BOOK PRICES: USED AND RARE, 1997

BOOK PRICES: USED AND RARE, 1997

Edited by

Edward N. Zempel

and

Linda A. Verkler

THE SPOON RIVER PRESS

Published by:
The Spoon River Press
2319-C West Rohmann Avenue
Peoria, Illinois 61604
(309) 672-2665
Fax: (309) 672-7853

ISBN 0-930358-15-5

Manufactured in the United States of America

This book is printed on acid-free paper meeting the standards of the American National Standard for Permanence of Paper for Library Materials.

Introduction

Book Prices: Used and Rare, 1997 is the fifth volume in a series of book price guides. Published annually, *Book Prices: Used and Rare* is a reference for the secondhand and antiquarian book dealer, general and rare book librarian, and the private collector seeking to place a value on a book. The nearly 32,000 titles in the present volume have been selected from the 1996 catalogs of 180 book dealers and auction houses in the United States and the United Kingdom. The dealers and auction houses who provided catalogs—and kindly gave their permission to reproduce their entries—represent a broad spectrum of the American and British book trade, not only geographically, but in the subject matter range and the price range of the books offered.

With a large variety of possible subject categories, we have attempted to balance the entries in this guide. Our general goal has been to provide pricing information on books in those subject categories and that price range most likely to be found in the day-to-day trade of the average generalist bookseller. However, in response to the suggestions of many, we have also included information on some more expensive books. This volume, then, contains entries on books in a wide variety of subject areas. Among them are modern first editions, travel and voyages, Americana and the West, natural history, science, medicine, art, architecture, children's literature, and books on books. Only books published in English have been listed. Though this guide includes several entries for books priced over $5,000 and some entries for books priced under $20, 85 percent of the titles listed in this guide are priced between $20 and $300.

All prices are given in both U.S. dollars and pounds sterling.

Entry Alphabetizing

Entries have been alphabetized word-for-word by the author's surname. Every effort has been made to present the correct spelling of surnames. However, variant spellings were sometimes found, especially in names beginning with de and De, le and Le, Mac and Mc, etc. (Such inconsistencies extend also to the entry of such names in reference works and library catalog files.)

Names preceded by de or de la should correctly be alphabetized under the family surname. For example, Simone de Beauvoir should be alphabetized under B—i.e., Beauvoir, Simone de. However, in the interests of clarity, ease of reference, and in anticipation of where many readers would first look, we have alphabetized such names under D. The same practice was used for surnames beginning with di, le, la, von, etc. Please take this into consideration when searching for a title by an author with such a name. If not in one place, the name may be in another.

In the case of U.S. government publications such as House and Senate documents, the user is advised to check under the title of the work, as well as under the work's author. Some works have been entered with the government agency as the author. For example, annual reports of the Bureau of American Ethnology (BAE) have generally been alphabetized under BAE. Bulletins of the Bureau of American Ethnology have been alphabetized under the author.

An entry for which the author is unknown has been alphabetized in the general list by its title. Pseudonymous entries give, if known, the author's real name in parentheses after the pseudonym. Generally, in the interest of more efficient alphabetizing, military ranks and other titles have been deleted from the author's name.

Some edited works (letters, diaries, and journals, especially) were listed in catalogs under the name of the author; others were listed under the name of the editor. In searching such titles in this guide, check first under the name of the author, and then under the name of the editor. Though there are exceptions, translated works have generally been entered under the name of the author, not the translator.

Entry Information

Each entry in *Book Prices: Used and Rare* includes the following information (when offered in the catalog): author's name (in CAPITAL letters), title of book, publisher and/or place and date of publication, condition, the price at which the book was cataloged or sold at auction, and the name (perhaps shortened) of the dealer or auction house that cataloged or auctioned the book. The key to these dealer and auction house abbreviations is found in the listing of contributing book dealers and auction houses, which begins on page 8.

If the condition of the book is not noted, it may be assumed that the book is in good or better collectible condition. Specific faults are usually listed in parentheses following the general condition of the book or its dust jacket. In the case of modern first editions, careful attention was given to noting those defects, both of the dust jacket and the book itself, affecting the book's value. The following are general definitions applying to a book's condition.

As New: In "as published" condition. The dust jacket (dj), if issued with the book, must be flawless.

Very Fine (VF): Nearly as new.

Fine: Without defect, but not "as new."

Near Fine (NF): Approaching Fine condition.

Very Good (VG): Minimal wear with no defects.

Good: In average condition.

Poor: Text complete, but book worn and binding defective.

Ex-library copies and book club editions are noted.

First editions are so noted. All titles are hardcover, unless the entry mentions otherwise. Every book is presumed to be in its original binding unless the entry mentions otherwise.

A dust jacket (dj) is mentioned when present. The dust jacket is assumed to be in the same general condition as the book unless the entry mentions otherwise. Slipcases are noted.

In the case of certain older books, where collation is a factor in determining the book's edition, the collation (if given in the dealer's catalog) has been provided. Generally, if mentioned in the dealer's catalog description, folding maps, folding plates, and folding illustrations have been noted in the entry, regardless of the value of the book. In the case of entries for limited editions, the number of copies in the edition has been noted, if included in the catalog entry.

When a "point" (a typographical or binding feature bearing on the edition of the book and thus on its value) was mentioned in the book dealer's catalog entry, we have included that "point" in our entry. For some Americana entries we have also included the Howes reference number included in the dealer's catalog entry (for example, Howes E 231). These numbers are keyed to entries in the second edition of *U.S.iana* by Wright Howes. Similarly, some entries carry numbers referencing the *Bibliography of American Literature* (BAL), e.g., BAL 14356.

For some titles we have provided multiple entries, suggesting a price agreement or a price range, usually across a range of conditions or editions. As mentioned, most of the entries provide information on books in the $20-$300 price range. Generally, then—though there are exceptions—this guide does not contain entries for unique copies, association copies, or books published in very small limited editions. While most of the books listed are hardcovers, prices on some vintage paperback first editions also have been included.

The prices listed are retail prices at which the books were cataloged or sold at auction in 1996.

Auction Prices

Those books sold at auction are identified by an asterisk following the name of the auction house. In the case of books sold by the following auction houses, the prices listed in this guide include the buyer's premium: Christie's South Kensington; Metropolitan Book Auction; Sotheby's; and Swann Galleries, Inc. In the case of books sold by the other auction houses, the price listed is the "hammer price," which is the price called out by the auctioneer when sale is made to the successful bidder. These hammer prices do not include the buyer's premium charged by the auction house. The buyer's premium charged is as follows: Baltimore Book Company, Inc., 10%; Kane Antiquarian Auction, 5%; New Hampshire Book Auctions, 10%; Oinonen Book Auctions, 10%; Pacific Book Auction Galleries, 15%; and Zubal Auction Company, 10%.

Identifying First Editions

First Editions: A Guide to Identification is the standard reference for identifying first editions. To receive information on this book, now in its third edition, send your name and address to the publisher: The Spoon River Press, 2319-C West Rohmann Avenue, Peoria, IL 61604. The Spoon River Press also publishes and distributes a wide range of books about books. Write, call (309-672-2665), or fax (309-672-7853) for our free catalog.

Abbreviations

To allow the inclusion of as much useful information as possible, certain standard abbreviations were used. A list of those abbreviations is on page 14.

A Caution

The prices listed in this guide are not the prices that book dealers will pay for the books listed. The prices listed are the prices at which dealers offered books for sale in 1996 or the prices at which auction houses sold books at auction in 1996. See Auction Prices (above).

Like any other retail business, the selling of rare, scarce, and used books depends on a markup for its profitability. The price a dealer is willing to pay for a book depends on its condition and scarcity, as well as the demand for the book.

In the case of cataloged books, the catalog prices listed in this guide are the prices at which the books were advertised for retail sale. The books may not have sold at these prices.

Standing Orders

Book Prices: Used and Rare is published annually in March. Annual volumes may be placed on standing order *at preferential discounts well below the post-publication price.*

Annual volumes on standing order will be shipped in March each year. To place *Book Prices: Used and Rare* on standing order, contact the publisher for an order form: The Spoon River Press, 2319-C West Rohmann Avenue, Peoria, IL 61604. Send no payment. An invoice will be enclosed with the book when it is shipped.

We are intent on making *Book Prices: Used and Rare* the most comprehensive, affordable, and useful book price guide obtainable. If you have suggestions on how future annual editions might be improved regarding focus or coverage, please let us know.

Contributing Book Dealers and Auction Houses

We are grateful to the book dealers and auction houses listed below. They generously provided copies of their 1996 catalogs (and, in the case of auction houses, prices realized lists) for our use in compiling this price guide. The name in parentheses below the name of the dealer or auction house is the name by which the catalog entries of that dealer or auction house are identified in this guide. Names followed by an asterisk are the names of auction houses.

Richard H. Adelson
(ADELSON)
North Pomfret, VT 05053
(802) 457-2608

Charles Agvent
(AGVENT)
291 Linden Road
Mertztown, PA 19539
(610) 682-4750

American Booksellers
(AMERICAN BOOKSELLERS)
102 W. 11th Street,
Aberdeen, WA 98520
(360) 532-2099

Antic Hay Rare Books
(ANTIC HAY)
P.O. Box 2185
Asbury Park, NJ 07712
(908) 774-4590

Any Amount of Books
(ANY AMOUNT)
62 Charing Cross Road
London WC2H 0BB
United Kingdom

Appelfeld Gallery
(APPELFELD)
1372 York Avenue
New York, NY 10021
(212) 988-7835

Archaeologia
(ARCHAEOLOGIA)
707 Carlston Avenue
Oakland, CA 94610
(510) 832-1405

Archer's Used and Rare Books
(ARCHER)
104 S. Lincoln Street
Kent, OH 44240
(216) 673-0945

Argonaut Book Shop
(ARGONAUT)
786-792 Sutter Street
San Francisco, CA 94109
(415) 474-9067

Argosy Book Store, Inc.
(ARGOSY)
116 East 59th Street
New York, NY 10022
(212) 753-4455

Ars Artis
(ARS ARTIS)
31 Abberbury Road
Oxford OX4 4ET
United Kingdom

Ash Rare Books
(ASH)
25 Royal Exchange
Threadneedle Street
London EC3V 3LP
United Kingdom

The Associates
(ASSOCIATES)
P.O. Box 4747
Falls Church, VA 22044-0747
(703) 578-3810

Authors of the West
(AUTHORS OF THE WEST)
191 Dogwood Drive
Dundee, OR 97115
(503) 538-8132

Gene W. Baade
(BAADE)
824 Lynnwood Avenue NE
Renton, WA 98056
(206) 271-6481

Gary A. Backman
(BACKMAN)
1005 Woodland Drive
Santa Paula, CA 93060
(805) 525-2647

Baltimore Book Company, Inc.
(BALTIMORE*)
2114 N. Charles Street
Baltimore, MD 21218
(410) 659-0550

Beasley Books
(BEASLEY)
1533 W. Oakdale
Chicago, IL 60657
(312) 472-4528

Benchmark Books
(BENCHMARK)
3269 S. Main Street
Suite 250, 2nd floor
Salt Lake City, UT 84115
(801) 486-3111

Steven C. Bernard
(BERNARD)
15011 Plainfield Lane
Darnestown, MD 20874
(301) 948-8423

Between the Covers
(BETWEEN THE COVERS)
35 W. Maple Avenue
Merchantville, NJ 08109
(609) 665-2284

David Bickersteth
(BICKERSTETH)
4 South End
Bassingbourn, Royston
Hertsfordshire SG8 5NG
United Kingdom

Matthew Biscotti & Company
(BISCOTTI)
481 Route 45 South
Austinburg, OH 44010
(216) 275-1310

Black Sun Books
(BLACK SUN)
157 East 57th Street
New York, NY 10022
(212) 688-6622

Blackwell's Rare Books
(BLACKWELL'S)
38 Holywell Street
Oxford OX1 3SW
United Kingdom

Frederick C. Blake
(BLAKE)
11 Oakway Drive
Stony Brook, NY 11790-1231
(516) 689-3754

Blue Mountain Books
(BLUE MOUNTAIN)
P.O. Box 363
Catskill, NY 12414
(518) 943-4771

Bohling Book Company
(BOHLING)
P.O. Box 204
Decatur, MI 49045
(616) 423-8786

Nelson Bond
(BOND)
4724 Easthill Drive
Roanoke, VA 24018
(540) 774-2674

The Book Block
(BOOK BLOCK)
P.O. Box 11090
Greenwich, CT 06831
(203) 532-1980

The Book Broker
(BOOK BROKER)
P.O. Box 1283
Charlottesville, VA 22902
(804) 296-2194

The Book Market
(BOOK MARKET)
Box 74
Altadena, CA 91003-0074
(818) 797-9527

Bookcell Books
(BOOKCELL)
Box 506
Haverford, PA 19041
(610) 649-4933

Bookfinders International
(BOOKFINDERS)
216 Ringwood Lane
Elgin, SC 29045
(803) 788-1368

Bookmark, Children's Books
(BOOKMARK)
Fortnight, Wick Down
Broad Hinton, Swindon
Wiltshire SN4 9NR
United Kingdom

Meyer Boswell Books, Inc.
(BOSWELL)
2141 Mission Street
San Francisco, CA 94110
(415) 255-6400

Judith Bowman—Books
(BOWMAN)
Pound Ridge Road
Bedford, NY 10506
(914) 234-7543

Bromer Booksellers
(BROMER)
607 Boylston Street
Boston, MA 02116
(617) 247-2818

Brooks Books
(BROOKS)
P.O. Box 21473
Concord, CA 94521
(510) 672-4566

Michael Brown
(BROWN)
4421 Osage Avenue
Philadelphia, PA 19104
(215) 387-2290

Richard Cady
(CADY)
1927 North Hudson Avenue, #1
Chicago, IL 60614
(312) 944-0856

Andrew Cahan
(CAHAN)
3000 Blueberry Lane
Chapel Hill, NC 27516
(919) 968-0538

The Captain's Bookshelf, Inc.
(CAPTAIN'S BOOKSHELF)
31 Page Avenue
Asheville, NC 28801
(704) 253-6631

Cattermole 20th Century
Children's Books
(CATTERMOLE)
9880 Fairmount Road
Newbury, OH 44065
(216) 338-3253

Chapel Hill Rare Books
(CHAPEL HILL)
P.O. Box 456
Carrboro, NC 27510
(919) 929-8351

Christie's South Kensington
(CHRISTIE'S*)
85 Old Brompton Road
London SW7 3LD
United Kingdom

Stan Clark Military Books
(CLARK)
915 Fairview Avenue
Gettysburg, PA 17325
(717) 337-1728

Clearwater Books
(CLEARWATER)
19 Matlock Road
Ferndown
Dorset BH22 8QT
United Kingdom

G. W. Connolly
(CONNOLLY)
2810 Kansas Avenue
Joplin, MO 64804-2931
(417) 624-5602

Claude Cox
(COX)
College Gateway Bookshop
3 & 5 Silent Street
Ipswich IP1 1TF
United Kingdom

Thomas Cullen
(CULLEN)
Box 134
Cattaraugus, NY 14719
(716) 257-5121

James Cummins, Bookseller
(CUMMINS)
699 Madison Avenue
New York, NY 10021
(212) 688-6441

Ursula C. Davidson, Books
(DAVIDSON)
134 Linden Lane
San Rafael, CA 94901
(415) 454-3939

Dawson's Book Shop
(DAWSON)
535 N. Larchmont Blvd.
Los Angeles, CA 90004
(213) 469-2186

Joseph A. Dermont
(DERMONT)
P.O. Box 654
Onset, MA 02558
(508) 295-4760

The Doctor's Library
(DOCTOR'S LIBRARY)
P.O. Box 423
Jersey City, NJ 07303-0423
(800) 225-0912

Dramatis Personae
(DRAMATIS)
P.O. Box 1070
Sheffield, MA 01257
(413) 229-7735

Dumont Maps & Books of the West
(DUMONT)
P.O. Box 10250
Santa Fe, NM 87504
(505) 988-1076

I. D. Edrich
(EDRICH)
17 Selsdon Road
London E11 2QF
United Kingdom

Francis Edwards
(EDWARDS)
The Old Cinema
Castle Street, Hay-on-Wye
Via Hereford HR3 5DF
United Kingdom

Francis Edwards of London
(EDWARDS)
13 Great Newport Street
Charing Cross Road
London WC2H 7JA
United Kingdom

Else Fine Books
(ELSE FINE)
P.O. Box 43
Dearborn, MI 48121
(313) 582-1080

Europa Books
(EUROPA)
15 Luttrell Avenue
London SW15 6PD
United Kingdom

Explorer Books
(EXPLORER)
Fallow Chase, Durfold Wood
Plaistow, W. Sussex RH14 0PL
United Kingdom

Fair Meadow Books
(FAIR MEADOW)
36 Rucum Road
Roxbury, CT 06783
(860) 354-9040

Joseph J. Felcone, Inc.
(FELCONE)
P.O. Box 366
Princeton, NJ 08542
(609) 924-0539

Fine Books
(FINE BOOKS)
781 E. Snell Road
Rochester, MI 48306
(810) 651-8799

Five Quail Books
(FIVE QUAIL)
8540 N. Central Avenue, #27
Phoenix, AZ 85020-3577
(602) 861-0548

Forest Books
(FOREST)
Knipton, Grantham
Lincs NG32 1RF
United Kingdom

W. Bruce Fye
(FYE)
1607 N. Wood Avenue
Marshfield, WI 54449
(715) 384-8128

John Gach Books
(GACH)
5620 Waterloo Road
Columbia, MD 21045
(301) 465-9023

Michael Ginsberg Books, Inc.
(GINSBERG)
Box 402
Sharon, MA 02067
(617) 784-8181

Edwin V. Glaser Rare Books
(GLASER)
P.O. Box 1765
Sausalito, CA 94966
(415) 332-1194

Glenn Books
(GLENN)
4503 Genessee, 2nd floor
Kansas City, MO 64111
(816) 561-9989

Gravesend Books
(GRAVESEND)
Box 235
Pocono Pines, PA 18350
(717) 646-3317

David A. H. Grayling
(GRAYLING)
Verdun House, Shap
Penrith, Cumbria CA10 3NG
United Kingdom

Green Meadow Books
(GREEN MEADOW)
2 Bellair House, Bellair Road
Madron, Penzance TR20 8SP
United Kingdom

John R. Gretton
(GRETTON)
5 Quebec Road
Dereham
Norfolk NR19 2DP
United Kingdom

Peter J. Hadley
(HADLEY)
132 Corve Street
Ludlow
Shropshire SY8 2PG
United Kingdom

E. Chalmers Hallam
(HALLAM)
"Trees", 9 Post Office Lane
St. Ives, Ringwood
Hampshire BH24 2PG
United Kingdom

Emmett Harrington
(HARRINGTON)
P.O. Box 27326
San Francisco, CA 94127
(415) 587-4604

Hartfield Fine and Rare Books
(HARTFIELD)
117 Dixboro Road
Ann Arbor, MI 48105
(313) 662-6035

Heinoldt Books
(HEINOLDT)
1325 W. Central Avenue
South Egg Harbor, NJ 08215
(609) 965-2284

John Henly
(HENLY)
Brooklands, Walderton
Chichester
West Sussex PO18 9EE
United Kingdom

Heritage Book Shop, Inc.
(HERITAGE)
8540 Melrose Avenue
Los Angeles, CA 90069
(310) 659-3674

The Hermitage Bookshop
(HERMITAGE)
290 Fillmore Street
Denver, CO 80206-5020
(303) 388-6811

High Latitude
(HIGH LATITUDE)
P.O. Box 11254
Bainbridge Island, WA 98110
(206) 842-0202

Hobbyhorse Books
(HOBBYHORSE)
P.O. Box 591
Ho-Ho-Kus, NJ 07423
(201) 327-4717

R. F. G. Hollett & Son
(HOLLETT)
6 Finkle Street, Sedbergh
Cumbria LA10 5BZ
United Kingdom

David J. Holmes
(HOLMES)
230 S. Broad Street, 3rd floor
Philadelphia, PA 19102
(215) 735-1083

Houle Rare Books & Autographs
(HOULE)
7260 Beverly Blvd.
Los Angeles, CA 90036-2537
(213) 937-5858

J. & J. House Booksellers
(HOUSE)
731 Unionville Road
Kennett Square, PA 19348
(610) 444-0490

James Jaffe Rare Books
(JAFFE)
P.O. Box 496
Haverford, PA 19041
(610) 649-4221

Janus Books
(JANUS)
P.O. Box 40787
Tucson, AZ 85717
(520) 881-8192

Kane Antiquarian Auction
(KANE*)
1525 Shenkel Road
Pottstown, PA 19465
(610) 323-5289

Kenneth Karmiole
(KARMIOLE)
P.O. Box 464
Santa Monica, CA 90404
(310) 451-4342

John K. King Books
(KING)
901 W. Lafayette Blvd.
Detroit, MI 48226
(313) 961-0622

Darwin Labordo, Books
(LABORDO)
738 Valle Vista Drive
Sierra Madre, CA 91024
(818) 355-0647

Lame Duck Books
(LAME DUCK)
90 Moraine Street
Jamaica Plain, MA 02130
(617) 522-6657

Edward J. Lefkowicz, Inc.
(LEFKOWICZ)
P.O. Box 630
Fairhaven, MA 02719
(508) 997-6839

George Lenz
(LENZ)
336 New York Avenue
Huntington, NY 11743
(516) 427-3744

Barry R. Levin
(LEVIN)
720 Santa Monica Blvd
Santa Monica, CA 90401
(310) 458-6111

Lien's Book Shop
(LIEN)
57 South 9th Street
Minneapolis, MN 55402
(612) 332-7081

Robert F. Lucas
(LUCAS)
P.O. Box 63
Blandford, MA 01008
(413) 848-2061

M & S Rare Books
(M & S)
Box 2594, East Side Station
Providence, RI 02906
(401) 421-1050

MacDonnell Rare Books
(MACDONNELL)
9307 Glenlake Drive
Austin, TX 78730
(512) 345-4139

Maggs Bros. Ltd.
(MAGGS)
50 Berkeley Square
London W1X 6EL
United Kingdom

Marlborough Rare Books, Ltd.
(MARLBOROUGH)
144-146 New Bond Street
London W1Y 9FD
United Kingdom

C. J. Martin
(MARTIN)
45 New Mill Lane
Mansfield
Woodhouse NG19 9BU
United Kingdom

David A. McClintock
(MCCLINTOCK)
1454 Sheridan Avenue NE
Warren, OH 44483
(330) 372-4425

Metropolitan Book Auction
(METROPOLITAN*)
123 W. 18th Street, 4th floor
New York, NY 10011
(212) 929-4488

Middle Earth Books
(MIDDLE EARTH)
251 Crestone Way,
Livermore, CO 80536
(970) 224-5650

Frank Mikesh
(MIKESH)
1356 Walden Road
Walnut Creek, CA 94596
(510) 934-9243

Mordida Books
(MORDIDA)
P.O. Box 79322
Houston, TX 77279
(713) 467-4280

Nicholas C. Morrell, Ltd.
(MORRELL)
77 Falkland Road
Kentish Town
London NW5 2XB
United Kingdom

V. J. Moss
(MOSS)
83 Chaigley Road
Longridge
Preston PR3 3TQ
United Kingdom

Howard S. Mott, Inc.
(MOTT)
P.O. Box 309
Sheffield, MA 01257

Murder by the Book
(MURDER)
1281 North Main Street
Providence, RI 02904
(401) 331-9140

My Bookhouse
(MY BOOKHOUSE)
27 S. Sandusky Street
Tiffin, OH 44883
(419) 447-9842

New Hampshire Book Auctions
(NEW HAMPSHIRE*)
P.O. Box 460
Weare, NH 03281
(603) 529-7432

Oak Knoll Books
(OAK KNOLL)
414 Delaware Street
New Castle, DE 19720
(302) 328-7232

October Farm
(OCTOBER FARM)
2609 Branch Road
Raleigh, NC 27610
(919) 772-0482

Oinonen Book Auctions
(OINONEN*)
P.O. Box 470
Sunderland, MA 01375
(413) 665-3253

Other Worlds Bookstore
(OTHER WORLDS)
1281 N. Main Street
Providence, RI 02904-1827
(401) 331-9140

Pacific Book Auction Galleries
(PACIFIC*)
133 Kearny Street, 4th floor
San Francisco, CA 94108
(415) 989-2665

Parmer Books
(PARMER)
7644 Forrestal Road
San Diego, CA 92120-2203
(619) 287-0693

Dick Perier—Books
(PERIER)
P.O. Box 1
Vancouver, WA 98666
(360) 696-2033

The Petersfield Bookshop
(PETERSFIELD)
16A Chapel Street
Petersfield
Hampshire GU32 3DS
United Kingdom

R & A Petrilla, Booksellers
(PETRILLA)
Box 306
Roosevelt, NJ 08555-0306
(609) 426-4999

Pettler & Lieberman Booksellers
(PETTLER)
8033 Sunset Blvd, #977
Los Angeles, CA 90046
(310) 474-2479

Pharos Books
(PHAROS)
P.O. Box 17, Fair Haven Station
New Haven, CT 06513
(203) 562-0085

Phillip J. Pirages
(PIRAGES)
P.O. Box 504
McMinnville, OR 97128
(800) 962-6666

R. Plapinger
(PLAPINGER)
P.O. Box 1062
Ashland, OR 97520
(541) 488-1220

Polyanthos Park Avenue Books
(POLYANTHOS)
P.O. Box 343
Huntington, NY 11743
(516) 271-5558

Wallace D. Pratt, Bookseller
(PRATT)
1801 Gough Street, #304
San Francisco, CA 94109
(415) 673-0178

Larry W. Price Books
(LARRY PRICE)
353 NW Maywood Drive
Portland, OR 97210-3333
(503) 221-1410

Suzanne & Truman Price
(PRICE)
7210 Helmick Road
Monmouth, OR 97361
(503) 838-5452

Quest Rare Books
(QUEST)
774 Santa Ynez
Stanford, CA 94305
(415) 324-3119

William Reese Co.
(REESE)
409 Temple Street
New Haven, CT 06511
(203) 789-8081

Jo Ann Reisler, Ltd.
(REISLER)
360 Glyndon Street NE
Vienna, VA 22180
(703) 938-2967

Alice Robbins, Bookseller
(ROBBINS)
3002 Round Hill Road
Greensboro, NC 27408
(910) 282-1964

Rostenberg & Stern, Rare Books
(ROSTENBERG & STERN)
40 East 88th Street
New York, NY 10128
(212) 831-6628

John Rybski, Bookseller
(RYBSKI)
2319 W. 47th Place
Chicago, IL 60609
(312) 847-5082

Sadlon's
(SADLON)
1207 Fox River Drive
De Pere, WI 54115
(414) 336-6665

Sagebrush Press
(SAGEBRUSH)
P.O. Box 87
Morongo Valley, CA 92256
(619) 365-5671

Savona Books
(SAVONA)
9 Wilton Road
Hornsea
East Yorkshire HU18 1QU
United Kingdom

Andrew Sclanders
(SCLANDERS)
11 Albany Road
Stroud Green
London N4 4RR
United Kingdom

Second Life Books, Inc.
(SECOND LIFE)
P.O. Box 242
Lanesborough, MA 01237
(413) 447-8010

Ed Smith Books
(SMITH)
P.O. Box 66
Oak View, CA 93022
(805) 649-2844

A. Sokol Books
(SOKOL)
P.O. Box 2409
London W1A 2SH
United Kingdom

Sotheby's
(SOTHEBY'S*)
34-35 New Bond Street
London W1A 2AA
United Kingdom

Henry Sotheran Ltd.
(SOTHERAN)
2 Sackville Street
Piccadilly
London W1X 2DP
United Kingdom

Andrew Stewart
(STEWART)
11 High Street
Helpringham
Lincolnshire NG34 9RA
United Kingdom

Sumner & Stillman
(SUMNER & STILLMAN)
P.O. Box 973
Yarmouth, ME 04096
(207) 846-6070

Raymond M. Sutton, Jr.
(SUTTON)
P.O. Box 330, 430 Main Street
Williamsburg, KY 40769
(606) 549-3464

Swann Galleries, Inc.
(SWANN*)
104 E. 25th Street
New York, NY 10010
(212) 254-4710

Michael Taylor Rare Books
(MICHAEL TAYLOR)
The Gables, 8 Mendham Lane
Harleston
Norfolk IP20 9DE
United Kingdom

Peter Taylor & Son
(PETER TAYLOR)
1, Ganders Ash
Leavesden, Watford
Hertfordshire WD2 7HE
United Kingdom

Robert Temple
(TEMPLE)
65 Mildmay Road
London N1 4PU
United Kingdom

Tiger Books
(TIGER)
Yew Tree Cottage
Westbere, Canterbury
Kent CT2 0HH
United Kingdom

Truepenny Books Inc.
(TRUEPENNY)
2509 N. Campbell Avenue
Tucson, AZ 85719
(520) 881-4822

Turtle Island Booksellers
(TURTLE ISLAND)
2041 Center Street
Berkeley, CA 94704
(510) 540-5422

The Typographeum Bookshop
(TYPOGRAPHEUM)
246 Bennington Road
Francestown, NH 03043
(603) 547-2425

Ulysses Bookshop
(ULYSSES)
31 & 40 Museum Street
London WC1A 1LH
United Kingdom

Len Unger Rare Books
(UNGER)
P.O. Box 5858
Sherman Oaks, CA 91413
(818) 990-7569

T. S. Vandoros Rare Books
(VANDOROS)
5827 Highland Terrace
Middleton, WI 53562
(608) 836-8254

Virgo Books
(VIRGO)
Little Court
South Wraxall, Bradford-on-Avon
Wiltshire BA15 2SE
United Kingdom

Patrick Walcot
(WALCOT)
60 Sunnybank Road
Sutton Colfield
West Midlands B73 5RJ
United Kingdom

Wantagh Rare Book Co.
(WANTAGH)
Box 605
Neversink, NY 12765-0605
(914) 985-7482

Rob Warren of Skyline Books
(WARREN)
13 West 18th Street
New York, NY 10011
(212) 759-5463

Andrew D. Washton
(WASHTON)
411 East 83rd Street
New York, NY 10028
(212) 481-0479

Jeff Weber Rare Books
(WEBER)
P.O. Box 3368
Glendale, CA 91221-0368
(818) 848-9704

F. E. Whitehart, Rare Books
(WHITEHART)
40 Priestfield Road
Forest Hill
London SE23 2RS
United Kingdom

Edna Whiteson
(WHITESON)
301 Mutton Lane, Potters Bar
Hertfordshire EN6 2AT
United Kingdom

Avril Whittle, Bookseller
(WHITTLE)
Swarthgill House
Garsdale, Nr. Sedbergh
Cumbria LA10 5PD
United Kingdom

Nigel Williams
(WILLIAMS)
22 Cecil Court
London WC2N 4HE
United Kingdom

Gary W. Woolson Bookseller
(WOOLSON)
2514 Western Avenue
Newburgh, ME 04444
(207) 234-4931

Worldwide Antiquarian
(WORLDWIDE)
P.O. Box 410391
Cambridge, MA 02141-0004
(617) 876-6220

Young's Antiquarian Books
(YOUNG)
Tillingham, Essex CM0 7ST
United Kingdom

Zubal Auction Company
(ZUBAL*)
2969 W. 25th Street
Cleveland, OH 44113
(216) 241-7640

ABBREVIATIONS

To present the maximum amount of information, we have used the following abbreviations in editing the entries in this guide. Most of these abbreviations are standard.

4to	a book with a height of approximately 12"	extrem(s)	extremities	OUP	Oxford University Press
8vo	a book with a height of approximately 9"	facs	facsimile	pb	paperback
12mo	a book with a height of approximately 7-8"	fep	free end paper, front end paper, front free end paper, flyleaf	perf	perforated
add'l	additional	fig(s)	figure(s)	Phila	Philadelphia
aeg	all edges gilt	fldg	folding, fold-out, folded	pict	pictorial
adv	advance	fr	front	prelims	preliminary pages
als	autograph letter, signed	frontis	frontispiece	plt(s)	plate(s)
assoc	association	FSG	Farrar, Straus, and Giroux	pg/pp	page(s)
BAE	Bureau of American Ethnology	G&D	Grosset & Dunlap	port(s)	portrait(s)
BAL	Bibliography of American Literature	GC	Garden City	promo	promotional
Balt	Baltimore	GPO	Government Printing Office	pseud	pseudonym
bd(s)	board(s)			ptd	printed
bkpl(s)	bookplate(s)	grn	green	ptg	printing
brn	brown	hb	hardback, hardcover	ptr	printer
b/w	black and white	hist	historical	pub's	publisher's
C&W	Chatto & Windus	HMSO	Her (His) Majesty's Stationery Office	rev	revised, reviser
ca	circa	illus	illustration(s), illustrated, illustrator	rev copy	review copy
cat(s)	catalog(s)	imp	impression	rep	rear end paper, rear free end paper
CCC	Collins Crime Club	incl	included, including	rt	right
cent	century	inscrip	non-authorial inscription	rmdr mk	remainder mark
cl	cloth	L.A.	Los Angeles	rpt	reprint
comp	compiler/complimentary	LEC	Limited Editions Club	rptd	reprinted
contemp	contemporary	lib	library	S&S	Simon & Schuster
CUP	Cambridge University Press	litho	lithograph, lithographic	SF	San Francisco
cvr(s)	cover(s)	lg	large	sig(s)	non-authorial signature(s); signature(s) (gathering of book pages)
cvrd	covered	ll	leaves		
dbl	double	ltd	limited	sl	slight, slightly, minor, marginally
DCC	Doubleday Crime Club	lt	light, lightly, moderately	sm	small
dec	decorative, decorated	mk(s)	mark(s), marking(s)	soc	society
diag(s)	diagram(s)	mkd	marked	SPCK	Society for the Promotion of Christian Knowledge
dj	dust jacket, dust wrapper	MMA	Metropolitan Museum of Art		
dk	dark	mod	modern	subs	subscription
dknd	darkened	MOMA	Museum of Modern Art	supp	supplement
dkng	darkening	ms	manuscript	teg	top edge gilt
dup	duplicate	mtd	mounted	tls	typed letter, signed
dwgs	drawings	n.d.	no date	tp	title page
ed(s)	editor(s), edited by, edition(s)	n.p.	no place, no publisher	trans	translated, translator, translation
emb	embossed	NAL	New American Library	univ	university
engr(s)	engraving(s), engraved	NF	near fine	unptd	unprinted
enlgd	enlarged	#	number	VF	very fine
ep(s)	endpaper(s)	NY	New York	VG	very good
esp	especially	NYGS	New York Graphic Society	vol(s)	volume(s)
et al	and others	o/w	otherwise	w/	with
ex-lib	ex-library	OJ	Orange Judd	w/o	without
ex-libris	bookplate present	orig	original		

A

A KEMPIS, THOMAS. Of the Imitation of Christ. Boston/London: L.C. Page/Kegan Paul, Trench, Trubner, 1899. One of 660 ptd. Teg, untrimmed. Plain vellum wraps, gilt. (Lt rubbed, handled, sl dusty.) *Baltimore**. $35/£22

A'BECKET, GILBERT ABBOTT. The Comic History of England [with] The Comic History of Rome. London: Bradbury & Evans, 1847-8 (and n.d.). 1st eds. 3 vols. Tall 8vo. Half-titles present, xii,308; xvii,320; 304pp; 30 hand-colored steel plts by John Leech. Marbled eps; teg. Crushed morocco, gilt. Fine set (sl rubbed). *Hartfield*. $495/£309

A., J. Y. Tales of Other Days. London: Effingham Wilson, 1830. 1st ed. 6 b/w plts by George Cruikshank. Marbled eps; aeg, untrimmed. Later full crimson calf by Zaehnsdorf, raised bands, gilt. (Sl aged, lg bkpl; sl rubbed, spine sl dknd.) Text Good. *Baltimore**. $70/£44

AARDEMA, VERNA. Who's in Rabbit's House? NY: Dial, 1977. 1st ed. 10.25 sq. Leo & Diane Dillon (illus). 32pp. Pict bds. Poster signed by artists. Fine in dj. *Cattermole*. $35/£22

AARONS, EDWARD S. Assignment—Madeleine. Greenwich: Fawcett, 1958. 1st ed. Pb orig. VG in wrappers. *Mordida*. $25/£16

AARONS, EDWARD S. Assignment—Stella Marni. Greenwich: Fawcett, 1957. 1st ed. Pb orig. VG in wrappers. *Mordida*. $25/£16

ABBE, DOROTHY. The Dwiggins Marionettes. NY: Abrams, (1970). 1st ed. Thick folio. 22 tipped-in color plts. Black cl, gilt. Very Clean in clear plastic dj (lt worn, dusty). *Baltimore**. $75/£47

ABBE, DOROTHY. The Dwiggins Marionettes. NY: Abrams, 1969. 32 tipped-in color plts. Dec cl, gilt. Fine in unptd cellophane dj (nicked). *Ulysses*. $200/£125

ABBE, ELFRIEDE. An Introduction to Hand-Made Paper. Manchester: Southern VT Art Center, 1972. 1st ed. One of 150 ptd. (Sl soiled), else NF in paper wrappers. *Pacific**. $52/£33

ABBEY, BARBARA. The Complete Book of Knitting. Thames & Hudson, 1972. 1st UK ed. VG in dj. *Whittle*. $40/£25

ABBEY, EDWARD. Black Sun. NY: S&S, (1971). 1st ed. Fine in dj. *Pacific**. $115/£72

ABBEY, EDWARD. Cactus Country. Time/Life Books, 1973. 1st ed. VG. *Five Quail*. $35/£22

ABBEY, EDWARD. Desert Solitaire. NY: McGraw Hill, (1968). 1st ed. Fine in Fine dj. *Lenz*. $300/£188

ABBEY, EDWARD. The Fool's Progress. NY: Henry Holt, (1988). 1st ed, 1st bk. Blue cl, yellow bds, gilt. Fine in dj. *Heritage*. $50/£31

ABBEY, EDWARD. The Fool's Progress. NY: Henry Holt, (1988). 1st ed. Signed, inscribed. Fine in dj. *Pacific**. $138/£86

ABBEY, EDWARD. Good News. NY: Dutton, (1980). 1st ed. Fine in Fine dj. *Lenz*. $75/£47

ABBEY, EDWARD. Jonathan Troy. NY: Dodd, Mead, 1954. 1st ed. Black cl. (Ex-lib, ink stamp, glue residue fr pastedown; spine sl skewed.) Dj (spine top chipped, rear panel soiled, sl edgeworn). *Heritage*. $750/£469

ABBEY, EDWARD. The Journey Home. NY: E.P. Dutton, (1977). 1st ed. Signed. Fine in dj. *Pacific**. $207/£129

ABBEY, EDWARD. The Monkey Wrench Gang. Phila: Lippincott, (1975). 1st ed. (Ex-lib, stamps, sl adhesion residue from tape to fr cvrs), else VG in VG dj. *Pacific**. $35/£22

ABBEY, EDWARD. The Monkey Wrench Gang. Salt Lake City: Dream Garden Press, 1985. One of 250 signed and w/unpublished print by R. Crumb laid in. Red cl, gilt. As New in openend slipcase w/color pict label. *Heritage*. $500/£313

ABBEY, EDWARD. One Life at a Time, Please. NY: Henry Holt, 1988. 1st ed. Fine in Fine dj. *Unger*. $125/£78

ABBEY, EDWARD. Slumgullion Stew. NY: Dutton, 1984. 1st ed. Fine in dj. *Smith*. $85/£53

ABBEY, EDWARD. Vox: Clamantis in Deserto—Some Notes from a Secret Journal. Santa Fe: Rydal, 1989. 1st ed. One of 250. 1/4 cl, paper spine label. Fine in slipcase. *Pacific**. $138/£86

ABBEY, JOHN R. Life in England in Aquatint and Lithography 1770-1860. Privately ptd, 1953. 1st ed. Color frontis, 32 plts. Teg. Buckram, leather spine label (sl rubbed). *Forest*. $280/£175

ABBEY, JOHN R. Scenery of Great Britain and Ireland in Aquatint and Lithography. Privately ptd, 1952. One of 500. Teg. Dj (sl soiled). *Sotheby's**. $275/£172

ABBOT, ANTHONY. About the Murder of Geraldine Foster. NY: Covici Friede, 1930. 1st ed, 1st bk. VG + in dj (chip replaced, lt worn). *Else Fine*. $175/£109

ABBOT, WILLIS J. Carter Henry Harrison: A Memoir. NY: Dodd, 1895. 1st ed. (4),254pp. *Ginsberg*. $100/£63

ABBOT, WILLIS J. Panama and the Canal in Picture and Prose. NY, 1914. Folio. Fldg map, 16 full-pg color plts. (1 plt torn, repaired; lt dampstain bottom edge of margin; rebound w/fr cvr, spine transposed.) *Heinoldt*. $35/£22

Abbot. By the Author of 'Waverley.' (By Walter Scott.) Edinburgh: Longman, 1820. 1st ed. 3 vols. Contemp plum 1/2 calf, raised bands, gilt, morocco labels. Sound set (no 1/2-title vol 1; vols 2, 3 misbound after the titles; sl rubbed, spotted). *Young*. $104/£65

ABBOTT, BERENICE. The View Camera Made Simple. Chicago/NY: Ziff-Davis Pub, 1948. 1st ed. Photo-illus glazed paper over bds. NF (inked-out name). *Cahan*. $150/£94

ABBOTT, BERENICE. The World of Atget. NY: Horizon, (1964). 1st ed. VG in dj (tears, chips). *Pacific**. $58/£36

ABBOTT, BERENICE. The World of Atget. NY, (1964). 1st ed. Folio. 180 repros by Eugene Atget. Dj (price-clipped, rubbed, yellowed). *Swann**. $92/£58

ABBOTT, CHARLES CONRAD. Notes of the Night and Other Outdoor Sketches. NY: Century, 1896. 1st ed. 231pp. Teg. Grn cl (spine dull). VG. *Lucas*. $20/£13

ABBOTT, CHARLES D. Howard Pyle: A Chronicle. NY: Harper, 1925. 1st ed. NF in dj. *Pacific**. $115/£72

ABBOTT, E. C. and HELENA HUNTINGTON SMITH. We Pointed Them North. NY: Farrar & Rinehart, 1939. 1st ed. Fine in dj. *Labordo*. $225/£141

ABBOTT, E. C. and HELENA HUNTINGTON SMITH. We Pointed Them North. Ron Tyler (ed). Chicago: Lakeside, 1991. Frontisport, color map. Brn cl. Fine. *Argonaut*. $25/£16

ABBOTT, E. C. and HELENA HUNTINGTON SMITH. We Pointed Them North. Ron Tyler (ed). Chicago: R.R. Donnelley, 1991. Frontis. VG. *Lien*. $30/£19

ABBOTT, ELEANOR HALLOWELL. Molly Make-Believe. N.p.: Woolly Whale, 1931. One of 250. Teg. 1/2 morocco. (Spine, upper morocco dknd), else VG. *Pacific**. $63/£39

ABBOTT, FRANCES M. Birds and Flowers About Concord, New Hampshire. Concord: Privately ptd, 1906. 1st ed. Brn cl, gilt. VG. *Larry Price*. $40/£25

ABBOTT, HENRY. Fish Stories. NY: Privately ptd, 1919. 1st ed. Signed, inscribed. Good (spine ends worn, extrems rubbed). *Pacific**. $86/£54

ABBOTT, HENRY. Fishing Brook. NY: Privately ptd, 1925. 1st ed. Signed, inscribed. Fldg map at rear. Dec bds. NF. *Pacific**. $161/£101

ABBOTT, J. Marco Paul in Vermont. Harper, 1852. 1st ed. (Spine spotted), else VG. *Fine Books*. $45/£28

ABBOTT, JACOB. A Description of the Mount Vernon School in 1832. Boston: Peirce & Parker, (1832). 1st ed. 18mo. 72pp. Orig calf-backed ptd bds (fr cvr detached). *M & S.* $500/£313

ABBOTT, JACOB. The History of King Charles the Second of England. Harper, (1849). 1st ed. Sm 8vo. Full-pg wood-engr frontis, x,304pp + 10pp list; full-pg engr port, tissue guard, 11 full-pg engrs. Buff eps. Tooled red linen on bds, gilt spine. VG (pencil dated sig; chipped, worn, line crack at spine, extrems sl rubbed). Internally Fine. *Hobbyhorse.* $70/£44

ABBOTT, JACOB. History of Xerxes the Great. NY: Harper, 1854. Full-pg wood-engr frontis, add'l extra chromolitho tp, tissue guard, map, 6 full-pg engrs. Buff eps. Dec tooled red linen on bds, gilt spine. Fine (eps lt foxed; sl shelfworn). *Hobbyhorse.* $75/£47

ABBOTT, JACOB. Rollo in Naples. Boston, 1858. 1st ed. 219pp. (Cvrs rubbed), else Good. *King.* $20/£13

ABBOTT, JOHN. Exposition of the Principles of Abbott's Hydraulic Engines...Together with an Illustration of the Power of Wheels, Heretofore Used. Boston, 1835. 1st ed. 7 plts. Orig cl-backed bds, paper cvr label. (Lt dampstained, foxed; worn, stained.) *Oinonen*.* $30/£19

ABBOTT, LEE K. A Tale Twice Told. OH: Logan Elm, 1992. 1st ed. 'Artist's Proof' of 300. Signed by Abbott and Brent Riley (illus). 3/4 cl, gilt. (Sl soiled), else Fine. *Pacific*.* $35/£22

ABBOTT, MAUDE E. (ed). Appreciations and Reminiscences of Sir William Osler, Bart., with a Classified Annotated Bibliography. (Binding title.) Montreal: Privately issued, 1926. 1st ed. Ltd to 1500 numbered. Frontisport. VG (spine sl dull, lt shelfworn). *Glaser.* $185/£116

ABC of Horses. London: Raphael Tuck & Sons, (ca 1890). Lg 4to. Harry Payne (illus). Color pict wrappers (lt worn, spine chipped). *Reisler.* $175/£109

ABC of Your Story Book Friends. London: Raphael Tuck & Sons, (ca 1940s). Obl 4to. Dbl-pg centerfold. Stiff paper wrappers, color paste label. Good. *Reisler.* $85/£53

ABC. London: Daily Express, n.d. (1933). 17x23 cm. 6 VG dbl-pg pop-ups. Pict bds (extrems bumped, worn; fr hinge sl weak). *Bookfinders.* $100/£63

ABC. A Comic Alphabet. London: Charles Tilt, 1836. George Cruikshank (illus). Panorama fldg sheet w/hand-colored illus. Pict yellow paper (skillfully rebacked, orig spine relaid). VG. *Davidson.* $320/£200

ABDILL, GEORGE B. Rails West. Seattle: Superior Pub, (1960). 1st ed. Fine in dj (sl rubbed). *Argonaut.* $35/£22

ABDILL, GEORGE B. This Was Railroading. Seattle: Superior Pub, (1958). 1st ed. Gray cl. Fine in pict dj (lt worn). *Argonaut.* $25/£16

ABDILL, GEORGE B. This Was Railroading. Seattle, (1958). One of 250. Signed. Frontis. Padded cl. VG (lower rt corner of cvr bumped, affecting 1/3 of pp) in VG + dj. *Sagebrush.* $75/£47

ABEL, ANNIE HELOISE. Tabeau's Narrative of Loisel's Expedition to the Upper Missouri. Norman: Univ of OK, (1968). 2nd ed in English. VG in dj (spine ends sl rubbed, sm tear upper fr panel). *Pacific*.* $23/£14

ABEL, CLARKE. Narrative of a Journey in the Interior of China, and of a Voyage...in the Years 1816 and 1817. London: Longman, Hurst et al, 1818. 1st ed. 4to. xvi,errata,420pp; 4 maps, 19 plts (blank margin 1 plt repaired), incl 8 hand colored. Mod 1/2 morocco (rebacked, rubbed). *Adelson.* $1,575/£984

ABERCROMBIE, JOHN. Inquiries Concerning the Intellectual Powers and the Investigation of Truth. Edinburgh/London, 1833. 4th ed. xv,441pp (lt spotting, fr hinge sl tender). 1/2 calf, marbled bds (extrems sl worn, tail of upper joint sl tender, spine faded). *Edwards.* $128/£80

ABERCROMBIE, L. A. and FLETCHER PRATT. My Life to the Destroyers. NY: Holt, 1944. 1st ptg. VG in dj. *American Booksellers.* $25/£16

ABERCROMBIE, LASCELLES. Interludes and Poems. London/NY: John Lane, 1908. 1st ed, 1st issue binding, 1st bk. VG in grn cl, spine gilt. *Cady.* $60/£38

ABERCROMBIE, LASCELLES. Interludes and Poems. John Lane, Bodley Head, 1908. 1st ed, 1st bk. Teg. VG (prelims, edges spotted, feps browned; spine ends sl bumped) in dj (worn, torn, chipped, creased, dusty, browned, lacks several sm pieces). *Ulysses.* $88/£55

ABERNATHY, BYRON R. (ed). Private Elisha Stockwell, Jr. Sees the Civil War. Norman: Univ of OK, (1958). 1st ed. Signed. Fine in pict dj (sl chipped). *Argonaut.* $40/£25

ABERNETHY, JOHN. The Surgical and Physiological Works of John Abernethy. Volume I. London, 1825. 6th ed. 414pp. Orig full leather. Good (foxed; extrems worn, spine chipped, hinges cracked). *Doctor's Library.* $40/£25

ABERT, JAMES W. Through the Country of the Comanche Indians in the Fall of the Year 1845. John Galvin (ed). (SF): John Howell Books, 1970. One of 5000 ptd. Fine. *Pacific*.* $40/£25

ABERT, JAMES W. Through the Country of the Comanche Indians in the Fall of the Year 1845. John Galvin (ed). (SF): John Howell Books, 1970. 2nd ed. Ltd to 5000 ptd. Folio. Color frontis, 21 color plts, 3 maps (2 fldg). Tan cl, gilt. VF. *Argonaut.* $50/£31

ABERT, JAMES W. Through the Country of the Comanche Indians in the Fall of the Year 1845. John Galvin (ed). (SF): John Howell Books, 1970. One of 5000 ptd. Fine in dj. *Pacific*.* $63/£39

ABERT, JAMES W. Western America in 1846-1847. John Galvin (ed). (SF): John Howell Books, 1966. One of 3000 ptd. 2 fldg maps. Pict cl, gilt. Fine in acetate. *Pacific*.* $52/£33

ABERT, JAMES W. Western America in 1846-1847. John Galvin (ed). (SF): John Howell Books, 1966. One of 3000 ptd. 2 fldg maps. Pict cl, gilt. Fine in acetate dj. *Pacific*.* $75/£47

ABNEY, W. DE W. Thebes and Its Five Greater Temples. London: Sampson, Low, Marston et al, 1876. 40 Woodburytype repros. Aeg. (Foxed, plts affected; fr hinge starting, extrems worn.) *Swann*.* $1,380/£863

ABOUT, EDMOND. The Man with the Broken Ear. Henry Holt (trans). NY: Holt & Williams, 1872. Early Amer ed. Ep ads dated November 4, 1872. Cream cl. VG (bkpls or labels removed, few ink notes; sl worn, sl soiled). *Sumner & Stillman.* $35/£22

ABRAHAM, GEORGE D. First Steps to Climbing. Mills & Boon, 1923. 1st ed. 24 plts. (Eps sl spotted.) *Hollett.* $64/£40

ABRAHAM, GERALD. Eight Soviet Composers. OUP, 1943. 1st ed. VG in dj. *Hollett.* $24/£15

ABRAHAM, GERALD. A Hundred Years of Music. Duckworth, 1938. 1st ed. (Spine sl faded.) *Hollett.* $32/£20

ABRAHAM, KARL. Selected Papers on Psychoanalysis. London: Hogarth, 1949. 4th ptg. Fine in NF dj (spine sl dknd, sm chips). *Beasley.* $40/£25

ABRAHAMS, PETER. Mine Boy. Dorothy Crisp, n.d. (1946). 1st Eng ed. VG (spine ends, corner sl bumped) in dj (rubbed, chipped, spine ends defective). *Ulysses.* $104/£65

ABRAMS, ALBERT. Spondylotherapy: Physio and Pharmaco-Therapy and Diagnostic Methods Based on a Study of Clinical Physiology. SF, 1910. 1st ed. VG (extrems sl worn). *Doctor's Library.* $150/£94

ABRANTES, LAURE SAINT-MARTIN JUNOT. Memoirs of Napoleon, His Court and Family. NY: D. Appleton, 1854. 2 vols. 16 steel-engr ports, incl frontis each vol. Marbled eps, edges. Contemp 1/2 calf, marbled sides, raised bands, black/olive morocco labels. VG (lt offsetting, 1859 inscrip vol 1; corners worn, paper sides sl chafed, joints, spine ends sl worn). *Pirages.* $175/£109

Abroad. London: Marcus Ward, (1882). 1st ed. 4to. Thos. Crane & Ellen Houghton (illus). 56pp. Cl-backed color pict bds (edges sl worn). *Reisler.* $250/£156

ABSE, DANNIE. A Small Desperation. London: Hutchinson, 1968. 1st Eng ed. Signed. NF (spine foot sl bumped) in dj (sl creased, spine sl faded). *Ulysses*. $40/£25

Abstract Art in England, 1913-1915. London, 1969. One of 2000 ptd. Lewis' 'Red Duet' tipped in. VG in orig wraps. *Edrich*. $32/£20

Abstract of Infantry Tactics; Including Exercises and Manoeuvres Light-Infantry and Riflemen; for the Use of the Militia of the United States. Phila: Moss & Bro, 1853. 138pp; 30 plts. Fair (stained, worn). *Pacific**. $92/£58

Account of the European Settlements in America.... (By Edmund Burke.) London, 1758. 2nd ed. 2 vols. 2 maps (1 defective). Contemp sheep (worn). Howes B974. *Swann**. $201/£126

Account of the Russian Discoveries Between Asia and America to Which are Added the Conquest of Siberia, and the History of the Transactions and Commerce Between Russia and China. London: J. Nichols for T. Cadell, 1780. 1st ed. 4to. 4 engr fldg maps, 1 engr view. Old brn calf bds (expertly rebacked), raised bands, red/grn leather spine labels. Fine. *Appelfeld*. $1,250/£781

Account of the Terrific and Fatal Riot at the New York Astor Place Opera House, on the Night of May 10th, 1849.... NY: H.M. Ranney, 1849. Frontis, 32pp. VG in ptd wrappers. *Brown*. $75/£47

Account of the Terrific and Fatal Riot at the New-York Astor Place Opera House. NY, 1849. 3/4 morocco (orig wrappers bound in). *Swann**. $103/£64

ACCUM, FREDERICK. A Practical Essay on the Analysis of Minerals. Phila: Kimber & Conrad, 1809. 1st Amer ed. 2 copper engrs, incl frontis. (Stained, foxed; lacks feps, spine.) *Metropolitan**. $230/£144

ACCUM, FREDERICK. System of Theoretical and Practical Chemistry. Phila: Kimber & Conrad, 1808. 1st Amer ed. 2 vols. Complete w/7 plts (sl stained). Contemp calf (rubbed), leather labels. *M & S*. $350/£219

ACERBI, JOSEPH. Travels Through Sweden, Finland and Lapland to the North Cape in...1798 and 1799. London: Jos. Mawman, 1802. 2 vols. Port, 15 plts, lg fldg map. 1/2 calf. (Lt foxed, marginal stains; sl rubbed, vol 1 spine reglued.) *Kane**. $375/£234

ACHEBE, CHINUA. Things Fall Apart. NY: McDowell, Obolensky, (1959). 1st ed, 1st bk. NF in dj (spine ends sl chipped). *Pacific**. $104/£65

ACKERLEY, J. R. My Father and Myself. London: Bodley Head, (1968). 1st ed. Frontis. (Sm blind-stamped name fep), o/w NF in dj (lt edgeworn, sm nicks). *Reese*. $60/£38

ACKERLEY, J. R. The Prisoners of War. London, 1925. 1st Eng ed. Signed. (Few grubby margins, 1 central joint weak, mark on fep; sl bumped, handled, spine label rubbed.) *Clearwater*. $192/£120

ACKERMAN, CARL W. Germany, the Next Republic? NY: George H. Doran, (1917). 1st ed. Frontis. (Bkpl), else NF in VG dj (few closed tears). *Reese*. $25/£16

ACKERMANN, RUDOLPH. A History of the University of Oxford, Its Colleges, Halls and Public Buildings. R. Ackermann, 1814. 1st ed. 2 vols. 4to. Half-titles, 1 uncolored port (sl spotted), 81 hand-colored aquatint plts. Gilt edges. Contemp crimson morocco, gilt. (1st plt loose, offsetting; leather scraped away in a few places; hinges, edges rubbed.) *Sotheby's**. $4,416/£2,760

ACKROYD, PETER. Chatterton. London: Hamish Hamilton, (1987). 1st Eng ed. Signed. Fine in dj. *Cady*. $40/£25

ACKROYD, PETER. Chatterton. NY: Grove, (1988). 1st Amer ed. Adv reading copy. VG in heavy pict paper wrappers. *Cady*. $35/£22

ACKROYD, PETER. Chatterton. Hamilton, 1987. 1st UK ed. Signed. Fine in Fine dj. *Martin*. $29/£18

ACKROYD, PETER. Dickens. London: Sinclair-Stevenson, 1990. 1st ed. One of 150 specially bound, signed. Fine in cl-backed marbled bds, gilt. *Vandoros*. $195/£122

ACKROYD, PETER. Diversions of Purley. Hamilton, 1987. 1st UK ed. Fine in Fine dj. *Martin*. $22/£14

ACKROYD, PETER. First Light. London: Hamish Hamilton, (1989). 1st Eng ed. Signed. Fine in dj. *Cady*. $35/£22

ACKROYD, PETER. First Light. Hamilton, 1989. 1st UK ed. Signed. Fine in Fine dj. *Martin*. $27/£17

ACKROYD, PETER. Hawksmoor. Hamish Hamilton, 1985. 1st Eng ed. (Pp browned), else Fine in dj. *Ulysses*. $72/£45

ACKROYD, PETER. The Last Testament of Oscar Wilde. NY, (1983). 1st Amer ed. VG in dj. *King*. $25/£16

ACKROYD, PETER. The Last Testament of Oscar Wilde. NY: Harper & Row, (1983). 1st Amer ed. Black cl-backed paper bds. NF in dj. *Cady*. $30/£19

ACKROYD, PETER. The Last Testament of Oscar Wilde. London: Hamish Hamilton, (1983). 1st Eng ed. VG in dj. *Cady*. $35/£22

ACKROYD, PETER. Notes for a New Culture. London: Vision, 1976. 1st ed. Fine in dj (spine sl faded, edges lt worn). *Lame Duck*. $125/£78

ACRES, MARK. Sniper! Viet Rampage. Lake Geneva, WI: TSR, 1987. 1st ed. Pb orig. (Eps tanned), else Fine. *Associates*. $25/£16

Across the Plains. (Hillsborough: L-D Allen, 1950.) One of 200. Dec bds. (Bkpl; spine head bump), else VG. *Pacific**. $127/£79

ACTON, ELIZA. Poems. Ipswich: R. Deck, 1826. 1st ed. Sm 8vo. Half-title, tipped-in slip w/add'l names for 'Subscribers' List' present, xx,140pp. Untrimmed. Orig blue glazed cotton-backed gray bds, ptd paper label. VG (contemp pencil name, prelims lt foxed; cvrs lt foxed). *Blackwell's*. $640/£400

ACTON, HAROLD and PETER QUENNELL (eds). Oxford Poetry 1924. Oxford: Basil Blackwell, 1924. 1st ed. Good in dk blue wrappers (label, sl creased). *Maggs*. $48/£30

ACTON, HAROLD. Aquarium. London: Duckworth, 1923. 1st ed, 1st bk. 8vo. Red/white/black patterned bds. (Fr joint split.) Tissue dj. *Maggs*. $560/£350

ACTON, HAROLD. The Last Bourbons of Naples (1825-1861). London: Methuen, 1961. 1st Eng ed. 15 b/w plts. VG (spine ends bumped) in dj (nicked, rubbed, dusty, sl mkd, creased, spine sl dknd, edges browned). *Ulysses*. $120/£75

ACTON, HAROLD. Memoirs of an Aesthete. London: Methuen, (1948). 1st ed. Frontis. Fine in NF dj (dknd). *Agvent*. $150/£94

ACTON, HAROLD. Modern Chinese Poetry. Ch'en Shih-hsiang (trans). London: Duckworth, 1936. 1st Eng ed. Teg. Dec cl, gilt. VG (eps browned; spine ends, corners sl bumped, spine, cvr edges sl dknd) in dj (nicked, torn, rubbed, chipped, dusty; spine, edges faded, price-clipped, tape repairs, chipped, sl creased). *Ulysses*. $200/£125

ACTON, HAROLD. More Memoirs of an Aesthete. London: Methuen, (1970). 1st ed. Fine (initials) in VG dj (tears at rear). *Agvent*. $50/£31

ACTON, HAROLD. Prince Isidore. (London): Methuen, (1950). 1st ed. Fine in dj (spine tips sl frayed). *Reese*. $100/£63

ACTON, HAROLD. Tit for Tat. London: Hamish Hamilton, 1972. 1st Eng ed. NF (spine ends sl bumped) in dj (sl creased). *Ulysses*. $58/£36

Acts of the Apostles. Theodore Schultz (trans). NY: American Bible Soc, 1850. 1st Amer ed. 119pp. (Sl worn, spine gone; foxing.) *Oinonen**. $90/£56

Acts of the General Assembly of the Commonwealth of Virginia, Passed in 1861.... [with] Appendix. Ordinances Adopted by the Convention of Virginia.... Richmond: William F. Ritchie, public ptr, 1861. 379; 75pp. Contemp sheep, marbled bds. (Text lt spotted, stained; hinges tender, spine worn), else Good. *Brown*. $50/£31

ADAIR, GILBERT. Vietnam on Film. NY: Proteus Pub, 1981. 1st ed. Fine in dj. *Associates.* $30/£19

ADAIR, JOHN. The Navajo and Pueblo Silversmiths. Norman: Univ of OK, 1944. 1st ed. VG. *Book Market.* $50/£31

ADAIR, JOHN. The Pilgrim's Way. Thames & Hudson, 1978. VG in dj. *Hadley.* $24/£15

ADAMIC, LOUIS. RJ: Robinson Jeffers, a Portrait.... (Covelo: Yolla Bolly, 1983.) 2nd ed, 1st bk. One of 265 numbered (of 280), signed by Garth Jeffers (foreword). Gray cl, paper labels. Fine. *Reese.* $65/£41

ADAMS, ALEXANDER B. Sitting Bull. NY, 1973. Good in dj. *Dumont.* $30/£19

ADAMS, ALICE. Beautiful Girl. NY: Knopf, 1979. 1st ed. Top edge stained pink. Cream cl, gilt. (Rmdr mk top edge, w/ink on 1 bd edge; edges sl bumped), o/w Fine in dj. *Heritage.* $75/£47

ADAMS, ALICE. Families and Survivors. NY: Knopf, 1974. 1st ed. (Sm smudge fep), else Fine in Fine dj. *Pettler.* $25/£16

ADAMS, ALICE. Families and Survivors. NY: Knopf, 1974. Rev copy w/slip. Fine in Fine dj. *Agvent.* $100/£63

ADAMS, ALICE. Return Trips. NY: Knopf, 1985. 1st ed. Fine in Fine dj. *Agvent.* $30/£19

ADAMS, ALICE. Rich Rewards. NY: Knopf, 1980. 1st ed. Cream cl. Fine in dj (backstrip faded). *Heritage.* $75/£47

ADAMS, ANDY. The Corporal Segundo. Austin: Encino Press, 1968. 1st ed. One of 750. Signed by Wilson M. Hudson (ed). Pict bds. Fine. *Harrington.* $40/£25

ADAMS, ANDY. The Log of a Cowboy. Boston: Houghton, Mifflin, 1903. 1st ed. 6 plts (lacks plt). No map. Pict tan cl, gilt. Good + (cvrs soiled, extrems rubbed). Howes A45. *House.* $25/£16

ADAMS, ANDY. The Log of a Cowboy. Boston: Houghton Mifflin, 1903. 1st ed, 2nd state, w/'Map Showing the Trail' in list of illus and on p28. NF. *Labordo.* $175/£109

ADAMS, ANDY. The Outlet. Boston: Houghton, Mifflin, 1905. 1st ed. 6 plts. Pict tan cl, gilt. VG (edges lt worn). *House.* $50/£31

ADAMS, ANDY. Reed Anthony, Cowman. Boston, (1907). 1st ed. Frontis. VG (ex-lib, lt worn). *Woolson.* $20/£13

ADAMS, ANSEL and EDWIN CORLE. Death Valley: The Creek Called Furnace. L.A.: Ward Ritchie, (1962). NF in dj. *Pacific*.* $104/£65

ADAMS, ANSEL and EDWARD JOESTING. An Introduction to Hawaii. SF: 5 Associates, (1964). 1st ed. 12x9. Fine in dj. *Pacific*.* $58/£36

ADAMS, ANSEL and EDWARD JOESTING. An Introduction to Hawaii. SF: 5 Associates, (1964). 1st ed. Fine in Fine dj. *Book Market.* $60/£38

ADAMS, ANSEL and NANCY NEWHALL. This Is the American Earth. SF: Sierra Club, (1960). 1st ed. 84 b/w photos. (Spine foot lt worn), else Fine in dj (sl chipped). *Argonaut.* $100/£63

ADAMS, ANSEL. Ansel Adams. Hastings-on-Hudson, (1972). Signed. 117 repros. Dj (sl soiled). *Swann*.* $161/£101

ADAMS, ANSEL. The Land of Little Rain. Text by Mary Austin. Cambridge, 1950. 1st ed. (Extrems worn.) Dj (worn, reverse inexpertly taped). *Swann*.* $138/£86

ADAMS, ANSEL. My Camera in the National Parks. Yosemite/Boston: Virginia Adams/Houghton Mifflin, 1950. 1st ed. Signed. Spiral-bound flexible bds. Fine. *Pacific*.* $207/£129

ADAMS, ANSEL. My Camera in the National Parks. Boston, 1950. 1st ed. Signed. Folio. 30 repros. Spiral bound, ptd bds. Clean in dj. *Swann*.* $345/£216

ADAMS, ANSEL. The Pageant of History and the Panorama of Today in Northern California: A Photographic Interpretation. Text by Nancy Newhall. SF: (American Trust Co), 1954. 1st ed. (Few scratches), else VG in spiral-bound photo-pict wrappers. *Pacific*.* $69/£43

ADAMS, ANSEL. The Print. Boston: NYGS/Little Brown, (1983). 1st ed thus. Dj. *Truepenny.* $35/£22

ADAMS, ANSEL. Sierra Nevada: The John Muir Trail. Berkeley: Archetype Press, 1938. 1st ed. One of 500. Signed. Folio. 16x12.25. 49 tipped-in plts. Fine. *Pacific*.* $1,955/£1,222

ADAMS, ANSEL. Taos Pueblo. (Boston): NYGS, 1977. One of 950. Signed. 17 x 12 1/4. 1/2 blind-lettered calf. Fine in slipcase (irregularly sunned). *Pacific*.* $690/£431

ADAMS, ANSEL. Taos Pueblo. Text by Mary Austin. Boston: NYGS, (1977). One of deluxe ed of 950. Signed. Folio. 12 repros. Orange cl, 1/4 leather. Clean in slipcase. *Swann*.* $805/£503

ADAMS, ANSEL. Volume I, The Eloquent Light. Text by Nancy Newhall. SF, (1963). 1st ed. Folio. (Marginal yellowing, ink stain 1 leaf.) Dj (rubbed, chipped). *Swann*.* $57/£36

ADAMS, ANSEL. Yosemite and the Range of Light. Boston: NYGS, 1979. 1st trade ed. Signed ptd label, mtd at fep. Obl folio. Crimson buckram, blue cl (lt dusty, sunned), gilt. Internally VG in dj (sl rubbed). *Baltimore*.* $80/£50

ADAMS, ANSEL. Yosemite and the Range of Light. Boston, 1979. 1st ed. Signed. Obl folio. Clean in dj (wrinkled, sm tears). *Swann*.* $126/£79

ADAMS, B. M. Sons of a Seaman. London: Kegan Paul, Trench, Trubner, 1904. Blue cl. VG. *American Booksellers.* $25/£16

ADAMS, B. M. G. (Pseud of Bride Scratton.) England. Paris: Three Mountains, 1923. 1st, only ed. One of 150. 8vo. Victorian patterned wallpaper over bds, paper cvr label. (Spine sl rubbed.) *Pharos.* $750/£469

ADAMS, C. C. and T. L. HANKINSON. The Ecology and Economics of Oneida Lake Fish. Syracuse, 1928. 4 color plts, fldg map. Wrappers (chipped, soiled, backstrip tears repaired w/tape). *Sutton.* $40/£25

ADAMS, CHARLES C. Boontling: An American Lingo. Austin: Univ of TX, (1971). 1st ed. VG in dj (sm tears spine ends, extrems). *Pacific*.* $23/£14

ADAMS, CHARLES FRANCIS, JR. The Double Anniversary: '76 and '63. Boston: Wm. Parsons Lunt, 1869. Presentation copy. 22-pg pamphlet. VG in orig wraps (sl nicked). *Brown.* $15/£9

ADAMS, DOUGLAS. The Hitchhiker's Guide to the Galaxy. NY, 1979. 1st Amer ed, 1st bk. VG (sl cocked) in VG dj. *Warren.* $30/£19

ADAMS, DOUGLAS. The Hitchhiker's Guide to the Galaxy. Arthur Barker, 1979. 1st UK ed. Fine in dj. *Williams.* $120/£75

ADAMS, DOUGLAS. The Restaurant at the End of the Universe. Arthur Barker, 1980. 1st UK ed. NF in dj. *Williams.* $96/£60

ADAMS, E. Francis Danby: Varieties of Poetic Experience. Yale Univ, 1973. 6 color, 160 b/w plt illus. Good in dj. *Ars Artis.* $120/£75

ADAMS, ELIZABETH LAURA. Dark Symphony. NY: Sheed & Ward, 1942. 1st ed. Gift card mtd on tp. VG in ptd dj. *Petrilla.* $35/£22

ADAMS, EMMA H. To and Fro in Southern California, with Sketches in Arizona and New Mexico. Cincinnati: W.M.B.C., 1887. 1st ed. 288pp. Gilt-dec cl. (Spine sl dull, ends rubbed), else NF. *Pacific*.* $115/£72

ADAMS, EVANGELINE. The Bowl of Heaven. NY: Dodd, 1926. VG + . *Middle Earth.* $45/£28

ADAMS, F. The Birth and Development of the Geological Sciences. Balt: William & Wilkins, c1938. 1st ptg. Signed, dated by Charles Mook. Good (fr bd top creased, old repair to fr joint top). *Blake.* $350/£219

ADAMS, F. C. Manuel Pereira; or, The Sovereign Rule of South Carolina. Washington, 1853. 1st ed. (4),(2),302,(2)pp. Uncut. Ptd wraps (sl chipped). *M & S.* $225/£141

ADAMS, F. W. Theological Criticisms, or Hints of the Philosophy of Man and Nature. Montpelier, (VT): J.E. Thompson, 1843. 1st ed. Inscribed presentation. 216,32pp. Orig cl. *M & S.* $125/£78

ADAMS, FREDERICK B. Radical Literature in America. Stamford: Overbrook, 1939. One of 650. Uncut. (Sl worn, soiled.) Slipcase (soiled, sl scuffed). *Oinonen**. $50/£31

ADAMS, GEORGE. Geometrical and Graphical Essays. London: The Author, 1791. 1st ed. Frontis (foxed), (iii),xvi,500pp; 32 VG fldg copperplts at rear. (Text sl browned; some plts w/old misfolds, few worn, chipped, 1 chipped along rt edge sl into plt, another w/tiny hole.) Old calf (recently rebacked in plain brn pebbled cl; leather cracking, paper adhesions along spine). *Baltimore**. $200/£125

ADAMS, GEORGE. A Treatise Describing the Construction, and Explaining the Use, of New Celestial and Terrestial Globes. London: The Author, 1769. 2nd ed. xxviii,345,7pp; 14 plts. New 1/4 tan calf, red label. VG. *Adelson.* $425/£266

ADAMS, HARRY. Beyond the Barrier with Byrd. Chicago: Donahue, c. 1932. 1st ed. VG (remains of dj laid in). *High Latitude.* $25/£16

ADAMS, HENRY. The Education of Henry Adams. LEC, 1942. Ltd to 1500 numbered, signed by Samuel Chamberlain (illus). Fine in slipcase. *Swann**. $69/£43

ADAMS, HENRY. Historical Essays. T. Fisher Unwin, 1891. 1st ed, Eng issue, ptd in America. 1/2-title not called for; single inset tp (a cancel), contents leaf; final blank; (iv),422,(ii)pp. Eps coated dk chocolate; uncut. 1/4 chocolate buckram, gilt, greenish-gray cl sides. (Spine ends sl worn), o/w Fine. *Temple.* $45/£28

ADAMS, HENRY. Mont-Saint Michel and Chartres. NY: LEC, 1957. One of 1500 ptd. Signed By Samuel Chamberlain (photos). Gray buckram. Fine in slipcase. *Pacific**. $46/£29

ADAMS, HENRY. Mont-Saint-Michel and Chartres. LEC, 1957. Ltd to 1500 numbered, signed by Samuel Chamberlain (illus). Fine in slipcase. *Swann**. $57/£36

ADAMS, JOEY. On the Road for Uncle Sam. NY: Bernard Geis Associates, 1963. 1st ed. Fine in dj (flaps sl foxed, sm chips, tears). *Associates.* $25/£16

ADAMS, JOHN QUINCY. Correspondence Between John Quincy Adams...and Several Citizens of Massachusetts Concerning...a Design to Dissolve the Union.... Boston, 1829. 1st ed. 80pp. Uncut. Contemp plain wrappers. (Sl foxed; frayed, soiled.) Howes A68. *Oinonen**. $40/£25

ADAMS, JOHN QUINCY. The Social Compact, Exemplified in the Constitution of the Commonwealth of Massachusetts...A Lecture, Delivered...at Providence, R.I., November 25, 1842. Providence, (RI): Knowles & Vose, 1842. 1st ed. 32pp. Sewn, uncut. (Soiled.) *M & S.* $125/£78

ADAMS, JOHN. An Analysis of Horsemanship; Teaching the Whole Art of Riding.... London, 1805. 3 vols. Port. Contemp 3/4 calf (worn, vol 1 spine chipped; foxing). *Oinonen**. $300/£188

ADAMS, JOHN. A View of Universal History, from the Creation to the Present Time. London: G. Kearsley, 1795. 1st ed. 3 vols. Tree calf, morocco spine labels. (Lacks 1/2-titles, old names; glue to joints), else VG. *Pacific**. $150/£94

ADAMS, JOSEPH. Salmon and Trout Angling: Its Theory, and Practice.... NY: E.P. Dutton, 1923. 1st Amer ed. Gilt-lettered brn cl. VG. *Pacific**. $40/£25

ADAMS, LEONIE. High Falcon and Other Poems. NY, 1929. 1st ed. VG. *Bond.* $75/£47

ADAMS, MAURICE B. Examples of Old English Houses and Furniture. London, 1888. Folio. 9pp; 35 plts (2 torn w/o loss, sm ink stain last plt, lt spotted). Teg. (New eps; sl soiled, rebacked in mod buckram.) *Edwards.* $120/£75

ADAMS, RAMON F. The Best of the American Cowboy. Norman, 1957. VG in dj. *Dumont.* $40/£25

ADAMS, RAMON F. Burs Under the Saddle. Norman: Univ of OK, 1964. 1st ed. Good in dj (sl worn). *Dumont.* $160/£100

ADAMS, RAMON F. and HOMER BRITZMAN. Charles M. Russell, the Cowboy Artist. Pasadena: Trail's End, (1948). 1st ed. Maroon cl, gilt. Clean (sl shelfworn) in pict dj (price-clipped, sl worn, chipped). *Baltimore**. $80/£50

ADAMS, RAMON F. and HOMER BRITZMAN. Charles M. Russell, the Cowboy Artist. Pasadena: Trail's End, (1948). 1st ed. Red cl, gilt. Fine in dj (sl edgeworn). *Pacific**. $207/£129

ADAMS, RAMON F. Cowboy Lingo. Boston, 1936. 1st ed. (Fep erasure, 1 cvr corner worn), else NF in dj (sl chipped, faded). *Baade.* $125/£78

ADAMS, RAMON F. The Cowman and His Philosophy. Austin: Encino, 1967. 1st ed. One of 750. Signed. Orig sketch by Bill Witliff (designer) on limitation pg, signed. Fine. *Labordo.* $150/£94

ADAMS, RAMON F. The Cowman Says It Salty. Tucson, 1971. VG in dj (chipped). *Dumont.* $40/£25

ADAMS, RAMON F. The Cowman Says It Salty. Tucson: Univ of AZ, 1971. 1st ed. Fine in dj. *Labordo.* $50/£31

ADAMS, RAMON F. A Fitting Death for Billy the Kid. Norman: Univ of OK, 1960. 1st ed. Fien in dj. *Labordo.* $65/£41

ADAMS, RAMON F. The Horse Wrangler and His Remuda. Austin: Encino, 1971. 1st ed. One of 850. Signed. VF. *Labordo.* $85/£53

ADAMS, RAMON F. The Language of the Railroader. Norman: Univ of OK, 1977. 1st ed. VG + in dj. *Labordo.* $50/£31

ADAMS, RAMON F. More Burs Under the Saddle. Norman: Univ of OK, (1979). 1st ed. VF in dj. *Argonaut.* $100/£63

ADAMS, RAMON F. More Burs Under the Saddle. Norman: Univ of OK, 1979. VG in dj. *Dumont.* $30/£19

ADAMS, RAMON F. The Old Time Cowhand. NY, 1961. 1st ed. VG in dj (worn, torn). *King.* $30/£19

ADAMS, RAMON F. The Old Time Cowhand. NY: Macmillan, 1961. 1st ed. Fine in dj. *Labordo.* $60/£38

ADAMS, RAMON F. The Rampaging Herd. Norman: Univ of OK, (1959). 1st ed. (Offset to eps), else VG in dj (rubbed, worn). *Pacific**. $46/£29

ADAMS, RAMON F. The Rampaging Herd. Univ of OK, 1959. 1st Amer ed. Fine. *Polyanthos.* $75/£47

ADAMS, RAMON F. Six-Guns and Saddle Leather. Norman: Univ of OK, (1954). 1st ed. Maroon buckram (edges, backstrip sl sunned, hinges w/later cl tape reinforcements),gilt. Text Good (brief pencil notes, underlining). *Baltimore**. $20/£13

ADAMS, RAMON F. Six-Guns and Saddle Leather. Norman: Univ of OK, (1954). 1st ed. VF in ptd dj. *Argonaut.* $125/£78

ADAMS, RAMON F. Six-Guns and Saddle Leather. Norman: Univ of OK, 1954. VG in dj. *Dumont.* $150/£94

ADAMS, RAMON F. Wayne Gard. Austin: Steck-Vaughn, 1970. 1st ed. Fine in wrappers. *Labordo.* $25/£16

ADAMS, RAMON F. Western Words. A Dictionary of the American West. Norman: Univ of OK, 1968. Rev ed. Fine in dj. *Labordo.* $50/£31

ADAMS, RANDOLPH G. The Passports Printed by Benjamin Franklin at His Passy Press. Ann Arbor: William L. Clements Library, 1925. Ltd to 505. Presentation copy. 3 plts. Marbled paper-cvrd bds, cl spine (rubbed; portion of feps yellowed). *Zubal**. $25/£16

ADAMS, RICHARD. The Day Gone By, Autobiography. NY, 1991. 1st ed. VG in dj. *Typographeum.* $15/£9

ADAMS, RICHARD. The Iron Wolf and Other Stories. Allen Lane, 1980. 1st UK ed. Mint in Mint dj. *Martin.* $14/£9

ADAMS, RICHARD. Nature Day and Night. Kestrel, 1978. 1st UK ed. Fine in Fine dj. *Martin.* $14/£9

ADAMS, RICHARD. The Ship's Cat. Knopf, 1977. 1st US ed. 4to. Alan Aldridge (illus). Unpaginated. VG in VG dj (2-inch tear to rear, lt rubbed). *Price.* $25/£16

ADAMS, RICHARD. The Ship's Cat. NY: Knopf, 1977. 1st Amer ed. Alan Aldridge (illus). 4to. Unpaginated. VG (ink inscrip) in VG dj. *Davidson.* $45/£28

ADAMS, RICHARD. The Tyger Voyage. NY: Knopf, 1976. 1st ed. 4to. 31pp; 15 full-pg color illus by Nicola Bayley. Fine in Fine dj. *Davidson.* $45/£28

ADAMS, RICHARD. Watership Down. (London): Penguin, (1976). 1st trade illus ed. Signed, dated. Fine in dj, slipcase. *Pacific*.* $109/£68

ADAMS, RICHARD. Watership Down. London: Rex Collings, 1972. 1st ed. (Cl sl insect-damaged), else VG in dj (spine head rubbed, tear to lower spine w/tape repair to verso). *Pacific*.* $489/£306

ADAMS, RICHARD. Watership Down. Collings, 1972. 1st ed. Crown 8vo. viii,413pp; color-ptd fldg map at end. Orange cl, gilt. Fine in dj. *Blackwell's.* $640/£400

ADAMS, ROBERT. Los Angeles Spring. NY: Aperture/A New Images Bk, 1986. 1st ed. 50 full-pg b/w photos. Fine in dj. *Cahan.* $60/£38

ADAMS, ROBERT. The Narrative of Robert Adams, a Sailor, Who Was Wrecked on the Western Coast of Africa, in the Year 1810.... London: John Murray, 1816. 1st ed. Lg fldg frontis map, xl,232pp. Old red calf (rebacked w/old spine laid down) over marbled bds (worn). *Karmiole.* $450/£281

ADAMS, ROBERT. Prairie. Denver: Denver Art Museum, 1978. 1st ed. 33 full-pg b/w photos. VG in ptd stiff wrappers (lt soiled, creased). *Cahan.* $45/£28

ADAMS, SAMUEL HOPKINS. Common Cause, a Novel of the War in America. Boston: Houghton Mifflin, 1919. 1st ed. Frontis, plt. Gray bds stamped in yellow. (Few fox mks at fore-edge), o/w NF in VG dj (sl nicked, smudged). *Reese.* $50/£31

ADAMS, THOMAS R. The American Controversy: A Bibliographical Study of the British Pamphlets About the American Disputes, 1764-1783. Providence, 1980. 2 vols. *Swann*.* $69/£43

ADAMS, VERDON R. Tom White: The Life of a Lawman. Joseph M. Ray (ed). El Paso: TX Western/Univ of TX, 1972. Signed. Fine in dj. *Lien.* $45/£28

ADAMS, VIRGINIA and ANSEL. Illustrated Guide to Yosemite Valley. SF: H.S. Crocker, 1940. 1st ed. 1 fldg diag, 45 photos. Fine in stiff blue wrappers (scratch rear cvr, 2 corners sl creased), spiral bound. *Argonaut.* $75/£47

ADAMS, W. I. LINCOLN. Sunlight and Shadow. NY: Baker & Taylor, (1897). 1st ed. 141,(i)pp. Aeg. Mustard cl (sl rubbed, worn), gilt. Cvrs Very Clean. *Baltimore*.* $50/£31

ADAMS, WILLIAM HOWARD. The French Garden 1500-1800. Scolar, 1979. Fine in dec wraps. *Hadley.* $24/£15

ADANSON, MICHEL. A Voyage to Senegal, the Isle of Goree, and the River Gambia. London: Nourse & Johnston, 1759. 1st Eng ed. xiv,337pp, errata; fldg map. Contemp calf (rubbed, spine ends chipped), gilt. *Adelson.* $385/£241

ADANSON, MICHEL. A Voyage to Senegal, the Isle of Goree, and the River Gambia. London, 1759. 8vo. Engr fldg map. Contemp sheep. (Ink lib stamp tp; needs rebinding.) *Swann*.* $575/£359

ADCOCK, A. ST. JOHN. For Remembrance. London, 1918. 1st Eng ed. 19 ports. (Cvrs sl mkd.) *Clearwater.* $48/£30

ADCOCK, FLEUR. The Eye of the Hurricane. Wellington, Auckland: A.H. & A.W. Reed, 1964. 1st Eng ed, 1st bk. VG (inscrip, feps spotted, top edge dusty; spine ends, corners sl bumped, cvrs bowed) in dj (nicked, rubbed, mkd, sl torn, creased, dusty, browned, lower panel scored). *Ulysses.* $104/£65

ADDAMS, CHARLES. Addams and Evil. NY: S&S, 1947. 12th ptg. (Top layer of spine gone), else Good in Good dj (worn). *Pettler.* $20/£13

ADDAMS, CHARLES. Black Maria. Hamish Hamilton, 1960. 1st Eng ed. Color pict eps. VG (spine ends sl bumped) in dj (rubbed, nicked, torn, spotted, price-clipped). *Ulysses.* $58/£36

ADDAMS, CHARLES. Homebodies. NY: S&S, 1954. 6th ptg. (1st cartoon has long tear), else Good in Good dj (lg chip to top edge of rear panel). *Pettler.* $20/£13

ADDAMS, CHARLES. My Crowd. NY, (1976). Signed, dated. Pict cl. Dj (few edge tears, cellotape repair on verso). *Swann*.* $92/£58

ADDICOTT, FREDRICK T. Abscission. Berkeley, 1982. Fine in dj. *Brooks.* $46/£29

ADDIS, STEPHEN. Nanga Paintings. London: Robert G. Sawers, (1975). Fld-out. NF in color illus wrappers. *Turtle Island.* $25/£16

ADDISON, JOSEPH. The Spectator. LEC, 1970. Ltd to 1500 numbered, signed by Lynton Lamb (illus). Fine in slipcase. *Swann*.* $34/£21

ADDISON, JOSEPH. The Works. Birmingham: John Baskerville/J.&R. Tonson, 1761. 1st ed thus. 4 vols. Engr frontisport, 3 plts, 13 woodcut plts. Sound contemp calf (expertly rebacked w/reinforced inner hinges each vol, twin labels). Very Clean set (last 4 ll vol 3 sl marginally repaired, not affecting text). *Young.* $400/£250

ADDISON, JOSEPH. The Works. John Baskerville for J. & R. Tonson, 1761. 4 vols. Engr frontis port, 3 engr plts, 9 plts of medals. Contemp tree-calf, gilt spines. (Bkpl, spotted; labels chipped, lower joints cracked, fr joint vol 4 weak, corners rubbed.) *Sotheby's*.* $459/£287

ADDISON, JOSEPH. The Works. NY, 1854. 6 vols. Engr frontispieces. Contemp 1/2 polished tan calf, gilt extra. *Swann*.* $103/£64

ADDISON, WILLIAM. English Fairs and Markets. London: Batsford, 1953. 1st Eng ed. VG (sl spotted; spine ends sl bumped) in dj (sl dusty, spotted, rubbed). *Ulysses.* $88/£55

Adelaide, or The Rainy Evening. A Moral Tale. Boston: Christian Register Office, 1827. 12mo. 34pp; 3 Fine 1/2-pg cuts in text. VG in pict buff paper wrappers (spine top chipped). *Hobbyhorse.* $100/£63

ADELBORG, QTTILIA. Clean Peter and the Children of Grubbylea. Ada Wallis (trans). NY: Longmans, Green, (n.d.). Obl 4to. Gray textured bds (worn, fr hinge cracked). *Reisler.* $225/£141

ADENEY, NOEL. No Coward Soul. Hogarth, 1956. 1st Eng ed. Later binding in blue cl, lettered in black. VG (1 edge faded) in dj (sl frayed). *Clearwater.* $48/£30

ADHEMAR, JEAN. Toulouse-Lautrec. London, 1965. 370 plts. Orange cl (sl soiled). *Edwards.* $64/£40

ADHEMAR, JEAN. Toulouse-Lautrec: His Complete Lithographs and Drypoints. NY: Abrams, n.d. Folio. Fine in pict dj. *Metropolitan*.* $69/£43

ADLARD, JOHN. Stenbock, Yeats and the Nineties. London: Cecil & Amelia Woolf, 1969. One of 750 numbered. B/w frontis, 2 b/w plts. Illus eps. Buckram. Fine in dj. *Ulysses.* $88/£55

ADLER, BILL. Love Letters to the Mets. S&S, 1965. 1st ed. VG in Good+ dj. *Plapinger.* $40/£25

ADLER, MORTIMER J. The Time of Our Lives: The Ethics of Common Sense. NY: Holt, (1970). 1st ed. Fine in dj (lt rubbed, price-clipped). *Captain's Bookshelf.* $25/£16

ADMIRARI, NIL. Trollopiad; or, Travelling Gentlemen in America. A Satire. (Pseud of F. W. Shelton.) NY: C. Shepard, 1837. 1st ed. 151pp (foxed). Orig cl. Howes S381. *Mott.* $50/£31

ADOLPH, E. F. Physiology of Man in the Desert. NY, 1947. 1st ed. NF in wrappers. *Sagebrush.* $45/£28

ADOLPH, E. F. Physiology of Man in the Desert. NY: Interscience Publishers, 1947. 1st ed. Fine in VG dj. *Book Market.* $60/£38

ADRIAN, ARTHUR A. Georgina Hogarth and the Dickens Circle. OUP, 1957. Good (bkpl) in dj (price-clipped, chipped, lacks sm pieces). *Tiger.* $19/£12

ADRIANI, GOTZ. Toulouse-Lautrec. London, 1987. 1st UK ed. 95 color plts. Dj. *Edwards.* $58/£36

ADRIANI, JOHN. Techniques and Procedures of Anesthesia. Springfield, 1949. 1st ed. Grn cl. VG (extrems sl worn). *Doctor's Library.* $45/£28

Adventures in Borneo. London: Henry Colburn, 1849. 1st ed. (iv),260pp. Orig plum blindstamped cl, leather spine label. Good (faded, tp sl soiled). *Morrell.* $256/£160

Adventures of a Pincushion Designed Chiefly for the Use of Young Ladies. Worcester, MA: Isaiah Thomas, 1788. 1st Worcester ed. 16mo. 100pp. Paper-cvrd bds (rubbed, fr cvr detached, lacks spine; lacks frontis, 1 pg w/marginal tear, 1 illus lt colored by owner). *Reisler.* $675/£422

Adventures of a Teddy Bear. London: Geographia, ca 1925. Obl 4to. H. R. Millar (illus). 14pp. Full color paper cvrs (worn, spine resewn; folds). *Reisler.* $385/£241

Adventures of Mother Hubbard and Her Dog. London: J.L. Marks, n.d. (ca 1840). 12mo. 15pp + 1pg ad on back wrapper, pp 2 and 15 pasted down on wrappers; 8 Fine half-pg hand-colored wood engrs. Internally Fine in ptd dec stiff buff-colored paper wrapper (sl soiled). *Hobbyhorse.* $255/£159

Adventures of Mr. Mouse. London: Collins Clear-Type Press, ca 1910. 4to. 16 full-pg color illus (incl tp) by W. E. Greenwood. Cl-backed color pict bds (edges rubbed, fr hinge cracked, spot to rear cvr). *Reisler.* $225/£141

Adventures of Roderick Random. (By Tobias Smollett.) A. Millar, 1763. 6th ed. 2 vols. 2 frontispieces, xvi,280; xii,316pp. Contemp sprinkled dk brn calf (rebacked to match), raised bands, polished morocco labels. Good (eps stained by turn-ins; corners rubbed, hinges split). *Blackwell's.* $120/£75

AESCHYLUS and PERCY BYSSHE SHELLEY. Prometheus Bound and Prometheus Unbound. NY: LEC, 1965. One of 1500. Fine in slipcase. *Pacific*.* $58/£36

AESCHYLUS. The Oresteia. LEC, 1961. Ltd to 1500 numbered, signed by Michael Ayrton (illus). Fine in slipcase. *Swann*.* $57/£36

AESOP. Aesop's Fables. NY: Frederick A. Stokes, (1908). 1st ed. Black cl, pict cvr label. VG. *Pacific*.* $69/£43

AESOP. Aesop's Fables. Phila: David McKay, (1929). 1st ed. 4to. 8 full-pg color plts by Nora Fry. Maroon cl, gilt, color paste label. Good in full color dj (worn, edges chipped). *Reisler.* $150/£94

AESOP. Aesop's Fables. London: Cassell, Petter & Galpin, (c. 1870s). 10.25x7.5. Ernest Griset (illus). Aeg. Pict blue cl, gilt. (Spine head lacks piece, fr joint, hinge cracking, spine sl leaning), else VG. *Pacific*.* $35/£22

AESOP. Aesop's Fables. London: J.M. Dent, 1895. 1st ed. Charles Robinson (illus). Tall thin 12mo. Teg. Yellow cl (dusty, ties missing). *Reisler.* $100/£63

AESOP. Aesop's Fables. V.S. Vernon Jones (trans). London: Heinemann, 1912. 1st ed. One of 1450 signed by Arthur Rackham (illus). 4to. 13 mtd color plts. Full grn morocco w/gilt panel device fr, rear cvrs; gilt animal heads at corners, gilt paneled spine w/gilt-stamped animal motifs, raised bands, inner wide gilt borders, aeg, by Bayntun-Riviere. Fine in slipcase. *Appelfeld.* $1,800/£1,125

AESOP. Aesop's Fables. LEC, 1933. Ltd to 1500 numbered, signed by Bruce Rogers (illus). 2 vols. Fine in slipcase. *Swann*.* $149/£93

AESOP. Aesop's Fables. Ithaca, NY: Elfriede Abbe, 1950. One of 500 numbered, signed by Abbe (illus). Folio. (72)pp. Black cl spine, 2 leather labels, marbled bds. Good. *Karmiole.* $200/£125

AESOP. The Fable of the Hare and the Tortoise from Aesop. Yellow Springs, OH: Ernest Morgan, (1931). 12mo. Eulalie (illus). 16pp. Good in grn pict wrappers (spine faded). *Reisler.* $85/£53

AESOP. Fables of Aesop and Others. London: J. Johnson...J. Harris, 1805. 17th ed. 12mo. Full-pg woodcut frontis, xxiv,(12),329,(7)pp. Old calf (worn, rebacked). Good (lacks rep, text soiled, 1st/last sigs sl sprung). *Karmiole.* $175/£109

AESOP. Fables of Aesop with a Life of the Author. NY: Hurd & Houghton, 1867. 8vo. xiii,311pp. Red tooled cl, gilt. VG (lt shaken; cvr rubbed, spine ends chipped). *Hobbyhorse.* $125/£78

AESOP. The Fables of Aesop. London: Hodder & Stoughton, (1909). 1st ed illus by Edward J. Detmold. 4to. xvi,152pp; 23 mtd color plts. Teg. 1/2 red polished morocco (recently rebound), spine w/raised bands, gilt. Orig pict cl cvr, spine bound in at rear. Fine. *Sotheran.* $749/£468

AESOP. The Fables of Aesop. Newcastle: T. Bewick & Son, 1818. 1st ed. xxiv,376pp; 188 wood-engr head-pieces, 136 vignettes by Thomas Bewick. Marbled eps, edges. Contemp calf (expertly rebacked). Very Nice. *Young.* $264/£165

AESOP. The Fables of Aesop. London: Hodder & Stoughton, 1909. One of 750. 4to. Unpaginated. 25 Spectacular tipped-in plts signed by E. Detmold (illus). Red cl, gilt. (Corners, spine ends lt worn, sm pinhole spine.) *Davidson.* $1,250/£781

AESOP. The Fables of Aesop. London: Hodder & Stoughton, 1909. Ltd to 750 signed. Sm folio. E.J. Detmold (illus). 25 mtd color plts. Teg. White cl (sl dusty, sm spot fr cvr), gilt. Internally Very Clean. *Reisler.* $1,250/£781

AESOP. The Fables of Aesop. Roger L'Estrange (trans). Golden Cockerel, 1926. One of 350 numbered. Royal 8vo. Edges untrimmed. 1/4 white buckram, gilt. Fine. *Sotheran.* $557/£348

AESOP. The Fables...Paraphras'd in Verse and Adorn'd with Sculpture. Ptd by Thomas Warren for Andrew Cook, 1651. 1st Ogilby ed. 4to. Frontis, add'l tp w/port, (xvi),64,55,(1),(blank),55,(1)pp; 80 plts. Gilt edges. Late 19th-cent crushed, polished dk grn morocco, by Riviere, backstrip w/gilt-ruled raised bands, gilt-paneled w/floral ornaments, central 'sunburst,' triple gilt fillet border on sides. Excellent (unobservable repairs to tail outer blank corners of frontis, 1st 5 leaves). *Blackwell's.* $7,600/£4,750

AESOP. A Hundred Fables of Aesop. London: John Lane, 1899. 1st ed. Percy J. Billinghurst (illus). 4to. Tan cl (lt edgeworn). *Reisler.* $250/£156

AESOP. Select Fables in Three Parts...to Which Are Prefixed, The Life of Aesop; and An Essay upon Fable. Newcastle: T. Saint, 1784. 1st ed thus. Thomas & John Bewick (illus). xii,308,(2)pp. Aeg. Morocco, gilt, by Riviere. (Old cat entry mtd to blank facing tp), else NF. *Pacific*.* $1,058/£661

AESOP. Some of Aesop's Fables with Modern Instances. NY: Macmillan, 1883. 1st Amer ed. R. Caldecott (illus). 4to. 79pp. Dec salmon bds. (Lt foxing), o/w VG. *Davidson.* $150/£94

AFLALO, F. G. (ed). A Book of Fishing Stories. London: J.M. Dent & Sons, 1913. 1st ed. Color frontis. (Foxed; sl spots fr cvr), else VG. *Pacific*.* $104/£65

AGASSIZ, ALEXANDER. Three Cruises of the United States Coast and Geodetic Survey Steamer 'Blake'...1877 to 1880. Boston: Houghton Mifflin, 1888. 1st ed. 2 vols. xxii,314; (3),220pp; map in rear cvr pocket vol 1. Good set (lib card pockets removed from rear pastedowns, fr hinge vol 1 cracked, spine sl spotted, ends rubbed). *Glaser.* $125/£78

AGASSIZ, LOUIS and MRS. LOUIS. A Journey in Brazil. London: Trubner, 1868. 1st UK ed. xix,540pp (corner 1st 100pp sl creased, marginal browning, fep notes, sl shaken). Gilt-illus cl (spine sl chipped, joints split, spine top fixed). *Edwards.* $144/£90

AGASSIZ, LOUIS and A. A. GOULD. Principles of Zoology.... Boston: Gould & Lincoln, 1864. Rev ed. 259+ pp. VG (nick rear bd). *Bookcell.* $40/£25

AGASSIZ, LOUIS. The Structure of Animal Life. NY, 1866. viii,128pp (browned). *Sutton.* $165/£103

AGEE, GEORGE W. Rube Burrow. Chicago: Henneberry, 1890. 1st ed. VG (spine ends tender, rear hinge weak). Howes A89. *Labordo.* $225/£141

AGEE, JAMES. A Death in the Family. NY: McDowell, Obolensky, (1957). 1st ed, 1st ptg, w/tp in blue, top edge stained blue, 'walking' on p80. NF in Good+ dj (lt edgeworn worn). *Reese.* $85/£53

AGEE, JAMES. A Death in the Family. NY, 1956. 1st ed. (Bkpl). Dj (edgeworn). *Swann*.* $69/£43

AGEE, JAMES. The Last Letter of James Agee to Father Flye. Boston: Godine, 1969. 1st ed. One of 500 numbered. Ptd label. (Fr corner sl bumped), else NF in plain wrappers. *Reese.* $50/£31

AGEE, JAMES. Let Us Now Praise Famous Men. Boston: HM, (1960). 2nd ed. Pamphlet laid in. VG (sig) in VG dj. *Agvent.* $45/£28

Aggression from the North: The Record of North Vietnam's Campaign to Conquer South Vietnam. Washington: Dept of State, 1965. 1st ed. Fine in wraps. *Associates.* $65/£41

AGNER, DWIGHT. The Books of WAD. A Bibliography.... SF: Alan Wofsy, 1977. 2nd ed. One of 700. 28 plts. Fine. *Harrington.* $40/£25

AGNEW, GEORGETTE. Let's Pretend. London: J. Saville, 1st ltd ed, 1927. One of 160 signed by Agnew and E. H. Shepard (illus). 11 full-pg illus. 1/4 white vellum, gilt. VG in slipcase. *Davidson.* $800/£500

AGNEW, JANET MARGARET. A Southern Bibliography; Historical Fiction 1929-1938. University, LA: LSU Press, 1940. (Lt soiled), else VG in wraps. *Dumont.* $30/£19

AGUILAR, GRACE. The Vale of Cedars. Phila: Jewish Pub Soc of America, 1902. 1st Amer ed. Pict cl, gilt. (Eps, rear joint sl damp-stained), else VG. *Pacific*.* $46/£29

AGUILERA-MALTA, DEMETRIO. Seven Serpents and Seven Moons. Austin: Univ of TX, 1979. 1st US ed. Fine in Fine dj. *Lame Duck.* $45/£28

AHARONI, YOHANAN (ed). Beer-Sheba I. Excavations at Tel Beer-Sheba, 1969-1971 Seasons. Tel Aviv: Tel Aviv Univ/Inst of Arch, 1973. 1st ed. VG in dj (sl torn). *Worldwide.* $65/£41

AHLEFELDT BILLE, G. Tandalla, a Danish Game Warden's Study of Native and Wildlife in Kenya and Tanganyika. London, 1951. 1st Eng ed. Map. *Hallam.* $80/£50

AIKEN, A. S. and J. M. ADAIR. A Biographical Sketch of the Rev. John Cuthbertson, the First Reformed Presbyterian Minister in America, from 1751 to 1791. Pittsburgh: Stevenson, Foster, 1878. Pamphlet. 36pp. Good in ptd wrappers (lacks portion at rear). *Brown.* $20/£13

AIKEN, CONRAD. Collected Poems. NY: Oxford, 1953. 1st ed. Port. NF in VG dj (few mended edge tears on verso). *Reese.* $35/£22

AIKEN, CONRAD. Costumes by Eros. NY: Scribner, 1927. 1st ed. Blue cl, gilt. VG in dj (dampstain rear panel). *Macdonnell.* $125/£78

AIKEN, CONRAD. A Heart for the Gods of Mexico. London: Martin Secker, 1939. 1st ed. One of 1000. Tan cl. (Edges sl dust dknd), o/w Fine in NF pict dj. *Reese.* $350/£219

AIKEN, CONRAD. Nocturne of Remembered Spring and Other Poems. Boston: Four Seas, 1917. 1st ed. Black cl, gilt. Good (ink inscrip; cl sl soiled). *Reese.* $40/£25

AIKEN, CONRAD. Punch: The Immortal Liar. NY: Knopf, 1921. 1st ed. Gray paper-cvrd bds, fr cvr label. Fine (spine dknd) in orange dj (edges sl worn). *Dramatis.* $65/£41

AIKEN, CONRAD. Skylight One. Fifteen Poems. London, 1951. 1st ed. Fine in NF dj. *Polyanthos.* $25/£16

AIKEN, JOAN. Black Hearts in Battersea. Doubleday, 1964. 1st US ed. Robin Jacques (illus). 239pp. Fine in VG dj (edges wrinkled). *Price.* $40/£25

AIKEN, JOAN. Mortimer Says Nothing. NY, 1985. 1st Amer ed. Fine in Fine dj. *Polyanthos.* $25/£16

AIKIN, JOHN. The Woodland Companion. Ptd for J. Johnson, 1802. (ii),92pp; 28 engr dbl-pg plts on guards. Old bds (corners worn, nicely rebacked in gilt calf). *Hollett.* $136/£85

AIKMAN, DUNCAN. Calamity Jane and the Lady Wildcats. NY: Henry Holt, 1927. 1st ed. VG+ in dj (worn). *Labordo.* $65/£41

AIMARD, GUSTAVE. The Pirates of the Prairies. Ward & Lock, 1861. viii,370pp. Contemp 1/2 calf, gilt, marbled bds (edges sl browned, fr joint cracked; faded, sl rubbed). *Hollett.* $64/£40

AINSLIE, KATHLEEN. Me and Catharine Susan Earns an Honest Penny. Castell Bros, c.1910. 12mo. (24)pp; 1 dbl-pg illus. VG in orig pict card wrappers (spine rubbed), sewn w/tasselled cord. *Hollett.* $72/£45

AINSLIE, KATHLEEN. Me and Catharine Susan. Castell Bros, c.1905. 12mo. (40)pp; 20 color illus. VG (edges sl browned, few spots) in orig pict card wrappers, sewn w/tasselled cord. *Hollett.* $104/£65

AINSWORTH, ED. The Cowboy in Art. NY: World, (1968). 1st ed. One of 1000. Aeg. Full gilt-dec leather. Fine in slipcase. *Pacific*.* $127/£79

AINSWORTH, KATHERINE. The McCallum Saga. Palm Springs: Desert Museum, 1973. 1st ed. Fine in Fine dj. *Book Market.* $60/£38

AINSWORTH, KATHERINE. The McCallum Saga. (Palm Springs, CA), 1973. 1st ed. Color frontis, facs. NF in VG dj. *Sagebrush.* $75/£47

AINSWORTH, W. F. (ed). All Around the World. NY: Selmar Hess, ca 1870s. 4 vols. 10 VG photogravure plts. Aeg. Dk brn cl. (Lt aged; rubbed, worn, spine gilt flaked, lost.) *Baltimore*.* $75/£47

AINSWORTH, WILLIAM HARRISON. Cardinal Pole: Or, The Days of Philip and Mary. Chapman & Hall, 1863. 1st ed. 3 vols. x,301; viii,305; viii,302pp (lt spotted). Mod 1/2 calf, gilt, raised bands. VG set. *Hollett.* $240/£150

AINSWORTH, WILLIAM HARRISON. John Law: The Projector. Chapman & Hall, 1864. 1st ed. 3 vols. vi,300; vi,303; vi,314pp. No 1/2-titles called for. Sprinkled edges. 20th-cent 1/2 blue morocco (lower edges sl worn), gilt. *Hollett.* $192/£120

AINSWORTH, WILLIAM HARRISON. The Lord Mayor of London: Or, City Life in the Last Century. Chapman & Hall, 1862. 1st ed. 3 vols. ix,304; vi,302; vi,316pp. No 1/2-titles called for. Early 20th-cent 1/2 morocco, gilt. VG. *Hollett.* $224/£140

AINSWORTH, WILLIAM HARRISON. Merry England; or, Nobles and Serfs. London: Tinsley Bros, 1874. 1st ed, 1st state of binding w/'Merry' spelled 'Merrie' on spines. 3 vols. Dk grn cl. Good (lt aged, lt foxed; sl worn, rubbed, spines sl turned). *Baltimore*.* $45/£28

AINSWORTH, WILLIAM HARRISON. Old Saint Paul's: A Tale of the Plague and the Fire. London: Parry, Blenkarn & Co, 1847. 1st 1-vol ed. Signed letter pasted to fep. Tall 8 vo. John Franklin & H. K. Browne (illus). (iv),(1-2),3,(4),(5),6-434pp. Crimson silk doublures, silk eps; teg. Full crimson French levant morocco. VG+. *Vandoros.* $525/£328

AINSWORTH, WILLIAM HARRISON. The Spanish Match or Charles Stuart at Madrid. Chapman & Hall, 1865. 1st ed. 3 vols. viii,293; vi,294; vi,324pp. No 1/2-titles called for. Old 1/2 calf, gilt, raised bands, spine labels. VG. *Hollett.* $240/£150

AINSWORTH, WILLIAM HARRISON. The Tower of London. Richard Bentley, 1840. George Cruikshank (illus). Marbled edges. Contemp 1/2 leather, marbled bds, raised bands (sl rubbed). Good (plts spotted). *Tiger.* $72/£45

AINSWORTH, WILLIAM HARRISON. Windsor Castle. London, 1844. New ed. Frontisports, extra engr tp, 21 plts by George Cruikshank and Tony Johannot. 11 parts, in orig wraps. (Few wraps chipped, few spines partly gone.) Cl slipcase. *Kane*.* $60/£38

Air War—Vietnam. Indianapolis: Bobbs-Merrill, 1978. 1st ed. Fine in dj (stamp rear flap). *Associates.* $35/£22

AIRLIE, COUNTESS (ed). With the Guards We Shall Go, a Guardsman's Letters in the Crimea. London, 1933. 1st ed. VG. *Gretton.* $19/£12

Airman's Wife. (By Aimee Bond.) (London): Herbert Jenkins, 1918. 1st ed. VG (paper grayed, 1918 ink inscrip) in Good pict dj (few tears, chip, ink blotch on rear). *Reese.* $50/£31

AITKEN, JONATHAN. The Young Meteors. Secker & Warburg, 1967. 1st ed. (Top edges sl dusty), o/w NF in dj (sl nicked). *Sclanders.* $32/£20

AKEHURST, RICHARD. Sporting Guns. London: Octopus Books, 1972. Fine (inscrip) in VG + dj. *Backman.* $25/£16

AKELEY, D. J. Jungle Portraits. NY, 1930. 1st ed. (Few pp, cvrs sl mkd), else VG. *Hallam.* $32/£20

AKENSIDE, MARK. The Poems of.... London: W. Bowyer & J. Nichols, 1772. 1st collected ed. xii,402pp. Period tree calf, gilt, morocco spine label. (Spine ends sl worn), else NF. *Pacific*.* $161/£101

AKERMAN, JOHN YONGE. Examples of Coffee House, Tavern, and Tradesmen's Tokens, Current in London in the Seventeenth Century. (N.p.), 1846-47. 2 parts. 18; 18pp, 6 plts. Unopened, uncut. Orig ptd wrappers (detached). *Forest.* $40/£25

AKERMAN, JOHN YONGE. Remains of Pagan Saxondom. London: John Russell Smith, 1855. 1st ed. xviii,84pp; 40 hand-colored plts. Contemp brn morocco over rust bds (extrems rubbed). *Karmiole.* $275/£172

AKERS, C. E. Argentine, Patagonian, and Chilian Sketches. London, n.d. (1893). 1st ed. vi,7-190pp. (Sig, lib stamp; water damage to bds.) *Maggs.* $216/£135

AKERS, FLOYD. (Pseud of L. Frank Baum.) The Boy Fortune Hunters in Alaska. Chicago: Reilly & Britton, (1908, but c. 1911). 1st ed, 3rd state. Quill & lamp device on tp, verso of 1/2-title lists bks through The Boy Fortune Hunters in the Yucatan, final paragraph p271 regarding the series, the cvr has no white stamping. Frontis by Howard Heath, 271 + (2)ad pp. Tan cl. (Sm spot to lower extrems of feps, following 2 pp; black spotty offset to fr cvr, spine, fr cvr lettering rubbed), else VG-. *Pacific*.* $115/£72

AKERS, FLOYD. (Pseud of L. Frank Baum.) The Boy Fortune Hunters in China. Chicago: Reilly & Britton, (1909). 1st, only ed. (325),(2)pp. Pict cl. Good (fr hinge cracked, lacks frontis, names; spine ends frayed, cvr design rubbed, shelfworn). *Pacific*.* $127/£79

AKERS, FLOYD. (Pseud of L. Frank Baum.) The Boy Fortune Hunters in Egypt. Chicago: Reilly & Britton, (1908, but c. 1911). 1st ed, 3rd state. Final paragraph p291 describes the series through The Boy Fortune Hunters in Yucatan, the cvr has no white stamping. Frontis by E. A. Nelson, 291 + (2)ad pp. Tan cl. (Spine ends chipped, spine tears, corners rubbed), else VG. *Pacific*.* $127/£79

AKERS, FLOYD. (Pseud of L. Frank Baum.) The Boy Fortune Hunters in Panama. Chicago: Reilly & Britton, (1908, but c. 1911). 1st ed, 2nd state w/open bk device on tp, 1/2-title verso lists bks through The Boy Fortune Hunters in Egypt, text concludes on p310 w/'of a mighty Prince.' Frontis by Howard Heath, 310 + (10)ad pp. Tan cl. Good (mold damage to extrems). *Pacific*.* $127/£79

AKERS, FLOYD. (Pseud of L. Frank Baum.) The Boy Fortune Hunters in Yucatan. Chicago: Reilly & Britton, (1910). 1st, only ed. Pub's 'File Copy,' so stamped on fore-edges, w/a pencil n on ep 'Register Copyright' & stamps to c. pg. Frontis by George A. Rieman, (8),343 + (1)ad pp. Pict cl. (Sl soiled), else NF. *Pacific*.* $690/£431

AL-BAYATI, BASIL. Basil Al-Bayati, Architect. NY: St. Martin's, 1988. 1st ed. Folio. NF in dj. *Worldwide.* $50/£31

Aladdin and the Wonderful Lamp. NY: McLoughlin Bros, n.d. (ca 1865). Sm 8vo. 8 leaves, 1pg list rear wrapper; 8 half-pg chromolithos. Pict stiff paper wrappers. VG (sm spots edges of 2 leaves; lower part of inner fold of wrappers reinforced). *Hobbyhorse.* $95/£59

ALAIN-FOURNIER. The Wanderer—Le Grand Meaulnes. Francoise Delisle (trans). Paul Elek, 1947. 1st ed. 8 b/w plts. VG (bkpl, pg edges browned, prelims, edges spotted; spine ends, corners sl bumped, cvrs sl bowed) in dj (nicked, chipped, torn, worn, sl creased, internally repaired, edges sl dknd). *Ulysses.* $154/£96

ALAIN-FOURNIER. The Wanderer. LEC, 1958. Ltd to 1500 numbered, signed by Andre Dignimont (illus). Fine in slipcase. *Swann*.* $34/£21

ALARCON. The Infant with the Globe. Robert Graves (trans). Trianon, 1955. 1st UK ed. Fine (bkpl) in VG dj (edges sl worn, sm scuff to spine). *Williams.* $72/£45

Alaska-Yukon Gold Book. (Seattle: Sourdough Stampede Assoc, 1930.) 1st ed. Pub's announcement laid in. Fine in wraps. *Perier.* $85/£53

ALBAUGH, WILLIAM A., III. More Confederate Faces. (Washington: ABS Printers, 1972.) 1st ed. Tan coated cl (sl shelf-worn). Internally NF in VG dj. *Baltimore*.* $80/£50

ALBEE, EDWARD. A Delicate Balance. NY, 1966. 1st Amer ed. Signed. Fine in Fine dj. *Polyanthos.* $45/£28

ALBEE, EDWARD. Malcolm. NY: Atheneum, 1966. 1st ed. VF in VF dj. *Between The Covers.* $125/£78

ALBEE, FRED H. Bone-Graft Surgery in Disease, Injury and Deformity. NY: D. Appleton-Century, 1940. Frontis. Fine (stamp). *Weber.* $175/£109

ALBEE, FRED H. Bone-Graft Surgery. Phila, 1915. 1st ed. (Inner hinges cracked; extrems worn), o/w Good. *Doctor's Library.* $250/£156

ALBEE, FRED H. Orthopedic and Reconstruction Surgery, Industrial and Civilian. Phila/London: W.B. Saunders, 1919. 1st ed. 6 plts (5 color). Green cl (sm to lt abrasive mk fr cvr), else Fine. *Weber.* $200/£125

ALBEMARLE, EARL OF and G. LACY HILLIER. Cycling. Longmans, Green, 1901. Rev ed. Pict brn cl (extrems sl rubbed), gilt. *Hollett.* $120/£75

ALBERS, JOSEF. Interaction of Color. NY, 1963. Folio. 80 silk-screened folders. Text vol in cl. Folders, booklet of commentary loose in cl fldg case (sl rubbed). *Swann*.* $1,265/£791

ALBERS, JOSEF. Poems and Drawings. New Haaven: Readymade, 1958. One of 500. Wrappers; dj. *Swann*.* $115/£72

ALBERT, ALPHAEUS H. Buttons of the Confederacy. Hightstown, 1963. 1st ed. (Cvr wear), o/w VG +. *Pratt.* $80/£50

ALBERTI, RAFAEL. The Lost Grove. Autobiography of a Spanish Poet in Exile. Univ of CA, 1976. 1st Amer ed. Fine in Fine dj. *Polyanthos.* $20/£13

ALBERTSON, CHRIS and GUNTHER SCHULLER. Bessie Smith: Empress of the Blues. NY: Schirmer Books, 1975. 1st ed. Wraps. *Beasley*. $40/£25

ALBERTSON, CHRIS. Bessie. NY: Stein & Day, (1972). 1st ed. Discography, port. VG in dj (lt worn). *Petrilla*. $35/£22

ALBIN, JOHN. A Companion to the Isle of Wight. London: Longman, Hurst & Reed, 1818. 8th ed. Tp, ii, 1f., 113pp, 3 (n.n.); 1 engr plt. Contemp tree calf (rubbed, hinges cracked, spine ends chipped). *Marlborough*. $56/£35

ALBION, ROBERT. The Rise of New York Port (1815-1860). NY: Scribner, (1970). New ed, 1st ptg. Grn cl. VG in dj (crease down backstrip). *House*. $20/£13

ALBRIGHT, HORACE M. Oh, Ranger! Stanford Univ, 1929. 2nd ed. Pict eps. (Name), o/w VG. *Five Quail*. $17/£11

ALBRIGHT, WILLIAM FOXWELL. The Excavation of Tell Beit Mirsim, Volume III (only). New Haven: ASOR, 1938. 56 plts. *Archaeologia*. $150/£94

ALCEDO, DON ANTONIO. The Geographical and Historical Dictionary of America and the West Indies.... George Alexander Thompson (trans). London: John Carpenter et al, 1812-15. 5 vols. 4to. 1/2-titles, list of subs and ad leaf at fr vol 1. (Lt spotting, inscrip on card mtd on verso of ad leaf.) Contemp 1/2 calf (worn, 1 bd lacking). *Christie's**. $990/£619

ALCOCK, C. W. (ed). Famous Cricketeers and Cricket Grounds. London, 1895-1897. (iv),287pp. Aeg. (Leaf torn, fr hinge cracked; extrems rubbed w/loss, spine chipped w/loss, tears repaired.) *Edwards*. $120/£75

ALCOCK, RUTHERFORD. The Capital of the Tycoon: A Narrative of a Three Years' Residence in Japan. NY: Harper, 1863. 1st Amer ed. 2 vols. 408; 436pp + 8pp ads; 2 fldg maps. Black patterned cl (spine extrems sl chipped). *Karmiole*. $175/£109

Alcoholics Anonymous. NY, 1942. 3rd ptg. Blue cl (edges lt frayed, spine rubbed, lettering partly effaced; eps dknd). *Swann**. $316/£198

Alcoholics Anonymous. The Story of How More Than Two Thousand Men and Women Have Recovered from Alcoholism. NY: Works Publishing, 1941. 1st ed, 2nd ptg. Tall thick 8vo. Lt blue cl, gilt spine. (Sl spotted, dusty along bulked edges; cvrs heavily spotted.) Text Good in 3rd ptg dj (sl worn, chipped, sm tears, creases; spine, rear cvr lt soiled). *Baltimore**. $900/£563

Alcoholics Anonymous. The Story of How More Than One Hundred Men Have Recovered from Alcoholism. NY: Works Publishing, 1939. 1st ed, 1st ptg, the only ed in red cl. Tall thick 8vo. (Lt pencil underlining, notes, few in ink, ink name, address; handled, rubbed, extrems sl soiled, lt frayed, sm tears spine head.) *Baltimore**. $1,900/£1,188

ALCOTT, A. B. The Letters of A. Bronson Alcott. Richard L. Herrnstadt (ed). Ames, IA: IA State Univ, (1969). 1st ed. Beige cl. VG in dj. *Lucas*. $50/£31

ALCOTT, A. B. Observations on the Principles and Methods of Infant Instruction. Boston, 1830. 1st ed. 8vo. 27pp (lacks blank portions of last leaf). New sewn pale blue wrappers. VG. BAL 101. *M & S*. $1,250/£781

ALCOTT, LOUISA M. Eight Cousins. NY: Saalfield, 1930. Lg 8vo. Frances Brundage (illus). Frontis by G. Lawson. VG in VG color dj by Lawson. *American Booksellers*. $25/£16

ALCOTT, LOUISA M. Flower Fables. Boston: George W. Briggs, 1855. 1st ed, 1st bk. Frontis, 182pp; 5 plts. (Lib handstamps; worn, shaken), else Good reading copy. BAL 142. *Brown*. $300/£188

ALCOTT, LOUISA M. Her Life, Letters and Journals. Ednah D. Cheney (ed). Boston: Roberts, 1889. 1st ed, 1st ptg, 1st state w/p44 ending '...with Goethe.' In Blanck's binding 1, in the style of Little Women. 8vo. 404 + ads pp. Brn cl. Good (hinge tender, sl rubbed). BAL 221. *Second Life*. $100/£63

ALCOTT, LOUISA M. Little Men: Life at Plumfield with Jo's Boys. Boston: Little, Brown, 1898. Brn cl, gilt. VG (corners bumped, edges sl worn, pages tight). *Price*. $35/£22

ALCOTT, LOUISA M. Little Women. LEC, 1967. Ltd to 1500 numbered, signed by Henry C. Pitz (illus). Fine in slipcase. *Swann**. $115/£72

ALCOTT, LOUISA M. An Old-Fashioned Girl. Phila, (1928). 4 full-pg color, 10 b/w plts by Clara M. Burd. (Bkpl), else very fresh in dj (chipped, edges torn). *King*. $35/£22

ALCOTT, LOUISA M. An Old-Fashioned Girl. Boston: Little Brown, 1927. Dk grn cl, stamped. Good. *Price*. $20/£13

ALDAM, W. H. A Quaint Treatise on 'Flees, and the Art a Artyfichall Flee Making.' London: John B. Day, 1876. 1st ed. 4to. 2 Fine chromolitho plts, 22 sunken mounts. Aeg. Grn cl, gilt. (Foxed, the 2 flies in the last 2 mounts loose; lt worn.) *Oinonen**. $1,000/£625

ALDERSON, E. A. H. Pink and Scarlet, or Hunting as a School for Soldiering. Hodder & Stoughton, 1913. Fore/lower edges uncut. 2-tone cl, gilt. (Upper hinge cracked, sl spotting; lower bd sl dented, spine faded, bumped, ends sl splitting.) *Edwards*. $72/£45

ALDIN, CECIL. An Artist's Models. London: H.F. & G. Witherby, (1930). 1st ed. Imperial 8vo. 20 Fine plts by Aldin. Grained cl. Fine in gray dj w/color onlaid plt by Aldin. *Sotheran*. $317/£198

ALDIN, CECIL. The Black Puppy Book. London: Henry Frowde/Hodder & Stoughton, n.d. 1st ed. 9x8. Cl-backed pict bds. (Lacks fep), else VG. *Pacific**. $98/£61

ALDIN, CECIL. Cathedrals and Abbey Churches of England. Eyre & Spottiswoode, 1929. 16 color plts. (Half-title spotted; cl sl used.) *Hollett*. $96/£60

ALDIN, CECIL. Just Among Friends. Eyre & Spottiswoode, 1935. 2nd ed. (Spine sl faded.) *Hollett*. $224/£140

ALDIN, CECIL. Old Inns. London, 1921. 1st ed. 16 full-pg color plts. Teg. (Bkpl; rear inside cvr creased, extrems frayed.) *King*. $75/£47

ALDIN, CECIL. Old Manor Houses. London: Heinemann, (1923). 1st ed. (Spine browned), else VG. *Pacific**. $52/£33

ALDIN, CECIL. Rough and Tumble. London: Henry Frowde/Hodder & Stoughton, (1909). 1st ed. Sq 4to. 24 full-pg color plts. Cl-backed bds, color paste label, gilt. (Prelims foxed, rep sl rippled; label sl chipped, sm repaired spine tear.) *Reisler*. $600/£375

ALDIN, CECIL. Time I Was Dead, Pages from My Autobiography. London: Eyre & Spottiswoode, 1934. 1st ed. 9 color plts. Very Bright. *Sotheran*. $157/£98

ALDINGTON, RICHARD (ed). Fifty Romance Lyric Poems. Alan Wingate, 1948. VG in dj (sl rubbed, soiled). *Cox*. $13/£8

ALDINGTON, RICHARD (trans). The Little Demon. London: Secker, 1916. 1st Eng ed. Good (fore-edge foxed; cvrs sl dust-mkd). *Clearwater*. $120/£75

ALDINGTON, RICHARD. At All Costs. London: Heinemann, (1930). 1st ed. One of 275 numbered, specially ptd and bound, signed. Cl, marbled bds. (Edges rubbed), o/w VG. *Reese*. $85/£53

ALDINGTON, RICHARD. At All Costs. London: Heinemann, 1930. One of 275 numbered, signed. Pub's presentation copy w/slip (sig) loosely laid in. Teg. 1/4 gray-grn buckram, gray marbled bds. (Bds rubbed), o/w Fine. *Temple*. $72/£45

ALDINGTON, RICHARD. Balls. And Another Book for Suppression. London: E. Lahr, 1931. 1st ed. Good in ptd wrappers (sl dusty). *Maggs*. $72/£45

ALDINGTON, RICHARD. The Colonel's Daughter. London: C&W, 1931. 1st ltd ed, One of 210 signed. Teg. Full buckram beveled bds (spine faded), o/w VG. *Virgo*. $88/£55

ALDINGTON, RICHARD. Death of a Hero. C&W, 1929. 1st Eng ed. (Extreme bottom edge rear cvr faded), o/w VG in dj (torn, soiled, defective at spine head, top of rear panel, foot of fr flap). *Ulysses.* $88/£55

ALDINGTON, RICHARD. Death of a Hero. Paris: Babou & Kahane, 1930. 1st ed. One of 300 numbered. 2 vols. Ptd stiff wrappers. Glassine djs, slipcase. *Swann*.* $172/£108

ALDINGTON, RICHARD. Death of a Hero. Paris, 1930. 1st expurgated ed. One of 300 numbered. 2 vols. VG (newly recased in fabric linen, orig wrappers retained). *Clearwater.* $320/£200

ALDINGTON, RICHARD. A Dream in the Luxembourg. London: C&W, 1930. 1st Eng ed. (Name), else VG in dj (sl worn, repaired). *Cady.* $25/£16

ALDINGTON, RICHARD. Images of Desire. Elkin Matthews, 1919. 1st Eng ed. Unopened. Wrappers. *Clearwater.* $152/£95

ALDINGTON, RICHARD. Images of War. London: Allen & Unwin, 1919. 1st ed thus. Untrimmed, partly unopened. Gray-tan bds, gilt. Fine in dj (extrems chipped, 1 at mid-spine). *Reese.* $150/£94

ALDINGTON, RICHARD. Last Straws. Paris: Hours Press, 1930. One of 500 (of 700) numbered. Uncut. Patterned paper bds. Fine in tissue wrapper. *Maggs.* $96/£60

ALDINGTON, RICHARD. Lawrence of Arabia: A Biographical Enquiry. London: Collins, 1955. 1st British ed. Port. Gilt black cl. (Few sm spots), o/w Nice in dj (rubbed, chip). *Reese.* $35/£22

ALDINGTON, RICHARD. Roads to Glory. London: C&W, 1930. 1st ed, trade issue. Brn cl, gilt. Fine in NF pict dj (spine crown lt frayed). *Reese.* $75/£47

ALDINGTON, RICHARD. Soft Answers. London: C&W, 1932. 1st Eng ed. VG in dj (sl worn). *Cady.* $30/£19

ALDINGTON, RICHARD. Two Stories. Paulton/London: Purnell & Sons, 1930. 1st ed. One of 530 numbered, signed. Patterned bds, blue cl spine. VG in patterned dj (spine head chipped, sl dust-mkd). *Maggs.* $40/£25

ALDINGTON, RICHARD. Two Stories: Deserter and The Lads of the Village. Elkin Matthews, 1930. One of 530 signed. Clbacked patterned bds. VG in dj (sl chipped, heavily reinforced). *Clearwater.* $80/£50

ALDINGTON, RICHARD. W. Somerset Maugham: an Appreciation. NY: Doubleday, 1939. 1st ed. (Fep top corner sl clipped), else Fine in stapled wrappers (sl rubbed). *Between The Covers.* $60/£38

ALDINGTON, RICHARD. War and Love (1915-1918). Boston: Four Seas Co, 1919. 1st Amer ed. NF (lt rubbed). *Polyanthos.* $35/£22

ALDINGTON, RICHARD. War and Love (1915-1918). Boston: Four Seas, 1919. 1st ed thus. Mottled brn bds, ptd labels. VF in dj w/pub's price label on spine. *Reese.* $150/£94

ALDISS, BRIAN and DAVID WINGROVE. Trillion Year Spree. The History of Science Fiction. Gollancz, 1986. 1st ed. One of 100 (of 126) signed by both. vii,511pp; 16 plts. Black cl, gilt, black silk marker. Fine in cl slipcase. *Blackwell's.* $144/£90

ALDISS, BRIAN. The Brightfount Diaries. London: Faber, 1955. 1st ed, 1st bk. (Fore-edge sl spotted, spine sl faded, corners, rear edges rubbed, sl cocked), else Good in dj (soiled, worn). *Virgo.* $48/£30

ALDISS, BRIAN. The Brightfount Diaries. Faber & Faber, 1955. 1st UK ed, 1st bk. NF (bkpl) in dj. *Williams.* $136/£85

ALDISS, BRIAN. Frankenstein Unbound. London: Cape, 1973. 1st Eng ed. NF (spine head sl bumped) in dj (nicked, sl rubbed, torn, browned, sm internal tape repair). *Ulysses.* $72/£45

ALDISS, BRIAN. Hothouse. Faber & Faber, 1962. 1st Eng ed. Fine in dj (sl mkd, rubbed, dusty). *Ulysses.* $152/£95

ALDRICH, CHILSON D. The Real Log Cabin. NY: Macmillan, 1945. 14th ptg. Good + (edgeworn). *Perier.* $15/£9

ALDRICH, HENRY. The Elements of Civil Architecture, According to Vitruvius and Other Ancients, and the Most Approved Practice of Modern Authors, Especially Palladio. Philip Smyth (trans). Oxford: D. Prince & J. Cooke, 1789. 1st ed in English. 55 copper plts. (Rebound in mod cl). *Pacific*.* $173/£108

ALDRICH, MILDRED. A Hilltop on the Marne. Boston: Houghton Mifflin, 1915. 1st ed. Frontis. VG. *Reese.* $30/£19

ALDRICH, MILDRED. The Peak of the Load. Boston: Small, Maynard, (1918). 1st ed. VG (lt soiled, rubbed). *Reese.* $30/£19

ALDRICH, MILDRED. Told in a French Garden, August 1914. Boston: Small, Maynard, 1916. 6th imp. Port. (Stain at port foreedge), else Good. *Reese.* $12/£8

ALDRICH, T. B. The Stillwater Tragedy. Boston: Houghton Mifflin, 1880. 1st ed. 324pp. Gilt-dec cvr. VG (shelfworn). *My Bookhouse.* $32/£20

ALDRIDGE, REGINALD. Life on a Ranch. London: Longmans, Green, 1884. 1st Eng ed. Blue pict cl. NF (pub's presentation blind-stamp; edges lt worn). Howes A110. *Labordo.* $750/£469

ALDRIDGE, RICHARD and JOSEPHINE. Reasons and Raisins. Berkeley: Parnassus, 1972. 1st ed. 6.25x8.25. John Larrecq (illus). VG in dj. *Cattermole.* $25/£16

ALEC-TWEEDIE, MRS. America As I Saw It: Or, America Revisited. NY: Macmillan, 1913. 1st Amer ed. Frontisport; 7 plts. Red cl, gilt. *Mott.* $25/£16

ALEGRIA, CIRO. Broad and Alien Is the World. NY: Farrar & Reinhart, 1940. 1st ed in English. VG + in dj (spine faded). *Lame Duck.* $175/£109

ALEGRIA, CIRO. The Golden Serpent. NY: Farrar & Reinhart, 1943. 1st ed. NF in VG dj. *Lame Duck.* $100/£63

ALEXANDER, DAVID. The Arts of War. (London, 1992.) Folio. Dj, bd slipcase. *Swann*.* $69/£43

ALEXANDER, E. P. Military Memoirs of a Confederate. NY: Scribner, 1907. 1st ed. Frontisport, fldg map. Grn cl. VG (spine top lt chipped). Howes A114. *Chapel Hill.* $275/£172

ALEXANDER, FRANCESCA. Christ's Folk in the Apennine. John Ruskin (ed). George Allen, Sunnyside, Orpington, Kent, 1887. Lg paper copy. x,264pp. Top edge uncut. Ribbed brn cl, gilt. NF. *Temple.* $64/£40

ALEXANDER, HENRY. The Cairngorms. S.M.C., 1928. 1st ed. Map. Mod cl, gilt. VG. *Hollett.* $48/£30

ALEXANDER, J. B. The History of Mecklenburg County from 1740 to 1900. Charlotte, NC: Observer Ptg House, 1902. 1st ed. Brn cl. VG + (sig; spine sl dull, edges lt spotted). *Chapel Hill.* $150/£94

ALEXANDER, J. J. G. Norman Illumination at Mont St. Michel 966-1100. Oxford: Clarendon, 1970. 55 plts. Grn cl. Dj. *Maggs.* $64/£40

ALEXANDER, JAMES EDWARD. Narrative of a Voyage of Observation Among the Colonies of Western Africa. In the Flag-Ship Thalia; and of a Campaign in Kaffir-Land.... London: Henry Colburn, 1837. 1st ed. 2 vols. 1/2 title,xxii,(i),(i blank),428; 1/2-title,xi,(i),352pp; 18 engr plts (3 color), 2 engr maps. (Leaf torn w/o loss; browned, foxed.) Contemp calf (rebacked w/new red/green spine labels, cvrs scratched). Sound. *Morrell.* $352/£220

ALEXANDER, JAMES EDWARD. Salmon-Fishing in Canada. London: Longman, 1860. 1st ed. Frontis, 350pp + ads. Blue cl, gilt. VG + (spine head lt worn). *Bowman.* $350/£219

ALEXANDER, JAMES M. The Islands of the Pacific. NY: American Tract Soc, 1895. 1st ed. 515pp. (Sl rubbed, soiled, spine ends frayed), o/w VG. *Worldwide.* $35/£22

ALEXANDER, JOHN H. Mosby's Men. NY/Washington: Neale, 1907. 1st ed. Als, 4pg prospectus (sm stain, crease) laid in. 8vo. Frontisport. Teg. Tan buckram. Fine (ink stamp). Howes A120. *Chapel Hill.* $700/£438

ALEXANDER, LLOYD. The First Two Lives of Lucas-Kasha. Dutton, 1978. 1st ed. 213pp. NF in VG dj (sm spine chips, sl dknd). *Price*. $30/£19

ALEXANDER, LLOYD. The High King. NY: Holt, 1968. Stated 1st ed. Inscribed. 285pp. Newberry medal sticker affixed. Fine in NF dj (price-clipped). *Price*. $145/£91

ALEXANDER, LLOYD. My Five Tigers. Crowell, (1956). 2nd ed. Peggy Bacon (illus). 118pp. VG (corner bumped, spine ends rubbed) in VG- dj (sm chips to corners, spine lacks 1/4-inch chips, rubbed). *Price*. $30/£19

ALEXANDER, LLOYD. My Five Tigers. NY: Thomas Crowell, (1956). 1st ed. NF in dj (spine ends sl rubbed). *Pacific**. $68/£43

ALEXANDER, LLOYD. Taran Wanderer. Holt, Rinehart, Winston, 1967. 1st ed. 256pp. NF (name stamp) in VG dj (spine dknd). *Price*. $40/£25

ALEXANDER, MARY CHARLOTTE. William Patterson Alexander in Kentucky, the Marquesas, Hawaii. Honolulu: Privately ptd, 1934. 2nd ptg. Errata slip laid in. 1/2 cl. NF. *Parmer*. $75/£47

ALEXANDER, ROY. The Cruise of the Raider Wolf. GC, 1941. Red cl. VG. *American Booksellers*. $22/£14

ALEXANDER, RUSSELL GEORGE. The Engraved Work of F.L. Griggs: Etchings and Dry-Points 1912-1928. Stratford-upon-Avon: Shakespeare Head, 1928. One of 325 numbered. Uncut. *Swann**. $161/£101

ALEXANDER, W. B. Birds of the Ocean. NY: Putnam, 1928. Black cl. VG. *American Booksellers*. $20/£13

ALEXANDER, W. B. Birds of the Ocean. NY/London: Putnam, 1928. 2nd imp. 88 photo plts. Blue ribbed cl, gilt. VF. *Explorer*. $88/£55

ALEXANDER, WILLIAM. The History of Women. London: W. Strahan & T. Cadell, 1779. 1st ed. 2 vols. (8),368,(14); (4),344,(14)pp. Mod vellum-like spine, marbled bds. Good. *Karmiole*. $450/£281

ALEXANDER, WILLIAM. Recreations with the Muses. London: Thomas Harper, 1637. Folio. (10),326pp. Checkered calf, gilt. (Old name, inscrip, lacks port, bkpl; joints cracked, spine worn, lacks label pieces), else VG. *Pacific**. $173/£108

ALEXINSKY, TATIANA. With the Russian Wounded.... Gilbert Canann (trans). London: T. Fisher Unwin, (1916). 1st ed in English. Red cl stamped in black. (Early ink name; lt sunned), o/w VG in white pict dj (dust-dknd, spine chips). *Reese*. $85/£53

ALFAU, FELIPE. Locos. NY: Farrar & Reinhart, 1936. 1st ed, 1st ptg. One of 1250 signed, numbered. (Few dk stains to top edge, dknd eps), else VG in VG dj. *Lame Duck*. $350/£219

ALFORD, M. Needlework as Art. London, 1886. Frontis, xxiii,422pp; 85 plts. Aeg. (Fr hinge cracked, sl shaken, soiled.) *Edwards*. $96/£60

Alfred, Lord Tennyson and His Friends. London: T. Fisher Unwin, 1893. One of 400. Folio. Frontis, 25 photogravure ports after J. M. and H. H. Hay Cameron's negatives, each w/ptd interleaving tissue. (Bkpls, eps foxed; soiled, spine sunned.) *Swann**. $1,725/£1,078

ALGER, HORATIO. Bertha's Christmas Vision. An Autumn Sheaf. Boston: Brown, Bazin, 1856. 1st ed, 1st bk. 8vo. Wood-engr frontis, pict tp, vii,248pp. Nice (pp lt soiled, foxed; wormholes to hinge) in red pub's cl, dec in gilt/blind. *Bromer*. $850/£531

ALGREN, NELSON. The Man with the Golden Arm. NY, 1949. 1st ed. One of unspecified # w/tipped-in sheet signed. Dj. *Swann**. $201/£126

ALGREN, NELSON. Nelson Algren's Own Book of Lonesome Monsters. (NY): Bernard Geis, (1962). 1st ed. Signed, inscribed w/dwg of cat by Algren. VG in dj (sm tear spine head, extrems sl rubbed). *Pacific**. $138/£86

ALGREN, NELSON. The Neon Wilderness. Andre Deutsch, 1965. 1st ed. NF in dj (rubbed, sm tear). *Ulysses*. $56/£35

ALGREN, NELSON. Never Come Morning. NY: Harper, (1942). 1st ed. Inscribed, signed, dated 1947. VG in Good dj (upper spine, rear panel lacks lg piece, sm tears to extrems, tape to rear flap). *Pacific**. $288/£180

ALGREN, NELSON. Somebody in Boots. NY: Vanguard, 1935. 1st ed, 1st bk. (Bds rubbed, sl edgeworn; lacks dj.) *Warren*. $250/£156

ALGREN, NELSON. A Walk on the Wild Side. NY: Farrar, Straus & Cudahy, (1956). 1st ed. Yellow/blue bds. (Spine ends sl rubbed), o/w NF in dj (edges sl soiled, worn, sm stain rear cvr). *Heritage*. $75/£47

Ali Baba and the Forty Thieves. London: Bancroft, 1960. 2 dbl-pg pop-ups. Pict bds. VG. *Bookfinders*. $100/£63

ALI, SALIM and S. DILLON RIPLEY. Handbook of the Birds of India and Pakistan. London: OUP, 1968-1974. 10 vols. 113 color plts. (Vols 1-3 cl sl worn), vols 4-10 in djs (chipped w/loss to spines). *Edwards*. $288/£180

Alice in Wonderland. London: Brown Watson, 1973. J. Pavlin & G. Seda (illus). 6 dbl-pg pop-ups. Glazed pict bds. VG. *Bookfinders*. $45/£28

Alice in Wonderland. London: Bancroft, n.d. (1961). 2 VG dbl-pg pop-ups, fr and back, by V. Kubasta. See-through circle on fr, showing white rabbit. Glazed pict bds (extrems worn). *Bookfinders*. $300/£188

ALINDER, JAMES (ed). New Landscapes. Untitled 24. Carmel, CA: The Friends of Photography, 1981. 1st ed. 40 full-pg photos by Robert Adams, et al. Fine in pict stiff wrappers. *Cahan*. $35/£22

ALINDER, JAMES. Collecting Light: the Photographs of Ruth Bernhard. Carmel: The Friends of Photography, 1979. 1st ed. 35 full-pg b/w plts. NF in stiff wrappers. *Cahan*. $45/£28

ALKEN, HENRY. The Analysis of the Hunting Field...Souvenir of the Season, 1845-6. London: Ackermann, 1846. Hand-colored tp, 6 hand-colored plts. Aeg. Full red morocco by Riviere, gilt. (Orig cvrs, spine bound in at end; lt rubbed, spine head sl worn; sl foxed, soiled.) *Oinonen**. $325/£203

ALKEN, HENRY. Scraps from the Sketch-Book. London: Thomas M'Lean, 1821. 42 hand-colored engrs. 3/4 leather, paper-cvrd bds, leather label on fr. (Marginal staining to plts; soiled, bumped.) *Metropolitan**. $460/£288

ALKEN, HENRY. Symptoms of Being Amused. Volume I. (All published.) London, 1822. 1st ed. Obl folio. 42 color engr plts, incl pict tp. Contemp roan-backed bds, red morocco cvr label. (Shelfworn, soiled, spine chipped, rear cvr detached; sl soiled, foxed.) Internally Sound. *Oinonen**. $425/£266

All About the Little Small Red Hen. NY: Cupples & Leon, (1917). 1st ed. 16mo. 48pp; 8 full-pg color plts by John B. Gruelle. Gray bds, full color paste label. Good in full color dj (spine worn, lacks pieces, marginal tears). *Reisler*. $175/£109

All Along the River. (By M. E. Braddon.) Simpkin, Marshall, Hamilton, et al, n.d. (c1890). Stereotyped ed. Pict bds (spine bumped, hinges, corners rubbed; bkpl). Good. *Tiger*. $48/£30

All Around the Christmas Tree. A Bonnie Book. Kenosha, WI: John Martin's House, 1949. 16x21 cm. 2 dbl-pg pop-ups. Pict bds (worn). Internally VG-. *Bookfinders*. $75/£47

ALLAN, JOHN R. North-East Lowlands of Scotland. Robert Hale, 1952. 1st ed. Map. (Cl sl rubbed, rear bd scratched, mkd.) *Hollett*. $24/£15

ALLAN, JOYCE. Australian Shells. Melbourne, 1950. 1st ed. Color frontis, 11 color, 32 b/w plts. Dj (sl chipped). *Edwards*. $56/£35

ALLAN, MEA. E. A. Bowles and His Garden at Myddelton House 1865-1954. London: R.U., 1973. 54 plts (8 color). VG in dj. *Hollett*. $32/£20

ALLAN, P. B. M. The Book Hunter at Home. London: Philip Allan, 1922. 2nd ed. Ltd to 500. Frontis, 3 plts. Canvas-backed bds (sl bumped). *Maggs.* $32/£20

ALLBEURY, TED. A Choice of Enemies. London: Peter Davies, 1973. 1st Eng ed. Purple bds, gilt. (Spine sl skewed), o/w Fine in dj. *Heritage.* $150/£94

ALLBUTT, T. C. and H. D. ROLLESTON (eds). A System of Medicine. London, 1905-11. 2nd ed. 9 vols, bound in 11. (Lt foxed; worn, vol 7 spine partly detached), o/w VG set. *Whitehart.* $192/£120

ALLBUTT, T. C. (ed). A System of Medicine. London, 1896-1899. 1st ed. 8 vols (of 9). xxxix,977; xiv,1176; xii,1001; xii,880; xii,1058; xi,944; xii,937; xii,998pp. (Lt foxed; worn, inner hinges cracked), o/w VG set. *Whitehart.* $128/£80

ALLDRIDGE, LIZZIE. By Love and Law. London, 1877. 1st ed. 3 vols. 1/2-titles present. Contemp 3/4 black polished calf (rubbed, lib mks). *Oinonen*.* $60/£38

ALLEGRO, JOHN. The End of a Road. MacGibbon & Kee, 1970. 1st ed. VG in dj. *Sclanders.* $19/£12

ALLEGRO, JOHN. The Sacred Mushroom and the Cross. GC: Doubleday, 1970. 1st ed. Good in dj. *Archer.* $25/£16

Allen Press Bibliography. (Greenbrae: Allen Press, 1981.) 1st ed. One of 140. 14 x 9 1/2. Dec cl. Fine in slipcase. *Pacific*.* $978/£611

ALLEN, AGNES. The Story of the Book. London: Faber & Faber, (1952). 1st ed. Fine in dj (tear). *Oak Knoll.* $30/£19

ALLEN, ALFRED. The Journal of the Postal Microscopical Society. London: W.P. Collins, 1882-1885. 4 vols. Grn cl. (Eps foxed; sl rubbed), else VG. *Weber.* $300/£188

ALLEN, B. SPRAGUE. Tides in English Taste (1619-1800). Cambridge: Harvard Univ, 1937. 2 vols. NF in VG djs. *Turtle Island.* $95/£59

ALLEN, BRASSEYA. Pastorals, Elegies, Odes, Epistles, and Other Poems. Abingdon, MD: Ptd by Daniel P. Ruff, 1806. 1st ed. 163pp. Contemp mottled calf-backed bds, morocco label. (Skillfully rebacked w/later calf; edges worn, scuffed), else VG. *Brown.* $125/£78

ALLEN, C. B. and LAUREN D. LYMAN. The Wonder-Book of the Air. Chicago: John C. Winston, (1936). 1st ed. VG in dj (panel crease, closed tear, extrems chipped). *Pacific*.* $58/£36

ALLEN, CHARLES DEXTER. American Book-Plates. London: George Bell, 1895. 1st ed. 437pp. (Spine extrems sl worn; bkpl.) *Dawson.* $50/£31

ALLEN, CHARLES DEXTER. American Book-Plates: A Guide to Their Study. London: George Bell & Sons, 1895. 1st ed. Olive cl, gilt, paper spine label. (Spine, extrems sunned; corners, extrems rubbed), else VG. *Pacific*.* $75/£47

ALLEN, CHARLES. Papier Mache. NY: Edward Arnold, 1896. 1st Amer ed. Mottled brn cl, gilt, beveled. Fine. *Sumner & Stillman.* $65/£41

ALLEN, D. L. Wolves of Minong. Boston: Houghton Mifflin, 1979. 1st ed. 16 maps, charts, graphs. NF in VG dj. *Mikesh.* $45/£28

ALLEN, E. M. Lafayette's Second Expedition to Virginia in 1781. Balt: MD Hist Soc, 1891. 50pp. Orig wrappers. (Sl chipped), else Good. *Brown.* $20/£13

ALLEN, FORREST C. My Basket-Ball Bible. Smith-Grieves, 1925. 3rd ed, 1st ptg. VG. *Plapinger.* $75/£47

ALLEN, GRANT. County and Town in England Together with Some Annals of Churnside. Grant Richards, 1901. Frontis map. Teg. Good (fore-edge spotted, new fep; spine bumped). *Tiger.* $26/£16

ALLEN, GRANT. The Evolutionist at Large. C&W, 1884. 2nd ed. Pub's cat dated Dec 1887. Pict cl (rubbed, spine bumped, rubbed, sunned). Good. *Tiger.* $16/£10

ALLEN, GRANT. Michael's Crag. Leadenhall, 1893. 1st ed. Good (pp browned; spine, edges faded, cl sl bubbled, soiled). *Ulysses.* $72/£45

ALLEN, GRANT. The People's Library. London/NY: SPCK/E. & J.B. Young, 1884. Correct 1st ptg, dated on tp. 1/2-title not called for; 191,(i)pp; 4pp inserted pub's ads. Ribbed brownish-olive cl, gilt. (Prelims lt foxed), o/w Fine. *Temple.* $51/£32

ALLEN, GRANT. What's Bred in Bone. Tit-Bits Office, 1891. Good (spine bumped, chipped, sunned, dull w/sm hole). *Tiger.* $32/£20

ALLEN, H. C. The Anglo-American Relationship Since 1783. London: A&C Black, (1959). 1st separate ed. Dj. *Mott.* $25/£16

ALLEN, HARRIS STEARNS. The Trail of Beauty. SF: L-D Allen Press, 1940. One of 100. Signed. 9 x 5 1/2. Orig tipped-in watercolor. Cl-backed dec bds, paper spine label. (Offset from glue of tipped-in illus to preceding few pp, foxing to p9), else VG. *Pacific*.* $1,093/£683

ALLEN, HERVEY. Action at Aquila. NY: Farrar & Rinehart, (1938). 1st ed. Blue cl. NF (spine crown lt rubbed) in pict dj. *Chapel Hill.* $45/£28

ALLEN, HERVEY. Anthony Adverse. NY: F&R, 1933. 1st ed. Tls laid in (folded as mailed) w/envelope present; inserted card not present. Fine in VG dj (price-clipped, soiled, lt stains). *Between The Covers.* $175/£109

ALLEN, HERVEY. Anthony Adverse. LEC, 1937. Ltd to 1500 numbered, signed by Edward A. Wilson (illus). 3 vols. Fine in slipcase. *Swann*.* $80/£50

ALLEN, HERVEY. It Was Like This. NY: Farrar & Rinehart, (1940). 1st ed. Red cl stamped in black. Fine in NF dj (spine lt sunned) w/pub's price increase stamped on flap. *Reese.* $50/£31

ALLEN, HERVEY. Toward the Flame. NY: Doran, (1926). 1st ed. Black cl stamped in red. VG in dj (spine lt sunned). *Reese.* $75/£47

ALLEN, I. N. Diary of a March Through Sinde and Afghanistan. London: Hatchard, 1843. Fldg frontis, 4pp ads; 7 lithos. New 1/2 red morocco, gilt. (Tp, frontis sl foxed.) *Petersfield.* $560/£350

ALLEN, JOHN EDWARD. Tales of the Print Shop. NY: Oswald, 1923. 1st ed. Paper spine label. (Cvrs faded.) *Oak Knoll.* $20/£13

ALLEN, JOHN LOGAN. Passage Through the Garden, Lewis and Clark and the Image of the American Northwest. Urbana: Univ of IL, (1975). 1st ed. Grn cl. Fine in dj (sl chipped). *Argonaut.* $150/£94

ALLEN, L. The Allen Press Bibliography. Tamal Land, 1985. One of 750. *Dawson.* $145/£91

ALLEN, L. Printing with the Handpress. NY: Van Nostrand Reinhold, (1969). (Bkpl.) Dj. *Oak Knoll.* $125/£78

ALLEN, LEE. The Cincinnati Reds. Putnam, 1948. 1st ed. VG+ in Good+ dj. *Plapinger.* $145/£91

ALLEN, LEE. The Hot Stove League. Barnes, 1955. 1st ed. VG+ in Good+ dj. *Plapinger.* $150/£94

ALLEN, LEWIS F. History of the Short-Horn Cattle. Buffalo: The Author, 1872. 1st ed. x,(13)-264,(2)pp; 10 litho plts. (Lacks eps, unnumbered ll after p.x, margins stained; stained, spine ends chipped), else Good+. *Pacific*.* $46/£29

ALLEN, MISS A. J. Ten Years in Oregon. Ithaca: Mack, Andrus & Co, ptrs, 1848. 2nd issue w/o port, but containing Fremont extracts. 430pp. Contemp calf, label. (Old lib bkpl; calf sl scuffed, worn), else Good. Howes A131. *Brown.* $200/£125

ALLEN, MISS A. J. Ten Years in Oregon. Ithaca, NY: Mack, Andrus, 1848. Contemp speckled calf. (Contents sl foxed; rear joint tender, fr joint cracked.) Howes A131. *Glenn.* $145/£91

ALLEN, MISS A. J. Ten Years in Oregon. Ithaca, 1850. Contemp sheep (fr cvr loose). Howes A131. *Swann*.* $80/£50

ALLEN, NATHAN. The Opium Trade. Lowell, (MA), 1853. 2nd ed. Signed. 80pp. Orig ptd wrappers. (Tp, fr wrap stained), o/w VG. *M & S.* $150/£94

ALLEN, PAUL. History of the American Revolution. Balt, 1822. 2nd ed. 2 vols. Full calf (worn, vol 2 hinges broken). (Vol 1 lacks fep, foxed), o/w contents VG. *New Hampshire*. $40/£25

ALLEN, R. M. The Microscope. London: Chapman & Hall, 1940. Frontis. VG. *Savona.* $40/£25

ALLEN, RICHARD. Stone Shelters. (MA): MIT, 1969. (Pencil dwgs), else Fine in dec bds. *Hadley.* $32/£20

ALLEN, ROBERT. Lucky Forward: The History of Patton's Third U.S. Army. NY, 1947. VG in dj (torn). *Clark.* $50/£31

ALLEN, THOMAS GASKELL, JR. and WILLIAM LEWIS SACHTLEBEN. Across Asia on a Bicycle. NY: Century, 1894. 1st ed. 1/2-title, frontis, xii,(iv),234pp. Teg. Blue cl, dec in blind, gilt. VG (ink stamp). *Morrell.* $168/£105

ALLEN, THOMAS GEORGE (ed). The Egyptian Book of the Dead. Chicago: Univ of Chicago, (1960). Folio. 131 plts. (2 edges lt bumped.) *Archaeologia.* $475/£297

ALLEN, WILLIAM. Five Years in the West. Nashville: Southern Methodist Pub House, 1884. 1st ed. 211pp. Stamped bds (extrems worn, spotted). Internally Clean. *Dumont.* $450/£281

ALLEN, WOODY. Getting Even. NY: Random House, (1971). 1st ed. Fine in Fine dj. *Lenz.* $75/£47

ALLEN, WOODY. Side Effects. NY: Random House, (1980). 1st ed. Fine in Fine dj. *Lenz.* $35/£22

ALLEN, WOODY. Side Effects. NY: Random House, (1980). 1st ed. Fine in dj (sm nick). *Reese.* $50/£31

ALLEN, WOODY. Without Feathers. NY: Random House, (1975). 1st ed. Fine in Fine dj. *Lenz.* $50/£31

ALLENDE, ISABEL. Eva Luna. NY: Knopf, 1988. 1st ed. Signed. Fine in Fine dj. *Robbins.* $45/£28

ALLENDE, ISABEL. Eva Luna. London: Hamish Hamilton, 1988. 1st UK ed. Fine in dj. *Lame Duck.* $65/£41

ALLENDE, ISABEL. The House of the Spirits. NY: Knopf, 1985. 1st ed. NF in NF dj. *Robbins.* $95/£59

ALLENDE, ISABEL. The Stories of Eva Luna. London: Hamish Hamilton, 1991. 1st UK ed. (Spine head bumped), else Fine in dj. *Lame Duck.* $50/£31

ALLERTON, R. G. Brook Trout Fishing. An Account of a Trip of the Oquossoc Angling Association to Northern Maine, in June, 1869. NY, 1869. 1st ed. Fine hand-colored fldg plt (loose; lacks fep; shelfworn). *Oinonen*. $450/£281

ALLEY, B. F. History of Clarke County, Washington Territory. Portland: Washington Pub Co, 1885. 399pp. (Top edge stained), else Good. *Perier.* $395/£247

ALLEY, R. Francis Bacon. London: Thames & Hudson, 1964. 27 mtd color illus, 1 pg laser print facs. Good in dj (sl frayed). *Ars Artis.* $2,000/£1,250

Allies' Fairy Book. London: Heinemann, (1916). 1st ed. Lg sq 8vo. xxii,121pp; 12 color plts by Arthur Rackham, guards. Slate-blue cl, gilt. (1st, last few ll sl browned), o/w Clean. *Sotheran.* $221/£138

Allies' Fairy Book. Edmund Gosse (intro). London: Heinemann, (1916). Ltd to 525 signed by Arthur Rackham (illus). 4to. 12 mtd color plts on brn paper. Teg. Pict blue cl, gilt. *Christie's*. $515/£322

ALLIN, ABBY. Home Ballads: A Book for New Englanders. Boston/Cambridge: Munroe, 1851. 1st ed. 288pp. Dec cl (lt soiled). *Ginsberg.* $75/£47

ALLINGHAM, MARGERY. Black Plumes. NY: DCC, 1940. 1st Amer ed. Proof copy. Fine in ptd wrappers. *Mordida.* $100/£63

ALLINGHAM, MARGERY. Dance of the Years. London: Michael Joseph, 1943. 1st ed. Inscribed. VG in dj (internal tape mends, 3/4-inch spine chip). *Mordida.* $95/£59

ALLINGHAM, MARGERY. The Fashion in Shrouds. Heinemann, 1938. 1st UK ed. VG + in Good dj (spine ends chipped, 2 other sm chips, couple closed tears). *Williams.* $312/£195

ALLINGHAM, MARGERY. The Mind Readers. London: C&W, 1965. 1st Eng ed. Black cl. Fine in dj. *Temple.* $38/£24

ALLINGHAM, MARGERY. The Mind Readers. NY: William Morrow, 1965. 1st ed. Fine in dj. *Mordida.* $45/£28

ALLINGHAM, MARGERY. The Mysterious Mr. Campion. Chatto, 1963. 1st UK ed. VG in dj (rear sl strengthened). *Williams.* $40/£25

ALLINGHAM, MARGERY. The Tiger in the Smoke. C&W, 1952. 1st ed. Teg. Buckram, beveled bds. (Offsetting to eps; fore-edge sl spotted, spine faded), o/w VG in dj (sl browned, soiled, chipped, edges reinforced, spine lacks sm piece). *Virgo.* $64/£40

ALLISON, DOROTHY. Bastard Out of Carolina. NY: Dutton, (1992). 1st ed. Press release laid in. Fine in dj. *Pacific*. $69/£43

ALLISON, WILLIAM. The British Thoroughbred Horse. London, 1901. 1st ed. Fldg color frontis. Uncut, unopened. Pict cvr label. (Sl worn, foxing.) *Oinonen*. $100/£63

ALLMAN, GEORGE JOHNSTON. Greek Geometry from Thales to Euclid. Dublin: Hodges, Figgis, 1889. 1st ed. Frontisport, xii,237,(2 ads)pp. VG (few faint lib mks). *Glaser.* $100/£63

ALLOTT, KENNETH. Poems. London: Hogarth, 1938. 1st Eng ed. One of 1000. VG (pastedown edges sl browned, rear one sl soiled; spine ends, corners sl bumped) in dj (nicked, rubbed, dusty, sl mkd, creased, dknd). *Ulysses.* $120/£75

ALLPORT, GORDON and PHILIP E. VERNON. Studies in Expressive Movement. NY: Macmillan, 1933. 1st ed. Chart in rear pocket. (Ex-lib; spine label.) *Beasley.* $25/£16

ALLRED, B. W. and JEFF C. DYKES. Flat Top Ranch. Norman: Univ of OK, 1957. 1st ed. NF in dj (chipped, lt soiled). *Labordo.* $50/£31

ALMACK, EDWARD (ed). Eikon Basilike or the King's Book. London: De la More, 1903. One of 290. Steel-engr port on tp, steel-engr pict general title 'The King's Library.' Aeg. Full brn niger w/inlaid panels of gilt-tooled dk brn morocco, raised spine bands, morocco lettering piece, gilt-ruled turn-ins, bound by Bumpus. (Eps dknd from turn-ins, eps sl foxed; sm mar to rear cvr), else NF. *Pacific*. $207/£129

ALMOND, LINDA STEVENS. Peter Rabbit and Little White Rabbit. Phila: Henry Altemus, (1923). 16mo. J. L. G. (illus). 63pp. Cl-backed pict bds, color paste label. Good in full color dj (spine worn, lt mkd). *Reisler.* $85/£53

ALPATOV, M. W. Art Treasures of Russia. Abrams, n.d. (1967?). Good. *Rybski.* $55/£34

Alphabet of Country Scenes. NY: McLoughlin Bros, (1873). Aunt Louisa's Big Picture Series. Folio. 12 leaves + 1pg list rear wrapper. Pict pink stiff paper wrappers. Fine (bkpl, label; sm creased corner fr wrapper). *Hobbyhorse.* $245/£153

Alpine Byways, Or, Light Leaves Gathered in 1859 and 1860, By a Lady. (By Jane Freshfield.) Longman, Green, Longman & Roberts, 1861. 1st ed. 8vo. viii,(i),232,24 ads pp; 8 tinted lithos, maps. Blind-stamped mauve cl, gilt. (Bds sl soiled), o/w Very Bright. *Sotheran.* $768/£480

ALSCHULER, ROSA and LA BERTA W. HATTWICK. Painting and Personality. A Study of Young Children. Chicago: Univ of Chicago, 1951. 1st ed. 2 vols. (Signs of plt removal vol 2; 2 mended pp vol 1), else NF in VG djs. *Beasley.* $60/£38

ALSTON, J. W. Hints to Young Practitioners in the Study of Landscape Painting. London: Longman, N.d. 3rd ed. 4 plts. Engr frontis (inner edge frayed), engr tp, 2ff,67pp; 4plts. Orig bds w/label (worn, rebacked). *Ars Artis.* $200/£125

ALSTON, M. Sunbirds and Jacarandas, a Bird Lover in Rhodesia. Cape Town, 1951. 1st ed. 9 plts (3 color). Dj. *Hallam.* $48/£30

ALTER, J. CECIL. James Bridger. Salt Lake City: Shepard Book, (1925). 1st ed. One of 1000 signed. Frontis, 17 full-pg illus. Pict blind-stamped fabricoid, gilt. *Dawson.* $225/£141

ALTER, J. CECIL. James Bridger: Trapper, Frontiersman, Scout, and Guide. Salt Lake City: Shepard Book, (1925). 1st ed. One of 1000 numbered. Signed. 18 plts. Teg. Emb fr cvr, gilt. VG. Howes A191. *Lien.* $300/£188

ALTHAUSEN, THEODORE L. et al (eds). Contributions in Medicine in Honor of William John Kerr, M.D., on the Occasion of His Sixtieth Birthday. Phila: Lippincott, (1950). Frontisport. Fine. *Weber.* $45/£28

ALTHER, LISA. Kinflicks. NY: Knopf, 1976. 1st ed. (Edge rubbed), o/w NF in dj. *Hermitage.* $40/£25

ALTIERI, JAMES. The Spearheaders. Indianapolis, 1960. 1st ed. VG. *Clark.* $35/£22

ALVAREZ, A. The Savage God. London: Weidenfeld & Nicolson, 1971. 1st ed. Maroon cl (sl faded). Dj (few sm tears). *Maggs.* $48/£30

ALVAREZ, WALTER C. The Mechanics of the Digestive Tract: An Introduction to Gastroenterology. NY, 1928. 2nd ed. Blue cl. NF. *Doctor's Library.* $75/£47

ALVERDES, F. The Psychology of Animals in Relation to Human Psychology. London: Kegan Paul, Trench, 1932. 1st ed. Fine (bkpl, sm home-made rear pocket). *Beasley.* $40/£25

ALVERDES, PAUL. Changed Men. London: Martin Secker, (1933). 1st Eng ed. (Edges sl sunned), o/w VG in pict dj (lt frayed, price-clipped). *Reese.* $40/£25

ALVERDES, PAUL. The Whistlers' Room. Basil Creighton (trans). London, 1929. 1st Eng ed. Nice (sl faded) in dj (sl rubbed, dusty). *Clearwater.* $56/£35

ALVERDES, PAUL. The Whistlers' Room. Basil Creighton (trans). NY: Covici-Friede, 1930. 1st US ed. Fine in NF dj (sm chip spine crown). *Reese.* $40/£25

ALVORD, CLARENCE W. and LEE BIDGOOD. The First Exploration of the Trans-Allegheny Region by the Virginians, 1650-1674. A.H. Clark, 1912. Partly unopened. (Ex-lib, internally waterstained; cvr badly waterstained, evidence of mildew.) Howes A194. *Book Broker.* $125/£78

ALVORD, CLARENCE W. (ed). Laws of the Territory of Illinois 1809-1811. Springfield, IL, 1906. Good+ ptd wraps (soiled). *Wantagh.* $40/£25

ALVORD, THOMAS. Paul Bunyan and Resinous Rhymes of the North Woods. NY: Derrydale, 1934. Ltd to 166 numbered. Blue cl. Fine. *Biscotti.* $225/£141

AMADO, JORGE. Dona Flor and Her Two Husbands. NY: Knopf, 1969. 1st US ed. NF in VG+ dj (fr flap-fld base torn, spine faded). *Lame Duck.* $45/£28

AMADO, JORGE. The Two Deaths of Quincas Wateryell. NY: Knopf, 1965. 1st US ed. NF in dj (price-clipped). *Lame Duck.* $85/£53

AMADO, JORGE. The Violent Land. NY: Knopf, 1945. 1st US ed. (Contemp inscrip), else VG+ in dj (verso sl stained). *Lame Duck.* $125/£78

AMARAL, ANTHONY A. Comanche: The Horse That Survived the Custer Massacre. L.A.: Westernlore, 1961. Fine in fabricoid, dj. *Pacific*.* $138/£86

AMARANT, JULES. Tall Baseball Stories. Association, 1948. 1st ed. Signed. Fine (pp browned) in VG dj. *Plapinger.* $175/£109

Amateur Poacher. By the Author of 'The Gamekeeper at Home.' (By Richard Jefferies.) London: Smith Elder, 1879. 1st ed. (viii),240pp. Brn blind/gilt-stamped cl. NF (extrems lt rubbed). *Young.* $144/£90

AMBLER, CHARLES HENRY. A History of Transportation in the Ohio Valley with Special Reference to Its Waterways, Trade, and Commerce from the Earliest Period to the Present Time. Glendale: A.H. Clark, 1932. 1st ed. One of 1498. Frontis, fldg map. Blue cl, gilt. (Name; corners, spine ends sl rubbed), else Fine. *Argonaut.* $225/£141

AMBLER, ERIC. Background to Danger. NY: Knopf, 1937. 1st US ed. Orange cl. VG (bkpl, paper sl browned) in dj (sl edgeworn, creased, rear panel lt soiled). *Heritage.* $500/£313

AMBLER, ERIC. The Care of Time. NY: FSG, (1981). One of 300 signed. Blue cl, gilt. Fine in slipcase. *Pacific*.* $75/£47

AMBLER, ERIC. A Coffin for Dimitrios. NY: Knopf, 1939. 1st US ed. Fine (corners sl worn) in VG+ dj (few sm closed tears, lt edgeworn, chipped). *Janus.* $400/£250

AMBLER, ERIC. The Jealous God. Stellar, (1964). One of 200. Sm bklet. VG in self-wrappers (fr wrapper lt stained). *Williams.* $152/£95

AMBLER, ERIC. Journey Into Fear. Hodder, 1940. 1st UK ed. VG (spine browned). *Williams.* $96/£60

AMBLER, ERIC. Journey into Fear. NY: Knopf, 1940. 1st US ed. Fine (name) in VG+ dj (spine extrems lt chipped, lt edgewear). *Janus.* $400/£250

AMBLER, ERIC. Judgement on Deltchev. Hodder & Stoughton, 1951. 1st UK ed. NF in VG dj (edges sl worn). *Williams.* $104/£65

AMBLER, ERIC. The Schirmer Inheritance. Heinemann, 1953. 1st UK ed. VG in dj (edges sl worn). *Williams.* $64/£40

AMBROSE, D. LEIB. History of the Seventh Regiment, Illinois Volunteer Infantry.... Springfield, IL, 1868. 1st ed. 391pp. (Spine defective.) *King.* $150/£94

AMBROSE, GORDON and GEORGE NEWBOLD. A Handbook of Medical Hypnosis. Balt: Williams & Wilkins, 1958. 2nd ed. Fine in brick-red cl. *Weber.* $20/£13

Ambulator; or, A Pocket Companion in a Tour Round London.... London: Bew & Wilkie, 1792. 4th ed. 311pp; engr fldg map colored in outline (repaired at fold). Contemp tree calf (sl rubbed). *Marlborough.* $160/£100

America and the Americans. (By James Boardman.) London: Longman, Rees, Orme et al, 1833. 1st ed. Inscribed. xvi,(2) ads,430pp. Uncut. Als tipped-in verifying inscription. Pub's cl (lt rubbed). Howes B561. *Mott.* $150/£94

America as I Found It. (By Mary Grey Lundie Duncan.) NY: Robert Carter & Bros, 1852. 1st ed. Engr frontisport, 440pp+12pp ads. Blind/gilt-stamped brn cl. (Text sl foxed.) *Karmiole.* $150/£94

America: Or a General Survey of the Political Situation of the Several Powers of the Western Continent. (By Alexander H. Everett.) London: Murray, 1828. 1st British ed. iv,356pp. 19th-cent bds, leather back, tips. (Sl foxed, soiled; rubbed.) *Oinonen*.* $70/£44

American Annual Cyclopaedia and Register of Important Events of the Year 1862. Volume II. NY: D. Appleton, 1866. 3/4 calf, marbled bds, gilt. NF. *Pacific*.* $92/£58

American Indian Legends. LEC, 1968. Ltd to 1500 numbered, signed by Everett Gee Jackson (illus). Fine in slipcase. *Swann*.* $115/£72

American Wild Life Illustrated. NY: Wise, 1940. 1st ed. (Lt worn), else VG. *Dumont.* $50/£31

Americans Against Liberty. (By Ambrose Serle.) London: J. Mathews, 1776. 3rd ed. 48pp. Mod cl. (Tp, last pg stained.) *Maggs.* $400/£250

AMES, FISHER, JR. By Reef and Trail. Boston: Brown & Page, 1909. 1st ed. 13 full-pg b/w plts. Navy cl. VG. *Bowman.* $35/£22

AMES, MRS. ERNEST. Little Red Fox. London: Duckworth, 1908. 1st ed. Sq 4to. 12 full-pg color plts. Cl-backed bds (rear cvr browned, cvrs fingered), color illus fr cvr. *Reisler.* $135/£84

AMES-LEWIS, FRANCIS and JOANNE WRIGHT. Drawing in the Italian Renaissance Workshop. London, 1983. Good+ in dj. *Washton.* $45/£28

AMESBURY, ROBERT. Nobles' Emigrant Trail. Susanville: Lassen Litho, 1967. Fine in wraps. *Perier.* $15/£9

AMHERST, AMELIA. A History of Gardening in England. Quaritch, 1896. 2nd ed. 405pp. (Extrems rubbed), else VG + in dec grn cl, gilt. *Hadley.* $184/£115

AMIS, KINGSLEY and ROBERT CONQUEST. The Egyptologists. London: Cape, 1965. 1st Eng ed. NF (name, feps sl spotted) in dj (price-clipped, spine sl faded). *Ulysses.* $56/£35

AMIS, KINGSLEY. The Alteration. London, 1976. 1st Eng ed. Inscribed. Fine in dj. *Clearwater.* $88/£55

AMIS, KINGSLEY. The Folks That Live on the Hill. Hutchinson, 1990. 1st UK ed. Signed. NF in dj. *Williams.* $40/£25

AMIS, KINGSLEY. I Like It Here. London: Gollancz, 1958. 1st ed. Fine in NF dj (sm rear gutter puncture, spine sl tanned). *Between The Covers.* $125/£78

AMIS, KINGSLEY. A Look Round the Estate: Poems 1957-67. London: Cape, 1967. 1st Eng ed. Parchment-backed cl. VG (top edge sl dusty; spine ends, corners sl bumped, cvrs sl cocked) in dj (nicked, sl rubbed, price-clipped, spine sl faded, edges sl browned). *Ulysses.* $96/£60

AMIS, KINGSLEY. Lucky Jim's Politics. CPC Summer School Studies, 1968. Fine in card wrappers. *Clearwater.* $40/£25

AMIS, KINGSLEY. My Enemy's Enemy. London, 1962. 1st Eng ed. VG in dj (sl nicked). *Clearwater.* $72/£45

AMIS, KINGSLEY. The Old Devils. London: London Ltd Editions, 1986. 1st Eng ed. One of 250 signed. Fine in tissue. *Clearwater.* $88/£55

AMIS, KINGSLEY. The Riverside Villas Murder. Cape, 1973. 1st UK ed. NF in VG dj (spine sl faded, edges sl worn). *Williams.* $29/£18

AMIS, KINGSLEY. That Uncertain Feeling. London: Gollancz, 1955. 1st ed. (Pg corner bent), else Fine in dj (spine sl tanned, sm nicks rear panel). *Between The Covers.* $100/£63

AMIS, MARTIN. Dead Babies. NY: Knopf, 1976. 1st Amer ed. Signed. Fine in dj (spine sl faded). *Pacific*.* $86/£54

AMIS, MARTIN. The Information. (London): Flamingo, (1995). 1st ed. One of 356. Signed. Black cl, gilt. Fine in slipcase. *Pacific*.* $98/£61

AMIS, MARTIN. London Fields. NY, 1989. 1st Amer ed. Signed. Fine in Fine dj. *Polyanthos.* $30/£19

AMIS, MARTIN. Money. NY, 1985. 1st Amer ed. Signed. Fine in NF dj. *Warren.* $60/£38

AMIS, MARTIN. Other People. London: Jonathan Cape, (1981). 1st ed. Signed, inscribed. Fine in dj. *Pacific*.* $92/£58

AMIS, MARTIN. Other People: A Mystery Story. NY: Viking, 1981. 1st US ed. Fine in Fine dj. *Beasley.* $60/£38

AMIS, MARTIN. The Rachel Papers. Cape, 1973. 1st ed. Fine in dj (edges chipped, 1/2-inch closed tear rear panel, sm scuffed tear edge of rear fold). *Virgo.* $288/£180

AMIS, MARTIN. The Rachel Papers. NY: Knopf, 1974. 1st Amer ed, 1st bk. Signed. Fine in dj. *Pacific*.* $109/£68

AMIS, MARTIN. Success. London: Jonathan Cape, (1978). 1st ed. One of 3700 ptd. Signed, inscribed. Dj. *Pacific*.* $150/£94

AMIS, MARTIN. Success. Cape, 1978. 1st ed. Fine in dj (spine sl faded). *Any Amount.* $144/£90

AMIS, MARTIN. Time's Arrow. NY, 1991. 1st Amer ed. Signed. Fine in Fine dj. *Warren.* $35/£22

AMIS, MARTIN. Time's Arrow. London, 1991. 1st Eng ed. Signed. Fine in dj. *Clearwater.* $40/£25

AMIS, MARTIN. Visiting Mrs. Nabokov. Cape, 1993. 1st UK ed. Signed. Mint in Mint dj. *Martin.* $32/£20

AMMONS, A. R. A Coast of Trees. NY: Norton, (1981). 1st ed. Fine in Fine dj. *Dermont.* $35/£22

AMMONS, A. R. The Snow Poems. NY: Norton, (1977). 1st ed. Fine in Fine dj. *Dermont.* $35/£22

AMOS, SHELDON. Political and Legal Remedies for War. NY: Harper & Bros, 1880. Sound (worn, rubbed). *Boswell.* $250/£156

AMOS, W. J. M.I.A.: Saigon. L.A.: Holloway House, 1986. 1st ed. Pb orig. Fine. *Associates.* $25/£16

AMSDEN, DORA. Impressions of Ukiyo-Ye: The School of the Japanese Colour-Print Artists. SF: Paul Elder, (1905). 1st ed. Dec thick cl, string ties. NF. *Pacific*.* $81/£51

AMUNDSEN, ROALD and LINCOLN ELLSWORTH. First Crossing of the Polar Sea. NY: George H. Doran, 1927. 1st ed in English. VG. *High Latitude.* $75/£47

AMUNDSEN, ROALD and LINCOLN ELLSWORTH. Our Polar Flight. NY: Dodd, Mead, 1925. 1st ed. Blue cl, gilt. (Inscrip; spine dull, rear hinge starting), else VG. *Pacific*.* $86/£54

AMUNDSEN, ROALD. My Life as an Explorer. London: Heinemann, 1927. 1st ed in English. Frontis port. (Sl foxed), else VG. *High Latitude.* $90/£56

AMUNDSEN, ROALD. My Polar Flight. London: Hutchinson, (1925). 1st Eng ed. 2 charts. Blue cl. Fine. *Maggs.* $80/£50

AMUNDSEN, ROALD. The North West Passage, Being the Record of a Voyage of Exploration of the Ship 'GJOA' 1903-1907. London: Constable, 1908. 1st Eng ed. 2 vols. 2 frontispieces, 43 photogravure plts, 3 maps, 2 fldg. (Lt spotting.) Leaflet tipped to fep. Orig pub's cl (spines lt faded, spine tail vol 2 chipped). *Christie's*.* $397/£248

AMUNDSEN, ROALD. The South Pole: An Account of the Norwegian Antarctic Expedition in the 'Fram,' 1910-1912. A.G. Chater (trans). London: John Murray, 1912. 2nd Eng ed, Dec 1912. 2 vols. 8vo. 5 maps (3 fldg). Teg. Maroon red pict cl. VG (sl foxed; spine sl faded). *Explorer.* $672/£420

AMUNDSEN, ROALD. The South Pole: An Account of the Norwegian Antarctic Expedition in the 'Fram,' 1910-1912. A.G. Chater (trans). London: John Murray, 1912. 1st Eng ed. 2 vols. 8vo. 2 fldg maps. Teg. Maroon red pict cl. VG (sl foxed). *Explorer.* $992/£620

AMUNDSEN, ROALD. The South Pole: An Account of the Norwegian Antarctic Expedition in the 'Fram,' 1910-1912. A. G. Chater (trans). London/NY: John Murray/Lee Keedick, 1913. 1st Amer ed. 2 vols. 8 vo. 1 fldg map vol 1; 2 in vol 2. Blue cl. VG + set (bottom edge rear bd vol 2 nicked). *Explorer.* $672/£420

AMUNDSEN, ROALD. The South Pole: An Account of the Norwegian Antarctic Expedition in the 'Fram,' 1910-1912. London: C. Hurst, 1996. Facs of 1st Eng ed of 1912. Map. Mint in dj. *Explorer.* $51/£32

ANACREON. 29 Odes. Doris Langley (trans). London: Gerald Howe, 1926. One of 105. Teg. Full vellum. NF (cvrs bowed) in slipcase (sl rubbed, dusty). *Ulysses.* $104/£65

Anastasius; or, Memoirs of a Greek. (By Thomas Hope.) John Murray, 1819. 1st ed. 3 vols. Contemp diced calf, gilt. (Lacks 1/2-titles, spotted; sl rubbed.) *Sotheby's*.* $275/£172

Anatomy of Melancholy.... (By Robert Burton.) London: Vernor, Hood, 1806. 11th ed. 2 vols. xxiv,461; 601,(12)pp. New lt tan 1/2 calf. *Young.* $125/£78

ANDERS, CURT. The Price of Courage. NY: Sagamore, 1957. 1st ed. VG in dj (shelfworn, sm chip). *Reese.* $40/£25

ANDERS, LESLIE. The Eighteenth Missouri. Bobbs, 1968. 1st ed. VG in dj. *Rybski.* $75/£47

ANDERSEN, HANS CHRISTIAN. Andersen's Fairy Tales. Chicago: Rand McNally, (1916). 14 full-pg color plts by Milo Winter. Grn textured cl, gilt, full color paste label. (1 pg spotted), o/w VG. *Reisler.* $200/£125

ANDERSEN, HANS CHRISTIAN. Andersen's Fairy Tales. (Phila: David McKay, 1932.) 1st Amer ed, w/British sheets, but David McKay on spine. 4to. Arthur Rackham (illus). 12 full-pg color plts. Teg. Rose-red cl, gilt. Good. *Reisler.* $275/£172

ANDERSEN, HANS CHRISTIAN. The Complete Andersen. LEC, 1949. Ltd to 1500 numbered, signed by Fritz Kredel (illus) and Jean Hersholt (trans). 6 vols. Fine in slipcase. *Swann*.* $230/£144

ANDERSEN, HANS CHRISTIAN. The Complete Andersen: All of the 168 Stories. NY: LEC, (1942/1949). One of 1500. Signed by Jean Hersholt (trans) and Fritz Kredel (illus). 6 vols. 1/2 blue buckram, dec bds, silver-lettered spine. Fine in glassine. *Pacific*.* $161/£101

ANDERSEN, HANS CHRISTIAN. Fairy Tales and Stories. H.W. Dulcken (trans). Routledge, n.d. ca 1910. Lg 8vo. 512pp; 60 illus (incl 4 color chromolitho plts) by A. W. Bayes. Pict slate-blue cl. Fr cvr design by Jessie M. King. (Edges rubbed, spine dknd), else VG. *Bookmark.* $88/£55

ANDERSEN, HANS CHRISTIAN. Fairy Tales by Hans Christian Andersen. London: George G. Harrap, (1916). Ltd to 125 signed by Harry Clarke (illus). 4to. 16 mtd color plts, 24 full-pg b/w dwgs. Teg. White vellum, gilt. Very Nice (spine sl rippled) in pub's cardbd box (lt worn, corners taped), felt-lined w/identifying label. *Reisler.* $9,000/£5,625

ANDERSEN, HANS CHRISTIAN. Fairy Tales by Hans Christian Andersen. LEC, 1942. Ltd 1500 numbered, signed by Fritz Kredel. 2 vols. Fine in slipcase. *Swann*.* $172/£108

ANDERSEN, HANS CHRISTIAN. Fairy Tales of Hans Andersen. London: George G. Harrap, (1932). Ltd to 525 signed. 4to. 12 full-pg color plts by Arthur Rackham. Teg. White vellum, gilt. VG. *Reisler.* $2,200/£1,375

ANDERSEN, HANS CHRISTIAN. Fairy Tales of Hans Christian Andersen. NY: Brentano's, (1916). 1st Amer ed. Lg 4to. 16 mtd color plts, 24 full-pg b/w illus by Harry Clarke. Teg. Gray cl (rear cvrs lt spotted, worn). Internally VG. *Reisler.* $485/£303

ANDERSEN, HANS CHRISTIAN. Fairy Tales. London: Thomas Nelson & Sons, (1920). 1st ed illus by Honor C. Appleton. 4to. (viii),9-178pp; 12 Fine color plts. Gray pict cl, gilt. VG (lower joint cracked, repaired, firm). *Sotheran.* $301/£188

ANDERSEN, HANS CHRISTIAN. Fairy Tales. Phila: David McKay, (1932). 1st Amer ed. 4to. 12 full-pg color plts by Arthur Rackham. Teg. Rose cl, gilt. Fine in full color pict dj, full color pict box (sl edgeworn). *Reisler.* $750/£469

ANDERSEN, HANS CHRISTIAN. Fairy Tales. London: George Harrap, (1932). One of 525 signed by Arthur Rackham (illus). 4to. 12 color plts. Teg. Full gilt-stamped vellum (sl rubbed, soiled). *Appelfeld.* $1,500/£938

ANDERSEN, HANS CHRISTIAN. Fairy Tales. London: Sampson Low, Marston, Low, & Searle, 1872. 1st ed. Sm folio. E.V.B. (illus). 12 full-pg color illus. Aeg. Grn cl. (Prelims sl foxed; sl worn.) *Reisler.* $1,650/£1,031

ANDERSEN, HANS CHRISTIAN. Fairy Tales. London: George G. Harrap, 1932. 1st trade ed. 4to. 8 color plts by Arthur Rackham. Russett pict cl, gilt. Fine in dj. *Christie's*.* $645/£403

ANDERSEN, HANS CHRISTIAN. Fairy Tales. London: Boots, ca 1913. 16 mtd color plts by W. Heath Robinson. Aeg by Sangorski & Sutcliffe. Full blue morocco (spine sl sunned), gilt paneled spine, raised bands. Fine. *Appelfeld.* $400/£250

ANDERSEN, HANS CHRISTIAN. The Fir Tree. NY: Harper & Row, (1970). 1st ed thus. 8vo. Nancy Ekholm Burkett (illus). Grn cl, color paste label fr cvr. Fine in full color dj. *Reisler.* $75/£47

ANDERSEN, HANS CHRISTIAN. Hans Andersen's Fairy Tales and Stories. London: Routledge, 1903. 1st ed. 8vo. Jessie M. King and A. W. Bayes (illus). 4 color plts, 60 b/w dwgs. Red cl, gilt. (Lt worn.) *Reisler.* $125/£78

ANDERSEN, HANS CHRISTIAN. Hans Andersen's Fairy Tales. H. Oskar Sommer (trans). T.C. & E.C. Jack, 1911. 1st ed thus. 4to. Cecile Walton (illus). 431pp. Dec golden eps; teg. Pict black cl, gilt. (Plt sl frayed, fr hinge reinforced; rubbed, wear), else VG. *Bookmark.* $104/£65

ANDERSEN, HANS CHRISTIAN. Hans Andersen's Fairy Tales. London: T.C. & E.C. Jack, 1911. 1st ed illus thus. 8vo. vii,431pp; 24 Fine color plts by Cecile Walton. Gold/black eps; teg, rest uncut. Dk blue cl, gilt. Lovely. *Sotheran.* $269/£168

ANDERSEN, HANS CHRISTIAN. Hans Andersen's Fairy Tales. London: Cobden-Sanderson, 1935. 1st ed illus thus. 8vo. Rex Whistler (illus). vii,470pp. Dec eps. Red cl stamped w/rococo design in cream. VF. *Sotheran.* $205/£128

ANDERSEN, HANS CHRISTIAN. Hans Andersen's Fairy Tales. NY: George H. Doran, n.d. (ca 1930). 1st ed. 320pp; 16 color plts by W. Heath Robinson. Dec yellow linen. (Final leaf, ep browned from old news clipping.) Illus dj (chipped). *Karmiole.* $150/£94

ANDERSEN, HANS CHRISTIAN. The Little Mermaid. Macmillan, 1939. 1st ed. 8x10. Dorothy Lathrop (illus). Unpaginated. Good+ (extrems sl worn). *Price.* $30/£19

ANDERSEN, HANS CHRISTIAN. The Nightingale and Other Stories. NY: Hodder & Stoughton, n.d. 9.75x7. 12 tipped-in color plts by Edmund Dulac. Dk blue/black cl, gilt. (Cvrs sl spotted), else VG. *Pacific*.* $104/£65

ANDERSEN, HANS CHRISTIAN. Rambles in the Romantic Regions of the Hartz Mountains. Charles Beckwith (trans). London: Richard Bentley, 1848. 1st Eng ed. 1/2-title, vii,(i blank),(9)-312pp. Blindstamped white/blue striped cl (sl grubby, faded, sm stain rear corner, fr cvr). Internally VG. *Morrell.* $152/£95

ANDERSEN, HANS CHRISTIAN. Seven Tales by Hans Christian Andersen. Eve Le Galliene (ed). London: World's Work, 1972. 1st UK ed. 7x9. Maurice Sendak (illus). 128pp. Fine in VG dj. *Price.* $60/£38

ANDERSEN, HANS CHRISTIAN. The Snow Queen. London: Blackie & Son, (ca 1950). Silver Thimble Series. Rie Cramer (illus). 12mo. Color illus bds (edgeworn; 2 black ink mks on ep). *Reisler.* $65/£41

ANDERSEN, HANS CHRISTIAN. Stories for the Household. London, 1893. Color frontis, iv, 316pp. Color pict cl-backed bds (lt soiled, edges sl worn, spine gilt rubbed, hinges cracked; margins browned, spotted, few sl thumbed). *Edwards.* $48/£30

ANDERSEN, HANS CHRISTIAN. Stories from Hans Andersen. London: Hodder & Stoughton, 1911. 1st ed illus thus. Deluxe ed. Ltd to 750 numbered, signed by Edmund Dulac (illus). 4to. (vi),7-250pp; 28 mtd color plts, guards. Dec eps. Teg, new silk ties. Orig full white vellum, gilt. Very Clean (lt speckling to few deckled edges). *Sotheran.* $1,920/£1,200

ANDERSEN, HANS CHRISTIAN. Thumbelina. London: Blackie & Son, (ca 1945). Rie Cramer (illus). 12mo. Illus red bds. Good in full color dj (rear wrinkled, few pieces of tape). *Reisler.* $75/£47

ANDERSEN, HANS CHRISTIAN. Thumbelina. Retold by Amy Ehrlich. Dial, 1979. 1st ed. 10x12. Susan Jeffers (illus). Unpaginated. Fine in Good dj. *Price.* $35/£22

ANDERSEN, HANS CHRISTIAN. Thumbelina. Vernon Ives (ed). (NY): Holiday House, 1939. One of 1200 colored by hand. Hilda Scott (decs). Sq 16mo. 28 leaves (1 loose leaf reglued at internal spine). Dec eps. Dec paper on bds, cl spine. Good. *Hobbyhorse.* $55/£34

ANDERSEN, HANS CHRISTIAN. The Ugly Duckling. NY: Grosset & Dunlap, (1945). 1st ed thus. 4to. F. Rojankovsky (illus). Color pict bds (edges lt rubbed). Full color dj. *Reisler.* $85/£53

ANDERSON IMBERT, ENRIQUE. The Other Side of the Mirror. Carbondale: Southern IL Univ, 1966. 1st ed in English. NF in dj (price-clipped). *Lame Duck.* $85/£53

ANDERSON, A. J. The ABC of Artistic Photography in Theory and Practice. NY: Dodd, Mead, 1913. 2nd ed. Frontisport. (Extrems rubbed, cl sl soiled), else VG. *Cahan.* $150/£94

ANDERSON, ALEX D. The Silver Country or the Great Southwest. NY: Putnam, 1877. 1st ed. 221pp; fldg map (tears repaired w/archival tape). Grn cl, pict map bds (extrems worn). Text VG. *Parmer.* $140/£88

ANDERSON, ANDREW A. Twenty-Five Years in a Wagon. London: Chapman & Hall, 1888. New 1 vol ed. 2,xiii,423 + 40pp ads; fldg map, 14 plts. (Cl lt rubbed.) *Adelson.* $195/£122

ANDERSON, ANNE. The Anne Anderson Fairy-Tale Book. NY: Thomas Nelson & Sons, (1923). 1st ed. Lg 4to. 190pp; 12 full-pg color plts. Blue cl, color paste label. Nice. *Reisler.* $350/£219

ANDERSON, ANNE. The Anne Anderson Fairy-Tale Book. NY: Thomas Nelson, (ca 1920s). 11.5x9. 12 color plts. Pict cvr label. (Old name; spine ends sl rubbed), else VG. *Pacific*.* $92/£58

ANDERSON, B. W. Gem Testing. London: Butterworths, 1971. 8th ed. Leatherette frontis, 5 color plts. VG in dj. *Savona.* $29/£18

ANDERSON, BARRY C. Lifeline to the Yukon. Seattle: Superior, 1983. 1st ed. Fine in dj. *American Booksellers.* $45/£28

ANDERSON, BERN. By Sea and by River. NY, 1962. 1st ed. Fine in dj (torn, repaired). *Pratt.* $37/£23

ANDERSON, C. W. Big Red. NY: Macmillan, 1943. 1st ed. VG in Good+ dj. *October Farm.* $48/£30

ANDERSON, C. W. Big Red. Macmillan, 1943. 1st ed. 9x11.5 oblong. 64pp. VG in Good- dj (5-inch tear through horse's face, 1-inch tear to rear, spine foot lacks 1 1/4-inch piece, sm chip from middle, other chips; edgeworn). *Price.* $85/£53

ANDERSON, C. W. Blaze and the Gypsies. NY: Macmillan, (1942). (Corners worn.) *October Farm.* $35/£22

ANDERSON, C. W. Bobcat. NY: Macmillan, 1949. 1st ed. Red cl. NF in color pict dj. *House.* $25/£16

ANDERSON, C. W. Heads Up, Heels Down. Macmillan, 1944. 1st ed. 144pp. VG (edges bds, spine worn; corners bumped, sm pull tears pp50-51). *Price.* $30/£19

ANDERSON, C. W. Thoroughbreds. Macmillan, 1942. 1st ed. 9x11.5 oblong. 64pp. VG in Good dj (three 3-inch tears, 1-inch tear to rear, spine foot lacks 1/4-inch piece, other chips; lt edgeworn). *Price.* $85/£53

ANDERSON, C. W. Tomorrow's Champion. NY: Macmillan, 1946. 1st ed. Brn cl. VG+ in pict dj (neat seamed tear fr cvr). *House.* $30/£19

ANDERSON, C. W. Tomorrow's Champion. Macmillan, 1946. 1st ed. 9x11.5 oblong. 64pp. VG in Good- dj (bottom fr cvr lacks 3-inch piece, other chips to rear, heavily edgeworn). *Price.* $45/£28

ANDERSON, CARL. Henry. Phila: David McKay, (1945). 12mo. Color pict bds (lt corner wear, edge dusting). Full color dj (sm chips along spine, dusting). *Reisler.* $85/£53

ANDERSON, CHARLES C. Fighting by Southern Federals. NY: Neale, 1912. 1st ed. Frontis map. Blue-grn cl. VG (spine sunned, sm hole above title, not affecting lettering). *Chapel Hill.* $275/£172

ANDERSON, E. L. Modern Horsemanship. Edinburgh, 1884. Uncut, teg. Pict bds, red roan back. (Sl worn.) *Oinonen*.* $60/£38

ANDERSON, E. L. Soldier and Pioneer. NY: Putnam, 1879. 63pp; fldg plt. (Ex-lib, fr hinge weak, cl worn, soiled.) *Brown.* $15/£9

ANDERSON, ELBERT. Skylight and the Darkroom: A Complete Text-Book on Portrait Photography. Phila: Benerman & Wilson, 1872. 1st ed. 234pp (foxed, stained, lib stamps); 12 mtd albumen prints. 1/2 leather (rubbed). *Cahan.* $400/£250

ANDERSON, EMILY. The Letters of Mozart and His Family. C. B. Oldman (ed). Macmillan, 1938. 1st ed. 3 vols. 40 plts, 5 facs. VG, vols 2 and 3 in djs. *Hollett.* $208/£130

ANDERSON, EVA GREENSLIT. Chief Seattle. Caldwell: Caxton, 1943. 1st ed. Fine in VG dj. *Perier.* $85/£53

ANDERSON, EVA GREENSLIT. Dog-Team Doctor: The Story of Dr. Romig. Caldwell: Caxton, 1947. 7th ptg. Signed presentation. Fine. *Perier.* $32/£20

ANDERSON, GARY CLAYTON and ALAN R. WOOLWORTH (eds). Through Dakota Eyes. St. Paul: MN Hist Soc, 1988. 1st ed. VG in dj. *Lien.* $30/£19

ANDERSON, GEORGE WILLIAM. A New, Authentic, and Complete Collection of Voyages Round the World.... Alex. Hogg, (c.1784-1786). Folio. 156 (of 157) plts & maps, incl engr frontisport, linen-backed fldg map, subs list. Contemp calf (rebacked preserving orig spine). *Sotheby's*.* $1,141/£713

ANDERSON, IAIN F. Scottish Quest. Herbert Jenkins, 1935. (Labels removed from eps; faded.) *Hollett.* $24/£15

ANDERSON, IAIN F. To Introduce the Hebrides. Herbert Jenkins, 1933. Map. (Cl faded, sl mkd.) *Hollett.* $32/£20

ANDERSON, J. The Course of Creation. Cincinnati: W. Moore, 1851. 1st ed. 384pp. (Lt foxed), else VG. *Mikesh.* $45/£28

ANDERSON, J. K. Ancient Greek Horsemanship. Berkeley: Univ of CA, 1961. 39 plts. (Owner stamp), o/w Fine in dj. *Archaeologia.* $65/£41

ANDERSON, J. R. L. High Mountains and Cold Seas. London: Gollancz, 1980. VG (ex-lib) in dj. *Explorer.* $22/£14

ANDERSON, JAMES. The Interest of Great Britain with Regard to Her American Colonies.... London: T. Cadell, 1782. (Some loss few pp, some tears, dampstaining; boardless.) *Metropolitan*.* $115/£72

ANDERSON, JOHN. The American Theatre and the Motion Picture in America. NY: Dial, 1938. 1st ed. VG in pict dj (frayed). *Dramatis.* $45/£28

ANDERSON, JOHN. Anderson Improved. Being an Almanack...for the Year of Our Lord 1773.... Newport, RI: Solomon Southwick, (1772). 1st ed. Frontis, (32)pp. Mod cl-backed binding. *M & S.* $85/£53

ANDERSON, JOHN. Zoology of Egypt: Mammalia. W.E. deWinton (rev). London: Rees, 1902. (Eps foxed; illus extracted from another work tipped-in before tp; worn.) *Oinonen*.* $475/£297

ANDERSON, KENNETH. The Black Panther of Sivanipalli and Other Adventures of the Indian Jungle. London, 1959. 1st ed. Frontisport, 4 plts, 2 maps. (Feps lt browned.) Dj (sl rubbed). *Edwards.* $40/£25

ANDERSON, KENT. Sympathy for the Devil. GC: Doubleday, 1987. 1st ed. Fine in dj. *Associates.* $30/£19

ANDERSON, L. A. Hunting the American Game Field. Chicago: Ziff-Davis Pub, (1949). 1st ed. Brn cl. VG+ in dj (lt chipped). *House.* $25/£16

ANDERSON, LAWRENCE. The Art of the Silversmith in Mexico. NY: Hacker, 1975. Rpt of 1941 1st ed. 2 vols in 1. 183 plts. Good. *Cullen.* $45/£28

ANDERSON, MARGARET J. In the Circle of Time. Knopf, 1979. 1st ed. 181pp. Fine in VG+ dj (sl edgeworn, 1/4-inch wrinkles to spine top). *Price.* $28/£18

ANDERSON, MARGARET J. Searching for Shona. Knopf, 1978. 1st ed. 159pp. Fine in VG dj (sm ding to top). *Price.* $25/£16

ANDERSON, MATTHEW. Presbyterianism, Its Relation to the Negro. Phila, (1897). 263pp. *Cullen.* $125/£78

ANDERSON, MAXWELL and ANDREW SOLT. Joan of Arc. NY: Sloane, (1948). 1st ed. VF in VF dj (sl rubbed). *Between The Covers.* $150/£94

ANDERSON, MAXWELL. Anne of the Thousand Days. (NY): Sloane, (1948). 1st ed. VF in VF dj. *Between The Covers.* $400/£250

ANDERSON, MAXWELL. Barefoot in Athens. NY: Sloane, (1951). 1st ed. VF in VF dj. *Between The Covers.* $350/£219

ANDERSON, MAXWELL. Key Largo. Washington: Anderson House, 1939. 1st ed. Top edge stained gray. Gray cl. (Spine dknd, sl skewed), o/w Fine in dj (spine lt browned, few sm edgetears, lt soiled). *Heritage.* $150/£94

ANDERSON, NELS. Men on the Move. Chicago: Univ of Chicago, 1940. 1st ed. Dorthea Lange, et al (photos). VG. *Cahan.* $150/£94

ANDERSON, POUL. The High Crusade. GC: Doubleday, 1960. 1st ed. (Eps sl dknd; spine sl bumped), o/w Fine in dj (spine ends sl bumped, rear cvr sl dust-soiled). *Levin.* $600/£375

ANDERSON, POUL. Tau Zero. GC: Doubleday, 1970. 1st ed. (2 sm tape spots eps; fr gutter margins sl dknd), o/w Fine in dj. *Levin.* $250/£156

ANDERSON, R. C. The Rigging of Ships in the Days of the Spritsail Topmast 1600-1720. Salem, MA: Marine Research Soc, 1927. 1st ed. Frontis, 24 plts. Blue cl. Fine. *Karmiole.* $75/£47

ANDERSON, ROBERT. Service for the Dead. NY: Arbor House, 1986. 1st ed. Fine in dj. *Associates.* $25/£16

ANDERSON, ROBERT. Silent Night, Lonely Night. NY: Random House, (1960). 1st ed. VF in VF dj (sm internal repair 1/8-inch short). *Between The Covers.* $85/£53

ANDERSON, ROBIN and LOUIS THOMAS BYARS. Surgery of the Parotid Gland. St. Louis: C.V. Mosby, 1965. Fine in blue cl. *Weber.* $40/£25

ANDERSON, SHERWOOD. Beyond Desire. NY: Liveright, (1932). One of 165 numbered, signed. VG (inscrip, sl rubbed; lacks slipcase). *Agvent.* $225/£141

ANDERSON, SHERWOOD. Dark Laughter. NY: Boni & Liveright, 1925. 1st ed. One of 350 signed. 1/4 vellum (spine sl spotted). Slipcase (worn, defective, lacks top panel). *Kane*.* $150/£94

ANDERSON, SHERWOOD. Hometown. NY, (1940). 1st ed. (Eps, pastedowns, cl stained.) Dj (torn). *Swann*.* $126/£79

ANDERSON, SHERWOOD. Hometown. NY: Alliance Book Co, 1940. 1st ed. 110 photogravures. (Cl edges sl faded), else Fine. *Cahan.* $85/£53

ANDERSON, SHERWOOD. Horses and Men. NY: Huebsch, 1923. 1st ed. Top edge stained orange. Fine in VG dj (chipped, spine tear). *Agvent.* $250/£156

ANDERSON, SHERWOOD. Nearer the Grass Roots, and...Account of a Journey: Elizabethton. SF: Westgate, 1929. 1st ed. One of 500. Signed. Grn patterned bds, black cl spine strip. NF. *Harrington.* $80/£50

ANDERSON, SHERWOOD. Nearer the Grass Roots. SF: Westgate, 1929. 1st ed. One of 500 signed. (Spine top sl worn.) *Kane*.* $85/£53

ANDERSON, SHERWOOD. Poor White. NY: B.W. Huebsch, 1920. 1st ed, 1st issue, w/top edges stained blue. Blue cl. Fine in dj (1.5 inch piece missing). *Cummins.* $200/£125

ANDERSON, SHERWOOD. Sherwood Anderson's Memoirs. NY: Harcourt Brace, 1942. 1st ed. VG (faint pencil note) in dj (edgeworn). *My Bookhouse.* $62/£39

ANDERSON, SHERWOOD. A Story Teller's Story.... NY: Huebsch, 1924. 1st ed. Brn cl (bkpl; sm ding fr cvr). Dj (sl worn). *Kane*.* $50/£31

ANDERSON, SHERWOOD. Tar. A Midwest Childhood. NY: Boni & Liveright, 1926. 1st ed. Nice (top edge stained dk brn). *Cady.* $30/£19

ANDERSON, SHERWOOD. Tar. A Midwest Childhood. NY: Boni & Liveright, 1926. 1st ed. VG + in dj (lg chips). *My Bookhouse.* $77/£48

ANDERSON, SHERWOOD. Winesburg, Ohio. NY: B.W. Huebsch, 1929. 1st ed, 1st issue w/top edges stained yellow. Yellow cl, paper spine label. (Label soiled), else NF. *Pacific*.* $104/£65

ANDERSON, SHERWOOD. Winesburg, Ohio. LEC, 1978. Ltd to 1500 numbered, signed by Ben F. Stahl (illus). Fine in slipcase. *Swann*.* $80/£50

ANDERSON, TEMPEST. Volcanic Studies in Many Lands. London: John Murray, 1903. 1st ed. 105 plts. Good (blindstamp on some plts; rubbed, lib #s removed from spine). *Glaser.* $95/£59

ANDERSON, W. ELLERY. Expedition South. London: Evans Bros, 1957. 1st ed. VG in dj. *High Latitude.* $25/£16

ANDERSON, WILLIAM. The Pictorial Arts of Japan. Boston, 1886. 1st Amer ed, in orig cl bound parts. Folio. 4 parts. 80 plts, incl 16 color. (Lacks ties, spine ends worn.) *Swann*.* $149/£93

ANDERSON, WILLIAM. The Scottish Nation; or the Surnames, Families, Literature, Honours, and Biographical History of the People of Scotland. London, 1860-63. 3 vols. 1/2 sheep (extrems worn; lt dampstained). *Swann*.* $80/£50

ANDERSON, WILLIAM. The Scottish Nation; or the Surnames, Families, Literature, Honours, and Biographical History of the People of Scotland. Edinburgh: A. Fullarton, 1863. 3 vols. 3/4 calf, gilt. (Joint starting, lacks spine labels), else VG set. *Pacific*.* $288/£180

ANDERSON, WINSLOW. Mineral Springs and Health Resorts of California. SF: Bancroft, 1892. 1st ed, 2nd ptg. xxx,384pp. Pict cl. VG. *Glaser.* $250/£156

ANDERSON-MASKELL, MRS. A. E. Children with the Fishes. Boston: D. Lothrop, (1887). 1st ed. Pict cl. (Spine head chip), else VG. *Pacific*.* $138/£86

ANDERSON-MASKELL, MRS. A. E. Four Feet, Wings, and Fins. Boston: D. Lothrop, (1879). 7 3/4 x 5 1/2. Cl-backed pict color litho bds, gilt spine. VG. *Pacific*.* $29/£18

ANDERSSON, CHARLES JOHN. Lake Ngami. London, 1856. 2nd ed. vii,546pp; 16 litho plts (1 fore-edge sl shaved not affecting image, lettering), fldg map (repair to verso). Blind-emb cl. (Lt browned; spine sl stained, faded; sympathetically recased w/repairs to spine ends.) *Edwards.* $360/£225

ANDERSSON, CHARLES JOHN. Lake Ngami. London: Hurst & Blackett, 1856. 1st ed. xviii,546pp + 24pp pub's list; fldg map, 16 litho plts. Brn blindstamped cl (faded, spine ends chipped, joints, hinges cracking; lt foxed, lt waterstain lower margin of plts). *Morrell.* $448/£280

ANDERSSON, CHARLES JOHN. The Okavango River. NY: Harper, 1861. Engr tp, xx,21-414pp, 2 ads; 16 plts, fldg map. Blue pict cl (spine faded, ends worn), gilt. *Adelson.* $185/£116

ANDERTON, H. O. Baldur. London: T. Fisher Unwin, 1893. Presentation copy inscribed to John Drinkwater. Untrimmed. VG in orig pict wraps, custom-made solander case. *Dramatis.* $50/£31

ANDERTON, H. O. Early English Music. 'Musical Opinion,' 1920. 1st ed. 5 ports. (Few ll carelessly opened; spine sl worn.) *Hollett.* $32/£20

ANDOVER, HENRY. Men Who March Away. London: Eyre & Spottiswoode, 1934. 1st ed. Orange cl stamped in black. (Edges sl dusty), o/w VG in pict dj. *Reese.* $75/£47

ANDRADE, E. N. da C. A Brief History of the Royal Society. London: Royal Soc, 1960. 1st ed. Signed presentation (recipient's name crossed out). VG in dj. *Glaser.* $60/£38

ANDRAE, ELSBETH. The Dear Old Boys in Blue. SF: Reynard, 1948. Ptd wrappers. *Dawson*. $30/£19

ANDRAL, GABRIEL. Medical Clinic; Diseases of the Abdomen. Phila, 1843. 418pp. White, grey bds (skillfully rebound), paper spine label. VG. *Doctor's Library*. $180/£113

ANDREAE, BERNARD. The Art of Rome. Robert Erich Wolf (trans). NY: Harry N. Abrams, (1977). 1st ed. 159 color plts. White cl, gilt. Fine in dj, slipcase. *Karmiole*. $100/£63

ANDREE, A. A. et al. The Andree Diaries, Being the Diaries and Records of A. A. Andree, Nils Strindberg and Knut Fraenkel.... John Lane, Bodley Head, 1931. 1st ed. 3 fldg maps (1 color). Red cl, gilt. Good (spine sl faded, rear bd sl scratched). *Sotheran*. $128/£80

ANDREEV, LEONID. The Dark. L. A. Magnus and K. Walter (trans). Hogarth, 1922. 1st Eng ed. VG in wrappers (nicked at overlapping fore-edges, sl dusty, creased). *Ulysses*. $152/£95

ANDRES, GLENN. The Art of Florence. NY, 1987. 2 vols. (Lt worn.) *Oinonen**. $130/£81

ANDREWS, ALLEN. The Pig Plantagenet. Viking, 1981. 1st ed. Michael Foreman (illus). Fine in VG + dj (sm chip top rear edge). *Price*. $35/£22

ANDREWS, ALLEN. The Pig Plantagenet. NY: Viking, 1981. 1st ed. 8vo. Full-pg frontis, 199pp; 11 full-pg illus by Michael Foreman. Pict eps. Gray paper, brn cl spine, gilt title. Mint in pict dj. *Hobbyhorse*. $95/£59

ANDREWS, C. E. Old Morocco and the Forbidden Atlas. NY: Doran, 1922. 1st ed. 17 tipped-in plts. (Ex-lib; spine frayed, faded, edges rubbed, lib spine #), o/w Good. *Worldwide*. $30/£19

ANDREWS, C. L. Sitka, the Chief Factory of the Russian American Company. Caldwell: Caxton, 1945. 3rd ed. VG in dj. *Perier*. $30/£19

ANDREWS, C. L. The Story of Alaska. Caldwell: Caxton, 1938. 1st ed. Map in pocket. VG. *Perier*. $30/£19

ANDREWS, C. L. The Story of Alaska. Caldwell, ID: Caxton, 1938. 1st ptg of enlgd ed. Fldg map in pocket. Nice in dj. *High Latitude*. $35/£22

ANDREWS, CHARLES W. A Monograph of Christmas Island. London: Ptd by Order of the Trustees, 1900. Fldg map, 21 plts at rear (7 color). (Margins lt browned, fore-edge of few plts sl spotted, bkpl; cl sl sunned, rubbed, sm paper spine label.) *Edwards*. $320/£200

ANDREWS, EDWARD D. The Community Industries of the Shakers. Albany: Univ of NY, 1933. 65 plts. (Inscrip), o/w VG in pict wrappers. *Hollett*. $48/£30

ANDREWS, FRED H. Wall Paintings from Ancient Shrines in Central Asia. London: OUP, 1948. 1st ed. 2 vols. Med 4to & folio. xxxiv,128pp, 3 plans, fldg map; 32 plts (12 color), 3 dbl-pg plts (1 color). Text vol in cl-backed paper bds (corners sl rubbed, sm nick top edge fr bd); plt portfolio in full lt blue buckram, as issued. VG set. *Ulysses*. $2,400/£1,500

ANDREWS, GRAEME. The Ferries of Sydney. Sydney: Reed, 1976. Pict cl. VG. *American Booksellers*. $35/£22

ANDREWS, J. CUTLER. The North Reports the Civil War. Pittsburgh: Univ of Pittsburgh, (1955). 1st ed. 16 plts, 2 maps (1 fldg). VF in pict dj. *Argonaut*. $45/£28

ANDREWS, JAMES. The Parterre; or, Beauties of Flora. London: T.H. & Bogue, 1842. Folio. 11 (of 12) hand-finished plts. Orig gilt-dec cl (spine laid down, sl dampstaining along outside edge, sl foxed). *Metropolitan**. $1,725/£1,078

ANDREWS, KEITH. The Nazarenes. Oxford: Clarendon, 1964. Frontis, 80 plts (10 color). Pub's cl. Dj. *Sotheran*. $136/£85

ANDREWS, KENNETH R. (ed). English Privateering Voyages to the West Indies 1588-1595. Cambridge: CUP, 1959. Blue cl. Fine. *Appelfeld*. $60/£38

ANDREWS, LUMAN. Flowering Plants and Ferns of Springfield, Massachusetts, Growing without Cultivation. Springfield: Museum of Natural History, 1924. 1st ed. 10 b/w plts. Grn cl, gilt. (Name), else VG. *Fair Meadow*. $25/£16

ANDREWS, RALPH W. Indians as the Westerners Saw Them. Seattle: Superior, (1963). 1st ed. Fine in dj. *Perier*. $40/£25

ANDREWS, RALPH W. Photographers of the Frontier West—Their Lives and Work—1875-1915. Seattle: Superior, (1965). 1st ed. Fine in VG dj. *Perier*. $45/£28

ANDREWS, RALPH W. Photographers of the Frontier West...1875-1915. Seattle: Superior Pub, 1965. 1st ed. Fine. *Cahan*. $60/£38

ANDREWS, WILLIAM LORING. Roger Payne and His Art. NY: De Vinne, 1892. One of 120. *Swann**. $172/£108

ANDRIST, RALPH K. The Long Death. The Last Days of the Plains Indian. NY: Macmillan, (1964). 1st ed. Fine in pict dj (spine dknd). *Argonaut*. $30/£19

ANDRONICOS, MANOLIS et al. The Greek Museums. Athens/New Rochelle: Ekdotike Athenon/Caratzas Bros, 1977. Sm folio. Dj. *Turtle Island*. $75/£47

Anecdotes of a Croat; or, The Castle of Serai. London, 1823. 2 vols. Orig bds (cvrs loose vol 1, spine labels chipped; bkpl). *Swann**. $115/£72

ANGAS, GEORGE FRENCH. South Australia Illustrated. London: Thomas M'lean, 1847. (Facsimile ed, 1967.) One of 1000 numbered. Lg folio. Colored 1/2-title, 60 color plts; facs of the 10 orig ptd wrappers. Period-style maroon morocco spine, heavy marbled bds. (Sl rubbed.) *Karmiole*. $350/£219

ANGAS, W. MACK. Rivalry on the Atlantic. NY: Lee Furman, 1939. Tan cl. VG. *American Booksellers*. $55/£34

ANGEL, MYRON (ed). History of Nevada with Illustrations and Biographical Sketches of Its Prominent Men and Pioneers. Oakland: Thompson & West, 1881. 1st ed. 680pp; 116 plts. (Recased in orig leather spine, dec cl.) VG. Howes A273. *Perier*. $625/£391

ANGEL, MYRON (ed). History of Nevada, 1881. Berkeley: Howell-North, 1958. Facs ed. Brn cl, gilt. Fine. Howes A273. *Harrington*. $100/£63

ANGEL, MYRON (ed). Thompson and West's Story of Nevada, 1881. Berkeley, CA: Howell-North, 1958. VG. Howes A273. *Lien*. $95/£59

ANGELO, VALENTI. Angelino and the Barefoot Saint. Viking, 1961. 1st ed. 63pp. NF (ex-lib, mkd) in NF dj. *Price*. $22/£14

ANGELOU, MAYA. I Know Why the Caged Bird Sings. NY, (1969). 1st ed, 1st bk. (Inscrip.) Dj. *Swann**. $138/£86

ANGELOU, MAYA. I Know Why the Caged Bird Sings. NY: Random House, (1969). 1st ed, 1st issue. Top edge stained magenta, untrimmed, bulked text measures 15/16 inches. Black cl. (Top edge sl dusty.) Internally Fine in VG dj. *Baltimore**. $150/£94

ANGELOU, MAYA. I Know Why the Caged Bird Sings. NY, (1969). 1st ed, 1st bk. Dj (sm closed tear bottom joint of fr panel). *Swann**. $172/£108

ANGELOU, MAYA. Oh Pray My Wings Are Gonna Fit Me Well. NY, 1975. 1st ed. NF in NF dj. *Warren*. $35/£22

ANGELOU, MAYA. Our Grandmothers. LEC, 1994. One of 400 signed by Angelou & John Biggers (illus). Fine in slipcase. *Swann**. $690/£431

Angels' Call, Woman and Fame and The Themes of Song. The Amulet, or Christian and Literary Romancer, 1829. Teg. Contemp full leather, raised bands. Good (adhesion of paper resulting in loss of several letters ptd tp, sl spotted). *Tiger*. $32/£20

ANGIER, R. H. Firearm Blueing and Browning. Harrisburg, 1936. 1st ed. Dj. *Hallam*. $45/£28

ANGLE, PAUL M. Here I Have Lived: A History of Lincoln's Springfield, 1821-1865. Rutgers, 1950. 2nd ptg. Good. *Rybski.* $25/£16

ANGLE, PAUL M. Lincoln 1854-1861. Being the Day-by-Day Activities of Abraham Lincoln from January 1, 1854 to March 4, 1861. Springfield, IL: A. Lincoln Assoc, (1933). 1st Amer ed. Fine (spine sl sunned). *Polyanthos.* $30/£19

Angler's Almanac and Pocket-Book for 1853. London: G. Cox, 1853. 1st ed. Period cl. NF. *Pacific*.* $127/£79

ANGLER'S CLUB OF NEW YORK. Angler's Club Story. NY: Privately ptd, 1956. One of 750 ptd. Inscribed presentation from Sparse Grey Hackle, w/presentation slip from Pete Hidy. Paper labels. (Lt worn.) Slipcase. *Oinonen*.* $475/£297

ANGLER'S CLUB OF NEW YORK. Best of the Angler's Club Bulletin 1920-1927. A. Ross Jones (ed). NY, 1972. 1st ed. One of 1000. (Lt worn.) Pict slipcase. *Oinonen*.* $90/£56

ANGLER'S CLUB OF NEW YORK. Well Dressed Lines Stripped from the Reels of Five New Englanders. NY: Privately ptd, 1962. One of 500. Ptd labels. (Lt worn.) *Oinonen*.* $100/£63

Angler's Vade Mecum: Or, a Compendious, Yet Full, Discourse of Angling.... London: Bassett, 1681. 1st ed. Sm 8vo. 4 leaves; 180(mis-numbered 166)pp; 6 leaves. Mod calf (sl soiled, browned). Bkpl of R.B. Barston inlaid to 2nd fep. *Oinonen*.* $1,900/£1,188

ANGLO, MICHAEL. Penny Dreadfuls and Other Victorian Horrors. Jupiter Books, 1977. 1st ed. Dj. *Forest.* $45/£28

ANGLUND, JOAN WALSH. In a Pumpkin Shell. NY: Harcourt, 1960. 4to. Fine in Fine dj. *American Booksellers.* $50/£31

ANGLUND, JOAN WALSH. Morning is a Little Child. NY: Harcourt, 1969. 1st ed. 4to. VG in VG dj. *American Booksellers.* $30/£19

ANGOLIA, JOHN R. Daggers, Bayonets and Fighting Knives of Hitler's Germany. (Mountain View, CA, 1971.) 1st ed. (Soiled.) *King.* $150/£94

Animals at Home. London: Frederick Warne, (c. 1900). 12.75x10. (Spine, extrems rubbed), else VG in pict chromolitho linen wrappers w/lg cat fr cvr, zebras on rear. *Pacific*.* $58/£36

Animals' Christmas. Gordon Stowell (designer). Oxford: A.R. Mowbray, 1972. 3 dbl-pg pop-ups (last one sl bent). Glazed pict bds. *Bookfinders.* $40/£25

Animated Animals. Akron: Saalfield, 1943. 4 moveables by Julian Wehr. Spiral-bound pict paper-cvrd bds (corners lt bumped). VG in dj. *Davidson.* $150/£94

Animated Noah's Ark. NY: G&D, (1945). 4 moveables by Julian Wehr. Spiral-bound. VG (1 tab worn but all working; ink name, lt soil) in dj (lt worn). *Davidson.* $225/£141

Animated Story Rhymes. GC Pub Co, 1944. 4 moveable pp by Julian Wehr. Spiral-bound pict paper-cvrd bds (corners bumped). VG. *Davidson.* $125/£78

ANNABEL, RUSSELL. Hunting and Fishing in Alaska. NY: Knopf, 1948. Color frontis. VG. *High Latitude.* $100/£63

ANNABEL, RUSSELL. Hunting and Fishing In Alaska. NY: Knopf, 1948. 1st ed. Burgundy cl. Fine in color pict dj (sl chipped). *Biscotti.* $140/£88

ANNABEL, RUSSELL. Tales of a Big Game Guide. NY: Derrydale, (1938). One of 950 numbered. (Backstrip sl faded.) *Swann*.* $287/£179

Annals of Kansas, 1886-1925. Topeka: KS State Hist Soc, (1954)/(1956). 1st ed. 2 vols. Nice set (lt edgeworn). *Glenn.* $75/£47

Annals of the Army of the Cumberland. (By John Fitch.) Phila: Lippincott, 1863. 1st ed. Steel-engr extra tp, 671pp (lt aging, sl dampstain bottom margin); 16 port plts, dbl-pg color litho map. Dk grn cl (sl worn, rippled). Cvrs VG. *Baltimore*.* $85/£53

ANNESLEY, GEORGE. Voyages and Travels to India, Ceylon, the Red Sea, Abyssinia, and Egypt. London: William Miller, 1809. 3 vols. 4to. 1/2-titles, 59 (of 60) engr plts, 9 fldg maps. (Sl offsetting from some plts, occasional lt spotting to some plts.) Marbled edges. Contemp calf (rebacked, cvrs scuffed, corners bumped). *Christie's*.* $757/£473

ANNIN, JIM. Eighty Years of Memories on the Banks of the Yellowstone. The Author, n.d. Signed presentation, 1977. Fine. *Perier.* $65/£41

ANNIXTER, PAUL. Wilderness Ways. Penn, 1930. 6.3x9.5. Navy cl, gilt, lg color plt on fr. VG (spine letters sl dknd, lg bkpl). *Price.* $35/£22

ANNO, MITSUMASA. Anno's Counting Book. NY: Crowell, 1977. 1st ed. 10 sq. 32pp. Pict bds. VG in dj. *Cattermole.* $35/£22

ANNO, MITSUMASA. Anno's Counting Book. NY: Thomas Y. Crowell, 1977. Obl 8vo. Unpaginated. VG in VG dj. *Davidson.* $45/£28

ANNO, MITSUMASA. Anno's Twice Told Tales. NY: Philomel, 1993. 1st US ed. 9x10. 64pp. Glossy bds. Fine in dj. *Cattermole.* $60/£38

ANNO, MITSUMASA. Anno's USA. NY: Philomel Books, 1983. 1st ed. One of 1000 signed. As New in slipcase. *Davidson.* $120/£75

Annual Report Major Gen. Nelson A. Miles, War Dept., Year Ending June 30, 1898. Washington: GPO, 1899. 720pp. (Rebound.) *Heinoldt.* $50/£31

Annual Report of the Adjutant General of the State of Michigan for the Years 1865-6. Lansing, 1866. 3 vols. 371; 895; 927pp. Calf spines. Good set (foxed, stamp; cvrs worn). *King.* $195/£122

Annual Report of the Board of Health of the City and County of San Francisco. SF: Hinton Ptg, 1898. 1st ed. Gilt-lettered blue cl. (Spine dknd, ends rubbed), else VG. *Pacific*.* $184/£115

Annual Report of the Board of Regents of the Smithsonian Institution...for the Year 1888. US Nat'l Museum, 1888. 225-386pp (sl waterstain to edge). Antique black cl (rebound). *Perier.* $125/£78

Annual Reports of the Department of the Interior, Indian Affairs. Washington: GPO, 1900-03. 6 vols. 10 fldg color litho maps. (Lib stamps; 1 vol dampstained, lt rubbed.) *Christie's*.* $198/£124

ANONYMOUS. (Pseud of Jean Cocteau.) The White Paper. NY: Macauley, (1958). 1st Amer ed. VF in VF black dj (extrems sl rubbed). *Between The Covers.* $75/£47

ANOUILH, JEAN. The Fighting Cock. Lucienne Hill (trans). NY: Coward-McCann, (1960). 1st Amer ed. VF in VF dj. *Between The Covers.* $100/£63

ANOUILH, JEAN. Legend of Lovers. Kitty Black (trans). NY: Coward-McCann, (1952). 1st Amer ed. VF in VF dj. *Between The Covers.* $150/£94

ANOUILH, JEAN. Mademoiselle Colombe. Louis Kronenberger (trans). NY: Coward-McCann, (1954). 1st Amer ed. VF in VF dj (sl rubbed). *Between The Covers.* $150/£94

ANOUILH, JEAN. Restless Heart. Lucieen Hill (trans). London: Methuen, (1957). 1st Eng ed. VF in dj (price-clipped), else VF. *Between The Covers.* $125/£78

ANOUILH, JEAN. Ring Round the Moon. Christopher Fry (trans). London: Methuen, (1950). 1st Eng ed. Fine in Fine dj (2 sm internal brn paper repairs, sl soiled). *Between The Covers.* $125/£78

ANOUILH, JEAN. Time Remembered. Patricia Moyes (trans). NY: Coward-McCann, (1958). 1st Amer ed. VF in VF dj (sm rubbed spot). *Between The Covers.* $125/£78

ANSCOMBE, ISABELLE. Omega and After: Bloomsbury and the Decorative Arts. London: Thames & Hudson, 1981. 1st ed. (Name), o/w VG in dj. *Virgo.* $56/£35

ANSON, ADRIAN C. A Ball Player's Career. Era, 1900. 1st ed. Good + . *Plapinger.* $400/£250

ANSON, GEORGE. A Voyage Around the World, in the Years MDCCXL, I, II, III, IV. Richard Walter (comp). London: The Author, 1748. 1st ed. 4to. Frontis, (34),417,(2)pp; 42 copper-engr maps, charts, views, etc. Period paneled calf (rebacked w/matching mod calf), raised bands, old leather spine label. (Few plts w/expert repairs, chart w/sm central tear, offset to plts, bkpl; lt worn), else VG. *Pacific*.* $1,610/£1,006

ANSON, GEORGE. A Voyage Round the World, in the Years MDCCXL, I, II, III, IV. London, 1748. 1st ed. 4to. 42 engr fldg maps, plans, views. Uncut. New bds. *Felcone.* $1,800/£1,125

ANSON, PETER F. Fashions in Church Furnishings 1840-1940. Studio Vista, 1960. VG in pub's cl. *Hadley.* $64/£40

ANSON, W. S. W. (ed). The Table-Talk of John Selden. London: Routledge, 1911? Grn cl (worn), extra gilt. Usable. *Boswell.* $45/£28

ANSTED, D. et al. Geology, Mineralogy, and Crystallography. London: Houlston and Stoneman/Wm. S. Orr, 1855. xx,587pp. Good (spine lettering lt rubbed). *Blake.* $100/£63

ANSTED, D. T. Scenery, Science, and Art. London, 1854. 1st ed. viii,323,4 ads; 4 tinted litho plts. (Rear joint starting to split.) *Henly.* $136/£85

ANSTEY, CHRISTOPHER. The Poetical Works.... 1808. 2 vols. 2 engr ports, 4 plts; this copy extra-illus, containing 53 contemp prints. Edges gilt. Panelled calf, gilt, by Zaehnsdorf. *Sotheby's*.* $1,011/£632

ANSTEY, F. Mr. Punch's Model Music Hall Songs and Dramas. NY, (1892). 1st Amer ed. Pict cvr. NF (sl rubbed, spine sl sunned). *Polyanthos.* $35/£22

ANTAL, FREDERICK. Florentine Painting and Its Social Background. The Bourgeois Republic Before Cosimo de'Medici's Advent to Power: XIV and Early XV Centuries. London, 1965. 2nd ed. 160 plts. (Sm spot lower fr cvr), o/w Nice. *Washton.* $85/£53

ANTHOENSEN, FRED. Types and Bookmaking Containing Notes on the Books Printed at the Southworth-Anthoensen Press. And a Bibliographical Catalogue by Ruth A. Chaplin. Portland, 1943. One of 500. Uncut. Leather spine label. (Lt worn.) *Oinonen*.* $100/£63

Anthology of Babyhood. Hutchinson, 1910. 1st ed thus. Sm 8vo. 186pp; 4 color plts by T.J. & E.A. Overnell. Pict pink eps. Pict red cl, gilt. (Spine faded), else VG. *Bookmark.* $40/£25

ANTHONY, CHARLES VOLNEY. Fifty Years of Methodism. SF: Methodist Book Concern, 1901. (Sl shelfworn, rubbed), o/w VG. *Brown.* $75/£47

ANTHONY, EDGAR W. Early Florentine Architecture and Decoration. Cambridge, 1927. Inscribed. 82 plts. (Corners sl rubbed.) *Washton.* $150/£94

ANTHONY, EDGAR W. A History of Mosaics. Boston, 1935. 80 plts. (Cl sl soiled, spine dknd.) *Washton.* $125/£78

ANTHONY, GORDON. Ballet Camera Studies. London: Bles, 1937. 1st ed. Frontis. 96 mtd photos. Uncut. Cl-backed bevelled bds. VF. *Europa.* $104/£65

ANTHONY, GORDON. Markova. A Collection of Photographic Studies. London: C&W, 1935. Frontis, 23 plts. Internally VF in dj (sl worn). *Europa.* $29/£18

ANTHONY, IRVIN. Paddle Wheels and Pistols. Phila: Macrae Smith, (1929). 1st ed. VG in pict cl. *Lien.* $20/£13

ANTHONY, KATHARINE. The Lambs: A Study of Pre-Victorian England. Hammond, Hammond, 1948. VG in dj (repaired w/closed tears). *Tiger.* $19/£12

ANTHONY, PIERS. Robot Adept. NY: Putnam, (1988). 1st ed. Fine in NF dj. *Antic Hay.* $20/£13

ANTHONY, PIERS. Unicorn Point. NY: Ace/Putnam, (1989). 1st ed. NF in dj (few sm tears). *Antic Hay.* $25/£16

Antiquarian Itinerary. (By James Sargeant Storer.) London, Wm Clarke, 1815-8. 7 vols. 334 copper-engr plts. Marbled eps; uncut. 1/2 morocco, marbled bds, gilt. (Bkpl, spotted; rubbed, lt soiled, sl worn, spine dknd.) *Edwards.* $400/£250

ANTONINUS, BROTHER. A Canticle to the Waterbirds. Berkeley: Eizo, 1968. One of 200. Signed by William Everson as Brother Antoninus and by Allen Say (illus). Gray cl. Fine. *Pacific*.* $69/£43

ANTONINUS, BROTHER. Who Is She That Looketh Forth as the Morning. Santa Barbara: Capricorn Press, 1972. One of 250. Signed by William Everson as Brother Antoninus. Prospectus laid in. Dk grn bds, gilt. Fine in acetate. *Pacific*.* $75/£47

APES, WILLIAM. Indian Nullification of the Unconstitutional Laws of Massachusetts Relative to the Marshpee Tribe. Boston: Press of Jonathan Howe, 1835. 1st ed. Woodcut frontis, 168pp. Orig red cl (faded), paper spine label. (Foxed; lt waterstain top/bottom corners through 1st 60pp.) *Karmiole.* $200/£125

APES, WILLIAM. A Son of the Forest: The Experience of William Apes, a Native of the Forest. NY: William Apes, 1831. 2nd ed. 214pp (pg 214 misnumbered 114). Period morocco-backed marbled bds, gilt. (Lacks frontis; spine sunned, extrems rubbed), else VG-. *Pacific*.* $98/£61

APFELBAUM, CHARLES and LOIS (eds). A Carl Sandburg Miscellany. Valley Stream, NY, 1977. 1st ed. One of 290. Signed. Good + in pict card cvrs. *Wantagh.* $45/£28

APOLLINAIRE, GUILLAUME. The Poet Assassinated. London: Rupert Hart-Davis, 1968. 1st ed. Signed, inscribed. (Stain to lower rear cvr), else VG- in dj (extrems sl yellowed, tape-repaired tears on verso). *Pacific*.* $52/£33

APOLLONIUS RHODIUS. The Argonautica. LEC, 1958. Ltd to 1500 numbered, signed by A. Tassos (illus). Fine in slipcase. *Swann*.* $115/£72

Apology for the Life of James Fennell. (By James Fennell.) Phila: Moses Thomas, 1814. 1st ed. Period calf (spine dry, crown chipped; lacks frontis port, foxed). *Dramatis.* $30/£19

Appeal to Pharaoh: The Negro Problem, and Its Radical Solution. NY: Fords Howard & Hulbert, 1889. 1st ed. 205pp. (Sl shelfwear, soil), o/w VG. *Brown.* $75/£47

Appeal to the Justice and Interests of the People of Great Britain, in the Present Disputes with America. (By Arthur Lee.) London: Almon, 1775. 3rd ed. Wrappers. Howes L183. *Rostenberg & Stern.* $125/£78

APPERLEY, CHARLES J. Nimrod Abroad. London: Colburn, 1842. 1st ed. 2 vols. Pub's cl. (Shelfwear, sl soil, foxing, etc.) *Oinonen*.* $80/£50

APPERSON, G. L. Bygone London Life. London, 1903. (Bkpls removed; corners, spine sl rubbed.) *Edwards.* $56/£35

APPLE, JACKI. Trunk Pieces. Rochester: Visual Studies Workshop, 1975. 1st ed. Ltd to 300. 40 photos. Patterned eps. Fine in illus stiff self wrappers (sm crease). *Cahan.* $50/£31

APPLE, MAX. The Oranging of America. NY: Viking, 1976. 1st ed, 1st bk. NF in dj (lt stain). *Agvent.* $45/£28

APPLEGATE, FRANK. Indian Stories from the Pueblos. Phila: Lippincott, 1929. 1st ed. VG. *Labordo.* $50/£31

APPLEGATE, FRANK. Indian Stories from the Pueblos. Phila, 1929. 1st ed. 7 color plts. Internally Good (bds sl soiled, worn). *Dumont.* $65/£41

APPLEGATE, FRANK. Native Tales of New Mexico. Phila, 1932. 1st ed. Dec cl. VG. *Baade.* $40/£25

APPLEGATE, FRANK. Native Tales of New Mexico. Phila: Lippincott, 1932. 1st ed. VG + . *Labordo.* $75/£47

APPLEGATE, JESSE and LAVINIA HONEYMAN PORTER. Westward Journeys. Martin Ridge (ed). Chicago: R.R. Donnelley, 1989. Frontis. VG. *Lien.* $30/£19

APPLEGATE, JESSE. A Day with the Cow Column in 1843. Portland: Champoeg, 1952. One of 225. VG. Howes A294. *Perier.* $97/£61

APPLEGATE, JESSE. A Day with the Cow Column. Chicago: Caxton Club, 1934. 1st ed. One of 300 ptd. NF. Howes A294. *Labordo.* $350/£219

Appleton's Cyclopaedia of American Biography. NY, 1887-89. 6 vols. Uniform 1/2 morocco (extrems rubbed). *Swann*.* $402/£251

APPLETON, E. H. Insurrection at Magellan. Boston: The Author, 1854. 1st ed. 1,l,228pp. Emb brn cl, gilt. (Foxed, soiled, esp prelims), else VG. *Parmer.* $250/£156

APPLETON, G. W. The Down Express. London: Lane, 1908. 1st ed. NF. *Else Fine.* $65/£41

APPLETON, VICTOR. The Movie Boys at the Big Fair. GC: GC, 1926. #16 in the Movie Boys series. 5x7. 214pp. VG+ (sl shelfworn) in color pict wraps. *My Bookhouse.* $32/£20

APPLETON, VICTOR. Tom Swift Among the Fire Fighters. NY: G&D, 1921. Tom Swift #24; lists 30 titles on dj flap. 5x7.5. 214pp + ads. (Lower edge worn), else VG in pale full color illus dj (sl edgeworn, dingy). *My Bookhouse.* $57/£36

APPONYI, FLORA H. The Libraries of California. SF: A.L. Bancroft, 1878. 1st ed. 304pp + 6pp ads. Black pebbled cl. (Emb seal tp; old marginal waterstain final ll; spine extrems frayed.) *Karmiole.* $150/£94

APPONYI, FLORA H. The Libraries of California. SF: A.L. Bancroft, 1878. 1st ed. One of 500, although not indicated. 304,(6)pp; 4 full-pg facs. Black leatherette (rebound in facs), gilt. Fine. *Argonaut.* $375/£234

APSLEY, LADY. Bridleways Through History. London: Hutchinson, 1936. 1st ed. 14 full-pg dwgs by Lionel Edwards. VG. *October Farm.* $65/£41

APULEIUS, LUCIUS. Cupid and Psyches. (London): Golden Cockerel, 1934. One of 150. (Ink inscrip; spine dknd.) *Kane*.* $120/£75

APULEIUS, LUCIUS. Cupid and Psyches. The Excellent Narration of Their Marriage.... William Adlington (trans). Nonesuch, 1923. One of 625. Patterned cream eps; untrimmed. 1/4 maroon parchment, gilt, patterned cream bds. VG (bkpl) in patterned cream bd slipcase. *Blackwell's.* $200/£125

APULEIUS, LUCIUS. The Golden Ass. William Addington (trans). NY: Scott-Thaw, 1904. One of 200 (of 210). Signed by pub. Uncut. Fine. *Polyanthos.* $95/£59

APULEIUS, LUCIUS. The Golden Ass. NY: LEC, 1932. One of 1500 signed by Percival Goodman (illus). VG (bkpl) in slipcase. *Williams.* $120/£75

APULEIUS, LUCIUS. The Marriage of Cupid and Psyche. LEC, 1951. Ltd to 1500 numbered, signed by Edmund Dulac (illus). Fine in slipcase. *Swann*.* $103/£64

APULEIUS, LUCIUS. The Marriage of Cupid and Psyche. NY: LEC, 1951. One of 1500. Signed by Edmund Dulac (illus). Full vellum, gilt. Fine in slipcase. *Pacific*.* $374/£234

APULEIUS, LUCIUS. The Metamorphosis, or Golden Ass, and Philosophical Works, of Apuleius. Thomas Taylor (trans). London: Robert Triphook & Thomas Rodd, 1822. 1st Taylor ed. With the 5pp of 'suppressed passages,' and their 1/2-title, ptd on 4 ll (2 blank, as issued). xxiv,400,(8)pp. Marbled eps. Teg. Mod 3/4 red levant morocco, marbled bds, gilt. (Sl rubbed), else Fine. *Pacific*.* $374/£234

APULEIUS, LUCIUS. The XI. Bookes of the Golden Asse...Translated Out of Latine into English, by William Adlington. (Chelsea: Ashendene), 1923. One of 165. 4to. Prospectus laid in. Linen-backed patterned bds. Cl slipcase. *Swann*.* $575/£359

AQUINAS, THOMAS. Writings of St. Thomas Aquinas. LEC, 1969. Ltd to 1500 numbered, signed by Reynolds Stone (illus). Fine in slipcase. *Swann*.* $161/£101

Arabian Nights Stories. London: Raphael Tuck & Sons, n.d. (193?). Sm 8vo. H. G. Theaker et al (illus). Color frontis, 156 + 4pp ads; dbl-pg pop-up. Glazed pict bds. Fine (lacks fep). *Bookfinders.* $75/£47

Arabian Nights' Entertainments. London: George Newnes Ld (sic), 1899. 1st ed. 4to. W. Heath Robinson et al (illus). viii,472pp. Aeg. Mid-blue pict cl, gilt. Very Clean (prelims lt speckled, few other ll lt browned; bds lt rubbed). *Sotheran.* $301/£188

Arabian Nights. London: Constable, ca 1920. Sm 4to. viii,298pp; 10 Fine mtd color plts by Rene Bull, guards. Grn cl stamped in dk grn w/onlaid pict label. (Tp, edges of bk block sl speckled), o/w VG. *Sotheran.* $221/£138

Arabian Nights. Tales from the Thousand and One Nights. London: Hodder & Stoughton, (1922). 1st ed. 4to. 12 full-pg mtd color plts by E. J. Detmold. White cl, gilt. (Sm ink spot on fore-edge), else Fine in ptd pub's box (worn, stained) w/full color paste label. *Reisler.* $1,000/£625

ARAGON, LOUIS. Aragon. Poet of the French Resistance. Malcolm Cowley and Hannah Josephson (eds). NY: Duell, Sloane & Pearce, (1945). 1st ed. Fine in VG dj (sl nicked, tanned). *Reese.* $45/£28

ARAGON, LOUIS. The Bells of Basel. Haakon M. Chevalier (trans). NY: Harcourt, (1936). 1st ed in English. Blue cl. Fine in pict dj (few scratches, 2 creased edge tears top of rear panel). *Reese.* $60/£38

Arbuckle's Illustrated Atlas of the United States of America. NY: Arbuckle Bros, 1889. Unpaginated (26); 48 color maps. Bound w/a tie. (Sl edgeworn, soiled), else VG. *Dumont.* $285/£178

ARBUS, DIANE. Diane Arbus: Magazine Work. NY: Aperture, (1984). 1st ed. Folio. Photo-pict bds (extrems sl worn). Dj (rubbed, tear). *Swann*.* $92/£58

ARBUTHNOT, J. The Life and Works of John Arbuthnot. G.A. Aitken (ed). Oxford, 1892. Frontisport, xii,516pp. Color eps. (1/2 title lt foxed, bkpl), o/w VG. *Whitehart.* $136/£85

ARBUTHNOT, J. Miscellaneous Works. London, 1770. 2nd ed. 2 vols. xvi,246; 310pp. 1/2 morocco (worn), marbled bds, gilt. VG. *Whitehart.* $224/£140

ARCAMBEAU, EDME. The Book of Bridges. London/Glasgow: Gowans/Gray, 1911. One of 1000. 17 full-pg plts w/guards. Teg. Illus laid on cvr. (Extrems lt worn), else Fine in grn cl, gilt spine. *Bromer.* $350/£219

Archer's Complete Guide. NY: Peck & Snyder, 1878. 26pp + 6pp ads; 4 full-pg plts. Blue cl, gilt. Fine. *Bowman.* $120/£75

ARCHER, JEFFREY. A Matter of Honour. London/Sydney/Auckland/Toronto: Hodder & Stoughton, 1986. 1st ed. Black cl-textured bds. Fine in dj. *Temple.* $26/£16

ARCHER, JEFFREY. The Prodigal Daughter. NY: Linden Press/S&S, 1982. 1st ed. Fine in dj (few sm creases rear flap). *Antic Hay.* $17/£11

ARCHER, M. Natural History Drawings in the India Office Library. London: HMSO, 1962. 1st ed. Color frontis. Pict cl, gilt. Fine in VG+ dj. *Mikesh.* $75/£47

ARCHER, S. A. (comp). A Heroine of the North. London: SPCK, 1929. Frontis. (Rebound; lib handstamps, shelf label), else Good. *Brown.* $25/£16

ARCHER, VINCENT W. The Osseous System. Chicago, 1945. 1st ed. VG (extrems sl worn). *Doctor's Library.* $30/£19

ARCHER, W. G. Indian Paintings from the Punjab Hills. London, 1973. 2 vols. Folio. Djs (torn). *Swann*.* $126/£79

ARCHER, WILLIAM and H. GRANVILLE BARKER. A National Theatre: Scheme and Estimates. London: Duckworth, 1907. 1st ed. (Spine sunned.) *Dramatis.* $65/£41

ARCHER, WILLIAM. America To-day: Observations and Reflections. London: Heinemann, 1900. 1st ed. (Sl bubbled, soiled.) *Mott.* $25/£16

ARCHIBALD, NORMAN. Heaven High, Hell Deep, 1917-1918. NY: Albert & Charles Boni, 1935. 1st ed. Blue cl, pict foil spine label. (1935 ink inscrip; edges sl sunned), o/w VG in pict foil dj (sl edgeworn, nicked). *Reese.* $65/£41

ARCTANDER, JOHN W. The Apostle of Alaska, the Story of William Duncan of Metlakahtla. NY: Fleming H. Revell, (1909). VG in dec cl. *Perier.* $65/£41

Arctic Bibliography. Washington: Dept of Defense, 1953-60. Vols I-VII. (Sl discoloration to lower spines vols. 6 & 7), else VG. *High Latitude.* $600/£375

Arctic Bibliography. Prepared for and in Cooperation with the Department of Defense Under the Direction of the Arctic Institute of North America. (Washington): Dept of Defense, 1953-1959. 8 vols. 8vo. Matching blue-gray cl. VG set (ex-lib, sm paper spine labels). *Explorer.* $512/£320

Arctic World. Its Plants, Animals and Natural Phenomena, with a Historical Sketch of Arctic Discovery. (By W.H. Adams.) Nelson, 1876. 1st ed. 276pp. Gilt-dec cl. Good (sl foxed). *Walcot.* $64/£40

ARDIZZONE, EDWARD. The Adventures of Tim. Chancellor, 1985. 1st ed thus. Sm 4to. 300pp. VG in dj. *Hollett.* $48/£30

ARDIZZONE, EDWARD. Diary of a War Artist. London: Bodley Head, 1974. 1st Eng ed. NF (spine tail sl bumped) in dj (edges sl rubbed). *Ulysses.* $72/£45

ARDIZZONE, EDWARD. Lucy Brown and Mr. Grimes. NY: OUP, (1937). 1st Amer ed. Sm folio. Cl-backed color illus bds (lower edges sl worn). Pict dj (tape repairs). *Reisler.* $575/£359

ARDIZZONE, EDWARD. Ship's Cook Ginger. NY: Macmillan, 1977. 1st US ed. 7.75x10.25. 48pp. Pict bds. Fine in dj. *Cattermole.* $25/£16

ARDIZZONE, EDWARD. Ship's Cook Ginger. Bodley Head, 1977. 1st ed. 4to. 48pp. Glossy pict bds. Fine. *Bookmark.* $48/£30

ARDIZZONE, EDWARD. Ship's Cook Ginger. Macmillan, 1978. 1st US ed. 8x10. 48pp. NF in NF dj. *Price.* $30/£19

ARDIZZONE, EDWARD. Tim and Ginger. NY: Walck, 1965. 1st US ed. 7.75x10.25. 48pp. VG in dj. *Cattermole.* $25/£16

ARDIZZONE, EDWARD. Tim and Lucy Go to Sea. OUP, (1938). Early Eng imp. Sm folio. Unpaginated. VG + (neat 1944 inscrip; bottom bd rubbed) in Good dj (edgeworn, rubbed, 4 medium chips not affecting text, 5-inch closed tear). *Price.* $150/£94

ARDLEY, PATRICIA B. Mr. and Mrs. Hedgehog. London: Collins, (1936). 1st ed. Obl 4to. 6 full-pg color plts by E. C. Ardley. Cl-backed pict bds (lt dusty). *Reisler.* $125/£78

ARGO, RONALD. Year of the Monkey. NY: S&S, 1989. 1st ed. Fine in dj. *Associates.* $25/£16

ARIAS, P. E. A History of 1000 Years of Greek Vase Painting. NY: Abrams, n.d. *Swann*.* $172/£108

ARIOSTO, LUDOVICO. Orlando Furioso. William Stewart Rose (trans). London: Bohn, 1858. 2 vols. 12 steel-engr plts, extra-illus. Teg, gilt inner dentelles. 19th cent full dk grn levant morocco, gilt, raised bands, bound by Bickers. (Bkpls; rubbed), else VG. *Pacific*.* $184/£115

ARISTOPHANES. The Birds. LEC, 1959. Ltd to 1500 numbered, signed by Marian Parry (illus). Fine in slipcase. *Swann*.* $34/£21

ARISTOPHANES. The Birds. NY: LEC, 1959. One of 1500. Signed by Marian Parry (illus). 1/2 leather, patterned bds. Fine in chemise, slipcase. *Pacific*.* $46/£29

ARISTOPHANES. The Frogs. LEC, 1937. Ltd to 1500 numbered, signed by John Austen (illus). Fine in slipcase. *Swann*.* $80/£50

ARISTOPHANES. Lysistrata. LEC, 1934. Ltd to 1500 numbered, signed by Pablo Picasso (illus). Fine in slipcase. *Swann*.* $2,760/£1,725

ARISTOPHANES. Lysistrata...A New Version by Gilbert Seldes. NY: LEC, 1934. One of 1500 numbered, signed by Pablo Picasso (illus). Sm folio. Glassine dj, bd slipcase, sleeve (spine faded). *Swann*.* $3,220/£2,013

ARISTOTLE. The Metaphysics of Aristotle...to Which Is Added, A Dissertation on Nullities and Diverging Series.... London: Thomas Taylor, 1801. 1st ed in English. 11.5x9. Period tree calf, gilt-stamped w/crest of 'The Society of Writers to the Signet.' (Rebacked w/orig spine strip laid-on, corners well rubbed), else VG. *Pacific*.* $1,035/£647

ARISTOTLE. Politics and Poetics. Lunenburg, VT: LEC, 1964. One of 1500. Signed by Leonard Baskin (illus). Cream/blue cl, gilt. Fine in slipcase. *Pacific*.* $127/£79

Arkansas. NY: Hastings House, 1941. 1st ed. VG + in dj (spine chipped). *Labordo.* $50/£31

ARKUS, LEON. John Kane, Painter. Catalogue Raisonne. Pittsburgh, 1971. (Lt worn.) Dj. *Oinonen*.* $60/£38

ARKWRIGHT, A. S. B. Return Journey. London: Seeley, Service, n.d. 1st Eng ed. NF (spine ends sl bumped) in dj (sl rubbed, dusty, nicked, edges creased). *Ulysses.* $58/£36

ARKWRIGHT, FRANCIS. Gossip and Glory of Versailles, 1692-1701. NY: Brentano's, n.d. 6 vols. Teg. 3/4 levant purple morocco, gilt, raised bands, bound by Whitman Bennett. (Spine ends, joints rubbed), else VG. *Pacific*.* $138/£86

ARKWRIGHT, RUTH. Brownikins and Other Fancies. NY: Frederick A. Stokes, (1910). 1st Amer ed. 4to. 5 mtd color plts by Charles Robinson. Color pict cl, color paste label. (Rear cvr stained, label sl chipped; wear, spotting within.) *Reisler.* $275/£172

ARKWRIGHT, WILLIAM. The Pointer and His Predecessors. An Illustrated History of the Pointing Dog from the Earliest Times. Arthur L. Humphreys, 1902. 1st ed. Ltd to 750 numbered. 4to. 39 plts, guards. Teg, rest uncut. 1/4 white buckram, grn cl sides, gilt. VG. *Sotheran.* $1,117/£698

ARMER, LAURA. Cactus. NY, 1934. Color frontis. VG in VG dj (torn). *Brooks.* $34/£21

ARMER, LAURA. Waterless Mountain. NY, 1931. 1st ed. Signed. Good in dj (chipped). *Dumont.* $45/£28

ARMES, ETHEL. Story of Coal and Iron in Alabama. Birmingham, 1910. Maroon cl. VG (sl soiled, dull). Howes A315. *Bohling.* $75/£47

ARMITAGE, ALBERT B. Cadet to Commodore. London: Cassell, 1925. Signed, inscribed. Frontis port. Blue 1/2 calf, red labels. Fine (pp sl spotted) in slipcase. *Explorer.* $384/£240

ARMITAGE, ALBERT B. Two Years in the Antarctic; Being a Narrative of the British National Antarctic Expedition. London: Edward Arnold, 1905. Fldg map. Contemp cl. VG- (sl loose). *Explorer.* $512/£320

ARMITAGE, HAROLD. Early Man in Hallamshire. London, 1939. 1st ed. (Browned; spine lt sunned.) *Edwards.* $61/£38

ARMITAGE, MERLE. The Aristocracy of Art. L.A.: Primavera Press, 1929. One of 500. Stiff wrappers, paper cvr label. *Dawson.* $75/£47

ARMITAGE, MERLE. Dance Memoranda. Edwin Corle (ed). NY, 1947. 1st Amer ed. Fine in NF dj. *Polyanthos.* $50/£31

ARMITAGE, MERLE. Igor Stravinsky. Edwin Corle (ed). NY: Duell, Sloan & Pearce, 1949. 2 color plts. Fine in dj (hinges sl rubbed). *Hollett.* $192/£120

ARMITAGE, MERLE. Martha Graham. L.A.: Merle Armitage, 1937. One of 1000. (Tips, spine extrems lt worn.) *Dawson.* $100/£63

ARMITAGE, MERLE. Pagans Conquistadores Heros and Martyrs. Fresno: Academy Guild Press, 1960. Ltd to 1500 w/add'l illus. NF in dj (clipped, sl soiled). *Dumont.* $55/£34

ARMITAGE, MERLE. Rendezvous with the Book. Brooklyn, 1949. Fine. *Truepenny.* $45/£28

ARMITAGE, MERLE. Rockwell Kent. NY: Knopf, 1932. One of 550. Gilt-stamped bds, cl spine. Dj (few sm tears, lower edge shelfworn). *Dawson.* $100/£63

ARMITAGE, MERLE. So-Called Abstract Art. NY: E. Weyhe, 1939. One of 500. Stiff wrappers (edges sunned, sm spine chip). *Dawson.* $50/£31

ARMOR, SAMUEL. History of Orange County California with Biographical Sketches of the Leading Men and Women of the County.... L.A.: Historic Record Co, 1921. 2nd ed. Black cl, gilt. NF (sl shelfworn). *Pacific**. $127/£79

ARMOUR, OGDEN. The Packers, the Private Car Lines, and the People. Phila: Henry Altemus, (1906). 1st ed. Yellow cl. VG. *Labordo.* $85/£53

ARMOUR, RICHARD. For Partly Proud Parents. NY, 1950. Stated 1st ed. Inscribed, dated. VF. *Bond.* $11/£7

ARMS, DOROTHY NOYES. Churches of France. NY, 1929. 51 plts, guards. Good. *Washton.* $50/£31

ARMS, DOROTHY NOYES. Churches of France. NY, 1929. (Lt worn.) Dj (frayed). *Oinonen**. $50/£31

ARMSTRONG, ANTHONY. The Trail of the Black King. Phila: Macrae-Smith, 1931. 1st Amer ed. (Hinges cracked), o/w VG in dj (sm chips at spine, corners). *Mordida.* $45/£28

ARMSTRONG, E. F. (ed). Chemistry in the Twentieth Century. London: Ernest Benn, 1924. 1st ed. *Argosy.* $75/£47

ARMSTRONG, EDWARD A. A Study of Bird Song. London: OUP, 1963. 1st ed. 17 plts. Dj (ragged). *Edwards.* $48/£30

ARMSTRONG, HAMILTON FISH. Where the East Begins. NY/London: Harper, 1929. 1st ed. Signed presentation. 3 plts, 5 maps. (Sl rubbed), o/w VG. *Worldwide.* $25/£16

ARMSTRONG, JOHN. Miscellanies. London: Cadell, 1770. 1st ed. 2 vols. Half-titles present, (vii),216; iv,279pp. Early polished calf, gilt, dbl leather labels. (Eps spotted), else Nice set. *Hartfield.* $385/£241

ARMSTRONG, JOHN. Practical Illustrations of Typhus Fever, of the Common Continued Fever, and of Inflammatory Disease, &c. NY: Evert Duyckinck et al, 1824. 1st Amer ed. 432pp. Mottled calf. Good+ (lacks 1/4 rep, text toned). *House.* $100/£63

ARMSTRONG, LILIAN. Renaissance Miniature Painters and Classical Imagery. Harvey Miller, (1981). Color frontis. (Rear cvr bumped.) Dj (worn). *Rybski.* $55/£34

ARMSTRONG, LILIAN. Renaissance Miniature Painters and Classical Imagery. London, 1981. Good. *Washton.* $60/£38

ARMSTRONG, MARGARET. Fanny Kemble. NY: Macmillan, 1938. 1st ed. Frontis port. Pict eps. (Spine sl dknd.) *Hollett.* $40/£25

ARMSTRONG, MARTIN. Adrian Glynde: A Novel. London: Gollancz, 1930. 1st ed. Glazed black buckram. Good. *Temple.* $16/£10

ARMSTRONG, MARTIN. Desert: A Legend. NY: Harper, 1926. 1st ed. Eric Ravilious (illus). Fine in Fine dj (sl worn). *Between The Covers.* $125/£78

ARMSTRONG, MARTIN. Mr. Darby. London, 1931. One of 50 numbered, signed. Orig 1/4 parchment, black cl. (Cl sl stained), o/w VG. *Temple.* $72/£45

ARMSTRONG, MARTIN. Saint Christopher's Day. London: Gollancz, 1928. 1st ed. Pale blue cl, gilt. Dj (unevenly browned). *Maggs.* $61/£38

ARMSTRONG, MARTIN. Sir Pompey and Madame Juno and Other Tales. London: Cape, (1927). 1st ed. VG in dj (sl worn). *Cady.* $20/£13

ARMSTRONG, MOSES K. The Early Empire Builders of the West. St. Paul: E.W. Porter, 1901. 1st ed thus. Later cl. (Few pp w/outer blank margins smoked; rebound), else Good. *Brown.* $35/£22

ARMSTRONG, MRS. M. F. and HELEN W. LUDLOW. Hampton and Its Students. Putnam, 1874. 255pp. Good+ (rear cvr edges waterstained). *Book Broker.* $45/£28

ARMSTRONG, T. R. My First and Last Buffalo Hunt. And a 'Sequel.' N.p.: T.R. Armstrong, 1918. 1st ed. VF in pict red wrappers. *Argonaut.* $75/£47

ARMSTRONG, TERENCE et al. Illustrated Glossary of Ice and Snow. Cambridge: Scott Polar Research Inst., Special Pub No.4, 1966. VG in ptd wrapper. *High Latitude.* $30/£19

ARMSTRONG, WALTER. Sir Henry Raeburn. London: Heinemann, 1901. Ltd ed. Folio. 61 lg plts, 8 sm plts. Teg, uncut. (Eps sl spotted; sl mkd.) *Hollett.* $192/£120

ARNALD, G. Picturesque Scenery on the River Meuse, from the City of Liege to That of Mezieres. London: B.B. King, ca 1827. Folio. Map, 30 plts. 3/4 leather. (Hinges weak, splitting, lt foxed.) *Metropolitan**. $345/£216

ARNALL, PHILIP. Portrait of an Airman. NY: Covici-Friede, 1932. 1st ed, US issue, comprised of sheets from 1931 British ed published by John Lane, bound in US, w/integral title leaf. Black cl. (Few smudges), o/w VG in pict dj (sl worn, 1/3-inch loss spine crown). *Reese.* $45/£28

ARNDT, KARL J. R. (ed). A Documentary History of the Indiana Decade of the Harmony Society, 1814-1824. Indianapolis: IN Hist Soc, 1975/1978. 2 vols. Fldg map laid in loose vol 2. VG. *Woolson.* $20/£13

ARNESON, ODD. The Polar Adventure. London: Gollancz, 1929. VG (sl dust soil). *High Latitude.* $45/£28

ARNO, PETER. Whoops Dearie. (NY): S&S, (1927). 1st ed. Signed. (Soiled), else VG. *Pacific**. $46/£29

ARNOLD, ANNA E. A History of Kansas. Topeka: State of Kansas, 1919. Rev ed. (Lower spine rubbed.) *Glenn.* $20/£13

ARNOLD, ARTHUR. Through Persia by Caravan. London: Tinsley Bros, 1877. 1st ed. 2 vols. Demy 8vo. xv,333; xi,325pp. (Lib stamps), else Fine set in mod 1/2 calf, marbled paper bds. *Ulysses.* $960/£600

ARNOLD, CHARLOTTE VIMONT. The Black and White Book. Chicago: Rand McNally, (1915). 1st ed. Pub's copy w/stamp, note, signature, sm pub's sticker to fr cvr. Pict black/white cl. Fine. *Pacific**. $40/£25

ARNOLD, EDWARD. The Light of Asia. LEC, 1976. Ltd to 1500 numbered, signed by Ayres Houghtelling (illus). Fine in slipcase. *Swann**. $69/£43

ARNOLD, EDWIN. East and West. Longmans, Green, 1896. Ad leaf precedes 1/2-title, 1/2-tone frontis, guard; (xii),373,(iii)pp; 11pts. Eps faced   brownish-charcoal; teg, rest uncut. Crimson art linen, gilt. VG (lt foxed, corners of 1st 2 sigs lt damp-mkd; spine sl faded, sides patchily so). *Temple.* $13/£8

ARNOLD, EDWIN. Japonica. NY: Scribner, 1891. 1st US ed. xv,128pp. Teg, untrimmed. Dk brn pict cl. (Sl edgeworn.) *Baltimore**. $80/£50

ARNOLD, EDWIN. Japonica. NY: Scribner, 1891. 1st Amer ed. VG in dec bds (spine ends lt frayed). *Captain's Bookshelf.* $100/£63

ARNOLD, EDWIN. The Light of Asia. London: John Lane, 1926. 1st ed thus. (Lt foxed), else NF in dec cl, VG dj. *Captain's Bookshelf.* $75/£47

ARNOLD, JULIAN BIDDULPH. Lawrence of Arabia. L.A., 1935. One of 500. Sewn wrappers. *Dawson.* $35/£22

ARNOLD, MATTHEW. Civilization in the United States: First and Last Impressions. Boston: Cupples & Hurd, 1888. 1st ed. pp192,(4) ads. Uncut. Red cl (spine lt faded). Fine. *Mott.* $125/£78

ARNOLD, MATTHEW. Discourses in America. London: Macmillan, 1885. 1st ed. xi(-xii),207pp. Fine. *Mott.* $75/£47

ARNOLD, MATTHEW. Discourses in America. Macmillan, 1885. 1st ed. Half-title present, xi,(iii),207pp. Dk grn cl, gilt. Good (eps foxed, lt browned; loss of color to cl). *Blackwell's.* $88/£55

ARNOLD, MATTHEW. Letters of Matthew Arnold, 1848-1888. George W.E. Russell (ed). Macmillan, 1895. 2 vols. Integral ad leaf at end vol 1; xii,402,(ii); (iv),379,(i blank)pp. Uncut. Dk blue buckram, gilt. (Eps sl foxed, sl offsetting), o/w Good. *Temple.* $104/£65

ARNOLD, MATTHEW. The Note-Books of.... London: Oxford, 1952. 1st ed. NF. *Agvent.* $50/£31

ARNOLD, MATTHEW. On the Study of Celtic Literature. London: Smith, Elder, 1867. 1st ed. Brn cl, gilt. (Spine ends chipped, corners sl worn), else VG. *Pacific*.* $127/£79

ARNOLD, MATTHEW. Poems. Longman, Brown, Green, & Longmans, 1855. 1st ed. v,(3),210,vi(ad)pp + 24-pg pub's cat. Brn eps; uncut. VG (sig dated 1856; spine ends sl worn). *Cox.* $72/£45

ARNOLD, RALPH. A Yeoman of Kent. London: Constable, 1949. 1st ed. Color frontis, 19 plts, pedigree. VG in dj (sl chipped). *Hollett.* $48/£30

ARNOLD, RICHARD. The Customs of London, Otherwise Called Arnold's Chronicle; Containing...the Original of the Celebrated Poem of the Nut-Brown Maid. London: F.C. & J. Rivington et al, 1811. (iii)-lii,300pp. Marbled eps; teg, gilt inner dentelles. 19th-cent calf, gilt, raised spine bands. (2 bkpls; joints rubbed), else NF. *Pacific*.* $138/£86

ARNOLD, S. G. Little Jenny Jarrold: One of Nine. Andrew Melrose, 1910. Good (prize-plt, bkpl; spine bumped). *Tiger.* $16/£10

ARNOTT, HOWARD J. The Seed, Germination, and Seedling of Yucca. Berkeley: Univ of CA, 1962. 33 plts. NF in wrappers. *Brooks.* $37/£23

ARNOW, HARRIETTE SIMPSON. Flowering of the Cumberland. Macmillan, (1963). 1st ed. Good in dj (worn, stained). *Rybski.* $30/£19

ARNOW, HARRIETTE SIMPSON. The Kentucky Trace. NY, 1974. 1st ed. Signed, dated. (Ink name, date), else VG in dj. *King.* $45/£28

ARNOW, HARRIETTE SIMPSON. Seedtime on the Cumberland. Macmillan, 1960. 1st ed. (Inscrip.) Dj (worn, stained). *Rybski.* $30/£19

ARORA, SHIRLEY L. What Then, Raman? Follett, 1960. 1st ed. 176pp. VG in VG dj (wrinkle, 1/2-inch chip on fr, scuffed). *Price.* $22/£14

ARRABAL, FERNANDO. Guernica and Other Plays. NY: Grove, 1969. 1st US ed, wraps issue. Signed. NF in illus wraps. *Lame Duck.* $100/£63

ARREOLA, JUAN JOSE. The Fair. Austin: Univ of TX, 1977. 1st ed. (Remainder dot bottom edge), else Fine in dj (sm spine base tear). *Lame Duck.* $45/£28

ARRINGTON, LEONARD J. Beet Sugar in the West. Seattle/London, 1966. VG in dj (chipped). *Benchmark.* $20/£13

ARROWSMITH, AARON. A Compendium of Ancient and Modern Geography, For the Use of Eton School. London: E. Williams, 1831. 1st ed. xviii,(i),(i blank),906pp; 5 engr charts, plans (4 fldg). Marbled edges. Contemp purple prize calf, gilt, black label. VG (sl offsetting from charts). *Morrell.* $72/£45

Art of Angling, Rock and Sea-Fishing: With the Natural History of River, Pond, and Sea-Fish. (By Richard Brookes.) London, 1740. 1st ed. (8)leaves; 249,(11)pp. Contemp calf (rubbed, sl soiled, browned). *Oinonen*.* $300/£188

Art of Brewing on Scientific Principles Adapted to the Use of Brewers and Private Families.... (By David Booth.) London: James Cornish, (1852). 2nd ed. xii,244,16 ads pp. Blind-stamped, coarse-grained cl, gilt. *Young.* $136/£85

Art of Cookery, Made Plain and Easy. By a Lady. (By Hannah Glasse.) London: A. Millar, 1785. 9th ed. (2),vi,(24),384,(24)pp. Period calf. (Hinge cracked before tp, ink blot to tp, 2 erasure holes to pp1-2, affecting lettering p2, sl foxed, soiled; rubbed, spine head chipped), else VG. *Pacific*.* $184/£115

Art of Modern Lace-Making. Butterick Pub Co, 1896. 136pp. Poor. *Whittle.* $56/£35

Art Work of Mississippi. Chicago: Gravure Illustration, 1901. 1st ed. Folio. 9 parts. VG set (1st 2 ll of 1st part sl stained; margins of several ll part 9 stained) in illus stiff wrappers (fr wrapper 1st part faded). *Cahan.* $450/£281

ARTAUD, ANTONIN. Collected Works, Volume 3. London: Calder & Boyars, 1972. Fine in wraps. *Beasley.* $40/£25

ARTHUR CHURCHILL LTD. A Catalogue of Old English and Other Glassware. London, 1937. 2nd ed. Inscribed. 16 plts. Orig wrappers (lt browned, edges chipped). *Edwards.* $72/£45

ARTHUR, STANLEY CLISBY. Jean Laffite, Gentleman Rover. Harmanson, 1952. Ltd to 750 signed. Good. *Rybski.* $85/£53

Artist and the Book, 1860-1960, in Western Europe and the United States. Boston: Museum of Fine Arts, (1961). 1st ed. Off-white cl, gilt. Text Nice, cvrs VG (sl rubbed) in dj (sl worn, chipped). *Baltimore*.* $90/£56

Artist's London, as Seen in Eight Contemporary Pictures. London: John Caastle, 1924. One of 200. Orig litho by Frank Brangwyn and orig etching by Robins, each signed; guards. 1/2 morocco, gilt-lettered cl. (Sl foxed), else VG. *Pacific*.* $316/£198

Artist's Repository; or, Encyclopedia of the Fine Arts. London: C. Taylor, 1808. 4 vols. Contemp red leather. (Sl worn; vol 1 lacks 5 plts, last plt repaired; frontisport, tps browned.) *Ars Artis.* $200/£125

Artistic Evolution of the English Home. Waring & Gillow, n.d. Ltd to 300. 25 photogravures. Full vellum, gilt. (Sl spotted, ll sl wrinkled, bkpl; fr bd sl warped.) *Edwards.* $200/£125

ARTLEY, ALEXANDRA. Hoorah for the Filth-Packets. Methuen, 1987. 1st ed. NF in dj. *Any Amount.* $26/£16

ARTRIP, LOUISE and FULLEN. Memoirs of (the late) Daniel Fore (Jim) Chisholm and the Chisholm Trail. N.p., 1959. 3rd ed. Signed by both authors. Frontis. Fine. *Baade.* $40/£25

ARTZIBASHEF, MICHAEL. War: A Play in Four Acts. NY: Knopf, 1916. 1st US ed. Dec cream bds stamped in plum/orange. Fine in dj (few sm nicks). *Reese.* $60/£38

ARTZYBASHEFF, BORIS. Poor Shaydullah. Macmillan, 1931. 1st ed. 7x7. Unpaginated. VG (name; spine, edges sunned). *Price.* $40/£25

ARTZYBASHEFF, BORIS. Poor Shaydullah. NY: Macmillan, 1931. 1st ed. Sq 8vo. VG in dj (nicked). *Houle.* $175/£109

ASBELL, MILTON B. A Bibliography of Dentistry in America 1790-1840. Cherry Hill, NJ: The Author, 1973. VG. *Dumont.* $45/£28

ASBURY, HENRY. Advice Concerning the Duties of Justices of the Peace and Constables. Quincy, IL et al: C.M. Woods/Newton Flagg et al, 1850. (v),294pp (sig). Orig full calf (outer hinges cracked, but holding, edgewear, 1cm of lower spine torn away), red leather label. *Wantagh.* $275/£172

ASBURY, HERBERT. Up from Methodism. NY, 1926. 1st Amer ed, 1st bk. Fine (sl rubbed). *Polyanthos.* $40/£25

ASCH, SHOLEM. America. James Fuchs (trans). NY: Alpha Omega, (1918). 1st Amer ed. Dec linen, paper-cvrd bds. Fine. *Between The Covers.* $250/£156

ASCH, SHOLEM. In the Beginning. NY, 1935. 1st Amer ed. Inscribed, signed. (Line whited-out bottom of tp; cvr sl rubbed.) *King.* $35/£22

ASH, CHRISTOPHER. Whaler's Eye. NY: Macmillan, 1964. 1st ed. VG in dj. *Walcot.* $22/£14

ASH, DOUGLAS. Dutch Silver. Cambridge: Golden Head, 1965. VG in dj (faded). *Hollett.* $24/£15

ASH, EDWARD C. Dogs: Their History and Development. Boston, (1927). 2 vols. Uncut. Cl-backed bds (shelfworn; sm cellotape stain tp foot vol 1), leather spine labels (sl scuffed). *Oinonen*.* $275/£172

ASH, EDWARD C. Dogs: Their History and Development. London: Ernest Benn, 1927. 1st ed. 2 vols. 160 plts. Rust cl. Good. *Karmiole.* $300/£188

ASH, EDWARD C. The New Book of the Dog. London: Cassell, (1938). 4 color, 24 half-tone plts. Blue linen. Good. *Karmiole.* $60/£38

ASH, JOHN. The Goodbyes. Manchester: Carcanet New Press, 1982. 1st Eng ed. VG (pp edges browned; spine foot bumped) in dj (sl browned, creased). *Ulysses.* $48/£30

ASHBAUGH, DON. Nevada's Turbulent Yesterday...a Study in Ghost Towns. (L.A., 1963.) 1st ed. Fine in Fine dj. *Sagebrush.* $50/£31

ASHBEE, C. R. A Book of Cottages and Little Houses.... London: Batsford, c. 1906. (Margins sl foxed.) *Petersfield.* $29/£18

ASHBERY, JOHN. April Galleons. Poems. NY, 1987. 1st Amer ed. Signed. Fine in Fine dj. *Polyanthos.* $30/£19

ASHBERY, JOHN. Houseboat Days. NY: Viking, 1977. 1st ed. Inscribed. Rev slip laid in. 1/4 cl. Fine in dj. *Cummins.* $200/£125

ASHBERY, JOHN. A Wave. Poems. NY, 1984. 1st Amer ed. Signed. Fine in Fine dj. *Polyanthos.* $30/£19

ASHBY, THOMAS A. Life of Turner Ashby. NY: Neale, 1914. 1st ed. 8vo. Frontisport. Grn cl. NF (bkpl; cvrs lt spotted). *Chapel Hill.* $550/£344

ASHBY, THOMAS A. The Valley Campaigns. NY: Neale, 1914. 1st ed. Grn cl. NF (cvrs sl soiled). *Chapel Hill.* $350/£219

ASHBY, W. ROSS. Design for a Brain. NY: John Wiley, 1952. 1st Amer ed. VG. *Glaser.* $150/£94

ASHBY, W. ROSS. Design for a Brain. London: Chapman & Hall, 1960. 2nd ed. NF in dj. *Glaser.* $150/£94

ASHDOWN, CHARLES H. Armour and Weapons in the Middle Ages. London/Calcutta/Sydney: George G. Harrap, (1925). 1st ed. Scarlet cl, gilt. Fine. *Glenn.* $25/£16

ASHDOWN, CHARLES H. British Castles. A&C Black, 1911. 1st ed. 32 color plts. Pict grn cl, gilt. (Feps browned; lower bd lt mkd), o/w Very Nice. *Hollett.* $80/£50

ASHE, GEOFFREY et al. The Quest for America. London: Pall Mall, (1971). 1st ed. 28 color plts, 157 b/w plts, 68 maps, charts. Maroon cl. Fine in color, pict dj. *House.* $25/£16

ASHER, DON. The Piano Sport. NY: Atheneum, 1966. 1st ed, 1st bk. Fine in NF dj. *Dermont.* $25/£16

ASHLEY, CLIFFORD W. Ashley Book of Knots. NY: Doubleday, 1944. VG (sm waterstain to bottom of some pp) in dj. *American Booksellers.* $50/£31

ASHLEY, CLIFFORD W. Whaleships of New Bedford. Boston: Houghton Mifflin, 1929. 1st ed. Ltd to 1035. 60 plts. VG. *Walcot.* $112/£70

ASHLEY, CLIFFORD W. Whaleships of New Bedford. Boston: Houghton Mifflin, 1929. 60 plts. VG (sl mkd). *High Latitude.* $170/£106

ASHLEY, CLIFFORD W. Whaleships of New Bedford. Boston, 1929. One of 1035. 60 plts. Dj (edges chipped), slipcase (defective). *Swann*.* $172/£108

ASHLEY, CLIFFORD W. Whaleships of New Bedford.... Boston, 1929. One of 1035 signed. 60 plts. *Swann*.* $138/£86

ASHLEY, CLIFFORD W. The Yankee Whaler. Boston, 1926. One of 1625. 1/4 cl. (Lt foxed; extrems worn.) *Swann*.* $258/£161

ASHLEY, WILLIAM H. The West of William H. Ashley. Dale L. Morgan (ed). Denver: Fred A. Rosenstock, 1964. 1st ed, trade issue. Pict cl. Fine. *Pacific*.* $115/£72

ASHLEY, WILLIAM H. The West of William H. Ashley. Dale L. Morgan (ed). Denver: Fred A. Rosenstock, 1964. One of 250 ptd. Signed by Morgan. 3/4 calf, morocco spine label. Fine in slipcase. *Pacific*.* $374/£234

ASHLEY, WILLIAM H. The West of William H. Ashley. Dale L. Morgan (ed). Denver: Fred A. Rosenstock, 1964. 1st ed. One of 250. Signed by Morgan. Prospectus laid in. 3/4 calf, cl, morocco spine label. (Spine sl rubbed), else NF in slipcase. *Pacific*.* $489/£306

ASHMEAD-BARTLETT, ELLIS. Port Arthor. London, 1906. 1st ed. Frontisport, 4 fldg maps, plans (2 in rear pocket). (Feps lt browned, marginal foxing, bkpl; spine faded, sl chipped.) *Edwards.* $136/£85

ASHTON, E. H. and R. L. HOLMES (eds). Perspectives in Primate Biology. London, 1981. Dj (sticker removed, worn). *Sutton.* $100/£63

ASHTON, JOHN. Chap-Books of the Eighteenth Century with Facsimiles, Notes, and Introduction by John Ashton. London: C&W, 1882. Lg paper ed. One of 100 (75 for sale, 25 for presentation). 4to. Full-pg wood-engr frontis w/guard, xvi,486pp. Untrimmed. Paper on bds, 3/4 vellum spine w/title label. Fine (cvrs soiled, corners rounded). *Hobbyhorse.* $250/£156

ASHTON, JOHN. Chap-Books of the Eighteenth Century. C&W, 1882. Dec cl (sl worn; new eps). *Moss.* $48/£30

ASHTON, JOHN. English Caricature and Satire on Napoleon I. NY, 1884. 2 vols. 290; 283pp. Marbled eps. Teg. 1/2 butterscotch morocco, marbled bds, gilt, blue/red leather spine labels. VG (bkpl; corner vol 1 bumped). *Truepenny.* $150/£94

ASHTON, JOHN. Florizel's Folly. C&W, 1899. Photogravure frontis ptd in sepia, xii,308pp; 6 half-tone plts, 6 line plts. Crimson buckram, gilt. (Eps browned, sl offsetting; spine sl dull, cvrs sl mkd), o/w Fine. *Temple.* $13/£8

ASHTON, JOHN. The History of Gambling in England. Chicago/NY: Herbert S. Stone, 1899. 1st Amer ed. (Rubbed, discolored, paper label worn.) Internally VG. *Dramatis.* $30/£19

ASHTON, THOMAS SOUTHCLIFFE. An Eighteenth Century Industrialist. Manchester: University Press, 1939. 1st ed. Frontis, map. (Eps browned; spine sl faded.) *Hollett.* $56/£35

ASHWORTH, EDMUND and THOMAS. A Treatise on the Propagation of Salmon and Other Fish. Stockport: E.H. King, 1853. 1st ed. Fldg plt. Orig bds. (Sm stamp to bottom of fldg plt; hinges reinforced; rebacked in cl), else VG. *Pacific*.* $104/£65

ASIMOV, ISAAC. The Asimov Chronicles. Martin H. Greenberg (ed). Arlington Heights: Dark Harvest, 1989. One of 52 lettered, signed by Asimov, Ron Lindahn and Val Lakey Lindahn (illus). Gilt-stamped simulated leather (sl worn). Wooden slipcase. *Oinonen*.* $90/£56

ASIMOV, ISAAC. The Death Dealers. NY: Avon, 1958. 1st ed. Pb orig. Fine in wrappers. *Mordida.* $75/£47

ASIMOV, ISAAC. Foundation's Edge. GC, 1982. 1st ed. Good in dj (edges torn). *King.* $17/£11

ASIMOV, ISAAC. Foundation. NY: Gnome, (1951). 1st ed, 2nd binding. Dk blue cl. 2nd state of dj listing numerous titles on rear panel. (Pp browned), else NF in dj (spine ends sl chipped, sm tears, lt creases to extrems). *Pacific*.* $86/£54

ASIMOV, ISAAC. The Gods Themselves. GC: Doubleday, 1972. 1st ed. VG in dj (spine ends rubbed). *Pacific*.* $69/£43

ASIMOV, ISAAC. Nemesis. NY: Doubleday, (1989). 1st ed, numbered state. Ltd to 500 numbered, signed. (Fr cvr sl rubbed), o/w Fine in slipcase, orig numbered mailing carton. *Levin.* $250/£156

ASIMOV, ISAAC. Only a Trillion. London/NY: Abelard-Schuman, (1957). 1st ed. (Sl soiled), else NF in dj (2 sm tears fr panel). *Pacific*.* $104/£65

ASIMOV, ISAAC. Pebble in the Sky. NY, 1950. 1st ed, 1st bk. Dj (2 sm nicks fr joint, spine head crinkled). *Swann**. $172/£108

ASIMOV, ISAAC. The Rest of the Robots. GC: Doubleday, 1964. 1st ed. VG in dj (spine ends chipped, price-clipped). *Pacific**. $92/£58

ASIMOV, ISAAC. Robots and Empire. GC, 1985. 1st ed. VG in dj. *King*. $17/£11

Ask Mamma; or, The Richest Commoner in England. (By Robert Surtees.) London: Bradbury, Agnew, (c. 1880s). 13 hand-colored plts. Pict red cl, gilt. NF. *Pacific**. $46/£29

ASLET, CLIVE. The Last Country Houses. Yale Univ, 1982. VG in dj. *Hadley*. $42/£26

ASLIN, ELIZABETH. The Aesthetic Movement. NY: Frederic A. Praeger, (1969). Orig ed. 121 plts (39 color). NF in dj. *Turtle Island*. $50/£31

ASOW, HEDWIG and E. H. VON MUELLER. Christoph Willibald Gluck. Stewart Thompson (trans). Barrie & Rockliff, 1962. 1st Eng ed. 19 plts. (Top margin of fr bd torn.) Dj (top edge sl creased, torn). *Hollett*. $40/£25

ASPIN, JEHOSHAPHAT. A Picture of the Manners, Customs, Sports, and Pastimes of the Inhabitants of England. London: J. Harris, 1825. Period calf-backed marbled bds. Fair (hinge cracked in middle, breaking bk in 1/2). *Pacific**. $98/£61

ASQUITH, CYNTHIA (ed). The Treasure Ship. NY: Scribner, (1926). 4 tipped-in color plts, 4 full-pg b/w illus. Tan cl. VG. *House*. $30/£19

ASQUITH, CYNTHIA. The Flying Carpet. NY: Scribner, (1925). 1st ed. 10 x 7 1/2. Pict cl. (Sl soiled, spine sl faded), else NF. *Pacific**. $92/£58

ASQUITH, HERBERT. The Volunteer and Other Poems. London: Sidgwick & Jackson, 1917. 2nd, enlgd ed. Grn cl, paper spine label. (Few lt mks, sm spine bump), o/w VG- in dj (rubbed, nicked, chip, sm stain lower edge). *Reese*. $45/£28

ASQUITH, HERBERT. Young Orland. NY: Scribner, 1927. 1st US ed. Grn cl. Fine in VG dj (loss of segment top of fr panel, 2 closed tears mended on verso). *Reese*. $45/£28

ASTAIRE, FRED. The Fred Astaire Dance Book and Record Rumba with Basic Mambo. NY: Arrowhead Books, (1955). 1st ed. Orig record laid-in to envelope at fr. Pict bds. (Extrems sl rubbed), else VG. *Pacific**. $40/£25

ASTLEY, HUBERT. My Birds in Freedom and Captivity. London, 1900. Lg paper copy. Ltd to 100. (Lt foxed, mainly to eps; bkpl.) *Edwards*. $64/£40

ASTON, F. W. Isotopes. London: Edward Arnold, 1922. 1st ed. 4 photo plts. (Lt foxed; rubbed, bubbled), else VG. *Glaser*. $250/£156

ASTON, HELEN I. Aquatic Plants of Australia. Carlton, Vic., 1977. 83 maps. VG in dj. *Brooks*. $55/£34

ASTON, JAMES. (Pseud of T.H. White.) First Lesson. Chatto, 1932. 1st ed. Signed, inscribed presentation. Yellow cl (stained, rubbed, spine dknd, top of lower hinge split). Good. *Any Amount*. $136/£85

ASTON, JAMES. (Pseud of T.H. White.) They Winter Abroad. NY: Viking, 1932. 1st US ed. Fine in dj (sm nicks at corners). *Reese*. $375/£234

ASTOR, BROOKE. Patchwork Child. NY: Harper & Row, 1962. 1st ed. Mulberry bds, brn cl spine. Fine in dj. *Cummins*. $75/£47

ASTRUP, EIVIND. With Peary Near the Pole. London: C. Arthur Pearson Ltd, 1898. 1st Eng ed. Frontis port, 362pp, fldg map. Teg. Brn cl (rubbed, spine chipped, faded; hinges cracked). VG (ll carelessly opened, sl dust-soiled). *Morrell*. $176/£110

ASTURIAS, MIGUEL ANGEL. The Bejeweled Boy. NY: Doubleday, 1971. 1st US ed. VG + in VG + dj (worn, extrems creased, sm spot surface loss fr panel). *Lame Duck*. $65/£41

ASTURIAS, MIGUEL ANGEL. The Cyclone. Darwin Flakoll and Claribel Alegria (trans). London: Peter Owen, 1967. 1st ed in English. (Stamp), else VG + in VG + dj (edgeworn), pub's wrap-around band (worn). *Lame Duck*. $150/£94

ASTURIAS, MIGUEL ANGEL. Men of Maize. NY: Delacorte/Seymour Lawrence, 1975. 1st US ed. NF in dj (spine sl faded). *Lame Duck*. $150/£94

ASTURIAS, MIGUEL ANGEL. Mulata. NY: Delacorte, 1967. 1st US ed. NF in VG + dj (edgeworn). *Lame Duck*. $75/£47

ASTURIAS, MIGUEL ANGEL. The President. London: Gollancz, 1963. 1st British ed. (Sig, date), else VG + in dj (soiled, fr cvr edge torn 3 inches). *Lame Duck*. $200/£125

ASTURIAS, MIGUEL ANGEL. The Talking Machine. GC: Doubleday, 1971. 1st US ed. Fine in illus paper-cvrd bds. NF dj (bottom edges sl torn). *Lame Duck*. $175/£109

At the Zoo. London: Bairns Books, n.d. (195?). 4 dbl-pg pop-ups. Glazed pict bds. VG. *Bookfinders*. $60/£38

ATCHLEY, SHIRLEY CLIFFORD. Wild Flowers of Attica. Oxford, 1938. 1st ed. Frontis, 21 color plts. VG in dj (repaired). *Cox*. $45/£28

ATGET, EUGENE. Atget Photographie de Paris. NY: E. Weyhe, (1930). 1st Amer ed (on French sheets). Sm 4to. Frontis, 96 collotype b/w plts. Red moire silk, gilt. (Bkpls; sl worn), else Fine. *Cahan*. $850/£531

ATGET, EUGENE. A Vision of Paris. NY: Macmillan, 1963. 1st ed. Red cl, gilt. Good in dj (sl chipped, soiled). *Karmiole*. $225/£141

ATHEARN, ROBERT G. The Coloradans. Albuquerque: Univ of NM, (1977). VG in dj (sl worn). *Lien*. $15/£9

ATHEARN, ROBERT G. The Mythic West in Twentieth-Century America. Lawrence, KS, 1986. 1st ed. Fine in dj. *Dumont*. $35/£22

ATHEARN, ROBERT G. Westward the Briton. NY: Scribner, 1953. 1st ed. Fair (ex-lib). *Lien*. $20/£13

ATHEARN, ROBERT G. Westward the Briton. NY: Scribner, 1953. 1st ed. Dj. *Mott*. $50/£31

ATHELING, WILLIAM, JR. (Pseud of James Blish.) More Issues at Hand. Chicago: Advent Publishers, Inc, 1970. 1st Eng ed. Inscribed presentation. VG (fore-edge sl mkd; bottom edge sl rubbed, spine ends sl bumped) in dj (nicked, dusty, sl rubbed, spotted, mkd, browned). *Ulysses*. $136/£85

Athenian Sport: or, Two Thousand Paradoxes Merrily Argued, to Amuse and Divert the Age...By a Member of the Athenian Society. (By John Dunton.) London: B. Bragg, 1707. 1st ed. xxxii,544pp. Period panel calf, morocco spine label. VG (bkpl). *Pacific**. $127/£79

ATHERTON, FAXON DEAN. The California Diary of Faxon Dean Atherton, 1836-1839. Doyce B. Nunis, Jr. (ed). SF: CA Hist Soc, 1964. Deluxe ed. One of 325. Signed by Nunis. Frontisport. Gilt-dec cl. Fine in slipcase (sl sunned). *Pacific**. $46/£29

ATHERTON, GERTRUDE. American Wives and English Husbands. NY: Dodd, Mead, 1898. 1st ed. Tan pict cl, gilt. (Spine sl flecked), else Good. *Macdonnell*. $35/£22

ATHERTON, GERTRUDE. A Daughter of the Vine. Bernhard Tauchnitz, 1904. Copyright ed. Sprinkled edges. Contemp 1/4 leather over cl. Good. *Tiger*. $26/£16

ATHERTON, GERTRUDE. The Jealous Gods. NY: Horace Liveright, 1928. 1st ed. Black cl, gilt. VF in NF dj. *Macdonnell*. $125/£78

ATHERTON, GERTRUDE. The Splendid Idle Forties. Kentfield: Allen, 1960. One of 150. Prospectus laid in. Brocade-design cl, paper spine label. NF. *Pacific**. $196/£123

ATHERTON, GERTRUDE. The White Morning. NY: Stokes, (1918). 1st ed. Gilt brn cl, pict onlay. VG + in dj (lt nicked, dust-smudged). *Reese*. $100/£63

ATHERTON, LEWIS. The Cattle Kings. IN Univ, (1961). 1st ed. *Heinoldt*. $25/£16

ATIL, ESIN. Suleymanname. Washington/NY: Nat'l Gallery of Art/Abrams, 1986. 1st ed. Folio. VG in dj. *Worldwide*. $65/£41

ATKINS, JOHN. A Voyage to Guinea, Brasil, and the West-Indies. Ward & Chandler, 1737. 2nd ed. Ad leaf before tp, 3 ll ads at end. (Stained, soiled, outer margins wormed.) Contemp paneled calf (spine partly restored). *Sotheby's*. $331/£207

ATKINSON, GEORGE FRANCKLIN. Curry and Rice, on Forty Plates. London: W. Thacker, 1911. 5th ed. 40 color plts, guards. Aeg. Dec brn linen. (Tp, 1st leaf foxed.) *Karmiole*. $100/£63

ATKINSON, J. A. (ed). The Shah Nameh of the Persian Poet Firdausi. London/NY: Warne, 1886. 1st ed. xxxii,412,2pp. Teg. (Sl rubbed), o/w VG. *Worldwide*. $125/£78

ATKINSON, JOSEPH. The History of Newark, New Jersey. Newark: William B. Guild, 1878. 1st ed. xiv,334pp. (Worn, spine ends sl frayed), o/w Good. *Brown*. $75/£47

ATKINSON, M. E. The Compass Points North. Bodley Head, 1938. 1st ed. Harold Jones (illus). VG+ in VG dj. *Green Meadow*. $32/£20

ATKINSON, THOMAS DINHAM. Local Style in English Architecture. London, 1947. Good in dj. *Washton*. $40/£25

ATKINSON, THOMAS W. Oriental and Western Siberia: A Narrative of Seven Years' Explorations and Adventures. NY, 1858. 1st Amer ed. Map. Pub's cl (spine ends frayed). *Swann*. $161/£101

ATKINSON, THOMAS W. Travels in the Regions of the Upper and Lower Amoor.... NY, 1860. 1st Amer ed. 448pp; lg fldg map. Black cl, gilt. (Spine professionally repaired), else Good+. *Larry Price*. $145/£91

ATKINSON, TI-GRACE. Amazon Odyssey. (NY): Links, (1974). 1st ed. (Corners bumped), else Fine in dj (sl stained; chip, tear). *Hermitage*. $50/£31

ATKYNS, ROBERT. The Ancient and Present State of Glostershire. London, 1712. 1st ed. Extra-illus w/over 15 engrs and tinted lithos, and an albumen photo. Folio. Engr frontisport, (10),859,(14)pp; 8 plts, dbl-pg map, 64 dbl-pg etched views. Early 19th-cent russia (rebacked retaining orig backstrip; spine bottom chipped, sm paper shelf label; fr cvr detached; lt early marginalia in text, port lt foxed, offsetting to tp w/paper repaired; bkpls). *Swann*. $5,290/£3,306

ATKYNS, ROBERT. The Ancient and Present State of Glostershire. Robert Gosling, 1712. Folio. 1 vol bound in 2. Engr frontisport, 8 engr plts, dbl-pg engr map, 64 dbl-pg engr plts. Aeg. Later paneled calf (rubbed). *Sotheby's*. $6,256/£3,910

ATMORE, CHARLES. Serious Advice, from a Father to His Children. Phila: J.H. Cunningham, 1819. 12mo. Full-pg VF wood engr frontis, 36pp + 1pg list on lower wrapper. (Ll lt browned; spine sl chipped, fore-edge upper cvr rubbed), else Fine in ptd blue paper wrappers. *Hobbyhorse*. $100/£63

ATTAWAY, WILLIAM. Blood on the Forge. GC, 1941. 1st ed. (Cvrs bumped, rubbed, soiled.) *King*. $35/£22

ATTAWAY, WILLIAM. Calypso Song Book. NY, (1957). 1st ed. 2-tone bds (spine ends sl worn), else Good in dj (edge-torn, chipped). *King*. $60/£38

ATTAWAY, WILLIAM. Calypso Song Book. NY: McGraw Hill, 1957. 1st ed. Fine in dj (sl edgeworn, tears). *Else Fine*. $85/£53

ATTAWAY, WILLIAM. Let Me Breathe Thunder. NY: Doubleday, Doran, (1939). 1st ed. VG in dj (split along rear joint, taped at bottom, lower rear panel; chipped, upper fr joint lacks piece). *Pacific*. $86/£54

ATTENBOROUGH, CHARLES L. The Law of Pawnbroking, with the Pawnbrokers' Act, 1872, and the Factors' Act, 1889. London: Jackson, Ruston & Keeson, 1897. Brn cl (worn, shaken). Usable. *Boswell*. $75/£47

ATTENBOROUGH, DAVID. Zoo Quest to Madagascar. London: Lutterworth, 1961. 1st ed. NF in VG dj. *Mikesh*. $30/£19

ATTOE, DAVID. Lion at the Door. Boston: Little, Brown, (1989). 1st ed. Fine in Fine dj. *Dermont*. $35/£22

ATTWELL, LUCIE MABEL. Lucie Attwell's Tiny Rhymes Pop-Up Book. London: Dean & Son, 1982. 3 dbl-pg pop-ups by Mabel Lucie Atwell. Glazed pict bds. VG. *Bookfinders*. $30/£19

ATTWELL, MABEL LUCIE. The Boo-Boos at Honey Sweet Farm. Dundee: Valentine & Sons, (ca 1920). 16mo. 14 full-pg color plts. Tan bds (edges rubbed), color paste label. *Reisler*. $375/£234

ATTWELL, MABEL LUCIE. Father Tuck's Storyland Pictures. London: Raphael Tuck & Sons, (ca 1920). 4to. 10pp + 4 full-pg color plts. Color pict stiff paper wrappers (lt marginal wear). *Reisler*. $675/£422

ATTWELL, MABEL LUCIE. The Lucie Attwell Annual. London: S.W. Partridge, (1922). 4to. Color paste labels on cvr/spine. VG (spine worn). *Reisler*. $800/£500

ATTWELL, MABEL LUCIE. The Lucie Attwell Annual. London: S.W. Partridge, (1923). 4to. Color paste labels on cvr/spine. (Rear cvr lt mkd, sm chip to spine edge.) *Reisler*. $685/£428

ATTWELL, MABEL LUCIE. Lucie Attwell's 'Happy Times Pop-Up Book.' London: Dean & Son, 1961. 8vo. 3 dbl-pg pop-ups. Full color pict bds (sl bowed from internal pop-up). *Reisler*. $125/£78

ATTWELL, MABEL LUCIE. Lucie Attwell's Book of Verse. London: Dean & Son, 1960. 1st ed. 4to. 20 leaves. Cl-backed color illus bds (lt corner bump). Color dj (lt worn). *Reisler*. $150/£94

ATTWELL, MABEL LUCIE. Lucie Attwell's Fairy Book. London: S.W. Partridge, (1932). 1st ed. Royal 8vo. (vi),7-255pp (sl thumbed); 12 color plts by Attwell. Bright blue cl (lt spotted, rubbed, spine faded). *Sotheran*. $397/£248

ATTWELL, MABEL LUCIE. Lucie Attwell's Fairy Book. London: S.W. Partridge, (1932). 1st ed. Thick 4to. 12 full-pg color plts. Tan cl (lt fingered; edges foxed). *Reisler*. $475/£297

ATTWELL, MABEL LUCIE. Lucie Attwell's Storytime Tales. London: Dean & Son, 1959. 4to. Full color pict bds. VG. *Reisler*. $85/£53

ATWATER, CALEB. Remarks Made on a Tour to Prairie du Chien Thence to Washington. Columbus, 1831. Contemp sheep (rebacked w/dk calf). Howes A379. *Swann*. $287/£179

ATWOOD, A. The Conquerors: Historical Sketches of the American Settlement of the Oregon Country. The Life and Works of Jason Lee. Jennings & Graham, (1907). 1st ed. Fine in dj (edges chipped). *Perier*. $30/£19

ATWOOD, EVANGELINE. We Shall Be Remembered. Anchorage: AK Methodist Univ, 1966. 1st ed. Fine in VG dj. *Perier*. $30/£19

ATWOOD, MARGARET. Good Bones. Toronto: Harbourfront Reading Series, 1992. One of 150 (of 500) numbered, signed. Fine in illus wrappers. *Dermont*. $40/£25

AUBREY, EDMUND. Sherlock Holmes in Dallas. NY: Dodd, Mead, 1980. 1st ed. NF in dj. *Zubal*. $20/£13

AUBURY, LEWIS E. Gold Dredging in California. SF: CA State Mining Bureau, 1910. 10 fldg maps. Ptd orange wrappers (backed). *Dawson*. $40/£25

AUCHINCLOSS, LOUIS. A World of Profit. Boston: Houghton Mifflin, 1968. 1st ed. VF in Fine dj. *Between The Covers*. $125/£78

AUDEN, W. H. About the House. London: Faber & Faber, 1966. 1st Eng ed. 4-line errata slip tipped onto Acknowledgements pg. Lt purplish-blue cl, gilt. VG in dj. *Vandoros*. $100/£63

AUDEN, W. H. The Age of Anxiety. NY, 1947. 1st ed. NF in NF dj. *Warren*. $60/£38

AUDEN, W. H. The Age of Anxiety. London: Faber & Faber, 1948. 1st Eng ed. Yellow cl. VG (inscrip) in dj (spine lt browned). *Maggs*. $40/£25

AUDEN, W. H. and CHRISTOPHER ISHERWOOD. The Ascent of F6: A Tragedy in Two Acts. London: Faber & Faber, (1936). 1st ed. VF in blue cl. Dj (lt soiled). *Bromer*. $385/£241

AUDEN, W. H. The Enchafed Flood. Faber, 1951. 1st UK ed. Fine in VG dj (dull, spine browned, closed tears). *Williams*. $40/£25

AUDEN, W. H. The Enchafed Flood; or, The Romantic Iconography of the Sea. London: Faber & Faber, 1951. 1st ed. Mottled bright blue cl. (Eps foxed), o/w VG in dj (sl frayed). *Temple*. $48/£30

AUDEN, W. H. For the Time Being. NY: Random House, (1944). 1st ed. Signed. (Eps sl tanned), else Very Nice in dj. *Reese*. $175/£109

AUDEN, W. H. For the Time Being. Faber, 1945. 1st UK ed. Fine in VG dj (edges sl worn, nicked). *Williams*. $72/£45

AUDEN, W. H. Homage to Clio. London: Faber & Faber, 1960. 1st ed. Fine in purple cl, gilt, Fine dj (price-clipped). *Vandoros*. $125/£78

AUDEN, W. H. and LOUIS MacNEICE. Letters from Iceland. NY: Random House, (1937). 1st Amer ed. One of 970 in 2nd binding. Gray cl w/pict paper labels. Nice in dj (sl worn). *Cady*. $45/£28

AUDEN, W. H. Louis MacNeice: A Memorial Address. London: Faber & Faber, 1963. One of 250. Ptd wrappers. *Maggs*. $192/£120

AUDEN, W. H. and CHESTER KALLMAN. The Magic Flute. NY: Random House, (1956). 1st ed. VF in VF dj (lt scratch rear cvr). *Between The Covers*. $250/£156

AUDEN, W. H. Mountains. Faber, 1954. 1st UK ed. NF in wrappers, envelope (lacks sm piece). *Martin*. $14/£9

AUDEN, W. H. The Old Man's Road. NY: Voyages, 1956. One of 700 (of 750). 2 publicity pieces loosely inserted. VG (cvr, pg edges browned) in dj (nicked, sl rubbed, mkd, browned). *Ulysses*. $232/£145

AUDEN, W. H. The Orators. Faber & Faber, 1932. 1st Eng ed. Very Nice (cvrs sl scuffed). *Ulysses*. $72/£45

AUDEN, W. H. Poems. NY, (1934). 1st ed. Dj (worn, spine extrems chipped). *Swann**. $115/£72

AUDEN, W. H. Poems. Faber & Faber, 1930. 1st ed. 8vo. Uncut, unopened. Pristine in blue wrappers ptd in black inside red rules. *Sotheby's**. $699/£437

AUDEN, W. H. Thank You, Fog. London, (1974). 1st ed. VG in dj. *King*. $25/£16

AUDEN, W. H. (ed). A Certain World, A Commonplace Book. London, 1971. (Name.) Dj (sl worn, soiled). *Typographeum*. $30/£19

AUDSLEY, G. A. and J. L. BOWES. Keramic Art of Japan. London, 1875. 2 vols. Folio. Orig brn morocco, gilt. (Lt foxed; spines sl faded, extrems worn.) *Swann**. $373/£233

AUDSLEY, G. A. and J. L. BOWES. Keramic Art of Japan. London, 1881. 33 plts. Mod cl w/orig cl backstrip, fr cvr laid down. *Swann**. $92/£58

AUDUBON, J. Audobon's Western Journal, 1849-50. Cleveland, OH: Clark, 1906. 1st ed. Lg fldg map. Orig pub's announcement and his reply to pre-order laid in. (Spine ends rubbed.) *Heinoldt*. $125/£78

AUDUBON, J. Audubon's Western Journal, 1849-1850. Cleveland, 1906. 1st ed. Port, fldg map, 10-pg A. H. Clark cat at rear. Untrimmed. (Sl worn, spine foot bumped.) Howes A390. *Woolson*. $225/£141

AUDUBON, J. Delineations of American Scenery and Character. NY: G.A. Baker, 1926. 1st 1-vol ed. Frontisport. Dk blue cl, gilt. Fine in pict dj (lt worn). Howes A389. *Argonaut*. $75/£47

AUDUBON, J. The Original Water-Color Paintings for the Birds of America. NY, 1966. 2 vols. Box. *Kane**. $70/£44

AUEL, JEAN. The Clan of the Cave Bear. NY: Crown, (1980). 1st ed. NF in dj. *Pacific**. $46/£29

AUEL, JEAN. The Clan of the Cave Bear. NY: Crown, 1980. 1st ed. NF in dj (spine head sl chipped, 2 sm tears fr panel top). *Pacific**. $23/£14

AUEL, JEAN. The Clan of the Cave Bear. NY: Crown, 1980. 1st ed. Signed on pub's label mtd to 1/2-title. NF (spine ends lt worn) in dj (price-clipped). *Pacific**. $63/£39

AUER, HARRY A. Camp Fires in the Yukon. Cincinnati: Stewart & Kidd, 1916. 1st ed. Grn cl. NF (lacks dj). *Biscotti*. $100/£63

AUER, MICHAEL. The Illustrated History of the Camera: from 1839 to the Present. NY: NYGS, 1975. 1st US ed. Fine in illus dj. *Cahan*. $150/£94

AUERBACH, ERNA. Nicholas Hilliard. London: Kegan Paul, 1961. Color frontis, 252 plts. Dec bds. (Ex-lib, few stamps), o/w Fine. *Europa*. $88/£55

AUGHEY, JOHN H. Tupelo. Lincoln, NE: Ptd by State Journal Co, 1888. 1st ed. 606pp. (Shelf-worn, extrems rubbed), else Good. *Brown*. $35/£22

AUGHINBAUGH, WILLIAM E. I Swear by Apollo. NY, 1938. 1st ed. VG in dj (tattered). *Doctor's Library*. $25/£16

AUGUSTINE, SAINT. The Confessions. Ipswich: LEC, 1962. One of 1500. Signed by Edy Legrand (illus). 1/2 leather, cl, gilt-lettered morocco cvr label. Fine in glassine, slipcase. *Pacific**. $75/£47

AUGUSTINE, SAINT. The Confessions. In Ten Books. Phila: Lippincott, 1900. One of 150. Frontis engr. Marbled eps; teg, uncut, yapped edges. Full vellum, gilt. VG (sl waterstained to prelims). *Hartfield*. $145/£91

AUMENT, SHARY. Unforgettable Faces. Kalamazoo, MI: Leaders, 1972. 1st ed. Signed. NF (lacks dj). *Associates*. $200/£125

Aunt Louisa's National Album. Frederick Warne, n.d. ca 1875. Lg 4to. 24pp; 4 dbl-pg spreads, 11 full-pg plts, 5 other plts, plain guarding ll. Illus ptd by Kronheim. Pict royal-blue cl, gilt. (Fep renewed, hinges pulled; spine, corners worn), else VG. *Bookmark*. $392/£245

Aunt Louisa's Old Nursery Friends. (By Laura Belinda Valentine.) London: Frederick Warne, n.d. (ca 1880). 4to. 18 VF full-pg chromolithos. Gilt pict bd, chromolitho label. (Corners lt rubbed, spine extrems chipped.) *Hobbyhorse*. $125/£78

Aunt Louisa's Sunday Picture Book. Frederick Warne, n.d. ca 1872. Lg 4to. 24pp; 24 plts, plain guarding ll. Dec royal-blue cl, gilt. (Hinges strained, sl rubbed, spine ends, corners worn), else VG. *Bookmark*. $192/£120

Aunt Louisa's Toy Book. Nine Niggers More. London: Frederick Warne, ca (1870). 1st ed. 4to. (16)pp. Color ptd cvrs. (Sl expert spine restoration), o/w VF. *Sotheran*. $477/£298

AURELIUS, MARCUS. Meditations. Meric Casaubon (trans). NY: LEC, 1956. One of 1500. Signed by Hans Alexander Mueller (illus). 1/2 black morocco, marbled bds. Fine in matching slipcase. *Pacific**. $63/£39

AURTHUR, ROBERT et al. The Third Marine Division. Washington, 1948. 1st ed. VG. *Clark*. $65/£41

AUSTEN, JANE. Emma. LEC, 1964. Ltd to 1500 numbered. Fine in slipcase. *Swann**. $69/£43

AUSTEN, JANE. Five Letters from Jane Austen to Her Niece Fanny Knight Printed in Facsimile. Oxford: Clarendon, 1924. One of 250. 5 facs letters. Gray linen-backed marbled bds, ptd fr cvr label. Good (feps browned, stamps). *Blackwell's*. $128/£80

AUSTEN, JANE. Jane Austen's Letters to Her Sister Cassandra and Others. R.W. Chapman (ed). London, 1952. 2nd ed. VG. *Gretton*. $32/£20

AUSTEN, JANE. Northanger Abbey and Persuasion. London: John Murray, 1818. 1st eds w/half-titles, biographical notice by Henry Austen, and 'Advertisement by the Authoress of Northanger Abbey'. 4 vols. 8vo. Contemp brn speckled calf, gilt ruled spines w/red morocco spine labels, sprinkled edges. Vols preserved in 2 half-morocco slipcases. *Appelfeld.* $8,500/£5,313

AUSTEN, JANE. Northanger Abbey. LEC, 1971. Ltd to 1500 numbered, signed by Clarke Hutton (illus). Fine in slipcase. *Swann*.* $46/£29

AUSTEN, JANE. The Novels. London: C&W, 1908. 10 vols. 8vo. A. Wallis Mills (illus). 3/4 green calf, gilt emblematic tooling on spines, raised bands, gilt tops. Fine set. *Appelfeld.* $1,600/£1,000

AUSTEN, JANE. Persuasion. Phila: Carey & Lea, 1832. 1st Amer ed, w/inserted cat at end vol 1. 2 vols. Uncut. Orig 1/4 purple muslin, buff bds. VG set (foxed, sl spotted, sig excised from blank at upper margin of each tp, inscrip; spine ends frayed). *Macdonnell.* $1,850/£1,156

AUSTEN, JANE. Persuasion. LEC, 1977. One of 1600 signed by Tony Buonpastore (illus). Fine in slipcase. *Swann*.* $57/£36

AUSTEN, JANE. Pride and Prejudice. NY/London: Macmillan/George Allen, 1894. 1st and ltd ed w/these dwgs. 250 copies for the English market. Royal 8vo. (xxvii),476pp; 98 engrs by Hugh Thomson. Uncut, unopened. Dk red buckram, gilt. (Spine sl sun-lightened), else Fine. *Sotheran.* $461/£288

AUSTEN, JANE. Pride and Prejudice. LEC, 1940. Ltd to 1500 numbered, signed by Helen Sewell (illus). Fine in slipcase. *Swann*.* $115/£72

AUSTEN, JANE. Sense and Sensibility. LEC, 1957. One of 1000. Helen Sewell (illus). Fine in slipcase. *Swann*.* $40/£25

AUSTEN, JANE. The Works. London: Richard Bentley, 1882. Illus ed. 6 vols. 8vo. 3/4 blue morocco over marbled bds, gilt lettering, raised bands, marbled edges. Fine. *Appelfeld.* $1,600/£1,000

AUSTEN, R. A. A Treatise of Fruit-Trees, Shewing the Manner of Planting, Grafting, Pruning, and Ordering of Them in all Respects, etc. Oxford: William Hall, 1665. 12mo. Mod marbled bds over brn morocco spine, leather label. Good. *Appelfeld.* $250/£156

AUSTER, PAUL. Disappearances. NY: Overlook, 1988. 1st ed. NF in NF dj. *Warren.* $35/£22

AUSTER, PAUL. Disappearances. Woodstock, NY: Overlook Press, 1988. 1st ed. Beige bds. Fine in dj (price-clipped). *Heritage.* $40/£25

AUSTER, PAUL. Ghosts. CA: Sun & Moon, 1986. 1st Amer ed. Fine in Fine dj. *Warren.* $95/£59

AUSTER, PAUL. In the Country of Last Things. (NY): Viking, (1987). 1st ed. Fine in Fine dj. *Between The Covers.* $45/£28

AUSTER, PAUL. In the Country of Last Things. Faber, 1987. 1st UK ed. Fine in dj. *Williams.* $29/£18

AUSTER, PAUL. Moon Palace. NY, 1989. 1st ed. Fine in Fine dj. *Warren.* $30/£19

AUSTER, PAUL. Moon Palace. London: Faber & Faber, 1989. 1st Eng ed. Signed. Fine (spine foot sl bumped) in dj. *Ulysses.* $104/£65

AUSTER, PAUL. Mr. Vertigo. Faber, 1994. 1st UK ed. Proof copy. Fine in oversized proof dj (sl creased). *Williams.* $26/£16

AUSTER, PAUL. The Music of Chance. London: Faber & Faber, 1991. 1st Eng ed. Fine in dj. *Ulysses.* $40/£25

AUSTERMAN, WAYNE R. Sharps Rifles and Spanish Mules. College Station, TX, 1985. VG in dj. *Dumont.* $40/£25

AUSTIN, AURELIA. Georgia Boys With 'Stonewall' Jackson. Athens, (1967). 1st ed. Inscribed. VG + . *Pratt.* $35/£22

AUSTIN, BENJAMIN. Constitutional Republicanism, in Opposition to Fallacious Federalism. Boston, 1803. Orig bds. Howes A396. *Swann*.* $92/£58

AUSTIN, C. R. (ed). The Mammalian Fetus In Vitro. London, 1973. 1st ed. Dj. *Edwards.* $24/£15

AUSTIN, F. BRITTEN. The War-God Walks Again. London: Williams & Norgate, 1926. 1st ed. Red cl stamped in gilt/black. VG (edges lt foxed, spine sl sunned). *Reese.* $25/£16

AUSTIN, J. P. The Blue and the Gray. Atlanta, GA, 1899. 246pp. Blind-stamped cl. (Spine badly speckled, cvrs heavily soiled.) *King.* $95/£59

AUSTIN, JOHN. The Province of Jurisprudence Determined. John Murray, 1832. 1st ed. xx,391,(1),lxxvipp (prelims, final pp foxed). Contemp sprinkled brn calf (expertly backed to match, corners repaired), smooth backstrip divided by gilt roll between blind, red morocco label, gilt. Good (hinges strengthened). *Blackwell's.* $360/£225

AUSTIN, L. The Metallurgy of the Common Metals. NY: Wiley, c1926. 6th ed. Good. *Blake.* $45/£28

AUSTIN, MARGOT. Gabriel Churchkitten. Dutton, 1942. 1st ed. 8.8x10. 32pp. VG- (pp fingerwrinkled; rear cvr soiled) in Good dj (soiled, tears poorly mended). *Price.* $35/£22

AUSTIN, MARY. The Arrow Maker: A Drama in Three Acts. NY: Duffield, 1911. 1st ed. Frontis. Tan bds, paper labels. (Bkpl; sl rubbed, spine label dknd.) *Dawson.* $75/£47

AUSTIN, MARY. The Children Sing in the Far West. Boston: Houghton Mifflin, 1928. 1st ed. Pict red cl. (Bkpl.) Dj (chipped). *Dawson.* $100/£63

AUSTIN, MARY. Experiences Facing Death. Bobbs-Merrill, (1931). 1st ed. Fine (name, year). *Authors Of The West.* $60/£38

AUSTIN, MARY. The Flock. Boston: Houghton Mifflin, 1906. 1st ed. NF. *Labordo.* $175/£109

AUSTIN, MARY. The Flock. Boston: Houghton, Mifflin, 1906. 1st ed. Frontis. Teg. Grn cl, gilt. VF in glassine wrapper, pub's box (both sl browned). *Heritage.* $450/£281

AUSTIN, MARY. The Green Bough. GC: Doubleday, Page, 1913. Frontis. Pict bds (hinges weak, tips rubbed; dknd). *Dawson.* $35/£22

AUSTIN, MARY. Indian Pottery of the Rio Grande. (Pasadena: Esto Pub, 1934.) Ptd wrappers. *Dawson.* $30/£19

AUSTIN, MARY. Isidro. Boston: Houghton Mifflin, 1905. 1st ed, 1st bk. VG. *Labordo.* $85/£53

AUSTIN, MARY. The Land of Journey's Ending. NY: Century, (1924). 1st ed. Pict cl (lt soiled; tips sl bumped). *Dawson.* $100/£63

AUSTIN, MARY. The Land of Journey's Ending. NY: Century, 1924. 1st ed. Pict cl. NF. *Labordo.* $95/£59

AUSTIN, MARY. The Land of Little Rain. Boston: Houghton Mifflin, 1903. 1st ed. Teg. Gilt-lettered pict grn cl. (Corners rubbed, sl insect damage; spine head, extrems chipped), else VG-. *Pacific*.* $69/£43

AUSTIN, MARY. The Land of Little Rain. Boston: Houghton Mifflin, 1950. 1st ed thus. Ansel Adams (illus). Yellow cl. NF in dj (rubbed). *Pacific*.* $115/£72

AUSTIN, MARY. The Land of Little Rain. Boston, 1950. 1st ed. Ansel Adams (photos). Buckram. VG (ink name) in VG dj. *Sagebrush.* $125/£78

AUSTIN, MARY. Mother of Felipe. Ward Ritchie, 1950. One of 450. *Dawson.* $37/£23

AUSTIN, MARY. Outland. Boni & Liveright, 1919. 1st ed. Signed. Pict cl. (Paper separated along fr hinge.) Dj (edges, spine ends chipped). *Dawson.* $200/£125

AUSTIN, MARY. Taos Pueblo. Boston: NYGS, 1977. Facs of orig 1930 ed. One of 950. Signed by Ansel Adams (photos). Folio. Valenti Angelo (woodcuts). 12 photo plts. Calf-backed adobe-colored cl. Orig matching cl box. *Kane**. $500/£313

AUSTIN, MARY. Western Trails. Reno: Univ of NV, 1987. 1st ed. Fine in Fine dj. *Book Market.* $30/£19

AUSTIN, PRONCIPAL. Glimpses of the Unseen. Toronto/Brantford: Bradley-Garretson, (1898). 504pp. Pict red cl (lt worn). *Cullen.* $200/£125

AUSTIN, SARAH. The Story Without an End. London: Sampson, Low, Son & Marston, 1868. 1st ed. Royal 8vo. (vi),40pp; 15 Fine color-ptd plts by E. V. B (Eleanor Vere Boyle). Aeg. Grn cl, onlaid ivorine label dec in gilt, colors inset into fr bd. VG (blue mk to rear cvr, ivorine label sl bowed); internally Fine. *Sotheran.* $205/£128

Authentic and Complete Trial of Lieut. Gen. Whitelocke. London, n.d. (1808). 1st ed. Engr frontisport, 96pp; port inlaid. Mod bds. (Tp, final 2 ll in facs.) *Maggs.* $192/£120

Authentic Records of the Court of England, for the Last Seventy Years. (By Anne Hamilton.) London: J. Phillips, 1832. 1st ed. Hand-colored frontis, viii,396pp. 19th-cent calf over bds (extrems worn, fr hinge split at head). Bkpl of Henry Gilpin. *Karmiole.* $200/£125

Autobiography of a Shaker, and Revelation of the Apocalypse. (By Frederick W. Evans.) NY: American News Co, (1869). 1st ed, 2nd ptg. 162pp. (1870 inscrip.) *M & S.* $150/£94

Autobiography of an English Soldier in the United States Army. (By George Ballentine.) NY: Stringer & Townsend, 1853. 1st Amer ed. xii,(12)-288pp; 2 plts. (Spotted, spine faded, sm worm hole.) Howes B77. *Mott.* $125/£78

Automobile Engineering. Chicago: American Technical Soc, 1923. 1st ed. 6 vols. Flexible black cl, gilt. NF set. *Pacific**. $81/£51

Automobile Year. Number 10, 1962-1963. Lausanne, Switzerland, (1962). (Inner fr hinge loose, sm edge dents), else Good in dj (stained, chipped). *King.* $125/£78

AVARY, MYRTA LOCKETT (ed). A Virginia Girl in the Civil War 1861-1865. NY: Appleton, 1903. 1st ed. 8vo. Teg. Blue-grn cl. NF (early sigs; sl cocked) in VG ptd dj (spine head chipped). *Chapel Hill.* $550/£344

AVEDON, RICHARD et al. Famous Photographers Course. Volume I. Lesson Assignment Material. Westport, CT: Famous Photographers School, 1964. Folio. Cl ring binder. (Intro pg soiled; binder lt worn), else VG. *Cahan.* $85/£53

AVEDON, RICHARD. Avedon: Photographs 1947-1977. (NY): FSG, (1978). 1st ed. Pict bds. (Sm ink notes rear pastedown), else NF in ptd glassine. *Pacific**. $127/£79

AVEDON, RICHARD. Avedon: Photographs 1947-1977. NY, (1978). 1st ed. Folio. 162 full-pg repros. (Sl yellowed; bds discolored.) Ptd plastic dj (rubbed). *Swann**. $287/£179

AVEDON, RICHARD. Avedon: Photographs 1947-1977. NY: FSG, 1978. 1st ed. Folio. 162 photos. Fine in pict bds. Ptd acetate dj. *Cahan.* $300/£188

AVEDON, RICHARD. In the American West 1979-1984. NY: Abrams, 1985. 1st ed. Signed in 1985. Folio. Photo illus cl cvr. Fine. *Smith.* $250/£156

AVEDON, RICHARD. In the American West. NY, (1985). 1st ed. Folio. Acetate wrapper. *Swann**. $126/£79

AVEDON, RICHARD. Nothing Personal. James Baldwin (text). NY, 1964. 1st Amer ed. Fine in box (spine sl creased). *Polyanthos.* $350/£219

AVEDON, RICHARD. Nothing Personal. Text by James Baldwin. NY, (1964). 1st ed. Folio. (Sl worn.) Slipcase (soiled, rubbed). *Swann**. $230/£144

AVEDON, RICHARD. Nothing Personal. Text by James Baldwin. NY: Atheneum, 1964. 1st ed. Folio. Fine in glazed bds in VG pub's slipcase. *Smith.* $250/£156

AVEDON, RICHARD. Observations. NY, 1959. 1st Amer ed. Fine in glassine dj (edge chips) in box (spine sl soiled, rear cvr rubbed). *Polyanthos.* $125/£78

AVEDON, RICHARD. Observations. Text by Truman Capote. NY, (1959). 1st ed. Folio. (Sl soiled; spine stained.) Slipcase (worn, soiled). *Swann**. $316/£198

AVEDON, RICHARD. Portraits. NY, (1976). 1st ed. (Notes fep.) Dj (age-dknd), acetate wrapper. *Swann**. $258/£161

AVEDON, RICHARD. Richard Avedon, Photographer. NY: Marlborough Gallery, 1975. 1st ed. 5 full-pg b/w photos, fold-out w/3 full-pg b/w photo sequence. Fine in pict stiff wrappers. *Cahan.* $35/£22

AVERILL, ESTHER. The Adventures of Jack Ninepins. NY: Harper, 1944. 1st ed. 6.25x8.5. 64pp. Good. *Cattermole.* $25/£16

AVERY, GILLIAN. Mouldy's Orphan. Collins, 1978. 1st ed. 8vo. Faith Jaques (illus). 79pp. Fine in pict dj. *Bookmark.* $24/£15

AWDRY, W. Edward the Blue Engine. Edmund Ward, 1954. 1st ed. Railway Series No. 9. VG in dj. *Green Meadow.* $40/£25

AWDRY, W. Henry the Green Engine. Edmund Ward, 1951. 1st ed. Railway Series No. 6. VG in dj. *Green Meadow.* $40/£25

AXE, JOHN WORTLEY. The Horse. Its Treatment in Health and Disease. London: Gresham, 1905. 9 vols. (Vol 1 frontis loose, frayed in margin; shelfworn, sl foxed, etc.) *Oinonen**. $140/£88

AXSOM, RICHARD. The Prints of Frank Stella: A Catalogue Raisonne 1967-1982. NY, (1983). Stiff wrappers. *Swann**. $57/£36

AYLING, ALAN. The Long Way Round. Whittington, 1977. One of 200, this copy unnumbered. Signed. Maroon cl. Fine in slipcase. *Michael Taylor.* $72/£45

AYLMER, FENTON (ed). A Cruise in the Pacific from the Log of a Naval Officer. London, 1860. 2 vols in 1. 2 plts. Mod lib buckram (lib #s on spine). *Swann**. $115/£72

AYRES, ATLEE B. Mexican Architecture. NY, 1926. Folio. (Cl sl soiled, rubbed, spine bumped, chipped w/sl loss.) *Edwards.* $72/£45

AYRES, GEORGE B. How to Paint Photographs in Water Colors. Phila: Benerman & Wilson, 1870. 2nd ed (so stated). (5)-148 + 20pp ads (lt aging, foxed) Dk grn cl (sl worn), gilt. Cvrs Good. *Baltimore**. $110/£69

AYRTON, EDWARD R. and W. L. S. LOAT. Pre-Dynastic Cemetery at El Mahasna. London: Kegan Paul, Trench, Trubner, Quaritch, 1911. 1st ed. Folio. 38 plts. Cl spine. (Ex-lib; sl rubbed, sm tear spine top, lib spine #), o/w VG. *Worldwide.* $75/£47

AYRTON, MICHAEL. Giovanni Pisano, Sculptor. NY, 1969. Good. *Washton.* £53

AYRTON, MICHAEL. Giovanni Pisano, Sculptor. London: Thames & Hudson, 1969. Color frontis, 370 plts. Good in dj. *Ars Artis.* $200/£125

AYRTON, MICHAEL. Golden Sections. London, 1957. 1st Eng ed. Nice in dj (sl rubbed). *Clearwater.* $64/£40

AYRTON, MICHAEL. The Maze Maker. Longmans, 1967. 1st ed. VG in dj (sl rubbed), w/wraparound band. *Ulysses.* $40/£25

AYSCOUGH, SAMUEL. An Index to the Remarkable Passages and Words Made Use of by Shakespeare. London, 1827. 3/4 leather. (Foxed; corners sl bumped.) *Argosy.* $75/£47

AZUELA, MARIANO. The Under Dogs. NY: Brentano's, 1929. 1st US ed, presumed later state of binding in blue cl. Fine in NF dj (sl worn, price-clipped). *Lame Duck.* $350/£219

B

B., B. The Fisherman's Bedside Book. London, 1946. Rpt. (Name), o/w Fine in dj. *Petersfield.* $48/£30

B., B. Monty Woodpig's Caravan. Ward, 1957. 1st ed. (Hand color to b/w illus), o/w VG in dj. *Green Meadow.* $64/£40

B., B. A Stream in Your Garden. Eyre & Spottiswoode, 1948. 1st ed. VG + in VG dj. *Green Meadow.* $56/£35

BAARS, DONALD L. Red Rock County. Doubleday, 1972. 1st ed. 34 maps. Brn cl. VG in full-color pict dj. *Five Quail.* $35/£22

BABB, DOT. In the Bosom of the Comanches. Amarillo, TX, (1923). 2nd ptg. Port. (Few pp, fr cvr fore-edge sl dampstained), else VG. *Sagebrush.* $85/£53

BABBITT, EDWIN D. The Principles of Light and Color. NY: Babbitt, 1878. 1st ed. 3 (of 4) chromolithos. (Adhesion residue to eps, w/pieces of rep lacking, stamp; spine ends sl rubbed), else VG. *Pacific*.* $92/£58

BABBITT, NATALIE. The Something. NY: FSG, 1970. 3rd ed. 6.25x7.25. 32pp. Fine in dj. *Cattermole.* $15/£9

BABCOCK, BERNIE. Hallerloogy's Ride with Santa Claus. Perry, AR: Rice Print Shop, 1943. Hand-set special ed. Signed. 8vo. 48pp; 9 photo illus. Blue ptd paper cvrs (lt stained), color paste label (worn). *Reisler.* $150/£94

BABCOCK, BERNIE. The Soul of Abe Lincoln. Phila, 1923. 1st Amer ed. Color frontis. NF (inscrip) in VG dj. *Polyanthos.* $25/£16

BABCOCK, HAVILAH. Tales of Quail N' Such. NY: Greenburg, 1951. 2nd ptg. Green-tan linen. Fine in Fine color pict dj. *Biscotti.* $40/£25

BABCOCK, LOUIS L. The Tarpon. N.p., 1930. 3rd ed. One of 250 numbered. Signed, inscribed presentation. Wrappers (edgewear), pict cvr label. *Oinonen*.* $375/£234

BABCOCK, PHILIP H. Falling Leaves; Tales from a Gun Room. NY: Derrydale, 1937. Ltd to 950 numbered. Brn cl. VF-. *Biscotti.* $200/£125

BABEL, ISAAC. Red Cavalry. London: Knopf, (1929). 1st British ed. Orange cl stamped in black. (Fore-edge foxed), o/w VF in dj w/T.L.S. blurb wraparound intact. *Reese.* $125/£78

BABER, D. F. and BILL WALKER. The Longest Rope. Caldwell: Caxton, 1940. 1st ed. Dj (lt chipped). *Dawson.* $60/£38

BABINGTON, ANTHONY. For the Sake of Example: Capital Courts-Martial 1914-1920. (London): Leo Cooper/Secker & Warburg, (1983). 1st ed. Gilt grn cl bds. (Sl bump), else NF in dj (nicked). *Reese.* $25/£16

BABINGTON, JOHN. Records of the Fife Fox-Hounds. Edinburgh/London, 1883. 1st ed. 29 plts. Red cl (corners bumped, spine worn, dknd), gilt. *Kane*.* $60/£38

BABITZ, EVE. Sex and Rage. NY: Knopf, 1979. 1st ed. Fine in dj. *Between The Covers.* $45/£28

Baby Talk. NY: Frederick A. Stokes, 1898. 1st ed. 4to. 6 full-pg color plts by Maud Humphrey & Elizabeth S. Tucker. Cl-backed color pict bds (stained, edges rubbed). *Reisler.* $250/£156

Baby's Bouquet. London: Frederick Warne, (ca 1900). Early ed. Sq 8vo. Walter Crane (illus). (viii),9-56pp. Dec bds. Fine. *Sotheran.* $109/£68

BACH, CARL PHILIPP EMANUEL. Essay on the True Art of Playing Keyboard Instruments. William J. Mitchell (ed). Cassell, 1949. 1st Eng ed. 4 plts. VG in dj. *Hollett.* $96/£60

BACHMAN, RICHARD. (Pseud of Stephen King.) The Long Walk. NY: Signet, 1979. 1st ptg. Pb orig. VG. *Warren.* $35/£22

BACHMAN, RICHARD. (Pseud of Stephen King.) Thinner. NY: New American Library, (1984). 1st ed. NF in dj (price-clipped). *Pacific*.* $69/£43

BACK, GEORGE. Narrative of the Arctic Land Expedition to the Mouth of the Great Fish River...1833-1835. London, 1836. Fldg map, 15 (of 16) plts on mtd India paper. Old bds (binding broken, spine gone). *Oinonen*.* $180/£113

BACK, GEORGE. Narrative of the Arctic Land Expedition...in the Years 1833, 1834, and 1835. London, 1836. Ad cat dated May 1836. Map, 16 plts. Early calf (skillfully rebacked; lt foxed). *Swann*.* $316/£198

BACKES, M. and R. DOLLING. Art of the Dark Ages. NY: Abrams, 1969. Yellow cl. Dj. *Maggs.* $29/£18

Background of the American Stud Book. (By Fairfax Harrison.) Richmond: Privately ptd at Old Dominion Press, 1933. Paper spine label. (Sl worn.) *Oinonen*.* $120/£75

BACKHOUSE, JAMES. Narrative of a Visit to Mauritius and South Africa. London: Hamilton, Adams, 1844. xvi,648,lvi pp; 2 fldg maps, 16 plts. Orig cl (rubbed, spine ends sl frayed). *Adelson.* $450/£281

BACKHOUSE, JANET. John Scottowe's Alphabet Books. London: Roxburgh Club, 1974. Sq folio. 28 facs plts. 1/2 morocco (rubbed, sl spotted). *Oinonen*.* $100/£63

BACON, EDWARD. Among the Cotton Thieves. Detroit, 1867. 1st ed. 299pp + errata. (Foxed; lacks bottom 1/3 spine cvr, cvr heavily worn.) *King.* $300/£188

BACON, FRANCIS. The Essayes or Counsels, Civill and Moral...Newly Enlarged. London, 1625. 1st complete ed, 1st issue. 4to. Sprinkled calf, gilt, by Bedford. *Felcone.* $3,000/£1,875

BACON, FRANCIS. The Essays. LEC, 1944. One of 1100 signed by Bruce Rogers (designer). Fine in slipcase. *Swann*.* $201/£126

BACON, FRANCIS. Essays. Sydney Humphries (ed). A&C Black, 1912. Sydney ed. 2 vols. Photogravure frontisport. Floral eps. VG in contemp full vellum, gilt, grn/red morocco labels. *Cox.* $136/£85

BACON, FRANCIS. History, Natural and Experimentall (sic), of Life and Death, or of the Prolongation of Life. William Rawley (trans). London: William Lee & Humphrey Moseley, 1650. 2nd ed of Rawley's trans. 2 prelims, 64pp. Old full polished blind-stamped calf (rebacked in later leather, rubbed, worn). *Kane*.* $375/£234

BACON, FRANCIS. Sylva Syvarum: Or, A Naturall Historie in Ten Centuries. William Rawley (ed). London: John Haviland for William Lee, 1635. 4th ed. 10.75x7. Dbl frontis, (20),260,(30),47,(3)pp. Period calf, raised bands, morocco spine label. (Bkpl), else NF. *Pacific*.* $575/£359

BACON, FRANCIS. The Two Bookes of Sr. Francis Bacon. Of the Proficience and Advancement of Learning. London, 1629. 2nd ed. 4to. Contemp sheep (rebacked). *Felcone.* $800/£500

BACON, FRANCIS. The Works of Francis Bacon, Baron of Verulam, Viscount St. Alban, and Lord High Chancellor of England. Thomas Birch (ed). London: A. Millar, 1765. 5 vols. 4to. Copper-engr frontispieces to vols I-IV, (12),xlii,(2),575; (5),658; (11),681,(74); xx,(2),529; vii,604pp; 2 fldg tables. Period full calf, gilt, morocco lettering pieces, raised bands. Very Nice set (vol I lacks fep, flyleaf, other vols w/few flyleaves loose, some offset to tp, bkpls; sl scuffed, worn, joints cracked). *Pacific*.* $690/£431

BACON, PEGGY. Starting from Scratch. Julian Messner, 1945. 1st ed. 8vo. 46pp. Paperbds spiral bound. VG (fep bottom edge worn, browned; bds lt rubbed, spine ends lack pieces) in Good dj (spine chips, 2.5x3-inch chip affecting dwg). *Price.* $65/£41

BACON-FOSTER, CORA. Early Chapters in the Development of the Patomac Route to the West. Washington: Columbia, 1912. 1st ed. Signed. (Ex-lib spine mks, few rubber stamps.) *Ginsberg.* $125/£78

BACOU, ROSELINE. Millet. Phaidon, 1975. 1st ed. 100 plts. Dj. *Edwards.* $72/£45

BADDELEY, JOHN F. The Rugged Flanks of Caucasus. London: Humphrey Milford/OUP, 1940. 1st ed. Super royal 8vo. xvi,272; x,318pp; 37 photogravure plts, 9 maps (8 fldg). Fore, lower edges uncut. Fine set (bkpls, neat contemp inscrip each vol; spine sl faded) in buff buckram. *Ulysses.* $960/£600

BADEN-POWELL, ROBERT. Adventures and Accidents. London, 1934. 1st ed. (Cl lt rubbed.) Contents VG. *Grayling.* $40/£25

BADEN-POWELL, ROBERT. Pig-Sticking or Hog-Hunting. London, 1924. 1st ed. Color frontis. *Petersfield.* $72/£45

BADHAM, C. DAVID. Prose Halieutics or Ancient and Modern Fish Tattle. London: John W. Parker & Son, 1854. 1st ed. Blind-stamped cl, gilt. NF (name, bkpl). *Pacific*.* $150/£94

BADHAM, C. DAVID. A Treatise on Esculent Funguses of England. Reeve Bros, 1847. 1st ed, w/9 more plts. 4to. x,138pp + 16pp cat dated March 1847 bound in; 21 litho plts (17 hand-colored), finished w/gum arabic, guards. Orig gray cl blocked in blind, lg gilt vignette fr cvr. (Joints, spine ends sl frayed, neatly repaired.) *Sotheran.* $637/£398

BAE. 2nd Annual Report. Washington, 1883. 174 plts (11 color), dbl-pg map. Dk grn cl, gilt. VG (spine ends worn). *Kane*.* $100/£63

BAE. 3rd Annual Report. Washington, 1884. 44 plts (2 color). Dk grn cl, gilt. VG (spine ends worn). *Kane*.* $110/£69

BAE. 4th Annual Report. Washington, 1886. 83 plts (11 color). Dk grn cl, gilt. VG (spine ends worn). *Kane*.* $90/£56

BAE. 5th Annual Report. Washington, 1887. 23 plts (8 color, 4 dbl-pg), 2 maps in rear pocket. Dk grn cl, gilt. VG (spine ends worn). *Kane*.* $140/£88

BAE. 6th Annual Report. Washington: GPO, 1888. 10 plts, 1 map in rear pocket. *Heinoldt.* $60/£38

BAE. 6th Annual Report. Wasshington, 1888. 10 maps, plts, 2 fldg maps in rear pocket. Dk grn cl, gilt. VG (spine ends worn). *Kane*.* $90/£56

BAE. 7th Annual Report. Washington, 1888. 26 plts, maps (6 color), fldg map in rear pocket. Dk grn cl, gilt. VG (spine ends worn). *Kane*.* $70/£44

BAE. 8th Annual Report. Washington, 1891. 123 plts (12 color, 2 dbl-pg), incl 3 in rear pocket. Dk grn cl, gilt. VG (spine ends worn). *Kane*.* $90/£56

BAE. 9th Annual Report. Washington, 1892. 2 maps, 6 color plts. Dk grn cl, gilt. VG (spine ends worn). *Kane*.* $65/£41

BAE. 10th Annual Report. Washington, 1893. 54 plts. Dk grn cl, gilt. VG (spine ends worn). *Kane*.* $70/£44

BAE. 11th Annual Report. Washington, 1894. 50 plts (18 color). Dk grn cl, gilt. VG (spine ends worn). *Kane*.* $70/£44

BAE. 12th Annual Report. Washington, 1894. 42 plts, incl 1 in rear pocket. Dk grn cl (sl spot fr cvr, spine ends worn), gilt. *Kane*.* $60/£38

BAE. 13th Annual Report. Washington, 1896. 60 plts. Dk grn cl, gilt. VG (spine ends worn). *Kane*.* $90/£56

BAE. 14th Annual Report. Washington, 1896. 2 vols. 122 plts, maps (7 color, 3 tinted). Dk grn cl, gilt. (Ex-lib, sl shaken, inner hinges weak; spine ends worn.) *Kane*.* $110/£69

BAE. 15th Annual Report. Washington, 1897. 125 plts. Black buckram (rebound; marginal tear 1 leaf). *Kane*.* $65/£41

BAE. 16th Annual Report. Washington, 1897. 81 plts. Dk grn cl, gilt. VG (spine ends worn). *Kane*.* $60/£38

BAE. 18th Annual Report. Washington, 1899. 2 vols. 107 plts, maps, 67 color maps. Dk grn cl, gilt. VG (spine ends worn). *Kane*.* $70/£44

BAE. 19th Annual Report. Washington, 1900. 2 vols. 79 plts, maps. Dk grn cl, gilt. VG (spine ends worn). *Kane*.* $90/£56

BAE. 20th Annual Report. Washington, 1903. 180 plts. Darker grn pebbled cl. (Ex-lib, inner joints opening.) *Kane*.* $65/£41

BAE. 22nd Annual Report. Washington, 1904. 2 vols. 91 plts. Dk grn cl, gilt. VG (spine ends worn). *Kane*.* $70/£44

BAE. 24th Annual Report. Washington, 1907. 24 plts (2 color). Dk grn cl, gilt. VG (spine ends worn). *Kane*.* $75/£47

BAE. 25th Annual Report. Washington, 1907. 131 plts. Dk grn cl (white paint spot on spine, ends worn), gilt. *Kane*.* $65/£41

BAE. 26th Annual Report. Washington, 1908. 58 plts. Dk grn cl, gilt. VG (spine ends worn). *Kane*.* $55/£34

BAE. 27th Annual Report. Washington, 1911. 66 plts, incl lg fldg map. Dk grn cl, gilt. VG (spine ends worn). *Kane*.* $60/£38

BAE. 28th Annual Report. Washington, 1912. 103 plts, incl lg fldg map. Dk grn cl, gilt. VG (spine ends worn). *Kane*.* $55/£34

BAE. 29th Annual Report. Washington: GPO, 1916. (Lib handstamps, spine #, sl shelfworn), else Good. *Brown.* $50/£31

BAE. 31st Annual Report. Washington: GPO, 1916. (Lib handstamps, spine #, fr inner hinge starting), else Good. *Brown.* $50/£31

BAE. 32nd Annual Report. Washington: GPO, 1918. (Lib handstamps, spine #, sl shelfworn), else Good. *Brown.* $45/£28

BAE. 33rd Annual Report. Washington: GPO, 1919. (Lib handstamps, spine #), else Good. *Brown.* $45/£28

BAE. 35th Annual Report. Washington: GPO, 1921. 2 vols. (Lib handstamps, spine #s), else Good set. *Brown.* $95/£59

BAE. 36th Annual Report. Washington: GPO, 1921. (Lib handstamps, spine #), else Good. *Brown.* $45/£28

BAE. 38th Annual Report. Washington: GPO, 1924. Map. (Lib handstamps, spine #), o/w Good. *Brown.* $45/£28

BAEDEKER, KARL. Great Britain. Leipzig, 1897. 4th ed. Good (used). *Gretton.* $19/£12

BAEDEKER, KARL. Italy from the Alps to Naples, a Handbook for Travellers. Leipzig: Karl Baedeker, 1909. 2nd ed. (Lt edgeworn, spine head tearing.) *Glenn.* $55/£34

BAEDEKER, KARL. London and Its Environs. Leipzig, 1911. 16th rev ed. 10 maps, 19 plans. All edges marbled. (Corners sl creased, spine sl rubbed.) *Edwards.* $40/£25

BAEDEKER, KARL. Northern Italy Including Florence. Leipzig, 1930. 15th ed. VG. *Gretton.* $24/£15

BAEDEKER, KARL. Southern Italy and Sicily. Leipzig, 1912. 16th ed. VG-. *Gretton.* $24/£15

BAER, ELIZABETH. Seventeenth Century Maryland. Balt, 1949. One of 300 ptd. (Lt worn.) Plain paper dj (turn-ins glued to pastedowns). *Oinonen*.* $110/£69

BAER, LUDWIG. The History of the German Steel Helmet 1916-1945. San Jose, 1985. 1st ed. VG. *Clark.* $40/£25

BAGBY, GEORGE. Bachelor's Wife. NY: Covici, Friede, 1932. 1st ed, 1st bk. VG (cvrs soiled, spine ends lt worn) in dj (rear lt soiled, lt worn). *Murder.* $175/£109

BAGBY, GEORGE. The Body in the Basket. Crime Club Dble, 1954. 1st ed. NF in dj (lt worn). *Murder.* $35/£22

BAGBY, GEORGE. The Twin Killing. Crime Club Dble, 1947. 1st ed. (Lt worn), else NF in dj (edges, spine ends chipped, lt soiled). *Murder.* $45/£28

BAGEHOT, WALTER. The English Constitution. Chapman & Hall, 1867. 1st ed. 8vo. Cream eps. Maroon cl (spine ends sl worn, fr hinge fragile; 1st, last ll sl foxed, fep sl stained). Collector's box. *Sotheby's*.* $827/£517

BAGGS, MAE LUCY. Colorado. Boston: Page, (1926). 3rd imp. 6 color plts. Teg. Gilt-dec cl. Fine. *Pacific**. $35/£22

BAGGS, THOMAS A. Back from the Front. London, 1914. 1st Eng ed. (Joints tender.) Card wrappers (sl rubbed). *Clearwater.* $40/£25

BAGLEY, CLARENCE B. The Acquisition and Pioneering of Old Oregon [with] Pioneer Seattle and Its Founders. Seattle: Argus Print, 1924. 1st ed thus. 17 plts, incl 2 photo engrs. Grn ptd wrappers. (Yapp edges chipped), o/w NF. *Harrington.* $100/£63

BAGLEY, DESMOND. The Spoilers. London: Collins, 1969. 1st ed. VF in dj. *Mordida.* $65/£41

BAGNOLD, ENID. A Diary Without Dates. London: Heinemann, (1918). 1st ed, 1st bk. Dec bds. (Bkpl; lt edgeworn), else VG. *Reese.* $75/£47

BAGNOLD, ENID. Early Poems. Whittington, 1987. One of 175. 1/4 hessian, patterned paper over bds. Fine. *Michael Taylor.* $72/£45

BAGNOLD, ENID. The Happy Foreigner. London: Heinemann, 1920. 1st ed. Gilt navy blue cl. (Sl foxed), else VG. *Reese.* $35/£22

BAGNOLD, ENID. Letters to Frank Harris and Other Friends. R. P. Lister (ed). Whittington, 1980. One of 370. Signed. Patterned cl, spine/fr labels. Fine in slipcase (sl rubbed). *Michael Taylor.* $64/£40

BAGNOLD, ENID. National Velvet. NY: William Morrow, 1935. 1st ed. (Spine sl faded), else VG in dj (spine ends sl chipped). *Pacific**. $86/£54

BAGOT, RICHARD. The Italian Lakes. A&C Black, 1912. 68 color plts, guards. VG in dec cl (sl mkd). *Cox.* $32/£20

BAGROW, LEO. History of Cartography. R. A. Skelton (ed). Chicago: Precedent, (1985). 2nd ed. NF in dj (sl worn). *Pacific**. $127/£79

BAHNEMANN, GUNTHER. New Guinea Crocodile Poacher. Adventurers Club, 1965. Fine in dj (repaired). *Hallam.* $19/£12

BAIGELL, MATTHEW. Thomas Hart Benton. NY, (1974). Dj. *Swann**. $138/£86

BAIKIE, JAMES. The Charm of the Scott Country. A&C Black, 1927. 1st ed. Pict cl, gilt. (Inscrips, label removed ep; fore-edge, fr panel sl spotted.) *Hollett.* $32/£20

BAIKIE, JAMES. Egyptian Antiquities in the Nile Valley. London: Methuen, (1932). 31 plts. (Spine faded, lt rubbed.) *Archaeologia.* $75/£47

BAIKIE, JAMES. A History of Egypt from the Earliest Times to the End of the XVIIIth Dynasty. London: A&C Black, 1929. 2 vols. 46 plts, 2 color maps. (Sigs; cvrs faded, discolored.) *Archaeologia.* $85/£53

BAIKIE, JAMES. Things Seen in the Scottish Highlands. Seeley Service, 1932. 1st ed. VG. *Hollett.* $24/£15

BAILES, KENDALL E. Rider on the Wind. Shawnee Mission: Wagon Wheel, 1962. 1st ed. Signed. VG. *Brown.* $20/£13

BAILEY, ALFRED M. Birds of Arctic Alaska. Colorado Museum of Natural History, April 1, 1948. 1st ed. VG in ptd wrapper. *High Latitude.* $70/£44

BAILEY, ALFRED M. and J. H. SORENSON. Subantarctic Campbell Island. (Denver): Museum of Natural Hist, 1962. Ptd color card binding, as issued. VG. *Explorer.* $54/£34

BAILEY, ALICE A. Telepathy and the Etheric Vehicle. NY: Lucis Pub, 1950. (Sl pencil underlining.) *Edwards.* $32/£20

BAILEY, ALICE A. A Treatise on Cosmic Fire. NY: Lucis Pub, 1951. 4th ed. *Edwards.* $40/£25

BAILEY, ALICE A. A Treatise on the Seven Rays. Esoteric Psychology. London/NY, 1950-1953. Various eds. 4 vols. *Edwards.* $96/£60

BAILEY, C. P. Practical Angora Goat Raising. San Jose, CA: Privately ptd, 1905. 1st ed. Grn cl, gilt. VG. *Larry Price.* $49/£31

BAILEY, CAROLYN S. Finnigan II: His Nine Lives. NY: Viking, 1953. 1st ed. 7x10. 95pp. Kate Seredy (illus). (Corners bumped), else VG + in dj (edgeworn). *My Bookhouse.* $42/£26

BAILEY, CAROLYN S. Homespun Playdays. Viking, 1941. 1st ed. Grace Paull (illus). 216pp. Beige cl, stamped. VG. *Price.* $25/£16

BAILEY, CAROLYN S. Tops and Whistles. Viking, 1937. 1st ed. Grace Paull (illus). 193pp. Gray cl. VG- (bkpl, 1/2-inch tear, wrinkle pg130; cl lt soiled). *Price.* $18/£11

BAILEY, DAVID and PETER EVANS. Goodbye Baby and Amen. NY: Coward-McCann, 1969. 1st Amer ed. Folio. Pub's cl. Fine in dj. *Sotheran.* $264/£165

BAILEY, DAVID. Mrs. David Bailey. NY: Rizzoli, 1980. 1st ed. 81 b/w photos. VG. *Cahan.* $85/£53

BAILEY, E. B. and J. WEIR. Introduction to Geology. Macmillan, 1939. 1st ed. Bkpl of Arthur Raistrick. *Hollett.* $32/£20

BAILEY, EDGAR H. (ed). Geology of Northern California. SF, (1968). VG + (lacks fldg map). *Sagebrush.* $45/£28

BAILEY, H. C. Dead Man's Effects. Macdonald, 1945. 1st UK ed. VG + in VG dj (sl rubbed, sm tears). *Williams.* $72/£45

BAILEY, H. C. The Life Sentence. London: Macdonald, (1946). 1st ed. Lt cerise cl. Fine in dj (chipped, rubbed, verso reinforced). *Temple.* $29/£18

BAILEY, H. C. Mr. Clunk's Text. CCD, 1939. 1st ed. (Edges lt worn), else NF in VG dj (few sm chips, rear rubbed, stained). *Murder.* $50/£31

BAILEY, H. C. Mr. Fortune Here. NY: Doubleday, Doran, 1940. 1st US ed. NF in VG + dj (extrems chipped, few sm closed tears). *Janus.* $50/£31

BAILEY, H. C. The Queen of Spades. GC: Doubleday, Doran, 1944. 1st US ed. VG + in dj (lt edgewear, chipped). *Janus.* $45/£28

BAILEY, HARRY. When New Mexico Was Young. Las Cruces, NM: Las Cruces Citizen, 1946. 1st ed. VG in pict wrappers. *Labordo.* $55/£34

BAILEY, J. O. Pilgrims Through Space and Time. NY: Argus Books, (1947). 1st ed. NF in dj (spine ends sl chipped). *Other Worlds.* $50/£31

BAILEY, JESSIE BROMILOW. Diego de Vargas and the Reconquest of New Mexico. Albuquerque, NM: Univ of NM, (1940). 1st ed. Red cl, gilt. (Spine sl faded), else Fine. *Argonaut.* $125/£78

BAILEY, KENNETH P. The Ohio Company of Virginia and the Westward Movement, 1748-1792. Glendale: A.H. Clark, 1939. 1st ed. 5 maps. Teg. *Dawson.* $75/£47

BAILEY, L. H. Cyclopedia of American Agriculture. NY: McMillian, 1907. 4 vols. 100 full-pg plates. Good (shelfworn, hinges starting). *Dumont.* $195/£122

BAILEY, L. H. The Forcing Book. NY: Macmillan, 1906. 6th ed. (Foxed, browned; spine edge worn in sm area, spotted), else VG. *Fair Meadow.* $18/£11

BAILEY, L. H. The Nursery-Manual. NY: Macmillan, 1928. 22nd ed. (Name), else VG in dec blue cl. *Fair Meadow.* $30/£19

BAILEY, L. H. The Pruning-Manual. NY, (1916). 18th ed. Dec cl. (Pp yellowed, inner hinge cracked; faded.) Dj (soiled). *Sutton.* $45/£28

BAILEY, L. H. The Standard Cyclopedia of Horticulture. NY: Macmillan, 1944. 7th ptg. 6 vols in 3. 96 full-pg cuts. (Eps browned; cl scuffed, corners bumped, spines sunned, cigarette burn fr bd, paint smudge rear bd of vol 3), else VG. *Fair Meadow.* $100/£63

BAILEY, L. H. (ed). The Cultivated Evergreens. NY: Macmillan, 1925. 58 full-pg plts. Uncut. 2-color buckram, gilt. (Lt cvr soil, spine dknd), else VG. *Quest*. $70/£44

BAILEY, L. R. (ed). The A.B. Gray Report. L.A., 1963. VG in dj. *Dumont*. $45/£28

BAILEY, LAWRENCE DUDLEY. Quantrell's Raid on Lawrence.... C. R. Green (ed). Lyndon, KS, 1899. 52pp. Sewn as issued. *Ginsberg*. $175/£109

BAILEY, MARGERY (ed). Boswell's Column, His 70 Contributions to the London Magazine Under the Pseudonym the Hypochondriak. London, 1951. 1st ed. Fine in dj. *Gretton*. $24/£15

BAILEY, PAUL. At the Jerusalem. London: Cape, 1967. 1st ed. VG in VG white dj (edges sl discolored, inside flds sl creased). *Virgo*. $64/£40

BAILEY, PAUL. Holy Smoke. L.A., 1978. 1st ed. (Inscrip), o/w Fine in dj. *Baade*. $37/£23

BAILEY, PAUL. Old Soldiers. London: Cape, (1980). 1st ed. Fine in dj. *Reese*. $22/£14

BAILEY, PAUL. Polygamy Was Better Than Monotony. L.A.: Westernlore, 1972. 1st ed. Signed, inscribed. Fine in VG dj. *Book Market*. $30/£19

BAILEY, PAUL. Sam Brannan and the California Mormons. L.A.: Westernlore, 1943. 1st ed. NF in dj (lt worn, spine sl sunned). *Pacific**. $52/£33

BAILEY, PAUL. Walkara, 'Hawk of the Mountains.' L.A.: Westernlore, (1954). 1st ed. Signed. Fine in VG dj. *Book Market*. $35/£22

BAILEY, PERCIVAL et al. Intracranial Tumors of Infancy and Childhood. Chicago: Univ of Chicago, 1939. 1st ed. (Bkpl, lib stamps, labels; spine label), o/w Nice. *Beasley*. $100/£63

BAILEY, PERCIVAL. Intracranial Tumors. Springfield, IL, 1948. 2nd ed. Frontis; 16 plts. Orig cl (recased w/new eps). *Whitehart*. $64/£40

BAILEY, PHILIP A. Golden Mirages. NY: Macmillan, 1940. 1st ed. 24 plts, 8 maps. Blue cl. Fine in VG+ dj (sl chipped). *Harrington*. $55/£34

BAILEY, ROBERT G. Hell's Canyon. Lewiston: The Author, 1943. 1st ed. One of 1500. Signed. (Ink name), else VG. *Perier*. $125/£78

BAILEY, VERNON. Life Zones and Crop Zones of New Mexico. Washington: GPO, 1913. Fldg map. (Lt soiled), else VG. *Dumont*. $50/£31

BAILEY, VERNON. Mammals of New Mexico. Washington: Bureau of Biological Survey, 1931. (Wraps lt soiled), else VG. *Dumont*. $100/£63

BAILEY, WILLIAM. The Angler's Instructor: A Treatise on the Best Modes of Angling in English Rivers, Lakes and Ponds. London/Nottingham, 1857. 1st ed. (4)leaves; 111pp. Pub's cl. (Worn, foxed, soiled.) *Oinonen**. $120/£75

BAILLIE SCOTT, M. H. Houses and Gardens. George Newnes, 1906. 4to. Color frontis, 16 color, 22 monochrome plts. Dec eps; teg. Pub's cl, gilt. (Spine faded), o/w VG. *Sotheran*. $504/£315

BAILLIE, G. H. and BRIAN LOOMES. Watchmakers and Clockmakers of the World. N.A.G., 1976. 2 vols. VG in djs. *Hollett*. $104/£65

BAILLIE, MRS. W. W. Days and Nights of Shikar. London, 1921. Color frontis. (1st 2pp lt foxed; spine sl discolored), o/w Fine. *Grayling*. $96/£60

BAILLIE-GROHMAN, W. A. Sport in the Alps in the Past and Present. London, 1896. Frontis, 16 plts. Teg, others uncut. Blue buckram (faded, sl damp mkd; note, sig). *Petersfield*. $104/£65

BAILY, LESLIE. Craftsman and Quaker. The Story of James T. Baily 1876-1957. London: Allen & Unwin, 1959. 1st ed. VG in dj. *Hollett*. $32/£20

BAILY, LESLIE. The Gilbert and Sullivan Book. Cassell, 1956. 4th ed rev. 12 color plts. VG in dj, custom-made slipcase. *Hollett*. $48/£30

BAIN, F. W.-(trans). The Indian Stories of F.W. Bain. London: Riccardi, 1913-20. One of 500. 13 vols. Blue-gray paper over bds, gray cl spine. (Lt soiled), else Fine in orig djs (some partly defective). *Cummins*. $400/£250

BAIN, H. (ed). More Recent Cyanide Practice. SF: Mining & Scientific, c1910. 2nd ed. Good (cvr spotted). *Blake*. $50/£31

BAIN, I. (ed). The Watercolours and Drawings of Thomas Bewick and His Workshop Apprentices. London: Gordon Fraser, 1981. 2 vols. Good in slipcase. *Ars Artis*. $216/£135

BAIN, R. NISBET. Cossack Fairy Tales. London: Lawrence & Bullen, 1894. 1st ed. 8vo. E. W. Mitchell (illus). xii,290pp. Teg, rest untrimmed. Pale grn linen cl. (Spine sl yellowed), o/w Very Clean. *Sotheran*. $93/£58

BAINBRIDGE, HENRY CHARLES. Peter Carl Faberge, Goldsmith and Jeweller to the Russian Imperial Court.... Batsford, 1949. Edition de Luxe. Ltd to 350. Teg, uncut. Blue 1/2 morocco, gilt. (Lib stamp tp; spine sl rubbed.) Slipcase (mkd). *Sotheby's**. $368/£230

BAINES, J. MAINWARING. Historic Hastings. Hastings, 1963. 2nd ed. 49 plts. Dj (sl chipped). *Edwards*. $56/£35

BAINES, THOMAS. Explorations in South-West Africa. London: Longman, Green, 1864. 8vo. xiv,535+24pp ads; 3 fldg maps, 10 plts. Mod 1/2 brn calf, black label. VG. *Adelson*. $650/£406

BAINES, THOMAS. The Gold Regions of South Eastern Africa. London, 1877. Mtd photo frontisport, xxiv,240pp (w/51pp ads at rear); 3 mtd plts, fldg facs letter, fldg map (w/sm fold tears) in rear pocket. Black emb cl w/gilt zebra (corners rubbed w/sl cl loss, spine sl chipped, joints repaired w/glue; bkpl). *Edwards*. $280/£175

BAIRD WARNER INCORPORATED. A Portfolio of Fine Apartment Homes. Evanston, IL, 1928. Folio. 1/4 cl. *Swann**. $431/£269

BAIRD, BILL. The Art of the Puppet. NY: Macmillan, (1965). NF (edges sl rubbed) in pict dj (price-clipped, fr fld of spine sl torn). *Blue Mountain*. $35/£22

BAIRD, G. W. A Report to the Citizens, Concerning Certain Late Disturbances on the Western Frontier.... Ashland, OR: Lewis Osborne, 1972. One of 600. Fine. *Pacific**. $29/£18

BAIRD, JOSEPH ARMSTRONG, JR. 1849-1869: California's Pictorial Letter Sheets. SF: David Magee, 1967. 1st ed. One of 475 ptd. Facs letter in rear pocket. 1/2 morocco, dec bds. Fine in plain dj. *Pacific**. $161/£101

BAIRD, JOSEPH ARMSTRONG, JR. Time's Wondrous Changes: San Francisco Architecture, 1776-1915. SF: CA Hist Soc, 1962. 1st ed. One of 1000 ptd. Signed, inscribed. (Bkpl; corners sl rubbed), else NF. *Pacific**. $52/£33

BAIRD, NEWTON D. and ROBERT GREENWOOD. An Annotated Bibliography of California Fiction, 1664-1970. Georgetown, CA, 1971. One of 500. VG in dj. *Dumont*. $75/£47

BAIRD, S. F. Pacific Railroad Survey. Volume 9. Birds. Washington, 1858. lvi,1005pp (browned). Cl over contemp bds (orig backstrip laid down, bds scuffed, worn). *Sutton*. $115/£72

BAIRD, S. F. et al. A History of North American Birds. Boston: Little, Brown, (1905). 3 vols. 64 color plts. Teg. VG. *Mikesh*. $300/£188

BAIRD, W. The Natural History of the British Entomostraca. London, 1850. 36 plts (17 color). (Rebacked, preserving spine.) *Henly*. $67/£42

BAIRNSFATHER, BRUCE. Carry on Sergeant! Indianapolis: Bobbs-Merrill, (1927). 1st US ed. Straw cl ptd in black. NF in pict dj. *Reese*. $75/£47

BAKELESS, JOHN. Daniel Boone. NY: William Morrow, 1939. 1st ed. VG in dj. *Labordo*. $45/£28

BAKELESS, JOHN. Lewis and Clark. Partners in Discovery. NY: William Morrow, 1947. 1st ed. VG in dj. *Labordo.* $45/£28

BAKELESS, KATHERINE and JOHN. Explorers of the New World. London: G. Bell & Sons, (1959). 1st British ed. One of 6 author's copies w/als from British publisher to Amer publisher Lippincott. Dbl-pg map, 16 plts. Grn bds. Fine in dj. *House.* $25/£16

BAKER, A. A. Geology of the Green River Desert-Cataract Canyon Region, Emery, Wayne, and Garfield Counties, Utah. Washington: USGS, 1946. 20 plts; 4 fldg maps boxed in separate map slipcase, w/string ties. Bulletin VG; maps, map case VG + (box worn). *Five Quail.* $75/£47

BAKER, A. A. Geology of the Monument Valley-Navajo Mountain Region, San Juan County, UT. Washington: USGS, 1936. 17 plts, incl 2 lg color foldouts in rear pocket. VG + . *Five Quail.* $45/£28

BAKER, CHARLES H. The South American Gentleman's Companion. NY: Crown, 1951. 1st ed. 2 vols. VG in slipcase. *Hollett.* $120/£75

BAKER, D. E. et al. Biographia Dramatica; or, a Companion to the Playhouse. London, 1812. 4 vols. (Bkpls.) Polished calf (fr bds detached on 3 vols, joints split), gilt, raised bands, black spine labels. *Maggs.* $248/£155

BAKER, E. C. STUART. The Fauna of British India, Including Ceylon and Burma—Birds. Arthur Shipley (ed). Taylor & Francis, 1922-30. 8 vols. Complete w/35 color, 3 plain plts, fldg map. VG set (few joints sl tender; extrems sl rubbed, corners bumped). *Hollett.* $360/£225

BAKER, E. C. STUART. The Indian Ducks and Their Allies. London, 1908. 30 color chromos. 1/2 leather. (Lt foxed, hinges splitting, spine heel bumped, affecting all pp.) *Metropolitan*.* $230/£144

BAKER, ERNEST A. Caving; Episodes of Underground Exploration. Chapman & Hall, 1932. 1st ed. Black cl, gilt. VG. *Sotheran.* $77/£48

BAKER, EZEKIEL. Remarks on Rifle Guns...with Specific Remarks in Fowling Pieces, the Percussion Lock, and Fire-arms in General. London, 1835. 11th ed. 17 plts, tables (8 hand-colored). Contemp bds, tips, mod backstrip (worn, sl browned). Bkpl of Howard E. French. *Oinonen*.* $200/£125

BAKER, FRANK. The Birds. Davies, 1936. 1st ed. Good + (worn). *Any Amount.* $38/£24

BAKER, GEORGE. Tenby, the Navy of England, and Other Occasional Poetry. J. Carpenter, 1807. 1st ed. (i)-iv,(5)-120pp. Contemp 1/2 brn calf (extrems rubbed, sl loss to spine end, lacks label), marbled bds. Internally VG (eps browned). *Blackwell's.* $72/£45

BAKER, H. BARTON. Our Old Actors. London: Richard Bentley & Son, 1881. Rev ed. Partly unopened. VG. *Dramatis.* $30/£19

BAKER, H. BARTON. Stories of the Streets of London. London, 1899. 2nd ed. xviii,426pp. (Lt browned, lacks fep; sl soiled, spine sl faded, rubbed.) *Edwards.* $32/£20

BAKER, J. G. A Flora of the English Lake District. London, 1885. 1st ed. viii,262,(i)pp. (Sm splits to joints, spine chipped.) *Edwards.* $88/£55

BAKER, JAMES. Pictures from Bohemia. Religious Tract Soc, n.d. Walter Crane (some illus). 192,8pp; map. Aeg. Pict cl, gilt. (Few spots.) *Hollett.* $104/£65

BAKER, JOSEPH E. (ed). Past and Present of Alameda County, California. Volume I only. Chicago: S.J. Clarke, 1914. 1st ed. 3/4 black morocco, grn cl (worn, esp extrems). Good; internally Fine. *Harrington.* $40/£25

BAKER, MARGARET. The Black Cats and the Tinker's Wife. Grant Richards, n.d. (1923). 1st ed, 1st bk. 8vo. Mary Baker (illus). (112)pp. Ribbed gray cl. (Sm stain fep; sl rubbed, corners sl bumped), else VG. *Bookmark.* $56/£35

BAKER, NICHOLSON. The Mezzanine. NY: Weidenfeld & Nicolson, 1988. 1st ed, 1st bk. Fine in Fine dj. *Beasley.* $125/£78

BAKER, NICHOLSON. The Mezzanine. Cambridge: Granta Books, 1989. 1st UK ed. Fine in dj. *Any Amount.* $32/£20

BAKER, NICHOLSON. The Mezzanine. London, 1989. 1st UK ed, 1st bk. NF in NF dj. *Warren.* $45/£28

BAKER, NICHOLSON. Room Temperature. London: Granta Books, 1990. 1st Eng ed. Fine (spine foot sl bumped) in dj. *Ulysses.* $56/£35

BAKER, NINA BROWN. Cyclone in Calico. The Story of Mary Ann Bickerdyke. Boston, (1952). Frontisport. VG. *Wantagh.* $35/£22

BAKER, PEARL. Trail on the Water. Boulder, n.d. (1970). 5 fldg maps (on 2 sheets) in rear pocket. Blue cl. VG in dj. *Five Quail.* $45/£28

BAKER, PEARL. The Wild Bunch at Robbers Roost. L.A.: Westernlore, 1965. 1st ed. Fabrikoid. VG + in dj. *Labordo.* $50/£31

BAKER, ROBERT JAMES. Fuel-Injected Dreams. NY, 1986. 1st ed. VG + in VG + dj. *Warren.* $30/£19

BAKER, SAMUEL W. The Albert N'Yanza. Macmillan, 1867. 2 vols. xxx,371; xii,372pp; lg fldg map, 35 maps, vignettes, full-pg illus. Uncut. Good set in grn cl (vol 1 sides badly faded by damp). *Cox.* $120/£75

BAKER, SAMUEL W. The Albert N'Yanza. London: Macmillan, 1867. 2nd ed. 2 vols. Frontisport, xxx,371; 1/2-title, tinted litho frontis, x,(ii),372pp; 2 maps (1 fldg), 12 engr plts. Grn dec cl, gilt. VG (fldg map torn, repaired; sl foxed; extrems sl stained, rubbed). *Morrell.* $152/£95

BAKER, SAMUEL W. The Albert N'Yanza. London, 1962. 2 vols. Djs. *Edwards.* $80/£50

BAKER, SAMUEL W. Cyprus as I Saw It in 1879. London, 1879. 1st ed. Frontis, xx,502,40pp (prelims lt foxed). Fine grn pict cl, gilt. *Maggs.* $400/£250

BAKER, SAMUEL W. Ismailia. NY, 1875. 1st Amer ed. 542pp. Dec cvr (mottled, spine ends worn; lt foxed). *Heinoldt.* $75/£47

BAKER, SAMUEL W. The Rifle and the Hound in Ceylon. London, 1884. 1/2 polished grn calf, gilt extra, red morocco label. (Bkpl.) *Swann*.* $172/£108

BAKER, VALENTINE. Clouds in the East: Travels and Adventures on the Perso-Turkoman Frontier. London: C&W, 1876. 2nd ed. 1/2-title, x,(i),(i blank),376pp + 36pp pub's list; 3 fldg maps (1 color), 8 chromolithos. (Stamp, 1 map sl foxed, another torn w/out loss.) Grn blindstamped cl (loose), gilt. Sound. *Morrell.* $320/£200

BAKER, W. S. Character Portraits of Washington.... Phila, 1887. One of 350. Extra-illus w/81 plts. Teg. 1/2 red morocco, marbled bds, gilt. (Edges sl rubbed.) *Kane*.* $150/£94

BAKER, W. S. Medallic Portraits of Washington. Phila: Robert M. Lindsay, 1885. 1st ed. Frontisport, 252pp. Mod 1/2 levant morocco, gilt, raised bands, spine label. A few letters loosely inserted. VG. *Hollett.* $240/£150

BAKEWELL, R. An Introduction to Geology: Intended to Convey a Practical Knowledge of the Science. London, 1833. 4th ed. Frontis, tp, xxxvi,589pp; 7 plts (2 hand-colored, 5 fldg). 1/2 calf (rebacked), gilt. *Henly.* $211/£132

BAKKEN, LAVOLA J. Lone Rock Free State. Myrtle Creek: Mail Printers, (1970). Fldg facs. VG in wraps. *Perier.* $25/£16

BAKST, LEON. Inedited Works of Bakst. NY: Brentano's, 1927. 1st Amer ed. One of 600. 13x9.75. 30 full-pg plts, ptd tissue guards. Cl-backed hand-colored pict bds. (Extrems rubbed, hinge cracked), else VG. *Pacific*.* $805/£503

BALABAN, JOHN. Vietnam Poems. Oxford: Carcanet, 1970. 1st UK ed. One of 40 numbered, signed. Ptd wrappers. *Maggs.* $48/£30

BALABAN, JOHN. Vietnam: The Land We Never Knew. SF: Chronicle Books, 1989. 1st ed. Fine in lg wraps. *Associates.* $35/£22

BALCH, EDWIN SWIFT. Glacieres or Freezing Caverns. Phila: Allen, Lane & Scott, 1900. 1st ed. Teg. Red/brn cl, gilt. (Rear bd sl soiled, extrems sl bumped, sm circular spine mk), o/w Good. *Sotheran.* $157/£98

BALCH, H. E. Wookey Hole, Its Caves and Cave Dwellers. OUP, 1914. Grey cl backstrip (dull, sl mkd w/red, blue ink) w/blue bd sides. *Petersfield.* $67/£42

BALDERSTON, K. C. A Census of the Manuscripts of Oliver Goldsmith. NY: Brick Row Book Shop, 1926. Uncut. Cl-backed marbled bds, paper spine/fr cvr labels. *Maggs.* $32/£20

BALDRY, A. L. Albert Moore: His Life and Works. London, 1894. 2 vols. (Scattered foxing; extrems rubbed.) *Swann*.* $287/£179

BALDRY, A. L. Sir John Everett Millais. George Bell & Sons, 1899. Teg. (Few mks; cl sl rubbed.) *Hollett.* $104/£65

BALDWIN, FAITH. Arizona Star. NY: F&R, (1945). 1st ed. Fine in VG dj (price-clipped, rubbed, lt worn). *Between The Covers.* $65/£41

BALDWIN, FAITH. Career by Proxy. NY: F&R, (1939). 1st ed. Inscribed. Fine in VG + dj (price-clipped, sm chips). *Between The Covers.* $125/£78

BALDWIN, HANSON W. Sea Fights and Shipwrecks. GC: Hanover House, c.1955. VG in dj (lt worn). *Parmer.* $30/£19

BALDWIN, JAMES MARK (ed). Dictionary of Philosophy and Psychology. NY, 1918/1920. Corrected eds, later ptgs. 2 vols. Vol 1 in brn buckram (rebound), vol 2 in olive-brn buckram. (Ex-lib, lacks 3rd vol.) *Gach.* $85/£53

BALDWIN, JAMES. Another Country. NY, 1962. 1st Amer ed. Fine (sl rubbed) in NF dj (price-clipped). *Polyanthos.* $60/£38

BALDWIN, JAMES. Blues for Mister Charlie. NY: Dial, 1964. 1st ed. Fine in NF dj (lt rubbed, sm tear). *Agvent.* $100/£63

BALDWIN, JAMES. The Evidence of Things Not Seen. NY: HRW, (1985). 1st ed. Fine in Fine dj. *Agvent.* $50/£31

BALDWIN, JAMES. Going to Meet the Man. NY: Dial, 1965. 1st ed. Fine in dj. *Smith.* $100/£63

BALDWIN, JAMES. Just Above My Head. NY: Dial, (1978). 1st ed. One of 500 signed. Aeg. Maroon cl, gilt. (Spine sl faded), o/w Fine in maroon cl open-end slipcase. *Heritage.* $150/£94

BALDWIN, JAMES. Little Man, Little Man. Michael Joseph, 1976. 1st UK ed. 7.7x10. Yoran Cazac (illus). 95pp. NF in VG + dj (2 sm chips). *Price.* $50/£31

BALDWIN, JAMES. Little Man, Little Man: A Story of Childhood. NY, (1976). 1st ed. Pict bds. Dj. *Swann*.* $57/£36

BALDWIN, JAMES. Nobody Knows My Name. NY: Dial, 1961. 1st ed. (Offset from bookmark to feps), else VG in dj (sm tears extrems, spine ends sl rubbed). *Pacific*.* $40/£25

BALDWIN, JAMES. Nobody Knows My Name. NY: Dial, 1961. 1st ed. Fine in dj (lt used). *Beasley.* $45/£28

BALDWIN, JAMES. Notes of a Native Son. NY, (1955). 1st ed. (Bkpl.) Dj (worn, cellotape repairs). *Swann*.* $230/£144

BALDWIN, JAMES. Tell Me How Long the Train's Been Gone. NY, 1968. 1st ed. NF in Fine dj. *Warren.* $60/£38

BALDWIN, JAMES. Tell Me How Long the Train's Been Gone. NY, 1968. 1st ed. Signed. (Sl shaken.) Dj. *Swann*.* $201/£126

BALDWIN, JOSEPH G. The Flush Times of Alabama and Mississippi. NY: Appleton, 1853. 1st ed. Frontis, x,330pp + ad leaf at fr, 18pp ads at rear; 3 b/w engr plts. Orig dk brn cl, gilt. (Sl aged, sm piece torn from top corner 2 leaves; fr hinge cracked, sl worn, spine sl turned, gilt sl dull, spine ends chipped.) Text Good. BAL 580. Howes B62. *Baltimore*.* $60/£38

BALDWIN, MARY H. and EVELYN G. HINDS. The Marigold Cook Book. NY: Doubleday, Doran, 1938. 1st ed. VG in hard cvr w/plastic comb binding. *Perier.* $60/£38

BALDWIN, RUTH. 100 Nineteenth-Century Rhyming Alphabets in English. Carbondale, IL, 1972. 1st ed. As New in dj. *Bond.* $35/£22

BALDWIN, WILLIAM CHARLES. African Hunting and Adventure. London: Richard Bentley, 1863. 2nd ed. Frontisport, x,451pp; fldg map, 6 tinted/sepia lithos, 10 plain plts. (Sl browned, pp39-43 cellotaped to inner margin, pp207-8 fore-edge chipped.) Mod 1/2 calf (rebound), marbled bds, gilt, raised bands, leather spine label. *Edwards.* $240/£150

BALDWIN, WILLIAM CHARLES. African Hunting; From Natal to the Zambesi...from 1852-1860. NY: Harper, 1863. 1st Amer ed. 397pp; fldg map. Brn, blind-stamped cl (cvrs worn, chipped). Internally NF. *Biscotti.* $90/£56

BALFOUR, E. B. The Living Soil and the Haughley Experiment. NY: Universe Books, 1976. 1st US ed. VG in dj. *Hollett.* $32/£20

BALFOUR, J. H. Introduction to the Study of Palaeontological Botany. Edinburgh: Black, 1872. 118pp; 4 litho plts. VG. *Savona.* $40/£25

BALFOUR, JAMES. Reminiscences of Golf on St. Andrews Links. Carlinville, IL: Chas. A. Dufner, 1982. Rpt of orig 1887 ed. One of 300. Fine (stamp) in ptd red wrappers. *Pacific*.* $109/£68

BALFOUR-KINNEAR, G. P. R. Flying Salmon. London: Longmans, (1937). 1st ed. 8 plts. (Binding faded.) *Petersfield.* $51/£32

BALISH, JACQUELYN (ed). Leica World. NY: American Photographic Bk Pub, 1957. 1st ed. Henri Cartier-Bresson, et al (photos). VG in dj (edges torn). *Cahan.* $50/£31

BALL, B. L. Rambles in Eastern Asia, Including China and Manilla. Boston: James French, 1855. 1st ed. 417 + 3pp ads; map. Brn blind-stamped cl, gilt. Good. *Karmiole.* $125/£78

BALL, C. J. Light from the East; or, The Witness of the Monuments. London et al: Eyre & Spottiswoode, 1899. 1st ed. xxxiv,256pp; color plt. Teg. (1st, last few ll sl foxed, sl shaken; edges rubbed, spine faded, ends chipped), o/w Good. *Worldwide.* $45/£28

BALL, EVE. Ma'am Jones of the Pecos. Tucson: Univ of AZ, 1969. 1st ed. Fine in dj. *Labordo.* $65/£41

BALL, JOHN W. An Introduction to Steelhead. Coburg, OR: Privately ptd, 1975. VF in grn illus wraps. *Bowman.* $65/£41

BALL, JOHN. In the Heat of the Night. NY: Harper, (1965). 1st ed. Fine in Fine dj (sm crown nick). *Between The Covers.* $350/£219

BALL, LARRY. Desert Lawmen. Albuquerque: Univ of NM, 1992. 1st ed. Fine in dj. *Labordo.* $45/£28

BALL, ROBERT S. The Story of the Heavens. Cassell, 1913. 24 color plts. All edges marbled, matching eps. Full brn calf prize binding (lt stain fr corner). *Hollett.* $104/£65

BALL, SUSAN L. Ozenfant and Purism. Ann Arbor: UMI Research, (1981). Fine (sm bkpl). *Turtle Island.* $55/£34

BALL, T. H. Lake County, Indiana, from 1834 to 1872. Chicago: Goodspeed, 1873. 1st ed. 264,(10)pp; color fldg map. Howes B79. *Ginsberg.* $175/£109

BALLANTINE, JAMES. The Life of David Roberts, R.A. Edinburgh, 1866. 4to. 9 etched plts. (Foxed, affecting 3 plts; cvrs sl blistered, tips, spine ends worn, repaired.) *Swann*.* $805/£503

BALLANTYNE, R. M. Dusty Diamonds Cut and Polished. James Nisbet, 1884. 1st ed. Frontis, add'l engr pict tp, vi,(ii),430pp,ad leaf; 4 plts. Brn cl. Fine (1883 inscrip). *Bickersteth.* $136/£85

BALLANTYNE, R. M. Gascoyne, the Sandalwood Trader. James Nisbet, 1872. 5th ed. Color frontis, viii,440pp + 16-pg pub's cat; 7 color plts. Grn cl (sl rubbed). *Bickersteth.* $35/£22

BALLANTYNE, R. M. The Lighthouse. James Nisbet, 1886. 20th thousand. Pict cl. Good (prize-plt, margins soiled, spotted, fore-edge mkd; spine bumped). *Tiger.* $19/£12

BALLANTYNE, R. M. The Red Man's Revenge. James Nisbet, 1880. 1st ed. viii,264pp, incl frontis, 3 full-pg illus. Grn cl. Fine. *Bickersteth.* $144/£90

BALLANTYNE, R. M. Rivers of Ice. James Nisbet, 1875. 1st ed. Frontis, add'l engr pict tp, vi,(ii),430pp,ad leaf, 16-pg inserted pub's cat; 4 plts. Blue-grey eps. Grn cl. Fine. *Bickersteth.* $128/£80

BALLANTYNE, R. M. The Settler and the Savage. James Nisbet, 1877. 1st ed. Frontis, engr pict add'l tp, (viii),421pp + ad leaf, 16-pg inserted pub's cat; 4 plts. Blue-grey eps. Brn cl. (1877 inscrip.) *Bickersteth.* $128/£80

BALLANTYNE, R. M. Under the Waves; or, Diving in Deep Waters. James Nisbet, 1876. 1st ed. Frontis, add'l engr pict tp, (viii),414pp + ad leaf, inserted 16-pg pub's cat; 4 plts. Blue-grey eps. Blue cl. Excellent (1876 inscrip, 1 section of text sl loose). *Bickersteth.* $128/£80

BALLANTYNE, R. M. Ungava: A Tale of Esquimaux-Land. T. Nelson & Sons, 1858. 1st ed. Wood-engr frontis, add'l wood-engr tp, viii,(9)-506pp; 6 wood-engr plts. Blue pebble cl. (Ink inscrip, sm ink spot top edge of tp, sewing loose in sig M, eps frayed on inner joints; spine gilt sl rubbed.) *Bickersteth.* $224/£140

BALLANTYNE, R. M. The World of Ice. London: Nelson, 1897. New ed. Frontis, 327pp. Blue cl, emb. Good+ (corners bumped). *Price.* $35/£22

BALLARD, J. G. The Atrocity Exhibition. London: Triad Panther, 1979. 1st pb ed. Signed. VG. *Warren.* $30/£19

BALLARD, J. G. The Atrocity Exhibition. CA: Re/Search, 1990. New rev ed. NF in tall wraps. *Warren.* $25/£16

BALLARD, J. G. The Day of Creation. Gollancz, 1987. One of 100 signed. Fine in cl slipcase (sl rubbed). *Ulysses.* $240/£150

BALLARD, J. G. High-Rise. London: Jonathan Cape, 1975. 1st ed. Fine in NF dj (price-clipped, sm edgetear). *Lame Duck.* $200/£125

BALLARD, J. G. Memories of the Space Age. Arkham House, 1988. 1st ed. Mint in Mint dj. *Martin.* $26/£16

BALLARD, J. G. Myths of the Near Future. Cape, 1982. Rev copy w/pub's slip loosely inserted. VG+ in dj. *Any Amount.* $32/£20

BALLARD, J. G. Running Wild. NY: FSG, (1988). 1st Amer ed. Fine in Fine dj. *Between The Covers.* $45/£28

BALLARD, J. G. The Unlimited Dream Company. London, (1979). 1st ed. Inscribed. Dj. *Swann*.* $69/£43

BALLENGER and BALLENGER. Diseases of the Nose, Throat and Ear. 1930. VG. *Doctor's Library.* $50/£31

BALLENTINE, GEORGE. Autobiography of an English Soldier in the United States Army. Chicago: R.R. Donnelley, 1986. Frontis, map. VG. *Lien.* $30/£19

BALLIETT, WHITNEY. Improvising. NY: Oxford, 1977. 1st ed. Fine in dj (lt used). *Beasley.* $30/£19

BALLY, ALBERT and A. PALMER (eds). The Geology of North America. Boulder: G.S.A., 1989. 1st ed. Pict bds. VG+ . *Archer.* $35/£22

BALMER, EDWIN and PHILIP WYLIE. When Worlds Collide. Phila: J.B. Lippincott, (1933). 7th ed. (Bkpl) else VG- in dj (lacks spine head piece; foot, corners chipped). *Pacific*.* $29/£18

BALSTON, THOMAS. The Cambridge University Press Collection of Private Press Types: Kelmscott, Ashendene, Eragny, Cranach. (Cambridge): CUP, 1951. 1st ed. One of 350 ptd. Grn cl, gilt. NF. *Pacific*.* $81/£51

BALSTON, THOMAS. Sitwelliana 1915-1927. (London): Duckworth, 1928. 1st ed. 3 ports. Patterned bds, paper cvr label. (Lt foxed; spine sunned), o/w Fine. *Pharos.* $75/£47

BALSTON, THOMAS. Staffordshire Portrait Figures. Massachusetts, (1960). 1st Amer ed. Dj (chipped). *Argosy.* $50/£31

Baltimore City Directory for 1876. Balt: John W. Woods, 1876. Upper/lower bds w/extensive ads. (Lacks spine.) Text VG. *Baltimore*.* $180/£113

Baltimore City Directory for 1880. Balt: John W. Woods, 1880. Dk brn cl, bds, gilt, w/extensive ads at bds. (Lacks tp; lower joint splitting.) *Baltimore*.* $50/£31

Baltimore City Directory for 1884. Balt: John W. Woods, 1884. Later plain black cl, marbled bds. (Lacks tp, business and Colored Persons sections, all display ads at fr/rear; worn, scuffed, spine ends frayed.) *Baltimore*.* $50/£31

Baltimore City Directory for 1897. Balt: R.L. Polk, 1897. Black cl, lettered bds w/ads. (Cvrs worn, cl tape repair upper joint and fr hinge, lower hinge cracked, old brass stud punched through corner rear cvr.) *Baltimore*.* $250/£156

BALTZ, LEWIS. Nation's Capital in Photographs, 1976. Washington: The Corcoran Gallery, 1976. 14 full-pg b/w photos. Fine in ptd wrappers. *Cahan.* $40/£25

BALTZ, LEWIS. Nevada. NY: Castelli Graphics, 1978. 1st ed. Ltd to 2000. 15 full-pg b/w photos. Fine in emb stiff wrappers. *Cahan.* $75/£47

BALTZ, LEWIS. Park City. Albuquerque/NY, 1980. 1st ed. 102 repros. (Lt spotted.) Dj (chipped, abraded), acetate wrapper. *Swann*.* $103/£64

BALZAC. See DE BALZAC

BALZER, ROBERT LAWRENCE. California's Best Wines. L.A.: Ward Ritchie, (1948). 1st ed. (Ink name), else VG in dj. *Perier.* $35/£22

BAMBARA, TONI CADE. Gorilla, My Love. NY: Random, (1972). 1st ed. NF in dj (sl edgeworn). *Robbins.* $100/£63

BAMBARA, TONI CADE. The Salt Eaters. NY: Random, 1980. 1st ed. Fine in NF dj. *Robbins.* $50/£31

BAMBARA, TONI CADE. The Sea Birds Are Still Alive. NY: Random House, 1977. 1st ed. (Rmdr stamp bottom pg edge), else NF in NF dj. *Pettler.* $60/£38

BAMBERGER, LOUIS. Memoirs of Sixty Years in the Timber and Pianoforte Trades. London: Sampson Low, Marston, n.d. 1st ed. Inscribed presentation. 90 ports. VG in dj (spine ends defective). *Hollett.* $104/£65

BANCOFF, CARL. A Forgotten Man. Ardmore, PA, 1987. 1st ed. Fine in dj. *Associates.* $35/£22

BANCROFT, ANNE. The Memorable Lives of Bummer and Lazarus (Citizens of San Francisco) 185?-1865. L.A.: Ward Ritchie, 1939. 1st ed. One of 500. Frontis. VG in dj. *Houle.* $65/£41

BANCROFT, EDWARD. Experimental Researches Concerning the Philosophy of Permanent Colours...by Dyeing, Calico Printing, &c. Phila: Thomas Dobson, 1814. 1st Amer ed. 2 vols. (3),xlv,(2),401,(2 ads); (3),394,(2 ads)pp. Early 1/2 morocco, marbled bds. VG set (browned, foxed; sl shelfworn). *Glaser.* $500/£313

BANCROFT, FREDERIC. Calhoun and the South Carolina Nullification Movement. Balt: Johns Hopkins, 1928. 1st ed. VG. *Cahan.* $50/£31

BANCROFT, FREDERIC. Slave-Trading in the Old South. Balt: J.H. Hurst, 1931. 1st ed. Purple cl, gilt. Fine (lt foxed) in dj (tattered). *Chapel Hill.* $375/£234

BANCROFT, GEORGE. History of the United States, from the Discovery of the American Continent to the Declaration of Independence. George Routledge & Sons, (n.d.) c. 1875. New ed. 7 vols. Sm 8vo. Marbled eps; all edges marbled. Contemp 1/2 polished calf, gilt, raised bands, contrasting leather labels. VG set. *Sotheran.* $720/£450

BANCROFT, HUBERT HOWE. California Inter Pocula. SF: History, 1888. 1st ed. 828pp. Brn lib cl. (Sm stamps), else Fine. *Argonaut.* $50/£31

BANCROFT, HUBERT HOWE. California Pastoral. 1769-1848. SF: History, 1888. 1st ed. 808pp. Brn lib cl. (Sm stamps), else Fine. *Argonaut.* $90/£56

BANCROFT, HUBERT HOWE. California Pioneer Register and Index, 1542-1848. Including Inhabitants of California, 1769-1800 and List of Pioneers. Balt: Clearfield, 1990. Rpt of 1964 ed. Blue cl. VF. *Argonaut.* $45/£28

BANCROFT, HUBERT HOWE. Essays and Miscellany. SF: History, 1890. 1st ed. vi,764pp. Orig full tan sheep, black leather spine labels. Fine (sl crack to extreme lower portion of fr hinge; extrems sl rubbed). *Argonaut.* $90/£56

BANCROFT, HUBERT HOWE. History of Alaska 1730-1885. NY: Antiquarian, 1960. Rpt Ltd to 750. Teg. VG (bkpl). *Perier.* $97/£61

BANCROFT, HUBERT HOWE. History of Alaska. 1730-1885. SF: History, 1886. 1st ed. xxxviii,775pp. Brn lib cl. (Sm stamps), else Fine. *Argonaut.* $90/£56

BANCROFT, HUBERT HOWE. History of Arizona and New Mexico, 1539-1888. SF: History, 1889. 1st ed. xxxvii,829pp; 1 fldg map. French cl, black leather labels. (Rubberstamp, lib mks; newly bound, new eps), else Fine. Howes H91. *Argonaut.* $125/£78

BANCROFT, HUBERT HOWE. History of California. Santa Barbara: Wallace Hebberd, (1963). Facs rpt. 7 vols. Mint set in djs. *Argonaut.* $350/£219

BANCROFT, HUBERT HOWE. History of Oregon. Volume I: 1834-1848. Volume II: 1848-1888. SF: History, 1886, 1888. 1st ed. 2 vols. xxxix,789; xv,808pp; fldg map. French cl (newly bound), black leather labels. (Rubberstamp, lib mks), else Fine set. *Argonaut.* $125/£78

BANCROFT, HUBERT HOWE. History of Utah, 1540-1886. SF: History Co, 1889. 1st ed. 808pp. Black cl (rebound), gilt. Fine. *Perier.* $100/£63

BANCROFT, HUBERT HOWE. History of Washington, Idaho and Montana, 1845-1889. SF: History, 1890. 1st ed. xxvi,836pp. Brn lib cl. (Sm stamps), else Fine. *Argonaut.* $90/£56

BANCROFT, HUBERT HOWE. Literary Industries, a Memoir. NY, 1891. 1st ed. Engr frontis, 446pp + index. (Tp separating at gutter; fr hinge loose, sl worn.) *King.* $35/£22

BANCROFT, HUBERT HOWE. Literary Industries. SF: History, 1890. 1st ed. Frontisport, vii,808pp. Orig full tan sheep, black leather labels, brn lib cl. (Sm stamps), else Fine. *Argonaut.* $60/£38

BANCROFT, HUBERT HOWE. The Native Races of the Pacific States of North America. NY, 1875-6. 5 vols. (Lib blindstamps, bkpls, cardholders; spines chipped w/sl loss to heads, spine # remains.) *Edwards.* $400/£250

BANCROFT, HUBERT HOWE. Popular Tribunals. SF: History, 1887. 1st ed. 2 vols. xiii,749; viii,772pp; fldg map, facs. Brn lib cl. (Sm stamps), else Fine set. *Argonaut.* $100/£63

BANCROFT, HUBERT HOWE. Some Cities and San Francisco and Resurgam. NY: Bancroft, 1907. 1st ed. Signed, inscribed. Teg. Gray cl, gilt. Fine. *Pacific*.* $75/£47

BANCROFT, LAURA. (Pseud of L. Frank Baum.) Babes in Birdland: A Fairy Tale. Chicago: Reilly & Britton, (1911). 1st ed. 8 3/4x6 3/8. 116,(1)+(3)ad pp; 8 color plts by Maginal Wright Enright. Cl-backed pict bds. (Insect discoloration to spine, corners rubbed), o/w VG. *Pacific*.* $219/£137

BANCROFT, LAURA. (Pseud of L. Frank Baum.) Bandit Jim Crow. Chicago: Reilly & Britton, (1906). 1st ed in cl. 6.75x4.75. Maginal Wright Enright (illus). Color pict cl. (New red eps; soiled), else VG. *Pacific*.* $184/£115

BANCROFT, LAURA. (Pseud of L. Frank Baum.) Mr. Woodchuck. Chicago: Reilly & Britton, (1906). 2nd ed in bds. 6.75x4.75. 14 color plts by Maginal Wright Enright. Color pict bds. (Inscrip dated 1916), else VG in VG- dj (chipped, torn, creased, dknd, flaps clipped). *Pacific*.* $431/£269

BANCROFT, LAURA. (Pseud of L. Frank Baum.) Mr. Woodchuck. Chicago: Reilly & Britton, (1906). 3rd ed w/ad for Twinkle Tales on rear cvr & rear dj panel. 6.75x4.75. 14 color plts by Maginal Wright Enright. Color pict bds. (Sm extrem tears, sl longer tear to fr panel w/crease), else VG in VG- dj (chipped, rear panel lacks sm pieces, flaps clipped). *Pacific*.* $460/£288

BANCROFT, LAURA. (Pseud of L. Frank Baum.) Policeman Bluejay. Chicago: Reilly & Britton, (1907). 1st ed, 1st state w/ the color pict bds having identical full-color illus on both fr & back cvrs, spine in blue cl lettered in black. 9x6.5. 116 + (3)ad pp; 8 color plts by Maginal Wright Enright. Cl-backed color pict bds. (Corners sl bumped, sl insect damage to spine), else VG in glassine. *Pacific*.* $489/£306

BANCROFT, LAURA. (Pseud of L. Frank Baum.) Prairie-Dog Town. Chicago: Reilly & Lee, n.d. 3rd ed, 1st issue. 6 3/8x4 3/8. Maginal Wright Enright (illus). Pict bds. (Spine foot, corners sl rubbed), else VG. *Pacific*.* $196/£123

BANCROFT, LAURA. (Pseud of L. Frank Baum.) Prince Mud-Turtle. Chicago: Reilly & Lee, (1906). 61pp; 14 color plts. Pict bds. (Spine taped, book shaken), o/w contents VG. *New Hampshire*.* $45/£28

BANCROFT, LAURA. (Pseud of L. Frank Baum.) Prince Mud-Turtle. Chicago: Reilly & Britton, (c. 1906). 2nd ptg (in bds). Tp is ptd from type, there is no c. notice and no ptr's imprint, blank eps of white stock, off-white paper-cvrd bds. VG in VG dj (pink spot to fr panel, chipped). *Pacific*.* $316/£198

BANDELIER, ADOLF F. The Delight Makers. NY: Dodd Mead, (1890). 1st ed. iv,490pp. (Ink names fr cvr, fr pastedown, tp; cvrs rubbed, worn; crease fr cvr), else VG. Howes B94. *Pacific*.* $86/£54

BANDELIER, ADOLF F. The Delight Makers. NY: Dodd, Mead, 1918. Later ed. VG in dj (sl chipped). *Dumont.* $50/£31

BANDELIER, ADOLPH F. and EDGAR L. HEWETT. Indians of the Rio Grande Valley. Albuquerque, 1937. 26 full-pg photos, 8 color plts. Good in dj (chipped). *Dumont.* $165/£103

BANDELIER, ADOLPHE F. The Gilded Man. NY: D. Appleton, 1893. iv,302, (10 ads) pp. (Faint spine #, lib stamps), else Good. *Dumont.* $135/£84

BANDINI, JOSE. A Description of California in 1828. Doris Marion Wright (trans). Berkeley: Friends of the Bancroft Library, 1951. One of 400 ptd. Frontisport. Fine. *Pacific*.* $52/£33

BANDINI, RALPH. Veiled Horizons: Stories of Big Game Fish of the Sea. NY: Derrydale, (1939). One of 950 numbered. 10 b/w photo plts, full-pg map. Untrimmed. Grn cl, gilt. (Spine sl sunned, dusted, lettering dull, cvrs lt worn.) *Baltimore*.* $60/£38

Banditti of the Rocky Mountains and Vigilance Committee of Idaho. Minneapolis, MN: Ross & Haines, 1964. Rpt ed. Fine in dj. Howes I1. *Labordo.* $30/£19

BANG, MOLLY. Dawn. NY: Morrow, 1983. 1st ed. 8.5x10.25. 34pp. 1/2 cl. Fine in dj. *Cattermole.* $25/£16

BANGS, JOHN KENDRICK. The Booming of Acre Hill. NY/London: Harper, 1900. 1st ed, 1st state w/'Joan of Arc' leading 1st ad pg. Inscribed, dated Oct 7, 1900. Blue-grn dec cl, gilt. Fine. *Sumner & Stillman.* $65/£41

BANGS, JOHN KENDRICK. The Idiot at Home. NY, 1900. 1st ed. Teg. (Ink initials, rep sl stained; cvrs sl dull, sl worn.) *King.* $35/£22

BANGS, JOHN KENDRICK. The Inventions of the Idiot. NY/London: Harper, 1904. 1st ed. Grn cl, gilt. Fine. *Sumner & Stillman.* $45/£28

BANGS, JOHN KENDRICK. Mr. Bonaparte of Corsica. Harper, 1895. Pict cl. VG (sig; spine bumped). *Tiger.* $29/£18

BANGS, JOHN KENDRICK. Mr. Munchausen: An Account of Some of His Recent Adventures. Boston: Noyes, Platt, 1901. 1st ed. Peter Newell (illus). Pict cl. (Rubbed, shelfworn), else VG. *Pacific*.* $46/£29

BANGS, JOHN KENDRICK. The Pursuit of the House-Boat. NY: Harper, 1897. 1st ed. NF (lacks dj). *Mordida.* $100/£63

BANGS, JOHN KENDRICK. R. Holmes and Co. NY, 1906. 1st ed, binding A. Pict cl (rear cvr sl stained, extrems rubbed). *King.* $125/£78

BANGS, JOHN KENDRICK. Toppleton's Client: A Spirit in Exile. NY: Harper, 1893. 1st ed. Inscribed in 1894. NF (few sm lt spots to bds). *Between The Covers.* $250/£156

Bankers' Directory of the United States and Canada. Chicago, July 1879. 399pp. (Cvr sl waterstained), else Good. *King.* $50/£31

BANKHEAD, TALLULAH. Tallulah: My Autobiography. NY: Harper, (1952). 1st ed. VF in VF dj (sl rubbed). *Between The Covers.* $85/£53

BANKS, IAIN. The Wasp Factory. London, 1984. Correct 1st ed. VG + (sl leaning) in VG + dj (internal spine stain). *Warren.* $75/£47

BANKS, JOSEPH. The Endeavor Journal of Joseph Banks, 1768-1771. J.C. Beaglehole (ed). (Sydney): Angus & Robertson, (1963). 2nd ed. 2 vols. Fldg map. NF in djs (sl rubbed). *Pacific*.* $219/£137

BANKS, LYNNE REID. The Indian in the Cupboard. NY: Doubleday, 1980. 1st ed. 5.5x8.5. Brock Cole (illus). 181pp. Fine in dj. *Cattermole.* $50/£31

BANKS, RUSSELL. Searching for Survivors. NY: Fiction Collective, 1975. 1st ed. Signed. Fine in Fine dj. *Pettler.* $50/£31

BANNER, ANGELA. (Pseud of Angela Maddison.) Ant and Bee and Kind Dog. London: Ward, 1963. 1st ed. 5x4. Bryan Ward (illus). 110pp. Glossy bds. VG in dj. *Cattermole.* $50/£31

BANNER, ANGELA. (Pseud of Angela Maddison.) Ant and Bee, an Alphabetical Story. Leicester: Edmund Ward, 1950. 1st ed, 1st issue. 4.75x3.75. 109pp. Good in wraps. *Cattermole.* $250/£156

BANNERMAN, D. A. and W. M. The Birds of Cyprus. London, 1958. 31 plts (16 color), fldg map. Buckram. Fine in dj. *Henly.* $224/£140

BANNERMAN, D. A. The Birds of the British Isles. London, 1953-1963. 12 vols. 387 color plts. Good in djs. *Henly.* $528/£330

BANNERMAN, D. A. The Birds of West and Equatorial Africa. Edinburgh, 1953. 2 vols. 54 plts (30 color). Djs (ragged, repaired w/cellotape, w/some loss). *Edwards.* $144/£90

BANNERMAN, HELEN. The Little Black Sambo Story Book. Phila: John C. Winston, (1930). Eunice Stephenson (illus). Pict cl (rear cvr stained; rubbed, dknd), color pict label. *King.* $65/£41

BANNERMAN, HELEN. Little Black Sambo. Platt & Munk, (1932). (Worn.) *King.* $75/£47

BANNERMAN, HELEN. Little Black Sambo. NY: Duenewald Ptg Corp, (1943). Julian Wehr (illus). 6 mechanical pp (one defective). Spiral pict bds (cvrs worn). *King.* $250/£156

BANNERMAN, HELEN. Little Black Sambo. NY: Duenewald Ptg Corp, (1943). Sq 8vo. 6 moveables by Julian Wehr. Spiral-bound pict bds. VG (sl worn). *Davidson.* $450/£281

BANNERMAN, HELEN. Little Black Sambo. NY: S&S, (1948). 2nd ed w/these illus. Issued as #57 in 'The Little Golden Library,' w/'B' at bottom corner of last pg. Gustaf Tenggren (illus). Slim 8vo. Paper-backed color pict bds (edges worn, scuffed; some pp sl rubbed). *Baltimore*.* $50/£31

BANNERMAN, HELEN. Little Black Sambo. Akron: Saalfield, (ca 1930). 8vo. 8 full-pg color plts by Florence White Williams. Full-color pict bds (edges lt rubbed). *Reisler.* $225/£141

BANNERMAN, HELEN. Little Black Sambo. Racine, WI: Whitman Pub, 1926. Clara Bell Thurston, Earnest Vetsch (illus). (Name erased; cvrs worn.) *King.* $95/£59

BANNERMAN, HELEN. Little Black Sambo. NY: E.P. Dutton, 1943. 17x22 cm. Julian Wehr (engineer). 7 tab-operated, movable plts. Pict bds. (Extrems lt worn), o/w VG. *Bookfinders.* $450/£281

BANNERMAN, HELEN. Little Black Sambo. NY: S&S, 1948. 1st ed thus. Gustaf Tenggren (illus). 'A' on last pg. VG (crown lt bumped). *Davidson.* $85/£53

BANNERMAN, HELEN. Little Black Sambo. Racine, WI: Whitman Pub, 1959. Violet LaMont (illus). Color pict bds (worn). *King.* $50/£31

BANNERMAN, HELEN. Little Degchie-Head; an Awful Warning to Bad Babas. London: James Nisbet, 1903. 1st ed. 16mo. 143pp. Grn pict cl (few spots, spine faded). *Reisler.* $600/£375

BANNERMAN, HELEN. The Story of Little Black Sambo. Chicago: Reilly & Britton, (1908). 1st ed thus. John R. Neill (illus). Red bds, pict cvr label. NF. *Pacific*.* $150/£94

BANNERMAN, HELEN. The Story of Little Black Sambo. London: Grant Richards, 1903. 1st 8vo ed. 109pp (1st sig sl loose). Aeg. Salmon-colored pict cl, white lettering (sl faded on spine). *Reisler.* $1,200/£750

BANNERMAN, HELEN. The Story of Little Black Sambo. NY: Frederick Stokes, n.d. Authorized Amer ed. Pict cvr label. (Fr cvr label sl rubbed), else VG. *Pacific*.* $161/£101

BANNERMAN, HELEN. The Story of Little White Squibba. London: C&W, (1966). 1st ed. 12mo. 64pp. Blue/white bds (edges rubbed) w/color illus. Color dj (margins, spine folds worn). *Reisler.* $90/£56

BANNING, WILLIAM and GEORGE HUGH. Six Horses. NY: Century, 1930. 1st ed. Pict cl. VG + in dj (spine head chipped). *Labordo.* $75/£47

BANNON, JOHN FRANCIS (ed). Bolton and the Spanish Borderlands. Norman: Univ of OK, (1964). 1st ed. Good. *Lien.* $35/£22

BANNON, LAURA. Watchdog. Whitman, 1948. 1st ed. 8.3x10.3. Unpaginated. NF (bkpl, 2 faint lib embossures) in VG dj (1/2-inch tear, sm chips). *Price.* $35/£22

BANTA, ARTHUR M. Selection in Cladocera on the Basis of Physiological Character. Carnegie Inst Pub, 1921. Good + in tan wraps (ex-lib). *Larry Price.* $25/£16

BANVILLE, JOHN. Doctor Copernicus. NY, 1976. 1st ed. NF in NF dj. *Warren.* $35/£22

BANVILLE, JOHN. Doctor Copernicus. London, 1976. 1st Eng ed. Fine in dj (sl scratched, spine faded). *Clearwater.* $64/£40

BANVILLE, JOHN. Long Lankin. Secker, 1970. 1st UK ed, 1st bk. NF in VG dj (sl worn, few sm closed tears, related crease to fr panel top). *Williams.* $792/£495

BANVILLE, JOHN. Mefisto. Martin Secker & Warburg, 1986. 1st Eng ed. VG (top edge dusty, spine ends sl bumped) in dj. *Ulysses.* $58/£36

BANVILLE, JOHN. The Newton Letter. Boston: Godine, (1987). 1st Amer ed. Fine in Fine dj. *Dermont.* $20/£13

BANVILLE, JOHN. The Newton Letter. Secker, 1982. 1st UK ed. VG in VG dj (sl dusty, spine faded). *Williams.* $64/£40

BARAKA, IMAMU AMIRI. Jello. Chicago: Third World Press, 1970. 1st ed. Fine in wraps. *Beasley.* $35/£22

BARBA, PRESTON ALBERT. Balduin Mollhausen, the German Cooper. Phila: Univ of PA, 1914. (Sl shelfworn), else VG. *Brown.* $50/£31

BARBAULD, A. L. Selections from Hymns in Prose. Phila: T. Ellwood Chapman, 1854. 12mo. Full-pg wood-engr frontis, iv,72pp; 10 VF full-pg engrs. Grn tooled cl on bds, gilt. VG (eps lt discolored, dated ink inscrip fep, stamped # rep). *Hobbyhorse.* $100/£63

BARBAULD. A Legacy for Young Ladies, Consisting of Miscellaneous Pieces, in Prose and Verse, by the Late Mrs. Barbauld. Boston: David Reed, 1826. 1st Amer ed, w/o plts. Sm 8vo. viii,151pp. 3/4 red roan, corners; marbled paper on bds, gilt. Good (eps foxed, owner label, lt water spot top margin fep, fading toward p9; cvrs lt soiled, rubbed, thin cracks along spine). *Hobbyhorse.* $125/£78

BARBAULD. Lessons for Children. London: Longman et al, 1867. New ed. 12mo. Full-pg copper engr frontis, iv,176pp. Speckled edges. Grn tooled cl, gilt spine. NF (lib ink stamp inside fr bd; #s, dry seal at lower margin 3 leaves; rep repaired). *Hobbyhorse.* $90/£56

BARBEAU, MARIUS. Pathfinders in the North Pacific. Caldwell: Caxton, 1958. 1st ed. VG in VG dj. *Perier.* $30/£19

BARBEAU, MARIUS. Totem Poles. Ottawa, 1950. 1st ed. 2 vols. Pict wraps (soiled, spine ends worn). Good+ (bkseller label vol 2 tp, sig on cvr, tp vol 2). *Baade.* $175/£109

BARBER, JOEL. Long Shore. NY: Derrydale, 1939. Ltd to 750 numbered, signed. Full red leather, issued boxed (red paper). NF. *Biscotti.* $500/£313

BARBER, NOEL. The White Desert. London: Hodder & Stoughton, 1958. Map. VG in dj (sl torn). *Explorer.* $13/£8

BARBER, RED. 1947: When All Hell Broke Loose in Baseball. Doubleday, 1982. 1st ed. Fine in VG+ dj. *Plapinger.* $65/£41

BARBIN, HERCULINE. Being the Recently Discovered Memoirs of a Nineteenth-Century French Hermaphrodite. NY, (1980). 1st Amer ed. Fine in dj (spine lt rubbed). *Polyanthos.* $25/£16

BARBOUR, THOMAS. That Vanishing Eden: A Naturalist's Florida. Boston: LB, 1944. 1st ed. Fine in VG dj (wrinkled tear). *Between The Covers.* $85/£53

BARBUSSE, HENRI. I Saw It Myself. Brian Rhys (trans). NY: E.P. Dutton, (1928). 1st US ed. Gilt black cl. Possibly pub's file copy, w/'File' rubberstamped on ep. (Spine gilt tarnished), o/w VG in dj (worn, chip fr panel edge). *Reese.* $45/£28

BARBUSSE, HENRI. Under Fire: The Story of a Squad. Fitzwater Wray (trans). London/Toronto/Paris: J.M. Dent & Sons/J.M. Dent & Fils, 1917. 1st British ed. Pale red cl stamped in gilt/blind. (Pencil erasure, offsetting to eps), o/w VG. *Reese.* $85/£53

BARCLAY, C. N. (ed). The History of the Duke of Wellington's Regiment 1919-1952. Clowes, (1953). Color frontis. (Lib # to tp verso sl showing through; backstrip # in white paint.) *Petersfield.* $48/£30

BARCLAY, CAPTAIN. Agricultural Tour in the United States and Upper Canada, with Miscellaneous Notices. Edinburgh: William Blackwood, 1842. 1st ed. pp xxiii,(1) blank,181,(1) blank,(2) ads. (Lt faded.) Howes B132. *Mott.* $250/£156

BARCLAY, EDGAR. Mountain Life in Algeria.... London: Kegan Paul, Trench, 1882. 1st ed. 1/2-title, xviii,119pp; 8 photogravures, 7 wood-engr plts (incl frontis). Turquoise dec cl. Good (sl foxed; recased w/new eps, spine label removed). *Morrell.* $144/£90

BARCLAY, EDGAR. Stonehenge and Its Earth-Works. London, 1895. 1st ed. 29 plts and plans. *Swann*.* $126/£79

BARCLAY, FLORENCE L. The Upas Tree: a Christmas Story for All Year Round. Putnam, 1912. Color frontis. Good (fore-edge lt spotted; spine bumped, sunned). *Tiger.* $16/£10

BARCLAY, JAMES. The Universal English Dictionary. London: London Ptg & Pub Co, n.d. Engr frontis, engr tp, 41 hand-colored engr maps, 14 plts and ports. (Corner ptd tp torn away, engr tp and frontis lt dampstained, clean long tear 1 plt, few short marginal tears, marginal dampstaining, dust-soiling some ll and plts.) Contemp 1/2 calf, cl (sl worn). *Christie's*.* $541/£338

BARCLAY, R. (ed). A Batch of Golfing Papers. Simpkin, Marshall, Hamilton, Kent, (c. 1892). 1st ed. Frontis, 2 full-pg illus. Wrappers (soiled, backstrip chipped). *Sotheby's*.* $221/£138

BARCLAY, THOMAS. Thirty Years. Anglo-French Reminiscences (1876-1906). London: Constable, 1914. Frontis. Good. *Stewart.* $48/£30

BARENHOLZ, EDITH (ed). The George Brown Toy Sketchbook. Princeton: Pyne Press, 1971. 1st ed. Folio. 60pp. NF in slipcase (lt soiled). *Davidson.* $125/£78

BARET, MICHAEL. An Hipponomie or the Vineyard of Horsemanship: Devided into Three Bookes.... London: George Eld, 1618. 1st ed. 3 parts in 1 vol, w/separate titles and pagination. 4to. (Shelfwear, soil, etc.; loose in casing, sl soiled, foxed, minor edge stains.) Internally Sound. *Oinonen*.* $850/£531

BARETTI, JOSEPH. An Account of the Manners and Customs of Italy.... London: T. Davies & L. Davis, 1769. 2nd ed. 2 vols. 2 engr plts vol 1. 1/2 calf, marbled bds, red leather spine labels, gilt. (Ink names, name cut out of each tp; rubbed, spine tops worn away.) *Kane*.* $120/£75

BARFIELD, OWEN. Poetic Diction. London, 1928. 1st Eng ed. (Cvrs dampstained.) Dj. *Clearwater.* $56/£35

BARHAM, WILLIAM. Descriptions of Niagara. Gravesend: The Compiler, n.d. (1847). 180pp (1st few ll sl dampstained at base; lt spotted); map, woodcut plt. Mod 1/2 levant morocco, gilt. Howes B136. *Hollett.* $440/£275

BARING, MAURICE (trans). Russian Lyrics. Heinemann, 1943. 1st ed. Ltd to 250. VG. *Whiteson.* $38/£24

BARING, MAURICE. Cecil Spencer. London, 1929. One of 525 signed. (Handled, chafed, dust-mkd.) *Clearwater.* $56/£35

BARING, MAURICE. R.F.C. H.Q. 1914-1918. London: G. Bell & Sons, 1920. 1st ed. Errata slip. Blue cl stamped in black. (Edges foxed, lt rubbed), o/w Nice. *Reese.* $85/£53

BARING, MAURICE. Sarah Bernhardt. Peter Davies, 1933. 1st ed. Signed presentation, dated Nov 1933. Frontisport. VG. *Any Amount.* $58/£36

BARING-GOULD, S. A Book of South Wales. London, (1905). 1st ed. VG. *King.* $35/£22

BARING-GOULD, S. A Book of the Rhine from Cleve to Mainz. Methuen, 1906. Pub's cat dated July 1906. Good (ink inscrip; spine bumped, chipped). *Tiger.* $34/£21

BARING-GOULD, S. Curious Myths of the Middle Ages. Rivingtons, 1874. New ed. Frontis. Good (blind-stamp; spine bumped, chipped, both hinge heads nicked). *Tiger.* $38/£24

BARING-GOULD, S. Old Country Life. Methuen, 1890. Blank before 1/2-title, frontis, guard, (2),x,258,(vi)pp; 3 integral ll of ads dated Dec 1889 at end, 1st/last pg blank. Eps coated dk gray-grn; teg, fore-edges uncut. Beveled navy blue buckram, gilt. VF reading copy (sl internal faults; cvrs dampstained, gilt rubbed). *Temple.* $19/£12

BARING-GOULD, S. The Silver Store. Longmans, Green, 1868. 1st ed. 197,(ii)pp. (Lib stamp, few marginal blindstamps; spine faded, neatly recased.) *Hollett.* $120/£75

BARING-GOULD, S. The Tragedy of the Caesars. Methuen, 1893. 2 vols. Pub's cat dated October 1892 vol 2. Good (fore-edge sl spotted; rebacked w/orig backstrips relaid, corners rubbed). *Tiger.* $48/£30

BARING-GOULD, WILLIAM. The Lure of the Limerick. NY, 1967. 1st ed. *Bond.* $25/£16

BARINGER, WILLIAM E. Lincoln's Vandalia: A Pioneer Portrait. New Brunswick, 1949. 1st ed. Fine. *Wantagh.* $20/£13

BARKER, A. L. Femina Real. London: Hogarth, 1971. 1st Eng ed. VG (top edge sl dusty; cvr edges sl faded) in dj (sl creased, mkd, spine sl faded). *Ulysses.* $40/£25

BARKER, A. L. A Heavy Feather. London: Hogarth, 1978. 1st Eng ed. VG (top edge sl mkd; spine ends, corners sl bumped, spine sl faded) in dj (sl creased, mkd, browned). *Ulysses.* $32/£20

BARKER, A. L. John Brown's Body. London: Hogarth, 1969. 1st Eng ed. VG (top edge sl dusty; spine ends, corners sl bumped) in dj (nicked, dusty, sl rubbed, creased, spotted, soiled, browned). *Ulysses.* $32/£20

BARKER, A. L. The Middling. London: Hogarth, 1967. 1st Eng ed. VG (top edge, spine head sl faded; tail, corner sl bumped) in dj (sl creased, mkd, browned). *Ulysses.* $40/£25

BARKER, BENJAMIN. Francisco, or the Pirate of the Pacific. Boston: F. Gleason, 1845. 1st ed. 50pp (later ll foxed). Ptd wraps (worn). VG. *M & S.* $125/£78

BARKER, CICELY MARY. The Book of the Flower Fairies. London: Blackie & Son, (1927). 1st ed. 8vo. Grn cl, gilt. Full color dj (rear cvr lacks piece). *Reisler.* $475/£297

BARKER, CICELY MARY. The Book of the Flower Fairies. Blackie, n.d., ca 1940. Grn cl, gilt. VG. *Green Meadow.* $152/£95

BARKER, CICELY MARY. Fairies of the Flowers and Trees. London: Blackie & Son, (1950). 1st ed. 8vo. Grn cl, gilt. Good in full color dj (margins sl worn). *Reisler.* $485/£303

BARKER, CICELY MARY. Fairies of the Trees. London: Blackie & Son, (1940). 16mo. 24 full-pg color plts. Tan-brn dec bds, color paste label. Full color dj. *Reisler.* $150/£94

BARKER, CICELY MARY. Fairies of the Trees. London: Blackie & Son, (1940). Stated 1st ed. 16mo. 24 full-pg color plts. Tan pict bds, full color paste label. Full color pict dj (dusty, chip at spine head). *Reisler.* $250/£156

BARKER, CICELY MARY. Flower Fairies of the Spring. Blackie, n.d. ca 1926. Early ed. 12mo. 24 color plts. Blue pict eps. Chequer-patterned bds, pict onlay. (Ends rubbed), else VG in pict dj (few sm tears, sm piece torn from top edge) w/protective film. *Bookmark.* $72/£45

BARKER, CICELY MARY. Flower Fairies of the Summer. (Tiny Tots series.) London: Blackie & Son, (1925). 1st ed. 16mo. B/w frontis, 24 full-pg color plts. Tan-brn dec bds (sl bowed), color paste label. Full color pict dj (lt mks rear cvr). *Reisler.* $185/£116

BARKER, CICELY MARY. A Flower Fairy Alphabet. London: Blackie & Son, (1934). 16mo. 24 full-pg color plts. Tan-brn dec bds, color paste label. Full color dj. *Reisler.* $175/£109

BARKER, CICELY MARY. Flower Songs of the Seasons. NY: Dodge, (c. 1930). 1st Amer ed. 9.75x7. Olive Linnell (music). Cl-backed bds, pict cvr label. VG. *Pacific*.* $40/£25

BARKER, CLIVE. Books of Blood V. L.A.: Scream, 1988. One of 333 numbered, signed by Barker and Harry O. Morris (illus). Simulated leather stamped in silver/red. (Sl worn.) Slipcase. *Oinonen*.* $30/£19

BARKER, CLIVE. The Damnation Game. London: Weidenfeld & Nicolson, (1985). 1st ed. One of 250 numbered, signed. (Sl worn.) Slipcase. *Oinonen*.* $80/£50

BARKER, CLIVE. The Great and Secret Show. London, 1989. One of 500 numbered, signed. Aeg. Simulated leather. (Sl worn.) Felt-lined case as issued. *Oinonen*.* $50/£31

BARKER, CLIVE. Imagica. NY, (1991). One of 500 numbered, signed. (Sl worn.) Slipcase. *Oinonen*.* $130/£81

BARKER, CLIVE. In the Flesh. NY, (1986). 1st Amer ed, signed. VG in dj. *King.* $60/£38

BARKER, CLIVE. Weaveworld. NY, (1987). One of 500 numbered, signed. Teg. (Sl worn.) Slipcase. *Oinonen*.* $90/£56

BARKER, CLIVE. Weaveworld. NY, (1987). 1st ed. Ltd to 500 numbered, signed. VG in slipcase. *King.* $150/£94

BARKER, EUGENE. The Life of Stephen E. Austin. Dallas: Cokesbury, 1925. 1st ed. Signed. Dk red cl, emb/gilt. NF. Howes B137. *Labordo.* $225/£141

BARKER, GEORGE. Calamiterror. Faber, 1937. 1st ed. (Offsetting to ep; ep, rear bd sl water-mkd), else NF in NF dj. *Any Amount.* $38/£24

BARKER, GEORGE. Poems. Faber, 1935. 1st ed. Fine in VG + dj. *Any Amount.* $48/£30

BARKER, GEORGE. Sacred and Secular Energies. CT: New Directions, 1943. 1st ed. VG in wraps. *Any Amount.* $22/£14

BARKER, GEORGE. The True Confession. (London): Parton Press, 1957. 2nd ed. VG in black cl, gilt. Dj. *Maggs.* $24/£15

BARKER, JAMES P. The Log of a Lime Juicer. NY: Macmillan, 1936. Blue-grn cl. VG. *American Booksellers.* $45/£28

BARKER, NICOLAS. Bibliotheca Lindesiana, the Lives and Collections of...25th Earl of Crawford and...26th Earl of Crawford. Roxburghe Club, 1978. VG. *Gretton.* $72/£45

BARKER, NICOLAS. The Oxford University Press and the Spread of Learning 1478-1978. London, 1978. 1st ed. Fine in dj. *Gretton.* $35/£22

BARKER, NICOLAS. Stanley Morison. London, 1972. VG in dj. *Typographeum.* $30/£19

BARKER, OMAR. Songs of the Saddlemen. Denver: Sage Books, 1954. 1st ed. Inscribed, signed. Fine in dj (spine ends chipped). *Labordo.* $95/£59

BARKER, PAT. The Ghost Road. Viking, 1995. 1st ed. Signed. Fine in dj. *Ulysses.* $104/£65

BARKER, T. C. A History of London Transport: Passenger Travel and the Development of the Metropolis. London: George Allen & Unwin, (1963)/1974. 2 vols. (Ex-lib, vol 1 w/sm tears to pg edges, faded; vol 2 upper fr hinge broken, bds bowed, rear hinge reinforced.) *Bohling.* $125/£78

BARKER, THOMAS. Barker's Delight: Or, The Art of Angling. London, 1657 (but 1820). 2nd ed. One of 100 ptd. (9)leaves,40pp + 2 leaves ads. Mod cl. (Lt worn; cracked behind 1st sig, tp sl soiled, browned.) *Oinonen*.* $200/£125

BARKER, W. BURCKHARDT. A Practical Grammar of the Turkish Language. London, 1854. 1st ed. Later paper spine label. *Swann*.* $80/£50

BARLOS, NORA (ed). Darwin and Henslow. The Growth of an Idea. Letters 1831-1860. London, 1967. 1st ed. Dj (sl chipped, creased). *Edwards.* $26/£16

Barlow's Journal of His Life at Sea in King's Ships, East and West Indiamen and Other Merchantmen from 1659 to 1703. London, 1934. 2 vols. 8 color plts. (1st/last few ll lt browned; spines sl rubbed.) *Edwards.* $120/£75

BARLOW, J. W. and D. P. HEAP. Letter from the Secretary of War, Accompanying an Engineer Report of a Reconnoissance of the Yellowstone River in 1871. Washington, 1871. 1st ed. 43pp; fldg map (few tears, 1 quite long, but no paper loss). Mod 1/2 cl. VG. Howes B145. *Pacific*.* $92/£58

BARLOW, NORA. Charles Darwin's Diary of the Voyage of H.M.S. 'Beagle.' NY/Cambridge: Macmillan/University Press, 1934. This copy signed, dated Oct 25, 1962. Port, 2 plts, map. Blue cl, gilt. (Cvrs sl worn, esp spine ends.) *Parmer.* $200/£125

BARMAN, CHRISTIAN. Early British Railways. Penguin Books, 1950. 1st ed. 16 color plts. Pict bds. VG in dj. *Hollett.* $48/£30

BARNARD, CHARLES H. Narrative of the Sufferings and Adventures of.... NY, 1829. 1st ed. 296pp. (Lacks 4 of 6 copperplts engrs, chart; foxed; rebound.) *Heinoldt.* $25/£16

BARNARD, CHRISTIAAN and CURTIS BELL PEPPER. One Life. (NY, 1970.) 1st Amer ed. Signed, dated April 30, 1970. Dj. *Argosy.* $175/£109

BARNARD, EVAN G. A Rider of the Cherokee Strip. Boston: Houghton Mifflin, 1936. 1st ed. Good. Howes B147. *Lien.* $45/£28

BARNARD, GEORGE. The Theory and Practice of Landscape Painting in Water Colours. London: William S. Orr, 1855. 1st ed. 24 chromolitho plts. Aeg. Gilt-lettered cl (professionally re-backed in later cl). (Few pp w/sm tears, not affecting plts; rear cvr sunned), else VG. *Pacific*.* $138/£86

BARNARD, J. G. The C. S. A. and the Battle of Bull Run. NY: D. Van Nostrand, 1862. 1st ed, w/errata leaf tipped in. 136pp + (8)pp ads; complete w/5 fldg maps. Red cl, gilt. VG + (few cvr stains). *Chapel Hill.* $200/£125

BARNARD, MRS. ALFRED. (ed). The Life of a Negro Slave. Norwich, (England): Charles Muskett, 1846. 1st Eng ed. 7,245pp (ep waterstained). Orig cl (spine worn). Howes B65. *M & S.* $200/£125

BARNARD, ROBERT. Death and the Princess. London: CCC, 1982. 1st ed. VF in dj. *Mordida.* $150/£94

BARNARD, ROBERT. Death on the High C's. London: CCC, 1977. 1st ed. VF in dj. *Mordida.* $350/£219

BARNARD, ROBERT. The Skeleton in the Grass. Collins, 1987. 1st UK ed. Fine in dj. *Williams.* $72/£45

BARNARD, SEYMOUR. A Child's Garden of Relatives. NY/Toronto: Rinehart, 1950. Tall 8vo. 84pp; 34 full-pg color lithos. Grn cl, gilt spine. Fine (cvr edges lt soiled). *Hobbyhorse.* $75/£47

BARNE, KITTY. Family Footlights. London: Dent, 1939. 1st ed. Ruth Gervis (illus). 244pp. Fine in Good dj (sm chips to spine ends). *Price.* $25/£16

BARNES, ALBERT C. The Art in Painting. Merion, PA: Barnes Foundation Press, 1925. 106 plts. *Argosy.* $50/£31

BARNES, CLARE. John F. Kennedy. Scrimshaw Collector. Boston/Toronto: Little, Brown, (1969). VG (cvr sl faded). *Explorer.* $32/£20

BARNES, DEMAS. From the Atlantic to the Pacific Overland. A Series of Letters.... NY: D. Van Nostrand, 1866. 1st ed. Litho frontis port, 136pp. VG + (text margins dknd; extrems rubbed). Howes B153. *Zubal*.* $65/£41

BARNES, DJUNA. The Book of Repulsive Women. NY: Guido Bruno, 1915. 1st ed, 1st bk. NF in ptd yellow wrappers (lt soiled). *Bromer.* $950/£594

BARNES, DJUNA. A Book. NY: Boni & Liveright, (1928). 1st ed. Black bds, paper spine label. (Spine sl faded), else VG. *Pacific*.* $75/£47

BARNES, DJUNA. Creatures in an Alphabet. NY: Dial, (1982). 1st ed. Blue cl, white bds, silver-lettered spine. Fine in dj (lt soiled). *Heritage.* $60/£38

BARNES, DJUNA. Nightwood. NY: Harcourt, Brace, (1937). 1st Amer ed. (Ownership 1st blank; spine, edge faded; lacks dj), o/w VG. *Hermitage.* $45/£28

BARNES, DJUNA. The Selected Works of Djuna Barnes. NY: Farrar, Straus & Cudahy, (1962). 1st ed. NF in dj (lt worn). *Hermitage.* $50/£31

BARNES, JAMES M. A Guide to Good Golf. NY: Dodd, Mead, 1925. 5th ed. Grn cl, pict cvr label. (Emb stamp, sig; cvr label sl rubbed), else NF. *Pacific*.* $29/£18

BARNES, JAMES. Through Central Africa from Coast to Coast. NY, 1915. Color frontis, map. Good (inner hinges strengthened, cvrs sl dull). *Hallam.* $72/£45

BARNES, JULIAN. Metroland. London: Jonathan Cape, (1980). 1st ed. One of 3000. Fine in dj (price-clipped). *Pacific*.* $92/£58

BARNES, JULIAN. Talking It Over. London: Cape, 1991. 1st ed. Signed. Fine in dj. *Virgo.* $24/£15

BARNES, LEONARD. Youth at Arms. (Ptd by Curwen Press), 1933. 1st Eng ed. VG (sm bkpl) in dj (sl dusty). *Clearwater.* $48/£30

BARNES, WILL C. Apaches and Longhorns. L.A., 1941. VG in dj. *Dumont.* $125/£78

BARNES, WILL C. Tales from the X-Bar Horse Camp. Chicago: Breeders Gazette, 1920. 1st ed. NF. *Labordo.* $250/£156

BARNES, WILL C. Tales from the X-Bar Horse Camp: The Blue-Roan 'Outlaw' and Other Stories. Chicago: Breeders' Gazette, 1920. 1st ed. 1/2 cl, gilt. (Tape residue to pastedowns), else NF. Howes B156. *Pacific*.* $150/£94

BARNES, WILL C. Western Grazing Grounds and Forest Ranges. Chicago, 1913. 1st ed. VG + (name). Howes B157. *Woolson.* $150/£94

BARNES, WILL C. Western Grazing Grounds and Forest Ranges. Chicago: Breeders Gazette, 1913. 1st ed. VG. Howes B157. *Labordo.* $175/£109

BARNES, WILLIAM H. The Fortieth Congress of the United States, 1867-69. NY, 1869-71. 2 vols. Morocco, gilt extra. (Backstrips sl faded.) *Swann*.* $201/£126

BARNES, WILLIAM HARRISON. The Contemporary American Organ. NY: J. Fischer, 1933. 2nd ed. Inscribed presentation, Feb 24, 1934. (Fr bd sl mkd.) *Hollett.* $136/£85

BARNES, WILLIAM. Early England and the Saxon-English. John Russell Smith, 1869. 1st ed. (ii),178pp + 56pp ads, w/errata slip. Orig cl (sl faded, neatly recased), gilt. *Hollett.* $288/£180

BARNES, WILLIAM. An Outline of English Speech-Craft. C. Kegan Paul, 1878. 1st ed. viii,92,32pp. Cl, beveled bds (spine top edges faded, extrems sl rubbed; joints just cracking). *Hollett.* $352/£220

BARNES, WILLIAM. Poems Grave and Gay. Giles Dugdale (ed). Dorchester: Longmans, 1949. 1st ed. Frontisport. VG in dj (top edges sl rubbed, sm nick, tear). *Hollett.* $48/£30

BARNES, WILLIAM. Poems of Rural Life in the Dorset Dialect. London: John Russell Smith, 1862. 3rd ed. xii,211pp + 16pp ads. Purple cl. Poor (lt stained; faded). *Marlborough.* $32/£20

BARNES, WILLIAM. Poems of Rural Life in the Dorset Dialect. Kegan Paul, Trench, 1888. ix,467pp (few spots to prelims; extrems sl rubbed). Untrimmed. *Hollett.* $136/£85

BARNES, WILLIAM. A Selection from Poems of Rural Life in the Dorset Dialect. Edited by His Son. London: Kegan Paul, Trench, Trubner, 1909. 1st ed. Frontisport, viii,132pp + 4pp ads. Pale blue cl, gilt. *Marlborough.* $48/£30

BARNETT, CORRELLI. The Desert Generals. NY, 1961. VG in VG dj. *Clark.* $25/£16

BARNETT, T. RATCLIFFE. Autumns in Skye, Ross and Sutherland. John Grant, 1946. Enlgd ed. (Spine faded.) *Hollett.* $32/£20

BARNEY, MARY (ed). A Biographical Memoir of the Late Commodore Joshua Barney. Boston: Gray & Bowen, 1832. 1st ed. xvi,328pp; port. Mod cl. (Foxed.) Howes B160. *Lefkowicz.* $100/£63

BARNHARDT, WILTON. Emma Who Saved My Life. NY: St. Martin's, (1989). 1st ed, 1st bk. Fine in Fine dj. *Agvent.* $45/£28

BARNITZ, ALBERT and JENNIE. Life in Custer's Cavalry. Robert M. Utley (ed). New Haven: Yale Univ, 1977. 1st ed. Dj (lt edgeworn). *Dawson.* $35/£22

BARNS, C. R. (ed). The Commonwealth of Missouri, a Centennial Record. St. Louis: Bryan, Brand, 1877. 1st ed. Grn cl (recased, rebacked, orig spine laid down). *Glenn.* $275/£172

BARNS, GEORGE C. Denver, the Man. Wilmington, OH, 1949. 1st ed. Good + . *Wantagh.* $65/£41

BARNUM, P. T. The Life of P. T. Barnum. London: Sampson Low & Son, 1855. 1st Eng ed, 3rd state in sm type, to be sold at 1/-. Contemp 1/2 roan (extrems rubbed, hinges tender). *Dramatis.* $50/£31

BARNUM, P. T. Struggles and Triumphs: or, Forty Years' Recollections of P.T. Barnum. London: Sampson, Low, Son, & Marston, 1870. 1st ed. Yellowback. viii,392,(10 ads)pp. Pict paper-cvrd bds (edges rubbed, spine creased, worn, hinges cracked). *Hollett.* $208/£130

BARNUM, P. T. Thirty Years of Hustling, or How to Get On. Rutland, IL, (1891). 1st ed. W. W. Denslow & Will Bradley (illus). Pict gray-blue cl (rubbed). *Swann**. $92/£58

BARNWELL. Game Fish of the Northern States of America, and British Provinces. NY: Carleton, 1862. 1st ed. Grn cl, gilt. (Shelfworn, spine ends frayed), else VG-. *Pacific**. $58/£36

BARO, GENE. Claes Oldenburg. London/NY, 1969. 368 plts. (Lib ink stamp, label, cellotape mk pastedown.) Dj (sl soiled). *Edwards*. $72/£45

BARON, JOSEPH. All About the English Lakes. Kendal: Atkinson & Pollitt, 1925. 1st ed. Frontis. VG. *Hollett*. $48/£30

BARON. (Pseud of Stirling Henry Nahum.) At the Ballet. London: Collins, 1950. Ltd to 150 numbered, signed by Baron and Arnold L. Haskell (intro). Full grn morocco. Good in cardboard slipcase (worn). *Karmiole*. $250/£156

BARONIO, JOYCE. Joyce Baronio: 42nd Street Studio. NY: Pyxidium, 1980. 1st ed. Folio. Illus paper over bds (rear bd tips sl rubbed, bumped), else VG in illus dj. *Cahan*. $125/£78

BARR, ALFRED H., JR. Fantastic Art, Dada, Surrealism. NY, 1936. (Cocked.) Dj (tears). *Swann**. $57/£36

BARR, ALFRED H., JR. Masters of Modern Art. NY: MOMA, (1954). 356 plts (77 tipped-in color). Fine in dj (chipped, edgeworn). *Turtle Island*. $65/£41

BARR, ALFRED H., JR. Matisse, His Art and His Public. NY: MOMA, (1951). VG in dj (sl frayed, soiled). *King*. $60/£38

BARR, ALFRED H., JR. Picasso. NY: MOMA, (1939). 2nd ed. VG (notes, underlining) in pict stiff wrappers (soiled). *Turtle Island*. $30/£19

BARR, ETHEL ELAINE. His Majesty the King: Our Baby's Biography. Chicago: George M. Hill, (1902). 4to. Red pict cl. Good. *Reisler*. $125/£78

BARR, NEVADA. Track of the Cat. NY: Putnam, 1993. 1st ed. Signed. VF in VF dj. *Unger*. $175/£109

BARR, STRINGFELLOW. Copydog in India. Viking, 1955. 1st ed. Kurt Wiese (illus). 125pp. VG (bottom edge sl worn) in Good dj. *Price*. $25/£16

BARRA, E. I. A Tale of Two Oceans; a New Story by an Old Californian. An Account of a Voyage.... SF: The Author, 1893. 1st ed. 198pp. 3/4 leather (newly bound). Fine. *Argonaut*. $225/£141

BARRATT, THOMAS J. The Annals of Hampstead. London: L. Leventhal, 1972. Rpts of 1912 ed. Ltd to 500 sets. 3 vols. Buckram. *Marlborough*. $240/£150

Barrel Mystery; or, the Career, Tragedy and Trial of Henry Jumpertz. Chicago: Norris & Hyde, 1859. 70pp; 2 ports. Good in wrappers (lacks rear wrapper, fr wrap detached, sl chipped). *Brown*. $95/£59

BARRELL, JOSEPH et al. The Evolution of the Earth and Its Inhabitants. Yale Univ, 1923. 17 plts. VG. *Larry Price*. $28/£18

BARRETT, ANGELA. Proud Knight, Fair Lady. Naomi Lewis (trans). NY: Viking, 1989. 1st US ed. 7.75x10.75. 100pp. Fine in dj. *Cattermole*. $25/£16

BARRETT, C. Reptiles of Australia. London: Cassell, 1950. 1st ed. Color frontis. VG. *Mikesh*. $37/£23

BARRETT, CHARLES (ed). The Pacific. Melbourne: N.H. Seward, n.d. (c. 1955). 1st ed. Tipped-in color frontis. (Spine sl faded), else NF. *Pacific**. $52/£33

BARRETT, ELLEN C. Baja California 1535-1956: A Bibliography.... L.A.: Bennett & Marshall, 1957. One of 550 ptd. Fac frontis. Blue cl, gilt. NF. *Pacific**. $127/£79

BARRETT, FRANKLIN A. and ARTHUR L. THORPE. Derby Porcelain 1750-1848. London: Faber & Faber, 1971. 1st ed. Color frontis, 7 color plts, 177 b/w plts. Dj. *Edwards*. $45/£28

BARRETT, JOHN G. The Civil War in North Carolina. Chapel Hill: Univ of NC, (1963). 1st ed. Blue cl. Fine in NF dj (price-clipped, few edge tears). *Chapel Hill*. $85/£53

BARRETT, NEAL. Long Days and Short Nights. (Mountain Home, TX: Y-O Press, 1980.) 1st ed. Brn cl, gilt. Fine in NF dj (sl insect damage). *Harrington*. $75/£47

BARRETT, TIMOTHY. Japanese Papermaking. NY/Japan: Weatherhill, 1983. 1st ed. 3 tipped-in samples. VG in dj. *Cox*. $48/£30

BARRETTO, LARRY. Horses in the Sky. NY: John Day, (1929). 1st ed. Gray cl stamped in red. NF in pict dj (chipped, torn). *Reese*. $100/£63

BARRIE, J. M. The Admirable Crichton. London: Hodder & Stoughton, (1914). 1st illus ed. 20 tipped-in color plts by Hugh Thomson, guards. (Spine sl sunned), else NF. *Pacific**. $98/£61

BARRIE, J. M. Courage. The Rectorial Address Delivered at St. Andrews University May 3rd 1922. London: Hodder and Stoughton, 1922. 1st ed, probable 2nd issue. Cream cl (bumped, sm creases). VG (1/2-title lt soiled, fep rubbed, rep dknd) in dj (lt soiled, creased; chipped; short tear). Fldg blue cl chemise in morocco-backed cl slipcase (spine rubbed). *Blue Mountain*. $25/£16

BARRIE, J. M. An Edinburgh Eleven. Office of the 'British Weekly,' 1889. 1st issue, w/author's name given as 'Gavin Ogilvy' on fr cvr. 4pp pub's ads at rear. VG (eps browned, spotted; spine ends, corners sl bumped). *Ulysses*. $152/£95

BARRIE, J. M. George Meredith, 1909. London: Constable, n.d. (1909). 1st ed. Uncut. Cream cl, gilt. VG. *Hollett*. $32/£20

BARRIE, J. M. The Little Minister. NY, (1891). 1st Amer ed. Pict cvrs, gilt. NF (spine sl rubbed). *Polyanthos*. $35/£22

BARRIE, J. M. The Little White Bird or Adventures in Kensington Gardens. NY: Scribner, 1902. 1st Amer ed. (Foxed), else VG. *Pacific**. $63/£39

BARRIE, J. M. The Little White Bird or, Adventures in Kensington Gardens. NY: Scribner, 1902. 1st Amer ed. Grn cl, gilt. NF. *Pacific**. $69/£43

BARRIE, J. M. Peter and Wendy. NY: Scribner, (1911). 1st Amer ed. F. D. Bedford (illus). Grn cl, gilt. NF. *Pacific**. $127/£79

BARRIE, J. M. Peter Pan and Wendy. Hodder & Stoughton, 1932. Sm 4to. 128pp; 12 color plts by Mabel Lucie Attwell. Pict blue cl, gilt. VG (lt spotted, finger-mks). *Hollett*. $120/£75

BARRIE, J. M. Peter Pan in Kensington Gardens. London, 1906. 1st trade ed. Arthur Rackham (illus). 50 tipped-in color plts w/ptd tissue guards, incl frontis. Orig cl (poorly rebacked w/leather, lettered portion of orig spine retained; corners bumped, lt worn). *Kane**. $300/£188

BARRIE, J. M. Peter Pan in Kensington Gardens. London: Hodder & Stoughton, 1906. 1st ed. Lg 4to. Arthur Rackham (illus). 50 mtd color plts. Brn cl, gilt. Good. *Reisler*. $900/£563

BARRIE, J. M. Peter Pan in Kensington Gardens. London: Hodder & Stoughton, 1906. 1st trade ed. 50 mtd color plts by Arthur Rackham on brn paper, bound at end. (Bkpl.) Russet pict cl, gilt. *Christie's**. $1,013/£633

BARRIE, J. M. Peter Pan in Kensington Gardens. London: Hodder & Stoughton, 1906. Ltd to 500 signed by Arthur Rackham (illus). 4to. 50 mtd plts on brn paper. Teg. Orig pict vellum, gilt. (Upper corner of 1/2-title lt soiled; fr cvr lt soiled, lacks ties.) *Christie's**. $2,208/£1,380

BARRIE, J. M. Peter Pan or the Boy Who Would Not Grow Up. London: Hodder & Stoughton, 1928. 1st ed. 8vo. (Lt offsetting to eps, fore-edges foxed), o/w Fine in dj (sl chipped, dust-soiled, sm closed tear). *Jaffe*. $225/£141

BARRIE, J. M. The Peter Pan Portfolio from Peter Pan in Kensington Gardens. NY: Brentano's, 1914. Ltd to 300. Folio. Arthur Rackham (illus). Tp, list of plts, limitation pg; 12 lg mtd plts (each 12x16 inches), ptd guards. Heavy bds cvrd w/yellow silk moire, tan cl back, corners. (Ties not present.) *Reisler*. $9,000/£5,625

BARRIE, J. M. Quality Street. London: Hodder & Stoughton, (1913). 1st ed illus thus. 4to. (xii),3-197pp; 22 mtd color plts by Hugh Thomson, guards. Purple cl, gilt. Fine in white dj (sl spine loss, sl browned, rubbed). *Sotheran*. $269/£168

BARRIE, J. M. Quality Street. London: Hodder & Stoughton, 1913. 1st Thomson ed. 22 mtd color plts by Hugh Thomson. 3/4 blue calf, marbled bds, raised bands, maroon leather label. Sound. *Appelfeld*. $200/£125

BARRIE, J. M. Tommie and Grizel. London, 1900. VG (no dj). *Typographeum*. $25/£16

BARRINGTON, ARCHIBALD. A Familiar Introduction to Heraldry. London: H.G. Bohn, 1848. 1st ed. Period 3/4 dk grn morocco, marbled bds. (Spine head, joints sl rubbed), else VG. *Pacific**. $58/£36

BARRINGTON, DAINES. The Possibility of Approaching the North Pole Asserted. London: T. & J. Allman, 1818. 2nd ed. xxiv,258pp,ad(iv); fldg map. Uncut. Orig bds. (New eps, map sl offset onto tp; bds very worn), else VG. *Explorer*. $320/£200

BARRINGTON, DAINES. The Possibility of Approaching the North Pole Asserted.... London, 1818. 2nd ed. Frontis map. 19th-cent 1/2 morocco (extrems worn; ink marginalia, bkpl). *Swann**. $172/£108

BARRINGTON, EMILIE ISABEL. The Life, Letters and Work of Frederick Leighton. London: George Allen, 1906. 1st ed. 2 vols. 158 plts mtd on grey card, guards. Teg, uncut. Dec cl (spines sl faded, mottled), gilt. *Hollett*. $224/£140

BARRINGTON, F. H. Kansas Day, Containing a Brief History of Kansas and a Collection by Kansas Authors. Topeka, 1892. 1st ed. Inscribed. 253pp. (Few sm edge tears; corners sl bumped), o/w VG. *Baade*. $250/£156

BARRON, EVAN MacLEOD. Prince Charlie's Pilot. Inverness: Robt. Carruthers & Sons, 1913. 1st ed. Frontis, fldg map tipped-in. Pict cl, gilt. VG. *Hollett*. $104/£65

BARROW, JOHN. Travels in China. London: T. Cadell & W. Davies, 1806. 2nd ed. 4to. Hand-colored frontisport, x,(ii),632pp; 4 hand-colored plts, 3 plain plts (2 dbl-pg). (Pp405-6 repaired to fore-edge, lt browned throughout.) Contemp marbled bds (surface wear), reinforced calf corners, rebacked in early morocco (head lacks sm piece), gilt, morocco label. *Edwards*. $880/£550

BARROW, JOHN. Travels in China.... Phila: W.F. M'Laughlin, 1805. 1st Amer ed. Engr frontis, 422pp. Contemp tree calf, gilt, red morocco label. Good. *Karmiole*. $300/£188

BARROW, JOHN. Visit to Iceland, by Way of Tronyem...in the Summer of 1834. London, 1835. Contemp 1/2 roan (needs rebinding). *Swann**. $201/£126

BARROW, JOHN. Voyages of Discovery and Research Within the Arctic Regions from the Year 1818 to the Present Time.... NY: Harper & Bros, 1846. xii,(13)-359pp; 2 maps incl lg fldg map. Uncut, unopened. Orig cl (Ex-lib; spine top chipped), but VG. *High Latitude*. $100/£63

BARROW, JOHN. Voyages of Discovery and Research Within the Arctic Regions, from the Year 1818 to the Present Time. London: John Murray, 1846. Frontisport, xiii,(i),530pp,16 ads; 2 maps (1 fldg). VG (rebacked, recornered). *Explorer*. $416/£260

BARROWS, DAVID PRESCOTT. The Ethno-Botany of the Coahuilla Indians of Southern California. Morongo: Malki Museum, 1967. 1st ed thus. Ltd to 750. Fine in Fine dj. *Book Market*. $60/£38

BARROWS, JOHN HENRY (ed). The World's Parliament of Religions. Chicago, 1893. 2 vols. 1600pp. (Sl worn, bindings dull.) *Woolson*. $30/£19

BARROWS, MARJORIE. Fraidy Cat. NY: Rand McNally, 1943. 'Glowing-Eye' bk. Barbara May-nard (illus). 8vo. Pict eps. Color pict bds (corners, spine ends sl rubbed). VG. *Houle*. $150/£94

BARROWS, MARJORIE. Jojo. Chicago: Rand McNally, 1946. Sq 12mo. Clarence Biers (illus). Color pict bds w/circular window. Good. *Reisler*. $55/£34

BARROWS, MARJORIE. The Pet Show. Kenosha, WI: Samuel Lowe, 1944. Ilona (illus). Fine in Fine dj. *American Booksellers*. $30/£19

BARRY, DAVID. Indian Notes on the Custer Battle. Usher L. Burdick (ed). Balt: Wirth Bros, 1949. 2nd enlgd ed. Fine in wrappers. *Labordo*. $40/£25

BARRY, JOHN WARREN. Studies in Corsica, Sylvan and Social. London, 1893. 1st ed. Frontis, xvi,302,(2)ads pp; 2 maps (1 fldg), 4 plts. *Maggs*. $280/£175

BARRY, JULIAN. Lenny. A Play Based on the Life and Words of Lenny Bruce. NY: Grove/Evergreen Black Cat, 1972. 1st ed. (Spine sl faded), o/w NF- in wraps. *Sclanders*. $11/£7

BARRY, LOUISE. The Beginnings of the West. Topeka: KS State Hist Soc, 1972. 1st ed. VG in dj. *Labordo*. $35/£22

BARRY, PHILIP. Second Threshold. NY: Harper, (1951). Rev ed. Robert E. Sherwood (rev). VF in Fine dj (sl rubbed, 1/8 inch short). *Between The Covers*. $85/£53

BARRY, T. A. and B. A. PATTEN. Men and Memories of San Francisco in the 'Spring of '50.' SF: A.L. Bancroft, 1873. 1st ed. 296pp. This copy w/o dbl frontis, which has apparently been removed (some copies probably issued w/o frontis). (Bkpl; rubbed, extrems worn, cvrs soiled), else VG. Howes B192. *Pacific**. $58/£36

BARRY, T. A. and B. A. PATTEN. Men and Memories of San Francisco in the 'Spring of '50.' SF: A.L. Bancroft, 1873. 1st ed. (6),7-296pp. Brn cl, gilt. (Bkpl; joints, spine sl rubbed), o/w Fine in later chemise, morocco slipcase. Howes B192. *Pacific**. $173/£108

BARRY, WILLIAM E. Journal of a Voyage for the Discovery of a Northwest Passage and Journal of a Second Voyage for the Discovery of a North-West Passage. NY, 1968. 2 vols. 132 plts, maps. (Shelfworn), else VG. *Dumont*. $165/£103

BARTECCHI, CARL E. Soc Trang: A Vietnamese Odyssey. Boulder, CO: Rocky Mountain Writers Guild, 1980. 1st ed. Fine in dj. *Associates*. $65/£41

BARTH, GUNTHER. City People. NY: OUP, 1980. 1st ed. Fine in Fine dj. *Book Market*. $35/£22

BARTH, HENRY. Travels and Discoveries in North and Central Africa. NY: Harper, 1857-9. 1st US ed. 3 vols. Thick 8vo. 1 fldg map. Mod cl, gilt. (Sm tape repair pp260, ink stamp vol 3 tp, sl soiled, browned; rebound.) *Edwards*. $560/£350

BARTH, JOHN. The End of the Road. GC: Doubleday, 1958. 1st ed. VG+ in VG dj (extrems worn). *Pettler*. $200/£125

BARTH, JOHN. Letters. NY: Putnam, (1979). 1st ed. Fine in NF dj w/gold lettering. *Agvent*. $20/£13

BARTH, JOHN. Letters: A Novel. NY: Putnam, 1979. 1st ed. One of 500 specially bound, signed. Mint in pub's slipcase. *Pirages*. $75/£47

BARTH, JOHN. The Sot-Weed Factor. GC: Doubleday, 1960. 1st ed. Yellow cl, blue bds. VG (bkpl; spine ends sl rubbed) in dj (sl chipped, soiled). *Heritage*. $400/£250

BARTHELME, DONALD. Come Back, Dr. Caligari. Eyre & Spottiswoode, 1966. 1st UK ed, 1st bk. Fine in dj. *Williams*. $56/£35

BARTHELME, DONALD. The Emerald. Hollywood: Sylvester & Orphanos, 1980. Ltd to 330 signed. Fine dec cl. *Truepenny*. $100/£63

BARTHELME, DONALD. Sixty Stories. NY, (1981). 1st ed. One of 500 numbered, signed. Slipcase. *Swann**. $103/£64

BARTHES, ROLAND. Arcimboldo. (Milan, 1980.) Folio. Cl fldg case. *Swann**. $161/£101

BARTHOLOMEW, ED. The Biographical Album of Western Gunfighters. Houston: Frontier, 1958. 1st ed. VG + . *Labordo.* $225/£141

BARTHOLOMEW, ED. Cullen Baker. Houston, 1954. Ltd to 1000. (Sig; rear cvr soiled), else Fine. *Baade.* $50/£31

BARTHOLOMEW, ED. Henry Plummer, Montana Outlaw Boss. From Old Newspaper Files.... Ruidoso, NM: Frontier Book, 1960. 1st ed. Signed. One of 500 ptd. Fine in yellow wrappers. *Labordo.* $60/£38

BARTHOLOMEW, ED. Kill or Be Killed. Houston: Frontier, 1953. 1st ed. VG + . *Labordo.* $75/£47

BARTHOLOMEW, ED. Western Hard Cases; Or, Gunfighters Named Smith. Ruidoso, NM: Frontier Book, 1960. 1st ed. NF in dj. *Labordo.* $75/£47

BARTHOLOMEW, ED. Wild Bill Longley, a Texas Hardcase. Houston: Frontier, 1953. 1st ed. VG. *Labordo.* $85/£53

BARTHOLOMEW, ED. Wyatt Earp, 1879 to 1882. Toyahvale, TX: Frontier Book Co, 1964. 1st ed. One of 1000. Signed. Brn cl. Dj. *Dawson.* $60/£38

BARTHOLOMEW, JOHN (ed). The Times Atlas of the World: Mid-Century Edition. London, 1955-59. 5 vols. Folio. Blue cl. Sound set, 4 vols in djs. *Argosy.* $400/£250

BARTHOLOW, ROBERTS. A Practical Treatise on Materia Medica and Therapeutics. NY, 1879. 3rd ed. 595pp. Tan textured cl (corners worn). VG. *Doctor's Library.* $65/£41

BARTHOLOW, ROBERTS. A Practical Treatise on Materia Medica and Therapeutics. NY: D. Appleton, 1884. 5th ed. xxii,738 + pp. VG (bds worn, spine top lt damaged). *Bookcell.* $35/£22

BARTLETT, D. W. The Heroes of the Indian Rebellion. Columbus, OH: Follett, Foster, 1860. 456pp. Marbled eps. Leather spine. VG- (Foxed; rubbed, scuffed, corners bumped). *My Bookhouse.* $52/£33

BARTLETT, DANA W. The Better City. L.A.: Nuener, 1907. 1st ed. Signed presentation. 32 plts. Blue cl, gilt. Fine. *Pacific*.* $58/£36

BARTLETT, DAVID W. What I Saw in London; or, Men and Things in the Great Metropolis. Auburn, 1853. Engr frontisport, x,327pp,3ff. *Marlborough.* $200/£125

BARTLETT, EDWARD EVERETT. The Typographic Treasures in Europe. NY/London, 1925. One of 585. Folio. 1/2 cl (backstrip dknd, extrems rubbed). *Swann*.* $57/£36

BARTLETT, HENRIETTA C. and ALFRED W. POLLARD. A Census of Shakespeare's Plays in Quarto 1594-1709. New Haven, 1916. One of 500. Uncut. Paper spine label. (Lt worn, soiled, corners bumped.) *Oinonen*.* $60/£38

BARTLETT, JOHN RUSSELL. Personal Narrative of Explorations and Incidents in Texas, New Mexico, California, Sonora and Chihuahua.... London: Routledge, 1854. 2 vols. 8vo. Fldg map, 16 plts (frontis belonging to vol 2 was placed in vol 1, only 1 geiser plt, not 2 as listed in vol 2, deficiency is made up by unlisted view of Tucson.) Nice set (sl foxed; faded, frayed, bumped). *Metropolitan*.* $546/£341

BARTLETT, JOHN RUSSELL. Personal Narrative of Explorations and Incidents in Texas, New Mexico, California, Sonora, and Chihuahua. NY, 1854. 1st ed. 2 vols bound in 1. Fldg map, 2 fldg litho plts. (Ex-lib, shelfworn, spine tips chipped). Howes B201. *Oinonen*.* $325/£203

BARTLETT, JOHN RUSSELL. The Progress of Ethnology. NY: American Ethnological Soc, 1847. 1st ed, 1st bk. 152pp. Brn cl (spine, corners chipped). *Karmiole.* $75/£47

BARTLETT, RICHARD A. Great Surveys of the American West. Norman: Univ of OK, 1962. VG in dj (price-clipped). *Dumont.* $60/£38

BARTLETT, RICHARD A. Great Surveys of the American West. Norman, 1966. 2nd ptg. VG in dj. *Dumont.* $45/£28

BARTLETT, ROBERT A. and RALPH T. HALE. The Last Voyage of the Karluk Flagship of Vilhjalmur Stefansson's Canadian Arctic Expedition of 1913-1916. Boston: Small, Maynard, c. 1916. 1st ed. Inscribed & signed by Bartlett, 1916. VG. *High Latitude.* $95/£59

BARTLETT, ROBERT A. Sails over Ice. NY: Scribner, 1934. VG in dj (soiled, spotted). *High Latitude.* $45/£28

BARTLETT, TRUMAN H. The Art Life of William Rimmer, Sculptor, Painter, and Physician. Boston, 1882. (Lib emb stamp on tp; eps renewed; recased.) *Swann*.* $161/£101

BARTLETT, W. P. More Happenings in California. Volume 2. Boston: Christopher, 1928. 1st ed. Fine in Fine dj. *Book Market.* $45/£28

BARTLETT, WILLIAM A. The History and Antiquities of the Parish of Wimbledon. London, 1865. xvi,222pp; fldg map. (Rep detached; joints splitting, spine chipped.) *Edwards.* $48/£30

BARTLETT, WILLIAM HENRY. Walks About the City and Environs of Jerusalem. London, ca 1845. Map. Pub's cl (worn; exlib, sm emb stamps, bkpl, rear pocket). *Swann*.* $103/£64

BARTLETTS, THE. Adios! NY: Morrow, 1929. 1st ed. Fine in VG dj. *Book Market.* $20/£13

BARTOK, BELA. Hungarian Folk Music. M. D. Calvocoressi (trans). Oxford: OUP, 1931. 1st Eng ed. (Cvrs mkd, corners bumped; no dj.) *Clearwater.* $88/£55

BARTON, LUCY. Historic Costume for the Stage. (Boston: Walter H. Baker, 1932.) Color frontis. VG. *Dramatis.* $60/£38

BARTON, R. T. (ed). Virginia Colonial Decisions. Boston Book, 1909. 2 vols. Rebound in lib buckram. VG. *Book Broker.* $75/£47

BARTON, WILLIAM P. C. A Flora of North America. Phila: M. Carey, 1821-1823. 1st ed. 3 vols. 4to. 104 (of 106) hand-colored stipple engrs. Red calf, marbled bds. (Foxed, spine split, rubbed, hinges weak, edges through, loose.) *Metropolitan*.* $1,265/£791

BARTRAM, ALAN. The English Lettering Tradition...1700 to the Present Day. London, 1986. Pict card. Fine. *Whittle.* $24/£15

BARTRAM, JOHN et al. A Journey from Pennsylvania to Onondaga in 1743. Barre, MA: Imprint Soc, (1973). Ltd to 1950 numbered, signed by Whitfield Bell, Jr. (illus). Fldg map. Orig leather-backed bds. VG (extrems sl rubbed). Howes B222. *New Hampshire*.* $45/£28

BARTRAM, WILLIAM. Botanical and Zoological Drawings, 1756-1788. Joseph Ewan (ed). Phila, 1968. Folio. Color frontis, 59 plts (19 color). Dj. *Sutton.* $200/£125

BARTRAM, WILLIAM. Travels Through North and South Carolina, Georgia, East and West Florida. Phila: James & Johnson, 1791. 1st ed. 8vo. 8 engr plts, fldg map. Mod calf. (Foxing, marginal dampstaining, upper outer corner torn off tp, 2T1 torn in outer margin, restored w/text in facs; bkpl, sig.) Howes B223. *Swann*.* $2,530/£1,581

BARTRAM, WILLIAM. William Bartram: Botanical and Zoological Drawings, 1756-1788. Joseph Ewan (ed). Phila: Amer Philo. Soc, 1968. 1st ed. Folio. Fine in VG dj. *Archer.* $185/£116

BARTRUM, DOUGLAS. Lilac and Laburnum. London: John Gifford, 1959. 1st ed. (Sunned), else VG. *Fair Meadow.* $20/£13

BARUCH, RUTH-MARION and PIRKLE JONES. The Vanguard: A Photographic Essay on the Black Panthers. Boston: Beacon, 1970. 1st ed. Rev slip laid in. NF in dj (dampstained). *Cahan.* $85/£53

BARWELL, MRS. Novel Adventures of Tom Thumb. London: Chapman & Hall, 1838. 1st ed. Sm 8vo. (iv),158,(ii)pp (sl browned); 4 engrs. Orig grn blind-stamped cl, gilt. *Sotheran.* $157/£98

BARZUN, JACQUES. Berlioz and the Romantic Century. Gollancz, 1951. 2 vols. 18 plts. VG in djs (sl chipped). *Hollett.* $104/£65

BASCOM, LOUISE RAND. The Bugaboo Men. NY: Sully & Kleinteich, (1914). 1st ed. Pict grn cl. Fine. *Pacific**. $109/£68

BASCOM, WILLARD. A Hole in the Bottom of the Sea. GC: Doubleday, 1961. VG in dj (rubbed). *Weber.* $25/£16

BASHKIRTSEFF, MARIE. The Journal of.... London, 1890. 2 vols. xl,424; 463pp; frontisports, extra-illus w/approx 100 plts. Aeg. Gilt-edged crushed morocco, raised bands, by Root & Son. (Spine heads, joints sl rubbed, bds sl worn.) *Edwards.* $400/£250

BASKERVILL, CHARLES READ. The Elizabethan Jig and Related Song Drama. Chicago: Univ of Chicago, (1929). Dj (chipped). *Argosy.* $50/£31

BASON, FRED. Fred Bason's Diary. Nicolas Bentley (ed). London: Wingate, 1951. Inscribed presentations. Frontis port. Apc loosely inserted. VG in dj. *Hollett.* $32/£20

BASS, RICK. The Deer Pasture. College Station: TX A&M Univ, (1985). 1st ed, 1st bk. As New in As New 1st issue dj priced at $12.50, pub's shrink-wrap. *Dermont.* $100/£63

BASS, RICK. The Deer Pasture. TX: TX A&M Univ, 1985. 1st ed, 1st bk. Signed. Fine in Fine dj. *Warren.* $200/£125

BASS, RICK. Oil Notes. Boston, 1989. 1st ed. Signed. Fine in Fine dj. *Warren.* $50/£31

BASS, RICK. Platte River. NY: HMC, 1994. 1st ed. Signed. Fine in Fine dj. *Unger.* $75/£47

BASS, RICK. The Watch. NY: Norton, (1989). 1st ed. Rev flyer, photo laid in. Fine in dj. *Reese.* $45/£28

BASS, RICK. The Watch. NY: Norton, 1989. 1st ed. Signed. Fine in Fine dj. *Unger.* $75/£47

BASSETT, JAMES. The Sky Suspended. NY: Delacorte, 1968. 1st ed. Fine in dj. *Associates.* $75/£47

BASSETT, JOHN Y. The Medical Reports of John Y. Bassett, M.D., The Alabama Student. Springfield, 1941. 1st ed. VG. *Doctor's Library.* $75/£47

BASSO, HAMILTON. Beauregard the Great Creole. NY, 1933. 1st ed. (Lt foxed; faded, stained). *Woolman.* $15/£9

BASTIN, BRUCE. Crying for the Carolines. London: Studio Vista, 1971. 1st ed. Fine in wraps. *Beasley.* $25/£16

BATCHELDER, MARJORIE H. Rod-Puppets and the Human Theatre. Columbus: OH State Univ, 1947. 1st ed. (Plt gutters sl dampstained; ends scuffed.) *Dramatis.* $40/£25

BATCHELOR, GEORGE KEITH. The Theory of Homogeneous Turbulence. Cambridge: CUP, 1953. VG in dj (lt worn). *Weber.* $20/£13

BATCHELOR, JOHN CALVIN. The Further Adventures of Halley's Comet. NY: Congdon & Lattes, 1980. 1st ed, 1st bk. Fine (sm stamp fep) in Fine dj. *Warren.* $300/£188

BATE, W. N. Frontier Legend. Texas Finale of Capt. William F. Drannan Pseudo Frontier Comrade of Kit Carson. New Bern, NC: Owen G. Dunn, 1954. 1st ed. Inscribed, signed. VG in stiff wrappers. *Labordo.* $40/£25

BATEMAN, C. S. L. The First Ascent of the Kasai. London: George Philip & Son, 1889. 1st ed. 8vo. 1/2-title, xx,192pp; 2 maps (1 fldg), 5 chromolithos, 6 etched plts, 6 engr plts. Beveled edges. Blue pict cl (bkpl, sl rubbed, corners bumped, fr hinge cracked, scratch), gilt. VG + (foxed). *Morrell.* $576/£360

BATEMAN, G. C. Freshwater Aquaria. London: Bazaar, (1890). 3rd rev ed. 352pp. Gilt dec cl. VG + . *Mikesh.* $35/£22

BATEMAN, NEWTON. Abraham Lincoln. Galesburg, IL: Cadmus Club, 1899. 1st ed. 46pp. Fine in ptd wraps. *Wantagh.* $75/£47

BATES, CHARLES FRANCIS. Custer's Indian Battles. Bronxville, NY: N.p., (1936). VG in pict wraps. *Lien.* $30/£19

BATES, CRAIG D. and MARTHA J. LEE. Tradition and Innovation: A Basket History of the Indians of the Yosemite-Mono Lake Region. Yosemite Nat'l Park: Yosemite Assoc, (1990). Ltd to 2000 ptd. Prospectus laid in. Charcoal linen, silver lettering. Fine in pict dj (sm defect). *Pacific**. $58/£36

BATES, EDMUND FRANKLIN. History and Reminiscences of Denton County. Denton, TX: McNitzky Ptg, (1918). 1st ed. Black cl, gilt. VG + (spine ends, bottom edges worn) in custom-made slipcase. *Labordo.* $650/£406

BATES, H. E. Achilles the Donkey. Dobson, 1962. 1st ed. Pict bds. (Sl foxed), o/w VG. *Green Meadow.* $72/£45

BATES, H. E. The Black Boxer. London: Pharos Editions, 1932. 1st Eng ed. Inscribed presentation. Sheet of orig ms loosely inserted. VG (top edge sl dusty; edges, eps sl spotted; cvrs sl mkd, dusty, edges sl soiled) in dj (sl creased, rubbed, dusty, sl browned). *Ulysses.* $600/£375

BATES, H. E. A Breath of French Air. London: Michael Joseph, (1959). 1st Eng ed. VG in pict dj. *Cady.* $30/£19

BATES, H. E. The Bride Comes to Evensford. Cape, 1943. 1st ed. VG (spine, edges sl faded, spine head sl bumped) in dj (nicked, sl rubbed, sl creased, spine faded, edges browned). *Ulysses.* $120/£75

BATES, H. E. Country Life. London: Penguin Books, 1943. 1st ed thus. (Pg edges browned; paper cvrs soiled, fr hinge cracked 3 inches), o/w Good in wrappers. *Virgo.* $56/£35

BATES, H. E. The Day of Glory. Michael Joseph, 1945. 1st ed. VG in dj (top edges sl chipped). *Hollett.* $48/£30

BATES, H. E. The Duet. Grayson Books, 1935. 1st Eng ed. One of 285 signed. VG (sl foxed; no dj). *Clearwater.* $176/£110

BATES, H. E. The Fallow Land. Cape, (1932). 1st ed. Inscribed, signed presentation, add'lly inscribed 'Oh: these collectors!' VG (edges sl foxed) in dj (lt worn). *Ash.* $400/£250

BATES, H. E. The Golden Oriole. Michael Joseph, 1962. 1st UK ed. NF in VG + dj (price-clipped). *Williams.* $40/£25

BATES, H. E. The Hessian Prisoner.... London: William Jackson, 1930. 1st ed. One of 550 numbered, signed. Frontis. Teg. Gilt red buckram. (Spine sunned, sm rub), o/w Nice. *Reese.* $125/£78

BATES, H. E. A House of Women. London: Cape, 1936. 1st Eng ed. Inscribed presentation. NF (edges spotted) in dj (sl rubbed, mkd, spine sl faded). *Ulysses.* $560/£350

BATES, H. E. Sally Go Round the Moon. White Owl, 1932. 1st Eng ed. VG (foxed) in dj (torn, partly defective at spine head). *Clearwater.* $120/£75

BATES, H. E. The Seekers. Bumpus, 1926. 1st UK ed. VG (lacks orig tissue wrapper). *Williams.* $45/£28

BATES, H. E. The Song of the Wren. London: Michael Joseph, (1972). 1st Eng ed. NF in dj. *Cady.* $20/£13

BATES, H. E. Through the Woods. NY, 1936. 1st Amer ed. 73 wood-engrs. Fine (3 sm nicks). *Polyanthos.* $30/£19

BATES, H. E. The Two Sisters. London: Cape, 1926. 1st Eng ed. Inscribed presentation. VG (feps partly browned, top edge sl spotted; spine ends, corners sl bumped, cvrs sl mkd) in dj (nicked, dusty, sl rubbed, creased, mkd, sl dknd). *Ulysses.* $632/£395

BATES, H. E. The Watercress Girl. London: Michael Joseph, 1959. 1st ed. (Eps sl offset, fore-edge sl browned, spotted; spine sl faded), o/w VG in dj (sl soiled, chipped, edges browned). *Virgo.* $24/£15

BATES, H. E. When the Green Woods Laugh. London: Michael Joseph, 1960. 1st Eng ed. VG in dj (sl worn). *Cady.* $25/£16

BATES, H. W. The Naturalist on the River Amazons. John Murray, 1863. 1st ed. 2 vols. 8vo. Fldg map, 9 wood-engr plts. (Vol 2 hinges sl weak.) *Sotheby's**. $1,288/£805

BATES, H. W. The Naturalist on the River Amazons. London, 1875. x,394pp (tanned, few corners creased). Gilt-dec cl (lt worn, fr cvr flecked, spine foot frayed, head partly missing). *Sutton.* $95/£59

BATES, JOSEPH D. The Art of the Atlantic Salmon Fly. Boston: Godine, 1987. Ltd to 250 numbered, signed. Color frontis; 24 color plts. Extra portfolio of the color plts in matching slipcase. Gray linen. Fine in Fine slipcase. *Biscotti.* $350/£219

BATES, JOSEPH D. The Atlantic Salmon Treasury. Montreal: Atlantic Salmon Assoc, 1975. 1st ed. One of 1000 signed. Color frontis. Lt blue morocco-grain leather, gilt. Pub's slipcase. *Swann*.* $230/£144

BATES, JOSEPH D. Streamer Fly Tying and Fishing. Harrisburg, PA, (1966). 1st ed. 8 color plts. Fine in dj. *Petersfield.* $26/£16

BATES, JOSEPH D. Streamers and Bucktails. The Big Fish Flies. NY: Knopf, 1979. 1st ed. 12 color plts. 1/4 brn cl, pict stamped paper-cvrd bds. Fine in NF pict color dj. *Biscotti.* $85/£53

BATES, KATHARINE LEE. From Gretna Green to Land's End. Grant Richards, 1908. Teg. Good (sig; spine bumped, chipped, sunned). *Tiger.* $26/£16

BATES, KATHARINE LEE. Spanish Highways and Byways. NY, 1900. Teg. (Bkpl.) Pict cl. Pict dj (sl frayed). *King.* $50/£31

BATES, WILLIAM. George Cruikshank. London, 1879. 2nd ed. Mtd India Proof repros. Roan-backed gilt-pict cl. W/prospectus. *Swann*.* $69/£43

BATESON, W. Mendel's Principles of Heredity. CUP, 1913. 3rd imp. 6 color plts, 3 ports. (Few spots to eps, prelims; sm snag spine base.) *Hollett.* $72/£45

BATSFORD, HARRY and CHARLES FRY. The English Cottage. London, 1938. 1st ed. VG in dj. *Typographeum.* $35/£22

BATSFORD, HARRY and CHARLES FRY. The Face of Scotland. Batsford, 1942. 4th ed. Color frontis, 4 maps. VG in dj (edges worn, sl spotted, price-clipped). *Hollett.* $24/£15

BATSFORD, HERBERT. English Mural Monuments and Tombstones. London: Batsford, 1916. 84 b/w plts. (Eps spotted, bkpl; edges, spine sl discolored.) *Edwards.* $120/£75

BATTEN, JOHN H. Skyline Pursuits. Clinton: Amwell, (1981). One of 1000 numbered, signed by Batten & Gordon Allen (illus). Frontis. Watered silk eps. Leather. Slipcase. *Swann*.* $149/£93

BATTEN, M. I. English Windmills. Architectural Press, 1930-32. 1st ed. 2 vols. (Sl faded.) Vol 2 in dj. *Hollett.* $104/£65

BATTEN, MARK. Stone Sculpture by Direct Carving. Studio, 1957. 1st ed. 80 half-tone plts. VG in dj (chipped). *Whittle.* $19/£12

BATTEY, THOMAS C. The Life and Adventures of a Quaker Among the Indians. Norman: Univ of OK, (1968). VG in dj. *Lien.* $17/£11

BATTEY, THOMAS C. The Life and Adventures of a Quaker Among the Indians. Boston: Lee & Shepard, 1876. xii,339pp. (Sm lib label fep; extrems worn, damped.) *Hollett.* $192/£120

BATTLE, R. J. V. Plastic Surgery. Washington: Butterworths, 1964. 1st Amer ed. Fine (bkpl). *Weber.* $75/£47

Battle-Fields of the Marne 1914. Michelin Tyre, 1919. 1st ed. Fep stamped 'complimentary copy.' VG (feps sl browned; spine ends sl bumped) in dj (dusty, sl creased). *Ulysses.* $104/£65

Battle-Fields of the South, from Bull Run to Fredericksburg. London: Smith, Elder, 1863. 1st ed. 2 vols. 8vo. 339; 399pp; complete w/2 fldg maps. Unopened. Purple cl. Nice set (spine ends rubbed, vol 2 head chipped). Howes B238. *Chapel Hill.* $600/£375

Battle-Fields of the South, from Bull Run to Fredericksburg. NY: John Bradford, 1864. 1st Amer ed. xxvii,517pp; 2 fldg maps. (Corners, spine worn.) Howes B238. *Mott.* $200/£125

BATTY, BEATRICE. Forty-Two Years Among the Indian and Eskimo. London: RTS, 1893. 1st ed. 223pp; map. Orig pict cl. Good. *Walcot.* $45/£28

BATTY, CAPTAIN. Welsh Scenery from Drawings. London: R. Jennings, 1825. viii,35 engr plts. Full crushed morocco, gilt. (Lt browned; extrems sl rubbed, sm repair to morocco on fr bd w/sl surface loss.) *Edwards.* $400/£250

BATTY, J. H. How to Hunt and Trap, Containing Full Instructions for Hunting the Buffalo, Elk, Moose.... NY, 1878. Pub's gilt-pict cl. (Lacks fep; spine ends sl frayed.) *Swann*.* $57/£36

BATTY, ROBERT. Campaign of the Left Wing of the Allied Army, in the Western Pyrenees and South of France, in the Years 1813-14. London, 1823. 25 plts. 1/2 sheep (needs rebinding; ex-lib, sm emb stamps). *Swann*.* $345/£216

BAUCHER, F. A Method of Horsemanship. Phila, 1851. 1st Amer ed. 254pp. (Name; bkpl removed, lacks rep; sl loose, worn.) *Woolson.* $35/£22

BAUDELAIRE, CHARLES. Flowers of Evil. LEC, 1971. Ltd to 1500 numbered. 2 vols. Fine in slipcase. *Swann*.* $69/£43

BAUER, CLYDE MAX. The Story of Yellowstone Geysers. Yellowstone Park/St. Paul: Haynes, (1937). Inscribed. Dbl-pg map. Pict cl. Dj. *Dawson.* $20/£13

BAUER, LOUIS HOPEWELL. Aviation Medicine. Balt: Williams & Wilkins, 1926. 1st ed. Grn cl. Fine. *House.* $100/£63

BAUGHAMN, ROLAND and ROBERT O. SCHAD. Great Books in Great Editions. San Marino: Huntington Library, 1954. 1st ed. Fine in paper wrappers. *Oak Knoll.* $10/£6

BAUGHMAN, THEODORE. The Oklahoma Scout. Chicago: Homewood, n.d. 2nd ed. VG. Howes B244. *Labordo.* $75/£47

BAUM, L. FRANK. American Fairy Tales. Chicago: George M. Hill, 1901. 1st ed. Issue w/red flowers at top & bottom of spine. 8.25x5.25. Ike Morgan et al (illus). Pict cl. (Old name fep, dated 1905; rubbed, scratched), else VG. *Pacific*.* $259/£162

BAUM, L. FRANK. The Army Alphabet. Chicago: Geo. M. Hill, 1900. 1st ed. 12.25x9.75. 27 color plts (and color c. pg) by Harry Kennedy. Cl-backed pict bds. (Bkpl; rubbed, scratched, spine ends expertly repaired), else VG. *Pacific*.* $1,265/£791

BAUM, L. FRANK. The Art of Decorating Dry Goods Windows and Interiors: A Complete Manual of Window Trimming, Designed as an Educator in all the Details of Art.... Chicago: Show Window Pub, 1900. 1st ed. 10.75x7.75. (5)-319,(4)pp. Dk grn cl lettered in silver. (Hinges cracking; spine rubbed w/lettering gone, cvr lettering faded), else VG-. *Pacific*.* $1,495/£934

BAUM, L. FRANK. Baum's American Fairy Tales. Indianapolis: Bobbs-Merrill, (1908). 2nd ed. 16 color plts. (Spine dknd.) *Kane*.* $170/£106

BAUM, L. FRANK. Baum's American Fairy Tales. Indianapolis: Bobbs-Merrill, (c.1920s). 3rd ed. 9x6.5. 8 color plts by George Kerr. Grn cl, pict cvr label. (Sm bump upper fr cvr edge), else VG. *Pacific*.* $207/£129

BAUM, L. FRANK. Baum's Own Book for Children. Chicago: Reilly & Britton, (1912). 1st ed thus, though essentially a rpt of Baum's 1910 Juvenile Speaker. Copyright notice has been extended to 1912, author's preface (p7) rewritten and titled from 'Oxcot,' and no ads. John R. Neill & Mabel Wright Enright (illus). 4to. Buckram-backed pict bds (rubbed). *Swann*.* $431/£269

BAUM, L. FRANK. Baum's Own Book for Children. Chicago: Reilly & Britton, (1912). 1st ed thus. 9x6.5. John R. Neill & Maginel Wright Enright (illus). 196pp. Cl-backed pict bds. (Old name crossed out fep; sm bump upper fr cvr), else NF. *Pacific*.* $633/£396

BAUM, L. FRANK. The Cowardly Lion of Oz. Toronto: Copp, Clark, (1923). 1st Canadian ed from Amer sheets, w/cancel tp and binding bearing imprint of Copp, Clark & Co. John R. Neill (illus). 4to. Grn cl (tips lt rubbed), pict fr cvr label. *Swann*.* $126/£79

BAUM, L. FRANK. The Cowardly Lion of Oz. Toronto: Copp, Clark, (1923). 1st Canadian ed from Amer sheets, w/cancel tp and binding bearing imprint of Copp, Clark & Co. John R. Neill (illus). 4to. Grn cl, pict fr cvr label. Dj (lt edgeworn, cracked at rear fold). Swann*. $1,840/£1,150

BAUM, L. FRANK. The Daring Twins: A Story for Young Folk. Chicago: Reilly & Britton, (1911). 1st ed. There was only 1 ptg, and this is the 1st binding state, showing the twins full-length. 7.5x5. 4 b/w plts by Pauline M. Batchelder, incl frontis. Pict blue/pink/black cl. (Spine ends sl rubbed), else NF. Pacific*. $184/£115

BAUM, L. FRANK. Dorothy and the Wizard in Oz. Chicago: Reilly & Britton, (1908). 1st ed, later state. 9 x 6 1/2. 12 (of 16) color plts by John R. Neill. Inserted pict eps in black/yellow. Lt blue cl, pict cvr label w/metallic gold background. (Hinges cracked, lacks 4 plts; spine rubbed, extrems soiled), else VG-. Pacific*. $75/£47

BAUM, L. FRANK. Dorothy and the Wizard in Oz. Chicago: Reilly & Britton, (1908). 1st ed, 1st state w/ad on verso of 1/2-title listing 3 titles; ownership pg showing a picture of Dorothy; final illus on p(257) of a dwg of Ozma w/the words 'The End'; plts captioned in black. 9x6.5. 256pp; 15 (of 16) color plts by John R. Neill. Inserted pict eps in black/yellow. Lt blue cl, pict cvr label. (Spine ends rubbed, cvrs scratched), else VG. Pacific*. $431/£269

BAUM, L. FRANK. Dot and Tot of Merryland. Indianapolis: Bobbs-Merrill, (1902, but 1903). 2nd ed. 9x6.75. W. W. Denslow (illus). (6),(13)-226pp. Orange/grn on eps, illus. No pub's ads, rear cvr is blank. Gray cl, pict stamped in dk grn/red/yellow. (Hinges, spine ends rubbed), else VG. Pacific*. $259/£162

BAUM, L. FRANK. Dot and Tot of Merryland. Chicago: M.A. Donohue, (ca 1913). 3rd ed. W. W. Denslow (illus). 4to. Pict pale gray-grn cl. Swann*. $230/£144

BAUM, L. FRANK. Dot and Tot of Merryland. Chicago: Geo. M. Hill, 1901. 1st ed. W. W. Denslow (illus). 4to. Gilt-pict cl. Sound (lt soiled, inner hinges cracked, rear hinge repaired). Swann*. $488/£305

BAUM, L. FRANK. Dot and Tot of Merryland. Chicago: George M. Hill, 1901. 1st ed. 8.5x6.25. W. W. Denslow (illus). Yellow cl pictorially stamped in gilt/red/brown. (Old inscrip, fr hinge reinforced, hinges cracked; soiled), else VG. Pacific*. $575/£359

BAUM, L. FRANK. The Emerald City of Oz. Chicago: Reilly & Britton, (1910). 1st ed, later state w/ad on verso of ownership leaf listing titles through The Tin Woodman of Oz. 9x6.5. 295,(1)pp; 16 color plts by John R. Neill. Pict eps in b/w. Dk grn cl, pict cvr label. VG. Pacific*. $345/£216

BAUM, L. FRANK. The Emerald City of Oz. Chicago: Reilly & Britton, (1910). 1st ed, 1st state w/ad on verso of ownership leaf listing titles through John Dough and the Cherub. The binding features the elaborate cvr label showing a number of characters traveling through the city, spine lettered in black w/picture of rabbit in black/silver. The striking use of metallic ink on the illus & cvr label can only be found in this state. 9x6.5. 295,(1)pp; 16 color plts by John R. Neill. Pict eps in black/orange. Lt blue cl, pict cvr label. (Spine ends, extrems rubbed), else VG. Pacific*. $805/£503

BAUM, L. FRANK. The Emerald City of Oz. Chicago: Reilly & Lee, (c. 1920). 12 color plts by John R. Neill. Grn cl, pict cvr label. (Soiled, discolored crease to bottom of cvr label), else VG-. Pacific*. $58/£36

BAUM, L. FRANK. The Enchanted Island of Yew. Indianapolis: Bobbs Merrill, (1903). 1st ed, 1st state, w/Braunworth imprint on tp verso and illus over text on p238 ptd upside-down. 4to. Fanny Y. Cory (illus). Pict cl. (Inner fr hinge partly cracked; spine extrems sl worn, fr cvr sl bubbled.) Swann*. $373/£233

BAUM, L. FRANK. The Enchanted Island of Yew. Chicago: M.A. Donohue, (1903; ca 1913). 3rd ed. 8 color plts. Gray cl. Fine (ink inscrip). Kane*. $75/£47

BAUM, L. FRANK. Father Goose's Year Book. Chicago: Reilly & Britton, (1907). 1st ed. Walter J. Enright (illus). 8vo. Pict eps (lt crayon coloring). Grn buckram, lg color pict label fr cvr. (Spine lt sunned, edges sl worn, label sl rubbed.) Text VG. Baltimore*. $130/£81

BAUM, L. FRANK. Father Goose's Year Book: Quaint Quacks and Feathered Shafts for Mature Children. Chicago: Reilly & Britton, (1907). 1st, only ed. 8.25x4.75. Walter J. Enright (illus). (128)pp. Grn buckram, pict cvr label. (Spine, upper extrems sunned, spine lettering worn off), else VG. Pacific*. $150/£94

BAUM, L. FRANK. Father Goose, His Book. Chicago: Geo. M. Hill, (1899). 1st ed. 11x8.5. W. W. Denslow (illus). Color pict bds. Good (old inscrip dated Oct 1899, pg margins soiled, hinges reinforced; shoddily rebacked, dknd, extrems rubbed). Pacific*. $127/£79

BAUM, L. FRANK. Glinda of Oz. Toronto: Copp Clark, (1920). 1st Canadian ed. W/ad on verso of 1/2-title listing 13 titles through Glinda of Oz, and ad for the Oz-Man Tales. 9x6.5. 279,(1)pp; 12 color plts by John R. Neill. B/w pict eps. Tan cl, pict cvr label. (Insect spotting to spine, extrems), else VG +. Pacific*. $127/£79

BAUM, L. FRANK. Glinda of Oz. Chicago: Reilly & Lee, (1920). 1st ed, 1st ptg. Ad on verso of 1/2-title lists 13 titles through Glinda of Oz. On p280 is an ad for the Oz-Man Tales. 9x6.5. 279,(1)pp; 10 (of 12) color plts by John R. Neill. B/w pict eps. Red cl, pict cvr label. (Faint spot to fr cvr label), else VG. Pacific*. $288/£180

BAUM, L. FRANK. Glinda of Oz. Chicago: Reilly & Lee, (1920). 1st ed. 12 color plts. Fine. Kane*. $325/£203

BAUM, L. FRANK. Jaglon and the Tiger Fairies. Chicago: Reilly & Lee, (1953). 1st ed thus. Dale Ulrey (illus). 4to. Grn cl, color paste label. Good in color illus dj (top edge sl worn). Reisler. $185/£116

BAUM, L. FRANK. John Dough and the Cherub. Chicago: Reilly & Britton, (1906). 1st ed, 3rd issue (variant), w/'cave' on p275, no contest blank, shortened pub's imprint at spine foot, w/cvr in tan cl stamped in yellow-grn/red/black. Color ep, color in text throughout. (Sl soiled, color ptg on binding worn.) Kane*. $60/£38

BAUM, L. FRANK. John Dough and the Cherub. Chicago: Reilly & Britton, (1906). 1st ed, 1st ptg. W/the rare detachable contest blank for 'the Great John Dough Mystery' on yellow paper facing p8 present. 1st state, w/misprint on p275, line 10 ('cage' for 'cave'); pub's imprint on spine reads to 'The Reilly &/ Britton Co.'; back cvr has picture of John Dough, Chick the Cherub, and a box on which is lettered 'THE GREAT/ JOHN DOUGH/ MYSTERY.' 9x6.5. John R. Neill (illus). 314,(2) + (4)ads pp. Color pict eps. Pict tan cl. (Sl soiled, upper rear cvr sl discolored, spine lettering, figure rubbed), else VG. Pacific*. $575/£359

BAUM, L. FRANK. John Dough and the Cherub. Chicago: Reilly & Britton, c. 1906. 1st ed, mixed 3rd/4th state, w/color pict eps, misprint 'cage' p275 corrected to 'cave,' and at start and end 'The Land of Oz' is advertised as 'Uniform with John Dough and the Cherub.' Spine-imprint Reilly & Britton conforms to shape of lettering used c1910-1913. John R. Neill (illus). 315pp + 4pp ads. Dbl-spread color pict eps. Buff cl. (Sm closed tear base of tp, fr hinge cracking, inscrip; lt dampstain on fr cvr through first dozen pp, spine rubbed, sl worn), o/w VG. Bookmark. $152/£95

BAUM, L. FRANK. L. Frank Baum's Juvenile Speaker: Readings and Recitations in Prose and Verse, Humorous and Otherwise. Chicago: Reilly & Britton, (1910). 1st ed. 9x6.5. John R. Neill & Maginel Wright Enright (illus). Pict cl. (Amateur hand-coloring to several illus, internal dkng to upper extrems from smoke damage?; irregular dkng, spine head rubbed, foot frayed), else VG-. Pacific*. $196/£123

BAUM, L. FRANK. The Land of Oz. Chicago: Rand McNally, 1939. Junior Editions. 12mo. 62pp + ads. Slick color pict cvrs (edges lt rubbed). *Reisler.* $45/£28

BAUM, L. FRANK. The Land of Oz: A Sequel to the Wizard of Oz. Chicago: Reilly & Britton, (1904, but c. 1914). 2nd ed, 2nd state. Tp has been type-set, w/author credits through Tik-Tok of Oz. Contains 12 color plts w/captions dropped. 9 x 6 1/2. 287pp; 12 color plts. Pict eps. Silver-lettered pict tan cl. VG (rear hinge starting; some plts chipped, torn; spine head rubbed). *Pacific*.* $75/£47

BAUM, L. FRANK. The Land of Oz: A Sequel to the Wizard of Oz. Chicago: Reilly & Lee, (c. 1931). 287pp; 12 color plts by John R. Neill. Pict eps. Orange cl, color pict cvr label. (Sm inscrip; extrems insect-damaged, cvr label rubbed w/scrape), else VG. *Pacific*.* $75/£47

BAUM, L. FRANK. The Life and Adventures of Santa Claus. Indianapolis: Bobbs-Merrill, (1902, but later). 8 color plts by Mary Cowles Clark. Lg pict cvr label. (Few pp w/spots, sm marginal tears; rubbed, few chips to cvr label), else VG-. *Pacific*.* $58/£36

BAUM, L. FRANK. The Life and Adventures of Santa Claus. Chicago: M.A. Donohue, (c. post-1913). 4th ed. 9x6.5. (10),206pp; 2 black/red plts by Mary Cowles Clark. Blank eps. Pict red cl. VG (p[207] w/no illus). *Pacific*.* $109/£68

BAUM, L. FRANK. The Life and Adventures of Santa Claus. Indianapolis, 1902. 1st ed, 1st state. 8vo. 206pp; 20 plts. Red pict cl. VG (plt loose, inner hinges cracked; cvrs worn). *New Hampshire*.* $110/£69

BAUM, L. FRANK. The Life and Adventures of Santa Claus. Indianapolis: Bowen-Merrill, 1902. 1st ed, 1st state. 9x6.75. (6),206pp; 12 color plts by Mary Cowles Clark. Pict red cl. (1 plt w/tape-repaired tear, sm name, rear hinge repaired; cvr illus sl rubbed; soiled, spine ends rubbed), else VG. *Pacific*.* $127/£79

BAUM, L. FRANK. The Life and Adventures of Santa Claus. Indianapolis: Bowen-Merrill, 1902. 1st ed, 1st state w/section headings as 'Book First,' 'Book Second,' & 'Book Third'; aside from the dedication leaf & 1st pg of the Table of Contents, there are no textural illus. 9x6.75. (6),206pp; 12 color plts by Mary Cowles Clark. Pict red cl. (Top of fr hinge cracking), else NF. *Pacific*.* $460/£288

BAUM, L. FRANK. Little Bun Rabbit and Other Stories. Chicago: Reilly & Britton, (1916). 1st ed, 2nd state w/ads on verso of ownership pg. 8.75x6.25. 4 color plts by John R. Neill. Pict bds. (Name heavily erased from ownership pg; upper corners sl rubbed), else VG. *Pacific*.* $345/£216

BAUM, L. FRANK. Little Bun Rabbit and Other Stories. Chicago: Reilly & Lee, (1920). 8.75x6.25. 4 color plts by John R. Neill. Pict bds. (Soiled, spine worn), else VG- in Fair dj (lacks upper half, other pieces, extrems chipped). *Pacific*.* $196/£123

BAUM, L. FRANK. The Lost Princess of Oz. Chicago: Reilly & Britton, (1917). 1st ed, 1st ptg w/the ad on verso of ownership pg listing 10 titles through The Lost Princess of Oz, dbl rules at top & bottom of spine. 9x6.5. 312pp; 12 color plts by John R. Neill. B/w pict eps. Lt blue cl, pict cvr label. (Spot fr cvr label, upper spine), else VG. *Pacific*.* $374/£234

BAUM, L. FRANK. The Lost Princess of Oz. Chicago: Reilly & Britton, (1917). 1st ed, 1st ptg w/the ad on verso of ownership pg listing 10 titles through The Lost Princess of Oz, dbl rules at top & bottom of spine. 9x6.5. 312pp; 12 color plts by John R. Neill. B/w pict eps. Lt blue cl, pict cvr label. (Name; spine ends sl rubbed), else NF. *Pacific*.* $633/£396

BAUM, L. FRANK. The Lost Princess of Oz. Chicago: Reilly & Britton, (1917). 1st ed, 1st state w/ads through Lost Princess of Oz. 4to. 12 full-pg color plts by John R. Neill. All edges tinted yellow. Lt blue cl w/full color paste label. VG in full color pict dj (worn, spine head chipped). *Reisler.* $5,000/£3,125

BAUM, L. FRANK. The Magic Cloak (Baum's Snuggle Tales). Chicago: Reilly & Britton, (1916). 1st ed, 2nd state (w/6 titles listed in ads, incl the 2 added in 1917). 8vo. Full color frontis by John R. Neill. Color pict bds (mks, corners worn). *Reisler.* $475/£297

BAUM, L. FRANK. The Magic of Oz. Toronto: Copp, Clark, (1919). 1st Canadian ed. W/ad on verso of ownership pg listing 11 titles through The Tin Woodman of Oz; no captions on the color plts. 9x6.5. 265,(1)pp; 12 color plts by John R. Neill. B/w pict eps. Grn cl, pict cvr label. (Insect damage to spine, extrems), else VG. *Pacific*.* $196/£123

BAUM, L. FRANK. The Magic of Oz. Chicago: Reilly & Lee, (1919). 1st ed, 1st state w/ad on verso of ownership pg listing 11 titles through The Tin Woodman of Oz; no captions on the color plts. 9x6.5. 265,(1)pp; 12 color plts by John R. Neill. B/w pict eps. Grn cl, pict cvr label. (Spine soiled, faded), else VG. *Pacific*.* $316/£198

BAUM, L. FRANK. The Magic of Oz. Chicago: Reilly & Lee, (1919). 1st ed, 1st state w/pub's ads listing 11 titles. 12 color plts. (Sm spot rear cvr, spine sl dknd), o/w Fine. *Kane*.* $350/£219

BAUM, L. FRANK. The Magical Monarch of Mo. Chicago: M.A. Donohue, (1903). 2nd ed, 1st issue w/reset tp in black only. 12 color plts. (Spine sl dknd, spine ends lt worn.) *Kane*.* $50/£31

BAUM, L. FRANK. The Marvelous Land of Oz. Chicago: Reilly & Britton, (1904). 1st ed, 2nd state. Binding B w/letters in 'Marvelous Land of Oz' on fr cvr embellished w/silver outlines. 2nd state w/the line 'Published, July, 1904' added below the c. notice on tp verso; illus p(4) has been considerably reduced: the box is 5 3/8-inches tall; illus on p(22) & (27) are transposed, and tailpieces on p82 & 158 are also transposed. 9x6.5. 287pp; 16 color plts by John R. Neill. Pict eps in dk grn on lt grn stock (faded to tan). Red cl stamped in navy blue/silver/grn. (Fr hinge cracked; spine ends sl rubbed, faint spot fr cvr), else VG. *Pacific*.* $546/£341

BAUM, L. FRANK. The Marvelous Land of Oz. London: J.M. Dent, (1969). 1st ed thus. 8vo. 4 full-pg color plts by B. S. Biro. Dec cl. Good in color dj (lt rubbed). *Reisler.* $75/£47

BAUM, L. FRANK. The Marvelous Land of Oz. Chicago: Reilly & Britton, 1904. 1st ed, 2nd state w/'Published, July, 1904' added below c. notice. Earliest issue, w/lt grn binding. 16 color plts. (Underlining; worn.) *Kane*.* $75/£47

BAUM, L. FRANK. The Marvelous Land of Oz. Chicago: Reilly & Britton, 1904. 1st ed, 1st state. 4to. 16 full-pg color plts by John R. Neill. Lt grn cl (casing A), dk blue lettering, vignette outlines (spine faded w/most color gone). Internally Clean (sl roughness to pp edges; cl edges worn, sl rubbed). *Reisler.* $900/£563

BAUM, L. FRANK. The Master Key: An Electrical Fairy Tale. Indianapolis: Bowen-Merrill, (1901). 1st ed, 1st state w/c. notice for 'The Bowen-Merrill Company' measuring 1-21/32 inches in length; comma in last line on c. pg incorrectly placed so it is immediately to the left of the 'N' of 'N.Y.'; 8 pg gatherings throughout. 8x5.25. 245pp; 12 color plts by Fanny Y. Cory. Olive-grn cl, gilt, pict cvr label. (Fr hinge starting, sm tear tp gutter; faint sm dampstains upper edges, spine ends rubbed), else VG. *Pacific*.* $138/£86

BAUM, L. FRANK. Mother Goose in Prose. Chicago: Way & Williams, (1897). 1st ed, 1st issue. Baum's 1st children's bk, 1st bk of fiction. 1st issue composed of 16pg sigs except for the last 2 gatherings of 8pp & 4pp, respectively, the terminal leaf concluding on p(268), (1) blank leaf at end, striped headbands. 11x8.75. 265pp; 12 b/w plts by Maxfield Parrish. Pict cl w/color cvr designs, gilt spine. (Spine ends chipped; sl soiled, cvr designs scratched), else VG. *Pacific*.* $2,300/£1,438

BAUM, L. FRANK. Mother Goose in Prose. Chicago: Way & Williams, (1897). 1st ed, 1st state. Lg 4to. 12 full-pg b/w illus by Maxfield Parrish. Pale gray cl (faded, shelfworn, corners worn), black lettering, color illus fr/rear, gilt spine. *Reisler.* $2,700/£1,688

BAUM, L. FRANK. The Navy Alphabet. Chicago: George M. Hill, 1900. 1st ed. (Lg piece torn from plt corner, affecting image; fr inner hinge open, worn, rubbed, bumped.) Kane*. $190/£119

BAUM, L. FRANK. The Navy Alphabet. Chicago: George M. Hill, 1900. 1st ed. 12.25x9.75. 27 color plts (& color c. pg) by Harry Kennedy. Pict bds (expertly backed in mod cl), orig spine strip laid on. (New eps, color plt on c. pg lacks sm marginal pieces, few plts soiled; corners, extrems rubbed, sl scratched), else VG. Pacific*. $489/£306

BAUM, L. FRANK. The Navy Alphabet. Chicago: George M. Hill, 1900. 1st ed. Lg 4to. Harry Kennedy (illus), Charles Costello (letters). Cl-backed color pict bds (edges rubbed, spine sl shelfworn). Internally Clean. Reisler. $1,500/£938

BAUM, L. FRANK. The New Wizard of Oz. Indianapolis: Bobbs-Merrill, (1903). 2nd ed, 2nd state, w/cvr title stamped 'The Wizard of Oz' (dropping the 'New'). Issue w/o a period following the author's name on spine, the crow's eye on fr cvr plain, the illus on p49 at bottom of pg, no type damage or resetting of type to the top of lines of p169 & (7). The c. pg w/pub's imprint at bottom. 9x6.75. 16 color plts by W. W. Denslow. Pict cl. VG- (few pp margins severely trimmed; tears, tape repairs to several pp; recased, joints, spine ends faded). Pacific*. $104/£65

BAUM, L. FRANK. The New Wizard of Oz. Indianapolis: Bobbs-Merrill, (1939). 8 inserted color plts by W. W. Denslow. Pict eps. Grn cl, gilt. NF in VG dj (spine ends, extrems creased, chipped, lower fr panel lacks sm piece). Pacific*. $109/£68

BAUM, L. FRANK. The New Wizard of Oz. Indianapolis: Bobbs-Merrill, (1939). 8 inserted color plts by W. W. Denslow. Pict eps. Pict grn cl, gilt. Fine in VG dj (spine ends, extrems creased, chipped, rubbed). Pacific*. $150/£94

BAUM, L. FRANK. The New Wizard of Oz. Indianapolis: Bobbs-Merrill, (c. 1925). Photoplay ed. 9x6.5. 8 plts by W. W. Denslow. Grn cl. NF. Pacific*. $207/£129

BAUM, L. FRANK. The New Wizard of Oz. Indianapolis: Bobbs-Merrill, (ca 1940s). Grn cl. VG. Pacific*. $58/£36

BAUM, L. FRANK. A New Wonderland: Being the First Account Ever Printed of the Beautiful Valley, and the Wonderful Adventures of Its Inhabitants. NY: R.H. Russell, 1900. 1st ed, 2nd binding, w/plain eps. 10.75x8.75. Frank Verbeck (illus). (6),170pp; 15 (of 16) color plts, incl tp, which is ptd on the same heavy stock as other plts. Pict cl. VG (lacks 1 plt [frontis?], bottom corners several pp in middle of bk stained, affecting a few plts; soiled, spine ends chipped, shelfworn). Pacific*. $748/£468

BAUM, L. FRANK. Ozma and the Little Wizard. Chicago: Reilly & Lee, (1932). Pict wraps. Kane*. $55/£34

BAUM, L. FRANK. Ozma of Oz. Chicago: Reilly & Britton, (1907). 1st ed, state 3. 4to. Blank eps, no color on p221. The 'O' in 'Ozma' in the Author's Note is missing. Ads at end of bk list titles through Patchwork Girl. Tan pict cl, red/yellow/black color illus. VG. Reisler. $800/£500

BAUM, L. FRANK. Ozma of Oz. Chicago: Reilly & Lee, (c. 1920). Ad pg lists titles through Glinda of Oz; lacks the 'O' in 'Ozma' on p11. John R. Neill (illus). 270pp. Dk brn cl, color pict cvr label. (Label sl discolored, spine ends rubbed), else VG. Pacific*. $92/£58

BAUM, L. FRANK. The Patchwork Girl of Oz. Chicago: Reilly & Britton, (1913). 1st ed, 1st state, w/'Chap. Three' on p35 overlapping the text. John R. Neill (illus). Lg sq 8vo. Top edge stained lt grn. Pict grn cl. VG (few finger smudges, ink inscrip, sig, address; sl dusty, worn). Baltimore*. $210/£131

BAUM, L. FRANK. The Patchwork Girl of Oz. Chicago: Reilly & Britton, (1913). 1st ed, 1st state binding. 9x6.5. John R. Neill (illus). 340,(2)pp + (6)pp ads at end, incl prelim ad w/photos of 5 cvrs & commencing w/'You Will be Glad to Know...', followed by 5pp synopses; later state of p35 w/the 'C' in 'Chapter' corrected so that it does not overlap text; 1st state binding in lt grn (rather than tan) cl stamped in dk grn/red/yellow. Color pict eps. (Name dated 1913; spine ends frayed, corners, extrems sl rubbed), else VG + . Pacific*. $219/£137

BAUM, L. FRANK. The Patchwork Girl of Oz. Chicago: Reilly & Britton, (1913). 1st ed, earliest state w/'Chap. Three' on p35 positioned so that 'C' overlaps the text. Earliest binding, lt grn cl. (Pencil name erased; sm spots top edge, spine sl dknd.) Kane*. $425/£266

BAUM, L. FRANK. Phoebe Daring: A Story for Young Folk. Chicago: Reilly & Britton, (1912). 1st ed, 1st state w/fr cvr illus of heroine writing. 7.5x5. 298,(2)pp + (8)ad ll; 4 halftones by Joseph Pierre Nuyttens. Pict blue cl. (Old names; upper fr cvr design rubbed, bump upper fr corner), else VG. Pacific*. $86/£54

BAUM, L. FRANK. The Purple Dragon of Oz and Other Fantasies. Lamont, GA: Fictioneer Books, 1976. 1st ed. One of 1500. Tim Kirk (illus). Illus eps. Purple cl. Fine in dj. Pacific*. $150/£94

BAUM, L. FRANK. Queen Zixi of Ix: Or, the Story of the Magic Cloak. NY: Century, 1905. 1st ed. 9x6.75. Frederick Richardson (illus). Pict cl. Pacific*. $52/£33

BAUM, L. FRANK. Rinkitink in Oz. Chicago: Reilly & Britton, (1916). 1st ed, 1st ptg. 9x6.5. 314pp; 11 (of 12) color plts by John R. Neill. B/w pict eps. Lt blue cl, pict cvr label. (Scratches fr cvr label, soiled, spine sl leaning), else VG. Pacific*. $219/£137

BAUM, L. FRANK. Rinkitink in Oz. Chicago: Reilly & Britton, (1916). 1st ed, 1st state, w/o pub's advert. 12 color plts. Fine. Kane*. $425/£266

BAUM, L. FRANK. Rinkitink in Oz. Chicago: Reilly & Britton, (1916). 1st ed, 1st ptg w/o ad on verso of ownership pg. 9x6.5. 314pp; 12 color plts by John R. Neill. B/w pict eps. Lt blue cl, pict cvr label. (Name dated 1917; cvr label sl scratched), else VG. Pacific*. $431/£269

BAUM, L. FRANK. The Road to Oz. Chicago: Reilly & Britton, (1909). 1st ed, 1st state w/2 ad pp at end; p(263) listing Baum bks pub under pseud 'Laura Bancroft;' p(264) listing the 4 Baum titles, The Land of Oz, Ozma of Oz, Dorothy and the Wizard of Oz, & John Dough and the Cherub; gatherings ptd on tinted stocks, arranged in the order called for by Hanff & Greene; rear cvr w/silhouette ports of Dorothy & Ozma; spine imprint ptd in upper & lower case letters; earliest copy w/o damaged type on p34, line 4 ('Toto on'); & w/the numeral & caption present beneath the illus on p129. 9x6.5. John R. Neill (illus). 261,(1) + (2)ad pp. Inserted pict eps. Lt grn cl, orig spine strip, cvrs laid-on. (Upper corner p129 lacks piece; expertly rebound, cvr designs rubbed), else VG. Pacific*. $288/£180

BAUM, L. FRANK. The Road to Oz. Chicago: Reilly & Britton, (1909). 1st ed, 1st state, w/perfect type on pp34, 121, 129. Fine (ink inscrip, sm tear p129; spine sl dknd). Kane*. $325/£203

BAUM, L. FRANK. The Road to Oz. Chicago: Reilly & Britton, (1918). 1st ed, 4th state w/ad listing titles through The Tin Woodman of Oz. Ptd on bulkier stock w/bk measuring about 1 1/4-inches thick (incl cvrs). 9x6.5. John R. Neill (illus). Plain eps. Lt tan cl. Fine. Pacific*. $127/£79

BAUM, L. FRANK. The Royal Book of Oz. Toronto: Copp, Clark, (1921). 1st Canadian ed, from 1st issue Amer sheets, w/Scarecrow's name misspelled on plt facing p255. John R. Neill (illus). 4to. Gray cl, pict fr cvr label. (Lacks fep, rear hinge repaired.) Swann*. $230/£144

BAUM, L. FRANK. The Royal Book of Oz. Ruth Plumly Thompson (ed). Chicago: Reilly & Lee, (1921). 1st ed, 1st state w/misspelled caption on plt facing p255 ('...Scarcorw's...'); plts coated 1 side only. Although Baum, who died in 1919, is listed as author on cvr and tp, bk was written entirely by Ruth Plumly Thompson. 9x6.5. 312pp; 12 color plts by John R. Neill. B/w pict eps. Gray-grn cl, pict cvr label. VG (few sm marginal tears, fr hinge weak; soiled). Pacific*. $288/£180

BAUM, L. FRANK. The Scarecrow of Oz. Chicago: Reilly & Lee, (1915). Early rpt. John R. Neill (illus). Sm 4to. Brn cl, lg color pict label. VG in dj (w/price of $1.75). Houle. $150/£94

BAUM, L. FRANK. The Scarecrow of Oz. Chicago: Reilly & Britton, (1915). 1st ed, 1st state, w/8 titles listed in pub's ad. 12 color plts. (Ink inscrip; sm waterstain rear cvr, 2 tears in spine.) Kane*. $160/£100

BAUM, L. FRANK. The Scarecrow of Oz. Chicago: Reilly & Britton, (1915). 1st ed, 1st state w/ad on verso of 1/2-title listing 8 titles through The Scarecrow of Oz, & w/12 inserted color plts by John R. Neill, w/o captions. 9x6.5. 288pp. B/w pict eps. Bright grn cl, pict cvr label. (Sl faded, spine head rubbed, sl scratches to cvr label), else VG. Pacific*. $230/£144

BAUM, L. FRANK. The Scarecrow of Oz. Chicago: Reilly & Lee, (c. post-1920s). 12 color plts by John R. Neill. Pict cvr label. Fair (1 plt detached; spine torn, rubbed). Pacific*. $29/£18

BAUM, L. FRANK. The Sea Fairies. Chicago: Reilly & Britton, (1911). 1st ed, 1st issue w/pub's imprint at spine foot in upper/lower case, color pict label on fr cvr showing 3 heads rising from sea. 12 color plts. (Sl rubbed, sm stain rear cvr.) Ink sig of Frank Haven McClurg. Kane*. $200/£125

BAUM, L. FRANK. The Sea Fairies. Chicago: Reilly & Britton, (1911). 1st ed, 2nd state w/fr cvr label illus Trot among the sea horses; last 2 lines p95, and lines 14&15 p105 transposed. 1st vol in the 'Trot' series. 9x6.5. 239,(1)pp; 12 duotone plts by John R. Neill. Color pict eps. Grn cl, pict cvr label. (Spine soiled, ends rubbed, cvr label sl scratched, lower corner fr cvr label lacks sm piece), else VG. Pacific*. $207/£129

BAUM, L. FRANK. Sky Island. Chicago: Reilly & Britton, (1912). 1st ed, 1st state w/pict cvr label edges in red; pub's ads on verso of 1/2-title lists 6 Baum titles. 12 color plts by John R. Neill. Color pict eps. Red cl, color pict cvr label. (Old names, rear hinge cracking; cvr label, spine soiled), else VG. Pacific*. $207/£129

BAUM, L. FRANK. Sky Island. Chicago: Reilly & Britton, (1912). 1st ed. 12 color plts. Color pict label. (Ink sig; lt smudged, sm spine tear.) Kane*. $275/£172

BAUM, L. FRANK. The Songs of Father Goose. Chicago/NY: George M. Hill, (1900). 1st ed. 4to. Red-brn cl, color pict buff bds (edges scraped, brief erasures fr cvr, sl worn). Text VG. Baltimore*. $70/£44

BAUM, L. FRANK. The Songs of Father Goose: For the Kindergarten, the Nursery and the Home. Chicago: George M. Hill, (1900). 1st ed. 10.75x8.25. Alberta N. Hall (music), W. W. Denslow (illus). 84pp. Orig pict cvrs laid on. Good (later eps, hand-coloring, hinges reinforced; cvr designs lack pieces). Pacific*. $46/£29

BAUM, L. FRANK. The Songs of Father Goose: For the Kindergarten, the Nursery and the Home. Chicago: George M. Hill, (1900). 1st ed. 11x8.5. Alberta N. Hall (music), W. W. Denslow (illus). 84pp. New patterned eps. Cl-backed pict bds. (Hinges starting, sl shelfworn, spine ends, corners rubbed), else VG. Pacific*. $173/£108

BAUM, L. FRANK. The Story of the Wizard of Oz. Racine: Whitman, 1939. 1st ed thus. 11x8.5. Henry E. Vallely (illus). (Pg extrems sl dknd), else VG in pict color wrappers. Pacific*. $98/£61

BAUM, L. FRANK. Strange Tale of Nursery Folk. (Douglasville, GA): Pamani, 1978. 1st ed in bk form. One of 150 ptd. Frontis. Fine in pict red wrappers. Pacific*. $161/£101

BAUM, L. FRANK. The Surprising Adventures of the Magical Monarch of Mo and His People. Indianapolis: Bobbs-Merrill, (1903). 1st ed, 2nd state w/Braunworth imprint on c. pg in unserified upper case; numeral on p50 faintly ptd; hand-lettered caption on p(121) in damaged type. 9x6.5. 236,(1)pp; 12 color plts by Frank Verbeck. Pict eps. Blue cl, pict cvr label. (Spine ends, extrems rubbed, lacks piece of cvr label), else VG. Pacific*. $86/£54

BAUM, L. FRANK. The Surprising Adventures of the Magical Monarch of Mo and His People. Indianapolis: Bobbs-Merrill, (1947). 1st ed thus. 9x6.5. Evelyn Copelman (illus). Grn cl, gilt. VG in dj (chipped, lacks sm piece, extrems dknd). Pacific*. $63/£39

BAUM, L. FRANK. Tik-Tok and the Nome King. Chicago: Reilly & Britton, (1913). 1st ed, binding state B (half-toned blue area below lion and tiger on ep). 12mo. Color pict bds (chipped; few pp sl water-stained). Reisler. $350/£219

BAUM, L. FRANK. The Tik-Tok Man of Oz. NY: Jerome H. Remick, (1913). Fr cvr signed Rowland. Lg 4to. Louis F. Gottschalk (music). Color pict wrappers (margins worn, few stains). Reisler. $85/£53

BAUM, L. FRANK. Tik-Tok of Oz. Chicago: Reilly & Britton, (1914). 1st ed, 1st state, w/6 titles listed in pub's ads. 12 color plts. Color pict label. (Pencil name erased, lt pencil mks 1 plt; label lt rubbed.) Kane*. $180/£113

BAUM, L. FRANK. Tik-Tok of Oz. Chicago: Reilly & Britton, (1914). 1st ed, 1st state. 9x6.5. 271,(1)pp; 12 color plts by John R. Neill. Inserted color pict eps of maps of Oz. Blue cl, pict cvr label. Good (hinges cracked; extrems rubbed, cvr label scratched). Pacific*. $184/£115

BAUM, L. FRANK. Tik-Tok of Oz. Chicago: Reilly & Britton, (1914). 1st ed, 1st state w/ads on verso of 1/2-title listing 6 titles through The Patchwork Girl of Oz, & w/horizontal dbl rules at top & bottom of spine. 9x6.5. 271,(1)pp; 12 color plts by John R. Neill. Inserted color pict eps of maps of Oz. Blue cl, pict cvr label. (Stamp, bkpl, hinge starting; spine ends rubbed, sm scrape fr cvr label), else VG. Pacific*. $431/£269

BAUM, L. FRANK. The Tin Woodman of Oz. Chicago: Reilly & Britton, (1918). 1st ed. 12 color plts. (Sm piece gone from color paste-down on fr cvr; hinges re-glued.) Kane*. $160/£100

BAUM, L. FRANK. The Tin Woodman of Oz. Chicago: Reilly & Britton, (1918). 1st ed, 1st state. Ad on verso of ownership pg lists 11 titles through The Tin Woodman of Oz. 9x6.5. 287,(1)pp; 12 color plts by John R. Neill. B/w pict eps. Red cl, pict cvr label. (Spine ends, corners sl rubbed), else VG. Pacific*. $546/£341

BAUM, L. FRANK. The Tin Woodman of Oz. Chicago: Reilly & Britton, (1918). 1st ed, 1st ptg. 12 full-pg color plts by John R. Neill. Red cl, illus color label, repeated on both fr/back of djs. (Few sm holes to spine), else Fine in dj (chip, sm closed tears). Bromer. $1,750/£1,094

BAUM, L. FRANK. The Tin Woodman of Oz. Chicago: Reilly & Lee, (c. 1930). 287,(1)pp; 12 color plts by John R. Neill. B/w pict eps. Blue cl, pict cvr label. (Book notice mtd to fep verso, hinges cracked; lacks piece of fr cvr label, extrems rubbed, lower fr joint torn), else VG-. Pacific*. $52/£33

BAUM, L. FRANK. The Tin Woodsman of Oz. Toronto: Copp, Clark, (1918). 1st Canadian ed from Amer sheets, w/cancel tp and Copp, Clark & Co. on spine. John R. Neill (illus). 4to. Color pict cvr label. Swann*. $115/£72

BAUM, L. FRANK. The Visitors from Oz.... Chicago: (1960). 1st ed, primary binding w/illus on cvrs in full color on grn background. Kane*. $60/£38

BAUM, L. FRANK. The Wishing Horse of Oz. Chicago: Reilly & Lee, (1935). 1st ed. 4to. 12 color plts by John R. Neill. Dk blue cl, color pict cvr label. (Name in ownership box.) Dj (few sm closed tears, sm chip rear panel). Swann*. $460/£288

BAUM, L. FRANK. The Wizard of Oz Picture Book. Racine: Whitman, 1939. 1st ed thus. 12.75x8.75. Leason (illus). (Extrems sl dknd), else VG in pict linen-like wrappers. *Pacific**. $81/£51

BAUM, L. FRANK. The Wizard of Oz Waddle Book. NY: Blue Ribbon Books, (c. 1934). 1st ed thus, 2nd state, w/no imprint on spine foot. Pp35-6, plt 7 lacks the 6 die-cut 'waddle toys' pictured on the fr cvr, '...the story book with characters that come out and walk.' Instructions for assembling waddles at rear. 9x7. 8 color plts by W. W. Denslow. Grn cl, color pict cvr label. (Old names), else Fine. *Pacific**. $127/£79

BAUM, L. FRANK. The Wizard of Oz. London: Hutchinson, (c. post-1920). 6.75x4.75. W. W. Denslow (illus). Red cl, pict cvr label. (Foxed, marginal worming; cvr label creased, sl rubbed, rear cvr dampstained), else VG-. *Pacific**. $69/£43

BAUM, L. FRANK. The Wizard of Oz. NY: Grosset & Dunlap, 1939. 1st ed thus. 6.75x8.75. Oskar Lebeck (illus). Cl-backed pict bds. (Extrems rubbed), else VG in dj (chipped, rubbed). *Pacific**. $104/£65

BAUM, L. FRANK. The Woggle-Bug Book. Chicago: Reilly & Britton, 1905. 1st (and only) ed, 2nd state w/a pale yellow background ptd on fr cvr & rear cvr decoratively ptd 'The Woggle-Bug Book' in yellow. 15x10.75. Ike Morgan (illus). VG in cl-backed pict wrappers (soiled, lacks lower corner fr wrapper, sm tears extrems). *Pacific**. $1,150/£719

BAUM, L. FRANK. The Wonderful Wizard of Oz. Chicago: George M. Hill, 1900. 1st ed, 2nd state w/'low wail of...' (p14, line 1); the word 'pieces' spelled correctly (p81, 4th line from bottom); p(227) begins w/the words 'While the woodman...'; imperfect type on last line of p100 & 186; tp verso w/press-ptd c. notice; color plt facing p34 w/o 2 dark-blue blots on the moon; plt facing p92 lacks red shading on the horizon. Variant 'C' spine imprint w/pub's name in serified type, stamped in red, the 'C' of 'Co.' encircling the 'o'. 8.25x6.25. 261pp; 22 (of 24) color plts by W. W. Denslow. Pict pastedowns. Lt grn cl. Fair (lacks fep, few plts scratched, 1 torn, repaired on verso, 2 plts detached, hinges cracked through; soiled, rubbed, spotted). *Pacific**. $489/£306

BAUM, L. FRANK. The Wonderful Wizard of Oz. Chicago: Geo. M. Hill, 1900. 1st ed, mixed state. State C of cvr: lt grn cl stamped in red/grn w/pub imprint in variant C (serifed type w/C encircling the o). All textual points are in earliest state: p(2), pub's ad enclosed in box; p14, line 1 has 'low wail on...'; p81, 4th line from bottom has 'peices'; p(227), line 1 begins 'While Tin Woodman...'; colophon at end of bk set in 11 lines, enclosed in box; pict self-eps; fr pastedown ep in black/gray; rear pastedown ep is black/red; pp facing pastedowns are blank; non-broken type on p100, last line, and p186, last line. 1 plt is 2nd state, others 1st state: plt facing p92 is 2nd state w/o red shading on horizon, but plt facing p34 has the 2 dk blue blots on the moon. Verso of inserted tp is intermediate state w/hand rubber stamped copyright notice rather than later ptd notice. 4to. VG (fr cvr sl stained, rear gutter of spine torn). *Reisler*. $9,000/£5,625

BAUM, VICKI. Headless Angel. GC: Doubleday, 1948. 1st ed. (Sm crease edge of fep), else NF in NF dj (sm tears, chip fr panel). *Between The Covers*. $50/£31

BAUMANN, GUSTAVE. Frijoles Canyon Pictographs. L.A.: William & Victoria Dailey, 1980. 1st ed. NF in dj. *Pacific**. $138/£86

BAUMGARTL, I. Sea Gods. Chicago: Kroch's, 1937. 1st ed. NF in dj. *Smith*. $30/£19

BAUR, JOHN et al. New Art in America. NYGS, (1957). Dj. *Argosy*. $125/£78

BAUR, JOHN. George Grosz. NY: Macmillan, 1954. 1st ed. 2 color plts. Yellow cl. VG + in VG dj (shelfworn, sm chip). *Any Amount*. $48/£30

BAWDEN, EDWARD. A Book of Cuts. Scolar, 1979. VG in orig wrappers (sl rubbed). *Hollett*. $32/£20

BAWDEN, NINA. The Robbers. NY: Lothrop, 1979. 1st ed. 5.5x8.5. 155pp. Fine (ex-lib) in dj. *Cattermole*. $20/£13

BAXT, GEORGE. A Parade of Cockeyed Creatures or Did Someone Murder Our Wandering Boy? NY: Random House, 1967. 1st ed. NF in dj (lt edgeworn). *Janus*. $35/£22

BAXT, GEORGE. A Queer Kind of Death. Cape, 1967. 1st Eng ed, 1st bk. NF (spine head sl bumped) in dj (sl rubbed, price-clipped). *Ulysses*. $104/£65

BAXTER, CHARLES. First Light. (NY): Viking, (1987). 1st ed. Rev copy w/press release laid in. Fine in Fine dj. *Robbins*. $50/£31

BAXTER, LUCY. The Life of William Barnes. Macmillan, 1887. 1st ed. Photo frontisport, xiv,358,(ii)pp. Orig cl (neatly recased), gilt. *Hollett*. $224/£140

BAXTER, WILLIAM T. Jewelry, Gem Cutting and Metalcraft. NY: McGraw-Hill, (1950). 3rd ed. Fine in Fine dj. *Book Market*. $15/£9

Bay Psalm Book. Univ of Chicago, 1956. Facs of 1st ed of 1640. 2 vols. Brn cl. Fine in slipcase. *Michael Taylor*. $48/£30

BAYER, HERBERT. Herbert Bayer: Painter, Designer, Architect. NY: Reinhold Pub, 1967. 1st ed. Fine in illus dj (lt worn). *Cahan*. $100/£63

BAYFIELD, HENRY WOLSEY. The St. Lawrence Survey Journals of Captain Henry Wolsey Bayfield, 1829-1853. Ruth McKenzie (ed). Toronto: Champlain Soc, 1984, 1986. 1st eds. Ltd to 1350. 2 vols. 10 plts, 4 maps. Red cl, gilt. Fine set. *Argonaut*. $90/£56

BAYLESS, MARGUERITE. Bolinvar. NY: Derrydale, 1937. Ltd to 950 numbered. 2 vols. Red cl. NF set in red slipcase (worn). *Biscotti*. $145/£91

BAYLEY, JOHN. The History and Antiquities of the Tower of London...etc. London: T. Cadell, 1825. 1st ed. 2 vols in 1. Old brn calf bds (expertly rebacked), gilt paneled spine, raised bands, marbled edges. Fine. *Appelfeld*. $350/£219

BAYLEY, NICOLA. Nicola Bayley's Book of Nursery Rhymes. Cape, 1979. Lg 8vo. (30)pp. Glazed pict bds. *Hollett*. $24/£15

BAYLEY, W. The Menominee Iron-Bearing District of Michigan. USGS, 1904. VG. *Blake*. $75/£47

BAYLOR, BYRD. The Way to Start a Day. NY: Scribner, 1977. 1st ed. 8.25x10.25. Peter Parnall (illus). 32pp. VG in dj. *Cattermole*. $25/£16

BAYLOR, FRANCES COURTENAY. Behind the Blue Ridge. Phila: Lippincott, 1887. 1st ed. 313pp + 10pp ads. (Ex-lib, blindstamp, bkpl; edgeworn, rubbed, soiled), else Good. *Brown*. $15/£9

BAYLOR, WALTER L. J. Last Man Off Wake Island. Cecil Carnes (ed). Indianapolis, (1943). Rpt. VG + . *Pratt*. $22/£14

BAYNE, SAMUEL G. On an Irish Jaunting Car Through Donegal and Connemara. NY: Harper, (1902). 1st ed. Inscribed. Pict gilt-dec grn cl. (Bkpl; spine ends sl rubbed), else VG. *Pacific**. $92/£58

BAYNTON-WILLIAMS, ROGER. Investing in Maps. London, 1969. 1st ed. Dj (sl rubbed). *Edwards*. $24/£15

BAZIN, G. The Natural History of Bees...Making Wax and Honey.... London: J&P Knapton, 1744. 12 copper plts. Old calf bds. (Lt foxed, lacks few index pp, hinges split; fr bd detached, rubbed, loss of leather.) *Metropolitan**. $287/£179

BEACH, REX. Big Brother. NY: Harper, 1923. 1st ed. Red cl, gilt. Fine in NF dj. *Macdonnell*. $100/£63

BEACH, REX. The Ne'er-Do-Well. NY: Harper, 1911. 1st ed, advance rev copy. Inscribed by Harper Brothers. Red bds, special label. VG (spine sunned, few nicks). *Macdonnell*. $85/£53

BEACH, REX. The Silver Horde. NY: Harper, 1909. 1st ed. Maroon pict cl. (Fep excised), else Fine in color pict dj (chip fr panel). *Macdonnell.* $100/£63

BEACH, REX. Too Fat to Fight. NY/London: Harper, (1919). 1st ed. Frontis. Pict brn bds. (Lg bkseller sticker rear pastedown), else NF in VG dj (lt edgeworn, sm nicks, tears). *Reese.* $30/£19

BEACH, SYLVIA. Shakespeare and Company. NY: HB & Co, (1959). 1st ed. VF in VF dj. *Between The Covers.* $85/£53

BEACH, SYLVIA. Ulysses in Paris. NY: Harcourt, Brace, (1956). 1st ed. Pict bds. Fine in glassine (chipped). *Pacific*.* $40/£25

BEACH, WALTER G. Oriental Crime in California...1900-1927. Stanford: Stanford Univ, 1932. 1st ed. Red cl. (Ex-lib, bkpl, margins dknd; sunned), else VG. *Pacific*.* $29/£18

BEADLE, ERASTUS F. To Nebraska in '57. A Diary by.... NY Public Library, 1923. Fine in ptd wraps. *Wantagh.* $40/£25

BEADLE, J. H. Life in Utah; or, The Mysteries and Crimes of Mormonism. Phila: National Pub Co, (1870). Frontis, 540pp + (4)pp ads; 29 plts. Grn cl, gilt. VG (lt toning; spine ends expertly repaired, spine gilt dull). *House.* $65/£41

BEADLE, J. H. Polygamy, or, The Mysteries and Crimes of Mormonism. N.p., (1904). Marbled eps, edges. Blue cl dec in black/gilt. VG + (sl shelfworn). *Pacific*.* $69/£43

BEAGLE, PETER S. A Fine and Private Place. NY: Viking, 1960. 1st ed, 1st bk. Fine in Fine dj. *Lenz.* $150/£94

BEAGLE, PETER S. A Fine and Private Place. NY: Viking, 1960. 1st ed, 1st bk. Inscribed, signed, dated 1982. (Spine sl sunned), else VG in NF dj (sm spine tear). *Pacific*.* $184/£115

BEAGLE, PETER S. I See by My Outfit. NY: Viking, (1965). 1st ed. (Lower corners sl bumped), o/w Fine in VG dj. *Agvent.* $50/£31

BEAGLE, PETER S. The Last Unicorn. NY: Viking, (1968). 1st ed. (Bkpl), else NF in dj (sm tear fr panel, sm ink price lower fr flap). *Pacific*.* $58/£36

BEAGLEHOLE, E. Social Change in the South Pacific. Aberdeen, 1957. 1st ed. (Lib stamp.) Dj (sl damaged, lib stamp). *Maggs.* $80/£50

BEAGLEHOLE, J. C. The Life of Captain James Cook. London, 1974. 1st ed. Frontisport, 43 plts, 5 sketch maps (1 fldg). Dj (sl rubbed). *Edwards.* $80/£50

BEAGLEHOLE, J. C. The Life of Captain James Cook. CA: Stanford Univ, 1983. 5 maps (1 fldg). VG in dj. *Explorer.* $80/£50

BEAGLEHOLE, J. C. Words for Music—Poems. London: Caxton, 1938. One of 150. VG (inscrip; prelims, edges, contents, eps spotted) in wrappers (sl creased, mkd; spine, edges browned). *Ulysses.* $120/£75

BEAL, GEORGE. Playing Cards and Their Story. NY: Arco, 1975. 1st ed. Black cl (corners sl frayed), gilt. NF in VG dj (lt soiled, sm stains, spine chipped). *Blue Mountain.* $20/£13

BEALE, LIONEL S. The Microscope in Its Application to Practical Medicine. London: John Churchill, 1867. 3rd ed. xxiii,(1),320,(44 ads)pp; 58 plts. VG (extrems worn). *Glaser.* $250/£156

BEALE, REGINALD. Lawns for Sports: Their Construction and Upkeep. London: Simpkin, Marshall, Hamilton, Kent, 1924. 1st ed. Frontisport. (Cvrs spotted, adhesion residue to lower spine, rear joint sl chipped), else VG. *Pacific*.* $173/£108

BEAM, PHILIP C. Winslow Homer's Magazine Engravings. NY, 1979. VG in dj. *Dumont.* $45/£28

BEAMISH, RICHARD. Memoir of the Life of Sir Marc Isambard Brunel. London: Longman, Green et al, 1862. 2nd ed. Frontis port, xx,357pp (tp sl browned, sm stamp verso; spine ends sl worn). *Hollett.* $88/£55

BEAN, JACOB. 100 European Drawings in the Metropolitan Museum of Art. NY, 1964. 100 plts. Good. *Washton.* $40/£25

BEAN, JACOB. 15th-18th Century French Drawings in the Metropolitan Museum of Art. NY, 1986. Good in dj. *Washton.* $30/£19

BEAN, W. J. Trees and Shrubs Hardy in the British Isles. London, 1936. 3 vols. 127 photo plts. Grn cl, gilt. VG. *Larry Price.* $75/£47

BEAN, W. J. Trees and Shrubs Hardy in the British Isles. G. Taylor et al (eds). London, 1970. 8th ed. Dj. *Sutton.* $95/£59

BEAR, BILLY. Billy-Boy Scout. NY: Samuel Gabriel, (1916). 1st ed. 4to. 4 color litho plts. Red cl, color pict glazed bds. Good (fr hinge detached). *Houle.* $125/£78

BEAR, LARRY ALAN (ed). Law, Medicine, Science—and Justice, the Proceedings of the First Interamerican Conference on Legal Medicine and Forensic Science. Springfield: Charles C. Thomas, 1964. VG in dj (sl worn). *Boswell.* $45/£28

BEARD, CHARLES A. The Devil Theory of War. NY: Vanguard, (1936). 1st ed. Black cl, paper labels. (Sm ink name), o/w Nice in dj (tanned). *Reese.* $25/£16

BEARD, D. C. Boat Building and Boating. NY: Scribner, 1931. Tan dec cl. VG (eps lt browned) in dj (chipped). *Bowman.* $50/£31

BEARD, JAMES. The Fireside Cook Book. S&S, 1949. 1st ed. VG-. *Book Broker.* $25/£16

BEARD, JAMES. The Fireside Cook Book: a Complete Guide to Fine Cooking for Beginner and Expert. NY: S&S, 1949. 1st ed. Fine in VG dj. *Perier.* $40/£25

BEARD, LINA and ADELIA. The American Girl's Handy Book. NY: Scribner, 1909. Pict cl (lt used). *Petrilla.* $35/£22

BEARD, PETER HILL. The End of the Game. NY: Viking, 1965. 1st ed. Frontis. VG (name; lower tips, spine lt rubbed) in dj (edgetorn, 1 tape-repaired tear). *Cahan.* $100/£63

BEARDSLEY, AUBREY. Letters from Aubrey Beardsley to Leonard Smithers. R. A. Walker (ed). First Edition Club, 1937. 1st ed. Photographic eps; fore/bottom edges untrimmed. Black cl, gilt. *Maggs.* $120/£75

BEARDSLEY, AUBREY. The Uncollected Work of Aubrey Beardsley. London: John Lane, Bodley Head, 1925. 1st ed. Frontisport, 162 plts (some loose). Uncut. Blue dec cl. Dj (spine ends torn, some loss, edges torn, frayed). *Maggs.* $400/£250

BEARDSLEY, AUBREY. The Uncollected Work of Aubrey Beardsley. London: John Lane, Bodley Head, 1925. 1st Eng ed. 4to. 162 plts, guards. Dec buckram. Fine (fep partly browned; spine foot sl bumped) in dj (sl rubbed, spine foot sl creased). *Ulysses.* $776/£485

BEARSE, RAY. Centerfire American Rifle Cartridges 1892-1963. South Brunswick/London: A.S. Barnes/Thomas Yoseloff, (1966). VG in dj (soiled, 1-inch closed tear). *Backman.* $20/£13

BEARSS, EDWIN C. Decision in Mississippi. Jackson, MS, (1962). 1st ed. Signed, inscribed. Fine in dj (lt worn). *Glenn.* $40/£25

BEARSS, EDWIN C. Steele's Retreat from Camden and the Battle of Jenkins' Ferry. (Little Rock, 1967.) 1st pub ed. Red cl. Fine in dj (price-clipped). *Chapel Hill.* $75/£47

BEATH, PAUL R. Febold Feboldson. Lincoln, 1948. 1st ed. Pict cl. Fine in dj (chipped, price-clipped). *Baade.* $35/£22

BEATON, CECIL. Ashcombe. The Story of a Fifteen-Year Lease. London: Batsford, 1949. 1st ed. Color frontis. (Feps lt browned; corner sl bumped, cl faded, spine sl stained; lacks dj.) *Edwards.* $24/£15

BEATON, CECIL. Ashcombe: The Story of a Fifteen-Year Lease. Batsford, 1949. 1st Eng ed. VG (feps partly browned; spine ends sl bumped) in dj (rubbed, nicked, corner browned). *Ulysses.* $88/£55

BEATON, CECIL. Ballet. GC: Doubleday, 1951. 1st ed. VF in VF dj. *Between The Covers.* $175/£109

BEATON, CECIL. The Best of Beaton. London, (1968). 1st ed. Folio. (Pencil notes; sl worn.) Dj (rubbed, torn, tape repair to reverse). *Swann**. $103/£64

BEATON, CECIL. Cecil Beaton's 'Fair Lady'. NY: HRW, (1964). 1st Amer ed. VF in VF dj. *Between The Covers*. $200/£125

BEATON, CECIL. Cecil Beaton's New York. NY, (1938). Signed (sl blurred). Dec yellow cl. *Argosy*. $50/£31

BEATON, CECIL. Cecil Beaton's New York. PA, 1938. 1st Amer ed. NF (spine sunned). *Polyanthos*. $35/£22

BEATON, CECIL. Cecil Beaton: Memoirs of the 40's. NY: McGraw-Hill, (1972). 1st Amer ed. Signed. Nice in dj. *Cady*. $25/£16

BEATON, CECIL. Diaries: 1944-48, the Happy Years. Weidenfeld & Nicolson, n.d. (c. 1972). 1st ed. VG in dj (sl soiled, faded, sm chips, nicks to edges, two 1-inch closed tears, top edge lacks sm piece). *Virgo*. $29/£18

BEATON, CECIL. The Face of the World. NY: John Day, (1957). 1st ed. VG in dj (edgeworn). *Cahan*. $65/£41

BEATON, CECIL. The Face of the World. NY, n.d. 1st Amer ed. Fine (spine sl rubbed) in NF dj. *Polyanthos*. $125/£78

BEATON, CECIL. I Take Great Pleasure. NY: John Day, (1956). 1st Amer ed. VF in VF dj. *Between The Covers*. $150/£94

BEATON, CECIL. It Gives Me Great Pleasure. Weidenfeld & Nicolson, 1955. 1st Eng ed. Fine (feps partly browned) in dj (sl rubbed, nicked). *Ulysses*. $104/£65

BEATON, CECIL. Photobiography. London: Odhams Press, (1951). 1st ed. VG in dj (nicked). *Houle*. $125/£78

BEATON, CECIL. Winged Squadrons. Hutchinson, n.d. (1942). 1st Eng ed. Wrappers. VG (tp, edges spotted; spine ends sl rubbed, nicked) in dj (nicked, rubbed, mkd, sl scratched, torn, creased, edges sl dknd). *Ulysses*. $200/£125

BEATON, GEORGE. (Pseud of Gerald Brenan.) Doctor Partridge's Almanack for 1935. C&W, 1934. 1st ed. (Eps foxed, offsetting; top edge dusty, fore-edge speckled, extrems rubbed), o/w VG in dj (internally reinforced, soiled, faded, extrems chipped, top edges lack pieces). *Virgo*. $144/£90

BEATON, K. DE P. A Warden's Diary. Nairobi, 1949. (Cvrs sl mkd.) *Hallam*. $29/£18

Beats and Company. A Portrait of a Literary Generation. NY, 1986. 1st Amer ed. Signed by Ann Charters (photos). Fine in NF dj (short closed tear top fr panel). *Warren*. $50/£31

BEATTIE, ANN. The Burning House. NY: RH, (1982). 1st ed. Fine in Fine dj. *Agvent*. $30/£19

BEATTIE, ANN. Chilly Scenes of Winter. GC: Doubleday, 1976. 1st ed, 1st bk. (Date), else VG in dj (spine ends sl rubbed). *Pacific**. $58/£36

BEATTIE, ANN. Falling in Place. Random House, 1980. 1st US ed. NF in dj. *Williams*. $32/£20

BEATTIE, ANN. Secrets and Surprises. NY: RH, (1978). 1st ed. Fine in Fine dj (fr flap sl creased). *Agvent*. $60/£38

BEATTIE, ANN. Where You'll Find Me and Other Stories. NY, 1986. 1st Amer ed. Signed. Fine in Fine dj. *Polyanthos*. $25/£16

BEATTIE, KIM. Brother, Here's a Man. NY: Macmillan, 1940. 1st ed. VG in dj. *Perier*. $35/£22

BEATTIE, OWEN and JOHN GEIGER. Frozen in Time: Unlocking the Secrets of the Franklin Expedition. Saskatoon: Prairie Books, (1988). 1st Canadian ed. Fine in dj. *Explorer*. $22/£14

BEATTIE, WILLIAM. Scotland Illustrated. London: George Virtue, 1838. 1st ed. 2 vols. Period 3/4 brn calf, marbled bds, gilt spine bands, morocco spine labels. (Bkpls; lt foxed; corners bumped, affecting interior vol II, vol II spine head scuffed), else VG. *Pacific**. $104/£65

BEATTIE, WILLIAM. Switzerland, Illustrated in a Series of Views Taken Expressly for This Work by W.H. Bartlett. London: George Virtue, 1836. 1st ed. 2 vols. Extra-engr tps, 105 (of 106) steel-engr plts, guards, fldg engr map at rear of Vol 2. Brn polished calf, marbled bds, raised bands, gilt, black leather spine labels. (Plts lt aged, map partly wrinkled, sl offsetting; text lt aged, extra tps sl foxed; extrems sl worn, scuffed.) *Baltimore**. $300/£188

BEATTIE, WILLIAM. Switzerland. London, 1836. 1st ed. 2 vols. 188; 152pp; 106 full-pg steel-engr plts by W.H. Bartlett; fldg map. 1/2 grn pebbled leather, marbled bds. (Extrems sl rubbed, sl foxed), else VG set. *King*. $600/£375

BEATTIE, WILLIAM. The Waldenses, or Protestant Valleys of Piedmont and Dauphiny. George Virtue, 1838. Engr frontisport, fldg map, engr add'l tp, 70 engr plts. Contemp 1/2 morocco, spine gilt. *Sotheby's**. $405/£253

BEATTY, CHARLES. His Country Was the World. London: C&W, 1954. 1st ed. 3 maps. NF in dj. *Worldwide*. $25/£16

BEATTY, DAVID L. Don't Tread on My Tire Rubber Sandals. N.p.: Seven Oceans, 1969. 1st ed. Fine in dj. *Associates*. $100/£63

BEATTY, HETTY BURLINGAME. Little Wild Horse. Boston: Houghton Mifflin, 1949. 1st ed. 4to. 32pp. Color pict bds. Nice in color pict dj (sl dusty). *Reisler*. $200/£125

BEATTY, JOHN. The Citizen-Soldier; or, Memoirs of a Volunteer. Cincinnati, 1879. 1st ed. 401pp + index. (Bkpl; extrems worn), else Nice. *King*. $135/£84

BEATTY, JOHN. Memoirs of a Volunteer, 1861-1863. Harvey S. Ford (ed). Norton, (c1946). 1st ed. VG (sl mildew spot to cvr) in Good dj. *Book Broker*. $35/£22

BEATY, RICHARD E. The Mountain Angels: Trials of the Mountaineers of the Blue Ridge and Shenandoah Valley. Front Royal, VA: R.E. Beaty, (1928). 1st ed. (Spine gilt sl rubbed.) *Sadlon*. $15/£9

BEAUCHAMP, WILLIAM M. Aboriginal Chipped Stone Implements of New York. NY State Museum, 1897. Vol 4. 102pp + plts. Black cl, gilt. VG (ex-lib). *Larry Price*. $49/£31

BEAUCHAMP, WILLIAM M. Metallic Implements of the New York Indians. NY State Museum, 1902. Black 1/2 leather, gilt. (ex-lib), else Good + . *Larry Price*. $49/£31

BEAUFORT, DUKE OF and MOWBRAY MORRIS. Hunting. London: Longmans, Green, 1906. Rev ed. Teg. 3/4 blue leather over orange buckram cvrd bds, gilt. VG + . *Biscotti*. $90/£56

BEAUFORT, HENRY SOMERSET and ALFRED E. T. WATSON (eds). The Badminton Library of Sports and Pastimes. London: Longmans, Green, (1885-96). Ltd to 250 lg paper copies. 28 (of 29) vols. 4to. Teg. Orig blue 1/2 morocco (lt rubbed, few spines lt faded or stained), gilt. *Christie's**. $3,421/£2,138

BEAUFOY, MARK. Mexican Illustrations Founded Upon Facts.... London: Carpenter & Son, 1828. 8vo. Fldg map, 6 plts. Full gilt-dec leather. VG (lt foxed, lib pocket residue rear fly, tp stamp; sl rubbed, spine split). *Metropolitan**. $603/£377

BEAUFOY, MARK. Nautical and Hydraulic Experiments, with Numerous Scientific Miscellanies. London: Henry Beaufoy, 1834. 1st ed. Vol 1 (of 1). Frontisport; 16 engr plts, 8 dbl-pg tables. (Lacks fep.) Uncut. Engr presentation leaf inscribed to the Grand Duke of Oldenburg tipped-in. Orig cl (shelfwear, inner joint broken; sl shaken), paper spine label (scuffed). *Oinonen**. $200/£125

BEAUMONT, CYRIL W. Ballet Design, Past and Present. London, 1946. Fine. *Europa*. $104/£65

BEAUMONT, CYRIL W. A Bibliography of Dancing. The Dancing Times, 1929. 1st ed. Buckram (faded). *Forest*. $61/£38

BEAUMONT, CYRIL W. The First Score. NY, 1980. 1st Amer ed. Fine in dj (spine sunned, 2 sm nicks). *Polyanthos*. $25/£16

BEAUMONT, FRANCIS and JOHN FLETCHER. Fifty Comedies and Tragedies. London: John Martyn et al, 1679. Folio. (10),578,557pp. Later 3/4 calf, marbled bds, spine tooled in blind, gilt, raised bands. VG (bkpl, lacks frontis port; ink inscrips, notes, tp gutter edge torn, soiled, margins stained, sl intruding into text; cvrs rubbed, extrems scuffed). *Pacific**. $173/£108

BEAUMONT, FRANCIS and JOHN FLETCHER. The Maides Tragedy. NY: Cheshire House, 1932. One of 1200. Teg. 1/2 grn calf, marbled bds. VG (rear evenly faded to brn, lt rubbed). *House*. $40/£25

BEAUMONT, FRANCIS and JOHN FLETCHER. The Works of Beaumont and Fletcher. Edinburgh: F.C. & J. Rivington et al, 1812. 14 vols. Period calf, gilt, red/grn morocco spine labels. (Bkpls, sm mar 1 spine head), else NF set. *Pacific**. $403/£252

BEAUMONT, FRANCIS and JOHN FLETCHER. The Works.... George Bell & A.H. Bullen, 1904-1912. Variorum ed. 4 vols. Photogravure frontisports vols 1 and 2, half-titles present. Grn eps; teg, rest untrimmed. Mod 1/2 pale grn morocco, morocco strip to bd fore-edges, raised bands, gilt, dated at foot, marbled bds. VF. *Blackwell's*. $320/£200

BEAUMONT, RICHARD. Purdey's. The Guns and the Family. London: David & Charles, 1985. VG in dj. *Hollett*. $48/£30

BEAUMONT, ROBERTS. Carpets and Rugs. Scott, Greenwood, & Son, 1924. 1st ed. 14 color plts. (Ink stamp.) Dj (chipped, stained). *Hollett*. $64/£40

BEAUMONT, WILLIAM. Experiments and Observations on the Gastric Juice, and the Physiology of Digestion. Boston: Lilly, Waite, 1834. 2nd ptg. Cancel title. 8vo. 280pp (sig clipped from ep, foxed). Orig cl-backed bds (edges sl worn), ptd paper label. *M & S*. $1,250/£781

BEAUMONT, WILLIAM. The Physiology of Digestion, with Experiments on the Gastric Juice. Burlington: Chauncey Goodrich, 1847. 2nd ed (so stated). 303,(i)pp, interleaved w/blanks throughout. Later plain tan buckram, red spine lettering. (Text severely browned, pp brittle, several pp w/tears, some w/lg old clear tape repairs, several tears to tp w/1 sm tear repaired by clear tape on verso; ex-lib, lib binding w/paper spine label, bkpl; sl worn.) *Baltimore**. $80/£50

BEAUREGARD, G. T. A Commentary on the Campaign and Battle of Manassas of July, 1861. NY/London: Putnam, 1891. 1st ed. 187pp; 2 fldg maps. Maroon cl. (Bkpl; extrems lt rubbed), else NF. *Chapel Hill*. $250/£156

Beauties of the Creation; or, A New Moral System of Natural History. London: G. Riley, 1793. 2nd ed. 5 vols. Sq 12mo. VF full-pg copper engr frontis, 1/2-title each vol, xiii,239; xvi,236; xiv,242,2; xiv,236; 252pp. Full marbled leather on bds, gilt, spine labels. Fine set (1 vol professionally rebacked w/orig spine and bds, facs dedication pg, 1 leaf preface; line cracking along spine folds, edges lt rubbed). *Hobbyhorse*. $650/£406

Beauty and the Beast. London: Sampson Low, Marston, Low & Searle, (1875). 1st ed. 4to. 10 full-pg color plts by E. V. B. Grn cl (sm area of pucker to rear cvr). *Reisler*. $485/£303

Beauty and the Beast. NY: McLoughlin Bros, 1893. Lg 4to. 6 flaps. Paper wrappered in form of a stage. Single back w/spines along each side. (Cl sl worn.) *Reisler*. $350/£219

BEAUVALLET, LEON. Rachel and the New World. NY: Dix, Edwards, 1856. 1st Amer ed. Mod buckram. Fine. *Dramatis*. $40/£25

BEAVER, HERBERT. Reports and Letters of Herbert Beaver, 1836-1838. Thomas E. Jessett (ed). (Portland, OR): Champoeg, 1959. One of 750 ptd. Frontis. Unopened. Fine. *Pacific**. $52/£33

BEAZLEY, C. RAYMOND. Prince Henry the Navigator. NY, 1895. 28 maps, plts. Contemp school prize binding: tan calf, gilt. (Prize certificate fr pastedown; spine dknd.) *Swann**. $80/£50

BEAZLEY, J. D. Attic Black-Figure Vase-Painters. NY: Hacker Art Books, 1978. Fine. *Archaeologia*. $150/£94

BECATTI, GIOVANNI. The Art of Ancient Greece and Rome. John Ross (trans). NY: Abrams, n.d. (ca 1967). 1st ed. VG in dj (torn). *Worldwide*. $95/£59

BECHDOLT, FREDERICK R. Tales of the Old-Timers. NY: Century, 1924. 1st ed. VG +. *Labordo*. $45/£28

BECHDOLT, FREDERICK R. When the West Was Young. NY, 1922. 1st ed. Pict cl. VG (pencil sig, address; cvrs lt worn). *Baade*. $45/£28

BECHDOLT, JACK. The Vanishing Hounds. NY: Oxford, 1941. Apparent 1st ed. Decie Merwin (illus). VG (sl edgeworn) in VG dj. *Price*. $25/£16

BECHSTEIN, J. M. The Natural History of Cage Birds. W.S. Orr, 1841. New ed. vi,311pp; 7 full-pg woodcuts. Aeg. Orig blind-stamped cl (neatly recased), gilt. *Hollett*. $104/£65

BECK, C. The Microscope—Part II. London: Beck, 1924. VG. *Savona*. $48/£30

BECK, C. The Microscope. London: Beck, 1930. 3rd ed. VG. *Savona*. $24/£15

BECK, HENRY C. Forgotten Towns of Southern New Jersey. NJ, 1936. 1st ed. 30 plts. *Heinoldt*. $25/£16

BECK, WARREN A. and YNEZ D. HAASE. Historical Atlas of New Mexico. Norman, 1969. 1st ed. 62 maps. VG in dj (sl worn). *Dumont*. $50/£31

BECKE, GEORGE LEWIS. The Settlers of Karossa Creek. London: RTS, (1907). 1st ed. 3 full-pg illus. Red dec cl (sl sunned). Nice. *Young*. $104/£65

BECKER, ETHEL ANDERSON. Klondike '98. Portland: Binfords & Mort, c. 1949. 1st ed. VG in dj. *High Latitude*. $25/£16

BECKER, MAY. Golden Tales of the Southwest. NY: Dodd Mead, 1939. 1st ed. Fine. *Labordo*. $35/£22

BECKER, ROBERT H. Designs on the Land; Disenos of California Ranchos and Their Makers. SF: Book Club of CA, 1969. One of 500 ptd. Obl folio. 64 maps. 1/2 leather. (Cl faded), else Very Nice. *Bohling*. $300/£188

BECKER, ROBERT H. Disenos of California Ranchos. Maps of Thirty-Seven Land Grants (1822-1846). SF: Book Club of CA, 1964. 1st ed. One of 400 ptd. Folio. 37 maps (24 fldg, 27 color). Dec bds, linen back. VF. *Argonaut*. $500/£313

BECKER, ROBERT H. (ed). Thomas Christy's Road Across the Plains: A Guide to the Route from Mormon Crossing, Now Omaha, Nebraska, to the City of Sacramento, California.... Denver: Fred A. Rosenstock, 1969. One of 2000 ptd. Frontisport. Cl w/map. Fine in dj (sunned, lt soiled). *Pacific**. $75/£47

BECKER, STEPHEN. The Season of the Stranger. NY: Harper, (1951). 1st ed, 1st bk. Fine in NF dj (price-clipped, 2 sm tears, spine sl tanned). *Between The Covers*. $45/£28

BECKER, WALTER. Italian Fascism and Its Great Originator. Monte Carlo: Continental Weekly, 1926. 1st ed. VG in stiff wraps (sl soiled). *Any Amount*. $29/£18

BECKETT, SAMUEL. All That Fall. NY: Grove, 1957. 1st US ed. Cream linen cl. (Top edge sl browned), o/w VG in dj (sl soiled, spine ends, corners chipped, 1-inch closed tear top edge rear panel, price-clipped). *Virgo*. $72/£45

BECKETT, SAMUEL. As the Story Was Told. Calder, 1990. 1st hb ed. Fine in dj. *Virgo*. $32/£20

BECKETT, SAMUEL. Au Loin un Oiseau. NY: Double Elephant, 1973. 1st ed. One of 130 numbered, signed. Lg 4to. 5 signed etchings by Avigdor Arikha. Contents loose in wrappers as issued. Cl fldg case. *Swann**. $747/£467

BECKETT, SAMUEL. Breath and Other Shorts. London, 1971. 1st ed. Fine in dj. *Petersfield*. $40/£25

BECKETT, SAMUEL. Come and Go. London, 1967. 1st Eng ed. (Stamp.) Card wrappers (sl dusty). *Clearwater*. $48/£30

BECKETT, SAMUEL. Echo's Bones and Other Precipitates. Paris: Europa, 1935. One of 327 signed. (Section at bottom of rep scraped), o/w Fine in tan wrappers. *Heritage.* $500/£313

BECKETT, SAMUEL. Eh Joe and Other Writings. Faber & Faber, 1967. 1st Eng ed. Fine in dj (sl rubbed, price-clipped). *Ulysses.* $72/£45

BECKETT, SAMUEL. Endgame. Faber, 1958. 1st UK ed. Fine (ink name) in VG dj (sm tape repairs to rear, sl stained). *Williams.* $96/£60

BECKETT, SAMUEL. Ends and Odds. NY: Grove, (1976). 1st ed. Fine in Fine dj. *Lenz.* $50/£31

BECKETT, SAMUEL. First Love and Other Shorts. NY: Grove, 1974. 1st Amer ed. Fine in Fine dj. *Polyanthos.* $25/£16

BECKETT, SAMUEL. Fizzles. NY: Grove, (1976). 1st ed. Fine in Fine dj. *Lenz.* $50/£31

BECKETT, SAMUEL. Footfalls. London, 1976. 1st Eng ed. Fine in card wrappers. *Clearwater.* $40/£25

BECKETT, SAMUEL. From an Abandoned Work. London: Faber & Faber, (1958). 1st ed. Fine in pict wraps. *Pharos.* $60/£38

BECKETT, SAMUEL. From an Abandoned Work. London, 1958. 1st ed. Pict wrappers. *Swann*.* $69/£43

BECKETT, SAMUEL. Happy Days. Faber, 1962. 1st UK ed. Fine in VG dj (sl rubbed). *Williams.* $72/£45

BECKETT, SAMUEL. How It Is. London: John Calder, 1964. 1st ed in English. Fine in VG dj (sl wrinkled along top, rear panel sl soiled). *Pirages.* $75/£47

BECKETT, SAMUEL. Ill Seen Ill Said. NY: Grove, 1981. 1st Amer ed. Fine in Fine dj. *Polyanthos.* $25/£16

BECKETT, SAMUEL. Ill Seen Ill Said. London, 1982. 1st Eng ed. Fine in dj. *Clearwater.* $48/£30

BECKETT, SAMUEL. Krapp's Last Tape. London, 1959. 1st ed. Limp bds. Fine in dj. *Petersfield.* $48/£30

BECKETT, SAMUEL. The Lost Ones. Calder & Boyars, 1972. 1st Eng ed. Fine in dj (rear partly dknd). *Ulysses.* $56/£35

BECKETT, SAMUEL. Malone Dies. NY: Grove, (1956). 1st ed thus. One of 500. White cl. (Extrems sl browned, sm red spot rear cvr), else VG. *Pacific*.* $161/£101

BECKETT, SAMUEL. Malone Dies. John Calder, 1958. 1st UK ed. Fine in VG + dj (spine head sl worn). *Williams.* $120/£75

BECKETT, SAMUEL. Mercier and Camier. NY: Grove, (1974). 1st ed. Fine in Fine dj. *Lenz.* $50/£31

BECKETT, SAMUEL. Molloy, Malone Dies, and the Unnamable: A Trilogy. Olympia, 1959. 1st ed thus. VG in wrapper. *Virgo.* $72/£45

BECKETT, SAMUEL. Molloy. Patrick Bowles (trans). Paris: Olympia/Editions Merlin, (1955). 1st ed. VF in plain white wrapper, ptd dj. *Pharos.* $250/£156

BECKETT, SAMUEL. Murphy. NY: Grove Press, (1957). 1st Amer ed. VG in dj (spine sl dknd, sm tears to head). *Pacific*.* $40/£25

BECKETT, SAMUEL. Murphy. Routledge, 1938. 1st ed. Crown 8vo. Good in mid grn cl (sl stained, ring stain fr cvr), gilt. *Blackwell's.* $2,160/£1,350

BECKETT, SAMUEL. Murphy. NY: Grove, n.d. (1938). Facs issue of 1st ed. One of 100 signed. 8vo. Cl-backed bds (edges sl dknd). VG. *Maggs.* $1,600/£1,000

BECKETT, SAMUEL. Nohow On. LEC, 1989. One of 550 signed by Beckett & Robert Ryman (illus). Fine in slipcase. *Swann*.* $1,840/£1,150

BECKETT, SAMUEL. Not I. London: Faber & Faber, 1973. 1st Eng ed. Signed. VG in wrappers (sl mkd, dusty). *Ulysses.* $232/£145

BECKETT, SAMUEL. Poems in English. John Calder, 1961. 1st Eng trade ed. (Offsetting to eps; spine, lower edges faded), o/w VG in dj (sl soiled, faded). *Virgo.* $96/£60

BECKETT, SAMUEL. Proust. London: C&W, 1931. 1st ed. Dec cream bds. Fine in dj (sl tanned, sm nicks). *Reese.* $250/£156

BECKETT, SAMUEL. Rockaby and Other Short Pieces. NY: Grove, 1981. 1st Amer ed. Fine in Fine dj. *Polyanthos.* $25/£16

BECKETT, SAMUEL. That Time. Faber, 1976. 1st ed. (Sm stain p14), o/w Fine in wrappers. *Virgo.* $11/£7

BECKETT, SAMUEL. Three Novels by Samuel Beckett - 'Molloy,' 'Malone Dies,' 'The Unnamable.' Calder, 1959. 1st UK ed. VG in Good+ dj (edges sl worn; faded, torn, creased). *Williams.* $72/£45

BECKEY, FRED. Mountains of North America. SF: Sierra Club Books, (1982). 1st ed. Frontis. Blue cl. (Corners bumped), else Fine in dj. *Argonaut.* $45/£28

BECKFORD, WILLIAM. The Episodes of Vathek. F. T. Marzials (trans). London, 1912. 1st ed. Purple cl (spine toned). VG. *Gretton.* $40/£25

BECKFORD, WILLIAM. The Journal of William Beckford in Portugal and Spain 1787-1788. Boyd Alexander (ed). Hart-Davis, 1954. 1st ed. VG in dj (sl soiled, chipped, spine browned, faded, price-clipped). *Virgo.* $56/£35

BECKFORD, WILLIAM. Life at Fonthill, 1807-1822. Boyd Alexander (ed). London, 1957. 1st Eng ed. VG in dj (sl torn, creased, mkd). *Clearwater.* $72/£45

BECKFORD, WILLIAM. Recollections of an Excursion to the Monasteries of Alcobaca and Batalha. London: Richard Bentley, 1835. 1st ed. 1/2-title, engr frontis port (sl offsetting from frontis). Later drab bds, paper spine label (partly torn away). *Christie's*.* $99/£62

BECKFORD, WILLIAM. Vathek. NY: John Day, 1928. 1st US ed. NF in dj (edges ragged), slipcase remains. *My Bookhouse.* $67/£42

BECKFORD, WILLIAM. Vathek. Nonesuch, 1929. Ltd ed. Teg. Gilt-dec bds, vellum spine. (Corners sl worn.) Internally NF. *Whiteson.* $56/£35

BECKFORD, WILLIAM. Vathek. Herbert B. Grimsditch (trans). Bloomsbury: Nonesuch, 1929. One of 1550. Marbled eps. Parchment-backed bds, gilt. Fine. *Pharos.* $125/£78

BECKFORD, WILLIAM. Vathek. LEC, 1945. Ltd to 1500 numbered, signed by Valenti Angelo (illus). Fine in slipcase. *Swann*.* $57/£36

BECKFORD, WILLIAM. Vathek. NY: LEC, 1945. One of 1500 ptd. Signed by Valenti Angelo (illus). Morocco, gilt. Fine in VG chemise, slipcase. *Pacific*.* $127/£79

BECKHAM, BARRY. Runner Mack. Morrow, 1972. 1st ed. VG + in VG + dj. *Plapinger.* $125/£78

BECKMAN, PETER. Kansas Monks: A History of St. Benedict's Abbey. Atchison, KS: Abbey Student Press, (1957). 1st ed. Black cl. Fine. *Glenn.* $25/£16

BECKWITH, B. K. Seabiscuit, the Saga of a Great Champion. N.p., (1940). (Spine chipped, cvrs lt soiled.) *King.* $35/£22

BECKWITH, JOHN. Ivory Carvings in Early Medieval England. Harvey Miller & Medcalf, 1972. 1st ed. Folio. Color frontis. VG in buckram. Dj (repaired). *Cox.* $56/£35

Becky Longnose and Other Stories. NY: McLoughlin Bros, 1882. 8vo. Ida Waugh (illus). 8pp. Good in full color pict paper wrappers (spine worn, lt dusty). *Reisler.* $110/£69

BECQUER, GUSTAVO. Rimas. NY: Appleton, 1881. 1st US ptd ed. VG in pub's cl. *Lame Duck.* $150/£94

BEDBROOK, GERALD STARES. Keyboard Music from the Middle Ages. Macmillan, 1949. 1st ed. 12 plts. VG in dj. *Hollett.* $40/£25

BEDDOES, THOMAS LOVELL. The Complete Works. Edmund Gosse (ed). Fanfrolico, 1928. 1st Eng ed. One of 750 numbered. 2 vols. Cl-backed patterned bds. Good (hinges of 1 vol weak; corner tips very worn). *Clearwater.* $152/£95

BEDDOES, THOMAS LOVELL. Letters. Edmund Gosse (ed). Elkin Mathews & John Lane, 1894. Ltd to 600. Teg. Beveled bds (spine bumped). VG. *Tiger.* $128/£80

BEDEAU, ADAM. Military History of Ulysses S. Grant from April, 1861 to April, 1865. NY: D. Appleton, 1868. 3 vols. Engr frontis port, 35 maps (6 loose in rear flap in vols 2, 3). Emb cl-cvrd bds. Fine. *Metropolitan*.* $103/£64

BEDFORD, HERBERT. The Heroines of George Meredith. (London): Hodder & Stoughton, (1914). 1st ed. One of 100. Signed. 20 mtd color miniatures. Teg. Vellum, gilt, pict cvr label, string ties. (Soiled, cvrs sl bowed; label, gilt rubbed), else VG. *Pacific*.* $69/£43

BEDFORD, JOHN. Talking About Teapots. Max Parrish, 1964. 1st ed. 4 color plts. VG in dj. *Hollett.* $24/£15

BEDICHEK, ROY. Adventures with a Texas Naturalist. Austin: Univ of TX, 1961. Rev ed. Fine in dj. *Labordo.* $35/£22

BEDICHEK, ROY. Karankaway Country. NY: Doubleday, 1950. 1st ed. VG + in dj. *Labordo.* $85/£53

BEDINI, SILVIO A. Thinkers and Tinkers: Early American Men of Science. NY: Scribner, (1975). Red cl. Fine in dj. *Weber.* $45/£28

BEE, JON. (Pseud of John Badcock.) Sportsman's Slang; a New Dictionary of the Terms Used in the Affairs of the Turf, the Ring, the Chase...and the Varieties of Life. London: The Author, 1825. Fldg color frontis, 4 plts. Uncut. Old cl-backed bds (shelfworn, shaken; sl browned, soiled, etc.). *Oinonen*.* $425/£266

BEEBE, LUCIUS and CHARLES CLEGG. The American West, the Pictorial Epic of a Continent. NY: E.P. Dutton, 1955. 1st ed. Fine in dj. *Labordo.* $55/£34

BEEBE, LUCIUS and CHARLES CLEGG. Hear the Train Blow. NY: E.P. Dutton, 1952. 1st ed. Natural buckram. Fine (inscrip) in VG pict dj (edges lt chipped). *House.* $35/£22

BEEBE, LUCIUS and CHARLES CLEGG. San Francisco's Golden Era. Berkeley: Howell-North, 1960. Pict eps. Tan cl. Fine in pict dj. *Pacific*.* $23/£14

BEEBE, LUCIUS and CHARLES CLEGG. Virginia and Truckee. Oakland, CA: Grahame H. Hardy, 1949. 1st ed. Map. Patterned bds. VG in pict dj (edge chipped). *House.* $25/£16

BEEBE, WILLIAM. Beneath Tropic Seas. NY: Putnam, 1928. 1st ed. VG. *Bookcell.* $30/£19

BEEBE, WILLIAM. Galapagos: World's End. NY, (1924). 1st ed, 2nd imp. 9 color plts (foxed). Illus eps. (Pp tanned, cartoon glued to fr blank, opposing pg browned; corners sl rubbed.) *Sutton.* $100/£63

BEEBE, WILLIAM. Pheasant Jungles. NY/London: Putnam/(Knickerbocker), 1927. 1st ed. (Sl rubbed, spine faded, ends frayed), o/w VG. *Worldwide.* $25/£16

BEEBE, WILLIAM. Pheasants. Their Lives and Homes. NY, 1936. 1st Amer ed. 2 vols in 1. Suede, 1/2 calf, gilt. Leather label. *Polyanthos.* $150/£94

BEEBY, DEAN. In a Crystal Land: Canadian Explorers in Antarctica. Toronto: Univ of Toronto, 1994. Fine in dj. *Explorer.* $24/£15

BEECHER, EDWARD. Narrative of Riots at Alton. Alton: George Holton, 1838. 1st ed. 159pp. Orig cl. (Lib handstamps, hinges weak, cl worn, parts of spine gone), else Good. Howes B307. *Brown.* $100/£63

BEECHER, HENRY W. Star Papers; or, Experiences of Art and Nature. NY: J.C. Derby, 1855. 1st ed. Plum cl, gilt. Good (bkpl, bksllr's description ep; spine faded, joint cracked). *Reese.* $60/£38

BEECHER, LYMAN. Lectures on Scepticism. Cincinnati: Corey & Fairbank, 1835. 1st ed. 160pp. Orig cl, ptd paper label. VG (ex-lib). *M & S.* $100/£63

BEECHEY, F. W. An Account of a Visit to California 1826-'27. SF: Book Club of CA, (1941). One of 350 ptd. 4 color plts, facs map. 1/2 linen, textured bds, paper spine label. (Lt offset eps; spine sl sunned), else NF. Howes B309. *Pacific*.* $173/£108

BEECHEY, F. W. An Account of a Visit to California, 1826-'27.... (SF): Book Club of CA, (1941). Ltd ed. One of 350 ptd. Color frontis, 3 color plts, map. 1/2 linen, gray-grn bds, paper spine label. Fine. Howes B309. *Harrington.* $200/£125

BEECHEY, F. W. Narrative of a Voyage to the Pacific and Beering's Strait.... London: Henry Colburn & Richard Bentley, 1831. 2 vols. (iii)-xxvi,(2),472; iv,452pp; 23 plts incl 4 dbl-pg lithos; 3 maps (2 fldg, 1 dbl-pg). 19th-cent 1/2 calf, marbled bds, gilt. (Bkpl, plts lt foxed; bds lt rubbed), else VG + . *Pacific*.* $863/£539

BEECHEY, F. W. Voyage to the Pacific and Beering's Strait, to Co-Operate with the Polar Expeditions.... Phila, 1832. Pub's 24-pg cat at end. Uncut. Orig 1/4 cl. (Lt foxed, lib stamp; backstrip damaged, fr cvr loose.) *Swann*.* $138/£86

BEECHEY, F. W. The Zoology of Captain Beechey's Voyage; Compiled from the Collections and Notes...Performed in His Majesty's Ship Blossom.... London: Henry G. Bohn, 1839. 1st ed. xii,180pp; 44 hand-colored copper-engr plts, 3 hand-colored engr maps (1 fldg). Mod full calf, raised spine bands, morocco label. (Sl soil to contents, lt dampstaining to text pp, not affecting color plts), else VG + . *Pacific*.* $8,625/£5,391

BEECHING, H. C. (ed). A Book of Christmas Verse. London: Methuen, 1895. 1st Eng ed. Walter Crane (illus). Teg. Pict buckram. VG (sm blindstamp fep, eps lt browned, edges sl spotted; spine, cvr edges dknd; spine ends, corners sl bumped). *Ulysses.* $136/£85

BEECKMAN, DANIEL. A Voyage to and from the Island of Borneo...Together with the Re-establishment of the English Trade There, An. 1714. T. Warner & J. Batley, 1718. 1st ed. Half-title w/ad on verso, 7 engr maps, plts (3 fldg), 3pg ad. (Discoloration.) Contemp blind-paneled calf (worn, rebacked). *Sotheby's*.* $2,024/£1,265

BEEDHAM, R. J. Wood Engraving. London: Faber & Faber, (1948). Rpt ed. VG in dj. *Turtle Island.* $30/£19

BEEDHAM, R. J. Wood Engraving. Hassocks: St. Dominic's, 1929. 3rd ed. 36 full-pg wood-engrs. Uncut. VG in cl-backed, ptd bds (lt soiled). *Cox.* $109/£68

BEEDING, FRANCIS. There Are Thirteen. London: Hodder & Stoughton, 1946. 1st ed. Red cl. Fine in dj (frayed). *Temple.* $26/£16

BEEDOME, THOMAS. Select Poems Divine and Humane. Meynell (ed). Nonesuch, 1928. One of 1250. Uncut. VG in orig full parchment w/pigskin thongs, card slipcase (lt soiled). *Cox.* $56/£35

BEELER, JOE. Cowboys and Indians. Norman: Univ of OK, 1967. 1st ed. Signed. Fine in dj (sl worn). *Labordo.* $95/£59

BEERBOHM, MAX. And Even Now. Heinemann, 1920. Good (pencil sig; spine bumped, sunned, paper label rubbed; lacks dj). *Tiger.* $24/£15

BEERBOHM, MAX. And Even Now. London, 1920. (Top cvr edge nicked.) Dj (worn, dknd). *Typographeum.* $45/£28

BEERBOHM, MAX. Around Theatres. London: Heinemann, 1924. Ltd to 780 sets (750 for sale). 2 vols. (Edges spotted, eps offset, browned, prelims sl foxed), o/w VG in djs (soiled, browned, corners chipped, spine ends lg chips missing). *Virgo.* $440/£275

BEERBOHM, MAX. Around Theatres. London: Hart-Davis, 1953. 1st 1-vol unltd ed. With proof. (Eps, fore-edge offset, spotted; spine ends, corners sl rubbed), o/w VG in dj (nicked, chipped, spine browned, price-clipped). *Virgo.* $40/£25

BEERBOHM, MAX. The Dreadful Dragon of Hay Hill. Heinemann, 1929. New imp. Color frontis. Good (ink inscrip; spine bumped, sm water stain fr cvr) in dj (chipped, closed tears). Tiger. $29/£18

BEERBOHM, MAX. Fifty Caricatures. London: Heinemann, 1913. 1st ed. (Corners, spine ends sl rubbed, spine sl faded), o/w VG (lacks dj). Virgo. $200/£125

BEERBOHM, MAX. Fifty Caricatures. Heinemann, 1913. 1st ed. 50 caricatures (48 mtd at large). Grn cl, gilt. VG in gray dj (chipped, repaired internally) repeating cvr design. Sotheran. $477/£298

BEERBOHM, MAX. The Happy Hypocrite. New Fairfield: Bruce Rogers/October House, 1955. One of 600. Cl-backed patterned bds. VF in glassine, slipcase. Pharos. $85/£53

BEERBOHM, MAX. Last Theatres: 1904-1910. Rupert Hart-Davis, 1970. 1st Eng ed. B/w frontis. VG (spine sl faded, ends sl bumped) in dj (sl creased, mkd, dusty, spine sl faded). Ulysses. $88/£55

BEERBOHM, MAX. Letters of Max Beerbohm 1892-1956. Rupert Hart-Davis (ed). NY: Norton, 1989. 1st Amer ed. Fine in dj. Virgo. $29/£18

BEERBOHM, MAX. The Mote in the Middle Distance. Berkeley: Hart Press, 1946. One of 100. Slip loosely inserted. VG (pp crinkled) in wrappers (sl mkd). Ulysses. $240/£150

BEERBOHM, MAX. Observations. Heinemann, 1925. Color frontis, 50 b/w plts, guards. Relevant newspaper cutting laid in. Good (bkpl, sl spotted, sl shaken; spine bumped, fr cvr mkd, lacks dj). Tiger. $104/£65

BEERBOHM, MAX. Observations. London: Heinemann, 1926. 1st ed. One of 250 (of 280) signed, numbered. 4to. Color frontis, 51 plts tipped-in, add'l signed color plt loosely inserted. Aeg. Grn bevelled cl, gilt. VG (spine ends, corners sl touched, rear panel sl mkd). Maggs. $560/£350

BEERBOHM, MAX. The Poets' Corner. NY: Dodd, Mead, 1904. 1st Amer ed. Folio. 22 sheets. VG (paper sl browned, margin of 2nd caricature sl frayed along fore-edge) in pict wrappers, stitched as issued (sl chipped, soiled). Heritage. $225/£141

BEERBOHM, MAX. Rossetti and His Circle. London: Heinemann, 1922. 1st ed. Frontis, 22 plts, guards. Blue cl, gilt. NF (eps browned, few lt fox mks) in dj (spine sl dknd, folds lt worn). Heritage. $350/£219

BEERBOHM, MAX. Rossetti and His Circle. Heinemann, 1922. One of 380 signed. Frontis, 22 tipped-in plts. Aeg. Fine (bkpl). Williams. $560/£350

BEERBOHM, MAX. A Survey. London, 1921. 1st ed. 51 tipped-in plts. Red cl. VG (foxed; lt worn). Truepenny. $75/£47

BEERBOHM, MAX. A Survey. London: Heinemann, 1921. One of 275 signed. Poor (eps very browned, guards sl browned; cvrs unevenly faded, corners bumped; edges, spine rubbed, spine faded; lacks dj). Internally Good. Virgo. $80/£50

BEERBOHM, MAX. A Survey. London: Heinemann, 1921. 1st ed. Red cl. Fine. Appelfeld. $100/£63

BEERBOHM, MAX. A Survey. NY: Doubleday, 1921. 1st Amer ed. VG in dj (soiled; stain, scorch mk on spine). Agvent. $125/£78

BEERBOHM, MAX. Things New and Old. Heinemann, 1923. 1st ed. Color frontis, 49 plts, guards. Good in buckram (sl mottled). Dj (lt soiled, frayed). Cox. $104/£65

BEERBOHM, MAX. A Variety of Things. NY: Knopf, 1928. 1st Amer ed, one of 2000. (Rear cvr, spine edge badly damp-mkd, corners knocked), o/w Good (lacks dj). Virgo. $16/£10

BEERBOHM, MAX. A Variety of Things. Heinemann, 1928. Vol 10 of Works of Max Beerbohm. Spare title label. VG (top edge dusty, ep edges browned; spine sl faded, ends sl bumped, rubbed). Ulysses. $152/£95

BEERBOHM, MAX. The Works of.... NY: Scribner, 1896. 1st Amer ed. Dec brn cl, gilt. (Foxed), else VG. Pacific*. $115/£72

BEERBOHM, MAX. Zuleika Dobson or an Oxford Love Story. London: Heinemann, 1912. New imp. (Bkpl, pg edges browned, fep offset; cvrs soiled, corners knocked, sm splits to spine ends), o/w Good (lacks dj). Virgo. $13/£8

BEERBOHM, MAX. Zuleika Dobson or, an Oxford Love Story. Oxford, 1975. One of 750 numbered, signed by Osbert Lancaster (illus). Sm folio. 12 color plts. Teg. Orig 1/4 Oxford blue morocco, gilt, 'Bullingdon' blue/white vertically striped bds. Fine. Blackwell's. $184/£115

BEERBOHM, MAX. Zuleika Dobson. London, 1911. 1st ed. Smooth brn cl. 1/4 morocco slipcase. Swann*. $373/£233

BEERBOHM, MAX. Zuleika Dobson. London: Folio Soc, 1966. 1st ed thus. (Spine sl faded, rubbed), o/w VG (lacks dj). Virgo. $22/£14

BEERS, HENRY PUTNEY. Spanish and Mexican Records of the American Southwest. Tucson: Univ of AZ, (1979). 1st ed. Fine. Book Market. $40/£25

BEERY, JESSE. A Practical System of Colt Training. Lima, OH: Parmenter Ptg, (1896). 1st ed. 272pp, 2 ads. Burgundy cl. Good (fr hinge cracked; dampstained; bumped, rubbed). Blue Mountain. $45/£28

Beeton's Book of Needlework. Ward Lock, n.d. (c. 1870). Color frontis, vi,584pp; 600 engrs, 5 pull-out pattern sheets. Aeg. Dec cl, gilt. VG. Whittle. $136/£85

BEETON, ISABELLA. Beeton's Housewife's Treasury of Domestic Information. Ward, Lock & Bowden, n.d. Gilt cl, beveled bds (damaged patch on fr bd; fr joint cracking). Hollett. $104/£65

BEETON, ISABELLA. The Book of Household Management. Ward, Lock, (c. 1950). 16 color plts. VG. Hollett. $80/£50

BEETON, ISABELLA. The Book of Household Management. S.O. Beeton, c. 1880. 325th thousand. 2 vols. xlvii,714; 715-1296pp; 12 color plts. Contemp 1/2 scarlet roan, gilt. (Lt spotting.) Sound. Hollett. $224/£140

BEETON, ISABELLA. The Book of Household Management. Ward, Lock, c. 1920. New ed. 32 color plts. 2-tone cl, gilt. VG (extrems sl worn). Hollett. $104/£65

BEGBIE, HAROLD. Shackleton: A Memory. London: Mills & Boon, 1922. Good+ (inscrip, sl foxed; rubbed). Explorer. $61/£38

BEGBIE, HAROLD. The Story of Baden-Powell. London: Grant Richards, 1900. 1st ed. 10 plts. Pict cl (sl soiled, spine faded, joints cracked; few spots, lacks fep). Hollett. $32/£20

BEGG, JOHN. Form and Format. NY, 1949. Fine. Truepenny. $30/£19

BEHAN, BRENDAN. Brendan Behan's Island: An Irish Sketch-Book. (NY): Bernard Geis Assoc, (1962). 1st ed. Signed by Behan and Paul Hogarth (illus). Fine in dj. Pacific*. $138/£86

BEHAN, BRENDAN. Brendan Behan's New York. Hutchinson, 1964. 1st UK ed. Signed by Paul Hogarth (illus). Fine in NF dj (extrems sl worn). Martin. $45/£28

BEHAN, BRENDAN. The Quare Fellow. Methuen, 1956. 1st UK ed, 1st bk. NF (ink name) in VG dj (spine, edges sl rubbed). Williams. $96/£60

BEHRENDT, WALTER C. Modern Building. NY: Harcourt, Brace, (1937). 1st ed. Signed presentation April 1937. All edges stained blue. Tan cl. Text NF (lt aged). Dj (sl worn, lt chipped, several scissor cuts to fr flap). Baltimore*. $30/£19

BEHRMAN, S. N. Conversation with Max. London: Hamish Hamilton, 1960. 1st ed. VG (prelims sl spotted, inscrip) in dj (soiled, browned, frayed). Virgo. $13/£8

BEHRMAN, S. N. The Incomparable Max. London: Heinemann, 1962. 1st ed. Adv rev copy. (Fore-edge sl spotted; cvrs sl rubbed), else Good (lacks dj). Virgo. $16/£10

BEIDELMAN, WILLIAM. The Story of the Pennsylvania Germans. Easton: Express Book Print, 1898. viii,254pp. VG +. *Zubal**. $40/£25

BEITZ, LES. Treasury of Frontier Relics. NY: Edwin House, 1966. 1st ed. Fine in dj. *Labordo*. $30/£19

BEKASSY, FRANC. Adriatica. Hogarth, 1925. 1st ed. One of 90. Marbled paper bds. Good (spotted, fep corner creased; top edge dusty, spine ends, corners bumped, spine worn, cvrs sl mkd, dusty). *Ulysses*. $248/£155

BEKE, X. (Pseud of G. H. Hawtayne.) West Indian Yarns. Demerara/London: J. Thomson/E.A. Petherick, 1890. New ed. 1/4 leather (very rubbed, soiled, spine worn; spotted). *Ulysses*. $152/£95

BEKEN, FRANK and KEITH. The Glory of Sail. NY: DeGraff, 1959. 1st ed. VG in dj. *American Booksellers*. $30/£19

BEKKER, PAUL. The Changing Opera. Arthur Mendel (trans). Dent, 1936. 1st Eng ed. 8 ports. VG in dj. *Hollett*. $40/£25

Belair Stud 1747-1761. (By Fairfax Harrison.) Richmond: Privately ptd at Old Dominion Press, 1929. Uncut. Paper spine label. (Sl worn.) *Oinonen**. $120/£75

BELCHER, JOHN and MERVYN E. MACARTNEY (eds). Later Renaissance Architecture in England. Volume I (only). London: Batsford, 1901. Lg folio. 83 plts. Marbled eps, teg. 1/2 morocco, cl bds, gilt. (Lib ink stamp tp verso, margins lt browned, few sl thumbed; lt soiled, rubbed, #s.) *Edwards*. $144/£90

BELDAM, GEORGE W. Great Golfers: Their Methods at a Glance. London: Macmillan, 1904. 1st ed. Gilt-dec cl. (Partial bkpl removed; spine ends chipped, corners sl bumped, joints sl chipped, rear hinge starting), else VG. *Pacific**. $115/£72

BELDAM, GEORGE W. Great Golfers; Their Methods at a Glance. Macmillan, 1904. 1st ed. Inscribed presentation. Teg. Pict cl, gilt. Good (sl shaken; sl rubbed, worn, sm split upper hinge, lower corners bumped). *Ash*. $472/£295

BELDAM, GEORGE W. and P. A. VAILE. Great Lawn Tennis Players. Macmillan, 1907. Teg. Grn cl, gilt. (Eps foxed, label removed fr pastedown, fr joint cracked; sl worn, mkd.) *Hollett*. $224/£140

BELDEN, DAVID. Souvenir of the Carnival of Roses...1901. Santa Clara: Carnival of Roses, (1901). 1st ed. Inscribed by Director of Rose Bowl Committee. 3/4 morocco, gilt-lettered cl. (Sl offset cvrs), else VG. *Pacific**. $58/£36

BELINAYE, HENRY. The Sources of Health and Disease in Communities. Boston: Allen & Ticknor, 1833. 1st Amer ed. 7,(1),160pp. Orig cl (faded), ptd paper label (chipped). *M & S*. $200/£125

Bell's British Theatre. London: British-Library, 1791-1797. Lg paper ed. 28 vols. Tall 8vo. Marbled eps. Full tree calf, gilt. Good set (worn, spine labels chipped, hinges weak, few professionally rehinged, 1 spine weak but holding). *Hartfield*. $995/£622

BELL, ADRIAN. Men and the Fields. Batsford, 1939. 1st ed. 6 color lithos. VG (prelims, edges sl spotted; spine ends sl bumped) in dj (nicked, sl creased, price-clipped). *Ulysses*. $120/£75

BELL, ALEX MELVILLE. Visible Speech: the Science of Universal Alphabetics, Self-Interpreting. London, 1867. 1st ed. 126 + pp. Good (loose tp; extrems sl worn). *Doctor's Library*. $145/£91

BELL, ANNE OLIVIER. Editing Virginia Woolf's Diary. London: Perpetua Press, 1989. One of 200 numbered, signed. Presentation copy. VG in wrappers (1pg, rear cvr sl soiled; cvrs sl creased). *Ulysses*. $58/£36

BELL, BENJAMIN. A System of Surgery. Edinburgh: Bell & Bradfute, 1791. 5th ed. 6 vols. 8vo. 99 copperplt engrs. Contemp full tree calf (joints cracked but holding, spine ends worn). Text Clean. *House*. $550/£344

BELL, BENJAMIN. A Treatise on the Theory and Management of Ulcers: With a Dissertation on White Swellings of the Joints. Edinburgh: Charles Elliot, 1789. 488pp. Contemp full tree calf. VG (fr joint repaired). *House*. $120/£75

BELL, CHARLES. The Anatomy and Philosophy of Expression as Connected with the Fine Arts. London: Bohn, 1872. 6th ed. viii,275pp; 4 engr plts. (Spine rebacked.) *Ars Artis*. $56/£35

BELL, CHARLES. The Hand: Its Mechanism and Vital Endowments as Evincing Design. London, 1837. 368pp. Marbled edges. Brn 1/2 calf, marbled bds, raised bands, gilt. Good +. *Larry Price*. $150/£94

BELL, CHARLES. Tibet, Past and Present. Oxford, 1924. 1st ed. Color port. (Sm inscrip.) *Petersfield*. $67/£42

BELL, CLIVE. An Account of French Painting. London: C&W, 1931. 1st ed. 32 plts. Top edge brn, lower edges uncut. Rough pink/white mixed-weave linen. Good (spine sl dknd). *Temple*. $32/£20

BELL, CLIVE. Art. London: C&W, 1949. This ed incl add'l 4pp Preface, and a few minor corrections in text. Pub's office copy. Half-tone frontis, 5 plts. Yellow Sundour cl. VG. *Temple*. $22/£14

BELL, CLIVE. The Legend of Monte Della Sibilla or Le Paradis de la Reine Sibille. Leonard & Virginia Woolf, 1923. 1st ed. Royal 8vo. Frontis, 25pp. Rough-trimmed. White bds. Fine in dj (lt sunned, few sm tears). *Blackwell's*. $616/£385

BELL, CLIVE. Old Friends. Personal Recollections. London: C&W, 1956. 1st ed. Frontis, 8 plts. VG in dj. *Cady*. $25/£16

BELL, CLIVE. On British Freedom. London: C&W, 1923. 1st Eng ed. VG (feps partly browned, top edge dusty, sl spotted; cvrs sl mkd, bowed, spine ends sl bumped, sm patch of fading) in dj (nicked, rubbed, dusty, sl creased, browned, price-clipped). *Ulysses*. $104/£65

BELL, CURRER. (Pseud of Charlotte Bronte.) The Professor, a Tale. London: Smith, Elder, 1857. 1st ed. 2 vols. 7.5x5.25. 2pp ads vol 1, 8pp ads (undated) vol 2. Contemp polished calf, gilt, raised bands, red/grn morocco labels. VG (text sl smudged, creased; recently rebacked, bds sl chafed, new eps). *Pirages*. $650/£406

BELL, CURRER. (Pseud of Charlotte Bronte.) The Professor. Smith, Elder, 1857. 2 vols. 8vo. Contemp 1/2 leather, marbled bds, raised bands. Good (rear cvr, ad ll vol 2 waterstained; corners sl rubbed). *Tiger*. $736/£460

BELL, CURRER. (Pseud of Charlotte Bronte.) The Professor.... NY, 1857. 1st Amer ed. Mod buckram. *Swann**. $230/£144

BELL, CURRER. (Pseud of Charlotte Bronte.) Villette. London: Smith, Elder, 1853. 1st ed. 3 vols. Blindstamped cl. (Old name; vol 1 expertly rebacked, orig spine strip laid-on; spine ends sl chipped), else VG. *Pacific**. $1,150/£719

BELL, ELIZABETH TURNER. Fifty Figure and Character Dances for Schools. Waverley Book, 1921. (Feps sl browned.) *Hollett*. $40/£25

BELL, F. JEFFREY. Catalogue of the British Echinoderms. London, 1892. xvii,202pp + 17pp ads; 16 plts. (Ex-lib w/labels, cardholders to eps; spine sl chipped, 3 sm holes to rear joint.) *Edwards*. $48/£30

BELL, FREDERIC J. Condition Red. NY: Longmans, Green, 1944. Tan cl. VG. *American Booksellers*. $20/£13

BELL, GEORGE. Rough Notes of an Old Soldier, During Fifty Years' Service.... London: Day & Son, 1867. 2 vols. Port. Red cl, blue cl spines, gilt. (Sl worn.) *Oinonen**. $250/£156

BELL, GEORGE. A Treatise on the Cow-Pox. Edinburgh: Longman, Hurst et al, 1807. 2nd ed. xii,143pp; 3 hand-colored engr plts. Untrimmed. Later 1/2 calf, gilt. (Extrems rubbed.) *Hollett*. $312/£195

BELL, GERTRUDE. The Arab War. London: Golden Cockerel, 1940. 1st ed. One of 500. Super royal 8vo. 52pp. Cream cl, backed w/grn niger. VG (sl mkd). *Ulysses*. $880/£550

BELL, GERTRUDE. The Letters of Gertrude Bell. Ernest Benn, 1927. 1st ed. 2 vols. Lg fldg map vol 2. Grn cl, gilt. VG set (bkpls; spines sl faded). *Sotheran.* $120/£75

BELL, GERTRUDE. The Letters of Gertrude Bell. Lady Bell (ed). NY: Liveright, n.d. (ca 1927). 1st US ed. 2 vols. 31 plts, 2 maps (1 fldg). (Sl rubbed), o/w VG. *Worldwide.* $65/£41

BELL, GERTRUDE. Syria, the Desert and the Sown. NY: Arno, 1973. Rpt of 1907 ed. 1 fldg map. VG. *Worldwide.* $30/£19

BELL, H. W. Sherlock Holmes and Doctor Watson. Constable, 1932. One of 500. Unopened. VG (fep, fr cvr sellotape-mkd; top edge sl faded, dusty; cvrs sl bowed; spine ends, corners sl bumped; edges sl rubbed) in dj (nicked, creased, sl rubbed, chipped, lacks 3-inch piece at spine tail, spine edges sl dknd). *Ulysses.* $120/£75

BELL, HORACE. On the Old West Coast. Lanier Bartlett (ed). NY: William Morrow, 1930. 1st ed. Good. *Lien.* $35/£22

BELL, HORACE. On the Old West Coast. Lanier Bartlett (ed). NY: William Morrow, 1930. 1st trade ed. Pict eps. Gray cl, red paper labels. NF in dj (chipped, rubbed, loss to corners, spine). *Harrington.* $45/£28

BELL, HORACE. Reminiscences of a Ranger or Early Times in Southern California. L.A.: Primavera, 1933. Rpt of 1927 Hebbard ed. 16 plts. Tan buckram, paper spine label. Fine. *Pacific*.* $23/£14

BELL, HORACE. Reminiscences of a Ranger or Early Times in Southern California. L.A.: Anderson, Ritchie & Simon, 1965-67. Ltd to 1200-1500. 3 vols. Tan cl-backed bds in 3 colors: vol 1 white, vol 2 brn, vol 3 red. As New; slipcases for vols 1, 3 (lacks vol 2 slipcase). *Pacific*.* $29/£18

BELL, HORACE. Reminiscences of a Ranger. Santa Barbara: W. Hebberd, 1927. Good in pict cl. Howes B325. *Lien.* $35/£22

BELL, J. H. B. Bell's Scottish Climbs. Gollancz, 1988. 1st ed. 11 maps, diagrams. VG in dj. *Hollett.* $32/£20

BELL, J. H. B. A Progress in Mountaineering. Oliver & Boyd, (1950). 1st ed. (Cvrs sl stained, worn.) *Rybski.* $25/£16

BELL, J. J. Scotland's Rainbow West. Harrap, 1933. VG in dj (edges chipped, torn, some loss). *Hollett.* $32/£20

BELL, J. MUNRO. The Furniture Designs of Chippendale, Hepplewhite and Sheraton. NY, 1912. 3 parts in 1 vol. (Eps foxed; sl worn, sl shaken, fr cvr spotted.) *Oinonen*.* $40/£25

BELL, JAMES (trans). The History of Gibraltar...Translated From the Spanish of Don Ignacio Lopez de Ayala. William Pickering, 1845. 1st ed in English. xx,234pp; lg fldg hand-colored map. Uncut. Orig brn cl. (Edges lt rubbed, paper label defective), o/w VG. *Cox.* $136/£85

BELL, JAMES B. The Homeopathic Therapeutics of Diarrhea, Dysentery, Cholera, Cholera Morbus, Cholera Infantum. Phila, 1869. 1st ed. 168pp. Black cl, gilt. Fine. *Doctor's Library.* $85/£53

BELL, JAMES S. Journal of a Residence in Circassia During the Years 1837, 1838 and 1839. London, 1840. 1st ed. 2 vols. 12 litho plts (dampstained in margins), fldg litho map hand-colored in outline. Orig cl (spine ends chipped; hinges cracked). *Swann*.* $316/£198

BELL, JOHN. Travels from St. Petersburg in Russia to Diverse Parts of Asia. Glasgow: Robert & Andrew Foulis, 1763. 1st ed. 2 vols. 4to. 1 fldg engr map. (Lacks 1/2-titles.) Contemp speckled calf, contrasting lettering pieces. (Spine heads chipped; fr/rear joints split but cords holding.) *Christie's*.* $630/£394

BELL, JULIAN (ed). We Did Not Fight. 1914-18 Experiences of War Resisters. Cobden-Sanderson, 1935. 1st Eng ed. (Cvrs mkd; no dj.) *Clearwater.* $48/£30

BELL, JULIAN. Winter Movement and Other Poems. C&W, 1930. 1st Eng ed. Buckram. Spare title label. VG (feps partly browned, pastedown edges sl dknd; spine ends, corner sl bumped, cvrs sl mkd) in dj (nicked, soiled, rubbed, dusty, sl torn, browned). *Ulysses.* $152/£95

BELL, KATHERINE M. Swinging the Censer. Santa Barbara: N.p., 1931. 2nd ptg. Teg. Red cl, gilt, black cl spine. Dj (spine tail chip). *Dawson.* $75/£47

BELL, MADISON SMARTT. The Washington Square Ensemble. NY, 1983. 1st ed, 1st bk. Inscribed, signed. NF in NF dj. *Warren.* $95/£59

BELL, THOMAS. A History of British Quadrupeds, Including the Cetacea. London: John van Voorst, 1837. 1st ed. xviii,526pp; pub's March 1850 cat tipped in at rear. Untrimmed. Orig dk grn cl, gilt spine. (Lt aged, hinges lt cracked; sl worn, lt rubbed, spine ends sl frayed, sm splits at ends of lower joints.) *Baltimore*.* $60/£38

BELL, W. H. The Quiddities of an Alaskan Trip. Portland, OR: C.A. Steel, 1873. Unpaginated (67pp). Gilt dec cl. (Sl marginal tear, no loss, 3 ll; new ep, cl spine strip), else VG. *High Latitude.* $290/£181

BELL, W. J. The Modern Book of Railways. London: A&C Black, 1935. 1st ed. 16 plts. (Rear bd dampstained.) *Edwards.* $32/£20

BELL, W. S. Old Fort Benton. Helena, 1909. (Sl worn, sm rear cvr spot.) Wrapper. *Woolson.* $70/£44

BELL, WILLIAM A. New Tracks in North America. A Journal of Travel and Adventure...During 1867-8. London: Chapman & Hall, 1870. 2nd ed. lxix,564,(1)pp; 2 maps, 24 plts. (Faded, flecked; spine very worn.) Howes B350. *Mott.* $150/£94

BELL, WILLIAM A. New Tracks in North America: A Journal of Travel and Adventure...1867-8. London: Chapman & Hall, 1869. 1st ed. 2 vols. (iii)-lxv,(2),236; (iii)-viii,(2),322pp; 20 color litho plts; 3 botanical plts; 1 (of 2) maps. This copy lacks the fldg map, but w/photo facs laid in, along w/map not belonging to the bk. Period 3/4 calf, morocco spine labels. (Dampstain vol 1 frontis, margins/corners of some plts, bkpls, sig, few ink notes; cvrs shelfworn), o/w VG. Howes B330. *Pacific*.* $863/£539

BELL, WILLIAM E. Carpentry Made Easy; or, the Science and Art of Framing, on a New and Improved System. Phila: Ferguson Bros., 1883. 2nd ed. 152pp; 44 plts. (Several sigs loose), else VG. *Glaser.* $175/£109

Bella Starr, the Bandit Queen. Austin, 1960. Steck rpt of 1889 ed. Steck Christmas card laid in. Pict cl (spine faded), else NF in slipcase (soiled). Howes S897. *Baade.* $32/£20

BELLAIRS, JOHN. The House with a Clock in Its Walls. Dial, 1973. 1st ed. NF in Good dj (chipped 1/2-inch at spine head). *Price.* $75/£47

BELLAIRS, JOHN. The Pedant and the Shuffly. NY: Macmillan, 1966. 1st ed. Marilyn Fitschen (illus). 79pp. VG (bottom edge rubbed) in VG dj. *Price.* $65/£41

BELLAIRS, NONA. Going Abroad. Charles J. Skeet, 1857. Tinted frontis. (Sig, fore-edge lt spotted; spine bumped, chipped; hinges nicked, cvrs waterstained, corners rubbed.) *Tiger.* $19/£12

BELLAMY, EDWARD. The Blindman's World. Boston/NY: Houghton Mifflin, 1898. 1st ed. Teg. Grn cl. VG. BAL 968. *Second Life.* $125/£78

BELLAMY, EDWARD. Equality. NY: D. Appleton, 1897. 1st ed. 8pp ads. Salmon cl. NF (sl soiled). *Sumner & Stillman.* $45/£28

BELLAMY, EDWARD. Looking Backward, 2000-1887. Boston: Ticknor, 1888. 1st ed, 1st issue w/'Press of J. J. Arkelyan' on c. pg. Gilt-dec gray cl. (Bkpl), else NF. *Pacific*.* $230/£144

BELLAMY, EDWARD. Looking Backward. LEC, 1941. Ltd to 1500 numbered, signed by Elise Cavanna (illus). Fine in slipcase. *Swann*.* $69/£43

BELLCHAMBERS, E. History of England. London: Allan Bell, 1839. 1st ed. 4 vols. 4 engr frontispieces. Orig grn cl, gilt/blind-stamped. Good. *Young.* $72/£45

Belle of the Fifties. (By Virginia Clay-Clopton.) Doubleday Page, 1905. Good+ (fixed fep torn; binding weak). *Book Broker.* $45/£28

BELLE, FRANCES P. Life and Adventures of the Celebrated Bandit Joaquin Murrieta [sic], His Exploits in the State of California. Chicago: Regan, 1925. 1st ed. Ltd to 975. Fine. *Labordo.* $95/£59

BELLE, FRANCES P. Life and Adventures of the Celebrated Bandit Joaquin Murrieta [sic], His Exploits in the State of California. Chicago: Charles Powner, 1937. 2nd ed. VG in dj. *Labordo.* $35/£22

BELLEW, CLARA (ed). The Merry Circle. Edinburgh: John Grant, n.d. (c.1875). Pict cl (sunned), gilt. *Dramatis.* $45/£28

BELLINGSHAUSEN, THADDEUS. The Voyage of Captain Bellingshausen to the Antarctic Seas 1819-1821. Frank Debenham (ed). London: Hakluyt Soc, 1945. 2 vols. 8vo. 11 maps vol 1; 9 maps vol 2. Fine. *Explorer.* $752/£470

BELLOC, HILAIRE. Avril. London: Sheed & Ward, 1945. 1st ed. Frontis. VG in dj (sl worn). *Hollett.* $40/£25

BELLOC, HILAIRE. The Battle Ground. Cassell, 1936. 1st Eng ed. 1 color map. VG (feps, pastedown edges sl browned; top edge sl dusty; spine ends, corners sl bumped) in dj (nicked, sl creased, dknd). *Ulysses.* $184/£115

BELLOC, HILAIRE. A Change in the Cabinet. Methuen, 1909. 1st ed. Good (inscrip, ep edges sl browned, spotted; bumped, mkd, edges rubbed, browned, top edge dusty). *Ulysses.* $88/£55

BELLOC, HILAIRE. The Chanty of the Nona. London: Ariel Poems, (1928). 1st Eng ed. Fine in pict card wrappers. *Clearwater.* $32/£20

BELLOC, HILAIRE. The Contrast. NY: Robert M. McBride, (1924). 2nd ptg. Blue cl. Dj (faded, lt chipped). *Mott.* $15/£9

BELLOC, HILAIRE. Cranmer. Cassell, 1931. 1st ed. B/w frontis. VG (top edge sl dusty, spine sl faded, spine ends sl bumped, edges spotted) in dj (nicked, sl creased, rubbed, dusty, sl mkd, torn, browned). *Ulysses.* $120/£75

BELLOC, HILAIRE. Cromwell. London: Cassell, 1934. 1st Eng ed. B/w frontis, 12 maps. VG (top edge sl dusty; prelims, edges, eps spotted; spine ends bumped) in dj (nicked, chipped, rubbed, spotted, dusty, sl torn, mkd, creased, browned, spine head sl defective). *Ulysses.* $72/£45

BELLOC, HILAIRE. Economics for Helen. (London): J.W. Arrowsmith, 1924. One of 265 numbered. Teg. Buckram. VG (eps sl spotted, half-title, final pg partly browned; spine ends, corners sl bumped) in dj (nicked, torn, rubbed, sl chipped, creased, mkd, dusty, browned, 2-inch tear spine head w/some loss). *Ulysses.* $248/£155

BELLOC, HILAIRE. The Elements of the Great War. NY: Hearst's Internat'l Library, (1916). 1st US ed. Dk grn cl, gilt. (Eps, edges sl smudged), o/w VG in pict dj (sl chipped, dust-mkd). *Reese.* $50/£31

BELLOC, HILAIRE. Esto Perpetua. Duckworth, 1906. 1st ed. Tipped-in color frontis. Teg. Dec cl, gilt. VG (feps sl browned; spine ends sl bumped). *Ulysses.* $120/£75

BELLOC, HILAIRE. The Eye Witness. Eveleigh Nash, 1908. 1st ed. Good (inscrip, eps sl mkd; edges sl rubbed, cvrs sl mkd, sl bumped, spine faded, top edge dusty, rear hinge cracked). *Ulysses.* $96/£60

BELLOC, HILAIRE. The Great Inquiry. Duckworth, n.d. (1903). 1st ed. Good (bottom edges of 1st 5pp dampstained, corners sl creased; mkd, rubbed, sl soiled, sm tear to top edge of fr cvr, spine foot split) in wrappers. *Ulysses.* $200/£125

BELLOC, HILAIRE. The Green Overcoat. J.W. Arrowsmith, 1912. 1st ed. 19 full-pg b/w dwgs. VG (bottom corner of 1 pg lacks sm piece, feps browned, edges sl browned; sl bumped, top edge dusty, spine browned). *Ulysses.* $96/£60

BELLOC, HILAIRE. The Haunted House. London: J.W. Arrowsmith, 1927. 1st Eng ed. 25 full-pg b/w dwgs by G. K. Chesterton. VG (spine ends, corners, top edge fr cvr sl bumped) in dj (nicked, rubbed, sl mkd, dusty, sl dknd). *Ulysses.* $560/£350

BELLOC, HILAIRE. The Highway and its Vehicles. Geoffrey Holme (ed). Studio, 1926. 1st ltd ed. 131 plts (24 color). Buckram. (Ex-lib.) *Forest.* $56/£35

BELLOC, HILAIRE. The Historic Thames. J.M. Dent, 1907. 1st ed. 59 color plts. Teg. Dec cl, gilt. Good (spotted, feps browned, rear hinge cracked; spine dknd, cvrs bowed, sl mkd, edges sl worn). *Ulysses.* $152/£95

BELLOC, HILAIRE. The Jews. Constable, 1922. 1st ed. (Edges sl faded), else Good. *Whiteson.* $38/£24

BELLOC, HILAIRE. The Man Who Made Gold. London: J.W. Arrowsmith, 1930. 1st Eng ed. 17 b/w dwgs by G. K. Chesterton. VG (feps partly browned; spine ends sl bumped) in later issue dj—w/price of 3/6 and pub's sticker on spine—(nicked, rubbed, internally repaired, sl mkd, dusty, dknd, clipped). *Ulysses.* $240/£150

BELLOC, HILAIRE. The Mercy of Allah. C&W, 1922. VG (feps partly browned, top edge dusty; spine ends sl bumped, edges sl rubbed) in dj (nicked, rubbed, chipped, dusty, sl mkd, creased, browned). *Ulysses.* $152/£95

BELLOC, HILAIRE. The Missing Masterpiece. London, 1929. 1st Eng ed. Nice (bkpl; 2 corners sl bumped; lacks dj). *Clearwater.* $72/£45

BELLOC, HILAIRE. New Cautionary Tales. Gerald Duckworth, 1930. 1st ed. Cl-backed pict bds. VG (prelims, final blanks, edges spotted, feps sl bumped; edges spotted, top edge dusty, corners sl bumped) in dj (nicked, rubbed, sl torn, mkd, creased, dusty, browned). *Ulysses.* $152/£95

BELLOC, HILAIRE. Nine Nines. Oxford, 1931. 1st Eng ed. Pict bds (dust-mkd, tanned, spine head sl torn; foxed; lacks dj). *Clearwater.* $56/£35

BELLOC, HILAIRE. On the Place of Gilbert Chesterton in English Letters. London, 1940. 1st Eng ed. Nice (stamp) in dj (sl dust-mkd). *Clearwater.* $72/£45

BELLOC, HILAIRE. The Path to Rome. Nelson, n.d. Pocket ed rpt. Inscribed 'To Mr. R. T. Hale from H. Belloc.' (Half-title hinge weak.) *Clearwater.* $72/£45

BELLOC, HILAIRE. Pongo and the Bull. Constable, 1910. 1st ed. Pict cl. VG (inscrip, eps spotted, sl browned; sl mkd, spine dknd, top edge sl mkd, dusty). *Ulysses.* $88/£55

BELLOC, HILAIRE. The Postmaster-General. London: J.W. Arrowsmith, 1932. 1st Eng ed. 30 full-pg b/w dwgs by G. K. Chesterton. VG (top edge dusty, bottom edges sl mkd; spine ends, corners sl bumped, spine sl faded) in dj (nicked, rubbed, dusty, sl mkd, creased, browned). *Ulysses.* $232/£145

BELLOC, HILAIRE. The Postmaster-General. London: Arrowsmith, 1932. 1st ed. G. K. Chesterton (illus). Grn cl, gilt. Fine in NF pict dj. *Vandoros.* $250/£156

BELLOC, HILAIRE. A Shorter History of England. George G. Harrap, 1934. 1st Eng ed. 11 maps. VG (spine ends, corner bumped) in dj (nicked, rubbed, sl creased, mkd, dusty, sl torn, browned). *Ulysses.* $136/£85

BELLOC, HILAIRE. Sonnets and Verses. Duckworth, 1923. One of 525. Teg, fore/lower edge untrimmed. (Sl foxed), o/w Fine in dj (worn, browned). *Any Amount.* $64/£40

BELLOC, HILAIRE. This and That and the Other. Methuen, 1912. 1st Eng ed. VG (eps browned, top edge dusty, bottom edge sl spotted; spine ends, corners sl bumped). *Ulysses.* $58/£36

BELLOC, HILAIRE. The Verse of Hilaire Belloc. W. N. Roughead (ed). London: Nonesuch, 1954. 1st collected ed. One of 1650. Fine in tan cl, gilt, Fine dj. *Vandoros.* $150/£94

BELLOC, HILAIRE. Verses. Duckworth, 1910. 1st Eng ed. Errata slip tipped in. Teg. Buckram. VG (feps, pastedown edges sl browned; fore-edge sl spotted; spine tail, corners bumped). *Ulysses.* $152/£95

BELLOW, SAUL. Dangling Man. NY: Vanguard, (1944). 1st ed, 1st bk. NF in VG + dj (edges sl dknd, few sm closed tears). *Reese.* $900/£563

BELLOW, SAUL. The Dean's December. (NY: Harper & Row, 1982.) 1st ed. One of 500 signed. Top edge stained red. Red cl. Fine in red blindstamped slipcase. *Heritage.* $125/£78

BELLOW, SAUL. Henderson the Rain King. NY, 1959. 1st ed. NF in NF dj (rear panel crinkled). *Warren.* $35/£22

BELLOW, SAUL. Henderson the Rain King. London: Weidenfeld & Nicolson, 1959. 1st British ed. VG+ in VG+ dj. *Pettler.* $60/£38

BELLOW, SAUL. Herzog. NY: Viking, 1964. 1st ed. VG+ in VG dj (edge lt chipped). *Pettler.* $35/£22

BELLOW, SAUL. Humbolt's Gift. NY: Viking, (1975). 1st ed. Fine in dj (sl worn). *Second Life.* $45/£28

BELLOW, SAUL. The Last Analysis. NY: Viking, 1965. 1st ed. NF in VG dj. *Pettler.* $40/£25

BELLOW, SAUL. Nobel Lecture. NY: Targ Editions, 1979. One of 350 signed. Fine. *Williams.* $128/£80

BELLOW, SAUL. Seize the Day. London: W&N, (1957). 1st British ed. VG in dj (lt worn, sm nick spine crown). *Reese.* $45/£28

BELLOW, SAUL. The Victim. London: John Lehmann, 1948. 1st Eng ed. VG (top edge dusty, edges spotted; spine ends, corners sl bumped; gilt sl oxidized) in dj (nicked, rubbed, dusty, sl soiled, torn, chipped, browned). *Ulysses.* $312/£195

BELLOWS, GEORGE. The Paintings. NY, 1929. Folio. (Spine dknd, corners worn.) *Swann*.* $161/£101

BELLOWS, HENRY W. Historical Sketch of Union League Club of New York, 1863-79. NY: Clubhouse, 1879. 200pp. (Cvrs spotted, bottom edge worn.) Contents VG. *Heinoldt.* $15/£9

BELMONT, AUGUST. Letters, Speeches and Addresses of.... N.p.: Privately ptd, 1890. 1st ed. Gilt-stamped blue cl (sl worn). *Oinonen*.* $30/£19

BELOE, WILLIAM. Anecdotes of Literature and Scarce Books. London: Rivington, 1807-1812. 1st Complete ed. 6 vols. Tall 8vo. 4pp pub's ads end of vol 2, 4-pg pub's leaflet dated 1812 tipped in at fr vol 6. Uncut. Orig pub's bds, paper spines, morocco labels, numerals. VG set. Each vol w/Rex Whistler bkpl; label of James Osborn 1st vol. *Hartfield.* $850/£531

BELOE, WILLIAM. The Attic Nights of Aulus Gellius. London: J. Johnson, 1795. 1st ed. 3 vols. Prize-bound calf, gilt, morocco spine labels. (Bkpls; extrems, spines dknd, joints cracked, lacks some spine labels), else VG set. *Pacific*.* $104/£65

BELSHAM, W. Memoirs of the Kings of Great Britain of the House of Brunswic-Lunenburg. London, 1793. 1st ed. 2 vols. 383; 386pp + index. Full speckled gilt-stamped calf. (Ink names, bkpls; extrems worn.) *King.* $125/£78

BELT, THOMAS. The Naturalist in Nicaragua. London/NY: J.M. Dent & Sons/E.P. Dutton, (c. 1920). New ed. Wood-engr add'l tp, surround, xxxiii,306pp; dbl-pg map. Teg. Recent crimson 1/2 morocco, gilt, sl raised bands. Fine. *Sotheran.* $157/£98

BEMAN, DAVID. The Mysteries of Trade, or the Great Source of Wealth. Boston: The Author, 1825. 1st ed, w/errata slip at end. Contemp sig of George H. Trumbull. Contemp tree calf (rubbed; sl foxed, soiled, sig). *Oinonen*.* $250/£156

BEMELMANS, LUDWIG. The Best of Times. NY: S&S, 1948. 1st ed. 10.5x13. 188pp. VG (corners, edges lt worn) in Fair dj (lacks 2-inch piece of flap). *Price.* $75/£47

BEMELMANS, LUDWIG. The Blue Danube. NY: Viking, 1945. 1st ed. Fine in dj. *Cummins.* $100/£63

BEMELMANS, LUDWIG. The Donkey Inside. NY: Viking, 1941. 1st ed. One of 175. Signed on the orig watercolor. NF in VG slipcase. *Pacific*.* $259/£162

BEMELMANS, LUDWIG. The Golden Basket. May Massee (ed). NY: Viking, 1936. 1st ed. 7 1/4 x 10. 96pp. Blindstamped vermilion cl. VG in dj (worn, sl chipped). *Cattermole.* $300/£188

BEMELMANS, LUDWIG. Hansi. NY: Viking, 1934. 1st ed, 1st bk. 9x12. 62pp. Cl spine, pict bds. VG (sl edgeworn) in dj (lacks few sm pieces). *Cattermole.* $375/£234

BEMELMANS, LUDWIG. The Happy Place. Boston: Little, Brown, 1952. 1st ed. 5 1/2 x 8 1/4. 58pp. VG in dj. *Cattermole.* $75/£47

BEMELMANS, LUDWIG. Italian Holiday. Boston: Houghton Mifflin, 1961. 1st ed. 9x11.5. 102pp. VG (spine foot worn) in VG dj (sl edgeworn). *Price.* $48/£30

BEMELMANS, LUDWIG. Madeline and the Bad Hat. NY: Viking, (1957). 1st ed. Lg 4to. Rose-red cl. Full color dj (spine chip, wear along edges, folds). *Reisler.* $200/£125

BEMELMANS, LUDWIG. Madeline's Christmas. McCall's, 1956. 1st issue. 12mo. 24 color pp (incl self-cvrs). Color illus paper wrappers. Nice (sl worn). *Reisler.* $175/£109

BEMELMANS, LUDWIG. Madeline's Rescue. NY: Viking, 1953. 1st ed. Lg 4to. Red cl, Madeline vignette fr cvr. Good in color dj (lt marginal wear). *Reisler.* $250/£156

BEMELMANS, LUDWIG. Madeline. NY: S&S, 1939. 1st ed. 9x12. 48pp. Pict bds. Fine in dj. *Cattermole.* $425/£266

BEMELMANS, LUDWIG. Madeline. NY: Simon & Schuster, 1939. 1st ed. Lg 4to. Full color pict bds (edges rubbed). Nice in pict dj (margins lt worn). *Reisler.* $450/£281

BEMELMANS, LUDWIG. Madeline. NY: Little Golden Book, 1954. 1st ed thus. 24pp. VG. *Cattermole.* $40/£25

BEMELMANS, LUDWIG. My War with the United States. NY: Viking, 1937. 1st ed. 6 3/4 x 9 1/2. 151pp. VG in dj. *Cattermole.* $100/£63

BEMELMANS, LUDWIG. Now I Lay Me Down to Sleep. NY: Viking, 1943. 1st ed, ltd issue. One of 500 numbered, signed. Gray cl, leather spine label. (Spine, label sl rubbed), o/w Nice in slipcase (cracked). *Reese.* $150/£94

BEMELMANS, LUDWIG. Parsley. NY: Harper, 1955. 1st ed. 12 x 10 1/4. 47pp. VG in dj. *Cattermole.* $200/£125

BEMELMANS, LUDWIG. Sunshine. NY: S&S, 1950. 1st ed. 42pp. NF (edges lt bumped) in NF dj. *Davidson.* $200/£125

BEMROSE, WILLIAM. Longton Hall Porcelain. London/Derby, 1906. Color frontis; 46 plts. Teg, rest uncut. (Feps browned; sl rubbed, spine sl faded.) *Edwards.* $136/£85

Ben Nicholson. London: Marlborough Galleries, October 1971. Ptd stiff wrappers. *Turtle Island.* $40/£25

BEN-ARI, RAIKIN. Habima. A. H. Gross and I. Soref (trans). NY: Thomas Yoseloff, (1957). VG in dec dj. *Dramatis.* $30/£19

BENCHLEY, NATHANIEL. Sweet Anarchy. NY: Doubleday, 1979. 1st ed. Signed presentation. VG+ in dj. *Any Amount.* $24/£15

BENCHLEY, PETER. Jaws. GC: Doubleday, 1974. 1st ed. VG+ in VG+ dj (extrems sl chipped, few scratches). *Unger.* $125/£78

BENDER, LAURETTA. Aggression, Hostility and Anxiety in Children. Springfield: Charles C. Thomas, 1953. 1st ed. Fine in NF dj. *Beasley.* $50/£31

BENDER, LAURETTA. Child Psychiatric Techniques. Springfield: Charles C. Thomas, 1952. 1st ed. Fine in dj (lt used). *Beasley.* $50/£31

BENDER, LAURETTA. A Dynamic Psychopathology of Childhood. Springfield: Charles C. Thomas, 1954. 1st ed. (Sm marginal stain several pp), else Fine in dj (lt used, sm chip). *Beasley.* $50/£31

BENEDETTI, MARIO. Truce. NY: Harper, 1969. 1st US ed. VG in dj. *Lame Duck.* $100/£63

BENEDICT, CARL. A Tenderfoot Kid on Gyp Water. Austin: Univ Press of Dallas, 1943. 1st ed. One of 550 ptd. VF. *Labordo.* $395/£247

BENEDICT, F. G. and R. C. LEE. Hibernation and Marmot Physiology. Washington, 1938. 2 plts. (Eps browned; lt worn, lower corners bumped, spine flecked.) *Sutton.* $80/£50

BENEDICT, LEONARD. Waifs of the Slums and Their Way Out. NY: Revell, 1907. 1st ed. (Homemade lib pocket, reading list tipped to fep), o/w Fine. *Beasley.* $50/£31

BENEDICT, LIBBY. The Refugees. Hogarth, 1938. One of 1222. VG (fore-edge sl spotted, sm dent fr cvr, spine head, corner sl bumped) in dj (sl rubbed, creased, dusty, spine, edges sl browned). *Ulysses.* $232/£145

BENEDICT, PINCKNEY. The Wrecking Yard and Other Stories. NY, 1992. 1st ed. NF in Fine dj. *Warren.* $30/£19

BENEDICTUS, DAVID. You're a Big Boy Now. NY, 1964. 1st Amer ed. VG in dj (sl rubbed). *King.* $20/£13

BENESCH, OTTO. The Drawings of Rembrandt. London, (1954-57). 1st complete ed. 6 vols. Folio. (Spines faded.) *Swann*.* $575/£359

BENET, STEPHEN VINCENT. The Barefoot Saint. NY: Doubleday, 1929. One of 367 ptd. Valenti Angelo (illus). VG + . *Pharos.* $150/£94

BENET, STEPHEN VINCENT. The Devil and Daniel Webster. NY: Dramatists Play Service, (1939). Correct 1st ed. Fine in wrappers. *Pharos.* $95/£59

BENET, STEPHEN VINCENT. The Headless Horseman. Music by Douglas Moore. Boston: Schirmer, (1937). 1st ed. Folio. Fine in cl-backed pict wrappers (head sl stained). *Pharos.* $250/£156

BENET, STEPHEN VINCENT. James Shore's Daughter. GC: Doubleday, Doran, 1934. 1st ed. One of 307 numbered, signed. Fine in glassine wrapper (chipped, browned), pub's slipcase. *Heritage.* $85/£53

BENET, STEPHEN VINCENT. John Brown's Body. LEC, 1948. Ltd to 1500 numbered. Fine in slipcase. *Swann*.* $57/£36

BENET, STEPHEN VINCENT. Johnny Pye and the Fool-Killer. Weston: Countryman, (1938). One of 700 (of 750). Signed by Benet and Charles Child (illus). Blue cl. Mint in acetate slipcase w/wraparound band, pub's box. *Pharos.* $350/£219

BENEZET, ANTHONY and JOHN WESLEY. Views of American Slavery, Taken a Century Ago. Phila: Assoc of Friends for Diffusion of Religious and Useful Knowledge, 1858. 138pp. Grn cl, gilt. (Ex-lib, bkpl; sm perforated stamp tp, 1pg; sm paper sticker fr cvr; sl worn.) Text Clean. *Baltimore*.* $30/£19

BENFORD, GREGORY. Jupiter Project. NY: Nelson, 1975. 1st ed. VG + (sl shelfworn) in dj (edgeworn). *My Bookhouse.* $37/£23

Bengo to the Rescue. (Somerset)/London: Purnell & Sons, 1956. 3 dbl-pg pop-ups by Tim. VG. *Bookfinders.* $50/£31

BENHAM, W. GURNEY. Playing Cards. London: Ward, Lock, (1931). 1st ed. VF in dj w/color repro mtd fr cvr. *Oak Knoll.* $125/£78

BENHAM, W. GURNEY. Playing Cards. London: Spring Books, n.d. Fine in dj (lt chipped). *Oak Knoll.* $65/£41

BENHAM, W. GURNEY. Playing Cards: History of the Pack and Explanations of Its Many Secrets. London: Ward, Lock, (1931). 1st ed. (Cvrs bowed), else VG- in dj (spine ends chipped, lacks piece, tape repair to verso). *Pacific*.* $92/£58

BENJAMIN, ASHER and DANIEL RAYNERD. The American Builder's Companion; or, A New System of Architecture: Particularly Adapted to the Present Style of Building in the United States of America.... Boston, 1806. 1st ed. 4to. 44 engr plts. Contemp sheep. *Felcone.* $1,500/£938

BENJAMIN, ASHER. The Practical House Carpenter.... Boston, 1830. 2nd ed. 64 engr plts. Contemp 1/2 sheep (quite worn; variously browned throughout). *Swann*.* $373/£233

BENJAMIN, ASHER. Practice of Architecture...for the Use of Carpenters and Practical Men.... Boston, 1840. 4th ed. 60 engr plts. Orig tree sheep (extrems rubbed; foxing, variously affecting plts). *Swann*.* $230/£144

BENJAMIN, RENE. Private Gaspard. A Soldier of France. Selmer Fougner (trans). NY: Brentano's, 1916. 1st ed in English, US issue. Khaki cl, tri-color border. NF in VG dj (lt foxed, lt ring mk, sm chips). *Reese.* $50/£31

BENKOVITZ, MIRIAM J. A Bibliography of Ronald Firbank. Soho Bibliographies XVI, 1982. 2nd ed. Dj. *Forest.* $40/£25

BENN, EDITH FRASER. An Overland Trek From India by Side-Saddle, Camel, and Rail. London: Longmans, Green, 1909. 1st ed. 48 half-tone plts, fldg route map (edge frayed, browned) at end. Beige dec, pict cl (hinges weak, spine faded, rubbed). Good (foxed, waterstained). *Morrell.* $152/£95

BENN, GEORGE. A History of the Town of Belfast. London: Marcus Ward, 1877. 1st ed. 2 vols in 1. Demy 8vo. x,770; 238pp; 3 plts. 8 fldg maps, plans (some repaired, w/o loss), fldg genealogical table contained in rear folder. Aeg. Full calf (recently recased), gilt, raised bands, panels, black title label. Fine (interior lt foxed). *Ulysses.* $1,008/£630

BENNET, J. HENRY. Winter and Spring on the Shores of the Mediterranean. NY: Appleton, 1870. xiv,621pp; 6 fldg maps, 12 plts. 1/2 calf, marbled bds (rubbed, spine worn). *Adelson.* $75/£47

Bennett's Hand-Book for Norway. London, 1884. 23rd ed. Good + (lacks fep). *Gretton.* $16/£10

BENNETT, ALAN. The Madness of George III. Faber, 1992. 1st UK ed. Fine pict pb. *Williams.* $29/£18

BENNETT, ARNOLD et al. The Art of E. A. Rickards. NY/London, 1920. Sm folio. *Swann*.* $92/£58

BENNETT, ARNOLD. Elsie and the Child. Cassell, 1929. 1st ed. Ltd to 750. Dec cl (few sm mks, sl dull). Internally VG in slipcase (dull). *Whiteson.* $176/£110

BENNETT, ARNOLD. Elsie and the Child. Cassell, 1929. One of 650 (of 750). 7 full-pg illus, 2 further illus, by E. McKnight Kauffer. Untrimmed. Fawn linen. VG (eps sl browned). *Blackwell's.* $224/£140

BENNETT, ARNOLD. Hilda Lessways. London: Methuen, (1911). 1st ed. (Backstrip faded, few tears, binding sl loose.) *Petersfield.* $35/£22

BENNETT, ARNOLD. Hilda Lessways. William Briggs, 1911. 1st ed, Canadian issue. VG + in VG dj (lt soiled, chipped). *Fine Books.* $225/£141

BENNETT, ARNOLD. Literary Taste. London: New Age Press, 1909. 1st ed. Dec cl (spine sl dknd), gilt. *Hollett.* $32/£20

BENNETT, ARNOLD. Lord Raingo. NY: George H. Doran, (1926). 1st US ed. Red cl (insect nibbling to hinges). Good in pict dj (lt chipped, creased, few old mends on verso). *Reese.* $25/£16

BENNETT, ARNOLD. Mediterranean Scenes. Cassell, 1928. 1st ed. (Top of limitation pg cut away), else VG in dj (discolored, sl mkd). *Whiteson.* $29/£18

BENNETT, ARNOLD. Mental Efficiency and Other Hints to Men and Women. Hodder & Stoughton, (1912). New ed. Good (spine bumped, waterstained). Good. *Tiger.* $13/£8

BENNETT, ARNOLD. Old Wives' Tale. LEC, 1941. Ltd to 1500 numbered, signed by John Austen (illus). 2 vols. Fine in slipcase. *Swann*.* $34/£21

BENNETT, ARNOLD. Piccadilly. Readers Library, 1929. 1st UK ed. VG + in pict dj (sl rubbed, spine ends strengthened w/tape). *Williams.* $120/£75

BENNETT, ARNOLD. The Pretty Lady. London: Cassell, (1918). 1st ed. Blue cl stamped in gilt/blind. Good (spine rubbed). *Reese.* $22/£14

BENNETT, ARNOLD. The Roll-Call. London: Hutchinson, 1918. 1st ed. Red cl stamped in black. VG in pict dj (lt worn). *Reese.* $100/£63

BENNETT, BONNIE A. and DAVID G. WILKINS. Donatello. London: Phaidon, 1984. 1st ed. Dj. *Edwards.* $40/£25

BENNETT, C. H. Shadows. London: D. Bogue, (1857). 1st ed. 24 hand-colored plts. Orig pict bds (corners worn, mod linen spine). *Appelfeld.* $200/£125

BENNETT, CHARLES. Nine Lives of a Cat. London: Griffith & Farran, Corner of St. Paul's Churchyard, 1860. 1st ed. 8vo. (vi),20,(ii),16pp pub's cat. Red red pebble-grained, blind-stamped cl, gilt. Nice (bkpl; spine rubbed, ends sl worn). *Sotheran.* $400/£250

BENNETT, DOROTHY A. The Golden Encyclopedia. S&S, 1946. 1st ed. 10.3x13. Cornelius DeWitt (illus). 126pp. VG (corners worn) in VG- dj (edgeworn, three 1.5-inch tears). *Price.* $65/£41

BENNETT, ESTELLINE. Old Deadwood Days. NY: J.H. Sears, 1928. 1st ed. NF in dj. Howes B356. *Labordo.* $65/£41

BENNETT, G. J. The Pedestrian's Guide Through North Wales. London: Henry Colburn, 1838. 1st ed. viii,391pp; add'l illus tp, 19 etched plts, 7 fldg plts. Orig blind-emb cl. (Foxed, shaken, bkpl; spine chipped, faded.) *Edwards.* $72/£45

BENNETT, H. S. English Books and Readers 1475-1557.... Cambridge: CUP, 1969. 2nd ed. Red cl. (Ex-lib, stamp; shelf mk to spine.) Dj (stuck down). *Maggs.* $29/£18

BENNETT, H. S. Life on the English Manor, a Study of Peasant Conditions 1150-1400. Cambridge, 1938. Dj (edges sl torn). *Petersfield.* $29/£18

BENNETT, JOHN. Madame Margot: A Grotesque Legend of Old Charleston. NY: Century, 1921. Possible rmdr copy. VG. *Cullen.* $45/£28

BENNETT, L. J. The Blue-Winged Teal. Ames: Collegiate, 1938. 1st ed. Color frontis. Pict cl. VG + . *Mikesh.* $60/£38

BENNETT, MARTIN. Rolls-Royce: The History of the Car. Arco, (1974). Good in dj (worn). *Rybski.* $40/£25

BENNETT, MILDRED R. The World of Willa Cather. NY, (1951). 1st Amer ed. Fine (sl rubbed) in NF dj. *Polyanthos.* $25/£16

BENNETT, N. The Science and Practice of Dental Surgery. London, 1931. 2nd ed. 2 vols. Fine set. *Whitehart.* $56/£35

BENNETT, RICHARD E. Mormons at the Missouri, 1846-1852. Norman: Univ of OK, (1987). 1st ed. Fine in dj. *Lien.* $25/£16

BENNETT, T. P. Architectural Design in Concrete. London, 1927. Lib morocco-backed cl bds. (Bkpl; lib ink stamps, spine #s, sl spotted; rebound, soiled, rubbed.) *Edwards.* $56/£35

BENNETT, WHITMAN. A Practical Guide to American Nineteenth Century Color Plate Books. NY, 1949. Frontis. Good. *Dumont.* $40/£25

BENNETT, WHITMAN. A Practical Guide to American Nineteenth Century Color Plate Books. NY: Bennett Book Studios, 1949. Errata pasted on inside fr cvr, 8pp Supplement No. 1 folded and inserted. VG. *Zubal*.* $50/£31

BENOIS, ALEXANDRE. The Russian School of Painting. NY, 1916. 32 plts. Patterned bds (spine ends, corners sl worn). *Swann*.* $103/£64

BENOIS, ALEXANDRE. The Russian School of Painting. T. Werner Laurie, 1916. 32 plts. Untrimmed. Dec paper-cvrd bds. Good (lib stamp, blind-stamps, sl fingering). *Hollett.* $120/£75

BENSON, A. C. et al. The Book of the Queen's Dolls' House Library. London: Methuen, (1924). 1st ed. One of 1500. 2 vols. 1/4 cl, bds, spine labels. NF in Fair djs (in pieces, laid in loose), VG slipcase. *Pacific*.* $431/£269

BENSON, ADOLPH (ed). Peter Kalm's Travels in North America: The English Version of 1770. NY: Wilson-Erickson, 1937. 2 vols. VG (sl dusty). *Pacific*.* $63/£39

BENSON, BERRY. Berry Benson's Civil War Book. Susan Williams Benson (ed). Athens: Univ of GA, (1962). 1st ed. Gray cl. Fine in VG dj. *Chapel Hill.* $100/£63

BENSON, C. E. British Mountaineering. Routledge, 1909. 1st ed. Grn speckled edges, rounded corners. Pict cl, gilt. Very Nice. *Hollett.* $136/£85

BENSON, D. R. Irene Good-Night. NY, 1982. 1st ed. One of 250 signed by Benson & Edward Gorey (frontis). Purple silk. Pict mylar dj. *Swann*.* $57/£36

BENSON, E. F. The Angel of Pain. London, 1906. 1st Eng ed. Good (foxed; cvrs sl mkd). *Clearwater.* $56/£35

BENSON, E. F. The Male Impersonator. Elkin Matthews & Marrot, 1929. One of 530 numbered, signed. Dec eps; unopened. Dec paper bds. VG (feps partly browned; spine ends, corners sl bumped) in dj (nicked, sl chipped, sl browned). *Ulysses.* $200/£125

BENSON, E. F. Mapp and Lucia. London, 1931. 1st Eng ed. (Few grubby ll; cvr sl mkd, faded; lacks dj.) *Clearwater.* $56/£35

BENSON, E. F. The Outbreak of War, 1914. (London): Peter Davies, 1933. 1st ed. Gilt straw cl. VG (ink name, edges dkng) in dj (lt used). *Reese.* $35/£22

BENSON, IVAN. Mark Twain's Western Years. Stanford: Stanford Univ, (1938). 1st ed. Gray cl, stiff bds. Fine (few ll dog-eared) in dj (chipped). *Macdonnell.* $50/£31

BENSON, LYMAN. The Cacti of Arizona. Tucson, 1969. 3rd ed. VG in dj. *Brooks.* $30/£19

BENSON, LYMAN. The Cacti of the United States and Canada. Stanford, 1982. Fine in dj. *Brooks.* $96/£60

BENSON, ROBERT (ed). The Holford Collection. Privately ptd, 1924. One of 300 signed. 98 plts. Dec eps; teg. 1/2 vellum, morocco label. (Fr cvr sl bowed), o/w Fine. *Europa.* $264/£165

BENSON, ROBERT (ed). The Holford Collection. Dorchester House/OUP, 1927. #XL/400. 2 vols. 200 plts. Marbled eps; teg. (Bkpl.) *Edwards.* $96/£60

BENSON, ROBERT. Sketches of Corsica. London: Longman, Hurst, Rees, Orme, Brown & Green, 1825. (vi),195pp; 5 aquatint plts. (Leading corner sl stained intruding on some margins.) Orig marbled bds (rebacked, recornered in gilt-edged mod calf), morocco spine label. *Edwards.* $400/£250

BENSON, THOMAS W. Fundamentals of Television. NY: Mancall Pub, (1930). 1st ed. Blue cl. VG. *Glaser.* $125/£78

BENT, A. C. Life Histories of North American Birds of Prey. Washington: Smithsonian, 1937-1938. 1st ed. 2 vols. Partly uncut. VG + (ex-lib) in wraps. *Mikesh.* $60/£38

BENT, A. C. Life Histories of North American Cuckoos Goatsuckers, Hummingbirds and Their Allies. Washington, 1940. 73 plts. Unopened. Rebound in cl w/orig wraps bound in to rear. (Bkpl.) *Edwards.* $80/£50

BENT, NEWELL. American Polo. NY, 1929. 1st ed. *Swann*.* $46/£29

BENTHAM, JEREMY. The Rational of Reward. London: John & H.L. Hunt, 1825. 1st ed. 8vo. viii,352pp. Orig grn ribbed cl (spine extrems rubbed, chipped), paper spine label (chipped). *Karmiole.* $650/£406

BENTINCK, HENRY. Letters. Robert Scott, 1919. 1st Eng ed. (Lacks fep; cvrs lt spotted.) *Clearwater.* $56/£35

BENTLEY, E. C. Clerihews Complete. Werner Laurie, 1951. 1st ed thus. (Foxed; edges sl soiled), else VG in dj (soiled, worn). *Virgo.* $24/£15

BENTLEY, E. C. Trent's Last Case. London: Thomas Nelson & Sons, n.d. (1913). 1st ed. Blind-stamped cl. VG (sl askew, spine head sl worn). *Sumner & Stillman.* $80/£50

BENTLEY, ERIC. In Search of Theater. NY: Knopf, 1953. 1st ed. Lt tan cl. VG (worn, sm tear rear cvr) in Fair dj (rubbed, soiled, chipped; piece out of spine, fr panel partially detached). *Blue Mountain.* $35/£22

BENTLEY, HARRY C. and RUTH S. LEONARD. Bibliography of Works on Accounting by American Authors. Boston, 1934-(1935). 2 vols. (Vol 2 lacks title-leaf, vol 1 inner joint strengthened; lt worn, spine gilt faded.) *Oinonen*.* $50/£31

BENTON, FRANK. Cowboy Life on the Sidetrack. Denver, 1903. 1st ed. Pict cl. VG (bkpls, pencil note; cvrs spotted, extrems sl worn). *Baade.* $80/£50

BENTON, FRANK. Cowboy Life on the Sidetrack.... Denver, CO, (1903). 1st ed. Pict cl. NF. *Sagebrush.* $85/£53

BENTON, J. G. Course of Instruction in Ordnance and Gunnery.... NY, 1862. 2nd ed. 550pp. (Outer spine material detached, included), o/w VG + . *Pratt.* $85/£53

BENWELL, J. An Englishman's Travels in America. London: Binns & Goodwin, (1853). 1st ed. Color frontis, pp vii,231,(20) ads (bkpl, sig). Orig red cl (rebacked), gilt. Howes B370. *Mott.* $300/£188

BENYON, JOHN. (Pseud of John Wyndham.) Planet Plane. Newnes, (1935). 1st UK ed. VG- (lt foxed; bds browned, sl mkd). *Williams.* $64/£40

Beowulf. LEC, 1952. Ltd to 1500 numbered. Lynd ward (illus). Fine in slipcase. *Swann*.* $138/£86

BERCKMAN, EVELYN. Nelson's Dear Lord. London: Macmillan, 1962. 1st ed. 12 plts. VG in dj (sl worn). *Hollett.* $40/£25

BERENDT, JOHN. Midnight in the Garden of Good and Evil. NY: Random House, 1994. 1st ed. Fine in NF dj. *Lame Duck.* $150/£94

BERENDT, JOHN. Midnight in the Garden of Good and Evil. NY: Random House, 1995. One of 2500 numbered, signed. Black cl. VF in VF pict slipcase. *Unger.* $200/£125

BERENGUER, M. Prehistoric Man and His Art. London: Souvenier, 1973. 1st ed. 73 maps, fig, 1 fldg plt. NF in VG dj. *Mikesh.* $25/£16

BERENS, S. L. (ed). The Fram Expedition. Nansen in the Frozen World.... Phila, (1897). (Fr hinge cracked; spine rubbed.) *Swann*.* $69/£43

BERENSON, BERNARD. The Drawings of the Florentine Painters. NY, 1903. One of 355. 2 vols. Tall folio. 1/2 leather (rubbed, chipped; sl worn). *Oinonen*.* $300/£188

BERENSON, BERNARD. The Drawings of the Florentine Painters. Chicago, 1938. Amplified ed. 3 vols. Sm folio. *Swann*.* $345/£216

BERENSON, BERNARD. The Drawings of the Florentine Painters. Chicago/London, 1970. 3 vols. As New in slipcase (sl worn). *Washton.* $200/£125

BERENSON, BERNARD. Homeless Paintings of the Renaissance. Hanna Kiel (ed). Bloomington: IN Univ, (1969). Color frontis, 422 b/w plts. Fine in dj. *Turtle Island.* $85/£53

BERENSON, BERNARD. Italian Painters of the Renaissance. London: Phaidon, (1952). Rev ed. Color frontis, 16 tipped-in color plts. VG. *Turtle Island.* $60/£38

BERENSON, BERNARD. Italian Pictures of the Renaissance. A List of the Principal Artists and Their Works with an Index of Places. Oxford, 1932. Good. *Washton.* $40/£25

BERENSON, BERNARD. The Passionate Sightseer. From the Diaries 1947 to 1956. NY, 1960. Color frontis, 2 color plts. Dj (sl chipped, sl loss). *Edwards.* $32/£20

BERESFORD, J. D. The Prisoners of Hartling. London/Glasgow/Melbourne/Auckland: W. Collins Sons, 1922. 1st ed. Midnight blue rough buckram. (Sm erasures fr pastedown), o/w Good. *Temple.* $19/£12

BERESFORD, JOHN. Gossip of the Seventeenth and Eighteenth Centuries. Richard Cobden-Sanderson, 1924. 4 plts. Paper spine label. (Lt spotted.) *Hollett.* $64/£40

BERG, WALTER G. Buildings and Structures of American Railroads. NY, 1893. 1st ed. 500pp. (Ink inscrip, corners bumped, hinges loose.) *King.* $350/£219

BERGER, JOHN. Art and Revolution. NY: Pantheon Books, (1969). 24 full-pg plts. VG. *Turtle Island.* $35/£22

BERGER, JOHN. G. NY: Viking, (1972). 1st Amer ed. Fine in Fine dj (sl worn). *Between The Covers.* $85/£53

BERGER, JOHN. G. Weidenfeld, 1972. 1st UK ed. Fine in dj. *Williams.* $77/£48

BERGER, JOHN. Once in Europa. Cambridge: Granta, 1989. 1st ed. Fine in dj. *Any Amount.* $16/£10

BERGER, KLAUS. Odilion Redon: Fantasy and Color. Michael Bullock (trans). NY/Toronto/London: McGraw-Hill, n.d. Fine in illus dj. *Metropolitan*.* $172/£108

BERGER, MARCEL and MAUDE BERGER. The Secret of the Marne. NY/London: Putnam, 1918. 1st US ed. Red cl. Nice in Good dj (spine crown chipped, lt soil). *Reese.* $50/£31

BERGER, MAURICE. Labyrinths. NY: Icon Editions/Harper & Row, (1989). VG. *Turtle Island.* $50/£31

BERGER, ROBERT W. (ed). In the Garden of the Sun King. Studies on the Park of Versailles Under Louis XIV. Washington: Dumbarton Oaks, 1985. xv,125pp + index. 120 illus, hors texte. VF in dj. *Europa.* $64/£40

BERGER, THOMAS. Being Invisible. Boston, 1987. 1st ed. VG in dj. *King.* $15/£9

BERGER, THOMAS. Little Big Man. NY: Dial, 1964. 1st ed. VG in dj (extrems, panels sl rubbed, spine sl sunned). *Pacific*.* $98/£61

BERGH, PETER. The Art of Ogden M. Pleissner. Boston: Godine, 1984. 1st ed. Ltd to 400 numbered, signed. Blue cl. Complete w/slipcase, suite of 4 prints in white envelope. VF. *Biscotti.* $175/£109

BERGH, PETER. The Art of Ogden M. Pleissner. Boston: Godine, 1984. Deluxe ed. Ltd to 400 numbered, signed by the author and Marion Pleissner (illus). Tan leather backed over grn buckram bds. Complete w/suite of 4 prints in white envelope, gray buckram slipcase, extra print numbered to ms. VF. *Biscotti.* $475/£297

BERGLER, EDMUND. The Psychology of Gambling. NY: Hill & Wang, 1957. 1st ed. (Sl slant; sunned edges), else Fine in dj (lt used, sm chips). *Beasley.* $30/£19

BERGLER, EDMUND. The Revolt of the Middle-Aged Man. NY: A. A. Wyn, 1954. 1st ed. Fine in dj (sl used). *Beasley.* $50/£31

BERGLER, EDMUND. Selected Papers of Edmund Bergler. NY: Grune & Stratton, 1969. 1st ed. Blue cl. VG + (tp wrinkled, bkpl; spine foot sl discolored). *Beasley.* $75/£47

BERGMAN, RAY. Fresh-Water Bass. NY: Knopf, 1945. 4th ptg, 1st Borzoi ed. 10 color plts. Burgundy cl. Fine in color pict dj (sl chipped). *Biscotti.* $35/£22

BERGMAN, RAY. Just Fishing. Phila: Penn Publishing, (1932). 1st ed. Signed. Fine in dj (spine head chipped; fr/rear panels lack pieces, closed tear, tips clipped). *Pacific*.* $63/£39

BERGMAN, RAY. Trout. NY: Knopf, 1952. 2nd, rev ed. 1st ptg. 22 color plts. 1/2 grn cl over red cl bds. Fine in NF color pict dj. *Biscotti.* $50/£31

BERGMAN, STEN. Sport and Exploration in the Far East. London: Methuen, 1933. VG (spine faded). *High Latitude.* $65/£41

BERGSTROM, INGVAR. Dutch Still-Life Painting in the Seventeenth Century. Christina Hedstrom & Gerald Taylor (trans). NY: Thomas Yoseloff, (1956). 1st ed. 8 color plts. Blue gilt cl, gilt. Good in dj. *Karmiole.* $150/£94

BERKELEY, EDMUND and DOROTHY SMITH BERKELEY. Dr. John Mitchell; the Man Who Made the Map. Chapel Hill, 1975. VG in dj. *Dumont.* $35/£22

BERKELEY, GRANTLEY F. Fact Against Fiction. The Habits and Treatment of Animals Practically Considered; Hydrophobia and Distemper. London, 1874. 2 vols. Pict red cl (lt shelf-worn, soiled), gilt. *Oinonen*.* $50/£31

BERKELEY, GRANTLEY F. Reminiscences of a Huntsman. London: Arnold, 1897. Sportsman's Library ed. 344pp. Teg. Orig 3/4 parchment vellum, marbled bds. VG. *Bowman.* $70/£44

BERKELEY, HASTINGS (ed). Japanese Letters. London: John Murray, 1891. 1st ed. 1/2-title (ink sig, sl browned), xvi,254,(1),(1)imprint. Maroon dec cl (sl rubbed), gilt. *Morrell.* $136/£85

BERKELEY, HENRY ROBINSON. Four Years in the Confederate Artillery. William H. Runge (ed). Chapel Hill: VA Historical Soc/Univ of NC, 1961. 1st ed. Frontisport. Red/black cl. (Few lt spots to fore-edge), else NF. *Chapel Hill.* $125/£78

BERKEY, HELEN. Mele and the Fire Woman. Honolulu: Tongg Pub, 1940. 1st ed. 7x12. Cornelia McIntyre Foley (illus). 47pp. Good+ (lg fr plt sl rubbed w/glass ring, 1/2-inch margin strip torn pg40; soiled; no dj). *Price.* $40/£25

BERKMAN, ALEXANDER. A.B.C. of Anarchism. Freedom Press, 1942. 1st Eng ed. VG (few ll sl dog-eared) in wrappers (partly dknd, sl rubbed, creased, spine ends scuffed). *Ulysses.* $56/£35

BERKO, PATRICK and VIVIANE. Dictionary of Belgian Painters Born Between 1750 and 1875. Brussels: Editions Laconti, 1981. 1st Eng ed. VG in dj. *Hollett.* $120/£75

BERKOFF, STEVEN. Gross Intrusion and Other Stories. London/Dallas: Calder/Riverrun, 1979. 1st ed. VG in dj (price-clipped). *Williams.* $48/£30

BERKOWITZ, HENRY J. The Fire Eater. Phila: Jewish Publication Soc of America, 1941. 1st ed. Inscribed. Brn cl. Fine in VG dj (lt edgeworn). *Reese.* $75/£47

BERLIN, SVEN. Alfred Wallis. London: Nicholson & Watson, (1949). Color frontis. (Cl soiled), else Sound. *Turtle Island.* $75/£47

BERLIN, SVEN. The Dark Monarch. Galley, 1962. 1st Eng ed. VG (eps, fore-edges sl foxed) in dj. *Clearwater.* $200/£125

BERMAN, LOUIS. The Religion Called Behaviorism. NY: Boni & Liveright, 1927. Black cl, paper labels. NF in dj. *Gach.* $100/£63

BERNACCHI, LOUIS. The Polar Book. London: Allom, (1930). Fldg map. Illus card cvrs. VG (sl foxed). *Explorer.* $104/£65

BERNACCHI, LOUIS. Saga of the 'Discovery.' London: Blackie, 1938. 2 fldg maps. VG (sig). *Explorer.* $61/£38

BERNACCHI, LOUIS. A Very Gallant Gentleman. Thornton Butterworth, 1933. 1st ed. Map. VG in dj (torn, repaired). *Walcot.* $56/£35

BERNANOS, GEORGES. The Diary of a Country Priest. LEC, 1986. One of 1000 signed by Fritz Eichenberg (illus). Fine in slipcase. *Swann*.* $172/£108

BERNARD, BRUCE. The Sunday Times Book of Photodiscovery. London, 1980. 1st UK ed. Dj (sl chipped). *Edwards.* $48/£30

BERNARD, CLAUDE. An Introduction to the Study of Experimental Medicine. NY, 1927. VG (ex-lib). *Doctor's Library.* $75/£47

BERNARD, J. Fly-Dressing. London, (1932). 1st ed. 2 color plts. *Petersfield.* $29/£18

BERNARD, JOHN. Retrospection of America, 1797-1811. Mrs. Bayle Bernard (ed). NY: Harper, 1887. 1st ed. Frontis, xiii,(2),380pp. Brn cl. Fine. *Mott.* $75/£47

BERNARD, JOHN. Retrospections of the Stage. London: Henry Colburn & Richard Bentley, 1830. 1st ed. 2 vols. Engr frontis. Orig 1/4 cl, bds (rubbed, lacks spines, bds loose). *Dramatis.* $55/£34

BERNARD, L. L. Instinct. A Study in Social Psychology. NY: Holt, 1924. 1st ed. NF (bkpl). *Beasley.* $60/£38

BERNARD, OLIVER P. Cock Sparrow. London, 1936. 1st Eng ed. VG (inscrip) in dj (sl frayed, dusty). *Clearwater.* $40/£25

BERNERS, JULIANA. An American Edition of the Treatyse of Fysshinge with an Angle. Geo. W. Van Siclen (ed). NY, 1875. 1st Amer ed. (Lt dampstain lower portion of gutter margin throughout; shelfworn.) *Oinonen*.* $90/£56

BERNERS, JULIANA. The Boke of Saint Albans.... London: Elliot Stock, 1899. Parchment-cvrd bds. (Foxing, piece of parchment lacking), else VG. *Pacific*.* $58/£36

BERNERS, JULIANA. A Treatyse of Fysshynge wyth an Angle.... London: Elliot Stock, (1880). Flexible parchment-cvrd wrappers. (Spine ends chipped), else VG. *Pacific*.* $58/£36

BERNERS, LORD. Count Omega. London, 1941. 1st Eng ed. VG in dj (dust-mkd, sl torn). *Clearwater.* $56/£35

BERNERS, LORD. First Childhood [together with] A Distant Prospect. Constable, 1934/1945. 1st eds. 2 vols. (Vol 1 cvrs, spine faded, lacks dj; vol 2 pp sl browned), o/w VG; vol 2 in dj (sl chipped). *Virgo.* $80/£50

BERNERS, LORD. First Childhood. London, 1934. 1st Eng ed. Frontis by Rex Whistler. Good (extrems sl faded) in Whistler dj (chipped, rubbed). *Clearwater.* $120/£75

BERNHARD, RUTH. The Eternal Body: a Collection of Fifty Nudes. Text by Margaretta Mitchell. Carmel: Photography West Graphics, 1986. 1st ed. Frontis; 50 full-pg b/w photos. Prospectus laid in. Fine in pink cl in illus dj (sl rubbed). *Cahan.* $275/£172

BERNHARD, THOMAS. Gargoyles. NY, 1970. 1st Amer ed. VG in VG dj (5-inch closed slice rear panel). *Warren.* $50/£31

BERNHEIMER, CHARLES L. Rainbow Bridge. GC: Doubleday, Page, 1924. 1st ed. Teg. Blue cl, gilt. NF (spine ends sl worn). *Harrington.* $80/£50

BERNIER, J. E. Report on the Dominion of Canada Government Expedition to the Arctic Islands and Hudson Strait on Board the D. G. S. 'Arctic'. Cttawa: Gov't Ptg Bureau, 1910. 4 fldg maps (sl tape repairs). VG (several sl spots, mks to binding). *High Latitude.* $95/£59

BERRA, TIM. William Beebe; an Annotated Bibliography. Hamden, CT: Shoestring, 1977. 1st ed. Grn cl. Fine in Fine ptd dj. *Biscotti.* $45/£28

BERRA, YOGI and ED FITZGERALD. Yogi. Doubleday, 1961. 1st ed. Signed by Berra. VG+ in VG dj. *Plapinger.* $75/£47

BERRALL, JULIA S. The Garden: An Illustrated History.... Thames & Hudson, 1966. (Inscrip), else NF in NF dj. *Hadley.* $48/£30

BERRIGAN, DANIEL. May All Creatures Live. Nevada City: Harold Berliner, (1984). Ltd to 250. 3-piece cl. *Truepenny.* $100/£63

BERRIGAN, TED. The Morning Line. (Santa Barbara): Immediate Editions, (1982). 1st ed. VG+ in stapled wrappers. *Pharos.* $15/£9

BERRIGAN, TED. The Sonnets. NY, 1982. 1st Amer ed. Signed. Fine in pict wraps. *Polyanthos.* $25/£16

BERRY, JOHN J. (ed). Life of David Belden. NY: Belden Bros, 1891. 1st ed. Steel-engr frontisport, 472pp. Brn cl, beveled bds. NF. *Harrington.* $125/£78

BERRY, MICHAEL and D. W. E. BROCK. Hunting by Ear. Text, Sound, Pictures. London: Witherby, (1937). Internally Sound in dj. Housed in orig box (worn) w/pict cvr label together w/'Two 10-inch Parlophone Gramophone Records of the Sounds of Fox-hunting.' *Oinonen*.* $50/£31

BERRY, R. J. and J. L. JOHNSTON. The Natural History of Shetland. Collins, 1980. True 1st ed. Mint in dj. *Hollett.* $208/£130

BERRY, WENDELL. Clearing. NY: Harcourt, (1977). 1st ed. Fine in dj. *Second Life.* $75/£47

BERRY, WENDELL. Nathan Coulter. Boston: HM, 1960. 1st ed. NF in NF dj (sl tape residue to edges). *Agvent.* $350/£219

BERRY, WENDELL. November Twenty Six Nineteen Hundred Sixty Three. NY: George Braziller, (1964). 1st ltd ed. One of unspecified #, signed by Berry and Ben Shahn (illus). 1 tipped-in color plt. Brown eps; untrimmed. White cl. Fine in black cl-cvrd bd slipcase (sl rubbed) w/ptd paper label. *Baltimore*.* $50/£31

BERRY, WENDELL. Remembering. SF: North Point, 1988. 1st Amer ed. Signed. Fine in Fine dj. *Polyanthos.* $25/£16

BERRY, WENDELL. To What Listens. (Crete, NE: Best Cellar, 1975.) 1st ed. Fine in stapled wrappers. *Between The Covers.* $75/£47

BERRYMAN, JOHN. 77 Dream Songs. London, 1964. 1st ed. Fine in Fine dj. *Polyanthos.* $35/£22

BERRYMAN, JOHN. Berryman's Sonnets. London: Faber & Faber, (1968). 1st British ed. One of 1500 ptd. Fine in VG dj (lt rubbed, worn). *Reese.* $30/£19

BERRYMAN, JOHN. The Dispossessed. NY: Sloane, (1948). 1st ed. NF in VG dj (spine sunned, sl edgeworn). *Agvent.* $225/£141

BERRYMAN, JOHN. The Dispossessed. NY: William Sloan, (1948). 1st ed. (Extrems sl rubbed), else Fine in dj (sl chipped, spine faded). *Bromer.* $275/£172

BERRYMAN, JOHN. Homage to Mistress Bradstreet. Faber, 1959. 1st UK ed. NF in NF- dj (sl frayed, nicked, sl sunned). *Any Amount.* $56/£35

BERRYMAN, JOHN. Stephen Crane. (NY): William Sloan, (1950). 1st ed. (Pp 246-7 sl browned), else Fine in dj (sl chipped). *Bromer.* $250/£156

BERTHOLD, VICTOR. The Pioneer Steamer California, 1848-1849. Boston/NY: Houghton Mifflin, 1932. Ltd to 550. 6 plts. Blue cl, paper spine label. Fine in slipcase (worn). *Pacific*.* $86/£54

BERTHOLD, VICTOR. The Pioneer Steamer California, 1848-1849. Boston: Houghton Mifflin, 1932. 1st ed. One of 550. Frontis. Blue cl, paper spine label. VF in orig glassine dj, slipcase (lt worn). *Argonaut.* $125/£78

BERTHONG, DONALD J. The Southern Cheyennes. Norman: Univ of OK, 1972. VG in dj (sl worn). *Dumont.* $30/£19

BERTO, HAZEL. North to Alaska's Shining River. Indianapolis: Bobbs-Merrill, (1959). 1st ed. VG in dj. *Perier.* $30/£19

BERTON, PIERRE. The Arctic Grail: The Quest for the North West Passage and the North Pole, 1818-1909. Toronto: McClelland & Stewart, 1988. Fine in dj. *Explorer.* $35/£22

BERTON, PIERRE. The Great Railway, 1871-1885. McClelland & Stewart, 1974/1971. 2 vols. Good in djs (worn). *Rybski.* $45/£28

BERTON, PIERRE. The Klondike Quest: A Photographic Essay, 1897-1899. Boston: Little Brown, (1983). 1st Amer ed. Fine in dj (chipped). *Perier.* $95/£59

BERTRAM, ANTHONY. Paul Nash. London, 1955. 1st Eng ed. VG (sl shelfworn) in dj (sl torn, nicked). *Clearwater.* $72/£45

BERTRAND, KENNETH J. Americans in Antarctica 1775-1948. NY: American Geographical Soc, 1971. Fine. *Explorer.* $64/£40

BERVE, HELMUT and GOTTFRIED GRUBEN. Greek Temples, Theatres and Shrines. NY: Harry N. Abrams, n.d. (ca 1962). 1st ed. 36 mtd color plts. Blue linen. Good in dj. *Karmiole.* $250/£156

BESANT, WALTER. London in the Eighteenth Century. London: A.& C. Black, 1925. Frontisport, lg fldg map. Patterned red cl (spine sl sunned, extrems sl scuffed). *Dramatis.* $75/£47

BESKOW, ELSA. Pelle's New Suit. NY: Platt & Munk, 1930. 6x8. Eulalie (illus). Unpaginated. Blue cl w/picture paste on. VG + (sl shelfworn) in dj (torn, chipped). *My Bookhouse.* $37/£23

BESKOW, ELSA. The Tale of the Wee Little Old Woman. NY: Harper, 1935. 10x10.5. 22pp. Cl spine, pict bds. Good. *Cattermole.* $90/£56

BESSE, J. (ed). An Account of the Life, Travels, and Christian Experiences in the Work of the Ministry of Samuel Bownas. London: James Phillips, 1795. 3rd ed. vii,196pp. Contemp speckled calf (hinges cracking, cvr tops sl defective). *Hollett.* $72/£45

BESSIE, ALVAH. Inquisition in Eden. NY: Macmillan, 1965. 1st ed. Fine in Fine dj (spine sl sunned, sm chip to rear panel foot). *Beasley.* $45/£28

BESSIE, ALVAH. The Symbol. NY: Random House, (1966). 1st ed. VF in VF dj. *Between The Covers.* $100/£63

BESSON, MAURICE. The Scourge of the Indies. London: Routledge, 1929. One of 960. 5 hand-colored age-treated dwgs, maps. VG in dj (chipped). *Parmer.* $195/£122

BEST, GERALD M. Nevada Country Narrow Gauge. Berkeley, CA, 1965. 1st ed. Frontis, fldg chart. Ptd eps. Dec cl. NF in VG + dj. *Sagebrush.* $60/£38

BEST, GERALD M. Ships and Narrow Gauge Rails. Berkeley, CA, 1964. 1st ed. Frontis, fldg map. Pict eps. VG + (name, 2 sm spots) in VG dj (chipped). *Sagebrush.* $60/£38

BEST, THOMAS. A Concise Treatise on the Art of Angling. London: C. Stalker, n.d. (1789). 2nd ed. Frontis (neatly hand-colored by an early owner), 6 leaves; 170pp (new eps). Old calf (neatly rebacked, rubbed, sl stained, soiled, foxed). *Oinonen*.* $225/£141

BESTER, JOHN. Tiger! Tiger! Sidgwick & Jackson, n.d. (1956). 1st Eng ed. VG (pg edges sl browned; cvrs sl mkd, bowed) in dj (nicked, sl creased, rubbed, dusty, edges sl dknd). *Ulysses.* $200/£125

BESTERMAN, THEODORE. Early Printed Books to the End of the Sixteenth Century. NY: Rowman & Littlefield, 1969. 2nd ed. Dk blue-grn cl, gilt. VG (sl shelfworn, rubbed). *Baltimore*.* $20/£13

BETENSON, LULA PARKER. Butch Cassidy, My Brother. Provo: Brigham Young Univ, (1975). 3rd ptg. White-ptd brn cl. Dj (sl edgeworn). *Dawson.* $50/£31

BETENSON, LULA PARKER. Butch Cassidy, My Brother. Provo, 1975. 2nd ed. Map. VG in dj (worn). *Benchmark.* $35/£22

BETHAM-EDWARDS, M. Snow Flakes, and Stories They Told the Children. London: Sampson Low, Son, (1862). 1st ed. 8vo. Dbl-pg chromolitho frontis, tp, (vi),7-46pp; 10 color plts by H. K. Browne, guards. Aeg. Brn grained cl, gilt pict device to fr cvr. VG (new blank fep). *Sotheran.* $205/£128

BETHEA, OSCAR W. Practical Materia Medica and Prescription Writing. Phila, 1919. 3rd ed. (Margins lt browned, hinges tender; corners, spine sl rubbed.) *Edwards.* $48/£30

BETJEMAN, JOHN. Antiquarian Prejudice. London: Hogarth, 1939. 1st Eng ed. Card wrappers (sl dust-mkd). *Clearwater.* $72/£45

BETJEMAN, JOHN. The Book Collectors Fair at the National Book League. London, 1966. 1st Eng ed. Fine. *Clearwater.* $32/£20

BETJEMAN, JOHN. Collected Poems. Earl of Birkenhead (ed). London: John Murray, 1958. 1st ed. Fine in dj. *Reese.* $50/£31

BETJEMAN, JOHN. Continual Dew. London: John Murray, 1937. 1st Eng ed. Signed. Aeg. Dec cl, gilt. NF (sl rubbed, spine ends sl bumped) in dj (sl rubbed, dusty, price-clipped). *Ulysses.* $440/£275

BETJEMAN, JOHN. Cornwall. London: Faber, 1964. 1st Eng ed. Very Nice in dj. *Clearwater.* $48/£30

BETJEMAN, JOHN. English Cities and Small Towns. 1943. 1st ed. VG in VG dj. *Whiteson.* $24/£15

BETJEMAN, JOHN. The English Town in the Past Hundred Years...The Rede Lecture. Cambridge: CUP, 1956. 1st ed. VG ptd wrappers (sl sunned, soiled). *Reese.* $30/£19

BETJEMAN, JOHN. First and Last Loves. London: John Murray, 1952. 1st Eng ed. Fldg panorama. Buckram. NF (spine ends, corner sl bumped) in dj (sl rubbed, spine sl dknd). *Ulysses.* $200/£125

BETJEMAN, JOHN. Ghastly Good Taste or A Depressing Story of the Rise and Fall of English Architecture. NY, 1971. 1st Amer ed. 9-foot long fldg illus. Fine in Fine dj. *Polyanthos.* $30/£19

BETJEMAN, JOHN. Ghastly Good Taste. London: Anthony Blond, 1970. One of 200 signed. 1/4 leather (spine sl mkd). Fine in cl slipcase. *Ulysses.* $312/£195

BETJEMAN, JOHN. London's Historical Railway Stations. London, 1972. 1st Eng ed. Fine in dj. *Clearwater.* $56/£35

BETJEMAN, JOHN. Mount Zion, or In Touch With the Infinite. London: James Press, (1931). 1st ed. Signed. 8vo. Dec bds (spine browned, head torn w/loss). *Christie's*.* $589/£368

BETJEMAN, JOHN. A Nip in the Air. NY: Norton, (1974). 1st US ed. Fine in dj. *Reese.* $20/£13

BETJEMAN, JOHN. A Nip in the Air. London: John Murray, 1974. 1st ed. One of 175 numbered, signed. VG in yellow buckram. *Maggs.* $360/£225

BETJEMAN, JOHN. Old Lights for New Chancels. John Murray, 1940. 1st UK ed. Fine (lacks dj). Bkpl of John Carter. *Williams.* $51/£32

BETJEMAN, JOHN. An Oxford University Chest. London: John Miles, 1938. 1st Eng ed. Teg. Buckram-backed marbled paper bds. NF (edges, eps, prelims sl spotted) in dj (torn, rubbed, sl chipped, internally spotted, tape repairs at top of fr/rear panels). *Ulysses.* $360/£225

BETJEMAN, JOHN. A Pickwick Portrait Gallery. London: Chapman & Hall, 1936. 1st Eng ed. Very Nice (initials, name) in dj (sl dusty, rubbed). *Clearwater.* $120/£75

BETJEMAN, JOHN. Uncollected Poems. (London): John Murray, (1982). 1st ed. Fine in dj. *Reese.* $25/£16

BETJEMAN, JOHN. Vintage London. London: Collins, 1942. 1st ed. (Eps sl foxed), else Nice in VG dj (sm tears). *Reese.* $50/£31

BETTEX, ALBERT. The Discovery of the World: The Great Explorers and the Worlds They Found... NY: S&S, (1960). 1st Amer ed. NF in dj (sl shelfworn). *Pacific*.* $40/£25

BETTINA. Angelo and Rosaline. London: Collins, 1957. 1st ed. 8x11. 48pp. NF in Good dj (top edge tears, .5-inch chip). *Price.* $45/£28

BEULAH HISTORICAL SOCIETY. From Mace's Hole, the Way It Was, To Beulah, the Way It Is. Colorado Springs, 1969. 1st ed. Pict cl. Fine in dj (edgeworn). *Baade.* $30/£19

BEUYS, EVA et al. Joseph Beuys. Mosel, (1990). Dj. *Swann*.* $69/£43

BEUYS, JOSEPH. Joseph Beuys in America. NY: Four Walls Eight Windows, (1990). 1st ed. Fine in dj. *Turtle Island.* $35/£22

BEVERIDGE, THOMAS J. English Renaissance Woodwork 1660-1730. London, (1921). Folio. 80 plts. 1/4 cl (lt soiled, tips bumped w/some loss, extrems rubbed.) *Swann*.* $69/£43

BEVERIDGE, THOMAS J. English Renaissance Woodwork 1660-1730. London: Technical Journals, 1921. 1st ed. Lg folio. 80 plts. VG. *Pacific*.* $184/£115

BEVERIDGE, W. I. B. Influenza: The Last Great Plague. NY: Prodist, 1977. 1st Amer ed. Fine in dj. *Glaser.* $30/£19

BEVERLEY, ROBERT. The History of Virginia. London, 1722. 2nd ed. This copy bears the imprint: Ptd for F. Fayram & J. Clarke.... 8vo. Frontis, tp, (vi),284,24pp + 4pp pub's ads; 14 engr plts. Marbled eps; aeg. Full crimson morocco, gilt. (Spine top lt frayed, sl split fr cvr joint.) Internally VF. Howes B410. *Truepenny.* $750/£469

BEWICK, THOMAS and JOHN. Poems by Goldsmith and Parnell. Shakespeare Ptg Office for Bulmer & Co, 1795. Lg copy. 4to. 5 full-pg wood engrs. Teg. 19th-cent 1/2 tan morocco, gilt, marbled bds. (Sl foxing early/final ll, discoloration to tissue guards.) *Sotheby's*.* $883/£552

BEWICK, THOMAS. Figures of British Land Birds...to Which Are Added, a Few Foreign Birds. Newcastle-upon-Tyne: R. Beilby & T. Bewick, 1800. 1st ed. Vol 1 (all published). (Marginal soil, few stains.) Contemp blind-stamped morocco (extrems rubbed). *Christie's*.* $235/£147

BEWICK, THOMAS. A General History of Quadrupeds. London, 1790. 1st ed. viii,456pp. 200 woodcuts, lower margin A3. signed. 1/2 calf. (Rebacked; lower margin A4 repaired, several other marginal tears also repaired, bkpl). *Henly.* $352/£220

BEWICK, THOMAS. A General History of Quadrupeds. London, 1791. 2nd ed. x,483pp. Calf (rebacked preserving label; 2 tears repaired at 284-285). *Henly.* $192/£120

BEWICK, THOMAS. A General History of Quadrupeds. Newcastle: S. Hodgson et al, 1800. 4th ed. Contemp 1/2 sheep (corners worn, rebacked; prelim ad leaf rehinged). *Swann*.* $126/£79

BEWICK, THOMAS. A General History of Quadrupeds. Newcastle-upon-Tyne, 1820. 7th ed. 527pp. Teg. Later leather-backed cl. (Bkpl, sl foxed, worn.) *King.* $125/£78

BEWICK, THOMAS. A History of British Birds. London, 1797-1804. 1st eds. 2 vols, one demi 8vo, the other royal 8vo. xxx,335, ad, 117 woodcuts; xx,400pp, 101 woodcuts. 1/2 calf (rebacked), gilt. Good (bkpl, vignette inked vol 1). *Henly.* $352/£220

BEWICK, THOMAS. A History of British Birds. Newcastle, 1826. 2 vols. xliv,382; xxii,432pp. 2 extra illus bound into vol 2. (Lt spotting, tp vol 2 supplied in ms and loosely inserted.) 1/2 calf (rebound; spines sl rubbed), marbled bds, gilt, raised bands. *Edwards.* $104/£65

BEWICK, THOMAS. A Memoir of Thomas Bewick. Newcastle-on-Tyne/London, 1862. 1st ed. 17 plts (last plt is a copper engr, signed in the plt). Grn cl, gilt. (Bkpl; spine, extrems dull), else VG. *Pacific*.* $138/£86

BEWICK, THOMAS. Works. Newcastle-upon-Tyne: Bernard Quaritch, 1884-87. New ed. One of 750 signed by pub. 5 vols. Royal 8vo in 4's. Marbled eps; teg, rest uncut. Orig 1/2 mid-brn morocco (extrems sl rubbed), backstrip w/raised bands, gilt, sand-grain brn cl sides. Good. *Blackwell's.* $960/£600

BEWSHER, PAUL. The Dawn Patrol and Other Poems of an Aviator. London, 1917. 1st Eng ed. (Paper acid; binding cracked.) Card wrappers (chafed, dusty). *Clearwater.* $40/£25

BEWSHER, PAUL. The Dawn Patrol and Other Poems of an Aviator. London: Erskine MacDonald Ltd, 1917. 1st ed. Tan wrappers ptd in dk brn. (Lt use at overlap edges), o/w Nice. *Reese.* $55/£34

BEY, PILAFF. (Pseud of Norman Douglas.) Venus in the Kitchen, or Love's Cookery Book. Viking, 1953. VG in Fair dj. *Book Broker.* $25/£16

BEYER, WILLIAM GRAY. Minions of the Moon. NY: Gnome Press, (1950). 1st ed. (Edgeworn), else Good in dj (frayed, tear). *King.* $25/£16

BEYER, WILLIAM GRAY. Minions of the Moon. NY: Gnome, 1950. 1st ed. VG + (sl shelfworn) in dj (tape-repaired, rubbed). *My Bookhouse.* $32/£20

BEZZERIDES, A. I. Long Haul. NY, (1938). 1st ed, 1st bk. VG in dj (sl chipped, worn). *King.* $60/£38

Bhagavad Gita: The Song Celestial. Edwin Arnold (illus). Bombay: LEC, 1964. One of 1500 ptd. Signed by Y. G. Srimati (illus). Dec silk. Fine in fldg silpcase (sl sunned). *Pacific*.* $52/£33

BIANCHI, JOHN. Blue Steel and Gunleather. North Hollywood, CA: Beinfeld Pub, (August 1979). VG in dj. *Lien.* $25/£16

BIANCHI, LEONARDO. A Text-Book of Psychiatry for Physicians and Students. James H. MacDonald (trans). NY: William Wood, 1906. 1st ed in English. Black cl, gilt. VG (worn). *House.* $200/£125

BIANCHI, MARTHA DICKINSON. The Life and Letters of Emily Dickinson. London, 1924. 1st ed. NF (spine sl sunned). *Polyanthos.* $30/£19

BIANCO, MARGERY. Winterbound. Viking, 1936. 1st ed. 234pp. Good + (cl faded, sl leaning, bumped; no dj). *Price.* $25/£16

BIANCO, PAMELA. Beginning with A. NY: OUP, 1947. 1st ed. 4to. Blue cl. Good in color dj (worn). *Reisler.* $150/£94

BIANCO, PAMELA. The Valentine Party. Phila: Lippincott, 1954. 1st ed. 6.5x8.25. 28pp. Fine in dj. *Cattermole.* $40/£25

Bibliotheca Diabolica; Being a Choice Selection of the Most Valuable Books Relating to the Devil.... NY: Scribner, Welford & Armstrong, 1874. 40pp; 2 facs. Mod cl-backed bds. *Forest.* $56/£35

Bibliotheca Stevensiana. London: J. Barker, 1800. vi,125pp. Contemp hand-ruled w/prices inked in. Period 3/4 calf, marbled bds, gilt spine. (Rubbed), else VG. *Pacific*.* $75/£47

BICHAT, XAV. A Treatise on the Membranes in General, and on Different Membranes in Particular. John C. Coffin (trans). Boston: Cummings & Hilliard, 1813. 1st Amer ed. 260pp (foxed). Uncut, unopened. Orig bds (worn, stained). *House.* $500/£313

BICKERDYKE, JOHN. Days of My Life on Waters Fresh and Salt, and Other Papers. London: Longmans, Green, 1895. 1st ed. Frontis photogravure port. Dec grn cl, gilt. (Spine ends rubbed), else NF. *Pacific*.* $40/£25

BICKNELL, RALPH EDMUND. Ralph's Scrap Book, Containing His Writings and Illustrated Stories of Travel. Lawrence, (MA): Privately published, 1905. Ltd ed ptd by Andover Press. Satin eps; aeg. Black morocco, raised bands, gilt. Fine. *Pacific*.* $345/£216

BIDDLE, ANTHONY J. DREXEL. Shantytown Sketches. Phila: Drexel Biddle, 1898. Stated 5th ed (?). Frontis, 67pp + (7) ads; 10 full-pg illus. Pict cl. VG. *Petrilla.* $100/£63

BIDDLE, ELLEN McGOWAN. Reminiscences of a Soldier's Wife. Phila: Lippincott, 1907. 1st ed. Inscribed. Frontis, 13 full-pg photo illus. Teg. Blue cl, gilt (spine sunned). *Dawson.* $100/£63

BIDDLE, NICHOLAS (ed). The Journals of the Expedition Under the Command of Capts. Lewis and Clark to the Sources of the Missouri.... NY: Heritage, (1962). 2 vols. Buckram-backed bds. (Spines sl faded), else NF set in slipcases. *Pacific*.* $75/£47

BIDDLE, NICHOLAS (ed). The Journals of the Expedition Under the Command of Capts. Lewis and Clark...1804-05-06. NY: Heritage, (1962). 2 vols. Fine in slipcase. *Perier.* $65/£41

BIDDLECOMBE, GEORGE. The Art of Rigging. Salem, MA: Marine Research Soc, 1925. 1st ed. 17 plts. Grn cl. Fine. *Karmiole.* $65/£41

BIDDLECOMBE, GEORGE. The Art of Rigging. NY: Sweetman, 1979. Tan cl. VG. *American Booksellers.* $35/£22

BIDWELL, JOHN. Echoes of the Past. (Chico, CA: Chico Advertiser, 1914.) 3 full-pg photo illus. (Contents dknd), else NF in ptd wrappers (sl worn). *Pacific*.* $86/£54

BIDWELL, JOHN. A Journey to California, with Observations About the Country...A Day-by-Day Record of the Journey from May 18, 1841, to November 6, 1841. SF: John Henry Nash, 1937. 2nd ed. Cl-backed bds, paper spine label. (Bkpl), else NF in dj (sl edgeworn, spine label lt rubbed). *Pacific*.* $40/£25

BIDWELL, JOHN. A Journey to California. SF, 1937. Ltd to 650. Prospectus laid in. NF (bkpl) in VG dj. *Sagebrush.* $150/£94

BIE, OSCAR. A History of the Pianoforte and Pianoforte Players. E. E. Kellett & E. W. Naylor (trans). London: J.M. Dent, 1899. 1st ed. Frontis, xii,336pp; 22 plts. Grn cl, gilt. Good. *Karmiole.* $85/£53

BIEBER, RALPH P. and LE ROY R. HAFEN (eds). The Southwest Historical Series. Glendale: A.H. Clark, 1931-1943. 12 vols. Teg. Red cl, gilt. Fine. *Pacific*.* $1,265/£791

BIERCE, AMBROSE. Battle Sketches. Oxford: First Edition Club, 1930. 1st ed. One of 350. Folio. 8 wood-engrs by Thomas Derrick. Largely unopened. VG in projecting parchment (sl spotted, cvrs splaying), gilt. *Maggs.* $80/£50

BIERCE, AMBROSE. Black Beetles in Amber. SF: Western Authors Publishing, 1892. 1st ed. Inscribed 1892. Frontisport, 280pp. Gray cl, gilt. (Spine dknd, ends sl rubbed), else NF. BAL 1111. *Pacific*.* $431/£269

BIERCE, AMBROSE. The Devil's Dictionary. LEC, 1972. Ltd to 1500 numbered, signed by Fritz Kredel (illus). Fine in slipcase. *Swann*.* $80/£50

BIERCE, AMBROSE. In the Midst of Life. Tales of Soldiers and Civilians. NY: Putnam, 1898. 1st US ed thus. Red cl, gilt. Very Nice (sl foxed; edges sl rubbed). BAL 1119. *Reese.* $85/£53

BIERCE, AMBROSE. The Letters of.... Bertha Clark Pope (ed). SF: Book Club of CA, 1922. 1st ed. One of 415. Tipped-in frontisport. Uncut. Black cl, marbled bds, gilt, black paper spine label. VG. *Houle.* $125/£78

BIERCE, AMBROSE. The Monk and the Hangman's Daughter. LEC, 1967. Ltd to 1500 numbered, signed by Michel Ciry (illus). Fine in slipcase. *Swann*.* $34/£21

BIERCE, AMBROSE. A Son of the Gods and A Horseman in the Sky. SF: Paul Elder, 1907. One of 1000. Photo frontis. Vellum spine, bds. Fine. *Smith.* $45/£28

BIERCE, AMBROSE. Tales of Soldiers and Civilians. SF: E.L.G. Steele, 1891. 1st ed. Gray cl (worn, rubbed, soiled). 1/4 morocco slipcase w/chemise. BAL 1109. *Cummins.* $250/£156

BIERCE, AMBROSE. Tales of Soldiers and Civilians. SF: E.L.G. Steele, 1891. 1st ed. Gray cl, gilt (dull). (Fep excised; rubbed.) BAL 1109. *Macdonnell.* $275/£172

BIERCE, AMBROSE. Tales of Soldiers and Civilians. SF: E.L.G. Steele, 1891. 1st ed. Inscribed in ink 'With compliments of The Author.' 12mo. 300pp. Grn cl, gilt. Very Nice. BAL 1109 binding format B. *M & S.* $1,500/£938

BIERCE, AMBROSE. Tales of Soldiers and Civilians. LEC, 1943. Ltd to 1500 numbered, signed by Paul Landacre (illus). Fine in slipcase. *Swann*.* $80/£50

BIERSTADT, O. A. The Library of Robert Hoe. NY: Dupart, 1895. 1st ed. One of 350 numbered. 110 full-pg illus. Uncut. (Sl rubbed.) *Forest.* $120/£75

Big Book of Fables. London/Glasgow: Blackie & Son, (1912). 1st ed. Charles Robinson (illus). 4to. Teg. Red pict cl, gilt spine. VG (sl bowed). *Glenn.* $250/£156

BIGELOW, ERASTUS B. The Tariff Question Considered in Regard to the Policy of England and the Interests of the United States. Boston: Little, Brown, 1862. 1st ed. Folio. xii,104,242pp. Brn cl (spine faded, extrems lt frayed). *Karmiole.* $150/£94

BIGELOW, H. B. and W. C. SCHROEDER. Fishes of the Gulf of Maine. Washington, 1953. 2nd ed. (Names, tear to pg repaired w/tape; lt scuffed, soiled, spine faded.) *Sutton.* $40/£25

BIGELOW, H. B. and W. C. SCHROEDER. Fishes of the Gulf of Maine. Washington: GPO, 1953. 1st revision. Red cl. VG + . *Bowman.* $65/£41

BIGELOW, H. B. et al. Fishes of the Western North Atlantic. New Haven: Yale Univ, 1963. 1st ed. One of 1500. 139 maps, dwgs. Fine in VG dj. *Mikesh.* $95/£59

BIGELOW, HORATIO. Gunnerman. NY: Derrydale, 1939. Ltd to 950 numbered. Red cl. Fine. *Biscotti.* $200/£125

BIGELOW, JACOB. Brief Expositions of Rational Medicine: to which is prefixed The Paradise of Doctors, a Fable. Boston, 1858. 1st ed. 75pp. *M & S.* $85/£53

BIGELOW, JOHN. The Campaign of Chancellorsville. (Dayton: Morningside House, 1984.) Photo facs of orig 1910 ed. 9 fldg maps loose in rear pocket, as issued. Crimson cl (sl rubbed), gilt. Clean. *Baltimore*.* $260/£163

BIGELOW, JOHN. France and the Confederate Navy 1862-1868. NY: Harper, 1888. 1st ed. 247pp + 4pp ads. Olive grn cl. (Spine extrems sl rubbed), else Fine. *Chapel Hill.* $125/£78

BIGELOW, JOHN. Jamaica in 1850. NY/London: Putnam, 1851. 1st ed. (2),3,4,214pp. (Reps stained; cl faded.) *M & S.* $100/£63

BIGELOW, JOHN. Memoir of the Life and Public Services of John Charles Fremont.... NY: Derby & Jackson, 1856. 1st ed. Steel-engr frontisport, 480pp; 7 wood-engr plts. Brn cl, gilt. (Spine sl faded, ends sl bumped), else Fine. *Argonaut.* $125/£78

BIGGERS, EARL DERR. Keeper of the Keys. Indianapolis, (1932). 1st ed. Dj (creased, inner flap edges reinforced w/archival tape). *Swann*.* $80/£50

BIGGERS, EARL DERR. Seven Keys to Baldpate. Indianapolis, (1913). 1st ed. VG. *Mcclintock.* $35/£22

BIGGLE, JACOB. Biggle Berry Book: A Condensed Treatise on the Culture of Berries. Phila: Wilmer Atkinson, 1894. 1st ed. 126,(2)pp; 20 chromolitho plts. Dec cl. VG (ends sl rubbed). *Cahan.* $100/£63

BIGGS, JOHN R. Woodcuts, Wood-Engravings, Linocuts and Prints by Related Methods of Relief Print Making. Blandford, 1958. 1st ed. Frontis. Dj. *Forest.* $40/£25

BIGHAM, CLIVE. A Year in China, 1899-1900. London, 1901. 4 maps. Uncut. (Lt spotted, fr hinge tender, lib bkpl; edges sl rubbed, spine lt faded, ends sl bumped.) *Edwards.* $120/£75

BIGLAND, EILEEN. In the Steps of George Borrow. Rich & Cowan, 1951. Frontisport. Good (sig; spine bumped, dulled; lacks dj). *Tiger.* $13/£8

BIGLAND, RALPH. Historical, Monumental and Genealogical Collections Relative to the County of Gloucester. Ptd by John Nichols, 1791. 1st ed. 2 vols. Folio. Later calf (rubbed), gilt. *Sotheby's*.* $478/£299

BIGLY, CANTELL A. (Pseud of George W. Peck.) Aurifodina; or, Adventures in the Gold Region. NY: Baker & Scribner, 1849. 1st ed. 103pp + 4pp ads at rear. Recent brn textured cl tape, plain rough bds (edges sl scuffed), mtd crimson spine label w/lg lettering. Text VG (browned, few pp w/lt pencil marginal notes). Recent buckram-covered bd fldg box w/similar label. *Baltimore*.* $100/£63

BIGMORE, E. C. and C. W. H. WYMAN. A Bibliography of Printing with Notes and Illustrations. NY: Duschnes, 1945. Rpt of 1880-1886, 1st ed. 2 vols. (Bkpl; newspaper review inserted causing some yellowing.) *Oak Knoll.* $135/£84

BIHALJII-MERIN, OTO. Masters of Naive Art. McGraw-Hill, n.d. (1970?). Good in slipcase. *Rybski.* $65/£41

BILL, ALFRED HOYT. The Beleaguered City, Richmond 1861-1865. NY, 1946. 1st ed. Fldg map. VG in dj (piece torn from spine). *Pratt.* $30/£19

BILL, PLATINUM. Under the Northern Lights. Portland: Columbia Ptg, 1916. 1st ed. Wraps (most of edge overhang gone). *Perier.* $65/£41

BILLEB, EMIL W. Mining Camp Days. Berkeley: Howell-North Books, 1968. 1st ed. Fine in Fine dj. *Book Market.* $25/£16

BILLING, ARCHIBALD. The Science of Gems, Jewels, Coins, and Medals. Daldy, Isbister, 1875. New ed. Inscribed presentation. 226pp; 22 plts, guards. Aeg. Dec blue cl gilt, beveled bds, photo port inset in fr bd. (Extrems sl rubbed.) *Hollett.* $192/£120

BILLING, GRAHAM and GUY MANNERING. South. Man and Nature in Antarctica. London: Hodder & Stoughton, 1965. 1st Eng ed. VG. *High Latitude.* $35/£22

BILLINGS, JOHN D. Hardtack and Coffee. Time-Life, 1982. Collector's Library of Civil War ed. Leather. Fine. *Pratt.* $30/£19

BILLINGS, JOHN D. Hardtack and Coffee. Richard Harwell (ed). Chicago: R.R. Donnelley, 1960. Frontis. VG. *Lien.* $30/£19

BILLINGS, JOHN SHAW. Selected Papers. Frank Bradway Rogers (comp). N.p.: Medical Library Assoc, 1965. 1st collected ed. Signed by Rogers. Frontisport. VG. *Glaser.* $75/£47

BILLINGS, ROBERT WILLIAM. Architectural Illustrations, History and Description of Carlisle Cathedral. London, 1840. 45 steel-engr plts. Contemp 3/4 calf (rubbed, fr joint weak; foxed). *Oinonen*.* $110/£69

BILLINGSLEA, CHARLES (comp). The Addison Reunion Papers. Balt: Wm. J.C. Dulany, 1871. 1st ed. viii,270pp. (Pp143-144 torn across, into text; shelfworn, rubbed, spine ends frayed), else Good. *Brown.* $40/£25

BILLINGTON, RAY ALLEN. The Reinterpretation of Early American History: Essays in Honor of John Edwin Pomfret. San Marino: Huntington Library, 1966. 1st ed. Inscribed, signed by Jack Pomfret. Blue cl. Fine in VG + ptd dj. *House.* $25/£16

Billy the Kid. Las Vegas Newspaper Accounts of His Career, 1880-1881. Waco, TX: W.M. Morrison, 1958. 1st ed. Ltd to 1000. VG + in wrappers. *Labordo.* $45/£28

BINDMAN, DAVID (ed). John Flaxman. London, 1979. 1st ed. 4 color plts. Dj (sl chipped). *Edwards.* $40/£25

BINDMAN, DAVID. The Complete Graphic Works of William Blake. NY, (1978). Folio. (Lt worn.) Dj. *Oinonen*.* $110/£69

BINDMAN, DAVID. The Complete Graphic Works of William Blake. London: Thames & Hudson, 1978. Good in dj. *Ars Artis.* $120/£75

BINGHAM, CLIFTON. The Animals' Rebellion. Ernest Nister/E.P. Dutton, (c.1900). Obl 4to. 52,(ii)pp; 8 Fine full-pg color plts by C. H. Thompson. Cl-backed pict bds. VG (sl loose, odd sm inner-edge tear, sl fingered; sl scratched, corners worn). *Hollett.* $240/£150

BINGHAM, CLIFTON. Something New for Little Folk. London: Ernest Nister, (1899). 4to. 7 round transformation plts by A. E. Jackson (illus) that are turned w/a cord to revolve w/in slats to change the picture (wheels worn, repaired). Cl-backed color pict bds (lt edgeworn, mkd, hinges reinforced). *Reisler.* $975/£609

BINGHAM, J. The Double Agent. Gollancz, 1966. 1st UK ed. (Sm tear, crease to corner), o/w Fine in VG dj. *Martin.* $13/£8

BINGHAM, J. A Fragment of Fear. Gollancz, 1965. 1st UK ed. Fine in NF dj (sl worn). *Martin.* $14/£9

BINGHAM, MILLICENT TODD. Ancestors' Brocades. NY: Harper, 1945. 1st ed. Grn cl, gilt, blindstamped pub's device on fr cvr. NF (red ink note 1 pg; spine extrems rubbed) in dj (lt chipped, soiled, spine faded). *Heritage.* $150/£94

BINGLEY, W. Animal Biography. London: Richard Phillips, 1804. 2nd ed. 3 vols. (Lacks frontis?, tps, some text lt browned, news clipping adhered to p283 vol 1, corner through much of vol 3 wormed affecting few text letters, bkpl.) Full tree calf (sl rubbed, fr joints vols 1, 3 tender, spines sl rubbed, chipped w/sl loss), gilt, leather spine labels. *Edwards.* $120/£75

BINGLEY, WILLIAM. Travels in South Europe. London: Harvey & Darton, 1821. 1st ed. Engr tp, (xii),360pp; 5 plts. Unopened. Orig cl. (Sl foxed; sl rubbed, soiled, faded, spine ends frayed), o/w VG. *Worldwide.* $85/£53

BINION, RUDOLPH. Frau Lou. Princeton, NJ: Princeton Univ, 1968. Gray cl. *Gach.* $50/£31

BINKERD, A. D. The Mammoth Cave and Its Denizens. Cincinnati, 1869. 1st ed. 95pp. Orig ptd wrappers (sl worn, stained, soiled). Morocco-backed cl case provided. *Oinonen*.* $120/£75

BINNING, JOHN. Target Area. Sydney, (1943). 1st ed. 23 photos. (Ink name, corners bumped, cvrs dknd, spine bottom faded.) Dj (defective). *King.* $35/£22

BINNS, ARCHIE. Peter Skene Ogden; Fur Trader. Portland, (1967). 1st ed. VG in dj (sl worn). *Woolson.* $30/£19

BINSTEAD, ARTHUR M. Houndsditch by Day. Sands, 1899. Pict cl. VG (fore-edge lt spotted, bkpl, sig; spine bumped). *Tiger.* $16/£10

BINSWANGER, LUDWIG. Sigmund Freud: Reminiscences of a Friendship. NY: Grune & Stratton, 1957. 1st ed. Fine (spine lt sunned). *Beasley.* $75/£47

BINYON, H. Eric Ravilious, Memoir of an Artist. Lutterworth, 1983. Fine in dj. *Moss.* $29/£18

BINYON, LAURENCE and J. J. O'BRIEN SEXTON. Japanese Colour Prints. NY, 1923. 1st Amer ed. Fine (spine sl rubbed). *Polyanthos.* $95/£59

BINYON, LAURENCE and J. J. O'BRIEN SEXTON. Japanese Colour Prints. Basil Gray (ed). Boston: Boston Book & Art Shop, (1960). VG in dj (worn). *Pacific*.* $58/£36

BINYON, LAURENCE et al. Persian Miniature Painting, Including a Critical and Descriptive Catalogue.... London, 1933. Folio. Uncut. (Sl worn, spine sl scuffed.) Oinonen*. $275/£172

BINYON, LAURENCE. The Drawings and Engravings of William Blake. Geoffrey Holme (ed). London: Studio, 1922. One of 200. Folio. 104 plts (16 color), 2 ports. Full vellum, gilt. (Fr inner hinge starting; rear cvr scratched.) Orig fldg box (worn) w/partial ties. Kane*. $160/£100

BINYON, LAURENCE. The Engraved Designs of William Blake. London: Ernest Benn, 1926. Paste-grain design paper over bds, cream cl spine, gilt. NF in dj (soiled, spine ends chipped). Turtle Island. $175/£109

BINYON, LAURENCE. The George Eumorfopoulos Collection: Catalogue of the Chinese Frescoes. London, (1927). Folio. 50 mtd color plts. Swann*. $287/£179

BINYON, LAURENCE. Painting in the Far East. London: Arnold, 1913. 2nd ed. Color frontis, 41 plts. Teg. (Lib spine #, edges rubbed, spine sl torn, sl soiled), o/w VG. Worldwide. $45/£28

BINYON, LAURENCE. Second Book of London Visions. London: Elkin Mathews, 1899. 1st ed. No. X in the 'Shilling Garland Series.' NF (sl edgeworn) in dec blue-gray wrappers designed by Selwyn Image. Sumner & Stillman. $95/£59

BINYON, LAURENCE. The Winnowing-Fan: Poems on the Great War. London: Elkin Mathews, 1915. 1st Eng ed, 2nd ptg. One of 500. VG. Cady. $20/£13

Biographical Anecdotes of William Hogarth. (By John Nichols.) London: John Nichols, 1785. 3rd ed. (2),xx,530pp, extra engr tp. Old mottled calf (scuffed), gilt, black morocco spine label. Karmiole. $200/£125

Biographical Sketches of Some of the Early Settlers of the City of Chicago. Part One. Fergus, 1876. 48pp. New binding w/orig wraps bound in. Rybski. $40/£25

BIOY CASARES, ADOLFO. The Invention of Morel and Other Stories. Austin: Univ of TX, 1964. 1st ed in English. (Bottom pp forecorners sl dampstained), else NF in dj (price-clipped). Lame Duck. $125/£78

BIOY CASARES, ADOLFO. A Plan for Escape. NY: Dutton, 1975. 1st US ed. NF in NF dj (1-inch edge tear fr cvr). Lame Duck. $45/£28

BIRCH, A. G. The Moon Terror. Indianapolis: Popular Fiction Pub, (1927). 1st ed. Fine in VG dj (spine ends chipped, rear panel lacks sm piece, sm tear fr panel). Pacific*. $69/£43

BIRCH, LIONEL (ed). The History of the T. U. C. 1868-1968. London: General Council TUC, 1968. 1st ed. Fine (spine snag) in wraps. Beasley. $40/£25

BIRCH, S. Ancient History from the Monuments, Egypt from the Earliest Times to B.C. 300. SPCK, (n.d.) c. 1880, Wood-engr frontis, 192,(iv) ads pp. Brn pict cl, gilt. (Sl browned), o/w VG. Sotheran. $32/£20

BIRCH, SAMUEL. History of Ancient Pottery. London, 1858. 1st ed. Pict cvrs, gilt. NF (extrems, spine mended). Polyanthos. $100/£63

BIRD, ANNIE LAURIE. Boise the Peace Valley. Caldwell: Caxton, 1934. 1st ed. VG. Perier. $100/£63

BIRD, DR. The Hawks of Hawk-Hollow. London: J. Cunningham, 1839. 134pp (ptr's crease pg 1, affecting text). Contemp 3/4 leather. M & S. $100/£63

BIRD, GEORGE ROBERT. Tenderfoot Days. Boston, 1918. 1st ed. (Bkseller label, sm tear tp margin; backstrip dknd), o/w VG. Baade. $75/£47

BIRD, ISABELLA L. A Lady's Life in the Rocky Mountains. John Murray, 1879. 2nd ed. xii,296pp; 7 wood-engr plts. Marbled edges. VG (bkpl) in contemp crimson 1/2 calf, gilt, marbled sides. Cox. $88/£55

BIRD, ISABELLA L. A Lady's Life in the Rocky Mountains. NY: Putnam, 1881. Frontis, xii,296pp. Pict cl. Mott. $30/£19

BIRD, MARIA. Andy Pandy and Rocky Red. Somerset/London: Purnell & Sons, n.d. (1955). Matvyn Wright (illus). VG. Bookfinders. $35/£22

Birds and Their Uses to Man. London: Darton, c. 1852. 1st ed. 32pp; 8 hand-colored lithos. Brn blind-stamped cl, gilt. (Few sm mks to upper cvr), o/w Fine w/bright grn wrapper, gilt, bound in at fr. Sotheran. $205/£128

BIRDSONG, JAMES C. Brief Sketches of the North Carolina Troops in the War Between the States. Raleigh: Josephus Daniels, 1894. 1st ed. 213pp. (Fr wrap detached, glued to fr bd), else Nice in ptd wraps, bound in protective cardbd cvrs. Chapel Hill. $225/£141

BIRDWELL, CLEO. (Pseud of Don DeLillo.) Amazons. Toronto: Lester & Orpen Dennys, (1980). 1st Canadian ed. (Bottom edge sl soiled), else Fine in Fine dj (price-clipped). Between The Covers. $85/£53

BIRKBECK, MORRIS. Letters from Illinois. London: Taylor & Hessey, 1818. 2nd Eng ed. pp(4) ads,xv,114,(6) ads. Uncut. Orig bds (rebacked w/paper, new eps), orig paper label. Nice. Howes B467. Mott. $125/£78

BIRKBECK, MORRIS. Letters from Illinois. Dublin: Thomas Larkin, 1818. 1st Dublin ed. vii,(i),112pp. Uncut. Recent lt tan 1/2 calf, gilt, marbled sides, twin morocco labels. Good. Young. $240/£150

BIRKBECK, MORRIS. Notes on a Journey in America, from the Coast of Virginia to the Territory of Illinois. Phila: Caleb Richardson, 1817. 1st ed. 12mo. 2 prelim ll (incl 1 blank),4-189pp. Uncut. Orig ptd bds. (Rubbed, old spine repairs, sig.) VF. Howes B468. Mott. $650/£406

BIRKBECK, MORRIS. Notes on a Journey in America, from the Coast of Virginia to the Territory of Illinois. London: James Ridgway, 1818. 3rd Eng ed. Fldg frontis map. pp163,(4) ads. Contemp marbled bds, vellum corners, tree calf spine, leather label. VG (bkpl, sig, map offset on tp). Mott. $200/£125

BIRKBECK, MORRIS. Notes on a Journey in America, from the Coast of Virginia to the Territory of Illinois.... Dublin: Rptd for Thomas Larkin, 1818. Hand-colored fldg frontis map. Mod 1/4 leather, cl sides. (Map hinge torn 3 inches into image), else VG + . Howes B468. Zubal*. $95/£59

BIRKELAND, K. B. The Whalers of Akutan. New Haven: Yale Univ, 1926. VG (sl soil, mks). High Latitude. $70/£44

BIRKELAND, K. B. The World in Snap Shots. NY/London/Montreal: Abbey, 1901. New, rev ed. (Lacks 1 leaf; sl rubbed.) Worldwide. $25/£16

BIRKENHEAD, FIRST EARL OF (ed). Fifty Famous Fights in Fact and Fiction. London: Cassell, (1932). 1st ed. (Sl foxed), else NF. Pacific*. $46/£29

BIRKS, TONY. The Art of the Modern Potter. London: Country Life, (1969). 2nd ptg. Fine in VG dj. Turtle Island. $65/£41

BIRRELL, AUGUSTINE. Frederick Locker-Lampson, a Character Sketch. London: Constable, 1920. Engr frontisport. Uncut, partly unopened. 1/4 cl (sl worn, soiled). Marlborough. $128/£80

Birth, Life, and Acts of King Arthur of His Noble Knights of the Round Table...etc. NY/London: E.P. Dutton/J.M. Dent, 1909. 2nd Beardsley ed. One of 500 ptd. 4to. Orig grn gilt stamped cl (eps dknd). Sound in linen fldg box. Appelfeld. $650/£406

BIRYUKOVA, N. Y. The Hermitage, Leningrad: Gothic and Renaissance Tapestries. London, 1965. 128 color plts. (Sl soiled.) Washton. $50/£31

Bishop's Oakland Directory for 1876-7. Oakland: B.C. Vandall, 1876. 502pp + ads; 2 inserted ads on card stock. Orig leather-backed ptd bds. VG (tears to early ll incl tp; rubbed, worn, spine head chipped). Pacific*. $316/£198

BISHOP, C. K. K. Notes on Church Organs. Rivingtons, 1873. 52pp; 11 litho plts. Ptd bds (backstrip sl defective). Hollett. $120/£75

BISHOP, CHARLES. The Journal and Letters of Captain Charles Bishop on the North-West Coast of America in the Pacific and in New South Wales 1794-1799. Michael Roe (ed). Cambridge: Hakluyt Soc, 1967. Frontis, 6 maps (1 fldg). Blue cl, gilt. VG in dj (faded). *Parmer*. $60/£38

BISHOP, J. The Child's Toy Book; or Pleasing Tales in Words of One and Two Syllables. London: Dean & Munday/A.K. Newman, n.d. (ca 1830). 12mo. Full-pg color engr frontis, 25pp + 1pg list on lower wrapper; 16 Fine color engrs. Near Mint (pub's ink stamp inside fr wrapper; ink inscrip at top of fr cvr; sm hole throughout at edge near spine, not interfering w/text or engrs) in dec grn stiff paper wrappers (lt dusted). *Hobbyhorse*. $350/£219

BISHOP, J. A Visit to the Farm. London: Dean & Munday/A.K. Newman, n.d. (ca 1835). Sq 12mo. 30pp + 1pg bk list on rear wrapper; 8 VF hand-colored full-pg wood engrs, incl frontis. Fine in dec buff stiff paper wrappers (edges lt soiled). *Hobbyhorse*. $325/£203

BISHOP, JOHN PEALE. Minute Particulars. NY: Alcestis, 1935. Ltd to 135 (of 165) signed, numbered. Fine in ptd wrappers over stiff plain card stock. Plain glassine dj. *Cahan*. $300/£188

BISHOP, MORCHARD. Blake's Hayley. London: Gollancz, 1951. 1st Eng ed. VG (stamp; edges, eps spotted; spine ends sl bumped) in dj (chipped, rubbed, torn, spine sl dknd). *Ulysses*. $56/£35

BISHOP, NATHANIEL H. Four Months in a Sneak-Box. Edinburgh: David Douglas, 1880. 1st London ed. x,(ii),322,(2)ads; 4 engr plts (incl frontis), 5 maps. Grn cl. Sound (lt offsetting, mkd, lacks fep; hinges broken, cvrs sl stained, rubbed). *Morrell*. $120/£75

BISHOP, NATHANIEL H. Voyage of the Paper Canoe. Boston: Lee & Shepard, 1878. 1st ed. Frontis. Grn cl, gilt spine. (Repair to spine cl), else VG. *Pacific**. $75/£47

BISHOP, NATHANIEL H. Voyage of the Paper Canoe. Edinburgh: David Douglas, 1878. Frontis, xv,351,(i)pp + 16pp pub's list; 10 maps, 6 plts. (Lt marginal browning; recased, repairs to spine ends.) *Edwards*. $320/£200

BISHOP, RICHARD E. Bishop's Birds: Etchings of Water-Fowl and Upland Game Birds. Phila: Lippincott, 1936. 1st ed. One of 135. Signed. Frontis. Teg. Dec vellum, gilt. (Sl offset from tape to upper cvr edges), else NF. *Pacific**. $288/£180

BISHOP, RICHARD E. Bishop's Wildfowl. (St. Paul, 1948.) 1st ed. Folio. Orig pict leather. *Swann**. $126/£79

BISHOP, S. C. Handbook of Salamanders: The Salamanders of the U.S., Canada and Lower California. NY: Hafner, (1962). Color frontis. VG. *Mikesh*. $45/£28

BISHOP, WILLIAM HENRY. Old Mexico and Her Lost Provinces. NY, 1883. 1st ed. 509pp. Pict cl. (Name label, spine sunned, top chipped.) *King*. $35/£22

BISLAND, ELIZABETH. The Life and Letters of Lafcadio Hearn. Boston, 1906. 1st ed. One of 200 w/orig pg of Hearn's ms tipped in. 2 vols. Lg 8vo. Black cl, ptd spine labels. (Bkpls.) BAL 7944. *Swann**. $1,840/£1,150

BISSELL, ALFRED E. Tuscarora Recollections. Wilmington, 1965. 1st ed. 8vo. 4 mtd color plts. Gilt-lettered cl-backed bds. (Lt worn.) *Oinonen**. $700/£438

BISSET, J. Bisset's Magnificent Guide, or, Grand Copperplate Directory, for the Town of Birmingham. Birmingham, 1803. Engr frontis map, add'l tp, 51 plts; extra-illus w/18 contemp engr proofs of bank notes. Contemp 1/2 leather (extrems worn, joints starting). *Swann**. $460/£288

BISSET, PETER. The Book of Water Gardening. NY: De La Mare, 1907. 1st ed. 2 dbl-pg plts. (Name; worn, shaken), else VG. *Fair Meadow*. $70/£44

BITTING, KATHERINE. Gastronomic Bibliography. (London: Holland Press, 1981.) One of 500 numbered, this copy unnumbered. Crimson bds, gilt. Clean in VG dj (few short tears). *Baltimore**. $55/£34

BJORNSON, BJORNSTERNE. Arne. Augusta Plesner & S. Rugely-Powers (trans). Boston: Sever, Francis, 1869. 150pp. Recent cl. (Rebound), o/w VG. *Brown*. $15/£9

Black Beauty. London: Octopus Books, 1980. J. Pavlin & G. Seda (illus). 6 dbl-pg pop-ups. Glazed pict bds. (Inscrip, lt worn.) *Bookfinders*. $40/£25

BLACK HAWK. Autobiography of Ma-Ka-Tai-Me-She-Kiak, or Black Hawk, Embracing the Traditions of His Nation.... J. B. Patterson (ed). St. Louis, 1881. Frontis, 208pp. VG +. *Zubal**. $60/£38

Black Hole. A Pop-Up Book. NY: Harmony Books/Crown, 1979. 6 dbl-pg pop-ups, wheel. Glazed pict bds. VG. *Bookfinders*. $40/£25

Black's General Atlas of the World. Edinburgh: A&C Black, 1857. Folio. 56 color engr maps. (Margins discolored.) Contemp 1/2 morocco (worn, fr cvr detached). *Sotheby's**. $238/£149

Black's Guide to Killarney and the South of Ireland. Edinburgh: A&C Black, 1865. 1st ed. Wood-engr frontis, (2),111pp + 32pp pub's cat; lg fldg map (sl crumpled), dbl-pg plan. Good (inner hinges neatly reinforced) in limp cl, gilt. *Cox*. $40/£25

Black's Guide to North and South Wales. London, 1867. (Shaken.) *Gretton*. $40/£25

BLACK, ALEXANDER. Miss America: Pen and Camera Sketches of the American Girl. NY: Scribner, 1898. 1st ed. Teg, untrimmed, partly unopened. Light blue-grn cl (sunned), add'l sm mtd repro photo at fr cvr. Clean. *Baltimore**. $35/£22

BLACK, ELEANORA and SIDNEY ROBERTSON. The Gold Rush Song Book. SF: Colt Press, 1940. 1st ed. Blue paper bds, yellow cl spine. NF. *Harrington*. $55/£34

BLACK, ELEANORA and SYDNEY ROBERTSON. The Gold Rush Song Book. SF: Colt, 1940. Tan buckram-backed grn linen, gilt. (Cvrs sl soiled, corner bumped), o/w NF. *Pacific**. $29/£18

BLACK, EMMA. Impressions of Moray. W.G. Briggs, 1931. 32 color plts tipped on to gray card. (Bds sl scraped.) *Hollett*. $48/£30

BLACK, GEORGE F. A Gypsy Bibliography. Provisional Issue. Liverpool: Gypsy Lore Soc, 1909. One of 200 (?) ptd. Ptd wrappers (worn, soiled). *Oinonen**. $50/£31

BLACK, JOHN LOGAN. Crumbling Defenses, or Memoirs and Reminiscences of John Logan Black, Colonel CSA. Eleanor D. McSwain (ed). Macon, GA: Eleanor D. McSwain, (1960). 1st ed. Full-pg port. Gray cl. Fine. *Chapel Hill*. $75/£47

BLACK, M. Superior Cookery. William Collins, (c. 1893). 15th thousand. 200pp; 8 color plts. VG. *Hollett*. $56/£35

BLACK, MARY and JEAN LIPMAN. American Folk Painting. NY: Clarkson N. Potter, (1966). 1st ed. Tan cl. Fine in color, pict dj. *House*. $85/£53

BLACK, ROBERT. The Art of Jacob Epstein. Cleveland: World, (1942). 1st ed. 175 plts. Beige linen. (Blank prelim, 1/2-title foxed.) Dj (sl chipped). *Karmiole*. $75/£47

BLACK, W. An Historical Sketch of Medicine and Surgery from the Origin to the Present Time. London, 1782. vi,315pp; fldg chart. (Ink sig, stamps; marginal stains, pp41-44 missing, lib label; rebacked.) *Whitehart*. $288/£180

BLACK, WILLIAM. The Beautiful Wretch. The Four Macnicols. The Pupil of Aurelius. Macmillan, 1882. New ed. 1st 1-vol ed, half-title present, integral ads at end. (iv),400,(4),24pp, pub's list dated December 1881. Chocolate brn eps. Sand-grain royal blue cl (extrems lt rubbed), gilt backstrip, black blocked bands. Good. *Blackwell's*. $64/£40

BLACK, WILLIAM. Green Pastures and Piccadilly. Sampson Low, Marston, 1892. New, cheaper ed. Good (spine bumped w/sm head nick, hinges, corners rubbed). *Tiger.* $16/£10

BLACK, WILLIAM. Shandon Bells. Macmillan, 1883. 3 vols. Pub's cat vol 1 dated October 1882. Good (lt soiled, spotted; traces lib labels removed; spines bumped, dull; hinges, corners rubbed). *Tiger.* $128/£80

BLACKBURN, HENRY. The Art of Illustration. J. Grant, 1904. Good in 2-color cl. *Moss.* $32/£20

BLACKBURN, HENRY. Randolph Caldecott: A Personal Memoir of His Early Art Career. London: Sampson Low, Marston etc, 1886. Lg paper ed. Frontisport, xvi,216pp. Teg, uncut. Gilt cl over beveled bds (extrems sl worn, spine dull). *Hollett.* $88/£55

BLACKBURN, HENRY. Randolph Caldecott: A Personal Memoir of His Early Art Career. London: Sampson Low, Marston, 1887. 4th ed. Frontisport, xvi,216pp. 1/2 calf, raised bands. *Young.* $72/£45

BLACKBURN, HENRY. Randolph Caldecott: His Early Art Career. NY: Routledge, 1886. 1st ed. 8vo. 5(ads),216pp. Brn eps, aeg. Grn cl. NF in VG dj. *Davidson.* $150/£94

BLACKBURN, J. K. P. Reminiscences of the Terry Rangers. (Austin): Univ of TX, 1919. 1st ed. VG + in ptd blue wraps (faded, lt chipped, tape-repaired 1-inch tear fr wrap). *Chapel Hill.* $225/£141

BLACKBURN, JOHN. A Sour Apple Tree. NY: M.S. Mill, 1959. 1st ed. VG in dj (spine ends sl rubbed, sm tear to extrems). *Pacific*.* $40/£25

BLACKBURN, PAUL. Brooklyn-Manhattan Transit. NY: Totem, 1960. 1st ed. NF in wraps. *Beasley.* $25/£16

BLACKBURN, PHILIP C. and LIONEL WHITE. Logical Nonsense: The Works of Lewis Carroll. NY: Putnam, (1934). 1st ed. No. 'E' of 25 signed by both. Gilt-tooled red calf. (Spine ends sl rubbed), else VG. *Pacific*.* $173/£108

BLACKBURNE-MAZE, C. I. Journals of My African Travels. Maidstone: W.E. Thorpe, 1913. Signed. Numerous silver-gelatin photos mtd 1 per pg. Teg. Grn pict cl (worn). *Christie's*.* $541/£338

BLACKER, J. F. The A B C of Collecting Old English Pottery. Stanley Paul, n.d. 4th ed. Pict cl, gilt. VG. *Hollett.* $56/£35

BLACKER, J. F. The A B C of Nineteenth-Century English Ceramic Art. Stanley Paul, n.d. Color frontis. Uncut. Pict cl, gilt. VG. *Hollett.* $64/£40

BLACKER, L. V. S. On Secret Patrol in High Asia. London: Murray, 1922. 1st ed. 15 plts, 2 (of 3) maps. Lib buckram. (Lib spine #, sl rubbed, sl foxed), o/w Good. *Worldwide.* $75/£47

BLACKER, WILLIAM. Blacker's Art of Fly Making.... London, 1855. 12mo. Engr frontis, engr tp, 20 Fine plts. (Lt worn, foxed, diagonal piece clipped from blank margin of engr tp.) *Oinonen*.* $650/£406

BLACKERBY, A. W. and LINN A. FORREST. Tale of an Alaska Whale. Portland: Binfords & Mort, (1955). VG in pict cl. *Perier.* $20/£13

BLACKFAN, KENNETH D. Atlas of the Blood in Children. NY, 1944. 1st ed. VG. *Doctor's Library.* $95/£59

BLACKFORD, CHARLES M., JR. Annals of the Lynchburg Home Guard. Lynchburg, VA: Ptd by John W. Rohr, Elecric (sic) Power, 1891. 1st ed. 12mo. Frontisport, 185pp. Black cl. VG (ink lib stamps; spine faded, extrems rubbed). *Chapel Hill.* $600/£375

BLACKFORD, SUSAN LEIGH. Letters from Lee's Army; Or, Memoirs of Life in and Out of the Army in Virginia During the War Between the States. NY: Scribner, 1947. Best ed. Red cl. VG in dj (foxed). *Chapel Hill.* $75/£47

BLACKMORE, HOWARD L. Guns and Rifles of the World. NY: Viking, 1965. 1st ed. VG + (sl shelfworn) in dj (sl edgeworn). *My Bookhouse.* $52/£33

BLACKMORE, R. D. Fringilla, or, Tales in Verse. Cleveland: Burrows, 1895. One of 600. This copy un-numbered, annotated 'Review Copy.' 4pp prospectus laid in. (Foxed; worn, rubbed.) *Kane*.* $225/£141

BLACKMORE, R. D. The Maid of Sker. William Blackwood & Sons, 1890. New ed. Frontis. Sprinkled edges. Contemp 1/2 leather, marbled bds, raised bands. Good (sig). *Tiger.* $64/£40

BLACKMORE, R. D. Perlycross. Sampson Low, Marston, 1894. 1st 1-vol ed. Good (sig, sl spotted; spine bumped, chipped; hinges, corners sl rubbed). *Tiger.* $29/£18

BLACKMORE, R. D. Perlycross. Sampson Low, Marston, 1894. 1st single vol ed. Half-title, (ii),iv,465,(1)pp. Blue patterned eps. Blue cl, gilt. Good. *Blackwell's.* $64/£40

BLACKMORE, R. D. Tales from the Telling-House. Sampson Low, Marston, 1896. Teg. Dec cl. VG (fore-edge sl spotted; spine bumped). *Tiger.* $61/£38

BLACKMUR, R. P. Language as Gesture. George Allen & Unwin, 1954. 1st Eng ed. NF (spine ends, corner sl bumped) in dj (sl dusty, nicked, spine sl faded). *Ulysses.* $72/£45

BLACKMUR, R. P. The Second World. Cummington: Cummington Press, 1942. 1st ed. One of 300 numbered. Fine in dj (frayed, dknd, split down 1 fold). *Reese.* $85/£53

BLACKSTONE, ORIN. Index to Jazz. Fairfax, VA: Record Changer, 1945-1948. 1st ed, vol I 2nd ptg. 4 vols, complete. VG (ink ticking). *Beasley.* $85/£53

BLACKSTONE, WILLIAM. An Analysis of the Laws of England. To Which Is Perfixed [sic] an Introductory Discourse on the Study of the Law. Dublin: Elizabeth Watts, 1766. 5th ed. Contemp calf (neatly rebacked). Good. *Boswell.* $850/£531

BLACKSTONE, WILLIAM. Commentaries on the Laws of England...Together with Notes Adapting the Work to the American Student by John L. Wendell. NY: Harper, 1847. 4 vols. Contemp sheep. Sound set (foxed; rubbed). *Boswell.* $650/£406

Blackwater Chronicle. A Narrative of an Expedition into the Land of Canaan, in Randolph County, Virginia. By 'The Clerke of Oxenforde.' NY: Redfield, 1853. 1st ed. Frontis, extra engr tp, 223pp + 8 leaves ads. (Foxed, sl soiled; spine edges worn, head chipped.) *Oinonen*.* $250/£156

BLACKWELL, J. KENYON. Explosions in Coal Mines, Their Causes, and the Means Available for Their Prevention or Control.... London: Taylor & Francis, 1853. 1st ed. 38pp (tp dusty). Calf-backed bds. *Young.* $51/£32

BLACKWELL, ROBERT. Original Acrostics, by Robert Blackwell, on Some of the Southern States, Confederate Generals, and Various Other Persons and Things. St. Louis: The Author, 1869. 1st ed. 100,ivpp. (Parts of spine head gone affecting title), else Good. *Brown.* $35/£22

BLACKWOOD, ALGERNON. Dudley and Gilderoy: A Nonsense. NY: Dutton, (1929). 1st US ed. (Rear hinge cracked, corner worn), else VG. *Other Worlds.* $25/£16

BLACKWOOD, ALGERNON. Full Circle. Woburn Books, 1929. One of 530 signed. Patterned bds. Fine in dj. *Clearwater.* $80/£50

BLACKWOOD, ALGERNON. The Promise of Air. NY: Dutton, (1918). 1st US ed. (Spine spotted, dampstained), else VG + . *Other Worlds.* $35/£22

BLACKWOOD, ALGERNON. The Wave. An Egyptian Aftermath. NY, 1916. 1st Amer ed. Fine in Fine dj. *Mcclintock.* $350/£219

BLADES, WILLIAM. An Account of the German Morality-Play Entitled Depositio Cornuti Typographici, as Performed in the 17th and 18th Centuries. London: Trubner, 1885. 1st ed. xii, 116 pp. Uncut. Bds, paper sides, (hinges worn, bkpl). *Oak Knoll.* $125/£78

BLADES, WILLIAM. The Enemies of Books. London, 1881. 3rd ed. 114pp; 7 full-pg copper engrs. Marbled eps; teg. 1/2 grn morocco, gilt. (Orig wrappers bound in.) VG. *Truepenny.* $125/£78

BLAEU, WILLEM JANSZ. The Light of Navigation. (Cleveland/NY: World, 1964.) Facs of Amsterdam 1612 ed. Obl folio. (Inner hinges tender; cvrs rubbed.) *Lefkowicz.* $75/£47

BLAGROVE, WILLIAM (ed). Elements of Chess. Boston, 1805. Fldg frontis. Sheep. *Felcone.* $1,500/£938

BLAIKIE, WILLIAM GARDEN. The Personal Life of David Livingstone. London, 1880. Frontisport, xix,504pp + 24pp pub's cat; fldg map. (Sl bubbled, spine sl rubbed.) *Edwards.* $64/£40

BLAINE, DELABERE. Canine Pathology. T. & T. Boosey et al, 1832. 3rd ed. Frontis, iv,316pp (bkpl). Contemp 1/2 calf, gilt, marbled bds, raised bands, gilt spine panels. Nice. *Hollett.* $136/£85

BLAINE, DELABERE. Canine Pathology. London, 1841. 4th ed, rev, corrected enlgd. Frontis, iv,324pp. Uncut. (Margins lt browned, sl spotted, feps adhered to eps; sl soiled, rubbed; rear joint foot split, gilt spine sl bumped.) *Edwards.* $96/£60

BLAINE, DELABERE. An Encyclopedia of Rural Sports. London: Longman, Brown, Green & Longmans, 1852. 2nd ed. 1246pp. 3/4 grn calf, marbled bds, morocco spine labels. (Bkpl, fr joint starting), else NF. *Pacific*.* $316/£198

BLAINE, JAMES G. Twenty Years of Congress: from Lincoln to Garfield. Norwich: Henry Bill, 1884. 1st ed. 2 vols. 13 steel-engr port plts, fldg map. (Some pp roughly opened; vol 1 lacks fep.) Marbled edges. Pebbled lt brn cl, gilt. Cvrs VG. *Baltimore*.* $25/£16

BLAIR, CLAUDE. Pistols of the World. NY: Viking, 1968. VG + (sl shelfworn) in dj (sl worn). *My Bookhouse.* $52/£33

BLAIR, DOROTHY. A History of Glass in Japan. (NY, 1973.) 1st ed. Mylar dj. *Swann*.* $230/£144

BLAIR, ROBERT. The Grave. A Poem. London: Bensley, 1808. Folio. Extra pict tp, mtd port (both sl dampstained; other internal lt mostly marginal dampstaining), 11 engr plts. Uncut. Later 3/4 morocco (rubbed, stains). *Oinonen*.* $750/£469

BLAIR, WALTER A. and FRANKLIN J. MEINE (eds). Half Horse, Half Alligator. Chicago: Univ of Chicago, (1956). 1st ed. Fine in dj. *Argonaut.* $45/£28

BLAIR, WALTER A. A Raft Pilot's Log. Cleveland: A.H. Clark, 1930. 1st ed. Blue cl, gilt. Binding on this copy perhaps later issue, and top edges are not gilded as the Clark bibliography notes they should be. (Lower corner fr cvr bumped), else NF. *Pacific*.* $69/£43

BLAKE, A. H. Photography: Being Simple Chapters for Beginners on the Art and Practice of Photography. London: George Routledge & Sons, 1899. 3rd ed. Photo frontis, ix,115pp + (2)pp ad; 2 full-pg b/w photos. (Eps dknd; soiled, sl wrinkled), else VG. *Cahan.* $85/£53

BLAKE, E. VALE (ed). Arctic Experiences. NY, 1874. Later(?) cl. (Hinges cracked.) *Swann*.* $69/£43

BLAKE, GEORGE. The Path of Glory. London: Constable, (1929). 1st ed, 2nd imp. Orange cl. VG; dj fragments laid in. *Reese.* $35/£22

BLAKE, JAMES. The Joint. GC: Doubleday/Paris Review, 1971. 1st ed. VF in VF dj (sl rubbed). *Between The Covers.* $85/£53

BLAKE, NICHOLAS. (Pseud of Cecil Day-Lewis.) A Tangled Web. Collins, 1956. 1st UK ed. VG + in dj (spine head sl pushed). *Williams.* $61/£38

BLAKE, NICHOLAS. (Pseud of Cecil Day-Lewis.) The Worm of Death. Collins, 1961. 1st UK ed. NF in VG dj (edges sl worn, sm chip spine head). *Williams.* $45/£28

BLAKE, W.O. (comp). The History of Slavery and the Slave-Trade, Ancient and Modern.... Columbus: H. Miller, 1860. 832pp. Marbled eps. Orig blind black sheep (lt worn, scuffed), gilt. Internally Good (lt foxed, browned). *Baltimore*.* $50/£31

BLAKE, WILLIAM. The Book of Thel. NY: Payson & Clarke, 1928. 1st ed. One of 850 numbered. Fine in VG dj (chipped, sunned). *Turtle Island.* $75/£47

BLAKE, WILLIAM. Job. NY: United Book Guild, (1947). Folio. 21 tipped-in plts. Black cl, pict cvr label. VG. *Pacific*.* $69/£43

BLAKE, WILLIAM. The Land of Dreams: Twenty Poems. Northampton, MA: Hampshire Bookshop, 1928. Ltd to 350 signed by Pamela Bianco (illus). 8vo. Silver-dec bds (faded, sm spine chip). Cardbd slipcase (lt edgeworn), ptd paste label. *Reisler.* $150/£94

BLAKE, WILLIAM. Pencil Drawings by William Blake. Geoffrey Keynes (ed). (London): Nonesuch, 1927. Ltd to 1550 numbered. 82 collotype plts. Beige linen (sl dknd), cream bds. *Karmiole.* $150/£94

BLAKE, WILLIAM. The Poems of William Blake. LEC, 1973. Ltd to 1500 numbered, signed by John Dreyfus (designer). Fine in slipcase. *Swann*.* $80/£50

BLAKE, WILLIAM. Songs of Innocence. London: Medici Soc, 1927. 12 color plts. *Petersfield.* $38/£24

BLAKE, WILLIAM. William Blake's Designs for Edward Young's Night Thoughts. Oxford, 1980. Complete ed. 2 vols. Tall folio. Fine in dj, box. *Argosy.* $375/£234

BLAKE, WILLIAM. William Blake's Water-Colour Designs for the Poems of Thomas Gray. Geoffrey Keynes (intro, vol 3). William Blake Trust, 1972. 3 vols. Folio. Facs texts mtd on 116 full-pg facs water-color designs. 1/4 morocco, marbled paper bds. Fine set, each vol in separate morocco-edged marbled paper slipcase. *Ulysses.* $2,000/£1,250

BLAKE, WILLIAM. The Writings of William Blake. Geoffrey Keynes (ed). London: Nonesuch, 1925. 1st ed. One of 1500. Frontis photogravure port. 1/4 vellum, marbled bds, gilt. (Corners sl rubbed), else NF. *Pacific*.* $316/£198

BLAKE, WILLIAM. The Writings of William Blake. Geoffrey Keynes (ed). London: Nonesuch, 1925. One of 1500 numbered sets. 3 vols. Photogravure frontis. 1/4 vellum, marbled bds. (Eps sl foxed; spine sl dknd, sm spine nick), o/w VG + . *Reese.* $350/£219

BLAKENEY, JANE. Heroes—U.S. Marine Corps 1861-1955. Washington, 1957. 1st ed. 2 color fldg plts. VG. *Clark.* $250/£156

BLAKENEY, THOMAS S. Sherlock Holmes: Fact or Fiction? London, (1932). 1st ed. Dj (price-clipped, spine sl tanned). *Swann*.* $80/£50

BLAKESTON, OSWELL. Priests, Peters and Pussens. Fortune, n.d. (1947). 1st ed. Signed presentation. (Spine sl bubbled, edges sunned), else VG + . *Any Amount.* $48/£30

BLAKESTON, OSWELL. The Queen's Mate. Scorpion, 1962. 1st ed. Signed, inscribed presentation. Fine in NF pict dj (sl sunned). *Any Amount.* $48/£30

BLAKEY, G. The Diamond. London: Paddington, c1977. Fine in dj. *Blake.* $60/£38

BLAKEY, ROBERT. Historical Sketches of the Angling Literature of All Nations. London: John Russell Smith, 1856. 1st ed. Grn cl, gilt. NF. *Pacific*.* $104/£65

BLAKSTON, W. A. et al. The Illustrated Book of Canaries and Cage-Birds, British and Foreign. London: Cassell, n.d. (ca 1890). Pub's gilt-pict cl (recased, new eps; shelfwear). *Oinonen*.* $375/£234

BLANC, HENRY. A Narrative of Captivity in Abyssinia. London: Smith, Elder, 1868. 1st ed. 1/2 title, xii,409,(1)imprint,(1)erratum; 8 engr plts. Brn, dec cl (extrems sl rubbed), gilt. VG. *Morrell.* $208/£130

BLANC, JEAN-CHARLES. Afghan Trucks. Stonehill Pub, 1976. 1st ed. 106 color photos. VG in pict stiff wrappers (lt rubbed). *Cahan.* $20/£13

BLANCK, JACOB. Bibliography of American Literature. Volume IV. New Haven/London: Yale/Oxford, 1963. (Ex-lib, hinges repaired), else Sound. *Zubal*.* $35/£22

BLANCK, JACOB. Bibliography of American Literature. Volume V. New Haven/London: Yale/Oxford, 1969. (Ex-lib), else Sound. *Zubal*.* $45/£28

BLANCK, JACOB. Bibliography of American Literature. Volume VII. New Haven/London: Yale/Oxford, 1983. (Ex-lib), else Sound. *Zubal*.* $55/£34

BLANCK, JACOB. Peter Parley to Penrod: A Bibliographical Description of the Best-Loved American Juvenile Books. NY: R.R. Bowker, 1956. 2nd ed. Lt blue-gray buckram, gilt. (Ink sig, pp sl handled; sl rubbed.) Text VG, cvrs Clean. *Baltimore*.* $60/£38

BLAND, DAVID. A History of Book Illustration. Faber, 1969. Rev ed. VG in dj. *Moss.* $96/£60

BLAND, DAVID. The Illustration of Books. Faber & Faber, 1953. 2nd ed. Color frontis. Dj (torn). *Forest.* $29/£18

BLAND, J. O. P. and E. BACKHOUSE. China Under the Empress Dowager, Being the History of the Life and Times of Tzu Hsi.... Phila/London: Lippincott/Heinemann, 1910. 1st ed. 1 color facs plt. Teg. (Foxed; sl rubbed, soiled), o/w VG. *Worldwide.* $45/£28

BLAND, J. O. P. China, Japan and Korea. Heinemann, 1921. 1st ed. All edges uncut. Orange cl. (Sl foxed), o/w VG in dj (sl head loss). *Sotheran.* $157/£98

BLANDFORD, G. FIELDING. Insanity and Its Treatment: Lectures on the Treatment...of Insane Patients. Edinburgh: Oliver & Boyd, 1877. 2nd ed. VG (lib mks; cl sl bubbled). *Beasley.* $65/£41

BLANDING, DON. Drifter's Gold. NY, 1939. 1st Amer ed. Pict cvrs, gilt. NF (sl rubbed). *Polyanthos.* $25/£16

BLANDING, DON. Vagabond's House. NY, 1932. Signed. Frontis. Pict cl (spine sl faded). *Argosy.* $30/£19

BLANFORD, W. T. Observations on the Geology and Zoology of Abyssinia. London, 1870. 1st ed. 8vo. Fldg color frontis, xii,487pp; fldg color map, 6 plain plts, 6 hand-colored plts. Grn cl, gilt. (Pp yellowed; soiled, lt worn, spine dknd; lib bkpl w/withdrawal stamp, sm # stamp, sm nick to backstrip; paper on interior hinges broken, hinges solid), o/w Internally Clean. *Sutton.* $575/£359

BLANK, CLAIR. Beverly Gray's Secret. NY: G&D, 1951. 1st ed. Beverly Gray #21; lists to this title. 5x7.5. 212pp. (Fep marred where old price erased), else VG + in dj (edgeworn). *My Bookhouse.* $32/£20

BLANKENSHIP, RUSSELL. And There Were Men. NY: Knopf, 1942. 1st ed. Signed. Good in dj (sl worn). *Lien.* $30/£19

BLANKFORT, MICHAEL. I Met a Man. Indianpolis: Bobbs-Merrill, (1937). 1st ed. Signed, inscribed. NF in pict dj (lt edgeworn). *Reese.* $75/£47

BLASCO IBANEZ, VINCENTE. The Enemies of Women. Irving Brown (trans). NY: E.P. Dutton, (1920). 1st US ed. Blue cl. (Ink stamps), else Bright in pict dj (edgeworn, lt nicked, chipped). *Reese.* $50/£31

BLASCO IBANEZ, VINCENTE. The Four Horsemen of the Apocalypse. NY: A.L. Burt, (post. 1918). Rpt. Gilt blue cl. (Ink inscrip), else VG in pict dj (lt nicked). *Reese.* $25/£16

BLASCO IBANEZ, VINCENTE. The Four Horsemen of the Apocalypse. Charlotte B. Jordan (trans). NY: E.P. Dutton, 1918. 1st ed in English. Blue cl stamped in red. (Sm spots of adhesion residue rear cvr), else Nice. *Reese.* $85/£53

BLASDALE, HELEN ROGERS. Bibliography of the Eucalyptus Press, 1932-1950. Mills College, CA, 1950. 1st ed. One of 250. Tipped-in frontis. Grn bds. Fine. *Harrington.* $75/£47

BLASDALE, WALTER C. The Cultivated Species Primula. Berkeley/L.A.: Univ of CA, 1948. 1st ed. Color frontis, 41 b/w plts, map. VG in dj (lacks sm pieces). *Fair Meadow.* $55/£34

BLASER, WERNER. Mies Van Der Rohe: The Art of Structure. D. Q. Stephenson (trans). NY: Frederick A. Praeger, 1965. 1st US ed. (Spine lettering rubbed, cl dusty), else VG. *Cahan.* $50/£31

BLATTY, WILLIAM PETER. The Exorcist. NY: Harper & Row, (1971). 1st ed. VG in dj (spine head sl chipped). *Pacific*.* $46/£29

BLEACKLEY, HORACE. More Tales of the Stumps. London: Ward, Lock, 1902. 1st ed. 11 illus by Arthus Rackham, the rest by 'Rip.' Color pict cl (extrems lt rubbed, spine sl faded; bkpl). *Christie's*.* $920/£575

BLEDSOE, A. J. Indian Wars of the Northwest. Oakland: Biobooks, 1956. 1st ed thus. Ltd to 200. Red cl. Fine. Howes B529. *Labordo.* $75/£47

BLEILER, EVERETT F. (ed). The Checklist of Fantastic Literature. Chicago: Shasta, 1948. 1st ed. Inscribed. (Bkpl, pencil notes), else VG + in dj (edgeworn, badly browned). *Other Worlds.* $100/£63

BLESSINGTON, MARGUERITE. The Confessions of an Elderly Lady and the Confessions of an Elderly Man. Simms & McIntyre, 1848. Sprinkled edges. Contemp 1/2 leather over marbled bds. Good. *Tiger.* $38/£24

BLEW, WILLIAM C. A. Brighton and Its Coaches. A History of the London and Brighton Road. London: Nimmo, 1894. 1st ed. 20 color plts. Uncut, teg. Pict cl. (Sl foxing; sl worn, spine sl scuffed.) *Oinonen*.* $180/£113

BLEW, WILLIAM C. A. A History of Steeple-Chasing. London, 1901. 12 hand-colored plts. Teg, rest uncut. (Text between pp 256-257 cracked, few margins sl thumbed; cl edges sl soiled, rubbed; spine sl discolored, spine head sl worn.) *Edwards.* $240/£150

BLEWITT, MARY. Surveys of the Sea. London: MacGibbon & Kee, 1957. Folio. 60 map repros (1 color). (Sl shelfworn), else VG. *Dumont.* $150/£94

BLIGH, WILLIAM. The Bligh Notebook: Rough Account—Lieutenant Wm. Bligh's Voyage in the Bounty's Launch.... Canberra: Nat'l Library of Scotland, 1986. Both one of 500 handbound. 2 vols. 3 facs ll listing bounty mutineers laid in loose, as issued. Facs is full leather, gilt, morocco spine label. Transcript w/2 plts; 1/2 leather, gilt. Both set in slipcase w/closed compartment for facs vol. Fine (bkpls). *Pacific*.* $489/£306

BLIGH, WILLIAM. The Log of H.M.S. Bounty 1787-1789. Guildford: Genesis, 1975. One of 50 signed by Mountbatten of Burma, and specially bound, from a facs ed of 500. Folio. Watered silk eps; aeg. Full morocco gilt, by Zaehnsdorf. Cl case. *Sotheby's*.* $626/£391

BLIGH, WILLIAM. A Voyage to the South Sea, Undertaken by Command of His Majesty, for the Purpose of Conveying the Bread-Fruit Tree to the West Indies.... London: George Nicol, 1792. 1st ed. Stipple-engr frontisport, (10),264pp, 8 plts (5 fldg). Marbled eps, aeg, gilt inner dentelles. Mod full brn morocco, gilt, raised bands. Very Nice (4 plts mtd on linen backing, repairing tears, few chips; lt foxing to frontis, tp, few other pp; pp81-2 w/sm burnhole). *Pacific*.* $4,313/£2,696

BLIGH, WILLIAM. A Voyage to the South Seas. LEC, 1975. One of 2000 signed by Alan Villiers (illus) and Douglas A. Dunstan (designer). Fine in slipcase. *Swann*.* $115/£72

BLISH, JAMES. Earthman Come Home. NY: Putnam, 1955. 1st ed. NF (spine ends sl bumped) in dj (sl frayed, nicked, spine sl dknd). *Ulysses.* $152/£95

BLISH, JAMES. Earthman, Come Home. NY: Putnam, (1955). 1st ed. Fine in dj (rear cvr sl dust-soiled). *Levin.* $150/£94

BLISH, JAMES. Jack of Eagles. NY: Greenberg, (1952). 1st ed, 1st bk. (Eps sl foxed, lt offsetting; edges foxed), o/w Fine in dj. *Levin.* $150/£94

BLISS, CAREY S. Autos Across America. L.A., 1972. VG. *Dumont.* $45/£28

BLISS, DOUGLAS PERCY. A History of Wood Engraving. Spring Books, 1964. (Edges sl browned.) Dj (top edge sl worn). *Hollett.* $40/£25

BLISS, DOUGLAS PERCY. A History of Wood-Engraving. London: J.M. Dent, 1928. 1st ed. 120 woodcuts. VG in dj (spine dknd, ends chipped). *Pacific*.* $86/£54

BLISS, FRANK C. St. Paul, Its Past and Present.... St. Paul: F.C. Bliss, 1888. 1st ed. 224pp. Blue cl, gilt. VG- (cvrs rubbed). *Pacific*.* $63/£39

BLIXEN, KAREN. Out of Africa. Putnam, 1937. 1st UK ed. Fine in VG dj (edges sl worn; browned). *Williams.* $600/£375

BLOCH, E. MAURICE. The Drawings of George Caleb Bingham. With a Catalogue Raisonne. Columbia, 1975. Folio. Dj. *Swann*.* $172/£108

BLOCH, MARC. Memoirs of War, 1914-15. Ithaca/London: Cornell Univ, (1980). 1st ed in English. Fine in NF dj. *Reese.* $25/£16

BLOCH, ROBERT. Dragons and Nightmares: Four Short Novels. Balt: Mirage, 1968. 1st ed. VG in dj (sm tear, sl rubbed). *Pacific*.* $35/£22

BLOCH, ROBERT. Night of the Ripper. GC: Doubleday, 1984. Pub's file copy stamp on fep. (Top edge sl dusty), o/w Fine in dj. *Any Amount.* $48/£30

BLOCH, ROBERT. The Opener of the Way. Sauk City: Arkham House, 1945. 1st ed. (Ink sig.) Dj (price lined through in pen, rear panel sl dust-soiled). *Kane*.* $225/£141

BLOCH, ROBERT. The Opener of the Way. Sauk City: Arkham House, 1945. 1st ed. (Bkpl.) else VG + in dj. *Other Worlds.* $300/£188

BLOCH, ROBERT. The Opener of the Way. Sauk City, 1945. 1st ed, 1st bk. Fine in dj. *Swann*.* $345/£216

BLOCH, ROBERT. Psycho II. NY: Whispers, 1982. One of 750 signed by Bloch and Stuart Schiff (designer). Fine in dj in slipcase. *Williams.* $120/£75

BLOCH, ROBERT. Psycho. London, (1960). 1st Eng ed. Dj (price-clipped). *Swann*.* $69/£43

BLOCK, EUGENE B. Above the Civil War: The Story of Thaddeus Lowe, Balloonist, Inventor, Railway Builder. Berkeley: Howell-North Books, 1966. 1st ed. Pict eps. Brn cl. Fine in Fine dj. *Harrington.* $50/£31

BLOCK, EUGENE B. The Immortal San Franciscans for Whom the Streets Were Named. SF: Chronicle Books, (1971). 1st ed. Rust cl. Fine in dj (lt rubbed). *Argonaut.* $45/£28

BLOCK, HERBERT. Herblock's Special for Today. NY, 1958. 1st Amer ed. NF (spine sl sunned). *Polyanthos.* $35/£22

BLOCK, LAWRENCE. Ariel. NY, 1980. 1st ed. NF (inscrip) in NF dj (sl rubbed). *Warren.* $30/£19

BLOCK, LAWRENCE. Eight Million Ways to Die. NY: Arbor House, 1982. 1st ed. (Pg edges, eps spotted), o/w VG in dj (few tears, edges sl worn). *Mordida.* $150/£94

BLOCK, LAWRENCE. Markham. NY: Belmont Books, 1961. 1st ed. Orig pb. VG. *Warren.* $25/£16

BLOCK, LAWRENCE. The Thief Who Couldn't Sleep. NY: Otto Penzler Books, (1994). 1st hb ed. Fine in dj (sm tear). *Antic Hay.* $17/£11

BLOCK, LAWRENCE. The Topless Tulip Caper. Allison & Busby, 1984. 1st UK ed. VG in dj (sl mkd). *Williams.* $45/£28

BLOCK, LAWRENCE. When the Sacred Ginmill Closes. Arbor, 1986. 1st ed. (Edges lt worn), else NF in dj. *Murder.* $37/£23

BLOMFIELD, REGINALD. The Formal Garden in England. London/NY, 1901. (Lt spotting, feps lt browned; cl sl soiled.) *Edwards.* $48/£30

BLOMFIELD, REGINALD. The Formal Garden in England. London: Macmillan, 1901. 3rd ed. 67 full-pg illus. Gilt-dec cl, pict cvr. (Spine dknd, lt cvr soil), else VG. *Quest.* $80/£50

BLOOM, JAMES D. Left Letters. The Culture Wars of Mike Gold and Joseph Freeman. NY: Columbia Univ, 1992. 1st ed. Fine in Fine dj. *Beasley.* $30/£19

BLOOMFIELD, ARTHUR L. A Bibliography of Internal Medicine: Communicable Diseases. (Chicago): Univ of Chicago, (1958). 1st ed. Crimson cl, gilt. NF in VG dj. *Baltimore*.* $80/£50

BLOOMFIELD, ROBERT. The Farmer's Boy; a Rural Poem. Phila: James Humphreys, 1801. 141pp + 2pp ads. Full contemp calf, leather label. (Text lt toned; sl rubbed, scuffed), else VG. *Brown.* $30/£19

BLOOMFIELD, ROBERT. Rural Tales, Ballads and Songs. Vernor & Hood/Longman & Rees, 1802. 1st ed. Half-title, xi,105,(ii,contents)pp; port (spotted). Old cl-backed marbled bds (edges worn). *Hollett.* $288/£180

BLOOMFIELD, ROBERT. Wild Flowers; or, Pastoral and Local Poetry. London: Vernor, Hood, et al, 1806. Teg. 3/4 red morocco, marbled bds, gilt. (Extrems sl rubbed), else NF. *Pacific*.* $184/£115

BLOOMFIELD, ROBERT. Wild Flowers; or, Pastoral and Local Poetry. Vernor & Hood, 1806. 1st ed, 1st issue. x,(ii),132pp; 8 wood-engr plts. Untrimmed. Orig cream paper-backed gray bds, ptd paper label. Good (6 sm neat contemp in marginalia, eps browned, contemp inscrip; joints split, backstrip soiled w/sl loss at head, wax spots). *Blackwell's.* $200/£125

BLORE, EDWARD. The Monumental Remains of Noble and Eminent Persons. London, Harding, Lepard, 1826. Lg paper copy. 30 plts (sl spotted; bkpl). Marbled eps; aeg. Contemp morocco (extrems, joints sl rubbed, bds lt discolored), gilt. *Edwards.* $296/£185

BLOSS, ROY S. Pony Express—The Great Gamble. Berkeley, 1959. 1st ed. Fldg map. Fine in dj (edges sl dknd). *Baade.* $45/£28

BLOSSFELDT, KARL. Art Forms in Nature, Second Series. London: A. Zwemmer, 1932. Folio. 120 gravure repros. (Shaken; eps, 1/2-title foxed, marginal loss plt 29, plt unaffected; worn.) *Swann*.* $1,150/£719

Blossoms of Morality. Intended for the Amusement and Instruction of Young Ladies and Gentlemen. London: E. Newbery, 1796. 2nd ed, 1st John Bewick ed. 12mo. x,221pp. 19th-cent 3/4 red morocco, marbled bds. (Extrems lt rubbed), else Fine. *Bromer.* $550/£344

BLOUNDELLE-BURTON, JOHN. Fortune's My Foe. NY: D. Appleton, 1899. 1st Amer ed. 4pp undated ads. Lt blue dec cl. NF (sl soiled). *Sumner & Stillman.* $25/£16

BLOY, C. H. A History of Printing Ink Balls and Rollers 1440-1850. Wynkyn de Worde Soc, 1967. 1st ed. 12 plts. *Forest.* $40/£25

Blue Book: A Comprehensive Official Souvenir View Book Illustrating the Panama-Pacific International Exposition at San Francisco, 1915. SF: Robert Reid, 1915. 1st ed. Marbled eps. Blue cl, gilt. Fine. *Pacific*.* $35/£22

BLUEMEL, ELINOR. Florence Sabin: Colorado Woman of the Century. Boulder: Univ of CO, (1959). 1st ed. Fine in dj. *Hermitage.* $35/£22

BLUM, RICHARD et al (eds). Utopiates: The Use and Users of LSD-25. Tavistock, 1965. 1st UK ed. NF in dj (sl mkd, nicked). *Sclanders.* $40/£25

BLUME, FRIEDRICH. Two Centuries of Bach. Stanley Godman (trans). OUP, 1950. 1st Eng ed. VG in dj. *Hollett.* $24/£15

BLUMENBACH, JOHANN F. Elements of Physiology. Charles Caldwell (trans). Phila: Thomas Dobson, 1795. 1st US ed. 2 vols in 1. xvi,229; 247pp. Old calf, leather spine label. (Browned, foxed, portion of 1st sig loose, portions torn from bottom of 2 early text pp, section missing from margin of another pg, lacks separate tp for vol 2; sl worn, scuffed, spine ends snagged.) Text Good. *Baltimore*. \$120/£75

BLUNDEN, EDMUND. The Bonadventure. R. Cobden-Sanderson, 1922. 1st UK ed. VG + in dj (sl creased, edgeworn). *Williams*. \$77/£48

BLUNDEN, EDMUND. The Great Church of the Holy Trinity Long Melford. (Long Melford, Suffolk), 1966. 1st ed. White wrappers. Fine. *Temple*. \$24/£15

BLUNDEN, EDMUND. Near and Far. London, 1929. Inscribed. VG in dj (dknd). *Typographeum*. \$65/£41

BLUNDEN, EDMUND. Retreat. (London): Richard Cobden-Sanderson, (1928). 1st ed, trade issue. Paper spine label. Fine in dj (sl tanned, frayed at top edge). *Reese*. \$65/£41

BLUNDEN, EDMUND. Retreat. Cobden-Sanderson, 1928. 1st Eng ed. Nice (foxed; no dj). *Clearwater*. \$32/£20

BLUNDEN, EDMUND. Shelley, a Life Story. Collins, 1946. 1st Eng ed. VG (spine ends, corners sl bumped) in dj (sl nicked, creased, spine faded). *Ulysses*. \$40/£25

BLUNDEN, EDMUND. Shells By a Stream. Macmillan, 1944. 1st UK ed. VG in dj (sl worn, browned). *Williams*. \$32/£20

BLUNDEN, EDMUND. To Nature. Beaumont, 1923. One of 390 numbered. VG + . *Williams*. \$120/£75

BLUNDEN, EDMUND. To Themis. Beaumont, 1931. 1st ed. Ltd to 405. Presentation copy. *Whiteson*. \$64/£40

BLUNDEN, EDMUND. Undertones of War. London: Cobden-Sanderson, (1930). 9th ptg, issued in Nov. Black cl stamped in red. (Lt offset eps), o/w Fine in NF dj (few sl edgetears). *Reese*. \$75/£47

BLUNDEN, EDMUND. Undertones of War. Cobden-Sanderson, 1930. Rev 2nd ed. (No dj.) *Clearwater*. \$40/£25

BLUNDEN, EDMUND. The Waggoner and Other Poems. London: Sidgwick & Jackson, 1920. 1st ed, 1st issue. One of 500, of which only 250 bound thus. Cl, paper spine label. (Early ink inscrip, eps tanned, top edge lt discolored), o/w Nice in dj (sl frayed, few sm chips). *Reese*. \$175/£109

BLUNDEN, EDMUND. War Poets 1914-18. London, 1964. Rpt. Stapled into wrappers. VG. *Typographeum*. \$10/£6

BLUNT, ANTHONY and PHOEBE POOL. Picasso. (NY): NYGS, (1962). 173 plts. Fine in dj. *Turtle Island*. \$55/£34

BLUNT, ANTHONY. Francois Mansart and the Origins of French Classical Architecture. London: Warburg Institute Studies, 1941. Frontisport, 34 plts hors-texte (1 fldg). (Creased margin fldg plt, ex-lib w/sm stamps, fep thinned where label removed; cl sl soiled), o/w Sound. *Europa*. \$77/£48

BLUNT, BETTY BACON. Double Trouble. NY: Crowell, 1945. 8vo. VG. *American Booksellers*. \$25/£16

BLUNT, JOSEPH. The Shipmaster's Assistant, and Commercial Digest. NY: E. & G.W. Blunt, 1837. 2nd ed. xii,(9)-683pp (dk stains on eps, part of text lt dampstained). Orig calf (sl rubbed). Sound. *Lefkowicz*. \$135/£84

BLUNT, WILFRID and WILLIAM T. STEARN. The Complete Naturalist: a Life of Linnaeus. NY: Viking, 1971. 1st ed. 32 color plts. VG in dj (worn). *Fair Meadow*. \$50/£31

BLUNT, WILFRID. The Art of Botanical Illustration. Collins Sons, 1973. Color frontis. 46 color, 32 b/w plts. (Cl sl faded.) *Forest*. \$56/£35

BLUNT, WILFRID. The Compleat Naturalist. NY: Viking, 1971. Fine in dj (edgeworn). *Quest*. \$50/£31

BLY, ROBERT and DAVID RAY (eds). A Poetry Reading Against Vietnam War. Madison, MN: American Writers Against the Vietnam War, 1966. 1st ed, 1st issue w/poems by ee cummings excised (pp cut out or heavily blackened by grease pencil). Fine in wraps. *Associates*. \$100/£63

BLYTH, ALEXANDER W. Poisons: Their Effects and Detection. NY, 1885. 2nd ed. Vol 1 only. 333pp. VG. *Doctor's Library*. \$50/£31

BLYTHE, T. ROGER (ed). A Pictorial Souvenir and Historical Sketch of Tombstone, Arizona.... Tombstone: Tombstone Epitaph, 1946. 1st ed. VG in wrappers. *Labordo*. \$35/£22

BLYTON, ENID. ABC with Noddy. London: Sampson Low, Marston, 1959. 1st ed. 4to. Color pict bds. Good. *Reisler*. \$75/£47

BLYTON, ENID. Cheer Up, Little Noddy! Samson Low, Marston, c. 1960. Early ed. Noddy Book #20; list on dj flap extends to 24 titles. 8vo. 61pp. Pict bds. NF in pict dj. *Bookmark*. \$21/£13

BLYTON, ENID. The Circus of Adventure. Macmillan, 1952. 1st ed. VG + in dj. *Green Meadow*. \$72/£45

BLYTON, ENID. Enid Blyton's Animal Lovers' Book. Evans, 1952. 1st ed. VG + in Eileen Soper dj. *Green Meadow*. \$72/£45

BLYTON, ENID. Enid Blyton's Fifth Bedside Book. Arthur Barker, 1953. 1st ed. VG + in dj (sl chipped). *Green Meadow*. \$40/£25

BLYTON, ENID. Five Go to Mystery Moor. H&S, 1954. 1st ed. VG + in Nice dj. *Green Meadow*. \$48/£30

BLYTON, ENID. Five Have a Mystery to Solve. Hodder & Stoughton, 1962. 1st ed. 8vo. Eileen Soper (illus). VG in pict dj (edge worn). *Bookmark*. \$22/£14

BLYTON, ENID. House-at-the-Corner. Lutterworth, 1947. 1st ed. 8vo. Elsie Walker (illus). 220pp. (Lacks fep; edges rubbed), else VG. *Bookmark*. \$19/£12

BLYTON, ENID. The Marigold Story Book. Gifford, n.d. (1954). 1st ed. 4to. 128pp; 4 color plts by Hilda Boswell. Cl spine, pict bds. VG + . *Bookmark*. \$27/£17

BLYTON, ENID. The Mountain of Adventure. Macmillan, 1949. 1st ed. (Fep removed), o/w VG in dj (sl chipped). *Green Meadow*. \$48/£30

BLYTON, ENID. The Mystery of Banshee Towers. Methuen, 1961. 1st ed. VG + in VG dj. *Green Meadow*. \$72/£45

BLYTON, ENID. The Mystery of the Strange Messages. Methuen, 1957. 1st ed. VG in dj (sl rubbed). *Green Meadow*. \$40/£25

BLYTON, ENID. The Mystery of the Vanished Prince. Methuen, 1951. 1st ed. 9th in series. VG in Nice dj. *Green Meadow*. \$48/£30

BLYTON, ENID. Noddy and the Bumpy Dog. Samson Low, Marston, n.d. (1957). 1st ed. 8vo. Pict bds. VG + in pict dj (sm repaired tear, spine creased, ptd price 3s/6d). *Bookmark*. \$51/£32

BLYTON, ENID. The Three Naughty Children and Other Stories. Macmillan, 1950. 1st ed. 8vo. Eileen Soper (illus). 192pp. Pict cl. Fine. *Bookmark*. \$32/£20

BLYTON, ENID. You Funny Little Noddy. Samson Low, Marston, n.d. (1955). 1st ed. 8vo. 61pp. Pict bds. VG in pict dj (tattered, ptd price 3s/6d). *Bookmark*. \$45/£28

BOADEN, JAMES. The Life of Mrs. Jordan. London: Edward Bull, 1831. 3rd ed. 2 vols. Frontispieces (vol 2 fldg), fldg facs plt. Orig bds (respined w/patterned cl), paper labels. VG. *Dramatis*. \$100/£63

BOARDER, ARTHUR. Starting with Cacti. London, 1968. 1st ed. VG in dj. *Brooks*. \$22/£14

BOARDMAN, JOHN. Archaic Greek Gems. Evanston: Northwestern Univ, 1968. Dj. *Archaeologia*. \$45/£28

BOARDMAN, JOHN. Archaic Greek Gems. Evanston, IL: Northwestern Univ, 1968. 15 color plts. NF in dj. *Turtle Island*. \$60/£38

BOARDMAN, JOHN. The Cretan Collection in Oxford. Oxford: Clarendon, 1961. Frontis, 48 plts. Dj. *Archaeologia.* $250/£156

BOARDMAN, JOHN. Engraved Gems. Evanston: Northwestern, c1968. VG. *Blake.* $45/£28

BOARDMAN, JOHN. Greek Gems and Finger Rings Early Bronze Age to Late Classical. NY: Abrams, n.d. Fine in dj. *Blake.* $150/£94

BOARDMAN, PETER. The Shining Mountain. Hodder & Stoughton, 1978. 1st ed. VG in dj. *Hollett.* $80/£50

BOARDMAN, TIMOTHY. Log-Book of Timothy Boardman...in 1778.... Albany: Joel Munsell's Sons, 1885. 1st ed. 85,(3)pp. Contemp 1/2 leather, marbled bds. (Lib stamps; worn, scuffed, hinges cracked), else Good. Howes B562. *Brown.* $45/£28

BOATMAN, ALAN. Comrades in Arms. NY: Harper & Row, 1974. 1st ed. (Name), else Fine in dj. *Associates.* $75/£47

BOATRIGHT, MODY and DONALD DAY (eds). From Hell to Breakfast. Dallas, 1944. (Bds spotted), else Good. *Dumont.* $35/£22

BOATRIGHT, MODY. Folk Laughter on the American Frontier. NY: Macmillan, 1949. 1st ed. VG. *Labordo.* $35/£22

BOATRIGHT, MODY. Tall Tales from Texas Cow Camps. Dallas: Southwest, 1934. 1st ed. Rattlesnake pattern paper bds, cl spine. NF. *Labordo.* $150/£94

Bobby Bear. Racine, WI: Whitman, 1935. Magic-Action Book. 18x19 cm. 3 dbl-pg pop-ups. Pict bds. (Center pop-up loose from staples, tipped-in), o/w VG. *Bookfinders.* $90/£56

Bobby Bear. Racine: Whitman, 1935. 1st ed. 7.75x7.25. 3 pop-ups. Pict bds. NF. *Pacific*.* $104/£65

BOCCACCIO, GIOVANNI. The Decameron of Boccaccio. LEC, 1930. Ltd to 1500 numbered, signed by T. M. Cleland (illus). 2 vols. Fine in slipcase. *Swann*.* $258/£161

BOCCACCIO, GIOVANNI. The Decameron. John Payne (trans). NY: Boni & Liveright, 1925. One of 2000. 2 vols. Black cl, gilt. (Spine ends sl rubbed), else NF. *Pacific*.* $127/£79

BOCCACCIO, GIOVANNI. The Decameron. NY: A. Colish, 1930. Signed by T.M. Cleland (illus). 2 vols. Full russet buckram, black leather labels gilt-stamped. Fine. Boxed. *Appelfeld.* $150/£94

BOCK, CARL. The Head-Hunters of Borneo: A Narrative of Travel up the Mahakkam and down the Barito; Also Journeyings in Sumatra. Sampson Low, 1882. 2nd ed. Half-title, fldg map, 30 litho plts. Later brn buckram (rubbed). *Sotheby's*.* $294/£184

BOCK, CARL. Temples and Elephants. London: Sampson Low, Marston, 1884. 1st ed. Engr frontis, xvi,438,(2)ads; port, 2 tinted lithos, 4 engr plts. (Edges browned, 1 or 2 brn stains, lib stamps.) Maroon cl (edges damp-stained, spine repaired). Sound. *Morrell.* $272/£170

BODART, LUCIEN. The Quicksand War: Prelude to Vietnam. Patrick O'Brian (trans). Faber, 1967. 1st UK ed. Fine in dj. *Williams.* $240/£150

BODDAM-WHETHAM, J. W. Western Wanderings. London: Richard Bentley & Son, 1874. 1st ed. xii,(ii),364pp; 12 full-pg plts. Contemp mid-tan calf (extrems, spine rubbed, stained). Internally VG. *Young.* $120/£75

BODDAM-WHETHAM, J. W. Western Wanderings: A Record of Travel in the Evening Land. London: Richard Bentley, 1874. 1st ed. xii,(2),364pp; 11 plts. Blue cl (spine worn, corners rubbed). *Mott.* $75/£47

BODDE, DERK. Shakespeare and the Ireland Forgeries. Cambridge: Harvard Univ, 1930. 1st ed. VG in dec wraps. *Dramatis.* $30/£19

BODDY, E. MANCHESTER. Japanese in America. L.A.: E. Manchester Boddy, 1921. Frontis, 9 full-pg photo illus. (Extrems lt worn.) *Dawson.* $200/£125

BODE, WILLIAM. Lights and Shadows of Chinatown. (SF: H. S. Crocker, 1896.) (44)leaves; 32 tipped-in plts. VG + in pict wrappers, string ties. *Pacific*.* $115/£72

BODE, WINSTON. A Portrait of Pancho, the Life of a Great Texan: J. Frank Dobie. Austin: Pemberton, 1965. 1st ed. Ltd to 150 signed. Tp port. Orig announcement laid in. Full leather, gilt. VF in slipcase. *Argonaut.* $300/£188

BODENHEIM, MAXWELL. Introducing Irony. NY, 1922. 1st Amer ed. Uncut. NF (rebacked; edge rubbed). *Polyanthos.* $35/£22

BODENHEIM, MAXWELL. Replenishing Jessica. NY: Boni & Liveright, 1925. 1st ed. Fine in dj (lt chipped). *Beasley.* $100/£63

BODFISH, HARTSON H. Chasing the Bowhead. Cambridge: Harvard Univ, 1936. 1st ed. Sig dated 1936 tipped in. (Rebound.) *Perier.* $97/£61

BODICHON, BARBARA LEIGH SMITH. An American Diary 1857-8. Joseph W. Reed, Jr. (ed). London: Routledge & Kegan Paul, (1972). Fine in dj. *Mott.* $25/£16

BODINE, A. AUBREY. The Face of Virginia. Balt: Bodine & Associates, 1963. 1st ed. Fine in illus dj (sl edgeworn). *Cahan.* $50/£31

BODLEY, THOMAS. Letters of Sir Thomas Bodley to Thomas James, First Keeper of the Bodleian Library. G.W. Wheeler (ed). Oxford: Clarendon, 1926. Frontis. Unopened. Cream paper-cvrd bds (edges sl soiled). *Maggs.* $80/£50

BOELTER, HOMER and S. E. HUSSEY. The Desert Thematic Portrait. Hollywood, 1945. 1st ed. Fine. *Book Market.* $40/£25

BOETHIUS, BERDA. Anders Zorn. An International Swedish Artist-His Life and Work. Stockholm: Nordisk-Rotogravyr, (1954). 1st ed. One of 1200 ptd. Full brn morocco, raised bands, gilt top. Fine. *Appelfeld.* $450/£281

BOETTICHER, JACOB GOTTLIEB. A Geographical, Historical, and Political Description of the Empire of Germany, Holland, the Netherlands.... London, 1800. 3 fldg maps, fldg index map, 23 city maps. Lib buckram. (Fldg maps reinforced on verso along folds, ink stamps; shelf #s on backstrip.) *Swann*.* $287/£179

BOGAN, LOUISE. Collected Poems 1923-53. NY: Noonday, (1954). 1st ed. Errata slip laid in. Fine in dj (edge, spine tanned). *Reese.* $30/£19

BOGARDE, DIRK. A Postillion Struck by Lightning. C&W, 1977. VG in dj. *Tiger.* $45/£28

BOGARDE, DIRK. West of Sunset. Allen Lane, 1984. 1st UK ed. Signed. Fine in dj. *Williams.* $40/£25

BOGARDUS. Field, Cover, and Trap Shooting. Charles J. Foster (ed). NY: OJ, 1881. Frontisport. Grn cl, gilt. (Spine ends frayed, spot fr cvr), else VG-. *Pacific*.* $46/£29

BOGER, A. J. The Road I Travelled. London, 1936. (Cvrs discolored.) Contents VF. *Grayling.* $56/£35

BOGG, EDMUND. A Thousand Miles of Wandering Along the Roman Wall.... Leeds: Edmund Bogg & James Miles, 1898. xii,256pp. (Feps sl browned), o/w VG. *Hollett.* $80/£50

BOGGS, KATE DOGGETT. Prints and Plants of Old Gardens. Richmond: Garrett & Massie, (1932). 1st ed. Dec cl. (Spine sl used, sunned), o/w VG. *Pharos.* $60/£38

BOGGS, KATE DOGGETT. Prints and Plants of Old Gardens. Richmond: Garrett & Massie, 1932. 1st ed. 39 plts. Dec grn, rust cl. VG in dj. *Fair Meadow.* $95/£59

BOHLIN, DIANE. Prints and Related Drawings by the Carracci Family. Washington: National Gallery of Art, 1979. Good + in wrappers (sl soiled). *Washton.* $125/£78

BOHLKE, J. E. and C. C. CHAPLIN. Fishes of the Bahamas and Adjacent Tropical Waters. Wynnewood: Livingston, 1968. 1st ed. 35 color plts. Pict bds. VG + in Good dj. *Mikesh.* $95/£59

BOHN, DAVE. Rambles Through an Alaskan Wild: Katmai and the Valley of the Smokes. Santa Barbara: Capra, 1979. 1st ed. One of 5000. Inscribed. Tipped-in color frontis. Pict eps. Brn cl, gilt. Fine in Fine dj. *Harrington*. $35/£22

BOHN, HENRY G. (ed). The Hand-Book of Games. Henry G. Bohn, 1850. 1st ed. xiv,617pp. Red cl. Good (sm slits starting in lower joint). *Bickersteth*. $96/£60

BOHR, NIELS. The Theory of Spectra and Atomic Constitution. Cambridge, 1922. 1st ed in English. *Argosy*. $100/£63

BOIME, ALBERT. Thomas Couture and the Eclectic Vision. Yale Univ, 1980. Color frontis. (Ink notes; upper hinge shaken, cracked.) *Edwards*. $56/£35

BOISSEVAIN, C. H. and C. DAVIDSON. Colorado Cacti. Pasadena, 1940. One of 2000 ptd. Tipped-in color frontis. Tan buckram. VG + . *Brooks*. $55/£34

BOIX, EMILE. The Liver of Dyspeptics, and Particularly the Cirrhosis Produced by Auto-Intoxication of Gastro-Intestinal Origin. NY, 1897. 133pp. Grn cl. VG (extrems sl worn). *Doctor's Library*. $40/£25

BOJER, J. The Prisoner Who Sang. Century, 1924. 1st Amer ed. Fine in NF dj. *Fine Books*. $35/£22

BOLINGBROKE, HENRY ST. JOHN. The Works. London, 1754-1779. 11 vols. 8vo. Full polished calf (worn), gilt, facs ptd labels, silk markers. Text VG (bkpls). *Hartfield*. $495/£309

BOLITHO, HECTOR. Albert the Good. London: Cobden-Sanderson, 1932. 1st ed. 5 color plts, incl frontis w/lift-up flap. Uncut. (Sm label upper bd, sl spotted.) *Hollett*. $40/£25

BOLITHO, HECTOR. The Queen's Tact. London, 1938. 1st ed. Signed. Fine in ptd wraps. *Polyanthos*. $25/£16

BOLL, HEINRICH. Acquainted with the Night. Richard Graves (trans). Hutchinson, 1955. 1st Eng ed. VG (rear cvr edges sl dented, spine tail sl bumped) in dj (sl nicked, edges rubbed). *Ulysses*. $88/£55

BOLLER, HENRY A. Among the Indians. Milo Quaife (ed). Chicago: R.R. Donnelley, 1982. Frontis, fldg map. VG. *Lien*. $30/£19

BOLLES, EDWIN C. Collectors and Collecting, an Essay. Melrose, (MA): Privately ptd, 1898. 300 ptd and type distributed. (61)pp. Stiff paper wrappers (dknd, sm chips). *Zubal**. $50/£31

BOLT, ROBERT. A Man for All Seasons. London, (1960). French's Acting ed. NF in ptd wraps. *Polyanthos*. $25/£16

BOLTON, A. C. Game Shooting in Africa. Carlisle, 1919. Frontis. (Fr cr sl soiled), else Good. *Hallam*. $296/£185

BOLTON, ARTHUR T. The Architecture of Robert and James Adam. Country Life, 1922. 1st ed. 2 vols. Folio. Color frontis. Pub's cl. Good (lacks djs). *Sotheran*. $880/£550

BOLTON, CHARLES KNOWLES. The Founders: Portraits of Persons Born Abroad Who Came to the Colonies in North America Before the Year 1701. Boston: Athenaeum, 1919-26. 3 vols. Teg. *Marlborough*. $312/£195

BOLTON, G. DOUGLAS. Scotland's Western Seaboard. Oliver & Boyd, 1958. 2nd ed. VG in dj (sl worn). *Hollett*. $32/£20

BOLTON, H. Follies of Science at the Court of Rudolph II. 1576-1612. Milwaukee: Pharmaceutical Review, c1904. Pict cl. VG. *Blake*. $85/£53

BOLTON, HERBERT E. Anza's California Expeditions. Berkeley: Univ of CA, 1930. 1st ed. 5 vols. Blue cl, gilt. (Extrems sl rubbed), o/w Fine set. Howes B583. *Pacific**. $460/£288

BOLTON, HERBERT E. Anza's California Expeditions. Berkeley: Univ of CA, 1930. 1st ed. 5 vols. 14 maps, 106 plts, 47 facs. Blue cl, gilt. VG set (spines sl rubbed, dull). Howes B583. *Argonaut*. $500/£313

BOLTON, HERBERT E. Anza's California Expeditions. Berkeley: Univ of CA, 1930. 1st ed. 5 vols. Blue cl, gilt. (Sl worn), o/w Fine set in djs. Howes B583. *Pacific**. $546/£341

BOLTON, HERBERT E. Coronado on the Turquoise Trail. Albuquerque: Univ of NM, 1949. Frontis, 3 fldg maps. Internally VG (spine faded, ends worn). *Dumont*. $145/£91

BOLTON, HERBERT E. Coronado on the Turquoise Trail: Knight of Pueblo and Plains. George P. Hammond (ed). Albuquerque: Univ of NM, 1949. 1st ed. Frontis, 3 fldg maps. Uncut. Maroon cl, gilt. VF in pict dj (spine ends sl chipped). *Argonaut*. $275/£172

BOLTON, HERBERT E. Coronado: Knight of Pueblos and Plains. NY/Albuquerque: Whittlesey House/Univ of NM, (1949). 2nd ed. Black cl, gilt. Fine (bkpl). *Argonaut*. $125/£78

BOLTON, HERBERT E. Fray Juan Crespi, Missionary Explorer on the Pacific Coast 1769-1774. Berkeley: Univ of CA, 1927. 1st ed. Blue cl, gilt. (Ink name, address label, repair to rear hinge at eps; extrems sl rubbed), else VG. Howes B586. *Pacific**. $115/£72

BOLTON, HERBERT E. Fray Juan Crespi: Missionary Explorer on the Pacific Coast. Berkeley: Univ of CA, 1927. 1st ed. Frontis, 10 maps, plts. Blue cl, gilt. Fine. *Argonaut*. $250/£156

BOLTON, HERBERT E. The Padre on Horseback. A Sketch of Eusebio Francisco Kino, S. J., Apostle to the Pimas. SF: Sonora, 1932. 1st ed. Paper spine label. (Bkpl; lower corners sl showing), else Fine in pict dj. *Argonaut*. $60/£38

BOLTON, HERBERT E. Pageant in the Wilderness. The Story of the Escalante Expedition to the Interior Basin, 1776. Salt Lake City: UT State Hist Soc, 1951. 1st bk ed. 2 fldg maps in rear pocket. VF in pict dj (sl chipped). *Argonaut*. $175/£109

BOLTON, HERBERT E. Pageant in the Wilderness: The Story of the Escalante Expedition to the Interior Basin, 1776. Salt Lake City: UT State Hist Soc, 1950. 1st trade ed. Color plt. Red cl, gilt. (Lower cvr edges faded), else VG in dj (sm edge tears). *Pacific**. $109/£68

BOLTON, HERBERT E. Rim of Christendom. NY: Macmillan, 1936. 8 maps. Black cl, gilt. (Scuff mks rear cvr), o/w VG. Howes B587. *Five Quail*. $75/£47

BOLTON, HERBERT E. Rim of Christendom. A Biography of Eusebio Francisco Kino, Pacific Coast Pioneer. NY: Russell & Russell, 1960. 2nd ed. 25 plts, 3 facs, 8 maps. Fine (bkpl) in dj. *Argonaut*. $100/£63

BOLTON, HERBERT E. Rim of Christendom: A Biography of Eusebio Francisco Kino, Pacific Coast Pioneer. NY: Macmillan, 1936. 1st ed. 8 fldg maps. NF. Howes B587. *Pacific**. $69/£43

BOLTON, HERBERT E. Rim of Christendom: A Biography of Eusebio Francisco Kino, Pacific Coast Pioneer. NY: Macmillan, 1936. 1st ed. Signed, dated Oct 5, 1936. 8 fldg maps. Fine in dj (edges worn, price-clipped). Howes B587. *Pacific**. $127/£79

BOLTON, HERBERT E. (ed). Font's Complete Diary: A Chronicle of the Founding of San Francisco. Berkeley: Univ of CA, 1933. 2nd ptg. Fldg map. Blue cl, gilt. Fine. Howes B585. *Pacific**. $81/£51

BOLTON, HERBERT E. (ed). Font's Complete Diary: A Chronicle of the Founding of San Francisco. Berkeley: Univ of CA, 1933. 1st separate ed, 2nd ptg. Signed by ed. Fldg map. Blue cl, gilt. NF (sl waterstain affecting mostly dj, few pg edges) in VG dj. Howes B585. *Harrington*. $85/£53

BOLTON, HERBERT E. (ed). Spanish Exploration in the Southwest, 1542-1706. NY: Scribner, (1916). Early ptg. 3 fldg maps. Black cl, gilt. Fine (cvrs lt soiled). Howes B588. *Argonaut*. $100/£63

BOLTON, HERBERT E. (ed). Spanish Exploration in the Southwest, 1542-1706. NY: Scribner, 1916. 1st ed. 2 fldg maps. Blue cl, gilt. (Ink name, hinge cracked before tp, at reps), else VG. Howes B588. *Pacific**. $288/£180

BOLTON, REGINALD P. Indian Life of Long Ago in the City of New York. NY: (Joseph Graham), 1934. 1st ed. One of 500. 30 plts, 5 maps. NF (spine sl faded, edgeworn). *Harrington*. $60/£38

BOLTON, REGINALD P. Relics of the Revolution. NY: The Author, 1916. 1st ed. Inscribed presentation. Frontis; inscribed 2nd frontis tipped-in; 3 photos mtd on prelim blanks. Tan linen (sl soiled). *Karmiole*. $85/£53

BOLTON, THEODORE. Early American Portrait Draughtsmen in Crayons. NY, 1923. One of 325. 1/4 cl. *Swann**. $57/£36

BOLTON, THEODORE. Early American Portrait Draughtsmen in Crayons. NY, 1923. One of 325. Uncut. Cl-backed bds, paper spine label. (Sl worn.) Slipcase. *Oinonen**. $70/£44

BOLTON, THEODORE. Early American Portrait Painters in Miniature. NY, 1921. One of 300. Uncut. Cl-backed bds, paper spine label. (Chipped; shelfworn; 1 pg torn, no loss.) *Oinonen**. $70/£44

BOLUS, HARRY. The Orchids of the Cape Peninsula. Cape Town, 1888. 1st ed. Inscribed. 36 litho plts partially hand-colored. Teal cl, gilt. NF. *Pacific**. $690/£431

BOMBAL, MARIA-LUISA. House of Mist. NY: FSG, 1947. 1st US ed. VG + in dj (price-clipped). *Lame Duck*. $85/£53

BONATTI, WALTER. On the Heights. Lovett F. Edwards (trans). London: Rupert Hart-Davis, 1964. 1st Eng ed. Black cl. (Sm stamp), else Fine in dj (worn). *Argonaut*. $150/£94

BONATUS, GUIDO. Anima Astrologiae; Or a Guide for Astrologers. Gnostic, 1918. Fldg chart. (Lt mkd), o/w VG. *Middle Earth*. $75/£47

BOND, FRANCIS. Gothic Architecture in England. London: Batsford, 1905. 1st ed. Teg. (1 prelim gathering detached, lacks feps, bkpl; lt dampstained, spine faded.) *Edwards*. $56/£35

BOND, J. R. Farm Implements and Machinery. London, 1923. *Petersfield*. $32/£20

BOND, JAMES H. From Out of the Yukon. Portland: Binfords & Mort, (1948). Signed presentation. VG in Poor dj (torn). *Perier*. $30/£19

BOND, MARSHALL, JR. Gold Hunter: The Adventures of Marshall Bond. U.N. Mes., 1969. 1st ed. Good in dj. *Rybski*. $30/£19

BOND, MICHAEL. Paddington on Top. Collins, 1974. 1st ed. 8vo. Peggy Fortnum (illus). 124pp. VG + in pict dj (frayed). *Bookmark*. $32/£20

BOND, MICHAEL. Paddington Takes the Test. William Collins Sons, 1979. 1st ed. Peggy Fortnum (illus). VG (feps sl soiled; fore-edge sl mkd, spine foot bumped) in dj (worn). *Ulysses*. $40/£25

BOND, MICHAEL. Paddington's Pop-Up Book. London: William Collins, 1977. 6 pop-ups by Ivor Wood. Glazed pict bds. VG. *Bookfinders*. $35/£22

BOND, MICHAEL. Thursday Rides Again. George G. Harrap, 1968. 1st ed. 128pp. NF in VG color dj (spine ends worn, sl edgeworn). *Price*. $50/£31

BOND, NANCY. A String in the Harp. Atheneum, 1976. 1st ed. 370pp. Fine in NF dj (edges sl bumped). *Price*. $50/£31

BOND, NELSON. The Remarkable Exploits of Lancelot Biggs: Spaceman. GC: Doubleday, 1950. 1st ed. VG in dj (spine ends sl chipped). *Pacific**. $40/£25

BOND, NELSON. The Thirty-First of February. NY: Gnome, (1949). 1st ed. NF in VG + dj (sm edge tears). *Other Worlds*. $40/£25

BOND, NELSON. The Thirty-First of February. NY: Gnome, (1949). 1st ed. 'Armed Services Edition,' paperbound binding. NF in pict wrappers (sm chips). *Other Worlds*. $100/£63

BOND, R. C. Prisoners Grave and Gay. London, 1934. 1st Eng ed. (Monograms on ll; spine, edges faded.) *Clearwater*. $32/£20

BONE, D. D. Fifty Years Reminiscences of Scottish Cricket. Glasgow: Aird & Coghill, 1898. 1st ed. 290,(xiv)pp; 26 plts. Teg. Beveled bds. VG (sl shaken; spine faded, sl mkd). *Hollett*. $192/£120

BONE, DAVID. Landfall at Sunset. London: Duckworth, 1955. 1st ed. VG in dj. *American Booksellers*. $30/£19

BONE, MUIRHEAD. The Western Front. NY: George H. Doran, 1917. 1st Amer ed. 2 vols. NF. Portfolios in wrappers in cl-backed ptd bds, spine labels, slipcases. (Spine labels sl chipped, piece of slipcase spine lacking from vol 2.) *Pacific**. $58/£36

BONE, MUIRHEAD. The Western Front: Drawings by.... London: Published by Authority of the War Office, 1917. 1st ed in bound form. 2 vols. Khaki linen-backed bds, leather labels. VG set (edges, eps lt foxed; corners nicked). *Reese*. $125/£78

BONE, STEPHEN and MARY ADSHEAD. The Little Boy and His House. J.M. Dent, 1936. 1st ed. Obl 4to. 60pp; 14 full-pg color plts. Pict bds (edges sl rubbed). *Hollett*. $72/£45

BONER, CHARLES. Chamois Hunting in the Mountains of Bavaria. London: Chapman & Hall, 1853. 1st ed. 6 two-tone litho plts. Blue cl, gilt. (Fr hinge cracked, rear starting; name, spot to fr cvr), else VG. *Pacific**. $40/£25

BONER, HAROLD A. The Giant's Ladder: David H. Moffat and His Railroad. Milwaukee: Kalmbach, 1962. (Sl shelfworn), else NF in dj (sl worn). *My Bookhouse*. $42/£26

BONHOMME, BERNARD. The Fine Feathered Friend of My Very Best Friends. Harlin Quist, 1971. 1st ed. 9x11.3. Nicole Claveloux (illus). Unpaginated. Fine in VG dj. *Price*. $22/£14

BONHOTE, J. LEWIS. Birds of Britain and Their Eggs. A&C Black, 1930. Rpt. 82 color plts. Dec cl. (Bkpl; sl worn.) *Edwards*. $40/£25

BONI, ALBERT (ed). Photographic Literature, Volume I. NY, (1962). 1st ed. (Prelims, eps, rear pastedowns lt foxed, fore-edge soiled.) Dj (spine panel sunned, chipped, torn). *Swann**. $69/£43

BONINGTON, CHRISTIAN. Annapurna South Face. Cassell, 1971. 1st ed. 48 color plts. (Edges sl faded.) Dj (price-clipped). *Hollett*. $64/£40

BONKER, FRANCES and JOHN J. THORNBER. The Sage of the Desert and Other Cacti. Boston, 1930. 1st ptg. 8 full-pg b/w photos. VG-. *Brooks*. $29/£18

BONN, FRANZ. The Children's Theatre. London: Kestrel, 1978. 4 3-D scenes. Glazed pict bds. VG. *Bookfinders*. $45/£28

BONNELLI, WILLIAM G. Billion Dollar Blackjack. Beverly Hills: Civic Research, (1954). 1st ed. Fine in wraps. *Book Market*. $50/£31

BONNER, HYPATIA BRADLAUGH. The Christian Hell, from the First to the Twentieth Century. London: Watts, 1913. 1st ed. (Sm hole fr joint), else VG in dj (upper fr panel lt chipped). *Pacific**. $35/£22

BONNER, WILLIAM HALLAM. Captain William Dampier. Stanford Univ/London: Stanford Univ, c.1934. Burgundy cl, gilt. (Fore-edge sl foxed; head dusty), else NF in dj (very worn). *Parmer*. $75/£47

BONNEY, CECIL. Looking Over My Shoulder. Roswell, NM: Hall-Poorbaugh, 1971. NF in dj (sl worn). *Dumont*. $60/£38

BONNEY, ORRIN H. and LORRAINE. Battle Drums and Geysers. Chicago, (1970). 1st ed. VG in dj (lacks sm piece at spine foot). *Woolson*. $40/£25

BONNEY, T. G. The Alpine Regions of Switzerland and the Neighbouring Countries. Cambridge, 1868. 1st ed. xvi,351pp + (i)pp pub's ads; 5 plts. Mod 1/2 morocco, marbled bds, gilt, raised bands, morocco spine label. (Mainly marginal foxing; rebound.) *Edwards*. $240/£150

BONNEY, T. G. Volcanoes: Their Structures and Significance. NY, 1899. 1st ed. Frontis, guard, xiv,(i),332,(ii)pp; fldg map. Dec cl. VG + . *Sagebrush*. $75/£47

BONNEY, T. G. (ed). Cathedrals, Abbeys, and Churches of England and Wales. London, 1891. 2 vols. 1/2 morocco. *Swann**. $92/£58

BONNEY, THERESE. Europe's Children 1939-1943. N.p.: n.p., 1943. One of unspecified # signed. 62 full-pg photo illus. Fine in stiff photo-illus wrappers, dj. *Smith*. $125/£78

BONNEY, W. P. History of Pierce County, Washington. Chicago: Pioneer Hist Pub, 1927. 1st ed. 3 vols. Frontisport vol 1. Brn cl, gilt. (1st vol cvrs sl spotted), else Fine set. *Argonaut*. $225/£141

BONNYCASTLE, JOHN. An Introduction to Astronomy. J. Johnson, 1796. 3rd ed. Engr frontis (offset onto tp), vi,(ii),437,(i)pp,ad leaf; 19 fldg plts. Orig speckled calf (sm spine chip). Very Nice. *Bickersteth*. $128/£80

BONSPENSIERE, LUIGI. New Pathways to Piano Technique. NY: Philosophical Library, 1953. 1st ed. VG in dj (sl creased, chipped). *Hollett*. $32/£20

BONTE, LOUISE QUARLES and GEORGE WILLARD BONTE. ABC in Dixie: A Plantation Alphabet. London: Ernest Nister, (1904). 1st ed. 4to. Cl-backed color pict bds (rubbed, worn, hinges weak). *Reisler*. $2,000/£1,250

BONTEMPS, ARNA and JACK CONROY. Slappy Hooper. Boston: HMCo, 1946. 1st ed. 9.25x8.75. Ursula Koering (illus). 44pp. Good. *Cattermole*. $50/£31

BONTEMPS, ARNA. Chariot in the Sky. Phila: Winston, (1951). 1st ed. Fine in dj (price-clipped). *Agvent*. $100/£63

BONVALOT, GABRIEL. Through the Heart of Asia, Over the Pamir to India. London, 1889. 8vo. 2 vols. (3 rubber stamps to each tp), o/w VG. *Petersfield*. $600/£375

BONY, JEAN. The English Decorated Style: Gothic Architecture Transformed 1250-1350. Cornell Univ, 1979. 1st ed. VG in dj. *Hadley*. $109/£68

BONY, JEAN. French Gothic Architecture of the 12th and 13th Centuries. Berkeley: Univ of CA, 1983. NF in dj. *Turtle Island*. $125/£78

Book of Baby Dogs. Charles Kaberry (descriptions). London: Henry Frowde/Hodder & Stoughton, (1915). 1st ed. 4to. 19 full-pg mtd color plts by E. J. Detmold. Circular color paste label. (Corner lt rubbed, lower spine bumped.) *Reisler*. $485/£303

Book of Birds. Nat'l Geographic Soc, 1925. VG. *Larry Price*. $60/£38

Book of Chivalry and Romance. London/Bombay/Sydney: George G. Harrap, (1933). 1st ed. Pub's forest grn cl, color pict pastedown. *Glenn*. $70/£44

Book of Common Prayer, and Administration of the Sacraments, and Other Rites and Ceremonies of the Church, According to the Use of the Church of Ireland. Dublin: George Grierson, 1785. Contemp calf. VG (few tears to pp). *Pacific**. $69/£43

Book of Common Prayer...Together with the Psalms of David, etc. Oxford: T. Wright, 1767. Full black 19th-cent diced calf, gilt raised bands, red leather label. Fine. *Appelfeld*. $125/£78

Book of Costume. (By Mary Wilton.) London, 1847. New ed. Litho tp, 482pp. Teg. 3/4 brn leather. (Edges bumped), else VG. *King*. $175/£109

Book of Ecclesiastes. LEC, 1968. Ltd to 1500 numbered, signed by Edgar Miller (illus). Fine in slipcase. *Swann**. $80/£50

Book of Fables. Worcester: J. Grout, Jr., n.d. (ca 1840). 12mo. 1/2-pg woodcut frontis, 24pp + 1pg ad lower wrapper; 1 woodcut signed K. VG (some ll lt foxed) in blue dec stiff paper wrappers (shelfworn). *Hobbyhorse*. $95/£59

Book of Fairy Tales. London: Frederick Warne, (1914). 24 full-pg color plts by H. M. Brock. Tan pict cl, gilt. Good. *Reisler*. $250/£156

Book of Fairy Tales. NY: Frederick A. Stokes, 1897. 4to. 12 full-pg color plts by Maud Humphrey. Cl-backed color pict bds (rubbed, lt mkd; eps replaced, margins of few pp at end stained). *Reisler*. $650/£406

Book of Fun; or Laugh and Learn for Boys and Girls. London: James Gilbert, n.d. (ca 1850). 8vo. Tinted full-pg copper engr 1/2-title, iv,215pp. Marbled eps. 3/4 leather w/corners, marbled paper on bds, 5 raised bands, gilt title. Fine (sm bklabel inside fr cvr; spine, corners lt rubbed). *Hobbyhorse*. $225/£141

Book of Job According to the Authorized Version of MDCXI, Following the Arrangement of the Temple Bible. (SF: Grabhorn, 1926.) One of 210. Color block print frontis signed in pencil by Valenti Angelo (illus). 1/2 buckram, dec bds. NF in Good dj (chipped, torn, sunned). *Pacific**. $196/£123

Book of Job. LEC, 1946. One of 1950 signed by Arthur Szyk (illus). Fine in slipcase. *Swann**. $402/£251

Book of Mormon. Salt Lake City: Deseret News, 1888. xii,623pp. Dec eps; aeg. Period morocco, gilt. VG (ink sig). *Pacific**. $127/£79

Book of Old Sundials and Their Mottoes. London/Edinburgh/Boston: Foulis, (1914). 1st ed. Color plts tipped onto gray paper matching the eps. Teg. Limp leather, blind-stamped fr and rear w/illus by Jessie M. King. (Extrems lt worn), else Fine. *Bromer*. $300/£188

Book of Parlour Games; Comprising Explanations of the Most Approved Games for the Social Circle. Phila: H.C. Peck & Theo. Bliss, 1853. 1st ed. (Spine ends chipped, corners rubbed), else VG. *Pacific**. $52/£33

Book of Proverbs. NY: LEC, 1963. One of 1500. Signed by Valenti Angelo (decs). Full red leather, gilt. Fine in slipcase. *Pacific**. $98/£61

Book of Psalms. NY: LEC, 1960. One of 1500. Signed by Valenti Angelo (decs). Full orange morocco, gilt. Fine in chemise, slipcase. *Pacific**. $127/£79

Book of Ruth. London: J.M. Dent, 1896. W.B. MacDougall (illus). Teg. 3/4 levant black morocco, marbled bds, gilt. Bound by Bumpus. Fine. *Pacific**. $138/£86

Book of Ruth. LEC, 1948. One of 1950 signed by Arthur Szyk (illus). Fine in slipcase. *Swann**. $460/£288

Book of St. Andrews Links, Containing Plan of Golf Courses, Descriptions of the Greens, Bye-Laws of the Links, Regulations for Starting, Golfing Rhymes, &c. (London): Ellesborough, (1984). Facs ed. One of 200. Signed by J. Stewart Larson. Aeg. Full dk grn morocco, gilt, raised bands, gilt-tooled calf cvr label. (Spine sl sunned), else Fine in slipcase. *Pacific**. $230/£144

Book of the Atmosphere. Boston: Lilly, Wait, 1833. 1st ed. 140pp. Orig cl (sl waterstained), paper label. *M & S*. $450/£281

Book of the Dead. Raymond O. Faulkner (trans). LEC, 1972. Ltd to 1500 numbered. 2 vols. Fine in slipcase. *Swann**. $161/£101

Book of the Flyfishers Club, 1883-1934. (England, 1934.) 1st ed. Color frontis, guard. Teg. 3/4 morocco, gilt-stamped cl. (Bkpl, frontis guard clipped, foxing), else NF. *Pacific**. $196/£123

Book of the Piscatorial Society 1836-1936. London: The Piscatorial Society, (1936). 1st ed. Color frontis. Teg. Grn cl, gilt. Fine. *Pacific**. $138/£86

Book of the Prophet Isaiah, the King James Version. LEC, 1979. One of 2000 signed by Chaim Gross (illus). Fine in slipcase. *Swann**. $201/£126

Book of Tiny Tots. London: Ernest Nister, (1903). Royal 8vo. Mtd chromolitho frontis, (66)pp; dbl-pg line dwg. Color-ptd cl-backed pict bds. Fine. *Sotheran*. $125/£78

Bookano Annual, with Pictures That Spring up in Model Form. Number One. London: Strand Pub, (1934). 1st ed. Sm sq 4to. 6 pop-up dbl-spread models. Pict eps. Dec pict bds. Internally VF (1 sm repaired tear, 1 crease to a movable figure), externally NF (spine lt creased). *Sotheran*. $589/£368

BOOKER, ANTON S. Wildcats in Petticoats. Girard, 1945. Wraps. (Upper corner partly bent/creased, cvrs faded), o/w VG. *Baade*. $17/£11

BOOKER, MOLLY. Embroidery Design. The Studio, 1935. 1st ed. 31 mtd photos. Good+ (fr hinge cracking; worn). *Whittle.* $19/£12

Bookman's Holiday: Notes and Studies Written and Gathered in Tribute to Harry Miller Lydenberg. NY: NY Public Library, 1943. 1st ed. *Dawson.* $35/£22

BOOLE, GEORGE. An Investigation of the Laws of Thought, on Which are Founded the Mathematical Theories of Logic and Probabilities. London: Macmillan, 1854. 1st ed. 8vo. v,iv,(1),424,(1)pp, complete w/errata, leaf of notes at end. Unopened. Pebbled grn cl (edges rubbed). VG (skillful paper repair to upper outside 2-inch of tp and dedicatory leaf; foxed). *Glaser.* $2,000/£1,250

BOOLE, GEORGE. A Treatise on Differential Equations. NY: Chelsea, n.d. (c.1959). 5th ed. Fine. *Glaser.* $45/£28

BOON, J. Under Six Reigns. Waterlow & Sons, 1925. Cream bds (sl age-dknd). VG. *Moss.* $43/£27

BOOTES, HENRY H. Deep-Sea Bubbles or the Cruise of the Anna Lombard. Ernest Benn, 1928. 1st ed. VG-. *Walcot.* $35/£22

BOOTH, STEPHEN. The Book Called Holinshed's Chronicles...with a Leaf from the 1587 Edition. SF: Book Club of CA, 1968. One of 500 ptd. Orig leaf tipped-in. Prospectus laid in. Paper spine label. Fine. *Pacific*.* $104/£65

BOOTH, WILLIAM STONE. Subtle Shining Secrecies. Boston, 1925. Ltd ed. Signed. Teg. NF (sl rubbed). *Polyanthos.* $45/£28

BOOTHBY, G. Dr. Nikola's Experiment. Appleton, 1899. 1st Amer ed. (Closed tear rear panel), else VG in wraps. *Fine Books.* $100/£63

BOOTHBY, G. Pharos the Egyptian. Appleton, 1899. 1st Amer ed. (Spine extrems lt rubbed), else VG-. *Fine Books.* $65/£41

BOOTHBY, GUY. A Bid for Fortune. NY: D. Appleton, 1895. 1st Amer ed. No. 179 in 'Town and Country Library.' 12pp undated ads. Lt blue-gray dec cl. Fine (mk p12). *Sumner & Stillman.* $80/£50

BOOTHBY, GUY. The Kidnapped President. London: Ward Lock, 1902. 1st ed. (Pg edges foxed), o/w VG in cl-cvrd bds, gilt. *Mordida.* $75/£47

BOOTHBY, ROBERT. I Fight to Live. Gollancz, 1947. 1st ed. Signed presentation. VG-. *Any Amount.* $24/£15

BOOTHROYD, B. The History of the Ancient Borough of Pontefract.... Pontefract: The Author/J. Fox, 1807. 1st ed. Engr frontis, xvi,496,xxiv pp; 4 plts, fldg plan. Mid 19th-cent 1/2 mid-brn calf, gilt, raised bands, dk red label, watered fine-horizontal-grain dk grn cl. Good (contents browned). *Blackwell's.* $176/£110

BORDEN, JOHN W. and JANET S. KRUGER. Thomas Bewick and the Fables of Aesop. SF: Book Club of CA, 1983. One of 518 ptd. Incl orig leaf from the 1st ed (1818) of The Fables of Aesop & a new imp from 1 of Bewick's orig wood engrs. Prospectus laid in. Fine. *Pacific*.* $127/£79

BORDEN, MARY. The Forbidden Zone. London: Heinemann, (1929). 1st ed. Inscribed presentation. Frontis. Gilt black cl. (Lt offset eps), else NF in VG dj (clean split at 1 fold). *Reese.* $65/£41

BORDEN, MARY. The Tortoise. NY: Knopf, 1921. 1st US ed. Blue cl. Good in dj (worn, largely intact). *Reese.* $25/£16

BORDEN, SPENCER. The Arab Horse. NY, Doubleday Page, 1906. 1st ed. VG. *October Farm.* $125/£78

BORDEN, SPENCER. What Horse for the Cavalry? Fall River: Franklin, 1912. 1st ed. Good. *October Farm.* $85/£53

Border and Bastille. NY: W.I. Pooley, (1863). 1st ed. xii,291pp. (Lib stamps, bkpl, name excised from fep; shelf-worn, edges, spine worn), else Good. *Brown.* $35/£22

Border Beagles; A Tale of the Mississippi. Phila: Carey & Hart, 1840. 1st ed, BAL's binding A. 2 vols. Orig plum P cl, ptd paper spine labels. VG set (lt foxed; sig starting, lt sunned, soiled). BAL 18068. *Reese.* $650/£406

BORG, CARL OSCAR. The Great Southwest Etchings. Text by Gustavus A. Eisen et al. Everett C. Maxwell (ed). (Santa Ana: Fine Arts), 1936. 1st ed. Signed. Frontis. 1/2 cl. (Sl shelfworn), else NF. *Pacific*.* $161/£101

BORGES, JORGE LUIS and ADOLFO BIOY-CASARES. Chronicles of Bustos Domecq. NY: Dutton, 1976. 1st ed. Fine in NF dj. *Lame Duck.* $45/£28

BORGES, JORGE LUIS and ADOLFO BIOY-CASARES (eds). Extraordinary Tales. Anthony Kerrigan (trans). NY: Herder & Herder, 1971. 1st US ed. NF in dj. *Lame Duck.* $75/£47

BORGES, JORGE LUIS. The Aleph and Other Stories. NY: Dutton, 1970. 1st US ed. Fine in NF dj. *Pettler.* $45/£28

BORGES, JORGE LUIS. The Book of Imaginary Beings. London: Jonathan Cape, 1970. 1st British ed. Fine in NF dj (author, title in lt marker to verso of spine, rear cvrs). *Lame Duck.* $125/£78

BORGES, JORGE LUIS. The Book of Sand. NY: Dutton, 1977. 1st US ed. NF in NF dj. *Lame Duck.* $50/£31

BORGES, JORGE LUIS. Dr. Brodie's Report. NY: Dutton, 1972. 1st US ed. Fine in Fine dj. *Lame Duck.* $65/£41

BORGES, JORGE LUIS. Evaristo Carriego. NY: Dutton, 1984. 1st US ed. NF in dj. *Lame Duck.* $45/£28

BORGES, JORGE LUIS. Ficciones. NY: Grove, 1962. 1st US ed. VG+ in VG dj (1-inch edge tear, triangular chip to lower fr cvr edge). *Lame Duck.* $125/£78

BORGES, JORGE LUIS. Ficciones. LEC, 1984. Ltd to 1500 numbered, signed by Sol LeWitt (illus). Fine in slipcase. *Swann*.* $402/£251

BORGES, JORGE LUIS. Ficciones. Anthony Kerrigan (ed). London: Weidenfeld & Nicolson, 1962. 1st Eng ed. NF (inscrip, stamp; spine head, fore-edge rear cvr sl bumped) in dj (sl creased, 3-inch tear fr panel). *Ulysses.* $152/£95

BORGES, JORGE LUIS. The Gold of the Tigers. NY: Dutton, 1977. 1st ed. Fine in dj (price-clipped). *Lame Duck.* $65/£41

BORGES, JORGE LUIS. Labyrinths. Norfolk: New Directions, 1962. 1st US ed. NF in VG dj (price-clipped, spinal extrems sl chipped). *Lame Duck.* $250/£156

BORGES, JORGE LUIS. Other Inquisitions 1937. Ruth L. C. Simms (trans). London: Souvenir Press, 1973. 1st Eng ed. Fine in dj. *Ulysses.* $40/£25

BORGES, JORGE LUIS. A Personal Anthology. NY, (1967). 1st Amer ed. VG in dj (sl rubbed w/few sl tears). *King.* $35/£22

BORGES, JORGE LUIS. A Personal Anthology. Anthony Kerrigan (ed). London: Cape, 1968. 1st Eng ed. Fine in dj (edges sl rubbed). *Ulysses.* $120/£75

BORGES, JORGE LUIS. Selected Poems 1923-1967. London: Allen Lane/Penguin, 1972. 1st British ed. (Bkpl, sig), else Fine in dj (price-clipped, 2 sm tape-repaired tears on spine head, rear cvr). *Lame Duck.* $100/£63

BORGES, JORGE LUIS. Selected Poems 1923-1967. NY: Delacorte, 1972. 1st US ed. NF in dj. *Lame Duck.* $150/£94

BORGES, JORGE LUIS. A Universal History of Infamy. NY: Dutton, 1972. 1st US ed. (Sm abrasion to cl bottom edge of rear bd), else NF in dj. *Lame Duck.* $65/£41

BORLASE, WILLIAM COPELAND. Niphon and Its Antiquities. Plymouth: W. Brendon and Son, 1876. 1st, only ed. 86,(1)pp. VG (sm lib stamp) in mod wrappers, ptd spine label. *Morrell.* $216/£135

BORRAS, MARIA LLUISA. Picabia. NY, (1985). Dj. *Swann*.* $172/£108

BORRER, WILLIAM. The Birds of Sussex. London, 1891. 1st ed. xviii,385,(iv),subscribers, + (viii)pp ads; 6 chromo plts. (Hinges cracked, sl shaken; spine chipped, fore-edge of bds damp-stained.) *Edwards*. $104/£65

BORROW, GEORGE. Lavengro. John Murray, 1900. New, enlarged ed. B/w frontisport, 10 full-pg b/w illus. Teg. Dec cl. VG (fep sl browned; fr hinge cracked, spine ends sl bumped, extrems sl rubbed). *Ulysses*. $120/£75

BORSI, FRANCO. Leon Battista Alberti. Rudolf G. Carpanini (trans). NY: Harper & Row, (1977). Brn linen, gilt. Good in dj, pub's slipcase. *Karmiole*. $100/£63

BORTHWICK, J. D. Three Years in California. Edinburgh: William Blackwood, 1857. 1st ed. vi,(2),384pp; 8 duotone litho plts. Orig red cl. (1x3-inch piece cut from top of tp and following leaf, w/replacement paper expertly reinserted; title sl marred by adhesive; contents dknd, few marginal dampstains; re-backed, orig spine strip laid on, extrems worn, cvr reglazed), else VG. Howes B622. *Pacific**. $196/£123

BORUP, GEORGE. A Tenderfoot with Peary. NY: Frederick A. Stokes, 1911. Fldg map. VG (rubbed). *Explorer*. $88/£55

BOS, K. J. et al. The Zoological Taxa of William H. Dall. Washington: Smithsonian, 1968. 1st ed. Fine in wraps. *Mikesh*. $30/£19

BOSANQUET, MRS. R. C. Days in Attica. London, 1914. 1st ed. Color frontis, 16 plts, 1 fldg plan (1 plt detached). (Lt browned; corners rubbed w/sl loss, spine faded.) *Edwards*. $48/£30

BOSANQUET, THEODORA. Paul Valery. London: Hogarth, 1933. 1st ed. One of 1000 ptd. Orange cl. VG (edges sl spotted, eps sl tape- mkd; spine, fr cvr faded; lacks tissue wrapper). *Virgo*. $40/£25

BOSQUI, EDWARD. Memoirs of Edward Bosqui. Oakland: Holmes Book Co, 1952. One of 350 ptd. Color frontis. 1/2 cl, patterned bds, paper spine label. (Spine faded), else NF in dj. Howes B623. *Pacific**. $63/£39

BOSSE, M. J. The Journey of Tao Kim Nam. GC: Doubleday, 1959. 1st ed. Fine in dj. *Associates*. $100/£63

BOSSERT, HELMUTH. Folk Art of Europe. NY: Praeger, (1953). 1st Amer ed. Fine (lt rubbed). *Polyanthos*. $125/£78

BOSSERT, HELMUTH. Ornament in Applied Art. NY, 1924. Folio. 122 color plts. (Spine, part of cvrs faded; dampstain along joints.) *Swann**. $201/£126

BOSTOCK, FRANK C. The Training of Wild Animals. NY: Century, 1907. Pict cl. (Name; spine sunned, ends rubbed), else VG. *Pacific**. $35/£22

BOSTOCK, H. S. Yukon Territory. Selected Field Reports...1898 to 1933. Ottawa, 1957. 3 fldg maps in pocket. VG in ptd wrapper. *High Latitude*. $75/£47

Boston Directory for...1806.... Boston: Adams, Sampson, July 1, 1859. 1st ed. (5),540,88,(3)pp. Cl-backed ptd paper-cvrd bds (rubbed). VG. *M & S*. $125/£78

BOSTON, BERNARD (ed). History of the 398th Infantry Regiment in World War II. Washington, 1947. VG. *Clark*. $75/£47

BOSTON, LUCY. A Stranger at Green Knowe. London: Faber, 1961. 1st ed. 5.5x8.25. Peter Boston (illus). 158pp. VG (ex-lib) in dj. *Cattermole*. $25/£16

BOSTON, N. and E. PUDDY. Dereham, the Biography of a Country Town. London, 1952. 1st ed. Map. VG in dj. *Gretton*. $43/£27

BOSTON, NOEL. Old Guns and Pistols. Ernest Benn, 1958. 1st ed. VG in dj. *Hollett*. $24/£15

BOSWELL, JAMES. An Account of Corsica. London: Edward & Charles Dilly in the Poultry, 1768. 2nd ed. Engr fldg frontis map. Contemp full calf (spine rebacked in leather) w/orig spine laid down. VG. *Gretton*. $256/£160

BOSWELL, JAMES. Boswell in Holland (1763-1764). Frank Brady and Frederick A. Pottle (eds). London: Heinemann, 1952. 1st ed. 3 plts, 2 facs. VG in dj (edges chipped, sl creased). *Hollett*. $40/£25

BOSWELL, JAMES. Boswell on the Grand Tour: Germany and Switzerland 1764. Frank Brady and Frederick A. Pottle (eds). London: Heinemann, 1953. 1st ed. 9 plts. VG in dj (sl worn, torn). *Hollett*. $48/£30

BOSWELL, JAMES. Boswell's London Journal (1762-1763). Frank Brady and Frederick A. Pottle (eds). London: Heinemann, 1950. 1st ed. 1 plt, 2 facs. VG. *Hollett*. $32/£20

BOSWELL, JAMES. Boswell's London Journal 1762-1763, Together with Journal of My Jaunt Harvest 1762. London: Heinemann, 1951. Ltd to 1050. 18 plts, 2 fldg maps. Vellum over blue cl (spine sl soiled), leather spine label. Slipcase. *Karmiole*. $85/£53

BOSWELL, JAMES. The Hypochondriack. Essays from the London Magazine. Margery Bailey (ed). CA: Stanford Univ, 1928. 2 vols. VG set. *Clearwater*. $240/£150

BOSWELL, JAMES. Journal of a Tour to the Hebrides with Samuel Johnson, L.L.D. NY, 1810. Calf (newly rebacked), marbled cvrs (sl rubbed), gilt, leather title label. NF (2 sm lib stamps). *Polyanthos*. $125/£78

BOSWELL, JAMES. A Journal of a Tour to the Hebrides with Samuel Johnson. LEC, 1974. One of 2000. Thomas Rowlandson (illus). Fine in slipcase. *Swann**. $34/£21

BOSWELL, JAMES. The Journal of a Tour to the Hebrides. Dublin: White, Byrne & Cash, 1785. 1st Dublin ed. vii,(i),524,(i)pp (tp sl soiled, corners rounded). Uncut. Early 20th-cent linen-backed bds. *Hollett*. $288/£180

BOSWELL, JAMES. The Life of Samuel Johnson and Journal of a Tour to the Hebrides.... NY: Doubleday, Page, 1922. Temple Bar ed. One of 785 sets. 10 vols. Engr frontisport each vol. Teg, rest untrimmed. White paper vellum, brn paper over bds, ptd spine labels. NF (sl soiled). *House*. $150/£94

BOSWELL, JAMES. The Life of Samuel Johnson, Including a Journal of a Tour to the Hebrides. NY: Alexander V. Blake, 1841. New ed. 2 vols. Frontisport. Period calf, leather spine labels. (Sl foxed; spines aged), else VG. *Pacific**. $104/£65

BOSWELL, JAMES. The Life of Samuel Johnson, L.L.D. [with] a Journal of a Tour to the Hebrides. Percy Fitzgerald (ed). London, 1891. 2nd ed thus. 3 vols. Recent 1/2 calf (expertly re-backed), marbled bds. Fine. *Gretton*. $120/£75

BOSWELL, JAMES. The Life of Samuel Johnson, LL. D. LEC, 1938. Ltd to 1500 numbered. Fine in slipcase. *Swann**. $138/£86

BOSWELL, JAMES. The Life of Samuel Johnson, LL.D. London: John Murray, 1835. 10 vols. 10 engr frontispieces, 1 fldg plt. Contemp 1/2 calf, gilt, gilt-dec spine panels. (Plts lt spotted; sl worn, few sm chips.) *Hollett*. $280/£175

BOSWELL, JAMES. The Life of Samuel Johnson, LL.D. Together with a Journal of a Tour to the Hebrides.... Percy Fitzgerald (ed). London: Bickers & Son, 1874. 3 vols. Lg 8vo. Extra-illus w/hand-colored frontis for each vol, 19 engr ports, facs, 1 fldg map. Full polished calf (expertly rebacked, few scuffs), gilt. VG set. *House*. $450/£281

BOSWELL, JAMES. The Life of Samuel Johnson. Charles Dilly, 1793. 2nd ed. 3 vols. Engr frontis, 2 fldg plts. Contemp tree calf. (Spotted; spines cracked, sl chipped.) *Sotheby's**. $442/£276

BOSWELL, JAMES. The Life of Samuel Johnson. London: T. Cadell, 1811. 6th ed. 4 vols. Frontisport; fldg facs plt. Tree calf, leather spine labels. (Joints cracked), else VG. *Pacific**. $109/£68

BOSWELL, JAMES. On the Profession of a Player. London: Elkin Mathews & Marrot, 1929. One of 600 numbered. Cl-backed dec paper bds. VG (tp sl mkd; spine tail, top corners sl bumped) in dj (sl nicked, mkd, dusty, browned). *Ulysses*. $88/£55

BOSWELL, JOHN and RON BARRETT. The Pop-Up White House. NY: Bantam Books, 1983. Ron Barrett & Gary Hallgren (illus). Dbl-pg pop-up w/envelope underneath containing ready-to-assemble furniture, MX missile. VG. *Bookfinders*. $50/£31

BOSWELL, THOMAS. Why Time Begins on Opening Day. Doubleday, 1984. 1st ed. Fine in VG+ dj. *Plapinger*. $35/£22

BOSWORTH, CLARENCE. Breeding Your Own. NY: Derrydale, 1939. Ltd to 1250 numbered. 1/4 cream linen, blue cl-cvrd bds. VF (tape mks). *Biscotti*. $100/£63

BOTHWELL, JEAN. Little Boat Boy. Harcourt Brace, 1945. 1st ed. 252pp. VG (bkpl; spine faded) in VG dj. *Price*. $20/£13

BOTKIN, B. A. (ed). Folk-Say, a Regional Miscellany, 1930. Norman: Univ of OK, 1930. 1st ed. NF. *Labordo*. $75/£47

BOTKIN, B. A. (ed). Lay My Burden Down. Chicago: Univ of Chicago, (1945). 1st ed, advance rev copy. Probable advance binding of fr/back bds w/o spine. (Fr cvr detached.) Dj (chipped, soiled). *Heritage*. $100/£63

BOTT, ALAN. The Londoner's England. London, 1947. 1st ed. 89 plts (32 color). (Bkpl.) *Edwards*. $32/£20

BOTTOME, PHYLLIS. The Second Fiddle. NY: Century, 1917. 1st US ed. Frontis. Pict grn cl. VG. *Reese*. $30/£19

BOTTOME, PHYLLIS. Stella Benson. SF: Albert Bender, 1934. One of 250. Ptd label. VG+ (bkpl). *Bohling*. $30/£19

BOTTOMLEY, GORDON. The Gate of Smaragdus. London: Elkin Mathews, 1904. Folio. 8 grn-tinted plts. Untrimmed. Gray flecked bds, grn cl spine (faded), ptd paper label (sl rubbed). *Maggs*. $200/£125

BOTTOMS, DAVID. Shooting Rats at the Bibb County Dump. NY: Morrow, 1980. 1st ed. Fine in Fine dj. *Pettler*. $40/£25

BOTTRALL, RONALD. The Collected Poems of Ronald Bottrall. Sidgwick & Jackson, 1961. 1st ed. Signed presentation. Fine in dj. *Any Amount*. $26/£16

BOUCHER, ANTHONY. The Case of the Baker Street Irregulars. NY: S&S, 1940. 1st ed. Red cl. Fine in Good+ dj (chipped). *Sumner & Stillman*. $95/£59

BOUCHETTE, JOSEPH. The British Dominions in North America. London: Longman, Reese, Orme et al, 1832. 2 vols. 4to. Engr frontis, 33 plts, plans and tables. (Occasional spotting, browning; bkpl.) Contemp diced calf gilt, red/grn morocco labels. *Christie's**. $685/£428

BOUDINOT, ELIAS. A Star in the West. Trenton: D. Fenton et al, 1816. 1st ed. iv,312pp. Early scarlet sheep, marbled bds, gilt. (Sl browned, foxed, fr hinge cracked; scuffed, crack forming at upper joint.) Text Good. Howes B643. *Baltimore**. $140/£88

BOUGHTON, V. T. (ed). History of the Eleventh Engineers, United States Army.... NY: (Trustees Eleventh Engineers Fund), 1926 (1927). 1st ed. 7 fldg maps, plts. Red cl, gilt, fr cvr medallion. Very Clean (sl aged). *Baltimore**. $40/£25

BOULDIN, POWHATAN. The Old Trunk. Danville, VA: Blair & Boatwright, 1896. 1st ed thus. (4),70pp. Orig ptd peach wraps. VG (spine soiled, ends chipped, fr spine edge cracked, sm chip rear corner). *Chapel Hill*. $85/£53

BOULGER, DEMETRIUS CHARLES. England and Russia in Central Asia. London: W.H. Allen, 1879. 1st ed. 2 vols. Demy 8vo. xvi,348pp, 2 fldg maps; vii,426pp. (Eps cracked at hinges, few tears to maps w/o loss; fr cvrs sl stained), o/w VG set in grn cl. *Ulysses*. $1,120/£700

BOULGER, G. S. Familiar Trees. Cassell, (1892). xvi,160,(xvi); xvi,168,(xvi)pp; 40 color plts. VG. *Hollett*. $104/£65

BOULLE, P. The Bridge Over the River Kwai. Vanguard, 1954. 1st Amer ed, 1st bk. NF in VG dj. *Fine Books*. $38/£24

BOURKE, JOHN G. Bourke's Diary: From Journals...June 27-Sept 15, 1876.... La Mirada, CA: James Willert, (1986). 1st ed. Ltd ed. Inscribed, signed presentation by James Willert (notes). Fabricoid. Fine. *Pacific**. $92/£58

BOURKE, JOHN G. On the Border with Crook. NY, 1891. 1st ed. 491pp. Silver stamped pict, dec cl. (Fr/rear hinges, backstrip top/bottom w/sm splits; corners sl worn.) Internally Sound. Howes B654. *Baade*. $175/£109

BOURKE, JOHN G. On the Border with Crook. NY: Scribner, 1891. 1st ed. xiii,(2),491pp + 4pp ads; 7 photo plts. Burgundy cl. (Tp w/offset from tissue guard, stain to dedication pg from newsclipping previously affixed to verso; fr hinge cracked, partly repaired w/glue, extrems rubbed), else VG. Howes B654. *Pacific**. $288/£180

BOURKE, JOHN G. Scatalogic Rites of All Nations. Washington: W.H. Lowdermilk, 1891. 1st ed. xi,496pp. Teg, untrimmed. Dk brn cl, gilt. (Sl aging, both hinges cracked, splitting; sl worn, sl chipped.) Cvrs VG. *Baltimore**. $75/£47

BOURKE, JOHN G. The Snake-Dance of the Moquis of Arizona. NY: Scribner, 1884. 1st ed. xvii,371pp; 33 Fine full-pg plts (1 fldg), tissue guards. Untrimmed. Dk grn cl, gilt. (Sl edgeworn, new eps.) Cvrs VG. Howes B655. *Baltimore**. $320/£200

BOURKE, JOHN G. The Snake-Dance of the Moquis of Arizona.... Chicago, 1962. Rpt. Fine. Howes B655. *Wantagh*. $45/£28

BOURKE, JOHN G. With General Crook in the Indian Wars. Palo Alto: Lewis Osborne, 1968. One of 2100. 2 photo plts, 2 fldg color maps. Red linen, gilt. (Bkpl partly removed from fep verso), else NF. *Pacific**. $52/£33

BOURKE-WHITE, MARGARET and ERSKINE CALDWELL. Say, Is This the U.S.A.? NY, (1941). 1st ed. Photo-pict glazed bds (spine browned, rubbed; foxed). *Swann**. $115/£72

BOURKE-WHITE, MARGARET. Portrait of Myself. London: Collins, 1964. 1st Eng ed. VG (spine ends sl bumped) in dj (rubbed, nicked, creased). *Ulysses*. $56/£35

BOURKE-WHITE, MARGARET. They Called It 'Purple Heart Valley': A Combat Chronicle of the War in Italy. NY: S&S, 1944. 1st ed. Frontis. (Stamp; sl soiled), else VG. *Cahan*. $40/£25

BOURNE, GWEN. The Wonder World Fairy Tale Book. London: Cecil Palmer, (1931). 1st ed. 4to. 9 full-pg color, 4 b/w plts by Harold Gaze. Blue pict cl. Good. *Reisler*. $290/£181

BOURNE, H. Flores Poetici. The Florist's Manual: Designed as an Introduction to Vegetable Physiology and Systematic Botany, for Cultivators of Flowers. Boston: Munroe, 1833. 1st ed. 8vo. 288pp. Old lib cl. *M & S*. $2,000/£1,250

BOURNE, RANDOLPH. History of a Literary Radical and Other Essays. Van Wyck Brooks (ed). NY, 1920. 1st Amer ed. Frontis. NF (name). *Polyanthos*. $25/£16

BOURNE, WESLEY. Mysterious Waters to Guard: Essays and Addresses on Anaesthesia. Oxford: Blackwell Scientific, (1955). Color frontis. Fine in dj. *Weber*. $100/£63

BOUTELL, CHARLES. Arms and Armour in Antiquity and the Middle Ages. London: Reeves & Turner, 1893. 1st ed. Brn cl, gilt. Fine. *Glenn*. $40/£25

BOUTELL, CHARLES. The Monumental Brasses of England: A Series of Engravings upon Wood.... London, 1849. xii,53,(14)pp; 150 plts. 1/4 leather, marbled bds (sl rubbed, fr bd corner gnawed). (Foxed, tips of some pp gnawed), else Internally VG. *Washton*. $100/£63

BOUVET, F. Bonnard, the Complete Graphic Work. London: Thames & Hudson, 1981. 60 color plts. Good in dj. *Ars Artis*. $61/£38

BOVA, BEN. The Star Conquerors. Phila: John C. Winston, (1959). 1st ed, 1st bk. VG in dj (spine head chipped, foot, corners rubbed, flaps clipped, not affecting price). *Pacific**. $161/£101

BOWDEN, CHARLES and LEW KREINBERG. Street Signs Chicago: Neighborhood and Other Illusions of Big City Life. Chicago: Chicago Review, (1981). 1st ed. Fine in NF dj (2 sm tears). *Between The Covers*. $125/£78

BOWDICH, T. EDWARD. An Account of the Discoveries of the Portuguese in the Interior of Angola and Mozambique. London: J. Booth, 1824. 1st ed. 8vo. (ii),186pp; 2 fldg maps. Orig bds. Very Clean. *Maggs.* $1,200/£750

BOWDICH, T. EDWARD. Mission from Cape Coast Castle to Ashantee. London: John Murray, 1819. 1st ed. 4to. 3 engr maps and plans (1 fldg), 8 plts, all but 1 hand-colored, 5pp of music. (Offsetting from plts, 2 plts spotted; bkpls.) Sprinkled edges. Contemp 1/2 calf, marbled bds. (Fr inner hinges cracked, extrems lt rubbed.) *Christie's*.* $685/£428

BOWDICH, T. EDWARD. Mission from Cape Coast to Ashantee. W. E. F. Ward (ed). Frank Cass, 1966. 3rd ed. Map, 10 plts (1 color, fldg). (Spine sl faded.) *Edwards.* $120/£75

BOWDITCH, HAROLD. A Catalogue of a Special Exhibition of Manuscripts, Books, Portraits and Personal Relics of Nathaniel Bowditch. Salem, MA: Peabody Museum, 1937. 8 plts. VG in gray wraps. *Larry Price.* $20/£13

BOWDITCH, N. T. Suffolk Surnames. London, 1861. 3rd ed. 25,757pp. (Rebound.) *Heinoldt.* $30/£19

BOWDITCH, NATHANIEL. Bowditch's Useful Tables. NY: E. & G.W. Blunt, 1866. 5th ed. vii,67,(2),131-147,160-229,(9),(2)ads pp. (Fr inner hinge tender; spine chipped.) *Lefkowicz.* $75/£47

BOWDITCH, NATHANIEL. Memoir of Nathaniel Bowditch. Cambridge: John Wilson & Son, 1884. 3rd ed. Inscribed presentation. (4),178pp; 8 plts. (Spine ends chipped, sl tear upper joint.) *Lefkowicz.* $150/£94

BOWDITCH, NATHANIEL. The New American Practical Navigator. Newburyport: Edmund M. Blunt, 1807. 2nd ed. xiv,15-312,(284 tables), 613-679,(1)ad pp; 11 plts. Orig calf, leather label. (Frontis chart loose, last few ll nearly loose, wrinkled; lacks feps.) Contemp calf dj. *Lefkowicz.* $750/£469

BOWDITCH, NATHANIEL. The New American Practical Navigator. NY: E. & G.W. Blunt, 1864. 32nd new stereotype ed. (2),8,(iii-xx),289,(1 blank),460,(2)ads pp; 15 charts, plts, incl uncalled for plt at p452. Orig calf. (Spine dried, chipped, cvrs loose.) *Lefkowicz.* $275/£172

BOWDLER, MISS. Poems and Essays by the Late Miss Bowdler. Bath, 1815. 15th ed. vi,274pp. Later tree calf. (Ink sig; new leather spine label), o/w VG. *Whitehart.* $224/£140

BOWDOIN, W. G. The Rise of the Book-Plate. NY, 1901. 1st Amer ed. Signed presentation. Uncut. NF (stenciled bkpl; sl soiled). *Polyanthos.* $95/£59

Bowen's New Guide to the City of Boston and Vicinity. Boston: James Munroe, (1849). 1st ed. 36pp; fldg map, 2 plts. Orig flexible black cl. VG. *Chapel Hill.* $125/£78

BOWEN, A. V. Lyrics of Death. Fortune, 1943. 1st ed. Signed. Frontis. (Sl dull), else VG in dj (sl dull). *Whiteson.* $24/£15

BOWEN, ELIZABETH. Ann Lee's: And Other Stories. London: Sidgwick & Jackson, 1926. 1st ed. Inscribed, signed May 1926. Brn cl, gilt. Good (bkpls, lt foxed, sl shaken; cl soiled, lt spotted). *Reese.* $450/£281

BOWEN, ELIZABETH. Bowen's Court. NY: Knopf, 1942. 1st Amer ed. Fine in Fine dj (spine sl dknd). *Between The Covers.* $85/£53

BOWEN, ELIZABETH. Collected Impressions. London, 1950. 1st ed. Fine in Fine dj. *Polyanthos.* $45/£28

BOWEN, FRANK. London Ship Types. East Ham Echo, 1938. 1st ed. (Sl spotted.) Dj. *Hollett.* $48/£30

BOWEN, J. J. The Strategy of Robert E. Lee. NY: Thomas Y. Crowell, (1914). 1st ed. Blue cl. (Cvr lt spotted), else VG. *Chapel Hill.* $60/£38

BOWEN, MARJORIE. Black Magic. Alston Rivers, 1909. 1st UK ed. VG (ink name, spine ends sl nicked, fep sl scuffed) in illus bds. *Williams.* $104/£65

BOWEN, PETER. Kelly Blue. NY: Crown, 1991. 1st ed. Signed. VF in dj. *Mordida.* $50/£31

BOWEN, STEPHEN. Forsaken. London: Williams & Norgate, 1931. 1st ed. Grn cl. Fine in dj (lt edgeworn). *Reese.* $50/£31

BOWER, B. M. Open Land. Boston: Little, Brown, 1933. 1st ed. Fine in illus dj (sl chipped). *Unger.* $125/£78

BOWER, B. M. The Wind Blows West. Boston: Little, Brown, 1938. 1st ed. Fine in NF illus dj (lt chipped). *Unger.* $125/£78

BOWER, DONALD E. Fred Rosenstock. Flagstaff: Northland, 1976. 1st ed. Inscribed. VG in dj. *Dumont.* $40/£25

BOWER, DONALD E. Fred Rosenstock. N.p.: Northland, 1976. 1st ed. Fine in dj. *Labordo.* $40/£25

BOWER, F. O. Botany of the Living Plant. London, 1923. 2nd ed. Grn cl, gilt. VG. *Larry Price.* $30/£19

BOWER, JOHN. Description of the Abbeys of Melrose and Old Melrose. Kelso: The Author, 1813. 1st ed. Fldg litho frontis (sl offset), 100pp. Uncut. Mod 1/2 levant morocco, gilt. *Hollett.* $152/£95

BOWERMAN, MARY L. The Flowering Plants and Ferns of Mount Diablo, California. Berkeley, 1944. Frontis; fldg chart. Fine in dj. *Brooks.* $95/£59

BOWERS, CLEMENT G. Rhododendrons and Azaleas. NY, 1936. 1st ed. VG. *Woolson.* $50/£31

BOWERS, F. and R. B. DAVIS. George Sandys. A Bibliographical Catalogue of Printed Editions in England to 1700. NY: NY Public Library, 1950. Wrappers. *Maggs.* $29/£18

BOWIE, WALTER RUSSELL. The Story of Jesus for Young People. NY: Scribner, 1937. 1st ed. 6 full-pg color plts by Robert Lawson. Blue-grn cl, gilt. Nice. *Reisler.* $50/£31

Bowker Lectures on Book Publishing: First Series. George Grady, 1943. One of 600. *Dawson.* $15/£9

BOWLAN, MARIAN. City Types. Chicago: Denison, (1916). 1st ed. Untrimmed, partly unopened. VG. *Second Life.* $45/£28

BOWLBY, JOHN. Attachment. NY: Basic Books, 1969. 1st US ed. Fine in NF dj. *Beasley.* $50/£31

BOWLES, JANE. In the Summer House. NY: Random House, (1954). 1st ed. Frontis. Fine in VG + dj (price-clipped, sm chip, tear to joint, extrems sl dknd). *Reese.* $125/£78

BOWLES, PAUL. The Delicate Prey and Other Stories. NY: Random House, (1950). 1st ed. (Sl adhesion residue rear pastedown), else VG in dj (spine ends chipped, joint foot lacks sm piece). *Pacific*.* $81/£51

BOWLES, PAUL. In the Red Room. Hollywood: Sylvester & Orphanos, 1981. Ltd to 330 signed. Fine dec cl. *Truepenny.* $100/£63

BOWLES, PAUL. Let It Come Down. NY, 1952. 1st ed. Dj (spine extrems lt worn). *Swann*.* $69/£43

BOWLES, PAUL. A Little Stone. London: Lehmann, (1950). 1st ed. Signed. Fine in dj (sl worn). *Lenz.* $300/£188

BOWLES, PAUL. A Little Stone. Lehmann, 1950. 1st ed, 1st issue w/bright grn cl, gilt backstrip. VG in dj (backstrip panel ends sl chipped). *Blackwell's.* $160/£100

BOWLES, PAUL. Next to Nothing. Kathmandu, Nepal: Starstreams 5, 1976. One of 500 numbered. Fine in wrappers. *Lenz.* $125/£78

BOWLES, PAUL. The Spider's House. NY, 1955. 1st ed. NF in VG + dj. *Warren.* $85/£53

BOWLES, PAUL. Things Gone and Things Still Here. Santa Barbara: Black Sparrow, 1977. 1st Amer ed. Fine in wraps. *Polyanthos.* $25/£16

BOWLES, PAUL. Without Stopping: An Autobiography. NY: Putnam, (1972). 1st ed. NF in dj (spine ends sl rubbed). *Pacific*.* $40/£25

BOWLES, PAUL. Yallah. NY, 1957. 1st ed. NF in VG + dj. *Warren.* $120/£75

BOWLES, SAMUEL. Our New West. Hartford, 1869. 1st ed. 524pp; map. Chocolate-brn beveled bds, gilt. (Bd edges scuffed), o/w VG + . *Five Quail.* $125/£78

BOWLKER, CHARLES. The Art of Angling: A Compleat Fly-Fishing...To Which Are Added, Directions for Making Artificial Flies. Birmingham: Swinney, 1786. 4th ed. Frontis, xii,120pp. Old calf (worn, broken, soiled, foxed, sl stained). Internally Sound. *Oinonen**. $120/£75

BOWLKER, CHARLES. Bowlker's Art of Angling, Greatly Enlarged and Improved.... Ludlow: Procter & Jones, 1826. Hand-colored frontis. (Old news-clipping tipped to verso of 1/2-title.) Later 3/4 calf (rubbed, soiled, foxed), spine gilt. *Oinonen**. $160/£100

BOWMAN, DAVID. Let the Dog Drive. NY: NY Univ, 1992. 1st ed. Fine in Fine dj. *Warren.* $125/£78

BOWMAN, GERALD. From Scott to Fuchs. London: Evans Bros, 1958. VG in dj. *Explorer.* $18/£11

BOWMAN, HEATH and STIRLING DICKINSON. Death Is Incidental. Chicago: Willett, Clark, (1937). 1st ed. Signed print tipped on fep. Fine in VG dj. *Book Market.* $35/£22

BOWMAN, ISAIAH (ed). Limits of Land Settlement. NY, 1937. 1st ed. Fldg map. Grn cl, gilt. VG. *Larry Price.* $49/£31

BOWMAN, J. N. and ROBERT F. HEIZER. Anza and the Northwest Frontier of New Spain. L.A.: Southwest Museum, 1967. (Shelfworn), else NF. *Dumont.* $55/£34

BOWMAN, LYNN. Los Angeles: Epic of a City. (Berkeley): Howell-North Books, (1974). 1st ed. Dj. *Dawson.* $40/£25

BOWMAN, SAMUEL M. and R. B. IRWIN. Sherman and His Campaigns: A Military Biography. NY: Charles B. Richardson, 1865. 1st ed. Steel-engr frontisport, 512pp (ink stamp; sl shaken, lt aging, foxed). Blind grn cl (sl spotted, lt worn; frayed). Internally Good. *Baltimore**. $25/£16

BOWNAS, SAMUEL. An Account of the Life, Travels, and Christian Experiences in the Work of the Ministry. London, 1756. 1st ed. 19th-cent bds, recent leather back. (Browning, tp sl frayed, soiled.) Howes B668. *Oinonen**. $120/£75

BOWNESS, ALAN and LUIGI LAMBERTINI. Victor Pasmore: A Catalogue Raisonne of the Paintings, Constructions and Graphics 1926-1979. NY, (1980). Dj. *Swann**. $46/£29

BOWNESS, ALAN (ed). The Complete Sculpture of Barbara Hepworth, 1960-1969. London: Lund Humphries, 1971. 1st Eng ed. Very Nice in dj (sl nicked). *Clearwater.* $88/£55

BOWRA, C. M. Edith Sitwell. London: Lyrebird, 1947. Orig stiff wraps (sl frayed). *Edrich.* $13/£8

BOWRING, JOHN. The Kingdom and People of Siam; with a Narrative of the Mission to That Country in 1855. London: John W. Parker & Son, 1857. 2 vols. 8vo. xi,482,2 ads; vii,446pp,8 ads (lib stamps to frontis versos); fldg map, 18 plts. Grn cl (spines faded). *Adelson.* $550/£344

BOWYER, ROBERT. An Illustrated Record of Important Events in the Annals of Europe...Comprising a Series of Views of the Principal Places.... R. Bowyer, 1816. Folio. Plain engr map, facs plt, 10 hand-colored aquatint views (some fldg). Watermks dated 1816 (text), 1811 and 1814 (plts). Recent 1/2 calf, marbled bds. *Sotheby's**. $1,011/£632

BOWYER, ROBERT. An Impartial Historical Narrative of Those Momentous Events Which Have Taken Place in This Country from the Year 1816 to 1823. T. Bensley, 1823. 1st ed. Folio. 5 engr plts, 3 hand-colored aquatints. Uncut. Orig bds (spine defective), fr cvr w/ptd label, neatly inscribed 'Proof.' *Sotheby's**. $275/£172

BOX, EDGAR. (Pseud of Gore Vidal.) Death Likes It Hot. London, 1955. 1st Eng ed. Dj (sl worn). *Swann**. $46/£29

BOX, MICHAEL. Capt. James Box's Adventures and Explorations in New and Old Mexico. NY, 1869. Pub's cl. (Lib label fr pastedown.) Howes B671. *Swann**. $149/£93

BOXER, C. R. The Christian Century in Japan, 1549-1650. Berkeley/L.A./London: Univ of CA, 1974. 3rd ptg. Frontis, 16 plts, fldg map. VG. *Worldwide.* $50/£31

BOXER, C. R. (ed). The Tragic History of the Sea 1589-1622. Cambridge: CUP, 1959. Blue cl. Fine. *Appelfeld.* $60/£38

Boy Mechanic, Book 3. Chicago: Popular Mechanics Press, (1919). 476pp. Blue cl, gilt. VG. *Davidson.* $35/£22

BOY SCOUTS OF AMERICA. Handbook for Boys. NY, (1940). 676pp. Pict wraps (fr cvr vertically creased). *King.* $22/£14

Boy Scouts. NY: McLaughlin Bros, 1912. 6 chromolithos. Pict chromolitho wrappers. (Spine chipped, hinges cracked through, offset from tape along spine, fr wrapper lacks top corner), else VG. *Pacific**. $98/£61

Boy's Own Annual. Volume 22, 1899-90. Boys Own Paper, 1890. 4to. 14 full-pg chromolitho plts (incl 5 fldg). Lib cl, gilt. (Upper joint cracked.) *Hollett.* $72/£45

BOYD, ARTHUR. Arthur Boyd: Etchings and Lithographs. London: Lund Humphries, (1971). One of 2000. Fine in dj. *Turtle Island.* $45/£28

BOYD, BELLE. Belle Boyd in Camp and Prison. NY: Blelock, 1865. 1st Amer ed. 464pp. Grn cl. (Spine sl faded, ends, hinges sl worn), else Good + . Howes H190. *Chapel Hill.* $100/£63

BOYD, E. Popular Arts of Spanish New Mexico. Santa Fe: Museum of NM, 1974. 1st ed. VG in dj (sl soiled). *Pacific**. $86/£54

BOYD, JAMES P. Life and Public Services of Hon. James G. Blaine, the Illustrious American Orator, Diplomat and Statesman. N.p.: Pub's Union, 1893. Salesman's sample w/leather spine sample pasted inside fr cvr. Pict cl (sl soiled, sl rubbed), gilt. *Sadlon.* $15/£9

BOYD, JAMES. Drums. NY, (1928). 14 full-pg color plts. (Corners bumped, label lt scratched, cvrs sl worn), else Good. *King.* $40/£25

BOYD, JAMES. Marching On. NY, 1927. 1st ed. VG + . *Pratt.* $40/£25

BOYD, JAMES. Roll River. NY: Scribner, 1935. 1st ed. Inscribed. Navy blue cl stamped in gilt/grn. (Few sm smudges fr cvr), o/w NF in VG dj (extrems lt worn). *Reese.* $85/£53

BOYD, JULIA. Bewick Gleanings: Being Impressions from Copperplates and Wood Blocks Engraved in the Bewick Workshop.... Newcastle-Upon-Tyne: Andrew Reid, 1886. Signed. xxiv,108,104pp; 53 full-pg engrs. Teg. Leather spine, tips. (Cat descrip pasted in, sm sig; expertly rebacked.) *Dawson.* $500/£313

BOYD, LOUISE. The Coast of Greenland...The Louise A. Boyd Arctic Expeditions of 1937 and 1938. NY: American Geographical Soc, 1948. 1st ed. 5 fldg panoramic photo plts, 7 fldg maps & charts loose in separate slipcase, as issued. (Sl shelfworn, spines sl sunned), else VG + . *Pacific**. $63/£39

BOYD, LOUISE. The Coast of North-East Greenland with Hydrographic Studies in the Greenland Sea. NY: American Geographical Soc, 1948. 1st ed. Good. Separate slipcase of maps, panoramas. *Walcot.* $67/£42

BOYD, ROBERT. History of the Synod of Washington of the Presbyterian Church in the United States of America. 1835-1909. Synod, 1910?. (Ink name), else VG. *Perier.* $45/£28

BOYD, ROBIN. New Directions in Japanese Architecture. Studio Vista, 1968. VG in dj (chipped, torn). *Hadley.* $32/£20

BOYD, THOMAS. Through the Wheat. NY, 1927. 1st Amer ed, 1st bk. Fine (spine sl sunned). *Polyanthos.* $35/£22

BOYD, WILLIAM. The Blue Afternoon. London: Sinclair-Stevenson, (1993). One of 150 numbered, signed. Cl, marbled bds. Fine in tissue dj, as issued. *Dermont.* $100/£63

BOYD, WILLIAM. The Blue Afternoon. Sinclair-Stevenson, 1993. 1st Eng ed. Signed, dated 13.9.93. VG (reps glued in sl askew; corners sl bumped) in dj. *Ulysses.* $104/£65

BOYD, WILLIAM. Brazzaville Beach. London: Sinclair-Stevenson, (1990). One of 150 numbered, signed. Cl, marbled bds. Fine in tissue dj, as issued. *Dermont.* $100/£63

BOYD, WILLIAM. A Good Man in Africa. NY, 1982. 1st Amer ed, 1st bk. Fine in dj. *Clearwater.* $96/£60

BOYD, WILLIAM. An Ice Cream War. London: Hamish Hamilton, (1982). 1st ed. Gilt blue cl bds. VF in dj (price-clipped). *Reese.* $50/£31

BOYD, WILLIAM. An Ice Cream War. Hamilton, 1982. 1st UK ed. NF in dj. *Williams.* $64/£40

BOYD, WILLIAM. The New Confessions. NY: Morrow, (1988). 1st Amer ed. Fine in Fine dj (sl rubbed). *Between The Covers.* $50/£31

BOYD, WILLIAM. On the Yankee Station. NY: William Morrow, 1984. 1st Amer ed. Fine in dj. *Associates.* $20/£13

BOYD, WILLIAM. Stars and Bars. London, 1984. 1st ed. Fine (pp browned) in Fine dj. *Warren.* $30/£19

BOYD, WILLIAM. Stars and Bars. Hamilton, 1984. 1st UK ed. Fine in dj. *Williams.* $48/£30

BOYDELL, JOHN and JOSIAH. A Collection of Prints, from Pictures Painted for the Purpose of Illustrating the Dramatic Works of Shakespeare by the Artists of Great Britain. London, 1803. Lg folio. 2 ports, 94 (of 96) plts, 1 add'l plt ('Shakespeare Nursed by Tragedy and Comedy') inserted. 3/4 leather (worn, dried; foxed, sl soiled). Internally Sound. *Oinonen*.* $3,500/£2,188

BOYER, GLENN. An Illustrated Life of Doc Holliday. Glenwood Springs, CO: Reminder, 1966. 1st ed. Fine in stiff pict wrappers. *Labordo.* $45/£28

BOYER, GLENN. Suppressed Murder of Wyatt Earp. San Antonio, TX: Naylor, 1967. 1st ed. VG + in dj. *Labordo.* $75/£47

BOYER, RICK. Billingsgate Shoal. Boston: Houghton Mifflin, 1982. 1st ed. (Pg edges lt spotted), o/w Fine in dj (2 sm internal tape mends). *Mordida.* $60/£38

BOYER, RICK. The Penny Ferry. Houghton, 1984. 1st ed. Fine in dj. *Murder.* $40/£25

BOYKIN, EDWARD. Ghost Ship of the Confederacy: The Story of the Alabama and Her Captain, Raphael Semmes. NY: Funk & Wagnalls, (1957). 1st ed. Signed. Cl-backed gray bds. NF in VG dj. *Chapel Hill.* $75/£47

BOYKIN, RICHARD M. Captain Alexander Hamilton Boykin. NY: Privately ptd, 1942. 1st ed. One of unspecified ltd ed. This copy signed, dated Nov 1942. Author's ptd note laid in. Blue cl. VG. *Chapel Hill.* $250/£156

BOYLE, FREDERICK. The Culture of Greenhouse Orchids, Old System and New. London: Chapman & Hall, 1902. 1st ed. 3 chromolitho plts. Teg. Pict red cl, gilt. (Sl soiled, spine dull, ends rubbed), else VG. *Pacific*.* $58/£36

BOYLE, FREDERICK. The Woodlands Orchids. London: Macmillan, 1901. 16 color chromo plts. 3/4 leather, marbled paper bds. Fine. *Metropolitan*.* $230/£144

BOYLE, KAY. Pinky in Persia. NY: Crowell Collier, (1968). 1st ed. Lilian Obligado (illus). Thin 8vo. Fine in Fine dj. *Between The Covers.* $125/£78

BOYLE, KAY. Pinky in Persia. Crowell, 1968. 1st ed. Lilian Obligado (illus). Unpaginated. White w/ochre, red, gray pict binding. Fine. *Price.* $40/£25

BOYLE, KAY. Words That Must Somehow Be Said. Selected Essays 1927-1984. SF: North Point, 1985. 1st Amer ed. Fine in Fine dj. *Polyanthos.* $25/£16

BOYLE, MARTIN. Yanks Don't Cry. NY, 1963. 1st ed. VG in VG dj. *Clark.* $35/£22

BOYLE, T. CORAGHESSAN. Budding Prospects. NY, 1984. 1st ed. Fine in Fine dj. *Warren.* $75/£47

BOYLE, T. CORAGHESSAN. Budding Prospects: A Pastoral. London: Gollancz, 1984. 1st Eng ed. Signed. Fine in dj. *Between The Covers.* $85/£53

BOYLE, T. CORAGHESSAN. Descent of Man. Gollancz, 1980. 1st UK ed, 1st bk. NF in dj (spine foot sl bumped). *Williams.* $80/£50

BOYLE, T. CORAGHESSAN. Descent of Man. London: Gollancz, 1980. 1st Eng ed, 1st bk. Signed. Fine in Fine dj. *Between The Covers.* $125/£78

BOYLE, T. CORAGHESSAN. The Road to Wellville. NY, 1993. 1st ed. Signed, dated 1993. Fine in Fine dj. *Warren.* $45/£28

BOYNTON, MARY FUERTES. Louis Agassiz Fuertes: His Life Briefly Told and His Correspondence Edited. NY: OUP, 1956. 1st ed. Black buckram. Fine in VG color pict dj. *Biscotti.* $65/£41

BOZ. (Pseud of Charles Dickens.) Memoirs of Joseph Grimaldi. Edited by 'Boz.' London: Richard Bentley, 1838. 1st ed, 2nd issue, w/p(xxi) vol 1 'Embellishments,' the 6th plt is properly recorded as at p182, last plt vol 2 at p238 does have the 'grotesque' border added around George Cruikshank's (illus) plt. 2 vols. 36pp undated ads cat vol 2 present. Orig purple-brn vertically-ribbed cl w/gilt clowns decorating spines. NF (bkpls, ink stamps; 1 sm nick at 1 spine head, lower fore-corners sl shelfworn, spine cl faded, cvrs sl mottled) in cl clamshell case w/leather label. *Sumner & Stillman.* $1,950/£1,219

BOZ. (Pseud of Charles Dickens.) Oliver Twist; or, The Parish Boy's Progress. By 'Boz.' London: Richard Bentley, 1838. True 1st ed, 1st issue w/'Boz' on tps and w/'fireside' plt at end of vol 3. Does not have 'Bentley | London' imprinted at foot of spines. 3 vols. George Cruikshank (illus). 4pp undated ads vol 1, w/list of illus; 2pp prelim undated ads vol 3. Orig eps. Orig horizontally ribbed reddish-brn cl, of the same color, but w/different arabesque design, as the fine-diaper cl sets. NF (fep vol 1 cracked, reglued; plts browned; 2 vols w/fr cvrs sl discolored) in 3 morocco-backed slipcases. *Sumner & Stillman.* $7,750/£4,844

BRACE, CHARLES LORING. The New West: Or, California in 1867-1868. NY, 1869. 1st ed. 373pp + 1 leaf ads. Pub's cl (shelfworn). *Oinonen*.* $50/£31

BRACE, JOHN P. Fawn of the Pale Faces; or, Two Centuries Ago. NY: Appleton, 1853. 1st ed. (2),288pp. Dec cl. *Ginsberg.* $100/£63

BRACKEN, HENRY. Farriery Improved; or, A Complete Treatise on the Art of Farriery.... Phila: Lang & Ustick for Carey, 1796. New ed. 144pp; 10 plts (piece of 1 fldg plt torn off but present). Contemp calf-backed bds (shelfworn; sl foxed, soiled). *Oinonen*.* $250/£156

BRACKENBURY, HENRY. The Ashanti War. Edinburgh: Wm. Blackwood & Sons, 1874. 2 vols. xii,428; vii,367pp; 6 maps, 1 plt. New 1/2 red morocco, gilt. VG. *Adelson.* $450/£281

BRACKENRIDGE, HENRY. Voyage to South America, Performed by Order of the American Government in the Years 1817 and 1818.... Balt: The Author, 1819. 2 vols. xvi,17-351,errata; iv,5-381pp; fldg map (repaired). Orig calf (rebacked, exlib), red labels. *Adelson.* $475/£297

BRACKETT, LEIGH. The Starmen. NY: Gnome, (1952). 1st ed. NF in NF dj. *Other Worlds.* $125/£78

BRADAM, TONY and COLIN HAWKINS. See You Later, Alligator. NY: Dial Books for Young Readers, 1986. 5 tab-operated mechanicals. Glazed pict bds. VG. *Bookfinders.* $25/£16

BRADBURN, JOHN. Breeding and Developing the Trotter. Boston, 1906. 1st ed. (Sl worn.) *Woolson.* $40/£25

BRADBURY, MALCOLM. All Dressed Up and Nowhere to Go. London, 1962. 1st Eng ed. Very Nice in dj. *Clearwater.* $56/£35

BRADBURY, MALCOLM. Eating People Is Wrong. London: Secker & Warburg, 1959. 1st ed, 1st bk. Fine in dj. *Pharos*. $45/£28

BRADBURY, MALCOLM. Evelyn Waugh. Edinburgh: Oliver & Boyd, 1964. 1st Eng ed. VG (edges sl rubbed) in wrappers. *Ulysses*. $72/£45

BRADBURY, MALCOLM. Phogey! Parrish, 1960. 1st UK ed. Fine in VG dj (sl nicked, dusty). *Williams*. $40/£25

BRADBURY, MALCOLM. Phogey! London: Max Parrish, 1960. 1st ed. 4pp flyer for The Regent Institute loosely laid in as issued. Blue cl-textured bds. (Fore-edges sl foxed, spine gilt sl dull), o/w Fine in dj (price-clipped). *Temple*. $48/£30

BRADBURY, MALCOLM. Rates of Exchange. Secker, 1983. 1st UK ed. Fine (ink date on fep) in dj. *Williams*. $48/£30

BRADBURY, MALCOLM. Stepping Westward. Martin Secker & Warburg, 1965. 1st Eng ed. VG (feps partly browned, top edge rubbed; spine tail sl bumped) in dj (sl rubbed, creased, dusty, sl browned). *Ulysses*. $152/£95

BRADBURY, RAY. Dandelion Wine. NY: Knopf, 1992. Later ed. Inscribed, signed, dated 1994. NF in dj. *Pacific**. $52/£33

BRADBURY, RAY. Fahrenheit 451. NY: Ballantine Books, (1953). 1st ed. Joe Mugnaini (illus). VG in dj (sm tears to extrems, sm bump to spine head). *Pacific**. $575/£359

BRADBURY, RAY. Fahrenheit 451. Hart-Davis, 1954. 1st UK ed. VG (ink name, bds sl dknd) in Nice dj (sl stained). *Williams*. $200/£125

BRADBURY, RAY. Fahrenheit 451. LEC, 1982. One of 2000 signed by Bradbury and Joe Mugnaini (illus). Fine in slipcase. *Swann**. $230/£144

BRADBURY, RAY. The Golden Apples of the Sun. GC: Doubleday, 1953. 1st ed. May 1953 signed ink presentation. Gray bds, yellow spine lettering. VG in VG dj (spine sl sunned, few sm scrapes fr panel). *Baltimore**. $220/£138

BRADBURY, RAY. The Halloween Tree. NY: Knopf, (1972). 1st ed. Fine in dj. *Levin*. $75/£47

BRADBURY, RAY. The Illustrated Man. NY, 1951. 1st ed. Inscribed, signed. VG+ (erasure on sig pg; cvrs worn) in VG dj. *Warren*. $185/£116

BRADBURY, RAY. The Martian Chronicles. GC: Doubleday, 1950. 1st ed. Signed. NF in dj (spine foot, flap creases sl rubbed, 1.5-inch closed tear upper spine). *Pacific**. $863/£539

BRADBURY, RAY. The Martian Chronicles. GC: Doubleday, 1950. 1st ed. Fine (sl faded) in Fine dj (chip to bottom tip rear panel). *Unger*. $875/£547

BRADBURY, RAY. The Martian Chronicles. LEC, 1974. One of 2000 signed by Bradbury and Joe Mugnaini (illus). Fine in slipcase. *Swann**. $230/£144

BRADBURY, RAY. Old Ahab's Friend, and Friend to Noah, Speaks His Piece. N.p.: Apollo Year Two, (1971). 1st ed. Fine in wraps; in a Philip Duschenes, Inc. envelope. *Cullen*. $75/£47

BRADBURY, RAY. R Is for Rocket. GC: Doubleday, (1962). 1st ed. NF in dj (spine ends sl rubbed). *Pacific**. $207/£129

BRADBURY, RAY. Something Wicked This Way Comes. NY: S&S, 1962. 1st ed. Signed, inscribed, dated 1988. NF in dj (spine ends rubbed, sm stain on rear). *Pacific**. $259/£162

BRADBURY, RAY. The Toynbee Convector. NY, 1988. 1st ed. Signed. NF in NF dj (sm internal stain). *Warren*. $35/£22

BRADDON, M. E. The Doctor's Wife. John Maxwell, 1865. 6th ed. Frontis. Sprinkled edges. Contemp cl. Good (sl spotted; spine bumped). *Tiger*. $72/£45

BRADDON, M. E. London Pride. Simpkin, Marshall, Hamilton, et al, (c1910). New ed. Pict cl. Good (lt spotted; joints cracked, spine bumped, chipped; rubbed). *Tiger*. $29/£18

BRADDY, HALDEEN. Cock of the Walk. Legend of Pancho Villa. Albuquerque, 1955. 1st ed. NF in NF dj. *Sagebrush*. $50/£31

BRADFORD, ALDEN. History of Massachusetts, for Two Hundred Years: from the Year 1620 to 1820. Boston: Hilliard & Gray, 1835. 1st ed. Fldg map. Orig drab bds over brn linen spine (extrems worn), paper label. Good. *Appelfeld*. $150/£94

BRADFORD, EDWARD H. and R. W. LOVETT Orthopedic Surgery. NY, 1915. 5th ed. Grn cl, gilt. Good (inner hinges cracked). *Doctor's Library*. $75/£47

BRADFORD, GAMALIEL, JR. Lee the American. Boston, 1912. 1st ed. (Bkpl, name; worn.) *Woolman*. $20/£13

BRADFORD, JOHN. Historical &c. Notes on Kentucky. From the Western Miscellany Compiled by G. W. Stipp, in 1827. Douglas Watson (ed). SF: Grabhorn, 1932. One of 500. Fldg color map. Unopened. Bds dec w/a map, paper spine label. (Spine sl dull), else NF. *Pacific**. $52/£33

BRADFORD, ROARK. This Side of Jordan. NY: Harper, 1929. 1st ed. VG in dj (spine foot lacks piece). *Smith*. $35/£22

BRADFORD, THOMAS LINDSLEY (comp). The Bibliographer's Manual of American History. Phila, 1907-10. 5 vols, incl index. *Swann**. $138/£86

BRADFORD, WILLIAM. History of the Plimoth Plantation. London: Ward & Downey, 1896. One of unstated ltd ed. (4),18pp + 536pp facs; 2 photolitho plts. Tan/burgundy linen (sl rubbed, soiled). *Karmiole*. $275/£172

BRADLEE, FRANCIS B. C. Blockade Running During the Civil War and the Effect of Land and Water Transportation on the Confederacy. Salem, MA: Essex Inst, 1925. 1st ed. Gray cl. VG (rear inner hinge cracked, fr hinge tender; spine sl browned). *Chapel Hill*. $300/£188

BRADLEE, FRANCIS B. C. Piracy in the West Indies and Its Suppression. Salem, MA: Essex Inst, 1923. 1st ed. Color frontis, 36 plts. Dec red linen. Good. *Karmiole*. $75/£47

BRADLEY, A. G. Other Days: Recollections of Rural England and Old Virginia, 1860-1880. London: Constable, 1913. Port. VG-. *Book Broker*. $50/£31

BRADLEY, BRUCE. James Joyce's Schooldays. Dublin: Gill & Macmillan, 1982. 1st Eng ed. NF (spine ends, corner sl bumped) in dj (sl creased). *Ulysses*. $40/£25

BRADLEY, DAVID. The Chaneysville Incident. NY: Harper & Row, (1981). 1st ed. NF in dj (sl edgeworn, sm tear). *Agvent*. $50/£31

BRADLEY, DAVID. South Street. NY: Grossman, 1975. 1st ed, 1st bk. Fine in dj. *Pacific**. $86/£54

BRADLEY, H. DENNIS. And After. London, 1931. 1st ptg. VG (ex-lib). *Middle Earth*. $28/£18

BRADLEY, HELEN. Miss Carter Came with Us. Boston: Little, Brown, 1974. Obl 4to. Fine in Fine dj. *American Booksellers*. $25/£16

BRADLEY, JAMES A. The Story of John Murray. Asbury Park Ptg House, 1889. 2nd ed. 38-pg pamphlet. (Spine worn), else Good in wraps. *Brown*. $15/£9

BRADLEY, JAMES H. The March of the Montana Column. Edgar I. Stewart (ed). Norman: Univ of OK, (1961). Dbl-pg map. NF in VG dj (rubbed, edgeworn). *Pacific**. $52/£33

BRADLEY, JOHN HODGDON. Farewell, Thou Busy World. L.A.: Primavera, 1935. 1st ed. Cl-backed dec bds. (Bkpl, inscrip, soiled), else VG. *Pacific**. $58/£36

BRADLEY, JOHN W. A Dictionary of Miniaturists, Illuminators, Calligraphers, and Copyists...to the Eighteenth Century. London: Bernard Quaritch, 1887-89. 3 vols. Uncut. Pub's 1/2 morocco (rubbed; foxing). *Oinonen**. $300/£188

BRADLEY, JOSHUA. Accounts of Religious Revivals in Many Parts of the United States from 1815 to 1818. Albany, 1819. 1st ed. 300pp. Orig full leather. (Rubbed, damp-stained), o/w VG. Howes B707. *New Hampshire**. $110/£69

BRADLEY, MARY HASTINGS. On the Gorilla Trail. NY, 1922. 1st ed. *Hallam*. $120/£75

BRADLEY, VAN ALLEN. The Book Collector's Handbook of Values. NY, (1972). 1st ed. VG in dj. *King*. $35/£22

BRADLEY, VAN ALLEN. Gold in Your Attic. NY: Fleet Pub, 1958. 2nd ptg. VG + in dj (extrems worn). *Smith*. $45/£28

BRADLEY, WILL. Peter Poodle, Toy Maker to the King. NY: Dodd, Mead, 1906. 1st ed. 4to. 25 color plts. Brn pict bds over linen spine (extrems sl worn, inner hinges expertly reinforced). Good in linen fldg box. *Appelfeld*. $800/£500

BRADMAN, ARTHUR. A Narrative of the Extraordinary Suffering of Mr. Robert Forbes...in the Year 1784. Phila, 1794. Mod 3/4 speckled calf. (Ink stamp tp.) *Swann**. $460/£288

BRADNER, ENOS. Northwest Angling. NY: Barnes, 1950. 1st ed. VG. *Bowman*. $30/£19

BRADSHAW, ANGELA. World Costumes. A&C Black, 1961. 3rd rpt. 16 plts. NF in dj (sl torn). *Whittle*. $32/£20

BRADSHAW, OLIVE. Dead Man's Body. Adelphi: Diamond, 1927. 1st ed. 1/4 orange buckram. (Top edge of rear bd scraped, rear bd sl mkd), o/w Fine in dj (sl chipped, torn, creased). *Temple*. $29/£18

BRADY, CYRUS TOWNSEND. Indian Fights and Fighters. NY: McClure, Phillips, 1904. Pict cl. (Spine sl sunned, top corners sl bumped), else NF. Howes B712. *Pacific**. $69/£43

BRADY, CYRUS TOWNSEND. Northwestern Fights and Fighters. NY: McClure, 1907. 1st ed. xxv,373pp + (1)ad pg. Pict cl. (Pp85-6 torn across center), else NF. Howes B713. *Pacific**. $58/£36

BRADY, DONALD. Theatre in Early El Paso. 1881-1905. El Paso: TX Western College, 1966. Fine in wraps. *Perier*. $15/£9

BRADY, JOHN. Kaddish in Dublin. London: Constable, 1990. 1st ed. Fine in dj. *Murder*. $40/£25

BRADY, ROBERT. A Complete History of England, from the First Entrance of the Romans...unto the End of the Reign of King Henry III.... London: Samuel Lowndes, 1685. 1st ed. Folio. Frontisport, (1),(10),lxviii,(8),675,(1),254 + 67 index pp. Old mottled calf, morocco spine label. (Bkpl, old notes, offset to fep; rebacked), else VG. *Pacific**. $489/£306

BRADY, ROBERT. An Historical Treatise of Cities, and Burghs or Buroughs. London: A.L., 1704. 2nd ed. Folio. (2),iv,88 (misnumbered from pp84,89,90,91,88),(2),41pp. Mottled calf. (Tp dknd, possibly lacks prelims; fr joint cracked), else VG. *Pacific**. $144/£90

BRAGG, W. and W. X Rays and Crystal Structure. NY: Harcourt Brace, 1924. 4th ed. VG. *Blake*. $65/£41

BRAGGE, WILLIAM. Bibliotheca Nicotiana; a Catalogue of Books About Tobacco, Together with a Catalogue of Objects.... London: Privately ptd, 1880. One of 200 numbered, signed. 251pp. Uncut. Lg paper, orig ptd wrappers bound in. *Forest*. $312/£195

BRAID, JAMES. Advanced Golf or, Hints and Instruction for Progressive Players. Phila: George W. Jacobs, (1908). 1st Amer ed. Frontisport. (Emb stamp, sig; sl insect-damaged), else VG. *Pacific**. $138/£86

BRAID, JAMES. et al. A Book of Golf. E. F. Benson and Eustace H. Miles (eds). London: Hurst & Blackett, 1903. 1st ed. Red dec cl. (Name; rear hinge starting, spine ends chipped, soiled), else VG-. *Pacific**. $259/£162

BRAIN, LORD and JOHN N. WALTON. Brain Diseases of the Nervous System. London, 1969. 7th ed. VG in dj (worn). *Doctor's Library*. $75/£47

BRAINE, JOHN. Room at the Top. Boston: Houghton Mifflin, 1957. 1st Amer ed, 1st bk. NF in dj. *Cady*. $40/£25

BRAINE, JOHN. The Vodi. London: Eyre & Spottiswoode, 1959. 1st ed. Signed. Navy blue glazed bds. NF in dj (creased, frayed, browned). *Temple*. $26/£16

BRAITHWAITE, E. R. Paid Servant. NY, (1962). 1st Amer ed. (Edges sl soiled), else Good in dj (sl worn). *King*. $45/£28

BRAITHWAITE, J. BEVAN (ed). Memoirs of Joseph John Gurney. Norwich: Fletcher & Alexander, 1854. 1st ed. 2 vols. xii,542; vii,551pp. Blind-stamped cl (spines evenly faded). *Young*. $96/£60

BRAITHWAITE, J. BEVAN. Memoirs of Anna Braithwaite...1830-59. London: Headley Bros, 1905. 1st ed. Frontisport. Teg, others uncut. Blue cl. Fine. *Mott*. $50/£31

BRAITHWAITE, R. The British Moss-Flora. London, 1887-1905. 3 vols. 128 plts. (Ends foxed, sporadically elsewhere.) *Henly*. $224/£140

BRAIVE, MICHEL F. The Photograph: A Social History. NY: McGraw-Hill, 1966. 1st Amer ed. NF in dj (lacks sm chip). *Cahan*. $185/£116

BRALEY, BERTON. In Camp and Trench: Songs of the Fighting Forces. NY: George H. Doran, (1918). 1st ed. Als from H. Edwards-Ficken laid in, also inscribed by H.E.-F. Tan bds. (Sm chip spine foot), else VG. *Reese*. $30/£19

BRAMAH, ERNEST. The Eyes of Max Carrados. London, (1923). 1st ed. (Tips bumped, spine lt rubbed.) *Swann**. $126/£79

BRAMAH, ERNEST. Kai Lung Beneath the Mulberry-Tree. London: Richards, 1940. 1st Eng ed. Nice (name stamp) in pict dj (chipped, sl rubbed). *Clearwater*. $88/£55

BRAMAH, ERNEST. Kai Lung Unrolls His Mat. NY: Doubleday, Doran, 1928. Cl-backed pict paper bds. VG (edges, eps sl spotted; cvrs sl mkd, spine ends sl bumped, sm dent rear cvr). *Ulysses*. $104/£65

BRAMAH, ERNEST. The Return of Kai Lung. NY, (1937). 1st Amer ed. (Eps, edges sl stained), else Good in dj (badly chipped). *King*. $25/£16

BRAMAH, ERNEST. The Wallet of Kai Lung. NY: George H. Doran, (1923). 2nd Amer ed. (Top of spine label sl worn), else Nice. *Cady*. $25/£16

BRAMBLE, FORBES. The Strange Case of Deacon Brodie. London: Hamish, 1975. 1st ed. Fine in dj (price-clipped, lt soiled). *Murder*. $65/£41

BRANCH, E. DOUGLAS. The Cowboy and His Interpreters. NY: Appleton, 1926. 1st ed. VG. Howes B721. *Pacific**. $431/£269

BRANCH, E. DOUGLAS. Hunting of the Buffalo. NY, 1929. 1st ed. (Cvr w/discolored spots.) *Heinoldt*. $35/£22

BRANCH, EDGAR M. (ed). Clemens of the 'Call.' Univ of CA, 1969. 1st Amer ed. Fine in dj (price-clipped). *Polyanthos*. $25/£16

BRANCH, LOUIS LEON. Los Bilitos. NY, 1980. NF in dj. *Dumont*. $45/£28

BRAND, CHRISTIANNA. London Particular. London: Michael Joseph, 1952. 1st ed. (Eps, pg edges foxed), o/w VG in dj (spine ends, corners chipped, rear panel sl soiled, folds lt worn). *Mordida*. $45/£28

BRAND, CHRISTIANNA. The Rose in Darkness. Joseph, 1979. 1st ed. Signed presentation. Fine in NF dj (top edge sl creased). *Any Amount*. $56/£35

BRAND, JOHN. Observations on Popular Antiquities, Including the Whole of Mr. Bourne's Antiquitates Vulgares.... William Baynes, 1810. 3rd ed. Engr tp, xvi,424pp. Orig 1/2 calf (joints cracked). *Bickersteth*. $120/£75

BRAND, MAX. The Long Chase. NY: Dodd Mead, 1960. 1st ed. Fine in dj. *Mordida*. $65/£41

BRAND, MAX. Mistral. NY: Dodd Mead, 1929. 1st ed. Fine in VF dj. *Mordida.* $450/£281

BRAND, MAX. Pillar Mountain. NY: Dodd Mead, 1928. 1st ed. Fine in VF dj. *Mordida.* $450/£281

BRAND, MAX. Tenderfoot. NY: Dodd Mead, (1952). 1st ed. Fine in NF dj (sm date fr panel). *Between The Covers.* $85/£53

BRAND, MAX. The Thunderer. NY: Derrydale, 1933. Ltd to 950 numbered. Red cl. Fine. *Biscotti.* $100/£63

BRANDAU, ROBERT (ed). De Meyer. NY: Alfred A. Knopf, 1976. 1st ed. 72 photos. Fine in gilt-emb illus dj. *Cahan.* $75/£47

BRANDE, W. T. Outlines of Geology. London, 1829. 2nd ed. Frontis, xiv,234pp; fldg hand-colored section. Calf (neatly re-backed preserving most of spine). Fine. *Henly.* $144/£90

BRANDEL, MARC. Rain Before Seven. NY: Harper, (1945). 1st ed, 1st bk. Fine in NF dj (crown lt worn, sm tears). *Between The Covers.* $75/£47

BRANDES, RAY. The Constanso Narrative of the Portola Expedition. Newhall, 1970. Facs rpt. Fine. Howes C795. *Baade.* $50/£31

BRANDON, RAPHAEL and J. ARTHUR. An Analysis of Gothic Architecture. Edinburgh: John Grant, 1903. New ed. 2 vols. Tp, 153 engr plts. *Marlborough.* $80/£50

BRANDON, RAPHAEL and J. ARTHUR. The Open Timber Roofs of the Middle Ages. London: Bogue, 1849. 43 litho plts. Orig cl (worn, spine frayed). *Oinonen*.* $120/£75

BRANDT, BILL. Camera in London. London/NY: Focal Press, 1948. 1st ed. Fldg table, 59 b/w photos. NF in pict dj (extrems rubbed). *Cahan.* $350/£219

BRANDT, BILL. The English at Home. London: B.T. Batsford, 1936. 1st ed, 1st bk. 63 b/w plts. Pict eps. Photo-illus glazed bds. (Inscrip; extrems sl rubbed), else Fine, issued w/o dj. *Cahan.* $475/£297

BRANDT, BILL. Perspective of Nudes. NY, (1961). 1st ed. (Sig; extrems worn.) Dj (worn, soiled, badly chipped). *Swann*.* $345/£216

BRANDT, BILL. Shadow of Light. NY: Viking, 1966. 1st ed. 128 full-pg photos. (Inscrip), else NF in dj (closed tear one corner). *Cahan.* $325/£203

BRANDT, HARRY A. Christopher Sower and Son. Elgin, IL: Brethren Pub House, (1938). 1st bk ed. Maroon cl. VG (lt soiled, pp110-11 lt foxed from something formerly laid in) in dj. *Chapel Hill.* $50/£31

BRANDT, HERBERT. Arizona and Its Bird Life. Cleveland, OH, 1951. 1st ed. 20 color plts. (Sl worn.) *Woolson.* $225/£141

BRANKSTON, A. D. Early Ming Wares of Chingtechen. Hong Kong/London, 1970. Reissue. Ltd to 1050. Color frontis, 44 b/w plts, map. Dj (sl soiled, sl spine loss). *Edwards.* $72/£45

BRANNER, JOHN CASPER. Casper Branner of Virginia and His Descendants. Stanford Univ, 1913. Facs, map. (Spine dog-chewed, cl insect spotted, corners rubbed.) Internally Sound. *Book Broker.* $65/£41

BRANNER, ROBERT. Manuscript Painting in Paris During the Reign of Saint Louis. Berkeley: Univ of CA, (1977). 25 color plts. NF in dj. *Turtle Island.* $125/£78

BRANNT, WILLIAM T. A Practical Treatise on the MAnufacture of Vinegar and Acetates, Cider, and Fruit Wines.... Phila: Henry Carey Baird, 1890. 1st ed. 79 engrs. Purple cl, gilt. (Lacks feps; lacks spine head piece; foot, corners rubbed, spine sunned), else VG. *Pacific*.* $92/£58

BRANT, TOBY L. Journal of a Combat Tanker. NY: Vantage, 1988. 1st ed. Adv rev copy, slip laid in. Fine in dj. *Associates.* $75/£47

BRASHLER, WILLIAM. Bingo Long Traveling All Stars. Harper & Row, 1973. 1st ed. VG+ in VG dj. *Plapinger.* $50/£31

Brassai. NY: MOMA, (1968). 1st ed. (Sl soiled, ex-libris stamp; extrems faded.) Dj (price-clipped, sl yellowed). *Swann*.* $115/£72

BRASSAI. Camera in Paris. London/NY: Focal, 1949. 1st ed. Fine in illus dj (few short closed tears repaired w/archival tissue). *Cahan.* $350/£219

BRASSAI. Paris by Night. NY: Pantheon Books, 1987. 1st Amer ed. 64 b/w heliogravure plts. As New in illus dj. *Cahan.* $85/£53

BRASSEY, MRS. In the Trades, the Tropics, and the Roaring Forties. London: Longmans, Green, 1885. One of 250. xiv,532pp; 9 maps incl 2 fldg, chart. Marbled eps; teg. Gilt-edged 1/2 vellum, cl bds. (Prelims lt browned; soiled.) *Edwards.* $240/£150

BRASSEY, MRS. The Last Voyage. NY: Longmans, Green, 1889. 1st ed. xxiv,490pp; 1 fldg color map. Teg. Blue cl, gilt. VF. *Sotheran.* $157/£98

BRATT, JOHN. Trails of Yesterday. Lincoln: University, 1921. 1st ed. Pict cl. Fine. Howes B725. *Labordo.* $385/£241

BRAUN, ANNE. Historical Targets. London: Roydon Pub, 1983. Fine in Fine dj, orig shipping box. *Backman.* $32/£20

BRAUN, HUGH. Historical Architecture. Faber, 1963. VG in dj. *Hadley.* $48/£30

BRAUN, HUGH. An Introduction to English Mediaeval Architecture. Faber, 1968. Rev ed. NF in dj. *Hadley.* $40/£25

BRAUND, STEPHEN R. The Skin Boats of Saint Lawrence Island, Alaska. Seattle: Univ of WA, (1988). VG in dj. *Perier.* $45/£28

BRAUTIGAN, RICHARD. The Galilee Hitch-Hiker. (SF: David Sandberg, 1966.) 2nd ed. One of 700 ptd. (Corners lt creased), else VG. Stitched into red illus wrappers. *Cahan.* $300/£188

BRAUTIGAN, RICHARD. In Watermelon Sugar. SF: Four Seasons Foundation, 1968. 1st ed. Fine in illus wrappers. *Smith.* $75/£47

BRAUTIGAN, RICHARD. In Watermelon Sugar. Cape, 1970. 1st UK ed. NF in dj. *Sclanders.* $40/£25

BRAUTIGAN, RICHARD. The Pill Versus the Springhill Mine Disaster. SF: Four Seasons Foundation, 1968. 1st ed, pb orig. VG+ in wrappers. *Pettler.* $50/£31

BRAUTIGAN, RICHARD. The Pill Versus the Springhill Mine Disaster. SF: Four Seasons Foundation, 1968. 1st ed. Fine in illus wrappers. *Smith.* $75/£47

BRAUTIGAN, RICHARD. Rommel Drives on Deep into Egypt. NY: Delacorte, (1970). 1st ed. Pict bds. Fine in dj. *Pacific*.* $81/£51

BRAUTIGAN, RICHARD. Rommel Drives on Deep into Egypt. NY, 1970. 1st ed. Fine in NF dj (rubbed, sm separation at rear flap). *Warren.* $75/£47

BRAUTIGAN, RICHARD. The Tokyo-Montana Express. NY: Targ Editions, (1979). 1st ed. One of 350. Signed. Gray cl, gilt. Fine in glassine dj. *Pacific*.* $150/£94

BRAUTIGAN, RICHARD. Trout Fishing in America. Cape, 1970. 1st UK ed. NF in dj (spine tail sl worn). *Sclanders.* $48/£30

BRAWNE, FANNY. Letters of Fanny Brawne to Fanny Keats, 1820-1824. Fred Edgcumbe (ed). NY, 1937. Very Nice (name)in dj (heavily reinforced). *Clearwater.* $56/£35

BRAY, MARTHA COLEMAN. Joseph Nicollet and His Map. Phila, 1994. 2nd ed. 2 fldg maps in rear pocket. NF in dj. *Dumont.* $35/£22

BRAYLEY, EDWARD WEDLAKE. The History and Antiquities of the Abbey Church of St. Peter, Westminster. London, 1818. 2 vols. (vi)pp subs. 60 engr plts, incl add'l illus tps, frontispieces. Marbled eps. Contemp 1/2 calf, raised bands, morocco spine label. (Bkpls; loss to corners, rebacked.) *Edwards.* $240/£150

BRAYLEY, EDWARD WEDLAKE. London and Middlesex. Vol X, Part I. London: Ptd by W. Wilson, 1810. Engr frontis, illus tp. Contemp diced calf, gilt, raised bands. (Browned; sl rubbed.) *Edwards.* $64/£40

BRAYTON, MATTHEW. The Indian Captive: A Narrative of the Adventures and Sufferings of.... Fostoria: Gray Ptg, 1896. 2nd ed. 70pp. Off-white cl, lettered bds (smudged, dusty, sl worn, cvrs once detached, reconnected by thin thread). Text Good (tp browned, edges discolored). Howes B736. *Baltimore**. $85/£53

BRAZIL, ANGELA. For the School Colours. Blackie, n.d. (inscrip dated 1919). 1st ed. Lg 8vo. 288pp; 6 mono plts by Balliol Salmon. Dec cl. VG. *Bookmark*. $48/£30

BRAZIL, ANGELA. Joan's Best Chum. Blackie, n.d. (1926). 1st ed. Lg 8vo. 320pp; 3 (of 6) mono plts by W.E. Wightman. Pict cl. VG-. *Bookmark*. $24/£15

BREADALBANE, MARCHIONESS. The High Tops of Blackmount. London, 1907. 2nd imp. (Spine mottled), o/w VF. *Grayling*. $112/£70

BREAKENRIDGE, WILLIAM M. Helldorado. Richard M. Brown (ed). Chicago: R.R. Donnelley, 1982. Frontis. VG. *Lien*. $30/£19

BREAKENRIDGE, WILLIAM M. Helldorado: Bringing Law to the Mezquite. Boston: Houghton Mifflin, 1928. 1st ed. Fine. Howes B739. *Pacific**. $58/£36

BREAN, HERBERT. The Traces of Merrilee. Morrow, 1966. 1st ed. (Cvrs lt discolored), else NF in dj (lt worn, sm closed tear). *Murder*. $35/£22

BREASTED, JAMES HENRY. A History of Egypt from the Earliest Times to the Persian Conquest. NY: Scribner, (1924). 2nd ed. Color frontis, 13 maps. Pict cl, gilt. (Inscrip.) *Archaeologia*. $75/£47

BREASTED, JAMES HENRY. A History of Egypt from the Earliest Times to the Persian Conquest. London: Hodder & Stoughton, 1906. 1st Eng ed. Color frontis, 13 maps. Pict cl, gilt. (Sig, bkpl.) *Archaeologia*. $125/£78

BREASTED, JAMES HENRY. Oriental Forerunners of Byzantine Painting. Chicago: Univ of Chicago, (1924). Folio. 23 plts (4 color). Dj (lt chipped). *Archaeologia*. $175/£109

BREAZEALE, JOHN M. Color Schemes of Cacti. Tucson, 1930. 4 color plts. VG in wrappers. *Brooks*. $29/£18

BREBNER, PERCY JAMES. The Master Detective: Being Some Further Investigations of Christopher Quarles. Dutton, 1916. 1st ed. (Spine lt faded, edges sl worn), else NF. *Murder*. $60/£38

BRECHT, BERTOLT. Threepenny Novel. Desmond I. Vesey & Christopher Isherwood (trans). Bernard Hanison, 1958. 1st UK ed. NF in dj (sm scuffed patch spine foot). *Williams*. $136/£85

BRECHT, BERTOLT. The Threepenny Opera. LEC, 1982. One of 2000 signed by Desmond Vessey (trans) and Jack Levine (illus). Fine in slipcase. *Swann**. $126/£79

BRECKINRIDGE, MARY. Wide Neighborhoods: A Story of the Frontier Nursing Service. NY, 1952. 1st ed. VG in dj (soiled). *Doctor's Library*. $30/£19

BREEN, PATRICK. The Diary of.... SF: Book Club of CA, 1946. One of 300 ptd. (Bkpl), else Fine. *Pacific**. $58/£36

BREIHAN, CARL W. and CHARLES A. ROSAMOND. The Bandit Belle. Seattle, 1970. 1st ed. NF. *Baade*. $40/£25

BREIHAN, CARL W. Great Lawmen of the West. London: John Long, 1963. 1st ed. VG + in dj. *Labordo*. $40/£25

BREIHAN, CARL W. The Man Who Shot Jesse James. Cranbury, NJ: A.S. Barnes, 1979. 1st ed. VG + in dj. *Labordo*. $40/£25

BRELIS, DEAN. The Face of South Vietnam. Boston: Houghton Mifflin, 1968. 1st ed. Fine in dj (sl used). *Associates*. $125/£78

BREMER, F. America of the Fifties. Letters of.... Adolph Benson (ed). NY: Amer-Scandinavian Foundation, 1924. 1st ed. Frontis-port; 3 plts. Teg. Maroon cl. VG + . *House*. $35/£22

BREMER, F. Travels in the Holy Land. Mary Howitt (trans). Hurst & Blackett, 1862. 1st Eng ed. 2 vols. Contemp calf. (Lacks 1/2-titles, sl spotted; sl rubbed.) *Sotheby's**. $275/£172

BREMER, L. Guide to New Orleans and Environs. (New Orleans: The Author, 1936.) 1st ed. Frontis, 7 photo views, 7 maps, fldg map at rear. VG in stiff wraps, gilt. *Petrilla*. $25/£16

BRENAN, GERALD. Best of Friends: The Brenan-Partridge Letters. Xan Fielding (ed). London: C&W, 1986. 1st Eng ed. Fine (spine tail sl bumped) in dj. *Ulysses*. $48/£30

BRENAN, GERALD. A Holiday by the Sea. NY: Farrar, Straus & Cudahy, 1962. VG (spine ends bumped) in dj (sl torn, rubbed, soiled, dusty, browned). *Ulysses*. $56/£35

BRENAN, GERALD. The Literature of the Spanish People. CUP, 1951. 1st Eng ed. VG (top edge dusty; spine ends, corners bumped; gilt partly oxidized, cvr sl cocked) in dj (nicked, rubbed, dusty, sl mkd, creased, chipped, browned). *Ulysses*. $104/£65

BRENAN, GERALD. Personal Record, 1920-1972. NY: Knopf, 1975. VG (fep sl rubbed, mkd; top edge partly faded; spine ends, 2 corners sl bumped; cvrs sl cocked, mkd) in dj (nicked, creased, sl torn, dusty, bottom edge frayed, soiled). *Ulysses*. $40/£25

BRENAN, GERALD. St. John of the Cross. CUP, 1973. 1st Eng ed. Fine (top corner 1 pg creased; spine ends sl bumped) in dj (nicked, sl creased, dusty, sl torn, price-clipped, spine browned). *Ulysses*. $72/£45

BRENCHLEY, CHAC. The Refugee. London: Hodder & Stoughton, 1989. 1st ed. Fine in dj. *Murder*. $40/£25

BRENDON, PIERS. Hawker of Morwenstow, Portrait of a Victorian Eccentric. London, 1975. 1st ed. VG + in dj. *Gretton*. $24/£15

BRENET, MICHEL. Haydn. C. Leonard Leese (trans). OUP, 1926. 1st Eng ed. (Sl pencil marginalia; spine faded.) *Hollett*. $24/£15

BRENNER, ANITA. A Hero by Mistake: The Story of a Frightened Indian. NY: William R. Scott, (1953). 1st ed. Jean Charlot (illus). 4to. Color-illus bds (edges lt chipped). Illus dj (tape mk, top edge chipped). *Reisler*. $85/£53

BRENT, JOHN. Canterbury in the Olden Time. Canterbury, 1879. viii,312pp + (iv) subs; 31 litho plts (2 color). (Ink lib stamps, several plts cropped to tail, no loss; cl faded, spine sl chipped.) *Edwards*. $72/£45

BRENT-DYER, E. M. Chudleigh Hold. Chambers, 1954. 1st ed. VG + in Fine dj. *Green Meadow*. $104/£65

BRENT-DYER, E. M. Joey and Co. in Tirol. Chambers, 1960. 1st ed. VG + in dj (sl chipped). *Green Meadow*. $120/£75

BRENTANO, CLEMENS. The Tale of Gockel, Hinkel, and Gackeliah. NY: Random, 1961. 1st ed. Maurice Sendak (illus). 7 3/4 x 9 1/4. 144pp. Fine in dj. *Cattermole*. $135/£84

BRERETON, FREDERICK (Pseud of Frederick T. Smith.) (comp). An Anthology of War Poems. London: W. Collins Sons, (1930). 1st ed, trade issue. NF in dj (lt worn, soiled, old inner reinforcements). *Reese*. $50/£31

BRERETON, ROBERT MAITLAND. Reminiscences of an Old English Civil Engineer, 1858-1908. Portland, OR: Irwin-Hudson, 1908. 1st ed. *Ginsberg*. $300/£188

BRESLAUER and FOLTER. Bibliography. Its History and Development. NY: Grolier Club, 1984. One of 600. (Lt worn.) *Oinonen**. $60/£38

BRETON, ANDRE. Yves Tanguy. NY: Pierre Matisse, (1946). One of 1150 numbered. *Swann**. $488/£305

BRETT, DOROTHY. Lawrence and Brett—a Friendship. Martin Secker, 1933. 1st Eng ed. Color frontis. VG (cvrs sl dusty, spine ends sl bumped, top edge rear cvr sl dented). *Ulysses*. $56/£35

BRETT, R. DALLAS. History of British Aviation 1908-1914. John Hamilton, (1933). 1st ed. Frontis, 64 plts. (Cl faded.) *Forest*. $72/£45

BREWER, E. COBHAM. Character Sketches of Romance, Fiction and the Drama. NY, 1892. 4 vols. 1/2 morocco (extrems rubbed). *Swann**. $69/£43

BREWER, GIL. Satan Is a Woman. NY: Fawcett, 1951. 1st ed. Pb orig. (Fr panel corner creased), o/w NF in wrappers. *Mordida.* $65/£41

BREWER, LUTHER A. Some Lamb and Browning Letters to Leigh Hunt. Cedar Rapids: Privately ptd, 1924. One of 300 ptd. Dec paper-cvrd bds, vellum spine. VG + . *Zubal*.* $35/£22

BREWER, WILLIAM H. and WILLIAM ALSUP. Such a Landscape! Yosemite: Yosemite Assoc, Sequoia Natural History Assoc, 1987. Ltd to 500 ptd. 39 plts. Linen-backed pict bds, gilt spine. Fine. *Pacific*.* $58/£36

BREWER, WILLIAM H. Up and Down California in 1860-1864. Francis Farquhar (ed). New Haven: Yale Univ, 1930. 1st ed. Frontisport, map, 32 plts. Black cl. Fine in dj (lacks sm piece of spine top). Howes B754. *House.* $200/£125

BREWERTON, GEORGE D. Incidents of Travel in New Mexico. Ashland: Lewis Osborne, 1969. 1st bk ed. One of 1400. Fine. *Argonaut.* $45/£28

BREWERTON, GEORGE D. Overland with Kit Carson, a Narrative of the Old Spanish Trail in '48. NY: Coward-McCann, 1930. Fldg map. Good (simply rebound w/orig title patch laid down on spine). *Bohling.* $25/£16

BREWERTON, GEORGE D. A Ride with Kit Carson. Palo Alto, 1969. One of 1400 numbered. VG in plain paper dj. *Dumont.* $50/£31

BREWINGTON, M. V. Chesapeake Bay Log Canoes. Newport News, VA: Mariners' Museum, 1937. 1st ed. Good (few rear pp sl rippled) in grn wraps. *American Booksellers.* $40/£25

BREWINGTON, M. V. and DOROTHY. Kendall Whaling Museum Prints. Sharon, 1969. Signed by Dorothy Brewington. (Sl worn.) *Oinonen*.* $70/£44

BREWINGTON, M. V. and DOROTHY. Marine Paintings and Drawings in the Peabody Museum. Salem, 1981. Ltd to 3000. (Lt worn.) Dj. *Oinonen*.* $90/£56

BREWSTER, A. B. The Hill Tribes of Fiji. Seeley, Service, 1922. 1st ed. Lg fldg map. Black pict cl. (Edges sl spotted.) *Sotheran.* $256/£160

BREWSTER, DAVID. Plates Illustrative of Ferguson's Astronomy.... London: John Murray/Robert Scholey, 1811. 1/2-title, 8pp; 24 engr plts. Orig full calf (gilt lib stamp cvrs, rebacked, inner hinges repaired), mod black leather label. VG. *Weber.* $165/£103

BREWSTER, DAVID. The Stereoscope: Its History,.... Hastings-on-Hudson, NY: Morgan & Morgan, (1971). Fine in dj. *Cahan.* $50/£31

BREWSTER, DAVID. A Treatise on the Microscope, Forming the Article under that Head in the Seventh Edition of the Encyclopaedia Britannica. Edinburgh: A&C Black, 1837. 1st ed. 14 plts. Later blue cl, gilt. (Sig.) *Weber.* $275/£172

BREWSTER, HAROLD S. Madness of War. NY: Harper, 1928. 1st ed. (Fore-edge lt foxed), o/w NF in pict dj. *Reese.* $35/£22

BREWSTER, WILLIAM. Concord River. Selections from the Journals of William Brewster. Smith O. Dexter (ed). Cambridge: Harvard Univ, 1937. 1st ed. 12 plts (3 in color). Grn cl. Fine in dj. *House.* $50/£31

BREWTON, JOHN E. Gaily We Parade. NY: Macmillan, 1940. 1st ed. 8vo. Robert Lawson (illus). Orange cl. Good in color dj (worn, edges chipped). *Reisler.* $85/£53

BREYER, SIEGFRIED. Battleships and Battle Cruisers, 1905-1970. Alfred Kurti (trans). NY: Doubleday, 1973. Fine in dj. *American Booksellers.* $50/£31

BREYTENBACH, BREYTEN. Mouroir. NY: FSG, (1984). 1st US ed. As New in dj. *Bernard.* $20/£13

BREYTENBACH, BREYTEN. The True Confessions of an Albino Terrorist. NY: FSG, (1985). 1st US ed. As New in dj. *Bernard.* $25/£16

Bridge of the Iconoclast. (By Benjamin Paul Blood.) Boston/Cambridge: James Munroe, 1854. 1st ed. 131pp. (Spine ends chipped.) *M & S.* $250/£156

Bridge Over the Delaware River Connecting Philadelphia, Pa. and Camden, N.J. (Camden, 1927.) Obl folio. 24 full-pg plts. VG. *Cullen.* $350/£219

BRIDGE, HORATIO. Journal of an African Cruiser. Nathaniel Hawthorne (ed). NY: Putnam, 1853. viii,179pp. (Spine ends very chipped.) *Lefkowicz.* $200/£125

BRIDGE, R. A Compendious Treaty on the Theory and Solution of Cubic and Biquadratic Equations, and of Equations of the Higher Orders. London: Ptd by R. Watts, 1821. 1st ed. (xii),155pp. 1/2 calf. *Young.* $80/£50

BRIDGES, HAL. Lee's Maverick General, Daniel Harvey Hill. NY, (1961). 1st ed. Fine in dj (lt worn, repaired). *Pratt.* $60/£38

BRIDGES, ROBERT. Eden. An Oratorio. London, 1891. 1st ed. One of 110 numbered. Uncut. (Lt worn.) *Oinonen*.* $30/£19

BRIDGES, ROBERT. Now in Wintry Delights. Oxford: (Daniel Press), 1903. 1st ed. One of 300. Untrimmed. Fine in blue-gray wrappers. *Maggs.* $160/£100

BRIDGES, ROBERT. Poems. London: Basil Montagu Pickering, 1873. 1st ed, 1st bk. Lt blue cl, ptd spine label. Horace Pym bkpl. VG (feps dknd, bkseller's description affixed to fr pastedown; spine sl faded, label edge sl worn). *Sumner & Stillman.* $850/£531

BRIDGES, ROBERT. The Testament of Beauty. Oxford, 1930. 1st ed. (Corners worn; no dj.) *Typographeum.* $15/£9

BRIDGES, ROBERT. The Testament of Beauty. NY, 1930. 1st US trade ed. As New. *Bond.* $20/£13

BRIDGES, ROY. From Silver to Steel. Melbourne: George Robertson, 1920. 1st ed. 67 Fine plts. (Soiled, fr bd ring-mkd.) *Hollett.* $224/£140

BRIDGMAN, CLARE. The Bairn's Coronation Book. London: J.M. Dent, (1902). Charles Robinson (illus). 16mo. Color illus cl (worn, rubbed, rear hinge cracked). *Reisler.* $50/£31

BRIDGMAN, L. J. More Happy Proverbs for Happy Children. NY: Dodge, (1927). 4to. Cl-backed color pict bds (edges lt rubbed). *Reisler.* $185/£116

BRIDWELL, J. W. The Life and Adventures of Robert McKemie, Alias 'Little Reddy,' from Texas. Houston: Frontier, 1955. Rpt ed. Ltd to 1000. Fine in wrappers. Howes B765. *Labordo.* $35/£22

Brief History of the Life of Mary Queen of Scots. London: Cockerell, 1681. Folio. Wrappers (sl damaged). *Rostenberg & Stern.* $425/£266

Brief Journal of the Life, Travels, and Labours of Love, in the Work of the Ministry, of...Thomas Wilson.... (By Thomas Wilson.) London: Ptd by James Phillips, 1784. New ed. xlviii,98,(2)pp. Old sheep (rebacked). *Young.* $56/£35

BRIEGER, PETER et al. Illuminated Manuscripts of the Divine Comedy. Princeton, (1969). 2 vols. *Swann*.* $172/£108

BRIEGER, PETER et al. Illuminated Manuscripts of The Divine Comedy. Princeton: Princeton Univ, (1969). 2 vols. 16 color plts vol 2. Fine set in djs, pub's slipcase. *Turtle Island.* $350/£219

BRIEGER, PETER. English Art 1216-1307. OUP, 1957. VG in dj (creased). *Hadley.* $51/£32

BRIFFAULT, ROBERT. Europa in Limbo. NY: Scribner, 1937. 1st US ed. Red cl stamped in gilt/black. (Splash mk top edge), o/w NF in VG dj (spine rubbed). *Reese.* $55/£34

Brigand Captain. Beadle's New Dime Novel. #328. Ca 1880. Last # listed on rear is 382. VG in wraps (chips, 2 pieces cut out). *Book Market.* $30/£19

BRIGGS, CLARE. Golf: The Book of a Thousand Chuckles—The Famous Golf Cartoons by Briggs. Chicago: P.F. Volland, (1916). 1st ed. 1/2 cl, pict bds. (Bkpl, smudge to fep, fr hinge starting; fore-edges rubbed), else VG. *Pacific**. $173/£108

BRIGGS, ERNEST E. Angling and Art in Scotland: Some Fishing Experiences Related and Illustrated. London: Longmans, Green, 1908. 1st ed. 32 color plts (incl frontis), guards. Teg. Gilt-dec pict cl. (Spine dknd), else VG. *Pacific**. $184/£115

BRIGGS, HAROLD E. Frontiers of the Northwest. A History of the Upper Missouri Valley. NY: D. Appleton-Century, 1940. 1st ed. Bkpl of Ernest Osgood. VG. *Labordo*. $75/£47

BRIGGS, L. VERNON. Around Cape Horn to Honolulu on the Bark 'Amy Turner' 1880. Boston, 1926. 1st ed. One of 550 numbered. *Ginsberg*. $125/£78

BRIGGS, MARTIN S. Baroque Architecture. London, 1913. 1st ed. Teg. (Feps lt browned; corners sl rubbed, sm nick.) Dj (lt soiled, chipped). *Edwards*. $72/£45

BRIGGS, MARTIN S. The English Farmhouse. Batsford, 1953. 1st ed. Color frontis. (Fep pulled, sl foxed), o/w Good +. *Whittle*. $35/£22

BRIGGS, RAYMOND. Fungus the Bogeyman Plop-Up Book. London: Hamish Hamilton Children's Books, 1982. 7 dbl-pg 'plop-ups.' Glazed pict bds. VG. *Bookfinders*. $50/£31

BRIGGS, RAYMOND. Fungus the Bogeyman. Hamish Hamilton, 1977. 1st ed. Glazed bds. VG. *Green Meadow*. $27/£17

BRIGGS, RAYMOND. Ring-a-Ring O'Roses. NY: Coward-McCann, 1962. 1st US ed. 7.5x10. 48pp. Fine in dj. *Cattermole*. $20/£13

BRIGGS, RAYMOND. The Snowman. Hamilton, 1978. 1st ed. Tall 4to. 40pp. Glossy pict bds. VG. *Bookmark*. $64/£40

BRIGGS, WALTER. Without Noise of Arms: The 1776 Dominguez-Escalante Search for a Route from Santa Fe to Monterey. Flagstaff: Northland Press, (1976). One of 100 leatherbound. Signed by Briggs and Wilson Hurley (illus). 10 color plts. Full leather, gilt. Fine in slipcase (sl soil). *Pacific**. $161/£101

BRIGHAM, CLARENCE. Paul Revere's Engravings. NY, 1969. Dj. *Swann**. $46/£29

BRIGHT, HENRY ARTHUR. Happy Country This America: The Travel Diary of.... Anne Henry Ehrenpreis (ed). Columbus: OH Univ, (1978). 1st ed. Fine in dj. *Mott*. $25/£16

BRIGHT, ROBERT. Miss Pattie. NY: Doubleday, 1954. 1st ed. 8x10.25. 36pp. Pict bds. VG in dj. *Cattermole*. $20/£13

BRILEY, JOHN. The Traitors. NY: Putnam, 1969. 1st ed. Fine in dj (sm tears). *Associates*. $100/£63

BRILL, CHARLES J. Conquest of the Southern Plains. Oklahoma City, (1938). 1st ed. Signed. Fine. *Pratt*. $150/£94

BRILL, EDITH. The Golden Bird. Franklin Watts, 1970. 1st Amer ed. Jan Pienkowski (illus). 151pp. VG + (recent tear/wrinkle pg57) in NF dj. *Price*. $40/£25

BRILLAT-SAVARIN, J. A. The Handbook of Dining. L.F. Simpson (trans). NY: D. Appleton, 1865. 1st Amer ed. 200pp. (Sl worn.) *M & S*. $175/£109

BRILLAT-SAVARIN, J. A. The Physiology of Taste. M.F.K. Fisher (trans). Heritage, (c1949). VG in box. *Book Broker*. $25/£16

BRILLAT-SAVARIN, J. A. The Physiology of Taste. NY: Boni & Liveright, 1926. Frontis port. (Sm split top of upper joint, extrems sl rubbed.) *Hollett*. $56/£35

BRILLAT-SAVARIN, J. A. The Physiology of Taste. NY: LEC, 1949. One of 1500. 1/4 calf, dec bds. Fine in glassine (chipped), slipcase. *Pacific**. $173/£108

BRILLAT-SAVARIN, J. A. The Physiology of Taste. M.F.K. Fisher (trans). Arion, 1994. Ltd to 200 numbered, signed by Wayne Thiebaud (illus). 356pp + 9 color lithos. Dec cl slipcase. *Truepenny*. $2,500/£1,563

BRIMLOW, GEORGE. The Bannock Indian War of 1878. Caldwell: Caxton, 1938. 1st ed. Dj. *Dawson*. $75/£47

BRIMLOW, GEORGE. Harney County, Oregon, and Its Range Land. Portland, OR: Binfords & Mort, 1951. 1st ed. VG + in dj (chipped). *Labordo*. $85/£53

BRIMMER, F. E. Motor Campcraft. NY: Macmillan, 1923. 1st ed. VG in dj (chipped, lacks spine pieces). *Pacific**. $46/£29

BRIN, DAVID. The River of Time. Niles: Dark Harvest, 1986. One of 400 numbered, signed by Brin and Paul Sonju (illus). (Sl worn.) Dj, slipcase. *Oinonen**. $50/£31

BRIN, DAVID. Startide Rising. West Bloomfield: Phantasia, (1985). 1st hb ed, trade state. Signed. Fine in dj. *Levin*. $125/£78

BRINDLE, ERNEST. With Russian, Japanese and Chunchuse. London: John Murray, 1905. 1st ed. 1/2-title, fldg map. Red cl, gilt. VG (fore-edge sl foxed; spine sl faded). *Morrell*. $72/£45

BRININSTOOL, E. A. Crazy Horse. L.A.: Wetzel, 1949. 1st ed. Red cl, gold paper cvr label. (Lt offset to cvr label from dj), else Fine in dj (chip to spine head). *Pacific**. $98/£61

BRININSTOOL, E. A. Crazy Horse. L.A.: Wetzel, 1949. 1st ed. Inscribed, signed. VG in dj. *Labordo*. $175/£109

BRININSTOOL, E. A. The Custer Fight. Hollywood, CA: E.A. Brininstool, 1933. 1st ed. Inscribed, signed. Fine in wrappers. *Labordo*. $250/£156

BRININSTOOL, E. A. Fighting Red Cloud's Warriors. Columbus, OH: Hunter-Trader-Trapper, 1926. 1st ed. Red pict cl. Fine (bold sig, few sm unobtrusive rubber/blindstamps). *Pacific**. $207/£129

BRININSTOOL, E. A. Troopers with Custer. Harrisburg, PA: Stackpole, (1952). Rev ed. VG in dj. *Lien*. $50/£31

BRINKLEY, F. Japan: Described and Illustrated by the Japanese. Boston: J.B. Millet, (1897). Thin lg folio. 15 sections. 30 mtd full-pg hand-colored albumen prints, 15 color collotypes, guards, 15 full-pg woodcuts. Orig lt gray pict wrappers w/reinforced red cl spines, bound in Japanese manner. (Wraps on 1st few parts chipped, top corner rear wrapper section 1 missing lg piece, another piece taped on.) Other *Baltimore**. $325/£203

BRINLEY, GORDON. Away to the Gaspe. NY: GC Pub, (1940). 24 plts. Blue cl. VG in color, pict dj. *House*. $15/£9

BRINNIN, JOHN MALCOLM. No Arch, No Triumph. NY: Knopf, 1945. 1st ed. Inscribed. Fine in dj (used). *Pharos*. $125/£78

BRINNIN, JOHN MALCOLM. Skin Diving in the Virgins and Other Poems. NY: Delacorte, (1970). 1st ed. Inscribed, signed 'John Malcolm.' Rev copy w/slip laid in. Fine in dj. *Pharos*. $95/£59

BRINNIN, JOHN MALCOLM. The Sorrows of Cold Stone. Dodd, 1951. 1st ed. VG (extrems rubbed) in dj (chipped, worn). *My Bookhouse*. $47/£29

BRINNIN, JOHN MALCOLM. The Third Rose, Gertrude Stein and Her World. Boston, 1959. VG in dj (sl worn). *Typographeum*. $32/£20

BRINSMEAD, H. F. Seasons of the Briar. OUP, 1965. 1st ed. William Papas (illus). 202pp. NF (price tag tape pull fep) in NF dj. *Price*. $45/£28

BRINTON, DANIEL G. The Lenape and Their Legends; with the Complete Text and Symbols of the Walam Olum, a New Translation, and an Inquiry into Its Authenticity. Phila: D.G. Brinton, 1885. (Traces of removed bkpl, tp erasure; corner bumped), else VG. *Pacific**. $92/£58

BRINTON, JOHN. Tour in Palestine and Syria.... London: Chapman & Hall, 1893. 1st ed. Photogravure frontis, xii,173,(1)imprint; 12 plts, dbl-pg map. (1/2-title cut away; few thumb mks, sl soiled, 1 plt frayed w/brittle edges.) Maroon beveled cl (spine faded, loose but firm, spine ink spots, extrems sl rubbed). Clean. *Morrell*. $80/£50

BRION, MARCEL. Ernst Fuchs. NY, (1979). Dj. Swann*. $57/£36

BRION, MARCEL. The Story of the Huns. Frederick H. Martens (trans). NY: McBride, 1929. 2nd ptg. 8 plts. (Bkpl; sl rubbed), o/w VG. Worldwide. $24/£15

BRISBANE, ALBERT. Social Destiny of Man; or, Association and Reorganization of Industry. Phila, 1840. 1st ed. Signed. 2 plts. Pub's cl, orig label. (Lt browned, foxed, few pencil notes; faded, stained, sm tear in backstrip.) Swann*. $316/£198

BRISBIN, JAMES. The Beef Bonanza; Or How to Get Rich on the Plains. Phila: Lippincott, 1881. 1st ed. VG. Howes B780. Labordo. $300/£188

BRISBIN, JAMES. Belden, the White Chief; or Twelve Years Among the Wild Indians of the Plains. Cincinnati, 1870. 1st ed, 1st state. 513pp. (Tp, edge of frontis w/few brn spots; rebound w/fr, rear cvrs transposed.) Heinoldt. $45/£28

BRISSOT DE WARVILLE, J. P. and ETIENNE CLAVIERE. The Commerce of America with Europe.... NY: T. & J. Swords, 1795. 1st US ed. Frontisports. Coarse brn cl, red spine label. (Pp lt browned, name torn from tp top, 1st few ll w/chipped edges; rebound.) Kane*. $95/£59

BRISTOL, SHERLOCK. The Pioneer Preacher. Chicago: Fleming H. Revell, (1887). 1st ed. Signed. Frontis, 330pp. Good. Lien. $150/£94

BRISTOL, SHERLOCK. The Pioneer Preacher. Chicago: Fleming Revell, (1898). 336pp; 6 plts. Maroon ribbed cl, gilt. VG (extrems worn). Howes B1210. House. $40/£25

BRISTOW, GWEN and BRUCE MANNING. The Invisible Host. Mystery League, 1930. 1st ed. NF in dj (lt used, sm piece out at spine head). Murder. $22/£14

BRITE, POPPY Z. Drawing Blood. Huntington Beach: James Cahill, 1993. One of 274. Signed. 1/2 cl, marbled bds. As New in slipcase. Pacific*. $40/£25

British Hunts and Huntsmen. Containing a Short History of Each Fox and Stag Hunt in the British Isles, Together with Biographical Records of Masters Past and Present.... London, 1908-1911. 4 vols. Thick folio. 3/4 red morocco. (Rubbed, top corner foreedge 3 vols sl chewed.) Oinonen*. $300/£188

British Topography. London: T. Payne & Son & J. Nichols, 1780. 2 vols. lii,792; (lix),822pp + (lxi); 8 fldg maps on 9 (1 w/fold split). Early 1/2 calf, marbled bds. (Contemp notes, browned; bds worn, rebacked in morocco w/raised bands.) Edwards. $400/£250

BRITTAIN, VERA. Born 1925. NY: Macmillan, 1949. 1st US ed. VG in dj (wrinkled, sl worn). Second Life. $65/£41

BRITTAIN, VERA. Honourable Estate. London: Gollancz, 1936. 1st ed. Blue cl stamped in dk blue. VG (ink name, date) in dj (sl soiled, creased, price-clipped). Reese. $60/£38

BRITTAIN, VERA. Testament of Friendship. Macmillan, 1940. 1st Eng ed. Color frontis. VG (feps partly browned; edges sl rubbed) in dj (rubbed, nicked, dusty, spine dknd). Ulysses. $72/£45

BRITTAIN, VERA. Twice a Stranger. London: Gollancz, 1938. 1st ed. VG in dj (chipped, worn). Second Life. $75/£47

BRITTEN, F. J. Old Clocks and Watches and Their Makers. Batsford, 1911. 3rd ed. (Unevenly dknd; hinges worn.) Hollett. $120/£75

BRITTEN, F. J. Old Clocks and Watches and Their Makers. Bloomsbury Books, 1986. 9th ed. VG in dj (creased). Hollett. $104/£65

BRITTON, JOHN. The Architectural Antiquities of Great Britain. London, 1807-26. 5 vols. Aeg. Full old grn morocco (rubbed, sl stained; sl foxed, soiled), gilt. Internally Sound. Oinonen*. $400/£250

BRITTON, N. L. and J. N. ROSE. The Cactaceae. Volume 1 (of 4). Washington, 1919. 1st ed. 36 plts (28 chromolitho). (Rear corner bumped.) Brooks. $195/£122

BRITZMAN, HOMER and LONNIE HULL. The West in Bronze. (L.A.), 1950. One of 100 numbered. 1/4 morocco. (Stamp, sig.) Swann*. $92/£58

BROADBENT, ELLINOR LUCY. Alpine Valleys of Italy. Methuen, 1928. 1st ed. (Tp sl spotted.) Hollett. $56/£35

BROADFOOT, W. et al. Billiards. Longmans, Green, 1896. 1st ed. xi,(i),(456)pp. Pict cl. Nice (few sm mks, 1 leaf sl creased). Ash. $120/£75

BROADLEY, A. M. Chats on Autographs. London, 1910. 1st ed. Fore-edge uncut. (Feps sl browned.) Dj (sl soiled, ragged). Edwards. $56/£35

BROADLEY, A. M. The Last Punic War: Tunis, Past and Present. Edinburgh: William Blackwood & Sons, 1882. 1st ed. 2 vols. 2 photogravure frontispieces, xvi,358; viii,400pp; 18 plts, fldg plan, lg 2-color fldg map. Grn cl. (1/2-titles foxed; lt rubbed.) Karmiole. $150/£94

BROCH, HERMANN. The Sleepwalkers. Boston: Little, Brown, 1932. 1st ed, US issue. Black cl stamped in red/silver. NF in VG dj (spine faded, lt soiled, nicked). Reese. $60/£38

BROCK, HENRY IRVING. Colonial Churches in Virginia. Dale, (c1930). One of 1980. Signed. Book Broker. $50/£31

BROCK, LYNN. The Slip-Carriage Mystery. Harper, 1928. 1st ed. (Pp edges lt soiled; spine sunned), else VG. Murder. $35/£22

BROCK, R. A. (ed). Documents...Relating to the Huguenot Emigration to Virginia and to the Settlement at Manakin-Town. V.H.S., 1886. 247pp. Good (ex-lib; spine frayed, label worn). Book Broker. $75/£47

BROCK, R. A. (ed). General Robert Edward Lee, Soldier, Citizen, and Christian Patriot. Atlanta: H.C. Hudgins, (1897). Salesman's dummy of 1st ed, w/cl and morocco binding samples inside fr cvr. (86)leaves. Gray cl. VG. Chapel Hill. $150/£94

BROCK, S. E. Hunting in the Wilderness, Big Game Hunting North of the Amazon. London, 1963. 1st Eng ed. (Cvrs sl mkd.) Hallam. $40/£25

BROCK, SAMUEL (ed). Injuries of the Skull, Brain and Spinal Cord. Balt: Williams & Wilkins, 1940. 1st ed. Fine (mks tp) in dj. Glaser. $75/£47

BROCKEDON, WILLIAM. Egypt and Nubia. London: Francis Graham Moon, 1846-1849. 1st ed. 3 vols. Lg folio. Engr map of Nile Valley, 3 tinted litho tps, 61 full pg tinted litho plts, 60 litho vignettes in text, by Louis Haghe after drawings by David Roberts. Teg. 3/4 19th-cent red morocco over marbled bds, gilt paneled spines, raised bands. Fine (few plts sl to lt foxed). Appelfeld. $30,000/£18,750

BROCKEDON, WILLIAM. Illustrations of the Passes of the Alps. London: The Author, 1828. 1st ed. 2 vols. 4to. 96 steel-engr plts, 1 fldg, 12 full-pg engr maps, hand-colored highlights. Marbled eps, edges. Contemp dk grn morocco, marbled bds, gilt, raised bands. Good (lt aged, sl foxed, fep vol 1 detached; plts lt aged, foxed; sl worn, scuffed, some hinges cracked). Baltimore*. $650/£406

BROCKHAUS, ALBERT. Netsukes. E. G. Stillman (ed). NY: Duffield, 1924. 1st ed. Frontis, 16 multiple image plts. Brn cl, gilt. Good. Karmiole. $100/£63

BROCKLEHURST, THOMAS UNETT. Mexico To-Day. London: John Murray, 1883. 2nd ed. xv,(i)blank,259,(1)imprint, incl 1/2-title; 16 color lithos, 35 engr plts (1 dbl-pg), map; early photo of author tipped to fep. Red cl (spine repaired, cvrs sl rubbed, damp-stained), gilt. Good. Morrell. $176/£110

BROCKLEHURST, THOMAS UNETT. Mexico To-day: a Country with a Great Future, and a Glance at the Prehistoric Remains and Antiquities of the Montezumas. London, 1883. 2nd ed. xv,259pp; 55 plts (last plt torn w/loss across fr leading corner affecting illus). 1/2 leather (amateurishly rebound), gilt. (Margins browned.) Edwards. $120/£75

BROCKWELL, MAURICE W. A Catalogue of Some of the Paintings in the Collection of Henry Edwards Huntington at San Marino, California. NY, 1925. Inscribed by Joseph Duveen. (Binding sl dirty.) *Woolson.* $30/£19

BRODER, PATRICIA J. Bronzes of the American West. NY, 1973. Signed. 48 color plts. NF in dj. *Dumont.* $350/£219

BRODER, PATRICIA J. Bronzes of the American West. NY: Abrams, n.d. (1974). 1st ed. 48 color plts. Grn cl, gilt. Fine in pict dj (sl soiled, spine faded). *Argonaut.* $300/£188

BRODER, PATRICIA J. Dean Cornwell, Dean of Illustrators. NY: Watson-Guptill, (1978). Fine in pict dj. *Metropolitan*.* $115/£72

BRODER, PATRICIA J. Great Paintings of the Old American West. NY, 1979. Folio. VG in dj. *Dumont.* $65/£41

BRODSKY, JOSEPH. A Part of Speech. NY: Farrar, (1980). 1st ed. Signed. Fine in dj. *Reese.* $55/£34

BRODSKY, JOSEPH. A Part of Speech. Oxford: OUP, 1980. 1st British ed. NF in glossy illus wraps. *Lame Duck.* $45/£28

BRODZKY, HORACE (ed). Gaudier-Brezeska Drawings. London: Faber & Faber, (1946). 1st ed. 3 color, 114 b/w plts. NF (notes) in VG dj. *Turtle Island.* $40/£25

BRODZKY, HORACE. Henri Gaudier-Brzeska—1891-1915. Faber & Faber, 1933. 1st ed. Inscribed presentation. 24 full-pg line dwgs. Unopened. VG (top edge sl dusty, spine ends, corners sl bumped) in dj (nicked, sl rubbed, creased, torn, chipped, spine faded, edges sl dknd). *Ulysses.* $152/£95

BROEL, A. Frog Raising for Pleasure and Profit. New Orleans: Marl. House, 1950. 1st ed. VG. *Mikesh.* $95/£59

BROGER, KARL. Pillbox 17: The Story of Comradeship-in-Arms. Oakley Williams (trans). London: Thornton Butterworth, (1930). 1st British ed. Brn cl stamped in black. (Prelims, edges lt foxed), else NF in NF pict dj (narrow chip spine crown). *Reese.* $85/£53

BROKE, PHILIP B. V. Admiral Sir P. B. V. Broke, Bart.... F. G. Brighton (ed). London: Sampson, Low, Son, & Marston, 1866. 1st ed. Frontis, xvi,488pp,8pp ads; 14 plts, 1 fldg facs. (Joints worn, short tear to fr joint.) *Lefkowicz.* $125/£78

BROME, VINCENT. The International Brigades, Spain 1936-39. NY, 1966. 1st ed. VG in dj. *Typographeum.* $25/£16

BROMFIELD, LOUIS. A Good Woman. NY: Stokes, 1927. 1st ed. Fine in Fine dj (spine sl tanned). *Between The Covers.* $125/£78

BROMFIELD, LOUIS. It Takes All Kinds. NY: Harpers, 1939. 1st ed. (Corner sl bumped), else Fine in VG dj (few sm chips). *Between The Covers.* $50/£31

BROMFIELD, LOUIS. Out of the Earth. NY: Harper, 1948. 1st ed. VG + (sl shelfworn) in dj (edges ragged). *My Bookhouse.* $30/£19

BROMFIELD, LOUIS. The Strange Case of Miss Annie Spragg. London: Jonathan Cape, 1928. 1st ed. Charcoal cl. Nice. *Temple.* $16/£10

BROMFIELD, LOUIS. Until the Day Break. NY: Harper, (1942). 1st ed. (Sl worn), else Fine in VG + dj (crown chip, sm tears). *Between The Covers.* $65/£41

BROMLEY, A. NELSON. A Fly Fisher's Reflection 1860-1930. London: The Fishing Gazette, 1930. 1st ed. Grn cl, gilt. Fine. *Pacific*.* $127/£79

BROMLEY, GEORGE TISDALE. The Long Ago and the Later On, or Recollections of Eighty Years. SF: A.M. Robertson, 1904. 1st ed. Frontisport. Black pict red cl. VG + . *House.* $50/£31

BRONAUGH, W. C. The Youngers' Fight for Freedom. Columbia, MO: The Author, 1906. (Worn, discoloration, hinges starting), else Good. *Dumont.* $125/£78

BRONAUGH, W. C. The Youngers' Fight for Freedom. Columbia: Privately ptd, 1906. 1st ed. Good (fr, rear hinges, extrems worn). *Baade.* $125/£78

BRONK, WILLIAM. The Empty Hands. New Rochelle, NY, (1969). 1st ed. (Sm snag bottom fr cvr), else VG in dj (edges sl frayed, torn). *King.* $25/£16

BRONK, WILLIAM. The Meantime. New Rochelle: Elizabeth Press, (1976). 1st ed, issue in bds. One of 400 ptd. Fine in slipcase. *Reese.* $85/£53

BRONOWSKI, J. The Ascent of Man. BBC, 1973. 1st UK ed. Signed, dated. NF in dj. *Williams.* $77/£48

BRONSON, BERTRAND H. Joseph Ritson, Scholar-at-Arms. Berkeley: Univ of CA, 1938. 1st ed. 2 vols. 2 ports. Fine set in djs, slipcase. *Glaser.* $200/£125

BRONSON, EDGAR BEECHER. Cowboy Life on the Western Plains. NY: G&D, (1910). 19 b/w plts. Red cl, color pict plt on upper side. (Color plt w/few nicks; cl speckled), o/w VG. *House.* $35/£22

BRONSON, EDGAR BEECHER. Cowboy Life on the Western Plains. NY: G&D, 1910. Frontis. (Soiled.) Internally Good. Dj (chipped). *Dumont.* $75/£47

BRONSON, EDGAR BEECHER. The Love of Loot and Women. NY: Privately ptd, 1917. One of 100 numbered. Port. Untrimmed. (Inner fr hinge split, bottom pg edges lt dampstained; worn, stained.) *Woolson.* $125/£78

BRONSON, EDGAR BEECHER. Red Blooded. Chicago: A.C. McClurg, 1910. 1st ed. Inscribed, signed. VG in dj (chipped). *Labordo.* $150/£94

BRONSON, EDGAR BEECHER. The Red-Blooded Heroes of the Frontier. NY; G&D, 1910. Frontis. Pict bds (sl worn). Dj (soiled, chipped). *Dumont.* $75/£47

BRONSON, EDGAR BEECHER. Reminiscences of a Ranchman. NY: McClure, 1908. 1st ed. VG. *Labordo.* $95/£59

BRONSON, WILLIAM. How to Kill a Golden State. GC: Doubleday, 1968. 1st ed. Red/white cl. NF in pict dj (sl worn). *Pacific*.* $69/£43

BRONSON, WILLIAM. The Last Grand Adventure. NY: McGraw Hill, (1977). VG in dj. *Perier.* $30/£19

BRONTE SISTERS. The Novels of the Sisters Bronte. Edinburgh: John Grant, 1907. 1st UK ed. 12 vols. Fine set (spine sl faded). *Williams.* $632/£395

BRONTE, CHARLOTTE. Jane Eyre. London, 1898. 2 vols. Frontis port vol 1. Teg. 1/2 grn morocco. *Swann*.* $103/£64

BRONTE, EMILY. Wuthering Heights. LEC, 1993. One of 300 signed by Balthus (illus). Fine in slipcase. *Swann*.* $1,380/£863

BROOK, G. and G. MATTHAI. Catalogue of the Madreporarian Corals in the British Museum (Natural History). London, 1893-1928. 7 vols. 242 plts. (Lib stamps; vol 1 rebacked preserving spine, vol 7 fr cvr waterstained.) *Henly.* $352/£220

BROOKE, DINAH. Death Games. NY: Harcourt, Brace, Jovanovich, 1976. 1st ed. Fine in dj. *Associates.* $100/£63

BROOKE, GEOFFREY. Good Company. London: Constable, 1954. 1st ed. 3 plts. VG in dj. *Hollett.* $32/£20

BROOKE, HENRY. The Tryal of the Roman Catholics of Ireland. T. Davies, 1764. 2nd ed. Half-title present, (i)-viii,(9)-234pp. Contemp sprinkled mid-brn calf, raised bands, gilt. Good (eps stained by turn-ins). *Blackwell's.* $96/£60

BROOKE, IRIS. English Costume of the Seventeenth Century. A&C Black, 1950. 2nd ed. Blue cl. VG. *Whittle.* $11/£7

BROOKE, IRIS. Four Walls Adorned. Methuen, 1952. 1st ed. Frontis, 7 full-pg color plts. (Ex-lib, sl adhesion mks, stamps), o/w VG in dj. *Whittle.* $19/£12

BROOKE, JAMES. Narrative of Events in Borneo and Celebes. London: Murray, 1848. 1st ed. 2 vols. Demy 8vo. xvii,385; xi,395pp; 18 plts (7 tinted litho, 11 woodcut), 5 fldg maps (1 color). Orig cl (recently rebacked w/orig spine laid on), gilt. VG set (plts sl foxed). *Ulysses.* $960/£600

BROOKE, JOCELYN. The Crisis in Bulgaria. London, 1956. 1st Eng ed. Very Nice in dj (sl rubbed, price-clipped, lacks lg piece rear panel). *Clearwater.* $56/£35

BROOKE, JOCELYN. The Dog at Clambercrown. London, 1955. 1st Eng ed. (Cvrs sl sunned.) Dj (repaired, strengthened). *Clearwater.* $56/£35

BROOKE, JOCELYN. A Mine of Serpents. London, 1949. 1st Eng ed. Inscribed. VG in dj (sl torn, nicked). *Clearwater.* $120/£75

BROOKE, JOCELYN. Ronald Firbank and John Betjeman. (London): British Council/Nat'l Book League, (1962). 1st ed. Fine in ptd wrappers, 1/2 morocco slipcase. *Reese.* $40/£25

BROOKE, JOCELYN. Ronald Firbank. London: Arthur Barker, 1951. 1st ed. VG in dj (soiled, rubbed; sm close edge tears). *Virgo.* $24/£15

BROOKE, JOCELYN. The Wild Orchids of Britain. London: The Bodley Head, 1950. 1st ed. One of 1140. 40 color plts. Dj (spine ends sl chipped w/couple sm tears along upper edge). *Edwards.* $192/£120

BROOKE, LESLIE. The Golden Goose Book. London: Warne, 1905. 1st ed, stated '1st ptd 1905'. 8x10. Unpaginated. Grn cl, stamped. NF (spine, edges sl faded). *Price.* $250/£156

BROOKE, LESLIE. The Golden Goose Book. London: Warne, stated 1st ptg 1905. 8x10. Unpaginated. Gray in pict lib binding, stamped illus. VG (ex-lib, neat stamps, neat pocket, tape pulls; 1 faint stain to bd, fep). *Price.* $150/£94

BROOKE, LESLIE. Johnny Crow's New Garden. NY: Frederick Warne, (1939). 8 1/4 x 6 1/4. Blue cl, pict cvr label. (Lacks fep), else Fine. *Pacific*.* $52/£33

BROOKE, LESLIE. Johnny Crow's New Garden. NY: Frederick Warne, 1935. 1st Amer ed. 8vo. 8 full-pg color plts. Blue cl (edges faded), color paste label. Very Nice in dj (margins sl worn), color paste label. *Reisler.* $300/£188

BROOKE, LESLIE. Little Bo-Peep, a Nursery Rhyme Picture Book. London: Frederick Warne, (1922). 4to. 6 full-pg color plts. Nice in stiff paper pict wrappers. *Reisler.* $125/£78

BROOKE, LESLIE. Ring o' Roses. London: Frederick Warne, (1922). 1st ed. Sm 4to. (124)pp; 32 color plts. Dec blue linen. Good in illus dj (1/2-inch chip spine foot). *Karmiole.* $100/£63

BROOKE, LESLIE. Ring O'Roses. London: Warne, n.d. Early rpt. 8x10. Unpaginated. Blue cl, stamped. VG + (gentle bends 1st few pp; spine sl faded). *Price.* $75/£47

BROOKE, LESLIE. Ring O'Roses: A Nursery Rhyme Picture Book. London: Frederick Warne, n.d. 9.75x7.5. Pict cl. VG. *Pacific*.* $98/£61

BROOKE, LESLIE. The Story of the Three Bears. London/NY: Frederick Warne, (c. 1920s). 10x8. 8pp full-pg color illus. Pict bds. NF. *Pacific*.* $58/£36

BROOKE, LESLIE. The Story of the Three Little Pigs. London: Frederick Warne, n.d. 10x7.5. Pict cl. (Sm tear bottom of 1 pg), else VG. *Pacific*.* $52/£33

BROOKE, LESLIE. The Three Bears. London: Frederick Warne, ca 1935. 4to. 8 color plts. Pict bds. Fine. *Appelfeld.* $65/£41

BROOKE, RUPERT. 1914 and Other Poems. London, 1915. 1st ed. Frontisport. Dk blue cl, paper spine label. VG (bkpl). *Truepenny.* $175/£109

BROOKE, RUPERT. 1914 and Other Poems. London: Sidgwick & Jackson, 1915. 1st ed. One of 1000 ptd. Port. Dk blue cl, paper spine label. Fine in NF dj (few sm nicks, short edge tear, shallow loss spine crown w/no loss to lettering, narrow chip top of rear joint). *Reese.* $850/£531

BROOKE, RUPERT. The Bastille. Rugby, 1905. 2nd ed. 8vo. 8pp. Fine in self-wrappers. *Truepenny.* $850/£531

BROOKE, RUPERT. Democracy and the Arts. London, 1946. 1st ed. One of 240 numbered. Engr port. 1/4 morocco. *Swann*.* $92/£58

BROOKE, RUPERT. Letters from America. NY: Scribner, 1916. 1st ed. Photogravure frontisport. Sheets bulk 1 inch; no broken type. Fine. *Mott.* $40/£25

BROOKE, RUPERT. The Letters of Rupert Brooke. Geoffrey Keynes (ed). London: Faber & Faber, (1968). 1st ed. Blue cl stamped in brn/gilt. (Smudges to fore-edge), o/w Fine in dj. *Reese.* $60/£38

BROOKE, RUPERT. Letters. Geoffrey Keynes (ed). London, 1968. 1st Eng ed. VG in dj. *Clearwater.* $72/£45

BROOKE, RUPERT. Lithuania. London, 1935. 1st Eng ed. One of 2000 ptd. (Dust-mkd; no dj.) *Clearwater.* $64/£40

BROOKE, RUPERT. Selected Poems. London, 1917. 1st ed. Dj (sm nicks spine extrems). *Swann*.* $161/£101

BROOKE, SYLVIA. Queen of the Head Hunters. London, 1971. 3rd imp. VG- in dj. *Gretton.* $11/£7

BROOKER, W. D. (ed). A Century of Scottish Mountaineering. Scottish Mountaineering Trust, 1988. Pict glazed bds. VG. *Hollett.* $40/£25

BROOKES, JOHN. Manners and Customs of the English Nation, from the Invasion of Julius Caesar to the Present Time. London: James Blackwood, (1859). 1st ed. (viii),280pp. Blind-stamped cl (sl rubbed). *Young.* $24/£15

BROOKES, JOHN. A Place in the Country. Thames & Hudson, 1984. NF in dj. *Hadley.* $24/£15

BROOKES, R. and JOSEPH COLLYER. A Dictionary of the World. London: T. Carnan & F. Newbery, Junior, 1772. 2 vols. Tall folio. Later full dk brn calf, red/grn cl spine labels. (Text sl handled, sl aged, browned; cvrs sl worn, lt spotted.) Text Good. *Baltimore*.* $160/£100

BROOKES, R. The General Dispensatory. London, 1765. 2nd ed. Vol 2 (only). 390pp. Old leather. (Eps, tp sl torn, ink notes, foxed; inner hinges sl cracked.) *Whitehart.* $144/£90

BROOKES, RICHARD. The Art of Angling, Rock and Sea-Fishing. London: Watts, 1740. 1st ed. 249pp + index + ads. Orig cl-backed bds. Good (lacks fep, tp relaid, p21 edgetorn w/sl loss). *Bowman.* $250/£156

BROOKFIELD, MRS. ARTHUR. Aesop's Fables for Little Readers. London: T. Fisher Unwin, (1888). 1st ed. 4to. H. J. Ford (illus). Red cl, gilt. Good. *Reisler.* $275/£172

BROOKNER, ANITA. Family and Friends. Cape, 1985. 1st UK ed. Fine in NF dj. *Williams.* $24/£15

BROOKNER, ANITA. A Friend from England. NY: Pantheon, (1987). 1st ed. Fine in Fine dj. *Robbins.* $20/£13

BROOKNER, ANITA. A Friend from England. Cape, 1987. 1st Eng ed. NF (spine ends, 2 corners sl bumped) in dj. *Ulysses.* $40/£25

BROOKNER, ANITA. Hotel du Lac. London, 1984. 1st Eng ed. Nice (bottom edges of cvrs sl faded) in dj (price-clipped, lamination at spine sl wrinkled) *Clearwater.* $56/£35

BROOKNER, ANITA. Lewis Percy. Cape, 1989. 1st Eng ed. NF (spine tail bumped) in dj (si creased). *Ulysses.* $32/£20

BROOKNER, ANITA. A Private View. NY: Random House, (1994). 1st Amer ed. Signed. Fine in Fine dj. *Dermont.* $25/£16

BROOKNER, ANITA. A Private View. Cape, 1994. 1st UK ed. NF in dj. *Williams.* $22/£14

BROOKS, ALFRED MANSFIELD. From Holbein to Whistler. New Haven: Yale Univ, 1920. 1/4 buckram, pale blue bds. VG (corners lt bumped). *Truepenny.* $45/£28

BROOKS, BRYANT BUTLER. Memoirs of Bryant B. Brooks.... Glendale: Privately ptd, 1939. 1st ed. Ltd ed. VF. Howes B814. *Labordo.* $325/£203

BROOKS, CHARLES E. The Henry's Fork. NY: Lyons/Winchester, (1986). One of 500 numbered, signed. Full leatherette (lt worn). Slipcase. *Oinonen*.* $170/£106

BROOKS, CHARLES WOLCOTT. Origin of the Chinese Race, Philosophy of Their Early Development.... SF, 1876. 1st separate ed. Fldg frontis map, 30pp. Orig ptd lt olive wraps (lt soiled). NF. *Chapel Hill.* $125/£78

BROOKS, CLEANTH. A Shaping Joy. Methuen, 1971. 1st Eng ed. Fine in dj (price-clipped, internally repaired nick). *Ulysses.* $48/£30

BROOKS, GWENDOLYN. Annie Allen. NY: H&R, (1949). 1st ed. Inscribed in 1994. Rev copy, pub's slip laid in; in dj. *Agvent.* $750/£469

BROOKS, GWENDOLYN. Selected Poems. NY: H&R, (1963). Inscribed in 1994. NF (corner sl bumped) in NF dj (spine sl sunned). *Agvent.* $225/£141

BROOKS, H. ALLEN. The Prairie School. Univ of Toronto, 1975. 2nd ed. VG in dj. *Hadley.* $80/£50

BROOKS, J. BARLOW. Lancashire Bred. Oxford: Privately published by Church Army Press, (1949). 1st ed. Inscribed. VG in dj (sl chipped, mkd). *Hollett.* $48/£30

BROOKS, J. TYRWHITT. (Pseud of Henry Vizetelly.) Four Months Among the Gold-Finders in Alta California. London: David Bogue, 1849. 1st ed. Frontis map, xviii,207pp (lt foxed). Orig red cl (sl worn). *Mott.* $250/£156

BROOKS, JUANITA. John Doyle Lee: Zealot-Pioneer Builder-Scapegoat. Glendale: Clark, 1973. New ed. Red cl. VG + in dj. *Five Quail.* $65/£41

BROOKS, JUANITA. The Mountain Meadows Massacre. Stanford: Stanford Univ, (1950). 1st ed. VF (sm bkpl) in dj (spine ends, corners sl rubbed). *Argonaut.* $150/£94

BROOKS, JUANITA. The Mountain Meadows Massacre. Norman, 1962. New ed, 1st ptg. Fine (label) in dj. *Baade.* $40/£25

BROOKS, NOAH. First Across the Continent. NY, 1901. 1st ed. Fldg map. (Bkpl; cvr, backstrip edges worn.) *Woolson.* $60/£38

BROOKS, VAN WYCK. The Flowering of New England. LEC, 1941. Ltd to 1500 numbered, signed by Raymond J. Holden (illus). Fine in slipcase. *Swann*.* $80/£50

BROOKSHAW, GEORGE. Groups of Flowers, Groups of Fruit and Six Birds. Thomas McLean, 1819. 2nd ed. 3 parts bound in 1 vol. Folio. 18 hand-colored plts. Leather framing w/center tile cartouche, else exposed bds. (Lt foxed, sl rubbed, edges worn.) *Metropolitan*.* $1,955/£1,222

BROOKSHAW, GEORGE. A New Treatise on Flower Painting. London: John Booth, 1816. 22 plts (1 torn, repaired). Orig old cl, spine laid down. (Sl soiled, edges worn, foxing.) *Metropolitan*.* $402/£251

BROOKSHIER, FRANK. The Burro. Norman, 1974. VG in dj. *Dumont.* $30/£19

BROPHY, BRIGID. Hackenfeller's Ape. NY: Random House, (1954). 1st ed. (Bottom corners bumped), o/w VG in dj (price-clipped, lt soiled). *Bernard.* $20/£13

BROPHY, BRIGID. Hackenfeller's Ape. London: Rupert Hart-Davis, 1953. 1st ed. NF in pict dj. *Cady.* $30/£19

BROPHY, JOHN and ERIC PARTRIDGE (comps). Songs and Slang of the British Soldier: 1914-1918. London: Eric Partridge Ltd at Scholartis Press, 1930. 1st ed. Orange cl, gilt. VG (humidity spotting toward cvr fore-edges) in NF dj. *Reese.* $75/£47

BROPHY, JOHN. The Bitter End. NY: E.P. Dutton, (1928). 1st US ed. Blue cl stamped in black. (Spine crown sl faded), else VG in dj (lt worn, chip, spine crown discolored). *Reese.* $60/£38

BROPHY, JOHN. The Nimble Rabbit. London: C&W, 1955. 1st ed. Moss-grn fine beaded linen-grain bds. Fine in dj (sl frayed). *Temple.* $19/£12

BROPHY, JOHN. The World Went Mad. London: Jonathan Cape, (1934). 1st ed. Orange cl stamped in black. NF in VG dj (tanned, dust-mkd, sl loss spine crown). *Reese.* $65/£41

BROPHY, TRUMAN WILLIAM. Oral Surgery, a Treatise on the Diseases, Injuries and Malformations of the Mouth and Associated Parts. Phila: P. Blakiston's Son, (1915). 1st ed. 39 plts. Fine in maroon cl. *Weber.* $300/£188

BROSNAN, C. J. History of the State of Idaho. NY, 1918. 1st ed. Pict cl. VG- (fep, frontis sl creased, old price stamp fr pastedown; cvr soiled). *Baade.* $75/£47

BROSNAN, C. J. Jason Lee, Prophet of the New Oregon. NY: Macmillan, 1932. 1st ed. VG in dj. *Brown.* $20/£13

BROSSARD, CHANDLER. A Chimney Sweep Comes Clean. CA: Realities Library, 1985. 1st ed. Signed. NF in wrappers. *Warren.* $40/£25

BROTHERS, MARY HUDSON. Billy the Kid. Farmington, NM: Hustler, 1949. NF in stiff wraps tied w/leather thong. *Dumont.* $60/£38

BROUGHAM, JOHN and JOHN ELDERKIN (eds). Lotus Leaves. Boston: William F. Gill, 1875. 1st ed, 2nd ptg, w/Rockwell & Churchill device on c. pg, variant version w/tp set in 19 lines (rather than 20 or 21). Text contains initial publication of 'An Encounter with an Interviewer' by Mark Twain. Aeg, marbled eps. Pub's full dk brn morocco, beveled bds, raised bands, gilt. (Foxing at fr/rear blanks; hinges cracked; scuffed.) BAL 3363. *Baltimore*.* $35/£22

BROUGHTON, JAMES. The Playground. (SF): Centaur, 1949. 1st ed. One of 1000. Good + (bumped, warped, spine head rubbed) in dj (extrems dknd, chipped; small piece out fr panel, short tears to rear panel, spine torn, partially repaired w/tape). *Blue Mountain.* $30/£19

BROUGHTON, RHODA. Scylla or Charybdis? Richard Bentley, 1895. Pub's cat dated Autumn 1895. Good (pencil sig, sl cocked; spine bumped, chipped; rubbed). *Tiger.* $48/£30

BROUGHTON, WILLIAM ROBERT. A Voyage of Discovery to the North Pacific Ocean. London: T. Cadell & W. Davies, 1804. 1st ed. 4to. xx,392,(1)pp + (2)pp ads; 9 plts incl 3 fldg charts, 4 fldg copper plts, 2 other copper-engr plts. Mod 3/4 calf, marbled bds, gilt, raised bands, morocco lettering piece. (Soil to contents, lt dampstains to lower portions of many pp and plts, 2 lg charts backed w/paper repaired several tears, 1 fldg plt backed w/tissue also affecting several repairs). Overall VG. Howes B821. *Pacific*.* $4,888/£3,055

BROUN, HEYWOOD. Collected Edition of Heywood Broun. NY, 1941. 1st Amer ed. Fine. *Polyanthos.* $25/£16

BROWER, CHARLES D. Fifty Years Below Zero. NY: Dodd, Mead, 1942. 3rd ptg. Inscribed, signed, 1943. VG in dj (chipped, taped, shabby). *High Latitude.* $45/£28

BROWER, J. V. The Mississippi River and Its Source. Minneapolis, MN: Harrison & Smith, 1893. 360pp. Fair (cvrs worn). *Lien.* $50/£31

BROWER, KENNETH. Galapagos: The Flow of Wildness: Discovery, Prospect. SF: Sierra Club, (1968). 1st ed. 2 vols. VF set in djs (spines lt sunned), pub's slipcase. *Argonaut.* $225/£141

BROWER, KENNETH. Kauai and the Park Country of Hawaii. SF: Sierra Club, (1967). 1st ed. Folio. Red cl. Fine in pict dj (sl chipped). *Argonaut.* $75/£47

BROWN, ABBIE FARWELL. The Lonesomest Doll. Boston: Houghton Mifflin, (1928). 1st ed thus. 8vo. Tp, 3 full-pg plts. Arthur Rackham (illus). Tan cl. VG. *Reisler.* $485/£303

BROWN, ABBIE FARWELL. The Lonesomest Doll. Boston/NY: Houghton Mifflin, 1928. 1st ed illus by Arthur Rackham. 4to. Color tp, 3 color plts, 26 illus. Pict tan cl. Fine. *Christie's*.* $589/£368

BROWN, ALAN K. Sawpits in the Spanish Red Woods, 1787-1849. San Mateo, CA: San Mateo County Hist Assoc, 1966. 1st ed. One of 750 ptd. Frontis map, 2 plts. Grn cl, gilt. Fine. *Harrington.* $40/£25

BROWN, ALEC (trans). The Voyage of the Chelyuskin, by Members of the Expedition. NY: Macmillan, 1935. 1st ed. VG in Poor dj (torn). Perier. $45/£28

BROWN, BOB. Readies for Bob Brown's Machine. Cagnes-sur-Mer: Roving Eye, 1931. 1st ed. Ltd to 300. (P197 corner torn, repaired tear to p101, neither affecting text; spine sl worn), else Nice in ptd wrappers. Bromer. $850/£531

BROWN, C. and H. HORWOOD. Death on the Ice. Toronto: Doubleday Canada, 1972. VG in dj. Explorer. $16/£10

BROWN, C. BARRINGTON and WILLIAM LIDSTONE. Fifteen Thousand Miles on the Amazon and Its Tributaries. London, 1878. 1st ed. 8vo. xiii,520pp; fldg map, 9 plts. Fine. Maggs. $760/£475

BROWN, C. BARRINGTON. Canoe and Camp Life in British Guiana. London: Edward Stanford, 1876. 1st ed. Fldg map at end, 10 Fine color litho plts. VG (prelims, end lt foxed) in 3/4 calf, marbled paper (sl edgeworn, expertly rehinged). Parmer. $395/£247

BROWN, CARTER. The Blonde. NY: NAL, 1958. 1st Amer ed. Pb orig. Fine in wrappers. Mordida. $30/£19

BROWN, CHARLES H. Insurrection at Magellan. Boston: The Author, 1854. 1st ed. Frontis, 228pp; plan. Black cl, gilt. Good. Karmiole. $175/£109

BROWN, CHRISTY. My Left Foot. London, 1954. 1st Eng ed. VG in dj (chipped, torn, faded, rubbed). Clearwater. $80/£50

BROWN, CHRISTY. My Left Foot. NY: S&S, 1955. 1st Amer ed. (Sm lib stamp), else Fine in NF dj (sl rubbed, soiled). Between The Covers. $85/£53

BROWN, D. ALEXANDER. The Bold Cavaliers. Morgan's 2nd Kentucky Cavalry Raiders. Phila: Lippincott, (1959). 1st ed. Red bds, gray cl back. Fine in dj. Chapel Hill. $80/£50

BROWN, D. ALEXANDER. Grierson's Raid. Urbana, 1954. 2nd ptg. (Sl worn), o/w Fine in dj (sl worn). Pratt. $45/£28

BROWN, D. MACKENZIE (ed). China Trade Days in California: Selected Letters from the Thompson Papers, 1832-1863. Berkeley: Univ of CA, 1947. 1st ed. Frontisport, plt. Red cl. Fine in NF dj (lt chipped). Harrington. $45/£28

BROWN, D. S. Freshwater Snails of Africa and Their Medical Importance. London: Taylor & Francis, 1980. Fine in dj. Savona. $40/£25

BROWN, DEE and MARTIN F. SCHMITT. Fighting Indians of the West. NY: Scribner, 1948. 1st ed. Color pict black cl. VG in dj (edges lt chipped, worn). House. $65/£41

BROWN, DEE and MARTIN F. SCHMITT. The Settlers' West. NY: Scribner, 1955. 1st ed. Grn cl. Fine in NF dj. House. $75/£47

BROWN, DEE and MARTIN F. SCHMITT. Trail Driving Days. NY: Scribner, 1952. 1st ed. Black pict cl. VG in Good dj (worn). Labordo. $50/£31

BROWN, DEE and MARTIN F. SCHMITT. Trail Driving Days. NY: Scribner, 1952. 1st ed. Black cl. Fine in VG + dj. House. $75/£47

BROWN, DEE. Fort Phil Kearny. NY: Putnam, (1962). 1st ed. Fine in dj. Pacific*. $40/£25

BROWN, DEE. Hear That Lonesome Whistle Blow. NY, 1977. (Spine faded), else NF in dj. Dumont. $35/£22

BROWN, DEE. They Went Thataway. Putnam, (1960). 1st ed. Fine (name, date) in VG + dj. Authors Of The West. $35/£22

BROWN, ELIJAH. The Real Billy Sunday. Otterbein, 1914. Rpt. VG in Good + dj. Plapinger. $250/£156

BROWN, FREDRIC. Angels and Spaceships. NY: E.P. Dutton, 1954. 1st ed. NF in dj. Pacific*. $184/£115

BROWN, FREDRIC. The Late Lamented. NY: E.P. Dutton, 1959. 1st ed. Fine in NF dj (price-clipped, sm tear top edge rear panel). Bernard. $200/£125

BROWN, FREDRIC. Space on My Hands. Chicago: Shasta, (1951). 1st ed. Signed. (Erasure bottom corner tp), o/w NF in dj (rear panel lt soiled). Bernard. $375/£234

BROWN, FREDRIC. Space on My Hands. Chicago: Shasta, 1951. 1st ed. Fine in dj. Mordida. $350/£219

BROWN, FREDRIC. What Mad Universe. NY: E.P. Dutton, 1949. 1st ed. VG in dj (sm tears to upper fr panel). Pacific*. $173/£108

BROWN, GEORGE MACKAY. Andrina and Other Stories. Chatto/Hogarth, 1983. 1st UK ed. Fine in dj (price-clipped). Williams. $29/£18

BROWN, GEORGE MACKAY. Fishermen with Ploughs. London: Hogarth, 1971. 1st Eng ed. NF (spine ends sl bumped) in dj (sl rubbed). Ulysses. $40/£25

BROWN, GEORGE MACKAY. Magnus. Hogarth, 1973. 1st UK ed. VG in dj. Williams. $40/£25

BROWN, GEORGE MACKAY. Poems: New and Selected. London: Hogarth, 1971. 1st Eng ed. NF (spine head, corner bumped) in dj (sl creased, sl rubbed). Ulysses. $40/£25

BROWN, GEORGE MACKAY. A Spell for Green Corn. Hogarth, 1970. 1st UK ed. NF (ink inscrip) in VG dj. Williams. $56/£35

BROWN, GEORGE VAN INGEN. The Surgery of Oral Diseases and Malformations; Their Diagnosis and Treatment. Phila/NY: Lea & Febiger, (1918). 3rd ed. 20 plts. Maroon cl. (Ex-lib w/rear pocket removed; stamps, blackened; sm tears), else Good. Weber. $50/£31

BROWN, GEORGE VAN INGEN. The Surgery of Oral Diseases and Malformations; Their Diagnosis and Treatment Including Plastic Surgical Reconstruction. Phila: Lea & Febiger, 1938. 4th ed. 12 color plts. Maroon cl. VF. Weber. $100/£63

BROWN, H. P. Trees of Northeastern United States. Boston, 1938. 2nd ed. (Pp tanned; spine faded.) Sutton. $55/£34

BROWN, H. RAP. Die Nigger Die! NY: Dial, 1969. 1st ed, 1st bk. Fine in NF dj (lt worn). Agvent. $125/£78

BROWN, HAMISH. Hamish's Groats End Walk. Gollancz, 1981. 1st ed. VG in dj. Hollett. $32/£20

BROWN, HOLMES and DON LUCE. Hostages of War. Washington: Indochina Mobile Education Project, 1973. 1st ed. NF (sl mk to text) in wraps. Associates. $100/£63

BROWN, IVOR. Conan Doyle: A Biography of the Creator of Sherlock Holmes. London: Hamish Hamilton, (1972). 1st ed. NF (ink name) in VG dj (price-clipped). Gravesend. $50/£31

BROWN, J. LEWIS. Golf at Glens Falls. Glens Falls, NY: Glens Falls Country Club, (1923). 1st ed. Frontis map. Pict cvr label. NF. Pacific*. $115/£72

BROWN, J. R. Unusual Plants. Pasadena, 1954. Ltd to 1650. 110 full-pg b/w photos. VG. Brooks. $46/£29

BROWN, JAMES BALDWIN (ed). Memoirs of John Howard, Compiled from His Diary, His Confidential Letters, and Other Authentic Documents. Boston: Lincoln & Edmonds, 1831. 1st Amer ed. Engr frontis port, xx,(iv),(xvii),xx,(21),352pp; 1 plt. Paper spine label. VG (foxed, joints sl worn). Gach. $65/£41

BROWN, JAMES BARRETT and FRANK McDOWELL. Neck Dissections. Springfield, IL: Charles C. Thomas, (1954). (Dj lt worn), else Fine. Weber. $75/£47

BROWN, JAMES BARRETT and FRANK McDOWELL. Skin Grafting. Phila: Lippincott, (1949). 2nd ed. (Few ll underlined in red pencil), else Fine. Weber. $50/£31

BROWN, JAMES BARRETT and FRANK McDOWELL. Skin Grafting. Phila: Lippincott, (1958). 3rd ed, rev. 6 color plts. Fine (bkpl). Weber. $50/£31

BROWN, JAMES. The Forester; or A Practical Treatise on the Planning, Rearing and General Management of Forest Trees. William Blackwood, 1871. 4th ed. xiv,835pp + ads. Uncut. Good (bkpl) in grn cl, gilt. Cox. $64/£40

BROWN, JANE (ed). Fulbrook...The Sketchbook, Letters, Specification of Works and Accounts for a House by Edwin Lutyens, 1896-1899. (Marlborough): Libanus, 1989. 2 vols. 1/4 morocco. Cl slipcase. Swann*. $149/£93

BROWN, JEANNIE ALBERT. Doctor Tom Brown Memories. NY, 1949. 1st ed. VG in good dj. Doctor's Library. $30/£19

BROWN, JESSE and A. M. WILLARD. The Black Hills Trails. Milek (ed). Rapid City, 1924. 1st ed. (Stamps; fr hinge, extrems worn), else VG. Howes B850. Baade. $150/£94

BROWN, JOHN HENRY. Reminiscences and Incidents of 'The Early Days' of San Francisco. SF: Mission Journal Pub Co, (1886). 1st ed. (106)pp; fldg plan. Tan cl, gilt. (Bkpl; fr hinge cracked; fr cvr, few pp lt soiled), o/w VG. Howes B853. Pacific*. $374/£234

BROWN, JOHN HENRY. Reminiscences and Incidents of Early Days of San Francisco (1845-50). SF: Grabhorn, (1933). One of 500 (of 525). 7 repros, fldg facs map. Prospectus laid in. Tan cl, marbled bds, paper labels. Fine. Karmiole. $100/£63

BROWN, JOHN HENRY. Reminiscences and Incidents of Early Days of San Francisco (1845-50). SF: Grabhorn, (1933). 2nd ed. One of 500. Fldg plan. Cl-backed marbled bds, paper spine/cvr labels. NF. Howes B853. Harrington. $125/£78

BROWN, JOHN J. The American Angler's Guide. NY, 1876. 5th ed. 428pp. Gilt-stamped cl. (Name label, inner hinge cracked, extrems rubbed.) King. $150/£94

BROWN, JOHN. Autobiography of Pioneer John Brown, 1820-1896.... Salt Lake City, 1941. 1st ed. Inscribed. Ginsberg. $175/£109

BROWN, JOHN. A Brief Concordance to the Holy Scriptures. Worcester: Isaiah Thomas, 1792. 322pp. Mod cl. (Browned, dampstained.) Swann*. $57/£36

BROWN, JOHN. John Leech and Other Papers. Edinburgh: David Douglas, 1882. 1st ed. x,442,(2)pp. Smooth cl (rubbed, extrems sl worn), paper label (browned). Cox. $19/£12

BROWN, JULIAN (ed). Fossils of the World. Hamlyn, 1988. VG in dj. Hollett. $48/£30

BROWN, KENNETH. The Medchester Club. NY: Derrydale, 1932. Ltd to 950 numbered. Red cl. Fine. Biscotti. $100/£63

BROWN, LARRY. Big Bad Love. Chapel Hill: Algonquin Books, 1990. 1st ed. Fine in Fine dj. Agvent. $35/£22

BROWN, LARRY. Dirty Work. Chapel Hill: Algonquin Books, 1989. 1st ed. Fine in Fine dj. Agvent. $45/£28

BROWN, LARRY. Joe. Chapel Hill: Algonquin Books, 1991. 1st ed. Fine in Fine dj. Pettler. $20/£13

BROWN, MAGGIE. Two Old Ladies, Two Foolish Fairies and a Tom Cat. London: Cassell, 1897. 1st ed. 8vo. Half-title; 4 color plts by Arthur Rackham (1 plt torn at margin w/o loss; lt spotted, stained). Mod cl w/orig upper red gilt-pict cl cvrs, spine labels laid down (new eps). Christie's*. $314/£196

BROWN, MARCIA. Felice. NY: Scribner, 1958. 1st ed. 8.25x10.25. 32pp. Pict cl. VG. Cattermole. $30/£19

BROWN, MARGARET WISE. Baby Animals. NY: Random House, (1941). 1st ed. 4to. 11 full color illus by Mary Cameron. Cl-backed color illus bds (corners sl worn). Full color dj (edges sl worn). Reisler. $110/£69

BROWN, MARGARET WISE. Black Tuppenny. (London): Heinemann, (1932). 4to. Sheila Hawkins (illus). Cl-backed color illus bds (rubbed, spine, eps replaced). Reisler. $250/£156

BROWN, MARGARET WISE. Doctor Squash the Doll Doctor. NY: S&S, 1952. 1st ed. Little Golden Book. 6.75x8. J. P. Miller (illus). 28pp. Pict bds. Fine. Cattermole. $20/£13

BROWN, MARGARET WISE. Little Chicken. NY: Harper, 1943. 1st ed. 8x7. Leonard Weisgard (illus). 32pp. VG. Cattermole. $30/£19

BROWN, MARGARET WISE. Little Pig's Picnic and Other Stories. Boston: D.C. Heath, 1939. 1st ed. 8vo. (vi),102pp; 69 color Walt Disney illus from orig cells. Pict cl. (Few mks on eps), o/w VG. Sotheran. $205/£128

BROWN, MARGARET WISE. The Noisy Book. NY: Harper, 1939. 1st ed. 7x8.75. Leonard Weisgard (illus). 32pp. Pict bds. Good. Cattermole. $75/£47

BROWN, MARGARET WISE. The Noon Balloon. NY: Doubleday, 1952. 1st ed. 7.5x10. Leonard Weisgard (illus). 32pp. Pict bds. VG in dj. Cattermole. $100/£63

BROWN, MARGARET WISE. The Streamlined Pig. Harper, 1938. 1st ed. 11x8. Kurt Wiese (illus). Unpaginated. Good (2-inch closed tear fep; cl speckled w/waterspots, corners rubbed). Price. $150/£94

BROWN, MARGARET WISE. Wheel on the Chimney. Phila: Lippincott, (1954). 1st ed. Tibor Gergely (illus). 4to. Gray cl. Good in color pict dj. Reisler. $150/£94

BROWN, MARK H. and W. R. FELTON. Before Barbed Wire. NY: Henry Holt, 1956. 1st ed. Pub's prospectus, 2 als by Brown (one w/Felton's sig) laid in. VG in dj (sl worn, clipped). Dumont. $75/£47

BROWN, MARK H. and W. R. FELTON. The Frontier Years. NY, 1955. VG in dj. Dumont. $50/£31

BROWN, MARK H. The Plainsmen of the Yellowstone. NY: Putnam, (1961). 1st ed. Inscribed presentation. Typed errata sheet, 'complied (sic) by the Author,' laid in loose. (Sl offset to eps, lower cvrs from earlier dj protector), else NF in dj (extrems sl rubbed, spine sl faded). Pacific*. $52/£33

BROWN, MONTY. Where Giants Trod. London: Quiller, 1989. 1st ed. Frontis, fldg map. Fine in Fine dj. Backman. $38/£24

BROWN, MRS. HUGH. Lady in Boomtown. Miners and Manners on the Nevada Frontier. Palo Alto: Amer West Pub, (1968). VG in dj. Perier. $25/£16

BROWN, P. HUME (ed). Our Journal into Scotland. Edinburgh: David Douglas, 1894. 56,(xvi)pp; facs. (Spine sl faded.) Hollett. $120/£75

BROWN, P. HUME. History of Scotland to the Present Time. CUP, 1911. 1st ed. 3 vols. Frontisports, 129 plts, 11 maps. Teg. 1/2 morocco, cl bds, raised bands, gilt. (Lt dampstains fr bd vol 3.) Edwards. $240/£150

BROWN, PAUL. Aintree: Grand Nationals Past and Present. NY: Derrydale, 1930. Ltd to 850 numbered. Folio. Fine orig prospectus laid in. Red cl. NF in ptd pict dj. Biscotti. $325/£203

BROWN, PAUL. Aintree; Grand Nationals Past and Present. NY: Derrydale, 1930. One of 850. (Shelfworn.) Oinonen*. $325/£203

BROWN, PAUL. Hits and Misses. (NY: Derrydale, 1935.) One of 950 numbered, signed. Pict cl (worn, stained, spine ends frayed; bkpl removed fr pastedown, glue remaining). Swann*. $103/£64

BROWN, PAUL. Mick and Mac: The Perkins' Pups. NY: Scribner, 1937. 1st ed. 4to. Cl-backed bds (edges lt rubbed). Dj (margins worn, chipped). Reisler. $110/£69

BROWN, PAUL. Piper's Pony. NY: Scribner, 1935. 1st ed. 11 1/4 x 8 3/4. 120pp. Cl spine, pict bds. Good. Cattermole. $75/£47

BROWN, PHILIP F. Reminiscences of the War of 1861-1865 [cover title]. (Roanoke, VA: Union Ptg, 1912.) 1st ed. Inscribed presentation. Frontisport, 2 plts. Ptd card laid in. Errata sheet affixed to inside fr cvr. NF in ptd tan wraps. Chapel Hill. $400/£250

BROWN, R. J. Windmills of England. Robert Hale, 1976. 1st ed. VG in dj. Hollett. $48/£30

BROWN, R. N. RUDMOSE. A Naturalist at the Poles. Seeley Service, 1923. 1st ed. VG. Walcot. $88/£55

BROWN, R. N. RUDMOSE. The Polar Regions: A Physical and Economic Geography.... London: Methuen, 1927. 23 maps (2 fldg color). NF. *Explorer.* $80/£50

BROWN, RITA MAE. Southern Discomfort. NY: Harper & Row, (1982). 1st ed. Fine in dj (1-inch tear top fr panel). *Agvent.* $35/£22

BROWN, ROBERT R. History of Kings County. Hanford, CA: A.H. Cawston, 1940. 1st ed. Red cl, gilt. Fine. *Harrington.* $85/£53

BROWN, RODERICK (ed). The Architectural Outsiders. Waterstones, 1985. NF in dj. *Hadley.* $40/£25

BROWN, SAMUEL R. Views of the Campaigns of the North-Western Army.... Burlington, VT: Samuel Mills, 1814. 156pp. Orig sheep (rubbed, worn). Howes B866. *Adelson.* $225/£141

BROWN, SOLYMAN. A Comparative View of the Systems of Pestalozzi and Lancaster. NY: Gray & Bunce, 1825. 1st ed. 24pp (margins sl foxed). Later cl. *M & S.* $275/£172

BROWN, SUSAN JENKINS. Robber Rocks: Letters and Memories of Hart Crane, 1923-1932. Middletown: Wesleyan, (1969). 1st ed. Fine in NF dj. *Reese.* $30/£19

BROWN, T. The Taxidermist's Manual. NY: Putnam, (1876). 27th ed. 150pp; 6 engr plts. VG. *Mikesh.* $45/£28

BROWN, THOMAS. Amusements Serious and Comical Calculated for the Meridian of London. London, 1702. 2nd ed. Orig old calf. (Lt foxed, names; fr bd detached, rubbed, sm loss of leather.) *Metropolitan*.* $115/£72

BROWN, THOMAS. Illustrations of the Recent Conchology of Great Britain and Ireland. London: Smith, Elder, n.d. (1844). 2nd ed, enlgd. Tall 4to. 62 Fine hand-colored plts. Contemp 3/4 morocco (rubbed, lt foxed, soiled). *Oinonen*.* $700/£438

BROWN, VARINA DAVIS. A Colonel at Gettysburg and Spotsylvania. Columbia, SC: State Co, 1931. 1st ed. Frontisport, fldg map, 2 full-pg maps. Blue cl. NF. *Chapel Hill.* $325/£203

BROWN, W. NORMAN. The Story of Kalaka. Washington: Smithsonian Inst, 1933. 1st ed. Folio. 15 plts (5 color). VG in stiff wraps. *Worldwide.* $75/£47

BROWN, WARREN. The Chicago White Sox. Putnam, 1952. 1st ed. VG in VG dj (spine lt worn). *Plapinger.* $100/£63

BROWN, WILLIAM H. Portrait Gallery of Distinguished American Citizens. (NY, 1931.) One of 600 numbered. Folio. *Swann*.* $149/£93

BROWN, WILLIAM R. The Horse of the Desert. NY: Derrydale, 1929. One of 750. Folio. Color frontis. (Cvrs stained.) *Swann*.* $258/£161

BROWN, WILLIAM R. The Horse of the Desert. NY: Derrydale, 1967. Ltd ed. Maroon cl, gilt. (Lacks frontis), else VG. *Larry Price.* $95/£59

BROWN, WILLIAM WELLS. The Negro in the American Rebellion. Boston: Lee & Shepard, 1867. 1st ed. 16,380pp. *M & S.* $300/£188

BROWNE, B. H. The Conquest of Mount McKinley. NY: Putnam, 1913. 1st ed. 4 color plts. Fldg map. Dec cl (sl mkd, sl mottling), teg. VG. *High Latitude.* $350/£219

BROWNE, B. H. Guns and Gunning. Dan Beard (ed). Chicopee Falls, MA: J. Stevens Arms & Tool, (1908). 1st ed. VG (bkpl). *Pacific*.* $138/£86

BROWNE, DOROTHEA GORE. Sweetbriar. A Pastoral with Songs. London: Elkin Matthews, 1905. 1st ed. 8vo. (vii),8-64pp + 30pg pub's cat; 13 hand-colored engrs by Edith Calvert. Uncut. Mid-grn cl. (Feps sl browned.) *Sotheran.* $141/£88

BROWNE, EDGAR. Phiz and Dickens. London: James Nisbet, 1913. 1st ltd ed. One of 175 signed and numbered by Browne. Frontis port, 38 plts. Teg, untrimmed. White cl, beveled bds (edges, spine ends sun-dknd, cvrs lt dusty, rubbed), gilt. Text VG (eps foxed). *Baltimore*.* $180/£113

BROWNE, G. WALDO. Japan: The People and the Place. Boston: Dana Estes, 1904. 2nd imp. 76 full-pg photo plts (16 color). Recent red 1/2 calf (orig cl spine bound in), red cl sides, gilt. Very Clean. *Sotheran.* $317/£198

BROWNE, HOWARD. Thin Air. NY: S&S, 1954. 1st ed. Fine in dj. *Else Fine.* $250/£156

BROWNE, HOWARD. Warrior of the Dawn. Chicago: Reilly & Lee, 1940. 1st ed. VF in dj (corners sl rubbed). *Else Fine.* $175/£109

BROWNE, J. ROSS. A Dangerous Journey. Ashland: Lewis Osborne, 1972. One of 600. (Ink name, spine faded), else VG. *Perier.* $30/£19

BROWNE, J. ROSS. Muleback to the Convention. Black Vine, 1950. One of 400. *Dawson.* $30/£19

BROWNE, J. ROSS. Report on the Debates in the Convention of California, on the Formation of the State Constitution, in September and October, 1849. Washington: John T. Towers, 1850. 479pp. Fair (ex-lib; rebacked, spine, corners worn). *Lien.* $60/£38

BROWNE, JANE EUPHEMIA. The Child from the Dove in the Cross. London: Day & Son, (1860). 1st ed. Slim 4to. (18),(ii)ads pp; 8 Fine color-ptd plts heightened w/gold. Aeg. Brn cl, gilt. Attractive (plt guards browned, inner hinge cracked; sl rubbed). *Sotheran.* $317/£198

BROWNE, K. R. G. How to Make a Garden Grow. London: Hutchinson, n.d. (1938). Inscribed presentation from W. Heath Robinson (illus). Good (name, address; edges spotted; cvrs cocked, rubbed; spine ends, corners sl bumped). *Ulysses.* $360/£225

BROWNE, MAGGIE. The Surprising Adventures of Tuppy and Tue. London: Cassell, 1904. Sm 4to. 4 color plts by Arthur Rackham. Blue pict cl. (Margins lt stained; extrems lt rubbed, spine faded; bkpl.) *Christie's*.* $258/£161

BROWNE, MAGGIE. Two Old Ladies Two Foolish Fairies and a Tom Cat: The Surprising Adventures of Tuppy and Tue. London: Cassell, 1897. 1st ed, 1st issue. 8vo. 190pp + ads; 4 full-pg color, 19 b/w plts by Arthur Rackham. Teg. Dk blue cl (lt worn), gilt. *Reisler.* $750/£469

BROWNE, THOMAS. A Letter to a Friend Upon Occasion of the Death of His Intimate Friend. Geoffrey Keynes (ed). Boston: David R. Godine, 1971. Ltd to 750 numbered. Marbled eps. Orig black calf, olive bds. Fine in pub's slipcase. *Karmiole.* $100/£63

BROWNE, THOMAS. Religio Medici. London: For R. Scot et al, 1678. 7th ed. 3 parts in 1. Engr frontis, (14),371,(3)pp. Contemp sprinkled calf (rebacked, orig spine, label laid down). *Karmiole.* $250/£156

BROWNE, THOMAS. Religio Medici. Eugene: Univ of OR/John Henry Nash, 1939. Signed by Nash (pub). 1/4 linen, ptd label, marbled paper sides. Box (worn). *Appelfeld.* $125/£78

BROWNE, THOMAS. The Works of Sir Thomas Browne. Charles Sayle (ed). Edinburgh: John Grant, 1927. 3 vols. Buckram-backed bds, leather spine labels. Fine set. *Ulysses.* $200/£125

BROWNE, THOMAS. The Works of Sir Thomas Browne. Geoffrey Keynes (ed). London: Faber & Gwyer, 1928. 1st ed thus. 6 vols. (Spines sunned), else Fine set in dec blue cl. *Captain's Bookshelf.* $150/£94

BROWNE, THOMAS. The Works of Sir Thomas Browne. Simon Wilkin (ed). London: George Bell, 1900-1901. Later ed. 3 vols. Frontisport. Maroon cl, gilt. VG +. *House.* $60/£38

BROWNE, THOMAS. The Works, Including His Unpublished Correspondence, and a Memoir. Simon Wilkin (ed). Henry G. Bohn, 1846. 4 vols. 1/2-titles absent, probably not called for; tps are cancels; Vol 1: engr frontisport, lg fldg facs, 2 lg fldg genealogies, engr plt; Vol 4: 2 engr plts. Brn faced eps. Contemp full calf, gilt, raised bands, red labels, burnished edges. (Margins lt browned; plts in vol 4 and adjacent ll dampstained in margins; 2 joints broken; spine tops chipped away or torn). Internally NF. *Temple*. $120/£75

BROWNE, THOMAS. The Works. London: Basset, Chiswell et al, 1686. 1st collected ed. Tall thick folio. Full-pg engr frontisport. Orig calf bds (worn, serviceably rebacked w/new leather label). Contents Fine (tp dusty). *Hartfield*. $895/£559

BROWNING, COLIN ARROTT. The Convict Ship. London: Smith, Elder, 1844. 2nd ed. xv,(i)blank,324pp, errata slip. Brn blindstamped cl (faded, stained, spine repaired), gilt. Internally Good (lt marks). *Morrell*. $288/£180

BROWNING, ELIZABETH BARRETT. Napoleon III in Italy. NY: C.S. Francis, 1860. 1st Amer ed. Black cl, gilt. Good (sm crown chip). *Macdonnell*. $100/£63

BROWNING, ELIZABETH BARRETT. Poems Before Congress. London: Chapman & Hall, 1860. 1st ed. Blind-stamped red cl, gilt. VG (bkpl, label; edges bumped, sl worn, spine rubbed, lt stained). *Hermitage*. $225/£141

BROWNING, ELIZABETH BARRETT. Sonnets from the Portuguese. Oxford: Shakespeare Head, 1945. Rpt of 1933 ed. Later 1/2 lambskin, red cl sides. *Cox*. $29/£18

BROWNING, ELIZABETH BARRETT. Sonnets from the Portuguese. NY: LEC, 1948. One of 1500. Signed by Valenti Angelo (decs). Gilt-stamped blue cl. Fine in slipcase. *Pacific**. $137/£86

BROWNING, OSCAR. Impressions of Indian Travel. H&S, 1903. 1st ed. Signed, dated 1903. VG (prelims sl foxed; spine head sl worn). *Any Amount*. $58/£36

BROWNING, R. A History of Golf, the Royal and Ancient Game. London: Sportsmans Book Club, 1956. Fine (emb stamp). *Pacific**. $161/£101

BROWNING, ROBERT and ELIZABETH BARRETT. Letters of Robert Browning and Elizabeth Barrett Browning 1845-1846. London, 1899. 1st ed. 2 vols. Nice set. *Gretton*. $40/£25

BROWNING, ROBERT. Paracelsus. Effingham Wilson, 1835. 1st ed. Sm 8vo. Half-title (sm hole near gutter margin, natural paper fault), ix,(iii),216pp. Marbled eps; gilt edges. Late 19th-cent crushed polished russet morocco (sl rubbed, sm repair to rep gutter margin), by Bagguley, backstrip w/gilt raised bands, date at tail. *Blackwell's*. $880/£550

BROWNING, ROBERT. The Pied Piper of Hamelin. London: George G. Harrap, (1934). 1st ed. 8vo. 4 full-pg color plts by Arthur Rackham. Pict eps. Limp bds (lt dusty). Nice in matching color dj. *Reisler*. $125/£78

BROWNING, ROBERT. The Pied Piper of Hamelin. London: George G. Harrap, 1934. 1st ed illus by Arthur Rackham. 8vo. (x),11-44pp; 4 full-pg color plts, 15 line dwgs. Pict eps. NF (spine head sl rubbed) in pict card wraps, preserved in orig pict wrapper. *Sotheran*. $269/£168

BROWNING, ROBERT. The Poems of Robert Browning. LEC, 1969. Ltd to 1500 numbered, signed by Peter Reddick (illus). Fine in slipcase. *Swann**. $69/£43

BROWNING, ROBERT. The Ring and the Book. L.A.: Plantin, 1949. Signed by Carl Schultheiss (illus). 2 vols. 1/4 red sheepskin gilt-stamped w/ptd Fabriano paper sides. Boxed. *Appelfeld*. $125/£78

BROWNLEE, RICHARD S. Gray Ghosts of the Confederacy. Guerrilla Warfare in the West, 1861-1865. Baton Rouge: LA State Univ, (1958). 1st ed. Brn cl. NF in dj. *Chapel Hill*. $75/£47

BROWNMILLER, SUSAN. Femininity. NY, 1984. 1st Amer ed. NF in dj (2 sm spine nicks). *Polyanthos*. $25/£16

BROWNSON, O. A. New Views of Christianity, Society, and the Church. Boston: James Munroe, 1836. 1st ed, 1st bk. Inscribed ink presentation, 'with the Respects of the Author.' 12mo. 116pp. Orig cl (edge sl rubbed). *M & S*. $925/£578

BROWNSON, O. A. Social Reform. Boston: Waite, Peirce, 1844. 1st ed. 42pp. Fine in orig ptd wrappers. *M & S*. $200/£125

BROWSE, LILLIAN (ed). Barbara Hepworth: Sculptress. London: Shenval/Ariel Books on the Arts, 1946. 1st Eng ed. Very Nice in dj (dust-mkd). *Clearwater*. $64/£40

BRUCCOLI, MATTHEW J. and C. W. FRAZER CLARK, JR. Hemingway at Auction, 1930-1973. Detroit: Gale Research, (1973). 1st ed. Grn cl, gilt. Text Good (crease fep, ex-lib, stamps, ink notes), cvrs Nice (sl handled). *Baltimore**. $25/£16

BRUCE, ALEXANDER BALMAIN. The Life of William Denny, Ship-Builder, Dumbarton. London, 1889. 2nd ed. Frontisport, xvi,479pp; fldg color map. Mainly unopened. (Lib ink stamp tp, bkpl, remains of another.) *Edwards*. $72/£45

BRUCE, C. Twenty Years in Borneo. London: Cassell, n.d. (1924). 1st ed. 16 half-tone plts. Grn cl. VG (lt foxed). *Morrell*. $128/£80

BRUCE, C. Twenty Years in the Himalaya. London, 1910. Map. (Sl rubbed.) *Petersfield*. $176/£110

BRUCE, DAVID. Bird of Jove. NY: Putnam, 1971. 1st ed. Pict cl. VG + in VG dj. *Mikesh*. $30/£19

BRUCE, DAVID. Sun Pictures. London, 1973. Dj. *Edwards*. $61/£38

BRUCE, EDWARD and FORBES WATSON. Art in Federal Buildings, Volume I: Mural Designs, 1934-1936. Washington: Art in Federal Buildings, 1936. 1st ed. 1/4 cl, gilt. (Rear cvr sl sunned), else NF. *Pacific**. $219/£137

BRUCE, IAN (ed). The Nun of Lebanon. London, 1951. Frontisport, 3 plts. Dj (chipped w/loss). *Edwards*. $40/£25

BRUCE, J. M. British Aeroplanes 1914-1918. NY: Funk & Wagnalls, (1969). 2nd ed. (Ex-lib, tape to pastedowns, adhesion residue fep), else VG. *Pacific**. $46/£29

BRUCE, JAMES. Travels to Discover the Source of the Nile in the Years 1768, 1769, 1770, 1771, 1772 and 1773. Edinburgh/London: Archibald Constable/Manners & Miller/Longman, Hurst, Rees et al, 1805. 2nd ed. 7 vols. 4to plt vol; rest 8vo. Engr frontis, 57 engr plts, 3 lg fldg maps. Full contemp diced calf, gilt, raised bands, tooling; recent 1/2 calf on plt vol, blue marbled bds. (Prelim text ll of plt vol lt foxed, maps sl browned, repairs; calf rebacked), o/w VG set. *Sotheran*. $1,920/£1,200

BRUCE, JAMES. Travels to Discover the ████████ Nile. J. Ruthven for G.G.J. & J. Robinson, 1████ ███ls, incl 1 vol of maps & plts. Vols 1-4 1st ed; vol 5 ████ 4to. 94 plts (some spotted, sl dampstained, 1 detach███ ███ut. Mod cl-backed bds (rubbed, some hinges broke██████eby's**. $736/£460

BRUCE, JOHN. Gaudy Century. NY: Random House, (1948). 1st ed. Gray cl. Fine in NF dj. *Harrington*. $35/£22

BRUCE, LENNY. How to Talk Dirty and Influence People. Peter Owen, 1966. 1st UK ed. VG in dj. *Sclanders*. $19/£12

BRUCE, PETER HENRY. Memoirs of...a Military Officer...Containing an Account of His Travels in Germany, Russia.... Dublin, 1783. Mod sheep. *Swann**. $103/£64

BRUCE, ROBERT V. Lincoln and the Tools of War. Indianapolis, (1956). 1st ed. Signed. 2-tone cl. (Inner fr hinge cracked, cvrs dull, rubbed.) *King*. $35/£22

BRUCE-MITFORD, RUPERT. The Sutton Hoo Ship-Burial. Volume 3, Parts 1 and 2. London, 1983. 1st ed. 2 vols. *Gretton*. $48/£30

BRUEHL, ANTON. Photographs of Mexico. NY: Delphic Studios, (1933). 1st ed. One of 1000. Folio. Leather-backed linen (spine worn; sl foxed throughout). Bd slipcase (panels detached). *Swann**. $230/£144

BRUEHL, ANTON. Photographs of Mexico. NY, (1945). Sq folio. (Bkpl; spine faded.) Dj (fully separated at spine panel). *Swann**. $92/£58

BRUEHL, ANTON. Tropic Patterns. Hollywood, FL: Dukane, 1970. 1st ed. Folio. 24 full-pg color plts. Illus eps. (Inscrip), else NF in dj. *Cahan*. $85/£53

BRUETTE, WILLIAM. Guncraft. Chicago: Privately ptd, 1912. 1st ed. Burgundy dec buckram, gilt. NF. *Biscotti*. $75/£47

BRUGUIERE, FRANCIS. San Francisco. SF: H.S. Crocker, 1918. 1st ed. Pict cvr label. (Tp, following pp foxed; spine sl chipped), else VG. *Pacific**. $63/£39

BRUN, SAMUEL JACQUES. Tales of Languedoc. SF: Doxey, 1896. 1st ed. Lg 8vo. Ernest Peixotto (illus). 240pp. Brn cl, full stamped pict, titles gilt. VG (foxed, 1/2-inch scrape top edge). *Price*. $95/£59

BRUN, T. The Haunted Heart. John Westhouse, 1946. 1st Eng ed. (Corners sl bumped), o/w VG in dj (rubbed, worn, price-clipped). *Ulysses*. $58/£36

BRUNHOUSE, ROBERT L. The Counter-Revolution in Pennsylvania 1776-1790. Harrisburg: PA Hist & Museum Comm, 1971. 2nd ptg. Blue cl. Fine in VG + dj (lt soiled). *House*. $15/£9

BRUNHOUSE, ROBERT L. Sylvanus G. Morley and the World of Ancient Mayas. Norman: Univ of OK, 1971. 1st ed. (Stamp), else VG in dj (sl worn). *Dumont*. $35/£22

BRUNNER, D. B. The Indians of Berks County, PA. Reading, 1897. 2nd ed. (Fep separating at fr inner hinge.) *Kane**. $100/£63

BRUNNER, JOHN. The Whole Man. NY: Walker, (1969). 1st Amer hb ed. Signed. Fine in NF dj. *Levin*. $200/£125

BRUNO, ANTHONY. Bad Guys. NY, 1988. 1st ed, 1st bk. Inscribed, signed. Fine in Fine dj. *Warren*. $50/£31

BRUNO, ANTHONY. Bad Moon. (NY): Delacorte, (1992). 1st ed. Signed. Fine in dj. *Between The Covers*. $45/£28

BRUSHFIELD, T. N. A Bibliography of Sir Walter Raleigh Knt. Exeter: James G. Commin, 1908. 2nd rev, enlgd ed. Frontisport, 14 plts. Red cl (rubbed, faded, headcaps bumped). *Maggs*. $104/£65

BRYAN, BRUCE. Archaeological Explorations on San Nicolas Island. L.A.: Southwest Museum Papers, 1970. 1st ed. Fine. *Book Market*. $35/£__

BRYAN, C. D. B. _____ Source of th_____ 790__. 3rd ed: Putnam, 1976. 1st ed. Fine in dj. *Associates*. $35/£__

BRYAN, GEORGE. Ch_____ Olden and Present Times. Chelsea: The Author, 1____, 2ff, 224pp. (Tear to spine top.) *Marlborough*. $80/£50

BRYAN, MICHAEL. Bryan's Dictionary of Painters and Engravers. London: George Bell, 1903. New ed. 5 vols. 1/2 cl. VG. *Pacific**. $161/£101

BRYAN, MICHAEL. Bryan's Dictionary of Painters and Engravers. London, 1918-19. New ed. 5 vols. (Shaken.) *Swann**. $287/£179

BRYAN, WILLIAM ALANSON. A Monograph of Marcus Island. Honolulu, HI, 1903. Uncut. (Ink name; rear cvr, many pg margins gnawed.) Wraps. *King*. $35/£22

BRYANT, BILLY. Children of Old Man River.... NY: Lee Furman, (1936). 1st ed. Signed, dated presentation. Fldg broadside. Dj. *Cullen*. $65/£41

BRYANT, H. STAFFORD, JR. Georgian Locomotive: Some Elegant Locomotive Steam Power in the South and Southwest, 1918-1945. Barre Gazette, 1962. 1st ed. Good in dj (worn). *Rybski*. $35/£22

BRYANT, J. R. M. Address Delivered Before the Philomathean Society, of Wabash College, July 13, 1836. Crawfordsville, IN: Harland & Holmes, (1836). 1st ed. 23pp. Contemp plain wraps. (Ex-lib.) *M & S*. $175/£109

BRYANT, JACOB. A Dissertation Concerning the War of Troy.... London, 1799. 2nd ed. Fldg map. Partly unopened. Orig wrappers (needs rebinding). *Swann**. $201/£126

BRYANT, JACOB. A New System; or, An Analysis of Antient Mythology. London: J. Walker et al, 1807. 3rd ed. 6 vols. 9.25x5.5. 41 plts, fldg maps. Period gilt-ruled calf. VG set (bkpls). *Pacific**. $575/£359

BRYANT, SARA CONE. Epaminondas and His Auntie. London: George G. Harrap, (1939). 1st ed thus. 8vo. Inez Hogan (illus). 16pp. Color pict bds set against a bright yellow background (edges sl rubbed). Color pict dj (dusty, margin torn). *Reisler*. $200/£125

BRYANT, WILLIAM CULLEN and HENRY D. THOREAU. Unpublished Poems by Bryant and Thoreau. Boston: Bibliophile Soc, 1907. 1st ed, 1st ptg. White bds. NF (lacks glassine, slipcase). *Lucas*. $150/£94

BRYANT, WILLIAM CULLEN (ed). Picturesque America. D. Appleton, (c. 1872). 2 vols. Lg 4to. viii,568; vi,576pp; 17 steel-engr plts. Contemp full black morocco, gilt, raised bands. (Fr joint foot both vols sl weak), o/w VG set. *Sotheran*. $720/£450

BRYANT, WILLIAM CULLEN. The Poems of... LEC, 1947. Ltd to 1500 numbered, signed by Thomas W. Nason (illus). Fine in slipcase. *Swann**. $57/£36

BRYANT, WILLIAM CULLEN. Poems. Cambridge: Hilliard & Metcalf, 1821. 1st ed. Inscribed in ink by Edward T. Channing (ed). Contemp 3/4 calf, plain paper-cvrd sides (spine very worn, fr cvr nearly loose). Sheets trimmed about 1/4-inch. BAL 1587. *M & S*. $950/£594

BRYCE, GEORGE. The Siege and Conquest of the North Pole. London: Gibbings, 1910. 9 maps, charts. Fine. *Explorer*. $93/£58

BRYCE, JAMES. The American Commonwealth. London: Macmillan, 1891. 2nd ed. 2 vols. Blue cl (fr hinge vol 1 cracked). *Mott*. $50/£31

BRYDEN, H. ANDERSON (ed). Great and Small Game of Africa. London: Rowland Ward, 1899. One of 500 signed. 4to. 15 hand-colored litho plts. Partly unopened. Orig pub's cl (spine lt faded, sl stained). *Christie's**. $1,171/£732

BRYDEN, H. ANDERSON. Kloof and Karroo: Sport, Legend, and Natural History in Cape Colony.... London: Longmans, Green, 1889. xv,435pp; 17 plts. Grn pict cl (rubbed, few spots, spine ends frayed). *Adelson*. $350/£219

BRYDONE, P. A Tour Through Sicily and Malta. W. Strahan/T. Cadell, 1773. 1st ed. 2 vols. 8vo. (xii),374; (viii),297pp. Marbled eps; all edges speckled. Contemp mottled calf (rebacked), burgundy leather labels, gilt, center tooling, spine date. VF set. *Sotheran*. $560/£350

BRYHER. (Pseud of Annie Winifred Ellerman.) Development. NY: Macmillan, 1920. 1st Amer ed. NF (lacks dj). *Captain's Bookshelf*. $200/£125

BRYHER. (Pseud of Annie Winifred Ellerman.) Roman Wall. NY, (1954). 1st Amer ed. NF (spine sl cocked; sl rubbed) in dj (spine torn). *Polyanthos*. $25/£16

BRYK, FELIX. Voodoo-Eros. NY: Privately ptd, 1933. 1st ed. One of 500. Brn cl, gilt. VG. *Larry Price*. $95/£59

BRYMER, JOHN. Games and Gambols. London: Blackie & Son, (1902). 1st ed. 4to. (98)pp; 24 color-tinted plts by Harry B. Neilson. Red pict cl, gilt. (Spine sunned, ends knocked), o/w Clean. *Sotheran*. $157/£98

Bubbles from the Brunnens of Nassau by an Old Man. (By Francis Bond Head.) Paris: Baudry's European Library, 1834. 3rd ed. Extra engr tp, (4),201pp; plt. Marbled eps. Morocco-backed grained paper sides (corners, fore-edges worn, ends lt foxed), leather tips. *Cox*. $56/£35

Bubbles of Canada. (By Thomas Chandler Haliburton.) Phila: Lea & Blanchard, 1839. 1st ed. (2)pp ads, 262pp. Orig purple patterned cl, paper spine label. (Foxed.) *Karmiole*. $200/£125

BUCHAN, JAMES WALTER. A History of Peeblesshire. Glasgow: Jackson, Wylie, 1925. 1st ed. One of 100. Initialed by Buchan on limitation pg. 3 vols. Fldg map. Bkpls of Joseph T. Hawden. Teg. 1/2 vellum, red cl, gilt. NF set. *Pacific**. $58/£36

BUCHAN, JOHN. Andrew Jameson Lord Ardwall. Blackwood, 1913. 1st UK ed. VG (sm bkpl; spine sl faded). *Williams*. $56/£35

BUCHAN, JOHN. The Battle of the Somme. NY: George H. Doran, (1917). 1st US ed, advance issue. Frontis. Gathered and trimmed sigs, bound in pict dj (flaps blank). Good (spine chipped, old mends, rear wrapper neatly detached). *Reese*. $75/£47

BUCHAN, JOHN. Castle Gay. London: Hodder & Stoughton, 1930. 1st ed. (Name, date; fore-edge spotted), o/w Fine in dj (lt soiled). *Mordida*. $200/£125

BUCHAN, JOHN. Greenmantle. London: Hodder & Stoughton, 1916. 1st ed. Blue cl stamped in gilt/blind. (Sl foxing early, late; spine extrems sl rubbed), else Good. *Reese*. $125/£78

BUCHAN, JOHN. A History of the Great War. London/Edinburgh/NY: Thomas Nelson & Sons, (1921-22). 1st ed thus. Vol 1 inscribed. 4 vols. Navy blue cl, gilt (except for vol 2, which is in greenish cl). VG set. *Reese*. $500/£313

BUCHAN, JOHN. Huntingtower. London: Hodder & Stoughton, 1922. 1st ed. Lt blue cl. (Joints lt worn), o/w Fine. *Maggs*. $72/£45

BUCHAN, JOHN. The Island of Sheep. London: Hodder & Stoughton, 1936. 1st ed. (Inscrip), o/w Fine in VG dj (closed tears). *Mordida*. $85/£53

BUCHAN, JOHN. The Long Traverse. London: Hodder & Stoughton, 1941. 1st ed. Lt blue cl. Fine in dj (sm closed tear fr panel, few nicks). *Maggs*. $192/£120

BUCHAN, JOHN. Mr. Standfast. Toronto, (1919). 1st Canadian ed. (Spine dull, cvr rubbed.) *King*. $35/£22

BUCHAN, JOHN. The Novel and the Fairy Tale. London: OUP, July, 1931. 1st ed. Pamphlet. Fine in lt gray heavy ptd paper wrappers. *Cady*. $25/£16

BUCHAN, JOHN. The Power House. Blackwood, 1916. 1st UK ed. VG (sm ink name; bds sl worn, stained). *Williams*. $120/£75

BUCHAN, JOHN. Scholar Gypsies. London/NY: John Lane, Bodley Head/Macmillan, 1906. 16pp pub's cat at rear. 7 etchings. Dec cl, gilt. Good (eps spotted, hinges cracked, top edge dusty; spine ends, corners bumped, bruised, cvrs sl mkd). *Ulysses*. $152/£95

BUCHAN, JOHN. The Scottish Tongue. Cassell, 1924. 1st ed. (Spine faded), else VG. *Whiteson*. $26/£16

BUCHAN, JOHN. Sick Heart River. Hodder & Stoughton, 1941. 1st UK ed. VG + in dj (rear strengthened). *Williams*. $72/£45

BUCHAN, LAURA and JERRY ALLEN. Hearth in the Snow. NY: Wilfred Funk, (1952). 1st ed. Fine in Fine dj. *Perier*. $30/£19

BUCHANAN, JAMES and GAIL STUART (eds). History of the Panama-Pacific International Exposition...San Francisco, 1915. SF: Pan-Pacific, (1915). 1st ed. Grn cl, gilt. VG. *Pacific**. $40/£25

BUCHANAN-BROWN, JOHN. Phiz: The Book Illustrations of Hablot K. Browne. D&C, 1978. 1st ed. Fine in dj (sl chipped). *Whittle*. $19/£12

BUCHANAN-JARDINE, JOHN. Hounds of the World. Methuen, 1937. 1st ed. 20 color, 24 collotype plts. Red cl (spine sl faded), gilt. *Hollett*. $192/£120

BUCHER, GEORG. In the Line, 1914-1918. Norman Gullick (trans). London, 1932. 1st Eng ed. Nice (spine sl faded; no dj). *Clearwater*. $48/£30

BUCHERL, W. et al. Venomous Animals and Their Venoms. Volume 1: Venomous Vertebrates. NY: Academic, 1968. (Couple short tears in dj), else Fine. *Weber*. $50/£31

BUCHERL, W. et al. Venomous Animals and Their Venoms. NY, 1968-71. 3 vols. xxii,707; xxiv,687; xxii,537pp. (Inked-out name eps.) Djs (chipped). *Sutton*. $225/£141

BUCHHEIM, LOTHAR-GUNTER. The Graphic Art of German Expressionism. NY: Universe Books, 1960. (Lt worn), else Sound. *Turtle Island*. $150/£94

BUCHSBAUM, RALPH. Animals Without Backbones. Univ of Chicago, 1947. 1st ed. Blue dec cl. VG. *Larry Price*. $15/£9

Buck Rogers (in the 25th Century). NY: Random House, 1980. Chuck McVicker (illus). 4 dbl-pg pop-ups, revolving wheel. Glazed pict bds. VG. *Bookfinders*. $40/£25

BUCK, CARL DARLING. A Dictionary of Selected Synonyms in the Principal Indo-European Languages. Chicago: Univ of Chicago, (1949). 1st ed. Dj (lt chipped). *Argosy*. $75/£47

BUCK, FRANK. Bring 'Em Back Alive. NY, 1930. Black cl, gilt. VG. *Larry Price*. $19/£12

BUCK, FRANKLIN A. A Yankee Trader in the Gold Rush. The Letters of Franklin A. Buck. Katherine A. White (comp). Boston/NY: Houghton Mifflin, 1930. 1st ed. Fine in pict dj (chipped, lacks sm piece). *Argonaut*. $50/£31

BUCK, PEARL S. The Good Earth. Methuen, 1931. 1st Eng ed. (Fore-edge, reps lt foxed; offsetting to fr cvr, rear cvr lt soiled), else NF in Fine dj. *Fine Books*. $375/£234

BUCK, PEARL S. One Bright Day. NY: John Day, (1950). 1st ed. (1st few pp sl foxed), else NF in Fine dj. *Between The Covers*. $100/£63

BUCK, PEARL S. (trans). All Men Are Brothers. LEC, 1948. Ltd to 1500 numbered, signed by Miguel Covarrubias (illus). 2 vols. Fine in slipcase. *Swann**. $126/£79

BUCK, PETER H. Explorers of the Pacific: European and American Discoveries in Polynesia. Honolulu: Bishop Museum, 1953. 1st ed. (Lower corners bumped, sm chip spine foot), else VG in color pict wrappers. *Pacific**. $23/£14

BUCK, ROBERT et al. Richard Diebenkorn. Buffalo: Albright-Knox Gallery, (1976). Fine in color illus wrappers. *Turtle Island*. $55/£34

BUCK, SAMUEL D. With the Old Confeds: Actual Experiences of a Captain in the Line. Balt: H.E. Houck, 1925. 1st ed. Signed in ink by Buck's widow. Tall slim 8vo. Frontis, 3 b/w photo ports. Lt blue-gray cl (sl rubbed), navy lettering. Text VG (eps lt foxed), cvrs Very Clean. *Baltimore**. $700/£438

BUCK, SOLON JUSTUS. Travel and Description 1765-1865. NY, 1971. Rpt of 1914 ed. VG. *Dumont*. $45/£28

BUCKBEE, EDNA BRYAN. The Saga of Old Tuolumne. NY: Press of the Pioneers, 1935. 1st ed. Red cl. Fine. *Argonaut*. $150/£94

BUCKE, RICHARD MAURICE. Notes and Fragments: Left by Walt Whitman.... (Ontario): Ptd for Private Distribution, 1899. 1st ed. One of 225 numbered, signed. Dk grn cl (tip rubbed), gilt. *Swann**. $161/£101

BUCKERIDGE, A. Jennings Again. Macmillan, 1991. 1st UK ed. Signed. Mint in Mint dj. *Martin*. $22/£14

BUCKERIDGE, A. The Jennings Report. Collins, 1970. 1st ed. VG in dj (sl worn). *Green Meadow*. $72/£45

BUCKINGHAM, JAMES SILK. America, Historical, Statistic, and Descriptive. NY: Harper, 1841. 1st Amer ed. 2 vols. Frontisport, 514,(1) (old tape repair 1 pg, no loss); 516pp. Orig cl (worn). Howes B921. *Mott.* $200/£125

BUCKINGHAM, JAMES SILK. The Eastern and Western States of America. London: Fisher, Son, (1842). 1st ed. 3 vols. 573; 536; 495pp; 15 plts. Orig cl (sm expert repairs spines). Internally Fine. Howes B922. *Mott.* $250/£156

BUCKINGHAM, JAMES SILK. Travels in Mesopotamia. Henry Colburn, 1827. 1st ed. 4to. 2 litho plts, fldg map (backed w/linen). 1/2 calf. *Sotheby's*.* $1,011/£632

BUCKINGHAM, NASH. The Best of Nash Buckingham. George Bird Evans (ed). NY: Winchester, 1973. 1st ed. VG + in VG dj (few sm edge tears, few sm edge pieces torn). *Backman.* $50/£31

BUCKINGHAM, NASH. De Shootinest Gent'man. NY: Derrydale, 1934. 1st ed. Ltd to 950 numbered. 8vo. Blue cl w/circular medallion. Fine. *Biscotti.* $525/£328

BUCKINGHAM, NASH. De Shootinest Gent'man. NY: Scribner, 1941. 1st ed thus. Frontis. Tan cl. Fine in NF ptd dj. *Biscotti.* $65/£41

BUCKINGHAM, NASH. Game Bag; Tales of Shooting and Fishing. NY: Putnam, 1945. 1st trade ed. Photo frontis. Red cl. NF in ptd dj (tattered). *Biscotti.* $35/£22

BUCKINGHAM, NASH. Hallowed Years. Harrisburg: Stackpole, 1953. 1st ed. Gray cl. Fine in NF pict dj. *Biscotti.* $125/£78

BUCKINGHAM, NASH. Mark Right! NY: Derrydale, 1936. Ltd to 1250 numbered. Burgundy cl. Fine. *Biscotti.* $300/£188

BUCKINGHAM, NASH. Ole Miss'. NY: Derrydale, 1937. Ltd to 1250 numbered. Dk burgundy cl. Fine. *Biscotti.* $300/£188

BUCKLAND, FRANK. Curiosities of Natural History. London: Richard Bentley, 1873. 2 vols. 4 wood-engr plts (incl frontispieces). Marbled eps, edges. Period full gilt-ruled polished tan calf, raised bands, morocco labels. (Cvrs scuffed, worn), o/w VG. *Pacific*.* $29/£18

BUCKLAND, FRANK. Curiosities of Natural History. London, 1891-3. Popular ed. 3 vols. Uncut. (Lt spotted, hinges cracked, sl shaken, lacks feps; spines sl rubbed, worn.) *Edwards.* $40/£25

BUCKLAND, FRANK. Notes and Jottings from Animal Life. Smith, Elder, 1886. 2nd ed. Photo frontisport, viii,414pp. Contemp full blue calf, gilt. VG. *Hollett.* $72/£45

BUCKLAND, GAIL (ed). First Photographs: People, Places, and Phenomena as Captured for the First Time by the Camera. NY: Macmillan, 1980. 1st ed. NF in VG dj. *Cahan.* $85/£53

BUCKLAND, W. Geology and Mineralogy. London: Pickering, 1836. 1st ed. 2 vols. 599;128pp; 69 plts. 1/2 leather, marbled bds. (Few plts, cvrs dampstained on vol 2), else VG. *Mikesh.* $175/£109

BUCKLAND-WRIGHT, JOHN. Etching and Engraving. Studio Publications, 1953. 1st ed. Frontis. *Forest.* $40/£25

BUCKLE, RICHARD. Jacob Epstein: Sculptor. Cleveland, (1963). Dj (few chips, tears at edges). *Swann*.* $69/£43

BUCKLEY, FRANCIS. A History of Old English Glass. London, 1925. 1st ed. 60 plts. (Bkpl; lib stamps, spine #s; sl soiled, fr joint sl rubbed.) *Edwards.* $64/£40

BUCKLEY, M. B. Diary of a Tour in America. By...of Cork, Ireland. Kate Buckley (ed). Dublin: Sealy, Bryers & Walker, 1889. 1st ed. 2 prelim ll, frontisport, ii,(2),384pp. Brn cl. Fine. *Mott.* $50/£31

BUCKLEY, WILLIAM F., JR. Stained Glass. GC, 1978. 1st ed. Signed. Dj. *Argosy.* $35/£22

BUCKLEY, WILLIAM F., JR. A Very Private Plot. NY: Morrow, (1994). 1st ed. Signed. Fine in dj. *Cady.* $25/£16

BUCKMASTER, HENRIETTA. Let My People Go. NY, (1941). 1st ed. (Spine badly dented, cvrs sl bent.) *King.* $25/£16

BUCKMASTER, HENRIETTA. Let My People Go.... NY: Harper, (1941). 3rd ed. Frontis, xii,398pp; map. VG in pict dj. *Petrilla.* $25/£16

BUDAY, GEORGE. The History of the Christmas Card. Rockliff, 1954. 1st ed. Fldg color frontis (sm split to 1 fold), 16 color, 201 half-tone plts. Good. *Cox.* $56/£35

BUDD, GEORGE. Diseases of the Liver. Phila, 1857. 3rd Amer ed. 499pp. Marbled bds (skillfully rebound) w/buckram spine, leather spine label. VG. *Doctor's Library.* $165/£103

BUDD, WILLIAM. Typhoid Fever. NY: (Delta Omega Soc/Amer Public Health Assn), 1931. One of 800. Port, 4 plts. Blue cl, leather lettering piece. VG (inner fr hinge repaired; lt soiled, worn). *House.* $50/£31

BUDDEN, LIONEL B. (ed). The Book of the Liverpool School of Architecture. Univ of Liverpool/Hodder & Stoughton, 1932. Ltd to 1000. Frontisport; 148 plts. (Lib ink stamps, spine #s; plt margins lt browned, bkpl; blind stamp fr bd, soiled, rubbed.) *Edwards.* $80/£50

BUDGE, E. A. WALLIS (ed). The Chronography of Gregory Abu'l Faraj. London: OUP, 1932. 1st ed. 2 vols. Med 8vo. lxiii,582pp; liii + 201pp facs. Fine set in brick red cl. Gray ptd djs (sl torn, chipped). *Ulysses.* $1,040/£650

BUDGE, E. A. WALLIS. Amulets and Talismans. New Hyde Park: University, 1961. VG in dj. *Blake.* $65/£41

BUDGE, E. A. WALLIS. The Book of the Cave of Treasures. London: Religious Tract Soc, 1927. Frontis, 15 plts. (Fr bd stained.) *Archaeologia.* $65/£41

BUDGE, E. A. WALLIS. The Book of the Dead: The Papyrus of Ani in the British Museum. London: British Museum, 1895. 1st ed in English. Teg. 3/4 morocco, gilt. (Faint lib stamp, sm discard sticker to tp verso), else VG. *Pacific*.* $259/£162

BUDGE, E. A. WALLIS. The Dwellers on the Nile. Religious Tract Soc, 1910. Frontis. (Joints separated, extrems rubbed.) *Archaeologia.* $35/£22

BUDGE, E. A. WALLIS. An Egyptian Hieroglyphic Dictionary. NY: Frederick Ungar, (1960). 2 vols. (Sig.) *Archaeologia.* $200/£125

BUDGE, E. A. WALLIS. The Egyptian Sudan, Its History and Monuments. Kegan Paul, Trench, Trubner, 1907. 2 vols. 57 plts (10 fldg). Teg. (Hinges cracked vol 1, spines sl rubbed, faded.) *Edwards.* $400/£250

BUDGE, E. A. WALLIS. Legends of the Gods. London: Kegan Paul, Trench, Trubner, 1912. Fldg frontis, 18 plts. *Archaeologia.* $125/£78

BUDGE, E. A. WALLIS. The Life and Exploits of Alexander the Great, Being a Series of Ethiopic Texts. London, 1896. One of 250 numbered sets. 2 vols. Port plt. Pub's 1/2 morocco (extrems rubbed), gilt. *Swann*.* $201/£126

BUDGE, E. A. WALLIS. Tutankhamen: Amenism, Atenism and Egyptian Monotheism. NY: Dodd, Mead, 1923. 1st ed. 3/4 cl, paper spine label. (Extrems rubbed), else VG. *Pacific*.* $40/£25

BUDGE, FRANCES ANNE. Annals of the Early Friends. Phila, 1880. 'First series' on cvr. xii,45pp. Blue cl, gilt. VG (lib mks). *Bohling.* $20/£13

BUDGEN, FRANK. Myselves When Young. London: OUP, 1970. 1st ed. 15 b/w plts. NF in dj. *Turtle Island.* $55/£34

BUECHNER, FREDERICK. A Long Day's Dying. NY: Knopf, 1950. 1st ed, 1st bk. VG + in VG dj (price-clipped, extrems chipped). *Pettler.* $40/£25

BUECHNER, FREDERICK. Treasure Hunt. NY: Atheneum, 1977. 1st ed. Fine in Fine dj. *Pettler.* $20/£13

BUEL, J. W. The Border Outlaws, an Authentic and Thrilling History of the Most Noted Bandits. St. Louis: Historical Pub Co, 1881. 1st ed. (New eps; cvrs worn, rebacked, old spine laid down.) Howes B933. *Glenn.* $175/£109

BUEL, J. W. Heroes of the Plains, or Lives and Wonderful Adventures of Wild Bill, Buffalo Bill, Kit Carson.... St. Louis: N.D. Thompson, 1882. 548pp; 16 color plts. Navy calf (rebound), color pict leather inlay port, red leather lettering piece. Fine. Howes B934. *House*. $500/£313

BUELER, L. E. Wild Dogs of the World. London, 1974. Fine in protected dj. *Grayling*. $40/£25

BUFF, MARY and CONRAD. Magic Maize. Cambridge: Houghton Mifflin, 1953. 1st ed. 8x11. 76pp. VG (sl shelfworn) in dj (edges ragged). *My Bookhouse*. $32/£20

BUFF, MARY MARSH. Dancing Cloud. NY: Viking, 1945. 3rd ptg. Conrad Buff (illus). Obl 8vo. 80pp. VG in dj (tattered). *Davidson*. $32/£20

Buffalo Bill's Wild West and Congress of Rough Riders of the World. (By William F. Cody.) Buffalo, NY: Courier Co, (c. 1900). 7th ed. (Spine tearing, chip to lower corner fr cvr), else VG in chromolitho wrappers. *Pacific**. $184/£115

Buffalo Bill's Wild West and Congress of Rough Riders of the World. NY: Fless & Ridge Ptg, 1895. 7th ed. Good in chromolitho wrappers (chipped, worn, fr wrapper lacks top corner). *Pacific**. $138/£86

BUFFET, BERNARD. Lithographs, 1952-1966. Fernand Mourlot (text). NY, (1968). 4to. 11 litho plts. Wrappers, plastic outer wrapper, slipcase. *Swann**. $546/£341

Buffon's Natural History Abridged. London, 1821. 2 vols. iv,viii,352; iv,426,1pp. 2 tps, 98 plts, as called for, all hand-colored. 1/2 calf, gilt. (Sl rubbed), o/w Fine. *Henly*. $288/£180

BUFFUM, E. GOULD. Six Months in the Gold Mines. London: Richard Bentley, 1850. 1st Eng ed. xi,244pp. Blindstamped cl. (Spine sl dknd, head chipped, foot sl rubbed w/1-inch tear along fr joint), else NF. Howes B943. *Pacific**. $288/£180

BUFFUM, E. GOULD. Six Months in the Gold Mines. L.A.: Ward Ritchie, 1959. 1st ed thus. VG. *Houle*. $50/£31

BUFFUM, E. GOULD. Six Months in the Gold Mines. From a Journal of Three Years' Residence in Upper and Lower California, 1847-8-9. (L.A.): Ward Ritchie, 1959. Cl-backed black/yellow dec bds. Fine. *Argonaut*. $90/£56

BUFORD, BILL. Among the Thugs. NY, 1993. 1st Vintage pb ed. NF. *Warren*. $25/£16

BUICK, T. L. The Mystery of the Moa. New Plymouth: T. Avery, 1931. 1st ed. 7 maps. NF in Good+ dj. *Mikesh*. $150/£94

BUKOWSKI, CHARLES. Barfly: The Continuing Saga of Henry Chinaski. Sutton West: Paget, (1984). 1st ed. One of 200. Signed. 1/4 cl, paper spine label. Fine. *Pacific**. $173/£108

BUKOWSKI, CHARLES. Confessions of a Man Insane Enough to Live with Beasts. Bensenville: Mimeo, 1965. 1st ed. One of about 475 (of 500). Signed by Blazek (pub). Fine in dec wrappers. *Smith*. $450/£281

BUKOWSKI, CHARLES. Crucifix in a Deathhand. NY: Lyle Stuart/Loujon, 1965. 1st ed. One of 3100 ptd on Linweave Spectra paper. Signed. Wrap-around band laid in. (One bump to corner), o/w Fine in wrappers. *Smith*. $350/£219

BUKOWSKI, CHARLES. Dangling in the Tournefortia. Santa Barbara: Black Sparrow, 1981. 1st trade ed. One of 750 signed. Fine in acetate dj. *Smith*. $150/£94

BUKOWSKI, CHARLES. The Days Run Away Like Wild Horses Over the Hills. L.A.: Black Sparrow, 1969. One of 250 numbered, signed. VG (pg, bd edges soiled) in unptd acetate dj as issued. *Between The Covers*. $250/£156

BUKOWSKI, CHARLES. Erections, Ejaculations, Exhibitions and General Tales of Ordinary Madness. Gail Chiarrello (ed). SF: City Lights, (1972). 1st ed. VF (few dk specks top edge) in photo illus wrappers. *Smith*. $300/£188

BUKOWSKI, CHARLES. Going Modern. (Fremont: Ruddy Duck Press, n.d.) 1st ed. One of 500. NF in wrappers. *Pacific**. $63/£39

BUKOWSKI, CHARLES. In the Shadow of the Rose. Santa Rosa: Black Sparrow, 1991. Only ed. One of 750 numbered, signed. Fine in turquoise plain paper dj, as issued. *Smith*. $175/£109

BUKOWSKI, CHARLES. Living on Luck. Selected Letters 1960s-1970s. Volume 2. Seamus Cooney (ed). Santa Rosa: Black Sparrow, 1995. One of 200 w/signed bound-in sheet. Fine in acetate dj, as issued. *Smith*. $300/£188

BUKOWSKI, CHARLES. Mockingbird Wish Me Luck. L.A.: Black Sparrow, 1972. One of 250 numbered, signed. Fine in acetate dj. *Smith*. $275/£172

BUKOWSKI, CHARLES. Play the Piano Drunk Like a Percussion Instrument Until the Fingers Begin to Bleed a Bit. Santa Barbara: Black Sparrow, 1979. 1st ed. One of 300. Signed. Prospectus laid in. 1/2 cl, dec bds, paper spine label. Fine. *Pacific**. $138/£86

BUKOWSKI, CHARLES. Poems Written Before Jumping Out of an 8 Story Window. (Glendale: Poetry X/Change, 1968.) Litmus 1st ed. Signed, w/sm dwg. Fine in pict wrappers. *Pacific**. $259/£162

BUKOWSKI, CHARLES. Post Office. L.A.: Black Sparrow, 1971. One of 250 numbered, signed. VG + (pg edges sl soiled) in unptd acetate dj as issued. *Between The Covers*. $300/£188

BUKOWSKI, CHARLES. Pulp. Santa Rosa: Black Sparrow, 1994. One of 300 signed w/orig silkscreen print by the author bound in. Fine in acetate dj, as issued. *Smith*. $150/£94

BUKOWSKI, CHARLES. The Roominghouse Madrigals. Santa Rosa: Black Sparrow, 1988. 1st trade ed. One of 500. Fine in acetate dj. *Smith*. $100/£63

BUKOWSKI, CHARLES. Run with the Hunted. Santa Rosa: Black Sparrow, 1993. One of 26 lettered, signed. Fine in acetate dj, as issued. *Smith*. $300/£188

BUKOWSKI, CHARLES. Shakespeare Never Did This. SF: City Lights, 1979. 1st ed. One of 300 hb, signed by Bukowski and Michael Montfort (photos). Fine in Fine dj. *Smith*. $450/£281

BUKOWSKI, CHARLES. Shakespeare Never Did This. Santa Rosa: Black Sparrow, 1995. 1st ed thus. One of 326 deluxe copies, signed by Michael Montfort (photos). Orig photo of Bukowski laid in. Fine in acetate dj. *Smith*. $65/£41

BUKOWSKI, CHARLES. Talking to My Mailbox. Santa Barbara: Black Sparrow, 1984. One of 100 numbered, signed. NF (folded neatly in 1/2, few creases at edges). *Beasley*. $60/£38

BUKOWSKI, CHARLES. There's No Business. Santa Barbara: Black Sparrow, 1984. One of 400 numbered, signed by Bukowski and R. Crumb (illus). Fine in acetate wrapper, as issued. *Smith*. $150/£94

BUKOWSKI, CHARLES. War All of the Time: Poems 1981-1984. Santa Barbara: Black Sparrow, 1984. 1st ed. One of 100. Signed in colophon and on his painting. Orig painting tipped to pg after tp. 1/2 cl, pict bds. Fine. *Pacific**. $460/£288

BULEY, R. CARLYLE. The Old Northwest, Pioneer Period 1815-1840. Bloomington: IN Univ, (1978). 2 vols. VG in djs. *Lien*. $30/£19

BULEY, R. CARLYLE. The Old Northwest. Pioneer Period, 1815-1940. Bloomington: IN Univ, 1951. 2nd ptg. 2 vols. (Bkpl), else VG. *Perier*. $47/£29

BULFINCH, THOMAS. The Age of Fable, or Stories of Gods and Heroes. NY: LEC, 1958. One of 1500 ptd. Signed by Joe Mugnaini (illus). 1/2 vellum, patterned bds. NF in slipcase. *Pacific**. $104/£65

BULKELEY, JOHN. A Voyage to the South-Seas in the Years 1740-1. Jacob Robinson, 1743. 1st ed. Contemp calf (rebacked, rubbed, bkpl; spotted, soiled, contemp sig). *Sotheby's**. $515/£322

BULL, DEBORAH and DONALD LORIMER. Up the Nile, a Photographic Excursion: Egypt, 1839-1898. NY: Clarkson N. Potter, 1979. 1st ed. 130 photos. NF in pict dj (sm closed tear, sl worn). *Cahan*. $50/£31

BULLARD, ASA. The Good Scholar. Boston: Lee & Shepard, 1863. 16mo. Engr frontis by Kilburn, 64pp + 1pg ad. Emb brn cl. VG (spot at edge of p9; corners sl rubbed). *Hobbyhorse*. $50/£31

BULLEN, FRANK T. The Cruise of The 'Cachalot' Round the World After Sperm Whales. London: Smith, Elder, 1898. 1st ed. xx,379pp; fldg map. VG. *High Latitude*. $225/£141

BULLEN, FRANK T. The Cruise of the 'Cachalot,' Round the World After Sperm Whales. Smith, Elder, 1899. 2nd ed. xx,379pp; 8 wood-engr plts, 1 fldg map. Blue cl, gilt. Good (extrems sl rubbed). *Sotheran*. $77/£48

BULLETT, GERALD. The Elderbrook Brothers. London: J.M. Dent, 1945. 1st ed. Top edge dk gray-grn. Cerise cl. (Fr cvr sl damp-mkd), o/w Fine in dj (frayed, chipped, verso sl stained). *Temple*. $13/£8

BULLETT, GERALD. The Panther. London: Heinemann, 1926. 1st ed. Gilt black cl. (Eps sl tanned, faint ink name), else NF in pict dj (lt frayed, nicked). *Reese*. $55/£34

BULLFINCH, THOMAS. The Age of Fable. LEC, 1958. Ltd to 1500 numbered, signed by Joe Mugnaini (illus). Fine in slipcase. *Swann**. $80/£50

BULLINS, ED. The Hungered One: Early Writings. NY: William Morrow, 1971. 1st ed. VG + in pict dj. *Petrilla*. $35/£22

BULLOCK, CHARLES J. and FREDERICK W. JARRAD (eds). China Sea Directory. London: Ptd for the Hydrographic Office, 1873-1874. 2 vols. (xi),632; (ix),386pp. Contemp bds. (Ex-lib, tps stamped.) *Maggs*. $560/£350

BULLOCK, WILLIAM. Six Months' Residence and Travels in Mexico. London: John Murray, 1824. 1st ed. xii,524pp (emb stamp); 16 plts (4 hand-colored, lg fldg view), fldg table, 2 fldg maps (repaired tear). 19th-cent calf, marbled bds (rubbed). Sound. *Karmiole*. $500/£313

BULMAN, H. F. and R. A. S. REDMAYNE. Colliery Working and Management. London, 1951. 5th ed. 32 plts. (Ex-lib, ink stamp, label.) *Edwards*. $48/£30

BULWER-LYTTON, EDWARD. The Last Days of Pompeii. Verona: Officina Bodoni, 1956. Signed by Kurt Craemer (illus) and Mardesteig (ptr). Grey cl blocked in Roman design, red/gilt label. Boxed. *Appelfeld*. $125/£78

BULWER-LYTTON, EDWARD. The Wooing of Master Fox. O. D. Martin (ed). Phila: Ashmead & Evans, 1866. 1st ed. 7.5x5.5. White (illus). Blue cl, gilt. (Interior sl soiled; spine ends chipped), else VG. *Pacific**. $58/£36

BUMPUS, T. FRANCIS. The Cathedrals of France. London: T. Werner Laurie, 1927. New ed. Color frontis, 90 plts. (Spine faded), else VG. *Turtle Island*. $75/£47

BUNBURY, CHARLES. Journal of a Residence at the Cape of Good Hope. London, 1848. (Bkpl; cl soiled, spine ends sl frayed.) *Swann**. $172/£108

BUND, J. W. WILLIS. Oke's Game Laws, Containing the Whole Law as to.... London: Butterworth, 1897. 4th ed. Grn cl (worn, hinges cracked), gilt. Usable. *Boswell*. $125/£78

BUNN, ALFRED. Old England and New England, in a Series of Views Taken on the Spot. Phila: A. Hart, 1853. 1st Amer ed. 2 vols in 1. pp315,(24) ads. Grn cl (faded, spine lt worn). *Mott*. $75/£47

BUNN, ALFRED. Old England and New England, in a Series of Views Taken on the Spot. London: Richard Bentley, 1853. 1st ed. 2 vols. Tinted litho frontis, xxi,313; viii,328pp. Grn cl, gilt. NF. *Mott*. $150/£94

BUNNELL, LAFAYETTE HOUGHTON. Discovery of the Yosemite and the Indian War of 1851, Which Led to That Event. Chicago: Fleming H. Revell, (1880). 2nd ed, 1st ptg. 'J.L. Regan & Co., Printers and Binders, 226 & 228 Lake Street, Chicago' is ptd on tp verso; 4pp of ads at rear; 22 chapters. Frontisport, (4),349,(1 blank),(4 ads)pp; map, 6 plts. Brn cl, gilt. (Spine faded, ends frayed, rear cvr stained), o/w VG. *Pacific**. $86/£54

BUNNELL, PETER C. Emmet Gowin: Photographs, 1966-1983. Washington: Corcoran Gallery of Art, 1983. One of 2000. Signed by Gowin. 20 plts. Fine in pict stiff wrappers. *Cahan*. $100/£63

BUNNELL, PETER C. (ed). A Photographic Vision...1889-1923. Salt Lake City: Peregrine Smith, 1980. 1st ed. (Sl rubbed), else Fine in illus stiff wrappers. *Cahan*. $40/£25

BUNNELL, STERLING (ed). Hand Surgery in World War II. Washington: U.S. Army Medical Dept Hist Unit, 1955. (Lib stamps, bkpls; rear pocket removed), else Fine. *Weber*. $100/£63

BUNNELL, STERLING. Surgery of the Hand. Phila: Lippincott, (1944). 1st ed, 3rd imp. Color frontis. VG (stamp, bkpl; extrems sl worn). *Glaser*. $135/£84

BUNNELL, STERLING. Surgery of the Hand. Phila/Montreal: Lippincott, (1956). 3rd ed. 9 color plts. Fine. *Weber*. $50/£31

BUNT, CYRIL G. E. Byzantine Fabrics. Leigh-on-Sea: F. Lewis, 1967. Sm folio. 56 b/w plts. *Turtle Island*. $45/£28

BUNTING, BAINBRIDGE. Taos Adobes. Santa Fe, 1964. 1st ed. One of 2000. Inscribed. NF in dj. *Dumont*. $85/£53

BUNTING, BASIL. Loquitur. Fulcrum, 1965. One of 1000. VG in glassine wrapper. *Clearwater*. $104/£65

BUNTING, BASIL. What the Chairman Told Tom. Cambridge, MA: Pym-Randall, 1967. One of 200 (of 226) numbered, signed. Fine in wrappers. *Ulysses*. $200/£125

BUNTING, EVE. Demetrius and the Golden Goblet. NY: HBJ, 1980. Obl 4to. Michael Hague (illus). Fine in Fine dj. *American Booksellers*. $30/£19

BUNTING, JOSIAH. The Lionheads. NY: George Braziller, 1972. 1st ed. Fine in dj. *Associates*. $100/£63

BUNTLINE, NED. (Pseud of Edward Z.C. Judson.) The Mysteries and Miseries of New York: A Story of Real Life. Parts I, II & IV (of 5). NY: Berford, 1848. 1st ed. 3 vols (of 5). Untrimmed. Sewn. Good (foxed, soiled) in rear wrapper of part II, part IV wrappers (detached). *Reese*. $85/£53

BUNTON, MARY TAYLOR. A Bride on the Old Chisholm Trail in 1886. San Antonio: Naylor, 1939. Frontis. Good in dj (sl faded). *Dumont*. $75/£47

Bunty. Racine: Whitman, (1935). Magic-Action Book. 12mo. 28pp; 3 dbl-pg pop-ups. VG in pict wraps. *Davidson*. $85/£53

BUNYAN, JOHN. The Complete Works. Phila: Bradley, Garretson, 1874. 9 1/2 x 6. Aeg. Emb brn morocco, gilt. VG. *Pacific**. $46/£29

BUNYAN, JOHN. The Doctrine of the Law and Grace Unfolded.... London: W. Johnston, 1765. 6th ed. (12),270,(2) + (2)ad pp. Mod calf, gilt. (Bkpl, notes, repairs to tp gutters, following pg), else VG. *Pacific**. $127/£79

BUNYAN, JOHN. The Holy War, Made by Shaddai upon Diabolus, for the Regaining of the Metropolis of the Word. London: The Book Society, n.d. (ca 1890). 16mo. Full-pg wood-engr frontis w/caption by W. Cheshire, xii,191pp + 1pg list on lower wrapper; 3 full-pg illus signed by Cheshire. Partly uncut. Internally Fine in brn stiff paper wrappers (lt soiled, edges chipped, rebacked w/matching color paper). *Hobbyhorse*. $125/£78

BUNYAN, JOHN. The Pilgrim's Progress and The Life and Death of Mr. Badman. G. B. Harrison (ed). Nonesuch, 1928. One of 1600. 8 wood-engr plts. Teg on the rough, rest untrimmed. Orig marbled fawn, brn/blue linen, cream parchment label. VG (feps browned; fore-edges sl foxed). *Blackwell's*. $160/£100

BUNYAN, JOHN. The Pilgrim's Progress from This World to That Which Is to Come. London: Ward, Lock, Tyler, n.d. (ca 1860). New ed. Sm 4to. Full-pg frontis, xix,304pp; 100 VF engrs by Thomas Dalziel. Marbled eps, edges. Full leather on bds, gilt, 5 raised bands, spine label. VG (sm tear top edge 1st 3 leaves; upper cvr dampstained, shelfworn). *Hobbyhorse*. $150/£94

BUNYAN, JOHN. The Pilgrim's Progress, from This World to That Which Is to Come. London/Edinburgh/NY, 1856. Aeg. Red morocco, gilt. Fine. *Glenn.* $100/£63

BUNYAN, JOHN. Pilgrim's Progress. London: Ernest Nister, (ca 1900). 1st ed illus thus. 5 Fine chromolitho plts by Walter Paget. Aeg. Gray pict cl. Fine. *Sotheran.* $125/£78

BUNYAN, JOHN. The Pilgrim's Progress. (London: Essex House, 1899.) Frontis, 426pp. Full vellum. (Cvrs sl soiled, warped), else Nice. *King.* $195/£122

BUNYAN, JOHN. The Pilgrim's Progress. NY: Payson & Clarke, 1928. Facs copy of King's Library of the British Museum. VG +. *Pharos.* $60/£38

BUNYAN, JOHN. Pilgrim's Progress. LEC, 1941. Ltd to 1500 numbered. Fine in slipcase. *Swann*.* $138/£86

BUNYAN, JOHN. The Pilgrim's Progress. London, 1947. Edward Ardizzone (illus). (Tp, eps sl foxed). Dj (torn). *Petersfield.* $67/£42

BUNYAN, JOHN. Pilgrim's Progress. London: A. Fullarton, n.d. (ca 1850). 1st ed. Frontisport, add'l engr tp, xlviii,148pp; 40 engr plts. 19th-cent calf, marbled bds (spine extrems sl chipped, hinges rubbed). *Karmiole.* $150/£94

BUNYAN, PAUL. The Wonderful Adventures of Paul Bunyan. Louis Untermeyer (retold by). NY: Aldus Ptrs, 1945. Signed by Everett Jackson (illus). Linen spine. Fine in slipcase. *Appelfeld.* $125/£78

BUNYARD, EDWARD. Old Garden Roses. London/NY: Country Life/Scribner, 1936. 1st ed. Color frontis, 32 b/w plts. Fine in dj (chipped). *Quest.* $95/£59

BUNYARD, EDWARD. Old Garden Roses. Country Life, 1936. 1st ed. Color frontis, 32 plts. VG (fore-edges spotted). *Hollett.* $104/£65

BURBANK, LUTHER. Luther Burbank: His Methods and Discoveries and Their Practical Application. NY: Luther Burbank Press, 1914. 12 vols. Teg. Red cl, oval port each fr cvr, gilt spines. (Spines sl faded, rubbed), else NF. *Pacific*.* $127/£79

BURBANK, LUTHER. The Training of the Human Plant. NY, 1907. 1st Amer ed. Frontisport. NF (name). *Polyanthos.* $25/£16

BURBANK, W. H. The Photographic Negative. NY: Scovill Manufacturing, 1888. 1st ed. Frontis, ii,198pp + (3),xviiipp ads. Pict emb cl. (Stamp, lt foxed; sl soiled, rubbed), else VG. *Cahan.* $175/£109

BURBIDGE, F. W. Cool Orchids and How to Grow Them. London: Robert Hardwicke, 1874. 1st ed. Aeg. Grn cl, gilt. (Lt spotted), else VG. *Pacific*.* $81/£51

BURBIDGE, F. W. The Gardens of the Sun: Or, A Naturalist's Journal.... London: John Murray, 1880. 1st ed. 1/2-title, xviii,(i),(i)blank,364 + 24 pub's list; 8 engr plts (incl frontis). Dec gray cl. Good (sl foxed; fr hinge split; spine ends, corners rubbed, cvrs sl stained). *Morrell.* $272/£170

BURBRIDGE, BEN. Gorilla. Tracking and Capturing the Ape-Man of Africa. London, 1928. 1st ed. (Sl rubbed, spine sl creased.) *Edwards.* $48/£30

BURCH, JOHN P. Charles W. Quantrell [sic], a True History of His Guerrilla Warfare on the Missouri and Kansas Border.... Vega, TX, 1923. 1st ed. VG in dj. *Labordo.* $50/£31

BURCHARD, PETER. Whaleboat Raid. NY: Coward, McCann, Geoghean, 1977. Brn cl. VG. *American Booksellers.* $25/£16

BURCHETT, JOSIAH. A Complete History of the Most Remarkable Transactions at Sea...Wherein Is Given an Account of the Most Considerable Naval Expeditions.... London, 1720. 1st ed. Folio. Frontisport, 9 dbl-pg fldg maps. Contemp paneled calf. *Felcone.* $1,500/£938

BURCHETT, WILFRED. Grasshoppers and Elephants. NY: Urizen Books, 1977. 1st ed. Fine in NF dj. *Associates.* $45/£28

BURCHETT, WILFRED. North of the Seventeenth Parallel. Hanoi: Red River Pub, 1957. 2nd enlgd ed. (Ex-lib), else VG in wraps. *Associates.* $100/£63

BURCHETT, WILFRED. Vietnam: Inside Story of the Guerilla War. NY: International Pub, 1965. 1st ed. Fine (3 sm bumps, 1 nick) in dj (price-clipped). *Associates.* $65/£41

BURCKHARDT, JOHN LEWIS. Notes on the Bedouins and Wahabys, Collected During His Travels in the East. London, 1830. 1st ed. 4to. Frontis map, ix,(ii),439pp. Contemp 1/2 calf. *Maggs.* $3,840/£2,400

BURCKHARDT, JOHN LEWIS. Travels in Arabia, Comprehending an Account of Those Territories in Hedjaz Which the Mohammedans Regard as Sacred. London: Henry Colburn, 1829. 2 vols. 8vo. Fldg map, 4 fldg plans. 3/4 mod red morocco, gilt paneled spines. VG (sl spotted, sl marginal tears). *Appelfeld.* $1,200/£750

BURCKHARDT, JOHN LEWIS. Travels in Nubia. London: John Murray, 1819. 1st ed. 4to. Frontisport, (vi),xcii,543pp; map, 2 fldg maps (1 sl torn). (Lacks pp523/4, lib ink stamps on frontis, tp, prelim, some text; pp465-6 fore-edge repaired, pp500 onwards w/lt stain to corner, pp95-180 fore-edges lt browned.) Morocco-backed marbled bds (rebound), raised bands, gilt. *Edwards.* $1,200/£750

BURCKHARDT, JOHN LEWIS. Travels in Syria and the Holy Land. William Leake (ed). London: John Murray, 1822. 1st ed. 4to. Litho frontisport, 6 engr maps, plans (2 fldg). Contemp tan polished calf, gilt paneled spine w/crescent emblems in gilt, raised bands, marbled edges. VG (marginal dampstain few plts). *Appelfeld.* $1,500/£938

BURCKHARDT, T. Siena. M. M. Brown (trans). London: OUP, 1960. 28 tipped-in color plts, 16 b/w plts. Red cl. Dj (few tears). *Maggs.* $29/£18

BURDETT, CHARLES. Life of Kit Carson. Phila: Potter, (1869). 382pp. VG. *Book Market.* $25/£16

BURDETT, CHARLES. Life of Kit Carson. Phila: J. Edwin Potter, 1866. 374,2pp. Stamped bds (worn, sl shaken). Good. *Dumont.* $80/£50

BURDETT, CHARLES. The Life of Kit Carson. NY: G&D, 1902. Frontis. VG in dj (worn). *Dumont.* $30/£19

BURDETT-COUTTS, W. The Brookfield Stud of Old English Breeds of Horses, Hackneys, Cleveland Bays...Ponies. London, 1891. Color plan, 6 color litho plts. Pict cl (sl worn, soiled; sl foxed). *Oinonen*.* $150/£94

BURDICK, ARTHUR J. The Mystic Mid-Region. NY: Putnam, 1904. 1st ed. Frontis. Teg. Tan pict cl. (Bkpl; sl soiled), else Fine. *Argonaut.* $175/£109

BURDICK, J. R. The American Card Catalog. Kistler, 1960. 1st ed. VG (lacks dj, as issued?). *Plapinger.* $125/£78

BURDICK, USHER L. and EUGENE D. HART. Jacob Horner and the Indian Campaigns of 1876 and 1877. Balt: Wirth Bros, 1942. 1st ed. Frontisport, map. Fine in ptd wrappers (sm address label taped to foot of fr wrapper, sm rubberstamps). *Pacific*.* $81/£51

BURDICK, USHER L. The Last Battle of the Sioux Nation. Stevens Point, WI: Worzalla Pub, (1929). 1st ed. Fine. *Pacific*.* $150/£94

BURDICK, USHER L. Tales from Buffalo Land: The Story of Fort Buford. Balt: Wirth Bros, 1940. 1st ed. Red cl, gilt. (Spine sl dull), else NF. *Pacific*.* $63/£39

BURGER, JOHN. Horned Death. Huntington, 1947. Pict cl (lt worn; edges, tips sl rubbed). *Oinonen*.* $110/£69

BURGER, WILLIAM. Families of Flowering Plants in Ethiopia. Stillwater: OSU Press, 1967. 1st ed. Fine. *Archer.* $35/£22

BURGES, TRISTAM. Battle of Lake Erie with Notices of Commodore Elliot's Conduct in That Engagement. Phila: Wm. Marshall, 1839. 132pp. Orig cl. (Foxed.) *Lefkowicz.* $300/£188

BURGESS, ALAN. Seven Men at Daybreak. NY, 1960. 1st ed. Map. VG + in dj (sl worn). *Pratt.* $17/£11

BURGESS, ANTHONY. 99 Novels. Alison & Busby, 1984. 1st ed. Fine in dj. *Any Amount.* $26/£16

BURGESS, ANTHONY. Beard's Roman Women. Hutchinson, 1977. 1st UK ed. NF in dj (torn). *Williams.* $45/£28

BURGESS, ANTHONY. A Christmas Recipe. Ptd for Friends of the Participants, Natale, 1977. One of 180 ptd. Fine in plain ptd wrappers. *Maggs.* $400/£250

BURGESS, ANTHONY. A Clockwork Orange. Heinemann, 1962. 1st issue in black cl. VG (top edge spotted, dusty, sl soiled, spine ends, corner bumped) in dj (nicked, sl torn, creased, rubbed, dusty, spine faded, lower panel, spine soiled). *Ulysses.* $632/£395

BURGESS, ANTHONY. A Clockwork Orange. NY: Norton, 1963. 1st US ed. NF in NF dj (sl soiled, bumped). *Unger.* $200/£125

BURGESS, ANTHONY. Coaching Days of England. London: Paul Elek, 1966. 1st ed. 24 color plts. Illus edps. (Top edges sl dirty) in dj (sl worn). *Woolson.* $125/£78

BURGESS, ANTHONY. Earthly Powers. Hutchinson, 1980. 1st ed. Fine in dj. *Any Amount.* $38/£24

BURGESS, ANTHONY. Enderby Outside. Heinemann, 1968. 1st UK ed. Fine in dj. *Williams.* $120/£75

BURGESS, ANTHONY. Here Comes Everybody. London: Faber and Faber, 1965. 1st Eng ed. VG (edges, eps sl spotted; spine foot sl bumped) in dj (sl rubbed, nicked, creased, mkd, spine sl dknd). *Ulysses.* $88/£55

BURGESS, ANTHONY. The Kingdom of the Wicked. Hutchinson, 1985. 1st UK ed. Fine in dj. *Williams.* $22/£14

BURGESS, ANTHONY. Language Made Plain. London: English Universities Press, 1964. 1st Eng ed. VG (spine ends sl bumped; spine, cvr edges sl browned) in dj (nicked, rubbed, sl creased, mkd, browned). *Ulysses.* $136/£85

BURGESS, ANTHONY. Little Wilson and Big God. Heinemann, 1987. 1st UK ed. Fine in NF dj. *Williams.* $32/£20

BURGESS, ANTHONY. Napoleon Symphony. London: Jonathan Cape, (1974). 1st ed. NF in NF dj. *Agvent.* $35/£22

BURGESS, ANTHONY. Nothing Like the Sun. London: Heinemann, 1964. 1st Eng ed. Fine (corner sl bumped) in dj (edges sl rubbed). *Ulysses.* $120/£75

BURGESS, ANTHONY. The Novel To-Day. Longmans, Green, 1963. 1st Eng ed. Fine in wrappers. *Ulysses.* $72/£45

BURGESS, ANTHONY. Shakespeare. Cape, 1970. 1st UK ed. NF (sl worn) in NF dj. *Martin.* $26/£16

BURGESS, ANTHONY. A Vision of Battlements. Sidgwick & Jackson, 1965. 1st ed. Purple bds, gilt backstrip. Fine in 2nd issue dj (edges sl foxed). *Blackwell's.* $96/£60

BURGESS, ANTHONY. You've Had Your Time. Heinemann, 1990. 1st UK ed. Fine in dj. *Williams.* $29/£18

BURGESS, F. F. R. Sporting Fire-Arms for Bush and Jungle. London, 1884. 1st ed. (Lt worn.) *Oinonen*.* $90/£56

BURGESS, FRED. Antique Jewellery and Trinkets. London: Routledge, 1919. 1st ed, 1st ptg. Pict cl. VG (pp browned). *Blake.* $125/£78

BURGESS, FRED. Antique Jewelry and Precious Stones. NY: Tudor, (1919). VG in dj (sl worn, torn, spine faded). *Hollett.* $48/£30

BURGESS, GELETT and BURGES JOHNSON. The Cat's Elegy. Chicago: McClurg, 1913. 1st ed. Pict cvrs. (Corners sl worn), else VG + . *Any Amount.* $32/£20

BURGESS, JOHN CART. An Easy Introduction to Perspective. London: The Author, 1840. 7th ed. 26pp,1f., frontis, 11 litho plts. (Rebacked, dampstained.) *Marlborough.* $192/£120

BURGESS, N. G. The Ambrotype Manual. NY: J.M. Fairchild, 1857. 3pp ads at rear. Red cl. (Name, foxed; spine top rubbed through, corners bumped), o/w Good. *Metropolitan*.* $230/£144

BURGESS, THORNTON W. The Adventures of Bobby Coon. Boston: Little, Brown, 1944. 1st ed thus (part of newly issued series of Bedtime Story-books). 8vo. 8 full-pg color plts by Harrison Cady. Cl-backed color illus bds (lt edgeworn). Color dj (worn, spine lacks piece). *Reisler.* $85/£53

BURGESS, THORNTON W. The Adventures of Buster Bear. Boston: Little, Brown, 1945. Inscribed. Harrison Cady (illus). 1/2 cl, pict bds. VG in VG dj. *Davidson.* $185/£116

BURGESS, THORNTON W. The Adventures of Johnny Chuck. Boston: Little, Brown, 1923. Signed 1923. Harrison Cady (illus). (Soil, name), else VG. *Pacific*.* $81/£51

BURGESS, THORNTON W. The Adventures of Poor Mrs. Quack. Boston: Little, Brown, 1917. 1st ed. 12mo. 6 full-pg plts by Harrison Cady. Gray pict cl. Good. *Reisler.* $150/£94

BURGESS, THORNTON W. Bill Mink. Boston: Little, Brown, 1924. 1st ed. 8vo. 8 full-pg color illus by Harrison Cady. Grn cl, color paste label. (Early sig sl shaken), o/w Nice. *Reisler.* $100/£63

BURGESS, THORNTON W. The Burgess Sea Shore Book for Children. Boston: Little, Brown, 1929. 1st ed. W. H. Southwick & George Sutton (illus). Gilt-lettered cl, pict cvr label. (Sl foxed), else NF. *Pacific*.* $58/£36

BURGESS, THORNTON W. Mother West Wind's Animal Friends. Boston: Little, Brown, 1912. 1st ed. 12mo. Frontis, guard (both foxed), 6 full-pg b/w illus by George Kerr. Tan pict cl. *Reisler.* $100/£63

BURGESS, THORNTON W. Mother West Wind's Neighbors. Boston: Little, Brown, 1913. 1st ed. 12mo. 6 full-pg b/w plts by George Kerr. Tan pict cl. Good. *Reisler.* $100/£63

BURGESS, THORNTON W. Old Mother West Wind. Boston: Little, Brown, 1960. Golden Anniversary ed. 8vo. Harrison Cady (illus). Fine in Fine dj. *American Booksellers.* $25/£16

BURGESS, THORNTON W. On the Green Meadows. Boston: Little, Brown, 1944. 1st ed. Harrison Cady (illus). 8vo. Red pict cl. Good in color dj. *Reisler.* $100/£63

BURGESS, THORNTON W. Peter Rabbit Puts on Airs, Jerry Muskrat Wins Respect, Jumper the Hare Cannot Sleep, Unc' Billy Possum Has a Fright, Buster Bear Invites Old Mr. Toad to Dine, Grandfather.... NY: John H. Eggers, (1928). 28cm high. Each bk 12pp incl cvrs. VG set, each vol in color pict wrappers (spines lt chipped). Pub's box cvrd w/color dec paper (lt worn, taped corner). *Reisler.* $475/£297

BURGESS, THORNTON W. Tales from the Storyteller's House. Boston: Little Brown, 1937. 1st ed. 195pp. 8 color plts by Lemuel Palmer. VG in Good- dj (chips, waterstained). *Price.* $45/£28

BURGESS, THORNTON W. Tommy and the Wishing Stone. NY: Century, 1915. 1st ed. Harrison Cady (illus). Gilt-lettered pict cl. Fine in dj (spine dknd, head chipped). *Pacific*.* $150/£94

BURGESS, THORNTON W. Whitefoot the Wood Mouse. Boston: Little, Brown, 1922. 1st ed. 8vo. 8 full-pg color plts by Harrison Cady. Blue cl, color paste label (edges lt worn). *Reisler.* $175/£109

BURGH, JAMES. Thoughts on Education.... Boston: Rogers & Fowle, 1749. (Browned throughout; lacks bds), else Good. *Metropolitan*.* $230/£144

BURK, MARGARET TANTE. Are the Stars Out Tonight? L.A.: Round Table West, (1980). Signed. Fabricoid. *Dawson.* $50/£31

BURKE, A. L. The Mayberry Murder Mystery of Bonito City. Alamogordo, NM, (1938). (Stained throughout.) Custom folder. *Dumont.* $350/£219

BURKE, BERNARD. Vicissitudes of Families. London: Longmans, Green, 1883. Inscribed presentation dated 1889. 2 vols. Blue cl. *Appelfeld.* $150/£94

BURKE, CLIFFORD. Printing Poetry. SF: Scarab, 1980. Ltd to 2000. Fine in dj. *Truepenny.* $95/£59

BURKE, EDGAR. American Dry Flies: and How to Tie Them. NY: Derrydale, 1931. One of 500. Inscribed. (Rebacked), o/w Fine. *Biscotti.* $400/£250

BURKE, EDMUND. On Conciliation with America and Other Papers on the American Revolution. LEC, 1975. One of 2000 signed by Lynd Ward (illus). Fine in slipcase. *Swann*.* $80/£50

BURKE, EDMUND. The Works. London: Ptd for J. Dodsley, 1792-1802. 1st collected ed. 4 vols. 4to. Contemp maroon diced calf (expertly rebacked w/new leather spines), raised bands, edges stained yellow. *Appelfeld.* $900/£563

BURKE, JAMES LEE. Dixie City Jam. NY: Hyperion, (1994). 1st ed. Signed. As New in dj. *Between The Covers.* $50/£31

BURKE, JAMES LEE. In the Electric Mist with Confederate Dead. NY: Hyperion, 1993. 1st ed. VF in dj. *Mordida.* $45/£28

BURKE, JAMES LEE. The Lost Get Back Boogie. Baton Rouge: LSU, 1986. 1st ed. Signed. Fine in Fine dj. *Between The Covers.* $300/£188

BURKE, JAMES LEE. The Lost Get-Back Boogie. NY: Holt/Owl Paperback, 1986. 1st trade pb ed. Fine in wraps. *Warren.* $35/£22

BURKE, JAMES LEE. The Neon Rain. NY: Holt, 1987. 1st ed. Signed. Fine in dj. *Lame Duck.* $250/£156

BURKE, JAMES LEE. To the Bright and Shining Sun. (Huntington Beach: James Cahill, 1992.) One of 400. Signed. Black/white cl, gilt. As New in slipcase. *Pacific*.* $98/£61

BURKE, JAMES LEE. Two for Texas. NY, 1982. 1st ed. Pb orig. VG- (2 stamps). *Warren.* $35/£22

BURKE, JAMES LEE. Two for Texas. (Huntington Beach: James Cahill, 1992.) One of 400. Signed by Burke and Joe Servello (illus). As New in slipcase. *Pacific*.* $86/£54

BURKE, JAMES LEE. Winter Light. Huntington Beach: James Cahill, 1992. 1st hb ed. One of 300 numbered, signed by Burke & Phil Parks (illus). VF. *Mordida.* $135/£84

BURKE, JOHN and JOHN BERNARD. A General Armory of England, Scotland, and Ireland. London, 1842. Early cl (hinges tender, corners sl rubbed, spine sl chipped). *Edwards.* $72/£45

BURKE, JOHN. A Hard Day's Night. Pan Books, 1964. 1st ed. VG in pict wrappers (sl creased). *Hollett.* $40/£25

BURKE, KENNETH. Attitudes Toward History. NY: New Republic, 1937. 1st ed. 2 vols. Flexible grey cl. VG set (sl dknd, rubbed). *Reese.* $60/£38

BURKE, THOMAS (ed). Children in Verse. Fifty Songs of Playful Childhood. London: Duckworth, 1913. 1st ed. 8vo. (xii),135pp; 8 mtd color plts by Honor C. Appleton. Teg, untrimmed. Blue cl, gilt. *Sotheran.* $237/£148

BURKE, THOMAS (ed). The Small People, a Little Book of Verse About Children for Their Elders. Chapman & Hall, 1910. 1st ed thus. 8vo. Sm port mtd as frontis, 220pp. Patterned cl. NF (ink #, initials). *Bookmark.* $24/£15

BURKE, THOMAS. The English Inn. London: Longmans, Green, 1930. 1st ed. Grn linen-grain cl. Fine. *Temple.* $16/£10

BURKE, THOMAS. Limehouse Nights. NY: McBride, 1926. 1st US ed. 14 color plts. (Bkpl; sl rubbed, soiled), o/w VG. *Worldwide.* $35/£22

BURKE, THOMAS. Limehouse Nights: Tales of Chinatown. London: Grant Richards, 1916. 1st ed. VG. *Pacific*.* $115/£72

BURKE, THOMAS. The London Spy. London: Thornton Butterworth, 1922. 1st ed. (Pg edges lt foxed, feps sl dknd), o/w NF in dj (sm chips). *Mordida.* $175/£109

BURKE, THOMAS. Murder at Elstree. Longmans, Green, 1936. 1st ed. VG (spine ends, corners sl bumped, top edge rear cvr sl mkd) in dj (nicked, sl creased, dusty, price-clipped, spine, edges sl dknd). *Ulysses.* $264/£165

BURKE, THOMAS. Whispering Windows. Grant Richards, 1921. 1st ed. NF (edges spotted) in pict dj (extrems rubbed). *Ulysses.* $600/£375

BURKE, W. S. The Indian Field Shikar Book. Calcutta, 1920. 5th ed. (Sl loose, cvrs sl soiled.) *Hallam.* $80/£50

BURKE, W. S. The Indian Field Shikar Book. Calcutta/Simla, 1928. 6th ed. (Cvrs sl worn.) *Petersfield.* $72/£45

BURKLEY, FRANK J. The Faded Frontier. Omaha, 1935. 1st ed. VG (few sm spots rear cvr). Howes B989. *Baade.* $75/£47

BURKS, ARTHUR J. Black Medicine. Sauk City: Arkham House, (1966). 1st ed. Fine in Fine dj (spine head sl worn). *Other Worlds.* $65/£41

BURKS, ARTHUR J. The Great Mirror. (London: Swann, 1952.) 1st ed. VG (few flaws) in pict wrappers. *Other Worlds.* $20/£13

BURLAMAQUI, J. J. The Principles of Natural Law. Mr. Nugent (trans). London: For J. Nourse, 1752. 1st ed in English. xvi,(xxiv),312pp. Old calf, leather spine label, gilt. (Sl browned, ep edges dknd from binding adhesive; fr cvr detached, old wear, scuffing, spine label dknd.) *Baltimore*.* $170/£106

BURLAND, C. A. Magic Books from Mexico. Penguin, 1953. 1st ed. King Penguin series No 64. Pict bds. VG in dj. *Hollett.* $152/£95

BURLEIGH, THOMAS D. Georgia Birds. Univ of OK, (1958). (Exlib, mkd, worn.) *Rybski.* $40/£25

BURLINGAME, ROGER. Engines of Democracy. NY, 1940. 1st ed. *Argosy.* $60/£38

BURLINGTON FINE ARTS CLUB. Catalogue of Specimens of Japanese Lacquer and Metal Work Exhibited in 1894. London, 1894. Contemp 1/2 mottled sheep (joints worn), gilt. *Swann*.* $57/£36

BURLINGTON, C. et al. The Modern Universal British Traveller. J. Cooke, 1779. Folio. Engr frontis, 2 fldg maps, 105 plts. Contemp tree calf (sl worn, lower joint split; bkpl), gilt. *Sotheby's*.* $920/£575

BURMEISTER, EUGENE. Early Days in Kern. Bakersfield: Cardon House, (1963). 1st ed. Fine in wraps. *Book Market.* $25/£16

BURN, JACOB HENRY. A Descriptive Catalogue of the London Traders, Tavern, and Coffee-House Tokens Current in the Seventeenth Century.... Ptd for the Use of the Members, 1853. 1st ed. Frontisport, 1 plt. Uncut. (Lacks spine.) *Forest.* $104/£65

BURN, RICHARD. The Justice of the Peace, and Parish Officer. (London): A. Millar, 1755. 1st ed. 2 vols. Contemp calf (rebacked), gilt. *Boswell.* $1,250/£781

BURNABY, FRED. A Ride to Khiva: Travels and Adventures in Central Asia. London, 1876. 2nd ed. 1/2 calf, gilt dec backstrip, red label. Fine. *Petersfield.* $96/£60

BURNE-JONES, EDWARD COLEY. The Flower Book. Reproductions of Thirty-Eight Watercolour Designs. London: Henry Piazza, 1905. Ltd to 300. Initialled by the pub. 4to. 38 color plts. Teg. Orig grn morocco (fr cvr, spine faded), gilt. In orig padded case (scuffed). *Christie's*.* $4,416/£2,760

BURNE-JONES, EDWARD. Fifty-Seven Plates. Newnes, (n.d.). 1st Eng ed. VG. *Clearwater.* $120/£75

BURNE-JONES, EDWARD. Letters to Katie. Macmillan, 1925. 1st ed. xiv,30pp (feps spotted); 24 illus. Holland-backed bds, paper spine label. *Hollett.* $64/£40

BURNE-JONES, EDWARD. Pictures of Romance and Wonder. NY: R.H. Russell, 1902. 1st ed thus. Teg. Cream cl, gilt. (Frontis lacks sm piece; soiled), else VG. *Pacific*.* $109/£68

BURNE-JONES, PHILIP. Dollars and Democracy. NY: D. Appleton, 1904. 1st ed. Color pict label. *Mott.* $40/£25

BURNES, A. Cabool: A Personal Narrative of a Journey...in the Years 1836, 7, and 8.... London: John Murray, 1843. 2nd ed. Engr frontisport, xii,398,(2)ads; 11 plts (2 fldg). Grn blind-stamped cl. Fine (edges sl browned; cvrs lt stained, cracked hinges). *Morrell.* $320/£200

BURNES, A. Travels into Bokhara. London: Murray, 1834. 3 vols. Frontis (stained), 8 plts (last plt stained). Full diced leather, gilt (sl damp-mkd). VG set. *Petersfield.* $680/£425

BURNET, THOMAS. The Theory of the Earth. London, 1697. 3rd ed. (xv),223,(xi),188pp; addt'l engr tp, port, 2 fldg plts. Folio. Recent 1/2 calf. Good. *Henly.* $384/£240

BURNETT, E. K. and FORREST E. CLEMENTS. The Spiro Mound Collection in the Museum and Historical Sketch of the Spiro Mound. NY, 1945. 94 plts. (Couple pp w/highlighting.) Wraps. *Dumont.* $40/£25

BURNETT, FRANCES HODGSON. Dolly. Warne, 1893. 1st ed. Pub's file copy label on eps, fldg stock sheet tipped-in, stamp on half-title. Frontis. Blue pict cl, gilt. (Top edge sl dusty; spine head sl bumped), else Fine. *Any Amount.* $120/£75

BURNETT, FRANCES HODGSON. Editha's Burglar. NY, (1888). 7.5x5. 66pp. Cl-backed pict bds. (Very loose, lacks 1 illus.) Fragments of ptd dj. *King.* $35/£22

BURNETT, FRANCES HODGSON. Giovanni and the Other. NY: Scribner, 1892. 1st ed. 6.5x8.5. 193 + ads pp. Reginald Birch (illus). Grn cl, gilt. VG- (worn, spotted, soiled). *My Bookhouse.* $52/£33

BURNETT, FRANCES HODGSON. In Connection with the De Willoughby Claim. Warne, 1899. 1st ed, later issue w/cancel tp. Pub's file copy stamps, ink note fep. Red dec cl, gilt. (Eps offsetting; spine ends sl bumped), o/w Fine in VG color pict dj (sl soiled, nicked). *Any Amount.* $128/£80

BURNETT, FRANCES HODGSON. A Little Princess. London: Frederick Warne, 1905. 1st ed. 8vo. Harold Piffard (illus). (xii),302,(vi)pp. Dec eps; edges uncut. Grn cl, gilt, sm rectangular pict label onlaid to fr cvr. VG. *Sotheran.* $237/£148

BURNETT, FRANCES HODGSON. The One I Knew the Best of All. Scribner, 1893. 1st ed. Teg. Pict cl, gilt. (Few pp sl creased), else VG + . *Any Amount.* $48/£30

BURNETT, FRANCES HODGSON. Racketty-Packetty House. NY: Century, 1906. 1st ed. 12mo. 20 full-pg color plts by Harrison Cady. Blue cl, color paste label. Good. *Reisler.* $150/£94

BURNETT, FRANCES HODGSON. Sara Crewe or What Happened at Miss Minchin's. NY: Scribner, 1888. 1st ed. 83,(16)ads. Pict gray cl, gilt. VG (few internal smudges; lt worn, soiled). *House.* $60/£38

BURNETT, FRANCES HODGSON. The Secret Garden. Phila: Lippincott, (1962). 1st Tudor ed. Tasha Tudor (illus). (Name), else VG in dj (extrems sl rubbed, sm tears, spot to spine head, price-clipped). *Pacific*.* $52/£33

BURNETT, FRANCES HODGSON. The Secret Garden. NY: Lippincott, 1985. Sm 4to. Tasha Tudor (illus). Fine in Fine dj. *American Booksellers.* $30/£19

BURNETT, FRANCES HODGSON. The Secret Garden. Boston: Godine, 1987. 4to. Graham Rust (illus). Fine in Fine dj. *American Booksellers.* $25/£16

BURNETT, FRANCES HODGSON. The Spring Cleaning, as Told by Queen Crosspatch. NY: Century, 1911. 1st ed. 6.25x4.75. Harrison Cady (illus). Pict cvr label. Fine. *Pacific*.* $86/£54

BURNETT, FRANCES HODGSON. Two Little Pilgrims' Progress. NY: Scribner, 1895. 1st ed. 7x8.5. 191 + ads pp. Reginald B. Birch (illus). Blue cl, gilt. VG (shelfworn). *My Bookhouse.* $57/£36

BURNETT, FRANCES HODGSON. The Way to the House of Santa Claus. NY: Harper & Bros, 1916. 1st ed. Lg Obl 4to. Red cl, color paste label (sl rubbed; names). *Reisler.* $375/£234

BURNETT, GEORGE. Specimens of English Prose-Writers. London: Longman, Hurst, et al, 1807. 1st ed. 3 vols. Teg. 3/4 dk grn morocco, marbled bds, gilt. (Extrems sl rubbed), else NF. *Pacific*.* $58/£36

BURNETT, PETER H. Recollections and Opinions of an Old Pioneer. NY: D. Appleton, 1880. 1st ed. xiii,448pp + (6)pp ads. Brn cl, gilt. (Ex-lib, bkpl, mks, tp browned, remargined, tape-repaired, new eps; rebacked w/orig spine strip laid on), else VG. *Pacific*.* $81/£51

BURNETT, W. R. The Asphalt Jungle. NY, 1949. 1st ed. Fine in black dj. *Swann*.* $149/£93

BURNETT, W. R. High Sierra. NY: Knopf, 1940. 1st ed. NF in VG + dj (price-clipped, extrems sl worn) in black cl slipcase. *Lame Duck.* $450/£281

BURNETT, W. R. Nobody Lives Forever. Heinemann, 1944. 1st UK ed. VG in dj (worn, browned, sl chipped). *Williams.* $22/£14

BURNEY, CHARLES. An Account of the Musical Performances in Westminster-Abbey, and the Pantheon...in Commemoration of Handel. London: Payne & Robinson, 1785. Ad at end; 8 full-pg plts (lt foxed). 1/4 calf (weak). *Rostenberg & Stern.* $450/£281

BURNEY, CHARLES. The Present State of Music in France and Italy. London: T. Becket, 1771. 1st ed. vii,(1),396,(11),(1)pp. Calf. (Fr cvr detached, rear joint cracked), else VG. *Pacific*.* $138/£86

BURNEY, CHARLES. The Present State of Music in Germany, the Netherlands, and United Provinces. London: T. Becket, J. Robson & G. Robinson, 1773. 1st ed. 2 vols. viii,376; iv,(2),352pp. Period calf, gilt. (Bkpls, worming to pp), else VG. *Pacific*.* $173/£108

BURNEY, FANNY. Evelina. London: Macmillan, (1903). 1st ed illus thus. Hugh Thomson (illus). Dk grn cl, gilt. *Sotheran.* $77/£48

BURNHAM, CLARA LOUISE. Tobey's First Case. Boston, 1926. 1st ed. (Sm dent), else VG in dj (heavily rubbed, edges chipped). *King.* $35/£22

BURNHAM, FREDERICK RUSSELL. Taking Chances. Mary Nixon Everett (ed). L.A.: Haynes, 1944. 1st ed. 'This book was privately ptd in a sm ed and is now quite scarce...' (Six-Guns). Presentation inscription by a member of Burnham's family, signed by Major Burnham. Dk blue cl, gilt. Fine (bkpl, foxed, mainly to eps). *Argonaut.* $300/£188

BURNHAM, JOHN B. The Rim of Mystery. NY: Putnam, 1929. 1st ed. Fldg map. Red buckram. NF. *Biscotti.* $165/£103

BURNHAM, JOHN C. Jelliffe: American Psychoanalyst and Physician and His Correspondence with Sigmund Freud and C. G. Jung. William McGuire (ed). Chicago: Univ of Chicago, (1983). Orange cl. VG in dj. *Gach.* $25/£16

BURNHAM, S. Precious Stones. Boston: Bradlee Whidden, c1886. 400pp. (Stamp, 4 sm notations; rebound, title portion of orig spine laid down), else Good. *Blake.* $75/£47

BURNIM, KALMAN A. (ed). The Letters of Sarah and William Siddons to Hester Lynch Piozzi in the John Rynalds Library. Manchester, 1969. Inscribed. Card wrappers. *Clearwater.* $40/£25

BURNINGHAM, JOHN. Cannonball Simp. London: Cape, 1966. 4th ed. 8.25x10.75. 32pp. Pict bds. VG. *Cattermole.* $25/£16

BURNLEY, JAMES. The History of Wool and Woolcombing. Sampson Low, Marston et al, 1889. 1st ed. xvi,487pp; 8 plts. Bkpl of Arthur Raistrick. (Lib stamps, label on pastedown, fr bd; extrems sl worn.) *Hollett.* $120/£75

BURNS, ESTHER. Mrs. Peregrine and the Yak. Holt, 1938. 1st ed. 5.5x7.5. Eloise Wilkin (illus). Unpaginated. Pict paper on cl. VG (1/2-inch tape pull on fr, 2-inch crack fr hinge). *Price.* $45/£28

BURNS, ROBERT H. et al. Wyoming's Pioneer Ranches. Laramie: Top-of-the-World, 1955. 1st ed. One of 1000. Speckled edges. Red cl. Fine. *Harrington*. $325/£203

BURNS, ROBERT IGNATIUS. The Jesuits and the Indian Wars of the Northwest. New Haven: Yale Univ, 1966. 1st ed. Color frontis by Charles M. Russell. VF in pict dj. *Argonaut*. $75/£47

BURNS, ROBERT. The Complete Writings...in Ten Volumes. Waverley Book Co, 1927. Lg paper copy, one of 250 for Great Britain. 10 vols. 9 ports, 6 fldg facs, guards. Russet eps; teg. Orig 1/4 red morocco, gilt, fine-diagonal-grain red cl sides, red cl hinges. VF. *Blackwell's*. $400/£250

BURNS, ROBERT. Illustrated Songs. Roy. Assoc Prom. Fine Arts Scot., 1861. Folio. (vi)pp; 6 steel-engr plts. Grn blind-stamped cl, gilt. Fine. *Hollett*. $136/£85

BURNS, ROBERT. The Life and Works. Robert Chambers (ed). Edinburgh/London, 1896. New ed. 4 vols. Teg, rest uncut. (Sl spotted, feps lt browned.) *Edwards*. $96/£60

BURNS, ROBERT. The Merry Muses. SF: City Lights, 1962. 1st ptg. One of 500. Fine in wraps. *Beasley*. $25/£16

BURNS, ROBERT. The Poems of.... Glasgow: LEC, 1965. One of 1500. Signed by Joan Hassall (illus). 1/2 grn morocco, lt grn cl, emb port medallion fr cvr. Fine in slipcase. *Pacific**. $75/£47

BURNS, ROBERT. Poems, Chiefly in the Scottish Dialect. Edinburgh: The Author, 1787. 2nd ed, 2nd issue w/'stinking' on p263 instead of 'skinking;' it is the variant w/'Boxburgh' rather than 'Roxburgh' in the list of subs. Stipple-engr frontisport, xlviii, 368pp (foxing, lt soil). Period calf. (Rebacked, w/much of orig spine, morocco label; joints starting to recrack, worn, spine discolored), else VG in full morocco slipcase, cl chemise. Bkpl of Thomas Philip Earl de Gray. *Pacific**. $403/£252

BURNS, ROBERT. Reliques of Robert Burns; Consisting Chiefly of Original Letters, Poems, and Critical Observations on Scottish Songs. R. H. Cromek (ed). London: T. Cadell & W. Davies, 1808. 1st ed. xxiii,(1),453,(1) + 6 ad pp. Calf, gilt, older fr and rear panels laid-on. (Binding lt faded), else VG. *Pacific**. $184/£115

BURNS, ROBERT. Tam O' Shanter. NY: W.J. Widdleton, 1868. Alexander Gardner (photos). Slim 4to. Mtd frontis; 7 mtd plts. Marbled eps; aeg. Grn cl, beveled bds, gilt. VG (lt foxed, letterpress credit on each mount, sl worn, hinges lt cracked). *Baltimore**. $550/£344

BURNS, ROBERT. The Works. William Allason et al, 1819. 4 vols. Engr port. Full polished calf, gilt. VG (feps sl spotted; hinges, extrems sl rubbed, hinges sl tender). *Hollett*. $192/£120

BURNS, ROBERT. The Works. Poetry; Prose. William Paterson, 1891. One of 500. 6 vols. Uncut. (Ex-lib; lt soiled, spine ends sl bumped.) *Edwards*. $136/£85

BURNS, WALTER NOBLE. Robin Hood of El Dorado. NY: Coward-McCann, (1932). 1st ed. Good. *Lien*. $15/£9

BURNS, WALTER NOBLE. The Robin Hood of El Dorado.... NY: Coward-McCann, 1932. 1st ed. Tan cl. VG in dj. *Labordo*. $85/£53

BURNS, WALTER NOBLE. Tombstone, an Iliad of the Southwest. GC: Doubleday, Page, 1927. 1st ed. Grn cl, gilt. NF (spine gilt faded). *Labordo*. $95/£59

BURNSIDE, H. M. The Childrens Wonderland (Moveable). London: Ernest Nister, (1900). Sq 4to. 7 full-pg rotating transformations by Florence Hardy, each activated by a silk ribbon (1 replaced) to turn the wheel. Cl-backed color illus bds (few sl stains). *Reisler*. $2,000/£1,250

BURR, ANNA ROBESON. Weir Mitchell, His Life and Letters. NY: Duffield, 1929. 1st ed. Frontisport. 2-toned cl. VG in dj (sl shelfworn, spine faded). *Glaser*. $60/£38

BURR, NELSON R. A Critical Bibliography of Religion in America. Princeton: Princeton Univ, (1968-1971). 5 parts in 2 vols. 3rd ptg vol 1, 4th ptg vol 2. Dk gray buckram, gilt. VG set (sl handled, shelfworn). *Baltimore**. $70/£44

BURRAGE, HENRY SWEETSER. Gettysburg and Lincoln: The Battle, the Cemetery, and the National Park. NY, 1906. 1st ed. Pict cl (Sl worn), o/w Fine. *Pratt*. $45/£28

BURRARD, G. Big Game Hunting in the Himalayas and Thibet. Herbert Jenkins, 1925. 1st ed. 8vo. 23 photo plts, 8 maps. Blue cl, gilt. Fine. *Sotheran*. $589/£368

BURRARD, G. Fly Tying. London: Jenkins, 1945. 2nd ed. Blue cl. VG in dj. *Bowman*. $30/£19

BURRARD, G. In the Gunroom. London, 1930. Fine in dj. *Petersfield*. $32/£20

BURRARD, G. The Modern Shotgun. NY, 1931/1932. 3 vols. (Edges foxed; lt worn.) *Oinonen**. $150/£94

BURRARD, G. Notes on Sporting Rifles. London, 1920. *Petersfield*. $29/£18

BURRARD, S. G. Records of the Survey of India. Volume VI. Completion of the Link Connecting the Triangulations of India and Russia 1913. Office of the Trionometrical Survey, 1914. Presentation ticket from Surveyor General fr pastedown. Sm folio, 20 plts (incl 7 photogravures), 4 charts, diagrams (2 fldg). Ptd cl-backed bds, cl spine label (frayed). VG (sl foxed, ink sig; sl rubbed, browned). *Morrell*. $720/£450

BURRIS-MEYER, HAROLD and EDWARD C. COLE. Theatres and Auditoriums. NY: Reinhold, (1964). 2nd ed. VG in dj. *Dramatis*. $30/£19

BURRITT, ELIJAH H. The Geography of the Heavens and Class-Book of Astronomy. NY: Huntington & Savage, 1844. xxiv,305 + pp. Good + (foxed, rebound). *Bookcell*. $100/£63

BURROUGHS, EDGAR RICE. Apache Devil. Tarzana: Edgar Rice Burroughs, (1933). 1st ed. Blue cl. Fine in dj. *Pacific**. $345/£216

BURROUGHS, EDGAR RICE. At the Earth's Core. Chicago: McClurg, 1922. 1st ed. Gray-grn ribbed cl (spine sl rubbed, dusty, edges sl worn). Text Good (eps lt foxed). *Baltimore**. $50/£31

BURROUGHS, EDGAR RICE. At the Earth's Core. Chicago: McClurg, 1922. 1st ed. 9 plts by J. Allen St. John. Gray cl, lettered in black. Fine in VG dj (1-inch chip to spine foot, head, corners chipped). *Pacific**. $2,070/£1,294

BURROUGHS, EDGAR RICE. At the Earth's Core. McClurg, 1922. 1st ed. Inscribed. (Pg edges lt dust-soiled), else VG in VG dj (sl worn, torn). *Fine Books*. $5,500/£3,438

BURROUGHS, EDGAR RICE. Back to the Stone Age. Tarzana: Edgar Rice Burroughs, (1937). 1st ed. 8vo. 7 b/w plts (incl frontis). Blue cl. NF (text sl browned; spine ends sl rubbed) in dj (supplied). *Heritage*. $600/£375

BURROUGHS, EDGAR RICE. Back to the Stone Age. Tarzana: Burroughs, (1937). 1st ed. 7 plts by John Coleman Burroughs. (Bkpl, rubberstamp; spine ends sl worn), else VG in Fine dj. *Pacific**. $748/£468

BURROUGHS, EDGAR RICE. Back to the Stone Age. Tarzana, (1937). 1st ed. 8vo. Blue cl. Fine in dj (backed w/non-acidic rice paper); slipcase. *Swann**. $805/£503

BURROUGHS, EDGAR RICE. The Bandit of Hell's Band. Chicago: A.C. McClurg, 1925. 1st ed. Frontis by M. Stein. Blue cl. (Rubberstamps; sl shelfworn), else NF in VG dj (expert repairs). *Pacific**. $2,070/£1,294

BURROUGHS, EDGAR RICE. The Beasts of Tarzan. NY: A.L. Burt, 1916. VG (corners bumped) in dj (worn, faded). *My Bookhouse*. $47/£29

BURROUGHS, EDGAR RICE. The Beasts of Tarzan. Chicago: McClurg, 1916. 1st Amer ed. VG (fr hinge starting, spine sl sunned). *Polyanthos*. $50/£31

BURROUGHS, EDGAR RICE. The Beasts of Tarzan. Chicago: McClurg, 1916. 1st ed. Grn cl. (Fr cvr cl sl creased, spine ends rubbed), else VG. *Pacific**. $115/£72

BURROUGHS, EDGAR RICE. The Beasts of Tarzan. Chicago: McClurg, 1916. 1st ed. Grn cl, gilt. Fine in dj (restored w/portions of image, lettering painted on). *Pacific**. $3,111/£1,944

BURROUGHS, EDGAR RICE. Beyond Thirty and the Man-Eater. South Ozone Park, (NY): Science-Fiction & Fantasy, 1957. 1st ed. One of 3000. (Sl offset to eps), else Fine in NF dj (sl soiled). *Pacific**. $75/£47

BURROUGHS, EDGAR RICE. Carson of Venus. Tarzana: Burroughs, (1939). 1st ed. (Cl lt faded, spotted), else VG in VG dj (spine head sl rubbed). *Pacific**. $288/£180

BURROUGHS, EDGAR RICE. The Cave Girl. Chicago: McClurg, 1925. 1st ed. Frontis by J. Allen St. John. Blue cl, lettered in dk grn. (Spine faded), else VG in VG dj (lower left corner fr panel lacks piece, sl worn). *Pacific**. $2,300/£1,438

BURROUGHS, EDGAR RICE. The Chessmen of Mars. Chicago: McClurg, 1922. 1st ed. Red cl. (Sl aged, eps lt foxed; sl rubbed, dusty, lt shelfworn.) Text Good. *Baltimore**. $60/£38

BURROUGHS, EDGAR RICE. The Chessmen of Mars. Chicago: McClurg, 1922. 1st ed. 8 plts by J. Allen St. John. Red cl, black lettering. (Bkpl, ink name, dated December 1922; sl shelfworn), else NF in VG dj (chipped, few sm edge tears, verso tape reinforcements). *Pacific**. $2,070/£1,294

BURROUGHS, EDGAR RICE. The Deputy Sheriff of Comanche County. Tarzana: Edgar Rice Burroughs, (1940). 1st ed. 8vo. Frontis. Top edge stained red. Gray cl. NF (bkpl, eps lt browned; spine ends lt rubbed) in dj (spine ends sl worn, rear panel sl soiled). *Heritage*. $750/£469

BURROUGHS, EDGAR RICE. The Efficiency Expert. Kansas City, MO: House of Greystoke, 1966. 1st ed. Frontis. NF in pict wrappers (sl worn). *Pacific**. $150/£94

BURROUGHS, EDGAR RICE. Escape on Venus. Tarzana: Edgar Rice Burroughs, (1946). 1st ed. 5 b/w plts. Blue cl. NF (spine ends sl rubbed, few sl white spots on cvrs) in dj (lt soiled, sl edgeworn), black cl open-end slipcase. *Heritage*. $400/£250

BURROUGHS, EDGAR RICE. Escape on Venus. Tarzana: Edgar Rice Burroughs, 1946. 5 b/w plts. Fine (spine ends bumped) in dj (sl rubbed, dusty, sl browned, spine tail lacks sm piece). *Ulysses*. $400/£250

BURROUGHS, EDGAR RICE. The Eternal Lover. Chicago: McClurg, 1925. 1st ed. Frontis. Blue cl. (Foxed, name label; soiled, spine sunned, ends rubbed), else VG. *Pacific**. $58/£36

BURROUGHS, EDGAR RICE. The Eternal Lover. Chicago, 1925. 1st ed. Frontis, 316pp. (Spine sl sunned, worn.) *King*. $65/£41

BURROUGHS, EDGAR RICE. The Eternal Lover. Chicago: McClurg, 1925. 1st ed. Frontis by J. Allen St. John. Blue cl, lettered in black. (Top spine ends sl rubbed), else Fine in NF dj (spine ends sl worn, sl chipped, sl edgeworn). *Pacific**. $1,840/£1,150

BURROUGHS, EDGAR RICE. A Fighting Man of Mars. NY: Metropolitan Books, (1931). 1st ed, 1st binding. Frontis. (Rear inner hinge cracked, edges rubbed, spine corner sl frayed), o/w VG. *Bernard*. $125/£78

BURROUGHS, EDGAR RICE. A Fighting Man of Mars. NY: Metropolitan, (1931). 1st ed. Frontis by Hugh Hutton. Red cl. (Inscrip), else Fine in VG dj (rubbed, edges sl worn, spine foot, corners chipped). *Pacific**. $1,380/£863

BURROUGHS, EDGAR RICE. The Girl from Farris's. Kansas City, MO: House of Greystoke, 1965. 1st ed. Frontis. NF in pict wrappers (sl worn). *Pacific**. $150/£94

BURROUGHS, EDGAR RICE. The Girl from Hollywood. NY: Macaulay, (1923). 1st ed, 2nd binding. Currey's 'A' binding in coarse mesh weave, but 'B' ptg w/caption 'The director's eyes snapped.... Only a camera man and myself are here.' Frontis. Coarse mesh weave red cl lettered in yellow-grn. Fine. *Pacific**. $58/£36

BURROUGHS, EDGAR RICE. The Girl from Hollywood. NY: Macaulay, (1923). 1st ed, 1st binding. Currey's 'A' binding, 1st issue w/frontis caption including the words 'he said.' Coarse mesh weave red cl lettered in yellow-grn. VG in dj (worn, creased, inch-long closed tears, spine ends lack pieces, spine stained). *Pacific**. $316/£198

BURROUGHS, EDGAR RICE. The Girl from Hollywood. NY: Macaulay, (1923). 1st ed, 2nd ptg, 1st binding, 1st issue dj. W/sigs triple-sewn & w/frontis lacking the words 'he said.' Frontis by P. J. Monahan. Course mesh weave red cl, lettered in yellow-grn. Fine in Nice dj (rubbed, extrems lt worn, sl chipped, sl torn, several verso tape repairs or stains from them). *Pacific**. $2,588/£1,618

BURROUGHS, EDGAR RICE. The Gods of Mars. Chicago: McClurg, 1918. 1st ed. Frontis. Red cl. (Rubberstamp; spine ends sl rubbed, joints sl dknd), else NF. *Pacific**. $150/£94

BURROUGHS, EDGAR RICE. The Gods of Mars. Chicago: McClurg, 1918. 1st ed. Frontis by Frank E. Schoonover. Red cl lettered in black. Fine (bkpl) in VG dj (lt chipped, 1/2-inch chip to foot, folds sl splitting). *Pacific**. $4,888/£3,055

BURROUGHS, EDGAR RICE. I Am a Barbarian. Tarzana: Burroughs, (1967). 1st ed. One of 1800. Frontis. Fine in dj. *Pacific**. $104/£65

BURROUGHS, EDGAR RICE. The Illustrated Tarzan Books No. 1. NY: G&D, (1929). Cl-backed pict bds. (Edges rubbed, lt shelfworn), else VG. *Pacific**. $460/£288

BURROUGHS, EDGAR RICE. John Carter of Mars. NY: Canaveral, 1964. 1st ed. Dk blue cl, gilt. Fine in dj (extrems sl rubbed). *Pacific**. $52/£33

BURROUGHS, EDGAR RICE. Jungle Girl. Tarzana: Burroughs, (1932). 1st ed. Studley Burroughs (illus). Blue cl. Fine in dj (faint crease along spine). *Pacific**. $1,725/£1,078

BURROUGHS, EDGAR RICE. Jungle Girl. London, (1933). 1st Eng ed. Dj (lt soiled, few sm closed tears top of panels). *Swann**. $126/£79

BURROUGHS, EDGAR RICE. Jungle Tales of Tarzan. Chicago: McClurg, 1919. 1st ed, 1st ptg. Currey's 'A' binding w/spine imprint in 3 lines; W.F. Hall imprint on c. pg. 5 plts by J. Allen St. John. Orange cl lettered in grn. (Fr joint dknd), else NF in NF dj (sl chipped, edgetorn). *Pacific**. $863/£539

BURROUGHS, EDGAR RICE. Jungle Tales of Tarzan. Chicago: McClurg, 1919. 1st ed, later ptg (or state?). Inscribed presentation, dated 4.26.28. 5 plts by J. Allen St. John. Grn cl. (Sl worn), else VG in cl slipcase. *Pacific**. $1,035/£647

BURROUGHS, EDGAR RICE. The Lad and the Lion. Tarzana, CA: Erb, (1938). 1st ed in 1st state (laminated) dj. 5 b/w plts. Fine in NF pict dj (few sm edge tears). *Bernard*. $550/£344

BURROUGHS, EDGAR RICE. Land of Terror. Tarzana: Edgar Rice Burroughs, (1944). 1st ed. Blue cl. VG (ink bkseller stamp, sm brn stains on eps; cl sl faded, spine extrems bumped) in dj (spine faded, edges lt chipped). *Heritage*. $500/£313

BURROUGHS, EDGAR RICE. The Land That Time Forgot. Chicago: McClurg, 1924. 1st ed. 4 plts by J. Allen St. John. Grn cl, lettered in blue. (Lower corner fr cvr lt bumped), else NF in Fine dj (spine foot, corners sl worn). *Pacific**. $6,325/£3,953

BURROUGHS, EDGAR RICE. Llana of Gathol. Tarzana: Edgar Rice Burroughs, (1948). 1st ed. 5 b/w plts. Blue cl. Fine (bkpl) in dj (spine lt browned), open-end slipcase of marbled bds, cl. *Heritage*. $200/£125

BURROUGHS, EDGAR RICE. Lost on Venus. Tarzana: Burroughs, (1935). 1st ed. NF in dj. *Pacific**. $374/£234

BURROUGHS, EDGAR RICE. The Mad King. Chicago: McClurg, 1926. 1st ed. Frontis by J. Allen St. John. Dk blue cl, lettered in orange. (Spine sl rubbed), else NF in VG dj (sm edge tears, few chips, few repairs). *Pacific**. $1,840/£1,150

BURROUGHS, EDGAR RICE. The Master Mind of Mars, Being a Tale of Weird and Wonderful Happenings on the Red Planet. Chicago: McClurg, 1928. 1st ed. Frontis. Orange cl. (Lt soiled, spine ends sl rubbed), else VG. *Pacific**. $150/£94

BURROUGHS, EDGAR RICE. The Master Mind of Mars, Being a Tale of Weird and Wonderful Happenings on the Red Planet. Chicago: McClurg, 1928. 1st ed. 5 plts (incl frontis) by J. Allen St. John. Orange cl, lettered in grn. (Spine ends sl crimped), else NF in VG dj (spine ends, extrems chipped, sl edgetorn, neat verso repairs to folds). *Pacific**. $1,265/£791

BURROUGHS, EDGAR RICE. The Monster Men. Chicago, 1929. 1st ed. 304pp. (Cvrs soiled, spine ends sl frayed.) *King*. $50/£31

BURROUGHS, EDGAR RICE. The Monster Men. Chicago: McClurg, 1929. 1st ed. Tan cl, grn lettering. (Blindstamp), else Fine in NF dj (extrems sl worn, folds sl rubbed, spine sl dknd, spot of adhesion damage to rear panel). *Pacific**. $1,495/£934

BURROUGHS, EDGAR RICE. The Moon Maid. Chicago: McClurg, 1926. 1st ed. Frontis by J. Allen St. John. Blue cl, lettered in brn. (Spine sl faded, sm stain to fr cvr), else VG in Good dj (lt stained, chipped, top rear panel lacks lg piece, old tape repairs to verso). *Pacific**. $2,185/£1,366

BURROUGHS, EDGAR RICE. The Mucker. Chicago: McClurg, 1921. 1st ed. 5 plts by J. Allen St. John. Green-blue cl, red lettering. (Lower corners sl bumped), else NF in NF dj (spine ends, corners sl worn, sl chipped, folds lt rubbed, worn). *Pacific**. $4,600/£2,875

BURROUGHS, EDGAR RICE. The New Adventures of Tarzan 'Pop-Up.' Chicago: Pleasure Books, (1935). 3 full-color dbl-pg pop-ups. Color pict bds. (Extrems, spine sl rubbed), else NF. *Pacific**. $403/£252

BURROUGHS, EDGAR RICE. The New Adventures of Tarzan 'Pop-Up.' Chicago: Pleasure Books, 1935. Illustrated Pop-Up Edition. 20x24 cm. 3 dbl-pg pop-ups. Pict bds (corners bumped). Internally VG. *Bookfinders*. $250/£156

BURROUGHS, EDGAR RICE. The Oakdale Affair and the Rider. Tarzana: Burroughs, (1937). 1st ed. 2 plts (incl frontis). VG in dj (spine sl sunned, ends rubbed, corners sl bumped). *Pacific**. $460/£288

BURROUGHS, EDGAR RICE. Official Guide of the Tarzan Clans of America. Tarzana: Tarzan Clans of America, 1939. 1st ed. Fine in orange wrappers. *Pacific**. $345/£216

BURROUGHS, EDGAR RICE. The Outlaw of Torn. Chicago: A.C. McClurg, 1927. 1st ed, 1st ptg. NF. *Bernard*. $250/£156

BURROUGHS, EDGAR RICE. The Outlaw of Torn. Chicago: McClurg, 1927. 1st ed. Red cl, gilt. Fine in NF dj (sl chipped, sl torn, old price partly erased from spine). *Pacific**. $1,495/£934

BURROUGHS, EDGAR RICE. The Outlaw of Torn. Chicago: A.C. McClurg, 1927. 1st ed. 8vo. Red cl, gilt. NF (eps lt browned; spine lt soiled, creased) in pict dj (expertly restored at folds, edges), brn cl slipcase w/fldg cl chemise. *Heritage*. $3,000/£1,875

BURROUGHS, EDGAR RICE. Pellucidar. Chicago: McClurg, 1923. 1st ed. Red cl. (Spine lt sunned, edges sl rubbed; text sl aged, eps lt foxed.) *Baltimore**. $60/£38

BURROUGHS, EDGAR RICE. Pellucidar: A Sequel to 'At the Earth's Core' Relating the Further Adventures of David Innes in the Land Underneath the Earth's Crust. NY: G&D, (1924). 4 plts. Red cl. (Ink name, sl soiled), else VG in VG dj (spine soiled, sl chipped, lt worn). *Pacific**. $196/£123

BURROUGHS, EDGAR RICE. Pellucidar: A Sequel to 'At the Earth's Core' Relating the Further Adventures of David Innes in the Land Underneath the Earth's Crust. Chicago: McClurg, 1923. 1st ed. 4 plts by J. Allen St. John. Red cl, lettered in black. (Spine ends sl frayed), else Fine in VG dj (expertly restored, heavily at spine, repairs to earlier chips). *Pacific**. $2,185/£1,366

BURROUGHS, EDGAR RICE. Pirates of Venus. Tarzana: Edgar Rice Burroughs, (1934). 1st ed. 8vo. 5 plts. Top edge stained red. Blue cl. (Spine sl sunned), o/w Fine in dj, grn cl slipcase. *Heritage*. $600/£375

BURROUGHS, EDGAR RICE. A Princess of Mars. Chicago: McClurg, 1917. 1st ed. (Old tape repairs to pp155-156 along marginal tear; lower gutters, upper right margins sl dampstained; possibly recased), else VG. *Pacific**. $81/£51

BURROUGHS, EDGAR RICE. A Princess of Mars. Chicago: McClurg, 1917. 1st ed. 5 plts (incl color frontis). This copy has a duplicate of the 5th plt substituted for the 4th plt. Brn cl. (Corners sl bumped), else NF. *Pacific**. $460/£288

BURROUGHS, EDGAR RICE. A Princess of Mars. Chicago: A.C. McClurg, 1917. Advance copy. 8vo. NF in pict wrappers (expertly restored), full red morocco clamshell case. *Heritage*. $6,500/£4,063

BURROUGHS, EDGAR RICE. The Return of Tarzan. NY: A.L. Burt, (1916). Grn cl. (Spine lettering sl flaked, head sl torn), else NF in N.C. Wyeth dj (spine sunned, soiled, chipped, fr panel rubbed, verso tape repairs or stains from them). *Pacific**. $127/£79

BURROUGHS, EDGAR RICE. The Return of Tarzan. Chicago: McClurg, 1915. 1st ed. Advance rev copy. Paper label affixed to fr cvr reads 'The Return/ of Tarzan/ The Sequel to/ 'Tarzan of the Apes'/ Will Be Published March 10' and it is illus w/2 of the chapter decs by J. Allen St. John. Above the label is rubberstamped 'Advance Sheets.' (Sl worn, spine sl creased), else NF in stiff paper wrappers. *Pacific**. $6,325/£3,953

BURROUGHS, EDGAR RICE. Savage Pellucidar. NY: Canaveral, 1963. 1st ed. Fine in NF dj (spine ends, corners sl rubbed). *Pacific**. $98/£61

BURROUGHS, EDGAR RICE. The Son of Tarzan. NY: G&D, 1917. VG (spine bumped) in dj (edgeworn, sm spine chip). *My Bookhouse*. $52/£33

BURROUGHS, EDGAR RICE. The Son of Tarzan. Chicago: A.C. McClurg, 1917. 1st ed. Frontis. Grn cl, gilt. Good (few sm wormholes fr hinge, cvrs worn). *Heritage*. $200/£125

BURROUGHS, EDGAR RICE. The Son of Tarzan. Chicago: A.C. McClurg, 1917. 1st ed. Frontis by J. Allen St. John. Grn cl, gilt. (Old bkpl, rubberstamp; cvr rippled along fore-edge), else NF in Good+ dj (rubbed, worn at folds, extrems, tape repairs on verso, spine sunned w/some retouching, horizontal lines from previous dj protector). *Pacific**. $2,588/£1,618

BURROUGHS, EDGAR RICE. Synthetic Men of Mars. Tarzana: Edgar Rice Burroughs, (1940). 1st ed. Frontis,4 plts. Blue cl. NF (spine ends sl rubbed) in later issue dj (crease fr panel, spine foot sl chipped). *Heritage*. $300/£188

BURROUGHS, EDGAR RICE. Synthetic Men of Mars. Tarzana: Edgar Rice Burroughs, (1940). 1st ed. Frontis, 4 plts. Blue cl. VG (eps browned, ink bkseller stamp; spine ends sl rubbed) in dj, apparently in pre-pub state, which was issued loose for promotional purposes (sl edgeworn, lt soiled). *Heritage*. $350/£219

BURROUGHS, EDGAR RICE. Tanar of Pellucidar. NY: Metropolitan, (1930). 1st ed. Frontis by Paul F. Berdanier. Blue cl, lettered in black. (Rubberstamp; spine ends, corners sl rubbed), else Fine in flawless dj. *Pacific**. $2,070/£1,294

BURROUGHS, EDGAR RICE. Tarzan and 'The Foreign Legion.' Tarzana, CA: Edgar Rice Burroughs, Inc, (1947). 1st ed. 5 plts. Blue cl stamped in red. Good in color illus dj (sl worn). *Karmiole*. $75/£47

BURROUGHS, EDGAR RICE. Tarzan and the Ant Men. NY: G&D, 1924. VG+ in dj (edges sl worn). *My Bookhouse*. $52/£33

BURROUGHS, EDGAR RICE. Tarzan and the Ant Men. Chicago: McClurg, 1924. 1st ed. Frontis. Brn cl lettered in dk brn. Fine in NF dj (extrems lt worn, sm chip to spine head, 1/2-inch tears to lower edge fr panel, top edge of rear panel, spine imprint w/rubbed spot). *Pacific**. $1,495/£934

BURROUGHS, EDGAR RICE. Tarzan and the Castaways. NY: Canaveral, 1965. 1st ed. Fine in dj (price-clipped). *Pacific**. $115/£72

BURROUGHS, EDGAR RICE. Tarzan and the City of Gold. Tarzana: Edgar Rice Burroughs, (1933). 1st ed. 5 plts (incl frontis) by J. Allen St. John. Fine in VG dj (spine head sl chipped, extrems, fr panel sl torn, creased). *Pacific**. $1,495/£934

BURROUGHS, EDGAR RICE. Tarzan and the Forbidden City. Tarzana, 1938. 1st ed. 8vo. Fine in dj (backed w/non-acidic rice paper, sm paper restorations to a few spots); slipcase. *Swann**. $575/£359

BURROUGHS, EDGAR RICE. Tarzan and the Forbidden City. Tarzana: Burroughs, 1938. 1st ed. Full color frontis by John Coleman Burroughs. Fine (spine ends lt bumped) in NF illus dj (sm closed tear). *Unger*. $600/£375

BURROUGHS, EDGAR RICE. Tarzan and the Foreign Legion. Tarzana: Edgar Rice Burroughs, 1947. 5 b/w plts. Fine (spine ends sl bumped) in dj (sl creased, sl browned). *Ulysses*. $360/£225

BURROUGHS, EDGAR RICE. Tarzan and the Golden Lion. NY: G&D, (1927). Photoplay ed. 4 plts from movie stills. Orange cl. Fine (ink name dated Feb. 20, 1929) in NF dj (spine sunned, ends sl worn, sl edgetorn). *Pacific**. $575/£359

BURROUGHS, EDGAR RICE. Tarzan and the Golden Lion. Chicago: McClurg, 1923. 1st ed. 8vo. Dj (backed w/non-acidic rice paper, few paper restorations); slipcase. *Swann**. $920/£575

BURROUGHS, EDGAR RICE. Tarzan and the Golden Lion. Chicago: McClurg, 1923. 1st ed. 8 plts by J. Allen St. John. Mustard cl. (Insect damage to spine), else NF in dj (chips, damage, expertly restored). *Pacific**. $1,380/£863

BURROUGHS, EDGAR RICE. Tarzan and the Jewels of Opar. NY: G&D, (1927). Frontis by J. Allen St. John. Red cl. Fine in VG dj (sl worn, sm tears neatly repaired w/tape on verso). *Pacific**. $196/£123

BURROUGHS, EDGAR RICE. Tarzan and the Jewels of Opar. Chicago: McClurg, 1918. 1st ed. 8 plts by J. Allen St. John. Grn cl, gilt. (Sticker, fr hinge sl starting before frontis), else NF. *Pacific**. $184/£115

BURROUGHS, EDGAR RICE. Tarzan and the Jewels of Opar. Chicago: McClurg, 1918. 1st ed. 8 plts by J. Allen St. John. Grn cl, gilt. Fine in NF dj (sm edge tears, lt worn). *Pacific**. $1,840/£1,150

BURROUGHS, EDGAR RICE. Tarzan and the Leopard Men. Tarzana: Burroughs, (1935). 1st ed. 4 plts. (Removed bkpl fr pastedown), else VG+ in dj (extrems sl worn, spine sl faded, price-clipped). *Pacific**. $173/£108

BURROUGHS, EDGAR RICE. Tarzan and the Leopard Men. Tarzana: Burroughs, (1935). 1st ed. 4 plts by J. Allen St. John. (Name), else VG in dj (spine head sl rubbed, corners sl bumped). *Pacific**. $345/£216

BURROUGHS, EDGAR RICE. Tarzan and the Lion Man. Tarzana: Edgar Rice Burroughs, (1934). 1st ed. J. Allen St. John (illus). (Spine ends sl worn), else Fine in dj. *Pacific**. $518/£324

BURROUGHS, EDGAR RICE. Tarzan and the Lost Empire. NY: Metropolitan, (1929). 1st ed, 1st binding. 8vo. Frontis. Fine in dj (backed w/non-acidic rice paper, several archival paper restorations to a few spots); slipcase. *Swann**. $920/£575

BURROUGHS, EDGAR RICE. Tarzan and the Lost Empire. NY: Metropolitan, (1929). 1st ed. Frontis by A. W. Sperry. Orange cl lettered in black. (Ink name dated St. Louis, Mo., Oct. 4, 1929), else Fine in Fine dj (spine ends, corners sl rubbed, spine sl faded). *Pacific**. $1,035/£647

BURROUGHS, EDGAR RICE. Tarzan and the Madman. NY: Canaveral, 1964. 1st ed. (Upper corners, spine head sl bumped), else NF in NF dj. *Pacific**. $86/£54

BURROUGHS, EDGAR RICE. Tarzan and the Tarzan Twins with Jad-Bal-Ja, the Golden Lion. Racine, WI: Whitman, (1936). 1st ed. Color pict bds. (Contents dknd, brittle, few pp w/sm tears, sticker fr pastedown; wear, abrasions to joints, edges), else VG. *Pacific**. $115/£72

BURROUGHS, EDGAR RICE. Tarzan and the Tarzan Twins. NY: Canaveral, 1963. 1st ed thus. Fine in NF dj (extrems sl worn, sm chip spine foot, price-clipped). *Pacific**. $98/£61

BURROUGHS, EDGAR RICE. Tarzan at the Earth's Core. NY: Metropolitan, (1930). 1st ed. Frontis by J. Allen St. John. Grn cl lettered in black. (Corner sl bumped), else Fine in NF dj (chip to spine head, corners sl chipped, 1.5-inch tear to rear panel, few sm tears). *Pacific**. $1,380/£863

BURROUGHS, EDGAR RICE. Tarzan Lord of the Jungle. Chicago: McClurg, 1928. 1st ed. 8vo. Grn cl. Dj (backed w/non-acidic rice paper, few archival paper restorations at spine, edges); slipcase. *Swann**. $920/£575

BURROUGHS, EDGAR RICE. Tarzan of the Apes. NY: A.L. Burt, (1915). 1st popular ed. Ads at end do not include this title. 8vo. Frontis, 6pp pub's ads at end. Grn cl. VG (sig, date) in dj (nicked, long closed tear along fr spine edge, across fr cvr; rubbed). *Houle*. $950/£594

BURROUGHS, EDGAR RICE. Tarzan of the Apes. NY: G&D, (c.1927). Frontis. Red cl. Fine in VG dj (few sm chips, tears, fr panel sl rubbed). *Pacific**. $150/£94

BURROUGHS, EDGAR RICE. Tarzan of the Apes. Chicago: McClurg, 1914. 1st ed. 8vo. Red cl, gilt. (Spine faded, binding sl skewed.) Facs dj; slipcase. *Swann**. $920/£575

BURROUGHS, EDGAR RICE. Tarzan of the Apes. Chicago: McClurg, 1914. 1st ed, 1st ptg, 1st binding, w/A.C. McClurg set in 1 line in spine imprint, no acorn device, and the 1st ptg (or state), w/'W.F. Hall Printing Co./Chicago' on c. pg set in 2 lines of Old English type. This copy in orig dj designed by Fred J. Arting. Red cl, gilt. (Pencil initials, sl dknd; spine sl leaning, gilt sl rubbed, foot sl bumped), else NF in VG+ dj (spine head, corners rubbed, sm chip to foot, rear joint rubbed, spine sl dknd). *Pacific**. $19,550/£12,219

BURROUGHS, EDGAR RICE. Tarzan the Invincible. Tarzana, (1931). 1st ed. (Spine faded.) Supplied rmdr dj; slipcase. *Swann**. $230/£144

BURROUGHS, EDGAR RICE. Tarzan the Invincible. Tarzana: Burroughs, (1931). 1st ed. Frontis by Stanley O. Burroughs. Blue cl. NF in NF dj (spine ends sl chipped, sm tear to fr crease, verso foxed). *Pacific**. $546/£341

BURROUGHS, EDGAR RICE. Tarzan the Magnificent. Tarzana: Burroughs, (1939). 1st ed. (Ink name, mostly erased), o/w NF in dj (laminated). *Pacific**. $345/£216

BURROUGHS, EDGAR RICE. Tarzan the Terrible. Chicago: McClurg, 1921. 1st ed. 9 plts, map. Dec red cl. (Hinges cracked), else VG-. *Pacific**. $69/£43

BURROUGHS, EDGAR RICE. Tarzan the Terrible. Chicago: McClurg, 1921. 1st ed. 9 plts, map by J. Allen St. John. Red cl. (Sl leaning), else NF in Good dj (worn, chipped, lacks piece from lower fr joint, adhesion damage to top fr panel affecting 'AN' in 'TARZAN,' few neat tape repairs to verso). *Pacific**. $633/£396

BURROUGHS, EDGAR RICE. Tarzan the Untamed. Chicago: McClurg, 1920. 1st ed. 9 plts. Lt grn cl. (Hinges cracked, repaired w/yellowing tape, spine ends, joints rubbed), else VG-. *Pacific**. $35/£22

BURROUGHS, EDGAR RICE. Tarzan the Untamed. Chicago: McClurg, 1920. 1st ed. 8vo. Dj (backed w/non-acidic rice paper, several archival paper restorations to spine panel, edges); slipcase. *Swann**. $920/£575

BURROUGHS, EDGAR RICE. Tarzan the Untamed. Chicago: McClurg, 1920. 1st ed. 9 plts by J. Allen St. John. Lt grn cl lettered in dk brn. (Tp sl soiled), else Fine in VG + dj (sl rubbed, lt edgeworn, sl chipped, spine sl dknd, faint stain to foot). *Pacific**. $1,035/£647

BURROUGHS, EDGAR RICE. Tarzan Triumphant. Tarzana: Burroughs, (1932). 1st ed. 5 plts by Studley Burroughs. Fine in dj. *Pacific**. $518/£324

BURROUGHS, EDGAR RICE. The Tarzan Twins. Joliet: P.F. Volland, (1927). 2nd ed. Cl-backed pict bds. (Spine ends frayed, corners, extrems rubbed), else VG, issued w/o a dj, originally in a box (not present). *Pacific**. $40/£25

BURROUGHS, EDGAR RICE. The Tarzan Twins. Joliet: P.F. Volland, (1927). 4th ed. 8vo. 126pp. (1 pg w/marginal tear). Cl-backed color illus bds. Color pict box (edges lt worn). *Reisler*. $300/£188

BURROUGHS, EDGAR RICE. The Tarzan Twins. Joliet: P.F. Volland, (1927). 1st ed. 8.25x6. Douglas Grant (illus). Cl-backed pict bds. (Ink name; edges rubbed), else VG. *Pacific**. $575/£359

BURROUGHS, EDGAR RICE. The Tarzan Twins. Joliet: P.F. Volland, (1927). 2nd ed. Cl-backed pict bds. (Ink date, sl spots of adhesion damage to 1/2-title; corners sl rubbed, 1 sl showing), else Fine in NF orig 2-part box (top sl split at 2 corners, sides sl rubbed). *Pacific**. $805/£503

BURROUGHS, EDGAR RICE. Tarzan's Quest. Tarzana: Burroughs, (1936). 1st ed. 5 plts. NF in dj (spine ends sl rubbed, fr flap creased). *Pacific**. $403/£252

BURROUGHS, EDGAR RICE. Tarzan's Quest. Tarzana: Burroughs, 1936. 1st ed. J. Allen St. John (illus). Fine (fep sl offset) in Fine dj (few nicks spine ends). *Unger*. $650/£406

BURROUGHS, EDGAR RICE. Tarzan, Lord of the Jungle. Chicago: McClurg, 1928. 1st ed. 5 plts. Grn cl. Good (child's pencil dwgs to eps, feps, verso of frontis, smudge to frontis, tear to 1/2-title; hinges cracked, spine sunned). *Pacific**. $23/£14

BURROUGHS, EDGAR RICE. Tarzan, Lord of the Jungle. Chicago: McClurg, 1928. 1st ed. 5 plts by J. Allen St. John. Grn cl lettered in black. NF (plt detached but present; spine ends sl rubbed) in NF dj (folds, joints sl rubbed; spine sl dknd, 1.5-inch split to top fr joint). *Pacific**. $1,265/£791

BURROUGHS, EDGAR RICE. Tarzan. NY: Random House, 1984. Jon Townley & Bill Selby (illus). 3 dbl-pg pop-ups. Glazed pict bds. VG. *Bookfinders*. $35/£22

BURROUGHS, EDGAR RICE. Thuvia, Maid of Mars. NY: G&D, (1920, but c.1921). 4 plts (incl frontis). Red cl. Fine in VG dj (edges worn, folds rubbed, spine sunned). *Pacific**. $173/£108

BURROUGHS, EDGAR RICE. Thuvia, Maid of Mars. Chicago: McClurg, 1920. 1st ed. Olive cl stamped in black. Text Good (lt aged, sl spotting to bulked edges; cvrs rubbed, sl dusty, edges sl worn, spine sl spotted, hinges severely cracked). *Baltimore**. $60/£38

BURROUGHS, EDGAR RICE. Thuvia, Maid of Mars. Chicago: McClurg, 1920. 1st ed. 8vo. Grn cl. Dj (backed w/non-acidic rice paper, few paper restorations at edges, spine); slipcase. *Swann**. $920/£575

BURROUGHS, EDGAR RICE. Thuvia, Maid of Mars. Chicago: McClurg, 1920. 1st ed. 10 plts (incl frontis) by J. Allen St. John. Grn cl lettered in black w/black circle design on fr cvr. (Offset to reps; spine ends sl rubbed), else Fine in VG dj (lower edge of fr panel, spine foot chipped, foot torn; sl dknd, soiled). *Pacific**. $1,495/£934

BURROUGHS, EDGAR RICE. The War Chief. Chicago: McClurg, 1927. 1st ed. Orange cl stamped in red. Fine in dj (creased vertically 3 times from being folded). *Pacific**. $1,495/£934

BURROUGHS, EDGAR RICE. The Warlord of Mars. Chicago: McClurg, 1919. 1st ed, 1st ptg w/imprint of W. F. Hall on c. pg & pub's imprint at base of spine set in 3 lines. Frontis. Red cl, gilt. (Sticker; spine ends sl rubbed), else NF. *Pacific**. $58/£36

BURROUGHS, EDGAR RICE. The Warlord of Mars. Chicago: McClurg, 1919. 1st ed. Frontis. Crimson cl, gilt; Currey's State A, w/spine imprint in 3 lines, ptr's credit of W.F. Hall on copyright pg. (Lt aged, eps lt foxed, fr hinge split; lt rubbed, sl abrasion along upper joint.) *Baltimore**. $65/£41

BURROUGHS, EDGAR RICE. The Warlord of Mars. Chicago: McClurg, 1919. 1st ed, 1st ptg w/imprint of W.F. Hall on c. pg, pub's imprint at spine base set in 3 lines. Frontis. Red cl, gilt. (Spine sl faded, ends sl rubbed), else VG. *Pacific**. $127/£79

BURROUGHS, EDGAR RICE. The Warlord of Mars. Chicago: McClurg, 1919. 1st ed, 1st ptg w/imprint of W. F. Hall on c. pg & pub's imprint at base of spine set in 3 lines. Frontis by J. Allen St. John. Red cl, heavily gilt. Fine in dj (chip, sm tear to spine foot, tear to rear panel, sl worn). *Pacific**. $3,450/£2,156

BURROUGHS, JOHN et al. Harriman Alaska Expedition—Alaska. Volumes 1 and 2. NY: Doubleday, Page, 1901. 1st ed. Fldg map. NF in cl djs (lt worn). *Woolson*. $450/£281

BURROUGHS, JOHN ROLFE. Guardian of the Grasslands.... Cheyenne: Pioneer Ptg & Stationary, 1971. 1st trade ed. Fabricoid. Fine in dj. *Labordo*. $165/£103

BURROUGHS, JOHN ROLFE. Where the Old West Stayed Young. NY, 1962. 1st ed. Pict bds, cl. NF in dj (edgeworn, sl chipped, price-clipped). *Baade*. $57/£36

BURROUGHS, JOHN. Camping and Tramping with Roosevelt. Boston: Houghton, Mifflin, 1907. 1st ed. One of 250. Paper spine label. (Sl soiled), else NF. *Pacific**. $69/£43

BURROUGHS, JOHN. Camping with President Roosevelt. NY: Houghton Mifflin, 1906. Photo frontis. Fine in paper wrappers (sl soiled, chipped). *Biscotti*. $30/£19

BURROUGHS, JOHN. Under the Apple-Trees. Boston: Houghton Mifflin, 1916. 1st ed. Frontis. Fine in NF dj (sl rubbed). BAL 2192. *Agvent*. $150/£94

BURROUGHS, RICHARD. A Treatise on Trigonometry and Navigation.... Middlebury: Ptd by J.D. Huntington, 1807. 81pp; 7 plts. Contemp calf. (Text dampstained; fr cvr detached, calf worn), else Good. *Brown*. $15/£9

BURROUGHS, STEPHEN. Sketch of the Life of the Notorious Stephen Burroughs. Otsego: Ptd by M. & E. Phinney, 1810. 2nd ed (?). 100pp. Contemp 1/4 calf, marbled bds. (Name, lt stained(?); rubbed.) Howes B1022. *Cahan*. $225/£141

BURROUGHS, WILLIAM and KEITH HARING. Apocalypse. NY: George Mulder Fine Arts, 1988. 1st Amer ed. Fine in NF dj (lt rubbed). *Warren*. $50/£31

BURROUGHS, WILLIAM and BRION GYSIN. The Third Mind. NY: Viking, 1978. 1st ed. Fine in dj. *Smith*. $100/£63

BURROUGHS, WILLIAM and BRION GYSIN. The Third Mind. Calder, 1979. 1st UK ed. NF in dj. *Sclanders*. $32/£20

BURROUGHS, WILLIAM, JR. Speed. London: Olympia, 1971. 1st UK, 1st hb ed. NF in dj. *Sclanders*. $40/£25

BURROUGHS, WILLIAM. Ah Pook Is Here. John Calder, 1979. 1st Eng ed. Signed. VG (spine ends, corners, top edge fr cvr sl bumped) in dj (sl mkd, creased). *Ulysses*. $136/£85

BURROUGHS, WILLIAM. Cities of the Red Night. NY: Holt, Rinehart & Winston, (1981). 1st ed. Pict eps. Orangish cl. (Bds sl faded at top/bottom edges), o/w Fine in dj (top edge sl browned). *Heritage*. $75/£47

BURROUGHS, WILLIAM. Junkie. (London): Olympia/New English Library, (1966). 1st ed. Fine in wrappers. *Lenz*. $75/£47

BURROUGHS, WILLIAM. The Last Words of Dutch Schultz. Calder, 1986. 1st UK ed of enlgd version. Fine in wraps. *Sclanders*. $10/£6

BURROUGHS, WILLIAM. The Naked Lunch. NY: Grove, (1959). 1st Amer ed. (Sig), o/w Fine in dj (sm edge tears). *Agvent.* $200/£125

BURROUGHS, WILLIAM. The Naked Lunch. Paris: Olympia, 1959. 1st ed. VG (cancelled price w/new stamped price; lacks dj). *Warren.* $125/£78

BURROUGHS, WILLIAM. The Naked Lunch. NY: Grove, 1959. 1st Amer ed. 3500 ptd. NF in dj (couple closed tears). *Smith.* $200/£125

BURROUGHS, WILLIAM. The Place of Dead Roads. NY: Holt, Rinehart & Winston, (1984). 1st ed. Brn cl. Fine in dj. *Heritage.* $50/£31

BURROUGHS, WILLIAM. Queer. Pan/Picador, 1986. 1st UK ed. Fine in dj. *Sclanders.* $24/£15

BURROUGHS, WILLIAM. Sinki's Sauna. (NY): Pequod Press, (1982). One of 500. Fine in wrappers. *Heritage.* $75/£47

BURROUGHS, WILLIAM. The Soft Machine. Paris: Olympia, 1961. 1st ed, 2nd issue (w/new price rubberstamped on rear cvr). Inscribed by Burroughs and Maurice Girodias (pub). (Strip of glue residue rear cvr, spine corners sl worn; lacks dj), else NF in ptd wrappers. *Smith.* $200/£125

BURROUGHS, WILLIAM. The Soft Machine. Paris: Olympia, 1961. 1st ed. Fine in card wrappers in VG dj. *Williams.* $256/£160

BURROUGHS, WILLIAM. The Soft Machine. Paris: Olympia, 1961. 1st ed. Ptd price of 15 new francs on rear cvr stamped over w/new price of 18 new francs. Fine (sm mk to fore-edge) in dj (sl rubbed, mkd, spine browned), wrappers. *Ulysses.* $472/£295

BURROUGHS, WILLIAM. The Ticket That Exploded. Paris: Olympia, 1962. 1st ed. (Wrappers lt rubbed at spine; lacks dj), else NF. *Smith.* $75/£47

BURROUGHS, WILLIAM. The Ticket That Exploded. Paris: Olympia, 1962. 1st ed. Fine in card wrappers in VG+ dj. *Williams.* $240/£150

BURROWES, JOHN FRECKLETON. The Piano-Forte Primer; Containing the Rudiments of Music.... London: The Author, 1819. 2nd ed. ix,(iii),56pp + (3)ads. Contemp calf (neatly re-backed). *Young.* $176/£110

BURROWS, GUY. The Curse of Central Africa.... London: R.A. Everett, 1903. 1st ed. Frontisport; 6 photogravures; fldg color map. Blue dec cl. Sound (foxed; rubbed edges, rear cvr marked, gatherings loose). *Morrell.* $152/£95

BURROWS, JACK. John Ringo. Tucson, 1987. 1st ed. Map. Photocopy of earlier magazine article by author on Ringo laid in. Fine in dj (price-clipped). *Baade.* $32/£20

BURROWS, JACK. John Ringo. Tucson: Univ of AZ, 1987. 1st ed. VF in dj. *Labordo.* $35/£22

BURRUS, ERNEST J. Kino and Manje Explorers of Sonora and Arizona, Their Vision of the Future. Rome: Jesuit Hist Inst, 1971. 1st ed. Loose map. Fine. *Book Market.* $60/£38

BURRUS, ERNEST J. Kino and Manje, Explorers of Sonora and Arizona. Rome, Italy: Jesuit Hist Inst, 1971. 1st ed. 2 facs on 1 plt; fldg map laid in loose. Fine. *Pacific*.* $92/£58

BURRUS, ERNEST J. Kino and the Cartography of Northwestern New Spain. Tucson: AZ Pioneers' Hist Soc, 1965. One of 750 ptd. 17 map repros. NF. *Dumont.* $325/£203

BURRUS, ERNEST J. (ed). Ducrue's Account of the Expulsion of the Jesuits from Lower California (1767-1769). Rome: Jesuit Hist Inst, 1967. 1st ed. Fine. *Book Market.* $25/£16

BURRUS, ERNEST J. (ed). Kino Reports to Headquarters [with] Supplement. Rome: Institutum Historicum S.J., 1954. 1st ed. 2 vols. 2 fldg maps. VG+ in gray ptd wrappers (corners, spine ends chipped). *Harrington.* $45/£28

BURRUS, ERNEST J. (ed). Kino Writes to the Duchess. Rome: Jesuit Hist Inst, 1965. 1st ed. Fine. *Book Market.* $30/£19

BURSEY, JACK. Antarctic Night. London/NY/Toronto: Longmans, Green, 1958. 1st ed. VG. *Explorer.* $19/£12

BURSILL, HENRY. Hand Shadows to Be Thrown upon the Wall. Griffith & Farran, 1859. 2nd ed. 4to. Complete w/18 hand-colored plts (coloring probably later). Mod cl-backed bds. VG. *Hollett.* $152/£95

BURSTYN, HAROLD L. At the Sign of the Quadrant. Mystic, CT, 1957. 1st ed. Ptd wrappers. *Lefkowicz.* $30/£19

BURT, HENRY M. Burt's Illustrated Guide of the Connecticut Valley. Northampton, 1867. Fldg map. Pub's cl. *Swann*.* $57/£36

BURT, MAXWELL STRUTHERS. In the High Hills. Boston: Houghton Mifflin, 1914. 1st ed, 1st bk. Linen, ptd bds. (Sig; tips sl bumped), else Nice. *Reese.* $50/£31

BURT, MAXWELL STRUTHERS. Powder River; Let 'Er Buck. NY: Farrar & Rinehart, 1938. 1st ed. NF. *Labordo.* $45/£28

BURT, S. W. and E. L. BERTHOUD. The Rocky Mountain Gold Regions. Denver: Old West Pub Co, 1962. Facs ed of 1861 orig. One of 320 ptd. 3 maps, 2 tables in rear pocket. Unopened. Facs of orig wrappers bound in. Brn cl. Fine. Howes B1026. *Harrington.* $75/£47

BURTON, E. F. An Indian Olio. Spencer Blackett, (c.1880). 1st ed. xii,388pp. Aeg. Pict cl (spine dknd, chipped, neatly recased), gilt. *Hollett.* $136/£85

BURTON, ISABEL and W. H. WILKINS. The Romance of Isabel Lady Burton. NY: Dodd, Mead, 1904. 8 plts. Teg. 1/2 morocco. (Sl rubbed, sl silverfished), o/w VG. *Worldwide.* $85/£53

BURTON, JOHN HILL. The Book-Hunter etc. Edinburgh: William Blackwood & Sons, 1882. Ltd to 1000 numbered. Etched frontis, civ,(428)pp. Nice (sl rubbed). *Ash.* $120/£75

BURTON, JOHN HILL. Narratives from Criminal Trials in Scotland. London: Chapman & Hall, 1852. 2 vols. Emb cl (worn, stained). *Boswell.* $450/£281

BURTON, KATHERINE. Paradise Planters. London, 1939. 1st ed. NF (name) in dj (sl rubbed). *Polyanthos.* $25/£16

BURTON, M. et al (eds). The New Larousse Encyclopedia of Animal Life. NY: Bonanza, (1981). Fine in VG+ dj. *Mikesh.* $30/£19

BURTON, MILES. Bones in the Brickfield. Collins, 1958. 1st UK ed. Fine in dj. *Williams.* $64/£40

BURTON, RICHARD F. Book of the Sword. C&W, 1884. Lg 8vo. xxxix,299pp. Partly uncut. Later grn 1/2 morocco by Morrell, gilt, gray/gilt cl spine pasted on rep, raised bands. VG. *Sotheran.* $1,920/£1,200

BURTON, RICHARD F. The Book of the Thousand Nights and a Night. H.S. Nichols, 1897. New ed. 12 vols (incl 4 'Supplemental Nights' vols). Royal 8vo. 71 repros. Teg. (Edges sl foxed), o/w VG set in pub's 3/4 crushed red morocco (sl rubbed), gilt, w/the vaguely mkd pale grn art linen sides, 5 raised bands. *Ulysses.* $1,920/£1,200

BURTON, RICHARD F. The Book of the Thousand Nights and One. (Denver: Burton Soc, 1900.) One of 1000. 16 vols (10 + 6 suppl). Teg. 3/4 red morocco, marbled bds, gilt, raised bands, bound by Phister. (Spines sl dknd, few joints cracked), else VG set. *Pacific*.* $633/£396

BURTON, RICHARD F. The City of the Saints and Across the Rock Mountains to California. London: Longman, Green, Longman & Roberts, 1861. 1st ed. Thick 8vo. Frontis, x,(1),701,(1)pp; fldg map, 8 plts. Grn cl (sm spine repair), gilt. Fine. Howes B1033. *Mott.* $600/£375

BURTON, RICHARD F. Explorations of the Highlands of Brazil. London: Tinsley Bros, 1869. 1st ed, 2nd issue. 2 vols. 8vo. xii,443; viii,478pp (lacks 1/2-title, lib stamps); fldg map. Mod 1/2 red calf. *Adelson.* $635/£397

BURTON, RICHARD F. Explorations of the Highlands of the Brazil. Tinsley Bros, 1869. 1st ed. 2 vols. 8vo. Wood-engr frontispieces, add'l vignette tps both vols, x,443; viii,478pp; fldg map (sm tear to inner margin). Marbled eps; teg. Early 20th-cent 1/2 dk brn morocco, raised bands, gilt, pale brn linen cl sides. Good (foxed; orig cl backstrips laid down, bound in at end, extrems rubbed). *Blackwell's*. $1,280/£800

BURTON, RICHARD F. First Footsteps in East Africa; or, an Exploration of Harar. Longman et al, 1856. 1st ed, 2nd issue. 2 engr maps, 4 chromolitho plts, 24pp pub's ads. (Lacks 2pp 4th Appendix; few pp coming loose.) Mod red morocco. *Sotheby's**. $736/£460

BURTON, RICHARD F. The Highlands of Brazil. Tinsley Bros, 1869. 1st ed. 2 vols. 8vo. Half-titles present, wood-engr frontispieces, add'l vignette tps, xii,443; viii,478pp (shaken, browned), (2) ads; fldg map (sm tear at gutter margin, some creases). Orig 1st issue sand-grain grn cl (recased), gilt backstrips (vol 1 worn at head w/sl loss, tail rubbed, gilt dull). *Blackwell's*. $880/£550

BURTON, RICHARD F. The Lands of Cazembe. London, 1873. 1st ed. vii,272pp; lg fldg map. (Cl sl soiled, corners bumped.) *Maggs*. $360/£225

BURTON, RICHARD F. A Mission to Gelele, King of Dahome. London, 1864. 1st ed. 2 vols. 8vo. xvii,386; vi,412pp; 2 plts. Dk purple pict cl, gilt. (Headcaps sl chipped, corners bumped.) *Maggs*. $1,920/£1,200

BURTON, RICHARD F. A Mission to Gelele. London, 1893. Memorial ed. 2 vols. xxiv,256; viii,306pp; 2 plts. Black pict cl (spines sl faded, fr bd vol 1 lt rubbed), gilt. *Maggs*. $280/£175

BURTON, RICHARD F. Personal Narrative of a Pilgrimage to El-Medinah and Meccah. Longman, Brown, Green & Longmans, 1855-6. 1st ed. 3 vols. 8vo. xiv,(i errata),388; iv,426; x,(i list of plts),448pp; 13 litho plts (7 color), 4 maps, plans (3 fldg). Full contemp calf, gilt, contrasting leather labels, raised bands. VG set (browned between pp 2 & 3, 388 & rep; 3 bkpls each vol; joints sl tender, extrems, gilt sl worn). *Sotheran*. $4,792/£2,995

BURTON, RICHARD F. and CHARLES F. TYRWHITT DRAKE. Unexplored Syria. Tinsley Bros, 1872. 1st ed, 3rd issue. 2 vols. 8vo. 2 frontispieces, fldg map, 25 plts (11 fldg). Orig dec cl. (Lacks 1/2-title vol 2, lower half of 1/2-title vol 1; lt rubbed, soiled.) *Sotheby's**. $920/£575

BURTON, RICHARD F. (trans). Arabian Nights Entertainments. LEC, 1954. Ltd to 1500 numbered. 4 vols. Arthur Szyk (illus). Fine in slipcase. *Swann**. $230/£144

BURTON, RICHARD F. (trans). Arabian Nights: The Book of the Thousand Nights and a Night. Benares: Kamashastra Soc, 1894-(98). Library ed. 12 vols. Teg. Dec cl (extrems lt rubbed). *Christie's**. $349/£218

BURTON, RICHARD F. (trans). Il Pentamerone; or, the Tale of Tales. London: Henry, 1893. 2 vols. xvi,282; vi,283-562pp. Orig black cl (rebacked, lt rubbed). *Adelson*. $325/£203

BURTON, RICHARD F. (trans). The Kasidah of Haji Abdu El-Yezdi. Phila: David McKay, (1931). 1st ed illus by Willy Pogany. 9.75x7.5. Silver/black cl, pict cvr label. (Bkpl mtd to fep; spine ends sl rubbed, spine dull), else VG. *Pacific**. $63/£39

BURTON, RICHARD F. (trans). Kasidah of Haji Abdu El-Yezdi. LEC, 1937. Ltd to 1500 numbered, signed by Valenti Angelo (illus). Fine in slipcase. *Swann**. $80/£50

BURTON, RICHARD F. (trans). The Kasidah. NY: Knopf, 1924. One of 2000 numbered. 12 plts. Cl-backed dec bds (edges rubbed, headcap chipped). *Maggs*. $120/£75

BURTON, RICHARD F. (trans). Persian Stories from the Arabian Nights. Greenbrae: Allen, 1980. One of 140. Prospectus laid in. Loose sigs in 3 wrappers vols, clamshell box. Fine. *Pacific**. $489/£306

BURTON, RICHARD. Meeting Mrs. Jenkins. NY: Morrow, 1966. 1st ed. VF in VF dj (price-clipped w/new stamped price). *Between The Covers*. $150/£94

BURTON, ROBERT. The Anatomy of Melancholy. Boston, 1859. New ed. 3 vols. Marbled eps, edges. 1/4 sheep, marbled bds, red morocco spine labels. NF set (spine chip). *Doctor's Library*. $250/£156

BURTON, ROBERT. The Anatomy of Melancholy. Floyd Dell and Paul Jordan-Smith (eds). NY: George H. Doran, (1927). One of 500. Vol 1 inscribed, signed. 2 vols. Teg. 1/2 vellum, gilt. (Spines soiled), else VG. *Pacific**. $86/£54

BURTON, VIRGINIA LEE. Life Story. Boston: Houghton Mifflin, 1962. 1st ed. Lg 4to. Yellow pict cl. Fine. *American Booksellers*. $75/£47

BURTON, VIRGINIA LEE. Mike Mulligan and His Steam Shovel. Boston: Houghton Mifflin, 1939. 1st ed. Obl 4to. Tan pict cl. Good. *Reisler*. $250/£156

BURTON, VIRGINIA LEE. Mike Mulligan and His Steam Shovel. Boston: HMCo, 1939. 1st ed. 9.5x8.75. 32pp. VG in dj. *Cattermole*. $2,000/£1,250

BURTON, WILLIAM. Josiah Wedgwood and His Pottery. NY/London, 1922. One of 1500. 32 color, 72 b/w plts. NF in dj (edgeworn). *New Hampshire**. $70/£44

BURY, ADRIAN. Water-Colour Painting of To-Day. C. G. Holme (ed). London: The Studio, 1937. 8 tipped-in color plts. (Lt spotting; spine lt faded.) *Edwards*. $40/£25

BURY, THOMAS TALBOT. Coloured Views on the Liverpool and Manchester Railway, with Plates of Coaches, Machines, &c. London: R. Ackermann, 1831. 1st ed. 4to. 13 hand-colored aquatint plts (occasional lt marginal dust-soiling, o/w Clean). Contemp roan-backed bds (spine lt rubbed). *Christie's**. $3,240/£2,025

BUSCH, MORITZ. Travels Between the Hudson and the Mississippi, 1851-1852. (Lexington): Univ Press of KY, (1971). 1st ed in English. Blue cl. Fine in NF dj. *Harrington*. $40/£25

BUSCH, WILHELM. Max and Mortiz. London: Siegle, Hill, (ca 1890). Early ed. 8vo. (iv),53pp. Red pict cl. Fine. *Sotheran*. $237/£148

BUSH ROMERO, P. My Adventure with Tigers and Lions. Mexico, ca 1958. 1st ed. One of 1000. Inscribed. 3 maps. (Edges sl dknd; lt rubbed.) *Sutton*. $195/£122

BUSH, ELIZA C. My Pilgramage to Eastern Shrines. London: Hurst and Blackett, 1867. 1st ed. Engr frontis, xii,317,(1),12,(4) pub's lists. Beveled edges. Maroon cl, gilt. Good (sl foxed; extrems rubbed, hinges cracked). *Morrell*. $64/£40

BUSH, MARTIN H. The Passion of Sacco and Vanzetti. Syracuse Univ, 1968. One of 200 signed by Bush and Ben Shahn (illus). Sq 8vo. Fine in pict dj (extrems lt worn). *Bromer*. $525/£328

BUSHELL, S. W. Oriental Ceramic Art. NY, 1899. xiii,942pp. Teg, partly unopened. Maroon cl (rebound; new eps). *Edwards*. $96/£60

BUSHELL, STEPHEN W. and WILLIAM M. LAFFAN. Catalogue of the Morgan Collection of Chinese Porcelains. NY: MMA, 1910. Ltd to 500. VG in wraps (sl rubbed, soiled). *Worldwide*. $45/£28

BUSHNELL, G. H. S. and ADRIAN DIGBY. Ancient American Pottery. Faber & Faber, 1955. 1st ed. Color frontis; 3 color, 80 b/w plts, 2 maps. (Lib ink stamp.) Dj. *Edwards*. $45/£28

BUSHNELL, GEORGE HERBERT. From Papyrus to Print, a Bibliographical Miscellany. London: Grafton, 1947. 1st ed. (Cvrs faded.) *Oak Knoll*. $20/£13

BUSNEL, R. G. and J. F. FISH (eds). Animal Sonar Systems. NY, 1980. (Lt worn.) *Sutton*. $125/£78

BUSS, H. Wanderings in the West, During the Year 1870. London: Thomas Danks, 1871. Only ed. Inscribed presentation. viii,196pp. Aeg. Blue cl (lt soiled), gilt. *Mott*. $125/£78

BUSSELL, JAN and ANN HOGARTH. Marionettes. How to Make Them. Ditchling: Pepler & Sewell, 1934. 1st ed. Dec bds. VG. *Dramatis.* $16/£10

BUSSEY, GEORGE MOIR. History of Napoleon. London: Joseph Thomas, 1840. Aeg. Contemp morocco, spine gilt w/an 'N' stamped on each cvr. Good. Bkpl of P. Flamank. *Stewart.* $400/£250

BUSWELL, LESLIE. Ambulance No. 10. Boston/NY, 1916. (Sl mkd, shelfworn, extrems rubbed.) *Clearwater.* $48/£30

BUTCHER, S. D. Butcher's Pioneer History of Custer County. Broken Bow, NE: Purcells, 1965. 2nd ed. Fine. Howes B1048. *Labordo.* $35/£22

BUTEN, HARRY M. Wedgwood and Artists. Merion, PA: Buten Museum of Wedgwood, (1960). Frontis. Illus bds. *Turtle Island.* $50/£31

BUTLER, A. J. Sport in Classic Times. London: Ernest & Benn, 1930. 1st ed. (Red binding faded), o/w VG. *October Farm.* $45/£28

BUTLER, A. S. G. The Architecture of Sir Edwin Lutyens. Antique Collector's Club, 1984. Ltd to 1500 (out of series). 3 vols. Folio. Buckram. Djs (few sm tears). *Marlborough.* $440/£275

BUTLER, A. S. G. The Architecture of Sir Edwin Lutyens. Volume III (only). London: Country Life, 1950. 1st ed. Folio. Frontis, 107 plts. Dj (sl soiled, chipped). *Edwards.* $120/£75

BUTLER, A. S. G. The Substance of Architecture. London, 1926. 8 plts. Fore-edge uncut. (Eps, fore-edge sl spotted, bkpl.) *Edwards.* $64/£40

BUTLER, ARTHUR G. Foreign Finches in Captivity. London: Reeve, 1894. 60 Fine hand-colored plts. Gilt-pict cl (shelfwear). *Oinonen*.* $100/£63

BUTLER, ARTHUR G. Illustrations of Typical Specimens of Lepidoptera Heterocera in the Collection of the British Museum. London: British Museum, 1877-93. 8 vols only (of 9, lacks vol IV). 4to. 157 chromolitho plts. Orig brn cl (spines chipped w/loss, stitching weak). *Christie's*.* $864/£540

BUTLER, BENJAMIN F. Butler's Book. Boston: A.M. Thayer, 1892. 1st ed. Signed inserted typed presentation leaf bound in. 1154 + 4pp ads (orig bkpl removed from orig binding & remtd at fep; lt aging; 5 dbl-pg plts. Aeg. Later brn cl, later leather spine label. Internally VG. *Baltimore*.* $50/£31

BUTLER, FRANCES ANNE. Journal. Phila: Carey, Lea & Blanchard, 1835. 1st Amer ed. 2 vols. pp252,(12) ads; 218,(32) ads. (Lt foxed.) Orig cl (faded), paper labels. *Mott.* $125/£78

BUTLER, FREDERICK. The Farmer's Manual. Hartford: Samuel Goodrich, 1819. 1st ed. 224pp. Orig leather-backed bds. (1st few ll w/tide mk), o/w VG. *New Hampshire*.* $90/£56

BUTLER, HARCOURT. A Big Game Shoot in Upper Burma, 1923. Rangoon, 1923. One of 200 ptd. Ptd bds, cl backstrip. *Petersfield.* $192/£120

BUTLER, HOWARD RUSSELL. Painter and Space or the Third Dimension in Graphic Art. NY, 1923. 1st Amer ed. Fine (bkpl; spine top sl rubbed). *Polyanthos.* $40/£25

BUTLER, JULIA. Singing Paddles. Portland: Binfords & Mort, 1952. 8vo. Dorothea Cooke (illus). VG. *American Booksellers.* $25/£16

BUTLER, OCTAVIA. Survivor. GC: Doubleday, 1978. 1st ed. Fine in dj. *Levin.* $125/£78

BUTLER, OCTAVIA. Wild Seed. GC: Doubleday, 1980. 1st ed. Fine in dj. *Levin.* $125/£78

BUTLER, RAGAN. Captain Nash and the Wroth Inheritance. London: Harwood-Smart, 1975. 1st ed. (Pp edges stained; cvr corners stained), else VG in dj. *Murder.* $35/£22

BUTLER, ROBERT OLEN. The Alleys of Eden. NY: Horizon, 1981. 1st ed. NF (edges spotted) in NF dj (lt rubbed). *Warren.* $125/£78

BUTLER, ROBERT OLEN. The Alleys of Eden. NY, 1981. 1st Amer ed, 1st bk. Signed. Fine in Fine dj. *Polyanthos.* $150/£94

BUTLER, ROBERT OLEN. Countrymen of Bones. NY, 1983. 1st ed. Fine in Fine dj. *Warren.* $85/£53

BUTLER, ROBERT OLEN. A Good Scent from a Strange Mountain. NY, 1992. 1st ed. Signed. Fine in Fine dj. *Warren.* $75/£47

BUTLER, ROBERT OLEN. On Distant Ground. NY, 1985. 1st Amer ed. Signed. Fine in Fine dj. *Polyanthos.* $45/£28

BUTLER, ROBERT OLEN. On Distant Ground. NY, 1985. 1st ed. Fine in Fine dj. *Warren.* $50/£31

BUTLER, ROBERT OLEN. Sun Dogs. NY, 1982. 1st ed. Fine in NF dj (sl rubbed). *Warren.* $60/£38

BUTLER, ROBERT OLEN. Sun Dogs. NY, 1982. 1st ed. Signed. Fine in Fine dj. *Warren.* $85/£53

BUTLER, ROBERT OLEN. They Whisper. Huntington Beach: James Cahill, 1993. 1st ed. One of 150. Signed. 1/4 blue morocco, marbled bds. As New in slipcase. *Pacific*.* $52/£33

BUTLER, ROBERT OLEN. Wabash. NY: Knopf, 1987. 1st ed. Fine in Fine dj. *Agvent.* $85/£53

BUTLER, SAMUEL. Erewhon. NY: LEC, 1934. One of 1500 ptd. Signed by Rockwell Kent (illus). Dec cl. (Spine rubbed, cl sl dull), else VG in slipcase. *Pacific*.* $86/£54

BUTLER, SAMUEL. Hudibras, in Three Parts: Written in the Time of the Late Wars. Troy: Wright, Goodenow & Stockwell, 1806. 1st Amer ed. Calf, morocco spine label. VG. *Pacific*.* $75/£47

BUTLER, SAMUEL. Hudibras, in Three Parts; Written at the Time of the Late Wars. London: C. Hitch et al, 1764. 2nd Grey ed. 2 vols. Period calf, diced, raised bands, morocco spine labels. (Bkpls; spines dknd, joints starting), else VG. *Pacific*.* $150/£94

BUTLER, SAMUEL. The Way of All Flesh. London: Grant Richards, 1903. 1st ed. Teg. Red cl. VG (sm ink name, inner hinges strengthened; hint of label removal fr bd) in early custom red cl slipcase. *Dermont.* $275/£172

BUTLER, SAMUEL. The Way of All Flesh. New Haven: Yale Univ, 1936. Signed by Robert Ward Johnson (illus). 2 vols. Full black sheep-skin, gilt/blind-stamped. Boxed. *Appelfeld.* $150/£94

BUTLER, WILLIAM. The Land of the Veda. NY/Cincinnati: Eaton & Mains/Jennings & Graham, 1906. Pict red cl. (Rear joint cracked.) *Hollett.* $224/£140

BUTLER-STONEY, T. The Old Man Who Lived in a Wood. London: George Allen, 1902. 1st ed. Obl royal 8vo. (31)pp; 11 full-pg color photolitho plts. Brn cl, color pict bds. Very Attractive (upper edge of lower bd sl knocked). *Sotheran.* $205/£128

BUTLIN, MARTIN and E. JOLL. The Paintings of J. M. W. Turner. New Haven: Yale Univ, 1977. 2 vols. 556 plts. Fine in djs. *Turtle Island.* $125/£78

BUTLIN, MARTIN and E. JOLL. The Paintings of J. M. W. Turner. Yale Univ, 1984. Rev ed. 2 vols. 572 plts. Paper in card slipcase. *Ars Artis.* $120/£75

BUTLIN, MARTIN et al. Turner at Petworth. London: Tate Gallery, 1989. 135 plts. Dj. *Edwards.* $56/£35

BUTLIN, MARTIN. The Paintings and Drawings of William Blake. New Haven/London, 1981. 2 vols. Sm folio. Djs. *Swann*.* $149/£93

BUTLIN, MARTIN. The Paintings and Drawings of William Blake. Yale Univ, 1981. 2 vols. 1193 plt illus. Good. *Ars Artis.* $360/£225

BUTLIN, MARTIN. William Blake. London: Tate Gallery, 1978. 17 color plts. Dj. *Edwards.* $48/£30

BUTOR, MICHEL. Degrees. Richard Howard (trans). Methuen, 1962. 1st ed. NF in dj. *Ulysses.* $56/£35

BUTTERWORTH, BENJAMIN. The Growth of Industrial Art. Washington: GPO, 1888. 1st ed. Lg folio. 200 VG b/w composite plts. Brn cl, gilt. Text Good (hinges split, eps heavily chipped, 1st few ll worn, chipped; faint dampstain bottom margin 1st few plts, all plts lt aged at margins, lacks plts #135-142; worn, scuffed). Baltimore*. $350/£219

BUTTERWORTH, W. E. Stop and Search. Boston: Little, Brown, 1969. 1st ed. Fine in dj. Associates. $125/£78

BUTTS, MARY. Traps for Unbelievers. London: Desmond Harmsworth, 1932. 1st Eng ed. VG (rep partly browned, top edge dusty; corners sl bumped) in dj (nicked, sl rubbed, chipped, dusty, sl creased, browned). Ulysses. $360/£225

BUXBAUM, FRANZ. Cactus Culture Based on Biology. London, 1958. Fold-out section w/7 maps. (Sm tears to spine head.) Brooks. $44/£28

BUXTON, THOMAS FOWELL. The African Slave Trade. London, 1839. 2nd ed. 240pp. (Contemp notes mtd on fep; rebacked retaining orig backstrip; rubbed, spine chipped.) King. $225/£141

BUXTON, THOMAS FOWELL. Memoirs. London: John Murray, 1848. 1st ed. Engr frontisport, xvi,600pp,8 pub's list. Orig blindstamped plum cl. Sound (foxed, ink inscrips; stained, faded, rubbed, hinges cracked). Morrell. $48/£30

BUXTON, THOMAS FOWELL. Memoirs. Charles Buxton (ed). London: John Murray, 1866. 5th ed. Engr frontisport, xvi,614pp. Marbled eps, edges. Full early calf, gilt, raised bands, leather spine label. Edwards. $120/£75

BYAM, GEORGE. Wanderings in Some of the Western Republics of America. London, 1850. 1st ed. xii,264pp; map, litho frontis, 2 plts. (Pencil lines in margins; lt worn.) Maggs. $400/£250

BYATT, A. S. Angels and Insects. London: C&W, 1992. 1st Eng ed. Signed. VG (spine ends sl bumped) in dj (sl torn, price-clipped). Ulysses. $88/£55

BYATT, A. S. Degrees of Freedom. London: C&W, 1965. 1st Eng ed. Fine in dj (spine, edges sl dknd). Ulysses. $152/£95

BYATT, A. S. Iris Murdoch. London: Longman Group, 1976. 1st Eng ed. Frontisport. VG in wrappers (sl mkd, dusty). Ulysses. $72/£45

BYATT, A. S. The Virgin in the Garden. London: C&W, 1978. 1st ed. NF in dj (spine foot sl water stained). Virgo. $56/£35

BYATT, A. S. Wordsworth and Coleridge in Their Time. London: Thomas Nelson & Sons, 1970. 1st Eng ed. VG (spine head sl bumped, edges sl spotted) in dj (sl creased, edges sl faded). Ulysses. $152/£95

BYERLY, WESLEY GRIMES, JR. Nam Doc. NY: Vantage, 1981. 1st ed. Fine in dj. Associates. $85/£53

BYFIELD, NATHANAEL. An Account of the Late Revolution in New England. NY: Joseph Sabin, 1865. Rpt. 26,(1)pp. 3/4 leather (deteriorated, fr hinge split, lacks top inch of backstrip), marbled bds. Wraps retained (worn, soiled). Bohling. $35/£22

BYINGTON, LEWIS FRANCIS and OSCAR LEWIS. The History of San Francisco. Chicago/SF: S.J. Clarke Pub, 1931. 1st ed. 3 vols. Grn cl, gilt. VF set. Argonaut. $250/£156

BYJ, CHARLOT. Christmas on Stage. Polygraphic Co of America, 1950. 5 pop-ups. VG in pict wraps. Bookfinders. $100/£63

BYNE, ARTHUR and MILDRED STAPLEY. Majorcan Houses and Gardens. NY, 1928. Folio. VG (ex-lib; spine faded). Swann*. $402/£251

BYNE, MILDRED STAPLEY and ARTHUR. Spanish Gardens and Patios. Phila/NY, 1924. 1st ed. Blue buckram, gilt. VG. Truepenny. $195/£122

BYNE, MILDRED STAPLEY and ARTHUR. Spanish Gardens and Patios.... Phila/NY: Lippincott/Architectural Record, 1928. 1st ed. 4 color plts. VF in dj. Pharos. $125/£78

BYNNER, WITTER. Book of Lyrics. NY: Knopf, 1955. 1st ed. Ltd to 1750 numbered. VF in Fine dj (internally repaired tear). Between The Covers. $85/£53

BYNUM, LINDLEY and IDWAL JONES. Biscailuz, Sheriff of the New West. NY: Morrow, 1950. 1st ed. Signed by Biscailuz, Bynum & Jones. VG in VG dj. Book Market. $30/£19

BYRD, RICHARD E. Alone. NY, 1938. 1st ed. Signed. (Bkpl; spine sunned), else Good. King. $50/£31

BYRD, RICHARD E. Discovery. The Story of the Second Byrd Antarctic Expedition. NY, 1935. 1st ed. Frontisport, 2 maps incl 1 ep. (Edges discolored.) Dj (ragged). Edwards. $64/£40

BYRD, RICHARD E. Discovery: The Story of the Second Byrd Antarctic Expedition. NY: Putnam, 1935. 1st ed. One of 500. Signed twice. Frontis port. 3/4 cl, morocco spine label. Fine in VG slipcase. Pacific*. $161/£101

BYRD, RICHARD E. Little America: Aerial Exploration in the Antarctic.... NY/London: Putnam/Knickerbocker, 1930. Author's Autograph ed of 1000 signed by Byrd and pub, specially bound. 2 fldg maps. NF. Explorer. $304/£190

BYRD, RICHARD E. Skyward. William R. Anderson (ed). Chicago: R.R. Donnelley, 1981. Frontis. VG. Lien. $30/£19

BYRD, WILLIAM. The Secret Diary of William Byrd, of Westyover, 1709-1712. Louis B. Wright and Marion Tinling (eds). Richmond, VA, 1941. 1st ed. Good+. Wantagh. $30/£19

BYRD, WILLIAM. The Writings of Colonel William Byrd of Westover in Virginia Esqr. John Spencer Bassett (ed). NY, 1901. One of 500 numbered. Uncut. Bds, paper parchment back, paper spine label. (Piece torn rep, sl lib mks; sl worn.) Cl dj (worn, soiled). Howes B1077. Oinonen*. $80/£50

BYRNE, BERNARD JAMES. A Frontier Army Surgeon. NY, 1962. 2nd ed. NF in dj. Howes B1078. Baade. $45/£28

BYRNE, J. F. Silent Years. NY: Farrar, Straus & Young, 1953. 1st US ed. VG (spine ends sl bumped) in dj (torn, nicked, creased, spine sl dknd). Ulysses. $72/£45

BYRNE, OLIVER. The First Six Books of the Elements of Euclid in Which Coloured Diagrams and Symbols Are Used Instead of Letters for the Greater Ease of Learners. London: William Pickering, 1847. 1st ed. 4to. xxix,268pp. Marbled eps. Red edges. Contemp 1/2 morocco, morocco-grain cl. VG (sm tear top of leaf ii3, not obscuring text; scattered foxing; extrems sl worn). Glaser. $3,500/£2,188

BYRON, GEORGE ANSON. Voyage of H.M.S. Blonde to the Sandwich Islands, in the Years 1824-1825. London: John Murray, 1826. 1st ed. 4to. xi,260pp; 13 plts, complete. Marbled eps. Contemp calf, marbled bds, gilt, raised bands. (Lt foxed, incl plts; joints cracked, weak, spine sl scuffed, edges worn, scuffed.) Text VG. Baltimore*. $1,350/£844

BYRON, JOHN. The Narrative of the Honourable John Byron...Containing an Account of the Great Distresses Suffered by Himself and His Companions on the Coast of Patagonia. London: S. Baker, G. Leigh & T. Davies, 1768. 2nd ed. 1/2-title, engr frontis (lt browned). Contemp speckled calf (joints strengthened, 1 corner bumped). Christie's*. $163/£102

BYRON, JOHN. A Voyage Round the World. London: T. Pridden, 1776. Rpt. 172pp. Contemp calf (rubbed, fr hinge cracked), red morocco spine label. Sound. Karmiole. $175/£109

BYRON, LORD. Byron's Letters and Journals. Leslie A. Marchand (ed). London: John Murray, 1973/1982. 1st eds. 12 vols incl index. (3 1/2-inch x 1 1/2-inch piece white paper pasted to vol 2 fep), o/w NF set in djs (vol 2 price-clipped). Virgo. $384/£240

BYRON, LORD. The Corsair, a Tale. Phila: Moses Thomas, 1814. Old calf bds (spine replaced), red spine label. Nice. Metropolitan*. $86/£54

BYRON, LORD. Marino Faliero. London: John Murray, 1821. 1st ed, 2nd issue. Contemp blue cl, gilt. VG. Macdonnell. $75/£47

BYRON, LORD. Mazeppa, a Poem. London: John Murray, 1810. 1st ed, 2nd issue, lacks final leaf w/imprint on verso. 70pp. W/half-title. Contemp 1/2 calf over marbled bds (lacks top inch of spine). *Cullen.* $125/£78

BYRON, LORD. Mazeppa, a Poem. John Murray, 1819. 1st ed, 2nd issue. 71,(i)pp. Mod 1/2 calf, gilt. (Sl spotted.) *Hollett.* $224/£140

BYRON, LORD. Mazeppa. London: John Murray, 1819. 1st ed. Later red cl, gilt. VG. *Macdonnell.* $75/£47

BYRON, LORD. The Ravenna Journal by George Gordon Byron 6th Lord Byron. London: First Edition Club, 1928. 1st ed in bk form. One of 500. Dec cl. VF in Fine tissue dj. *Maggs.* $80/£50

BYRON, LORD. The Siege of Corinth. A Poem. Parisina. A Poem. London: John Murray, 1816. 1st ed. 8vo. (2)ll,89,(3)pp + 2 ll ads. Aeg. Full grey morocco. (Spine sl dknd, joints sl rubbed), else VG. *Cummins.* $500/£313

BYRON, LORD. A Venetian Story. Kentfield: Allen, 1963. One of 150. 35 full-pg repros. Prospectus laid in. Loose sheets in dec cl chemise, box. (Box fr sl smudged), else Fine. *Pacific*.* $316/£198

BYRON, LORD. The Works of...with His Letters and Journals, and His Life, by Thomas Moore, Esq. London: John Murray, 1832-1833. 17 vols. Sm 8vo. Engr frontis, tp each vol. Teg. 3/4 blue morocco, marbled bds, gilt, gilt date foot of spines. VG set (frontispieces browned; few sl scuffs). *House.* $1,000/£625

BYRON, LORD. The Works. John Murray, 1832-1833. 17 vols. 12mo. Engr frontispieces, add'l tps. Teg. Later 1/2 vellum, marbled bds, gilt spines. (Bkpl, sl browned.) *Sotheby's*.* $773/£483

BYRON, LORD. The Works. Ernest Hartley Coleridge (ed). London: John Murray, 1898. 15 vols. Blue gilt-stamped cl, gilt tops. Fine set. *Appelfeld.* $350/£219

BYRON, MAY. Cat's Cradle: A Picture-Book for Little Folk. London: Blackie & Son, (1908). 8vo. 6 full-pg color plts by Louis Wain. Cl-backed dk tan pict bds, color paste label. Nice (lt worn, rear hinge weak). *Reisler.* $900/£563

BYRON, MAY. Friday and Saturday: The Adventures of Two Little Pickles. London: Henry Frowde/Hodder & Stoughton, (1910). Obl 4to. John Hassall (illus). 12 full-pg color illus. (Eps replaced.) Illus bds (edgeworn). *Reisler.* $185/£116

BYRON, MAY. The Peek-a-Boo Farmers. London: Humphrey Milford, (1918). 1st ed. Sm 4to. 6 Fine color plts by Chloe Preston. Buff bds. (Sm corner tear lower edge 1 leaf), o/w NF. *Sotheran.* $128/£80

BYRON, ROBERT. The Appreciation of Architecture. London: Wishart, 1932. 1st Eng ed. 15 plts. Cl-backed patterned paper bds. NF (eps sl spotted) in ptd tissue dj (chipped, torn, creased). *Ulysses.* $216/£135

BYRON, ROBERT. An Essay on India. London: Routledge, 1931. 1st Eng ed. VG (neat inscrip, eps, prelims lt spotted; cvrs sl cocked, spine sl faded; no dj). *Ulysses.* $392/£245

BYRON, ROBERT. First Russia then Tibet. London, 1933. Color frontis. Dj (sl torn). *Petersfield.* $152/£95

C

CABELL, JAMES BRANCH. The Line of Love. NY: Harpers, 1905. 1st ed, 1st state binding. 10 full-pg color plts. VG (cvrs rubbed). *Agvent.* $90/£56

CABELL, JAMES BRANCH. The Silver Stallion. NY: McBride, 1926. 1st ed. VG + (sl shelfworn) in dj (chipped). *My Bookhouse.* $47/£29

CABELL, JAMES BRANCH. Something About Eve. A Comedy of Fig-Leaves. NY: Robert M. McBride, 1929. 1st illus ed. 12 full-pg engrs by Frank C. Pape. Pict eps. NF in gold dj (fragile, internal repairs to few short tear). *Cady.* $60/£38

CABELL, JAMES BRANCH. Sonnets from Antan. NY: Fountain Press, 1929. One of 718 signed. Patterned bds, cl spine (extrems lt worn), paper spine label. *Dawson.* $45/£28

CABELL, JAMES BRANCH. The Way of Ecben. A Comedietta Involving a Gentleman. NY: Robert M. McBride, 1929. Lg paper issue. Ltd to 850 signed. Uncut, unopened. Vellum spine, corners, blue paper bds, spine gilt. Fine in pub's paper bd slipcase (sl rubbed). *Cady.* $60/£38

CABELL, JOHN BRANCH. Jurgen: A Comedy of Justice. LEC, 1976. One of 2000 signed by Virgil Burnett (illus). Fine in slipcase. *Swann*.* $69/£43

CABELL, MARGARET A. Sketches and Recollections of Lynchburg by the Oldest Inhabitant...1858. Lynchburg Hist Foundation, 1974. One of 1000 signed by Louise A. Blunt. VG in VG- dj. *Book Broker.* $50/£31

Cabinet-Maker and Upholsterer's Director. NY, 1912. 3 vols. Folio. (Cl worn; few cvrs faded, hinges cracked.) *Swann*.* $92/£58

CABLE, BOYD. (Pseud of Ernest A. Ewart.) Grapes of Wrath. NY: Dutton, (1917). 1st US ed. Gray blue cl. (Pencil erasures ep; spine crown sl soft), else Good. *Reese.* $30/£19

CABLE, GEORGE W. Old Creole Days. NY: Scribner, 1879. 1st ed, 1st issue w/pagination thus: (i-viii),229,(1) blank leaf. (Spine ends, corners rubbed), else VG in later box. BAL 2330. *Pacific*.* $115/£72

CABLE, GEORGE W. Old Creole Days. LEC, 1943. Ltd to 1500 numbered, signed by John O'Hara Cosgrave II (illus). Fine in slipcase. *Swann*.* $46/£29

CABOT, W. B. In Northern Labrador. Boston: R. Badger, 1912. 1st ed. Good + (sl rubbed). *Walcot.* $112/£70

CABRERA INFANTE, G. Infante's Inferno. S. J. Levine (trans). Faber, 1984. 1st UK ed. Signed presentation. Fine in dj. *Any Amount.* $112/£70

CABRERA INFANTE, G. Three Trapped Tigers. NY: Harper & Row, 1971. 1st US ed. NF in dj. *Lame Duck.* $200/£125

CABRERA INFANTE, G. View of Dawn in the Tropics. London: Faber & Faber, 1988. 1st British ed. Fine in dj. *Lame Duck.* $75/£47

CADY, HARRISON. Jack Frost Arrives on Butternut Hill. Racine, WI: Whitman Pub, (1929). 12mo. Full color pict bds. Good in color dj (margins sl worn). *Reisler.* $110/£69

CADY, HARRISON. Ol' Teacher Owl's School on Butternut Hill. Racine: Whitman, (1929). 16mo. Full color pict bds. (Loose in stapled binding), else VG in full color pict dj (dusty). *Reisler.* $110/£69

CADY, JOHN H. Arizona's Yesterday...John H. Cady, Pioneer. (Patagonia, AZ: John H. Cady, 1916.) Frontis (loose), 7 full-pg photo illus. Grn cl (tips bumped), gilt. *Dawson.* $100/£63

CADZOW, DONALD A. Archaeological Studies of the Susquehannock Indians of Pennsylvania. Harrisburg: PA Historical Commission, 1936. 3 fldg plts. Good in wraps. (lacks spine portion). *Brown.* $25/£16

CAEN, HERB and DONG KINGMAN. San Francisco: City on Golden Hills. GC: Doubleday, 1967. One of 350. Signed by both. White linen. Fine in matching linen-cvrd slipcase w/ptd side label. *Pacific*.* $98/£61

CAEN, HERB. Don't Call It Frisco. NY: Doubleday, 1953. 1st ed. Signed. Yellow cl. VF in pict dj. *Argonaut.* $25/£16

CAEN, HERB. Don't Call It Frisco. GC: Doubleday, 1953. 1st ed. Signed, inscribed. Top edges stained. Yellow cl. Fine in pict dj. *Pacific*.* $29/£18

CAEN, HERB. Only in San Francisco. GC: Doubleday, 1960. 1st ed. Inscribed, signed. VG in dj. *Pacific*.* $58/£36

CAESAR, JULIUS. The Gallic Wars. John Warrington (trans). Verona: LEC, 1954. One of 1500. Signed by Bruno Bramanti (illus) & Giovanni Mardersteig (ptr). 1/2 linen, patterned bds. NF in dj, VG slipcase. *Pacific**. $81/£51

CAFFIN, CAROLINE. Vaudeville. NY: Mitchell Kennerly, 1914. Color frontis. (Spine dull.) *Dramatis.* $45/£28

CAGNOLO, C. The Akikuyu. Nyeri: Mission Ptg School, 1933. 1st Eng ed. Presentation copy. Fldg map. *Maggs.* $392/£245

CAHEN, EDWARD and WILLIAM ORD WOOTON. The Mineralogy of the Rarer Metals. London: Charles Griffin, 1920. 2nd ed. VG (eps sl damp; corners rounded, extrems sl rubbed, cl sl cockled). *Hollett.* $120/£75

CAHILL, HOLGER. Max Weber. NY, 1930. (Fr joint repaired.) *Swann**. $126/£79

CAHILL, PATRICK. The English First Editions of Hilaire Belloc. Patrick Cahill, 1953. 1st ed. Ptd wrappers. *Forest.* $35/£22

CAIGER-SMITH, A. English Medieval Mural Painting. OUP, 1963. 1st ed. Color frontis, 25 plts. (Sl soiled.) *Edwards.* $56/£35

CAILLIE, RENE. Travels Through Central Africa to Timbuctoo...in the Years 1824-1828. London, 1968. New imp of 1830 Eng ed. 2 vols. Frontisports. 2 fldg maps, plts. *Edwards.* $120/£75

CAIN, J. et al. Lithographs of Chagall 1962-1968. Volume III. Boston, 1969. 2 orig color lithos as frontis and dj (sm tear). VG. *Ars Artis.* $560/£350

CAIN, JAMES M. The Butterfly. NY, 1947. 1st ed. NF in VG dj (closed spine tear, rear panel rubbed). *Warren.* $35/£22

CAIN, JAMES M. Galatea. NY, 1953. 1st ed. (Glue stains outer hinge gutters), else VG in dj (sl used, chip rear corner). *King.* $25/£16

CAIN, JAMES M. Galatea. NY: Knopf, 1953. 1st ed. Fine in NF dj (few sm tears). *Beasley.* $60/£38

CAIN, JAMES M. Our Government. NY, 1930. 1st ed. Pict dj (sm chip spine head). *Swann**. $103/£64

CAIN, JAMES M. The Postman Always Rings Twice. Cape, 1934. 1st British ed. Yellow cl. Nice (press clippings pasted, tipped to eps; top edge lt spotted) in dj (lt worn, chipped). *Ash.* $320/£200

CAIN, JAMES M. Serenade. NY: Knopf, 1937. Fine in Fine illus dj (few sm closed edge tears, spine sl dknd). *Cahan.* $350/£219

CAIN, JAMES M. Three of a Kind: Three Short Novels. NY: Knopf, 1944. 4th ed. Signed, inscribed, dated 1944. VG in dj. *Pacific**. $86/£54

CAINE, HALL. Capt'n Davy's Honeymoon, The Last Confession, The Blind Mother. Heinemann, 1893. Good (erasure traces of ink inscrip, bkpl, lt spotted; spine bumped, lt sunned). *Tiger.* $42/£26

CAIRD, JAMES. Prairie Farming in America. London: Longman, Brown, Green et al, 1859. 1st ed. 'Presented by the Publishers' blindstamp on tp. Fldg frontis map, viii,128pp. Grn cl (faded). Howes C19. *Mott.* $150/£94

CAIRNES, J. E. The Slave Power. NY: Carleton, 1862. 1st Amer ed. 172pp. Grn patterned cl. (Bkpl removed.) *Karmiole.* $100/£63

CAIRNES, J. E. The Slave Power. London: Parker, Son, & Bourn, 1862. 1st ed. Signed presentation. xviii,304pp. Contemp 1/2 calf, gilt, red leather label, marbled bds. (Rubbed, scuffed, shelfworn), else VG. *Brown.* $200/£125

CAJORI, FLORIAN. William Oughtred, a Great Seventeenth-Century Teacher of Mathematics. Chicago: Open Court, 1916. 1st ed. Fine in dj. *Glaser.* $45/£28

CALAS, NICOLAS. Confound the Wise. NY, (1942). 1st Amer ed. NF in NF dj. *Polyanthos.* $25/£16

CALDECOTT, RANDOLPH. R. Caldecott's Picture Book. London: Routledge, (c. 1880). 5.5x4.5. Edmund Evans (illus). Pict cl. (Spine torn, splitting), else VG. *Pacific**. $35/£22

CALDECOTT, RANDOLPH. A Sketch-Book of R. Caldecott's. London: Routledge, (1883). 1st ed. Obl 4to. 48pp of illus. Dec cl-cvrd bds. Good. *Reisler.* $125/£78

CALDER, RITCHIE. Men Against the Frozen North. London/Toronto: George Allen & Unwin/Thomas Nelson & Sons, 1957. Fine in dj (chipped). *Explorer.* $16/£10

CALDER-MARSHALL, ARTHUR. Dead Centre. London, 1935. 1st Eng ed. Bright in dj (rubbed, dust-mkd). *Clearwater.* $72/£45

CALDER-MARSHALL, ARTHUR. The Magic of My Youth. London: Rupert Hart-Davis, 1951. 1st Eng ed. Fine in dj (sl nicked, sl rubbed). *Ulysses.* $72/£45

CALDER-MARSHALL, ARTHUR. The Scarlet Boy. London: Rupert Hart-Davis, 1961. 1st Eng ed. VG (sl abrasion fep, edges sl spotted; spine ends sl bumped) in dj (sl spotted, sl rubbed). *Ulysses.* $56/£35

CALDINS, DICK and PHIL NOWLAN. Buck Rogers: 25th Century Featuring Buddy and Allura in 'Strange Adventures in the Spider-Ship.' Chicago: Pleasure Books, (1935). 4to. 3 dbl-pg full color pop-ups. Full color pict bds. VG. *Reisler.* $600/£375

CALDWELL, CHARLES. The Autobiography of Charles Caldwell, M. D. (Phila), 1968. Rpt. *Doctor's Library.* $55/£34

CALDWELL, CHARLES. A Discourse on the Genius and Character of the Rev. Horace Holley.... Boston: Hilliard, Gray, Little, & Wilkins, 1828. 1st ed. Engr frontis, 8,294pp; litho. Uncut. Orig muslin-backed bds, ptd paper label. VG (marginal staining). *M & S.* $175/£109

CALDWELL, ERSKINE. All-Out on the Road to Smolensk. NY, (1942). 1st ed. Signed. (Cl sl discolored), else VG in dj (sl frayed, chipped). *King.* $50/£31

CALDWELL, ERSKINE. The Bastard. NY: Heron Press Inc, 1929. One of 200 (of 1100) signed by Caldwell & Ty Mahon (illus). Royal 8vo. Pink cl, gilt. (Spine faded, sl cocked.) *Heritage.* $600/£375

CALDWELL, ERSKINE. Claudelle. London: Heinemann, 1959. 1st Eng ed. Orange salmon bds. Fine in dj (sl frayed, strengthened on verso w/ghost-tape). *Temple.* $14/£9

CALDWELL, ERSKINE. Journeyman. NY: Viking, 1935. 1st ed. Ltd 1475 numbered. Fine in glassine dj, pub's slipcase (lt worn). *Cahan.* $85/£53

CALDWELL, ERSKINE. Kneel to the Rising Sun, and Other Stories. NY: Viking, 1935. 1st ed. Signed. NF in dj. *Karmiole.* $300/£188

CALDWELL, ERSKINE. Poor Fool. NY: Rariora, 1930. One of 1000 numbered, issued w/o dj. NF (edge, spine sunned, spine ends sl worn). *Beasley.* $200/£125

CALDWELL, ERSKINE. The Sacrilege of Alan Kent. Portland, ME: Falmouth Book House, 1936. Rev ed. One of 300 signed. 8 wood-engrs. White cl, red bds, gilt. NF (spine lt dknd) in red cardboard slipcase. *Heritage.* $225/£141

CALDWELL, ERSKINE. Say, Is This the U.S.A. NY: Duell, Sloan & Pearce, (1941). 1st ed. Pict bds. NF. *Agvent.* $150/£94

CALDWELL, ERSKINE. Stories by Erskine Caldwell. NY: DSP, (1944). 1st ed. Fine in VG dj (crown chip). *Between The Covers.* $85/£53

CALDWELL, ERSKINE. The Sure Hand of God. NY: Duell, Sloan, (1947). 1st ed. Fine in color dj (spine tips sl worn). *Agvent.* $75/£47

CALDWELL, ERSKINE. The Sure Hand of God. NY: DSP, (1947). 1st ed. Fine in Fine dj (sl rubbed, 3 sm tears). *Between The Covers.* $100/£63

CALDWELL, MARY FRENCH. Andrew Jackson's Hermitage. Nashville: Ladies Hermitage Assoc, 1933. 1st ed. 9 plts. Red cl, gilt. Fine. *House.* $20/£13

CALDWELL, TAYLOR. The Listener. GC: Doubleday, 1960. 1st ed. Black cl, gilt. NF (spine sl cocked, extrems rubbed) in dj (lt chipped, browned). *Heritage.* $50/£31

Caleb in Town. (By Jacob Abbott.) Boston: Crocker & Brewster, 1839. 1st ed. Frontis view. Orig blind-stamped purple-brn cl. NF (date, inscrip, sl foxed; sl worn, spine sl faded). *Sumner & Stillman.* $165/£103

CALEF, ROBERT. Wonders of the Invisible World or Salem Witchcraft. Boston: Timothy Bedlington, 1828. Woodcut frontis, 333pp (lt browned, bkpl). Orig calf (broken, needs repairing), gilt. *Cullen.* $100/£63

Calendar of Annual Events in New Mexico. Santa Fe, 1937. Wraps. (Sl age tone), else NF. *Dumont.* $85/£53

CALHOUN, ARTHUR W. A Social History of the American Family from Colonial Times to the Present. Cleveland: A.H. Clark, 1917-18-19. 1st ed, w/errata slip vol 2. 3 vols. Uncut. (Shelfworn; vol 3 ex-lib.) Howes C27. *Oinonen*.* $160/£100

CALHOUN, EDWIN. Reminiscences of a Confederate Soldier [cover title]. (Abbeville, SC?, ca 1910.) 1st ed. 8vo. Frontisport, 3 ports (1 full-pg), 2 add'l illus. Gray cl. (Eps, cvrs lt foxed), else Very Nice. *Chapel Hill.* $1,750/£1,094

CALHOUN, JOHN. Digest of the Ordinances and Resolutions of the Second Municipality of New-Orleans, in Force May 1, 1840. New-Orleans: Cook & Levy, 1840. (2)leaves,392pp. Later buckram. (Ex-lib, sl stains, browning, foxing.) *Oinonen*.* $50/£31

CALHOUN, W. L. History of the 42nd Regiment, Georgia Volunteers. Atlanta: (Ptd by Sisson, 1900). 1st ed. Frontisport. (Edges lt spotted), else VG in crate-paper wraps, custom 3/4 calf clamshell box, protective folder. Howes C33. *Chapel Hill.* $475/£297

CALIFF, JOSEPH M. Notes on Military Science and the Art of War. Iowa City: Republican Pub, 1889. 1st ed. 160pp, errata slip. (2 sigs misbound, pagination erratic; shelfworn, edges worn, cl sl spotted), else Good. *Brown.* $45/£28

California Column: Its Campaigns and Services in New Mexico, Arizona and Texas, During the Civil War.... Santa Fe: NM Ptg Co, 1908. Fine in ptd wrappers. *Pacific*.* $173/£108

California Gold Rush Miscellany.... (SF): Grabhorn, 1934. 1st ed. Ltd to 550. Color frontis, 16 plts, facs 2 fldg maps. Cl-backed burgundy bds, gilt, leather spine label (faded, abrasion). VG (edges, extrems lt worn, rubbed). *Harrington.* $95/£59

California. NY, 1939. 1st ed, 1st state. Fldg map. (Corner badly bumped, cvrs, map worn.) *King.* $35/£22

California. NY: Hastings House, 1939. 1st ed. VG+ in dj (chipped). *Labordo.* $60/£38

CALIN, HAROLD. Search and Kill. NY: Belmont Books, 1967. 1st ed. Pb orig. (Name), else Fine. *Associates.* $45/£28

CALKINS, F. WELLES. The Cougar Tamer and Other Stories of Adventures. Chicago: Herbert S. Stone, 1899. Fine. *Perier.* $50/£31

CALL, HUGHIE. Golden Fleece. Boston: Houghton Mifflin, 1942. 1st ed. Signed. Dj (edgeworn). *Labordo.* $150/£94

CALLAHAN, HARRY. Callahan. John Szarkowski (ed). NY, (1976). 1st ed. Folio. Mtd 1/2 tone repro. (Age-dknd; bumped.) *Swann*.* $92/£58

CALLAHAN, HARRY. Photographs. Santa Barbara, CA: El Mochuelo Gallery, (1964). 1st ed. One of 1500. Folio. 126 repros. (Pastedowns, eps stained, fore-edge foxed; lt spotted.) Slipcase (top panel spotted). *Swann*.* $431/£269

CALLAHAN, SEAN (ed). The Photographs of Margaret Bourke-White. (Greenwich), 1972. 1st ed. (Corner creased last few pp.) Dj, acetate wrapper (inner flap creased). *Swann*.* $115/£72

CALLISON, JOHN. Bill Jones of Paradise Valley, Oklahoma. Chicago: M.A. Donohue, 1914. 1st ed. Signed. Red cl. VG. Howes C74. *Labordo.* $450/£281

CALMOUR, ALFRED C. Fact and Fiction About Shakespeare. Stratford-on-Avon: George Boyden, n.d. (1894). Inscribed presentation. Frontis port. Deckled edges. Vellum spine (dknd; shelfworn). *Dramatis.* $75/£47

CALMOUR, ALFRED C. Rumbo Rhymes or The Great Combine. London: Harper, 1911. 1st ed. 8vo. Dbl-pg illus tp, (xiv),15-(101)pp; 22 color plts by Walter Crane. Dec eps. Pict cl. (Narrow red stain to edge of rear cvr corner), o/w Fine. *Sotheran.* $253/£158

CALTHORPE, DION CLAYTON (ed). Diary of an XXVIIIth Century Gardener. London: Williams & Norgate, (ca 1920). Color frontis. Uncut. Fine. *Quest.* $40/£25

CALTHROP, DION CLAYTON. The Charm of Gardens. A&C Black, 1910. 1st ed. 16 color plts. Ruled cl (spine sl faded, rubbed; bkpl). *Edwards.* $24/£15

CALVERLEY, C. S. The Literary Remains of.... London: Bell, 1885. 2nd ed. Port, plt. VG. *Agvent.* $30/£19

CALVERLEY, C. S. The Literary Remains. London, 1885. (Corners worn.) *Typographeum.* $28/£18

CALVERLEY, ELEANOR T. My Arabian Days and Nights. NY, 1958. 1st ed. VG in Good dj. *Doctor's Library.* $30/£19

CALVERT, A. F. Southern Spain. London: A&C Black, 1908. 1st ed, 1st issue. One of 3000 ptd. 75 plts. Teg. NF in dec cl. *Ulysses.* $440/£275

CALVERY, A. F. Spanish Arms and Armour. London/NY: John Lane, Bodley Head, 1911. Teg. Red cl, gilt. Fine. *Glenn.* $50/£31

CALVIN, ROSS. River of the Sun. UNM Press, 1946. Pict eps. Reddish-brn cl, gilt. (Name; corners, spine ends rubbed), o/w Good+. *Five Quail.* $30/£19

CALVIN, ROSS. Sky Determines. Albuquerque: (Univ of NM, 1948). Rev ed. VG (ink name) in dj (torn). *Perier.* $30/£19

CALVINO, ITALO. The Castle of Crossed Destinies. NY: Harcourt Brace, 1977. 1st US ed. (Part of inner fr hinge split), else VG+ in VG dj (price-clipped). *Pettler.* $25/£16

CALVINO, ITALO. Marcovaldo. NY, 1983. 1st Amer ed. Fine in NF dj. *Warren.* $30/£19

CALVINO, ITALO. T Zero. NY, 1969. 1st Amer ed. NF in VG dj (few sm tears). *Warren.* $40/£25

CALVINO, ITALO. Under the Jaguar Sun. SD: HBJ, (1986). 1st Amer ed. Fine in Fine dj (sm crease). *Between The Covers.* $35/£22

CALVINO, ITALO. The Watcher. William Weaver & Archibald Colquhoun (trans). NY: Harcourt Brace Jovanovich, 1971. 1st ed. VG (spine ends sl bumped) in dj (edges rubbed). *Ulysses.* $72/£45

CAMARD, FLORENCE. Ryhlman, Master of Art Deco. David Macey (trans). NY: Abrams, (1984). 1st US ed. Charcoal cl. NF in VG dj. *Baltimore*.* $60/£38

CAMBELL, MARY MASON. The New England Butt'ry Shelf Cookbook. NY: World, (1968). 1st ed. Signed presentation by Tasha Tudor (illus). Thick 8vo. 16 full-pg color plts. Orange-brn cl, gilt. Fine in full color dj. *Reisler.* $135/£84

Cambria Depicta: A Tour Through North Wales, Illustrated with Picturesque Views. By a Native Artist. (By Edward Pugh.) London, 1816. 70 (of 71) plts, views. Old 3/4 calf. (Rebacked w/orig spine; worn, sl stained, spine-label chipped; foxing, soiled.) *Oinonen*.* $150/£94

Cambrian Traveller's Guide...in the Principality of Wales, and Bordering Districts.... (By George Nicholson.) Stourport/London, 1813. 2nd ed. Engr fldg map (sm clean tear along gutter). Orig bds (needs rebinding). *Swann*.* $80/£50

Cambridge of 1776. Cambridge: Lockwood, Brooks, 1876. 1st ed. Engr frontis, guard, (x),123pp + 5pp ads. Brn eps; teg. VG. *Connolly.* $65/£41

Camera in the Gold Rush. SF: Book Club of CA, 1946. 13 4-pg folders. Folders all laid in cl chemise, matching morocco/cl slipcase, gilt-stamped morocco spine labels. (Leather spine lt worn), o/w Fine. *Pacific*.* $81/£51

CAMERER, DAVE. A Hand in Sport. (As told by Willard Mullin.) Barnes, 1958. 1st ed. VG in Good+ dj. *Plapinger.* $130/£81

CAMERON, ELEANOR. The Court of the Stone Children. Dutton, 1973. 1st ed. 191pp. Fine in NF ivory, brn dj (.3-inch spine tear). *Price.* $80/£50

CAMERON, ELEANOR. A Spell Is Cast. Boston: Little Brown, 1964. 1st ed. Beth & Joe Krush (illus). 271pp. NF (spine head bumped) in NF dj. *Price.* $48/£30

CAMERON, JULIA MARGARET. Victorian Photographs of Famous Men and Fair Women. Tristam Powell (ed). Boston: David R. Godine, 1973. Folio. 44 photo plts. NF in illus dj. *Cahan.* $75/£47

CAMERON, LOU. The Dragon's Spine. NY: Avon Books, 1969. 1st ed. Pb orig. NF. *Associates.* $45/£28

CAMERON, MARGUERITE. This is the Place: Words Ascribed to Brigham Young.... Caldwell: Caxton, 1941. 3rd ptg. Brown cl. VG (stamps to fr, rear eps; bumped, spine foot dknd) in Good color pict dj (rubbed, chipped w/few short edge tears). *Blue Mountain.* $50/£31

CAMERON, NORMAN. The Collected Poems of Norman Cameron, 1905-1953. London: Hogarth, 1957. 1st Eng ed. NF (edges lt spotted; spine ends sl bumped) in dj (sl torn, creased, spine sl faded). *Ulysses.* $72/£45

CAMERON, NORMAN. Collected Poems. London, 1957. 1st Eng ed. One of 750. Very Nice (bkpl; spine head sl rubbed) in dj. *Clearwater.* $64/£40

CAMERON, ROBERT and HAROLD GILLIAM. Above Yosemite: A New Collection of Aerial Photographs.... SF: Cameron & Co, 1984. 2nd ptg. White linen. Fine in pict dj. *Pacific*.* $52/£33

CAMERON, ROBERT. Above Los Angeles. SF: Cameron, (1976). 1st ptg. Orange cl, gilt spine. Fine in pict dj. *Pacific*.* $23/£14

CAMERON, V. L. Across Africa. London, 1877. 2 vols. xvi,389,(iv)pp; xii,366pp + 8pp pub's ads; 29 plts, 4 facs (3 fldg), fldg map in rear pocket. Partly unopened. (Rear sig vol 1 detached, hinges reinforced w/morocco.) Orig gilt-illus cl (spines sl rubbed, sl discolored, corners reinforced w/pigskin). *Edwards.* $240/£150

CAMERON, V. L. Across Africa. London, 1877. 1st Eng ed. 2 vols. 33 plts, fldg map in rear pocket. Very clean set. (Inner hinges sl weak; label removed fr cvr vol 1, corners sl bumped.) *Hallam.* $336/£210

CAMFIELD, WILLIAM. Francis Picabia: His Art, Life and Times. Princeton, (1979). Dj. *Swann*.* $258/£161

CAMINOS, RICARDO A. Literary Fragments in the Hieratic Script. Oxford: OUP, 1956. 1st ed. Atlas folio. 30 plts. VG (sl rubbed, cvrs affected by dampness). *Worldwide.* $75/£47

CAMP, CHARLES L. Earth Song. Berkeley/L.A.: Univ of CA, 1952. 1st ed. Brn cl-backed tan bds, gilt spine. Fine in pict dj. *Pacific*.* $23/£14

CAMP, CHARLES L. (ed). James Clyman, American Frontiersman, 1792-1881. SF: CA Hist Soc, 1928. 1st bk ed. Tipped-in frontisport, 1 facs, 1 plt, 3 maps (1 fldg). Blue cl. NF (lt glue residue corner of fr pastedown, rep; spine sl dknd). Howes C81. *Harrington.* $300/£188

CAMP, CHARLES L. (ed). James Clyman, American Frontiersman, 1792-1881. The Adventures of a Trapper and Covered Wagon Emigrant.... SF: CA Hist Soc, 1928. 1st ed in bk form. Ltd to 300. Frontisport tipped in, full-pg port, full-pg facs, 3 maps (1 fldg). Blue cl, gilt. (2 sm tape stains fep), else Fine. Howes C81. *Argonaut.* $375/£234

CAMP, CHARLES L. et al. From Land's End to the Ferry. SF: Black Vine, (1942). One of 200. 1/2 cl. (Eps offset; sl sunned), else VG. *Pacific*.* $35/£22

CAMP, JOHN. The Fool's Run. Holt, 1989. 1st ed, 1st bk. Fine in Fine dj (couple sm closed tears, lt rubbed). *Murder.* $27/£17

CAMP, PHINEAS. Poems of the Mohawk Valley, and on Scenes in Palestine.... Utica: Curtiss & White, 1859. 1st ed. 204pp. (Rubbed, scuffed, edgeworn), else Good. *Brown.* $35/£22

CAMP, WALTER. The Substitute. NY: D. Appleton, 1908. 1st ed. Pict cvr label. (Fr hinge starting; cvrs sl discolored), else VG. *Pacific*.* $29/£18

CAMP, WALTER. The Substitute. Appleton, 1908. 1st ed. (Stain to pastedown), else VG. *Fine Books.* $45/£28

Campaigns of the Civil War. NY: Scribner, 1881-83. All vols 1st eds, except for I, II and IV, which are 2nd eds (but issued w/the others as part of the series). 13 vols. 8vo. Blue cl. Fine in pub's box (lt worn). *Chapel Hill.* $700/£438

CAMPBELL and DUNN. The Child's First Book. Richmond: Ayres & Wade, 1864. 48pp, stitched. Orig ptd buff wraps. VG (browned, sl foxed, few sm spots; wraps separated from text, browned, edges sl brittle). *Baltimore*.* $225/£141

CAMPBELL, BEBE MOORE. Sweet Summer. NY: Putnam, 1989. 1st ed. (Rear corner sl bumped), else Fine in Fine dj. *Pettler.* $30/£19

CAMPBELL, BRUCE D. Where the High Winds Blow. NY: Scribner, 1946. 1st ed. VG in dj (edges torn). *Perier.* $20/£13

CAMPBELL, CHARLES. Bats, Mosquitoes and Dollars. Stratford, (1925). (Foxed; sl faded.) *Rybski.* $45/£28

CAMPBELL, DONALD. A Journey over Land to India.... Phila: T. Dobson, 1797. 1st US ed. Contemp full calf, red morocco spine label, gilt. (Foxed; hinges tender; spine top chipped.) *Kane*.* $130/£81

CAMPBELL, DOUGLAS HOUGHTON. The Structure and Development of the Mosses and Ferns (Archegoniatae). London: Macmillan, 1895. 1st ed. vi-viii,2-544pp. VG (foxed, name). *Fair Meadow.* $80/£50

CAMPBELL, GEORGE. White and Black: The Outcome of a Visit to the United States. London: C&W, 1879. 1st ed. Inscribed. xvii,441,40pp. (1-inch fade line fr cvr; spine very worn.) Internally Fine. Howes C91. *Mott.* $100/£63

CAMPBELL, GWLADYS. The Web of Fortune. London: Neville Spearman, 1965. 1st ed. 22 plts. VG in dj. *Hollett.* $40/£25

CAMPBELL, HEYWORTH (ed). The Body Beautiful. Volume III. NY: Dodge Pub, 1937. 1st ed. 89 full-pg b/w nudes. NF in color pict spiral bound stiff wrappers (lt rubbed). *Cahan.* $125/£78

CAMPBELL, J. M. Notes on the Natural History of the Bell Rock. Edinburgh: David Douglas, 1904. 1st ed. xv,112,(8) ads pp. (Cl stained.) *Young.* $38/£24

CAMPBELL, JOHN L. Highland Songs of the Forty-Five. Edinburgh: John Grant, 1933. 1st ed. Color fldg map. Untrimmed. Buckram-backed cl, gilt. (Fep lt creased), o/w Very Nice. *Hollett.* $136/£85

CAMPBELL, JOHN W., JR. Islands of Space. Reading: Fantasy, (1956). 1st ed, trade issue. (Stamps), else VG+ in Fine dj. *Other Worlds.* $40/£25

CAMPBELL, JOHN W., JR. Islands of Space. Reading: Fantasy, (1956). 1st ed. NF in dj (bottom edge rear panel sl smudged). *Pacific*.* $58/£36

CAMPBELL, JOHN W., JR. The Mightiest Machine. Providence: Hadley Publishing, (1947). 1st ed. Red pebbled cl. (Bkpl), else VG in dj (tape repairs to top edge, spine head, fr flap crease; spine ends chipped). *Pacific*.* $86/£54

CAMPBELL, JOHN W., JR. Who Goes There? Chicago: Shasta, 1948. 1st ed. NF in Fine Bok wraparound dj. *Levin.* $225/£141

CAMPBELL, JOHN. How to See Norway. London, 1871. Map, plt. (Cl dknd.) *Swann*.* $115/£72

CAMPBELL, JOHN. Travels in South Africa. London: The Author, 1815. 1st ed. Frontisport, xvi,582pp; fldg hand-colored map (verso repaired), 8 plts (1 fldg). (Last leaf repaired; plts lt browned, sl affecting text; bkpl.) Mod buckram (rebound). *Edwards.* $240/£150

CAMPBELL, JOHN. Travels in South Africa.... London: Francis Westley, 1822. 2 vols bound together. Fldg color map, 12 color plts. 3/4 leather, marbled paper bds. (Sl foxed; bumped, spine sunned.) *Metropolitan*.* $575/£359

CAMPBELL, JOSEPH and HENRY MORTON ROBINSON. A Skeleton Key to Finnegans Wake. London: Faber & Faber, (1947). 1st British ed. (Edges lt sunned), else Nice in dj (sl chipped, nicked). *Reese.* $55/£34

CAMPBELL, JOSEPH. The Flight of the Wild Gander. NY, 1969. 1st ed. Inscribed, signed. Fine in NF dj. *Warren.* $50/£31

CAMPBELL, JOSEPH. The Hero with a Thousand Faces. NY: Bollingen Series, (1949). Inscribed, signed, dated May 1953. (Corners, spine bumped, edges worn.) *Argosy.* $40/£25

CAMPBELL, JOSEPH. The Hero with a Thousand Faces. NY: Bollingen/Pantheon, 1949. 1st ed. Fine in dj (torn, lt chipped). *Beasley.* $85/£53

CAMPBELL, JOSEPH. The Mythic Image. Princeton, (1974). 1st ed. Good in dj. *Rybski.* $65/£41

CAMPBELL, JOSEPH. The Mythic Image. Princeton: Princeton Univ, (1974). Orig ed. NF in dj. *Turtle Island.* $125/£78

CAMPBELL, MARIA. Revolutionary Services and Civil Life of General William Hull. NY: D. Appleton, 1848. 1st ed. xx,482pp. 1/2 calf, raised spine bands. VG (lt foxed, bkpl). *Cahan.* $125/£78

CAMPBELL, MARJORIE WILKINS. The North West Company. Toronto: Macmillan, 1957. 4plts. VG in dj. *High Latitude.* $35/£22

CAMPBELL, P. J. In the Cannon's Mouth. London: Hamish Hamilton, (1979). 1st ed. Map. Fine in NF dj. *Reese.* $30/£19

CAMPBELL, PATRICK. Travels in the Interior Inhabited Parts of North America in the Years 1791 and 1792. H. H. Langton (ed). Toronto: Champlain Soc, 1937. One of 550, this copy not numbered. Gilt-stamped red buckram (shelfworn). *Oinonen*.* $75/£47

CAMPBELL, ROY. The Flaming Terrapin. NY: Dial, 1924. 1st US ed, 1st bk. Fine in dj (lt used, sl chipped). *Beasley.* $85/£53

CAMPBELL, ROY. Flowering Rifle. London, 1939. 1st Eng ed. VG (name; spine foot sl bumped) in dj (sl chipped, nicked, torn, creased). *Clearwater.* $80/£50

CAMPBELL, ROY. The Georgiad, A Satirical Fantasy in Verse. London: Boriswood, 1931. 1st ed. Fine in dj. *Polyanthos.* $30/£19

CAMPBELL, ROY. The Georgiad. London, 1931. 1st ed. Inscribed. (Backstrip faded, sl worn; no dj.) *Typographeum.* $100/£63

CAMPBELL, ROY. The Gum Trees. London: Faber & Faber, 1930. Lg paper ed. One of 400 signed. Good in salmon-pink bds (sl soiled), gilt. *Maggs.* $136/£85

CAMPBELL, ROY. Talking Bronco. Faber & Faber, 1946. 1st ed. Unopened, partly uncut. VG (top corners of 1st few pp creased; spine foot sl bumped) in dj (worn). *Ulysses.* $58/£36

CAMPBELL, RUTH. The Cat Whose Whiskers Slipped. Joliet: P.F. Volland, 1925. 5th ed. 8vo. Ve Elizabeth Cadie (illus). Color pict bds (edges lt rubbed). Color pict box (edges rubbed). *Reisler.* $90/£56

CAMPBELL, THOMAS MONROE. The Movable School Goes to the Negro Farmer. Tuskegee, AL: Tuskegee Inst, (1936). 1st ed. Fine in Fine dj. *Agvent.* $300/£188

CAMPBELL, THOMAS. The Journal of a Residence in Algiers. London: Henry Colburn, 1837. 2 vols. xx,354; 358,2pp; plan, 10 plts. 1/4 brn calf, marbled bds (rubbed), black labels, spines gilt. *Adelson.* $425/£266

CAMPBELL, THOMAS. Letters from the South. London: Henry Colburn, 1837. 1st ed thus. 2 vols. xx,354; xi,358,(ii)pp; 10 aquatint plts (3 fldg), fldg plan. (Pp.vii-x, pp183-7 partly detached vol 1; plts browned, offset; prelims foxed.) Early cl (rebacked w/much of orig faded spines laid down). *Edwards.* $280/£175

CAMPBELL, THOMAS. The Poetical Works. London: Henry Colburn, 1828. 1st Eng ed. 2 vols. Engr frontisport vol 1 (offset), (iv),238; viii,237pp. Uncut. Orig bds (spine feet sl damaged), ptd labels. VG set. *Young.* $232/£145

CAMPBELL, VICTOR. The Wicked Mate. H. G. R. King (ed). England: Bluntisham Books, 1988. Map. VF in dj. *High Latitude.* $37/£23

CAMPBELL, WALTER DOUGLAS. Beyond the Border. London: Archibald Constable, 1898. 1st ed. 8vo. Helen Stratton (illus). xiv,456,(8)pp + pub's cat. Aeg. Dk grn cl, gilt. Very Bright. *Sotheran.* $141/£88

CAMPBELL, WALTER. The Old Forest Ranger. London, 1842. xi,444pp; add'l sepia litho tp, 7 sepia litho plts. (Pp439-43 margin stained; sl soil.) Contemp cl rebacked in mod leather, raised bands, spine label. *Edwards.* $120/£75

CAMPBELL, WILFRED. Canada. London: A&C Black, 1907. Rear fldg map. Red, grn, gilt pict cl. (Ep hinges cracking; spine strip faded), else VG. *Turtle Island.* $55/£34

CAMPBELL, WILL. Forty Acres and a Goat. Atlanta, (1986). 1st ed. Fine in VG dj. *Agvent.* $25/£16

CAMPBELL, WILL. The Glad River. NY: HR&W, (1982). 1st ed. NF in NF dj. *Agvent.* $25/£16

CAMPBELL, WILLIAM C. From the Quarries of Last Chance Gulch. (Helena), 1951/1964. 1st eds. Vol 2 signed. 2 vols. NF in Fine dj. *Baade.* $95/£59

CAMPBELL, WILLIAM W. Annals of Tryon County. Cherry Valley: Cherry Valley Gazette Print, 1880. 3rd ed. 312pp. Contemp 1/2 leather, marbled bds. (Scuffed, shelfworn), else Good. Howes C103. *Brown.* $50/£31

CAMPBELL, WILLIAM W. The Life and Writings of Dewitt Clinton. NY: Baker & Scribner, 1849. 381pp (sl foxed); port. 1/2 calf, marbled bds, gilt, dbl black spine labels. *Cullen.* $175/£109

CAMPBELL, WILLIAM. Arctic Patrols. Milwaukee: Bruce Pub, 1939, 4th ptg. VG in dj (tattered). *High Latitude.* $35/£22

CAMUS, ALBERT. Caligula and Cross Purpose. (NY): New Directions, (1947). 1st Amer ed from Eng sheets. VF in VF dj. *Between The Covers.* $250/£156

CAMUS, ALBERT. Exile and the Kingdom. NY, 1958. 1st Amer ed. NF in dj (spine sunned; sl chipped). *Polyanthos.* $25/£16

CAMUS, ALBERT. Exile and the Kingdom. Justin O'Brien (trans). London: Hamish Hamilton, 1958. 1st Eng ed. NF (spine foot sl bumped) in dj (price-clipped, sl rubbed). *Ulysses.* $88/£55

CAMUS, ALBERT. Lyrical and Critical Essays. P. Thody (ed). E. Kennedy (trans). NY, 1968. 1st ed. (Few sm ink mks to ep.) Dj (frayed). *Typographeum.* $28/£18

CAMUS, ALBERT. The Outsider. Stuart Gilbert (trans). London: Hamish Hamilton, 1946. 1st Eng ed, 1st bk. VG (edges sl spotted; spine tail sl bumped) in dj (sl torn, rubbed, chipped, nicked, spotted, dusty, spine sl dknd). *Ulysses.* $248/£155

CAMUS, ALBERT. The Stranger. LEC, 1971. Ltd to 1500 numbered, signed by Daniel Maffia (illus). Fine in slipcase. *Swann*.* $92/£58

Canadian Guide Book, with a Map of the Province. Montreal: Armour & Ramsay, 1849. 1st ed. (i),154pp + ad leaf; lg fldg engr map. Orig blind grn cl, gilt. (Feps detached, 2 leaves w/lengthy vertical tear at margin, sl browned, few ll brittle; map separating along folds, several sections detached; cvrs once cracked along joints w/good repairs, sl edgewear, few sm spots fr cvr.) *Baltimore**. $120/£75

Canadian Handbook and Tourist's Guide Giving a Description of Canadian Lake and River Scenery and Places of Historical Interest with the Best Spots for Fishing and Shooting. Montreal, 1867. 8 photos by William Notman. (Eps renewed, pencil notes fep, sl age-dknd, soiled; heavily worn, rebacked.) *Swann**. $103/£64

Canadian Handbook and Tourist's Guide Giving a Description of Canadian Lake and River Scenery and Places of Historical Interest with the Best Spots for Fishing and Shooting. (By H. B. Small.) Montreal: Longmoore, 1867. 10 actual mtd photo plts by Netman (copies appear w/varying # of photos). (Foxed, soiled; shelfworn, spine tips frayed.) *Oinonen**. $250/£156

CANBY, COURTLANDT (ed). Lincoln and the Civil War. NY, 1960. VG + in dj (sl worn). *Pratt*. $17/£11

CANBY, HENRY SEIDEL. Thoreau. Boston: Houghton Mifflin, 1939. 1st ed, 1st ptg. One of 260 signed. Teg. White cl, red leather labels. Fine in box (extrems rubbed). *Lucas*. $150/£94

CANDEZE, ERNEST CHARLES. The Curious Adventures of a Field Cricket. N. D'Anvers (trans). London: Sampson Low, 1881. 2nd ed. viii,272pp. Black-stamped blue cl, gilt. Good. *Young*. $136/£85

CANE, PERCY. The Creative Art of Garden Design. London: Country Life, 1967. 1st ed. Color frontis. (Name), else VG in dj (chipped, tape repaired). *Fair Meadow*. $55/£34

CANE, PERCY. Garden Design of Today. London: Methuen, 1934. 1st ed. (Lt browned; corners bumped), else VG. *Fair Meadow*. $60/£38

CANFIELD, CHAUNCEY L. (ed). The Diary of a Forty-Niner. Stanford: James Ladd Delkin, (1947). Fine in VG dj. *Book Market*. $20/£13

CANFIELD, CHAUNCEY L. (ed). The Diary of a Forty-Niner. NY: Morgan Shepard, 1906. 1st ed. Frontis map. 1/2 cl, pict bds, gilt spine. (Ink name; cvrs rubbed; edges, corners worn), else VG. Howes C111. *Pacific**. $52/£33

CANFIELD, DOROTHY. Bonfire. NY: HB&Co, (1933). 1st ed. Fine in dj (long snag tear fr panel that has been flattened). *Between The Covers*. $85/£53

CANFIELD, DOROTHY. The Deepening Stream. NY: Harcourt Brace, (1930). 1st ed. Blue cl. Fine in NF dj. *Reese*. $40/£25

CANFIELD, DOROTHY. Tell Me a Story. Lincoln, NE: University Pub, 1940. 1st ed. 8.5x11. Tibor Gergely (illus). 64pp. Pict bds. VG (ex-lib). *Cattermole*. $25/£16

CANIN, ETHAN. Emperor of the Air Stories. Boston, 1988. 1st Amer ed, 1st bk. Signed presentation. Fine (spine sl rubbed) in Fine dj. *Polyanthos*. $75/£47

CANIN, ETHAN. Emperor of the Air. Boston: Houghton Mifflin, 1988. 1st ed, 1st bk. Fine in Fine dj. *Beasley*. $40/£25

CANIN, ETHAN. Emperor of the Air. Boston: Houghton Mifflin, 1988. 1st ed, 1st bk. Fine in NF dj. *Pettler*. $40/£25

CANNON, GEORGE Q. The Life of Joseph Smith, the Prophet. Salt Lake City: Juvenile Instructor Office, 1888. 1st ed. Signed, inscribed. Aeg. Gilt-lettered morocco. Good (bkpl, stamp; joints cracked through, spine worn, repaired). *Pacific**. $98/£61

CANNON, IDA M. On the Social Frontier of Medicine. Cambridge, 1952. VG. *Doctor's Library*. $20/£13

CANNON, MILES. Toward the Setting Sun. Portland, OR: Columbian, 1953. 1st ed. Fine in wrappers. *Labordo*. $60/£38

CANNON, RICHARD. Historical Record of the Thirty-Sixth or the Herefordshire Regiment of Foot. London: G. Eyre & W. Spottiswoode, 1853. 135pp; 3 color plts. Good. *Cullen*. $165/£103

CANNON, T. G. Old Spode. London, n.d. Color frontis, (xii),82pp; 56 b/w plts. Fore/lower edge uncut. Japon-backed bds, gilt. (Spotting, text leaf for last plt almost detached; bds sl soiled, corners bumped.) *Edwards*. $40/£25

CANSE, JOHN M. Pilgrim and Pioneer: Dawn in the Northwest. NY: Abingdon, (1930). 1st ed. Port, map, 11 plts. Ptd wrappers. *Ginsberg*. $60/£38

CANTON, FRANK. Frontier Trails. Edward Everett Dale (ed). Boston: Houghton Mifflin, 1930. 1st ed. Fine in dj. Howes C118. *Labordo*. $225/£141

CANTON, WILLIAM. The Invisible Playmate. London: Isbister, 1894. 1st ed. Lt brn cl. NF (spine head sl worn). *Sumner & Stillman*. $45/£28

CANTRELL, DALLAS. Younger's Fatal Blunder. San Antonio, TX: Naylor, 1973. 1st ed. Pict fabricoid. NF in dj. *Labordo*. $50/£31

CANTWELL, ROBERT. The Real McCoy. Vertex, 1971. 1st ed. Fine in VG + dj. *Plapinger*. $50/£31

CAPEK, KAREL. How a Play Is Produced. London, (1928). 1st Eng ed. (Bkpl, rep discolored; cvrs sl soiled), else Good in dj (tattered, incomplete). *King*. $75/£47

CAPEK, KAREL. Krakatit. NY, 1925. 1st Amer ed. (Worn, paper spine label partially lifted.) *King*. $20/£13

CAPEK, KAREL. Krakatit. Lawrence Hyde (trans). NY, 1925. 1st Amer ed. Fine (spine label rubbed). *Polyanthos*. $40/£25

CAPEK, KAREL. War with the Newts. NY: Putnam, (1937). 1st ed. VG (name, offsetting to eps from flaps; bds sl foxed) in VG dj (spine lt tanned, 1 longish tear). *Between The Covers*. $250/£156

CAPERS, HENRY D. Belleview. NY: E.J. Hale & Son, 1880. 1st ed. Signed, inscribed. 165pp. (Cl sl worn, soiled; fr cvr spotted), else Good. *Brown*. $50/£31

CAPERS, HENRY D. The Life and Times of C.G. Memminger. Richmond, VA, 1893. 1st ed. 604pp + index. Speckled sheep (rebacked; blank spine). (Eps chipped), else Good. *King*. $95/£59

CAPERS, WALTER B. The Soldier-Bishop. Ellison Capers. NY: Neale, 1912. 1st ed. Frontisport. Teg. Purple cl, gilt. (Neat sig), else As New. *Chapel Hill*. $500/£313

Capitals of the World. London, 1892. 2 vols. viii,181pp; 58,vii-ipp. Marbled eps, edges. 1/2 calf (worn w/surface loss), gilt, morocco spine labels. *Edwards*. $136/£85

CAPONIGRO, PAUL. Megaliths. Boston, (1986). 1st ed. (Ink stamp.) Dj (extrems sl worn). *Swann**. $80/£50

CAPONIGRO, PAUL. Megaliths. Boston: NYGS, 1986. 1st ed. Fine in dj. *Smith*. $125/£78

CAPOTE, TRUMAN and E. and F. PERRY. Trilogy: An Experiment in Multimedia. NY: Macmillan, (1969). 1st ed. Pict bds. NF (lt ink underlining) in NF dj (price-clipped). *Agvent*. $75/£47

CAPOTE, TRUMAN. Answered Prayers. London: Hamish Hamilton, (1986). 1st ed. Fine in dj. *Antic Hay*. $35/£22

CAPOTE, TRUMAN. Breakfast at Tiffany's. NY: Random House, (1958). 1st ed. Fine in NF dj (spine sl faded). *Between The Covers*. $300/£188

CAPOTE, TRUMAN. Breakfast at Tiffany's. NY: Random House, 1958. 1st ed. NF in NF dj (price-clipped, nicked, rubbed). *Unger*. $250/£156

CAPOTE, TRUMAN. A Christmas Memory. NY: Random House, (1966). 1st ed, trade issue. (Lt bkpl mk), else NF in slipcase. *Reese*. $45/£28

CAPOTE, TRUMAN. Christmas Memory. NY: Random House, (1966). 1st ed. Beige/blue bds. Fine in slipcase. *Appelfeld.* $65/£41

CAPOTE, TRUMAN. A Christmas Memory. NY: Random House, (1966). One of 600 numbered, signed. Grn cl. Fine in red cardbd slipcase (sl worn). *Antic Hay.* $450/£281

CAPOTE, TRUMAN. In Cold Blood. NY: RH, (1965). One of unspecified #, signed on tipped-in leaf. NF in NF dj. *Agvent.* $450/£281

CAPOTE, TRUMAN. In Cold Blood. NY: RH, (1965). One of 500 numbered, signed. 8vo. Fine in glassine, slipcase (sm strip sunned). *Agvent.* $600/£375

CAPOTE, TRUMAN. In Cold Blood. NY, 1965. 1st ed. Inscribed. Dj (worn). *Swann*.* $172/£108

CAPOTE, TRUMAN. Local Color. NY, (1950). 1st ptg. (Corners sl worn.) Dj (sm tears). *Woolson.* $80/£50

CAPOTE, TRUMAN. The Muses Are Heard. NY: Random House, 1956. 1st ed. Signed. NF in VG + dj. *Lame Duck.* $275/£172

CAPOTE, TRUMAN. Music for Chameleons. NY: Random House, (1980). 1st ed. Fine in dj. *Antic Hay.* $25/£16

CAPOTE, TRUMAN. Music for Chameleons. NY: RH, (1980). One of unspecified #, signed on tipped-in leaf. Fine in Fine dj. *Agvent.* $250/£156

CAPOTE, TRUMAN. One Christmas. NY: RH, (1983). 1st ed. Fine in NF slipcase. *Agvent.* $75/£47

CAPOTE, TRUMAN. One Christmas. NY: Random House, (1983). 1st ed, ltd issue. One of 500 numbered, signed. Black cl, gilt. Fine in slipcase. *Reese.* $250/£156

CAPOTE, TRUMAN. One Christmas. NY, 1983. 1st Amer ed. Mint in Mint box. *Polyanthos.* $45/£28

CAPOTE, TRUMAN. Other Voices Other Rooms. NY, (1968). 20th anniversary issue, signed on tipped-in leaf. Dj (2 sm closed tears). *Swann*.* $230/£144

CAPOTE, TRUMAN. Selected Writings of Truman Capote. NY: Random House, (1963). 1st ed. Yellow-orange cl. NF (eps lt browned; cl sl soiled) in VG dj (flaps browned, spine sl sunned). *Antic Hay.* $100/£63

CAPOTE, TRUMAN. Selected Writings of Truman Capote. NY: Random House, (1963). 1st ed. VF in VF dj. *Between The Covers.* $200/£125

CAPOTE, TRUMAN. The Thanksgiving Visitor. NY, (1967). 1st ed. One of 300 numbered, signed. Slipcase. *Swann*.* $258/£161

CAPOTE, TRUMAN. The Thanksgiving Visitor. NY, 1967. 1st Amer ed. Fine in Fine box. *Polyanthos.* $35/£22

CAPOTE, TRUMAN. The Thanksgiving Visitor. NY: Random House, 1967. 1st ed, 1st ptg. Fine in pub's slipcase. *Cady.* $35/£22

CAPP, B. Astrology and the Popular Press. English Almanacs 1500-1800. London: Faber & Faber, 1979. 8 plts. Red cl. Dj. *Maggs.* $61/£38

CAPPON, LESTER J. The Adams-Jefferson Letters. Univ of NC, (c1959). 2 vols. (Edges, eps foxed; cvrs stained, spotted.) *Book Broker.* $45/£28

CAPPS, BENJAMIN. The Warren Wagon Train Raid. NY: Dial, 1974. VG in dj (clipped). *Dumont.* $35/£22

CAPRON, E. S. History of California, from Its Discovery to the Present Time.... Boston: John P. Jewett, 1854. 1st ed. Fldg frontis hand-colored litho map, xii,356pp. Blindstamped cl, gilt. (Sm tape-repaired tear to map; rebacked, w/sm gilt seal from orig spine cl laid on spine), else VG. Howes C127. *Pacific*.* $92/£58

Captain Charles M. Weber, Pioneer of the San Joaquin and Founder of Stockton, California. Berkeley: Friends of the Bancroft Library, 1966. One of 700. Fine. *Pacific*.* $58/£36

Captain Lightfoot, the Last of the New England Highwaymen, a Narrative of His Life and Adventures, with Some Account of the Notorious Captain Thunderbolt. Topsfield: Wayside, 1926. Cl-backed crimson bds (worn). Sound. *Boswell.* $50/£31

CAPUTO, PHILIP. Horn of Africa. NY: Holt, Rinehart & Winston, (1980). One of 250 numbered, signed. White cl. NF in slipcase. *Antic Hay.* $100/£63

CAPUTO, PHILIP. Means of Escape. NY, 1991. 1st Amer ed. Fine in Fine dj. *Polyanthos.* $20/£13

Car: Watch It Work! NY: Viking Kestrel, 1984. Pop-up by John Bradley. Paper model intact. Glazed pict bds. VG. *Bookfinders.* $45/£28

CARDENAL, ERNESTO. Homage to the American Indians. Balt: Johns Hopkins, 1973. 1st US ed. NF in VG dj (worn). *Lame Duck.* $45/£28

CARDINAL, ROGER. Outsider Art. NY: Praeger, (1972). NF (crease fr cvr) in color illus stiff wrappers. *Turtle Island.* $50/£31

CARDUS, NEVILLE. A Composer's Eleven. Cape, 1958. 1st ed. 2-tone cl. VG in dj. *Hollett.* $32/£20

CARELL, PAUL. Scorched Earth: The Russian-German War, 1943-1944. Little, (1970). 1st Amer ed. Good in dj. *Rybski.* $40/£25

CAREW, BAMPFYLDE MOORE. An Apology for the Life of Mr. Bampfylde-Moore Carew. London, n.d. (1760?). 5th ed. Engr frontis, 344pp. Full calf. (Ink names; frontis torn, repaired w/thread; hinges cracked; worn.) *King.* $125/£78

CAREW, BAMPFYLDE MOORE. The Life and Adventures of Bampfylde-Moore Carew. J. Buckland et al, 1793. 2nd ed. 235,(5)pp. Mod 1/2 levant morocco, gilt. VG. *Hollett.* $136/£85

CAREW, JAN. Children of the Sun. Boston: Little Brown, 1980. 1st ed. 9x11.5. Leo & Diane Dillon (illus). Unpaginated. NF in NF dj. *Price.* $36/£23

CAREW, THOMAS. A Rapture. Great Britain: Golden Cockerel, 1927. One of 375. VG + (sl shelfworn) in dj (ragged, soiled). *My Bookhouse.* $112/£70

CAREY, A. A. On the Track of Murder. London: Jarrolds, n.d. (1930). Frontis. VG. *Savona.* $24/£15

CAREY, CHARLES H. A General History of Oregon Prior to 1861. Portland: Metropolitan, 1935/1936. 2 vols. VF in dj. *Perier.* $125/£78

CAREY, CHARLES H. History of Oregon. Chicago: Pioneer Hist Pub, 1922. Author's ed. VG. *Perier.* $95/£59

CAREY, CHARLES H. History of Oregon. Chicago: Pioneer Hist Pub, 1922. Pub's ed. 3 vols. VG set. *Perier.* $150/£94

CAREY, CHARLES H. (ed). Journals of...1843 and 1849-52. (By Theodore Talbot.) Portland: Metropolitan, 1931. 1st ed. VG + (sm booklet pasted to fep). *Book Market.* $75/£47

CAREY, HENRY. The Poems of.... F.T. Wood (ed). London: Scholartis, (1930). One of 560. NF. *Agvent.* $75/£47

CAREY, PATRICIA. Bobby Bluegum Plays Father Christmas. London: Methuen, (1947). 1st ed. 8vo. Lt gray cl, red lettering and illus. Good in color dj (wear, sm tears). *Reisler.* $75/£47

CAREY, PETER. Bliss. Faber, 1981. 1st UK ed. Fine in NF dj (sl creased). *Williams.* $45/£28

CAREY, PETER. The Fat Man in History. Faber, 1980. 1st UK ed. NF in dj (sm label spine foot). *Williams.* $45/£28

CAREY, PETER. Illywhacker. Faber, 1985. 1st UK ed. Signed. NF in dj (price-clipped). *Williams.* $56/£35

CAREY, PETER. Oscar and Lucinda. Faber, 1988. 1st UK ed. Fine in Fine dj. *Martin.* $22/£14

CAREY, PETER. Oscar and Lucinda. Faber, 1988. 1st UK ed. Signed. Fine in dj. *Williams.* $64/£40

CAREY, PETER. Oscar and Lucinda. Univ of Queensland Press, 1988. 1st Australian ed. (Edges sl browned), o/w VG in dj. *Virgo*. $64/£40

CAREY, PETER. The Unusual Life of Tristram Smith. Faber, 1994. 1st UK ed. Signed, dated. Mint in Mint dj. *Martin*. $26/£16

CARLETON, JAMES HENRY. Diary of an Excursion to the Ruins of Abo, Quarra and Grand Quivira in New Mexico in 1853. Santa Fe: Stagecoach Press, 1965. One of 750. Black cl. Dj. *Dawson*. $40/£25

CARLETON, WILL. Farm Ballads. Routledge, 1879. Aeg. Dec beveled bds. Good (inscrip cut from 1/2-title, not affecting text; spine bumped). *Tiger*. $58/£36

CARLISLE, D. T. The Belvidere Hounds. NY: Derrydale, 1935. One of 1250. Cl-backed pict bds. Glassine dj (top/bottom edges sl chipped). *Swann**. $92/£58

CARLISLE, ROBERT (ed). An Account of Bellvue Hospital with a Catalogue of the Medical and Surgical Staff from 1736 to 1894. NY, 1893. 381pp. As New. *Doctor's Library*. $50/£31

CARLSON, JOHN ROY. Under Cover. NY, 1943. 1st ed. VG in VG dj. *Warren*. $40/£25

CARLYLE, THOMAS. Chartism. Boston: Little & Brown, 1840. 1st Amer ed. Orig blue muslin, paper cvr label. Good. *Macdonnell*. $200/£125

CARLYLE, THOMAS. Collected Works. Chapman & Hall, (1869)-1882. Lib ed. 34 vols. 8vo. 19th-cent tree calf by Riviere, gilt. (Bkpl, prelims spotted.) *Sotheby's**. $2,576/£1,610

CARLYLE, THOMAS. Critical and Miscellaneous Essays. London: Chapman & Hall, (1869). 3 vols. Engr frontis, port. Full tan polished calf, gilt emblematic shields on cvrs, richly gilt paneled spines, raised bands; maroon, green leather spine labels, marbled edges. Fine set. *Appelfeld*. $400/£250

CARLYLE, THOMAS. Critical and Miscellaneous Essays. Phila: A. Hart, 1852. 1st ed thus. Frontis port. Dk brn cl (foxed). VG. *Houle*. $75/£47

CARLYLE, THOMAS. The French Revolution. London: Chapman & Hall, 1910. 1st ltd ed w/these illus. One of 150 numbered, signed by Edmund J. Sullivan (illus). 2 vols. 33 b/w plts. Teg, untrimmed. White vellum, tan buckram, gilt. (Ex-lib, ink handstamps; sl worn, rubbed.) *Baltimore**. $45/£28

CARLYLE, THOMAS. The French Revolution: A History. NY: LEC, 1956. One of 1500. Signed by Bernard Lamotte (illus). 1/2 morocco. Fine in slipcase. *Pacific**. $63/£39

CARLYLE, THOMAS. The French Revolution: A History. NY: Peter Beilenson, 1956. Signed by Bernard Lamotte (illus). 1/4 red morocco, stamped in gilt, blue linen sides. Boxed. *Appelfeld*. $150/£94

CARLYLE, THOMAS. Reminiscences.... Charles Eliot Norton (ed). London: Macmillan, 1887. 1st ptg. One of 1000 ptd sets. 2 vols. Olive cl, gilt. (Bkpl, ink name), else Nice. *Reese*. $85/£53

CARLYLE, THOMAS. Reminiscences.... James Anthony Froude (ed). London: Longman, Green, 1881. 1st ed. 2 vols. Frontis. Grn cl, gilt. (Bkpl, ink, pencil inscrips; lt rubbed), o/w VG. *Reese*. $85/£53

CARLYLE, THOMAS. Sartor Resartus: The Life and Opinions of Herr Teufelsdroekh. (London: Doves, 1907.) One of 300. Presentation, signed, inscribed by T.J. Cobden-Sanderson, November 1911. (Eps sl frayed, dusty.) Limp vellum (sl bowed, lt worn, soiled), gilt. *Oinonen**. $180/£113

CARLYLE, THOMAS. Shooting Niagara: And After? Chapman & Hall, 1867. Contemp 1/2 leather over cl (orig wrappers bound in). Good (sig; lacks spine label, cvrs sl mkd). *Tiger*. $51/£32

CARLYLE, THOMAS. Works. Chapman & Hall, 1895. Ashburton ed. 17 vols. Lg 8vo. 13 frontisports, guards. Marbled eps; teg, rest untrimmed. Contemp 1/2 dk red polished morocco, raised bands, gilt, marbled bds. VG set (sl rubbed, spines evenly faded). *Blackwell's*. $1,040/£650

CARNAHAN, JOHN G. et al. Tales of a Prairie Town as Told to Howard C. Gillespie. Oxford, IN: Craw, (1935). 1st ed. *Ginsberg*. $75/£47

CARNAP, RUDOLF. Meaning and Necessity, a Study in Semantics and Modal Logic. Univ of Chicago, (1947). Grn cl. Fine. *Weber*. $25/£16

CARNE, JOHN. Syria, the Holy Land, Asia Minor, &c. Illustrated. London: Fisher Son & Co, (1836-38). 3 vols. 2 maps, 117 plts. (Spotting, browning; bkpl.) Contemp grn 1/2 morocco (lt rubbed), gilt. *Christie's**. $451/£282

CARNE, JOHN. Syria, the Holy Land, Asia Minor, &c. Illustrated. London/Paris: Fisher, 1837. 1st ed. 3 vols in 2. 3 engr title vignettes, 2 maps, 117 litho plts. (Lacks 1 ptd title, prelims vols 2-3.) Contemp 1/2 calf, marbled bds (few sm wormholes spine vol 2; cvrs lt scuffed.) *Christie's**. $469/£293

CAROSSA, HANS. A Roumanian Diary. London: Martin Secker, (1929). 1st British ed. Yellow cl, gilt label. (Sl offsetting from feps), o/w VF in dj. *Reese*. $50/£31

CARPENTER, CHARLES K. The Early History of Northern Illinois. (Mount Morris, IL): Ogle Co Federation of Women's Clubs, 1948. 1st ed. Port, map. Good + . *Wantagh*. $25/£16

CARPENTER, DON. Hard Rain Falling. NY: Harcourt, Brace, (1966). 1st ed. (Eps, extrems lt soiled, worn), else Fine in dj. *Bromer*. $135/£84

CARPENTER, G. D. H. A Naturalist on Lake Victoria. NY, 1920. 2 color plts, fldg map, fldg chart. *Sutton*. $250/£156

CARPENTER, W. B. Elements of Physiology, Including Physiological Anatomy. Phila, 1851. 2nd ed. 566pp (foxed, ex-lib, sm burn mk bottom edge 1st 40pp, few eps removed, writing on fore-edge). Full calf (scuffed, worn). *Doctor's Library*. $50/£31

CARPENTER, W. B. Introduction to the Study of the Foraminifera. London, 1862. Folio. xxii,319pp; 22 plts. (Pp yellowed; stained, edgeworn, spine chipped.) *Sutton*. $135/£84

CARPENTER, WILLIAM. The Angler's Assistant: Comprising Practical Directions for Bottom-Fishing, Trolling, &c. London: Bogue, 1848. 1st ed. Pub's gilt-pict cl (lt worn). *Oinonen**. $200/£125

CARPENTIER, ALEJO. Explosion in a Cathedral. London: Gollancz, 1963. 1st British ed. VG + in dj (sl offsetting to flap versos). *Lame Duck*. $150/£94

CARPENTIER, ALEJO. The Kingdom of This World. NY: Knopf, 1957. 1st US ed. (Sig), else VG + in paper-cvrd bds. VG dj (spinal extrems chipped). *Lame Duck*. $75/£47

CARPENTIER, ALEJO. The Kingdom of This World. London: Gollancz, 1967. 1st British ed. (Top edge soiled), else VG + in dj (spine sl tanned). *Lame Duck*. $150/£94

CARPENTIER, ALEJO. The Kingdom of This World. LEC, 1987. One of 750 signed by Carpentier and Roberto Juarez (illus). Fine in slipcase. *Swann**. $138/£86

CARPENTIER, ALEJO. The Lost Steps. NY: Knopf, 1956. 1st US ed. VG + in dj (sm chip to spine head, spine tanned). *Lame Duck*. $100/£63

CARPENTIER, ALEJO. The Lost Steps. London: Gollancz, 1956. 1st Eng ed. (Pp top edges soiled), else NF in dj (spine dknd). *Lame Duck*. $150/£94

CARPENTIER, ALEJO. Reasons of State. London: Gollancz, 1976. 1st ed in English. Fine in NF dj. *Lame Duck*. $85/£53

CARPENTIER, ALEJO. The War of Time. London: Gollancz, 1970. 1st British ed. (Sig, date), else NF in VG + dj (few sm edge-tears). *Lame Duck*. $85/£53

CARR, CALEB. The Alienist. NY, 1994. 1st ed. Fine in Fine dj. *Warren*. $50/£31

CARR, CALEB. Casing the Promised Land. NY: Harper, (1980). 1st ed. Fine in Fine dj (sl worn). *Between The Covers*. $300/£188

CARR, CLARK E. The Illini. A Story of the Prairies. Chicago: A.C. McClurg, 1906. 5th ed. Inscribed. (Binding soiled.) *Zubal**. $15/£9

CARR, CLARK E. Lincoln at Gettysburg. Chicago, 1909. 3rd ed. VG. *Wantagh*. $35/£22

CARR, D. J. (ed). Sydney Parkinson: Artist of Cook's Endeavor Voyage. Canberra: Australian Nat'l Univ, 1983. 1st ed. Gilt-dec bds. (Lower corners sl bumped, worm damage to top of rear joint), else VG in dj. *Pacific**. $92/£58

CARR, GERALD L. Frederick Edwin Church, Catalogue Raisonne of Works of Art at Olana State Historic Site. CUP, 1994. 2 vols. New in pub's box. *Metropolitan**. $80/£50

CARR, J. COMYNS. Essays on Art. Smith, Elder, 1879. (viii),253,(i blank),(2)pp; integral ad leaf at end. Top edge uncut. Dk grn buckram, gilt. NF. *Temple*. $45/£28

CARR, J. L. The Battle of Pollocks Crossing. London: Viking, 1985. 1st Eng ed. Signed. VG (sm mk fep; spine ends sl bumped) in dj (sl creased). *Ulysses*. $104/£65

CARR, J. L. The Harpole Report. London, 1972. 1st Eng ed. Inscribed. Fine in dj (closed tear). *Clearwater*. $104/£65

CARR, J. L. A Month in the Country. (Brighton): Harvester, (1980). 1st ed. Red cl. Fine in dj. *Reese*. $25/£16

CARR, JOHN DICKSON. The Life of Sir Arthur Conan Doyle. NY: Harper & Bros, (1949). 1st ed. VG (bkpl) in Good+ dj (edges worn, price-clipped). *Gravesend*. $35/£22

CARR, JOHN. The Stranger in France: Or, A Tour from Devonshire to Paris. Hartford: Oliver D. Cooke, 1804. 1st Amer ed. Period calf. (Old name; spine worn), else VG. *Pacific**. $46/£29

CARR, JOHN. The Stranger in Ireland. London, 1806. Hand-colored map, 15 (of 16) aquatint plts. Contemp 1/2 sheep. (Lt foxed, browned; needs rebinding.) *Swann**. $373/£233

CARR, JOHN. A Tour Through Holland, Along the Right and Left Banks of the Rhine, to the South of Germany...in 1806. London: Richard Phillips, 1807. 1st ed. 4to. Map, 20 hand-colored acquatint views. Old brn calf bds (expertly rebacked), gilt paneled spine, red leather label. Good (sl spotted). *Appelfeld*. $750/£469

CARR, ROBERT SPENCER. Beyond Infinity. Reading: Fantasy, 1951. 1st ed, trade issue. Grn binding. VG+ in NF dj. *Other Worlds*. $40/£25

CARR, ROBERT SPENCER. Beyond Infinity. Reading, PA: Fantasy, 1951. 1st ed. VG in dj (sl worn). *King*. $45/£28

CARR, ROBERT SPENCER. The Room Beyond. NY, (1948). 1st ed. (Extrems worn), else VG in dj (rubbed, inside tape repairs). *King*. $35/£22

CARR, WARNER. Little Lost Lammie. Chicago: Whitman, 1916. 8vo. Color paste-on. Blue cl. Fine. *American Booksellers*. $25/£16

CARR, WILLIAM H. Desert Parade. NY: Viking, 1947. 1st ed. Brn cl. VG in dj (lt soiled). *House*. $25/£16

CARRAHER, RONALD G. and JACQUELINE B. THURSTON. Optical Illusions and the Visual Arts. London, 1966. (Ex-lib, label fep.) Dj (sl chipped). *Edwards*. $26/£16

CARRET, PHILIP L. The Art of Speculation. Boston/NY/Phila: Barron's, 1927. 1st ed. (Corners sl bumped.) *Glenn*. $25/£16

CARRICK, EDWARD. The Georgics of Virgil. R. D. Blackmore (trans). London: George W. Jones, 1931. Folio. Teg, others uncut. Fine in plain paper dj (sl soiled). *Maggs*. $112/£70

CARRICK, ROBERT W. and RICHARD HENDERSON. John G. Alden and His Yacht Designs. Camden: Intl. Marine, 1983. 1st ed. Fine in dj. *American Booksellers*. $120/£75

CARRINGTON, CHARLES. Rudyard Kipling, his Life and Work. London, 1955. 1st ed. Fine in dj. *Gretton*. $19/£12

CARRINGTON, DORA. Carrington: Letters and Extracts from Her Diaries. NY: Holt, Rinehart & Winston, (1971). 1st Amer ed. NF in VG dj. *Hermitage*. $40/£25

CARRINGTON, FRANCES C. My Army Life and the Fort Phil. Kearney Massacre with an Account of the Celebration of 'Wyoming Opened.' Henry B. Carrington (ed). Phila: Lippincott, 1910. 1st ed. Inscribed presentation. (Sl shelfworn), else NF. Howes C172. *Pacific**. $403/£252

CARRINGTON, MARGARET L. Asaraka, Home of the Crows. Milo Milton Quaife (ed). Chicago, 1950. Lakeside Classics ed. Pict cl. Fine. *Pratt*. $40/£25

CARRINGTON, MRS. HENRY B. Ab-Sa-Ra-Ka, Home of the Crows.... Phila: Lippincott, 1868. 1st ed. 284pp; fldg map. (Tears, non-archival tape repairs to map; rubbed, spine ends frayed, binding apparently reinforced w/glue, sig askew), else VG. Howes C175. *Pacific**. $150/£94

CARROLL, CAMPBELL. Three Bar. The Story of Douglas Lake. Vancouver, 1958. Ltd to 500. Signed by Victor Spencer. Fine, no dj as issued. *Baade*. $150/£94

CARROLL, JOHN M. 4 on Custer by Carroll. N.p.: Guidon, (1976). One of 126. Signed by Carroll and Lorence Bjorklund (illus). 1/2 cl, marbled bds, gilt. Fine. *Pacific**. $69/£43

CARROLL, JOHN M. Buffalo Soldiers West. Fort Collins, CO: Old Army, 1971. NF in dj. *Dumont*. $50/£31

CARROLL, JOHN M. Custer in Periodicals: A Bibliographic Checklist. (Ft. Collins, CO): Old Army, (1975). 1st ed. One of 500. Signed. 1/2 cl, linen. Fine in wrappers. *Pacific**. $40/£25

CARROLL, JOHN M. To Set the Record Straight! The Real Story of Wounded Knee. N.p.: The Author, 1980. One of 50 signed. (Fr wrap stained), else VG. *Dumont*. $150/£94

CARROLL, JOHN M. (ed). The Black Military Experience in the American West. NY: Liveright, (1971). 1st ed. One of 300. Tls laid in. Fine in dj (price-clipped), slipcase. *Pacific**. $345/£216

CARROLL, JOHN M. (ed). Custer in Texas. NY, 1975. (Bkpl removed), else Good in dj (sl soiled). *King*. $25/£16

CARROLL, JOHN M. (ed). Custer in Texas. NY: Sol Lewis & Liveright, 1975. VG in dj. *Lien*. $40/£25

CARROLL, JOHN M. (ed). Custer in the Civil War: His Unfinished Memoirs. San Rafael: Presidio, (1977). 1st ed thus. 2 full-pg illus (incl frontis). Fine in dj. *Pacific**. $63/£39

CARROLL, JOHN M. (ed). General Custer and the Battle of the Washita: The Federal View. Bryan, TX, (1978). 1st ed. Frontis. Fine in Fine dj. *Sagebrush*. $75/£47

CARROLL, JOHN M. (ed). A Graphologist Looks at Custer and Some of His Friends (and a Few Enemies). Bryan, TX: Privately pub, (1977-1978). 3 vols. Each one of 100. Each signed. Fine in pict wrappers. *Pacific**. $104/£65

CARROLL, JOHN M. (ed). Papers of the Order of Indian Wars. (Fort Collins, CO): Old Army Press, (1975). 1st collected ed. Blue cl. Fine in dj (1 closed hairline cut on spine, sl penetrating cl). *Harrington*. $50/£31

CARROLL, JOHN M. (ed). The Two Battles of the Little Big Horn. NY: Liveright, (1974). 1st ed. One of 1000. Signed. Rev copy w/slip laid in. Fldg color plt. Blue cl, gilt. (Spine sunned), else NF in slipcase. *Pacific**. $86/£54

CARROLL, KAY. Han Solo's Rescue. Star Wars—Return of the Jedi. NY: Random House, 1983. 6 dbl-pg pop-ups by Bryant Eastman. Glazed pict bds. VG. *Bookfinders*. $30/£19

CARROLL, LEWIS. (Pseud of C. L. Dodgson.) Alice in Wonderland and Through the Looking Glass. NY: Platt & Munk, (1937). 10x7.75. John Tenniel (illus). Frontis by Ninon MacKnight. VG in dj (tears, creases). *Pacific**. $63/£39

CARROLL, LEWIS. (Pseud of C. L Dodgson.) Alice in Wonderland with 'Come to Life' Panorama. London: Raphael Tuck & Sons, (1932). Thick 8vo. 152pp + ads (text foxed); 2 full-pg color plts by A. L. Bowley. Cl-backed color pict bds. *Reisler.* $275/£172

CARROLL, LEWIS. (Pseud of C. L. Dodgson.) Alice in Wonderland. Chicago: Rand McNally, (1916). 1st ed thus. 8vo. 14 full-pg color plts by Milo Winter. Olive textured cl, gilt, full color paste label. VG. *Reisler.* $375/£234

CARROLL, LEWIS. (Pseud of C. L. Dodgson.) Alice in Wonderland. London: Birn Bros, (1946). 1st ed. 4to. 140pp (bkpl); 4 full-pg color plts. Orange cl-backed color pict bds (corners lt rubbed). Full color pict dj (edges worn). *Reisler.* $125/£78

CARROLL, LEWIS. (Pseud of C. L. Dodgson.) Alice in Wonderland. London: Collins, (1951). 1st ed. 4to. 128pp; 8 full-pg color plts by G. W. Backhouse. Cl-backed color pict bds. Good. *Reisler.* $85/£53

CARROLL, LEWIS. (Pseud of C. L. Dodgson.) Alice in Wonderland. Dennis Dobson, 1967. 1st ed. 4to. Ralph Steadman (illus). NF (spine head sl bumped) in dj (price-clipped, edges sl creased, spine sl faded). *Ulysses.* $120/£75

CARROLL, LEWIS. (Pseud of C. L. Dodgson.) Alice in Wonderland. London: Octopus Books, 1980. J. Pavlin & G. Seda (illus). 6 pop-ups. Glazed pict bds. VG. *Bookfinders.* $45/£28

CARROLL, LEWIS. (Pseud of C. L. Dodgson.) Alice Through the Looking Glass. MacGibbon & Kee, 1972. 1st ed. Ralph Steadman (illus). VG (spine ends sl bumped) in dj (edges sl creased). *Ulysses.* $120/£75

CARROLL, LEWIS. (Pseud of C. L. Dodgson.) Alice's Adventures in Wonderland and Through the Looking Glass. Boston: Lothrop Pub Co, (1898). 4to. 4 full-pg color plts by uncredited artist, 92 illus by John Tenniel. Cl-backed color pict bds (edge-worn). *Reisler.* $100/£63

CARROLL, LEWIS. (Pseud of C. L. Dodgson.) Alice's Adventures in Wonderland and Through the Looking-Glass. Phila: John C. Winston, (1925). 8vo. xiv,319pp; 89 b/w illus by John Tenniel, 4 color plts by Edwin Prittie. Color pict eps. Blue cl, gilt, color plt on fr cvr. VF in NF color pict dj. *House.* $55/£34

CARROLL, LEWIS. (Pseud of C. L. Dodgson.) Alice's Adventures in Wonderland and Through the Looking-Glass. NY: Grosset & Dunlap, (1934). 8vo. 16 full-pg photo plts. Blue cl. (Tp separated; overall wear.) *Reisler.* $135/£84

CARROLL, LEWIS. (Pseud of C. L. Dodgson.) Alice's Adventures in Wonderland and Through the Looking-Glass. London: Macmillan, 1911. 1st ed w/color plts by John Tenniel. 8vo. (xii),291pp; 16 color plts. Teg. 1/2 dk red calf gilt over red cl sides (recently rebound, orig cl cvr bound in at rear), spine gilt. Fine. *Sotheran.* $269/£168

CARROLL, LEWIS. (Pseud of C. L. Dodgson.) Alice's Adventures in Wonderland and Through the Looking-Glass. Winston, 1923. Early ptg. 4 plts by Prittie; 89 illus by Tenniel. Blue cl bds w/lg Prittie plt of Alice, Rabbit, title. VG (spine gilt faded; plts, corners sl rubbed; sl leaning, edges soiled). *Price.* $45/£28

CARROLL, LEWIS. (Pseud of C. L. Dodgson.) Alice's Adventures in Wonderland. London: Cassell, (1907). 1st ed thus. 8vo. 8 full-pg color plts by Charles Robinson. Teg. Blue cl (lt rubbed, binding sl loose), gilt. *Reisler.* $950/£594

CARROLL, LEWIS. (Pseud of C. L. Dodgson.) Alice's Adventures in Wonderland. NY: Doubleday Page, (1907). Ltd to 550 for America. 4to. 13 mtd color plts by Arthur Rackham. Teg. Grn cl-backed bds (fore-edges sl faded), mtd color picture, gilt. *Reisler.* $1,600/£1,000

CARROLL, LEWIS. (Pseud of C. L. Dodgson.) Alice's Adventures in Wonderland. NY: Cupples & Leon, (1917). 9.5x7. Julia Greene & Helen Pettes (illus). 1/4 cl, pict bds. NF in Good dj. *Pacific*.* $184/£115

CARROLL, LEWIS. (Pseud of C. L. Dodgson.) Alice's Adventures in Wonderland. NY: Dodd, Mead, (1922). 1st Amer ed thus. 181pp; 12 tipped-in color illus by G. Hudson, guards. Emb grn pict bds, gilt. VG (fep lt foxed, ink name). *Davidson.* $375/£234

CARROLL, LEWIS. (Pseud of C. L. Dodgson.) Alice's Adventures in Wonderland. NY: E.P. Dutton, (1929). 1st ed thus. Willy Pogany (illus). 8vo. Purple cl, gilt (lt faded). Color illus dj (sm spine chips). *Reisler.* $385/£241

CARROLL, LEWIS. (Pseud of C. L. Dodgson.) Alice's Adventures in Wonderland. London: Macmillan, 1866. 1st Eng, 2nd pub ed. 8vo. Aeg. Orig gilt-pict red cl (recased, rebacked, preserving orig spine; inner hinges reinforced w/archival paper). Fldg cl case, morocco label. *Swann*.* $1,610/£1,006

CARROLL, LEWIS. (Pseud of C. L. Dodgson.) Alice's Adventures in Wonderland. NY: D. Appleton, 1866. 1st Amer ed, comprised of orig rejected sheets from London 1865 issue w/cancelled tp. Sm 4to. Orig gilt-pict red cl (rebacked, recased, new eps; 1 sig partly sprung when repaired). Fldg cl case, morocco label. *Swann*.* $5,980/£3,738

CARROLL, LEWIS. (Pseud of C. L. Dodgson.) Alice's Adventures in Wonderland. Boston: Lee & Shepard, 1869. 1st Amer ed. 42 illus by John Tenniel. Aeg. Grn cl (rubbed, spine frayed), gilt. Internally Fine. *Cummins.* $450/£281

CARROLL, LEWIS. (Pseud of C. L. Dodgson.) Alice's Adventures in Wonderland. London: Macmillan, 1882. Early ed. 8vo. (x),192,(ii)pp; 42 illus by John Tenniel. Aeg. 1/2 red calf gilt over red cl sides (recently rebound, orig cl cvr bound in at rear), spine gilt. (Sl browned, mkd.) Externally Fine. *Sotheran.* $269/£168

CARROLL, LEWIS. (Pseud of C. L. Dodgson.) Alice's Adventures in Wonderland. Riccardi, 1914. 1st ed thus. One of 1012. Dec bds. Fine in dj (faded). *Williams.* $576/£360

CARROLL, LEWIS. (Pseud of C. L. Dodgson.) Alice's Adventures in Wonderland. LEC, 1932. Ltd to 1500 numbered, signed by Frederic Warde (designer). John Tenniel (illus). (Spine sl faded.) Slipcase. *Swann*.* $138/£86

CARROLL, LEWIS. (Pseud of C. L. Dodgson.) Alice's Adventures in Wonderland. NY: LEC, 1932. One of sm # (of 1500) signed by Alice Hargreaves on specially inserted pg. 8vo. Full red morocco, gilt. Slipcase. *Swann*.* $546/£341

CARROLL, LEWIS. (Pseud of C. L. Dodgson.) Alice's Adventures in Wonderland. NY: LEC, 1935. One of 1500 numbered, signed by Frederic Warde (designer). Also signed by Alice Hargreaves on tipped-in leaf at fr. Tall 8vo. John Tenniel (illus). Aeg. Crimson morocco, gilt. (Spine ends sl scuffed), o/w Fine in red cl-cvrd bd slipcase (sl rubbed). *Baltimore*.* $600/£375

CARROLL, LEWIS. (Pseud of C. L. Dodgson.) Alice's Adventures in Wonderland. NY: Maecenas, 1969. One of 2500 signed by Salvador Dali (illus). Folio. Orig etching as color frontis, signed on plt. 150pp; 12 illus each w/orig remarque. Loose, as issued, in silk-cvrd wrappers, box. *Bromer.* $1,850/£1,156

CARROLL, LEWIS. (Pseud of C. L. Dodgson.) Alice's Adventures in Wonderland. NY, 1969. One of 2500. Signed by Salvador Dali (illus) in pencil. Folio. Etched frontis in 3 colors, 12 color plts. Contents loose in cl-covered wrappers as issued. 1/4 leather fldg case w/ivory clasps. *Swann*.* $2,300/£1,438

CARROLL, LEWIS. (Pseud of C. L. Dodgson.) Alice's Adventures in Wonderland. NY: Delacorte, 1980. 6 pop-ups by Jenny Thorne. Glazed pict bds. VG. *Bookfinders.* $40/£25

CARROLL, LEWIS. (Pseud of C. L. Dodgson.) Alice's Adventures Under Ground. London: Macmillan, 1886. 1st ed. 8vo. 37 dwgs. Aeg. Red cl (corners sl worn), gilt. *Reisler.* $250/£156

CARROLL, LEWIS. (Pseud of C. L. Dodgson.) Alice's Adventures Under Ground. London: Macmillan, 1886. 12mo. 37 illus by Carroll. Red cl, gilt. (Spine lt dknd), else Fine. *Cummins.* $750/£469

CARROLL, LEWIS. (Pseud of C. L. Dodgson.) Alice's Adventures Under Ground. Being a Facsimile of the Original Ms. Book.... Macmillan, 1886. Only ed. 8vo. viii,(viii),95,(4)pp; facs. White feps (browned); gilt edges. Red cl (mk w/loss to surface color, faded backstrip), gilt, rear cvr w/mock turtle. Good (inscrip, dated 1908). *Blackwell's.* $440/£275

CARROLL, LEWIS. (Pseud of C. L. Dodgson.) Alice's Adventures Underground. London: Macmillan, 1886. 1st ed. Inscribed Feb 1887. 8vo. 1/2 red calf (rebound). *Swann*.* $2,530/£1,581

CARROLL, LEWIS. (Pseud of C. L. Dodgson.) The Collected Verse of Lewis Carroll. London: Macmillan, 1932. 8vo. John Tenniel et al (illus). 446pp. Teg. Blue cl, gilt. Pub's box (corners lt worn). *Reisler.* $200/£125

CARROLL, LEWIS. (Pseud of C. L. Dodgson.) The Complete Alice [and] The Hunting of the Snark. Topsfield: Salem House, 1987. 1st ed. 1st collected ed. Ralph Steadman (illus). Fine in dj. *Smith.* $75/£47

CARROLL, LEWIS. (Pseud of C. L. Dodgson.) The Complete Works.... London: Nonesuch, (1939). Sm 8vo. Aeg. Full polished red calf by Bayntun of Bath, gilt, blue spine label. *Swann*.* $517/£323

CARROLL, LEWIS. (Pseud of C. L. Dodgson.) Feeding the Mind. London: C&W, 1907. 1st ed. Orig cl-backed wrappers. VG (sl frayed, stained). *M & S.* $175/£109

CARROLL, LEWIS. (Pseud of C. L. Dodgson.) The Game of Logic. Macmillan, 1887. 1st trade ed. Game board envelope dated 1886, game board insert, 8 (of 9) game mkrs present. (Spine extrems lt worn), else VG-. *Fine Books.* $875/£547

CARROLL, LEWIS. (Pseud of C. L. Dodgson.) The Hunting of the Snark and Other Poems and Verses. NY: Harper, 1903. 1st ed thus. 4to. Tinted frontis. Teg. White bds, gilt. Good in stiff grn dj (spine sl faded), gilt. *Reisler.* $385/£241

CARROLL, LEWIS. (Pseud of C. L. Dodgson.) The Hunting of the Snark, an Agony in Eight Fits. London: Macmillan, 1876. 1st ed. One of 100 in special binding by request from Carroll. 8vo. xi,(iii),83,(iii)pp; 9 full-pg illus by Henry Holiday. W/1 pg pub's ads for other Carroll titles. Aeg. Red cl, gilt illus on both cvrs. VF (faint foxing few ll; sm bump 1 corner) in cl drop-back box. *Bromer.* $2,000/£1,250

CARROLL, LEWIS. (Pseud of C. L. Dodgson.) The Hunting of the Snark, An Agony, in Eight Fits. London: Macmillan, 1900. 9 illus by Henry Holiday. Red cl, gilt. Fine in orig dj. *Cummins.* $400/£250

CARROLL, LEWIS. (Pseud of C. L. Dodgson.) The Hunting of the Snark. Macmillan, 1910. xi,(iii),83pp; 9 illus by Henry Holiday. Aeg. Pict cl. *Hollett.* $48/£30

CARROLL, LEWIS. (Pseud of C. L. Dodgson.) The Hunting of the Snark. London: Heinemann, 1970. 1st ed. 8.5x11.25. Helen Oxenbury (illus). 48pp. Pict bds. Good. *Cattermole.* $25/£16

CARROLL, LEWIS. (Pseud of C. L. Dodgson.) The Hunting of the Snark. Michael Dempsey, 1975. 1st ed. 4to. VG (spine ends bumped) in dj (sl creased, price-clipped, spine faded). *Ulysses.* $88/£55

CARROLL, LEWIS. (Pseud of C. L. Dodgson.) Letters of... Morton N. Cohen (ed). NY: OUP, 1979. 1st US ed. 2 vols. Navy cl, gilt. Fine set in bd slipcase (sl worn). *Baltimore*.* $50/£31

CARROLL, LEWIS. (Pseud of C. L. Dodgson.) Lewis Carroll and the Kitchins. Morton N. Cohen (ed). NY: Argosy, 1980. Ltd ed. 4to. Patterned bds over brn leather spine. Fine in box. *Appelfeld.* $200/£125

CARROLL, LEWIS. (Pseud of C. L. Dodgson.) Novelty and Romancement. Boston: B.J. Brimmer, 1925. 1st ed. (Bds, spine ends rubbed), else VG-. *Pacific*.* $29/£18

CARROLL, LEWIS. (Pseud of C. L. Dodgson.) Phantasmagoria and Other Poems. London: Macmillan, 1869. 1st ed. Aeg. Blue cl, gilt. (Sm spot fr cvr; spine ends, joints sl rubbed), else VG. *Pacific*.* $230/£144

CARROLL, LEWIS. (Pseud of C. L. Dodgson.) Phantasmagoria and Other Poems. London: Macmillan, 1869. 1st ed. Jan 1869 presentation. 12mo. Gilt-pict blue cl. (Spine extrems worn w/loss, rear joint repaired w/cellotape.) *Swann*.* $2,760/£1,725

CARROLL, LEWIS. (Pseud of C. L. Dodgson.) Rhyme? and Reason? London: Macmillan, 1883. 1st ed. Falconer Madan's sig. Arthur B. Frost & Henry Holliday (illus). 8vo. Gilt-pict grn cl (lt rubbed, shaken). *Swann*.* $316/£198

CARROLL, LEWIS. (Pseud of C. L. Dodgson.) Rhyme? and Reason? NY: Macmillan, 1888. 8vo. 214pp, 12pp ads. 65 illus by A. Frost, 9 by Henry Holiday. Red cl, gilt. (Spots on p37/38 not affecting text.) *Davidson.* $150/£94

CARROLL, LEWIS. (Pseud of C. L. Dodgson.) A Selection from the Letters of Lewis Carrol to His Child-Friends. Evelyn M. Hatch (ed). Macmillan, 1933. 1st ed. 8vo. 268pp; 8 collotype plts. Blue cl. Blue ribbon bkmk within. NF. *Bookmark.* $45/£28

CARROLL, LEWIS. (Pseud of C. L. Dodgson.) A Selection from the Letters of Lewis Carroll to his Child-Friends.... E.M. Hatch (ed). London, 1933. 1st ed. Teg. VG-. *Gretton.* $35/£22

CARROLL, LEWIS. (Pseud of C. L. Dodgson.) Songs from 'Alice's Adventures in Wonderland' [cover title]. London: Weekes & Co, (1870). 1st ed, variant ptg w/title in dk brn ink, rather than gold. Obl 8vo. Pict wrappers (foxed, spine perished). *Swann*.* $1,610/£1,006

CARROLL, LEWIS. (Pseud of C. L. Dodgson.) Sylvie and Bruno Concluded. London: Macmillan, 1893. 1st ed. Harry Furniss (illus). 8vo. Aeg. Gilt-pict red cl. *Swann*.* $46/£29

CARROLL, LEWIS. (Pseud of C. L. Dodgson.) Sylvie and Bruno Concluded. London: Macmillan, 1893. 1st ed, w/ad leaf preceding Preface. Harry Furniss (illus). 8vo. Aeg. Gilt-pict red cl. Fine. *Swann*.* $115/£72

CARROLL, LEWIS. (Pseud of C. L. Dodgson.) Sylvie and Bruno Concluded. Macmillan, 1893. 1st ed. xxiii,423,(vi)pp; 46 illus by Harry Furniss. Aeg. Red cl (sl mkd, dknd), gilt. *Hollett.* $136/£85

CARROLL, LEWIS. (Pseud of C. L. Dodgson.) A Tangled Tale. London: Macmillan, 1885. 1st ed. 6 illus by Arthur B. Frost. Red cl (bkpl; lt worn, foxed), gilt. *Cummins.* $250/£156

CARROLL, LEWIS. (Pseud of C. L. Dodgson.) Through the Looking Glass and What Alice Found There. NY: Dodge, (1900). 8x5.75. Bessie Pease Gutmann (illus). Pict cl. NF. *Pacific*.* $98/£61

CARROLL, LEWIS. (Pseud of C. L. Dodgson.) Through the Looking Glass and What Alice Found There. Phila: Henry Altemus Co, (ca 1929). Wee Folks Edition. 16mo. 125pp + 4pp ads; 30 color illus by John Tenniel. Red cl-backed purple bds, grn lettering, color paste label. (Eps cracked.) *Reisler.* $125/£78

CARROLL, LEWIS. (Pseud of C. L. Dodgson.) Through the Looking Glass. NY: Frederick A. Stokes, (1905). 1st ed. 8vo. 12 full-pg color plts by Kirk, 50 b/w dwgs by Tenniel. Illus purple-gray cl, gilt. Good. *Reisler.* $175/£109

CARROLL, LEWIS. (Pseud of C. L. Dodgson.) Through the Looking Glass. London: Macmillan, 1962. 8vo. 50 illus by John Tenniel. 3/4 grn morocco w/emblematic figures gilt on spine, raised bands, aeg, by Sangorski & Sutcliffe. Fine. *Appelfeld.* $350/£219

CARROLL, LEWIS. (Pseud of C. L. Dodgson.) Through the Looking Glass. Roselle Ross (ed). NY: Maxton, 1947. 1st ed thus. 4to. Marjorie Collison (illus). Full color eps. Cl-backed full color pict bds. Good in full color dj (margins sl worn, sm tear top edge). *Reisler.* $90/£56

CARROLL, LEWIS. (Pseud of C. L. Dodgson.) Through the Looking-Glass and What Alice Found There. NY: Dodge, (1909). 1st ed. 8vo. 10 full-pg color plts by Bessie Pease Gutmann. Blue cl (sl shelfworn). *Reisler.* $250/£156

CARROLL, LEWIS. (Pseud of C. L. Dodgson.) Through the Looking-Glass and What Alice Found There. London: Macmillan, 1872. 1st ed. 8vo. 50 illus by John Tenniel. Orig gilt-pict red cl (recased, rebacked, preserving orig spine; inner hinge reinforced w/archival paper). Fldg cl case, morocco label. *Swann**. $460/£288

CARROLL, LEWIS. (Pseud of C. L. Dodgson.) Through the Looking-Glass and What Alice Found There. NY: LEC, 1935. One of 1500 numbered, signed by Alice Hargreaves. 8vo. John Tenniel (illus). Aeg. Blue morocco, gilt. (Spine ends chipped, scuffed.) Text Fine in cl-cvrd bd slipcase (sl worn, cracks starting at ends of several edges) w/matching dec spine. *Baltimore**. $425/£266

CARROLL, LEWIS. (Pseud of C. L. Dodgson.) Through the Looking-Glass, and What Alice Found There. London: Macmillan, 1872. 1st ed, 1st issue, w/'wade' on p21. John Tenniel (illus). Pg of ads at rear. Aeg, dk blue-grn coated eps. Orig gilt-stamped red cl later recased w/spine laid down. (Lt aged; worn, frayed, gilt rubbed, spine dknd.) *Baltimore**. $225/£141

CARROLL, LEWIS. (Pseud of C. L. Dodgson.) To All Child-Readers of 'Alice's Adventures in Wonderland' [cover title]. (Oxford), 1871. 1st ed. 24mo. Single sheet folded to form 4pp. Fine. *Swann**. $230/£144

CARROLL, LEWIS. (Pseud of C. L. Dodgson.) Verses from Alice. London: Collins, (1944). 1st ed thus. 4to. Unpaginated. Blue cl, gilt Humpty. VG in VG dj. *Davidson*. $225/£141

CARROLL, MARY BOWDEN. Ten Years in Paradise. (San Jose: The Author, 1903.) 1st ed. 28 plts. Beige cl. Compliments slip tipped to fep. Fine. *Pacific**. $29/£18

CARROLL, RUTH R. Chessie. NY: Julian Messner, 1936. 1st ed. 4to. Unpaginated. Grn cl. VG (bkpl). *Davidson*. $50/£31

CARROLL, W. The Angler's Vade Mecum, Containing a Descriptive Account of the Water Flies.... Edinburgh: Archibald Constable, 1818. 1st ed. 12 hand-colored copper-engr plts. Later gilt-lettered black calf. (Fr hinge w/old glue stain), else VG. *Pacific**. $288/£180

CARRYL, GUY WETMORE. Fables for the Frivolous (with Apologies to La Fontaine). NY: Harper, 1898. 1st ed. Dec cl, gilt. (Mild pink offset to fep extrems, hinge starting in middle w/pp47-48 detached; fr cvr sl discolored, spine ends rubbed), else VG. *Pacific**. $63/£39

CARRYL, GUY WETMORE. Fables for the Frivolous. NY: Harper, 1898. 1st ed. Peter Newell (illus). Red/grn cl, gilt. (Spine dknd, ends chipped), else VG. *Pacific**. $81/£51

CARRYL, GUY WETMORE. Mother Goose for Grown-Ups. NY: Harper, 1900. 1st ed. Peter Newell (illus). Teg. Pict cl, gilt. (Spine ends sl rubbed, hinges tight), else VG. *Pacific**. $104/£65

CARSE, ADAM. 18th Century Symphonies. Augener, 1951. 1st ed. Frontis. VG in glassine dj remains. *Hollett*. $24/£15

CARSE, ADAM. The History of Orchestration. Kegan Paul et al, 1925. 1st ed. VG. *Hollett*. $48/£30

CARSE, ADAM. Musical Wind Instruments. Macmillan, 1939. 1st ed. 30 plts. VG in dj (sm edge tear). *Hollett*. $104/£65

CARSE, ROBERT. Blockade. The Civil War at Sea. NY: Rinehart, (1958). 1st ed. Grn cl. Fine in NF dj. Edward Boykin's copy, signed by him. *Chapel Hill*. $65/£41

CARSON, KIT. Kit Carson's Own Story of His Life. As Dictated to Col. and Mrs. D. C. Peters About 1856-57, and Never Before Published. Blanche C. Grant (ed). Taos, NM: (Blanche C. Grant), 1926. 1st ed. Signed by Grant. 13 plts. Newer cl (orig grn wrappers bound in), gilt. (Bkpl, withdrawn, few rubberstamps.) Howes C182. *Argonaut*. $150/£94

CARSON, L. M. KIT. David Holzman's Diary. NY: FSG, 1970. 1st ed. Fine in wraps. *Associates*. $50/£31

CARSON, RACHEL. The Edge of the Sea. Boston: HM, 1956. 1st ed. Fine in Fine dj (spine sl scraped). *Between The Covers*. $100/£63

CARSON, RACHEL. The Sea Around Us. LEC, 1980. One of 2000 signed by Alfred Eisenstaedt (photos). Fine in slipcase. *Swann**. $316/£198

CARSON, RACHEL. Silent Spring. Boston: Houghton Mifflin, 1962. 1st ed. Clean (bkpl which covers pen mks) in dj (bump). *Smith*. $85/£53

CARSON, RACHEL. Silent Spring. Boston: Houghton Mifflin, 1962. 1st ed. VG in dj (extrems sl rubbed). *Pacific**. $92/£58

CARTER, ANGELA. American Ghosts and Old World Wonders. Chatto, 1993. 1st ed. Fine in dj. *Any Amount*. $26/£16

CARTER, ANGELA. Black Venus. London, 1985. 1st Eng ed. Fine in dj (price-clipped). *Clearwater*. $32/£20

CARTER, ANGELA. The Infernal Desire Machines of Doctor Hoffman. London, 1972. 1st Eng ed. Very Nice in dj (price-clipped). *Clearwater*. $56/£35

CARTER, ANGELA. The Passion of New Eve. NY: HBJ, (1977). 1st Amer ed. Fine in dj. *Hermitage*. $65/£41

CARTER, ANGELA. Several Perceptions. London: Heinemann, (1968). 1st ed. (Edges lt foxed), else Fine in dj. *Hermitage*. $125/£78

CARTER, CHARLES. The Complete Practical Cook.... London: W. Meadows, C. Rivington, R. Hett, 1730. 1st ed. 10x7.75. Complete w/last 4 leaves present. 60 copper plts, 5 fldg. Period paneled calf, raised bands, new morocco spine label. VG. *Pacific**. $3,163/£1,977

CARTER, CHARLES. The London and Country Cook: Or, Accomplished Housewife, Containing Practical Directions and the Best Receipts.... London, 1749. 3rd ed. Engr frontis, 48 plts (few strengthened, w/sl loss). Mod leather (browned, stains, soiled, few tears). *Oinonen**. $275/£172

CARTER, FORREST. The Education of Little Tree. N.p.: Delacorte/Eleanor Friede, 1976. 1st ed, '1st ptg' on c. pg. Fine in dj. *Labordo*. $300/£188

CARTER, FORREST. Gone to Texas. NY: Delacorte, 1973. 1st ed. Fine in Fine dj. *Unger*. $250/£156

CARTER, HARVEY LEWIS. Dear Old Kit. Norman: Univ of OK, (1968). 1st ed. Fine in Fine dj. *Book Market*. $75/£47

CARTER, HODDING. The Angry Scar. NY: Doubleday, 1959. 1st ed. Signed. Facs. VF in dj (sl rubbed). *Argonaut*. $40/£25

CARTER, HOWARD and A. C. MACE. The Tomb of Tut Ankh Amen. London, 1923. 3 vols. (Ex-lib, bkpls, ink stamps; warped, hinges cracked, sl stained, dknd, spines chipped.) *Edwards*. $200/£125

CARTER, JIMMY. The Blood of Abraham. Boston: HM, 1985. 2nd ptg. Signed. NF (lacks dj). *Agvent*. $125/£78

CARTER, JIMMY. Keeping Faith. NY: Bantam, (1982). 1st ed, 3rd ptg. Signed. NF in VG dj (sl edgeworn). *Agvent*. $100/£63

CARTER, JOHN and GRAHAM POLLARD. An Enquiry into the Nature of Certain Nineteenth Century Pamphlets. London: Constable, 1934. 1st ed. 4 plts. (Top corners rubbed), else VG. *Pacific**. $149/£93

CARTER, JOHN and PERCY H. MUIR. Printing and the Mind of Man. NY: Holt, Rinehart & Winston, (1967). 1st US ed. Redbrn cl, gilt. Good (sl handled, shelfworn). *Baltimore**. $150/£94

CARTER, JOHN and MICHAEL SADLEIR. Victorian Fiction. An Exhibition of Original Editions...January to February 1947. Cambridge: CUP for Nat'l Book League, 1947. Illus ed. 16 plts. (Spine tail bumped.) *Zubal**. $35/£22

CARTER, JOHN (ed). New Paths in Book-Collecting. London: Constable, (1934). 1st ed. Gilt forest grn cl. VG (spine crown sunned) in dj (price-clipped, sm chips, tears). *Reese*. $45/£28

CARTER, JOHN. Taste and Technique in Book Collecting. CUP, 1948. 1st UK ed. VG in dj (sl browned, closed tear to spine head repaired to rear). *Williams*. $45/£28

CARTER, JOHN. Taste and Technique in Book-Collecting. Cambridge: CUP, 1948. 1st ed. (Eps lt foxed; top edge of cl sl soiled), o/w NF in dj (foxed, sl defective; spine, fr joint torn, short tears). *Pirages.* $50/£31

CARTER, JOSEPH. The History of the 14th Armored Division. Atlanta, 1946. Fine. *Clark.* $125/£78

CARTER, NICHOLAS. The False Claimant. NY: Street & Smith Corp, (1907). (Bottom edge sl stained, pp browned; sl worn.) Pict wraps. *King.* $20/£13

CARTER, NICHOLAS. The Hole in the Vault. NY: Street & Smith Corp, 1903. (Pp browned; cvrs chipped, creased.) Pict wraps. *King.* $15/£9

CARTER, NICHOLAS. The Mystic Diagram. NY: Street & Smith Corp, (1903). (Pp browned, cvrs detached), else Good in pict wraps (sl chipped). *King.* $15/£9

CARTER, NICHOLAS. A Trap of Tangled Wire. Street & Smith Corp, (1906). (Pp browned; cvrs sl chipped.) Pict wraps. *King.* $20/£13

CARTER, PETER. The Gates of Paradise. London: Oxford, 1974. 1st ed. Fermin Rocker (illus). 134pp. Fine in VG dj. *Price.* $25/£16

CARTER, R. BRUDENELL et al. Our Homes, and How to Make Them Healthy. Shirley Forster Murphy (ed). London: Cassell, 1883. Color frontis, xii,947pp (ink stamp 1pg). Teg. Mod 1/2 morocco, marbled bds, gilt. *Edwards.* $224/£140

CARTER, ROBERT GOLDTHWAIT. On the Border with MacKenzie. Washington: Eynon Ptg, 1935. 3 plts. (5 pp clipped at top, others chipped; rebound), o/w internally Good. Howes C195. *Dumont.* $850/£531

CARTER, THOMAS FRANCIS. The Invention of Printing in China and Its Spread Westward. L. Carrington Goodrich (ed). NY: Ronald Press, (1955). Rev ed. (Bkpl). *Oak Knoll.* $145/£91

CARTER, W. H. Horses, Saddles and Bridles. Balt: Lord Baltimore, 1906. 3rd ed. Good+ (edges worn). *October Farm.* $65/£41

CARTER, W. H. Old Army Sketches. Balt: Lord Baltimore, 1906. VG+ (shelfworn). *Dumont.* $275/£172

CARTIER-BRESSON, HENRI. Beautiful Jaipur. (Bombay: Times of the India Press, 1948.) 1st ed, 1st bk. Illus red cl. (Spine, rear edge sunned), else VG in illus dj (lacks few sm chips, lt soiled). *Cahan.* $450/£281

CARTIER-BRESSON, HENRI. The Decisive Moment. NY, (1952). 1st Amer ed. Folio. 126 repros. Pamphlet of captions laid in. (Soiled, foxed, sl bowed, cellotape on spine.) Dj (torn, soiled). *Swann*.* $575/£359

CARTIER-BRESSON, HENRI. The Decisive Moment. NY: S&S, 1952. 1st Amer ed. Folio. 126 photos, bklet of captions laid in. Ptd bds. Fine in illus dj (sm chip at crown, lt soiled). *Cahan.* $675/£422

CARTIER-BRESSON, HENRI. The People of Moscow. NY, 1955. 1st Amer ed. NF (name; sl sunned) in dj (spine sunned, chips). *Polyanthos.* $125/£78

CARTIER-BRESSON, HENRI. The Photographs of Henri Cartier-Bresson. NY: MOMA, (1947). 1st ed. (Sl foxed; sl soiled.) *Swann*.* $172/£108

CARTLAND, BARBARA. Barbara Cartland's Princess to the Rescue. London: Hamlyn, 1984. 5 pop-ups by Jane Longmore. Glazed pict bds. VG. *Bookfinders.* $50/£31

CARTLAND, BARBARA. The Little Pretender. London: Rich & Cowan, 1950. 1st ed. Sky-blue cl. Fine in dj. *Temple.* $13/£8

CARTWRIGHT, EDMUND. The Prince of Peace; and Other Poems. London: Murray, 1779. Lg 4to. Morocco, bds. *Rostenberg & Stern.* $525/£328

CARTWRIGHT, GEORGE. A Journal of Transactions and Events, During a Residence of Nearly Sixteen Years on the Coast of Labrador. Newark, 1792. 1st ed on lg paper. 3 vols. Lg 4to. Plt, 3 fldg maps. Contemp bds. *Felcone.* $3,000/£1,875

CARTWRIGHT, H. MILLS. Photogravure: a Text Book.... Boston: American Photographic Pub, 1930. 1st ed. NF. *Cahan.* $85/£53

CARUTHERS, WILLIAM. Loafing Along Death Valley Trails. Shoshone, CA: Death Valley, 1951. 1st ed. Map. Grn cl. Fine in VG dj (lacks sm piece at spine foot). *House.* $20/£13

CARUTHERS, WILLIAM. Loafing Along Death Valley Trails. Ontario, CA, 1951. Map. VG. *Dumont.* $65/£41

CARVALHO, SOLOMON NUNES. Incidents of Travel and Adventure in the Far West. Phila: Jewish Pub Soc, 1954. Good in dj (faded). *Dumont.* $60/£38

CARVALHO, SOLOMON NUNES. Incidents of Travel and Adventure in the Far West. Bertram Wallace Korn (ed). Phila: Jewish Pub Soc of America, 1954. Centennial rpt of orig ed. Facs tp. Fine (spine ends sl rubbed). *Argonaut.* $75/£47

CARVER, RAYMOND. Carnations: A Play in One Act. William L. Stull (ed). (Vineburg, 1992.) Ltd to 124. Full taupe cl, paper title label. As New. *Truepenny.* $95/£59

CARVER, RAYMOND. Cathedral. NY: Knopf, 1983. 1st ed. Signed, dated October 31, 1983. Fine in Fine dj. *Smith.* $250/£156

CARVER, RAYMOND. If It Please You. Northridge: Lord John, 1984. 1st ed. One of 200 numbered (of 226), signed. Dec bds. Fine. *Reese.* $100/£63

CARVER, RAYMOND. What We Talk About When We Talk About Love. NY, 1981. 1st ed. Fine in NF dj. *Warren.* $75/£47

CARVER, RAYMOND. Where I'm Calling From. NY: Atlantic Monthly, 1988. 1st ed. Inscribed, dated May 29, 1988. Fine in Fine dj. *Smith.* $175/£109

CARY, ANNE and PERCIVAL MANDSLAY. A Glimpse at Guatemala, and Some Notes on the Ancient Monuments of Central America. London: John Murray, 1899. Lg 4to. Orig dec paper-cvrd bds (sl edgeworn, sl soiled). *Metropolitan*.* $1,035/£647

CARY, DIANA SERRA. Hollywood Posse. Houghton, 1975. 1st ed. Good in dj. *Rybski.* $40/£25

CARY, E. L. The Works of James McNeill Whistler. NY: Moffat, Yard, 1907. 31 plts. 1/2 cl. Good. *Ars Artis.* $120/£75

CARY, G. The Medieval Alexander. D. J. A. Ross (ed). Cambridge: CUP, 1967. Rpt of 1956 ed. Frontis, 8 plts. Black cl. Dj. *Maggs.* $32/£20

CARY, JOYCE. The Horse's Mouth. London, 1957. 1st illus ed. Port. Marbled cvrs, vellum spine, red gilt title label. Fine. *Polyanthos.* $30/£19

CARY, JOYCE. The Horse's Mouth. Folio Soc, 1969. 1st ed. VG (backstrip sl faded) in slipcase. *Cox.* $16/£10

CARY, JOYCE. Not Honour More. London: Joseph, (1955). 1st ed. (Eps sl foxed), else Nice in dj. *Reese.* $20/£13

CARY, JOYCE. To Be a Pilgrim. London: Michael Joseph, 1942. 1st ed. Brn fine rough buckram, thin bds. VG. *Temple.* $35/£22

CARY, LORENE. The Price of a Child. NY: Knopf, 1995. 1st ed. Fine in Fine dj. *Pettler.* $20/£13

CASAL, LOURDES. Everyone Has Their Moncada. NY: Center for Cuban Studies, 1982. 1st ed in English. VG in stapled gray wraps (loss, presumably due to insect damage). *Lame Duck.* $35/£22

CASANOVA, JACQUES. The Memoirs of Casanova. LEC, 1972. Ltd to 1500 numbered, signed by Rene Ben Sussan (illus). Fine in slipcase. *Swann*.* $34/£21

CASANOVA, JACQUES. The Memoirs of Jacques Casanova. LEC, 1940. Ltd to 1500 numbered. 8 vols. Fine in slipcase. *Swann*.* $80/£50

CASANOVA, JACQUES. Memoirs. Arthur Machen (trans). Edinburgh: R.& R. Clark, 1940. 8 vols. Patterned bds over linen spines. Fine. Boxed. *Appelfeld*. $250/£156

Case of Impotency Debated, in the Late Famous Tryal at Paris; Between the Marquis de Gesures and His Lady, Mademoiselle de Mascranny. London: C. Curll, 1715. 2nd ed. 2 vols. (4),326,(2); 197,(3)pp. Period calf (expertly rebacked), gilt, morocco spine labels. (Bkpls, vol 1 fr joint cracking), else VG. *Pacific**. $196/£123

CASE, E. C. New Reptiles and Stegocephalians from the Upper Triassic of Western Texas. Washington, 1922. 14 plts. Orig wrappers. (Pp tanned; soiled; top corner of wrappers, tp gone; sm tears near spine; Call #s, lib stamp on fr wrapper.) *Sutton*. $60/£38

CASE, JOSEPHINE Y. Freedom's Farm. Boston, 1946. 1st ed. VG in dj (sm tears). *Woolson*. $15/£9

CASEBIER, DENNIS G. Background to Historic and Prehistoric Resources of the East Mojave Desert Region. Riverside: US Dept of Interior Bureau of Land Mgmt, 1976. 1st ed. Fine. *Book Market*. $100/£63

CASEBIER, DENNIS G. Camp El Dorado, Arizona Territory. Tempe: AZ Hist Foundation, 1970. 1st ed. Fine in wraps. *Book Market*. $25/£16

CASEY, BERNIE. Look at the People: Poems and Paintings. GC: Doubleday, 1969. 1st ed. Inscribed, signed. Color frontis, 8 b/w plts. Offprint of 1968 Newsweek article laid in. VG + in pict dj. *Petrilla*. $45/£28

CASEY, ROBERT J. The Black Hills and Their Incredible Characters. Indianapolis: Bobbs-Merrill, 1949. 1st ed. Fine in dj. *Labordo*. $55/£34

CASKEY, LACEY DAVIS et al. The Erechtheum. Cambridge, 1927. 2 vols. Text vol 4to, cl; plt vol folio, contents loose in cl folder as issued. 54 plts. VG set (ex-lib). *Swann**. $230/£144

CASLER, JOHN O. Four Years in the Stonewall Brigade. Jed Hotchkiss (ed). Guthrie, OK: State Capital Ptg, 1893. 1st ed. 8vo. 495pp; fldg facs. Pict blue cl, gilt. VG (sig on top edge; spine lt sunned, gilt sl rubbed). *Chapel Hill*. $750/£469

CASLER, JOHN O. Four Years in the Stonewall Brigade. Jed Hotchkiss (ed). Girard, KS: Appeal Pub, 1906. 2nd ed. Frontisport. Gray cl. VG (fep almost unnoticeably replaced; lt rubbed). *Chapel Hill*. $500/£313

CASSADY, NEAL. The First Third and Other Writings. (SF): City Lights, (1971). 1st ed, 1st bk. VG in wrappers (sl worn). *Lenz*. $60/£38

CASSELL, LAFAYETTE. Thrilling Experiences of Frontier Life in the Early Days of Western Oklahoma.... Cincinnati: God's Bible School & Revivalist, (c.1910). 1st ed. (Dknd; few hinges cracked; worn, spine repaired), else Good + . Howes C223. *Pacific**. $40/£25

CASSIDY, JOHN. A Station in the Delta. NY: Scribner, 1979. 1st ed. Fine in dj. *Associates*. $65/£41

CASSIRER, ERNST. The Philosophy of Symbolic Forms. Ralph Manheim (trans). Yale Univ, 1953-1955. 2 vols (vols 1,2 only of 3). Djs (sl soiled, chipped). *Edwards*. $56/£35

CASSON, LIONEL. Ships and Seamanship in the Ancient World. Princeton: Princeton Univ, 1971. Dj. *Archaeologia*. $65/£41

CASSON, STANLEY. Steady Drummer. London: G. Bell & Sons, 1935. 1st ed. Frontis. Red cl stamped in black. NF in pict dj (sl worn, closed edge tear). *Reese*. $65/£41

CASSOU, JEAN and JEAN LEYMARIE. Fernand Leger: Drawings and Gouaches. Greenwich, (1973). Folio. Dj (price-clipped). *Swann**. $161/£101

CASSOU, JEAN et al. The Sources of Modern Art. London, 1962. 1st UK ed. Tipped-in color frontis, 51 tipped-in color plts, 333 b/w plts. (Lib ink stamps; corners sl rubbed.) *Edwards*. $64/£40

CASTANEDA, CARLOS E. The Catholic Heritage in Texas. Austin: Von Boeckmann-Jones, 1936-1958. 1st ed. 7 vols (complete set). Royal 8vo. 48 plts, 9 maps (8 fldg). Blue/gold fabricoid. Good. *Karmiole*. $1,500/£938

CASTIGLIONE, BALDASSARE. The Book of the Courtier, (1528). Leonard Eckstein Opdycke (trans). NY: Scribner, 1901. Ltd to 500 numbered. 74 full-pg plts. Orig vellum-like bds. Good. *Karmiole*. $100/£63

CASTLE, AGNES and EGERTON. The Pride of Jennico Being a Memoir of Captain Basil Jennico. NY, 1899. 1st Amer ed. Dec cvrs, gilt. NF (sm dampstain rear cvr, spine sl rubbed). *Polyanthos*. $25/£16

CASTLEDEN, LOUISE DECATUR. George Frederick Castleden, Etcher-Painter. NY: Exposition, (1953). 1st ed. Signed presentation. Frontis. VG. *Turtle Island*. $55/£34

CASTLEMAN, JOHN B. Active Service. Louisville, KY: Courier-Journal Job Ptg, 1917. 1st ed. Frontisport. Gray cl. NF (inner hinges cracked). Howes C231. *Chapel Hill*. $325/£203

Catalogue of a Collection of Early Printed Books in the Library of the Royal Society. London: Royal Soc, 1910. 1st ed. 1/4 vellum, beige cl, gilt. Fine. *Weber*. $150/£94

Catalogue of Books on Angling.... (By John Bartlett.) Cambridge, MA, 1882. 1st ed. Signed, inscribed presentation. (1)leaf; 77pp (ex-lib, perf stamp tp). Ptd bds (shelfworn, soiled). *Oinonen**. $150/£94

Catalogue of Books Printed in the XVth Century Now in the British Museum. Part V. Venice. British Museum, 1925. Folio. 41 facs. *Forest*. $120/£75

Catalogue of Carvings in Ivory. Victoria & Albert Museum, 1927/1929. 2 vols. 76 plts; frontis, 96 plts. Pub's ptd wrappers (sl browned, chipped). *Peter Taylor*. $61/£38

Catalogue of Some Five Hundred Examples of the Printing of Edwin and Robert Grabhorn, 1917-1760: Two Gentlemen from Indiana Now Resident in California. SF: David Magee, (1961). One of 250 ptd. 1/2 cl, paper spine label. (Top corners lt bumped), else NF in dj (soiled). *Pacific**. $150/£94

Catalogue of the Celebrated Library, the Property of Major J.R. Abbey. Part II. London: Sotheby, (1966). 4 plts. Prices realized loosely inserted. Fine. *Oak Knoll*. $60/£38

Catalogue of the Collection of Dutch and Flemish Still-Life Pictures Bequeathed by Daisy Linda Ward. Oxford: Ashmolean Museum, 1950. Good + . *Washton*. $75/£47

Catalogue of the Library of the West India Committee. London: West India Committee, 1941. 1st ed. Blue linen, gilt. Good. *Karmiole*. $75/£47

Catalogue of the Montague Guest Collection of Badges, Tokens and Passes. London, 1930. (Lib ink stamps, label; blind-emb stamp fr bd.) *Edwards*. $64/£40

Catalogue of the Pictures in the Garrick Club. London: Garrick Club, 1936. 6 sepia-toned plts, guards. Teg. Vellum-backed bds. VG. *Dramatis*. $120/£75

Catalogue of the Printed Books in the Library of the University of Edinburgh. Edinburgh Univ, 1918-23. 3 vols. (Lt worn.) *Oinonen**. $80/£50

CATE, CURTIS WOLSEY. Camping with Kate Cate. (L.A.: Ward Ritchie), 1961. 1st ed. VG in stiff blue wrappers. *Houle*. $37/£23

CATHASAIGH, P. O. (Pseud of Sean O'Casey.) The Story of the Irish Citizen Army. Dublin/London: Manusel, 1919. Ptd wraps (nicked). *Metropolitan**. $230/£144

CATHER, THOMAS. Thomas Cather's Journal of a Voyage to America in 1836. Rodale, (1955). 1st ed. Pict bds. Ptd glassine dj. *Mott*. $25/£16

CATHER, WILLA. Death Comes for the Archbishop. London: Heinemann, (1927). 1st Eng ed. NF in dj (spine chipped, dknd). *Pacific**. $316/£198

CATHER, WILLA. A Lost Lady. NY: Knopf, 1923. 1st ed. One of 200. Signed. 1/2 cl, blue bds, paper spine label. (Bds sl rubbed), else VG in slipcase (rubbed). *Pacific**. $546/£341

CATHER, WILLA. A Lost Lady. LEC, 1983. Ltd to 1500 numbered, signed by William Bailey (illus). Fine in slipcase. *Swann**. $80/£50

CATHER, WILLA. Lucy Gayheart. NY: Knopf, 1935. 1st ed. Fine in NF dj. *Macdonnell*. $100/£63

CATHER, WILLA. Lucy Gayheart. NY: Knopf, 1935. 1st ed. (Lt faded), else Fine in grn cl, ptd label. Dj (sm chips). *Bromer*. $125/£78

CATHER, WILLA. My Mortal Enemy. NY: Knopf, 1926. 1st Trade ed. Cl-backed dec bds. VG in dj (spine, extrems dknd), slipcase. *Pacific**. $150/£94

CATHER, WILLA. Obscure Destinies. NY: Knopf, 1932. 1st ed. One of 260. Signed. Teg. 1/2 vellum, grn cl, gilt, gold cvr label. Fine. *Pacific**. $546/£341

CATHER, WILLA. Sapphira and the Slave Girl. NY, 1940. 1st Amer ed. NF (spine sunned). *Polyanthos*. $25/£16

CATHER, WILLA. Sapphira and the Slave Girl. NY: Knopf, 1940. 1st ed. NF in dj. *Pacific**. $81/£51

CATHER, WILLA. Sapphira and the Slave Girl. NY: Knopf, 1940. 1st ed. (Spine sl sunned), else VF in grn cl. NF dj. *Bromer*. $165/£103

CATHER, WILLA. Shadows on the Rock. NY: Knopf, 1931. 1st ed. (Spine sunned), else Fine in grn cl, ptd label. Ptd dj (spine lt toned). *Bromer*. $200/£125

CATHER, WILLA. Shadows on the Rock. NY: Knopf, 1931. 1st ed. Ltd to 619 signed. Lg paper ed. Uncut. Marble paper-cvrd bds, leather label (sl scuffed). VG. *Second Life*. $400/£250

CATHER, WILLA. Willa Cather in Europe: Her Own Story of the First Journey. NY: Knopf, 1956. 1st ed. (Sm ink name; words, sticker fep), o/w NF in dj (price-clipped, sl worn). *Hermitage*. $65/£41

CATLIN, GEORGE. Catlin's North American Indian Portfolio. (NY, 1989.) Facs ed. One of 950 numbered. Folio. 1/2 morocco, morocco cvr label. *Swann**. $920/£575

CATLIN, GEORGE. Episodes from Life Among the Indians and Last Rambles. Marvin C. Ross (ed). Norman: Univ of OK, (1959). 1st ed thus. Color frontis. Fine in dj. *Pacific**. $29/£18

CATLIN, GEORGE. Episodes from Life Among the Indians and Last Rambles. Marvin Ross (ed). Norman: Univ of OK, (1959). 1st ed. Color frontis. Grn cl. Fine in VG+ pict dj. *House*. $65/£41

CATLIN, GEORGE. Illustrations of the Manners, Customs, and Condition of the North American Indians. Henry G. Bohn, 1866. 10th ed. 2 vols. 8vo. 180 plts, incl lg fldg map. Gilt edges. Contemp 1/2 crimson morocco, gilt. (Sl spotting; sl rubbed.) *Sotheby's**. $9,568/£5,980

CATLIN, GEORGE. Illustrations of the Manners, Customs, and Condition of the North American Indians.... London, 1845. 5th ed. 2 vols. Later 1/2 morocco, gilt, by The Atelier Bindery. (Foxed throughout; extrems sl rubbed.) *Swann**. $488/£305

CATLIN, GEORGE. Unparalleled Exhibition. London, 1844. 1st ed. 12mo. 28pp. 1/2 calf (rebacked; stain on tp, inner margin throughout affecting only tp, following leaf). *Maggs*. $720/£450

CATLIN, MARK. Fly Fishing for Trout. Appleton, WI: Badger, 1930. 1st ed. (Lt worn.) *Oinonen**. $160/£100

CATLOW, AGNES and MARIA E. Sketching Rambles; or, Nature in the Alps and Apennines.... London: James Hogg, n.d. (1862). 1st ed. 2 vols. 1/2-title, color frontis, xii,(ii),374,2 ads; 1/2-title, color frontis, viii,(ii),368pp; 18 tinted lithos. Red grained cl, gilt. (Hinge cracked, lt ink spots), o/w VG. *Morrell*. $368/£230

CATTO, J. I. and R. EVANS (eds). The History of the University of Oxford. Volume I: The Early Oxford Schools. Oxford: Clarendon, 1986. Rpt of 1984 ed w/corrections. Frontis, 12 plts, 10 maps, plans. Blue cl. Dj. *Maggs*. $64/£40

CATTON, BRUCE. A Stillness at Appomattox. Franklin Center, PA: Franklin Library, 1977. Ltd ed. Signed. Aeg. Gilt-stamped leather. As New. *King*. $50/£31

CAUDILL, REBECCA. A Certain Small Shepherd. Holt, 1965. 1st ed. 7.5x7.5. William Pene Du Bois (illus). 48pp. NF in NF dj. *Price*. $70/£44

CAUGHEY, JOHN WALTON. Gold Is the Cornerstone. Berkeley: Univ of CA, 1948. 1st ed. VG in dj. *Lien*. $25/£16

Causes of the Decay of Christian Piety. (By Richard Allestree.) London: R. Norton for Edward Pawlet, 1694. 1st ed. (24),450pp + 2pp ads; 2 engr plts. Old calf (rebacked), grn morocco spine label. (Brown stains final ll.) *Karmiole*. $200/£125

CAUTE, DAVID. The Demonstration. London: Andre Deutsch, 1970. 1st Eng ed. NF (spine ends sl bumped) in dj (spine sl faded). *Ulysses*. $40/£25

CAVAFY, C. P. Poems. John Mavrogordato (trans). London, 1951. 1st Eng ed. Nice in dj (sl foxed). *Clearwater*. $72/£45

CAVALLY, FREDERICK L., JR. Mother Goose's Teddy Bears. Indianapolis: Bobbs-Merrill, 1907. 4to. Dk red cl, gilt, color paste label. (Overall dkng, chip in cl at edge.) *Reisler*. $575/£359

CAVE, C. J. P. Roof Bosses in Medieval Churches, an Aspect of Gothic Sculpture. CUP, 1948. Pub's cl (sl damp-spotted). Interior Clean. *Peter Taylor*. $46/£29

CAVE, EDWARD. The Boy's Camp Book. GC: Doubleday, Page, 1914. 1st ed. 12mo. 4 full-pg b/w plts by Norman Rockwell. Grn pict cl (stain rear cvr). *Reisler*. $65/£41

CAVE, RODERICK. The Private Press. Faber & Faber, 1971. 1st ed. 72 plts. VG in dj (lt soiled). *Cox*. $77/£48

CAVE, RODERICK. Rare Book Librarianship. Clive Bingley, 1976. 1st ed. 10 plts. VG in dj. *Moss*. $29/£18

CAVELER, WILLIAM. Select Specimens of Gothic Architecture. London: The Author, 1835. 3pp subs. 74 plts (6 dbl-pg, 1 tinted). Gilt-edged full morocco, gilt. (Some foxing to plts; sl worn, spine lt sunned.) *Edwards*. $152/£95

CAVENDISH, LADY FREDERICK. The Diary of Lady Frederick Cavendish. John Bailey (ed). London: John Murray, 1927. 1st ed. 2 vols. 16 plts. (Spotted; sl soiled, extrems sl frayed.) *Hollett*. $56/£35

CAXTON, WILLIAM. The Fifteen D's and Other Prayers. (London): Griffith & Farran, 1869. Pict bds. (Name, cat entry fr pastedown; rear joint cracking, spine ends sl worn), else VG. *Pacific**. $46/£29

CAYLEY, NEVILLE W. Australian Parrots in Field and Aviary. London: Angus and Robertson, 1973. Rev ed. 13 color plts. Dj (lower part of wrap torn). *Edwards*. $40/£25

CAYTON, HORACE R. Long Old Road. NY: Trident, 1965. 1st ed. VG in ptd dj (lt edgeworn). *Petrilla*. $25/£16

CECIL, DAVID. Max. A Biography. London: Constable, 1964. 1st ed. VG in dj. *Hollett*. $48/£30

CECIL, DAVID. The Stricken Deer, the Life of Cowper. London, 1929. 1st ed. Rev copy. VG (pencil notes). *Gretton*. $11/£7

CECIL, DAVID. Two Quiet Lives. London, 1948. 1st ed. VG in dj. *Typographeum*. $18/£11

CECIL, EDWARD. The Leisure of an Egyptian Official. London: Hodder & Stoughton, 1921. 2nd ed. Frontis. (Bds lt soiled.) *Archaeologia*. $75/£47

CECIL, HENRY. Settled Out of Court. Michael Joseph, 1959. 1st UK ed. Inscribed, dated March 1959. VG in dj (rear panel sl stained). *Williams*. $40/£25

CECIL, HENRY. A Woman Named Anne. NY: Harper & Row, (1967). 1st ed. VG in dj. *Antic Hay*. $20/£13

CECIL, MRS. EVELYN. London Parks and Gardens. London: Constable, 1907. 1st ed. x,384pp; 25 color-ptd plts. Teg. Pict cl, gilt. VG. *Marlborough.* $216/£135

CELA, CAMILO JOSE. The Hive. NY, 1953. 1st Amer ed. Fine in VG + dj (2 short closed tears). *Warren.* $40/£25

CELA, CAMILO JOSE. The Hive. London: Gollancz, 1953. 1st British ed. VG + in dj (name). *Lame Duck.* $75/£47

CELA, CAMILO JOSE. Journey to the Alcarria. Madison: Univ of WI, 1964. 1st ed in English. (Bds, pp top edges foxed), else Fine in NF dj (sm edge-tear rear panel). *Lame Duck.* $100/£63

CELANT, GERMANO. Art Povera. NY: Praeger Pub, (1969). Photo-illus stiff wrappers. *Turtle Island.* $85/£53

Celebrated Collection of Americana Formed by the Late Thomas Winthrop Streeter. Volume 7. NY: Parke-Bernet Galleries, 1969. *Dawson.* $75/£47

Celebrated Collection of Americana...of Thomas Winthrop Streeter. NY, 1966-70. 8 vols, incl index. 8vo. *Swann*.* $575/£359

Celebrated Library of Bois Penrose...Travel and Exploration, Navigation and Trade. London: Sotheby, 1971. 2 vols. (Bd binding bowing), else VG + . *Zubal*.* $30/£19

Celebrated Trials and Remarkable Cases of Criminal Jurisprudence. (By George Henry Borrow.) Knight & Lacey, 1825. 6 vols. 8vo. Fldg engr frontispieces. 19th-cent calf gilt by Bickers & Son. (Bkpl; some joints cracked; spines sl rubbed, chipped.) *Sotheby's*.* $736/£460

Celebrated Trials, and Remarkable Cases of Jurisprudence, from the Earliest Records to the Year 1825. (By George Borrow.) Knight & Lacey, 1825. 1st ed. 6 vols. 35 engr plts. (Sl waterstaining at end of vol 3.) Orig bds (sl chipped, vol 5 spine foot sl defective). *Sotheby's*.* $1,104/£690

CELLI, ROSE (retold by). Baba Yaga: A Popular Russian Tale. Poughkeepsie, NY: Artists & Writers Guild, 1935. 1st Amer ed. Lg 4to. Nathalie Parain (illus). 16pp. Very Nice in stiff color pict paper wrappers (sl edgeworn). *Reisler.* $125/£78

CELLINI, BENVENUTO. The Life of Benvenuto Cellini. LEC, 1937. Ltd to 1500 numbered, signed by Fritz Kredel (illus). Fine in slipcase. *Swann*.* $172/£108

CELLINI, BENVENUTO. The Life of.... John Addington Symonds (trans). (London: Vale Press, 1900.) 2 vols. Untrimmed. Tan cl, blue bds, ptd paper spine/fr cvr labels. (Corners, spines worn, labels partly chipped w/loss; cl worn, dusty; few ll lt foxed.) Texts Clean. *Baltimore*.* $60/£38

CELLINI, BENVENUTO. The Life. NY, (1906). 2 vols. 3/4 morocco, gilt. *Swann*.* $57/£36

CELLINI, BENVENUTO. The Treatises of Benvenuto Cellini on Goldsmithing and Sculpture. (London: Essex House, 1898.) One of 600 numbered. 11 plts. (Cl worn, spine faded, stained.) *Swann*.* $373/£233

CENDRARS, BLAISE. A Night in the Forest. MO: Univ of MO, 1985. 1st ed in English. Fine in Fine dj. *Warren.* $35/£22

CENDRARS, BLAISE. Panama; or, The Adventures of My Seven Uncles. NY, 1931. 1st ed thus. One of 300 numbered, signed by Cendrars and John Dos Passos (trans, illus). Pict stiff wrappers. Glassine dj; slipcase (defective). *Swann*.* $201/£126

Centennial of the US Military Academy at West Point, New York. Washington, 1904. House Exec Doc No 789. Tan lib buckram. *Kane*.* $65/£41

Century of Dishonor: A Sketch of the United States Government's Dealings with Some of the Indian Tribes. (By Helen Hunt Jackson.) NY: Harper, (1881). x,457pp + 6pp ads. Brn cl, gilt. (Sm rubberstamps, inscrip; extrems sl rubbed), else NF. *Pacific*.* $81/£51

Century of the English Book Trade. London: Bibliographical Soc, 1948. 1st Eng ed. Linen-backed paper bds. Fine in dj (sl creased). *Ulysses.* $88/£55

CERAM, C. W. The First American. NY: Harcourt Brace Jovanovich, (1971). 1st ed. Brn/orange cl. Fine in NF dj. *Harrington.* $30/£19

Ceramics—The World's Great Collections. Oriental Ceramics, Volumes 1-10 [of 11] only. Kodansha, Japan, 1980-1982. 10 vols. Folio. Slipcases. *Sotheby's*.* $920/£575

CERF, BENNETT. Bennett Cerf's Pop-Up Riddles. NY: Random House, 1966. 3 dbl-pg pop-ups by Art Leonardi. Glazed pict bds. VG. *Bookfinders.* $60/£38

CERF, BENNETT. Bennett Cerf's Pop-Up Silliest Riddles. NY: Random House, 1967. Glazed pict bds. VG. *Bookfinders.* $50/£31

CERIO, EDWIN. That Capri Air. London, n.d. One of 530. Teg, uncut. Fine (corner crease). *Polyanthos.* $35/£22

CERRUTI, HENRY. Ramblings in California: The Adventures of Henry Cerruti. Margaret Mollins and Virginia Thickens (eds). Berkeley: Friends of the Bancroft Library, 1954. 1st ed. One of 500 ptd. Port. Fine. *Argonaut.* $60/£38

CERVANTES. Don Quixote de la Mancha. London: Nonesuch, (1930). One of 1475 numbered sets. 2 vols. 21 photogravure plts by McKnight Kauffer, stenciled in color by Curwen Press. Teg, untrimmed. Orig full natural niger morocco, raised bands, dk brn morocco spine labels. Text Clean, cvrs VG (spine, edges sl sun-dknd, cvrs lt rubbed, sm scrap fr cvr vol 2). *Baltimore*.* $170/£106

CERVANTES. Don Quixote, the Ingenious Gentleman of La Mancha. LEC, 1950. Ltd to 1500 numbered, signed by Edy Legrand (illus). 2 vols. Fine in slipcase. *Swann*.* $115/£72

CERVANTES. The First [-Second] Part of the History of...Don Quixote of the Mancha. Chelsea: (Ashendene), 1927-28. One of 225 sets. 2 vols. Folio. Grn levant, gilt. *Swann*.* $2,530/£1,581

CERVANTES. The History and Adventures of the Renowned Don Quixote. T. Smollett (trans). London: Effingham Wilson, 1833. 1st George Cruikshank ed. 3 vols. Teg. Caramel calf, gilt. Bound by Morrell. (Lacks spine labels), else VG. *Pacific*.* $259/£162

CERVANTES. The History of the Most Renowned Don Quixote of Mancha: and His Trusty Squire Sancho Panza. London: Thomas Hodgkin, 1687. 1st illus ed in English. Folio. (18),616,(4)pp; 8 full-pg copper plts, later guards. Teg. Bound by H. Jackel in 3/4 levant lime grn morocco, marbled bds, gilt, spine w/flowers inlaid w/blue & red morocco, raised bands. (Bound w/o frontis [frequently lacking, possibly a 1st issue point], tp margins expertly replaced; tp, extrems of following few pp stained), else VG. *Pacific*.* $690/£431

CESARESCO, E. M. The Place of Animals in Human Thought. NY: Scribner, 1909. 1st ed. 34 plts. Good (card pocket removed rear pastedown; lib #s removed from spine). *Glaser.* $75/£47

CESCINSKY, HERBERT and ERNEST R. GRIBBLE. Early English Furniture and Woodwork. London: Routledge, 1922. 2 vols. Teg. Pub's gilt-stamped black leather (rubbed). *Oinonen*.* $130/£81

CESCINSKY, HERBERT and ERNEST R. GRIBBLE. Early English Furniture and Woodwork. Routledge, 1922. 1st ed. 2 vols in 1. 2 color frontispieces. Buckram-backed cl, gilt. VG. *Hollett.* $240/£150

CESCINSKY, HERBERT. English Furniture of the Eighteenth Century. Waverley Book Co, (1909-11). 3 vols. Teg. Orig 1/2 black morocco, gilt. VG set. *Hollett.* $520/£325

CEZANNE, PAUL. Paul Cezanne Letters. John Rewald (ed). London, 1941. (Sl soiled.) Dj (soiled, chipped, spine loss). *Edwards.* $32/£20

CHABON, MICHAEL. The Mysteries of Pittsburgh. NY, (1988). 1st ed, 1st bk. VG in dj. *King.* $50/£31

CHABOT, FREDERICK C. The Almo-Mission, Fortress and Shrine. San Antonio, March 1936. Centennial ed. VG in wraps. *Perier.* $12/£8

CHABOT, FREDERICK C. (ed). The Perote Prisoners, Being the Diary of James L. Trueheart. San Antonio: Naylor, 1934. 1st ed. Frontisport. Grn cl, gilt. Fine. *Pacific*. $75/£47

CHADWICK, JABEZ. New Light on the Subject of Christian Baptism, Presented in Three Parts.... Ithaca: Ptd by Mack & Andrus, 1832. 1st ed. 201pp. Orig cl spine, bds. (Lacks spine label, worn, sides rubbed), else Good. *Brown*. $15/£9

CHADWICK, MRS. ELLIS H. In the Footsteps of the Brontes. Isaac Pitman, 1914. 1st ed. (Spotted.) *Hollett*. $56/£35

CHAFFERS, WILLIAM. Gilda Aurifabrorum. London: Reeves & Turner, n.d. (c.1890). 267pp. (Shaken), o/w Good. *Europa*. $32/£20

CHAFFERS, WILLIAM. Hall Marks on Gold and Silver Plate. Reeves & Turner, 1905. 9th ed. Fldg facs, plt. Teg. (Lt spotted.) *Hollett*. $64/£40

CHAGALL, MARC. The Biblical Message. NY, (1973). Folio. Color litho frontis. Dj. *Swann**. $103/£64

CHAGALL, MARC. The Graphic Work. London: Thames & Hudson, (1957). 1st British ed. 6 color plts, 147 full-pg b/w repros. Gray pict cl. VG (edges of 1st/last ll sl aged; lt sunned, shelfworn) in color pict dj (price-clipped, extrems worn, chipped, torn). *Baltimore**. $60/£38

CHAGALL, MARC. The Jerusalem Windows. NY/Monte-Carlo, (1962). Lg 4to. 2 lithos. Dj (2 sm closed tears, sl edgewear, sl dampstain to inner portion). *Swann**. $1,265/£791

CHAGALL, MARC. The Lithographs of.... Maria Jolas (trans). Monte Carlo/NY: Andre Sauret/George Braziller, (1960). 1st US ed. Lg 4to. 11 full-pg color lithos. Tan cl. Perfect, as issued, in VG dj (bottom edge sl chipped), VG orig clear plastic wrapper. *Baltimore**. $1,300/£813

CHAGALL, MARC. The Lithographs of...1957-1962. Maria Jolas (trans). Monte Carlo/Boston: Andre Sauret/Boston Book & Art Shop, (1963). 1st Us ed. Sm folio. 11 NF full-pg lithos. Tan cl. (Spine top, top edge rear cvr sl worn, few lt spots.) Text VG (few finger smudges, sm stain to one bulked edge) in dj (lacks flaps). *Baltimore**. $650/£406

CHAGALL, MARC. The Lithographs of...1962-1968. George Lawrence (trans). Boston: Boston Book & Art Shop, (1969). 1st US ed. Color litho frontis. Tan cl. Perfect, as issued, in Mint color litho dj, Fine clear plastic dj, orig plain thin cardboard slipcase. *Baltimore**. $240/£150

CHAGALL, MARC. The Lithographs of...1962-1968. Boston: Boston Book & Art Shop, (1969). 1st Amer ed. Orig color litho frontis. Fine in litho dj, slipcase. *Pacific**. $316/£198

CHAGALL, MARC. The Lithographs of...1969-1973. NY: Crown, (1974). 1st Amer ed. Frontis litho. Fine in dj. *Pacific**. $259/£162

CHAGALL, MARC. Lithographs, 1980-1985. John Ottaway (trans). NY: Crown, (1986). 1st US ed. Tan cl. Mint in color litho dj (edges sl worn), VG clear plastic dj. *Baltimore**. $90/£56

CHALFANT, W. A. Death Valley, The Facts. CA: Stanford Univ, 1930. 1st ed. VG in pict bds. *Lien*. $25/£16

CHALFANT, W. A. Death Valley: The Facts. Stanford: Stanford Univ, (1947). 3rd rev ed. 18 b/w photo plts. Yellow/purple cl. Fine in VG+ pict dj. *House*. $20/£13

CHALFANT, W. A. Gold, Guns, and Ghost Towns. Stanford: University Press, (1947). 1st ed. Fine. *Book Market*. $15/£9

CHALFANT, W. A. Outposts of Civilization. Boston, (1928). 1st ed. Dec cl. NF. *Sagebrush*. $80/£50

CHALFANT, W. A. The Story of Inyo. N.p., 1933. Rev ed. Frontis map. NF. *Sagebrush*. $65/£41

CHALFANT, W. A. Tales of the Pioneers. Stanford, CA, (1942). 1st ed. Dec cl. Fine in NF dj. *Sagebrush*. $65/£41

CHALFANT, WILLIAM Y. Dangerous Passage. Norman: Univ of OK, (1994). 1st ed. As New in dj. *Lien*. $30/£19

CHALIAND, GERARD. The Peasants of North Vietnam. Middlesex, England: Penguin Books, 1969. 1st ed. Pb orig. (Eps offset; cvrs sl rubbed), else NF. *Associates*. $35/£22

CHALKLEY, A. P. Diesel Engines for Land and Marine Work. Constable, 1912. 1st ed. 15 fldg figs. Fair (1/2-title pasted down; cl sl soiled, worn, sm splits in lower hinge). *Cox*. $40/£25

CHALKLEY, THOMAS. The Journal of.... NY, 1808. 7,555pp. Contemp calf bds rebacked in mod calf, leather label. (Lib label tp, lt browned; surface loss.) *Edwards*. $144/£90

CHALKLEY, THOMAS. A Journal, or, Historical Account of the Life, Travels and Christian Experiences.... London, 1751. 2nd ed. Contemp calf (fr cvr loose). Howes C262. *Swann**. $258/£161

CHALLAMEL, AUGUSTIN. The History of Fashion in France. NY, 1882. 21 color plts. Cl-backed bds (shaken; inscrip tp). *Swann**. $161/£101

CHALMERS, MARY. A Hat for Amy Jean. NY: Harper, 1956. 1st ed. 5.5x6.25. 32pp. Cl spine, pict bds. VG. *Cattermole*. $35/£22

CHALMERS, PATRICK. Birds Ashore and A-Foreshore. London, 1935. 1st ed. 16 color plts. (Lt spotted; cl edges lt faded) in dj (browned, chipped, spine ends repaired). *Edwards*. $72/£45

CHALMERS, PATRICK. A Dozen Dogs or So. London: Eyre & Spottiswoode, 1928. 1st ed. Tall 4to. (viii),47pp; 13 color plts by Cecil Aldin. Brn cl. Fine. *Sotheran*. $205/£128

CHALMERS, PATRICK. (ed). Kenneth Grahame. Life, Letters and Unpublished Work. Methuen, 1933. 1st ed. 10 plts, facs of 3 letters, repro of frontis, fldg pedigree. Untrimmed. Pale blue cl, gilt. VG (eps lt browned) in dj. *Blackwell's*. $104/£65

CHALMERS, THOMAS. On the Power, Wisdom, and Goodness of God as Manifested in the Adaption of External Nature to the Moral and Intellectual Constitution of Man. London: William Pickering, 1839. 1st ed. 302pp. Contemp calf (extrems rubbed). *Young*. $96/£60

CHAMALES, TOM T. Never So Few. NY: Scribner, 1957. 1st ed. NF in NF dj. *Unger*. $50/£31

CHAMBAUD, LEWIS. A Grammar of the French Tongue; with a Preface, Containing an Essay on the Proper Method of Teaching.... London: Ptd by D. Cock, 1814. 17th ed. xxxii,466pp; fldg table. Contemp sheep (joints worn). *Young*. $120/£75

CHAMBERLAIN, ARTHUR. Hans Holbein the Younger. London: George Allen, 1913. 2 vols. Teg, uncut. Red cl (spines rubbed). *Argosy*. $275/£172

CHAMBERLAIN, BASIL HALL. A Practical Introduction to the Study of Japanese Writing. London/Shanghai: Sampson, Low, Marston/Kelly & Walsh, 1899. 1st ed. viii,482pp + errata leaf & slip. VG (recently recased in cl w/orig cl cvrs, spine laid on). *Ulysses*. $480/£300

CHAMBERLAIN, BERNARD P. A Treatise on the Making of Palatable Table Wines. (Charlottesville): The Author, 1931. 1st ed. One of 400 numbered, signed. Untrimmed. Tan buckram, lt blue bds, ptd paper labels. (Eps sl aged; spine label lt chipped). Text Clean, cvrs VG. *Baltimore**. $80/£50

CHAMBERLAIN, G. A. African Hunting Among the Thongas. NY: Harper, 1923. 1st ed. VG in pict cl. *Mikesh*. $75/£47

CHAMBERLAIN, NEWELL. The Call of Gold. (Mariposa: Gazette Press, 1936.) 1st ed. Tan cl. Dj (top edge worn). *Dawson*. $60/£38

CHAMBERLAIN, NEWELL. The Call to Gold. (Mariposa, CA: Gazette, 1936.) 1st ed. (Fr cvr sl stained), else NF. *Pacific**. $63/£39

CHAMBERLAIN, SAMUEL. Etched in Sunlight: Fifty Years in the Graphic Arts. Boston, 1968. Folio. Dj. *Swann**. $57/£36

CHAMBERLAINE, WILLIAM W. Memoirs of the Civil War Between the Northern and Southern Sections of the United States of America, 1861 to 1865. Washington: Byron S. Adams, 1912. 1st ed. Sm 8vo. Frontisport. Red cl, gilt. Fine. *Chapel Hill*. $900/£563

CHAMBERLAYNE, HAM. Ham Chamberlayne, Virginian: Letters and Papers of an Artillery Officer in the War for Southern Independence, 1861-1865. Richmond, VA: Dietz Ptg, 1932. 1st ed. One of 1000. Frontisport, dbl-pg map, fldg map. 2-toned cl. (Fore-edge lt spotted), else Fine in NF dj. *Chapel Hill*. $250/£156

CHAMBERLIN, HARRY D. Riding and Schooling Horses. NY, (1934). One of 950 numbered. Dj (price-clipped). *Swann**. $57/£36

CHAMBERLIN, T. C. (ed). Geology of Wisconsin: Survey of 1873-1879. (Madison): Commiss. of Public Ptg, 1883. 1st ed. 2 vols. Grn cl, gilt. (Extrems rubbed, sl torn), else VG. *Pacific**. $81/£51

CHAMBERS, CHARLES E. S. Golfing: A Handbook to the Royal and Ancient Game, with List of Clubs, Rules, &c. Edinburgh: W. & R. Chambers, 1887. 1st ed. Chromolitho frontisport. Pict blue cl, gilt. (Stamp, tape to verso), else Fine. *Pacific**. $1,093/£683

CHAMBERS, DANA. Rope for an Ape. NY: Dial, 1947. 1st ed. Fine in dj (lt chipped). *Murder*. $37/£23

CHAMBERS, DAVID and CHRISTOPHER SANDFORD. Cock-A-Hoop. Chatham, UK, 1962. Only trade ed. Frontis. As New in dj. *Bond*. $60/£38

CHAMBERS, E. Cyclopaedia; or, An Universal Dictionary of Arts and Science.... London, 1778. Plt vol only. Folio. 141 copperplts. Full calf. (1st few ll, cvrs detached; worn, rubbed.) *Kane**. $350/£219

CHAMBERS, E. K. The Elizabethan Stage. Oxford: Clarendon, 1923. 1st ed. 4 vols. VG in djs (spines, extrems sl dknd, 1 spine head chipped). *Pacific**. $75/£47

CHAMBERS, E. K. William Shakespeare: A Study of Facts and Problems. Oxford: Clarendon, 1930. 2 vols. Frontis. Dj (sl chipped). *Argosy*. $75/£47

CHAMBERS, E. T. D. The Ouananiche and Its Canadian Environment. NY, 1896. *Swann**. $138/£86

CHAMBERS, GEORGE F. The Story of the Comets. OUP, 1909. 1st ed. 27 photo plts. Blue cl, gilt. VG. *Larry Price*. $60/£38

CHAMBERS, HENRY A. Diary of Captain Henry A. Chambers, May 4, 1861 to April 24, 1865, Fredericksburg to Appomattox. T. H. Pearce (ed). Wendell, 1983. 1st ed. Fine in Fine dj. *Pratt*. $32/£20

CHAMBERS, JOHN. Autobiography of John Chambers. John C. Parish (ed). Iowa City, 1908. 1st ed. One of 400 numbered. *Ginsberg*. $125/£78

CHAMBERS, LENOIR. Stonewall Jackson. NY, 1959. 1st ed. 2 vols. Fine in slipcase (lt worn). *Pratt*. $115/£72

CHAMBERS, ROBERT W. The King in Yellow. NY/London, 1938. 'Memorial ed.' (Lt damp mk spine edge), else VG in VG dj. *Mcclintock*. $85/£53

CHAMBERS, ROBERT W. The Maid-at-Arms. NY/London: Harper, 1902. 1st ed. 8vo. Frontis, vi,(vi),342,(1)pp + 4pp pub's cat (fore-edge sl soiled); 7 plts by Howard Chandler Christy. Grn cl, gilt. Good (name, plt creased; bumped, rubbed, sm stain). *Blue Mountain*. $20/£13

CHAMBERS, ROBERT W. The Maker of Moons. NY, 1896. 1st ed. Frontis. Gilt-pict blue cl. (Bkpl, contemp inscrip.) Fine. *Swann**. $103/£64

CHAMBERS, ROBERT. The Picture of Scotland. Edinburgh: William Tait, 1830. 2 vols. Teg. 1/2 morocco, marbled bds, gilt. *Glenn*. $300/£188

CHAMBERS, WILLIAM and ROBERT. Chambers' Encyclopaedia: A Dictionary of Universal Knowledge. London: W. & R. Roberts, 1888. New ed. 10 vols. 3/4 morocco, gilt. (1 rear cvr detached), else VG. *Pacific**. $69/£43

CHAMBERS, WILLIAM. A Treatise on the Decorative Part of Civil Architecture. W. H. Leeds (ed). London: Lockwood, 1862. viii,336pp; 54 Good full-pg b/w litho plts. Blind crimson cl recently rebacked in crimson buckram, gilt. (Lt aged, few ll w/sm edge tears; lt worn, new eps.) *Baltimore**. $50/£31

CHAMBERS, WILLIAM. A Treatise on the Decorative Part of Civil Architecture. W. H. Leeds (ed). London, 1862. 3/4 calf (rubbed, dried, spine sl singed). Internally Sound. *Oinonen**. $90/£56

CHAMBLESS, EDGAR. Roadtown. NY: Roadtown, (1910). 1st ed. Purple cl, pict insert fr cvr. (Lettering sl chipped, shelf label on spine), else Fine. *Cummins*. $250/£156

CHAMETZKY, JULES and SIDNEY KAPLAN (eds). Black and White in American Culture. N.p. (Amherst?): Univ of MA, 1969. 1st ed. Fldg plt. Underscoring, marginalia of Julius Lester. VG in ptd dj. *Petrilla*. $40/£25

Champions of the Round Table. London: George Newnes, 1905. 1st Eng ed illus by Howard Pyle. Royal 8vo. (xviii),322pp; 32 full-pg b/w illus. Beige pict cl. Nice (gilt school stamp, rubbed, lt soiled). *Sotheran*. $240/£150

CHAMPNEY, ELIZABETH W. and FRERE. Romance of Old Japan. NY, 1917. 1st Amer ed. Color frontis. Teg. Pict cvrs, gilt. NF. *Polyanthos*. $35/£22

CHAMSON, ANDRE. A Mountain Boyhood. John Rodker (trans). John Lehmann, 1947. 1st ed. VG (feps browned; sl bowed, top edge dusty, spine, edges sl faded) in dj (nicked, sl rubbed, dusty, sl creased, torn, edges browned). *Ulysses*. $72/£45

CHAMSON, ANDRE. Roux the Bandit. Van Wyck Brooks (trans). London, 1929. 1st Eng ed. (Fore-edges foxed; cvrs sl bowed, corner sl bumped.) Dj (chipped, tanned). *Clearwater*. $40/£25

CHAMSON, ANDRE. Roux the Bandit. Van Wyck Brooks (trans). NY: Scribner, 1929. 1st US ed. Gilt forest grn cl. Fine in NF dj. *Reese*. $50/£31

CHANCE, JOHN NEWTON. The Devil in Greenlands. London: Gollancz, 1939. 1st ed. Black glazed cl. Nice. *Temple*. $35/£22

CHANCE, JOHN NEWTON. The Red Knight. London: Macdonald, n.d. (1945). 1st ed. Black cl. Nice in dj (frayed). *Temple*. $21/£13

CHANCE, JOHN NEWTON. Screaming Fog. London: Macdonald, (1944). 1st ed. Sky blue silk weave cl. (Inscrip), o/w Fine in dj (frayed, spine chipped). *Temple*. $21/£13

CHANCELLOR, E. BERESFORD. London Recalled. Oxford, 1937. 1st ed. 9 color plts. Teg. *Edwards*. $45/£28

CHANDLER, JOHN GREENE. The Remarkable History of Chicken Little, 1840-1940. South Lancaster: College Press, (1940). 1st ed thus. Inscribed, signed, dated by Herbert H. Hosmer, Jr. (great, great nephew of Chandler & writer of biographical chapter). VG (inscrip) in dj (sm scrape fr panel, sl soiled). *Pacific**. $40/£25

CHANDLER, JOSEPH EVERETT. The Colonial Architecture of Maryland, Pennsylvania and Virginia. Boston, 1900. 50 full-pg photos, loose as issued. 1/2 cl, marbled bds folder. (Lt foxed, extrems soiled; folder rubbed, dknd, lacks ties.) *King*. $150/£94

CHANDLER, MELBOURNE C. Of Garry Owen and Glory: The History of the Seventh United States Cavalry. Annandale, VA: Turnpike, (1960). Fine in dj. *Pacific**. $92/£58

CHANDLER, RAYMOND. Backfire. Robert Parker (ed). Santa Barbara, 1984. 1st ed. One of 126 specially bound, signed. This copy lettered 'C.' Red cl, black pict inlay. Slipcase. *Swann**. $40/£25

CHANDLER, RAYMOND. The Big Sleep. NY, (1946). 1st movie ed. Dj (sl edgeworn). *Swann**. $126/£79

CHANDLER, RAYMOND. The Big Sleep. NY, 1939. 1st ed, 1st bk. (Offset at fr/rear gutters; lib stamp; cl lt soiled.) *Swann**. $316/£198

CHANDLER, RAYMOND. The Big Sleep. NY: Knopf, 1939. 1st ed. Top edge stained gray. Orange cl. (Lt shelfworn, minor hinge repair), o/w Fine in dj (expertly restored), 1/4 morocco clamshell case. *Heritage.* $5,000/£3,125

CHANDLER, RAYMOND. The Big Sleep. Cleveland: World, 1946. Photoplay ed. VG in VG dj (worn). *Unger.* $100/£63

CHANDLER, RAYMOND. Farewell, My Lovely. NY: Knopf, 1940. 1st ed. Orange cl, blue lettering, topstain blue/grn. VG (extrems rubbed; w/o dj). *Smith.* $100/£63

CHANDLER, RAYMOND. Farewell, My Lovely. NY, 1940. 1st ed. 8vo. Red cl. VG (spine extrems lt rubbed) in dj (sl chipped, browned, minor restoration). *Heritage.* $2,500/£1,563

CHANDLER, RAYMOND. Farewell, My Lovely. NY: Knopf, 1940. 1st ed. 8vo. Top edge stained blue. Red cl. VG (eps lt browned; spine sl cocked, extrems lt rubbed) in dj (sl chipped, browned, some restoration). *Heritage.* $2,500/£1,563

CHANDLER, RAYMOND. The Finger Man and Other Stories. NY: Avon, 1946. 1st ed. Pb orig. (Fr cvr sl creased), o/w Fine in wrappers. *Mordida.* $200/£125

CHANDLER, RAYMOND. Five Sinister Characters. NY: Avon, 1945. 1st ed. Pb orig. (Sm nicks at spine ends), o/w Fine in wrappers. *Mordida.* $250/£156

CHANDLER, RAYMOND. The High Window. NY: Knopf, 1942. 1st ed. (Name; lacks dj), o/w VG. *Mordida.* $100/£63

CHANDLER, RAYMOND. The High Window. NY, 1942. 1st ed. 8vo. Grayish-brn cl. NF in dj (price-clipped, backstrip extrems lt chipped, rear panel sl soiled). *Heritage.* $2,500/£1,563

CHANDLER, RAYMOND. Killer in the Rain. Boston, (1964). 1st ed. Fine in dj. *Swann**. $201/£126

CHANDLER, RAYMOND. Killer in the Rain. London, 1964. 1st Eng ed. Nice (spine sl creased) in dj (stained). *Clearwater.* $72/£45

CHANDLER, RAYMOND. The Lady in the Lake. NY, 1943. 1st ed. 8vo. Grn cl. VG (sm brn stain to fr cvr) in dj (minor restoration to head, foot of backstrip, minimal edgewear, lt soiling). *Heritage.* $2,000/£1,250

CHANDLER, RAYMOND. The Little Sister. Boston: HM, 1949. 1st Amer ed. NF (spine ends sl worn) in VG + dj (long tear, few sm holes). *Between The Covers.* $350/£219

CHANDLER, RAYMOND. The Little Sister. Boston: Houghton Mifflin, 1949. 1st Amer ed. Orange cl blocked in blue. VG in dj (price-clipped, extrems sl rubbed). *Sotheran.* $477/£298

CHANDLER, RAYMOND. The Long Goodbye. London: Hamish Hamilton, (1953). 1st ed. Purple cl. NF in Fine dj (trimmed). *Cummins.* $275/£172

CHANDLER, RAYMOND. The Midnight Raymond Chandler. Boston: Houghton Mifflin, 1971. 1st ed thus. Fine in dj (1 sm closed tear). *Cahan.* $50/£31

CHANDLER, RAYMOND. Pick-Up on Noon Street. Pocket Books, 1952. 1st ptg. (Spine edges lt worn, fr, rear creased), else NF in wraps. *Murder.* $40/£25

CHANDLER, RAYMOND. Playback. NY, 1958. 1st Amer ed. Fine in NF dj. *Warren.* $150/£94

CHANDLER, RAYMOND. Smart-Aleck Kill. London: Hamish Hamilton, 1953. 1st ed. Pb orig. (Fr cvr creased, rubbed), o/w Fine in wrappers. *Mordida.* $300/£188

CHANDLER, RAYMOND. The Smell of Fear. London, (1965). 1st Eng and only ed. Dj. *Swann**. $316/£198

CHANDLER, SAMUEL. The History of Persecution...Among the Heathens...Under the Christian Emperors.... London: J. Gray, 1736. 9 fldg plts. 1/2 calf. (2 plts sl torn, old waterstains; worn.) *Kane**. $100/£63

Change for the American Notes: in Letters from London to New York. By an American Lady. (By Henry Wood.) London: Wiley & Putnam, 1843. 1st ed. xii,(9)-392pp. Orig cl (sl faded). *Mott.* $75/£47

CHANNING, ELLERY. Poems of Sixty-Five Years. F. B. Sanborn (ed). Phila/Concord: James H. Bentley, 1902. 1st ed. One of 300. Frontis. Brn cl spine, plain brn bds. Good (brn offset on tp; spine top worn). *Lucas.* $45/£28

CHANNING, W. E. Analysis of the Character of Napoleon Bonaparte. Boston/London, 1828. 2nd ed. 52pp. Calf-backed bds. *Young.* $80/£50

CHANNING, W. E. Remarks on the Character and Writings of John Milton. Boston/London: Edward Rainford, 1828. 2nd ed. 48pp. Calf-backed bds. *Young.* $72/£45

CHANNING, W. E. Thoreau: The Poet-Naturalist. Boston: Roberts Bros, 1873. 1st ed. 357pp. Reddish-brn cl (spine ends sl chipped). VG. *Lucas.* $175/£109

CHANSLOR, ROY. The Ballad of Cat Ballou. Boston: Little, Brown, (1956). 1st ed. Inscribed, signed. NF in dj (extrems, spine head sl rubbed). *Pacific**. $92/£58

CHAPEL, CHARLES EDWARD. Finger Printing. NY: Coward-McCann, 1941. VG (smells musty, sl shelfworn) in dj (ragged, limp). *My Bookhouse.* $27/£17

CHAPEL, CHARLES EDWARD. Guns of the Old West. NY: Coward-McCann, 1961. 1st ed. VG in dj. *Labordo.* $50/£31

CHAPELLE, HOWARD I. The Baltimore Clipper. Salem, MA: Marine Research Soc, 1930. 1st ed. Frontis, 35 plts, 48 plans. Textured blue cl, gilt. Fine. *Karmiole.* $125/£78

CHAPELLE, HOWARD I. The History of American Sailing Ships. NY: W.W. Norton, 1935. 2nd ptg. Frontis, 16 plts. Beige cl, blue spine, cvr titles. (Sl foxed, soiled), else VG in dj (worn). *Parmer.* $45/£28

CHAPELLE, HOWARD I. Yacht Designing and Planning. NY: Norton, 1936. 1st ed. Tan cl. VG. *American Booksellers.* $60/£38

CHAPIN, ANNA ALICE. The Now-A-Days Fairy Book. NY: Dodd, Mead, 1911. 1st ed. Tall 4to. 6 full-pg mtd plts by Jessie Wilcox Smith. Brn cl, full color paste label, white spine lettering (rubbed). VG. *Reisler.* $450/£281

CHAPIN, FREDERICK H. Mountaineering in Colorado. Boston, 1889. Pict cl. *Swann**. $258/£161

CHAPIN, FREDERICK H. Mountaineering in Colorado: The Peaks About Estes Park. Boston: Appalachian Mountain Club, 1889. 1st ed. (2),168pp; 11 collotype plts. (Stain to top edge of cvrs), else NF. *Pacific**. $69/£43

CHAPIN, JOHN B. A Compendium of Insanity. Phila: Saunders, 1898. 1st ed. VG (ex-lib; hinges tender, spine label removed). *Beasley.* $50/£31

CHAPLIN, CHARLES. My Autobiography. London: Bodley Head, 1964. VG in dj. *Hollett.* $32/£20

CHAPLIN, RALPH. Bars and Shadows. NY: Leonard, 1922. 1st ed. Fine in dj (lt soiled). *Beasley.* $75/£47

CHAPMAN, ABEL. The Borders and Beyond. London, 1924. 19 color plts by W. H. Riddell; 2 fldg sketch maps. *Edwards.* $120/£75

CHAPMAN, ABEL. Memories of Fourscore Years Less Two 1851-1929. London, 1930. 1st ed. (Feps lt foxed.) *Edwards.* $72/£45

CHAPMAN, ABEL. On Safari, Big-Game Hunting in British East Africa. London, 1908. 1st ed. Edges uncut except for top. (New eps; backstrip, corners sl rubbed.) *Petersfield.* $384/£240

CHAPMAN, ABEL. Savage Sudan, Its Wild Tribes, Big Game and Bird-Life. London, 1921. 1/2 dk grn calf, marbled bds, gilt. (1 plt torn, repaired), o/w contents VF. *Grayling.* $288/£180

CHAPMAN, ABEL. Wild Norway: With Chapters on Spitsbergen, Denmark.... London: Arnold, 1897. 16pp ads. (Backstrip sl dampstained.) *Petersfield.* $125/£78

CHAPMAN, ABEL. Wild Spain. London, 1893. Map. (Lt foxed; spine sunned.) *Oinonen*.* $80/£50

CHAPMAN, ARTHUR. The Pony Express. NY: Putnam, 1932. 1st ed. Fine (spine sl faded, sm spot fr cvr). Howes C291. *Argonaut.* $75/£47

CHAPMAN, ARTHUR. The Pony Express. NY: Putnam, 1932. 1st ed. Tan/grn cl. Fine in NF dj (sl chipped). Howes C291. *Harrington.* $125/£78

CHAPMAN, ARTHUR. The Story of Colorado. Chicago: Rand McNally, (1924). 1st ed. Color frontis. Blue pict cl, gilt. Fine. *Harrington.* $45/£28

CHAPMAN, CHARLES. The Ocean Waves: Travels by Land and Sea. London, 1875. 1st ed. (Shelfworn.) *Oinonen*.* $80/£50

CHAPMAN, CHARLES. The Ocean Waves: Travels by Land and Sea. London: George Berridge, 1875. 1st ed. 1876 inscribed presentation (erasure). Frontis, 2 prelim ll, 323pp; 4 inserted plts, chart. (Shelfworn, soiled.) *Mott.* $250/£156

CHAPMAN, F. M. Bird-Life. NY: Appleton, (1900). 75 full-pg 1/2-tone repros, b/w dwgs by E. T. Seton. Pict cl. (Spine ends rubbed), else VG. *Mikesh.* $37/£23

CHAPMAN, F. SPENCER. Lhasa, the Holy City. London, 1938. 1st ed. Color frontisport, 7 color plts. Dec cl (spine sl faded, rubbed). *Edwards.* $80/£50

CHAPMAN, F. SPENCER. Northern Lights. London: C&W, 1932. 1st ed. Frontis, 4 fldg maps, 63 plts. Dj (sl worn, soiled). *Maggs.* $136/£85

CHAPMAN, F. SPENCER. Watkins' Last Expedition. London: C&W, 1934. 48 photo plts; fldg map. VG (sl dknd spine). *High Latitude.* $45/£28

CHAPMAN, GEORGE. Bussy D'Ambois. Nicholas Brooke (ed). Methuen, 1964. 1st Eng ed. Fine in dj. *Ulysses.* $32/£20

CHAPMAN, GUY. A Passionate Prodigality. London: Ivor Nicholson & Watson, 1933. 1st ed. Emerald cl stamped in red. (Cl lt foxed), o/w VG in dj (sl foxed, edge-used). *Reese.* $200/£125

CHAPMAN, GUY. A Passionate Prodigality. NY, 1966. VG in dj. *Typographeum.* $18/£11

CHAPMAN, HAY. Law of the Links: Rules, Principles and Etiquette of Golf. SF: Privately ptd, 1922. 1st ed. Ptd bds (Emb stamp; spine, extrems sunned, spine ends chipped), else VG. *Pacific*.* $150/£94

CHAPMAN, HENRY C. A Manual of Medical Jurisprudence, Insanity and Toxicology. Phila, 1904. 3rd ed. Good (inner hinges cracked; extrems sl worn). *Doctor's Library.* $60/£38

CHAPMAN, JOHN JAY. Treason and Death of Benedict Arnold. NY: Moffet, Yard, 1910. 1st ed. Inscribed. VG (inscrip) in grn paper-cvrd bds (spine, fr cvr labels tanned, spine ends worn). *Lame Duck.* $175/£109

CHAPMAN, JOHN. Broadway's Best 1957: The Complete Record of the Theatrical Year. GC: Doubleday, 1957. 1st ed. VF in VF dj (sl rubbed). *Between The Covers.* $85/£53

CHAPMAN, JOHN. Broadway's Best 1958: The Complete Record of the Theatrical Year. GC: Doubleday, 1958. 1st ed. VF in VF dj (sl rubbed). *Between The Covers.* $85/£53

CHAPMAN, JOHN. Theater '53. NY: Random House, (1953). 1st ed. VF in VF dj (sl rubbed). *Between The Covers.* $100/£63

CHAPMAN, KENNETH M. The Pottery of San Ildefonso Pueblo. Albuquerque: Univ of NM, 1970. 1st ed. 174 color plts. Good in dj (sl soiled). *Dumont.* $100/£63

CHAPMAN, MARIA WESTON. Right and Wrong in Massachusetts. Boston: Dow & Jackson's Anti-Slavery Press, 1839. 1st ed. (Spine foot chipped.) *Rostenberg & Stern.* $275/£172

CHAPMAN, VICTOR. Letters from France. NY, 1917. (Sl mkd, corners sl bumped.) *Clearwater.* $64/£40

CHAPONE, HESTER. The Posthumous Works of Mrs. Chapone. London/Edinburgh: John Murray/A. Constable, 1808. 2nd ed. 2 vols. xii,190; (iv),216,217-224 ads pp. Rebound in gray/brn paper-cvrd bds, new labels. Good set. *Young.* $192/£120

CHAPPE D'AUTEROCHE, JEAN. A Journey into Siberia...in 1761. London, 1770. Engr fldg map, 11 plts. Mod lib buckram. (Ink lib stamps.) *Swann*.* $488/£305

CHAPPELL, EDWARD. Voyage of His Majesty's Ship Rosamond to Newfoundland and the Southern Coast of Labrador. London: J. Mawman, 1818. 8vo. (x),xix,270,(ii)pp; fdlg color map. Contemp full calf (skillfully rebacked). Fine (bkpl). *Explorer.* $880/£550

CHAPPUIS, ADRIEN. The Drawings of Paul Cezanne: A Catalogue Raisonne. Greenwich, (1973). 2 vols. Folio. (Spines rubbed.) *Swann*.* $230/£144

CHAPUT, DON. Virgil Earp: Western Peace Officer. Encampment, WY: Affiliated Writers of America, (1994). 1st ed. Fine in dj. *Lien.* $25/£16

CHARAKA CLUB. Proceedings of.... Volume IX. NY: Richard R. Smith, 1938. White cl-backed tan bds. VG (lacks fep; lt soiled). *House.* $65/£41

CHARAKA CLUB. Proceedings of.... Volume V. NY: Paul B. Hoeber, 1919. One of 500. Teg. White cl-backed gray bds. VG +. *House.* $65/£41

CHARCOT, J. M. Clinical Lectures on Diseases of the Nervous System. Vol III. London: New Sydenham Soc, 1889. 1st ed in English. Nice (lib stamps; spine head frayed). *Beasley.* $275/£172

CHARCOT, J. M. Lectures on the Diseases of the Nervous System. Vol I. London: New Sydenham Soc, 1877. 1st ed in English. VG (lib stamps; hinges tender, spine head joints torn, 1 clear tape spine mend, spine frayed, sl chipped). *Beasley.* $250/£156

CHARCOT, JEAN. The Voyage of the 'Why Not?' London, (1911). 1st Eng ed. 4to. Fldg frontis. Pict cl, gilt. Fine. *Maggs.* $880/£550

CHARCOT, JEAN. The Voyage of the 'Why Not?' in the Antarctic. Toronto: Musson Book, n.d. (1911). 1st ed in English. Fldg frontis; map. Dec cl. VF. *High Latitude.* $600/£375

CHARDIN, JOHN. Sir John Chardin's Travels in Persia. London: Argonaut, 1927. One of 975 numbered. 2 fldg illus. Gilt vellum over aqua cl. Good. *Karmiole.* $150/£94

CHARDIN, JOHN. Travels in Persia. London: Argonaut, 1927. One of 975. 1/2 vellum, blue cl, gilt. Nice (corners bumped, lt soiled). *Parmer.* $250/£156

CHARHADI, DRISS BEN HAMED. A Life Full of Holes. Paul Bowles (trans). NY: Grove, 1964. 1st Amer ed. Fine in dj (sm tear). *Polyanthos.* $30/£19

CHARLES II. An Account of the Preservation of King Charles II after the Battle of Worcester; Drawn up by Himself. London: S. Gosnell, 1803. 5 copper plts (incl frontisport). Period calf, gilt. Fine. *Pacific*.* $69/£43

CHARLES, C. J. Elizabethan Interiors. London, (1912). One of 800 numbered. Folio. Later 1/4 morocco. *Swann*.* $69/£43

CHARLES, MRS. TOM. Tales of the Tularosa. Alamogordo, NM, 1954. Rev ed. Signed. Frontisport, dbl-pg map. Rose buckram. Fine in pict map dj. *House.* $45/£28

CHARLES, ROBERT H. A Roundabout Turn. London: Frederick A. Warne, (1930). 1st ed. 4 full-pg color plts by L. Leslie Brooke. 8vo. Orange cl, brn dec, gilt. (Marginal tear in pg mended w/tape; lt dusting.) *Reisler.* $100/£63

CHARLES-ROUX, EDMONDE. Chanel and Her World. Weidenfeld & Nicolson, 1982. 1st pb ed. Pict card. Good+ (sl margin tears, bend-mks to pp). *Whittle*. $19/£12

Charleston South Carolina in 1883: With Heliotypes of the Principal Objects of Interest in and Around the City. Boston: Heliotype Ptg Co, 1883. 1st ed. vi,(2),39pp; 39 heliotype plts. VG (hinges weak or cracking; extrems worn, stain fr cvr). *Pacific**. $259/£162

CHARLETON, T. W. The Art of Fishing: A Poem. North Shields: The Author, 1819. 1st ed. Errata slip tipped in at rear. Period hand-lettered parchment-backed wrappers. (Sm old label fr wrapper, sm pieces of spine lacking, lt foxing), else VG. *Pacific**. $115/£72

CHARLOT, JEAN. Charlot Murals in Georgia. Univ of GA, (1945). One of 2500. NF in dj (tape-reinforced). *Agvent*. $85/£53

CHARLOT, JEAN. Picture Book II. L.A., 1973. One of 1000 numbered, signed. 32 color lithos. Wrappers, slipcase. *Swann**. $345/£216

CHARLTON, MOYRA. The Midnight Steeplechase. Methuen, 1932. 1st ed. Lg 8vo. Color frontis, 132pp; 6 mono plts by Gilbert Holiday. NF in pict dj (chipped). *Bookmark*. $32/£20

CHARNAS, SUZY McKEE. Walk to the End of the World. Gollancz, 1979. 1st ed, 1st bk. (Extrems sl faded), else Fine in dj. *Any Amount*. $45/£28

CHARNOCK, RICHARD STEPHEN. On Ancient Manorial Customs, Tenures, Services, Privileges, Serjeanties, Grants, Fines, Etc., in the County of Essex. London: Longmans, 1870. 1st ed. 38pp. Calf-backed bds. *Young*. $67/£42

CHARRIERE, HENRI. Papillon. Patrick O'Brian (trans). Hart-Davis, 1970. 1st UK ed. VG in dj. *Williams*. $56/£35

CHARTERIS, LESLIE. The Ace of Knaves. Hodder, 1937. 1st UK ed. VG (spine sl faded) in VG dj (sl chipped, stained). *Williams*. $1,200/£750

CHARTERIS, LESLIE. Call for the Saint. NY: Crime Club, 1948. 1st Amer ed. Fine (sl rubbed) in dj (sm edge tear, spine sl sunned). *Polyanthos*. $25/£16

CHARTERIS, LESLIE. Count on the Saint. Hodder, 1980. 1st UK ed. VG in dj (edges sl worn). *Williams*. $24/£15

CHARTERIS, LESLIE. The Happy Highwayman. London: Hodder & Stoughton, 1939. 1st ed. Cerise cl. (Sl restoration to cl rear joint corner, gilt oxidized, sm mk rear cvr.) Internally Fine. *Temple*. $48/£30

CHARTERIS, LESLIE. The Saint on Guard. London: Hodder & Stoughton, (1945). 1st ed. Blue cl. (Spine sl cocked, extrems sl rubbed), o/w NF in dj (lt soiled, edgeworn). *Heritage*. $300/£188

CHARTERIS, LESLIE. The Saint on the Spanish Main. London: Hodder & Stoughton, (1956). 1st ed. Blue cl, gilt. (Spine sl cocked, extrems sl rubbed), o/w Fine in dj (lt chipped, soiled). *Heritage*. $100/£63

CHARTERIS, LESLIE. The Saint Sees It Through. London: Hodder & Stoughton, (1947). 1st ed. Blue cl. VG (eps lt browned; spine sl cocked, extrems sl rubbed) in dj (lt chipped, soiled). *Heritage*. $300/£188

CHARTERIS, LESLIE. The Saint Steps In. GC: Doubleday, Doran, 1943. Red cl. (Bkpl removed, eps browned, ink # rear pastedown; spine extrems sl rubbed.) Dj (chipped). *Heritage*. $150/£94

CHARTERIS, LESLIE. The Saint to the Rescue. London: Hodder & Stoughton, (1961). 1st ed. Red cl, gilt. (Ink name, 1st/last few ll lt browned), o/w Fine in dj (soiled). *Heritage*. $100/£63

CHARTERIS, LESLIE. Senor Saint. London: Hodder & Stoughton, 1959. 1st Eng ed. Fine in dj. *Mordida*. $65/£41

CHARTERIS, LESLIE. Thanks to the Saint. London: Hodder & Stoughton, 1958. 1st Eng ed. Fine in dj. *Mordida*. $65/£41

CHARTERS, ANN (ed). The Portable Beat Reader. NY, 1992. 1st ed, 1st ptg. NF in Fine dj. *Warren*. $40/£25

CHARTERS, ANN (ed). Scenes Along the Road. NY: Portents/Gotham Book Mart, 1970. 1st ed. Fine (sm spine chip) in wraps. *Beasley*. $35/£22

CHARTERS, SAMUEL. The Country Blues. NY: Rinehart, (1959). 1st ed. VG in pict dj. *Petrilla*. $45/£28

CHARTERS, SAMUEL. The Poetry of the Blues. NY: Oak Pub, 1963. 1st ed. VG in wraps (3/4-inch closed tear). *Warren*. $30/£19

CHASE, A. W. Dr. Chase's Recipes; or, Information for Everybody. Ann Arbor: R.A. Beal, 1870. Later ed. 384pp. Full red morocco, gilt. (Spine dknd, ends worn, shelfworn), else Good. *Brown*. $25/£16

CHASE, J. SMEATON. California Desert Trails. Boston: Houghton Mifflin, 1919. 1st ed. 35 plts. Grn pict cl, gilt. NF (extrems sl worn). *Harrington*. $55/£34

CHASE, J. SMEATON. Cone-Bearing Trees of the California Mountains. Chicago: McClurg, 1911. 1st ed. 21 plts. Orange pict cl. Fine. *Pacific**. $40/£25

CHASE, J. SMEATON. Our Araby: Palm Springs and the Garden of the Sun. Pasadena: Star News, 1923. New ed. Map in pocket. VG. *Book Market*. $25/£16

CHASE, JOHN. Frenchmen, Desire, Good Children and Other Streets of New Orleans. New Orleans, LA, 1949. 1st ed. Signed, w/cartoon. VF in VF dj. *Bond*. $17/£11

CHASE, WILL H. Alaska's Mammoth Brown Bears. Kansas City: Burton Pub Co, (1947). VG (worn). *Perier*. $45/£28

CHASE, WILL H. Reminiscences of Captain Billie Moore. Kansas City: Burton Pub Co, (1947). Signed. VG. *Perier*. $50/£31

CHASE-RIBOUD, BARBARA. From Memphis and Peking. Poems. NY: Random House, 1974. 1st ed. Signed, inscribed. Fine in dj. *Smith*. $75/£47

CHASE-RIBOUD, BARBARA. Sally Hemings. NY: Viking, 1979. 1st ed. Fine in NF dj (few sm tears). *Beasley*. $35/£22

CHASTEL, ANDRE. A Chronicle of Italian Renaissance Painting. Ithaca: Cornell Univ, 1984. 1st ed. NF (sl shelfworn) in dj (sl worn). *My Bookhouse*. $42/£26

CHATEAUBRIAND, FRANCOIS-RENE. An Autobiography. Simms & McIntyre, 1849. Sprinkled edges. Contemp 1/2 leather, marbled bds (sl rubbed, spotted; sig). Good. *Tiger*. $22/£14

CHATELAIN, JEAN. The Biblical Message. Marc Chagall. NY, (1973). Color litho frontis. Dj, mylar outer wrapper, bd slipcase. *Swann**. $92/£58

CHATFIELD, C. Teutonic Antiquities, or...Sketches of Roman and Barbarian History. London: Hurst, Chance & Co., 1828. 270pp + 13ff tables. Orig paper-cvrd bds. (Spine faded, lt foxing.) *Cullen*. $85/£53

CHATTERTON, E. KEBLE. Captain John Smith. NY/London: Harper, 1927. 1st ed. Frontisport, 3 maps. Blue cl. NF in dj (lt worn). *Parmer*. $85/£53

CHATTERTON, E. KEBLE. Sailing Ships. London: Sidgwick & Jackson, 1909. Color frontis. Color pict inlay to fr cvr. *Petersfield*. $51/£32

CHATTERTON, E. KEBLE. Whalers and Whaling. London: T. Fisher Unwin, 1925. 1st ed. (Sl worn), else VG. *High Latitude*. $35/£22

CHATTERTON, E. KEBLE. The Yachtsman's Pilot to the Harbours of England, Wales, Scotland, Ireland; and the Continent of Europe from Ymuiden to Bordeaux. London: Hurst & Blackett, (1933). 1st ed. 32 plans. (Cl soiled, spine faded.) *Lefkowicz*. $75/£47

CHATTERTON, THOMAS. Poems Supposed to Have Been Written at Bristol by Thomas Rowley and Others. Cambridge: B. Flower for the Editor, 1794. 5th ed. Lg paper ed. xxix,329pp; engr plt (incorrectly placed opposite p192, as in variant copy). Marbled eps. 1/2 red morocco (nicely rebound), gilt, marbled bds. VG (ex-lib, mks, prelims professionally strengthened). *Hartfield.* $295/£184

CHATTERTON, THOMAS. The Rowley Poems of Thomas Chatterton. Maurice Evan Hare (ed). Oxford: Clarendon, 1911. 1st Eng ed. Dec gilt buckram. VG (feps partly browned, top edge sl mkd; spine ends sl bumped) in 1932 dj (price-clipped, sl nicked, rubbed, browned). *Ulysses.* $104/£65

CHATTO, WILLIAM ANDREW. A Treatise on Wood Engraving. London, 1861. 2nd ed. (Spine ends worn, fr hinge cracked.) *Swann*.* $69/£43

CHATWIN, BRUCE and PAUL THEROUX. Patagonia Revisited. Michael Russell, 1985. One of 250 numbered, signed. Dec cl. Fine in unptd tissue dj (nicked, sl torn, creased). *Ulysses.* $440/£275

CHATWIN, BRUCE. In Patagonia. Cape, 1977. 1st UK ed. NF in dj (price-clipped). *Williams.* $600/£375

CHATWIN, BRUCE. On the Black Hill. London, (1982). 1st ed. Dj. *Swann*.* $80/£50

CHATWIN, BRUCE. The Songlines. London: Cape, 1987. 1st Eng ed. VG (spine ends sl bumped) in dj (sl mkd, creased, internally sl dknd). *Ulysses.* $152/£95

CHATWIN, BRUCE. The Songlines. Franklin Center, PA: Franklin Lib, 1987. Signed ltd ed. Fine in full leather, gilt. *Clearwater.* $320/£200

CHATWIN, BRUCE. The Songlines. NY: Viking Penguin, 1987. Signed. VG (rmdr stripe on fore-edge, spine foot; production fault at bottom edges of feps; spine ends sl bumped) in dj (spine sl faded). *Ulysses.* $440/£275

CHATWIN, BRUCE. Utz. Cape, 1988. 1st ed. Fine in dj. *Virgo.* $40/£25

CHATWIN, BRUCE. The Viceroy of Ouidah. NY: Summit Bks, 1980. 1st Amer ed. Fine in dj. *Cady.* $30/£19

CHAUCER, GEOFFREY. The Booke of the Duchesse. F. J. Furnivall (ed). (Lexington): Anvil, (1954). One of 225 numbered. *Black Sun.* $400/£250

CHAUCER, GEOFFREY. The Canterbury Tales. NY, (1934). 1st Amer ed. Rockwell Kent (illus). NF in dj (rear cvr torn, sl sunned). *Polyanthos.* $35/£22

CHAUCER, GEOFFREY. The Canterbury Tales. Frank Ernest Hill (trans). NY: LEC, (1946). One of 1500. Signed by Arthur Szyk (illus). 1/2 morocco, dec bds, gilt. Fine in slipcase. *Pacific*.* $150/£94

CHAUCER, GEOFFREY. The Canterbury Tales. London: William Pickering, 1830. 5 vols. 8vo. Engr frontis, ccxxii,122; 354; 290; 348; 296pp; engr port. Teg. Bound in full calf by Zaehnsdorf, 2 morocco lettering pieces, gilt. VF. *Bromer.* $750/£469

CHAUCER, GEOFFREY. The Canterbury Tales. LEC, 1934. Ltd to 1500 numbered, signed by George W. Jones (designer/ptr). 2 vols. Fine in slipcase. *Swann*.* $103/£64

CHAUCER, GEOFFREY. The Canterbury Tales. LEC, 1946. Ltd to 1500 numbered, signed by Arthur Szyk (illus). Fine in slipcase. *Swann*.* $287/£179

CHAUCER, GEOFFREY. The Poetical Works of.... London, 1782. 14 vols. Engr frontispieces. Contemp tree calf, flat spines w/red labels (dulled; few joints tender, spine extrems worn). *Swann*.* $230/£144

CHAUCER, GEOFFREY. Troilus and Cressida. LEC, 1939. Ltd to 1500 numbered, signed by George W. Jones (designer). Fine in slipcase. *Swann*.* $46/£29

CHAUNCY, CHARLES. A Compleat View of Episcopacy...Until the Close of the Second Century. Boston: Kneeland for Leverett, 1771. 1st ed. x,474pp; 2 leaves. Contemp calf (rubbed, joints broken; sl browned). Internally Sound. *Oinonen*.* $100/£63

CHAUVENET, WILLIAM. A Manual of Spherical and Practical Astronomy. Phila, 1908. 5th ed. 2 vols. 15 plts. Blue cl, gilt. VG (ex-lib; rebound, non-matched set). *Larry Price.* $95/£59

CHAYEFSKY, PADDY. Altered States. Hutchinson, 1978. 1st UK ed. NF in dj. *Williams.* $45/£28

CHEESMAN, R. E. In Unknown Arabia. London, 1926. 3 maps. VG. *Petersfield.* $99/£62

CHEETHAM, F. H. Louis Napoleon and the Genesis of the Second Empire. London: J. Lane, 1909. Frontis; 24 plts. Teg, uncut. (Spine faded.) *Stewart.* $48/£30

CHEEVER, DAVID W. Surgical Cases in 1867, Reprinted from the Boston Medical and Surgical Journal. Boston, 1867. 37pp. Fair (lacks paper wrappers). *Doctor's Library.* $40/£25

CHEEVER, GEORGE B. The Guilt of Slavery and the Crime of Slaveholding. NY, 1860. 1st ed. Brn cl, gilt. (Spine ends worn, cl piece at head replaced), else VG. *Pacific*.* $46/£29

CHEEVER, JOHN. The Brigadier and the Golf Widow. NY, (1964). 1st ed. VG in Nice dj. *King.* $50/£31

CHEEVER, JOHN. The Enormous Radio and Other Stories. NY: Funk & Wagnalls, 1953. 1st ed. NF in VG 1st state dj ($3.50 price, port). *Warren.* $75/£47

CHEEVER, JOHN. The Leaves, the Lion Fish, and the Bear. Hollywood: Sylvester & Orphanos, 1980. Ltd to 330 signed. Fine dec cl. *Truepenny.* $100/£63

CHEEVER, JOHN. The National Pastime. Hollywood: Sylvester & Orphanos, 1982. Ltd to 330 signed. Fine dec cl. *Truepenny.* $100/£63

CHEEVER, JOHN. The Way Some People Live. NY: Random House, (1943). 1st ed, 1st bk. (Sm sticker removed fep), else Fine (lacks dj). *Between The Covers.* $125/£78

CHEKHOV, ANTON. The Letters of Anton Chekhov. Simon Karlinsky (ed). Michael Henry Heim (trans). Bodley Head, 1973. 1st Eng ed. NF (spine ends sl bumped) in dj (price-clipped, edges sl creased). *Ulysses.* $104/£65

CHEKHOV, ANTON. The Short Stories. LEC, 1973. Ltd to 1500 numbered, signed by Lajos Szalay (illus). Fine in slipcase. *Swann*.* $57/£36

CHEKHOV, ANTON. Two Plays: The Cherry Orchard and Three Sisters. LEC, 1966. Ltd to 1500 numbered, signed by Lajos Szalay (illus). Fine in slipcase. *Swann*.* $46/£29

CHELIUS, J. M. A System of Surgery. Phila, 1847. 3 vols. 2168pp. Full calf. Good (foxed, rear ads removed vol II; scuffed, wear, nibbled at edges). *Doctor's Library.* $130/£81

CHELIUS, J. M. A System of Surgery. John F. South (trans). Phila: Lea & Blanchard, 1847. 1st Amer ed. 3 vols. Orig sheep (sl rubbed). *M & S.* $175/£109

CHENERY, WILLIAM H. The Fourteenth Regiment Rhode Island Heavy Artillery (Colored), in the War to Preserve the Union, 1861-1865. Providence: Snow & Farnham, 1898. 1st ed. Frontisport, 343pp. Red cl. (Spine faded, few lt stains to fr cvr), else VG. *Chapel Hill.* $325/£203

CHENEY, SHELDON. The New Movement in the Theatre. NY: Mitchell Kennerly, 1914. Frontis. (Ends rubbed, hinges starting.) *Dramatis.* $45/£28

CHEREPANOV, A. I. Cerambycidae of Northern Asia. Volume 3, Lamiinae, Parts I-III. New Delhi: Amerind Pub, 1990. 1st ed. 3 vols. Fine in NF djs. *Archer.* $60/£38

CHERKOVSKI, NEELI. Hank. The Life of Charles Bukowski. NY: Random House, 1991. 1st trade ed. Signed by Cherkovski and Bukowski. Fine in dj. *Smith.* $250/£156

CHERRY, P. P. The Western Reserve and Early Ohio. Akron: R.L. Fouse, 1921. (Shelfworn), else Good. *Dumont.* $45/£28

CHERRY-GARRARD, APSLEY. The Worst Journey in the World. London: Constable, 1922. 1st ed. 2 vols. 8vo. Blue-gray paper bds, spare labels tipped in. Very Nice. *Explorer.* $1,520/£950

CHERRY-GARRARD, APSLEY. The Worst Journey in the World. London, 1922. 1st ed. 2 vols. 8vo. 5 maps (4 fldg), 6 color plts. Linen-backed pale blue cl, ptd paper labels, spare labels tipped to feps each vol. *Maggs.* $1,760/£1,100

CHERRY-GARRARD, APSLEY. The Worst Journey in the World. C&W, 1937. 10 plts, 4 maps. VG (fore-edges sl spotted; spine sl faded, rear bd sl mkd, bumped). *Hollett.* $104/£65

CHERRY-GARRARD, APSLEY. The Worst Journey in the World. London, 1937. 4th ed. 4 fldg maps, 10 plts. Dj (torn w/loss). *Maggs.* $192/£120

CHERRY-GARRARD, APSLEY. The Worst Journey in the World. London: C&W, 1939. Rpt of 1-vol ed. NF in dj. *Explorer.* $72/£45

CHERRY-GARRARD, APSLEY. The Worst Journey in the World. Harmondsworth: Penguin Books, 1948. Penguin Books Double Volume #100. 4 maps. Ptd card binding. VG. *Explorer.* $13/£8

CHERRY-GARRARD, APSLEY. The Worst Journey in the World. London: C&W, 1952. 4 maps (2 fldg). Fine (spine sl faded). *Explorer.* $48/£30

CHERRY-GARRARD, APSLEY. The Worst Journey in the World. London: Constable, n.d. (1922). 1st ed. 2 vols. 8vo. 5 maps (4 fldg), 58 plts (6 color, 10 fldg). Holland-backed blue bds (spines sl rubbed, cvrs sl soiled, blue paper torn away from Vol 1 cvr, repaired), paper spine labels, spare labels tipped in. Internally VG. *Morrell.* $1,056/£660

CHESBRO, GEORGE C. Shadow of a Broken Man. NY: S&S, (1977). 1st ed. NF in Fine dj. *Other Worlds.* $35/£22

CHESELDEN, WILLIAM. The Anatomy of the Human Body. Boston: Ptd by Manning & Loring, 1795. 1st Amer ed. vi,350pp; 40 copperplt engrs. Recent 1/4 calf, marbled bds. (Text browned, lt spotted; rebound), o/w Good. *Brown.* $350/£219

CHESLEY, HERVEY E. Adventuring with the Old-Timers. B. Byron Price (ed). Midland, TX: Nita Stewart Haley Memorial Lib, (1979). 1st ed. VG in dj. *Lien.* $30/£19

CHESNEY, LIEUT.-COLONEL. The Expedition for the Survey of the Rivers Euphrates and Tigris,...in the Years 1835, 1836, and 1837. London: Longman, Brown, Green, et al, 1850. 1st ed. W/o slipcase containing 14 maps issued separately. 2 vols. Royal 8vo. xxvii,(ii),799pp; xvi,78pp. 49 litho plts incl dbl-pg frontis. Blind-emb cl. (Ex-lib, bkpls, plt margins ink stamped w/exception of 2 plts not affecting image; joint heads frayed vol 2, spine #s.) *Edwards.* $720/£450

CHESNUT, MARY BOYKIN. A Diary from Dixie. Isabella D. Martin and Myrta Lockett Avary (eds). London: Heinemann, 1905. 1st Eng ed. Frontisport. Grn cl, gilt. NF. *Chapel Hill.* $175/£109

CHESSON, W. H. (ed). Eliza Brightwen. London: Unwin, n.d. (ca 1910). (Spine faded, rubbed), else Good + . *Mikesh.* $20/£13

CHESTER, ALFRED. The Exquisite Corpse. NY: S&S, (1967). 1st ed. VF in VF dj. *Between The Covers.* $150/£94

CHESTERFIELD, EARL OF. The Elements of a Polite Education. G. Gregory (ed). Dublin, 1802. Contemp sheep, new calf backstrip. (Corners sl bumped) o/w VG. *Petersfield.* $56/£35

CHESTERFIELD, EARL OF. Miscellaneous Works. London: Edward & Charles Dilly, 1779. 2nd ed. 4 vols. 4 engr frontispieces, 375pp; 2ff., 411pp; 2ff., 401pp; 1f. (lacks half-title), 106pp. Contemp calf (hinges sl worn, spines chipped; bkpls). *Marlborough.* $240/£150

CHESTERTON, G. K. Charles Dickens. Methuen, 1906. 1st ed. 2 photogravure ports (sl foxed, ads spotted; spine sl faded). *Hollett.* $56/£35

CHESTERTON, G. K. Christendom in Dublin. Sheed & Ward, 1932. 1st Eng ed. Buckram. VG (spine faded) in dj (sl rubbed, dusty, sl browned). *Ulysses.* $136/£85

CHESTERTON, G. K. The Club of Queer Trades. Harpers, 1905. 1st UK ed. VG (spine sl faded, rubbed). *Williams.* $152/£95

CHESTERTON, G. K. The Coloured Lands. NY: Sheed & Ward, 1938. 1st Amer ed. NF in NF dj. *Agvent.* $90/£56

CHESTERTON, G. K. The Coloured Lands. London: Sheed & Ward, 1938. 1st ed. Royal 8vo. (vii),9-238; 18 full-pg color plts. Bright yellow cl-backed dec bds. Fine in pict wrapper (sl mkd). *Sotheran.* $109/£68

CHESTERTON, G. K. The Crimes of England. NY, 1916. 1st Amer ed. NF in dj (spine chips). *Polyanthos.* $30/£19

CHESTERTON, G. K. Five Types: A Book of Essays. London: Arthur L. Humphreys, 1910. 1st ed. (Spine sl faded), o/w Fine in wrappers, slipcase. *Jaffe.* $65/£41

CHESTERTON, G. K. The Flying Inn. NY: John Lane, 1914. VG (sm stains reps, top edge dusty; spine ends, corners sl bumped, cvr edges sl dampstained) in dj (nicked, chipped, rubbed, sl mkd, dusty, browned, ends lack sm pieces). *Ulysses.* $264/£165

CHESTERTON, G. K. Four Faultless Felons. London: Cassell, 1930. 1st Eng ed. NF (spine ends, corners sl bumped) in dj (nicked, chipped, sl rubbed, dusty, browned, 3-inch tear bottom edge between spine and rear panel, sm pieces missing). *Ulysses.* $600/£375

CHESTERTON, G. K. Heretics. London: John Lane, Bodley Head, 1908. VG. *Hollett.* $40/£25

CHESTERTON, G. K. The Incredulity of Father Brown. London: Cassell, 1926. 1st Eng ed. VG (feps partly browned; spine ends, corners sl bumped) in dj (nicked, sl creased, rubbed, dusty, sl browned, sl tear in rear fold). *Ulysses.* $2,680/£1,675

CHESTERTON, G. K. The Innocence of Father Brown. J. Lane, 1911. 1st Amer ed. (Sl worn), else VG-. *Fine Books.* $40/£25

CHESTERTON, G. K. The Judgement of Doctor Johnson. London: Sheed & Ward, 1927. 1st Eng ed. VG (spine foot sl bumped) in dj (nicked, sl rubbed, dusty). *Ulysses.* $200/£125

CHESTERTON, G. K. Magic. Secker, (1920). New ed. Ltd to 150 signed. Good (all ll at central joint, bottom cvr edges waterstained). *Clearwater.* $120/£75

CHESTERTON, G. K. The Man Who Knew Too Much. NY: Harper, 1922. 1st US ed. (Bkpl, date; spine head rubbed), o/w NF. *Beasley.* $75/£47

CHESTERTON, G. K. The Man Who Was Thursday. London, (1908). 1st ed, 1st issue. (Fr cvr sl bowed.) *Swann*.* $172/£108

CHESTERTON, G. K. The Outline of Sanity. D-M, 1927. 1st Amer ed. (Spots to rear panel), else VG + . *Fine Books.* $15/£9

CHESTERTON, G. K. The Outline of Sanity. Leipzig: Bernhard Tauchnitz, 1927. VG in wrappers (sl mkd, spine dknd, sl rubbed). *Ulysses.* $40/£25

CHESTERTON, G. K. The Poet and the Lunatics. London: Cassell, 1929. 1st Eng ed. VG (spine ends, corner bumped) in dj (nicked, rubbed, dusty, sl creased, spine sl dknd, sm tear top edge fr panel). *Ulysses.* $1,760/£1,100

CHESTERTON, G. K. The Queen of Seven Swords. Sheed & Ward, 1926. 1st Eng ed. VG (1-inch tear to fore-edge p19; cvrs sl mkd, edges sl faded) in dj (nicked, chipped, sl mkd, browned). *Ulysses.* $120/£75

CHESTERTON, G. K. The Return of Don Quixote. Chatto, 1927. 1st UK ed. VG (ink name). *Williams.* $56/£35

CHESTERTON, G. K. The Return of Don Quixote. Chatto, 1927. 1st UK ed. NF in VG dj (edges sl worn, spine sl faded, short closed tear to fr panel). *Williams.* $192/£120

CHESTERTON, G. K. Robert Louis Stevenson. Hodder & Stoughton, n.d. (1927). 1st Eng ed. VG (some pg edges sl nicked; spine tail, bottom corners bumped) in dj (sl creased, rubbed, dusty, browned). *Ulysses*. $136/£85

CHESTERTON, G. K. The Scandal of Father Brown. London: Cassell, 1935. 1st Eng ed. VG (feps sl offset; spine foot, top corners sl bumped) in dj (torn, creased, chipped, sl rubbed, dusty, sl dknd, lacks sm piece top edge fr panel). *Ulysses*. $1,200/£750

CHESTERTON, G. K. The Secret of Father Brown. London: Cassell, 1927. 1st Eng ed. VG (top edge sl mkd; spine ends, corners sl bumped) in dj (nicked, sl rubbed, cresed, chipped, dusty, sl dknd, spine head sl frayed). *Ulysses*. $2,712/£1,695

CHESTERTON, G. K. The Superstitions of the Sceptic. Cambridge: W. Heffer & Sons, 1925. 1st Eng ed. Yapp edges (sl nicked, creased). VG in wrappers (sl mkd, dusty). *Ulysses*. $88/£55

CHESTERTON, G. K. The Surprise. NY, 1953. 1st Amer ed. Fine. *Polyanthos*. $25/£16

CHESTERTON, G. K. Tales of the Long Bow. London: Cassell, (1925). 1st ed. (Spine, extrems sl sunned), else VG. *Pacific**. $35/£22

CHESTERTON, G. K. Tales of the Long Bow. London: Cassell, (1925). 1st ed. (Fore-edge spotted, tape shadows on eps), o/w Fine in dj (few sm tears). *Captain's Bookshelf*. $225/£141

CHESTERTON, G. K. Tales of the Long Bow. London: Cassell, 1925. 1st Eng ed. VG (spine ends sl bumped) in dj (nicked, sl torn, rubbed, creased, dusty, sl dknd). *Ulysses*. $1,752/£1,095

CHESTERTON, G. K. Tremendous Trifles. Methuen, 1909. 1st Eng ed. Teg. Dec cl, gilt. VG (bottom edge fr cvr, fore-edge fep nicked; spine faded, ends sl bumped). *Ulysses*. $136/£85

CHESTERTON, G. K. William Blake. London: Duckworth, n.d. 1st ed. VG. *Pacific**. $40/£25

CHESTNUTT, CHARLES W. The Marrow of Tradition. Boston: Houghton Mifflin, 1901. 1st ed. Lt orange cl (soiled). Nice (erased inscrip). *Agvent*. $450/£281

CHESTNUTT, CHARLES W. The Marrow of Tradition. Boston: Houghton, Mifflin, 1901. 1st ed. 8vo. Orange cl. VG (extrems lt rubbed, cl sl soiled). *Heritage*. $600/£375

CHETTLE, E. M. Tiny Toddlers. London: Raphael Tuck & Sons, (ca 1890). 4to. Helen Jackson (illus). Cl-backed color illus bds (rubbed, edges worn). *Reisler*. $225/£141

CHEVALIER, MAURICE. My Paris. NY: Macmillan, 1972. 1st ed. Robert Doisneau (photos). (Dot on lower edge), else Fine in NF dj. *Cahan*. $60/£38

CHEVALIER, MICHAEL. Society, Manners and Politics in the U.S.... Boston, 1839. 1st US ed. Orig cl (sl worn, spotted, spine reglued). *Kane**. $45/£28

CHEVALIER, MICHAEL. Society, Manners and Politics in the United States. Boston: Weeks, Jordan, 1839. 1st US ed, 1st ed in English. iv,467pp + ad pg. Orig blind grn cl, gilt. (Sl foxed, hinges cracked; spine sunned, sm tears spine ends, scattered cracks at joints.) Howes C359. *Baltimore**. $80/£50

CHEVIGNY, HECTOR. Russian America. NY: Viking, 1965. Good in dj. *Dumont*. $25/£16

CHEVRILLON, ANDRE. England and the War (1914-1915). GC: Doubleday, Page 1917. 1st US ed. Gilt brn cl. (1917 ink name), o/w NF in dj (few sl tears). *Reese*. $50/£31

CHEYNEY, PETER. Dames Don't Care! NY: Coward McCann, n.d. 1st US ed, 2nd imp. (Lib stamp; cvr spotted), else VG in dj (chipped). *My Bookhouse*. $37/£23

CHEYNEY, PETER. Dark Bahama. London: Collins, 1950. 1st Eng ed. NF (name stamp; spine ends, 2 corners sl bumped) in dj (sl rubbed, creased). *Ulysses*. $40/£25

CHEYNEY, PETER. Dressed to Kill. London: Todd & George Harrap, (1952). Fine in color dj. *Glenn*. $25/£16

CHEYNEY, PETER. Ladies Don't Wait. London: Collins, 1951. 1st Eng ed. NF (name stamp; spine ends sl bumped) in dj (sl frayed). *Ulysses*. $40/£25

CHEYNEY, PETER. Lady, Behave! London: Collins, 1950. 1st Eng ed. NF (name stamp; spine ends sl bumped) in dj (sl rubbed, nicked). *Ulysses*. $40/£25

CHIARENZA, CARL. Aaron Siskind: Pleasures and Terrors. Boston, 1982. 1st ed. Signed by Siskind. Dj (rear panel lt soiled), acetate wrapper. *Swann**. $172/£108

Chicken World. (By E. Boyd Smith.) NY: Putnam, 1910. 1st ed. Obl 4to. Cl-backed color pict bds (worn, section of lifted paper fr cvr). *Reisler*. $175/£109

CHICKERING, ALLEN L. Wildflowers Around Soda Springs. (N.p.: Allen L. Chickering), 1953. 1st ed. 4 tipped-in orig photos (3 color). Grn cl. Fine. *Harrington*. $25/£16

CHICKERING, CAROL. Flowers of Guatemala. Norman: Univ of OK, 1973. 1st ed. 50 color plts. NF in VG dj. *Archer*. $45/£28

Child's Book of Old Verses. NY: Duffield, 1910. 1st ed. 4to. 10 full-pg color plts by Jessie Wilcox Smith. Teg. Dk blue cl, gilt, color paste label. (Sl shelfworn.) *Reisler*. $250/£156

Child's Pictorial Mentor for the Year Containing Amusing Instruction for Each Month to Which Is Appended A Sketch of the Solar System. Worcester: S.A. Howland, 1845. 2nd ed. 12mo. 58pp. Cl-backed illus wrappers (part of spine cl missing, overall wear, lt spotting). *Reisler*. $900/£563

CHILD, ANDREW. Overland Route to California; Description of the Route, Via Council Bluffs, Iowa.... L.A.: N.A. Kovach, 1946. One of 775. Rpt. Fldg map. VG in dj. Howes C378. *Brown*. $45/£28

CHILD, HEATHER and JOHN BROMLEY. The Armorial Bearings of the Guilds of London. London: Warne, 1960. 1st ed. 40 plts. VG in dj. *Michael Taylor*. $56/£35

CHILD, JULIA. Julia Child and More Company. Knopf, 1979. 1st ed. VG in VG dj. *Book Broker*. $25/£16

CHILD, L. MARIA. Isaac T. Hopper: A True Life. Boston: John P. Jewett, 1853. 1st ed. Frontisport, 493pp (ink name, stamp, lt foxed throughout). Aeg. Orig full leather (scuffed, rubbed, worn; fr joint, hinge starting), gilt. VG. *Hermitage*. $85/£53

CHILD. The Family Nurse; or Companion of the Frugal Housewife. Boston: Charles J. Hendee, 1837. 1st ed. Signed Bradley binding. 156pp. Orig cl (stained, worn). BAL 3136. *M & S.* $225/£141

CHILDE, EDWARD LEE. The Life and Campaigns of General Lee. C&W, 1875. 336pp; port, map. (Foxed, border of port waterstained; hinges broken.) Internally Sound. *Book Broker*. $85/£53

CHILDE, H. L. Manufacture and Uses of Concrete Products and Cast Stone. Concrete Publications Ltd, 1927. Frontis. Cl-backed pict bds. (Eps spotted, corner of 1 leaf torn neatly off.) *Hollett*. $48/£30

CHILDERS, ERSKINE. The Riddle of the Sands. London: Smith, Elder, 1903. 1st ed. 8vo. 2 maps (frontis map misbound but present), 2 charts. Uncut. Blue cl (joints sl rubbed, rear joint head split; sl shaken, inscrip). *Maggs*. $840/£525

CHILDERS, ERSKINE. The Times History of the War in South Africa. Volume V. 1899-1902. Sampson Low, Marston, 1907. 1st ed. 9 Rembrandt photogravure plts, 21 maps, plans, fldg map, 2 maps in rear pocket. Teg, unopened. VG (spotted; sl rubbed, mkd, spine ends, corners bumped, edges lt faded). *Ulysses*. $280/£175

Children's Hour Story Books: Mother Goose, Sleeping Beauty, Noah's Ark, the Three Bears. NY: Samuel Gabriel & Sons, (c. 1920). 4 vols. 8.25x7.25. A. E. Kennedy & R. A. Burley (illus). Fine in pict linen wrappers, VG slip-box. *Pacific**. $52/£33

Children's Mother Goose. Chicago: Reilly & Lee, (1921). 1st ed thus. 4to. 12 full-pg color plts by William Donahey. Brn cl (few sm edge chips), color paste label. Nice. *Reisler*. $350/£219

Children's Primer. John B. Doris and E. D. Colvin's Illustrated Gift-Book. NY: S. Booth & Co, 1887. Thin 8vo. 16pp + (2) + 1pg ad on lower wrapper. Buff pict stiff paper wrappers. 'The Book's Address to Good Boys and Girls' is ptd in full pg on verso of fr wrapper. VG (ink name fr wrapper, reinforced at inner folds, lt spotting at cvrs). *Hobbyhorse.* $155/£97

Children's Sampler. (NY), 1950. 8vo. (90)ff. VF in yellow cl; red slipcase. *Bromer.* $350/£219

Children's Songs with Pictures and Music. Marcus Ward, n.d. (1875). 1st ed. Obl 8vo. Kate Greenaway et al (illus). (32)pp. Gold-patterned pale turquoise eps. Mustard/turquoise cl w/panel of birds in foliage and little harp in gilt on fr. VG. *Bookmark.* $400/£250

CHILDRESS, MARK. V for Victor. NY, 1989. 1st Amer ed. Fine in Fine dj. *Polyanthos.* $25/£16

CHILDRESS, MARK. A World Made of Fire. NY: Knopf, 1984. 1st ed. VF in dj. *Pharos.* $35/£22

CHINARD, GILBERT (ed). The Letters of Lafayette and Jefferson. Balt/Paris: Johns Hopkins/Les Belles Lettres, 1929. 1st ed. One of 800. Frontisport. 3/4 cl, gilt bds. (Museum bkpl; sl shelfworn), else VG. *Pacific*.* $75/£47

CHIPPENDALE, THOMAS. The Gentleman and Cabinet-Maker's Director. London: Hodder Bros, 1894. Facs of 1762 ed. Contemp 1/2 mottled calf (fr joints sl weak, lt scuffed). *Christie's*.* $258/£161

CHISHOLM, JOE. Brewery Gulch. San Antonio: Naylor, 1949. 1st ed. VG + in dj (chipped). *Labordo.* $75/£47

CHISHOLM, LOUEY (ed). Nursery Rhymes. London: T.C. & E.C. Jack, (1905). 1st ed thus. 16mo. 118pp; 24 color plts. Pink bds, color paste. Good in dj, color paste label. *Reisler.* $135/£84

CHISHOLM, LOUEY. The Enchanted Land. London: T.C. & E.C. Jack, 1906. 1st ed. 8vo. (xv),211pp; 30 color plts by Katherine Cameron. Gold eps. Teg, rest uncut. Brn pict cl, gilt, w/onlaid pict label to upper cvr. *Sotheran.* $205/£128

CHISHOLM, LOUEY. The Enchanted Land: Tales Told Again. London: T.C. & E.C. Jack, 1906. 1st ed. 4to. 30 full-pg color plts by Katherine Cameron. Gold eps; teg. Brn cl, gilt, color paste label. Good. *Reisler.* $200/£125

CHISHOLM, LOUEY. In Fairyland. London: T.C. & E.C. Jack, (1904). 1st ed, 3rd imp. 8vo. xv,211pp; 30 color plts by Katherine Cameron. Teg, rest uncut. White cl, gilt, w/onlaid pict label to upper cvr. Clean. *Sotheran.* $157/£98

CHISLETT, RALPH. Northward Ho! Country Life, 1933. 1st ed. (Edges lt spotted.) *Hollett.* $56/£35

CHISLETT, RALPH. Northward Ho! London, 1933. 1st ed. 44 photo plts. Brn cl. Good +. *Larry Price.* $75/£47

CHITTENDEN, HIRAM MARTIN. The American Fur Trade of the Far West. NY, 1902. 1st ed. 3 vols. Lg fldg map inside vol 3 back cvr (folds starting to split). Uncut, partly opened. (Name inside cvr vols 1&2; cvrs sl spotted, backstrips sl worn at ends, upper corners vol 1 bumped.) Howes C390. *Woolson.* $800/£500

CHITTENDEN, HIRAM MARTIN. The American Fur Trade of the Far West. NY: Press of the Pioneers, 1935. 2nd ed. 2 vols. VG +. Howes C390. *Labordo.* $225/£141

CHITTENDEN, LUCIUS E. The Capture of Ticonderoga. Rutland: Tuttle, 1872. 1st ed. 127pp. (Sig, foxed; worn, faded.) *Cullen.* $60/£38

CHITTENDEN, NEWTON H. Health Seekers', Tourists' and Sportsmen's Guide to the Sea-Side, Lake-Side, Foothill, Mountain and Mineral Spring Health and Pleasure Resorts of the Pacific Coast. SF: C.A. Murdock, 1884. 2nd ed. (4)ads,(3)-311pp. (Bkpl; rear cvr stained, extrems worn), else VG. *Pacific*.* $173/£108

CHITTENDEN, RUSSELL H. History of the Sheffield Scientific School of Yale University, 1846-1922. Yale Univ, 1928. 1st ed. 2 vols. Good (lib stamps; traces of #s on spine). *Glaser.* $75/£47

CHITTENDEN, WILLIAM. Ranch Verses. NY: Putnam, 1893. 1st ed. Brn cl. Fine. *Labordo.* $350/£219

CHIVERS, T. H. Nacoochee; or, The Beautiful Star, with Other Poems. NY: W.E. Dean, 1837. 1st ed. 12mo. 10,(2),143pp (stamp, foxed). Orig reddish-brn cl. VF. BAL 3227. *M & S.* $425/£266

CHO-YO. Japanese Chess (Sho-Ngi). NY: Eurasiamerica, (1905). One of 999, this copy unnumbered, unsigned. Photo frontis. *Argosy.* $200/£125

CHOLMONDELEY-PENNELL, H. The Modern Practical Angler. London: Frederick Warne, 1870. 1st ed. Chromolitho frontis, guard. (Spine, extrems sunned), else VG. *Pacific*.* $58/£36

CHRISMAN, HARRY E. The Ladder of Rivers. Denver: Sage Books, (1962). 1st ed. Presentation copy. VG in dj (sl worn). *Lien.* $50/£31

CHRISMAN, HARRY E. The Ladder of Rivers. Denver, 1962. 1st ed. VG-. *Baade.* $30/£19

CHRISTENSEN, LARS. Such Is the Antarctic. Hodder & Stoughton, 1935. 1st Eng ed. 4 fldg maps. Blue cl (rebound). VG +. *Walcot.* $77/£48

CHRISTENSEN, LARS. Such Is the Antarctic. London: Hodder & Stoughton, 1935. VG (sm mk rear bd). *Explorer.* $120/£75

CHRISTIE, AGATHA. The Adventure of the Christmas Pudding and a Selection of Entrees. London, 1960. 1st ed. Fine in dj. *Petersfield.* $40/£25

CHRISTIE, AGATHA. Afternoon at the Seaside. London: Samuel French, 1963. 1st ed. NF in blue wrappers. *Janus.* $100/£63

CHRISTIE, AGATHA. The Agatha Christie Hour. London, 1982. 1st ed. Fine in dj. *Petersfield.* $19/£12

CHRISTIE, AGATHA. Akhnaton. Collins, 1973. 1st ed. VG (spine ends, 2 corners bumped) in dj (sl torn, edges rubbed). *Ulysses.* $56/£35

CHRISTIE, AGATHA. Appointment with Death. Collins, 1938. 1st UK ed. VG (sl faded) in VG + dj (professional restoration). *Williams.* $3,200/£2,000

CHRISTIE, AGATHA. By the Pricking of My Thumbs. London, 1968. 1st ed. Fine in dj. *Petersfield.* $29/£18

CHRISTIE, AGATHA. Cards on the Table. Collins, (1936). 1st ed. Orange cl (spine faded, fr cvr sm area rubbed; feps browned, name, lt foxed). *Blackwell's.* $160/£100

CHRISTIE, AGATHA. A Caribbean Mystery. London, 1964. 1st ed. Fine in dj. *Petersfield.* $29/£18

CHRISTIE, AGATHA. Cat Among the Pigeons. London, 1959. 1st ed. Fine in dj. *Petersfield.* $40/£25

CHRISTIE, AGATHA. The Clocks. London, 1963. 1st ed. Fine in dj. *Petersfield.* $29/£18

CHRISTIE, AGATHA. Crooked House. London, 1949. 1st ed. (Back faded; lacks dj.) *Petersfield.* $29/£18

CHRISTIE, AGATHA. Death Comes as the End. Collins, 1945. 1st UK ed. Fine in VG dj (edges sl worn, spine sl faded). *Williams.* $176/£110

CHRISTIE, AGATHA. Death on the Nile. Collins, 1937. 1st ed. Orange cl. Good (prelims, last few ll lt foxed; spine, rear cvr faded). *Blackwell's.* $200/£125

CHRISTIE, AGATHA. Death on the Nile. Collins, 1937. 1st UK ed. VG (spine sl faded) in dj (edges sl worn). *Williams.* $3,200/£2,000

CHRISTIE, AGATHA. Dumb Witness. Collins, 1937. 1st UK ed. VG (lt stained, dusty). *Williams.* $112/£70

CHRISTIE, AGATHA. Easy to Kill. NY: Dodd Mead, 1939. 1st Amer ed. (Name stamp), o/w Fine in VG dj (spine ends chipped, frayed; folds, corners worn). *Mordida.* $250/£156

CHRISTIE, AGATHA. Elephants Can Remember. London, 1972. 1st ed. Fine in dj (price-clipped). *Petersfield.* $29/£18

CHRISTIE, AGATHA. Endless Night. London, 1967. 1st ed. Fine in dj. *Petersfield*. $29/£18

CHRISTIE, AGATHA. Endless Night. London: Crime Club, 1967. 1st ed. Fine in dj (lt worn). *Glenn*. $45/£28

CHRISTIE, AGATHA. Five Little Pigs. Collins, 1942. 1st ed. Orange cl. VG (edges sl faded) in dj (finger-soiled). *Blackwell's*. $456/£285

CHRISTIE, AGATHA. Hallowe'en Party. London, 1969. 1st ed. Fine in dj. *Petersfield*. $29/£18

CHRISTIE, AGATHA. Hickory Dickory Dock. London, 1955. 1st ed. Fine in dj. *Petersfield*. $48/£30

CHRISTIE, AGATHA. The Hound of Death and Other Stories. Odhams, 1933. 1st ed. Maroon cl, gilt. Good (prelims, last few ll lt foxed; gilt tarnished, cvrs spotted) in dj (sl frayed). *Blackwell's*. $320/£200

CHRISTIE, AGATHA. The Hound of Death. Odhams, 1933. 1st ed. VG (top edge dusty, spine sl faded) in dj (nicked, sl torn, rubbed, creased, dusty, lower panel sl soiled). *Ulysses*. $520/£325

CHRISTIE, AGATHA. The Labours of Hercules. Collins, 1947. 1st UK ed. Fine (bkpl) in VG + dj (edges sl worn). *Williams*. $200/£125

CHRISTIE, AGATHA. The Mirror Crack'd. NY, 1963. 1st Amer ed. Fine in Fine dj. *Polyanthos*. $25/£16

CHRISTIE, AGATHA. The Mirror Crack's From Side to Side. London, 1962. 1st ed. Fine in dj. *Petersfield*. $40/£25

CHRISTIE, AGATHA. The Moving Finger. Collins, 1943. 1st Eng ed. Red cl. VG (corner rubbed) in dj (sl chipped). *Blackwell's*. $440/£275

CHRISTIE, AGATHA. The Murder at the Vicarage. Collins, (1930). 1st ed. Orange cl (sl finger-soiled; feps lt foxed). *Blackwell's*. $240/£150

CHRISTIE, AGATHA. Murder in Mesopotamia. Collins, 1936. 1st UK ed. VG (bds sl stained, spine faded). *Williams*. $112/£70

CHRISTIE, AGATHA. The Murder of Roger Ackroyd. Collins, 1926. 1st UK ed. Good + (fr hinge damaged, repaired; spine head creased). *Williams*. $264/£165

CHRISTIE, AGATHA. The Murder on the Links. Bodley Head, 1923. 1st UK ed. VG- (rear cvr sl stained, bds sl rubbed). *Williams*. $1,520/£950

CHRISTIE, AGATHA. The Mysterious Mr. Quin. Collins, (1930). 1st ed. Black cl (spine rubbed; prelims, last few ll lt foxed). *Blackwell's*. $304/£190

CHRISTIE, AGATHA. N or M? NY: Dodd, Mead, 1941. 1st Amer ed. (Adhesion residue fr pastedown), else VG in dj (spine ends, extrems chipped, sl sunned, flaps clipped). *Pacific**. $92/£58

CHRISTIE, AGATHA. Nemesis. London, 1971. 1st ed. Fine in dj. *Petersfield*. $29/£18

CHRISTIE, AGATHA. One, Two, Buckle My Shoe. Collins, 1940. 1st ed. Crown 8vo. 252 + (3)ads pp. Orange cl (spine ends, fr cvr edge lt faded). VG in dj (sl frayed, extrems chipped). *Blackwell's*. $1,040/£650

CHRISTIE, AGATHA. Passenger to Frankfurt. London, 1970. 1st ed. Fine in dj. *Petersfield*. $29/£18

CHRISTIE, AGATHA. The Patient. London: Samuel French, 1963. 1st ed. NF in blue wrappers. *Janus*. $100/£63

CHRISTIE, AGATHA. A Pocket Full of Rye. London, 1953. 1st ed. (Tp sl foxed; faded; lacks dj.) *Petersfield*. $22/£14

CHRISTIE, AGATHA. Poems. London: Collins, 1973. 1st Eng ed. Fine in ptd glassine dj. *Ulysses*. $88/£55

CHRISTIE, AGATHA. Poirot Investigates. Bodley Head, 1924. 1st UK ed. VG (ink inscrip, name rubbed out in ink on fep; spine sl faded). *Williams*. $1,200/£750

CHRISTIE, AGATHA. Poirot Loses a Client. NY: Dodd, Mead, 1937. 1st Amer ed. Orange cl (Spine sunned w/sl spot), else VG. *Pacific**. $46/£29

CHRISTIE, AGATHA. Poirot's Early Cases. London, 1974. 1st ed. Fine in dj. *Petersfield*. $29/£18

CHRISTIE, AGATHA. Postern of Fate. London, 1973. 1st ed. Fine in dj. *Petersfield*. $29/£18

CHRISTIE, AGATHA. The Rats. London: Samuel French, 1963. 1st ptg. NF in blue wrappers. *Janus*. $100/£63

CHRISTIE, AGATHA. The Road of Dreams. Bles, (1924). 1st ed. Untrimmed. 1/4 pale grn cl, ptd label, mid grn bds (cvrs faded, corners rubbed; feps browned). *Blackwell's*. $320/£200

CHRISTIE, AGATHA. The Secret Adversary. Bodley Head, 1922. 1st UK ed. VG (lacks fep). *Williams*. $1,400/£875

CHRISTIE, AGATHA. Sleeping Murder, Miss Marple's Last Case. London, 1976. 1st ed. Fine in dj. *Petersfield*. $29/£18

CHRISTIE, AGATHA. Sleeping Murder. NY, 1976. 1st Amer ed. Fine in Fine dj. *Polyanthos*. $25/£16

CHRISTIE, AGATHA. So Many Steps to Death. NY: Dodd, 1955. 1st US ed. Fine in dj (chipped). *Beasley*. $30/£19

CHRISTIE, AGATHA. Sparkling Cyanide. Collins, 1945. 1st UK ed. VG + in dj (few sm closed tears, edges sl worn). *Williams*. $144/£90

CHRISTIE, AGATHA. Spider's Web. London: Samuel French, 1956. 1st ed. NF (lt crease fr cvr, tp) in blue wrappers. *Janus*. $100/£63

CHRISTIE, AGATHA. Taken at the Flood. Collins, 1948. 1st Eng ed. Orange cl (spine foot lt faded). Good in dj (sl frayed, rear panel sl dust-soiled). *Blackwell's*. $160/£100

CHRISTIE, AGATHA. Ten Little Niggers. Collins, 1939. 1st UK ed. VG (ink stamp; spots to spine). *Williams*. $160/£100

CHRISTIE, AGATHA. Third Girl. London, 1966. 1st ed. Fine in dj. *Petersfield*. $29/£18

CHRISTIE, AGATHA. Thirteen at Dinner. NY: Dodd Mead, 1933. 1st Amer ed. (Pg edges spotted), o/w VG in dj (spine dknd, ends, corners chipped, sm tears). *Mordida*. $350/£219

CHRISTIE, AGATHA. Three Act Tragedy. Collins, (1935). 1st Eng ed. Orange cl (Backstrip faded, rear cvr inkstained; prelims, final few ll lt foxed). *Blackwell's*. $160/£100

CHRISTIE, AGATHA. Towards Zero. Collins, 1944. 1st UK ed. VG + in dj. *Williams*. $440/£275

CHRISTIE, AGATHA. Why Didn't They Ask Evans? Collins, (1934). 1st ed. Orange cl (spine faded, sm stain fr cvr; sm area of offsetting to Contents pg). *Blackwell's*. $240/£150

CHRISTIE, E. W. HUNTER. The Antarctic Problem. An Historical and Political Study. London, 1951. 1st ed. 24 plts, 5 maps (2 on 1 fld-out). Dj (ragged). *Edwards*. $48/£30

CHRISTIE, ELLA R. Through Khiva to Golden Samarkand. London, 1925. 1st ed. Map. (Tp detached at head; cl faded.) *Edwards*. $136/£85

CHRISTIE, MRS. ARCHIBALD. Embroidery and Tapestry Weaving. Pitman, 1933. 4th ed. 15 collotype plts. (Sl worn, sl faded), o/w VG. *Whittle*. $24/£15

CHRISTIE, MRS. ARCHIBALD. Samplers and Stitches. London: Batsford, 1920. 1st ed. Color frontis, 33 plts. Fore-edge uncut. (Lower hinge sl tender, 2 plts loose, bkpl; bds worn, spine ends sl frayed.) *Edwards*. $72/£45

Christmas Alphabet. NY: McLoughlin Bros, 1900. 4to. 6 full-pg color plts. Color pict wrappers (spine worn, lt marginal tears). *Reisler*. $275/£172

CHRISTO. Christo: The Accordion-Fold Book for the Umbrellas, Joint Project for Japan and U.S.A. SF, (1991). 1st ed. One of 400 numbered, signed, dated. Pict bds (Plt creased), else VG in clamshell box (1 spot, soiled). *King*. $350/£219

CHRISTY, HOWARD CHANDLER. The American Girl. NY: Moffat, Yard, 1906. 1st ed. 8vo. 157pp; 16 color plts. Grn cl w/color plt to fr cvr. (Cl lt rubbed), o/w VG. *House.* $225/£141

CHRISTY, THOMAS. Road Across the Plains. Robert H. Becker (ed). Denver, CO: Old West Pub, 1969. VG in dj. *Lien.* $50/£31

Chronicles of the City of Gotham, from the Papers of a Retired Common Councilman. (By J.K. Paulding.) NY: G. & C. & H. Carvill, 1830. 1st ed. 270pp (lt foxed). Uncut. Later 2-toned bds, paper label. BAL 15712. *M & S.* $200/£125

CHUQUET, ARTHUR. Human Voices from the Russian Campaign of 1812. H. M. Capes (trans). London: Melrose, n.d. (ca 1910). (Ex-lib, rep label; sl soiled.) *Stewart.* $48/£30

CHURCH, A. H. Colour Cassell's Technical Manuals. Cassell, Petter, & Galpin, (1872). 1st ed. 112pp,2 ad ll; 6 color plts. (Spine top sl worn.) *Bickersteth.* $77/£48

CHURCH, ALFRED J. The Story of the Persian War (from Herodotus). Seeley, 1888. 'Fifth thousand.' Color-ptd frontis, vi,(vi),292pp; 15 color full-pg illus. Marbled eps; all edges marbled. Contemp full calf prize binding, raised bands, gilt. VG (bkpl). *Sotheran.* $136/£85

CHURCH, PERCY. Chinese Turkestan with Caravan and Rifle. London, 1901. (White spine mks, spine tips frayed, fr cvr discolored.) Internally sound (ex-lib, stamp). *Oinonen*.* $130/£81

CHURCH, RICHARD. The Flood of Life. Fifield, 1917. 1st Eng ed, 1st bk. Signed, dated 1917. (Sl foxed.) Card wrappers (spine foot sl rubbed). *Clearwater.* $160/£100

CHURCHILL, CHARLES. The Duelist: A Poem in Three Books. London: G. Kearsly, W. Flexney et al, 1764. 1st ed. (4),49,(1)pp. Half-title, final blank present. Marbled bds. (Later eps, 1/2-title sl spotted; bkpl fr cvr, rubbed), else VG. *Pacific*.* $115/£72

CHURCHILL, CHARLES. Poems. John Churchill, 1765. 2nd ed. Vol 2 signed by John Churchill. 2 vols. Sprinkled edges. Contemp full leather, raised bands, leather spine labels. Good (labels chipped, 1 missing, hinges cracked but cords sound, corners rubbed). *Tiger.* $136/£85

CHURCHILL, CHARLES. Poems. London: John Churchill & W. Flexney, 1766. 3rd ed. 2 vols. Period calf, gilt, morocco spine labels. (Extrems, spines sl dknd), else VG. *Pacific*.* $150/£94

CHURCHILL, FLEETWOOD. On the Theory and Practice of Midwifery. Phila, 1848. 3rd ed. 525pp. Full calf, spine label. (Foxed; scuffed, nibbled), o/w Good. *Doctor's Library.* $40/£25

CHURCHILL, FLEETWOOD. Researches on Operative Midwifery. Dublin: Martin Keene & Son, 1841. 1st ed. 19 fldg litho plts. (Spine ends rubbed, cvrs sl discolored), else VG. *Pacific*.* $138/£86

CHURCHILL, RANDOLPH S. Winston Churchill Companion 1874-1914. London, 1967-1969. 1st eds. 5 vols. VG in djs. *Gretton.* $64/£40

CHURCHILL, ROBERT. Churchill's Shotgun Book. NY: Knopf, 1955. 1st Amer ed. VG (name; sl soiled) in Good+ dj (ragged, edges torn). *Backman.* $45/£28

CHURCHILL, WINSTON S. Addresses Delivered in the Year Nineteen Hundred and Forty to the People of Great Britain, of France, and to the Members of the English House of Commons.... SF: Ransohoffs, 1940. One of 250 ptd. 1/2 white linen, red cl. (Spine label faded, sl peeling), else NF. *Pacific*.* $104/£65

CHURCHILL, WINSTON S. Amid These Storms. NY: Scribner, 1932. 1st Amer ed. Red cl (spine faded). *Glenn.* $150/£94

CHURCHILL, WINSTON S. The Collected Works of Sir Winston Churchill. Library of Imperial History, 1973-76. Centenary ltd ed. Incl 4 vols of Collected Essays which were pub sl later but uniform w/the set. 8vo. 38 vols. Aeg. Orig full vellum, gilt, w/gilt-blocked arms on fr cvrs, gilt lettering on spines. Fine set (bklabels most vols), each vol in orig gilt-blocked slipcase. *Sotheran.* $7,200/£4,500

CHURCHILL, WINSTON S. The Collected Works.... Volumes 1-22 only (of 34). (London): Library of Imperial History, (1973-75). Centenary ltd ed. Ltd to 3000. Pub's limitation bkpls. 8vo. Gilt edges. Orig vellum, gilt. Orig grn cl slipcases. *Christie's*.* $1,197/£748

CHURCHILL, WINSTON S. First Journey. London, (1964). Ltd to 260 numbered, signed. 8vo. Pub's full red calf. Fine in cardbd slipcase. *Heritage.* $2,000/£1,250

CHURCHILL, WINSTON S. The Great War. London, (1933). 1st bk ed. 3 vols. Blue cl. Fine set. *Swann*.* $258/£161

CHURCHILL, WINSTON S. A History of the English-Speaking Peoples. London, 1956-1958. 1st eds. 4 vols. Djs (foxed). *Edwards.* $72/£45

CHURCHILL, WINSTON S. A History of the English-Speaking Peoples. London, 1956-1958. 1st ed. 4 vols. Djs (sl dknd, few sm closed tears). *Swann*.* $161/£101

CHURCHILL, WINSTON S. A History of the English-Speaking Peoples. London: Cassell, 1956-58. 1st ed. 4 vols. Fine in djs (lt chipped). *Glenn.* $280/£175

CHURCHILL, WINSTON S. History of the Second World War. London: Cassell, 1948-54. 1st ed. 6 vols. Djs. *Marlborough.* $184/£115

CHURCHILL, WINSTON S. Ian Hamilton's March. Longmans, Green, 1900. 1st ed. 8vo. Frontisport, fldg map. Dk red cl (spine sl faded, sm snag to head). VG (prelims foxed). *Sotheran.* $880/£550

CHURCHILL, WINSTON S. Ian Hamilton's March. NY: Longmans, Green, 1900. 1st US ed. 8vo. Frontis, 2 maps (1 fldg). Teg. Red buckram, gilt. VG (ink sig, hinges starting, lt marginal dampstain few ll; extrems sl rubbed) in 1/4 morocco dj. *Heritage.* $1,000/£625

CHURCHILL, WINSTON S. India. Speeches and an Introduction. London: Thornton Butterworth, 1931. 1st ed. 8vo. Pamphlet loosely inserted. VG in ptd orange wrappers. *Maggs.* $720/£450

CHURCHILL, WINSTON S. Into Battle. Cassell, 1941. Inscribed in the month of publication. Lt blue cl. *Sotheby's*.* $1,656/£1,035

CHURCHILL, WINSTON S. Liberalism and the Social Problem. London: Hodder & Stoughton, 1909. 1st ed. One of 5000 ptd. Plum cl, gilt. Sound (edges, eps sl foxed; lt rubbed, soiled; lower edge fr cvr, spine toe sunned). *Reese.* $650/£406

CHURCHILL, WINSTON S. London to Ladysmith via Pretoria. London, 1900. New imp. 4 maps (3 fldg). (Sl foxed, maps chipped; soiled, sm splits to joints, spine sl chipped.) *Edwards.* $56/£35

CHURCHILL, WINSTON S. London to Ladysmith via Pretoria. Longmans, Green, 1900. 1st ed. 8vo. Fldg color frontis map (repaired; feps browned), 2 fldg maps, plans. Pict cl (spine dull). VG. *Sotheran.* $797/£498

CHURCHILL, WINSTON S. Lord Randolph Churchill. London: Macmillan, 1906. 1st ed. 2 vols. Lg 8vo. Largely unopened. Plum cl, gilt. (Sl foxed), o/w NF in VG ptd djs (sl soiled, creased, sm chips spine ends). *Reese.* $1,250/£781

CHURCHILL, WINSTON S. Marlborough and His Times. London, (1933-1938). 1st ed. 4 vols. Frontispieces. Gilt-pict red cl (vol 1 spine faded, lt edgeworn). *Swann*.* $258/£161

CHURCHILL, WINSTON S. Marlborough, His Life and Times. Volume 1 only. Harrap, 1933. One of 155 signed. 8vo. Teg. Orig full morocco, gilt. *Sotheby's*.* $589/£368

CHURCHILL, WINSTON S. My African Journey. Hodder, 1908. 1st UK ed. VG (label removed fep). *Williams*. $472/£295

CHURCHILL, WINSTON S. My African Journey. Hodder & Stoughton, 1908. 1st ed. 8vo. 3 maps. Red pict cl, gilt. (Contemp inscrip; cvrs sl dull.) *Sotheran*. $637/£398

CHURCHILL, WINSTON S. My African Journey. London: Hodder & Stoughton, 1908. 1st ed. 61 photos. NF (pp, edges foxed; spine faded). *Bromer*. $650/£406

CHURCHILL, WINSTON S. My Early Life, a Roving Commission. London: Macmillan, 1941. 1st Macmillan ed. NF in dj (lt worn). *Glenn*. $80/£50

CHURCHILL, WINSTON S. The River War: An Historical Account of the Reconquest of the Soudan. F. Rhodes (ed). London: Longmans, Green, 1899. 1st ed. 2 vols. Aeg. Red calf, gilt, raised bands, bound by Bickers & Son. (Foxed; spines sl dknd, soiled, rubbed), else VG. *Pacific**. $920/£575

CHURCHILL, WINSTON S. The Second World War. London: Cassell, (1948-1954). 1st Eng ed. 6 vols. Top edges stained maroon. Black cl, gilt spines. NF set in djs (spines lt browned, some sl chipped, sm tears) in 3 dk blue open-end slipcases. *Heritage*. $450/£281

CHURCHILL, WINSTON S. The Second World War. Cassell, 1951-1954. 1st Eng ed. 6 vols. All inscribed presentation copies. 8vo. Djs (few sm tears). *Sotheby's**. $5,520/£3,450

CHURCHILL, WINSTON S. The Sinews of Peace, Post-War Speeches. Randolph Churchill (ed). London: Cassell, (1948). 1st ed. NF in dj (lt soiled, chipped). *Glenn*. $55/£34

CHURCHILL, WINSTON S. Step by Step 1936-1939. Thornton Butterworth, (1939). 1st ed. Nice (few sm mks). *Ash*. $152/£95

CHURCHILL, WINSTON S. The Story of the Malakand Field Force, an Episode of Frontier War. Longmans, Green, 1898. 1st ed, 1st bk. 8vo. Frontisport, xvi,336,32 ads pp; 6 maps, plans (2 fldg). Grn cl (sl soiled). VG. *Sotheran*. $5,200/£3,250

CHURCHILL, WINSTON S. The Story of the Malakand Field Force. Longmans, Green, 1898. 1st ed, 1st bk, 1st issue w/o errata slip. 8vo. Ads at end. Black eps. Apple grn cl (sl soiled; sl foxed). *Sotheby's**. $1,840/£1,150

CHURCHILL, WINSTON S. The Unrelenting Struggle. Boston: Little, Brown, 1942. 1st US ed. Red cl. NF (eps browned; spine extrems sl rubbed) in dj (lt edgeworn). *Heritage*. $225/£141

CHURCHILL, WINSTON S. The World Crisis. London, (1923-1931). 1st ed. 6 vols. 8vo. Blue cl, gilt. (Spines sl bumped), o/w Fine set. *Heritage*. $2,000/£1,250

CHURCHILL, WINSTON S. The World Crisis. Thornton Butterworth, 1923-1931. 6 vols in 5. 1st eds, the 1st 2 vols signed by Churchill (dated 1925, 1 inscribed to Charles Nickoll). 8vo. Errata slips. Navy blue cl (sl rubbed, sm lib label on 'The Eastern Front'). *Sotheby's**. $4,416/£2,760

CIARDI, JOHN. The King Who Saved Himself from Being Saved. Phila: Lippincott, 1965. 6x5. Edward Gorey (illus). Unpaginated. VG + in dj (sl edgeworn). *My Bookhouse*. $34/£21

CIARDI, JOHN. The King Who Saved Himself from Being Saved. Phila: Lippincott, 1965. 1st ed. 6.5x5.5. Edward Gorey (illus). Unpaginated. NF (inscrip) in VG dj (2-inch flattened wrinkle in upper fr panel). *Price*. $65/£41

CICERO. Five Books of Tusculan Disputations.... London: Jonas Brown & John Watts, 1715. xxiv,243 + (1)ad pg. 3/4 morocco, gilt. VG. *Pacific**. $46/£29

CICERO. The Orations and Essays. LEC, 1972. Ltd to 1500 numbered, signed by Salvatore Fiume (illus). Fine in slipcase. *Swann**. $57/£36

CICERO. Tully's Offices in Three Books. Roger L'Estrange (trans). London: Henry Brome, 1680. 1st ed thus. (16),208pp. Period blind-tooled calf, later morocco spine label. VG. *Pacific**. $345/£216

CICOGNARA, LEOPOLDO. The Works of Antonio Canova in Sculpture and Modelling. Boston, 1876-78. 2 vols. Morocco (extrems sl worn), gilt. *Swann**. $287/£179

Cincinnati Union Terminal. Cincinnati: Chamber of Commerce, 1933. 1st ed. Dec ptd wrappers. *Cox*. $56/£35

Cinderella and Other Fairy Stories with Realistic Pop-Up Pictures. England: Birn Bros, n.d. (195?). 5 dbl-pg pop-ups. (Hinges, misfolds strengthened.) *Bookfinders*. $60/£38

Cinderella and the Sleeping Beauty. Chicago: Reilly & Britton, 1905. 1st ptg. 4x3. Cl-backed pict bds, gilt. (Fr hinge cracked; fr cvr extrems rubbed), else VG. *Pacific**. $259/£162

Cinderella, or the Little Glass Slipper. NY: Nafis & Cornish, (ca 1860). 12mo. 8pp. Good in yellow pict wrappers (spine worn, partly resewn). *Reisler*. $200/£125

Cinderella. Northampton: W.F. Graham, (ca 1950). 4to. 16pp (6 w/full-pg illus). Willy Schermele (illus). Color pict bds. Good. *Reisler*. $55/£34

Cinderella. NY: Stephen Daye, 1945. 17x23 cm. Julian Wehr (engineer). 5 tab-operated plts. Pict bds (worn). Internally VG-. *Bookfinders*. $75/£47

Cinderella. London: Collins, n.d. (193?). 17x23 cm. Eulalie (illus). 6 opening panels. Pict bds. VG. *Bookfinders*. $280/£175

Cinderella. Boston: Houghton Mifflin, n.d. (195?). Roland Pym (illus). 6 fold-down scenes. Glazed pict bds. Ribbon intact. VG. *Bookfinders*. $200/£125

Cinderella. An All-Action Treasure Hour Pop-Up Book. England: Brown Watson, 1981. 6 dbl-pg pop-ups by V. Kubasta. Glazed pict bds. VG. *Bookfinders*. $32/£20

Cinderella. Pop-Ups with Moving Pictures. London: Murray Sales & Service, 1974. 6 dbl-pg pop-ups by V. Kubasta. Glazed pict bds. VG. *Bookfinders*. $60/£38

Cinderella: or, The Little Glass Slipper; an Amusing Tale. Edinburgh: Oliver & Boyd, n.d. (ca 1820). 12mo. Full-pg wood engr frontis, 355pp + 1pg ad on back wrapper; 14 VF half-pg cuts. Fine in pict stiff paper wrappers (lt soiled, discolored, chipping along spine; sm paper nicks top edge lower wrapper, last pg, not affecting text). *Hobbyhorse*. $175/£109

CIPRIANI, LEONETTO. California and Overland Diaries of Count Leonetto Cipriani from 1853 Through 1871.... Ernest Falbo (ed). (Portland): Champoeg, 1962. One of 750 ptd. Frontis. Red cl, gilt. (Spine sl sunned), else NF. *Pacific**. $23/£14

CISNEROS, SANDRA. Woman Hollering Creek. NY: Random House, 1991. 1st ed. Fine in dj. *Lame Duck*. $45/£28

Citation and Examination of William Shakespeare. (By Walter Savage Landor.) Saunders & Otley, 1834. 1st ed. Half-title, w/o duplicate of pp239-240, 2pp ads at end. Teg, rest uncut. Later full morocco, gilt, by Tout. *Sotheby's**. $368/£230

City and County Directory of San Joaquin, Stanislaus, Merced, and Tuolumne.... SF: L.M. McKenney, 1881. 1st ed. 514pp; orig albumen photo laid on inserted ptd card stock. Orig leather-backed ptd bds, gilt. (Offset to eps; bds stained, edges worn, spine rubbed.) *Pacific**. $1,035/£647

City of the Soul. (By Alfred Douglas.) Grant Richards, 1899. Orig vellum-backed bds (grubby, mkd, fore-edge lt spotted; margins soiled, new fep). *Tiger*. $38/£24

Civil War Naval Chronology. Parts I-VI. Washington: Naval History Division, Navy Dept, 1961-1966. Ink presentation on fr cvr Part V by E.M. Eller, Director of Naval History (comp). Nice set (sl handled) in wraps. *Baltimore**. $20/£13

CIXOUS, HELENE. The Exile of James Joyce. Sally A. J. Purcell (trans). NY: David Lewis, 1972. 1st Amer ed. NF in dj. *Hermitage*. $75/£47

CLAGETT, MARSHALL. The Science of Mechanics in the Middle Ages. Madison: Univ of WI, 1959. 9 plts. Fine in dj (corners lt worn). *Weber*. $75/£47

CLAIR, C. Christopher Plantin. London: Cassell, 1960. 16 plts. Brn cl. (Pencil inscrip.) Dj. *Maggs.* $56/£35

CLAIR, MAXINE. Coping with Gravity. Washington: Washington Writers, 1988. 1st ed, 1st bk. Fine in blue wrappers. *Robbins.* $85/£53

CLAIRE, WILLIAM F. (ed). Publishing in the West: Alan Swallow, Some Letters and Commentaries. Santa Fe: Lightning Tree, (1974). 1st ed. Port. Fine in NF dj. *Reese.* $35/£22

CLAMPITT, AMY. Westward. NY: Knopf, 1990. 1st ed. (Rmdr lines on bottom pg edge), else Fine in Fine dj. *Pettler.* $15/£9

CLANCY, FOG HORN. My Fifty Years in Rodeo. San Antonio: Naylor, (1952). 1st ed. Red cl. Good in illus dj (chipped). *Karmiole.* $75/£47

CLANCY, TOM. The Hunt for Red October. Annapolis, MD: Naval Institute Press, (1984). 1st ed. 8vo. Red cl, silver-lettered spine, ISBN # in silver on rear cvr. (Ink inscrip), o/w Fine in dj (lt soiled, sl edgeworn). *Heritage.* $600/£375

CLANCY, TOM. The Hunt for Red October. Annapolis: Naval Inst, (1984). 1st ed, 1st bk. (Inscrip), else Fine in NF dj (sm unobtrusive tear, extrems sl dknd). *Between The Covers.* $650/£406

CLANCY, TOM. Red Storm Rising. NY: Putnam, (1986). 1st ed. 1/4 black cl, black bds, gilt. Fine in dj. *Heritage.* $50/£31

CLANCY, TOM. Red Storm Rising. NY: Putnam, (1986). 1st ed. Signed. NF. *Cady.* $85/£53

CLANCY, TOM. Submarine, A Guided Tour Inside a Nuclear Warship. NY: Putnam, 1993. 1st ed. One of 300 numbered, signed. VF in pub's slipcase, shrinkwrapped. *Unger.* $250/£156

CLAPESATTLE, HELEN. The Doctors Mayo. Minneapolis, 1941. 1st ed. Red cl. VG (extrems sl worn). *Doctor's Library.* $30/£19

CLAPP, GEORGE WOOD. The Life and Work of James Leon Williams. NY, 1925. VG. *Doctor's Library.* $35/£22

CLAPPE, LOUISE. The Shirley Letters from the California Mines 1851-1852. NY, 1949. 1st ed. Dec cl, gilt. NF in VG + dj. *Sagebrush.* $50/£31

CLAPPERTON, R. and W. HENDERSON. Modern Paper Making. Oxford: Blackwell, 1941. Good in blue cl. *Moss.* $29/£18

CLARE, JOHN. Poems of John Clare's Madness. Geoffrey Grigson (ed). London: Routledge & Kegan Paul, 1949. 1st Eng ed. 3 b/w plts. VG (top edge sl dusty; spine ends, corners sl bumped) in dj (nicked, chipped, sl rubbed, mkd, dusty, price-clipped, sl browned). *Ulysses.* $88/£55

CLARE, JOHN. The Poems of John Clare. J. W. Tibble (ed). London: J.M. Dent, 1935. 1st Eng ed. 2 vols. Rev slip loosely inserted. VG set (eps spotted; spines faded, ends sl bumped). *Ulysses.* $152/£95

CLARE, JOHN. Sketches in the Life of John Clare by Himself Now First Published.... London: Cobden-Sanderson, 1931. 1st ed. NF in blue cl, ptd paper label, extra label tipped in at rear. Good dj (internally mended). *Captain's Bookshelf.* $50/£31

CLARE, JOHN. The Village Minstrel, and Other Poems. Taylor & Hessey, 1821. 1st ed. 12mo. Half-titles present, frontisport vol 1 (lt offset), xxviii,216,(4); (viii),211,(1) blank,(4)pp, ads at end both vols, those in vol 1 dated Sept. 1st, 1821. Unpressed, untrimmed. Orig gray bds (expertly rebacked to match, w/orig ptd labels laid down). VG (prelims, final ll sl foxed, feps browned, engr bkpl). *Blackwell's.* $1,120/£700

CLARE, MARTIN. The Motion of Fluids, Natural and Artificial; in Particular That of the Air and Water. For Edward Symon, 1735. 1st ed. 8vo. 9 engr plts. Gilt edges. Later morocco, gilt by Brian Frost & Co. (Ink note fep.) *Sotheby's*.* $515/£322

CLARENDON, EDWARD. The History of the Rebellion and Civil Wars in England. London, 1717. 3 vols in 6. Engr ports vols 1-4. Contemp full paneled calf (few heads chipped), spines gilt w/red labels. *Swann*.* $172/£108

CLARK, A. C. The Descent of Manuscripts. Oxford: Clarendon, 1918. Red cl. (Bklabel, inscrip; sl bumped.) *Maggs.* $56/£35

CLARK, ALAN. The Lion Heart. NY: William Morrow, 1969. 1st ed. Fine in dj (lt edgeworn). *Associates.* $85/£53

CLARK, ALFRED (ed). My Erratic Pal. London, 1918. 1st Eng ed. Cl-backed pict bds. (Fep damaged; chafed, corners bumped.) *Clearwater.* $40/£25

CLARK, BADGER. Sky Lines and Wood Smoke. Custer, SD: The Cronicle Shop, 1935. Fine in wraps. *Perier.* $45/£28

CLARK, BARRETT H. The Blush of Shame. NY: Gotham Book Mart, 1932. 1st ed. One of 500. VG in ptd wraps (top edges chipped) w/dec stitching. *Dramatis.* $18/£11

CLARK, CAROL. Thomas Moran: Watercolors of the American West. Austin: Univ of TX, 1980. VG in dj. *Dumont.* $50/£31

CLARK, CHARLES B., JR. Sun and Saddle Leather. Boston, 1917. 2nd ed. (Name.) *Wantagh.* $45/£28

CLARK, CUMBERLAND. Shakespeare and Dickens. London: Chiswick, 1918. 1st ed. (Corners bumped.) *Dramatis.* $30/£19

CLARK, CURT. (Pseud of Donald E. Westlake.) Anarchaos. NY: Ace, 1967. 1st ed. Pb orig. NF in NF wrappers. *Janus.* $15/£9

CLARK, DANIEL. Proofs of the Corruption of General James Wilkinson, and His Connection with Aaron Burr.... Phila: Ptd by Wm. Hall, Jr & Geo. W. Pierie, 1809. 199pp. Good (rebound, 1st 3pp encapsulated; foxed). Howes C431. *Dumont.* $850/£531

CLARK, E. WARREN. From Hong Kong to the Himalayas: or, Three Thousand Miles Through India. American Tract Soc, 1880. 1st ed. 368pp; 31 plts, 1 map. Blue pict cl, gilt. (Extrems sl rubbed), o/w VG. *Sotheran.* $136/£85

CLARK, ELEANOR. Rome and a Villa. GC: Doubleday Doran, 1952. 1st ed. (Sm stamp on dj fr flap, extending to fep), else NF in VG + dj. *Pettler.* $25/£16

CLARK, ELLA E. Indian Legends from the Northern Rockies. Norman, 1966. 1st ed. (Fr cvr sl bumped), o/w Fine in dj (edgeworn). *Baade.* $65/£41

CLARK, ERLAND FENN. Truncheons. Herbert Jenkins, 1935. 1st ed. VG in dj. *Hollett.* $104/£65

CLARK, GALEN. Big Trees of California. Yosemite Valley: Galen Clark, 1910. 2nd ed. Frontisport, 19 plts. Grn pict wrappers. (Fep removed, name, date), o/w NF. *Pacific*.* $86/£54

CLARK, GALEN. Early Days in the Yosemite Valley. L.A.: Docter, 1964. One of 70. Marbled bds w/paper spine label. *Dawson.* $100/£63

CLARK, GALEN. Indians of the Yosemite Valley and Vicinity. Yosemite Valley: Galen Clark, 1904. 1st ed. 27 full-pg illus. Pict tan cl. (Bkpl, lacks fep.) *Dawson.* $75/£47

CLARK, GALEN. The Yosemite Valley. Yosemite Valley: Nelson L. Salter, 1911. 2nd ed. 21 plts. Gray pict cl. (Water stain inner margins of 6 leaves; cvrs lt soiled, worn), o/w VG. *Pacific*.* $69/£43

CLARK, HARTLEY. Bokhara, Turkoman and Afghan Rugs. London, 1922. 17 color plts. 1/2 leather. (Wormholes to tp, prelims; rebound.) *Petersfield.* $38/£24

CLARK, J. W. The Care of Books. An Essay on the Development of Libraries...to the End of the Eighteenth Century. Cambridge: CUP, 1901. Frontis, 45 plts. (Inscrip; chipped, spine sl worn.) *Maggs.* $104/£65

CLARK, JAMES A. and MICHAEL T. HALBOUTY. Spindletop. NY: Random House, 1952. Stated 'Beaumont ed.' 1st ptg. Good in dj (edges worn). *Dumont.* $60/£38

CLARK, JAMES L. The Great Arc of the Wild Sheep. Norman: Univ of OK, 1964. *Petersfield.* $51/£32

CLARK, JOHN E. T. Musical Boxes. Cornish Bros, n.d. (c.1948). 1st ed. VG in dj. *Hollett.* $32/£20

CLARK, KENNETH and DAVID FINN. The Florence Baptistry Doors. London: Thames & Hudson, 1980. VF in dj. *Europa.* $72/£45

CLARK, KENNETH and C. PEDRETTI. Leonardo da Vinci: Anatomical Drawings in the Royal Library at Windsor Castle. Phaidon, 1969. 2nd rev ed. Vol 3 of 3-vol set of dwgs at Windsor Castle, but complete in itself. 150 collotype plts. Good in dj. *Ars Artis*. $80/£50

CLARK, KENNETH B. Dark Ghetto: Dilemmas of Social Power. NY: Harper & Row, (1965). 1st ed. VG + in ptd dj (sl mended). *Petrilla*. $25/£16

CLARK, KENNETH. The Drawings of Leonardo da Vinci in the Collection...at Windsor Castle. London/Oxford: Phaidon, 1968. 2nd ed. 3 vols. Uniform buckram. VF set (vol 1 w/mks) in djs. *Europa*. $440/£275

CLARK, KENNETH. Sidney Nolan. London, 1961. 199 plts (16 color). (Eps lt spotted; sl soiled, spine, edges faded.) *Edwards*. $77/£48

CLARK, L. PIERCE. Lincoln: A Psycho-Biography. NY: Scribner, 1933. 1st ed. Fine in dj (lt used). *Beasley*. $75/£47

CLARK, LARRY. Teenage Lust. (NY): Clark, (1987). 2nd ed (so stated). Internally VG in gray wraps (lt worn; spine creased, sl curled). *Baltimore**. $90/£56

CLARK, LARRY. Teenage Lust. NY, (1987). Signed. Pict wrappers. *Swann**. $460/£288

CLARK, LARRY. Tulsa. (NY: Larry Clark, 1971.) 1st ed. Signed w/star. 12x8.75. NF in dj. *Pacific**. $690/£431

CLARK, LEONARD. An Intimate Landscape. Nottingham Court, 1981. One of 400. W/added In Memorium leaf noting the death of Clark before he signed more than 50 copies. (7) wood engrs by Miriam Macgregor. 1/4 cl, marbled bds. Fine in slipcase. *Michael Taylor*. $104/£65

CLARK, MARGERY. The Poppy Seed Cakes. GC: Doubleday, Page, 1924. 1st ed. 8vo. 14 full-pg color plts by Maud & Miska Petersham. Black cl. Good. *Reisler*. $275/£172

CLARK, NEIL M. (ed). Campfires and Cattle Trails. Caldwell, 1970. 1st ed. NF in pict wraps. *Baade*. $35/£22

CLARK, O. S. Clay Allison of the Washita. Houston: Frontier, 1954. Stiff wraps (sl browned). *Dumont*. $35/£22

CLARK, O. S. Clay Allison of the Washita. Houston, 1954. Rpt. VG in wraps. Howes C445. *Baade*. $47/£29

CLARK, ROBERT (ed). Golf: A Royal and Ancient Game. London: Macmillan, 1875. 1st ed. Teg. Pict grn cl, gilt. (Emb stamp, fr hinge starting; spine head rubbed, cl torn along rear joint), else VG. *Pacific**. $3,163/£1,977

CLARK, ROBERT (ed). Golf: A Royal and Ancient Game. London: Macmillan, 1893. 3rd ed. Pict red cl, gilt. (Plts lt foxed, emb stamp; spine ends sl rubbed), else VG. *Pacific**. $316/£198

CLARK, ROBERT A. and PATRICK J. BRUNET. The Arthur H. Clark Company. Spokane, WA: A.H. Clark, 1993. Ltd to 500. As New, issued w/o dj. *Lien*. $200/£125

CLARK, ROLAND. Etchings. NY: Derrydale, (1938). One of 800 numbered. Folio. 70 plts, incl signed frontis etching. Pub's 2-piece box (lid corners cracked). *Swann**. $632/£395

CLARK, ROLAND. Gunner's Dawn. NY: Derrydale, 1937. Ltd to 950 numbered. Frontis, orig signed etching. Red cl. VG. *Biscotti*. $325/£203

CLARK, RONALD and EDWARD C. PYATT. Mountaineering in Britain. London, 1957. 1st ed. 104 plts. Dj (sl creased, chipped). *Edwards*. $72/£45

CLARK, RONALD. The Early Alpine Guides. London: Phoenix House, 1949. 1st ed. 4 maps. VG in dj. *Hollett*. $64/£40

CLARK, SAMUEL. The Life and Death of the Valiant and Renowned Sir Francis Drake. For Simon Miller, 1671. Engr frontis (cropped, repaired). Recent 1/2 calf (sl rubbed). *Sotheby's**. $405/£253

CLARK, STERLING. How Many Miles from St. Jo? SF: Privately ptd, 1929. 1st ed. 5 plts. Erratum slip. Red cl-backed marbled bds, pict inset on cvr. VG + (rubbed, corners worn). *Harrington*. $50/£31

CLARK, THOMAS BLAKE. Omai: First Polynesian Ambassador to England. (SF): Colt Press, 1940. One of 500. Screened gravure plt. 1/2 linen, batik bds, paper spine label. Fine. *Pacific**. $138/£86

CLARK, THOMAS CURTIS. Lincoln: Fifty Poems. Herrin, IL: Trovillion Private Press, 1943. 1st ed. Ltd to 488 numbered, signed by Clark and Hal W. Trovillion (intro). Silver/black cl. NF in glassine dj (chipped, browned). *Cahan*. $75/£47

CLARK, THOMAS D. Travels in the Old South, 1527-1860: A Bibliography. Norman, (1956-59). 3 vols. Djs. *Swann**. $287/£179

CLARK, THOMAS D. Travels in the Old South. Norman, 1956. 1st ed. 2 vols. Good in djs (soiled). *Dumont*. $195/£122

CLARK, TOM. Champagne and Baloney: The Rise and Fall of Finley's A's. NY: Harper, (1976). 1st ed. (Corners sl bumped), else Fine in VG dj (rubbed, lt worn). *Between The Covers*. $85/£53

CLARK, WALTER VAN TILBURG. The Track of the Cat. NY: Random House, 1949. 1st ed. Fine in NF dj (rubbed). *Unger*. $200/£125

CLARK, WALTER. The Papers of Walter Clark. Aubrey Lee Brooks and Hugh Talmage Lefler (eds). Chapel Hill: Univ of NC, (1948-50). 1st ed. 2 vols. Frontisports. Red cl, gilt. Fine in VG djs (edgeworn). *Chapel Hill*. $150/£94

CLARK, WILLIAM B. Gold Districts of California. SF: CA Division of Mines & Geology, 1970. Lg pocket map. Fine. *Book Market*. $40/£25

CLARKE, ARTHUR C. 2001: A Space Odyssey. (NY): NAL, (1968). 1st ed. (Names; spine ends lt bumped), else VG in dj (lt purple offset from former dj protector). *Pacific**. $127/£79

CLARKE, ARTHUR C. 2001: A Space Odyssey. Hutchinson, 1968. 1st Eng ed. NF (top edge sl spotted) in dj (top edge sl creased). *Ulysses*. $200/£125

CLARKE, ARTHUR C. Against the Fall of Night. (NY): Gnome, (1953). 1st ed. VG in dj (spine ends rubbed, sm tear upper fr panel, sm crease). *Pacific**. $104/£65

CLARKE, ARTHUR C. The City and the Stars. London: Frederick Muller, (1956). 1st British ed. VG in dj (spine ends, extrems chipped, sm tears, creases, spine head lacks sm piece). *Pacific**. $127/£79

CLARKE, ARTHUR C. The Coast of Coral. NY, 1956. 1st ed. 13 color plts, 32 b/w photo plts. VG. *Larry Price*. $20/£13

CLARKE, ARTHUR C. Interplanetary Flight: An Introduction to Astronautics. NY: L. Harper, (c. 1950). 1st Amer ed. VG in dj (spine ends, corners sl rubbed). *Pacific**. $127/£79

CLARKE, ARTHUR C. Sands of Mars. NY: Gnome Press, (1952). 1st Amer ed. (Sm nick lower fr joint), else VG in dj (spine head chipped, sm tear fr panel, price-clipped). *Pacific**. $161/£101

CLARKE, AUSTIN. Night and Morning. Dublin: Orwell, 1938. One of 300. VG (inscrip; fr cvr lt browned, edges sl creased, spine ends, corners bumped) in wrappers. *Ulysses*. $104/£65

CLARKE, BASIL. English Churches. Vista Books, 1964. 1st Eng ed. VG (spine tail sl bumped) in dj (price-clipped, sl rubbed, spine faded). *Ulysses*. $72/£45

CLARKE, COVINGTON. Aces Up. Chicago: Reilly & Lee, (1929). 1st ed. Brn cl. NF in VG pict dj (spine sunned, lt frayed). *Reese*. $35/£22

CLARKE, DENNIS C. Public School Explorers in Newfoundland. London: Putnam, (1934). VG (edges dusty) in dj (worn). *Explorer*. $24/£15

CLARKE, DORUS. Lectures to Young People in Manufacturing Villages. Boston: Perkins & Marvin, 1836. 1st ed. 220pp (stained). Orig cl. *M & S.* $150/£94

CLARKE, DWIGHT L. William Tecumseh Sherman: Gold Rush Banker. SF: CA Hist Soc, 1969. 1st ed. Inscribed, signed presentation. VF in pict dj. *Argonaut.* $50/£31

CLARKE, EDWARD DANIEL. Travels in Various Countries of Europe, Asia, and Africa. Part 2. Section 1 (only). NY: Whiting & Watson, 1813. 1st US ed. xvi,350,130pp. Contemp tree calf. (Foxed; rubbed, scuffed, sl wormholes), o/w VG. *Worldwide.* $85/£53

CLARKE, HERMAN FREDERICK. John Hull. Portland: Southworth-Anthoensen, 1940. One of 500 numbered. Prospectus, order form laid in. Uncut, unopened. (Lt worn.) Slipcase (scuffed). *Oinonen*.* $225/£141

CLARKE, HYDE. Serpent and Siva Worship and Mythology in Central America, Africa, and Asia. London: Trubner, 1876. Old paper bds, 1/2 leather. *Metropolitan*.* $69/£43

CLARKE, JAMES. A Survey of the Lakes of Cumberland, Westmorland and Lancashire. The Author, 1789. 2nd ed. Folio. 11 fldg engr maps, plans, 2 plts (tp, 1 plt repaired, few folds repaired or strengthened, lt offsetting). Uncut. Orig bds (bkpl). *Sotheby's*.* $883/£552

CLARKE, JOSEPH I. C. Japan at First Hand. NY, 1918. 1st Amer ed. Fine. *Polyanthos.* $30/£19

CLARKE, JOSEPH T. et al. Investigations at Assos...During the Excavations of 1881-1882-1883. London, 1902. Folio. Contents loose in cl-backed bd portfolio (worn) as issued. *Swann*.* $201/£126

CLARKE, KIT. The Practical Angler. NY: American News Co, 1892. 1st ed. (Hinges cracking, rep tear), else VG. *Pacific*.* $46/£29

CLARKE, KIT. Where the Trout Hide. NY, 1889. 1st ed. 116pp (lt dampstained in lower margin throughout, lacks the 8pp ads present in some copies). Contemp 3/4 morocco (rubbed). *Oinonen*.* $100/£63

CLARKE, L. LANE. Objects for the Microscope. Groombridge, 1889. 8th ed. Color litho frontis, viii,230,(2)pp; 7 plts. Cream eps; gilt edges. Fine diagonal-grain blue cl, gilt. Good. *Blackwell's.* $120/£75

CLARKE, PAULINE. The Twelve and the Genii. London: Faber, 1962. 4th ed. 5.5x8. Cecil Leslie (illus). 185pp. VG (ex-lib) in dj. *Cattermole.* $30/£19

CLARKE, PEYTON NEALE. Old King William Homes and Families. Louisville, 1897. 1st ed. (Part of fep torn away, few pp roughly opened, inner joint broken; shelfworn.) Howes C459. *Oinonen*.* $50/£31

CLARKE, SAVILE. Alice in Wonderland, a Dream Play. London: Ptd at the 'Court Circular' Office, 1886. 1st ed. 8vo. Ptd brn wrappers (fr cvr detached, lt foxing). *Swann*.* $1,092/£683

CLARKE, THOMAS. Sir Copp. Chicago: Clarke, 1865. 1st ed. Inscribed, 1866. 8,122pp. *M & S.* $375/£234

CLARKSON, PATRICK and ANTHONY PELLY. The General and Plastic Surgery of the Hand. Phila: F.A. Davis, (1962). 1st ed. Fine (bkpl). *Weber.* $60/£38

CLARY, WILLIAM W. History of the Law Firm of O'Melveny and Myers, 1885-1965. L.A., 1966. 2 vols. Good. *Rybski.* $100/£63

CLATER, FRANCIS. Every Man His Own Cattle Doctor. F. Warne, n.d. 2nd ed. 3 color plts. Orig morocco-backed cl, gilt. (Few pp sl soiled, sm piece of tp stuck to next leaf; sl worn.) *Hollett.* $72/£45

CLAUDEL, PAUL. The Book of Christopher Columbus. New Haven: Yale, 1930. 1st ed. 8.5x11.25. Jean Charlot (illus). 64pp. VG in dj. *Cattermole.* $200/£125

CLAUDET, F. G. Gold: Its Properties, Modes of Extraction.... Vancouver, BC: Robert Reid & Takao Tanabe, 1958. One of 275. Facs of orig title cvr tipped in, facs leaf of 1871 ads laid in. 1/4 oasis niger, marbled paper bds. Good. *Karmiole.* $200/£125

CLAUDY, C. H. The Battle of Baseball. Century, 1912. 1st ed. VG. *Plapinger.* $450/£281

CLAUDY, C. H. The Gold He Found. NY: Appleton, 1928. 1st ed. Frontis. NF (blindstamp) in NF vintage dj (rear panel soiled, 2 tears). *Unger.* $150/£94

CLAUDY, C. H. The Land of No Shadow. NY: G&D, 1933. Adventures in the Unknown #3; lists to #4. 5x7.5. 214pp. VG (shelfworn) in dj (edges ragged). *My Bookhouse.* $72/£45

CLAVELL, JAMES. Noble House. NY, (1981). 1st ed. One of 500 numbered, signed. Black leather. Matching slipcase. *Swann*.* $46/£29

CLAVELL, JAMES. Noble House. NY: Delacorte, 1981. 1st ed. (Sm inscrip), else NF in NF dj (price-clipped). *Pettler.* $25/£16

CLAVELL, JAMES. Noble House. Hodder, 1981. 1st ed. Signed. Fine in dj. *Any Amount.* $48/£30

CLAVELL, JAMES. Tai-Pan. NY: Atheneum, 1966. 1st ed. VG+ in dj (1-inch edge tear). *Lame Duck.* $175/£109

CLAY, JEAN. Romanticism. London: Phaidon, 1981. 367 color plts. Dj. *Edwards.* $56/£35

CLAY, JOHN. My Life on the Range. Norman: Univ of OK, (1962). New ed, 1st ptg. Tan cl. Fine in pict dj. Howes C470. *House.* $25/£16

CLAY, JOHN. My Life on the Range. Norman, (1962). New ed, 1st ptg. NF (ink inscrip) in VG dj. *Sagebrush.* $50/£31

CLAY, JOHN. My Life on the Range. Chicago: Privately ptd, 1924. 1st ed. Teg. Grn cl, gilt. VF. Howes C478. *Labordo.* $375/£234

CLAYBOURN, JOHN G. Dredging on the Panama Canal. Chicago, 1931. 1st ed. Signed by Claybourn and his wife. 158 photo plts. VG in dj. *Larry Price.* $49/£31

CLAYTON, JACQUELINE. The Georgie-Porgie Book. London: Thomas Nelson & Sons, ca 1914. 8vo. 12 full-pg color plts by Margaret Clayton. Blue cl, ruled lines around full color paste label. Good. *Reisler.* $175/£109

CLAYTON, JACQUELINE. The Twirly-Whirly Book. London: Thomas Nelson & Sons, ca 1914. 8vo. 12 full-pg color plts by Margaret Clayton. Blue cl, ruled lines around full color paste label. Good. *Reisler.* $150/£94

CLAYTON, P. B. Plain Tales from Flanders. London, 1929. 1st ed. VG (no dj). *Typographeum.* $28/£18

CLAYTON, W. F. A Narrative of the Confederate States Navy. Weldon, NC: Harrell's Ptg House, 1910. 1st ed. One of 100. 8vo. Frontisport. Gray cl. VG+. *Chapel Hill.* $800/£500

CLEARY, BEVERLY. Ralph S. Mouse. Morrow, 1982. 1st ed. Paul Zelinsky (illus). 160pp. Fine in VG+ dj (sm corner chips). *Price.* $34/£21

CLEARY, BEVERLY. Ramona Forever. Morrow, 1984. 1st ed. Alan Tiegreen (illus). NF (inscrip) in NF dj. *Price.* $32/£20

CLEARY, BEVERLY. Socks. NY: Morrow, 1973. 1st ed. 6x8. Beatrice Darwin (illus). 156pp. VG+ (sl shelfworn) in dj (sl worn, sl dingy). *My Bookhouse.* $27/£17

CLEARY, JON. You Can't See Around Corners. Scribner, 1947. 1st ed. (Pp edges browned), else NF in dj (rubbed, head chip, edges worn). *Murder.* $75/£47

CLEATOR, P. E. The Robot Era. NY: Crowell, (1955). 1st Amer ed. 23 plts. Fine. *Glaser.* $25/£16

CLEAVELAND, AGNES MORELAND. No Life for a Lady. Boston: Houghton Mifflin, 1941. 1st ed. (Name), else VG in dj (spine ends, extrems chipped, spine sl sunned). *Pacific*.* $46/£29

CLEAVELAND, NORMAN and GEORGE FITZPATRICK. The Morleys, Young Upstarts on the Southwest Frontier. Albuquerque: Calvin Horn, 1971. 1st ed. NF in dj. *Labordo*. $65/£41

CLEAVELAND, P. An Elementary Treatise on Mineralogy and Geology. Boston: Cummings and Hilliard, 1822. 2nd ed. 2 vols in 1. xii,818pp + errata. Mod grn cl, paper spine label. (Internally dampstained, sl cockled), else VG. *Blake*. $500/£313

CLEAVER, ELDRIDGE. Gangster Cigarettes. Stanford: CP Times, 1984. 1st ed. Signed. Fine in wraps (staples sl rusty). *Any Amount*. $35/£22

CLEAVER, ELDRIDGE. Idi and the Sultan. Stanford: CP Times, 1984. 1st ed. Signed. Fine in wraps (staples sl rusty). *Any Amount*. $38/£24

CLEAVER, ELDRIDGE. Post-Prison Speeches and Writings. NY: Ramparts/Random House, 1969. 1st ed. NF in dj (price-clipped). *Sclanders*. $19/£12

CLEAVER, ELDRIDGE. Soul on Ice. Cape, 1969. 1st UK ed. NF in dj. *Sclanders*. $16/£10

CLEETON, GLEN U. and CHARLES W. PITKIN. General Printing. Bloomingdale: McKnight & McKnight, 1953. 2nd ed. Fine. *Oak Knoll*. $30/£19

CLELAND, ROBERT. El Molino Viejo. L.A.: Ward Ritchie, 1951. 1st ed, 2nd ptg. Signed. VG. *Houle*. $75/£47

CLELAND, ROBERT. The Irving Ranch of Orange County 1810-1950. San Marino, (1953). 2nd ed. VG in dj. *Woolson*. $50/£31

CLELAND, ROBERT. The Pathfinders. L.A.: Powell, (1929). VG. *Book Market*. $35/£22

CLELAND, ROBERT. The Place Called Sespe. Chicago: Privately ptd, 1940. 1st ed. VG +. *Labordo*. $75/£47

CLEMENCEAU, G. Clemenceau. Milton Waldman (trans). London: Longmans & Green, 1930. Frontisport; 25 plts. Good. *Stewart*. $48/£30

CLEMENT, ERNEST W. A Handbook of Modern Japan. Chicago: A.C. McClurg, 1904. 2nd ed. 2 color maps (1 fldg). Grn pict cl, gilt. VG (spine sl faded). *Sotheran*. $104/£65

CLEMENT, HAL. Needle. GC: Doubleday, 1950. 1st ed. (Name), else VG in dj (spine foot chipped, sm tears upper fr panel, creases). *Pacific**. $86/£54

CLERGUE, LUCIEN. Eros and Thantos. Boston: NYGS, 1985. 1st ed. Inscribed by Marianne Fulton (essayist). Errata slip laid in. Fine in dj. *Smith*. $90/£56

CLERGUE, LUCIEN. Toros Muertos. NY, 1966. 1st ed. NF in VG + dj. *Warren*. $50/£31

CLERK, THOMAS. The Works of William Hogarth.... London: Scholey, 1810. 2 vols. Vol I: ptd 1/2 title, engr tp w/vignette of Hogarth's self-port, v,203pp; 55 engr plts; vol II; engr tp w/vignette of 'Boys Peeping at Nature,' 34 engr plts + 'Analysis of Beauty', marginal pagination following orig ed: (153pp) + the 2 plts. All plts guarded. Full mottled calf, gilt, blind dec spines. Generally Fine sets (marginal browning to plts; labels removed both vols; sl abrasion spine vol II). *Europa*. $224/£140

CLEVELAND, GROVER. Fishing and Shooting Sketches. NY: Outing Publishing, 1907. 1st ed. Frontisport. Gilt-lettered grn cl. (Spine sl sunned), else NF. *Pacific**. $63/£39

CLEVELAND, RICHARD. A Narrative of Voyages and Commercial Enterprises. Cambridge, (MA): John Owen, 1842. 1st ed. 2 vols. xvi,249; viii,240pp. Orig cl, paper spine labels. (Foxed, vol 2 w/sl dampstain at upper gutter margin of early pp, ink names; extrems worn, spine labels rubbed, chipped), o/w VG set. Howes C485. *Pacific**. $489/£306

CLIAS, PETER HENRY. An Elementary Course of Gymnastic Exercises; Intended to Improve the Physical Powers of Man. London: Sherwood, Jones, 1823. 1st ed in English. xx,111pp + 2 Sherwood cats (12 + 20pp) dated April 1823 at the end; 6 fldg engr plts. Uncut. Orig bds (shelfworn, sl foxed, spine chipped), ptd paper spine label (chipped). *Oinonen**. $160/£100

CLIFFORD, ELSIE M. Bagendon: A Belgic Oppidum. Cambridge, 1961. Frontis, 58 plts. Dj (sl worn). *Edwards*. $72/£45

CLIFFORD, ISIDORE. Crown, Bar, and Bridge-Work. N.p., 1887. 2nd ed. 24pp; 9 color litho plts, numbered 1-7,9,10. 'With the Author's Compliments' in ink on ffep. *Bickersteth*. $120/£75

CLIFFORD, JAMES L. (ed). Dr. Campbell's Diary of a Visit to England in 1775. CUP, 1947. 1st Eng ed. Frontis. NF (spine tail sl bumped) in dj (sl rubbed, nicked, tape-mkd). *Ulysses*. $72/£45

CLIFFORD, W. K. Lectures and Essays by the Late William Kingdon Clifford. Leslie Stephen and Frederick Pollock (eds). London: Macmillan, 1879. 2 vols. Frontis port, (vi),340; (vi),321,(1)pp + inserted cat dated March 1879. Panelled dk grn cl. Good + set (sl pencil lining; crowns frayed, hinges cracked). *Gach*. $100/£63

CLIFTON, MRS. TALBOT. Pilgrims to the Isles of Penance. London, 1911. 1st ed. Fldg map. (Lt foxed; extrems sl rubbed, faded.) *Edwards*. $120/£75

CLINCH, GEORGE. Bloomsbury and St. Giles's: Past and Present. London: Truslove & Shirley, 1890. Frontis map, xii,220pp; 23 photomezzotype plts. Red cl (spine sl faded), gilt. Bkpl of George Duckworth. *Marlborough*. $104/£65

CLINCH, GEORGE. Marylebone and St. Pancras. London: Truslove & Shirley, 1890. xii,235pp; 38 photomezzotype and other plts. Red cl (spine sl faded), gilt. Bkpl of George Duckworth. Fine. *Marlborough*. $120/£75

CLINTON-BAKER, H. Illustrations of Conifers. Hertford: Privately ptd, 1909-1913. 3 vols. 232 plts. Teg, marbled eps vols 1, 2. 1/2 crushed grn morocco, grn cl bds, raised bands, spines gilt. (Fore-edges sl spotted, bkpl; spine lt sunned). Vol 3 in orig wraps (joint partly split, backstrip sunned). *Edwards*. $480/£300

CLIVE, TERRY, JR. Damon. NY, 1975. 1st ed. Fine in Fine dj. *Warren*. $50/£31

CLOE, JOHN HAILE. Top Cover for America—The Air Force in Alaska 1920-1983. Pictorial Hist Pub, (1985). 2nd ptg. Signed. One of 260. Fine in Fine dj. *Perier*. $75/£47

CLOKE, KEN. A Pocket Manual on Draft Resistance. NY: Weekly Guardian Associates, 1968. 1st ed. (Faint stain rear cvr), else Fine in stapled wraps. *Associates*. $40/£25

CLOSSON, ERNEST. History of the Piano. Delano Ames (trans). Paul Elek, 1947. 1st Eng ed. 2-tone cl, gilt. VG in dj (few tears top edge). *Hollett*. $56/£35

Clouds Hill, Dorset: A Property of the National Trust. Country Life, 1955. 1st Eng ed. Wrappers. VG (browning inside fr cvr, edges sl rubbed). *Ulysses*. $40/£25

CLOUGH, ARTHUR HUGH. Letters and Remains of Arthur Hugh Clough. Blanche Smith Clough (ed). London: Spottiswoode, 1865. 1st ed. 1866 inscribed presentation. vi,328pp (feps cracked). Grn gilt/black stamped cl. *Mott*. $300/£188

CLOUGH, ARTHUR HUGH. The Poems and Prose Remains, with a Selection from His Letters. Macmillan, 1869. 1st Eng ed. 2 vols. Sound (cvrs mkd, rubbed, hinges cracked). *Clearwater*. $88/£55

CLOUSTON, BRIAN (ed). Landscape Design with Plants. London: Heinemann, 1977. 1st ed. VG in dj (lt worn). *Fair Meadow*. $60/£38

Cloven Foot, or Popery Aiming at Political Supremacy in the United States by the Rector of Oldenwold. NY, 1855. 1st ed. 400pp. (Ink name; extrems frayed.) *King*. $45/£28

CLOVER, SAM T. A Pioneer Heritage. L.A.: Saturday Night Pub Co, 1932. 1st ed. Blue cl, gilt, photo inset on fr cvr. Fine in Fine dj. *Harrington*. $50/£31

CLUCHEY, RICK. The Cage. CA: Barbwire, 1970. 1st Amer ed. Inscribed, signed. NF in wraps (rear panel lt sunned). *Warren*. $50/£31

CLUNESS, A. T. The Shetland Isles. Robert Hale, 1951. 1st ed. 49 plts, map. (Edges sl spotted.) Dj (sl spotted). *Hollett*. $40/£25

CLUTE, WILLARD N. Our Ferns in Their Haunts. NY: Stokes, 1901. Dec grn cl, gilt. (Corners bumped, spine sunned), else VG. *Fair Meadow.* $30/£19

CLUTTERBUCK, WALTER J. The Skipper in Arctic Seas. London: Longmans, Green, 1890. 1st ed. (viii),271pp; 19 plts. (Lib stamps on tp, frontis; fep loose.) *Lefkowicz.* $150/£94

CLUTTON, CECIL and GEORGE DANIEL. Watches. NY: Viking, (1965). 1st ed. VG in dj. *Pacific*.* $40/£25

CLYDE, NORMAN. Norman Clyde of the Sierra Nevada. SF: Scrimshaw Press, 1971. Ltd ed. Frontisport, 16 plts. Linen-backed pict bds, paper spine label. Fine. *Pacific*.* $230/£144

CLYNE, GERALDINE. The Jolly Jump-Ups ABC Book. Springfield, MA: McLoughlin Bros, 1948. 27x21 cm. 6 dbl-pg pop-ups. Pict bds (edges lt worn). *Bookfinders.* $80/£50

CLYNE, GERALDINE. The Jolly Jump-Ups and Their New House. Springfield: McLoughlin, 1939. 1st ed. Pop-up. 7 3/4 x 11. Cl-backed pict bds. (Sm pencil names fr cvr), else NF. *Pacific*.* $52/£33

CLYNE, GERALDINE. The Jolly Jump-Ups and Their New House. Springfield, MA: McLoughlin Bros, 1939. 27x19 cm. 6 dbl-pg pop-ups. Pict bds. (Sm break along perforation in 5th pop-up), o/w VG. *Bookfinders.* $80/£50

CLYNE, GERALDINE. Jolly Jump-Ups Favorite Nursery Stories. Springfield, MA: McLoughlin Bros, 1942. 6 dbl-pg pop-ups, incl Little Black Sambo. Pict bds. VG. *Bookfinders.* $150/£94

CLYNE, GERALDINE. The Jolly Jump-Ups Mother Goose. Springfield, MA: McLoughlin Bros, 1944. 19x27 cm. 6 dbl-pg pop-ups. Illus bds (extrems lt worn). *Bookfinders.* $100/£63

CLYNE, GERALDINE. Jolly Jump-Ups Vacation Trip. Springfield, MA: McLoughlin Bros, 1942. 1948 ptg. 19x27 cm. 6 dbl-pg pop-ups. Pict bds. VG. *Bookfinders.* $75/£47

COAKLEY, CORNELIUS G. A Manual of Diseases of the Nose and Throat. NY/Phila, 1905. 3rd ed. 118 engrs, 5 color plts. (Sl yellowed; spine faded, sm end tears), o/w VG. *Doctor's Library.* $30/£19

COAN, TITUS. Life in Hawaii. NY: Anson D.F. Randolph, 1882. Frontisport, viii,340pp. (Cl rubbed, spine ends worn.) *Adelson.* $150/£94

COATES, HENRY. A Perthshire Naturalist. T. Fisher Unwin, 1923. 1st ed. Map. 2-tone cl, gilt. (Feps lt browned.) *Hollett.* $104/£65

COATES, JOHN BOYD, JR. (ed). Surgery in World War II. Washington, 1956. 1st ed. Maroon leatherette cl bds, gilt. VG (sm water stain lower rt corner). *Doctor's Library.* $50/£31

COATES, JOHN BOYD, JR. (ed). Wound Ballistics in World War II. Washington, 1962. 1st ed. Maroon leatherette cl bds, gilt. VG. *Doctor's Library.* $50/£31

COATS, ALICE M. The Travels of Maurice. London: Faber, 1939. 1st ed. Illus bds. *Petersfield.* $13/£8

COATS, ALICE. The Book of Flowers. Phaidon, 1973. 1st ed. Folio. 40 full-pg color, 86 monochrome full-pg plts. VG in dj, thin card slipcase. *Hollett.* $104/£65

COATS, ALICE. Flowers and Their Histories. London: A&C Black, 1968. Rev ed. 4 color plts (incl frontis). NF in dj. *Quest.* $70/£44

COATS, PETER. Flowers in History. NY: Viking, 1970. 1st ed. VG in dj (worn). *Fair Meadow.* $45/£28

COATS, PETER. Great Gardens of Britain. NY: Putnam, c. 1967. 40 color plts. VG in dj (repaired, chipped). *Fair Meadow.* $40/£25

COATS, PETER. Great Gardens of the Western World. NY: Putnam, c. 1963. 40 color, 350 monochrome plts. (Rep creased w/sm punctures), else VG in dj (browned). *Fair Meadow.* $60/£38

COATSWORTH, ELIZABETH. Away Goes Sally. Macmillan, 1934. 1st ed. 122pp. VG (cvr soiled, browned; spine faded). *Price.* $30/£19

COATSWORTH, ELIZABETH. The Cat Who Went to Heaven. NY: Macmillan, 1930. 1st ed. Lynd Ward (illus). Sm 4to. VG in dj. *Houle.* $150/£94

COATSWORTH, ELIZABETH. The Cat Who Went to Heaven. NY: Macmillan, 1930. 1st ed. 4to. Lynd Ward (illus). Red cl. Good in color dj (dknd, edges rubbed) *Reisler.* $250/£156

COATSWORTH, ELIZABETH. The Wonderful Day. Macmillan, 1946. 1st ed. Helen Sewell (illus). 126pp. Yellow bds. VG (corners bumped, worn; bds lt soiled). *Price.* $20/£13

COBB, G. BELTON. Stand to Arms. London: Wells Gardner, Darton, (ca 1916). 1st ed, 1st bk. Frontis. Pict grn cl. (1922 school prize inscrip, sl rubbed), else VG. *Reese.* $95/£59

COBB, HUMPHREY. Paths of Glory. NY: Viking, 1935. 1st ed, only bk. Signed. VG + in dj. *Lame Duck.* $375/£234

COBB, IRVIN S. Speaking of Prussians. NY: George H. Doran, (1917). 1st ed. Frontis. Pict eps. Pict-stamped brn bds. (Spine ends sl worn), o/w VF in dj. *Reese.* $50/£31

COBB, IRVIN S. The Thunders of Silence. NY: George H. Doran, (1918). 1st ed. Frontis. Tan pict bds. NF in Good dj (sl chipped, lt soiled). *Reese.* $50/£31

COBB, JOHN N. Canning of Fishery Products. Seattle: Miller Freeman, 1919. (Corners worn), else VG. *Perier.* $50/£31

COBB, LYMAN. The North American Reader. Trenton/Balt: B. Davenport/Cushing & Sons, 1836. Frontis, 504pp. Contemp calf. (Lt spotted; rubbed, scuffed), else VG. *Brown.* $20/£13

COBBETT, G. T. B. and A. F. JENKIN. Indian Clubs. London, 1895. (v)ads,118pp,(v)ads. (Cl sl dknd.) *Edwards.* $32/£20

COBBETT, WALTER WILLSON. Cobbett's Cyclopedic Survey of Chamber Music. OUP, 1930. 1st ed. 2 vols. 2 frontispieces. VG. *Hollett.* $136/£85

COBBETT, WILLIAM. Cottage Economy. London: The Strand, 1843. 16th ed. Orig cl-backed bds, spine label (sl chipped). Good. *Clearwater.* $56/£35

COBBETT, WILLIAM. Life of Andrew Jackson, President of the United States of America. London: The Author, 1834. 1st ed. Litho frontis, 142pp. Old 1/2 calf, gilt. (Top edges sl stained, faded.) *Hollett.* $192/£120

COBBLEDICK, GORDON. Don't Knock the Rock. World, 1966. 1st ed. Fine in VG dj. *Plapinger.* $225/£141

COBBOLD, ELIZABETH. Poems...with a Memoir of the Author. Ipswich: J. Raw, 1825. (2nd ed?) 8vo. viii (for vi),(3)-192pp. Contemp 1/2 black calf, gilt, raised bands, morocco label, morocco-grain grn cl sides. Good (lacks 1/2-title; bkpls). *Blackwell's.* $232/£145

COBDEN, RICHARD. The American Diaries of.... Elizabeth Hoon Cawley (ed). Princeton, NJ: Princeton Univ, 1952. 1st ed. Fine in dj. *Mott.* $40/£25

COBLENTZ, STANTON A. The Planet of Youth. L.A.: F.P.C.I., 1952. 1st ed. NF in VG + dj (top edge lt chipped). *Other Worlds.* $20/£13

COBLENTZ, STANTON A. Under the Triple Suns. Reading: Fantasy Press, (1955). 1st ed. One of 300. Signed, inscribed. VG in dj (sm chip spine foot, sm tear fr panel). *Pacific*.* $52/£33

COBLENTZ, STANTON A. Villains and Vigilantes. NY: Wilson-Erickson, 1936. 1st ed. Grn cl. Fine in NF dj (sticker remains spine foot). *Harrington.* $50/£31

COBURN, ALVIN LANGDON. Alvin Langdon Coburn, Photographer, and Autobiography. Helmut and Alison Gernsheim (eds). London, (1966). 1st ed. 64 gravure repros. (Eps sl age-dknd; extrems sl worn.) Dj (rubbed, sl yellowed). *Swann*.* $126/£79

COBURN, ALVIN LANGDON. The Door in the Wall and Other Stories. Text by H. G. Wells. NY/London: Mitchell Kennerley, 1911. One of 300. Label affixed to pastedown indicates that Frederic W. Goudy designed the 'now famous Kennerley Type,' and that this vol contains the Aquatone plts. Folio. 10 aquatone illus. Magenta bds, gilt. (Fep notes; lt faded, spine label browned.) Contents Clean. *Swann**. $690/£431

COBURN, ALVIN LANGDON. New York. London/NY: Duckworth/Brentano's, (1910). 1st ed. Folio. 20 tipped-in photogravures. Morocco-backed bds (rebacked, fr cvr bowed, corners frayed; notes, inscrip), gilt. *Swann**. $6,670/£4,169

COCHRANE, ALEXANDER BAILLIE. The Theatre Francaise in the Reign of Louis XV. London: Hurst & Blackett, 1879. Marbled eps. 1/2 red morocco, spine gilt, marbled bds. (Spine crown worn.) Internally Fine. *Dramatis*. $40/£25

COCHRANE, J. A. Dr. Johnson's Printer. The Life of William Strahan. Routledge & Kegan Paul, 1964. 1st ed. 4 plts. Dj. *Forest*. $35/£22

COCHRANE, JOHN DUNDAS. Narrative of a Pedestrian Journey Through Russia and Siberian Tartary.... John Murray, 1824. 1st ed. 8vo. xvi,564pp; 2 lg fldg maps. All edges uncut. Orig brn paper bds (neatly rebacked in calf), label, gilt. VG (sm repairs to inner margin of 1/2-title; bds sl bumped, corners rubbed). *Sotheran*. $520/£325

COCHRANE, WILLIAM A. Orthopedic Surgery. NY, 1926. Grn cl. (Tears in text, none missing, fr inner hinge cracked; extrms worn, binding loose), o/w Good. *Doctor's Library*. $50/£31

Cockalorum. A Sequel to Chanticleer and Pertelote. Being a Bibliography of the Golden Cockerel Press June 1943-December 1948. Golden Cockerel, 1950. One of 250 signed by Christopher Sandford (foreword, notes). Teg, rest untrimmed. Orig 1/4 mid brn crushed morocco, gilt, raised bands. Fine. *Blackwell's*. $400/£250

COCKBURN, GEORGE. A Voyage to Cadiz and Gibraltar, Up the Mediterranean to Sicily and Malta, in 1810, and 11. London, 1815. 2 vols. W/errata leaf. Engr tp, 6 maps, plans, 23 hand-colored aquatint plts. Early 1/2 calf. (Sm emb lib stamps; worn, several cvrs loose.) *Swann**. $373/£233

COCKBURN, HENRY THOMAS. Life of Lord Jeffrey with a Selection from His Correspondence. Edinburgh: A&C Black, 1852. 2nd ed. 2 vols. Marbled edges. 1/4 crimson calf (rubbed). *Boswell*. $250/£156

COCKBURN, JAMES PATTISON. Swiss Scenery. London: Rodwell & Martin, 1820. 1st ed. Engr tp, 60 plts. (Lacks 1/2-title; tp, few plts spotted.) Mod 1/2 morocco, marbled bds. *Christie's**. $576/£360

COCKE, SARAH JOHNSON. Bypaths in Dixie: Folk Tales of the South. NY: Dutton, (1911). 1st ed. 7 plts. VG (hinges cracked but tight). *Agvent*. $150/£94

COCKER, MARK. Loneliness and Time. Secker & Warburg, 1992. 1st ed. Mint in dj. *Virgo*. $32/£20

COCKERAM, HENRY. The English Dictionary of 1623. NY: Huntington, 1930. 1st ed thus. One of 999. Frontis. Full brn suede, facs label. Nice (spine sl discolored) in slipcase w/red label, gilt. *Hartfield*. $165/£103

COCKERELL, CHARLES ROBERT. Iconography of the West Front of Wells Cathedral. John Henry Parker, 1851. 1st ed. Fldg frontis (sl spotted), xxiii,126,115pp; 8 plts (2 tinted lithos). Blind-ruled ribbed cl (neatly recased), gilt. *Hollett*. $200/£125

COCKERELL, DOUGLAS. Bookbinding, and the Care of Books. John Hogg, 1901. 1st ed. Frontis, 8 plts. (Sl faded.) *Forest*. $32/£20

COCKERELL, SIDNEY. Old Testament Miniatures. A Medieval Picture Book with 283 Paintings from the Creation to the Story of David. NY, n.d. (ca 1975). Folio. Good in dj (worn). *Washton*. $100/£63

COCKERELL, SYDNEY. The Best of Friends. Further Letters to Sydney Carlyle Cockerell. Viola Meynell (ed). London: Rupert Hart-Davis, 1956. 1st ed. 8 plts. VG in dj. *Cady*. $30/£19

COCKERELL, SYDNEY. Old Testament Miniatures: A Medieval Picture Book.... NY: George Braziller, (1969). 1st Amer ed. VG in dj (extrms rubbed, chipped). *Pacific**. $184/£115

COCKSHOOT, JOHN V. The Fugue in Beethoven's Piano Music. Egon Werllesz (ed). Routledge/Kegan Paul, 1959. 1st ed. VG in dj. *Hollett*. $40/£25

COCKTON, HENRY. The Life and Adventures of Valentine Vox, the Ventriloquist. Robert Tyas, 1840. 1st ed. Frontis, extra engr tp, xx,620pp; 58 etched plts. Sound (spotted, mostly to plt margins) in contemp 1/2 calf (rebacked, preserving orig backstrip), marbled sides, morocco label. *Cox*. $104/£65

COCKTON, HENRY. The Life and Adventures of Valentine Vox, the Ventriloquist. London: Robert Tyas, 1840. 1st ed. (iii)-xx,620pp; 60 etched plts (incl frontis, added tp) by J. Onwhyn. Marbled eps; aeg. Full polished tan calf, gilt, morocco labels. Bound by Riviere. (Lacks 1/2-title, lt foxed, offset, some plts marginally dknd; cvrs sl discolored), else NF. *Pacific**. $115/£72

COCTEAU, JEAN. 5 Plays. NY: Hill & Wang, (1961). 1st Amer ed. (Fep sl creased), else VF in VF dj (rear cvr sl rubbed). *Between The Covers*. $100/£63

COCTEAU, JEAN. The Blood of a Poet [and] The Testament of Orpheus. NY: Orion, (1968). 1st Amer ed. VF in dj. *Between The Covers*. $100/£63

COCTEAU, JEAN. Cocteau on the Film. NY: Roy Pub, 1954. 1st Amer ed. VF in VF dj. *Between The Covers*. $200/£125

COCTEAU, JEAN. The Difficulty of Being. Elizabeth Sprigge (trans). NY: Coward-McCann, 1967. 1st ed. Fine in NF dj (price-clipped, extrms rubbed). *Smith*. $25/£16

COCTEAU, JEAN. The Eagle Has Two Heads. Ronald Duncan (trans). NY: Funk & Wagnalls, (1948). 1st ed. VF in VF dj (less than 1/16 inch shorter than bk). *Between The Covers*. $175/£109

COCTEAU, JEAN. The Head of a Stranger. NY: Horizon, (1959). 1st Amer ed. VF in VF dj (rear cvr sl soiled). *Between The Covers*. $150/£94

COCTEAU, JEAN. The Human Voice. (London): Vision, (1951). 1st Eng ed. VF in VF dj (extrms sl rubbed). *Between The Covers*. $125/£78

COCTEAU, JEAN. The Imposter. Dorothy Williams (trans). London: Peter Owen, (1957). 1st ed. Gilt black cl (lt foxed), else NF in VG pict dj (lt soiled). *Reese*. $35/£22

COCTEAU, JEAN. The Infernal Machine and Other Plays. NY: New Directions, (1963). 1st ed. VF in VF dj. *Between The Covers*. $100/£63

COCTEAU, JEAN. Journals of Jean Cocteau. Wallace Fowlie (ed). NY: Criterion, (1956). 1st ed. (One corner sl bumped), else VF in Fine black dj (rubbed). *Between The Covers*. $65/£41

COCTEAU, JEAN. Maalesh: a Theatrical Tour of the Middle East. London: Peter Owen, (n.d. 1949). 1st Eng ed. Fine in Fine dj (price-clipped; trimmed 1/8 inch). *Between The Covers*. $125/£78

COCTEAU, JEAN. My Contemporaries. Phila: Chilton, (1968). 1st Amer ed. VF in VF dj. *Between The Covers*. $100/£63

COCTEAU, JEAN. Paris Album, 1900-1914. London: W.H. Allen, 1956. 1st Eng ed. VF in VF dj. *Between The Covers*. $100/£63

COCTEAU, JEAN. Three Screenplays. NY: Grossman, 1972. 1st Amer ed. VF in VF dj. *Between The Covers*. $100/£63

COCTEAU, JEAN. The Typewriter: a Play in Three Acts. Ronald Duncan (trans). London: Dobson, 1947. 1st Eng ed. (Bds sl splayed), else VF in VF dj. *Between The Covers*. $150/£94

CODRESCU, ANDREI. The History of the Growth of Heaven. NY, (1973). 1st (wraps) ed. Presentation copy. Inscribed, signed. Good. *King*. $22/£14

CODRESCU, ANDREI. The Life and Times of an Involuntary Genius. NY, 1975. 1st Amer ed. Signed. Fine (spine sl rubbed) in Fine dj. *Polyanthos*. $30/£19

CODY, LIZA. Head Case. Collins, 1985. 1st UK ed. Inscribed. Fine in dj. *Williams*. $77/£48

CODY, W. F. An Autobiography of Buffalo Bill. NY: Cosmopolitan, 1920. 1st Wyeth ed. N. C. Wyeth (illus). Pict cl. VG. *Pacific**. $138/£86

COE, CHARLES H. Juggling a Rope; Lariat Roping and Spinning, Knots and Splices.... Pendleton, OR: Harmley, 1927. 1st ed. VG + . *Labordo*. $85/£53

COE, GEORGE W. Frontier Fighter, the Autobiography of George W. Coe...As Related to Nan Hillary Harrison. Boston: Houghton Mifflin, 1934. 1st ed. VG + in dj. Howes C534. *Labordo*. $225/£141

COE, GEORGE W. Frontier Fighter. Albuquerque, 1951. 2nd ed. Pict cl. (Bottom cvr edges sl worn), else Fine in dj (worn, price-clipped). Howes C534. *Baade*. $45/£28

COE, GEORGE W. Frontier Fighter. D. B. Nunis, Jr. (ed). Chicago: R.R. Donnelley, (1984). Frontis. VG. *Lien*. $30/£19

COETZEE, J. M. Dusklands. Johannisberg: Ravan, 1974. 1st UK ed, 1st bk. NF in dj. *Williams*. $320/£200

COETZEE, J. M. Life and Times of Michael K. Secker, 1983. 1st UK ed. Fine (ink inscrip) in dj. *Williams*. $29/£18

COETZEE, J. M. Truth in Autobiography. (Cape Town): Univ of Cape Town, 1985. 1st ed. 6pp. As New in stapled blue wrappers. *Between The Covers*. $100/£63

COFFEY, BRIAN. Third Person. George Reavey/Europa, 1938. One of 300. VG + in VG- dj (frayed, tanned). *Any Amount*. $56/£35

COFFIN, LEVI. Reminiscences of Levi Coffin.... London/Cincinnati: Sampson, Low et al/Western Tract Soc, 1876. 1st Eng ed. (2 port plts), (tp), (v)-vi,i-iii,(blank),vii-viii,3-712pp apparently as issued. (Spine faded, fr joint splitting.) Howes C540. *Zubal**. $40/£25

COFFIN, MARIE M. The History of Nantucket Island. (Nantucket: Nantucket Hist Trust, 1970.) 1st ed, ltd ed. *Lefkowicz*. $35/£22

COFFINBERRY, ANDREW. The Forest Rangers: A Poetic Tale.... Columbus, 1842. 1st ed. 220pp (foxed, sl stained, soiled). Mod 1/2 morocco. *Oinonen**. $50/£31

COGGINS, J. C. Abraham Lincoln, a North Carolinian. Gastonia, NC: Carolina Ptg, 1927. 2nd ed. Grn cl. NF. *Chapel Hill*. $150/£94

COGHLAN, MARGARET. Memoirs of Mrs. Coghlan, Daughter of the Later Major Moncrieffe. NY: Privately published, 1864. One of 120. Later cl (sl worn). Contents VG. Howes C543. *New Hampshire**. $70/£44

COHEN, HARVEY. The Amphetamine Manifesto. NY, (1972). 1st Amer ed. NF (sl rubbed) in pict wraps. *Polyanthos*. $25/£16

COHEN, HOWARD. Ebenezer Cooke: The Sot-Weed Canon. Athens, GA, 1971. 1st ed. As New in dj. *Bond*. $20/£13

COHEN, I. BERNARD. Some Early Tools of American Science. Cambridge: Harvard Univ, 1950. 1st ed. VG (gilt dull). *Glaser*. $50/£31

COHEN, ISRAEL. The Ruhleben Prison Camp: A Record of Nineteen Months Internment. London: Methuen, (1917). 1st ed. Frontis. Dk blue cl stamped in gilt/blind. (Spine gilt perished, sl foxed, rear inner hinge cracking), o/w Good. *Reese*. $45/£28

COHEN, KATHLEEN. Metamorphosis of a Death Symbol. Berkeley: Univ of CA, (1973). NF in dj. *Turtle Island*. $70/£44

COHEN, LEONARD. The Energy of Slaves. London, 1972. 1st ed. Fine in dj. *Warren*. $40/£25

COHEN, LEONARD. The Favorite Game. NY, (1963). 1st Amer ed. Pict cl. VG in Nice dj (sl soiled). *King*. $175/£109

COHEN, LEONARD. The Spice-Box of Earth. NY: Viking, (1965). 1st Amer ed. Fine in VG dj (2 long tears rear panel, internally repaired). *Between The Covers*. $125/£78

COHEN, MARVIN. Baseball the Beautiful: Decoding the Diamond. NY: Links, (1974). 1st ed. Inscribed. Fine in NF dj (edges yellowing). *Between The Covers*. $100/£63

COHEN, MARVIN. Fables at Life's Expense. NY: Latitudes, 1975. 1st ed. Inscribed. NF in illus wraps (spine sl tanned). *Lame Duck*. $65/£41

COHEN, MARVIN. The Inconvenience of Living. NY: Urizen, 1977. 1st ed. NF in VG + dj. *Lame Duck*. $35/£22

COHEN, MORTON N. Lewis Carroll at Christ Church. (London): Nat'l Portrait Gallery, 1974. 1st ed. 28 b/w photos. (Stamp), else NF in pict stiff wrappers. *Cahan*. $30/£19

COHEN, NIK. King Death. NY: Harcourt Brace, 1975. 1st ed. Fine in Fine dj. *Pettler*. $15/£9

COHEN, SOLOMON SOLIS A. A System of Physiologic Therapeutics, Volume 1 Electrotherapy. Phila, 1901. 1st ed. VG (inner hinges starting; extrems sl worn). *Doctor's Library*. $40/£25

COHN, ALBERT. George Cruikshank: A Catalogue Raisonne. London, 1924. One of 500 numbered. *Swann**. $287/£179

COHN, LOUIS HENRY. A Bibliography of the Works of Ernest Hemingway. NY: Random House, 1931. 1st ed. Fldg frontis facs. Black cl, gilt spine. (Sl foxed), else NF. *Pacific**. $58/£36

COHN, WILLIAM. Chinese Painting. Phaidon, 1948. 1st ed. Sm folio. 224 plts. VG in dj. *Hollett*. $64/£40

COIGNEY, RODOLPHE L. (comp). Walton Izaak: A New Bibliography, 1653-1987. NY: James Cummins, 1989. 1st ed. One of 500 numbered, signed. Scarlet buckram, gilt. Fine in NF dj. *Baltimore**. $55/£34

COIT, DANIEL WADSWORTH. Digging for Gold—Without a Shovel. George P. Hammond (ed). (Denver): Fred Rosenstock, 1967. Ltd to 1250 ptd. Frontis, 16 plts. Red pict cl. Fine. *Harrington*. $60/£38

COKE, LAWRENCE and LUCILLE. Mining on the Trails of Destiny. NY, (1969). Inscribed, dated by both. VG in VG dj. *Sagebrush*. $55/£34

COKE, VAN DEREN and DIANA C. DU PONT. Photography: A Facet of Modernism. NY: Hudson Hills, 1986. 1st ed. 25 color, 130 b/w plts. Fine in dj. *Cahan*. $75/£47

COKE, VAN DEREN. Andrew Dasburg. Albuquerque, 1979. 1st ed. NF in dj (lt worn). *Dumont*. $90/£56

COKE, VAN DEREN. Photography in New Mexico. From the Daguerreotype to the Present. Albuquerque, (1979). 1st ed. Frontis. Fine in NF dj. *Sagebrush*. $65/£41

COKER, W. S. It Happened in Cow Country. Broken Bow, (NE), 1972. 1st ed. Dec cl. Fine in dj. *Baade*. $32/£20

COLBURN, WARREN. Arithmetic upon the Inductive Method of Instruction. NY/Boston: R. Lockwood/Hilliard, Gray, Little, & Wilkins, 1830. 1st ed. 245,(5)pp. Contemp calf. (Lib bkpl, shelf labels; scuffed, rubbed, lacks label), else Good. *Brown*. $30/£19

COLE, BABETTE. Don't Go Out Tonight. Hamish Hamilton, 1982. Pop-up bk. VG. *Green Meadow*. $40/£25

COLE, CYRENUS. I Am a Man: The Indian Black Hawk. St. Hist Soc of IA, 1938. VG. *Rybski*. $100/£63

COLE, DESMOND T. Lithops, Flowering Stones. Johannesburg, 1988. 1st ed. One of 2400. Fine in dj. *Brooks*. $160/£100

COLE, EMMA. The Life and Sufferings of Miss Emma Cole, Being a Faithful Narrative of Her Life. Boston: M. Aurelius, 1844. 1st ed. Frontis, 36pp. (Text dampstained; frontis, 1st few ll stained sl affecting text; lacks wrappers), else Good. *Brown*. $50/£31

COLE, ERNEST. House of Bondage. NY: Ridge/Random House, 1967. 1st ed. Fine in Fine dj. *Beasley*. $45/£28

COLE, HARRY ELLSWORTH. Stagecoach and Tavern Tales of the Old Northwest. Louise P. Kellogg (ed). Cleveland: Arthur C. Clark, 1930. 1st ed. Dbl-pg map at fr. Teg, untrimmed. Navy ribbed cl, gilt. Very Clean (lt aged, bkpl, sig; sl shelfworn). *Baltimore**. $35/£22

COLE, JOHN. Amaranth. Emmaus: Rodale, 1979. 1st ed. Fine in NF dj. *Archer*. $15/£9

COLE, M. ELIZ. Jottings from Overland Trip to Arizona and California. (Poughkeepsie, NY: Privately ptd, 1908.) 1st ed. Good + in ptd wraps. *Wantagh*. $100/£63

COLE, MARY COOK. Savage Gentlemen. George G. Harrap, 1929. 1st ed. Black cl, gilt. VF in brn dj (2 sm tears). *Sotheran*. $312/£195

COLE, S. W. The American Fruit-Book. Boston: John P. Jewett, 1849. 1st ed. xii,288pp. Calf, bds. Good (eps stained; spine damaged). *Bookcell*. $50/£31

COLE, WILLIAM. A Cat-Hater's Handbook. NY: Dial, 1963. 1st ed. 6x8.5. Tomi Ungerer (illus). 60pp. VG in dj. *Cattermole*. $50/£31

COLEGATE, I. The Blackmailer. London: Blond, 1958. 1st ed. (Eps offset, foxed; top-edge sl speckled), o/w VG in dj (spotted internally, corners sl chipped, spine faded, price clipped). *Virgo*. $136/£85

COLEGATE, I. The Blackmailer. Blond, 1958. 1st ed. (Eps foxed, offsetting; top edge speckled), o/w VG in dj (spotted, corners sl chipped, spine faded, price-clipped). *Virgo*. $136/£85

COLEGATE, I. The Shooting Party. Hamish Hamilton, 1980. 1st ed. Fine in dj. *Virgo*. $19/£12

COLEGATE, I. The Shooting Party. Hamilton, 1980. 1st UK ed. NF in dj. *Williams*. $24/£15

COLEMAN, A. P. Ice Ages, Recent and Ancient. NY: Macmillan, 1926. 1st ed. (Spine ends sl rubbed), else NF. *Pacific**. $63/£39

COLEMAN, ARTHUR and BOBBIE. The Texas Cookbook: Culinary and Campfire Lore from the Lone Star State. A.A. Wyn, 1949. 1st ed. VG- in VG- dj. *Book Broker*. $35/£22

COLEMAN, EDWARD D. (comp). The Bible in English Drama. NY: NYPL, 1931. VG in orig wraps. *Dramatis*. $30/£19

COLEMAN, H. T. J. A Rhyme for a Penny. Vancouver: Clarke, 1934. 1st ed. 6.3x9.3. Elisabeth Kerr (illus). 49pp. Fine in VG dj (1/2-inch chip). *Price*. $25/£16

COLEMAN, J. D. (ed). 1st Air Cavalry Division: Memoirs of the First Team, Vietnam, August 1965-December 1969. Tokyo: Dai Nippon Ptg, 1969. 1st ed. (Name), else NF. *Associates*. $200/£125

COLEMAN, LONNIE. Sam. NY: McKay, (1959). 1st ed. VF in Fine dj (sl rubbed). *Between The Covers*. $75/£47

COLEMAN-COOKE, JOHN. Discovery II in the Antarctic. London: Oldham, 1963. Map. VG in dj. *High Latitude*. $32/£20

COLENSO, JOHN W. Ten Weeks in Natal. Cambridge: Macmillan, 1855. 1st ed. (xxxi),271,(xvi)pp; fldg map, 4 litho plts. (Sl worn.) *Maggs*. $192/£120

COLERIDGE, G. Pan's People. London: T. F. Unwin, 1923. 1st ed. Pict cl (Spine faded), else VG. *Mikesh*. $25/£16

COLERIDGE, HARTLEY. Biographia Borealis; or Lives of Distinguished Northerns. London/Leeds: Whitaker, Treacher/F.E. Bingley, 1833. 1st ed. viii,732pp; 2 engr ports. Mod 1/2 levant morocco, gilt, w/raised bands, spine label. VG. *Hollett*. $256/£160

COLERIDGE, SAMUEL TAYLOR. The Ancient Mariner. London: George C. Harrap, (1910). 1st ed illus by Willy Pogany. 20 mtd color plts. Uncut. Gray cl, gilt. Very Nice (inner hinge cracked; sl speckled). *Sotheran*. $269/£168

COLERIDGE, SAMUEL TAYLOR. Biographia Literaria; or Biographical Sketches of My Literary Life and Opinions. Rest Fenner, 1817. 1st eds. 2 vols in 1. Lacks half-titles. Pub's ads at end of vol 2. Contemp polished speckled calf (rebacked, sl rubbed). *Sotheby's**. $368/£230

COLERIDGE, SAMUEL TAYLOR. Christabel, Kubla Khan, Fancy in Nubibus, and Song from Zapolya. London: Eragny, (1904). 1st ed thus. One of 226 (of 236). Lucien Pissarro (illus). (Hinge between 2 fr blanks reinforced w/paper), o/w Fine. *Agvent*. $400/£250

COLERIDGE, SAMUEL TAYLOR. Christabel; Kubla Khan, a Vision; The Pains of Sleep. John Murray, 1816. 1st ed, 1st ptg of all 3. 8vo. vi,64pp; w/o half-title and terminal ads present in some copies. Marbled eps; aeg, inner dentelles, by Riviere. Full tan calf (faded, joints sl rubbed), French fillet border to sides, fully gilt spine w/2 morocco labels. *Sotheran*. $1,597/£998

COLERIDGE, SAMUEL TAYLOR. Confessions of an Enquiring Spirit. Henry Nelson Coleridge (ed). William Pickering, 1840. 1st ed. Prelim ad leaf, (8),x,(2),95pp + 16pp pub's cat. Uncut. Good (sl browned) in blue cl (hinges splitting, spine ends chipped, paper label defective). *Cox*. $77/£48

COLERIDGE, SAMUEL TAYLOR. Confessions of an Enquiring Spirit. Henry Nelson Coleridge (ed). Boston: James Munroe, 1841. 1st Amer ed. Orig blue-grn cl, label. (Spine head chip), else Good. *Macdonnell*. $125/£78

COLERIDGE, SAMUEL TAYLOR. The Friend. Burlington: Chauncey Goodrich, 1831. 1st Amer ed. Orig 1/4 muslin, label. Good (worn). *Macdonnell*. $150/£94

COLERIDGE, SAMUEL TAYLOR. The Rime of the Ancient Mariner. NY: Thomas Crowell, (1910). 1st ed thus. Willy Pogany (illus). 20 tipped-in color plts. (Sm tear 1/2-title), else NF. *Pacific**. $196/£123

COLERIDGE, SAMUEL TAYLOR. The Rime of the Ancient Mariner. Bristol: Douglas Cleverdon, 1929. One of 400. 4to. 10 copper engrs. Fine in cl-backed bds. *Bromer*. $950/£594

COLERIDGE, SAMUEL TAYLOR. The Rime of the Ancient Mariner. London: C&W, 1971. 1st ed. 8x10. C. Walter Hodges (illus). c.48pp. Fine in Fine dj. *Price*. $35/£22

COLERIDGE, SAMUEL TAYLOR. The Rime of the Ancient Mariner. LEC, 1983. Ltd to 1500 numbered, signed by Edward A. Wilson (illus). Fine in slipcase. *Swann**. $69/£43

COLERIDGE, SAMUEL TAYLOR. Sibylline Leaves: A Collection of Poems. Rest Fenner, 1817. 1st ed. 8vo. 19th-cent full morocco, gilt. (Half-title, prelims sl foxed.) *Sotheby's**. $1,067/£667

COLERIDGE, SAMUEL TAYLOR. Specimens of the Table Talk of the Late Samuel Taylor Coleridge. (By Samuel Taylor Coleridge.) John Murray, 1835. 2 vols. Frontispieces. Aeg. Contemp full-vellum (yawing), leather spine labels. Good (sl spotted). *Tiger*. $106/£66

COLES, ABRAHAM. Wine in the World. NY, 1878. 1st ed. 48pp. VG (ex-lib, extrems sl worn) in ptd wrappers. *Doctor's Library*. $50/£31

COLES, ROBERT. The Darkness and the Light, Photographs by Doris Ulmann. NY, (1974). 1st ed. (Notes fep.) Dj (lt soiled). *Swann**. $149/£93

COLES, ROBERT. The Darkness and the Light. NY: Aperture, 1974. 1st ed. 65 b/w plts by Doris Ulmann. (Sig; illus stiff wrapper dusty), else VG. *Cahan*. $60/£38

COLES, ROBERT. The South Goes North. Volume III of Children of Crisis. Boston: Atlantic Monthly, (1971). 1st ed. Brn cl. VG + in dj (lt soiled). *House*. $20/£13

COLES. Recollections and Reflections by Coles Pasha, C.M.G., Late Inspector-General of Prisons, Egypt. London: Saint Catherine Press, (1918). Frontisport, 5 plts. *Archaeologia*. $45/£28

COLETTA, PAOLO E. William Jennings Bryan, 1860-1925. Univ of NE, 1964-1971. 3 vols. (Ex-lib, mkd, worn.) *Rybski*. $55/£34

COLETTE. The Break of Day. LEC, 1983. One of 2000 signed by Francoise Gilot (illus). Fine in slipcase. *Swann**. $138/£86

COLETTE. Mitsou and Music-Hall Delights. NY: FSG, (post 1957). Rpt. Purple cl, gilt. Fine in NF dj. *Reese*. $18/£11

COLETTE. Mitsou, or How Girls Grow Wise. Jane Terry (trans). NY: Albert & Charles Boni, 1930. 1st US ed. Violet cl, gilt. Good (sm bkshop stamp; spine sl dull, cocked) in pict dj (lt chipped, internal mend). *Reese*. $50/£31

Collection of All Such Public Acts of the General Assembly, and Ordinances of the Conventions of Virginia, Passed Since the Year 1768, As Are Now in Force.... Richmond: Thomas Nicholson & William Prentis, 1785. Folio. 235pp. Mod calf-backed marbled bds. (Faint rubberstamp, sl foxed, lacks few marginal lower corners of pp), else VG. *Pacific**. $489/£306

Collection of Familiar Quotations. (By John Bartlett.) Cambridge: John Bartlett, 1856. 2nd ed. viii,358pp. Blindstamped blue cl (faded). *Karmiole*. $125/£78

COLLIER, J. PAYNE. A Bibliographical Account of the Rarest Books in the English Language.... London: Joseph Lilly, 1865. 1st ed. 2 vols. (Pg extrems chipped), else VG in later marbled wrappers. *Pacific**. $58/£36

COLLIER, JEREMY. A Defence of the Short View of the Profaneness and Immorality of the English Stage, etc. London: S. Keble, R. Sare & H. Hindmarch, 1699. 1st ed. (4),139,(1)pp. Period calf. (Spotted; fr cvr nearly detached, extrems rubbed), else VG-. *Pacific**. $150/£94

COLLIER, JOHN. The Devil and All: Six Short Stories. (London): Nonesuch, 1934. One of 1000. Signed. Wood-engr frontis. Grn cl, gilt. Fine in Good acetate/foil dj (chipped). *Pacific**. $75/£47

COLLIER, JOHN. Fancies and Goodnights. GC: Doubleday, 1951. VG (spine ends, corners sl bumped, cvrs sl cocked) in dj (nicked, rubbed, dusty, sl torn, chipped, creased, spine edges sl dknd). *Ulysses*. $152/£95

COLLIER, JOHN. Witch's Money. NY: Viking, 1940. One of 350 numbered, signed. Ptd pub's slip laid in. Red cl. Fine in tissue dj (used). *Dermont*. $250/£156

COLLIER, RICHARD. 1940, the World in Flames. London, 1979. 1st ed. Fine in Fine dj. *Pratt*. $17/£11

COLLIER, WILLIAM ROSS and EDWIN VICTOR WESTRATE. The Reign of Soapy Smith. GC, 1935. 1st ed. Pict cl. (Top fr cvr sl bumped, extrems sl worn), else VG in dj (badly chipped, fr lacks piece). *Baade*. $40/£25

COLLING, JAMES KELLAWAY. Examples of English Mediaeval Foliage and Coloured Decoration from Buildings of the XIIth to the XVth Centuries. London: The Author/Batsford, 1874. 75 plts. (Lt worn, binding loose.) *Oinonen**. $40/£25

COLLINGS, ELLSWORTH and ALMA MILLER ENGLAND. The 101 Ranch. Norman: Univ of OK, 1938. 2nd ed. Pub's comp slip laid in. VG in dj (spine head chipped, extrems lack few sm pieces). *Pacific**. $52/£33

COLLINGS, ELLSWORTH. The Old Home Ranch. Stillwater, OK: Redlands, 1964. 1st ed. NF in dj. *Labordo*. $55/£34

COLLINGWOOD, STUART. The Life and Letters of Lewis Carroll. London: T. Fisher Unwin, 1898. 1st ed. xx,448,(xii)pp. Teg. Gilt cl over beveled bds (sl mkd, spine faded; upper joint cracked). *Hollett*. $64/£40

COLLINS, A. F. Book Crafts for Seniors. Dryad, 1959. Good. *Moss*. $19/£12

COLLINS, ASA W. Doctor Asa. L.A., (1941). Dj (few sm tears). *Dawson*. $100/£63

COLLINS, CECIL. The Vision of the Fool. Grey Walls, 1947. 1st Eng ed. Nice (lib rubberstamp blacked-out at foot of dedication pg, along fore-edges) in dj (sl chipped, torn). *Clearwater*. $88/£55

COLLINS, E. TREACHER. In the Kingdom of the Shah. London: T. Fisher Unwin, 1896. 1st ed. xii,300pp (incl 1/2-title, frontisport, map). Blue cl. VG (margins lt browned, thumb mks; cracked hinges, discolored spine, rubbed). *Morrell*. $176/£110

COLLINS, FRANCIS. Mountain Climbing. John Long, 1924. 1st Eng ed. (Spine, edges faded, sl frayed.) *Hollett*. $40/£25

COLLINS, GEORGE R. and JUAN BASSEGODA NONELL. The Designs and Drawings of Antonio Gaudi. Princeton, (1983). Folio. Dj. *Swann**. $69/£43

COLLINS, GREENVILLE. Great Britain's Coasting Pilot. London: Harrap, n.d. (ca 1968). Facs of 1753 ed. Folio. Pseudo-calf. Dj. *Marlborough*. $280/£175

COLLINS, HENRY B. et al. The Aleutian Islands: Their People and Natural History. Washington: Smithsonian Inst. War Background Studies No. 21, Feb 5, 1945. Fldg map. VG in ptd wrapper. *High Latitude*. $25/£16

COLLINS, HUBERT EDWIN. Warpath and Cattle Trail. NY: William Morrow, 1928. 1st ed. VG + . Howes C592. *Labordo*. $185/£116

COLLINS, JESS. Translations. L.A.: Black Sparrow, 1971. One of 250 signed by Collins and Robert Duncan (intro). Yellow cl w/color repro laid on. NF. *Turtle Island*. $150/£94

COLLINS, JOE G. The Last of Steam. Berkeley: Howell-North, 1960. 1st ed. VG + (sl shelfworn) in dj (edgeworn). *My Bookhouse*. $42/£26

COLLINS, W. WILKIE. Rambles Beyond Railways; or, Notes in Cornwall Taken A-Foot. Richard Bentley, 1852. 2nd ed. Tinted litho frontis, iv,(iv),304pp; 11 plts. Gray eps; polished red sprinkled edges. Contemp red morocco, gilt, raised bands. Good (lt foxed). *Blackwell's*. $216/£135

COLLINS, WILKIE. The Moonstone. LEC, 1959. Ltd to 1500 numbered, signed by Andre Dignimont (illus). Fine in slipcase. *Swann**. $57/£36

COLLINS, WILKIE. The Moonstone. NY: LEC, 1959. One of 1500. Signed by Andre Dignimont (illus). Gilt-dec blue buckram, red morocco spine label. Fine in glassine, slipcase. *Pacific**. $58/£36

COLLINS, WILKIE. The Woman in White. NY: Harper, 1860. True 1st ed; 1st issue binding. Dk brn blind cl. (Lt browned, foxed, lacks fep, lg bkpl, stain fr pastedown; sl worn, frayed, old stains.) *Baltimore**. $100/£63

COLLINS, WILKIE. The Woman in White. LEC, 1964. Ltd to 1500 numbered, signed by Leonard Rosoman (illus). Fine in slipcase. *Swann**. $57/£36

COLLINS, WILLIAM. The Poetical Works of William Collins. Alexander Dyce (ed). London: William Pickering, 1827. 1st ed. Marbled eps; gilt inner dentelles. Full red morocco, raised bands, gilt. Fine. *Pharos*. $150/£94

COLLINSON, RICHARD. Journal of H.M.S. Enterprise, on the Expedition in Search of Sir John Franklin's Ship by Behring Strait, 1850-55. London, 1889. 1st ed. 8vo. Color frontis, x,532,32ads pp; 6 maps, port. Pict cl (corners lt rubbed), gilt. *Maggs*. $2,000/£1,250

COLLISON, ROBERT. The Story of Street Literature. J.M. Dent, 1973. 1st ed. Dj. *Forest*. $29/£18

COLLODI, CARLO. Pinocchio, the Adventures of a Marionette. LEC, 1937. Ltd to 1500 numbered, signed by Richard Floethe (illus). Fine in slipcase. *Swann**. $115/£72

COLLODI, CARLO. Pinocchio, the Story of a Puppet. Phila: Lippincott, (1920). Deluxe ed. 4to. 14 mtd color plts by Maria L. Kirk. 2-tone linen bds, gilt top. *Appelfeld*. $85/£53

COLLODI, CARLO. Pinocchio. Phila: Lippincott, (1920). 8vo. 234pp; 14 tipped-in color illus by Maria L. Kirk. Blue cl, beige spine, gilt. VG. *Davidson*. $85/£53

COLLODI, CARLO. Pinocchio. NY: J.H. Sears, (1926). 1st ed thus. 9 1/2 x 7 1/2. Frontis color plt by Christopher Rule. Gilt-lettered olive cl, pict cvr label. VG. *Pacific**. $46/£29

COLLODI, CARLO. Pinocchio. NY: Blue Ribbon, (1933). 1st ed. Thick 4to. 96pp; 4 color pop-ups by Harold Lentz. Illus eps. Pict bds. VG + in pict dj. *Davidson*. $675/£422

COLLON-GEVAERT, SUZANNE et al. A Treasury of Romanesque Art. London, 1972. 83 plts (70 tipped-in color). (Cl sl soiled.) *Washton*. $250/£156

COLLYNS, CHARLES PALK. The Chase of the Wild Red Deer. London: Lawrence & Bullen, 1902. (Sl foxed.) *Oinonen**. $50/£31

COLMAN, BENJAMIN. David's Dying Charge to the Rulers and People of Israel, a Sermon. Boston, 1723. (2),6,41pp, stitched. Evidence of early wrappers. *Swann**. $287/£179

COLMAN, GEORGE. Broad Grins. London: T. Cadell, 1809. 4th ed. Engr/ptd tps, vii,128pp; 12 engr vignettes. Contemp mid-tan tree-calf, black morocco label, gilt. VG (sl rubbed). *Young*. $72/£45

COLNETT, JAMES. The Journal of Captain James Colnett Aboard the Argonaut from April 26, 1789 to Nov. 2, 1791. F.W. Howay (ed). Toronto: Champlain Soc, 1940. One of 550. Unopened; teg. Red buckram, gilt. (Spine sl faded), else Fine. *Pacific**. $184/£115

Colorado Springs. (By Helen Hunt Jackson.) Boston: Roberts Bros, 1883. Rpt. (4),92pp. (1st leaf well soiled, old name), o/w VG in ptd wrappers (soiled, few sm chips). *Pacific**. $81/£51

COLQUHOUN, A. R. The Mastery of the Pacific. London, 1902. 3 fldg maps. VG. *Hallam*. $48/£30

COLQUHOUN, JOHN. The Moor and the Loch. William Blackwood & Sons, 1878. 4th ed. 2 vols. xvi,(i),408; xii,(i),462pp; 15 woodcut plts. (Bkpl, sig each vol; hinges sl rubbed.) *Hollett*. $136/£85

COLQUHOUN, JOHN. Sporting Days. London, 1866. 1st ed. 255pp. (Pp lt browned; lt rubbed, top hinge w/1-inch split.) *Grayling*. $72/£45

COLSON, ELIZABETH. The Makah Indians: A Study of an Indian Tribe in Modern American Society. Manchester: Manchester Univ, (1953). VG in dj (chipped). *Perier*. $45/£28

COLSON, NATHANIEL. The Mariner's New Calendar. London: W. & J. Mount/T. & T. Page, 1754. (3)-136pp (lacks 1/2-title); 4 woodcuts. Orig full dk calf (spine hinge cracked, worn), gilt. *Weber*. $200/£125

COLT, MIRIAM DAVIS. Went to Kansas. Watertown: L. Ingalls, 1862. 1st ed. 294pp. Brn blindstamped cl. VG + (sig, date, lt foxed, soiled; gilt dull, extrems worn). Howes C616. *Harrington*. $425/£266

COLTART, J. S. Scottish Church Architecture. Sheldon, 1936. 1st ed. 90 plts. VG in dj. *Hollett*. $48/£30

COLTHURST, IDA. Familiar Flowering Trees in India. Calcutta: Thacker, Spink, 1924. 1st ed. Grn cl. (Sl silverfished), o/w VG. *Archer*. $25/£16

COLTON, CALVIN. Four Years in Great Britain. NY: Harper, 1836. New, improved ed. 360pp. Brn patterned cl (spine lt chipped). *Karmiole*. $75/£47

COLTON, HENRY E. Mountain Scenery. Raleigh, NC/Phila: W.L. Pomeroy/Hayes & Zell/C. Sherman, 1859. 1st ed. (5)-120pp; 4 full-pg lithos. (Sheets browned; cl soiled.) *M & S*. $250/£156

COLTON, RAY C. The Civil War in the Western Territories. Norman: Univ of OK, 1959. VG. *Dumont*. $45/£28

COLTON, WALTER. The California Diary. Oakland: Biobooks, 1948. One of 1000 ptd. 5 plts, fldg facs. Marbled eps. Red cl. Fine. *Argonaut*. $75/£47

COLTON, WALTER. Deck and Port. NY, 1850. 1st ed, 2nd issue, yet still w/ptd eps as called for in 1st issue. 408pp; 4 color litho plts, frontisport, map. (Plts foxed, spotted; cvrs worn), o/w VG. Howes C624. *New Hampshire**. $70/£44

COLTON, WALTER. Glances into California. L.A.: Glen Dawson, 1955. Ltd to 250 ptd. Grn cl, red leather spine label, gilt. Fine in plain white dj (soiled). *Argonaut*. $75/£47

COLTON, WALTER. The Sea and the Sailor, Notes on France and Italy, and Other Literary Remains.... NY/Cincinnati: A.S. Barnes/H.W. Derby, 1851. 1st ed. 437pp,8pp ads; 2 plts. (Extrems sl worn.) *Lefkowicz*. $85/£53

COLUM, MARY and PADRAIC. Our Friend James Joyce. NY, 1958. 1st Amer ed. NF in dj (sl rubbed). *Polyanthos*. $25/£16

COLUM, PADRAIC. The Frenzied Prince. Phila, (1943). 1st ed. 9.5x7.5. 196pp; 8 full-pg color plts by Willy Pogany. (Reps stained, extrems frayed.) Dj (chipped, stained). *King*. $35/£22

COLUM, PADRAIC. Orpheus, Myths of the World. NY, 1930. 1st ed. One of 350 numbered, signed by Colum & Boris Artzybasheff (illus). (Cvrs worn, esp spine.) *King*. $135/£84

COLUM, PADRAIC. Three Men. London: Elkin Mathews, 1930. 1st ed. One of 530 signed. Dec bds over linen spine, paper label. Fine. *Appelfeld*. $95/£59

Columbian Gallery: A Portfolio of Photographs from the World's Fair. Chicago: Werner, (1894). 1st ed. 3/4 morocco, gilt cl. (Spine ends lack pieces), else VG. *Pacific**. $98/£61

COLUMBUS, CHRISTOPHER. Journals and Other Documents on the Life and Voyages of Christopher Columbus. Samuel Eliot Morison (ed). NY: LEC, 1963. One of 1500. Signed by Lima de Freitas (illus). Blue buckram, emb bust set into fr cvr, leather spine label. Fine in glassine, slipcase. *Pacific**. $69/£43

COLUMBUS, CHRISTOPHER. Journals and Other Documents on the Life and Voyages of.... Samuel Eliot Morison (ed). NY: Heritage, 1963. Frontis; 5 dbl-pg color plts. 8 maps. Pict blue cl. Fine in slipcase. *House*. $25/£16

COLUMBUS, CHRISTOPHER. The Voyages of Christopher Columbus. London: Argonaut Press, 1930. One of 1050. 5 maps (1 fldg). Unopened. 1/2 vellum, gilt. NF. *Pacific**. $259/£162

COLVILE, EDEN. London Correspondence Inward, from Eden Colvile, 1849-1852. E. E. Rich (ed). London: Hudson's Bay Record Soc, 1956. 1st ed. Ltd ed. Frontis. Blue cl, gilt. (Spine sl faded), else Fine. *Argonaut*. $125/£78

COLVILE, HENRY. The Land of the Nile Springs. London: E. Arnold, 1895. 1st ed. (xv),312pp; 2 fldg maps, 17 plts. Pict cl, gilt. Fine. *Maggs*. $320/£200

COLVILLE, MRS. ARTHUR. 1,000 Miles in a Machilla. London/Felling on Tyne: Walter Scott Pub, 1911. 1st ed. Fldg map, 50 plts (4 color), incl frontis. Red cl, gilt. (Foxed.) *Morrell*. $112/£70

COLVIN, ROD. First Heroes. NY: Irvington Pub, 1987. 1st ed. Signed, dated 1987. Fine in dj. *Associates*. $65/£41

COLVIN, SIDNEY. Drawings of the Old Masters in the University Galleries and in the Library of Christ Church Oxford. Oxford: Clarendon, 1907. 3 vols. Lg folio. 3/4 morocco (worn). *Oinonen**. $250/£156

COLWIN, LAURIE. Dangerous French Mistress. London: C&W, 1975. 1st British ed, 1st bk. Fine in Fine dj. *Pettler*. $20/£13

COLWIN, LAURIE. Happy All the Time. NY: Knopf, 1978. 1st ed. Inscribed. (Sl cocked), else Fine in VG dj (few sm nicks, tears). *Between The Covers*. $100/£63

COLWIN, LAURIE. Shine on Bright and Dangerous Object. London, 1975. 1st UK ed. VG in VG dj. *Warren*. $30/£19

COLYER, CHARLES N. Flies of the British Isles. London: Warne, (1951). 1st ed. Fine in dj (sl mkd). *Petersfield*. $67/£42

COMBE, ANDREW. Observations on Mental Derangement. Boston: Marsh, Capen & Lyon, 1834. 1st ed. Period cl. (Sl foxed; spine lettered by hand, ends worn), else VG. *Pacific**. $69/£43

COMBE, ANDREW. The Physiology of Digestion Considered with Relation to the Principles of Dietics.... Edinburgh: MacLachlan & Stewart, 1836. 2nd ed. 1/2-title, xxviii,350,(8)pp. VG in orig cl-backed bds (label chipped). *Young.* $288/£180

COMBE, WILLIAM and THOMAS ROWLANDSON. The First [Second, Third] Tour of Dr. Syntax in Search of the Picturesque. Nattali & Bond, (n.d.). 9th ed. 3 vols. 2 hand-colored engr tps, 78 hand-colored engr plts. Aeg. 19th-cent calf (rebacked, preserving orig spines), gilt. *Sotheby's*.* $368/£230

COMBE, WILLIAM. The English Dance of Death and the English Dance of Life. London: Rudolph Ackermann, 1815, 1816, 1817. 1st eds. 3 vols. 8vo. 98 hand-colored plts by Thomas Rowlandson. Full maroon crushed levant morocco, gilt paneled spines, raised bands, gilt tops by Riviere & Son. Sound. *Appelfeld.* $1,750/£1,094

COMBE, WILLIAM. The Tour of Doctor Syntax, in Search of the Picturesque. London: Nattali & Bond, (c.1819-1821). 9th ed. 3 vols. 80 hand-colored aquatint plts by Thomas Rowaldson. Orig cl. (Expertly rebacked w/orig spine strips laid on, corners sl bumped, extrems sl faded), else VG. *Pacific*.* $259/£162

COMEAU, N. A. Life and Sport on the North Shore of the Lower St. Lawrence and Gulf. Quebec, 1909. 1st ed. Signed. Port, map. (Spine faded, cvrs mkd, sl loose.) *Hallam.* $88/£55

COMETTI, ELIZABETH (ed). Jefferson's Ideas on a University Library. McGregor Lib, 1950. One of 1000. VG (ex-lib). *Book Broker.* $25/£16

COMINI, ALESSANDRA. Egon Schiele's Portraits. Berkeley, (1974). Dj. *Swann*.* $57/£36

COMMAGER, HENRY STEELE. The Blue and the Gray. Indianapolis: Bobbs-Merrill, (1950). 1st ed. 2 vols. Gray cl. NF in VG djs (chipped), VG pub's slipcase (split along lower edge). *Chapel Hill.* $85/£53

Commercial Advertiser Directory for the City of Saint Paul (1858-1859). St. Paul: Newsen & Barton, 1858. (Bds detached, lacks spine, sm loss at edges, sl soiled.) Internally clean. *Metropolitan*.* $143/£89

COMMIRE, ANNE (ed). Yesterday's Authors of Books for Children. Detroit: Gale Research, (1977-1978). 1st ed. 2 vols. Orange cl. Nice set (fep vol 1 torn out; sl rubbed, shelfworn). *Baltimore*.* $95/£59

Comparative View of the Antient Monuments of India. (By Richard Gough.) London: Ptd by John Nichols, 1785. xvi,85pp + (iii)pub's ads; 10 plts (2 fldg). Uncut, unpressed. Mod gilt-edged 1/2 calf, morocco spine label. (Sl marginal browning, tp lt soiled; rebound.) *Edwards.* $416/£260

Compilation of Narratives of Exploration in Alaska. Washington: GPO, 1900. 33plts, 27 fldg maps. (Few spots, inner hinges taped), else VG. *High Latitude.* $450/£281

Compilation of Narratives of Explorations in Alaska. Washington: Senate, 1900. 27 maps, 33 full-pg illus. Sheep, red/grn/black leather spine labels. (Lib bkpl, 2 sm stamps eps and edges; call # partially removed, chip spine head.) Howes A102. *Dawson.* $500/£313

Complaint: or Night-Thoughts on Life, Death, and Immortality.... (By Edward Young.) R. Dodsley, 1743. 1st ed. Engr frontis, prelim blank present, (ii),30; (ii),5-44; (ii),5-34; (ii),ii,(3)-47,(1); (iv),(7)-60; v,(i),42,(2)ads pp. Red sprinkled/polished edges. Contemp mottled dk calf, raised bands, leather label, gilt. Sound (general tp sl soiled, bkpl; joints split but firm, fr bd/corners w/loss of calf). *Blackwell's.* $216/£135

Complete Cattle Doctor: a Treatise on the Diseases of Horned Cattle and Calves. Chicago: W.B. Sloan, 1848. 1st ed. 34 (of 36?)pp (probably lacks 1 ad leaf). Sewn. (Foxed, tp frayed, stained; lacks wrappers.) *M & S.* $475/£297

Complete Scotland. Ward Lock, (early 1940s). 3rd ed. 30 fldg maps, plans. VG in dj (worn, torn). *Hollett.* $24/£15

Complete Young Man's Companion; or, Self Instructor. Manchester: S. Russell, 1805. Engr frontis (ink inscrip verso), viii,496pp; 7 engr plts (1 hand-colored). Mod cl. *Ars Artis.* $240/£150

COMPTON, ARTHUR HOLLY. Atomic Quest, a Personal Narrative. NY: OUP, 1956. Dj (worn). *Weber.* $15/£9

COMPTON, HERBERT (comp). A Particular Account of the European Military Adventures of Hindustan from 1784 to 1803. London, 1892. Fldg frontis, 8 plts, map. Teg. (Notes, edges sl browned, early ms genealogy chart to fep; corners rubbed w/sl loss; spine, joints sl rubbed.) *Edwards.* $136/£85

COMPTON, R. H. (ed). Our South African Flora. Cape Town: Cape Times, n.d. 1st ed. VG. *Archer.* $35/£22

COMPTON-BURNETT, IVY. Dolores. London, 1911. 1st Eng ed, 1st bk. VG (eps partly browned, eps, edges spotted; spine tail sl bumped). *Ulysses.* $1,200/£750

COMPTON-BURNETT, IVY. The Mighty and Their Fall. London: Gollancz, 1961. 1st ed. VG in dj (sm nick). *Reese.* $20/£13

COMPTON-BURNETT, IVY. Pastors and Masters, a Study. London: Heath Cranton, 1925. 1st ed. NF in dj (dusty; chips fr, rear panels). *Reese.* $150/£94

COMPTON-BURNETT, IVY. The Present and the Past. NY: Messner, 1953. 1st ed, Amer issue. Dec bds. (Sl dusty), else Good in dj. *Reese.* $20/£13

COMSTOCK, FRANCIS ADAMS. A Gothic Vision: F.L. Griggs and His Work. Boston, 1966. One of 600 numbered, signed. *Swann*.* $69/£43

COMSTOCK, HENRY SMITH (ed). Hasty Recollections of a Busy Life. (Peoria, IL: The Transcript Co, 1896.) 1st ed. Frontisport, 296pp, index (2 sm marginal tears to 1 leaf). *Wantagh.* $35/£22

COMSTOCK, J. H. The Spider Book. NY: Doubleday, 1912. 1st ed. Teg. Full leather, gilt. VG. *Mikesh.* $60/£38

COMSTOCK, J. L. Elements of Mineralogy. Boston, 1827. 1st ed. 338pp. Full brn calf, gilt. VG. *Larry Price.* $395/£247

COMSTOCK, J. L. Grammar of Chemistry. Hartford, 1825. 2nd ed. 240pp. Contemp calf. VG (extrems sl worn). *Doctor's Library.* $50/£31

CONDIT, KENNETH and EDWIN TURNBLADH. Hold High the Torch. Nashville, 1989. Rpt. VG. *Clark.* $40/£25

CONDON, EDDIE and THOMAS SUGRUE. We Called It Music. NY: Holt, 1947. 1st ed. NF in dj (rear panel lacks lg piece). *Beasley.* $40/£25

CONDON, EDDIE. We Called It Music: A Generation of Jazz. NY: Henry Holt, (1947). 1st ed. Discography. VG in pict dj (chipped). *Petrilla.* $40/£25

CONDON, RICHARD. The Ecstasy Business. NY, 1967. 1st Amer ed. Fine in VG dj (price-clipped). *Polyanthos.* $25/£16

CONDON, RICHARD. The Manchurian Candidate. NY: McGraw-Hill, (1959). 1st ed. (Bkpl, spine ends rubbed), else VG in dj (spine ends lack pieces, greenish tint around edges, rear panel creased, corners chipped). *Pacific*.* $40/£25

CONDON, RICHARD. The Manchurian Candidate. NY: McGraw-Hill, 1959. 1st ed. (Stamp; spine sl sunned), o/w NF in Nice dj. *Smith.* $185/£116

CONDORCET, MARIE J. A. N. Outlines of an Historical View of the Progress of the Human Mind. London: For J. Johnson, 1795. 1st ed in English. (vii),iii,372pp. Old calf, leather spine label. (Lt foxed, aged; cvrs detached, worn, scuffed, spine ends chipped, vertical crack down entire spine.) *Baltimore*.* $220/£138

Conestoga Six-Horse Bell Teams of Eastern Pennsylvania. Published by John Omwake for Private Distribution. (By H. C. Frey et al.) Cincinnati: Ebbert & Richardson Co, 1930. 2nd ptg. VG +. *Zubal*.* $50/£31

CONFUCIUS. The Analects. LEC, 1933. Ltd to 1500 numbered. Fine in silk brocade wrappers, carved rosewood box (bottom sl warped, detached). *Swann**. $258/£161

CONFUCIUS. The Analects. L.A.: Plantin, 1970. Signed by Tseng Yu-Ho (illus). Full mottled Chinese red linen, silk-screened w/an all over pattern; oriental wood veneer label ptd in red. Fine in Chinese-stylized box. *Appelfeld*. $200/£125

CONFUCIUS. The Analects. LEC, 1970. Ltd to 1500 numbered, signed by Tseng Yu-Ho (illus). Fine in slipcase. *Swann**. $201/£126

CONFUCIUS. The Morals of Confucius, a Chinese Philosopher. London: Randal Taylor, 1691. 1st ed in English. Fldg frontis port, xx,183pp. Calf, gilt. VG (ex-lib rubber stamps to fep verso, frontis verso, tp). *Pacific**. $1,495/£934

CONGREVE, WILLIAM. The Way of the World. Haymarket, 1928. One of 875. Frontis, signed by A.R. Middleton Todd (illus). VG (edges sl rubbed, sl bumped) in dj (rubbed, soiled). *Ulysses*. $56/£35

CONGREVE, WILLIAM. The Way of the World. LEC, 1959. Ltd to 1500 numbered, signed by T. M. Cleland (designer). Fine in slipcase. *Swann**. $46/£29

CONKLIN, HAROLD C. Ethnographic Atlas of Ifugao. Yale Univ, 1980. 1st ed. Elephant folio. Mint. *Larry Price*. $145/£91

CONKLING, ROSCOE P. and MARGARET B. The Butterfield Overland Mail, 1857-1869. Glendale, CA: Arthur H. Clark, 1947. 1st ed. 3 vols. Frontis, 77 plts. Partly unopened. NF set (atlas vol fep w/opaqued box; 2 text vols w/sl rubbing on spines). *Sagebrush*. $975/£609

CONN, GEORGE KEITH THUBURN and F. J. BRADSHAW (eds). Polarized Light in Metallography. London: Butterworths Scientific Pub, 1952. Fine in dj. *Weber*. $25/£16

CONN, WILLIAM. Cowboys and Colonels. London: Griffith, Farran, Okeden & Welsh, (n.d., ca 1888). 2nd Eng ed. Lt blue cl, gilt. NF. Howes M246. *Labordo*. $150/£94

CONNELL, EVAN S. The Diary of a Rapist. NY: S&S, (1966). 1st ed. Fine in dj (sl rubbed). *Lenz*. $45/£28

CONNELL, EVAN S. Notes from a Bottle Found on the Beach at Carmel. NY: Viking, (1963). 1st ed. VG in dj (extrems sl sunned, chipped). *Pacific**. $52/£33

CONNELL, EVAN S. Son of the Morning Star, Custer and the Little Big Horn. SF, 1984. 1st ed. Fine in Fine dj. *Pratt*. $55/£34

CONNELLEY, WILLIAM E. The Life of Preston B. Plumb 1837-1891, United States Senator from Kansas...1877 to 1891. Chicago: Browne & Howell, 1913. 1st ed. Port. Teg. (Fr inner hinge opening), o/w VG. *Brown*. $65/£41

CONNELLEY, WILLIAM E. War with Mexico, 1846-1847. Topeka: The Author, 1907. 1st ed. VG. Howes C688. *Labordo*. $175/£109

CONNELLEY, WILLIAM E. Wild Bill—James Butler Hickok. Volume XVII. KS State Hist Soc, 1926-1928. 1st ed. Fine in wrappers. *Labordo*. $45/£28

CONNELLEY, WILLIAM E. (ed). Collections of the Kansas State Historical Society, 1915-1918; Volume XIV. Topeka: KS State Ptg Plant, 1918. (Inner hinges cracked; fr cvr fore-edge nicked), o/w Good. *Brown*. $30/£19

CONNELLY, MARC. The Green Pastures. NY, 1930. 1st ed thus. One of 550 numbered, signed by Connelly & Robert Edmond Jones (illus). Gilt-pict grn vellum (spine lt sunned). Slipcase. *Swann**. $57/£36

CONNELY, WILLARD. The Reign of Beau Brummell. London: Cassell, 1940. Frontis. VG in dj (sl worn, torn). *Hollett*. $24/£15

CONNER, DANIEL and LORRAINE MILLER. Master Mariner. London, 1978. 61 plts. Dj (torn w/o loss). *Edwards*. $32/£20

CONNER, DANIEL ELLIS. Joseph Reddeford Walker and the Arizona Adventure. Norman, 1956. 1st ed. VG in dj (sl worn, scuff to fr cvr). *Dumont*. $55/£34

CONNER, PATRICK. Oriental Architecture in the West. London, 1979. 1st ed. VG in dj. *Gretton*. $40/£25

CONNETT, EUGENE V. Any Luck? London: Hutchinson, 1935. 1st Eng ed. Grn cl. Fine. *Biscotti*. $40/£25

CONNETT, EUGENE V. A Decade of American Sporting Books and Prints: The Derrydale Press. NY: Derrydale, 1937. NF in red paper wraps (faded). *Biscotti*. $100/£63

CONNETT, EUGENE V. Duck Decoys. NY, (1953). 1st ed. VG in dj (chipped, sl spotted). *King*. $45/£28

CONNETT, EUGENE V. and EDGAR BURKE. Feathered Game From a Sporting Journal. NY: Derrydale, 1929. Ltd to 500 numbered. 1/2 black cl over brn mottled paper-cvrd bds (corners sl rubbed). Fine. *Biscotti*. $375/£234

CONNETT, EUGENE V. Fishing a Trout Stream. NY: Derrydale, 1934. Ltd to 950 numbered. Promo bkmk laid in. Blue cl (sl scuff mks). *Biscotti*. $325/£203

CONNETT, EUGENE V. Random Casts. NY: Derrydale, 1939. Ltd to 1075 numbered. Inscribed. Mottled blue-grn cl. Fine. *Biscotti*. $300/£188

CONNETT, EUGENE V. (ed). American Sporting Dogs. Princeton, NJ: D. Van Nostrand, 1948. 1st ed. Rust buckram. Fine in VG ptd dj. *Biscotti*. $125/£78

CONNETT, EUGENE V. (ed). Duck Shooting; Along the Atlantic Tidewater. NY: William Morrow, 1947. 1st ed. Red buckram. Fine in Good pict color dj. *Biscotti*. $125/£78

CONNETT, EUGENE V. (ed). Upland Game Bird Shooting in America. NY: Derrydale, 1930. One of 850. Folio. 64 plts (5 color). (Sm hole at top of rear joint.) *Swann**. $316/£198

CONNETT, EUGENE V. (ed). Wildfowling in the Mississippi Flyway. Princeton, NJ: D. Van Nostrand, 1949. 1st ed. Rust buckram. Fine in Good pict dj. *Biscotti*. $200/£125

CONNICK, CHARLES J. Adventures in Light and Color. NY, (1937). Paper labels. (Lt worn, cvrs sl bowed.) *Oinonen**. $80/£50

CONNICK, CHARLES J. Adventures in Light and Color. NY, (1937). 1st ed. One of 300. Signed, inscribed presentation. (Rubbed.) Leather back; remnant of dj. *Oinonen**. $90/£56

CONNOISSEUR, MADAM. The Complete Fortune-Teller: or An Infallible Guide to the Hidden Decrees of Fate. London, 1812. 1/2 calf, bds. (Spotted; bds rubbed), else VG. *Pacific**. $138/£86

CONNOLLY, CYRIL. Enemies of Promise. London, 1938. 1st Eng ed. Good (name; fr hinge cracked) in dj (rubbed, dust-mkd). *Clearwater*. $136/£85

CONNOLLY, CYRIL. The Rock Pool. NY: Scribner, 1936. 1st Amer ed. NF in VG dj (spine ends chipped, fr panel lacks pieces, sl pink stain to corners). *Pacific**. $29/£18

CONNOLLY, JAMES. Labour in Ireland; Socialism and Nationalism; Labour and Easter Week; The Worker's Republic. Dublin: At the Sign of the Three Candles, 1944-1951. Vol 1 rpt, rest 1st eds edited by Desmond Ryan. 4 vols. VG set (spine ends sl bumped) in dj (sl dusty, chipped, creased, spines sl dknd). *Ulysses*. $200/£125

CONNOR, J. TORREY. Saunterings in Summerland. L.A.: Ernest K. Foster, 1902. 1st ed. Fine in wraps over bds. *Book Market*. $75/£47

CONOLLY, L. W. and J. P. WEARING. English Drama and Theatre 1800-1900. Detroit: Gale Research, (1978). (Sl pencil mks; sl rubbed.) *Dramatis*. $50/£31

CONOLLY, M. F. Fifiana; or, Memorials of the East of Fife. Glasgow, 1869. Frontisport, viii,345pp + (iv)pp ads. (Contents leaf loose, lt browning, lt spotted, fr hinge cracked; cl sl soiled, rubbed; corners, spine sl bumped.) *Edwards*. $72/£45

CONRAD, EARL. Harriet Tubman. Washington, (1943). 1st ed. (Shelfworn), else Good. *King*. $35/£22

CONRAD, JESSE. Handbook of Cookery for a Small House. Heinemann, 1923. 1st ed. Cream cl. VG (feps partly browned). *Blackwell's.* $80/£50

CONRAD, JESSIE. Personal Recollections of Joseph Conrad. Privately ptd, 1924. 1st ed. One of 100 signed. Teg, rest untrimmed. Marbled red cl, ptd label. Good (edges lt foxed; sm unobtrusive dampstain fr cvr). *Blackwell's.* $320/£200

CONRAD, JESSIE. Simple Cooking Precepts for a Little House. (Privately ptd, 1921.) 1st ed. One of 100 signed, numbered by Joseph Conrad (preface). Crown 8vo. (4)pp. Good (sm tear to fore-edges) in ptd white stapled wrappers. *Blackwell's.* $640/£400

CONRAD, JOSEPH and RICHARD CURLE. Conrad to a Friend [with] The Last Twelve Years of Joseph Conrad. London: Sampson Low, 1928/1929. 1st Eng ed. 2 vols. Fldg facs letter frontis vol 1, frontis vol 2. VG set (spine ends, 2 corners bumped, cvrs sl mkd). *Ulysses.* $120/£75

CONRAD, JOSEPH. Almayer's Folly. NY: Macmillan, 1895. 1st Amer ed, 1st issue w/final gathering in 8 leaves, 1st bk. Blue cl, gilt. NF. *Macdonnell.* $500/£313

CONRAD, JOSEPH. Almayer's Folly. London: T. Fisher Unwin, 1895. 1st Eng ed, 1st issue, 1st bk. Teg. VG (spine ends bumped, cvrs sl mkd). *Ulysses.* $2,392/£1,495

CONRAD, JOSEPH. The Arrow of Gold. London: T. Fisher Unwin, (1919). 1st Eng ed, 1st state(?), w/running head intact on p67. Grn cl. Fine. *Cummins.* $150/£94

CONRAD, JOSEPH. The Arrow of Gold. A Story Between Two Notes. Fisher Unwin, 1919. 1st Eng ed. Crown 8vo. W/o fep as issued, ppix/x being conjugate w/fr pastedown. Mid grn cl, gilt. VG (eps sl browned) in dj (chipped, backstrip panel sl browned). *Blackwell's.* $584/£365

CONRAD, JOSEPH. Chance. A Tale in Two Parts. London: Methuen, 1914. 1st ed, 2nd issue. Fore/lower edges uncut. Grn cl, gilt. VG (prelims, fore-edge foxed, sm ink stain on spine; joints sl worn) in pict dj. *Maggs.* $120/£75

CONRAD, JOSEPH. Chance. A Tale in Two Parts. GC: Doubleday, Page, 1914. 1st Amer ed. Dk blue cl. VG. *Cummins.* $125/£78

CONRAD, JOSEPH. The Children of the Sea. A Tale of the Forecastle. NY: Dodd, Mead, 1897. 1st Amer ed of Nigger of the Narcissus. Blue grey pict cl. VG. *Cummins.* $400/£250

CONRAD, JOSEPH. Five Letters Written to Edward Noble in 1895. Privately ptd, 1925. 1st ed. One of 100 signed by Edward Noble (foreword). Untrimmed. VG in ptd tan wrappers (sl offsetting from sm removed bookticket). *Blackwell's.* $320/£200

CONRAD, JOSEPH. Heart of Darkness. NY: LEC, 1969. One of 1500 ptd. Signed by Robert Shore (illus). 1/2 vellum, dec bds, gilt. Fine in glassine, slipcase. *Pacific*.* $75/£47

CONRAD, JOSEPH. Heart of Darkness. LEC, 1992. One of 300 signed by Sean Scully (illus). Fine in slipcase. *Swann*.* $920/£575

CONRAD, JOSEPH. Last Essays. London, 1926. 1st ed. Leaf of Dent's ads for 1926 laid in. Dj (spine sl tanned). *Swann*.* $126/£79

CONRAD, JOSEPH. Last Essays. London/Toronto: J.M. Dent, 1926. 1st ed. Grn cl. Fine. *Cummins.* $150/£94

CONRAD, JOSEPH. Last Essays. Dent, 1926. 1st UK ed. NF in VG dj (sl foxed, spine extrems sl worn, fr panel sl stained). *Williams.* $152/£95

CONRAD, JOSEPH. Laughing Anne and One Day More. John Castle, 1924. 1st ed thus. Fine (sl foxed) in VG + dj (sm closed tear, sm spine stain). *Williams.* $240/£150

CONRAD, JOSEPH. Letters from Conrad 1895 to 1924. Edward Garnett (ed). Nonesuch, 1928. 1st ed. One of 925. 2 ports. Teg on the rough, rest untrimmed. Maroon buckram, gilt. VG (spine lt faded). *Blackwell's.* $96/£60

CONRAD, JOSEPH. Lord Jim. London/Edinburgh: William Blackwood, 1900. 1st ed. 8vo. Grey-grn cl ptd in black. (Spine sl dknd, inner hinge split), o/w VG. *Cummins.* $750/£469

CONRAD, JOSEPH. Lord Jim. LEC, 1959. Ltd to 1500 numbered, signed by Lynd Ward (illus). Fine in slipcase. *Swann*.* $126/£79

CONRAD, JOSEPH. The Mirror of the Sea. London, (1906). 1st ed, 1st issue. (Lt rubbed, sm ink spot fr cvr.) Bkpl of Lillian Ashley. *Swann*.* $201/£126

CONRAD, JOSEPH. The Mirror of the Sea. NY: Harper, 1906. 1st Amer ed. Blue/yellow/grey pict cl. Fine. *Cummins.* $200/£125

CONRAD, JOSEPH. The Nigger of the 'Narcissus.' London: Heinemann, 1898. 1st issue w/'Heinemann' in capital letters on spine. 32pp ads at rear. VG (inscrip, eps browned, edges sl spotted; spine ends, corners bumped, cvrs mkd, rubbed, sl cocked). *Ulysses.* $560/£350

CONRAD, JOSEPH. The Nigger of the Narcissus. L.A.: LEC, 1965. One of 1500. Signed by Millard Sheets (illus). 1/2 grn morocco, dec cl, gilt. Fine in slipcase. *Pacific*.* $63/£39

CONRAD, JOSEPH. Nostromo: A Tale of the Seaboard. SF: LEC, 1961. One of 1500. Signed by Lima de Freitas (illus). Dec aquamarine buckram backed w/burlap. Fine in glassine, slipcase. *Pacific*.* $81/£51

CONRAD, JOSEPH. Notes on My Books. GC: Doubleday, 1921. 1st ed. One of 250 signed. Cream parchment bds. (Corner sl bumped; spine nick, chip), o/w Fine in orig parchment dj. *Cummins.* $400/£250

CONRAD, JOSEPH. Notes on My Books. London: Heinemann, 1921. One of 250 signed. English issue. Parchment-backed bds (spine, edges sl tanned; label dull). VG. *Clearwater.* $680/£425

CONRAD, JOSEPH. One Day More. Beaumont, 1919. 1st trade ed. One of 250 (of 274). Cat slip pasted to rear pastedown. Untrimmed. 1/4 fawn canvas, ptd rear/fr cvr paper labels, blue/pale yellow,bds. Good (eps browned, offsetting from sm circular bk ticket). *Blackwell's.* $240/£150

CONRAD, JOSEPH. One Day More. GC: Doubleday, Page, 1920. One of 377 signed. 1/4 parchment, blue bds, gilt. (Spine sl dknd), o/w Fine. *Heritage.* $300/£188

CONRAD, JOSEPH. One Day More. NY, 1920. 1st Amer ed. One of 377 numbered, signed. Imitation vellum-backed bds. *Swann*.* $431/£269

CONRAD, JOSEPH. An Outcast of the Islands. NY: D. Appleton, 1896. 1st Amer ed. Lime grn cl. Fine. *Cummins.* $250/£156

CONRAD, JOSEPH. An Outcast of the Islands. Fisher Unwin, 1896. 1st ed. (vi),391,(1)pp. Cat cutting tipped to fr pastedown. Teg, rest untrimmed. Fine-ribbed dk grn cl, gilt. Good (bkpl, bkticket; spine head frayed, foot bumped). *Blackwell's.* $440/£275

CONRAD, JOSEPH. An Outcast of the Islands. Fisher Unwin, 1896. 1st UK ed. VG. *Williams.* $560/£350

CONRAD, JOSEPH. An Outcast of the Islands. Avon: LEC, 1975. One of 1500 signed by Robert Shore (illus). Dec cl. VF in glassine, slipcase. *Pharos.* $95/£59

CONRAD, JOSEPH. A Personal Record. J.M. Dent & Sons, 1919. 1st ed thus. Good (sig; spine bumped, sunned). *Tiger.* $22/£14

CONRAD, JOSEPH. Preface to the Nigger of the Narcissus. Lebanon, PA: E.U. Sowers, 1927. Frontisport. Untrimmed. Slate-blue vertically striped bds, ptd fr cvr label. Good (spine, adjacent area faded). *Blackwell's.* $320/£200

CONRAD, JOSEPH. The Rover. London, (1923). 1st ed. (Spine dknd, cvrs rubbed, rear outer hinge cracked, spine top chipped.) *King.* $60/£38

CONRAD, JOSEPH. The Rover. London: T. Fisher Unwin, (1923). 1st ed. 8vo. Grn cl, gilt. NF (eps lt browned; spine extrems lt rubbed, gilt faded, edges sl foxed) in dj (lt soiled, spine chip). *Heritage.* $750/£469

CONRAD, JOSEPH. The Secret Agent. A Drama in Three Acts. London, 1923. 1st ed thus. Ltd to 1000 signed, numbered. Parchment spine, paper label. Fine in dj (chipped). *Black Sun.* $400/£250

CONRAD, JOSEPH. The Secret Agent. A Drama in Three Acts. Werner Laurie, 1923. One of 1000 numbered, signed. VG in dj. *Williams.* $440/£275

CONRAD, JOSEPH. The Secret Agent: A Simple Tale. London: Methuen, (1907). 1st ed, 1st issue, 1st binding. 40-pg pub's cat at rear dated Sept 1907; repetition of 'be' in last line of p117. Ribbed crimson cl, gilt spine. (Lt aged; eps, edges of 1st few ll foxed.) Cvrs VG. *Baltimore*.* $450/£281

CONRAD, JOSEPH. The Secret Agent: A Simple Tale. London: Methuen, (1907). 1st ed. 8vo. Red cl (sl rubbed at edges). *Cummins.* $750/£469

CONRAD, JOSEPH. The Secret Sharer. LEC, 1985. Ltd to 1500 numbered, signed by Bruce Chandler (illus). Fine in slipcase. *Swann*.* $80/£50

CONRAD, JOSEPH. A Set of Six. London: Methuen, (1908). 1st ed, later (?) issue, w/verso of 1/2 title corrected, 1/2 title, tps integral ll, ads dated June 1908. Dk blue cl. Fine. *Cummins.* $100/£63

CONRAD, JOSEPH. The Shadow Line. NY: Doubleday, Page, 1917. 1st Amer ed. Dk blue cl, gilt. Fine. *Glenn.* $65/£41

CONRAD, JOSEPH. The Shadow Line. Dent, 1917. 1st UK ed. Fine (sm ink name, edges sl foxed). *Williams.* $216/£135

CONRAD, JOSEPH. The Shadow-Line. London: J.M. Dent & Sons, 1917. 1st ed. Lt grn dec cl. (Spine sl dknd, few ink-spots), o/w VG. *Maggs.* $120/£75

CONRAD, JOSEPH. The Sisters. NY: Crosby Gaige, 1928. 1st ed. One of 926 ptd. Marbled cl, leather label. VG. *Cullen.* $120/£75

CONRAD, JOSEPH. Suspense. NY, 1925. 1st ed. NF (sm bump bottom edge fr panel) in VG + dj (sl rubbed, few short tears). *Warren.* $150/£94

CONRAD, JOSEPH. Suspense. London/Toronto: J.M. Dent, 1925. 1st Eng ed. Frontis. Burgundy cl. *Cummins.* $225/£141

CONRAD, JOSEPH. Suspense. London: J.M. Dent & Sons, 1925. 1st ed. Maroon cl. Dj (sm tears, top sl crumpled, sl soiled). *Maggs.* $240/£150

CONRAD, JOSEPH. Tales of Hearsay. London: T. Fisher Unwin, (1925). 1st ed. Blue cl (rubbed, faded). Dj (worn, soiled). *Cummins.* $100/£63

CONRAD, JOSEPH. Tales of Hearsay. Fisher Unwin, 1925. 1st UK ed. Fine in NF dj. *Williams.* $144/£90

CONRAD, JOSEPH. Twenty Letters. London: Curwen Press, 1926. One of 220 sets. 12 vols. Foolscap 8vo, 8vo, 4to. Fine set in orig ptd, dec wrappers. Fold-over pocketed slipcase (sl rubbed, bubbled). *Maggs.* $560/£350

CONRAD, JOSEPH. Twixt Land and Sea. London: J.B. Dent, 1912. 1st ed, 3rd issue, w/'Secret' correct. Grn cl lettered in black. *Cummins.* $150/£94

CONRAD, JOSEPH. Typhoon and Other Stories. Heinemann, 1903. 1st Eng ed. Prelim ad leaf, Contents leaf present. Untrimmed. Slate-gray cl, gilt. Good (feps lt browned, bkpl; spine ends rubbed, rear cvrs sl bubbled, fr hinge weak). *Blackwell's.* $296/£185

CONRAD, JOSEPH. Typhoon. NY: Putnam, 1902. 1st Amer ed, 1st issue in dk grn pict cl, orange lettering. 6 plts. Fine. *Cummins.* $400/£250

CONRAD, JOSEPH. Under Western Eyes. NY, 1911. 1st Amer ed. (Spine worn, frayed.) *King.* $20/£13

CONRAD, JOSEPH. Victory. An Island Tale. GC: Doubleday, Page, 1915. 1st ed. Dk blue cl. VG. *Cummins.* $75/£47

CONRAD, JOSEPH. Victory: An Island Tale. GC: Doubleday, Page, 1915. 1st ed, 1st state (not always noted) w/quotation mark missing at beginning of line 3, p431. Navy cl, gilt. (Sl aged.) Dj (spine browned, chipped, sm tears, worn, now in portions w/complete separations along lower spine fold, rear flap fold). *Baltimore*.* $40/£25

CONRAD, JOSEPH. Within the Tides. London/Toronto: J.M. Dent, 1915. 1st ed. (Abrasion fep.) Grn cl (sl worn). *Cummins.* $75/£47

CONRAD, JOSEPH. The Works of.... NY: Doubleday, Doran, (1924). 24 vols. Full gray cl, ptd paper spine labels. VG set (news clipping affixed to fep, offset to pastedown; labels browned, chipped). *Heritage.* $300/£188

CONRAD, JOSEPH. The Works of.... NY: Doubleday, Doran, 1938. 21 vols. Grn cl, gilt, yellow emb circular port on fr cvrs. NF set. *Heritage.* $375/£234

CONRAD, JOSEPH. Youth and Two Other Stories. London, 1902. 1st ed. Grn cl. (Rear inner hinge partly cracked; sm stain rear cvr, corner bumped.) *Swann*.* $161/£101

CONRAD, JOSEPH. Youth, Typhoon and the End of Tether. LEC, 1972. Ltd to 1500 numbered, signed by Robert Shore (illus) and Ward Ritchie (designer). Fine in slipcase. *Swann*.* $57/£36

CONRAD, JOSEPH. Youth. (Kentfield: Allen, 1959.) One of 140. Dec bds. Fine in slipcase (rubbed, sl broken). *Pacific*.* $431/£269

CONROY, FRANK. Stop-Time. NY, (1967). 1st ed, 1st bk. VG in dj (sl frayed, torn). *King.* $50/£31

CONROY, FRANK. Stop-Time. NY, 1967. 1st Amer ed, 1st bk. NF in dj (price-clipped, 2 edge tears, rubbed; spine sl chipped). *Polyanthos.* $40/£25

CONROY, J. The Disinherited. Covici Friede, 1933. 1st ed. NF in VG + 1st issue pict dj (several long closed tears, 1/2-inch chip spine head). *Fine Books.* $195/£122

CONROY, PAT. The Lords of Discipline. Boston: HM, 1980. 1st ed. Inscribed in 1989. (Lower corner bumped), o/w Fine in 1st issue dj (price-clipped, spine tip lt wrinkled) w/Dickey blurb. *Agvent.* $275/£172

CONROY, PAT. The Prince of Tides. Boston: HMC, 1986. 1st ed. Signed. Fine in Fine dj. *Unger.* $125/£78

Conservation of Georgian Edinburgh. Edinburgh: Edinburgh Univ, 1972. VG (top edge sl spotted) in dj (nicked, sl torn, creased, mkd, dusty, price-clipped, spine faded). *Ulysses.* $58/£36

CONSTABLE, JOHN. English Landscape Scenery. London, 1855. 1st ed. Folio. 40 mezzotint plts by David Lucas. (Prelims heavily foxed, some plts marginally foxed.) Contemp 1/2 red morocco, gilt. *Swann*.* $805/£503

CONSTABLE, W. G. Canaletto, Giovanni Antonio Canal 1697-1768. Clarendon, 1962. 1st ed. 2 vols. Frontisport, 184 b/w plts. Marbled eps. (Sm ink stamp.) Fawn crushed morocco-backed cl bds, gilt. *Edwards.* $160/£100

CONSTANTINE, K. C. Always a Body to Trade. Hodder, 1983. 1st UK ed. Fine in dj. *Any Amount.* $32/£20

CONSTANTINE, K. C. The Man Who Liked to Look at Himself. NY: Saturday Review/Dutton, 1973. 1st ed. Fine in VG dj (rubbed, spine lt sunned). *Janus.* $35/£22

CONSTANTINO, HUMBERTO. The Long Night of Francisco Sanctis. NY: Harper & Row, 1985. 1st US ed. (Fr inner hinge of spine starting), else Fine in dj. *Lame Duck.* $45/£28

Constitution of the Commonwealth of Pennsylvania. Phila: Poulson, 1790. 29pp, stitched (few sm marginal tears). *Swann*.* $92/£58

Constitution of the State of North-Carolina, Together with the Ordinances and Resolutions...Jan. 14th, 1868. Raleigh, (NC): Joseph W. Holden, 1868. 1st ed. 129,4pp. Contemp law sheep (fr hinge weak). *M & S.* $300/£188

Constitution of the United States of America, Proposed by the Convention Held at Philadelphia, September 17, 1787...Approved, Setember 9, 1850. G.S.L. City, UT, 1852. 7.5x5.25. 48pp. Fine (removed from larger vol w/remains of stitching in spine). *Pacific*.* $690/£431

Contributions to Medical and Biological Research Dedicated to Sir William Osler. NY, 1919. One of 1600. 2 vols. *Fye.* $125/£78

Contributions to the Historical Society of Montana, Volume II. Helena: State Pub'g, 1896. 1st ed. Red cl (worn). NF. *Harrington.* $135/£84

Contributions to the Historical Society of Montana. Volume 6. Helena: Independent Pub, 1907. VG. *Perier.* $80/£50

Contributions to the Medical Sciences in Honor of Dr. Emanuel Libman by His Pupils, Friends and Colleagues. NY, 1932. 1st ed. 3 vols. (Extrems worn), o/w Good in protective djs. *Doctor's Library.* $100/£63

Convention Vindicated from the Misrepresentations of the Enemies of Our Peace. (By Horatio Walpole.) London: Roberts, 1739. 1/4 calf. (Bkpl.) *Rostenberg & Stern.* $150/£94

Conversations and Amusing Tales, Offered to the Publick for the Youth of Great Britain. (By Harriet English.) London: Charles Clarke, 1799. 1st ed. Copper frontis plt, xiv,385,(10)pp; 12 oval hand-colored yellow aquatint vignette plts. 1/2-title present. Period diced russia, gilt-roll borders, gilt-tooled spine, morocco spine labels. (Old cat entry mtd to fep verso, pg(95) w/type blurred [ptr's error]; extrems rubbed), else NF. *Pacific*.* $403/£252

CONVERSE, HARRIET MAXWELL. The Ho-De-No-Sau-Nee. The Confederacy of the Iroquois. NY/London: Putnam, 1884. 1st ed. 13pp. VG in wraps. *Brown.* $20/£13

CONVERSE, JOHN MARQUIS (ed). Reconstructive Plastic Surgery: Principles and Procedures in Correction, Reconstruction, and Transplantation.... Phila: W.B. Saunders, (1977). 2nd ed. 7 vols. Fine (sig). *Weber.* $300/£188

CONWAY, JAMES. Forays Among Salmon and Deer. London: Chapman & Hall, 1861. 1st ed. Frontis litho. Teg. 3/4 levant brn morocco, marbled bds, gilt, raised bands; bound by Birdsall. Fine. *Pacific*.* $316/£198

CONWAY, WILLIAM MARTIN. Aconcagua and Tierra del Fuego. Cassell, 1902. 1st ed. 27 plts, map. (Fr bd, spine dampmkd.) *Hollett.* $224/£140

CONWAY, WILLIAM MARTIN. Climbing and Exploration in the Karakoram-Himalayas. T. Fisher Unwin, 1894. 1st ed. xxviii,709,(i)pp; fldg map (some folds torn). Uncut. Pict cl, gilt. (Lib label, sm stamp; joints cracked, cl sl worn, bumped.) *Hollett.* $400/£250

CONWELL, RUSSELL H. Why and How. Why the Chinese Emigrate.... Boston: Lee & Shepard, 1871. Presumed 1st ed, although c. is dated 1870. Wood-engr frontis, (iv),283pp + ad pg. Recent orange-yellow eps. Plum cl, gilt. (Lt aged, lib spine sticker removed, sm ink stamps, ink # c. pg; spine sunned, sl edgeworn.) Text Nice. *Baltimore*.* $80/£50

Cook's Handbook for London. Thomas Cook & Son/Simpkin, Marshall, 1888. 118pp; 2 fldg maps. Mod 1/2 calf. Nice (few sm mks, creases), preserving orig wraps. *Ash.* $136/£85

Cook's Tourist's Handbook for Holland, Belgium and the Rhine. London, 1874. 1st ed. Red cl, gilt. VG. *Gretton.* $48/£30

COOK, CLARENCE. Art and Artists of Our Time. NY: Selmar Hess, (1888). 3 vols. Aeg. Orig dk brn morocco, brn pebbled cl, raised bands, gilt. (Sl scuffed.) Texts Nice, cvrs Clean. *Baltimore*.* $140/£88

COOK, CLARENCE. The House Beautiful: Essays on Beds and Tables, Stools and Candlesticks. NY: Scribner, Armstrong, 1878. 1st ed. Color frontis by Walter Crane, 336pp. Dk brn coated eps; teg. Dk blue cl, gilt. (Frontis detached, text lt aged; sl rubbed, sl worn, fr hinge split.) Cvrs VG. *Baltimore*.* $210/£131

COOK, EDWARD T. Studies in Ruskin. Sunnyside, Oprington: George Allen, 1890. 1st ed. *Argosy.* $100/£63

COOK, ELIZA. Poems. Routledge, Warne & Routledge, 1860. Engr frontisport, xii,564pp; 8 woodcut plts, guards. All edges gilt, gauffered. Full brn morocco, gilt, over blind-dec beveled bds. VG. *Hollett.* $120/£75

COOK, FRED. The Golden Book of the American Revolution. Golden Deluxe, c.1959. 8.8x11.3. 191pp. Fine in VG dj. *Price.* $30/£19

COOK, FREDERICK A. My Attainment of the Pole. NY: Polar Pub, 1911. 1st ed. Signed, presentation. Dec cl (extrems sl worn). VG. *High Latitude.* $225/£141

COOK, FREDERICK A. My Attainment of the Pole: Being the Record of the Expedition That First Reached the Boreal Center, 1907-1909. NY/London: Mitchell Kennerley, 1912. 1st trade ed. VG (sl sunned). *Explorer.* $80/£50

COOK, FREDERICK A. Through the First Antarctic Night 1898-1899. NY: Doubleday & McClure, 1900. Author's signed ed. One of 1000 numbered, signed in a special binding, w/limitation leaf, photogravure port of Cook not in trade ed. 4 color plts, map. Teg, rest uncut. Orig dec watered silk. VG (new eps; expertly rebacked, orig spine mtd). *High Latitude.* $1,500/£938

COOK, FREDERICK A. Through the First Antarctic Night 1898-1899. Montreal: McGill-Queen's Univ, c. 1980. Facs rpt. Map. VG. *High Latitude.* $37/£23

COOK, FREDERICK A. Through the First Antarctic Night 1898-1899. A Narrative of the Voyage of the 'Belgica'.... London: Heinemann, 1900. 8 vo. VG (lt foxed; sl worn, spine sl sunned). *Explorer.* $528/£330

COOK, G. H. Medieval Chantries and Chantry Chapels. Phoenix House, 1947. Orig ed. Good. *Peter Taylor.* $32/£20

COOK, GEORGE CRAM. Greek Coins. Poems and Memorabilia. NY: Doran, 1925. 1st ed. Fine in NF dj (sm chip to spine head). *Beasley.* $125/£78

COOK, JAMES and JAMES KING. A Voyage to the Pacific Ocean...for Making Discoveries in the Northern Hemisphere [Third Voyage]...Second Edition. London, 1785. 3 vols (lacks Atlas). 4to. 24 maps, charts. Early speckled calf (extrems worn). *Swann*.* $747/£467

COOK, JAMES H. Fifty Years on the Old Frontier as Cowboy, Hunter, Guide, Scout, and Ranchman. New Haven: Yale Univ, 1923. 1st ed, 2nd ptg. (Corners sl bumped), else NF. *Pacific*.* $52/£33

COOK, JAMES H. Fifty Years on the Old Frontier. New Haven, 1923. 1st ed. (Name, sl worn.) *Woolson.* $70/£44

COOK, JAMES H. Fifty Years on the Old Frontier. New Haven: Yale Univ, 1923. 1st ed. Signed. Fine in dj. *Labordo.* $450/£281

COOK, JAMES H. Fifty Years on the Old Frontier. Norman: Univ of OK, 1957. New ed. Fine in dj. *Labordo.* $50/£31

COOK, JAMES. The Explorations of Captain James Cook in the Pacific, as Told by Selections of His Own Journals, 1768-1779. A. Grenfell Price (ed). NY: LEC, 1957. One of 1500. Signed by Geoffrey C. Ingleton (illus) & Douglas Dunstan (ptr). 1/4 calf, tapa cl. Fine in slipcase. *Pacific*.* $196/£123

COOK, JAMES. The Journals of Captain Cook on His Voyages of Discovery. J.C. Beaglehole (ed). London: Hakluyt Soc, 1955-1974. 1st eds. 5 vols in 6 incl Atlas & Life of Cook. Each of 1st 3 vols w/'Addenda and Corrigenda' booklets laid in. Blue cl, gilt. Fine (sl shelfworn); last 3 in djs. *Pacific*.* $1,150/£719

COOK, JAMES. The Journals of Captain James Cook on His Voyages of Discovery. J. C. Beaglehole (ed). Glasgow: Hakluyt Soc, 1961-69. 1st ed thus. 3 vols, vol 3 in 2 parts. Thick 8vos, 15-inch portfolio of charts. 2 color ports, 49 maps, ports, views (4 color). Gilt-dec blue buckram. (Bkpls; sl spotted, scuffed.) *Parmer.* $995/£622

COOK, JAMES. The Journals of Captain James Cook on His Voyages of Discovery. J. C. Beaglehole (ed). Cambridge/London, 1967-74. 5 vols in 6, incl Beaglehole's bio of Cook and portfolio of 58 charts and views. Folio and 8vo. Text vols in djs. *Swann*.* $977/£611

COOK, JIM. Lane of the Llano. T. M. Pearce (as told to). Boston, 1936. 1st ed. Pict cl (Bottom rear cvr stained), else NF in VG dj (chipped, price-clipped). *Baade.* $30/£19

COOK, JOHN. Observations on Fox-Hunting, and the Management of Hounds in the Kennel and the Field. London, 1826. 1st ed. 3 litho plts. Uncut. Orig bds, paper spine label. (Sl foxed, soiled; shelfworn.) Protective cl case provided. *Oinonen*.* $160/£100

COOK, JOSEPH W. Diary and Letters of Reverend Joseph W. Cook. Laramie, WY: Laramie Republican Co, 1919. 1st ed. Fine in ptd wraps. Howes C730. *Chapel Hill.* $225/£141

COOK, MRS. E. T. Highways and Byways in London. London, 1902. Teg. (Feps lt browned; spine sl dknd, chipped.) *Edwards.* $32/£20

COOK, ROBIN. Fever. NY: Putnam, (1982). 1st ed. NF (spine sl cocked) in dj. *Antic Hay.* $15/£9

COOK, ROY BIRD. The Family and Early Life of Stonewall Jackson. Richmond: Old Dominion, 1925. 2nd ed. Frontisport. Red cl. NF. *Chapel Hill.* $125/£78

COOK, ROY BIRD. Washington's Western Lands. Shenadoah Pub, 1930. VG- (ex-lib). *Book Broker.* $45/£28

COOK, SAMUEL. The Jenolan Caves: An Excursion in Australian Wonderland. London, 1889. Map. Pub's gilt-pict cl (backstrip defective). *Swann*.* $57/£36

COOK, SPRUILL. J. Frank Dobie Bibliography. Waco, 1968. One of 500 numbered, signed by Cook & Bertha McKee Dobie. VG in dj. *Dumont.* $75/£47

COOK, THEODORE ANDREA. Old Touraine. The Life and History of the Chateaux of the Loire. London, 1906. 5th ed. 2 vols. Fldg table. (Corners, spines sl rubbed.) *Edwards.* $32/£20

COOK, THEODORE ANDREA. Twenty-Five Great Houses of France. London: Country Life, n.d. Folio. Tipped-in frontis, map. Teg. 1/2 cl (sl soiled), gilt. *Edwards.* $120/£75

COOK, THOMAS AND SON. India, Burma and Ceylon. London: Thos. Cook & Son, 1928. 1st ed. 4 fldg color maps. Gilt-stamped thin cl. Good. *Karmiole.* $75/£47

COOK, WARREN L. Flood Tide of Empire: Spain and the Pacific Northwest, 1543-1819. New Haven: Yale Univ, 1973. 1st ed. Fldg map in rear pocket. VF in pict dj. *Argonaut.* $90/£56

COOK, WILLIAM A. Through the Wildernesses of Brazil by Horse, Canoe and Float. NY, 1909. Grn dec cl. (Spine title faint), else VG. *Larry Price.* $49/£31

COOKE, C. J. BOWEN. British Locomotives, Their History, Construction, and Modern Development. London, 1900. 3rd ed. Marbled edges. Full leather. Good (prize bkpl, lib mks, frontis detached, 1 plt split; scuffed). *Bohling.* $25/£16

COOKE, FLORA J. Nature Myths and Stories for Young Children. Chicago: A. Flanagan, (1893). Sm 4to. 93pp, pub's ad. Blue cl, cream bds (bumped, rubbed, dknd) Good + overall (bkpl). *Blue Mountain.* $10/£6

COOKE, GEORGE WILLIS. The Poets of Transcendentalism, an Anthology. Boston/NY: Houghton Mifflin, 1903. 1st ed. Teg. Blue cl. VG. *Lucas.* $50/£31

COOKE, JOHN ESTEN. Outlines from the Outpost. Richard Harwell (ed). Chicago: R.R. Donnelley, 1961. VG. *Lien.* $30/£19

COOKE, JOHN ESTES. (Pseud of L. Frank Baum.) Tamawaca Folks: A Summer Comedy. (Macatawa, MI): Tamawaca, (1907). 1st ed. 185pp. Blue-gray pict cl. (Old name; spine ends, upper corners bumped), else NF. *Pacific*.* $1,265/£791

COOKE, JOHN HENRY. A Narrative of Events in the South of France, and of the Attack on New Orleans, in 1814 and 1815. London, 1835. 1st ed. iv,319pp + 2 leaves ads. Contemp calf (rubbed; foxed). Howes C736. *Oinonen*.* $100/£63

COOKE, JOSIAH P., JR. Elements of Chemical Physics. Boston: Little, Brown, 1860. xii,739pp. Brn blind-stamped cl. (Sigs; corners sl showing, top corner, spine bottom sl frayed.) *Weber.* $150/£94

COOKE, MATTHEW. Insects Injurious and Beneficial. Sacramento, 1883. 1st ed. 156pp. Grn cl, gilt. (Cvr lt flecked), else VG. *Larry Price.* $30/£19

COOLEY, TIMOTHY MATHER. Sketches of the Life and Character of the Rev. Lemuel Haynes.... NY: John S. Taylor, 1839. Frontis, 348pp. Orig cl (spine worn). *M & S.* $100/£63

COOLIDGE, CALVIN The Autobiography of.... NY, 1929. 1st trade ed. Presentation copy inscribed, signed. (Cvr lt rubbed), else Good. *King.* $295/£184

COOLIDGE, CALVIN. The Autobiography of Calvin Coolidge. NY: Cosmopolitan Book Corp, 1929. 2nd trade ed. Inscribed. Frontisport, 7 plts. Grn cl. VG (bkpl; spine ends chipped, sm tear fr joint). *Chapel Hill.* $150/£94

COOLIDGE, DANE and MARY. The Last of the Seris. NY: Dutton, (1939). 1st ed. Fine in VG dj. *Book Market.* $30/£19

COOLIDGE, DANE. Arizona Cowboys. NY: E.P. Dutton, 1938. 1st ed. VG in dj (chipped). *Labordo.* $80/£50

COOLIDGE, DANE. Old California Cowboys. NY: E.P. Dutton, 1939. 1st ed. NF in dj (lt chipped). *Labordo.* $80/£50

COOLIDGE, DANE. Texas Cowboys. NY: E.P. Dutton, 1937. 1st ed. VG in dj (lacks top section, 1.5 inches to fr, 3 inches to rear). *Labordo.* $80/£50

COOLIDGE, MARY ROBERTS. The Rain-Makers, Indians of Arizona and New Mexico. Boston: Houghton Mifflin, 1929. 1st ed. Frontis. (Spine ends lt rubbed), else Fine. *Argonaut.* $75/£47

COOLIDGE, SUSAN. (Pseud of Susan Chauncy Woolsey.) What Katy Did; What Katy Did at School. London: Ward, Lock & Tyler, (1873/4). 1st Eng eds. 2 vols in 1. 8vo. (viii),238; (iv),236pp (bound w/o half-titles). Speckled edges. Contemp 1/2 black calf, black cl sides, spine w/raised bands, red leather lettering label. Very Sound (thin 1-cm strip carefully cut from tp of 1st bk excising sig, neat 1874 ink sig in 2nd bk, sl internal mks). *Sotheran.* $1,040/£650

COOLIDGE, W. A. B. Alpine Studies. NY: Longmans, Green, 1912. 1st ed. Frontis; 15 plts. Grn cl. Good (sl foxed, prelims sl stained; bumped, soiled, lib spine #s). *Blue Mountain.* $35/£22

COOMBS, DAVID (comp). Churchill: His Paintings. London, 1967. 1st ed. Color frontis port, 72 color plts. Dj (sl chipped, price-clipped). *Edwards.* $29/£18

COONEY, BARBARA. Captain Pottle's House. Farrar, 1943. 1st ed. 192pp. Good (corners, spine worn, bumped; broken hinge, rear separating). *Price.* $30/£19

COONS, FREDERICA B. The Trail to Oregon. Portland: Binfords & Mort, (1954). Fldg map. VG in dj (sl worn). *Lien.* $25/£16

COONS, FREDERICA B. The Trail to Oregon. Portland: Binfords & Mort, (1954). Fine in VG dj. *Perier.* $30/£19

COOPER, A. and F. S. EDWARDS. Diseases of the Rectum and Anus. London, 1892. 2nd ed. xix,324pp; 11 plts. (Few sm lib stamps; cl dull, sl worn), o/w VG. *Whitehart.* $48/£30

COOPER, ABRAHAM. Impressions of a Series of Animals, Birds, Etc. London, 1821. 16 mtd India-proof plts, add'l engr tp. Contemp 3/4 calf (rubbing). *Oinonen*.* $200/£125

COOPER, ARTEMIS (ed). Mr. Wu and Mrs. Stitch, the Letters of Evelyn Waugh and Diana Cooper. London, 1991. 1st ed. Fine in dj. *Gretton.* $19/£12

COOPER, ASTLEY. The Anatomy and Surgical Treatment of Abdominal Hernia. Phila: Lea & Blanchard, 1844. 1st Amer ed. xvi,(17)-427pp; 26 engr plts, w/plt XII appearing as frontis. Mod cl. VG (ex-lib, stamps on all edges, foxed). *Glaser.* $250/£156

COOPER, ASTLEY. A Treatise on Dislocations and on Fractures of the Joints.... Phila: Carey & Lea, 1825. 1st Amer ed. vii,425,(3)pp; 21 plts. Contemp sheep. Good (marginal worming to 1st 20 ll, plt III partly separated at fold, no loss; browned, spotted). *Glaser.* $200/£125

COOPER, DOUGLAS. Great Family Collections. London, 1965. 1st ed. VG in dj. *Gretton.* $40/£25

COOPER, DOUGLAS. Nicolas de Stael. 1961. 1st ed. 69 plts. (Pp65-68, 97-100 loose; spine sl damaged), o/w Good. *Whittle.* $13/£8

COOPER, DOUGLAS. Picasso Theatre. NY, (1968). Pict cl (sl dknd). *Swann*.* $115/£72

COOPER, DUFF. Talleyrand. London: Arrow Bks, 1958. 1/4 morocco, marbled bds. Good. *Stewart.* $32/£20

COOPER, H. J. et al. Aircraft of the Fighting Powers. Volumes 1-7. Aircraft (Technical) Pub, 1940-1946. VG (few weak hinges). *Rybski.* $275/£172

COOPER, J. M. W. Game Fowls, Their Origin and History.... West Chester: The Author, 1869. Standard ed. 2 color frontispieces, 304pp. (Spine sunned, ends worn, shelfworn, lt soiled), o/w Good. *Brown.* $85/£53

COOPER, JAMES FENIMORE Lionel Lincoln; or, the Leaguer of Boston. Richard Bentley, 1832. Frontis (sl spotted). Marbled edges, ribbon marker. Orig 1/2 leather, marbled bds; pub's presentation binding. VG (vignette sl spotted). *Tiger.* $32/£20

COOPER, JAMES FENIMORE. The Borderers; or, the Wept of Wish-Ton-Wish. Richard Bentley, 1833. Frontis (sl spotted). Marbled edges, ribbon marker. Orig 1/2 leather, marbled bds; pub's presentation binding (sl rubbed). VG. *Tiger.* $32/£20

COOPER, JAMES FENIMORE. The Deerslayer. (Hartford): LEC, 1961. One of 1500. Signed by Edward A. Wilson (illus). 1/2 deerskin, marbled bds. Fine in glassine, slipcase. *Pacific*.* $52/£33

COOPER, JAMES FENIMORE. Excursions in Switzerland. Richard Bentley, 1836. 1st binding (later copies in full cl). 2 vols. (xvi),304; viii,314pp. Top/fore-edges cut, lower edges rough trimmed. Pink silk markers. 1/4 crimson fine diaper cl, drab bd sides, paper spine label. (One marker detached; chip, labels browned, sl chipped), o/w Nice. *Temple.* $192/£120

COOPER, JAMES FENIMORE. History of the Navy of the United States of America. Phila: Lea & Blanchard, 1839. 1st ed. 2 vols. xxxvi,(37)-394; 481,(1)pp; 2 maps. Good set (lt foxed, spine ends worn, splits over part of joints vol 2). BAL 3888. Howes C748. *Lefkowicz.* $300/£188

COOPER, JAMES FENIMORE. History of the Navy of the United States of America. Phila, 1840. 2nd eds, w/corrections. 2 vols. Frontis maps. 1/2 leather, marbled cvrs, gilt title labels. NF (sl rubbed). *Polyanthos.* $100/£63

COOPER, JAMES FENIMORE. History of the Navy of the United States of America...Continued to 1853.... NY: Putnam, 1854. Tp mtd, 276,248,100pp; 5 ports, 2 maps. Mod cl. Sound (waterstained). Howes C748. *Lefkowicz.* $50/£31

COOPER, JAMES FENIMORE. Homeward Bound. Phila: Carey, Lea & Blanchard, 1838. 1st ed. Orig purple cl. Good set (lacks labels, spine aged). BAL 3883. *Macdonnell.* $200/£125

COOPER, JAMES FENIMORE. Homeward Bound; or, The Chase. London, 1838. 1st ed. 3 vols. 12mo. Half-titles. Uncut. Orig 1/4 cl (spines faded, paper labels worn). BAL 3881. *Swann*.* $805/£503

COOPER, JAMES FENIMORE. The Last of the Mohicans. London: Hodder & Stoughton, (1919). 16 color illus by N. C. Wyeth, incl frontis, mtd tp plt. Lt blue pict cl, gilt. (Extrems lt worn, few scratches to cvr illus), else VG. *Glenn.* $150/£94

COOPER, JAMES FENIMORE. Lionel Lincoln; or, The Leaguer of Boston. Paris, 1825. 1st continental ed. 3 vols. Uncut. Orig wrappers (backstrip bottoms chipped, vol 1 fr cvr partly detached; lt foxed). *Swann*.* $230/£144

COOPER, JAMES FENIMORE. The Monikins. Phila, 1835. 1st Amer ed, w/'Monnikins' in running head on p17 vol 1. 2 vols. 12mo. 2 leaves pub's ads fr vol 1, 6 leaves ads fr vol 2. Orig 1/4 cl. (Lt foxed, top portion of feps excised; spines faded, paper labels sl rubbed.) BAL 3868. *Swann*.* $920/£575

COOPER, JAMES FENIMORE. Pages and Pictures from the Writings of James Fenimore Cooper. NY: James Miller, 1865. 1st ed. Aeg. Brn morocco, gilt. (Joints, extrems sl rubbed, fr lt discolored), else NF. *Pacific*.* $98/£61

COOPER, JAMES FENIMORE. The Pathfinder. LEC, 1965. Ltd to 1500 numbered, signed by Richard M. Powers (illus). Fine in slipcase. *Swann*.* $40/£25

COOPER, JAMES FENIMORE. The Pathfinder; or, The Inland Sea. Phila: Lea & Blanchard, 1840. 1st Amer ed. 2 vols. (i-iv),(13),14-240; (ii),(3),4-233,(234)pp. Orig brn cl, paper labels. VG (bkpls, sl foxed, spotted, lacks ads; labels chipped). *Vandoros.* $350/£219

COOPER, JAMES FENIMORE. The Pilot. LEC, 1968. Ltd to 1500 numbered, signed by Robert Quackenbush (illus). Fine in slipcase. *Swann*.* $57/£36

COOPER, JAMES FENIMORE. The Prairie. LEC, 1940. Ltd to 1500 numbered, signed by John Steuart Curry (illus). Fine in slipcase. *Swann*.* $46/£29

COOPER, JAMES FENIMORE. The Spy. NY, 1929. 3 vols. Teg. Fine. *Polyanthos.* $45/£28

COOPER, JAMES FENIMORE. The Spy: A Tale of the Neutral Ground. (Mt. Vernon, NY): LEC, 1963. One of 1500. Signed by Henry C. Pitz (illus). Patterned cl, leather spine label. Fine in glassine, slipcase. *Pacific*.* $40/£25

COOPER, JAMES FENIMORE. The Two Admirals. Baudry's European Library, 1842. 1st continental ed, 1st 1-vol ed. (Corners lt worn), else NF in 1/4 leather, marbled bds. *Fine Books.* $125/£78

COOPER, JEREMY. Nineteenth-Century Romantic Bronzes. David & Charles, 1975. 1st ed. (Corners bumped.) Dj. *Hollett.* $48/£30

COOPER, MR. The History of South America. London: E. Newbery, 1789. 1st ed. 12mo. Full-pg copper-engr frontis, x,168pp; 5 full-pg copper engrs. Full leather on bds, gilt. VG (dated ink sigs inside upper cvr, on tp; portion of spine professionally repaired; corners, edges lt rubbed). *Hobbyhorse.* $425/£266

COOPER, SUSAN. The Dark Is Rising. NY: Atheneum, 1973. 1st Amer ed. Fine in dj. *Pacific*.* $219/£137

COOPER, SUSAN. Greenwitch. NY: Atheneum, 1974. 1st Amer ed. Frontis. Fine in dj. *Pacific*.* $150/£94

COOPER, SUSAN. Over Sea, Under Stone. London: Jonathan Cape, (1965). 1st ed. Inscribed, signed, dated 1965. Margery Gill (illus). (Name), else NF in dj (spine ends sl rubbed, price-clipped). *Pacific*.* $978/£611

COOPER, THOMAS SIDNEY. New Drawing Book of Animals and Rustic Groups. Charles Tilt, 1837. 1st ed. Obl 4to. Complete w/tp, ad leaf at end, 32 litho plts (some foxed, spotted, 2 sm tears to 1 lower edge). Orig patterned cl (edges sl bumped, corners worn), gilt. *Hollett.* $720/£450

COOPER, THOMAS. Some Information Concerning Gas Lights. Phila, 1816. 1st ed. 190pp, (1)leaf. Full mod leather. (Sl worn, browned, sl stained.) *Oinonen*.* $400/£250

COOPER, THOMAS. Some Information Respecting America. London: J. Johnson, 1794. 1st ed. Fldg frontis map, pp iv,240,(1) errata. 19th-cent 1/2 calf. Howes C760. *Mott.* $350/£219

COOPER, THOMAS. A Treatise of Domestic Medicine...to which is added, a Practical System of Domestic Cookery.... Reading, (PA): George Getz, 1824. 1st ed. 128pp (lacks most of pp79/80, 111/12; foxed); 2 plts (of 3). Orig calf-backed ptd paper-cvrd bds (paper loose on edges). *M & S.* $250/£156

COOPER, W. T. and J. M. FORSHAW. The Birds of Paradise and Bower Birds. Sydney/London: Collins, 1977. 1st ed. Tall folio. 62 full-pg color repros, b/w dwgs, maps. VF in Fine dj, Fine slipcase. *Mikesh.* $300/£188

COOPER, W. T. Parrots of the World. Joseph Forshaw (text). London, 1973. 1st ed. Folio. Fine in dj. *Edwards.* $360/£225

COOPER, WALTER G. The Story of Georgia. NY: American Hist Soc, 1938. 4 vols. (Scuffed, rubbed), else Good set. *Brown.* $100/£63

COOPER, WENDY. Hair: Sex, Society, Symbolism. NY: Stein and Day, (1971). 1st Amer ed. VG (fep rubbed, contents pg sl soiled, 1st pp of text offset; black cl dusty) in Fair dj (soiled, chipped; piece out spine head, top edge fr panel; price-clipped). *Blue Mountain.* $25/£16

COOPER, WILLIAM M. A History of the Rod in All Countries from the Earliest Period to the Present Time. London, n.d. New ed. Uncut. (Eps, text lt spotted, few margins sl soiled, fore-edge some ll sl red-stained; edges soiled, rubbed.) *Edwards.* $48/£30

COOPER, WILLIAM. The History of North America; Containing a Review of the Customs and Manners of the Original Inhabitants; the First Settlement of the British Colonies.... Albany: Samuel Shaw, 1815. 264pp. Period sheep. (Old ink names, dknd, soiled; lt rubbed), else VG. *Pacific*.* $63/£39

COOTE, WALTER. The Western Pacific, Being a Description of the Groups of Island to the North and East of the Australian Continent. London, 1883. Map. Unopened. Pict cl. *Swann*.* $103/£64

COOVER, ROBERT. The Origin of the Brunists. NY: Putnam, (1966). 1st ed, 1st bk. Fine in NF dj (sl dk spot spine crown). *Reese.* $150/£94

COOVER, ROBERT. The Public Burning. Allen Lane, 1978. 1st UK ed. Fine in dj. *Williams.* $26/£16

COOVER, ROBERT. Spanking the Maid. London, 1987. 1st Eng ed. Fine in dj. *Clearwater.* $40/£25

COOVER, ROBERT. The Universal Baseball Association, Inc. NY, 1968. 1st ed. NF (sl leaning, sig) in NF dj (edgeworn). *Warren.* $75/£47

COPE, WENDY. Making Cocoa for Kingsley Amis. Faber, 1986. 1st pb ed. Good in wrappers. *Virgo.* $16/£10

COPELAND, FAYETTE. Kendall of the Picayune. Norman: Univ of OK, 1943. Good in dj (sl worn). *Dumont.* $50/£31

COPELAND, WALTER. Babes and Blossoms. London: Blackie & Son, (1908). 1st ed. 8vo. Charles Robinson (illus). (70)pp. Pict bds (2 waterstains, 1 is 2.5-inches wide). *Sotheran.* $205/£128

COPELAND, WALTER. Silly Submarine. London: Blackie & Son, (1907). 1st ed. Long slim obl 12mo. (30)pp folded ll; 30 color plts by Charles Robinson. Dec eps. Dk grn pict cl. VG (few lt internal mks; expertly recased, neat prize label to inner fr bd). *Sotheran.* $477/£298

COPELAND, WALTER. The Toy Shop. London: Blackie & Son, (1907). 1st ed. 3.2x2.6 inches. Charles Robinson (illus). Full color pict bds. (Facs rear cvr, ep.) *Reisler.* $200/£125

COPEMAN, FRED. Reason in Revolt. London, 1948. VG in dj. *Typographeum.* $18/£11

Copies as Originals. Translations in Media and Techniques. Princeton: Art Museum, Princeton Univ, 1974. Good + in wrappers. *Washton.* $25/£16

COPLAND, AARON. Copland on Music. NY, (1960). Signed. Dj. *Argosy.* $175/£109

COPLAND, SAMUEL. A History of the Island of Madagascar.... London: Burton & Smith, 1822. xv,369pp, errata; fldg map. Full brn morocco (lt rubbed), gilt. *Adelson.* $350/£219

COPP, ELBRIDGE J. Reminiscences of the War of the Rebellion, 1861-1865. Telegraph Pub, 1911. 1st ed. VG. *Rybski.* $135/£84

COPPARD, A. E. Cherry Ripe. Windham, CT: Ptd by Edmund B. Thompson, 1935. 1st ed. One of 300. Valenti Angelo (illus). Tissue wrapper, slipcase. *Maggs.* $48/£30

COPPARD, A. E. Cherry Ripe. Poems. Windham, CT: Hawthorn House, 1935. Amer ed. One of 300. Buckram-backed bds. Fine (sm label partly removed from ep) in slipcase. *Clearwater.* $72/£45

COPPARD, A. E. Collected Poems. London: Jonathan Cape, (1928). 1st ed. Signed, inscribed. VG in dj (soiled, rubbed, sl chipped). *Pacific*.* $40/£25

COPPARD, A. E. Count Stefan. Golden Cockerel, 1928. 1st ed. One of 600. 4 wood engrs (incl frontisport). Untrimmed. 1/4 lemon-yellow buckram, gilt, blue/grn marbled bds. Fine in dj. *Blackwell's.* $192/£120

COPPARD, A. E. Fearful Pleasures. Sauk City, WI: Arkham House, 1946. VG (inscrip, top edge dusty; sm figure stamped on fr pastedown, dj fr flap; spine ends, corners bumped) in dj (nicked, rubbed, dusty, sl torn, chipped, creased, browned, frayed). *Ulysses.* $72/£45

COPPARD, A. E. Fearful Pleasures. Sauk City, WI: Arkham House, 1946. 1st ed. VG + in dj (sl edgeworn). *My Bookhouse.* $77/£48

COPPARD, A. E. The Field of Mustard. (London, 1926.) 1st ed. One of 85. Signed. Full vellum, leather spine label. (Sl discolored, sl warped.) *Kane*.* $30/£19

COPPARD, A. E. Hips and Haws. Golden Cockerel, 1922. Amer issue, w/$ price on dj spine. One of 500. Unopened. Buckram. VG (feps lt browned, fore-edge sl dusty; top edge sl dusty, spine foot sl bumped) in dj (sl rubbed, mkd, dusty; spine, edges dknd). *Ulysses.* $152/£95

COPPARD, A. E. The Hundredth Story. Golden Cockerel, 1931. 1st ed. One of 1000. 4 wood engrs. W/'Notice to Subscribers' loosely inserted. Teg, rest untrimmed. Orig 1/4 emerald-grn morocco, gilt, patterned grn/white bds. Fine. *Blackwell's.* $192/£120

COPPARD, A. E. It's Me, O Lord! London, 1957. 1st Eng ed. Very Nice (spine foot, corner sl bumped) in dj (sl rubbed). *Clearwater.* $40/£25

COPPARD, A. E. The Man From Kilsheelan. London: William Jackson, 1930. One of 550 signed. (Spine, cvr top edge sl faded), o/w VG in glassine wrapper. *Virgo.* $64/£40

COPPARD, A. E. Nixey's Harlequin. London, 1931. 1st Eng ed. One of 305 signed. Full vellum (sl bowed), leather label (sl mkd). Very Nice. *Clearwater.* $88/£55

COPPARD, A. E. Pelagea and Other Poems. Golden Cockerel, 1926. 1st ed. One of 425. 6 wood engrs. Untrimmed. 1/4 white canvas, gilt, pink batik bds. VG (backstrip sunned). *Blackwell's.* $160/£100

COPPARD, A. E. Pelegea and Other Poems. Golden Cockerel, 1926. 1st ed. One of 425. 6 wood engrs. Uncut. VG in canvas-backed dec batik bds. Dj (sl frayed, spotted). *Cox.* $144/£90

COPPARD, A. E. Pink Furniture. Cape, 1930. 1st UK ed. VG in dj (browned, edges sl worn, minor loss to top edge). *Williams.* $51/£32

COPPARD, A. E. Pink Furniture. Cape, 1930. One of 260 signed. Unopened; teg. Full vellum. NF (spine tail sl bumped, cvrs sl bowed) in dj (sl rubbed, mkd, nicked, spine sl dknd). *Ulysses.* $152/£95

COPPARD, A. E. Silver Circus. London: Cape, 1928. 1st trade ed. Uncut. (Edges sl browned, spotted, 1/2-title, last pg sl offset), o/w VG in dj (soiled, chipped, nicked, sm closed tears). *Virgo.* $48/£30

COPPARD, A. E. Silver Circus. Jonathan Cape, 1928. 1st ed. Fine (feps, 1/2-title, final blank lt browned; spine ends sl bumped) in dj (sl creased, mkd, dusty). *Ulysses.* $88/£55

COPPARD, A. E. Tapster's Tapestry. London: Golden Cockerel, 1938. 1st trade ed. 5 full-pg wood engrs. Teg. VG (eps browned, spotted; spine ends, corners sl bumped; spine, cvr edges sl dknd) in dj (nicked, sl rubbed, spotted, dusty, sl mkd, sl dknd). *Ulysses.* $96/£60

COPPARD, A. E. Yokohama Garland and Other Poems. Phila: Centaur, 1926. One of 500 signed. Holland-backed patterned bds. Fine in wrapper, slipcase (sl stained). *Clearwater.* $104/£65

COPPENS, ARMAND. Memoirs of an Erotic Bookseller. Luxor, n.d. (c. 1969). 1st ed. VG in dj (sl soiled, nicked, price-clipped). *Virgo.* $29/£18

COPPOLA, ELEANOR. Notes. NY, 1979. 1st ed. NF (rmdr mk bottom edge) in VG+ dj. *Warren.* $35/£22

Coquet-Dale Fishing Songs, Now First Collected and Edited by a North-Country Angler. Edinburgh: William Blackwood & Sons, 1852. 1st ed. Grn cl, gilt. (Lt foxed, sl insect damage to paste-downs; spine, extrems sunned, spine ends frayed), else VG. *Pacific*.* $92/£58

Coquet-Dale Fishing Songs. (By Francis Doubleday.) William Blackwood & Sons, 1852. 1st ed. viii,168pp. Blind-stamped cl (spine dull, ends chipped), gilt. *Hollett.* $104/£65

CORBET, PHILIP S. et al. Dragonflies. London, 1960. 1st ed. New Naturalist #41. 58 color, 16 b/w plts. Fine in dj. *Petersfield.* $256/£160

CORBETT, EDWARD. An Old Coachman's Chatter with Some Practical Remarks on Driving. London, 1891. 2nd ed. 8 litho plts (lt dampstained). Uncut, teg. 3/4 morocco by Riviere. (Orig cvrs/spine bound in at end; rubbed.) *Oinonen*.* $130/£81

CORBETT, JAMES J. The Roar of the Crowd: The True Tale of the Rise and Fall of a Champion. NY: Putnam, 1925. 1st ed. Grn cl, gilt. (Prelims sl foxed, stamp), else VG. *Pacific*.* $63/£39

CORBETT, JIM. Man-Eaters of Kumaon. Madras, 1945. 2nd ed. Port. (Cvrs sl mkd), else Good in dj (very worn). *Hallam.* $56/£35

CORBETT, JIM. Man-Eaters of Kumaon. London, 1946. 1st Eng ed. Fine in dj (lt scuffed). *Grayling.* $40/£25

CORBETT, JIM. The Man-Eating Leopard of Rudraprayag. London, 1948. 1st Eng ed. VG. *Grayling.* $40/£25

CORBETT, JIM. The Man-Eating Leopard of Rudraprayag. London: OUP, 1948. 1st ed. VG+ in VG dj. *Mikesh.* $45/£28

CORBETT, SCOTT. The Case of the Silver Skull. Boston: Little Brown, 1974. 1st ed. Paul Frame (illus). 120pp. NF in NF dj (sm scuff spine foot). *Price.* $25/£16

CORBIERE, TRISTAN. Tristan Corbiere Poems. William A. Newsom (ed). C.F. MacIntyre (trans). Nevada City: Ptd by Harold Berliner, (1988). Ltd to 150. Frontis. 1/4 grn cl, marbled bds. Cl slipcase. *Truepenny.* $185/£116

CORCAO, GUSTAVO. Who If I Cry Out. Austin: Univ of TX, 1967. 1st US ed. NF in VG dj (edge tears, spinal extrems chipped). *Lame Duck.* $55/£34

CORDER, E. M. The Deer Hunter. NY: Jove Pub, 1978. 1st ed. Pb orig. Fine in wraps. *Associates.* $35/£22

CORDINGLY, DAVID. Marine Painting in England, 1700-1900. NY: Clarkson N. Potter, (1974). 1st Amer ed. Fine in dj. *Lefkowicz.* $75/£47

CORE, EARL. The Flora of the Erie Islands. Columbus: Ohio State Univ, 1948. 1st ed. VG in wraps. *Archer.* $20/£13

CORELLI, MARIE. Cameos. Hutchinson, n.d. (1896). Frontis. Good (shelf # recto of frontis, lacks 1/2-title; spine bumped, sl chipped). *Tiger.* $19/£12

CORELLI, MARIE. Poems. Hutchinson, n.d. (1925). Frontisport. Good (fore-edge sl spotted; bumped) in dj (lacks sm pieces). *Tiger.* $48/£30

COREMANS, P. B. Van Meegeren's Faked Vermeers and de Hooghs. London, 1949. Frontis; 76plts. (Lib stamps, #s.) *Ars Artis.* $40/£25

CORKRAN, ALICE. The Romance of Woman's Influence. Blackie, 1906. 1st ed. Frontis, 10 mono plts. Teg. Navy-blue cl, gilt. Fine. *Bookmark.* $32/£20

CORLE, EDWIN and ANSEL ADAMS. Death Valley and the Creek Called Furnace. L.A.: Ward Ritchie, (1962). 1st ed thus. Signed by Adams. 32 plts. Blue cl. NF in pict dj (sl worn). *Pacific*.* $161/£101

CORLE, EDWIN. Coarse Gold. NY/Boston, (1952). One of 1000. Signed by Coile and Ward Ritchie. VG in dj (spine ends sl rubbed, sm tear fr panel). *Pacific*.* $46/£29

CORLE, EDWIN. Fig Tree John. NY: Liveright, (1935). 1st ed. Fine in Fine dj (chipped). *Book Market.* $100/£63

CORLE, EDWIN. Fig Tree John. (L.A.): Ward Ritchie, (1955). Ltd to 550 numbered. Fine in Fine slipcase. *Book Market.* $125/£78

CORLETT, MARY LEE. The Prints of Roy Lichtenstein, a Catalogue Raisonne, 1948-1993. NY: Hudson Hills, (1994). 1st ed. Grn cl, silver spine lettering. Fine in color pict dj (sl rubbed). *Baltimore*.* $35/£22

CORLEY, EDWIN. Farewell, My Slightly Tarnished Hero. NY, (1971). 1st Amer ed. NF in NF dj. *Polyanthos.* $25/£16

CORLISS, CARLTON J. Trails to Rails. (Chicago, 1934.) Good+ in ptd card wraps. *Wantagh.* $25/£16

CORMACK, MALCOLM. Bonington. Oxford: Phaidon, 1989. 1st ed. Dj. *Edwards.* $40/£25

CORN, ALFRED. All Roads Are One. NY: Viking, (1976). 1st ed, 1st bk. VF in VF dj (faint scratch). *Between The Covers.* $100/£63

CORNELIUS, BROTHER (HERMAN EMANUEL BRAEG). Keith: Old Master of California. NY/(Fresno), (1942/1957). Vol 1 signed. 2 vols. Djs (vol 2 spine top chipped). *Swann*.* $201/£126

CORNELL, RALPH D. Conspicuous California Plants. Pasadena: San Pasqual, 1938. VG. *Dumont.* $35/£22

CORNER, CAROLINE. Ceylon: The Paradise of Adam. London: John Lane, 1908. 1st ed. 1/2-title, frontisport; 15 plts. Teg. Grn pict cl, gilt. VG (sl foxed, plts sl wrinkled). *Morrell.* $104/£65

CORNER, E. J. H. Wayside Trees of Malaya. Singapore: GPO, 1952. 2nd ed. 2 vols. VG (fr hinge vol 1 split; spines sunned). *Archer.* $100/£63

CORNER, JAMES M. and E. E. SODERHOLTZ. Examples of Domestic Colonial Architecture in New England. Boston, 1901. 50 full-pg photo plts, loose as issued. 1/2 cl, marbled bds folder. (Tp foxed, some margins sl soiled, foxed, lacks plt 27; folder worn, lacks ties.) *King.* $150/£94

CORNER, MISS. Careless James; or, the Box of Toys. London: Dean & Son, n.d. (ca 1855). 16mo. Full-pg wood engr frontis, 7ff+1pg list rear wrapper. Pict yellow paper wrappers. VG (pencil sig; wrapper lt soiled). *Hobbyhorse.* $95/£59

CORNER, WILLIAM. San Antonio de Bexar. San Antonio: Bainbridge & Corner, 1890. vi,166pp+27pp ads. Nice. Howes C784. *Dumont.* $185/£116

CORNEY, PETER. Voyages in the Northern Pacific: Narrative of Several Trading Voyages from 1813 to 1818.... Honolulu: Thomas G. Thrum, 1896. 1st ed. x,(2),134,vpp+1 ad pg. VG (few pg corners dog-eared) in ptd wrappers (soiled, extrems sl worn). *Pacific*.* $431/£269

CORNFORD, FRANCES. Death and the Princess, a Morality. Cambridge: Bowes & Bowes, 1912. 1st ed. Tipped-in frontis. VG in brn ptd paper wrappers (spine sl creased). *Maggs.* $120/£75

CORNFORD, FRANCES. Spring Morning. Poetry Bookshop, 1915. 1st Eng ed. Card wrappers (sl faded, edges creased). *Clearwater.* $120/£75

CORNISH, C. J. The Naturalist on the Thames. London: Seeley, 1902. Dec red cl, gilt. Good + . *Savona.* $40/£25

CORNISH, SAM. People Beneath the Window. (Balt: Sacco Pub, 1962.) 1st ed. (Lt used.) Illus wrappers. *Dermont.* $60/£38

CORNWELL, BERNARD. Redcoat. (NY): Viking, (1988). 1st Amer ed. Fine in dj. *Between The Covers.* $45/£28

CORNWELL, BERNARD. Sharpe's Company. Collins, 1982. 1st UK ed. NF in dj. *Williams.* $192/£120

CORNWELL, BERNARD. Sharpe's Devil. Harper Collins, 1992. 1st UK ed. Fine in dj. *Williams.* $32/£20

CORNWELL, BERNARD. Sharpe's Eagle. NY: Viking, 1981. 1st US ed. Fine in Fine dj (rear fold lt soiled). *Unger.* $100/£63

CORNWELL, BERNARD. Sharpe's Eagle. Collins, 1981. 1st UK ed. NF in dj. *Williams.* $288/£180

CORNWELL, BERNARD. Sharpe's Enemy. Collins, 1984. 1st UK ed. NF in dj. *Williams.* $136/£85

CORNWELL, BERNARD. Sharpe's Gold. London: Collins, 1981. 1st ed. Fine in Fine dj. *Unger.* $125/£78

CORNWELL, BERNARD. Sharpe's Gold. Collins, 1981. 1st UK ed. NF in dj (price-clipped). *Williams.* $136/£85

CORNWELL, BERNARD. Sharpe's Rifles. Collins, 1988. 1st UK ed. Fine in dj. *Williams.* $64/£40

CORNWELL, BERNARD. Sharpe's Rifles. Collins, 1988. 1st Eng ed. Signed. NF (spine ends sl bumped) in dj (sl creased). *Ulysses.* $72/£45

CORNWELL, BERNARD. Sharpe's Siege. Collins, 1987. 1st UK ed. Fine in dj (price-clipped). *Williams.* $77/£48

CORNWELL, BERNARD. Wildtrack. Michael Joseph, 1988. 1st UK ed. Fine in dj. *Williams.* $32/£20

CORNWELL, PATRICIA D. All That Remains. Scribner, 1992. 1st Amer ed. Fine in dj. *Murder.* $35/£22

CORNWELL, PATRICIA D. Body of Evidence. NY: Scribner, 1991. 1st ed. VF in dj. *Mordida.* $100/£63

Coronal; or Prose, Poetry and Art. London: Religious Tract Soc, ca 1868. 8 Good chromolitho plts (lt foxed). Aeg. Plum blind cl, gilt. (Sl foxed; sl worn, dusty.) Cvrs Nice. *Baltimore*.* $45/£28

CORREDOR-MATHEOS, J. Miro's Posters. NJ: Chartwell, n.d. (1980). 119 color plts. Good in dj. *Ars Artis.* $120/£75

CORRELL, J. LEE. Through White Men's Eyes: A Contribution to Navajo History—A Chronological Record of the Navajo People from Earliest Times to the Treaty of June 1, 1868. Window Rock: Navajo Heritage Center, 1979. 1st ed. 6 vols. B/w cl, gilt. (Joint ends sl rubbed), else NF set. *Pacific*.* $230/£144

CORREVON, HENRY and PHILIPPE ROBERT. The Alpine Flora. E. W. Clayforth (trans). Geneva: Atar, (1911). 1st Eng ed. Gilt/grn floral eps. (Fep separated; shelf-worn), else Good. *Fair Meadow.* $55/£34

CORREVON, HENRY. Rock Garden and Alpine Plants. NY: Macmillan, 1930. 1st ed. 8 color, 8 b/w plts. (Eps browned), else VG in dj (chipped). *Fair Meadow.* $45/£28

CORRIGAN, ANDREW J. A Printer and His World. London: Faber & Faber, 1944. (Cvrs sl warped.) *Oak Knoll.* $30/£19

CORRINGTON, JOHN WILLIAM. The Upper Hand. NY: Putnam, (1967). 1st ed. VF in Fine black dj (lt rubbed). *Between The Covers.* $65/£41

CORROTHERS, JAMES D. The Black Cat Club. NY: Funk & Wagnalls, 1902. 1st ed. Red cl. VG (ink inscrip; cvrs spotted, spine sl dknd). *Heritage.* $250/£156

CORSER, H. P. Totem Lore of the Alaska Indian and the Land of the Totem. Wrangel: Bear Totem Store, 1932. Rev ed. Pict color pastedown fr cvr. (Sl shelfworn), o/w VG. *Brown.* $30/£19

CORSO, GREGORY. The American Express. Paris: Olympia, 1961. 1st ed. Fine in wraps (sm loss to spine head; lacks dj). *Warren.* $50/£31

CORSO, GREGORY. Bomb. SF: City Lights, 1958. 2nd state w/o ad for Vestal Lady on rear panel. Fldg broadside. Fine. *Beasley.* $45/£28

CORTAZAR, JULIO. 62: A Model Kit. NY: Pantheon, 1972. 1st US ed. Fine in dj (price-clipped). *Lame Duck.* $50/£31

CORTAZAR, JULIO. All Fires the Fire. NY: Pantheon, 1973. (Top edge sl foxed), else Fine in dj. *Lame Duck.* $65/£41

CORTAZAR, JULIO. A Change of Light and Other Stories. NY: Knopf, 1980. 1st US ed. NF in dj. *Lame Duck.* $45/£28

CORTAZAR, JULIO. A Change of Light. London: Harvill, 1984. 1st British ed. NF in dj (price-clipped). *Lame Duck.* $75/£47

CORTAZAR, JULIO. Cronopios and Famas. NY: Pantheon, 1969. Fine in NF dj. *Lame Duck.* $150/£94

CORTAZAR, JULIO. End of the Game. NY, 1967. 1st Amer ed. NF in NF dj (price-clipped). *Warren.* $50/£31

CORTAZAR, JULIO. Hopscotch. Gregory Rabassa (trans). NY: Pantheon, 1966. 1st US ed. NF in dj. *Lame Duck.* $200/£125

CORTAZAR, JULIO. Hopscotch. London: Collins and Harvill, 1967. 1st British ed. NF in NF dj. *Lame Duck.* $150/£94

CORTAZAR, JULIO. A Manual for Manuel. NY: Pantheon, 1978. 1st US ed. Fine in dj. *Lame Duck.* $50/£31

CORTAZAR, JULIO. The Winners. NY: Pantheon, 1965. 1st US ed. (Bottom forecorners bumped), else VG + in VG dj (chip to spine head). *Lame Duck.* $85/£53

CORTES, HERNAN. Letters from Mexico. A. R. Pagden (ed). NY: Grossman Pub, 1971. VG in dj. *Lien.* $27/£17

CORTISSOZ, ROYAL. Monograph of the Work of Charles A. Platt. NY, 1913. Folio. (Lt worn, cvrs spotted.) *Oinonen*.* $190/£119

CORVO, BARON. (Pseud of Frederick Rolfe.) The Armed Hands and Other Stories and Pieces. Cecil Woolf (ed). London: Cecil & Amelia Woolf, 1974. 1st Eng ed. NF (spine foot sl bumped, rear cvr edge sl dented) in dj (edges sl creased). *Ulysses.* $40/£25

CORVO, BARON. (Pseud of Frederick Rolfe.) Hadrian the Seventh. London: C&W, 1904. 1st ed, 1st issue. 8vo. Pub's ads (browned), dated September 1903. Purple pict cl (joints, edges worn, sm ink stain to spine, head sl frayed, lib label removed from fr cvr; bkpl), gilt. *Maggs.* $680/£425

CORVO, BARON. (Pseud of Frederick Rolfe.) Nicholas Crabbe or the One and the Many. (Norfolk): New Directions, (1958). 1st ed, Amer issue. Nice. *Cady.* $27/£17

CORVO, BARON. (Pseud of Frederick Rolfe.) The Venice Letters. Cecil Woolf (ed). London: Cecil & Amelia Woolf, 1974. 1st Eng ed. NF in dj (edges sl creased). *Ulysses.* $40/£25

CORVO, BARON. See also ROLFE, FREDERICK

CORY, O. The Lionhounds. Leadore, ID: Privately ptd, 1977. 1st ed. VG + . *Mikesh.* $45/£28

CORYAT, THOMAS. Coryat's Crudities. Glasgow, 1905. 2 vols. 9 plts (4 fldg, 1 cut). Teg, partly unopened. (Ex-lib; spines sl rubbed, sl warped, edges sl dknd.) *Edwards.* $200/£125

COSENTINO, FRANK J. Edward Marshall Boehm, 1913-1969. (Chicago, 1970.) Sm folio. Red leatherette, gilt. Slipcase. *Swann*.* $103/£64

COSGRAVE, GEORGE. Early California Justice: The History of the U.S. District Court for the Southern District of California, 1849-1944. SF: Grabhorn, 1948. 1st ed. One of 400. 7 inserted facs. Red cl, paper spine label. NF (extrems sl worn). *Harrington.* $100/£63

COSGROVE, RACHEL R. The Hidden Valley of Oz. Chicago: Reilly & Lee, (1951). 1st ed. Dirk (Gringhuis) (illus). Blue cl w/pict cvr label. (Ink inscrip, hinges loose; cvrs worn, sl soiled; extrems bumped), else Good+ in dj (chipped, worn). *King.* $250/£156

COSINDAS, MARIE. Color Photographs. Boston: NYGS, (1978). 1st ed. 60 full-pg repros. Tan cl (sl worn), gilt. Internally VG in VG pict dj. *Baltimore*.* $20/£13

COSS, BILL (ed). Jazz 1956 Metronome Yearbook. NY: Metronome, 1956. 1st ed. NF in wraps. *Beasley.* $30/£19

COSSIO DEL POMAR, FELIPE. Peruvian Colonial Art, the Cuzco School of Painting. Genaro Arbaiza (trans). Mexico City: Wittenborn, (1964). Ltd to 2000. 80 plts (18 color). Dk grn cl. Good in color illus dj. *Karmiole.* $85/£53

COSTA DU RELS, ADOLFO. Bewitched Lands. NY: Knopf, 1945. 1st US ed. NF in VG+ dj (panel versos tanned). *Lame Duck.* $85/£53

COSTAIN, THOMAS B. The Silver Chalice. GC: Doubleday, 1952. 1st ed. One of 750 numbered, signed. Fine in pub's slipcase (sl soiled, flaked). *Unger.* $250/£156

COSTIGAN, JAMES. Little Moon of Alban [and] A Wind from the South. NY: S&S, (1959). 1st ed. VF in VF dj. *Between The Covers.* $125/£78

COTMAN, JOHN SELL and DAWSON TURNER. Architectural Antiquities of Normandy. London: John & Arthur Arch, 1822. 2 vols. 100 engr plts. (Lt spotting, staining, emb lib stamps, lib bkpl.) Later calf-backed bds (corners lt rubbed). *Christie's*.* $243/£152

COTTAM, CLARENCE et al. Whitewings: The Life History, Status, and Management of the White-wing Dove. Van Nostrand, 1968. Good in dj (worn). *Rybski.* $40/£25

COTTERILL, R. S. The Southern Indians. Norman: Univ of OK, (1954). 1st ed. Brick red cl. Fine in dj (spine faded, verso foxed). *Chapel Hill.* $65/£41

COTTESLOE, LORD. The Englishman and the Rifle. London, (1945). Color frontis. Fine in dj. *Petersfield.* $40/£25

COTTON, ALFRED J. Cotton's Sketch-Book. Portland: Thurston, 1874. 1st ed. 216pp; port. *Ginsberg.* $100/£63

COTTON, HENRY. Golf: Being a Short Treatise for the Use of Young People Who Aspire to Proficiency in the Royal and Ancient Game. London: Eyre & Spottiswoode, 1931. 1st ed. Red cl, gilt. (Emb stamp, name), else Fine. *Pacific*.* $138/£86

COUCH, JONATHAN. A History of the Fishes of the British Islands. Groombridge & Sons, 1864-1865. 4 vols. Lg 8vo. 4-pg als dated 9 Feb 1846 tipped in to vol 1. 252 color plts. Blue cl, gilt. (Vol 4 foot chipped.) *Sotheby's*.* $846/£529

COUES, E. and J. A. ALLEN. Monographs of North American Rodentia. Washington, 1877. xii,x,1091pp (tanned, tp lacks corner); 5 plts. New brn cl w/orig cl labels laid down on spine. *Sutton.* $200/£125

COUES, ELLIOTT (ed). The Journal of Jacob Fowler.... NY: Francis P. Harper, 1898. 1st ed. One of 950 numbered. Fldg frontis, xxiv,183pp. Untrimmed. Navy ribbed cl, gilt. Clean. Howes F298. *Baltimore*.* $110/£69

COUES, ELLIOTT (ed). On the Trail of a Spanish Pioneer: The Diary and Itinerary of Francisco Garces...1775-1776. NY: Francis Harper, 1900. 1st ed. Ltd to 950. 2 vols. Fine set. *Book Market.* $300/£188

COUHAT, JEAN LaBAYLE. Combat Fleets of the World, 1982-83. Naval Inst., 1983. VG in dj. *American Booksellers.* $85/£53

COULING, S. The Pageant of Peking. Shanghai: A.S. Watson, 1922. 3rd ed. Folio. 66 tipped-in plts. (Lt browned; gilt faded, corners, spine head sl frayed.) *Edwards.* $320/£200

COULSON, WILLIAM. Coulson on Diseases of the Bladder and Prostate Gland. NY, 1881. 6th ed. 393pp. Good (sl foxed). *Doctor's Library.* $50/£31

COULTER, E. MERTON. Travels in the Confederate States. Norman: Univ of OK, 1948. 1st ed. (Faint glue stain fep.) Dj (lt chipped). *Dawson.* $75/£47

COULTER, E. MERTON. Travels in the Confederate States: A Bibliography. Norman: Univ of OK, 1948. 1st ed. Good dj. *Mott.* $100/£63

COULTER, E. MERTON. William G. Brownlow, Fighting Parson of the Southern Highlands. Chapel Hill: Univ of NC, 1937. 1st ed. Advance reader's copy. Frontisport. Internally VG in blue wraps (spine ends chipped, cvrs lt worn, soiled). *Chapel Hill.* $35/£22

COULTER, J. and A. NELSON. New Manual of Botany of the Central Rocky Mountains. NY: Amer Book Co, n.d. Rev ed. Leather. Good. *Archer.* $45/£28

COULTER, JOHN. Adventures on the Western Coast of South America, and the Interior of California: Including a Narrative of Incidents at the Kingsmill Islands.... London: Longman, Brown, Green, & Longmans, 1847. 1st ed. 2 vols. Sm 8vo. xxiv,288; xii,278pp. 3/4 polished calf, gilt, leather labels, contemp bds. Fine set (bkpls). Howes C802. *Argonaut.* $750/£469

COULTON, G. G. Art and the Reformation. CUP, 1953. (Lib ink stamp fr pastedown; spine lt faded, #.) *Edwards.* $32/£20

COULTON, G. G. Life in the Middle Ages. Volume IV: Monks, Friars and Nuns. Cambridge: CUP, 1930. Frontis. Blue cl. *Maggs.* $13/£8

COULTON, G. G. A Victorian Schoolmaster: Henry Hart of Sedbergh. London: G. Bell, 1923. 1st ed. Orig buckram, gilt. VG. *Hollett.* $48/£30

Country Calendar. CA: Whittington, 1985. One of 115. 12 sm engrs by Gwenda Morgan. 1/4 cl, marbled bds. Fine in slipcase. *Michael Taylor.* $77/£48

COUPER, HEATHER and DAVID PELHAM. The Universe. NY: Random House, 1985. 6 dbl-pg pop-ups by Harry Wilcock. Glazed pict bds (sl worn). Internally Fine. *Bookfinders.* $40/£25

COUPER, WILLIAM. One Hundred Years at V.M.I. Richmond: Garrett & Massie, (1939). 1st ed. 4 vols. Brick-red cl (few spines sl sunned), gilt. Internally NF. *Baltimore*.* $180/£113

COUPIN, H. and JOHN LEA. The Romance of Animal Arts and Crafts. London, 1907. (Lt spotted; spine lt faded.) *Edwards.* $40/£25

COURAGE, JAMES. A Way of Love. NY: Putnam, (1959). 1st Amer ed. VF in VF dj. *Between The Covers.* $85/£53

COURLANDER, HAROLD. Negro Folk Music, U. S. A. NY: Columbia Univ, (1964). Orange cl. VG. *Petrilla.* $30/£19

COURSEY, O. W. Beautiful Black Hills; a Comprehensive Treatise on the Black Hills of South Dakota.... Mitchell, SD: Educator Supply, 1926. 1st ed. Signed. Red cl. Fine. *Labordo.* $50/£31

Courtship, Merry Marriage and Pic-Nic Dinner of Cock Robin and Jenny Wren. London: Griffith & Farran, n.d. (ca 1880). 12mo. 167pp + 1pg list on back wrapper, all pp mtd on linen back; 16 VF half-pg color wood engrs. Fine in ptd yellow paper wrappers (sl chipping along spine). *Hobbyhorse.* $125/£78

COUSINS, NORMAN. The Good Inheritance: The Democratic Chance. NY, (1942). Signed. Dj. *Argosy.* $25/£16

COUSSENS, PENRHYN. The Sapphire Story Book: Stories of the Sea. NY: Duffield, 1917. 1st ed. Color frontis by Maxfield Parrish. Blue cl. (Sl shelfworn), else VG. *Pacific*.* $52/£33

COUTANT, C. G. The History of Wyoming from the Earliest Known Discoveries. In Three Volumes. Volume I (all published). Laramie: Chaplin, Spafford & Mathison, 1899. 1st ed. xxiv,712pp; map, 76 plts. 16-pg prospectus laid in. Orig brn pebbled calf over gilt black cl. Good. Howes C816. *Karmiole.* $500/£313

COVARRUBIAS, MIGUEL. The Eagle, the Jaguar, and the Serpent. Indian Art of the Americas. North America: Alaska, Canada, the United States. NY: Knopf, 1954. 1st ed. 12 color plts. Pict black, cream cl. Fine in color, pict dj (lt edge worn). *House.* $150/£94

COVARRUBIAS, MIGUEL. Indian Art of Mexico and Central America. NY: Knopf, 1957. 13 color plts. Internally Fine (few sm stains to cl) in pict dj (chipped, bumped, worn, dampstained). *Metropolitan*.* $86/£54

COVARRUBIAS, MIGUEL. Island of Bali. NY: Knopf, 1937. 1st ed. Yellow cl, black cl spine, gilt. (Cl sl soiled), else VG. *Turtle Island.* $65/£41

COVARRUBIAS, MIGUEL. Negro Drawings. NY: Knopf, 1927. 56 plts. Buckram. VG (spine tail sl bumped). *Ulysses.* $200/£125

COVARRUBIAS, MIGUEL. Negro Drawings. NY, 1927. Sm 4to. Dj. *Swann*.* $1,092/£683

COVENTRY, FRANCIS. The History of Pompey the Little, or, The Life and Adventures of a Lap-Dog. Golden Cockerel, 1926. One of 400. Frontis, tail piece wood engr. Uncut, partly unopened. VG in buckram-backed bds. Ptd dj (spotted). *Cox.* $176/£110

COVEY, A. DALE. The Secrets of Specialists. Newark, 1911. 3rd ed. Fine. *Doctor's Library.* $35/£22

COWAN, BUD. Range Rider. GC, 1930. 1st ed. (Name, 1 worm hole bottom pp edges, not affecting text; sl worn.) *Woolson.* $30/£19

COWAN, BUD. Range Rider. GC: Doubleday, Doran, 1930. 1st ed. Fine in dj. *Labordo.* $85/£53

COWAN, ROBERT ERNEST and ROBERT GRANNISS COWAN. A Bibliography of the History of California, 1510-1930. L.A.: (Torrez), 1964. 4-in-1 ed. 4 vols in 1. 3/4 blue cl, patterned bds, paper spine label. Fine. *Harrington.* $125/£78

COWAN, ROBERT ERNEST and ROBERT GRANNISS COWAN. A Bibliography of the History of California. L.A., 1964. Rpt of 1933 ed. 4 vols in 1. (Shelfworn), else Good. *Dumont.* $125/£78

COWAN, ROBERT ERNEST et al. The Forgotten Characters of Old San Francisco.... N.p. (L.A., 1964). Frontis, 12 single-sided plts, map. Dec cl. VG+. *Sagebrush.* $40/£25

COWAN, ROBERT G. Ranchos of California. L.A.: Hist Soc of Southern CA, 1977. Signed. Fine. *Book Market.* $40/£25

COWARD, NOEL. Bon Voyage. GC: Doubleday, 1968. 1st Amer ed. VF in VF dj. *Between The Covers.* $100/£63

COWARD, NOEL. Future Indefinite. GC: Doubleday, 1954. 1st ed. VF in Fine dj (sl rubbed). *Between The Covers.* $85/£53

COWARD, NOEL. Middle East Diary. GC: Doubleday, 1944. 1st Amer ed. Fine (bd edges sl rubbed) in VF dj. *Between The Covers.* $100/£63

COWARD, NOEL. The Noel Coward Song Book. Michael Joseph, 1953. 1st ed. Color frontisport. VG in dj (extrems sl worn). *Hollett.* $120/£75

COWARD, NOEL. Not Yet the Dodo and Other Verses. London: Heinemann, (1967). 1st ed. VF in VF dj. *Between The Covers.* $125/£78

COWARD, NOEL. Not Yet the Dodo and Other Verses. GC: Doubleday, 1968. 1st Amer ed. VF in VF dj. *Between The Covers.* $85/£53

COWARD, NOEL. Nude with Violin. GC: Doubleday, 1958. 1st Amer ed. VF in VF dj. *Between The Covers.* $100/£63

COWARD, NOEL. Peace in Our Time. GC: Doubleday, 1948. 1st Amer ed. VF in Fine dj (lt rubbed). *Between The Covers.* $100/£63

COWARD, NOEL. Pomp and Circumstance. NY: Doubleday, 1960. 1st Amer ed. VG in dj. *Cady.* $30/£19

COWARD, NOEL. Present Laughter. GC: Doubleday, 1947. 1st Amer ed. (Couple finger smudges to bds), else Fine in Fine dj (sm scrape fr cvr). *Between The Covers.* $85/£53

COWARD, NOEL. Pretty Polly and Other Stories. GC: Doubleday, 1965. 1st Amer ed. VF in VF dj (sl rubbed). *Between The Covers.* $100/£63

COWARD, NOEL. Star Quality: Six Stories. GC: Doubleday, 1951. 1st ed. VF in VF dj (sl rubbed). *Between The Covers.* $100/£63

COWARD, NOEL. Suite in Three Keys. GC: Doubleday, 1967. 1st Amer ed. VF in VF dj (2 pin-prick size rubbed spots). *Between The Covers.* $100/£63

COWARD, NOEL. Waiting in the Wings. GC: Doubleday, 1961. 1st Amer ed. VF in VF dj. *Between The Covers.* $125/£78

COWARD, T. A. Life of the Wayside and Woodland. London, 1945. 5th imp. (Sl rubbed, soiled.) *Edwards.* $24/£15

COWELL, SYDNEY. The Enchanted Baseball. NY: Cosmopolitan, 1890. 1st ed. 3/4 morocco, marbled bds, gilt. VG. *Pacific*.* $98/£61

COWEN, D. V. Flowering Trees and Shrubs in India. Bombay: Thacker, 1965. 4th ed. VG (ex-lib; bumped) in dj (tape stains). *Archer.* $35/£22

COWLEY, ABRAHAM (trans). Anacreon. London: Nonesuch, 1923. Ltd to 725 w/7 new engrs by Stephen Gooden. Gold bds, linen backstrip. Fine. *Cullen.* $180/£113

COWLEY, ABRAHAM. The Mistress. John Sparrow (ed). London: Nonesuch, 1926. One of 1050 numbered. Buckram, leather spine label. VG (feps browned, pastedown edges spotted, top edge dusty; spine ends sl bumped, rear cvr sl soiled, extrems sl rubbed, label worn). *Ulysses.* $96/£60

COWLEY, ABRAHAM. The Works of Mr. A. Cowley.... Richard Hurd (ed). London: J. Sharpe, 1809. New ed. 3 vols. Uncut. Orig bds, paper title labels. Good+ (tps foxed). *Gretton.* $48/£30

COWLEY, MALCOLM. Blue Juniata: Poems. NY, 1929. 1st ed. Fine. *Bond.* $125/£78

COWLEY, MALCOLM. Exile's Return. LEC, 1981. One of 2000 signed. Fine in slipcase. *Swann*.* $103/£64

COWLEY, MALCOLM. Exile's Return. NY, 1981. One of 2000 numbered, signed by Cowley and Berenice Abbott (photos). Cl-backed patterned bds. *Swann*.* $201/£126

COWLEY, MALCOLM. The Literary Situation. NY: Viking, 1954. 1st ed. VF in VF- dj (couple tiny rubbed spots). *Between The Covers.* $125/£78

COWNING, ANDREW JACKSON. The Architecture of Country Houses. Phila, 1850. Later cl. (Lib stamp on tp.) *Swann*.* $230/£144

COWPER, WILLIAM. Poems, by William Cowper, of the Inner Temple, Esq.... London: J. Johnson, 1788. 4th ed. 2 vols. 367; 359pp. Contemp speckled-calf (neatly rebacked). *Young.* $96/£60

COWPER, WILLIAM. Poems, the Early Productions.... London: Baldwin, Craddock, Joy, 1825. 1st ed. viii,75pp. Orig bds (sm splits at joint ends, label sl soiled). VG. *Young.* $224/£140

COWPER, WILLIAM. The Works.... Robert Southey (ed). Baldwin & Cradock, 1835-37. 1st Southey ed. 15 vols. Engr frontispieces, add'l tps in each vol. Marbled eps, edges. Contemp dk blue morocco, gilt, marbled bds. VG (internally foxed). *Blackwell's.* $456/£285

COWTAN, ROBERT. Memories of the British Museum. Richard Bentley & Son, 1872. 1st ed. Photo frontis (loose). Uncut. Orig 1/4 morocco (upper cvr detached, lacks spine). *Forest.* $56/£35

COX, CHARLES E. John Tobias, Sportsman. NY: Derrydale, 1934. Ltd to 950 numbered. Blue cl. Fine in orig glassine wrapper. *Biscotti.* $250/£156

COX, DAVID. A Treatise on Landscape Painting in Water Colours. Geoffrey Holme (ed). London: The Studio, 1922. Facs tp. 72 plts (15 color/mtd). Teg. Contemp 1/2 morocco by Riviere (orig wrappers bound in), gilt. Fine. *Europa.* $104/£65

COX, EDWARD G. A Reference Guide to the Literature of Travel. Seattle: Univ of WA Publications, 1935-49. 1st ed. 3 vols. (Lt worn; rebound.) *Oinonen**. $100/£63

COX, EDWARD G. A Reference Guide to the Literature of Travel. Seattle: Univ of WA, 1948-1950. 3 vols. 1st ed vol 3, later ptgs vols 1-2. Lt brn cl, gilt. Good (hinges cracked; ex-lib, sl internal mks, each w/white paper shelf sticker on cvrs; sl worn). *Baltimore**. $160/£100

COX, GEORGE W. The Mythology of the Aryan Nations. London: Longmans, Green, 1870. 1st ed. 2 vols. Blue cl, gilt. (Spine ends, corners rubbed), else VG. *Pacific**. $81/£51

COX, GEORGE W. Tales of Ancient Greece. London: Longmans, Green, 1872. 2nd ed. lix,(1)pp,(1)leaf,461pp. Marbled eps, edges. Royal blue calf by Bickers & Son, gilt, raised bands, olive morocco label. VG (lg bkpl, inscrip, 2 leaves sl browned, few sl spots; spine evenly faded). *Pirages.* $45/£28

COX, JAMES R. (ed). Classics in the Literature of Mountaineering and Mountain Travel. L.A.: Univ of CA, 1980. 1st ed. Ltd to 500. Fine. *Book Market.* $75/£47

COX, PALMER. Brownie Year Book. NY: McLoughlin Bros, n.d. 12.25x9.5. Cl-backed chromolitho bds. (Lacks pieces of chromolitho plts due to sticking to facing pp; extrems sl rubbed), else VG. *Pacific**. $46/£29

COX, PALMER. The Brownies in the Philippines. NY: Century, (1904). 1st ed. 4to. 144pp. Tan-olive bds (edges lt rubbed). *Reisler.* $220/£138

COX, PALMER. The Brownies Many More Nights. NY: Century, (1913). 1st ed. 4to. 144pp. Tan-olive bds. Nice in ptd dj (margins worn, spine chip). *Reisler.* $285/£178

COX, PALMER. How Columbus Found America. NY: Art Ptg Establishment, (1877). 1st ed. Orig pict wraps (chipped, lower 1/4 of spine gone, spine neatly reinforced w/archival tape). *Kane**. $110/£69

COX, PALMER. Queer People with Paws and Claws and Their Kweer Kapers. Phila: Hubbard Bros, (1888). 1st ed. 4to. Full color pict bds (worn). Internally Clean. *Reisler.* $150/£94

COX, PALMER. Queer People, Such as Goblins, Giants, Merry-Men, and Monarchs, and Their Kweer Kapers. Phila: Hubbard Bros, (1888). 1st ed. 9.5x7.75. Pict bds. (Tp tear, inscrip; rubbed, spine ends chipped), else VG-. *Pacific**. $40/£25

COX, PALMER. Squibs of California, or Every-Day Life Illustrated. Hartford: Mutual Pub Co, 1874. 1st ed, 1st bk. 491pp. Brn cl, gilt. NF (spine ends professionally restored, corner wear stabilized). *Harrington.* $175/£109

COX, ROSS. The Columbia River. Norman: Univ of OK, 1957. 1st ed thus. VG in dj. *Labordo.* $50/£31

COX, SAMUEL S. Diversions of a Diplomat in Turkey. NY: Charles L. Webster, 1887. 1st US ed. Frontisport, xix,685pp; color chromolitho port. VG in red cl, gilt. *Ulysses.* $400/£250

COX, WILLIAM R. Address on the Life and Character of Maj. Gen. Stephen D. Ramseur.... Raleigh: E.M. Uzzell, 1891. 1st ed. Frontisport, 54pp. (Lib blindstamps; rebacked), else VG in ptd grn wraps. *Chapel Hill.* $175/£109

COX, WILLIAM. Luke Short and His Era. NY: Doubleday, 1961. 1st ed. Fine in dj. *Labordo.* $60/£38

COXE, EDWARD JENNER. Domestic Medicine. Phila, 1854. 1st ed. 300pp. Gilt. VG. *Doctor's Library.* $50/£31

COXE, GEORGE HARMON. The Glass Triangle. Knopf, 1940. 1st ed. (Eps lt soiled; edges worn, spine sl slanted), else VG. *Murder.* $20/£13

COXE, JOHN REDMAN. The American Dispensatory. Phila: Thomas Dobson, 1810. 2nd ed. 840pp; 6 plts. Orig calf (extrems rubbed), red morocco spine label. *Karmiole.* $250/£156

COXE, TENCH. A View of the United States of America, In a Series of Papers...Between the Years 1787 and 1794. London: J. Johnson, 1795. 1st Eng ed. xiv,512pp; 6 fldg tables. Later 1/2 calf, gilt, marbled bds. (Spine worn, bds sl rubbed, scuffed, else Good. Howes C833. *Brown.* $250/£156

COXE, WILLIAM. Account of the Russian Discoveries Between Asia and America. London: Ptd by J. Nichols for T. Cadell, 1780. 1st ed. 4to. xxii,344,(14)pp + (2)pp ads; 4 fldg copper-engr charts, fldg copper-engr view. Teg. Mod 3/4 calf, gilt, raised bands, morocco labels. (Offset from and lt foxing to maps/plt), else NF. Howes C834. *Pacific**. $1,610/£1,006

COXE, WILLIAM. Account of the Russian Discoveries Between Asia and America. London: Ptd by J. Nichols for T. Cadell, 1787. 3rd ed. 8vo. (2),xxviii,387,(22),(6),417-454,(2)pp; 4 fldg copper-engr charts, fldg copper-engr view. Period tree calf (rebacked w/mod calf), gilt, raised bands, morocco label. (Repaired tears to chart and view, sl staining to top margins, old ink name), else VG. Howes C834. *Pacific**. $518/£324

COXE, WILLIAM. Account of the Russian Discoveries Between Asia and America. To Which Are Added, the Conquest of Siberia, and the History of the Transactions and Commerce.... London: T. Cadell, 1787. 3rd ed. (2),xxviii,387,(22),(6),417-454,(2)pp; 4 fldg copper-engr charts, fldg copper-engr view. Period marbled bds. (Chart of Synd's voyage w/sm stub tear; this copy suffered a bit from being in a fire, w/rear cvr, pg edges, margins well-dknd; crudely rebacked w/paper), else Good + . Howes C834. *Pacific**. $184/£115

COXE, WILLIAM. Memoirs of the Life and Administration of Sir Robert Walpole, Earl of Oxford. London: T. Cadell & W. Davies, 1798. 1st ed. 3 vols. Copperplt frontisport, fldg chart, 4pp of facs. Marbled eps, edges. Contemp full calf later rebacked in matching calf, pairs of grn leather spine labels. (1 tp, half-title w/skilled repairs, ex-lib, sm spine labels, bkpls, ink stamps; worn, cracking.) Texts Nice. *Baltimore**. $35/£22

COXE, WILLIAM. Travels in Switzerland, and in the Country of the Grisons: In a Series of Letters to William Melmoth, Esq. London: T. Cadell, 1791. 2nd ed. 3 vols. xii,(blank),(1),410; iii,(1),431; xii,420,(27)index pp; fldg map, fldg view, 4 other plts (1 fldg). Full calf (dry, spine dknd, extrems rubbed; lacks General Map of Switzerland vol 1). *Zubal**. $95/£59

COXE, WILLIAM. Travels in Switzerland, and the Country of the Grisons. T. Cadell & W. Davies, 1801. 4th ed. 3 vols. 4 maps (3 fldg), 3 engr plts, 21 sepia aquatint plts. Dk blue-grn eps; yellow edges. Orig lt 1/2 brn morocco, marbled bds. Nice set (sides sl rubbed, spines dknd, sm slits starting at top of joints vol 1). *Bickersteth.* $352/£220

COXE, WILLIAM. Travels into Poland, Russia, Sweden, and Denmark. London, 1784-90. 1st ed. 3 vols. 4to. 12 plts, 14 maps, plans. Contemp tree calf (rubbed; sl foxed, soiled). *Oinonen**. $550/£344

COY, OWEN C. The Great Trek. L.A.: Powell, (1931). VG + . *Book Market.* $40/£25

COY, OWEN C. The Humboldt Bay Region, 1850-1875. L.A.: CA State Hist Assoc, 1929. 16 maps, plts. Buckram. *Dawson.* $100/£63

COY, OWEN C. (ed). Pictorial History of California. Berkeley: Univ of CA, (1925). 1st ed. Buckram, gilt. NF. *Pacific**. $150/£94

COY, SIMEON. The Great Conspiracy. Indianapolis, 1889. 261pp; port. (Heavily rubbed.) *King.* $25/£16

COYKENDALL, RALF. Duck Decoys and How to Rig Them. NY, (1955). 1st ed. VG in dj (frayed, chipped). *King.* $50/£31

COZZENS, FREDERIC S. The Sparrowgrass Papers: Or, Living in the Country. NY, 1856. 1st Amer ed. Frontispieces. NF (sl rubbed, spine sl chipped). *Polyanthos.* $35/£22

COZZENS, JAMES GOULD. Castaway. NY: Random House, 1934. 1st ed. NF (top edge stain sl splashed at top of pp; sl scuffed) in VG + dj (lt soiled). *Between The Covers*. $125/£78

COZZENS, JAMES GOULD. S. S. San Pedro. NY: Harcourt Brace, 1931. 1st ed. VG (inscrip) in VG dj (sl worn). *Unger*. $125/£78

COZZENS, SAMUEL WOODWORTH. The Marvellous Country. Boston: Henry L. Shepard, (1874). 532pp; map, 27 wood-engr plts. Grn cl dec in gilt/black. VG (rubbed, worn, possibly recased). Howes C838. *Pacific**. $316/£198

CRABB, GEORGE. The History and Postal History of Tristan da Cunha. Epsom: George Crabb, 1980. One of 600 ptd. 2-pg Addenda and Errata dated 24th June 1980 inserted. Comb-bound. VG. *Explorer*. $136/£85

CRABB, JAMES. The Gipsies' Advocate. Sold by Lindsay et al, 1831. 2nd ed. 167,(i)pp (lacks 1/2-title). Mod cl, gilt. *Hollett*. $88/£55

CRABB, RICHARD. Empire on the Platte. Cleveland: World Pub, 1967. 1st ed. VG in dj (sl worn). *Dumont*. $50/£31

CRABBE, GEORGE. Tales of the Hall. John Murray, 1819. 1st ed. 2 vols. Half-titles present, xxiv,326 (lacks blank Y4); viii,353,(1)pp (final leaf not present, perhaps as issued). Orig gray bds, ptd paper labels (chipped, rubbed). Good (lt foxed, early sigs; bds dust-soiled, corners rubbed). *Blackwell's*. $200/£125

CRABBE, GEORGE. Tales. J. Hatchard, 1812. 1st ed. xxii,(2),398,(2)ads pp. Marbled eps. New maroon 1/2 morocco, gilt, maroon cl sides. (Fore-edge of 1/2-title, tp lt waterstained), o/w VG. *Cox*. $56/£35

CRABBE, GEORGE. Tales. London: J. Hatchard, 1812. 1st ed. xxii,ii,398pp. 1/2 calf (neatly rebacked), gilt. Sound. *Young*. $112/£70

CRACE, JIM. Continent. Heinemann, 1986. 1st UK ed. Fine in dj (pub's sticker fr cvr). *Williams*. $24/£15

CRACKANTHORPE, HUBERT. Wreckage. London: Heinemann, 1893. 1st Eng ed. Dec cl. Good (eps browned; prelims, edges, eps spotted; spine ends, corners bumped, rubbed; cvrs sl rubbed, mkd, bubbled; fr hinge cracked). *Ulysses*. $136/£85

CRADDOCK, HARRY. The Savoy Cocktail Book. NY: Richard R. Smith, 1930. 1st ed. Cl-backed pict bds. (Rubbed, rear hinge cracking), else VG. *Pacific**. $115/£72

CRADDOCK, HARRY. The Savoy Cocktail Book. Constable, 1930. 1st ed. Cl-backed bds (sl rubbed). VF in glassine wrapper. *Sotheran*. $477/£298

CRADOCK, MRS. H. C. The Best Teddy Bear in the World, and, Robin's Friends. Nelson's 'Children's Own' series, n.d. ca 1950. 8vo. Honor Appleton (illus). 96pp. Grn bds. (Few pinpricks on fr), else VG + in pict dj. *Bookmark*. $24/£15

CRADOCK, MRS. H. C. Josephine and Her Dolls. London: Blackie & Son, 1916. 1st ed. 4to. 12 tipped-in color plts by Honor C. Appleton. Illus white cl (few spots). Internally Fine. *Reisler*. $285/£178

CRADOCK, MRS. H. C. Josephine's Birthday. London: Blackie & Son, (1920). 4to. Honor C. Appleton (illus). Color paste label. Good in color dj (worn, marginal tears). *Reisler*. $150/£94

CRAFTS, WILLIAM A. Pioneers in the Settlement of America. Boston, 1876. 2 vols. 86 full-pg engr plts. Aeg. Pub's 1/2 black morocco, pebbled maroon cl, gilt. Fine set. *Kane**. $160/£100

CRAIG, A. R. The Book of the Hand. London, 1867. viii,349pp + (ii)pp ads. Uncut. Emb cl (Blind emb stamp, sl spotted; edges, spine sl faded.) *Edwards*. $40/£25

CRAIG, ALEC. The Banned Books of England. London, 1937. 1st ed. Good + (sl rubbed). *Gretton*. $16/£10

CRAIG, ALEC. Suppressed Books. Cleveland, 1963. 1st Amer ed. NF (bkpl) in dj (sl soiled). *Polyanthos*. $25/£16

CRAIG, E. GORDON. Books and Theatres. London/Toronto: J.M. Dent & Sons, 1925. 1st ed. Buckram-backed bds (soiled, extrems rubbed). *Dramatis*. $35/£22

CRAIG, E. GORDON. Books and Theatres. J.M. Dent, 1925. 1st ed. Frontis, 31 plts. Cl-backed bds (sl soiled). *Forest*. $40/£25

CRAIG, E. GORDON. Gordon Craig's Paris Diary. Colin Franklin (ed). North Hills: Bird & Bull, 1982. One of 350. 8 color plts. 1/2 morocco patterned bds. Fine in glassine dj (sl torn). *Any Amount*. $136/£85

CRAIG, E. GORDON. On the Art of the Theatre. London: Heinemann, 1911. 1st trade ed. 1/4 cl, dec bds (scuffed, backstrip rubbed, upper joint worn; inscrip). *Dramatis*. $60/£38

CRAIG, E. GORDON. A Production, Being Thirty-two Collotype Plates...for The Pretenders of Henrik Ibsen and Produced at the Royal Theatre Copenhagen 1926. London: OUP, 1930. Ltd to 500. Folio. 32 color plts, guards. (Rebacked, cornered in cream calf; sl stained fr cvr near spine), o/w Fine. *Europa*. $280/£175

CRAIG, E. GORDON. Scene. London: Humphrey Milford/OUP, 1923. 1st trade ed. (Inscrip; bds, corners rubbed; spine dknd, ends sl frayed.) *Dramatis*. $80/£50

CRAIG, E. GORDON. The Theatre-Advancing. Boston: Little, Brown, 1920. (Spine dull.) Internally VG. *Dramatis*. $20/£13

CRAIG, NEWTON N. Thrills 1861 to 1887. Oakland, CA: N.N. Craig, 1931. 1st ed. Morocco. VG. *Labordo*. $75/£47

CRAIS, ROBERT. The Monkey's Raincoat. London: Platkus, 1989. 1st hb ed. Fine in Fine dj (price-clipped). *Unger*. $75/£47

CRAIS, ROBERT. Sunset Express. Huntington Beach: James Cahill, 1996. One of 200. Signed. Blue cl, gilt. Fine in slipcase. *Pacific**. $81/£51

CRAM, GEORGE F. Cram's Superior Reference Atlas of California, Nevada and the World. Chicago, 1908. Folio. (Shelfworn, hinges strengthened), else Good. *Dumont*. $125/£78

CRAM, GEORGE F. Cram's Unrivaled Atlas of the World. Chicago, 1889. 268pp. (Extrems worn, faded; hinges weak.) Internally Good. *Dumont*. $225/£141

CRAM, JACOB. Journal of a Missionary Tour in 1808 Through the New Settlements of Northern New Hampshire and Vermont. Rochester: Genessee Press, 1909. 1st pub ed. One of 200. (Spine #; rubbed, shelfworn), else Good. *Brown*. $20/£13

CRAM, RALPH ADAM. Impressions of Japanese Architecture and the Allied Arts. Boston: Marshall Jones, 1930. 1st ptg. (Edges rubbed), o/w VG. *Worldwide*. $45/£28

CRAMPTON, FRANK A. Deep Enough. Norman: Univ of OK, (1982). 1st of new ed. Fine in Fine dj. *Book Market*. $30/£19

CRANCH, WILLIAM. Reports of Cases Argued and Adjudged in the Supreme Court of the United States...Volume VII. Washington: Ptd by Daniel Rapine, 1816. 1st ed. Contemp sheep (worn, joints cracked). Usable. *Boswell*. $75/£47

CRANDALL, MARJORIE LYLE. Confederate Imprints. Boston: Athenaeum, 1955. 2 vols. (Lt worn.) Slipcase. *Oinonen**. $130/£81

CRANDALL, MARJORIE LYLE. Confederate Imprints. Boston, 1955. 2 vols. VG. *Dumont*. $150/£94

CRANE, HART. The Bridge. Paris: Black Sun, 1930. 1st ed. One of 200 numbered. 4to. 3 photos by Walker Evans. Wrappers (discolored where exposed by curved indentation in slipcase), silver slipcase. *Sotheby's**. $2,576/£1,610

CRANE, HART. The Bridge. LEC, 1981. One of 2000 signed by Richard Mead Benson (photos). Fine in slipcase. *Swann**. $69/£43

CRANE, HART. The Collected Poems. NY: Liveright, 1933. 1st ed. (Tips, spine edges worn; lacks dj). VG in 1st issue red cl. *Warren*. $50/£31

CRANE, JOAN. Willa Cather: A Bibliography. Lincoln: Univ of NE, (1982). 1st ed. Fine in dj. *Pacific**. $52/£33

CRANE, LEO. California Golf Directory. Fresno: CA Golf Directory, 1953. 1st ed. Fine (emb stamp) in wrappers. Pacific*. $58/£36

CRANE, LEO. Desert Drums. Boston: Little, Brown, 1928. Fldg map. Good in dj (chipped). Dumont. $85/£53

CRANE, LEO. Desert Drums: The Pueblo Indians of New Mexico, 1540-1928. Boston: Little, Brown, 1928. 1st ed. Fldg map. Teg. Blue cl, gilt. Fine (table of contents pg sl dknd from news clipping rev laid in loose; spine ends, corners sl rubbed). Pacific*. $52/£33

CRANE, LEO. Indians of the Enchanted Desert. Boston: Little, Brown, 1925. Good (spine faded). Dumont. $75/£47

CRANE, STEPHEN. Active Service. NY: Frederick Stokes, 1899. 1st Amer ed. Lt grn pict cl. (Spine sl sunned), o/w Good. BAL 4084. Macdonnell. $150/£94

CRANE, STEPHEN. George's Mother. NY: Edward Arnold, 1896. 1st ed. NF (sl cocked). BAL 4073. Agvent. $225/£141

CRANE, STEPHEN. The Little Regiment and Other Episodes of the American Civil War. NY: Appleton, 1896. 1st ed, 1st ptg, w/ad for 'Gilbert Parker's Best Books' on p(197). 8vo. 196pp + (6)pp ads. Tan cl. (1 leaf roughly opened, offsetting to eps from dj flaps; spine foot sl dampstained), else NF in ptd dj (spine soiled, top chipped 1/4-inch). BAL 4076. Chapel Hill. $2,900/£1,813

CRANE, STEPHEN. A Lost Poem. NY: Harvard Press, (1932). One of 100 numbered, signed by Harvey Taylor. Single sheet of laid paper French-folded to make 4pp. Fine. BAL 4105. Between The Covers. $85/£53

CRANE, STEPHEN. Maggie: A Girl of the Streets. LEC, 1974. One of 2000 signed by Sigmund Abeles (illus). Fine in slipcase. Swann*. $34/£21

CRANE, STEPHEN. The Monster and Other Stories. NY, 1899. 1st ed. Dec stamped brick-red cl (spine sl dknd). Swann*. $138/£86

CRANE, STEPHEN. The Open Boat. NY, 1898. 1st ed. Silver-pict grn cl. Swann*. $149/£93

CRANE, STEPHEN. The Red Badge of Courage. NY: Appleton, 1895. 1st ed, 1st ptg, w/last line of text on p225 in perfect type and w/p(235) of ads reading 'Gilbert Parker's Best Books.' 12mo. 233pp. Tan cl, stamped in red/black/gilt. Fine in custom brn cl chemise, 1/4 morocco slipcase. BAL 4071. Chapel Hill. $3,500/£2,188

CRANE, STEPHEN. The Red Badge of Courage. LEC, 1944. Ltd to 1500 numbered, signed by John Steuart Curry (illus). Fine in slipcase. Swann*. $149/£93

CRANE, STEPHEN. The Third Violet. NY, 1897. 1st ed. Dec-stamped tan cl. Dj (lt rubbed). Swann*. $431/£269

CRANE, STEPHEN. War Is Kind. (NY, 1899.) 1st ed. Pict bds (spine extrems worn, backstrip sl browned). Swann*. $373/£233

CRANE, STEPHEN. Whilomville Stories. NY: Harper, 1900. 1st ed. 34 plts. Grn cl. VG (eps, few ll lt browned; cvrs spotted, spine faded, few sl scuff mks rear cvr). BAL 4089. Heritage. $175/£109

CRANE, THOMAS and ELLEN HOUGHTON. Abroad. London: Marcus Ward, (c. 1884). 1st ed. Cl-backed pict bds. VG (extrems, spine ends rubbed). Pacific*. $69/£43

CRANE, W. J. E. Bookbinding for Amateurs. London: L. Upcott Gill, (1885). 156 engrs. Grn blindstamped cl, gilt. Maggs. $72/£45

CRANE, WALTER. The Absurd ABC. London: Routledge, (1874). #110 New Sixpenny Toy Books. 4to. 8pp. Good in color pict wrappers (resewn, lt worn). Reisler. $400/£250

CRANE, WALTER. The Alphabet of Old Friends. London: Routledge, (1875). #73 Shilling Toy Books. Lg 4to. 12pp. Good in stiff paper wrappers (worn, spine resewn, spotting). Reisler. $225/£141

CRANE, WALTER. The Baby's Bouquet. London/NY: Routledge, n.d. (1878). 1st ed. Sq 8vo. Orig cl-backed glazed pict bds. Glenn. $250/£156

CRANE, WALTER. The Baby's Opera. London/NY: Routledge, n.d. (1877). 1st ed. Sq 8vo. Cl-backed glazed pict bds (extrems, joints lt worn). VG. Glenn. $300/£188

CRANE, WALTER. Baby's Own Alphabet. London: Routledge, (1875). #114 New Sixpenny Toy Books. 4to. 8pp. Good in color pict wrappers (resewn). Reisler. $400/£250

CRANE, WALTER. Chattering Jack. London: Routledge, (1867). #64 New Sixpenny Toy Books. 4to. 8pp (lt foxed). Color pict wrappers (resewn). Reisler. $400/£250

CRANE, WALTER. The Fairy Ship. London: George Routledge & Sons, (1870). #95 of Routledge new Sixpenny Toy Books. 8vo. 8pp. Good in color pict stiff paper wrappers (spine sl chipped, sm splits starting). Reisler. $400/£250

CRANE, WALTER. Flora's Feast. Cassell, 1889. 1st ed. Sm 4to. 40,(i) ads. French-folded, unopened. Cl-backed dec bds. Good (label partly removed from tp sig, lt finger-mkd; corners worn, spine ends sl frayed, 1 hinge top sl splitting). Hollett. $224/£140

CRANE, WALTER. Flora's Feast; A Masque of Flowers. Cassell, 1899. 4to. 40pp,9pp ads. Uncut. Dec bds. (Fingermks; sl dusty, edges grazed), else VG. Bookmark. $136/£85

CRANE, WALTER. A Floral Fantasy in an Old English Garden. NY: Harper, 1899. 1st Amer ed. 4to. Color pict cl (fr section sl rippled). Reisler. $450/£281

CRANE, WALTER. A Flower Wedding. Cassell, 1905. 1st ed. Dbl ll, fldg Japanese style. Cl-backed pict bds. VG. Green Meadow. $312/£195

CRANE, WALTER. The Forty Thieves. George Routledge & Sons, (ca 1880). Royal 8vo. 16pp (incl self-wraps); 8 full-pg color plts. VG (sm tear corner of 1st leaf) in pict paper wraps (lower wrap sl soiled). Sotheran. $109/£68

CRANE, WALTER. A Gaping-Wide-Mouth Waddling Frog. London: Routledge, (1866). #61 New Sixpenny Toy Books. 4to. 8pp. Good in color pict wrappers (resewn). Reisler. $475/£297

CRANE, WALTER. Grammar in Rhyme. London: Routledge, (1868). #70 Aunt Mavor's Toy Books. 4to. 8pp. Good in color pict wrappers (resewn). Reisler. $400/£250

CRANE, WALTER. Mr. Michael Mouse. NY: Merrimack, 1956. 5.5x8. 36pp. Fine in wraps. Cattermole. $30/£19

CRANE, WALTER. The Noah's Ark Alphabet. London: Routledge, (1872). #100 New Sixpenny Toy Books. 4to. 8pp (foxed). Color pict wrappers (resewn, spine reinforced from underneath). Reisler. $350/£219

CRANE, WALTER. The Old Courtier. London: George Rogtledge [sic] & Sons, (1867). #62 New Sixpenny Toy Books. 4to. 8pp. Good in color illus wrappers (spine reinforced, resewn). Reisler. $400/£250

CRANE, WALTER. Queen Summer or The Journey of the Lily and the Rose. London/Paris/Melbourne: Cassell, 1891. 40pp + 9pp list. Dec orange eps. Dec paper on bds, cl spine. VG (ink sig; inner hinge top cracked; fr cvr spotted, bds lt soiled, edges sl rubbed). Hobbyhorse. $125/£78

CRANE, WALTER. Queen Summer or the Journey of the Lily and the Rose. London: Cassell, 1891. 1st ed. 4to. 40pp. White/brn eps. White cl-backed grn, brn/black pict paper over bds. VG (lt soiled, edges sl chipped). House. $200/£125

CRANE, WALTER. Renascence; A Book of Verse. Elkin Matthews, 1891. 1st ed. Ltd to 350 numbered on sm paper, in ink for England. 8vo. 163pp,2pp ads. Erratum slip present. Vellum spine, gray bds. VG (bkpl; spine rubbed, dknd). Bookmark. $112/£70

CRANE, WALTER. A Romance of the Three R's. London: Marcus Ward, 1886. 1st ed. Sq 8vo. Color pict bds (corners worn, esp lower fr; spine head lacks sm piece). Overall VG. *Glenn.* $300/£188

CRANE, WALTER. Sing a Song of Sixpence. London: Routledge, (1866). #60 New Sixpenny Toy Books. 4to. (Lt foxed), o/w Nice in color pict wrappers (resewn). *Reisler.* $475/£297

CRANE, WILLIAM CAREY. Life and Select Literary Remains of Sam Houston of Texas. Phila: Lippincott, 1885 (c.1884). 2nd issue, w/1885 date on tp. 2 vols in 1. 672pp; 6 plts. Grn cl (lt spotted). Howes C864. *Karmiole.* $125/£78

CRANTZ, DAVID. The History of Greenland. London, 1767. 1st Eng ed. 2 vols. Contemp calf. (Ex-lib, bkpls, ink/emb stamps; needs rebinding.) *Swann*.* $115/£72

CRANTZ, DAVID. The History of Greenland. London: Longman, Hurst, et al, 1820. Abridged, rev ed of 1st Eng trans of 1767, w/added material. 2 vols. xi,359; vi,323pp; 9 plts, fldg map. Old 1/2 calf, gilt. (Upper portion of both tps sl stained, discolored w/o loss), else Very Nice. *High Latitude.* $300/£188

CRARY, MARY. The Daughters of the Stars. London, 1939. One of 500 signed by Crary & Edmund Dulac (illus). 2 color plts. Vellum-backed bds (spotted), leather spine label. *Kane*.* $170/£106

CRASTER, EDMUND. History of the Bodleian Library. Oxford: Clarendon, 1952. 12 plts. Black cl. Dj (sl spotted, top edge chipped). *Maggs.* $40/£25

CRAVEN, AVERY O. The Growth of Southern Nationalism, 1848-1861. (Baton Rouge): LA State Univ, (1962). 3rd ptg. Red cl. NF (edges sl foxed) in dj. *Chapel Hill.* $35/£22

CRAVEN, JOHN J. Prison Life of Jefferson Davis. NY: Carleton, 1866. 1st ed. Wood-engr frontis, 377 + 6pp pub's ads (lt foxed). Blind grn cl (sl spotted), gilt. Cvrs VG. *Baltimore*.* $40/£25

CRAVEN, T. A Naval Campaign in the Californias, 1846-1849. (SF): Book Club of CA, (1973). One of 400. Frontisport, 3 color plts. Blue cl, gilt. Fine. *Pacific*.* $58/£36

CRAWFORD, F. MARION. Don Orsino. London: Macmillan, 1892. 1st ed. 3 vols. Contemp calf (fr bds vol 3 sl dampstained). *Young.* $72/£45

CRAWFORD, F. MARION. Mr. Isaacs. Macmillan, 1882. 1st ed. (ii),316pp. Contemp 1/2 roan (worn), marbled paper sides. *Cox.* $40/£25

CRAWFORD, J. H. From Fox's Earth to Mountain Tarn. John Lane, Bodley Head, 1907. 1st ed. Uncut. (Feps browned; sl mkd.) *Hollett.* $48/£30

CRAWFORD, J. MARSHALL. Mosby and His Men: A Record of That Renowned Partisan Ranger, John S. Mosby.... NY: G.W. Carleton, 1867. 1st ed. 375pp. Emb grn cl. VG (lt edgeworn, sl foxed). Howes C871. *Chapel Hill.* $350/£219

CRAWFORD, JOE (ed). The Black Photographers Annual. Volume 2. Brooklyn, 1974. 1st ed. Roy DeCarava, James Van Der-Zee, et al (photos). Fine in pict stiff wrappers. *Cahan.* $65/£41

CRAWFORD, JOHN F. and ANDREW HOYEM (trans). The Pearl...Including the Middle English Text Printed Interlinearly.... SF: Grabhorn-Hoyem, 1972. One of 225. 1/2 vellum, silk, gilt. Fine. *Pacific*.* $92/£58

CRAWFORD, LEWIS F. The Medora-Deadwood Stage Line. Bismarck: Capital Book Co, 1925. 1st ed. VG in wraps. *Lien.* $35/£22

CRAWFORD, LEWIS F. Rekindling Camp Fires: The Exploits of Ben Arnold. Bismark, ND: Capital Book, (1926). 1st ed. Map. Blue cl, gilt. (Cvrs soiled, extrems rubbed), else VG. Howes C872. *Pacific*.* $58/£36

CRAWFORD, M. A. (ed). Comparative Nutrition of Wild Animals. London, 1968. Dj (worn). *Sutton.* $85/£53

CRAWFORD, MARY M. The Nez Perces Since Spalding—Experiences of Forty-One Years at Lapwai, Idaho. Berkeley: Presbyterian Bookstore, 1936. (Ex-lib, handstamp, occasional underscoring), else Good in wraps. *Brown.* $25/£16

CRAWFORD, SAMUEL J. Kansas in the Sixties. Chicago: A.C. McClurg, 1911. 1st ed. (Cvrs lt worn, spine sl faded.) *Glenn.* $75/£47

CRAWFURD, JOHN. History of the Indian Archipelago. London, 1820. 1st ed. 3 vols. 8vo. 34 plts, fldg map hand-colored in outline. (Vol 1 pp211-12 lacks corner; pp377-8 w/sm tear; lt browned, lib ink stamps.) Mod calf-backed marbled bds (rebound), raised bands, gilt, spine labels. *Edwards.* $608/£380

CRAYON, GEOFFREY. (Pseud of Washington Irving.) Bracebridge Hall; or, The Humorists. London: John Murray, 1822. 1st ed. 2 vols. iv,(ii),393; iv,(ii),404pp. Full calf, gilt, raised bands. Good set (almost invisibly rehinged, extrems lt rubbed). *Young.* $120/£75

CREASY, EDWARD. The Fifteen Decisive Battles of the World. LEC, 1969. Ltd to 1500 numbered, signed by Joseph Domjan (illus). Fine in slipcase. *Swann*.* $115/£72

CREASY, JOHN. A Beauty for Inspector West. London: Hodder, 1954. 1st ed. (Lt foxed), else Fine in VG + dj. *Murder.* $45/£28

CREASY, JOHN. Murder, London—South Africa. NY: Scribner, 1966. 1st ed. (Pg edges, eps foxed), else NF in NF dj (sm tear). *Between The Covers.* $45/£28

Creative Photography, 1956. Lexington, KY: Lexington Camera Club/Dept of Art, Univ of KY, 1956. 1st ed. 34 photos. (Sm closed tears to ll edges, few creases, sl soiled), o/w VG- in pict wrappers. *Cahan.* $50/£31

CREEL, GEORGE. War Criminals and Punishment. NY: Robert McBride, 1944. Presentation copy. Grn cl, gilt. Well Preserved. *Boswell.* $45/£28

CREELEY, ROBERT. The Gold Diggers. (Palma de Mallorca): Divers Press, 1954. 1st ed. One of about 500. Signed, inscribed. (Soiling; sl adhesion residue along fr gutter), else NF in wrappers. *Pacific*.* $127/£79

CREELEY, ROBERT. Memories. Durham: Pig Press, 1984. One of 100 numbered, signed. Fine in illus wrappers. *Dermont.* $35/£22

CREELEY, ROBERT. Myself. Bedfordshire, England, 1977. 1st UK ed. One of 250. Fine in wrappers. *Warren.* $50/£31

CREELMAN, JAMES. Diaz. Master of Mexico. NY, 1911. 1st ed. Frontisport. Teg. VG + . *Sagebrush.* $75/£47

CREENY, W. F. Illustrations of Incised Slabs. London, 1891. Folio. vii,76pp; dec tp, 69 plts (1 color). Cl-backed illus bds (spine chipped, extrems sl worn, soiled.) *Edwards.* $136/£85

CREMER, W. H. (ed). The Magician's Own Book. London: John Camden Hotten, n.d. (c. 1871). Frontis. Pict blue cl (spine ends rubbed). *Dramatis.* $50/£31

CRESPELLE, JEAN-PAUL. The Fauves. Greenwich, CT: NYGS, n.d. Fine in pict dj (spine sunned). *Metropolitan*.* $34/£21

CRESSMAN, L. S. The Sandal and the Cave. Portland: Beaver Books, 1964. 2nd ptg. Fine in red wrappers. *Harrington.* $25/£16

CRESSWELL, BEATRICE F. The Royal Progress of King Pepito. London: SPCK, (1889). 1st ed. 8x6. 12 color plts by Kate Greenaway. Teg. 3/4 red morocco, dec bds, gilt spine. (Orig wrappers soiled, laid on backing paper, bound to rear), else VG. *Pacific*.* $92/£58

CRESSWELL, NICHOLAS. The Journal of Nicholas Cresswell 1774-1777. NY: Dial, 1924. 1st ed, 1st ptg. Fine in dj. *Mott.* $50/£31

CREWS, HARRY. Car. NY, 1973. 1st ed. NF in VG + dj (price-clipped). *Warren.* $95/£59

CREWS, HARRY. A Childhood. NY, 1981. 1st ed. NF (sl cocked) in NF dj. *Warren.* $95/£59

CREWS, HARRY. A Feast of Snakes. NY: Atheneum, 1976. 1st ed. Fine in NF dj. *Lame Duck.* $200/£125

CREWS, HARRY. The Gypsy's Curse. NY, 1974. 1st ed. NF in NF dj. *Warren.* $150/£94

CREWS, HARRY. This Thing Don't Lead to Heaven. NY: William Morrow, (1970). 1st ed. NF in dj. *Pacific*.* $98/£61

CRICHTON, KYLE S. Law and Order Ltd. Santa Fe: New Mexican Pub, 1928. (Shelfworn, sl cocked.) Internally Good. *Dumont.* $125/£78

CRICHTON, KYLE S. Law and Order, Ltd. The Rousing Life of Elfego Baca of New Mexico. Santa Fe: New Mexican Pub, 1928. 1st ed. One of 2000 ptd (375 of which were a signed issue). Fine. Howes C886. *Pacific*.* $63/£39

CRICHTON, MICHAEL. Eaters of the Dead. NY: Knopf, 1976. 1st ed. Fine in dj. *Pacific*.* $69/£43

CRICHTON, MICHAEL. Jasper Johns. NY: Abrams, 1977. 1st trade pb ed. Fine (bottom corner sl soiled). *Warren.* $35/£22

CRICHTON, MICHAEL. Jurassic Park. NY, 1990. 1st ed. Advance reader's copy. VG+. *Warren.* $30/£19

CRICHTON, MICHAEL. Jurassic Park. NY: Knopf, 1990. 1st ed. Fine in Fine dj. *Pettler.* $50/£31

CRICHTON, MICHAEL. Rising Sun. NY: Knopf, 1992. 1st ed. Fine in Fine dj. *Pettler.* $40/£25

CRICHTON, MICHAEL. Sphere. NY, 1987. Advance reader's ed. NF in glossy wraps. *Warren.* $25/£16

CRICHTON, MICHAEL. Sphere. Knopf, 1987. 1st US ed. Fine in dj. *Williams.* $48/£30

CRICHTON, MICHAEL. The Terminal Man. NY, 1972. 1st ed. Fine in Fine dj (price-clipped). *Warren.* $40/£25

CRIMMINS, JOHN D. St. Patrick's Day: Its Celebration in New York and Other American Places, 1737-1845. NY: The Author, 1902. 1st ed. Grn cl, gilt. Good. *Karmiole.* $65/£41

CRINKLE, C. Voyages of Captain Crinkle and the Good Ship Swan. SF: Crinkle, 1945. 7x10. Edith Lincoln (illus). 205pp; frontis, dedication pg tipped-in color plts w/sea fairies. Blue cl, stamped Crinkle. VG (corners sl bumped). *Price.* $20/£13

CRIPPEN, LEE F. Simon Cameron: Ante-Bellum Years. Oxford, OH: Mississippi Valley Press, 1942. 1st ed. Port. Dj. *Ginsberg.* $100/£63

CRIPPS, WILFRED JOSEPH. Old English Plate. John Murray, 1901. Best ed (library ed). 1/2 vellum (sl spotted), gilt. *Hollett.* $104/£65

CRIPPS-DAY, FRANCIS HENRY. A Record of Armour Sales 1881-1924. London, 1925. (Extrems lt rubbed.) *Swann*.* $201/£126

CRISP, QUENTIN and DONALD CARROLL. Doing It with Style. Eyre Methuen, 1981. 1st UK ed. NF in dj. *Williams.* $22/£14

CRISP, QUENTIN and A. F. STUART. Lettering for Brush and Pen. Frederick Warne, n.d. (1936). 1st Eng ed. B/w frontis. VG (prelims, edges, eps spotted; top edge sl dusty; cvrs sl bowed, bottom cvr edges dusty; spine ends, corners sl bumped) in dj (torn, chipped, rubbed, dusty, sl creased, mkd, clipped, browned). *Ulysses.* $58/£36

CRISP, QUENTIN. The Naked Civil Servant. Cape, 1968. 1st ed. NF (edges sl browned, sl mk to rear bd) in VG+ dj (sl soiled, creased, spine sl tanned). *Any Amount.* $35/£22

CRISP, QUENTIN. The Naked Civil Servant. Cape, 1968. 1st UK ed. Inscribed. VG in dj (browned, rubbed, sl stained). *Williams.* $96/£60

CRISPIN, EDMUND. Frequent Hearses. Victor Gollancz, 1950. 1st ed. VG (eps spotted; top edge sl mkd, dusty, spine ends, corners sl bumped) in dj (nicked, rubbed, chipped, mkd, spotted, sl torn, creased, browned). *Ulysses.* $152/£95

CRISPIN, EDMUND. Swan Song. Gollancz, 1947. 1st UK ed. Good in dj (browned, spine sl chipped). *Williams.* $120/£75

CRISPIN, EDMUND. Swan Song. Victor Gollancz, 1947. 1st ed. Good (prelims, edges, eps spotted; mkd, sl soiled, sl bumped, top edge dusty, fr hinge cracked, spine rubbed, faded) in dj (chipped, torn, rubbed, spotted, sl torn, frayed, creased, extrems browned, fr panel faded). *Ulysses.* $152/£95

CRISSEY, FORREST. Alexander Legge, 1866-1933. Chicago: Lakeside, 1936. 1st ed. Color frontis. Good+. *Wantagh.* $25/£16

CRIST, EDA and RICHARD. Chico. Westminster, 1951. 1st ed. Fine in VG+ dj. *Price.* $26/£16

CRISTIANI, R. S. A Technical Treatise on Soap and Candles. Phila: Henry Carey Baird, 1881. xvi,581pp. (Joints cracked; tp, rep browned; extrems worn), o/w VG. *Hollett.* $120/£75

CRISWELL, G. C. and C. L. Confederate and Southern State Currency. Pass-A-Grille Beach, FL, 1957. VG. *Book Broker.* $35/£22

Criticisms on the Rolliad. (By Joseph Richardson et al.) London: James Ridgway, 1785. Corrected & Enlarged ed. Copper-engr frontis, 196,(1)pp. 3/4 calf, marbled bds, morocco spine label. (Fr joint cracking), else VG. *Pacific*.* $46/£29

CROCE, BENEDETTO. History as the Story of Liberty. Sylvia Sprigge (trans). London: George Allen & Unwin, 1941. 1st Eng ed. NF (eps sl browned; spine ends, corner sl bumped) in dj (sl nicked, dusty, edges rubbed). *Ulysses.* $72/£45

CROCKER, JAMES F. Prison Reminiscences.... Portsmouth, VA: W.A. Fiske, 1906. 1st ed. 8vo. NF in ptd gray wraps. *Chapel Hill.* $1,250/£781

CROCKETT, S. R. The Men of the Moss-Hags. Isbister, 1895. Pub's cat dated Autumn 1895. Teg. Good (ink inscrip; spine bumped). *Tiger.* $22/£14

CROCKETT, S. R. Sir Toady Crusoe. Wells Gardner, Darton, 1905. 1st Eng ed. Frontis. VG (pg edges browned, feps partly browned, spotted; spine ends bumped, corners sl rubbed) in dj (rubbed, chipped, nicked, spine dknd). *Ulysses.* $120/£75

CROCKETT, W. S. In the Border Country. W. Shaw Sparrow (ed). London, 1906. 1st ed. 25 mtd color plts. Teg. (Lt marginal browning; spine faded.) *Edwards.* $45/£28

CROCKETT, WALTER HILL. A History of Lake Champlain. Burlington, VT: Hobart J. Shanley, 1909. 5 plts. 1/2 red morocco (rubbed, hinges worn; orig ptd wrappers bound in). *Adelson.* $160/£100

CROFT-COOKE, RUPERT. Port. London: Putnam, 1957. 1st ed. NF in dj (lt soiled, price-clipped). *Glenn.* $45/£28

CROFTS, FREEMAN WILLS. The Futile Alibi. NY: Dodd Mead, 1938. 1st Amer ed. VG in dj (internal tape mends, spine chipped, frayed; corners, folds worn, rear panel stained). *Mordida.* $75/£47

CROFTS, FREEMAN WILLS. The Mystery of the Sleeping Car Express and Other Stories. Hodder, 1956. 1st UK ed. Fine (lg stamp on fep) in dj. *Williams.* $109/£68

CROFTS, FREEMAN WILLS. Young Robin Brand, Detecive. Univ of London, 1947. 1st Eng ed. NF (bkpl; spine sl faded) in dj (sl rubbed). *Ulysses.* $312/£195

CROFUTT, GEORGE A. Crofutt's New Overland Tourist and Pacific Coast Guide. Chicago: Overland Pub Co, 1878. 1st ed. Frontis, 324pp; 18 dbl-pg views. Maroon cl (worn, soiled). Text clean. Howes C901. *House.* $200/£125

CROFUTT, GEORGE A. Crofutt's Trans-Continental Tourist. NY: Crofutt, 1874. 160pp. VG (cvr loose). *Book Market.* $35/£22

CROFUTT, GEORGE A. Crofutt's Trans-Continental Tourist. NY: Crofutt, 1874. 160pp. VG (cvr loose). *Book Market.* $35/£22

CROGHAN, GEORGE. Army Life on the Western Frontier. Francis Paul Prucha (ed). Norman: Univ of OK, (1958). 1st ed. VG in dj. *Lien.* $30/£19

CROKER, THOMAS CROFTON. A Walk from London to Fulham. T. F. Dillon Croker (ed). London: William Tegg, 1860. (xviii),256pp. 1/2 morocco. (Lacks half-title; respined.) *Marlborough*. $160/£100

CROMMELIN, MAY. Little Soldiers. London: Hutchinson, (1916). 4to. 95pp (marginal tears, rough edges); 39 illus by Louis Wain. Color pict bds (edges, spine worn). *Reisler*. $800/£500

CROMPTON, FRANCES E. Little Swan Maidens. Ernest Nister, n.d. c1900. 8vo. Evelyn Lance (illus). 40pp. Pict bds, gilt. (Lacks fep; sm hole spine top), else VG. *Bookmark*. $24/£15

CROMPTON, RICHMAL. William and the Masked Ranger. Newnes, 1966. 1st ed. VG in Nice dj. *Green Meadow*. $120/£75

CROMPTON, RICHMAL. William and the Space Animal. Newnes, 1956. 1st ed. Gilt dec grn cl. VG + in Fine dj. *Green Meadow*. $88/£55

CROMPTON, RICHMAL. William and the Tramp. Newnes, 1952. 1st ed. Grn cl, gilt. VG + in dj. *Green Meadow*. $104/£65

CROMWELL, THOMAS. Excursions Through Ireland...Forming a Complete Guide for the Traveller and Tourist. London, 1820. 2 vols. Orig 1/4 cl (backstrips worn). *Swann**. $138/£86

CRONE, RAINER. Andy Warhol. NY, (1970). 1st ed. (Ink inscrip), else VG in dj (defective, heavily repaired). *King*. $650/£406

CRONISE, TITUS FEY. The Natural Wealth of California.... SF: H.H. Bancroft, 1868. 1st ed. xvi,696pp + (2)pp ads. Grn cl, gilt. (Fr hinge cracked at eps), else NF. *Pacific**. $92/£58

CRONKHITE, DANIEL. Death Valley's Victims. Verdi, NV: Sagebrush, 1968. 1st ed. Ltd to 750 signed. Fine in wraps. *Book Market*. $20/£13

CRONKHITE, DANIEL. Death Valley's Victims: A Descriptive Chronology, 1849-1966. Verdi, (NV): Sagebrush, 1968. 1st deluxe ed. Ltd to 225. 13 plts. Pict eps. Brn linen, gilt spine. Fine in pict dj. *Pacific**. $46/£29

CROOK, RONALD E. A Bibliography of Joseph Priestley 1733-1804. Library Assoc, 1966. 1st ed. Dj. *Forest*. $88/£55

CROOK, WILLIAM H. Through Five Administrations. NY, 1910. 1st ed. (Lt worn, name erased fep.) *Woolman*. $15/£9

CROSBY, CARESSE. Crosses of Gold: A Book of Verse. Paris: (Privately ptd), 1925. 1st ed, 1st bk. One of 100. Tree calf, morocco spine label, bound by Lafon (as issued). Fine. *Pacific**. $748/£468

CROSBY, CARESSE. Painted Shores. Paris: Editions Narcisse, 1927. 1st ed. One of 222. 3 hand-colored illus. NF in ptd wrappers, glassine. *Pacific**. $345/£216

CROSBY, HARRY. Chariots of the Sun. Paris: Black Sun, 1931. 1st ed. One of 500. Ptd wrappers (1/2-inch chip spine base). Glassine dj. *Swann**. $161/£101

CROSBY, HARRY. Transit of Venus. Paris: BSP, 1929. 2nd ed. One of 200. NF in VG slipcase. *Any Amount*. $192/£120

CROSBY, HARRY. Transit of Venus: Poems. Paris: Black Sun, 1929. 2nd ed. One of 200. Fine in ptd wrappers, glassine, VG slipcase. *Pacific**. $207/£129

CROSBY, HENRY. War Letters. Paris: Black Sun, 1932. 1st ed. One of 125. Frontis. 1/2 tree calf, dec bds, raised bands, morocco spine labels. (Prelim creased; spine, extrems sl rubbed), else NF. *Pacific**. $460/£288

CROSFIELD, GEORGE. Memoirs of the Life and Gospel Labours of Samuel Fothergill, with Selections from His Correspondence. Liverpool: D. Marples, 1843. 1st ed. Engr frontis, vii,544pp. Orig blind-stamped cl. *Young*. $80/£50

CROSLAND, MARGARET. Colette: A Provincial in Paris. NY: British Book Centre, (1954). 1st ed. Rev slip laid in. NF (edges lt worn) in dj. *Hermitage*. $45/£28

CROSS, AMANDA. The Question of Max. NY: Knopf, 1976. 1st ed. Fine in dj (lt edgeworn). *Janus*. $50/£31

CROSS, ARTHUR LYON. Eighteenth Century Documents Relating to the Royal Forests, the Sheriffs and Smuggling. Ann Arbor: William L. Clements Library, 1928. 1st ed. One of 100 numbered, inscribed. Port. Untrimmed. Paper over bds, cl spine, paper label. (Lt worn, spotted, label discolored.) *Woolson*. $75/£47

CROSS, F. M. The Ancient Library of Qumran and Modern Biblical Studies. London: Gerald Duckworth, 1958. Frontis. Black cl. Dj (few sm tears). *Maggs*. $19/£12

CROSS, IRA B. Financing an Empire. SF: S.J. Clarke, 1927. 1st ed. 4 vols. Emb dec cl. Fine. *Pacific**. $127/£79

CROSS, IRA B. Financing an Empire: History of Banking in California. SF: S.J. Clarke, 1927. 1st ed. 4 vols. Teg. Gilt/silver emb dec cl. Fine. *Pacific**. $173/£108

CROSS, J. W. (ed). George Eliot's Life as Related in Her Letters and Journals. NY: Harper, 1885. 1st ed. 3 vols. Grn cl (Lt worn, rubbed), else VG set. *Robbins*. $85/£53

CROSS, JOE. Cattle Clatter; A History of Cattle from the Creation to the Texas Centennial in 1936. Kansas City, MO: Walker, 1938. 1st ed. Fine. *Labordo*. $225/£141

CROSS, M. I. and MARTIN J. COLE. Modern Microscopy. London, 1895. 2nd ed. 182pp. (Spine sl chipped.) *Edwards*. $40/£25

CROSS, ODO. The Snail that Climbed the Eiffel Tower and Other Stories. London: Lehmann, 1947. 1st Eng ed, 1st issue in cl-backed patterned bds. 8 full-pg dwgs. Dj (sl torn, rubbed). *Clearwater*. $360/£225

CROSS, RALPH HERBERT. The Early Inns of California, 1844-1869. SF: Privately ptd, 1954. 1st ed. One of 500. Fldg map. Cl-backed red patterned bds. Fine. *Harrington*. $65/£41

CROSS, RALPH HERBERT. The Early Inns of California, 1844-1869. SF: (Cross & Brandt), 1954. 1st ed. One of 500 ptd. 1/4 cl, dec bds, gilt. Fine. *Pacific**. $81/£51

CROSS, W. L. The History of Henry Fielding. New Haven: Yale Univ, 1918. 3 vols. 3 frontispieces, 35 plts. Maroon cl (headcaps bumped). *Maggs*. $224/£140

CROSS, W. L. The Life and Times of Laurence Sterne. New Haven: Yale Univ, 1925. New enlgd ed. 2 vols. 2 frontisports, 13 plts. Teg. Red cl (headcaps sl bumped). *Maggs*. $208/£130

CROSS, WILBUR. Ghost Ship of the Pole. Heinemann, 1960. 1st Eng ed. VG + in dj. *Walcot*. $27/£17

CROSSLEY, FRED H. English Church Craftsmanship. London, 1947. 2nd ed. Good in dj. *Washton*. $40/£25

CROSSLEY, FRED H. English Church Monuments A.D. 1150-1550. London, 1921. Good. *Washton*. $125/£78

CROSSLEY, FRED H. Timber Building in England. Batsford, 1951. 1st ed. (1st few ll spotted, feps sl browned.) Dj (sl chipped, edges, spine browned). *Edwards*. $88/£55

CROSSLEY-HOLLAND, KEVIN. The Wildman. Andre Deutsch, 1976. 1st ed. Obl sm 4to. Charles Keeping (illus). Illus bds. (Edges rubbed), else VG + in pict dj. *Bookmark*. $24/£15

CROSSMAN, EDWARD C. Military and Sporting Rifle Shooting. Onslow County, NC, (1932). Brochure for Noske Fieldscope present. (Bkpl; sl worn.) *King*. $40/£25

CROTTY, HOMER D. Glimpses of Don Quixote and La Mancha. L.A.: Zamorano Club, 1963. 1st ed. One of 250 ptd. Cl-backed marbled bds. Fine. *Pacific**. $40/£25

CROUCH, STEVE. Steinbeck Country. Palo Alto: American West Publishing, (1973). 1st ed. Fine in slipcase. *Pacific**. $23/£14

CROUCHER, JOHN H. Plain Directions for Obtaining Photographic Pictures by the Calotype and Energiatype, also, Upon Albumenized Paper and Glass, by Collodion and Albumen, etc. etc. Phila: A. Hart, 1853. 1st ed. 16mo. 224pp (foxed; spine chipped). *M & S*. $750/£469

CROWE, CATHERINE. The Night-Side of Nature or, Ghosts and Ghost-Seers. NY: Redfield, 1856. 1st ed. (Foxed; spine ends, fr joint chipped), else VG-. *Pacific*. $63/£39

CROWE, EARLE. Men of El Tejon: Empire in the Tehachapis. L.A.: Ward Ritchie, 1957. 1st ed. VG in brn dj. *Houle*. $45/£28

CROWE, J. A. and G. B. CAVALCASELLE. A History of Painting in North Italy. Tancred Borenius (ed). NY, 1912. 2nd ed. 3 vols. 75; 73; 59 plts. Good. *Washton*. $225/£141

CROWE, PHILIP K. Sport Is Where You Find It. NY: D. Van Nostrand, (1953). 1st ed. One of 1475. Signed. Grn cl, gilt. (Soiled, hinges sl weak), else VG. *Pacific*. $29/£18

CROWE, SAMUEL. Halsted of Johns Hopkins: The Man and His Men. Springfield, 1957. 1st ed. Good (sl fr, rear waterstain). *Doctor's Library*. $50/£31

CROWE, SYLVIA. Garden Design. NY: Hearthside, 1959. 61 half-tones. Fine in dj. *Quest*. $45/£28

CROWE, SYLVIA. The Landscape of Roads. London: Architectural Press, 1960. Dj. *Edwards*. $24/£15

CROWE, SYLVIA. Tomorrow's Landscape. London: Architectural, 1956. NF. *Quest*. $50/£31

CROWLEY, ALEISTER. Ambergris. Elkin Mathews, 1910. 1st Eng ed. VG (spine faded). *Clearwater*. $136/£85

CROWLEY, ALEISTER. The Argonauts. Inverness: Soc for the Propagation of Religious Truth, 1904. 1st ed. Fine in ptd thick wrappers, later chemise. *Pacific*. $173/£108

CROWLEY, ALEISTER. The City of God: A Rhapsody. London: O.T.O., 1943. 1st ed. Frontis photogravure port. Fine in ptd wrappers. *Pacific*. $138/£86

CROWLEY, ALEISTER. Magick in Theory and Practice by the Master Therion. London: For Subscribers Only, 1929. Teg. (Feps browned, sm lt brn mk to pp ix foot; lt soiled, spine sl, sl spotting intruding on fr bd joint.) *Edwards*. $144/£90

CROWLEY, ALEISTER. Moonchild. London, 1929. 1st ed. Pieces of dj laid in. *Swann*. $46/£29

CROWLEY, ALEISTER. Olla: An Anthology of Sixty Years of Song. London: O.T.O., (c. 1946). 1st ed. One of 500. Frontis-port. VG in dj (sl soiled, sm spine label). *Pacific*. $161/£101

CROWLEY, MART. The Boys in the Band. NY, (1968). 1st ed, 1st bk. (Ink marker scribbles, underlining), else Good in dj (sl worn). *King*. $25/£16

CROWQUILL, ALFRED. Seymour's Humorous Sketches Comprising Eighty-Six Caricature Etchings. London: T. Miles, 1888. Sm 4to. 173pp + 10pp bio notice, 6pp list of plts; 86 VF full-pg plts. Pict black/red linen. Good (heavy foxing tp, lt foxing some plts; water stain along fore-edge affecting some pp; dated inscrip; lt rubbed, spine faded, cracked along edge). *Hobbyhorse*. $125/£78

CROWTHER, J. The Microscope and Its Lessons. London: Caudwell, 1891. Frontis, 286pp. Aeg. Pict cl. Good+ (dust-stained, sl worn). *Savona*. $32/£20

CROWTHER, JOHN. Firebase. London: Constable, 1975. 1st ed. Fine in dj (price-clipped). *Associates*. $75/£47

CROWTHER, SAMUEL. Vocabulary of the Yoruba Language. London: Church Missionary Soc, 1843. 1st ed. vii,(194)pp. Uncut, largely unopened. VG 1/2 reddish-brn polished morocco, raised bands, gilt, red/grn title/author labels. *Young*. $352/£220

CROY, HOMER. Jesse James Was My Neighbor. NY: Duell, Sloan & Pearce, (1949). 1st ed. Signed, inscribed. Fine in dj (chipped). *Glenn*. $50/£31

CROY, HOMER. Star Maker. The Story of D. W. Griffith. NY: Duell, Sloane & Pearce, 1959. 1st ed. VG+ in dj (closed tears). *Labordo*. $45/£28

CROZIER, F. P. A Brass Hat in No Man's Land. London: Jonathan Cape, (1930). 1st ed. Port. Gilt reddish-brn cl (lt rubbed, soiled). VG in Fine dj (supplied?). *Reese*. $100/£63

CROZIER, F. P. A Brass Hat in No Man's Land. London, 1930. 1st Eng ed. VG (no dj). *Clearwater*. $40/£25

CROZIER, F. P. The Men I Killed. London: Michael Joseph, (1937). 1st ed. Brn cl stamped in red. (Edges, end blanks foxed), o/w VG in dj (sm edge tear, sl smudges). *Reese*. $85/£53

Cruelty to Children, Five Years with, a Review and Statement. London: Nat'l Soc for the Prevention of Cruelty to Children, 1889. 1/2 calf, raised bands, red/olive labels. Fine. *Petersfield*. $48/£30

CRUIKSHANK, GEORGE. The Comic Almanack an Ephemeris in Jest and Earnest. London: C&W, n.d. (ca 1870?). 2 vols. Contemp tree calf (rubbed, sl foxed), gilt spine. *Oinonen*. $110/£69

CRUIKSHANK, GEORGE. The Comic Almanack: An Ephemeris in Jest and Ernest. Horace Mayhew (ed). London: David Bogue, 1848. 1st ed thus, 1st issue w/date of 1848 ptd in black on fr cvr, the proper ads, and w/frontis plt 'A Good Pennyworth.' 6 engr plts. Orig ptd wrappers, mod gilt-lettered chemise. (Spine, extrems dknd), else NF. *Pacific*. $150/£94

CRUIKSHANK, GEORGE. Cruikshank at Home: A New Family Album of Endless Entertainment. London: Henry G. Bohn, 1845. 1st ed. 4 series in 2 vols. Red cl, gilt. (Spine ends rubbed, fr hinges cracked, fr cvr vol II nearly detached), else VG. *Pacific*. $161/£101

CRUIKSHANK, GEORGE. The Cruikshank Fairy Book. NY: Putnam, 1897. 8vo. (viii),216,(ii)ads pp; 25 engrs. Aeg. Dec red ribbed cl, gilt. Very Nice (thumbed; expertly recased retaining fep; inscrip). *Sotheran*. $205/£128

CRUIKSHANK, GEORGE. George Cruikshank's Omnibus. London: Tilt & Bogue, 1842. 1st ed. 3/4 dk grn morocco, gilt paneled spine, raised bands, gilt top by Zaehnsdorf. *Appelfeld*. $150/£94

CRUIKSHANK, GEORGE. George Cruikshank's Omnibus. Laman Blanchard (ed). London: Tilt & Bogue, 1842. 1st ed. vi,(4),300pp; 22 etched (stipple-engr) plts (incl port). Aeg. Full tan calf, gilt, morocco label. Bound by Riviere. (Lt foxed; faded, spotted), else NF. *Pacific*. $207/£129

CRUIKSHANK, GEORGE. George Cruikshank's Table-Book. Gilbert A. A'Beckett (ed). London: George Bell & Sons, 1878. New ed. 12 steel-engr plts, 116 wood engrs. Aeg. Gilt-dec grn cl. (Spine ends chipped), else VG. *Pacific*. $63/£39

CRUIKSHANK, GEORGE. Greenwich Hospital, a Series of Naval Sketches, Descriptive of the Life of a Man-of-War's Man. J. Robins, 1826. 1st ed. 4to. 12 hand-colored etched plts. Teg. Later blue 1/2 morocco,s pine gilt. (Sl offsetting from plts onto text; rubbed, faded.) *Sotheby's*. $552/£345

CRUIKSHANK, GEORGE. The Travels and Surprising Adventures of Baron Munchausen. London: William Tegg, 1869. Hand-colored frontis, 32 plts, 5 woodcuts. Teg. 3/4 maroon morocco, gilt paneled spine, raised bands. Fine. *Appelfeld*. $250/£156

Cruise of Her Majesty's Ship 'Bacchante' 1879-1882. London, 1886. 2 vols. xxviii,675pp; 16 plts, 28 charts (1 fldg). (Lt browned, hinges cracked, lib stamp fep vol 1; spines chipped, vol 1 head repaired.) *Edwards*. $256/£160

Cruise of the Midge. By the Author of 'Tom Cringle's Log.' (By Michael Scott.) Edinburgh: William Blackwood & Sons, 1836. 1st ed. 2 vols. 387;452pp (lacks 1/2-titles). Contemp mid-tan calf, raised bands, gilt, twin morocco lables. Very Nice set (extrems sl rubbed). *Young*. $152/£95

Cruise of the Revenue-Steamer Corwin in Alaska and the N.W. Arctic Ocean in 1881. Washington: GPO, 1883. 120pp; 12 plts (9 colored). (Eps sl foxed, damaged; worn.) *Explorer*. $96/£60

CRUMB, R. Fritz the Cat. NY: Ballantine, 1969. 1st ptg. VG in wraps (creased, soiled). *Warren*. $40/£25

CRUMB, R. Head Comix. NY, 1988. Signed, dated May 1988. Fine in wraps. *Warren.* $100/£63

CRUMB, R. Waiting for Food. Amsterdam: Oog & Blik, 1995. True 1st ed. Fine in cl illus bds. *Smith.* $45/£28

CRUMB, R. The Yum Yum Book. (SF): Scrimshaw, 1975. 1st ed. NF in dj. *Pacific*.* $58/£36

CRUMB, R. The Yum Yum Book. CA: Scrimshaw, 1975. 1st Amer ed. NF in NF dj. *Warren.* $75/£47

CRUMBINE, SAMUEL J. Frontier Doctor. Phila: Dorrance, 1948. 1st ed. Fine in dj (wear). *Labordo.* $75/£47

CRUMLEY, JAMES. The Last Good Kiss. NY: Random House, 1978. 1st ed. Inscribed. NF in dj (lt used). *Beasley.* $50/£31

CRUMLEY, JAMES. The Mexican Tree Duck. (NY): Mysterious Press, (1993). One of 150. Signed. Blue cl, gilt. Fine in slipcase. *Pacific*.* $46/£29

CRUMLEY, JAMES. One to Count Cadence. (NY): Random House, (1969). 1st ed, 1st bk. Top edge stained dk gray, untrimmed. Brn cl, silver spine lettering. Text Very Clean (sm spot fep, old price mkd in black fr pastedown), cvrs NF (top/bottom edges sl dusty). Dj (lt crease fr flap corner). *Baltimore*.* $160/£100

CRUMLEY, JAMES. One to Count Cadence. NY: Random House, (1969). 1st ed, 1st bk. Fine in dj. *Pacific*.* $288/£180

CRUMLEY, JAMES. One to Count Cadence. NY: Bantam Books, 1970. 1st pb ptg. NF. *Associates.* $25/£16

CRUMLEY, JAMES. The Pigeon Shoot. Santa Barbara: Neville, 1987. One of 350. Signed. Orange cl. Fine. *Pacific*.* $63/£39

CRUMLEY, JAMES. Whores. (Missoula: Dennis McMillan), 1988. One of 501. Signed. Fine. *Pacific*.* $69/£43

CRUMLEY, JAMES. The Wrong Case. NY: Random House, (1975). 1st ed. NF in dj (sm spot fr panel). *Pacific*.* $259/£162

CRUSE, A. J. Cigarette Card Cavalcade. London: Vawser & Wiles, (1948). 1st ed. Color frontis, 28 b/w plts. Tan cl (lt worn; hinges weak). Text Good in dj (chipped, torn, old clear tape repairs). *Baltimore*.* $35/£22

CRUTCHLEY, BROOKE. A Printer's Christmas Books. Cambridge: Privately ptd, 1974. 1st ed. Ltd to 500. Fldg illus. VG in cl-backed dec bds. *Cox.* $80/£50

CRUTWELL, MAUD. Luca and Andrea Della Robbia and Their Successors. London/NY, 1902. Good. *Washton.* $45/£28

Cuala Press 1903-73, an Exhibition. London, 1973. Stapled into wrappers (staples rusted). *Typographeum.* $25/£16

CUBBIN, THOMAS. The Wreck of the Serica. Dropmore Press, 1950. One of 300. Prospectus loosely inserted. Dj (sm cellotape stain). *Edwards.* $120/£75

CULIN, STEWART. Games of the North American Indians. BAE Bulletin 24. Washington, 1907. 21 plts (2 color). Tan lib buckram (rebound). *Kane*.* $85/£53

CULLEN, COUNTEE. The Ballad of the Brown Girl. NY: Harper, 1927. 1st ed. Dbl-pg plt. 1/4 black cl, yellow bds, ptd paper spine label. Fine in orig box (worn). *Heritage.* $175/£109

CULLEN, COUNTEE. The Ballad of the Brown Girl: An Old Ballad Retold. NY: Harper, 1927. 1st ed. 3/4 black cl, yellow bds, paper spine label. (Smoke damage upper fr cvr, and sl to internal upper extrems), else VG. *Pacific*.* $35/£22

CULLEN, COUNTEE. The Black Christ and Other Poems. NY, 1929. 1st ed. (Labels rubbed.) Dj (top edge reinforced on verso). *Swann*.* $92/£58

CULLEN, COUNTEE. My Lives and How I Lost Them. NY, (1942). 1st ed. (Bkpl.) Dj (chipped, cellotape repairs on verso). *Swann*.* $138/£86

CULLER, R. D. Boats, Oars and Rowing. Camden: Intl. Marine, 1979. VG in dj. *American Booksellers.* $35/£22

CULLETON, JAMES. Indians and Pioneers of Old Monterey. Fresno: Academy of CA Church History, 1950. 1st ed. Fine in dj (sl sunned, soiled, price-clipped). *Pacific*.* $69/£43

CULLINGFORD, C. H. D. British Caving. London: Routledge & Kegan Paul, 1953. 1st ed. 48 plts. (Extrems sl rubbed.) Dj (sl worn, spine creased). *Hollett.* $56/£35

CULLMANN, WILLY et al. The Encyclopedia of Cacti. OR: Timber, (1986). Fine in Fine dj. *Book Market.* $75/£47

CULPEPER, NICHOLAS. Culpeper's Complete Herbal, to Which Is Now Added, Upwards of One Hundred Additional Herbs.... London: Thomas Kelly, 1822. 10.5x8.25. Copper-engr frontis, vi,398,(4)pp; 40 hand-colored plts. Old tree calf (rebacked in old calf), gilt. NF. *Pacific*.* $978/£611

CULPEPER, NICHOLAS. Culpeper's Complete Herbal. Halifax: William Milner, 1848. Bijou ed. Fldg frontis, extra engr tp, 431pp; 24 hand-colored plts. Uncut. Orig red cl, gilt. Good (extrems sl worn). *Cox.* $56/£35

CULPEPER, NICHOLAS. Culpeper's English Physician; and Complete Herbal. London: Lewis and Hamblin et al, 1807. Old brn calf bds (expertly rebacked), raised bands, red leather labels. Good. *Appelfeld.* $400/£250

CULPEPER, NICHOLAS. Culper's Complete Herbal and English Physician. 1981. Facs ed. As New in dj. *Doctor's Library.* $50/£31

CULSHAW, JOHN. A Century of Music. Dennis Dobson, 1952. 1st ed. VG in dj (sl worn, piece torn from upper margin). *Hollett.* $24/£15

CULVER, DOROTHY CAMPBELL. Bibliography of Crime and Criminal Justice 1927-1931. NY, 1934. Russet cl. *Gach.* $30/£19

CULVER, HENRY B. Contemporary Scale Models of Vessels of the Seventeenth Century. NY, 1926. One of 1000. Folio. 50 plts. *Swann*.* $115/£72

CUMBERLAND, MARTEN. Policeman's Nightmare. GC, 1949. 1st ed. (Pp yellowed), else Good in dj (chipped, edgetorn). *King.* $20/£13

CUMBERLAND, RICHARD. Calvary. London: Lackington, Allen, 1800. 1st illus ed. 2 vols. 1/2-titles; (iv),171; (iv),169pp; 9 engr plts. Contemp 1/2 calf (rebacked). *Young.* $128/£80

CUMING, E. D. British Sport Past and Present. London, 1909. 31 mtd color plts. (Shaken.) *Swann*.* $115/£72

CUMING, E. D. The Three Jovial Puppies. London: Blackie & Son, (1908). 1st ed. Folio. J. A. Shepherd (illus). (36)pp. Grn cl, gray pict bds. Very Nice (sl speckled; corners rubbed w/sl loss of surface paper). *Sotheran.* $253/£158

CUMING, E. D. The Three Jovial Puppies. London: Blackie & Son, (1912). 1st ed in this smaller format. Royal 8vo. J. A. Shepherd (illus). Cl-backed paper-cvrd bds, onlaid pict label to upper cvr. *Sotheran.* $157/£98

CUMINGS, EDWARD M. Fly Fishing. (Flint, MI: Privately ptd, 1934.) 1st ed. Pict cl (lt worn). *Oinonen*.* $90/£56

CUMMING, C. F. GORDON. Granite Crags of California. Edinburgh/London: William Blackwood & Sons, 1886. New ed. x,384pp; 5 plts, fldg map. Lt blue pict cl, gilt spine. Fine (offset to eps; spine sl sunned). *Pacific*.* $127/£79

CUMMING, CONSTANCE FREDERICA. A Lady's Cruise in a French Man-of-War. Edinburgh: William Blackwood & Sons, 1882. New ed. Frontis, xiv,366pp; 7 plts, fldg map. Unopened. Dec grn cl. Good. *Karmiole.* $100/£63

CUMMING, GERSHOM. Views at Dunkeld, and Descriptive and Historical Sketches. Dundee: Sold by G. Cumming, 1839. 1st ed. 54pp (last gathering loose); 13 engr plts. Aeg. Orig brn blind/gilt-stamped cl. *Young.* $72/£45

CUMMING, KATE. Gleanings from Southland. Birmingham: Roberts & Son, 1895. Only ed. Frontisport, 277pp. Red cl. (Hinges sl tender, spine lettering faded), else VG. *Chapel Hill.* $200/£125

CUMMING, ROBERT. A Discourse on Domestic Disorder. (Orange, CA: Robert Cumming, 1975.) 13 b/w photos. Fine in stiff wrappers. *Cahan.* $50/£31

CUMMING, ROBERT. Picture Fictions. (N.p.: Robert Cumming, 1971.) 1st ed, 1st bk. VG in pict stiff wrappers (sm crease). *Cahan.* $75/£47

CUMMING, ROUALEYN G. Five Years of a Hunter's Life in the Far Interior of South Africa. NY, 1850. 1st Amer ed. 2 vols. Red cl (few sm cracks spine extrems; pp foxed). *Swann*.* $201/£126

CUMMING, WILLIAM P. The Southeast in Early Maps, with an Annotated Check List of Printed and Manuscript Regional and Local Maps of Southeastern North America During the Colonial Period. Chapel Hill: Univ of NC, (1973). VG +. *Pacific*.* $288/£180

CUMMING, WILLIAM P. The Southeast in Early Maps. Chapel Hill, 1962. (Name, sm notes), else Good. *Dumont.* $95/£59

CUMMING, WILLIAM P. et al. The Discovery of North America. NY, 1972. 1st Amer ed. VG in dj. *Dumont.* $65/£41

CUMMINGS, BYRON. Indians I Have Known. Tucson: AZ Silhouettes, 1952. 1st ed. Frontisport, 20 photo ports. Yellow cl. Fine. *House.* $30/£19

CUMMINGS, CHARLES A. A History of Architecture in Italy from the Time of Constantine to the Dawn of the Renaissance. Boston/NY, 1901. 2 vols. (Cl sl dknd, soiled.) Internally VG set. *Washton.* $85/£53

CUMMINGS, CHARLES L. The Great War Relic. Harrisburg, n.d. ca 1886. 48pp. VG in pict wraps (sl worn). *Brown.* $30/£19

CUMMINGS, E. E. 50 Poems. NY, (1940). 1st ed. One of 150 numbered, signed. Cl, leather label fr cvr. *Swann*.* $230/£144

CUMMINGS, E. E. CIOPW. NY: Covici Friede, 1931. One of 391. Signed. Silver-lettered burlap. (Spine dknd), else VG. *Pacific*.* $288/£180

CUMMINGS, E. E. E. E. Cummings, a Miscellany. George J. Firmage (ed). NY: Argophile, 1958. 1st ed, ltd issue. One of 75 signed. Gray cl. Fine. *Heritage.* $300/£188

CUMMINGS, E. E. Eimi. NY: Covici, Friede, 1933. 1st ltd ed. One of 1381 signed and numbered in ink. Untrimmed. Yellow cl. Text VG (few ll sl rippled, eps sl foxed; cvrs sl spotted). *Baltimore*.* $80/£50

CUMMINGS, E. E. The Enormous Room. London, 1928. 1st Eng ed, 1st bk. VG (sl chafed, extrems bumped). *Clearwater.* $96/£60

CUMMINGS, PAUL. Artists in Their Own Words. NY: St. Martin's, (1979). Fine (bkpl) in dj. *Turtle Island.* $40/£25

CUMMINGS, RAY. Brigands of the Moon. Chicago: McClurg, 1931. 1st ed. (Fr hinge cracked), else Good. *Other Worlds.* $25/£16

CUMMINGS, RAY. The Girl in the Golden Atom. NY: Harper, 1923. 1st US ed. (Spine sl leaned), else VG. *Other Worlds.* $65/£41

CUMMINGS, RAY. The Shadow Girl. Swan, 1946. 1st UK ed. NF in dj (price-clipped). *Williams.* $72/£45

CUMMINS, ELLA STERLING. The Story of the Files. SF, 1893. 1st ed. Beveled edges. Brn pict bds. VG (cvrs lt worn). *Labordo.* $185/£116

CUMMINS, ELLA STERLING. The Story of the Files: A Review of California Writers and Literature. (SF), 1893. 1st ed. 460pp. (Extrems, spine sl rubbed), else Fine. *Pacific*.* $259/£162

CUMMINS, JIM. Jim Cummins' Book Written by Himself. Denver, 1903. 1st ed. Red pict cl. (Last part of subtitle cut out, patched, facs of lacking piece affixed; narrow band of next prelim torn off; 1 corner torn off 1 blank, 2 sm pieces torn from top edge of other; bk resewn w/new eps.) Howes C951. *Baade.* $350/£219

CUNARD, NANCY. Grand Man: Memories of Norman Douglas. London: Martin Secker & Warburg, 1954. 1st Eng ed. VG (spine ends, corners sl bumped, cvrs sl mkd) in dj (nicked, rubbed, mkd, sl torn, creased, sl dknd). *Ulysses.* $77/£48

CUNARD, NANCY. Parallax. London: Hogarth, 1925. 1st ed. VG (uniformly sunned, spine lt worn). *Robbins.* $450/£281

CUNDALL, H. M. Birket Foster. A&C Black, 1906. Signed, ltd, de luxe ed (of 500?). Thick sm 4to. Frontisport, 73 color plts, extra etched plt (only in this ed). Marbled eps. Full dk grn levant morocco, gilt, beveled bds. VG. *Hollett.* $1,040/£650

CUNDALL, JOSEPH. A Brief History of Wood-Engraving from Its Invention. Sampson, Low, 1895. 1st ed. Frontis, ix,132pp. Teg. Pict cl, gilt, beveled bds (sl rubbed). *Hollett.* $56/£35

CUNEO, TERENCE. Sheer Nerve. Warne, 1939. 1st ed. Pub's file copy stamp on half-title. Frontis. Fine in stiff pict wraps (sl soiled). *Any Amount.* $29/£18

CUNEY-HARE, MAUD. Negro Musicians and Their Music. Washington: Associated Pub, (1936). 1st ed. 38 plts. Mod blue buckram, gilt. VG. *Petrilla.* $75/£47

CUNHA, F. Osler as a Gastroenterologist. SF, 1948. 1st ed. *Fye.* $50/£31

CUNLIFFE, BARRY. Excavations at Fishbourne 1961-1969. Leeds, 1971. 2 vols. 119 plts. Djs (chipped). *Edwards.* $120/£75

CUNLIFFE, MARCUS. Chattel Slavery and Wage Slavery. The Anglo-American Context 1830-1860. Athens: Univ of GA, (1979). 1st ed. Black cl. (Cvrs sl damp-stained), else VG + in dj. *Chapel Hill.* $35/£22

CUNNINGHAM, EDWARD. Dancer. The Colt Who Dreamed About Being Grown Up. Kansas City: Hallmark Children's Editions, n.d. (1976). 5 dbl-pg pop-ups by Rich Rudish. Glazed pict bds. VG. *Bookfinders.* $50/£31

CUNNINGHAM, EUGENE. Triggernometry. Caldwell, 1947. 5th ptg. Pict cl. VG in dj (faded, edgeworn). Howes C954. *Baade.* $45/£28

CUNNINGHAM, FRANK. General Stand Watie's Confederate Indians. San Antonio, TX: Naylor, (1959). 1st ed. Blue cl. Fine in NF dj. *Chapel Hill.* $85/£53

CUNNINGHAM, HARRY FRANCIS and JOSEPH ARTHUR YOUNGER. Measured Drawings of Georgian Architecture in the District of Columbia 1750-1820. NY: Architectural Book Pub, 1914. Folio. 66 plts. (Lt worn, cvrs soiled.) *Oinonen*.* $170/£106

CUNNINGHAM, IMOGEN. Imogen! Imogen Cunningham Photographs 1910-1973. Seattle/London, (1974). 1st ed. Signed, inscribed. (Fep creased.) Dj (spine sunned, lt soiled), acetate wrapper. *Swann*.* $161/£101

CUNNINGHAM, IMOGENE. After Ninety. Seattle: Univ of WA, 1977. 1st ed. VG + in dj. *Smith.* $65/£41

CUNNINGHAM, J. V. The Judge Is Fury. NY: Swallow, 1947. One of 1000 ptd. Fine in dj (lt edgeworn). *Agvent.* $150/£94

CUNNINGHAM, J. V. Poems and Epigrams Titled Aliquid Salis or If You Prefer English, Some Salt. (Mount Horeb, WI): Perishable, 1967. 1st ed. One of 200. Fine in plain mid grn sewn wrappers, ptd dj. *Blackwell's.* $112/£70

CUNNINGHAM, J. V. To What Strangers, What Welcome. Denver: Swallow, (1964). One of 1000. NF (inscrip) in wraps. *Agvent.* $35/£22

CUNNINGHAM, JAMES CHARLES. The Truth about Murietta [sic].... L.A.: Wetzel, 1938. 1st ed. Fine in dj. *Labordo.* $150/£94

CUNNINGHAM, PETER (intro). Extracts from the Accounts of the Revels at Court.... Shakespeare Soc, 1842. 1st Eng ed. 1/2 blue morocco, raised bands. VG (eps sl spotted; spine ends rubbed, damage to bottom; corners bumped). *Ulysses.* $72/£45

CUNNINGHAME GRAHAM, R. B. See GRAHAM, R. B. CUN-NINGHAME

CUNYNGHAME, FRANCIS. Lost Trail. London: Faber & Faber, (1953). Fine in dj (torn). *Perier.* $50/£31

CUPPLES, GEORGE. A Spliced Yarn. London: Gibbings, 1899. 1st Eng ed. Frank Brangwyn (illus). Dec buckram. VG (eps browned, sl spotted, some pp roughly opened; spine faded, ends sl bumped). *Ulysses.* $72/£45

CURIE, EVE. Madame Curie: A Biography by Her Daughter. Vincent Sheean (trans). London, 1938. 1st ed. VG in Good dj. *Doctor's Library.* $30/£19

Curiosities for the Ingenious. London: Thomas Boys, 1821. 1st ed. Engr frontis, 11 plts. Contemp patterned cl spine, marbled bds (scuffed). VG (sl foxed; spine label chipped). *Dramatis.* $185/£116

Curiosities of Human Nature. (By Samuel G. Goodrich.) Boston: Bradbury, Soden, 1843. Engr frontis. Orig patterned cl (extrems dusty, worn). *Dramatis.* $55/£34

CURLE, ALEXANDER O. The Treasure of Traprain. Glasgow: Maclehose, Jackson, 1923. Inscribed presentation dated 8th Feb 1923. 41 plts. Teg, uncut. Grn cl, gilt. VG. *Hollett.* $136/£85

CURLE, RICHARD. Collecting American First Editions. Indianapolis: Bobbs-Merrill, (1930). 1st ed. Ltd to 1250 signed. Fine in beveled blue cl, paper label. Cardbd slipcase. *Bromer.* $85/£53

CURLE, RICHARD. A Handlist of the Various Books, Pamphlets...Written About Joseph Conrad. Brookville, PA: Privately ptd, 1932. One of 250. This copy inscribed by Curle. (Mark on inside fr cvr, facing 1/2-title, probably from a leather bkpl now absent). Card wrappers (sl tanned). *Clearwater.* $144/£90

CURLE, RICHARD. Joseph Conrad. Kegan Paul, Trench, Trubner, 1914. Frontisport. Pub's slip. Good (newspaper cutting tipped on fep; spine bumped, chipped, dull). *Tiger.* $26/£16

CURR, EDWARD M. Pure Saddle-Horses, and How to Breed Them in Australia. Melbourne: Wilson & Mackinnon, 1863. 1st ed. Inscribed presentation. xviii,(i),299pp + (iv)pp ads. (Top 1/4 cut from dedication leaf, w/o text loss.) Orig roan-backed cl (sl mkd, rubbed), gilt. *Hollett.* $280/£175

CURRAN, J. J. Mr. Foley of Salmon. San Jose: The Author, 1907. 1st ed. Red cl. Good+ (rear hinge paper split, cvrs worn, soiled). *House.* $45/£28

CURRENT, WILLIAM. Pueblo Architecture of the Southwest. Text by Vincent Scully. Fort Worth: Amon Center Museum of Western Art, (1971). 1st ed. 65 full-pg b/w photos. Fine in NF dj. *Cahan.* $65/£41

CURREY, L. W. Science Fiction and Fantasy Authors: A Bibliography of First Printings of Their Fiction. Boston: G.K. Hall, (1979). 1st ed. Fine. *Pacific*.* $98/£61

CURREY, L. W. Science Fiction and Fantasy Authors: A Bibliography.... Boston: Hall, (1979). 1st ed. (Corners, spine ends lt worn.) *Other Worlds.* $50/£31

CURRIE, BARTON. Fishers of Books. Little, Brown, 1931. 1st US ed. VG in dj (few closed tears, amateur repairs). *Williams.* $45/£28

CURRIE, BARTON. Fishers of Books. Boston: Little, Brown, 1931. One of 365 signed. 2 vols. Gray paper bds, paper labels. Fine set in box. *Appelfeld.* $150/£94

CURRY, JANE LOUISE. Mindy's Mysterious Miniature. HBJ, 1970. 1st ed. Chs Robinson (illus). 157pp. Fine in VG+ dj (rear soil spot). *Price.* $20/£13

CURSHMANN, H. Typhoid Fever and Typhus Fever. William Osler (ed). Phila, 1905. 1st ed in English. *Fye.* $75/£47

CURTIN, L. S. M. By the Prophet of the Earth. Santa Fe, 1949. VG. *Dumont.* $100/£63

CURTIN, L. S. M. Healing Herbs of the Upper Rio Grande. Santa Fe: Rydal Press, 1947. VG in dj (sl worn). *Dumont.* $135/£84

CURTIN, WALTER R. Yukon Voyage. Caldwell, ID: Caxton, 1938. VG in dj (sl chipped). *High Latitude.* $80/£50

CURTIS, CHARLES H. Orchids: Their Description and Cultivation. London: Putnam, (1950). 1st ed. Color frontis. Grn cl, gilt. Fine. *Pacific*.* $40/£25

CURTIS, GEORGE W. Nile Notes of a Howadji. NY, 1851. 1st ed. 320pp. Olive cl, gilt. (Spine ends chipped, edgeworn), else Good. *Larry Price.* $65/£41

CURTIS, GEORGE WILLIAM (ed). The Correspondence of John Lothrop Motley. NY, 1889. 1st ed. 2 vols. VF set. *Bond.* $50/£31

CURTIS, MATTOON M. The Book of Snuff and Snuff Boxes. NY, (1935). 1st Amer ed. Fine. *Polyanthos.* $35/£22

CURTIS, MATTOON M. The Story of Snuff and Snuff Boxes. NY: Liveright, 1935. Fine. *Metropolitan*.* $46/£29

CURTIS, PAUL. Guns and Gunning. Phila: Penn Pub, 1934. True 1st ed, 1st ptg. Color frontis. VG (top edge last 40 pp sl damp-stained; lt soiled) in VG dj (soiled, edges sl torn). *Backman.* $75/£47

CURTIS, PAUL. Sportsmen All. NY: Derrydale, 1938. Ltd to 950 numbered. Black cl. Fine. *Biscotti.* $150/£94

CURTISS, DANIEL S. Western Portraiture and Emigrant's Guide. NY: J.H. Colton, 1852. 1st ed. 351pp + 18pp ads; fldg litho map. Orig cl, later gilt-stamped leather spine label. (Fldg map worn, split at folds, in 2 pieces; lib stamps, fr pastedown damaged; rebacked w/most of orig spine strip laid on), o/w Good. *Pacific*.* $81/£51

CURWEN, HENRY. A History of Booksellers, the Old and the New. C&W, (1873). 1st ed. Frontis. Mod buckram-backed bds. (Some illus sl stained; spine faded.) *Forest.* $32/£20

CURWOOD, JAMES OLIVER. The Country Beyond. Cosmopolitan, 1922. 1st ed. VG+ in Good dj. *Authors Of The West.* $50/£31

CURWOOD, JAMES OLIVER. Steele of the Royal Mounted. NY: Burt, 1911. Photoplay ed. VG in VG color dj (chipped). *Unger.* $100/£63

CURZON, DANIEL. Something You Do in the Dark. NY: Putnam, (1971). 1st ed. VF in VF dj (sm pinprick rubbed spot). *Between The Covers.* $100/£63

CURZON, GEORGE N. Russia in Central Asia in 1889 and the Anglo-Russian Question. London: Longmans, Green, 1889. 2nd ed. xxiv,477,24pp; fldg color map. (Lib spine label, edges rubbed, spine ends frayed, sm nick), o/w VG. *Worldwide.* $70/£44

CURZON, LOUIS HENRY. The Blue Ribbon of the Turf. Phila, 1890. 1st Amer ed. Frontis. (Tp taped in, name; fep, frontis lt foxed; lt worn.) *Woolson.* $50/£31

CURZON, ROBERT. Visits to Monasteries in the Levant. NY: Putnam, 1849. Woodcut frontis, tp, 15 plts. Later 1/2 morocco. (Deep repaired tear 1 leaf, spotted; rubbed.) *Christie's*.* $82/£51

CURZON, ROBERT. Visits to Monasteries in the Levant. London: John Murray, 1849. 1st ed. Frontis, xxxi,(i)blank,449pp; 14 plts, engr fldg plan. Orig ribbed/brn cl, gilt. VG (foxing on, adjacent to plts; corners sl rubbed, neat spine repairs). *Morrell.* $232/£145

CURZON, ROBERT. Visits to Monasteries in the Levant. London, 1955. VG. *Gretton.* $24/£15

CUSHING, FRANK H. Zuni Breadstuff. NY: Heye Foundation, 1920. (Bds soiled, hinges starting.) Internally VG. *Dumont.* $125/£78

CUSHING, FRANK H. Zuni Breadstuff. F. W. Hodge (ed). NY: Museum of the American Indian, Heye Foundation, 1920. 1st ed. 27 b/w plts. Tan cl, red lettering. Text VG (lg bkpl; cvrs rubbed, spine lettering dull). *Baltimore**. $90/£56

CUSHING, FRANK H. Zuni Folk Tales. NY: Putnam, 1901. 1st ed. (Sl shelfworn), else NF. *Dumont*. $250/£156

CUSHING, HARVEY. The Life of Sir William Osler. Oxford, 1925. 1st ed. 2 vols. Blue cl. Good (ex-lib; extrems sl worn, vol I rebound). *Doctor's Library*. $100/£63

CUSHING, HARVEY. The Life of Sir William Osler. Oxford, 1925. 1st ed, 3rd ptg. 2 vols. Blue cl. (ex-lib; sm spine tear, extrems worn), o/w Good. *Doctor's Library*. $150/£94

CUSHING, HARVEY. The Life of Sir William Osler. Oxford: Clarendon, 1925. 1st ed. 2 vols. Frontis, map. VG (few ll sl foxed). *Weber*. $200/£125

CUSHING, HARVEY. The Life of Sir William Osler. Oxford, 1925. 1st ed, 2nd ptg. 2 vols. VF. *Fye*. $200/£125

CUSHING, HARVEY. The Life of Sir William Osler. Oxford, 1925. 1st ed, 1st ptg. 2 vols. Full lt blue leather, gilt; red, black labels. Bound by Bayntun & Riviere. (Outer hinges cracked), o/w Fine. *Fye*. $400/£250

CUSHING, HARVEY. The Life of Sir William Osler. Clarendon, 1926. 4th imp. 2 vols. Frontisports. (Lower edge 1st few ll both vols waterstained; fr hinge cracked, w/half-title, frontis vol 1 sl detached; bkpl; sl rubbed; fr bd tail vol 2 sl waterstained.) *Edwards*. $152/£95

CUSHMAN, DAN. The Great North Trail. NY: McGraw Hill, 1966. 1st ed. Fine in VG dj. *Perier*. $20/£13

CUST, A. M. The Ivory Workers of the Middle Ages. George Bell, 1902. 1st ed. 37 plts. (Feps browned; spine lettering sl faded.) *Hollett*. $48/£30

CUST, LIONEL (comp). Catalogue of the Collection of Fans and Fan-Leaves Presented...by Lady Charlotte Schreiber. British Museum, 1893. viii,138pp. (Lib ink stamp; lt browned; spine sl creased, label.) *Edwards*. $104/£65

CUST, LIONEL. The Royal Collection of Paintings at Buckingham Palace and Windsor Castle. Fine Arts Pub Co, 1905-6. De luxe ed. 2 vols. (Tps, some edges dusty.) 180 photogravures, loose as issued. Cl portfolios (soiled, worn), gilt. *Hollett*. $120/£75

CUSTER, ELIZABETH B. Boots and Saddles or Life in Dakota with General Custer. NY: Harper, (1885). Frontisport, 312pp; map. Gilt-dec cl. VG (bkpl, newspaper clipping taped to fep; extrems rubbed, rear cvr stained). Howes C980. *Pacific**. $40/£25

CUSTER, ELIZABETH B. Boots and Saddles or Life in Dakota with General Custer. NY: Harper, 1885. 1st ed, 2nd issue, w/map and port added. Frontisport, 312pp; map. Gilt-dec cl. (Bkpl removed from fr pastedown; spine ends, corners lt rubbed), else VG + . Howes C980. *Pacific**. $115/£72

CUSTER, ELIZABETH B. Following the Guidon. NY: Harper, 1890. 1st ed. xx,341pp + (2)pp ads. Gilt-dec cl. (Bkpls, scotch tape repairs to pp179-182, w/creases to adjacent pp), o/w VG. *Pacific**. $52/£33

CUSTER, ELIZABETH B. Tenting on the Plains, or General Custer in Kansas and Texas. NY: Harper, 1895. Steel-engr frontisport. Dec cl. (Fr hinge repaired, shelfwear), else VG. *Pacific**. $92/£58

CUSTER, GEORGE A. My Life on the Plains. NY: Sheldon, 1874. 1st ed. Grn cl, gilt. Fine. Howes C981. *Labordo*. $400/£250

CUSTER, GEORGE A. My Life on the Plains. London: Folio Soc, 1963. 1st ed thus. (Spine dknd, label sl worn), else NF in VG box. *My Bookhouse*. $47/£29

CUSTER, GEORGE A. My Life on the Plains. Milo Milton Quaife (ed). Chicago: Lakeside Press, 1952. Teg. (Sl worn.) *King*. $35/£22

CUSTOT, PIERRE. Sturly. Richard Aldington (trans). London: Cape, 1924. 1st ed. Frontis. Cl-backed blue bds, paper label. Fine. *Maggs*. $120/£75

CUTBIRTH, RUBY NICHOLS. Ed Nichols Rode a Horse. J. Frank Dobie (ed). Dallas, 1943. 1st ed. Signed by Cutbirth and Ed Nichols. Frontis. VG in dj. *Dumont*. $100/£63

CUTCHINS, JOHN A. A Famous Command. Garrett & Massie, (c1934). Good (ex-lib; spine frayed, fr hinge tear, edges sl stained). *Book Broker*. $50/£31

CUTCLIFFE, H. C. The Art of Trout Fishing on Rapid Streams.... London: Sampson Low, 1883. xi,212pp. (Shelfworn.) *Oinonen**. $140/£88

CUTLER, CARL C. A Descriptive Catalogue of the Marine Collection at India House. Middleton: India House, 1973. 2nd ed. Ltd to 1250. 12 color, 39 monochrome plts. As New in slipcase. *Parmer*. $125/£78

CUTRIGHT, PAUL RUSSELL and MICHAEL BRODHEAD. Elliott Coues. Urbana: Univ of IL, 1981. 1st ed. Fine in dj. *Labordo*. $50/£31

CUTRIGHT, PAUL RUSSELL. A History of the Lewis and Clark Journals. Norman: Univ of OK, 1976. NF in dj. *Dumont*. $75/£47

CUTRIGHT, PAUL RUSSELL. Lewis and Clark: Pioneering Naturalists. Urbana: Univ of IL, 1969. 1st ed. VG in dj. *Pacific**. $98/£61

CUTTER, DONALD C. California in 1792. Norman: Univ of OK, (1990). 1st ed. Blue cl. Fine in dj. *House*. $25/£16

CUTTER, DONALD C. Malaspina in California. SF: John Howell Books, 1960. One of 1000 ptd. Frontis map, 2 color plts. Unopened. Gilt-dec cl. (Upper corners bumped), else NF. *Pacific**. $46/£29

CUTTER, DONALD C. (ed). The California Coast: A Bilingual Edition of Documents from the Sutro Collection. Norman: Univ of OK, (1969). 1st ed thus. Brn bds, cl backstrip. (Corners sl bumped), o/w Fine in Fine dj. *Harrington*. $60/£38

CUVIER, GEORGES. The Animal Kingdom. London: A. Fullarton, 1859. New ed. 34 hand-colored plts. Aeg. 3/4 calf & cl, gilt, morocco spine label. (Upper tp sl worn; extrems lt rubbed), else VG. *Pacific**. $138/£86

CZWIKLITZER, CHRISTOPHER (ed). Picasso's Posters. NY: Random House, (1971). 1st Amer ed. Thick folio. 55 tipped-in plts. Add'l cat of posters. Blue cl in dj. Good. *Karmiole*. $175/£109

D

D'ABRANTES, DUCHESSE. Memoirs of Madame Junot, Duchesse d'Abrantes. London: Richard Bentley, 1883. New rev ed. 3 vols. 8vo. 20 steel engr ports. Extra-illus w/95 engrs. Aeg. Finely bound in full red crushed morocco by Riviere, spines gilt tooled, cvrs gilt ruled, gilt dentelles. Fine. *Stewart*. $1,600/£1,000

D'AMICO, VICTOR E. Theatre Art. Peoria: The Manual Arts Press, (1931). 1st ed. Color frontis. Dec eps. Dec blue cl. (Lower corner p88 torn, affecting 2 or 3 words.) Dec dj. *Dramatis*. $35/£22

D'ANCONA, P. and E. AESCHLIMANN. The Art of Illumination. An Anthology...Sixth to the Sixteenth Century. Alison Stones (trans). London: Phaidon, 1969. Tipped-in color frontis, 146 plts (23 tipped-in color). Blue cl (sl bumped; several pp were stuck together at bottom once, not affecting plts). Dj. *Maggs*. $64/£40

D'ARBLAY, MADAME. Diary and Letters of Madame D'Arblay...Edited by her Niece. London: Henry Colburn, 1842. 7 vols. 8vo. Full blue polished calf, gilt mitre lines on cvrs, gilt paneled spines, raised bands; contrasting red, maroon leather spine labels, inner gilt dentelles, gilt tops by Zaehnsdorf. Fine. *Appelfeld*. $1,500/£938

D'AUBIGNE, J. H. MERLE. History of the Reformation in the Sixteenth Century. Blackie & Son, 1862. 3 vols. Contemp 1/2 calf, gilt, w/contrasting spine labels, marbled bds. VG set. *Hollett*. $192/£120

D'AULAIRE, INGRI and EDGAR PARIN. Animals Everywhere. NY: Doubleday, Doran, 1940. 1st ed. 4to. Panorama, w/12 panels. Red-orange cl (lower edge sl dkned). Very Nice in full color dj (lt mkd, margins worn, tear). *Reisler*. $600/£375

D'AULAIRE, INGRI and EDGAR PARIN. Benjamin Franklin. Doubleday, 1950. 8.7x10.7. Unpaginated. Pict bds w/cl spine. Good+ (1965 name; corners bumped). *Price*. $20/£13

D'AULAIRE, INGRI and EDGAR PARIN. Children of the North Lights. NY: Viking, 1935. 2nd ed. 9 x 12 1/4. 38pp. VG. *Cattermole*. $50/£31

D'AULAIRE, INGRI and EDGAR PARIN. Columbus. Doubleday, 1955. 1st ed. VG (name, few lt thumb-wrinkles) in VG dj. *Price*. $65/£41

D'AULAIRE, INGRI and EDGAR PARIN. D'Aulaire's Book of Greek Myths. Doubleday, 1962. 1st ed. 9x12.5. 192pp. Fine in VG dj (1x1.5-inch sticker pull on fr, spine end creases). *Price*. $80/£50

D'AULAIRE, INGRI and EDGAR PARIN. Foxie the Singing Dog. NY: Doubleday, 1969. 1st ed thus. 10.5x8.25. 48pp. Pict bds. Fine in dj. *Cattermole*. $50/£31

D'AULAIRE, INGRI and EDGAR PARIN. Leif the Lucky. GC: Doubleday, Doran, 1941. 1st ed. Tall 4to. Cl-backed color pict bds. Nice in full color pict dj (margins lt worn). *Reisler*. $120/£75

D'AULAIRE, INGRI and EDGAR PARIN. The Magic Meadow. NY: Doubleday, 1958. 1st ed. 4to. 55pp; 25 color lithos, 23 b/w illus. Illus eps. VG in VG dj. *Davidson*. $60/£38

D'AULAIRE, INGRI and EDGAR PARIN. The Two Cars. GC: Doubleday, 1955. 1st ed. Obl 4to. Color pict bds. VG in full color dj. *Reisler*. $155/£97

D'AULAIRE, INGRI and EDGAR PARIN. Wings for Per. Doubleday, 1944. Stated 1st ed. 4to. Unpaginated. Full color paper bds. VG- (lower corner 1/2 title missing to 2x1-inch). *Price*. $55/£34

D'AULNOY, MME and CHARLES PERRAULT. A Fairy Garland. London: Cassell, (1928). 1st ed, deluxe. One of 1000 signed by Edmund Dulac (illus). 4to. 251pp; 12 color plts. Gilt vellum-backed cl. NF. *Davidson*. $650/£406

D'AULNOY, MME. D'Aulnoy's Fairy Tales. Anne Thackeray Ritchie (trans). London: Lawrence & Bullen, 1892. 1st ed thus. Lg sq 8vo. Clinton Peters (illus). xxi,535pp (lt speckled). Dk blue cl, gilt. *Sotheran*. $141/£88

D'AULNOY, MME. Fortunia. NY: Frank Hallman, 1974. One of 300 signed by Richard Schaubeck (trans) and Maurice Sendak (illus). Fine. *Davidson*. $125/£78

D'AUTEROCHE, JEAN CHAPPE. A Voyage to California. (Richmond, England): Richmond Pub, 1973. Facs rpt of 1st Eng ed. Fldg map. Blue cl. Fine. *Argonaut*. $25/£16

D'AUVERGNE, EDMUND. The Prodigious Marshal. London: Selwyn & Blount, 1928. Frontisport; 13 plts. (Spine head torn.) *Stewart*. $48/£30

D'EWES, J. Sporting in Both Hemispheres. London: Routledge, 1858. 1st ed. 398pp. 1/2 morocco. Good (foxed; scuffed). *Cullen*. $95/£59

D'ISRAELI, I. The Literary Character. Henry Colburn, 1828. 4th ed, rev. 2 vols. Marbled eps. 19th-cent 1/2 calf, marbled bds. *Bickersteth*. $192/£120

D'OLLONE, VICOMTE. In Forbidden China. Bernard Miall (trans). London: Fisher, Unwin, 1912. 1st ed in English, 2nd imp. Frontisport, dbl-pg map, 31 plts. Blue pict cl, gilt. VG. *Morrell*. $80/£50

D'WOLF, JOHN. A Voyage to the North Pacific and a Journey Through Siberia More Than Half a Century Ago. Bristol, RI: Rulon-Miller, 1983. One of 225. Signed by Harold M. Turner (Commentary) and Anne Hughes (illus). 1/2 cl, gilt. Fine. *Pacific**. $127/£79

D., H. (Pseud of Hilda Doolittle.) Palimpsest. (Boston: Houghton, Mifflin, 1926.) 1st Amer ed. Ltd to 700. Cl-backed dec bds (extrems rubbed, sl faded, soiled). *Hermitage*. $200/£125

D., H. (Pseud of Hilda Doolittle.) Sea Garden. Constable, 1916. 1st Eng ed, 1st bk. VG (ep gutters sl dampstained, some pg edges sl nicked; spine, cvr edges dknd, ends nicked). *Ulysses*. $360/£225

D., H. (Pseud of Hilda Doolittle.) Tribute to Freud. Pantheon, (1956). 1st ed. VG in dj (edges torn, sl dknd). *King*. $35/£22

D., J. The Secrets of Angling...1613. London: W. Satchell, 1883. 1st ed thus. 1/4 morocco, cl. (Bkpl; name; spine morocco lacking), else VG-. *Pacific**. $46/£29

DA ORTA, G. Colloquies on the Simples and Drugs of India. C. Markham (trans). London: Sotheran, (1913). New ed. One of 250. 23 plts. Teg. VG. *Mikesh*. $95/£59

DA SILVA, OWEN. Mission Music of California. (L.A.: Warren F. Lewis, 1941.) Ltd to 1000. Signed. Brn burlap, grn bds. Good. *Karmiole*. $125/£78

DA VINCI, LEONARDO. Leonardo Da Vinci: Drawings of Textile Machines. Kenneth G. Ponting (ed). Wiltshire: Moonraker, 1979. Grn cl. VG in dj. *Weber*. $30/£19

DA VINCI, LEONARDO. On the Human Body. NY: Henry Schuman, (1952). Sm folio. NF in dj. *Turtle Island*. $95/£59

DABNEY, R. L. Life and Campaigns of Lieut.-Gen. Thomas J. Jackson.... NY: Blelock, 1866. 1st ed. Frontisport, xii,742pp + (1)pg ads. Pub's 1/2 calf, morocco spine labels. (Blank preceding frontis excised; cvrs sl rubbed.) *Chapel Hill*. $350/£219

DABNEY, R. L. A Memorial of Lieut. Colonel John T. Thornton, of the Third Virginia Cavalry, C.S.A. Richmond, 1864. 8vo. 22pp. Self-wrappers. *Swann**. $1,035/£647

DACUS, J. A. Illustrated Lives and Adventures of Frank and Jesse James and the Younger Brothers, the Noted Western Outlaws. St. Louis, 1881. 'New edition, revised & improved', 1st thus. Full sheep, leather labels. (1 leaf lacks piece torn affecting 30 words of text; sl soiled, foxed; sl edge chips last 2 ll; cvrs sl worn), o/w Good. Howes D6. *Baade*. $200/£125

DACY, GEORGE. Four Centuries of Florida Ranching. St. Louis: Privately ptd, 1940. 1st ed. Letter/postcard from author and pub notice laid in loose. Fine in dj. *Labordo*. $135/£84

DADLEY, J. Costume of the Russian Empire. London: William Miller, 1810. 1st ed. Folio. 73 hand-colored stipple-engr plts. Aeg. Full maroon ribbed mroocco, gilt. Fine (bkpls). *Pacific**. $575/£359

DAGLISH, E. F. Birds of the British Isles. London, 1948. Ltd to 1500. 48 woodcuts (25 hand-colored). Teg. Buckram, gilt. Fine in dj (chipped). *Henly*. $136/£85

DAHINDEN, JOSEF. The Art of Ski-ing. London: Faber & Gwyer, (1928). 1st ed. Grn cl, gilt. NF. *Pacific**. $75/£47

DAHL, LINDA. Stormy Weather: The Music and Lives of a Century of Jazzwomen. NY: Pantheon, (1984). 1st ed. VG in pict dj. *Petrilla*. $35/£22

DAHL, ROALD. The BFG. London: Cape, 1982. 1st ed. 6.25x9.5. Quentin Blake (illus). 224pp. Fine in dj. *Cattermole*. $75/£47

DAHL, ROALD. Charlie and the Great Glass Elevator. NY: Knopf, (1972). 1st ed. 8vo. Joseph Schindelman (illus). 163pp. Blue cl. VG+ in dj. *House*. $25/£16

DAHL, ROALD. Danny the Champion of the World. NY, (1975). 1st Amer ed. Fine in NF dj (price-clipped). *Polyanthos.* $25/£16

DAHL, ROALD. Going Solo. NY: FSG, 1986. 1st US ed. 6.25x9.5. 208pp. 1/2 cl. Fine in dj. *Cattermole.* $32/£20

DAHL, ROALD. Going Solo. Cape, 1986. 1st UK ed. Signed. Mint in Mint dj. *Martin.* $38/£24

DAHL, ROALD. The Gremlins. NY: Random House, (1943). 1st ed. Lg 4to. 14 full-pg color illus. Cl-backed color illus bds (edges rubbed). Color pict dj (worn, marginal tears). *Reisler.* $685/£428

DAHL, ROALD. The Gremlins: A Royal Air Force Story. NY: Random House, (1943). 1st ed, 1st bk. Slim 4to. Red cl, color pict red bds (sl worn, scuffed, dusty). Text Good (few pp w/sm edge tears, 1st few ll foxed). *Baltimore*.* $200/£125

DAHL, ROALD. The Magic Finger. London: George Allen & Unwin, 1968. 1st UK ed. Lg sq 8vo. Pene du Bois (illus). (vi),40pp. Color dec eps. Pict white bds (sl soiled). VG. *Sotheran.* $109/£68

DAHL, ROALD. Switch Bitch. Michael Joseph, 1974. 1st UK ed. Fine in dj. *Williams.* $29/£18

DAHL, ROALD. The Twits. Cape, 1980. 1st ed. Quentin Blake (illus). VG+ in dj. *Green Meadow.* $48/£30

DAHL, ROALD. The Wonderful Story of Henry Sugar. Cape, 1977. 1st ed. 8vo. 249pp. NF in pict dj. *Bookmark.* $64/£40

DAIKEN, LESLIE. Children's Games Throughout the Year. Batsford, 1949. 1st ed. Color frontis. Dj. *Forest.* $40/£25

DAIN, MARTIN J. Faulkner's County: Yoknapatawpha. NY: Random House, 1964. 1st ed. (Stamp), else VG in dj (edgetorn). *Cahan.* $50/£31

DAKIN, WILLIAM J. Whaleman Adventurers. Sydney: Angus & Robertson, 1934. 1st ed. Inscribed, signed. 2 maps. VG. *High Latitude.* $165/£103

DALBIEZ, ROLAND. Psychoanalytical Method and the Doctrine of Freud. Volume 1: Exposition. Volume 2: Discussion. T. F. Lindsay (trans). London: Longmans, Green, (1948). 1st ed in English, 2nd ptg. 2 vols. Blue cl. VG in djs. *Gach.* $50/£31

DALBY, MILTON A. The Sea Saga of Dynamite Johnny O'Brien.... Seattle: Lowman & Hanford, 1933. Signed. VG. *High Latitude.* $40/£25

DALE, DARLEY. The Great Auk's Eggs. Religious Tract Soc, (c.1886). 158,(ii),16pp. Dec cl (sl rubbed, mkd), gilt. *Hollett.* $120/£75

DALE, EDWARD EVERETT and GASTON LITTON. Cherokee Cavaliers: Forty Years of Cherokee History as Told in the Correspondence of the Ridge-Watie-Boudinot Family. Norman: Univ of OK, 1939. 1st ed. Frontisport, fldg genealogical table. Red cl. NF. *Chapel Hill.* $75/£47

DALE, EDWARD EVERETT. Frontier Ways. Austin: Univ of TX, 1959. 1st ed. NF in dj. *Labordo.* $50/£31

DALE, EDWARD EVERETT. The Indians of the Southwest. Norman: Univ of OK, 1949. 1st ed. Fine in VG dj. *Book Market.* $50/£31

DALE, EDWARD EVERETT. The Prairie Schooner and Other Poems. Guthrie, OK: Cooperative Pub, 1929. 1st ed, 1st bk. NF. *Labordo.* $75/£47

DALE, EDWARD EVERETT. The Range Cattle Industry. Norman: Univ of OK, (1960). New ed, 1st ptg. Tan cl. VG in dj (few sm scrapes). Howes D20. *House.* $30/£19

DALE, EDWARD EVERETT. The Range Cattle Industry. Norman: Univ of OK, 1930. 1st ed. (Hinges cracking at eps; lib #s pencilled at tp top; spine, top of cvrs faded; repair to top 3 inches of fr joint, trace from removed spine label), else VG. Howes D20. *Pacific*.* $52/£33

DALE, EDWARD EVERETT. The Range Cattle Industry. Norman: Univ of OK, 1930. 1st ed. Signed. (Spine fragile, faded, ends worn.) Howes D20. *Labordo.* $175/£109

DALE, EDWARD EVERETT. The Range Cattle Industry. Norman: Univ of OK, 1930. 1st ed. (Ink name; spine sl faded), else NF. Howes D20. *Pacific*.* $345/£216

DALE, HARRISON C. The Ashley-Smith Explorations and the Discovery of a Central Route to the Pacific, 1822-1829; with the Original Journals. Cleveland: A.H. Clark, 1918. 1st ed. Dbl-pg color frontis map, 4 plts. Teg. Red cl, gilt. (Top corner, fr cvr edge sl bumped), else NF. Howes D21. *Pacific*.* $345/£216

DALE, JONATHAN. Angling Days, and an Angler's Books. Scarbrough/London: The Angler, 1895. 1st ed. Gilt-lettered pink cl. (Bkpls; spine, extrems dull, soiled, fr cvr spots), else VG. *Pacific*.* $63/£39

DALE, WILLIAM. Tschudi the Harpsichord Maker. Constable, 1913. 1st ed. 17 plts. Fine in dj. *Hollett.* $104/£65

DALGLIESH, ALICE. The Bears on Hemlock Mountain. Scribner, 1952. 1st ed. 8vo. Helen Sewell (illus). Unpaginated. Fine in VG dj (corner clipped). *Price.* $30/£19

DALGLIESH, ALICE. Long Live the King! NY: Scribner, 1937. Lois Maloy (illus). Sm 4to. Frontis, 77pp; 27 full-pg b/w dwgs, 3 full-pg dbl spreads. Pict color litho eps. Pict paper on bds (lt worn along edges, sm chips; rebacked). Internally Fine. *Hobbyhorse.* $55/£34

DALI, SALVADOR and PHILIPPE HALSMAN. Dali's Mustache: a Photographic Interview. NY: S&S, (1954). 1st ed. Pict bds. VF (sl rubbed) in unptd dj. *Between The Covers.* $125/£78

DALI, SALVADOR. Dali on Modern Art. Haakon M. Chevalier (trans). NY: Dial, 1957. 1st ed in English. NF (name) in dj (chipped). *Turtle Island.* $150/£94

DALI, SALVADOR. Diary of a Genius. NY, 1965. 1st Amer ed. NF in NF dj. *Polyanthos.* $25/£16

DALI, SALVADOR. Hidden Faces. NY, 1944. 1st ed. Frontis. NF (bkpl, ink place, date) in dj (tape remnants). *Warren.* $95/£59

DALI, SALVADOR. Hidden Faces. London/Brussels: Nicholson & Watson, 1947. 1st Eng ed. Frontis. Black cl. Fine in dj (frayed, sl rubbed, chipped). *Temple.* $80/£50

DALLAWAY, JAMES. Anecdotes of the Arts in England. London: T. Cadell, 1800. Lg-paper copy. Engr tp, xxi,(iii),526,(i)ads pp (heavily spotted, bkpl, 1 margin repaired w/o loss). 1/2 calf (rebound), marbled bds, later spine laid down. *Edwards.* $160/£100

DALLAWAY, JAMES. Inquiries into the Origin and Progress of the Science of Heraldry in England. Gloucester, 1793. Early tree sheep (worn, rebacked in non-uniform calf; lt foxed, browned). *Swann*.* $103/£64

DALLAWAY, JAMES. Inquiries into the Origin and Progress of the Science of Heraldry in England. Gloucester: T. Cadell, 1793. 1st ed. xiii,424,(iii),cxiipp; 25 Nice full-pg copperplts. Untrimmed. Recent dk brn morocco, maroon cl, gilt. (Sl aged, foxed; new eps, blanks; ex-lib, spine label neatly removed, ink stamps; sl edgeworn.) Text Clean, cvrs VG. *Baltimore*.* $120/£75

DALOIAN, OSCAR. From Chickens to Prospecting. NY, (1958). 1st ed. NF in VG+ dj. *Sagebrush.* $37/£23

DALRYMPLE, ALEXANDER. A Collection of Charts and Memoirs. London, 1771-72. 4to. W/the full complement of the sectional tps and 1/2-titles. 11 fldg maps or charts (each w/sm portion excised from top edge). Contemp sheep (needs rebinding). *Swann*.* $2,070/£1,294

DALRYMPLE, WILLIAM. In Xanadu. London, 1989. 1st Eng ed. NF (name; extrems sl bumped) in dj. *Clearwater.* $40/£25

DALRYMPLE, WILLIAM. Travels Through Spain and Portugal in 1774. London, 1777. Fldg map, plt. Mod lib buckram. (Lt browned, soiled, ink lib stamps.) *Swann*.* $138/£86

Dalton Brothers and Their Astounding Career of Crime, by an Eyewitness. NY: Frederick Fell, 1954. Rpt ed. Fine in dj. Howes D39. *Labordo.* $35/£22

DALTON, EMMETT. When the Daltons Rode. GC: Doubleday, Doran, 1931. 1st ed. Pict cl. Fine. *Labordo.* $125/£78

DALTON, EMMETT. When the Daltons Rode. GC: Doubleday, Doran, 1931. 1st ed. NF. Howes D39. *Pacific*.* $138/£86

DALTON, EMMETT. When the Daltons Rode. NY, 1931. Signed, inscribed by Dalton & Jack Jungmeyer (co-author). 8vo. *Swann*.* $1,955/£1,222

DALTON, O. M. East Christian Art: A Survey of the Monuments. Oxford, 1925. Frontis, 69 plts. (Joints tender, spine top torn.) *Swann*.* $57/£36

DALVIMART, OCTAVIEN. The Costume of Turkey. William Miller, 1804. Rpt of 2nd ed. Sm folio. (xiv)pp; 60 hand-colored stipple engrs, each w/leaf of text in English. Aeg. Contemp full scarlet morocco, gilt, raised bands. (Bkpl, sl offsetting from plts; extrems sl worn, rubbed), o/w VF. *Sotheran.* $2,800/£1,750

DALY, LOUISE HASKELL. Alexander Cheves Haskell: The Portrait of a Man. Norwood, MA: Privately ptd at Plimpton, 1934. 1st ed. One of 300. Lg 8vo. Frontisport. Blue cl. Fine. *Chapel Hill.* $650/£406

DALYELL, J. G. (ed). Fragments of Scotish History. Edinburgh: Archibald Constable, 1798. 1st ed. (4),vii,(1),88,64,16,99pp. Contemp gilt-ruled diced russia, earlier morocco spine label. (Expertly rebacked, corners worn), else VG. *Pacific*.* $161/£101

DALZIEL, BROTHERS. Brothers Dalziel, a Record of Fifty Years Work in Conjunction with Many of the Most Distinquished Artists of the Period 1840-1890. London: Methuen, 1901. 1st ed. (Blotchy strip along spine edge), else VG in blue cl, new acetate wrapper. *Michael Taylor.* $96/£60

Dame Crump and Her Pig. NY: McLoughlin Bros, ca 1900s. 4to. 6 full-pg illus w/heavy gilt by J. H. Howard. Pict wraps (spine resewn, sm corner fr wrap missing). VG. *Davidson.* $250/£156

Dame Partlet's Farm; an Account of the Riches She Obtained by Industry, the Good Life She Led, and Alas! Good Reader, Her Death and Epitaph. London: Grant & Griffith, n.d. (ca 1840). New ed. 12mo. Full-pg frontis, 48pp + 1pg list; 12 VF half-pg hand-colored engrs. Fine (sl spotted, 1 plt sl affected, pencil sig fep) in yellow stiff paper wrappers (spine strengthened). *Hobbyhorse.* $150/£94

Dame Wiggens of Lee and Her Seven Wonderful Cats. London: Field & Tuer, Leadenhall Press, E.C., 1887. 1st ed thus. Early facs ed ptd from orig 1823 ed. 8vo. (iv),6-31,(vi)ads pp. Internally Clean in grn hand-colored paper wraps (sm crease lower corner, spine sl rubbed). *Sotheran.* $141/£88

DAME, WILLIAM MEADE. From the Rapidan to Richmond and the Spottsylvania Campaign. Balt: Green-Lucas, 1920. 1st ed. 3 photo ports. Tan cl, gilt. Good (smudges, dusty). *Baltimore*.* $75/£47

DAMPIER, WILLIAM. Voyages and Discoveries. London: Argonaut, 1931. One of 975, this copy unnumbered. 4 fldg facs maps. 1/2 vellum, gilt. (Shelfworn, spine foot, top corners bumped), else VG. *Pacific*.* $109/£68

Dan De Quille of the Big Bonanza. (By William Wright.) Philpotts, 1980. One of 650. *Dawson.* $35/£22

DANA, CHARLES A. (ed). The United States Illustrated. NY: Hermann J. Meyer, (c. 1855). 2 vols. 82 steel-engr plts incl added pict tps. Orig 1/2 morocco, mottled bds, gilt-lettered spines. (Many plts lt flecked to paper, mostly in margins; mild foxing; cvrs rubbed, worn), else VG. *Pacific*.* $863/£539

DANA, E. A Text-Book of Mineralogy. NY: Wiley, c1877. 1st ed, 1st ptg. viii,485pp + ads. (Cvrs faded, spotted.) Internally Good. *Blake.* $75/£47

DANA, H. W. L. Handbook on Soviet Drama. NY: Amer Russian Inst, 1938. 1st ed. Pict bds. VG in pict dj (shelfworn). *Dramatis.* $25/£16

DANA, JAMES. Manual of Geology. Phila, 1863. 1st ed. 798pp + color fldg map, illus. Black cl, gilt. (Inscrip; spine expertly repaired), else VG. *Larry Price.* $65/£41

DANA, JAMES. Manual of Mineralogy and Lithology Containing the Elements of the Science of Minerals and Rocks. London: Trubner, 1882. 4th ed. iii,474pp. VG (sl damage spine ends). *Bookcell.* $60/£38

DANA, JAMES. Manual of Mineralogy. New Haven: H.C. Peck, 1865. 2nd ed. xii,456pp. 1/4 calf. VG. *Blake.* $65/£41

DANA, JAMES. System of Mineralogy. NY: Putnam, c1850. 3rd ed. 712pp + 45pp ads. Good (lt foxed; sm dampstain top inside corner rear pp; old repair top 1 1/4 inches of joint, lt edgeworn). *Blake.* $450/£281

DANA, KATHERINE FLOYD. Our Phil and Other Stories. Boston/NY: Houghton Mifflin, 1889. 1st ed. E.W. Kemble (illus). viii,147pp. (Worn, spine sl dknd), o/w Good. *Brown.* $40/£25

DANA, MARSHALL N. Newspaper Story. Portland, 1951. 1st ed. Frontisport. Good. *Sagebrush.* $20/£13

DANA, MRS. WILLIAM STARR. How to Know the Wildflowers. NY: Scribner, 1912. New ed. 158 plts by Marion Satterlee and Elsie Louise Shaw. Dec grn cl, gilt. (Browned), else VG. *Fair Meadow.* $20/£13

DANA, RICHARD HENRY, JR. Two Years Before the Mast. Boston, 1840. 1st ed, 2nd ptg. 12mo. Black levant, gilt, by Sangorski & Sutcliffe. (Orig cl cvrs bound in.) BAL 4434. *Swann*.* $862/£539

DANA, RICHARD HENRY, JR. Two Years Before the Mast. London: Edward Moxon, 1841. 2nd Eng ed. (6),124pp. Contemp mottled calf, gilt. VG (rebacked to match mottled cvrs). Howes D49. BAL 4434. *House.* $200/£125

DANA, RICHARD HENRY, JR. Two Years Before the Mast. NY: Random House, 1936. Ltd to 1000 ptd. 14 plts, 1 facs. Orig cream calf over tan linen. (Bds, spine spotted), o/w Fine in orange dj (neatly repaired chip spine top). *Karmiole.* $175/£109

DANA, RICHARD HENRY, JR. Two Years Before the Mast. LEC, 1947. Ltd to 1500 numbered, signed by Hans Alexander Mueller (illus). Fine in slipcase. *Swann*.* $57/£36

DANA, RICHARD HENRY, JR. Two Years Before the Mast. John Haskell Kemble (ed). L.A: Ward Ritchie, 1964. Pict cl. Fine in slipcase. *Pacific*.* $109/£68

DANA, RICHARD HENRY, JR. Two Years Before the Mast: A Personal Narrative of Life at Sea. Chicago: Lakeside Press, 1930. One of 1000 ptd. Teg. Blue cl, white cl spine, gilt. Fine in slipcase (sl shelfworn). *Pacific*.* $58/£36

DANA, RICHARD HENRY. Poems and Prose Writings. Boston: Russell, Odiorne, 1833. 1st ed. 9,(1),450pp. Aeg. Full contemp emb red calf (detached). BAL 4426. *M & S.* $125/£78

DANA, RICHARD HENRY. Poems. Boston, 1827. 1st ed. 113pp. Aeg. Full polished calf, gilt-dec spine by Root. (Ink name; sl worn, top corners sl bumped.) *King.* $75/£47

DANA, SAMUEL L. A Muck Manual for Farmers. Lowell, MA: Bixby, 1842. 1st ed. 242pp, 1f. *Marlborough.* $192/£120

DANDOLO, VINCENT. The Art of Rearing Silkworms.... John Murray, 1825. 1st Eng ed. 8vo. xxiv,365pp; 3 engr plts (2 fldg), 2 fldg letterpress tables. Uncut, unopened. Orig bds. (Sl rubbed, stained, lt spotted.) *Sotheran.* $557/£348

Dandy-Andy Book. (By Anne Anderson.) London: Thomas Nelson, (ca 1915). 8vo. 12 full-pg color plts. Wheat buckram, color paste label. (Lt dusty.) *Reisler.* $200/£125

DANE, C. H. Geology of the Salt Valley Anticline and Adjacent Areas, Grand County, UT. Washington: USGS, 1935. 21 plts, incl 3 lg color foldouts in rear pocket. (Cvrs sunned, sl frayed), else VG. *Five Quail.* $35/£22

DANE, G. EZRA and BEATRICE J. Ghost Town.... NY: Knopf, 1941. 1st ed. Blue cl. Fine in VG + dj (sl tape on verso). *Harrington.* $45/£28

DANENHOWER, JOHN. Lieutenant Danenhower's Narrative of the 'Jeannette'. Boston: James R. Osgood, 1882. x(2)102pp; 2 plts, dbl pg map. VG (bkplt, repair to map w/no loss). *High Latitude.* $250/£156

DANERT, THOMAS. The History of Philip de Commines, Knight, Lord of Argenton. London: Samuel Mearne, 1674. 4th ed. Period calf, later morocco spine label. (Bkpls, hinges cracked, new pastedowns), else VG. *Pacific**. $196/£123

DANIEL, PRICE, JR. Books, Pamphlets, Articles, etc. Waco, n.d. One of 100 numbered. H.D. Bugbee (illus). Photo tipped-in. *Dumont.* $85/£53

DANIEL, PRICE, JR. Texas and the West Featuring Books Printed and/or Designed by Carl Hertzog. Waco, n.d. One of 125 numbered. Signed by Hertzog. VG. *Dumont.* $150/£94

DANIEL, PRICE, JR. Texas and the West Featuring the Writing of J. Frank Dobie. Waco, n.d. One of 210 numbered. Frontis. NF. *Dumont.* $125/£78

DANIEL, W. B. Rural Sports. London: Bunny & Lane/Philanthropic Soc, 1801. 1st ed. 3 vols. 526; 378; 356pp. All edges marbled. 3/4 brn calf (orig?) over marbled paper-cvrd bds w/black leather spine labels. Good (sl foxed; worn, cvrs detached vol 1). *Biscotti.* $375/£234

DANIEL, W. B. Rural Sports. (London): I. White, 1805. Lg paper ed. Deluxe edition. 3 vols. Foolscap folio. 66 hand-colored plts, 2 hand-colored pict tps, 3 engr charts/tables (heavily foxed). Gilt gauffered edges; gilt-ruled inner dentelles. Full burgundy crushed morocco, gilt. VG set (fr cvr vol 1 sl water-stained, affecting eps, some darkening to the leather; fr hinge vol 3 broken; all joints rubbed). *Glenn.* $3,000/£1,875

DANIEL, W. B. Rural Sports. London, 1812-13. 4 vols. Engr tps, 74 plts (variously foxed, offset). Mod 1/2 leather, gilt. *Swann**. $431/£269

DANIELL, A. E. London Riverside Churches. Westminster, 1897. xii,318pp + 6pp pubs ads. Teg. (Prelims lt browned; spine sl chipped, faded.) *Edwards.* $56/£35

DANIELL, L. E. Types of Successful Men of Texas. Austin: The Author, 1890. 1st ed. x,631pp. Later cl. (Old tape repairs to margins, spine sl sunned, rebound), o/w Good. *Brown.* $125/£78

DANIELLS, JOHN M. The Life of Stonewall Jackson. London/New York, 1863. 305pp + 44pp ads; engr port. (Lt spotted, extrems worn.) *Cullen.* $120/£75

DANIELS, JONATHAN. Prince of Carpetbaggers. Phila, (1958). 1st ed. VG in dj. *Pratt.* $30/£19

DANIELSON, RICHARD E. Martha Doyle: and Other Sporting Memories. NY: Derrydale, 1938. Ltd to 1250 numbered. Red cl. Fine. *Biscotti.* $100/£63

DANNENFELDT, KARL H. Leonhard Rauwolf Sixteenth Century Physician, Botanist, and Traveler. Cambridge: Harvard Univ, 1968. 1st ed. Gray cl. Fine in dj. *House.* $35/£22

DANTE. Dante's Inferno. Henry Francis Cary (trans). NY/London: Cassell, ca 1875. Gustave Dore (illus). Aeg. Gilt-stamped brn morocco (extrems worn). Good. *Appelfeld.* $150/£94

DANTE. The Divine Comedy. Boston/NY, 1906. One of 650 numbered sets of lg paper ed. 6 vols. Paper spine labels. (Edges sl worn.) *Swann**. $126/£79

DANTE. The Divine Comedy. Verona: Officina Bodoni, 1932. Signed by Hans Mardersteig (designer, ptr). Small folio. Full brocade specially woven by Fortuny of Venice. Fine in box. *Appelfeld.* $250/£156

DANTE. La Divina Commedia. Mario Casella (ed). H.F. Cary (trans). Nonesuch, 1928. Ltd to 1475. 4to. 42 hand-tipped dbl-spread plts after Sandro Botticelli. Teg. Full orange-stained vellum, gilt. VG + (bds sl bowed). *Truepenny.* $650/£406

DANTE. The New Life. Dante Gabriel Rossetti (trans). Portland, ME: Thomas B. Mosher, 1905. Ltd to 925. Pale blue bds, paper-parchment spine, overlapping fore-edges. Fine. *Truepenny.* $35/£22

DANTE. Purgatory and Paradise. Henry Francis Cary (trans). NY/London: Cassell, ca 1875. Gustave Dore (illus). Aeg. Gilt-stamped buckram. Good. *Appelfeld.* $150/£94

Danubian Principalities, the Frontier Lands of the Christian and the Turk. (By James Henry Skene.) London: Richard Bentley, 1854. 3rd ed. 2 vols. Litho plt, fldg map. Grn pub's cl. (1st few ll both vols spotted affecting plt, map, tps; spines faded.) *Christie's**. $258/£161

DANZIGER, JAMES (ed). Beaton. NY, 1980. 1st ed. Dj. *Edwards.* $40/£25

DARAN, G. H. The Chronicles of Barabbas 1884-1934. Methuen, 1935. 1st ed. Good in dj. *Moss.* $16/£10

DARBY, WILLIAM J. et al. Food: The Gift of Osiris. Academic Press, 1977. 2 vols. 10 color plts. Djs (chipped). *Edwards.* $72/£45

DARBY, WILLIAM. Memoir on the Geography, and Natural, and Civil History of Florida. Phila: T.H. Palmer, 1821. 8vo. Ads at rear; color fldg map. Untrimmed. (Eps replaced, lt stains, foxed.) Orig ptd paper-cvrd bds (cl spine replaced). *Metropolitan**. $2,070/£1,294

DARBY, WILLIAM. A Tour from the City of New-York, to Detroit, in the Michigan Territory. NY, 1819. 1st ed. 3 fldg maps. Orig bds (rebacked). Howes D77. *Swann**. $287/£179

DARBY, WILLIAM. A Tour from the City of New-York, to Detroit...Between the 2d of May and the 22d of September, 1818. NY, 1819. 1st ed. 228,lxiiipp,(4)ll; 3 fldg maps (1 color). Errata slip not present. Old calf (rebacked, rubbed; foxed, sl soiled, 1 map torn). Howes D66. *Oinonen**. $180/£113

DARK, ALICE ELLIOTT. Naked to the Waist. Boston: Houghton Mifflin, 1991. 1st ed, 1st book. Signed, dated 1991. Fine in dj. *Smith.* $45/£28

DARK, SIDNEY and ROWLAND GREY. W. S. Gilbert. His Life and Letters. London: Methuen, 1924. 2nd ed. 8 plts. (Ep gutters sl stained.) *Hollett.* $40/£25

DARLEY, GEORGE. The Life and Letters of George Darley, Poet and Critic. C. Colleer Abbott (ed). London: OUP, 1928. 1st Eng ed. Later presentation inscribed by Abbott. Nice (lacks dj). *Clearwater.* $64/£40

DARLEY, GEORGE. Sylvia. London: J.M. Dent, 1892. One of 500. Gilt-dec cl, beveled edges (extrems rubbed). *Dramatis.* $50/£31

DARLING, F. FRASER and J. MORTON BOYD. The Highlands and Islands. Collins, 1964. 1st ed thus. VG in dj (worn, defective). *Hollett.* $56/£35

DARLING, F. FRASER. A Naturalist on Rona. London, 1939. (Lt faded.) *Grayling.* $32/£20

DARLING, F. FRASER. West Highland Survey. OUP, 1956. Frontis, map. VG in dj. *Hollett.* $72/£45

DARLING, ROGER. A Sad and Terrible Blunder: Generals Terry and Custer.... Vienna, VA: Potomac-Western, (1990). 1st ed. Inscribed presentation. Fine. *Pacific**. $29/£18

DARLINGTON, MARY C. (ed). History of Colonel Henry Bouquet and the Western Frontiers of Pennsylvania, 1747-1764. (Pittsburgh): Privately ptd, (1920). 1st ed. One of 600 unnumbered. Frontisport. Crimson cl, gilt. VG (sl aged; spine sl abraded). Howes D71. *Baltimore**. $70/£44

DARLINGTON, WILLIAM. American Weeds and Useful Plants. George Thurber (ed). NY: OJ, 1880. Rev ed. vii-xvi,460pp + 4pp ads. (Browned; shelf-worn), else VG. *Fair Meadow.* $35/£22

DARNELL, A. W. Orchids for the Outdoor Garden. London, 1930. 1st ed. Color frontis, 21 plts. Dj (ragged w/loss). *Edwards.* $112/£70

DARRAH, H. Z. Sport in the Highlands of Kashmir. Rowland Ward, 1898. 2 maps. 1/4 grn morocco, gilt. (Staining mainly to prelim margins, few pp carelessly opened; recently rebound.) *Hallam*. $336/£210

DARRAH, H. Z. Sport in the Highlands of Kashmir. London: Rowland Ward, 1898. 1st ed. 8vo. Frontis, xviii,506,(9)ads pp; 2 fldg maps in rear pocket. Silvered cl. VG. *Maggs*. $1,200/£750

DARRAH, WILLIAM C. The World of Stereographs. Gettysburg, PA: W.C. Darrah, 1977. 1st ed. NF in Good dj. *Cahan*. $100/£63

DARROW, CLARENCE. Resist Not Evil. Chicago: Charles H. Kerr, 1903. 1st ed. Grn cl. VG (eps lt browned; extrems lt rubbed, sm spine hole, spine lt browned). *Heritage*. $150/£94

DARROW, CLARENCE. The Story of My Life. NY: Scribner, 1932. 1st ed. NF in Good dj (extrems chipped, sm tears, spine ends lack pieces). *Pacific**. $75/£47

DARROW, CLARENCE. The Story of My Life. NY: Scribner, 1932. 1st trade ed. Signed ink presentation dated Oct 17, 1932. Thick 8vo. Untrimmed. Dk blue cl, gilt. (Sl aged; sl edgeworn, sm dent fr cvr.) Text Nice. Dj (chipped, edgeworn, lacks top left corner rear panel, top several inches rear flap). *Baltimore**. $800/£500

DARTON, F. J. HARVEY (comp). Vincent Crummles, His Theatre and His Times. London: Wells Gardner, Darton, (1926). Ltd to 400. Hand-colored frontis, 14 plts. Red/beige cl, paper spine label. Good in dj (chipped). *Karmiole*. $100/£63

DARTON, F. J. HARVEY. Modern Book-Illustration in Great Britain and America. Studio, 1931. 1st ed. 8 color plts. Dec wrappers. *Forest*. $51/£32

DARTON, N. H. Geology and Water Resources of the Northern Portion of the Black Hills and Adjoining Regions in South Dakota and Wyoming. US Geol Surv Prof Paper, 1909. 22 photo plts. Grn cl (nicely rebound), gilt. VG. *Larry Price*. $70/£44

DARTON, N. H. Guidebook of the Western U.S., Part F. Washington: USGS, 1933. 29 fldg color maps, 40 plts. VG (spine foot chipped, sl surface wear). *Five Quail*. $40/£25

DARTON, N. H. A Reconnaissance of Parts of Northwestern New Mexico and Northern Arizona. Washington: USGS, 1910. 17 plts, map, fldg color map in rear pocket, 2 full-color foldouts. VG +. *Five Quail*. $75/£47

DARTON, WILLIAM. The Third Chapter of Accidents and Remarkable Events. Phila: J. Johnson, 1807. 16mo. (24)ff; 12 copper-engr illus. (Spot inside cvr), else Fine in orig stiff marbled wrappers. *Bromer*. $350/£219

DARWIN, BERNARD (ed). The Dickens Advertiser. London: Elkin Mathews & Marrot, 1930. 1st ed. Pict cl (worn, soiled). *Hollett*. $56/£35

DARWIN, BERNARD et al. A History of Golf in Britain. London: Cassell, (1952). 1st ed. Leather spine label. Fine (emb stamp, name) in VG dj (spine ends, corners chipped). *Pacific**. $288/£180

DARWIN, BERNARD. Golf Between Two Wars. London: C&W, 1944. 1st ed. NF (emb stamp). *Pacific**. $161/£101

DARWIN, BERNARD. The Golf Courses of Great Britain. London: Jonathan Cape, (1925). Rev ed. Color frontis. Teg. Grn cl, gilt. (Bkpl tipped-in, sig; rear hinge cracked, spine, extrems rubbed, sl adhesion residue to lower spine), else VG-. *Pacific**. $374/£234

DARWIN, BERNARD. The Golf Courses of the British Isles. London: Duckworth, (1910). 1st ed. 9x6.75. 64 color plts by Harry Rountree, guards. Teg. Grn cl, gilt. NF (emb stamp). *Pacific**. $1,265/£791

DARWIN, BERNARD. Green Memories. London: Hodder & Stoughton, (1928). 1st ed. Frontisport. Grn cl. (Emb stamp; spine ends rubbed, sm tear lower fr joint, crease to spine), else VG. *Pacific**. $259/£162

DARWIN, BERNARD. Second Shots: Casual Talks About Golf. London: George Newnes, 1930. 1st ed. (Emb stamp; spine ends sl rubbed), else NF. *Pacific**. $316/£198

DARWIN, BERNARD. The Tale of Mr. Tootleoo. London: Nonesuch, (1925). 1st ed. Obl royal 8vo. Unpaginated. 22 full-pg color plts by Eleanor Darwin. Brn paper-cvrd limp bds w/onlaid waxy relief ptd to fr bd, decs in similar brickish red to corners, spine. Fine in VG pale grn dj (sl faded). *Sotheran*. $360/£225

DARWIN, BERNARD. Tootleoo Two, a Sequel to The Tale of Mr. Tootleoo. London: Nonesuch, (1927). 1st ed. Obl royal 8vo. Pict beige/blue paper-cvrd limp bds. Fine in VG blue pict wrapper (sl faded, sm closed tears, nicks along bottom edge). *Sotheran*. $400/£250

DARWIN, CHARLES et al. Narrative of the Surveying Voyages of His Majesty's Ships Adventure and Beagle. Henry Colburn, 1839. 1st ed, vol 3 1st issue. 3 vols in 4, incl Appendix to vol 2. 55 engr plts, maps and plans, incl 7 (of 8) loose in pockets. Orig blue cl, Freeman's variant a w/authors' names on spines. (2 maps sl torn, foxing, vol 2 stitching loose; vol 2 spine head defective, others sl torn at spine heads.) *Sotheby's**. $4,784/£2,990

DARWIN, CHARLES. The Autobiography of Charles Darwin 1809-1882. Nora Barlow (ed). London: Collins, 1958. 1st complete ed, 2nd ptg. 4 plts. Grn cl. VG in dj. *Gach*. $35/£22

DARWIN, CHARLES. The Descent of Man and Selection in Relation to Sex. London: John Murray, 1888. 2nd rev, enlgd ed, later ptg. 2 vols. (ii),(xviii),507,(1); (ii),viii,528pp + inserted ad leaf each vol. Ruled gray-grn cl. Good + set (joints, spine ends shelfworn). *Gach*. $125/£78

DARWIN, CHARLES. The Descent of Man and Selection in Relation to Sex. LEC, 1971. Ltd to 1500 numbered, signed by Fritz Kredel (illus). Fine in slipcase. *Swann**. $138/£86

DARWIN, CHARLES. The Different Forms of Flowers on Plants of the Same Species. John Murray, 1877. 1st ed. 8vo. 32pp pub's ads dated March 1877 at end. Uncut, largely unopened. Grn cl. (Tp lt spotted.) *Sotheby's**. $589/£368

DARWIN, CHARLES. The Different Forms of Flowers on Plants of the Same Species. John Murray, 1892. 4th thousand. xxiv,352pp. Uncut, partly unopened. NF (ex-libris) in grn cl, gilt. *Cox*. $64/£40

DARWIN, CHARLES. The Effects of Cross and Self Fertilisation in the Vegetable Kingdom. John Murray, 1876. 1st ed. 3-line errata slip. Uncut, unopened. Grn cl (sl rubbed). *Sotheby's**. $552/£345

DARWIN, CHARLES. The Expression of the Emotions in Man and Animals. London: John Murray, 1872. 1st ed, 2nd issue. vi,374,4(ads)pp; 7 heliotype plts, 3 fldg. Later 3/4 calf, marbled bds, raised spine bands. NF (faded sig). *Glaser*. $450/£281

DARWIN, CHARLES. The Expression of the Emotions in Man and Animals. London: (John Murray), 1872. 1st ed, 2nd issue of text, 1st state of the 7 heliotype plts (w/Arabic, not Roman, numbers). Pub's grn cl dec in blind, gilt spine. *Book Block*. $575/£359

DARWIN, CHARLES. The Expression of the Emotions in Man and Animals. NY: Appleton, 1873. 1st ed. 374pp; 7 photo helio plts. VG. *Mikesh*. $175/£109

DARWIN, CHARLES. The Expressions of the Emotions in Man and Animals. London: John Murray, 1872. 1st ed, 1st issue. (Review tipped to feps; fr joint lt rubbed, spine ends sl worn), o/w NF. *Beasley*. $500/£313

DARWIN, CHARLES. The Formation of Vegetable Mold, Through the Actions of Worms, with Observations on Their Habits. London: John Murray, 1881. (Sl foxed; bumped, worn), else Nice. *Metropolitan**. $51/£32

DARWIN, CHARLES. The Formation of Vegetable Mould Through the Action of Worms with Observations on Their Habits. London: Murray, 1904. 10 plts. Grn cl. VG. *Savona*. $29/£18

DARWIN, CHARLES. The Formation of Vegetable Mould Through the Action of Worms. London, 1881. 3rd thousand. pp vii,errata,326,2 ads. Fine. *Henly.* $72/£45

DARWIN, CHARLES. The Formation of Vegetable Mould, Through the Action of Worms, with Observations on Their Habits. John Murray, 1881. 1st ed. Pub's ad leaf at end. Uncut. Grn cl (fr cvr sl mkd). *Sotheby's*.* $442/£276

DARWIN, CHARLES. Journal of Researches into the Geology and Natural History of the Various Countries Visited by H.M.S. Beagle.... Henry Colburn, 1839. 1st separate ed. 8vo. 2 fldg maps, half-title, 16-pg pub's list, 1-pg ad for 'The Zoology of the Voyage of H.M.S. Beagle' and 'Geological Observations' inserted at end. Ms notes affixed to eps. Orig plum cl (faded, spine head defective, bkpl pasted to fr cvr). *Sotheby's*.* $2,392/£1,495

DARWIN, CHARLES. Journal of Researches into the Natural History and Geology of the Countries Visited During the Voyage of H.M.S. 'Beagle' Round the World.... London, 1889. 20th thousand. xii,(13)-615pp (yellowed, eps browned, rear inner hinge paper cracked); port, 14 woodcuts. Grn cl (edges, corners rubbed, sm tears to spine head), gilt. *Sutton.* $125/£78

DARWIN, CHARLES. Journal of Researches into the Natural History and Geology of the Countries Visited During the Voyage of the H.M.S. Beagle Round the World. NY, 1846. 1st Amer ed. 2 vols. Uncut. Orig cl. (Lt foxed; spine ends worn.) *Swann*.* $402/£251

DARWIN, CHARLES. Journal of Researches into the Natural History and Geology of the Countries Visited During the Voyage Round the World of H.M.S. Beagle. NY: Appleton, 1890. New ed. Pict cl, gilt. (Emb stamp; extrems, spine ends rubbed), else VG. *Pacific*.* $69/£43

DARWIN, CHARLES. The Life and Letters of Charles Darwin Including an Autobiographical Chapter. Francis Darwin (ed). London: John Murray, 1887. 2nd corrected ed. 3 vols. Frontis each vol, (x),(396), 1 plt; (iv),(394), facs holograph ll; iv,418pp. Panelled grn-gray cl, gilt. VG set (ex-lib, lt mkd; edges foxed, rear pocket, spine #s each vol). *Gach.* $150/£94

DARWIN, CHARLES. Life and Letters of Charles Darwin. Francis Darwin (ed). NY: Basic Books, 1959. 2 vols. VG set (spines sl faded) in slipcase. *Glaser.* $60/£38

DARWIN, CHARLES. More Letters of Charles Darwin. Francis Darwin (ed). NY, 1903. 1st Amer ed. 2 vols. (Sl worn.) *Woolson.* $100/£63

DARWIN, CHARLES. On the Origin of Species by Means of Natural Selection, or the Preservation of Favoured Races in the Struggle for Life. Adelaide, South Australia: LEC, 1963. One of 1500. Signed by Paul Landacre (illus). 1/2 oasis morocco, wood veneer bds, gilt. Fine in glassine, slipcase. *Pacific*.* $138/£86

DARWIN, CHARLES. On the Origin of Species by Means of Natural Selection. NY: Appleton, 1860. 1st US ed, 2nd issue. Distinguishable from 1st issue only by # of quotations on the leaf opposite tp; 1st issue has 2 quotations, 2nd issue has 3. 432pp; fldg chart. Dotted brn cl, gilt. Good (sl browned, lt foxed, few sigs sl sprung, 1860 ink sig, few lt pencil notes, long pencil note rep; sl edgeworn, spine ends chipped, sm crack fr joint). *Baltimore*.* $230/£144

DARWIN, CHARLES. On the Origin of Species by Means of Natural Selection.... John Murray, 1860. 2nd ed, 2nd issue, 5th thousand. 8vo. 1/2-title, fldg diag at p117, 32pp pub's ads at end dated Jan 1860. Grn blind-stamped cl. (L2-M1 stained at lower corner; spine bumped, strengthened at ends.) *Sotheby's*.* $570/£356

DARWIN, CHARLES. On the Origin of Species, by Means of Natural Selection. London: John Murray, 1859. 1st ed. 8vo. Pub's 32-pg cat dated June 1859 (Freeman's 3rd variant); fldg litho chart. Freemans' binding variant b. Orig cl (expertly rebacked retaining orig backstrip; scattered minor marginal repairs). Cl slipcase. *Swann*.* $8,050/£5,031

DARWIN, CHARLES. On the Origin of Species. John Murray, 1859. 1st ed. Half-title, fldg diag at p117, 32pp of Murray's ads (3rd issue) dated June 1859 at end. (Sl spotted, inner hinges cracked, stain on rep.) Uncut. Orig grn blind-stamped cl, gilt spine (ends sl rubbed). VG in cl box. *Sotheby's*.* $23,920/£14,950

DARWIN, CHARLES. On the Origin of Species. London: John Murray, 1861. 3rd ed. 8vo. Grn cl. (Fep soiled; spine extrems sl frayed.) *Argosy.* $1,250/£781

DARWIN, CHARLES. On the Structure and Distribution of Coral Reefs. Ward Lock, 1890. xx,549pp. Contemp 1/2 calf, gilt. VG. *Hollett.* $104/£65

DARWIN, CHARLES. On the Various Contrivances by Which British and Foreign Orchids Are Fertilised by Insects.... John Murray, 1862. 1st ed. 8vo. Fldg plts at p18 (repaired along fold), 32pp pub's ads dated Dec 1861 at end. *Sotheby's*.* $1,104/£690

DARWIN, CHARLES. The Variation of Animals and Plants Under Domestication. NY, (1868). 1st Amer ed. 2 vols. x,(11)-494; viii,(9)-568pp; 43 woodcuts. (1st few pp vol 1 margins dampstained; bkpls, pp tanned, abrasions, paper residue from lib cards on pastedowns; fr inner joint vol 1 cracked; lt worn, spines sl torn.) *Sutton.* $225/£141

DARWIN, CHARLES. The Variation of Animals and Plants Under Domestication. NY: Appleton, (1900). 2 vols. VG + . *Mikesh.* $60/£38

DARWIN, CHARLES. The Variation of Animals and Plants Under Domestication. London, 1868. Vol 1: 1st ed, 1st issue (the 32pp of ads not present in this copy). Vol 2: 1st ed, 2nd issue w/the binding as the 1st issue (the imprint being in one line). viii,141; viii,486,2 ads. Good (vol 2 rebacked preserving spine, eps). *Henly.* $288/£180

DARWIN, CHARLES. The Variation of Animals and Plants Under Domestication. John Murray, 1868. 2 vols. 1st ed, 1st issue, w/5 errata in 6 lines on p.vi vol 1 and 9 errata in 7 lines on p.viii vol 2, 32pp of ads dated April 1867 at end of vol 1, 2pp ads dated Feb 1868 at end of vol 2. 1-pg unsigned ms note by Emma Darwin tipped in to vol 1. Uncut. Grn cl. *Sotheby's*.* $736/£460

DARWIN, CHARLES. The Variation of Animals and Plants Under Domestication. John Murray, 1875. 2nd ed, 4th thousand. 2 vols. xiv,473; x,495pp + 32pp pub's cat dated Jan 1876. Good set (prelims sl spotted) in grn cl (extrems rubbed, spine ends sl worn). *Cox.* $120/£75

DARWIN, CHARLES. The Voyage of the H. M. S. Beagle. LEC, 1956. Ltd to 1500 numbered, signed by Robert Gibbings. Fine in slipcase. *Swann*.* $172/£108

DARWIN, ERASMUS. A Plan for the Conduct of Female Education in Boarding Schools. Derby, 1797. 1st ed. 4to. Uncut. Stab-stictched w/o wrappers. VG (1/2-title w/sm piece cut away from corner) in 1/4 blue morocco slipcase. *Heritage.* $1,750/£1,094

DARWIN, ERASMUS. Zoonomia; or, The Laws of Organic Life. For J. Johnson, 1794-1796. 1st ed. 2 vols. 4to. 10 plts (6 color); directions to binder/errata leaf at end of vol 1. Contemp tree calf. (Foxed, offset; 1 plt stained at margin; rebacked, repaired.) *Sotheby's*.* $1,195/£747

DARY, DAVID. The Buffalo Book. Chicago, (1974). Frontis. Pict eps. (Edges soiled), else NF in VG + dj. *Sagebrush.* $30/£19

DARY, DAVID. Entrepreneurs of the Old West. NY: Knopf, 1986. 1st ed. Fine in dj. *Labordo.* $30/£19

DAS, SARAT CHANDRA. Journey to Lhasa and Central Tibet. W. W. Rockhill (ed). London: John Murray, 1902. 1st ed. 1/2 title, frontisport, x,(iv),285pp; 2 lg fldg maps, 4 plans, 3 other plts. Grn cl, gilt. VG (lib labels removed, cl sl cockled, extrems sl rubbed). *Morrell*. $312/£195

DAS, SARAT CHANDRA. Journey to Lhasa and Central Tibet. W. W. Rockhill (ed). NY, 1904. New ed. 8vo. 5 fldg plts. Dec cl, gilt. Fine. *Sotheby's**. $515/£322

DASENT, ARTHUR IRWIN. Nell Gwynne 1650-1687. London: Macmillan, 1924. 1st ed. 8 plts, incl color frontisport. Teg, uncut. VG. *Hollett*. $48/£30

DATER, JUDY. Imogen Cunningham: A Portrait. Boston, (1979). 1st ed. (Top edge faded.) Dj (sm tear to panels). *Swann**. $57/£36

DAUDET, ALPHONSE. Recollections of a Literary Man. Laura Ensor (trans). Routledge, 1892. Teg. Good (sigs; spine bumped, sm vents rear hinge, cvrs unevenly sunned w/sl mks). *Tiger*. $24/£15

DAUGHERTY, C. M. City Under the Ice, the Story of Camp Century. NY, 1963. 1st ed. VG in dj (torn). *Hallam*. $24/£15

DAUGHERTY, JAMES. Poor Richard. Viking, 1941. 1st ed. 8vo. 158pp. Brn cl. (Apparently set w/o last pg of text, name; corners sl bumped), else Good + . *Price*. $40/£25

DAUGHERTY, SONIA. The Broken Song. Nelson, 1934. 1st ed. Kate Seredy (illus). Fine (1/8-inch chips at corners, spine tips) in VG dj. *Price*. $100/£63

DAULBY, DANIEL. A Descriptive Catalogue of the Works of Rembrandt. Liverpool, 1796. Engr frontisport (spotted), xxii,(i),339pp + (ii)pp index. Marbled eps, edges. Calf (rebacked, orig spine laid down), gilt. (Tp sl browned, hinges repaired; rubbed.) *Edwards*. $176/£110

DAVENPORT, BISHOP. A Pocket Gazeteer, or Traveller's Guide Through North America and the West Indies. Trenton/Balt: The Author/Plaskitt, 1834. Fldg color map, 468pp, fldg profile plt at end. Orig calf (fr outer hinge opened, shelfworn, old ms shelf # on spine). *Brown*. $150/£94

DAVENPORT, CYRIL. Beautiful Books. Methuen, 1929. 1st ed. 15 plts. Good in dj. *Moss*. $32/£20

DAVENPORT, CYRIL. Byways Among English Books. Methuen, 1927. 1 plt. Good in dj. *Moss*. $32/£20

DAVENPORT, CYRIL. English Embroidered Bookbindings. Alfred Pollard (ed). Kegan Paul, Trench, Trubner, 1899. 1st ed. Color frontis, 52 plts. Teg, uncut. Buckram (spine faded). *Forest*. $176/£110

DAVENPORT, CYRIL. The English Regalia. London: Kegan Paul, Trench, Trubner, 1897. One of 500. 12 color plts, guards. Red cl, gilt. (Offset to tp, spine sl sunned), else NF. *Pacific**. $63/£39

DAVENPORT, CYRIL. Royal English Bookbindings. London: Seeley, 1896. Color frontis, 7 color plts. Maroon cl (sl worn, spine sl faded). *Maggs*. $120/£75

DAVENPORT, GUY (trans). Mimes of Herondas. SF: Grey Fox, 1981. 1st ed. Fine in brn cl. *Lame Duck*. $85/£53

DAVENPORT, JOHN S. German Talers 1700-1800. London: Spink, 1965. Orig rexine. Price list loosely inserted. Fine. *Europa*. $42/£26

DAVEY, NEIL K. Netsuke. Sotheby, 1982. Rev ed. VG in dj. *Hollett*. $120/£75

DAVEY, NEIL K. Netsuke: A Comprehensive Study Based on the M. T. Hindson Collection. London: Sotheby Parke Bernet, (1974). Dj. *Swann**. $149/£93

DAVEY, NORMAN. The Penultimate Adventure. London: Elkin Mathews, 1924. 1st ed. One of 300 signed. Nice in blue buckram backed bds. *Cady*. $35/£22

DAVID, ROBERT B. Malcolm Campbell Sheriff. Casper, 1932. 1st ed. Good (sig, date; sl shaken, backstrip faded). Howes D85. *Baade*. $95/£59

DAVID, ROBERT B. Malcolm Campbell, Sheriff. Caspar, WY: Wyomingana, 1932. 1st ed. VG (spine faded). *Labordo*. $150/£94

DAVIDIAN, H. H. The Rhododendron Species. Portland, 1982. 1st ed. VG in dj. *Woolson*. $45/£28

DAVIDIAN, H. H. The Rhododendron Species. Volume II: Elepidotes, Part 1: Arboreum-Lacteum. Portland, OR: Timber Press, 1989. 1st ed. Fine in dj. *Archer*. $40/£25

DAVIDS, ARLETTE. Flowers: Rock Plants. London: Hyperion, 1939. 1st ed. VG in dj (chipped, sm tears to extrems, spine dknd). *Pacific**. $63/£39

DAVIDSON, BRUCE. East 100th Street. Cambridge, MA, (1970). (Lt age-dknd.) Photo-pict stiff wrappers (lt soiled). *Swann**. $287/£179

DAVIDSON, BRUCE. Subway. NY: Aperture, 1986. 1st ed. 60 full-pg color photos. NF in pict dj. *Cahan*. $50/£31

DAVIDSON, DONALD. The Tennessee. NY, (1946, 1948). 1st eds. 2 vols. Good + . *Wantagh*. $65/£41

DAVIDSON, GEORGE. The Alaska Boundary. SF: Alaska Packers Assoc, 1903. 1st ed. Port, 2 lg fldg maps. Brn cl, gilt. Fine (corners, spine ends lt rubbed). *Argonaut*. $500/£313

DAVIDSON, HUGH COLEMAN. The Gargrave Mystery. Warne, 1889. 1st ed. Pub's file copy stamp on fep, ink notes on prelims. Pict glazed bds (rubbed, extrems worn), o/w VG-. *Any Amount*. $64/£40

DAVIDSON, JOHN. A Full and True Account of the Wonderful Mission of Earl Lavender, Which Lasted One Night and One Day. Ward & Downey, 1895. Frontis by Aubrey Beardsley. Good (spine bumped, dull; dusty). *Tiger*. $48/£30

DAVIDSON, JOHN. Miss Armstrong's and Other Circumstances. Methuen, 1896. 1st ed. Good (eps, cvrs soiled, spine very dknd, rubbed). *Ulysses*. $72/£45

DAVIDSON, LIONEL. A Long Way to Shiloh. Gollancz, 1966. 1st UK ed. VG + in dj (sl dusty). *Williams*. $29/£18

DAVIDSON, LIONEL. Smith's Gazelle. Cape, 1971. 1st UK ed. Fine in dj (price-clipped). *Williams*. $26/£16

DAVIDSON, ORLANDO. The Deadeyes. Washington, (1947). 1st ed. (Hinges loose, corner sl chewed, cvrs rubbed, spine sunned.) *King*. $75/£47

DAVIDSON, ORLANDO. The Deadeyes: The Story of the 96th Infantry Division. Washington, 1947. 1st ed. VG. *Clark*. $95/£59

DAVIDSON, W. T. and MARGARET GILMAN GEORGE. The Yellow Rose. Little Rock: C.A. Woodruff, 1929. 1st ed. Frontisport. Maroon cl, gilt, photo plt on fr cvr. VG (sl scuffed). *House*. $25/£16

DAVIE, W. GALSWORTHY and E. GUY DAWBER. Old Cottages and Farmhouses in Kent and Sussex. Batsford, 1900. 1st ed. 100 plts. Teg. Dec cl. Good (sl rubbed, sunned). *Ash*. $120/£75

DAVIE, W. GALSWORTHY. Old English Doorways. Batsford, 1903. 1st ed. 70 collotype plts. (Eps, 1/2-title spotted; cl sl mkd.) *Hollett*. $136/£85

DAVIES, CHARLES. A Treatise on Shades and Shadows, and Linear Perspective. NY: Harper, 1832. 157pp; 20 fldg engr plts. Contemp 1/2-leather, marbled bds (joints cracked, sl worn; sl foxed, waterstain blank upper margin last ff). *Ars Artis*. $152/£95

DAVIES, DAVID W. An Enquiry into the Reading of the Lower Classes. Pasadena: Grant Dahlstrom, 1970. Ltd to 750 ptd. Color frontis, 17 plts. Dec gray/brn linen. Fine. *Karmiole*. $50/£31

DAVIES, E. W. L. Algiers in 1857. London, 1858. *Swann**. $201/£126

DAVIES, J. H. Modern Methods of Welding: As Applied to Workshop Practice. Constable, 1921. 1st ed. (Spine tail, edges sl rubbed), o/w VG. *Whittle*. $24/£15

DAVIES, JAMES. Relation of a Voyage to Sagadahoc. B. F. De-costa (ed). Cambridge: John Wilson & Son, 1880. One of 'a small edition...for private distribution.' 43pp. Marbled eps. (Orig fr wrap bound in.) 3/4 leather. *Parmer.* $250/£156

DAVIES, JOHN. The History of the Tahitian Mission 1799-1830. C. N. Newbury (ed). Cambridge: Hakluyt Soc, 1961. Fldg fron-tis, fldg map. Blue cl. VG. *Parmer.* $85/£53

DAVIES, K. G. Northern Quebec and Labrador Journals and Cor-respondence 1819-35. London: Hudson's Bay Record Soc, 1963. 1st ed. Ltd ed. 2 fldg maps in rear pocket. Black cl, gilt. Fine in dj. *Argonaut.* $90/£56

DAVIES, K. G. (ed). Letters from Hudson's Bay, 1703-40. Lon-don: Hudson's Bay Record Soc, 1965. 1st ltd ed. Fine in VG dj. *Perier.* $60/£38

DAVIES, MARTIN. Paintings and Drawings on the Backs of Na-tional Gallery Pictures. London: The Trustees, 1946. NF in dj. *Turtle Island.* $35/£22

DAVIES, N. DE G. The Mastaba of Ptahhetep and Akhethetep at Saqqareh. London: EEF, 1900-1901. 2 vols. Folio. 64 plts. (Bkpls; sm hole vol 1 spine.) *Archaeologia.* $275/£172

DAVIES, R. TREVOR. Four Centuries of Witch Beliefs: With Spe-cial Reference to the Great Rebellion. London, 1947. 1st ptg. VG + in Good+ dj. *Middle Earth.* $60/£38

DAVIES, RAY. X-Ray. NY, 1995. Advance reading copy. Signed. Fine in glossy wraps. *Warren.* $50/£31

DAVIES, RHYS. Arfon. London: W. & G. Foyle, n.d. 1st ed. One of 400. Signed. Fine in dj (pieces of spine ends, dknd). *Pacific*.* $35/£22

DAVIES, RHYS. The Black Venus. London: Heinemann, 1944. 1st ed. Black cl. Fine. *Temple.* $16/£10

DAVIES, RHYS. Rings on Her Fingers. London: Harold Shaylor, 1930. One of 175, this copy numbered, signed. Grn coarse glazed linen. (Eps lt foxed), o/w NF in slipcase (sl worn). *Tem-ple.* $56/£35

DAVIES, RHYS. Tale. London, (1930). 1st ed. 16pp stapled into wrappers (staples rusted, cvrs sl soiled). *Typographeum.* $25/£16

DAVIES, ROBERTSON. Eros at Breakfast. Toronto: Clarke, Irwin, 1949. 1st ed. (Top edges of pp dknd), else NF in VG dj (edges sl torn, extrems worn). *Lame Duck.* $375/£234

DAVIES, ROBERTSON. The Lyre of Orpheus. NY, 1988. Later ptg. Inscribed, signed. Fine in Fine dj. *Warren.* $85/£53

DAVIES, ROBERTSON. The Manticore. NY: Viking, 1972. 1st US ed. Fine in NF dj. *Beasley.* $45/£28

DAVIES, ROBERTSON. Murther and Walking Spirits. (NY): Vi-king, (1991). 1st ed. 1/4 cream cl, gilt, black bds. Fine in dj. *Heritage.* $50/£31

DAVIES, ROBERTSON. Shakespeare's Boy Actors. Dent, 1939. 1st UK ed. NF (spine head sl pushed). *Williams.* $232/£145

DAVIES, ROBERTSON. Tempest-Tost. NY: Rinehart, 1952. 1st US ed. (Bkpl), else Fine in VG + dj (long tear rear panel). *Beasley.* $100/£63

DAVIES, ROBERTSON. World of Wonders. Toronto: Macmillan, (1975). 1st ed. (Sm paper loss fep corner), else Fine in dj (spine ends rubbed, sl chipped). *Pacific*.* $29/£18

DAVIES, ROBERTSON. World of Wonders. NY: Viking, 1975. 1st US ed. Fine in Fine dj. *Beasley.* $35/£22

DAVIES, THOMAS. The Preparation and Mounting of Micro-scopic Objects. NY, 1874. 2nd ed. 214pp. Good (ex-lib; ex-trems worn). *Doctor's Library.* $40/£25

DAVIES, W. H. The Adventures of Johnny Walker, Tramp. Cape, 1926. 1st ed. Ltd to 125 signed. (Spine, edges faded), else VG in dj (dull). *Whiteson.* $40/£25

DAVIES, W. H. The Hour of Magic and Other Poems. London: Cape, 1922. Teg, fore/lower edges uncut. Ptd label fr cvr. VG (bds sl foxed) in ptd dj (sl soiled). *Maggs.* $64/£40

DAVIES, W. H. Later Days. Cape, 1925. 1st ed. Ltd to 125 signed. Teg, partly unopened. Buckram. (Spine faded), else VG. *Whiteson.* $40/£25

DAVIES, W. H. Moss and Feather. London: Ariel Poems, (1928). 1st Eng ed. Fine in pict card wrappers. *Clearwater.* $32/£20

DAVIES, W. H. A Poet's Pilgrimage. Andrew Melrose, 1918. 1st Eng ed. VG (fep sl browned, top edge dusty; spine ends, cor-ners bumped, faded, cvrs sl cocked, fr cvr creased) in dj (chipped, torn, rubbed, creased, dusty, browned, dampstained at spine, ends frayed). *Ulysses.* $120/£75

DAVIES, W. H. Selected Poems Arranged by Edward Garnett. Gregynog, 1928. One of 310. Engr frontis, tp device in black/yellow, yellow (not pale red) page ruling. Black buckram back/fore-edge strip, Cockerell paper sides. VG (bkpl; sl rubbed). *Cox.* $216/£135

DAVIES, WILLIAM H. The Soul's Destroyer and Other Poems. Farmhouse, Marshalsea Road: The Author, (1905). 1st ed, 1st bk. Orig wraps (chipped, detached, spine flaked). *Kane*.* $95/£59

DAVILA, ENRICO CATERINO. The History of the Civil Wars of France. London: Henry Herringman, 1678. 2nd imp. Folio. (4),734,(18)pp. Orig calf (bkpl; hinges sl rubbed; fr hinges start-ing). *Karmiole.* $350/£219

Davis' Commercial Encyclopedia of the Pacific Southwest—Cali-fornia, Nevada, Utah, Arizona. (By Ellis A. Davis.) Berkeley: El-lis A. Davis, 1914. Expanded, rev ed. 4 lg color fldg maps, 10 full-pg or dbl-pg color maps. Black pebble-grain cl. Fine. *Har-rington.* $150/£94

DAVIS, BOB. Tree Toad: Adventures of a Big Brother. Stokes, 1942. 1st ed. Robert McCloskey (illus). 176pp. VG (browned; cvrs sl faded) in Good dj (spine ends, corners deeply chipped). *Price.* $75/£47

DAVIS, BRIAN LEIGH. Flags and Standards of the Third Reich: Army, Navy, and Air Force, 1933-1945. Arco, (1975). Good in dj. *Rybski.* $37/£23

DAVIS, BRITTON. The Truth About Geronimo. M. M. Quaife (ed). New Haven: Yale Univ, 1929. 1st ed. Frontis. (Top tips bumped.) Dj (lt edgeworn). *Dawson.* $100/£63

DAVIS, BURKE. The Billy Mitchell Affair. NY, (1967). 3rd ptg. Fine in dj (sl worn). *Pratt.* $22/£14

DAVIS, BURKE. Gray Fox, Robert E. Lee and the Civil War. NY, 1956. 1st ed. Signed. VG + in dj (sm tears, lt worn). *Pratt.* $40/£25

DAVIS, BURKE. Jeb Stuart. The Last Cavalier. NY: Rinehart, (1957). 1st ed. Gray cl. (Offsetting to fep), else NF in VG dj. *Chapel Hill.* $55/£34

DAVIS, BURKE. Marine: The Life of Lt. Gen Lewis B. 'Chesty' Puller, USMC. Boston, 1962. 1st ed. VG. *Clark.* $50/£31

DAVIS, CHARLES G. Shipping and Craft in Silhouette. Salem: Marine Research Soc, 1929. (Lt worn.) Dj. *Oinonen*.* $50/£31

DAVIS, CHARLES G. Ships of the Past. Salem: Marine Research Soc, 1929. 12 dbl-pg plans. (Prelim gutters lt dampstained; sl worn.) *Oinonen*.* $50/£31

DAVIS, CHARLES H. S. (ed). The Egyptian Book of the Dead. NY/London: Putnam/(Knickerbocker), 1901. Folio. 99 plts. (Worn, edges rubbed, sl shaken, spine ends torn), o/w Good. *Worldwide.* $195/£122

DAVIS, DEERING. The American Cow Pony. NY, (1962). 1st ed. VG in VG dj. Flyers laid in loose. *Woolson.* $25/£16

DAVIS, EDWIN ADAMS. Fallen Guidon. Santa Fe: Stagecoach, 1962. One of 1000. (Spine faded), else Fine in dj (few chips). *Dumont.* $75/£47

DAVIS, ELLIS A. Davis' Commercial Encyclopedia of the Pacific Southwest. Oakland: Ellis A. Davis, 1915. Folio. (Extrems worn, hinges cracked), else Good. *Dumont.* $165/£103

DAVIS, ELLIS A. Davis' Commercial Encyclopedia of the Pacific Southwest: California, Nevada, Utah, Arizona. Berkeley: Ellis Davis, 1911. 1st ed. Folio. Gilt-lettered black cl. (Extrems sl rubbed), else NF. *Pacific*. $161/£101

DAVIS, ELLIS A. Davis' Commercial Encyclopedia of the Pacific Southwest: California, Nevada, Utah, Arizona. Berkeley: Ellis A. Davis, 1914. 2nd expanded ed. Folio. 3 lg fldg maps. Pebbled black cl, gilt. Fine (fep soiled; spine ends rubbed, fr cvr scratch). *Argonaut.* $175/£109

DAVIS, EVANGELINE and BURKE. Rebel Raider. A Biography of Admiral Semmes. Phila: Lippincott, (1966). 1st ed. Grn cl. NF in dj. *Chapel Hill.* $40/£25

DAVIS, FREDERICK C. He Wouldn't Stay Dead. NY: Doubleday, Doran, 1939. Blue cl. NF (bkpl, spine ends rubbed) in dj (top edges lt worn, lt soiled). *Heritage.* $100/£63

DAVIS, GEORGE E. Practical Microscopy. London: Bogue, 1882. 2nd ed. Frontis, 335pp. VG. *Savona.* $48/£30

DAVIS, GLOVER. Bandaging Bread and Other Poems. West Branch: Cummington Press, 1970. 1st ed. One of 300. Fine in grn woven wrappers. *Pacific*. $29/£18

DAVIS, H. W. B. (ed). Mediaeval England. A New Edition of Barnard's Companion to English History. Oxford: Clarendon, 1924. 1st ed. Frontis. Blue cl (sl bumped), gilt. *Maggs.* $40/£25

DAVIS, HASSOLDT. Land of the Eye. NY: Holt, 1940. 1st ed. (Sl rubbed), o/w VG. *Worldwide.* $45/£28

DAVIS, HENRY E. The American Wild Turkey. Georgetown, (SC): Small Arms, 1949. 1st ed. Color frontis. (Spine sl dknd), else VG. *Bowman.* $250/£156

DAVIS, HENRY P. Training Your Own Bird Dog. NY: Putnam, 1948. 2nd ptg. Rust buckram. NF in pict dj (chipped). *Biscotti.* $25/£16

DAVIS, JEFFERSON. The Rise and Fall of the Confederate Government. Richmond, VA: Garrett & Massie, (1938). 2 vols. Gray cl. (Spines sl dull), else NF set. *Chapel Hill.* $75/£47

DAVIS, JEFFERSON. The Rise and Fall of the Confederate Government. NY, 1881. 1st ed. 2 vols. 707,index + ads; 808,index + ads. Full leather (bkpls, sl worn, vol 2 outer hinges cracked, some insect damage.) *Woolman.* $300/£188

DAVIS, JOHN FRANCIS. The Chinese: A General Description of China and Its Inhabitants. Charles Knight, 1844. New, enlgd, rev ed. 3 vols. 280; 283; 236pp. Contemp dk brn 1/2 calf, gilt, marbled bds. Good set (extrems sl worn). *Sotheran.* $317/£198

DAVIS, JOHN KING. Willis Island: A Stormwarning Station in the Coral Sea. Melbourne: Critchley Parker, 1923. 1st ed. Inscribed. Frontis, 15 plts. Blue cl, blind-stamped, gilt. (Mk from paperclip fr pastedown, fep, frontis recto; lt worn.) *Parmer.* $150/£94

DAVIS, JOHN KING. With the 'Aurora' in the Antarctic, 1911-1914. London: A. Melrose, n.d. (1919). 1st ed. Lg fldg map. Pict cl (faded, lt edgeworn; lib stamps). *Maggs.* $352/£220

DAVIS, JOHN. The American Turf. NY, 1907. Frontis (lt foxed); port. (Some pp opened roughly; edges, corners worn.) *Woolson.* $80/£50

DAVIS, JOHN. Personal Adventures and Travels of Four Years and a Half in the United States of America. London: J. Davis, 1817. 3rd ed. 96pp. Later 3/4 calf, marbled bds, gilt. (Sl foxed, soiled; spine worn), else VG. Howes D123. *Pacific*. $58/£36

DAVIS, JOHN. Travels in the United States of America 1798 to 1802. John Vance Cheney (ed). Boston: Bibliophile Soc, 1910. 1st ed. 2 vols. Unopened. Vellum-like spine, gray bds. Good. Howes D125. *Karmiole.* $125/£78

DAVIS, JOHN. Travels of...in the United States of America, 1798 to 1802. John Vance Cheney (ed). Boston: Privately ptd, 1910. 2 vols. Uncut. Orig 1/4 vellum over bds. (Foxed.) Howes D123. *Mott.* $50/£31

DAVIS, KEITH F. Wanderlust. Kansas City, MO: Hallmark Cards, 1987. 1st ed. 64 full-pg photos. NF in pict stiff wrappers. *Cahan.* $25/£16

DAVIS, LAVINIA. A Bibliography of the Writings of Edith Wharton. Portland: Southworth, 1933. One of 325. Uncut, unopened. (Lt worn, spine gilt sl faded.) *Oinonen*. $80/£50

DAVIS, LEONARD M. From Trail to Rail! Being a History of the City of Roseville, California 1864-1909. (Roseville, CA), 1964. 1st ed. Map. VG in pict wrappers. *Sagebrush.* $30/£19

DAVIS, LINDSEY. Last Act in Palmyra. Century, 1994. 1st ed. Fine in dj. *Virgo.* $48/£30

DAVIS, LINDSEY. Shadow in Bronze. London: Sidgwick & Jackson, 1990. 1st ed. Fine in dj. *Murder.* $175/£109

DAVIS, LINDSEY. Shadows in Bronze. Sidgwick & Jackson, 1990. 1st UK ed. Signed. Fine in dj. *Williams.* $312/£195

DAVIS, LINDSEY. The Silver Pigs. London: Sidgwick & Jackson, 1989. 1st Eng ed, 1st bk. VG (pg edges sl browned, edges sl spotted; cvrs sl string-mkd; spine ends, corners sl bumped) in dj (sl creased, rubbed, mkd). *Ulysses.* $440/£275

DAVIS, LINDSEY. Venus in Copper. London: Hutchinson, 1991. 1st ed. Signed. VF in dj. *Mordida.* $75/£47

DAVIS, M. E. M. The Wire Cutters. Boston: Houghton, 1899. 1st ed. VG (gilt lt rubbed). *Reese.* $150/£94

DAVIS, R. C. Reminiscences of a Voyage Around the World. Ann Arbor, MI, 1869. 1st ed. 331,(4)ads pp. Blindstamped grn cl. *Maggs.* $400/£250

DAVIS, REBECCA HARDING. Bits of Gossip. Boston/NY: Houghton Mifflin, 1904. 1st ed. (Extrems worn, spine repaired), o/w Good. *Second Life.* $45/£28

DAVIS, RICHARD BEALE (ed). William Fitzhugh and His Chesapeake World, 1676-1701. V.H.S., 1963. Port. VG- (rep stained from tape). *Book Broker.* $35/£22

DAVIS, RICHARD HARDING. Bar Sinister. NY: Scribner, 1903. 1st ed. Pict cl, gilt. *Glenn.* $35/£22

DAVIS, RICHARD HARDING. The Deserted. NY: Scribner, 1917. 1st separate ed, 1st this title. Cl, pict bds. Fine in dj (lt soiled, sm chip, tear). BAL 4577. *Reese.* $65/£41

DAVIS, RICHARD HARDING. Somewhere in France. NY: Scribner, 1915. 1st ed. Frontis. Pict grn cl. VG. BAL 4570. *Reese.* $25/£16

DAVIS, RICHARD HARDING. With the Allies. NY: Scribner, 1914. 1st ed. Port. Red cl. (Sm stamp, stamping sl rubbed), o/w VG in dj (lt worn, nicks, 2 creased tears). BAL 4565. *Reese.* $50/£31

DAVIS, RICHARD HARDING. With the French in France and Salonika. NY: Scribner, 1916. 1st ed, later issue, comprised of 1st ptg Scribner sheets and prelims bound in A.L. Burt binding. Frontis. Slate cl stamped in red/yellow. (1918 ink name, tears at gutter of prelim), else Good. *Reese.* $15/£9

DAVIS, ROBERT B. Malcolm Campbell, Sheriff. Casper: Wyomingana, (1932). 1st ed. Blue-grn cl. Good (spine dknd, cvrs rubbed, sl soiled; spine ends, corners sl worn; rear hinge repaired). Howes D85. *Harrington.* $90/£56

DAVIS, TENNEY L. The Chemistry of Powder and Explosives. NY: John Wiley, 1941-1943. 1st ed. 2 vols. Crimson cl, gilt. (Bkpls, pencil notes vol 1 feps; sl rubbed.) Cvrs Good. *Baltimore*. $225/£141

DAVIS, TERRY. Vision Quest. NY: Viking, (1977). 1st ed. (Paper over fr hinge sl cracked in few spots), else Fine in NF dj (sm tear rear panel). *Between The Covers.* $75/£47

DAVIS, VARINA JEFFERSON. Jefferson Davis. NY, (1890). 1st ed. 2 vols. 699; 939pp. (Inner hinges broken; worn, bkpls.) Internally VG. *Woolman.* $200/£125

DAVIS, W. B. The Recent Mammals of Idaho. Caldwell, 1939. Frontis, map. (Eps browned, name stamp top edge of pp.) Dj (worn, chipped). *Sutton.* $68/£43

DAVIS, W. W. H. El Gringo; or New Mexico and Her People. NY: Harper & Bros, 1857. 432pp (foxed). Stamped bds (worn, faded). Good. Howes D139. *Dumont.* $225/£141

DAVIS, W. W. H. El Gringo; or New Mexico and Her People. Santa Fe: Rydal Press, 1938. Errata. (Dj sl chipped, spine faded), else NF in mod slipcase. *Dumont.* $185/£116

DAVIS, W. W. H. History of the 104th Pennsylvania Regiment. Phila, 1866. Presentation copy. 364pp. (Ex-lib; cvrs detached, lacks most of spine.) *King.* $145/£91

DAVIS, WILLIAM C. (ed). The Image of War, 1861-1865. GC, (1981-4). Vols 1-3: 2nd, 3rd ptgs; vols 4-6: 1st ptgs. 6 vols. VG in djs. *Woolman.* $150/£94

DAVIS, WILLIAM C. (ed). The Image of War: 1861-1865. Vols I-III (of 6). GC: Doubleday, 1981-82. 1st ed, initial ptg, on quality coated paper. VG (sl shelfworn, dusty) in djs (lt worn, chipped, torn). *Baltimore*.* $30/£19

DAVIS, WILLIAM HEATH. Seventy-Five Years in California, 1831-1906. SF: John Howell, 1929. One of 2250. Blue cl. (Ex-lib, bkpl, blindstamp; fr hinge cracked, offset from tipped-in facs; shelfworn, cl faded in gutters.) Howes D136. *Parmer.* $135/£84

DAVIS, WILLIAM HEATH. Seventy-Five Years in California. Harold A. Small (ed). SF: John Howell, 1967. 3rd ed. One of 2500. Brn cl, gilt. Fine in NF dj. Howes D136. *Harrington.* $50/£31

DAVIS, WILLIAM HEATH. Seventy-Five Years in California.... SF: John Howell-Books, 1929. 2nd ed. VG. Howes D136. *Labordo.* $200/£125

DAVIS, WILLIAM J. (ed). The Partisan Rangers of the Confederate States Army. (By Adam Rankin Johnson.) Louisville, KY: Geo. G. Fetter, 1904. 1st ed. 8vo. Frontisport. Red cl, gilt. NF. Howes J122. *Chapel Hill.* $550/£344

DAVIS, WINFIELD J. History of Political Conventions in California, 1849-1892. Sacramento: CA State Library, 1893. 1st ed. 711pp. Brn cl. (Sl soiled, spine ends lt worn), else Fine. *Argonaut.* $125/£78

DAVISON, LAWRENCE H. (Pseud of D.H. Lawrence.) Movements in European History. London: Humphrey Milford/OUP, 1921. 1st ed, 1st ptg; 1st binding. Brn cl lettered in black. (Bkpl, pub's rev stamp, lt foxed, eps offset), o/w VG. *Reese.* $450/£281

DAVISON, RALPH C. Concrete Pottery and Garden Furniture. NY, 1910. 1st ed. (Stamped names; worn, soiled.) *King.* $45/£28

DAVITT, MICHAEL. The Boer Fight for Freedom. London, 1902. 3rd ed. Frontisport, fldg map. Gilt-edged cl (fr bd lt damp-stained). *Edwards.* $240/£150

DAVY, HUMPHRY. Elements of Agricultural Chemistry, in a Course of Lectures for the Board of Agriculture. London: Longman, Hurst et al, 1813. 1st ed. viii,323,lxiii,(4)pp; 10 copper-engr plts (1 fldg). Untrimmed. Contemp bds (rebacked in early binders cl, worn; bkpl). VG (few plts sl foxed). *Glaser.* $500/£313

DAVY, HUMPHRY. On the Safety Lamp for Coal Miners. London: R. Hunter, 1818. 1st ed. 8vo. Fldg engr frontis by Lowry, viii,148pp. Orig 1/4 calf, dk grn cl, maroon leather spine label. (Lib stamps; joints, corners scuffed, lt worn.) *Weber.* $1,800/£1,125

DAVY, HUMPHRY. Salmonia; or, Days of Fly Fishing, with Some Account of the Habits of Fishes Belonging to the Genus Salmo. Boston: Roberts Bros, 1870. Grn cl, gilt. (Name, bkpl; spine ends sl rubbed), else VG. *Pacific*.* $58/£36

DAVY, JOHN. The Angler in the Lake District. London: Longman, Brown, Green et al, 1857. 1st ed. Grn cl. (Fr hinge starting; spine sl sunned), else VG. *Pacific*.* $46/£29

DAVY, JOHN. Memoirs of the Life of Sir Humphry Davy, Bart. London: Longman, Rees et al, 1836. 1st ed. 2 vols. Frontisport, xii,507; vii,419,(1)pp. New 1/2 calf, orig marbled bds, leather spine labels. VG (tp, port strengthened at gutter vol 1; lib stamps). *Glaser.* $375/£234

DAVY, JOHN. Notes and Observations on the Ionian Islands and Malta. London, 1842. 2 vols. 6 engr plts. Unopened. (Bkpl; fr joint splitting 1 vol.) *Swann*.* $201/£126

DAWE, GEORGE. The Life of George Morland. T. Werner Laurie, (c.1904). Sm folio. Color frontis, 55 plts. Teg. VG. *Hollett.* $120/£75

DAWS, GAVAN. Shoal of Time. NY: Macmillan, (1968). 1st ed. Fine in Fine dj. *Book Market.* $50/£31

DAWSON, CHARLES. Pioneer Tales of the Oregon Trail and of Jefferson Country (Nebraska). Topeka: Crane, 1912. 1st ed. VG in pict cl. Howes H150. *Perier.* $575/£359

DAWSON, CHARLES. Pioneer Tales of the Oregon Trail and of Jefferson County. Topeka, KS: Crane, 1912. 1st ed. VG. Howes D150. *Labordo.* $600/£375

DAWSON, CONINGSBY. Carry On: Letters in War-Time. NY/London/Toronto: John Lane/S.B. Gundy, 1917. 1st ed. Port. Gilt tan cl. (Fep excised), else Good. *Reese.* $12/£8

DAWSON, CONINGSBY. The Glory of the Trenches. Toronto/NY: S.B. Gundy/John Lane, 1918. 1st ed, Canadian issue. Port. Gilt red cl. (1921 ink name), o/w VG in dj (sl worn, dknd). *Reese.* $50/£31

DAWSON, CONINGSBY. The Test of Scarlet. NY/London: John Lane, 1919. 1st ed. Red cl stamped in black. (Edges lt foxed), else NF in pict dj (corners nicked). *Reese.* $85/£53

DAWSON, FIELDING. Krazy Kat/The Unveiling and Other Stories from 1951-1968. L.A.: Black Sparrow, 1969. Ltd to 1000. Signed. Fine pict wraps in Fine acetate dj. *Polyanthos.* $25/£16

DAWSON, GEORGE. Pleasures of Angling with Rod and Reel for Trout and Salmon. NY, 1876. 1st ed. Gilt-pict cl (shelfworn, spine tips sl frayed; sm tape stain on tp). *Oinonen*.* $200/£125

DAWSON, GEORGE. Pleasures of Angling with Rod and Reel for Trout and Salmon. NY: Sheldon, 1876. 1st ed. Frontis. Lt brn cl, gilt. NF. *Pacific*.* $288/£180

DAWSON, J. W. The Origin of the World According to Revelation and Science. Hodder & Stoughton, 1877. vii,438pp. Old 1/2 calf (sl worn), gilt. *Hollett.* $64/£40

DAWSON, JOSEPH. Peter Mackenzie. His Life and Labours. Charles H. Kelly, 1896. 2nd ed. xi, 348pp; 20 plts. Beveled bds. VG. *Hollett.* $40/£25

DAWSON, NICHOLAS. Narrative of Nicholas 'Cheyenne' Dawson (Overland to California in '41 and '49, and Texas in '51). SF: Grabhorn, 1933. 2nd ed. One of 500. (Offset to eps), else NF. Howes D159. *Pacific*.* $81/£51

DAWSON, SAMUEL E. The Saint Lawrence: Its Basin and Border-Lands. NY, 1905. 1st ed. 48 photo plts, fold-outs. Orange cl, gilt. (Fldg map needs repair, rebound, lib spine #s removed), else Good + . *Larry Price.* $25/£16

DAWSON, SAMUEL EDWARD. The Saint Lawrence Basin. London: Lawrence and Bullen, 1905. 1st ed. 2 fldg maps (1 color), 37 plts and maps (2 fldg), incl frontis. Grn cl, gilt. VG (cvrs sl stained, spine rubbed). *Morrell.* $96/£60

DAWSON, SIMON J. Report of the Exploration of the Country Between Lake Superior and the Red River Settlement.... Toronto: Legislative Assembly, 1859. 45pp; 3 lg fldg maps. Mod cl. VG. *Adelson.* $385/£241

DAWSON, WILLIAM LEON. The Birds of California. L.A.: South Moulton, 1923. Booklovers' ed. 4 vols. Emb cl. (Sl shelfworn), else Fine. *Pacific*.* $230/£144

DAWSON, WILLIAM LEON. The Birds of California. San Diego, CA: South Moulton, 1923. 1st ed. 3 vols. NF set. *Labordo.* $250/£156

Day in a Child's Life. London: Routledge, (1881). 1st ed, 1st issue. Kate Greenaway (illus), Myles B. Foster (music). 4to. All edges tinted grn. Cl-backed color pict bds (corners sl worn). Pict tan dj (few pieces missing). *Reisler.* $550/£344

DAY, BRADFORD M. (ed). Talbot Mundy Biblio.... NY: S-F & Fantasy Pub, 1955. 1st ed. (Notes.) Red ptd wrappers (worn, sunned along spine, top edge). *Other Worlds.* $20/£13

DAY, C. M. Pioneers of the Eastern Townships. Montreal: John Lovell, ptr, 1863. 171pp. Nice (edges sl worn). *Perier.* $75/£47

DAY, C. R. The Music and Musical Instruments of Southern India. Novello, Ewer/A&C Black, 1891. 1st ed. Ltd to 700. 17 chromolitho plts. Vellum, gilt. Wrapper. *Sotheby's*.* $368/£230

DAY, DONALD. Big Country Texas. Erskine Caldwell (ed). NY, 1947. 1st ed. (Sl browned), else Good in dj (chipped incl top 1/2-inch of spine). *Dumont.* $40/£25

DAY, HAROLD. East Anglian Painters. Eastbourne: Fine Art, 1968-9. Ltd to 1000. Each vol inscribed. 3 vols. Vol 1 in cl; vols 2, 3 in buckram; mtd illus fr bds each vol. Protective cellophane cvr cellotaped to pastedowns vols 2, 3. *Edwards.* $120/£75

DAY, HAROLD. John Constable, R.A. 1776-1837. Drawings. The Golden Age. Eastbourne: Fine Art Publishers, 1975. 218 b/w, 5 color plts. Dj. *Edwards.* $72/£45

DAY, J. WENTWORTH. Sport in Egypt. Country Life, 1938. 1st ed. Orange cl, gilt. Good (fr bd sl worn). *Sotheran.* $77/£48

DAY, JACK HAYS. The Sutton Taylor Feud. San Antonio, 1937. VG (corners sl bumped) in wraps. *Baade.* $50/£31

DAY, JAMES. Maps of Texas 1527-1900. Austin, 1964. (Spot on fr bd), else VG. *Dumont.* $85/£53

DAY, JEREMIAH. A Practical Application of the Principles of Geometry to the Mensuration of Superficies and Solids. New Haven, (CT): Oliver Steele, 1811. 1st ed. (4),96pp; 2 fldg plts. Uncut. Orig ptd wraps, dated 1816 (soiled). *M & S.* $200/£125

DAY, KENNETH (ed). Book Typography 1815-1965 in Europe and the United States of America. Chicago: Univ of Chicago, (1965). 1st Amer ed. VG in illus dj (extrems sl torn). *Pacific*.* $52/£33

DAY, LEWIS F. Ornamental Design. London, 1897. 4th ed. xi,56; xi,48; xi,76pp + 10pp ads; 130 plts. Teg. Dec cl. (Bkpl; hinges cracked, cl lt soiled, bumped.) *Edwards.* $64/£40

DAY, LOUIS F. Alphabets Old and New for the Use of Craftsmen. Batsford, 1906. 2nd ed. 219 plts. Dec tan cl. Good+ (lt worn, sl soiled). *Whittle.* $29/£18

DAY, MARY L. Incidents in the Life of a Blind Girl. Balt: James Young, (1859). Frontisport, 206pp. Blindstamped black cl, gilt (rebacked, orig spine laid down; corners worn). Internally Good. *House.* $35/£22

DAY, SAMUEL PHILLIPS. Down South; or, an Englishman's Experience at the Seat of the American War. London: Hurst & Blackett, 1862. 1st ed. 2 vols. Frontisport, x,328; frontisport, pp viii,327,(8) ads. Plum cl (lt stain fr cvr vol 1; spines faded). Howes D162. *Mott.* $650/£406

DAY, THOMAS. The history of Sandford and Merton. Phila: Lippincott, 1868. 8vo. 532pp; 6 VF full-pg stipple steel engrs. Brn eps. Burgundy tooled cl, gilt spine. (Spine faded), o/w VF. *Hobbyhorse.* $100/£63

DAY-LEWIS, C. The Magnetic Mountain. London: Leonard & Virginia Woolf, 1933. 1st trade ed. One of 500 ptd. Dec bds. VG (inscrip; spine sl dknd). *Maggs.* $72/£45

DAY-LEWIS, C. Noah and the Waters. Leonard & Virginia Woolf, 1936. 1st ed. Yellow cl (lt dust-soiled, backstrip dknd). *Cox.* $24/£15

DAY-LEWIS, C. Noah and the Waters. Hogarth, 1936. 1st Eng ed. VG (feps browned) in dj (sl spotted, spine sl dknd). *Ulysses.* $88/£55

DAY-LEWIS, C. Ten Singers, an Anthology. London: Fortune & Merriman, '1925' (i.e., 1924). 1st ed. Uncut. VG in tan ptd wrappers. *Maggs.* $64/£40

Days on the Hill by an Old Stalker. Nisbet, 1926. 1st ed. 8 plts, 4 sketch-maps. VG (sl spotted). *Hollett.* $120/£75

DAYTON, EDSON C. Dakota Days, May 1886-August 1898. Privately ptd, 1937. 1st ed. One of 300. VF. Howes D165. *Labordo.* $375/£234

DAYTON, FRED ERVING. Steamboat Days. NY: Tudor, (1939). Good. *Lien.* $35/£22

DAYTON, ISAAC. The Office of Surrogate, Surrogates, and Surrogates' Courts, and Executors, Administrators and Guardians, in the State of New-York.... NY: Banks, Gould, 1846. Contemp sheep. VG (ex-lib). *Boswell.* $125/£78

DAZEY, CHARLES. In Old Kentucky. Detroit: Fine Book Circle, 1937. 1st ed. One of 1000, 1st 350 signed. Linen. VG. *Dramatis.* $50/£31

DE ALARCON, PEDRO ANTONIO. The Three-Cornered Hat. Martin Armstrong (trans). L.A.: LEC, 1959. One of 1500. Signed by Roger Duvoisin (illus). 1/2 cl, dec bds. Fine in glassine, slipcase. *Pacific*.* $40/£25

DE AMICIS, EDMONDO. Morocco, Its People and Places. Maria Hornor Lansdale (trans). Phila, 1897. 2 vols. viii,253; viii,226pp; fldg map. Marbled eps. 1/2 calf, marbled bds (extrems rubbed, fr joint vol 1 split, spine tails sl rubbed, vol 1 spine head rubbed w/loss), gilt, morocco spine labels. *Edwards.* $120/£75

DE ANGELI, ARTHUR C. The Empty Barn. Phila: Westminster, 1966. 1st ed. 6.75x9.5. Marguerite de Angeli (illus). 60pp. VG in dj. *Cattermole.* $40/£25

DE ANGELI, MARGUERITE. Book of Nursery and Mother Goose Rhymes. GC: Doubleday, 1954. 4to. Fine in VG dj. *American Booksellers.* $50/£31

DE ANGELI, MARGUERITE. Bright April. GC: Doubleday, (1946). 1st ed. Sq 4to. 6 full-pg color plts. Grn cl. Good in full color dj (sl worn). *Reisler.* $85/£53

DE ANGELI, MARGUERITE. The Door in the Wall. GC: Junior Books, Doubleday, (1949). 1st ed. 8vo. 4pp full color illus (1 db-pg spread). Blue cl, silvered. Good in full color dj (sl edgeworn). *Reisler.* $85/£53

DE ANGELI, MARGUERITE. The Door in the Wall. Doubleday, 1949. 1st ed. 112pp. Blue cl. Good (ex-lib, rear pocket removed, lt stain 2 pp). Dj flaps tipped-in on eps. *Price.* $25/£16

DE ANGELI, MARGUERITE. The Door in the Wall. NY: Doubleday, 1949. 8vo. Fine in VG dj. *American Booksellers.* $40/£25

DE ANGELI, MARGUERITE. Elin's Amerika. GC: Junior Books, Doubleday, Doran, 1941. 1st ed. Sq 4to. Tan-gray dec cl w/red/blue/grn lettering. Good in full color dj (margins worn). *Reisler.* $85/£53

DE ANGELI, MARGUERITE. Henner's Lydia. NY: Doubleday, 1944. 8.5 sq. 68pp. Cl spine, pict bds. Good. *Cattermole.* $40/£25

DE ANGELI, MARGUERITE. Jared's Island. GC: Doubleday, (1947). 1st ed. 4to. Color frontis. Pumpkin-colored cl. Good in full color dj (margins lt worn). *Reisler.* $75/£47

DE ANGELI, MARGUERITE. Skippack School. GC: Junior Books, Doubleday, Doran, 1939. 1st ed. Sq 4to. Chocolate brn cl. Good in full color dj (edges lt rubbed). *Reisler.* $85/£53

DE ANGELI, MARGUERITE. Ted and Nina Have a Happy Rainy Day. GC: Doubleday, 1941. Early rpt. Lg 12mo. Good+. *American Booksellers.* $25/£16

DE ANGELI, MARGUERITE. Thee, Hannah. NY: Doubleday, 1941. 8vo. Good+ (ex-lib). *American Booksellers.* $25/£16

DE ANGELI, MARGUERITE. Turkey for Christmas. Phila: Westminster, 1949. 1st ed. 5x6.5. Unpaginated. Pict bds. (Sl shelfworn), o/w VG+ in dj (sl edgeworn). *My Bookhouse.* $52/£33

DE ANGELI, MARGUERITE. Up the Hill. GC: Junior Books, Doubleday, Doran, 1942. 1st ed. Sq 4to. Tan cl, grn lettering. Good in full color dj (margins lt worn). *Reisler.* $85/£53

DE ANGELI, MARGUERITE. Yonie Wondernose. NY: Doubleday, 1944. 1st ed. 9x10. 36pp. VG in dj. *Cattermole.* $75/£47

DE ANGELI, MARGUERITE. Yonie Wondernose. GC: Doubleday, Doran, 1944. 1st ed. 4to. 7 full-pg color plts. Cl-backed color pict bds. Good in full color dj. *Reisler.* $100/£63

DE ASSIS, JOACHIM MARIA MACHADO. Epitaph of a Small Winner. NY: Noonday, 1952. 1st US ed. NF in VG dj (price-clipped, fr spine-fld split). *Lame Duck.* $65/£41

DE ASSIS, JOAQUIM MARIA MACHADO. The Psychiatrist and Other Stories. Berkeley: Univ of CA, 1963. 1st ed. VG+ in VG+ dj. *Lame Duck.* $50/£31

DE ASSIS, JOAQUIM MARIA MACHADO. The Psychiatrist and Other Stories. London: Peter Owen, 1963. 1st British ed. (Eps, pg edges sl foxed), else NF in dj (lt foxed). *Lame Duck.* $55/£34

DE BACA, CARLOS C. Vincente Silva. N.p., 1968. Rpt. Fine in pict wraps. *Baade.* $35/£22

DE BACA, MANUEL C. Vicente Silva and His 40 Bandits. Washington: Libros Escogidos, 1947. 1st ed in English. One of 300 signed by trans & illus. Black paper-cvrd bds, red cl backstrip. NF (sl rubbed). Howes B10. *Harrington.* $125/£78

DE BALZAC, HONORE. The Alkahest. Routledge, 1887. Good (sl spotted; spine bumped; hinges, corners rubbed, cvrs sl mkd). *Tiger.* $32/£20

DE BALZAC, HONORE. Droll Stories. Jacques le Clercq (trans). NY: LEC, 1932. One of 1500 numbered sets, signed by W. A. Dwiggins (illus). 3 vols. Pict bds, gilt-dec cl spines. (Lt worn.) Slipcase. *Oinonen*.* $50/£31

DE BALZAC, HONORE. The Hidden Treasures, or, The Adventures of Maitre Cornelius. Kentfield: L-D Allen, 1953. One of 160. Plain, marbled bds. (Spine sl dull), else NF. *Pacific*.* $225/£141

DE BALZAC, HONORE. Old Goriot. LEC, 1948. Ltd to 1500 numbered, signed by Rene Ben Sussan (illus). Fine in slipcase. *Swann*.* $69/£43

DE BEAUFORT, J. M. Behind the German Veil. London, 1917. 1st Eng ed. (Sl spotted.) *Clearwater.* $88/£55

DE BEAUVOIR, SIMONE. The Blood of Others. NY: Knopf, 1948. 1st Amer ed. NF (edges lt soiled) in dj (rubbed, sunned, chipped). *Hermitage.* $95/£59

DE BECKER, J. E. The Nightless City, or The History of the Yoshiwara Yukwaku. Yokohama: Max Nossler, (1905). 4th ed. Pict red cl, gilt. (Corners bumped), else NF. *Pacific*.* $345/£216

DE BEER, G. R. Alps and Men. Edward Arnold, 1932. 1st ed. 16pp plts. (Spine sl faded, bds sl spotted, mkd, 2 sm bumps to edge of rear bd.) *Hollett.* $48/£30

DE BEER, G. R. Early Travellers in the Alps. Sidgwick & Jackson, 1930. 1st ed. 40 plts, 1 map. (Spine faded.) *Hollett.* $56/£35

DE BENAVIDES, ALONSO. The Memorial of Fray Alonso de Benavides. Chicago: Privately ptd, 1916. One of 300 numbered. (Newspaper clipping tipped to fep, cl title strip on spine as issued?), else NF. *Dumont.* $350/£219

DE BENAVIDES, ALONSO. The Memorial of Fray Alonso de Benavides. Albuquerque: Horn & Wallace, 1965. Rpt. NF. *Dumont.* $40/£25

DE BERNIERES, LOUIS. Senor Vivo and the Coca Lord. London, 1991. 1st UK ed. NF in NF dj. *Warren.* $50/£31

DE BIBIENA, JEAN-GALLI. Amorous Philandre. NY: Avon, (1948). 1st US ed. NF in pict wrappers. *Other Worlds.* $20/£13

DE BOSSCHERE, JEAN. Christmas Tales of Flanders. London: Heinemann, (1917). 1st ed. 4to. xii,144pp; 12 color plts, guards. Pict eps. Orange dec cl. VG in textured brn paper wrapper (sm nicks, sm triangular loss 1-inch deep to rear wrap at top edge), dj (internally strengthened). *Sotheran.* $360/£225

DE BOSSCHERE, JEAN. The City Curious. NY: Dodd, Mead, (1920). 1st US ed. 8vo. xii,178,(viii)ads; 8 color plts, guards. Pict eps. Pict yellow bds stamped in orange/black. VG (spine sl browned). *Sotheran.* $205/£128

DE BOSSCHERE, JEAN. The City Curious. London: Heinemann, (1920). 1st ed. 8 color plts, guards. Pict gray bds (spine sl browned). Very Nice. *Sotheran.* $240/£150

DE BOUGAINVILLE, LOUIS ANTOINE. A Voyage Round the World. Performed by Order of His Most Christian Majesty, in the Years 1766, 1767, 1768, and 1769. John Reinhold Forster (trans). London: J. Nourse, 1772. 1st ed in English. xxviii,476pp; 5 fldg charts, 1 fldg plt. Contemp calf, gilt, raised bands, red morocco title label. Fine (lt offset, last 2 blanks sl marginally dampstained; skillfully rebacked w/orig backstrip preserved). *Parmer.* $6,000/£3,750

DE BRUNHOFF, JEAN. A.B.C. of Babar. NY: Random House, (1936). 1st Amer ed. 8vo. Color illus bds (lt spotted, corners sl worn). *Reisler.* $300/£188

DE BRUNHOFF, JEAN. Babar and His Children. NY: Random House, (1938). 1st Amer ed. 4to. Pict bds (extrems worn). *Appelfeld.* $200/£125

DE BRUNHOFF, JEAN. Babar and His Children. Random House, 1938. Early ptg. 10.5x14.5. Unpaginated. Good (tiny pull tear fr edge, several pp have 2-inch tears; scuffed, loose; bd, spine edges worn w/corners rounded). *Price.* $75/£47

DE BRUNHOFF, JEAN. Babar and Zephir. NY: Random House, 1937. VG in glazed bds. *American Booksellers.* $30/£19

DE BRUNHOFF, JEAN. Babar the King. NY: H. Smith & R. Haas, 1935. 1st Amer ed. Folio. 47pp. Illus eps. Cl-backed illus bds. VG (ink inscrip). *Davidson.* $750/£469

DE BRUNHOFF, JEAN. Babar the King. London: Methuen, 1936. 1st Eng ed. 4to. Cl-backed color pict paper bds (sl rubbed, sl mkd, spine ends sl bumped). VG. *Ulysses.* $400/£250

DE BRUNHOFF, JEAN. Babar the King. NY: Random House, 1986. Folio. Fine in Fine dj. *American Booksellers.* $50/£31

DE BRUNHOFF, JEAN. The Story of Babar the Little Elephant. Merle S. Haas (trans). NY: Random House, (1933). 1st Amer ed. 4to. Pict bds (extrems worn). *Appelfeld.* $250/£156

DE BRUNHOFF, JEAN. Zephir's Holidays. Merle Haas (trans). NY: Random House, (1937). 1st Amer ed. Sm folio. Cl-backed color pict bds (edges rubbed). Full color pict dj (worn, spine lacks pieces). *Reisler.* $450/£281

DE BRUNHOFF, JEAN. Zephir's Holidays. Random House, 1937. Early ptg. 10.5x14.5. 40pp. Good (several pp w/1-inch tears, 1 pg lacks 1.5x2.5-inch piece from margin; hinge cracked, bd, spine edges worn w/corners rounded, 1-inch pull tear fr edge, edges scuffed). *Price.* $140/£88

DE BRUNHOFF, LAURENT. Babar Goes to America. M. Jean Craig (trans). London: Collins, (1969). 1st Eng ed. 4to. Full color pict bds. VG in full color pict dj. *Reisler.* $100/£63

DE BRUNHOFF, LAURENT. Babar the King. Merle Haas (trans). NY: Harrison Smith & Robert Haas, 1935. 1st Amer ed. Sm folio. Cl-backed yellow pict bds (edges lt rubbed). Color dj (dusty, lacks pieces). *Reisler.* $485/£303

DE BRUNHOFF, LAURENT. Babar's Book of Colour. London: Methuen Children's Books, 1985. 1st Eng ed. 4to. Full color pict bds. Fine. *Reisler.* $60/£38

DE BRUNHOFF, LAURENT. Babar's Cousin: That Rascal Arthur. Merle Haas (trans). NY: Random House, (1948). 1st Amer ed, 1st bk. Lg 4to. Cl-backed color pict bds (edges rubbed). Full color dj (spine worn). *Reisler.* $475/£297

DE BRUNOFF, JEAN. The Travels of Babar. NY: Random House, 1934. 8vo. Good +. *American Booksellers.* $30/£19

DE BUSBECQ, OGIER GHISELIN. Travels into Turkey. London: J. Robinson & W. Payne, 1744. 2nd Eng ed. 12mo. iv,290pp. Contemp speckled calf (spine rubbed, joints cracked). *Maggs.* $1,840/£1,150

DE CAMP, L. SPRAGUE and P. SCHUYLER MILLER. Genus Homo. Reading, PA: Fantasy, 1950. 1st ed. VG in dj (edges sl frayed, sl torn). *King.* $75/£47

DE CAMP, L. SPRAGUE and FLETCHER PRATT. The Incomplete Enchanter. NY: Henry Holt, (1941). 1st ed. NF in VG dj (chipped, flap tips clipped). *Pacific*.* $138/£86

DE CAMP, L. SPRAGUE. The Continent Makers and Other Tales of the Viagens. NY: Twayne, (1953). 1st ed. VG in dj (spine ends, extrems rubbed). *Pacific*.* $23/£14

DE CAMP, L. SPRAGUE. Divide and Rule. Reading: Fantasy, 1948. 1st ed. (Bkpl, bottom edge of text block stained), else Fine in Good + dj (edgeworn, soiled, sl chipped). *Other Worlds.* $40/£25

DE CAMP, L. SPRAGUE. An Elephant for Aristotle. GC: Doubleday, 1958. 1st ed. Fine in dj (sl worn, dust-soiled). *Levin.* $125/£78

DE CAMP, L. SPRAGUE. A Gun for Dinosaur and Other Imaginative Tales. GC: Doubleday, 1963. 1st ed. Fine in dj (sm closed tear, spine sl dknd, top edge worn). *Levin.* $200/£125

DE CAMP, L. SPRAGUE. The Tritonian Ring and Other Pusadian Tales. NY: Twayne Pub, (1953). 1st ed. VG in dj (fr panel lacks sm piece, spine sunned). *Pacific*.* $69/£43

DE CASTANEDA, PEDRO. The Journey of Francisco Vazquez de Coronado, 1540-1542.... George Parker Winship (ed). SF: Grabhorn, 1933. One of 500 ptd. Yellow-tan linen. NF (sm ink inscrip; spine head lt worn, foot lt rubbed; spine, top edge fr cvr sl dknd). *Argonaut.* $175/£109

DE CERVANTES. See CERVANTES

DE CHAIR, SOMERSET (trans). First Crusade. The Deeds of the Franks and Other Jerusalemites. London, 1945. One of 500 ptd. Gilt-dec bds, 1/4 vellum. *Cullen.* $100/£63

DE CHARLEVOIX, PIERRE-FRANCOIS-XAVIER. Letters to the Dutchess of Lesdiguieres; Giving an Account of a Voyage to Canada.... London: R. Baldwin, 1763. 2nd ed in English, w/new title. Sm 8vo. Lg fldg copperplt frontis map, xvi,384pp. Contemp full calf, gilt, leather spine label. (Lt browned, map edges sl aged; sl edgeworn, joints sl tender.) Cvrs VG. *Baltimore*.* $1,150/£719

DE CHASTELLUX, MARQUIS. Travels in North America in the Years 1780, 1781 and 1782. Chapel Hill: Univ of NC, (1963). 2 vols. (Spines sl faded), else VG in slipcase. *Pacific*.* $46/£29

DE CHIRICO, GIORGIO. Hebdomeros. NY: Four Seasons Book Soc, 1966. 1st ed in English. One of 500 numbered. (Name, address), o/w Fine in NF dj (sl staining verso). *Beasley.* $100/£63

DE CLAVIJO, GONZALEZ. Narrative of Embassy to Court of Timour, at Samarcand, 1403-6. London: Hakluyt Soc, 1859. 7,lvi,200pp; fldg map. Mod cl (ex-lib). *Adelson.* $70/£44

DE COCK, LILIANE (ed). Ansel Adams. (Hastings-on-Hudson): Morgan & Morgan, (1972). 1st ed. Signed by Adams. VG in dj (sm tear rear panel). *Pacific*.* $58/£36

DE COLANGE, LEO. Picturesque Russia and Greece. Boston, 1886. 144pp. Aeg. (Frontis detached, text between frontis/tp cracked, margins lt browned; cl sl soiled; corners, spine ends sl worn w/loss.) *Edwards.* $152/£95

DE CORONADO, FRANCISCO VAZQUEZ. The Journey of Francisco Vazques de Coronado, 1540-1542. George Parker Winship (ed). SF: Grabhorn, 1933. One of 500. VG (cvrs sl bowed, spine rubbed). Howes W572. *Pacific*.* $46/£29

DE COSTA, B. F. The Pre-Columbian Discovery of America. By the Northmen. Albany, NY: Joel Munsell's Sons, 1890. 2nd ed. 1890 signed presentation by 'the author.' 196pp; 2 maps. Black pebbled cl (spine foot sl frayed). *Karmiole.* $75/£47

DE CRESPIGNY, EYRE CH. A New London Flora. London, 1877. xxiv,179pp + 32pp pub's cat. (Sl shaken; sl rubbed, spine sl chipped.) *Edwards.* $24/£15

DE DEUX-PONTS, WILLIAM. My Campaigns in America: A Journal...1780-81. Samuel Abbott Green (trans). Boston: J.K. Wiggin & Wm. Parsons Lunt, 1868. 1st ed. One of 150. xvi,176pp. Paper spine label. (Edgeworn, corners sl bumped), else VG. Howes D291. *Brown.* $100/£63

DE FONTENELLE, BERNARD. A Plurality of Worlds. John Glanvill (trans). N.p.: Nonesuch, 1929. One of 1600 numbered. Teg, untrimmed. Limp vellum, gilt. Fine in slipcase (worn). *Glaser.* $150/£94

DE FREYTAS, NICHOLAS. The Expedition of Don Diego Dionisio de Penalosa. Albuquerque, 1964. VG in dj. *Dumont.* $30/£19

DE GAMEZ, TERA. The Yoke and the Star. Indianapolis: Bobbs Merrill, 1966. 1st ed. (Abrasion to fep from sticker removal), else Fine in VG + dj (rear cvr top edge chip). *Lame Duck.* $45/£28

DE GARDILANNE, GRATIANE and ELIZABETH WHITNEY MOFFATT. The National Costumes of Holland. London, 1932. Folio. 50 color plts, map. 2-tone cl. (Ex-lib, sm ink stamps all plts, bkpls; hinges reinforced; fore-edges sl dampstained; lt soiled, rubbed, spine lt faded.) *Edwards.* $200/£125

DE GARMO, W. B. Abdominal Hernia Its Diagnosis and Treatment. Phila, 1907. 1st ed. Red cl bds (top spine chipped). VG (inner rear hinge cracked; extrems sl worn). *Doctor's Library.* $100/£63

DE GAURY, GERALD. Arabia Phoenix. London/Sydney et al: Harrap, 1947. 2nd ptg. 64 half-tone plts, color ep maps. (Sl rubbed), o/w VG. *Worldwide.* $35/£22

DE GIAFFERRI, PAUL LOUIS. The History of French Masculine Costume.... NY, n.d. (1927). 119 color plts. (Rebound lib buckram; plts blind-stamped, one missing (?), one torn; cvrs worn.) *King.* $250/£156

DE GIAFFERRI, PAUL LOUIS. The History of the Feminine Costume of the World. (NY, 1926-1927.) 2 vols. 238 color plts. (Lib buckram; plts blind-stamped, many torn/tape-repaired; worn.) *King.* $400/£250

DE GIVRY, CHARLOTTE. Witchcraft Magic and Alchemy. J. Courtenay Locke (trans). London: George G. Harrap, 1931. Black cl, gilt. VG in dj (spine sl dknd). *Maggs.* $120/£75

DE GRAAFF, JAN and EDWARD HYAMS. Lilies. Funk & Wagnalls, 1968. 1st Amer ed. (Name, eps foxed), else VG in dj. *Fair Meadow.* $22/£14

DE GRAF, BELLE. Mrs. De Graf's Cookbook. SF: H.S. Crocker, 1922. Fine (recently rebound). *Perier.* $45/£28

DE GROOT, ROY ANDRIES. Feasts for All Seasons. Knopf, 1966. 1st ed. VG in VG dj. *Book Broker.* $20/£13

DE GRUNWALD, CONSTANTIN. Saints of Russia. Roger Capel (trans). London: Hutchinson, 1960. 1st ed. Color frontis. VG in dj (sl nicks). *Hollett.* $24/£15

DE HAAS, ARLINE. The Jazz Singer: A Story of Pathos and Laughter. NY: G&D, (1927). Photoplay ed. Frontis. Fine in VG dj (extrems lack sm piece, spine ends chipped). *Pacific*.* $46/£29

DE HAAS, ELSA. Antiquities of Bail, Origin and Historical Development in Criminal Cases to the Year 1275. NY: Columbia Univ, 1940. *Boswell.* $65/£41

DE HAVEN, TOM. Jersey Luck. NY: H&R, (1980). 1st ed. Fine in NF dj. *Agvent*. $35/£22

DE JONG, MEINDERT. Bells of the Harbor. Harper, 1941. 1st ed. Kurt Wiese (illus). 289pp. VG + in Good dj (soiled, worn). *Price*. $65/£41

DE KAY, CHARLES. Bird Gods. NY: A.S. Barnes, (1898). 1st ed, rev copy. Rev slip tipped to fr. Teg. Pict cl, gilt. (Spine foot sl rubbed), else NF. *Pacific**. $92/£58

DE KAY, JAMES. Zoology of New York, or the New-York Fauna. Albany: W. & A. White/J. Visscher, 1842. 1st ed. 102 litho plts. Orig gilt-stamped brn cl. (Spine ends chipped, corners rubbed), else VG. *Pacific**. $92/£58

DE KAY, JAMES. Zoology of New York. Part I. Mammalia. Albany, 1842. 33 hand-colored litho plts. 1/4 leather, marbled bds (rebound). *Kane**. $250/£156

DE KOCK, CHARLES PAUL. Works. Boston: Frederick J. Quinby, (1904). One of 1000 numbered sets. 25 vols. Teg, untrimmed. Red cl, ptd paper spine labels. Text Clean (sl aged, 1 vol w/dampstains to cvrs and partially to text; cl sl worn, spines sunned). *Baltimore**. $230/£144

DE LA BARCA, CALDERON. Life in Mexico. Howard T. and Marion Hall Fisher (ed). GC: Doubleday, 1966. 1st ed thus. NF in dj (chipped, worn). *Labordo*. $75/£47

DE LA CAMPA, MIGUEL. A Journal of Explorations Northward Along the Coast from Monterey in the Year 1775. John Galvin (ed). SF: John Howell Books, 1964. 1st ed. Floral-patterned cl, gilt. Fine. *Pacific**. $69/£43

DE LA CAMPA, MIGUEL. A Journal of Explorations Northward Along the Coast from Monterey in the Year 1775. John Galvin (ed). SF: John Howell, 1964. 1st ed. Ltd to 1000. Fine. *Book Market*. $75/£47

DE LA FONTAINE, JEAN. The Fables of Jean de la Fontaine. Joseph Auslander & Jacques Le Clercq (trans). NY: LEC, 1930. One of 1500 signed by Rudolph Ruzicka (illus). 2 vols. (Spines sl faded), else Fine in slipcase (rubbed). *Pharos*. $125/£78

DE LA FONTAINE, JEAN. The Fables. Heinemann, 1931. One of 525 numbered, signed by Stephen Gooden (illus) and Edward Marsh (trans). 2 vols. Royal 8vo. 26 Fine copper-engrs. Teg, rest uncut. 1/2 dk blue morocco (recently rebound), gilt. VG. *Sotheran*. $1,277/£798

DE LA FONTAINE, JEAN. Selected Fables. NY: Quadrangle, 1948. 1st ed. (Spine head sl bumped), else NF in dj. *Pacific**. $92/£58

DE LA FONTAINE. See also LA FONTAINE

DE LA MARE, WALTER. Alone. London: Ariel Poems, (1927). 1st Eng ed. Pict card wrappers (sl mkd). *Clearwater*. $40/£25

DE LA MARE, WALTER. The Captive and Other Poems. NY: Bowling Green, 1928. 1st ed. One of 600 ptd. Signed. Cl-backed gray bds. Fine. *Pacific**. $29/£18

DE LA MARE, WALTER. Down-Adown-Derry, a Book of Fairy Poems. London, 1922. (Backstrip sl frayed.) *Typographeum*. $75/£47

DE LA MARE, WALTER. Early One Morning in the Spring. Faber, 1935. 1st ed. One of 50 signed. 12 plts (incl frontis). Teg, rest untrimmed. White parchment, gilt. VG (cvrs sl spotted) in bd slipcase (sl cracked). *Blackwell's*. $424/£265

DE LA MARE, WALTER. Memoirs of a Midget. London: W. Collins Sons, (1921). 1st ed. One of 210. Signed. 1/2 cl, morocco spine label. (Sl offset from bkpl to fr pastedown), else NF. *Pacific**. $35/£22

DE LA MARE, WALTER. Mr. Bumps and His Monkey. Chicago: John C. Winston, 1942. 1st ed. Dorothy Lathrop (illus). 8vo. 67pp. VG in VG dj. *Davidson*. $120/£75

DE LA MARE, WALTER. O Lovely England. London, 1953. 1st ed. Fine in dj. *Petersfield*. $24/£15

DE LA MARE, WALTER. Peacock Pie, a Book of Rhymes. London: Constable, (1916). 1st ed illus thus. Sq 8vo. Color frontis, viii,178pp; 95 line dwgs by W. Heath Robinson. Pict eps. Dk grn cl, gilt, onlaid white cl label, gilt. (Half-title speckled, few places lt foxed; spine sl dknd.) *Sotheran*. $141/£88

DE LA MARE, WALTER. Peacock Pie. Chiswick for Constable, 1936. 1st ed w/these illus. 8vo. Jocelyn Crowe (illus). 112pp. Blue cl, gilt. (Edges rubbed), else VG. *Bookmark*. $40/£25

DE LA MARE, WALTER. The Return. W. Collins, 1922. One of 250 signed. Uncut. Holland-backed bds, morocco label. Good (backstrip dknd, sl rubbed). *Cox*. $40/£25

DE LA MARE, WALTER. Rhymes and Verses Collected Poems for Young People. Holt, 1947. 1st ed. 7x9.5. Elinore Blaisdell (illus). 344pp. Bluegrn cl, gilt. NF (bkpl) in Good dj (top edges worn, short tears; 1/2-inch chip). *Price*. $35/£22

DE LA MARE, WALTER. Self to Self. London: Ariel Poems, (1928). 1st Eng ed. Pict card wrappers (sl dusty). *Clearwater*. $40/£25

DE LA MARE, WALTER. Seven Short Stories. London: Faber & Faber, 1931. 1st ed deluxe. Ltd to 150 numbered, signed by de la Mare and John Nash (illus). 8vo. (xii),13-195pp; 8 color plts. Teg, rest uncut. Full cream parchment, gilt. Very Clean (spine sl yellowed, rubbed, cvrs sl mkd). *Sotheran*. $237/£148

DE LA METTRIE, JULIEN OFRAY. Man a Machine. Chicago: Open Court Pub, 1912. 1st ed in English. Frontis port. Dec ptd blue cl, gilt. *Gach*. $75/£47

DE LA MOTTE-FOUQUE, FREIDRICH H. K. Undine. NY: Doubleday, Page, 1919. Early Amer ed. Royal 8vo. (viii),136pp; 15 mtd color plts by Arthur Rackham, guards. Pict eps. Buckram-backed gray pict bds. NF. *Sotheran*. $205/£128

DE LA PARRA, TERESA. Mama Blanca's Souvenirs. Harriet de Onis (trans). Washington: Pan American Union, 1959. 1st ed in English. VG + in VG- dj. *Lame Duck*. $75/£47

DE LA PEROUSE, JEAN FRANCOIS GALAUP. A Voyage Round the World. (Amsterdam/NY, 1968.) 2 vols. *Swann**. $115/£72

DE LA ROCHE, MAZO. Ringing the Changes. London: Macmillan, 1957. 1st ed. Frontis, 7 dbl-sided plts. Grn buckram. Fine in dj (sl frayed). *Temple*. $14/£9

DE LABILLARDIERE, JACQUES JULIEN HOUTEN. Voyage in Search of La Perouse, Performed by Order of the Constituent Assembly, During the Years 1791, 1792, 1793, and 1794.... London: John Stockdale, 1800. 1st Eng ed. 4to. xviii,(2),(17)-476,65pp + (2)pp ads; copper-engr fldg chart, 45 copper-engr views, plts, etc. Period marbled bds (rebacked in mod calf), old leather spine label. VG + (lt foxing, offset, fldg chart w/repaired tear and sm unrepaired crease tear; corners sl worn). *Pacific**. $1,495/£934

DE LACOMBE, JEAN. A Compendium of the East. London: Golden Cockerel, 1937. 1st ed. One of 300 numbered. Sm folio. (Spine ends worn.) *Swann**. $201/£126

DE LAGUNA, F. The Archaeology of Cook Inlet, Alaska. Anchorage: AK Hist Soc, 1975. 2nd ed. 77 plts. VG (ex-lib) in wrapper. *Walcot*. $29/£18

DE LAMARTINE, A. Graziella. Ralph Wright (trans). London: Nonesuch, 1929. One of 1600 numbered. Teg, rest uncut. Red/grn patterned oatmeal cl, ptd paper spine label (sl rubbed). VG. *Maggs*. $104/£65

DE LATIL, PIERRE. Thinking by Machine. Y. M. Golla (trans). London, 1956. 1st Eng ed. Very Nice (stamp) in dj (sl nicked). *Clearwater*. $56/£35

DE LEE, JOSEPH B. The Principles and Practice of Obstetrics. Phila, 1929. 5th ed. Orig bl cl bds (extrems sl worn). VG (ex-lib). *Doctor's Library*. $50/£31

DE LEEUW, HENDRIK. Crossroads of the Buccaneers. Phila: Lippincott, 1937. Orange dec cl. VG. *American Booksellers*. $38/£24

DE LEIRIS, ALAIN. The Drawings of Edouard Manet. Berkeley, (1969). Sm folio. Dj. *Swann**. $126/£79

DE LESSEPS, JEAN BAPTISTE. Travels in Kamtschatka, During the Years 1787 and 1788. London, 1790. 2 vols. Contemp calf (skillfully rebacked; lacks map). *Swann**. $201/£126

DE LOCRE, ELIZABETH. Older Than Earth. Fanfrolico, 1930. 1st ed. One of 175 signed. Uncut. Good in cl-backed dec bds (lt rubbed). *Cox*. $45/£28

DE LONG, GEORGE W. M. The Voyage of the Jeannette. Emma De Long (ed). Boston: Houghton Mifflin, 1883. 1st ed. 2 vols. xii,x,911pp; 1 tinted litho plt, 2 steel-engr port plts, fldg map in rear pocket vol 1, 13 full-pg wood-engr illus. Orig pict dk brn cl, gilt. VG (few hinges cracked, fldg map partly separated along 1 fold, few pinholes at vol 2 fep corners; sl edgeworn). *Baltimore**. $160/£100

DE LONG, GEORGE WASHINGTON. The Voyage of the Jeannette. Boston, 1884. 2 vols. Fldg map laid in vol 1 rear pocket. (Vol 1 hinges cracked.) *Swann**. $172/£108

DE LONG, LIEUTENANT. Our Lost Explorers. Hartford: American Publishing, 1883. Silver-dec pict cl. (Fr hinge cracking; spine ends frayed, corners rubbed), else VG. *Pacific**. $63/£39

DE MADARIAGA, SALVADOR. Christopher Columbus. London: Hollis & Carter, 1949. 4 plts, 3 maps. VG in dj (sl worn). *Hollett*. $32/£20

DE MADARIAGA, SALVADOR. Morning Without Noon, Memoirs. Westmead, 1974. 1st ed. VG in dj. *Typographeum*. $15/£9

DE MARE, ERIC. Photography and Architecture. Architectural Press, 1961. 1st ed. (Eps sl spotted.) Dj (spotted, chipped). *Edwards*. $56/£35

DE MASSEY, ERNEST. A Frenchman in the Gold Rush. Marguerite Eyer Wilbur (trans). SF: CA Hist Soc, 1927. 1st ed. Gilt-lettered blue cl. Fine. *Pacific**. $86/£54

DE MAUPASSANT, GUY. Doctor Heraclius Gloss. Jeffrey E. Jeffrey (trans). Brentano's, 1923. One of 150. Uncut. Good in linen-backed bds, paper labels (rubbed, chipped). *Cox*. $61/£38

DE MAUPASSANT, GUY. Saint Anthony and Other Stories. Lafcadio Hearn (trans). NY: Albert & Charles Boni, 1924. VG (eps partly browned; spine tail, corners sl bumped) in dj (nicked, sl creased, spine faded). *Ulysses*. $240/£150

DE MAUPASSANT, GUY. The Tales of Guy de Maupassant. LEC, 1963. Ltd to 1500 numbered, signed by Gunther Bohmer (illus). Fine in slipcase. *Swann**. $34/£21

DE MILLE, AGNES. Lizzie Borden a Dance of Death. Boston: Little, Brown, (1968). 1st ed. Fine in dj. *Hermitage*. $40/£25

DE MILLE, AGNES. Lizzie Borden: A Dance of Death. Boston: Atlantic/LB, (1968). 1st ed. As New in dj. *Between The Covers*. $100/£63

DE MILLE, NELSON. By the Rivers of Babylon. NY: Harcourt Brace, 1978. 1st ed, 1st bk. Fine in Fine dj (spine ends wrinkled). *Unger*. $125/£78

DE MIRANDA, FRANCISCO. The New Democracy in America. Travels of Francisco de Miranda in the U.S. 1783-84. John S. Ezell (ed). Norman: Univ of OK, (1963). 1st ed. Blue cl. Fine in dj. *House*. $20/£13

DE MONTAIGNE, MICHEL. The Essays. NY: Aldus Ptrs, 1946. Signed by T.M. Cleland (illus). 4 vols. 1/2 white calf, gilt. Good set (spines sl faded) in box. *Appelfeld*. $250/£156

DE MONTAIGNE, MICHEL. Montaigne's Essays. London: Nonesuch, 1931. One of 1375 numbered sets. 2 vols. Full niger morocco (goat skin), raised bands, grn spine labels; grn, gilt-stamped oval onlay on cvrs. Good. *Karmiole*. $250/£156

DE MUSSET, ALFRED. The Complete Writings of.... NY: Privately ptd, 1908. One of 1000. 10 vols. Teg. 3/4 dk maroon morocco, gilt. (Spines sl sunned, ends rubbed), else VG. *Pacific**. $149/£93

DE MUSSET, PAUL. Mr. Wind and Madam Rain. Emily Makepeace (trans). NY: Putnam, 1904. 1st Bennett ed. Charles Bennett (illus). Red cl, gilt. (Soiled), else VG. *Pacific**. $69/£43

DE NAVARRO, ANTONIO. The Scottish Women's Hospital at the French Abbey of Royaumont. London, 1917. 1st Eng ed. (Sl mkd.) *Clearwater*. $40/£25

DE PACKMAN, ANA BEGUE. Early California Hospitality. Glendale: A.H. Clark, 1938. 1st ed. 3 plts. Orange cl. Fine in dj (chips to spine head, top of rear panel). *Harrington*. $140/£88

DE PACKMAN, ANA BEGUE. Early California Hospitality. 1953. VG. *Book Broker*. $25/£16

DE PACKMAN, ANA BEGUE. Early California Hospitality: The Cookery Customs of Spanish California, with Authentic Recipes.... Glendale: A.H. Clark, 1938. 1st ed. Prospectus laid in. Orange cl. NF. *Pacific**. $138/£86

DE PALOL, PEDRO and MAX HIRMER. Early Medieval Art in Spain. NY: Harry N. Abrams, (1966). 1st ed. 54 tipped-in color plts, 256 photo plts, map. Grn cl. Good in color illus dj. *Karmiole*. $150/£94

DE PAOLA, TOMIE. Giorgio's Village. London: Methuen Children's Books, 1982. 6 pull-down pop-ups. Fr cvrs tie together w/ribbon. VG. *Bookfinders*. $40/£25

DE PILES, ROGER. The Principles of Painting, Under the Headings of Anatomy, Attitude.... London: J. Osborn, 1743. 1st Eng ed. 8vo. Tp, xii+ 300pp; 2 engr plts. Contemp marbled eps. Mod full calf, restrained gilt/blind dec. Fine. *Europa*. $232/£145

DE PURUCKER, G. The Esoteric Tradition. CA: Theosophical Univ, 1935. 2 vols. Djs (lt soiled, ragged w/spine loss). *Edwards*. $72/£45

DE QUATREFAGES, A. The Pygmies. NY, 1895. 255pp. (Fr inner hinge cracked; cvrs worn, soiled.) *King*. $25/£16

DE QUEIROZ, ECA. The Relic. NY: Knopf, 1925. 1st ed. (Bkpl paper residue to fep), else NF in dj (shallow loss to extrems, spine panel faded, few sm dampstains). *Lame Duck*. $85/£53

DE QUILLE, DAN. Dan de Quille of the Big Bonanza. SF: Book Club of CA, 1980. One of 650 ptd. 3 ports, 5 pencil sketches. Orig prospectus in mailing envelope laid in. Linen-backed dec bds, gilt spine. Fine in plain dj. *Pacific**. $63/£39

DE QUILLE, DAN. History of the Big Bonanza. NY: Knopf, 1947. 2nd ptg this ed. Frontisport. Blue cl, gilt. (Gilt rubbed), o/w Fine. *Pacific**. $40/£25

DE QUILLE, DAN. A History of the Comstock Mines, Nevada and the Great Basin Region; Lake Tahoe and the High Sierras.... Virginia (City), NV: F. Boegle, (1889). 1st ed. 158pp (incl fr wrapper). (Contents dknd), else NF in ptd wrappers (rear corners sl chipped, spine ends lack sm pieces). Howes W711. *Pacific**. $173/£108

DE QUILLE, DAN. Snow-Shoe Thompson. L.A.: Dawson's Book Shop, 1954. 1st bk ed. One of 210 ptd. White paper spine over dec bds. VF. *Argonaut*. $450/£281

DE QUILLE, DAN. Washoe Rambles. Richard E. Lingenfelter (ed). L.A.: Dawson's Book Shop, 1963. Editor's ed of 50 ptd, specially bound. Signed by ed. 9 plts. Partly unopened. Full tan morocco, gilt. Fine. *Pacific**. $63/£39

DE QUINCEY, THOMAS. Confessions of an English Opium-Eater Together with Selections from the Autobiography. Edward Sackville-West (ed). London: Cresset, 1950. 1st ed thus. Orig buckram, gilt. VG in dj. *Hollett*. $32/£20

DE QUINCEY, THOMAS. A Diary Written in the Year 1803. NY, 1927. One of 1500 ptd. VG (cvrs sl faded). *Clearwater*. $88/£55

DE QUINCEY, THOMAS. Letters of the English Opium-Eater. Phila: John Pennington, 1843. Orig bds, paper label. Good (foxed; outer joint cracked, extrems sl rubbed). *Clearwater*. $160/£100

DE QUINCEY, THOMAS. The Posthumous Works of Thomas De Quincey. Alexander H. Japp (ed). Heinemann, 1891. 2 vols. Top edges red. Good (sl spotted; spines bumped, cvrs sl warped). *Tiger.* $54/£34

DE QUINCEY, THOMAS. Select Essays of Thomas de Quincey: Narrative and Imaginative. David Masson (ed). A&C Black, 1888. 2 vols. Frontisport vol 1. Good (inscrips; spines bumped, chipped, sunned, corners rubbed, rear cvr cl bubbled vol 1). *Tiger.* $51/£32

DE QUINCEY, THOMAS. The Works. Edinburgh: A&C Black, 1862-1863. 2nd ed. 15 vols. 8vo. Engr frontisport. Marbled eps; teg. 3/4 brn polished calf, marbled bds, raised bands, panelled spines, gilt, dbl leather labels. Fine set (sl rubbed). *Hartfield.* $895/£559

DE QUINCEY, THOMAS. The Works. Edinburgh: A&C Black, 1862-1871. Author's ed. 16 vols. Glazed blue close-grained cl, paper labels. (Sl foxed; shelfworn, few labels chipped.) *Marlborough.* $448/£280

DE QUINCEY, THOMAS. The Works. Edinburgh: A&C Black, 1862-1874. 3rd ed. 16 vols. 8vo. Engr port. Marbled eps, edges. Contemp 1/2 calf, gilt, marbled bds. VG set (lib label, stamps; sl rubbed, scuffed, nicely restored). *Hollett.* $720/£450

DE QUINCEY, THOMAS. The Works. Edinburgh: A&C Black, 1885. 4th ed. 16 vols. Marbled edges. 3/4 dk grn morocco, marbled bds, gilt, raised bands. (Bkpls; joints, spines rubbed), else VG set. *Pacific*.* $207/£129

DE RICCI, SEYMOUR. The Book Collector's Guide. Rosenbach, 1921. 1st ed. (Hinges shaken.) *Forest.* $40/£25

DE ROOS, JOHN FREDERICK FITZGERALD. Personal Narrative of Travels in the United States and Canada in 1826. London: William Harrison Ainsworth, 1827. 1st ed. Fldg frontis litho (sl foxed), xii,207pp; 11 litho plts, 2 maps. Uncut. Orig bds, ptd paper label (sl chipped). (Spine worn), else Fine. Howes D268. *Mott.* $400/£250

DE ROQUEFEUIL, CAMILLE. A Voyage Round the World, Between the Years 1816-1819. London: Richard Phillips, 1823. 1st Eng ed. 8vo. 112pp. Fine mod 1/2 calf, marbled bds, gilt. (Lt soil to tp, few other pp; few sl marginal chips, tears), else VG. Howes R438. *Pacific*.* $518/£324

DE RUPERT, A. E. D. Californians and Mormons. NY: John Wurtele Lovell, 1881. 166pp. VG (text dkng; binding sl rubbed). *Zubal*.* $45/£28

DE SAINT PIERRE, J. H. B. A Voyage to the Isle of France, the Isle of Bourbon, and the Cape of Good Hope. London, 1800. 334pp. 3/4 polished calf. (Ex-lib, flyleaf loose; corners bumped.) *Argosy.* $125/£78

DE SAINT-EXUPERY, ANTOINE. Le Petit Prince. NY: Reynal & Hitchcock, (1943). 1st ed. One of 260. Signed. 8.75x6.75. Fine in VG dj (soiled, rear panel, spine irregularly dknd). *Pacific*.* $2,070/£1,294

DE SAINT-EXUPERY, ANTOINE. The Little Prince. Katherine Woods (trans). NY: Reynal & Hitchcock, (1943). 1st ed, 5th ptg. Grn pict cl. VG in dj (sl nicked). *Houle.* $275/£172

DE SAINT-EXUPERY, ANTOINE. The Little Prince. Katherine Woods (trans). NY: Reynal & Hitchcock, (1943). 1st Amer ed. Rust-colored cl. VG (ink name; spine browned, ends sl rubbed) in dj (price-clipped, lt chipped, soiled, spine browned). *Heritage.* $350/£219

DE SAINT-EXUPERY, ANTOINE. Night-Flight. Stuart Gilbert (trans). London: Desmond Harmsworth, 1932. 1st Eng ed. VG (top edge dusty, prelims, edges, final pg of text spotted; spine faded, offset from spine-panel of dj) in dj (nicked, rubbed, chipped, mkd, sl torn, creased, spotted, dusty, edges browned). *Ulysses.* $680/£425

DE SAINT-EXUPERY, ANTOINE. Wind, Sand, and Stars. L. Galantiere (trans). NY: Reynal & Hitchcock, n.d (ca 1939). 1st Amer ed. (Spine ends sl rubbed), o/w VG in dj (sl soiled, worn; sm chips, tape repairs spine). *Virgo.* $80/£50

DE SAINT-EXUPERY, ANTOINE. The Wisdom of the Sands. Stuart Gilbert (trans). London: Hollis & Carter, 1952. 1st Eng ed. VG (edges, eps sl spotted; spine ends, corner sl bumped; 2 sm spots rear cvr) in dj (sl nicked, mkd, dusty, creased). *Ulysses.* $88/£55

DE SANDRAZ, COURTILZ. Memoirs of Monsieur D'Artagnan Captain-Lieutenant of the First Company of the King's Musketeers. Ralph Neville (trans). London, 1925. 3 vols. Frontisport. Uncut. (Lt soiled.) *Edwards.* $77/£48

DE TOCQUEVILLE, ALEXIS. Democracy in America. Henry Reeve (trans). NY: Adlard & Saunders, 1838. 1st Amer ed. xxx,464pp. Orig cl. (Internal foxing; recased w/cvrs refurbished), else VG. Howes T278. *Pacific*.* $173/£108

DE TOLDO, V. The Italian Art of Bookbinding. London: Batsford, 1925. 37 plts (last few plts edges sl flaking), of which 8 are color. Paper-cvrd bds (worn). *Maggs.* $48/£30

DE TOLNAY, C. The Drawings of Pieter Brueghel the Elder. London, 1952. Rev ed. (Sl worn.) *Ars Artis.* $96/£60

DE TOLNAY, C. Michelangelo. Princeton: Princeton Univ, (1975). NF in dj. *Turtle Island.* $50/£31

DE TOULOUSE-LAUTREC, HENRI. The Circus. NY, (1952). One of 1500 numbered. 39 color repros. Stiff wrappers. *Swann*.* $258/£161

DE TRAFFORD, HUMPHREY F. The Horses of the British Empire. London, (1907). 2 vols. Pub's 2-tone cl (sl worn, spines sl sunned, corners fraying). *Oinonen*.* $190/£119

DE VERE, AUBREY. The Foray of Queen Maeve. Kegan, Paul, Trench, 1882. 1st ed. Grn dec cl, gilt. (Eps, few pp sl foxed; spine sl dknd, sl rubbed), o/w VG + . *Any Amount.* $48/£30

DE VERE, AUBREY. May Carols. Longman, 1857. 1st ed. Pub's presentation stamp on tp. Grn blind dec cl, gilt. VG + (spine sunned, ends sl mkd, bumped, corners sl bruised). *Any Amount.* $88/£55

DE VERE, AUBREY. St. Thomas of Canterbury. Henry S. King, 1876. 1st ed. Grn dec cl, beveled bds, gilt. (2 sm ink mks to half-title verso; sl scratched, spine ends sl bumped), else NF. *Any Amount.* $72/£45

DE VINNE, THEODORE. Notable Printers of Italy During the Fifteenth Century. NY: De Vinne Press, 1910. 1st ed. Inscribed presentation on De Vinne's bkpl. Sm folio. 41 plts. Olive linen, gilt tan bds. (Lt rubbed.) *Karmiole.* $200/£125

DE VINNE, THEODORE. The Plantin-Moretus Museum: A Printer's Paradise. (SF): Grabhorn, 1929. One of 425 ptd. Color frontis. Cl-backed patterned bds, paper spine label. Fine. *Pacific*.* $127/£79

DE VINNE, THEODORE. The Plantinmoretus Museum. SF: Grabhorn, 1929. One of 425. Prospectus laid in. Bound in vellum, slipcase. Fine. *Smith.* $60/£38

DE VOTO, BERNARD. Across the Wide Missouri. Boston: Houghton Mifflin, 1947. Tan cl. NF in color pict dj. *House.* $25/£16

DE VOTO, BERNARD. Across the Wide Missouri. Boston, 1947. 1st ed. Ltd to 265 signed. Full red buckram. Fine in slipcase (soiled, lt worn). Howes D296. *Truepenny.* $300/£188

DE VOTO, BERNARD. Mark Twain's America. Boston: Little, Brown, 1932. 1st ed. 13 woodcuts. Blue cl. (Spine foot sl faded), else Fine in pict dj. *Argonaut.* $100/£63

DE VOTO, BERNARD. The Year of Decision, 1846. Boston: Little, Brown, 1943. 1st ed. (Few sm fade spots to spine), else Fine in pict dj (sl chipped). *Argonaut.* $75/£47

DE VRIES, HUGO. Species and Varieties. Chicago/London: Open Court/Kegan Paul, Trench, Trunber, 1906. 2nd ed, corrected, rev. Frontisport. Teg. Red cl, leather spine label. (Lt waterstain to outer edges), else VG. *Weber.* $125/£78

DE VRIES, LEONARD (ed). Flowers of Delight. Pantheon, 1965. 7.75x10.5. 230pp. Fine in Good+ (long taped tear). *Price.* $30/£19

DE VRIES, PETER and JOSEPH FIELDS. The Tunnel of Love. Boston: LB, (1957). 1st ed. VF in Fine dj (sl rubbed, 1/16 inch short). *Between The Covers.* $125/£78

DE VRIES, PETER. But Who Wakes the Bugler? Boston, 1940. 1st ed, 1st bk. VG+ in VG dj. *Warren.* $150/£94

DE VRIES, PETER. Comfort Me with Apples. Boston, 1956. 1st ed. VG+ in VG+ dj. *Warren.* $50/£31

DE WAAL, RONALD B. The World Bibliography of Sherlock Holmes and Dr. Watson. Boston: NYGS, 1974. 1st ed. Issued w/o dj. Fine in houndstooth slipcase (sm bump). *Janus.* $85/£53

DE WINDT, HARRY. Through the Gold-Fields of Alaska to Bering Straits. C&W, 1898. 1st ed. viii,312pp + 32pp ads dated Jan 1898; 32 plts, lg fldg map. (Mkd, bumped.) *Hollett.* $256/£160

DE WORMS, PERCY. Perkins Bacon Records. John Easton and Arnold Strange (eds). Royal Philatelic Soc, 1953. 2 vols. 50 plts. Teg. Djs (sl soiled, chipped). *Edwards.* $240/£150

DEACON, RENEE M. Bernard Shaw as Artist-Philosopher. London: A.C. Fifield, 1910. 1st ed. Uncut, unopened. (1/2-title head lt dampstained.) Pink ptd wraps (edges dusty). *Dramatis.* $50/£31

DEAKIN, EDWIN. The Twenty-One Missions of California. Berkeley: (Edwin Deakin), 1899. 1st ed. 6 prelim, 2 final pp + 21 full-pg repros w/guards. Blue-ptd gray bds (worn, stained). *Dawson.* $175/£109

Dean's Pop-Up Book of Animals. A Playtime Pop-Up Book. London: Deans, 1979. 3 dbl-pg pop-ups. Glazed pict bds. VG. *Bookfinders.* $30/£19

Dean's Pop-Up Book of Motor Cars. London: Dean & Son, 1961. 3 dbl-pg pop-ups. Glazed pict bds. VG. *Bookfinders.* $25/£16

DEAN, BASHFORD. Catalogue of European Court Swords and Hunting Swords. NY, 1929. Sm folio. 1/2 cl. (Bkpl.) *Swann*.* $201/£126

DEAN, BASHFORD. Notes on Arms and Armour. NY: MMA, 1916. Blue cl. Fine. *Glenn.* $30/£19

DEAN, PHILLIP HAYES. Paul Robeson. GC: Nelson Doubleday, (1978). Book Club ptg. Inscribed presentation, signed in full. NF in dj. *Reese.* $35/£22

DEAN, S. F. X. Nantucket Soap Opera. Athenium, 1987. 1st ed. Fine in dj. *Murder.* $30/£19

DEAN, S. F. X. Such Pretty Toys. Walker, 1982. 1st ed. Fine in dj. *Murder.* $37/£23

DEANE, RUTH and L. L. WEEDON. Happy Families and Their Tales. London/NY: Ernest Nister/E.P. Dutton, (1898). Obl 4to. (13)ff; 5 stories have full-pg color pop-up scenes. VF in illus cl-backed bds. *Bromer.* $1,350/£844

DEARBORN, HENRY. Revolutionary War Journals...1775-1783. Lloyd A. Brown and Howard H. Peckham (eds). Chicago: Caxton Club, 1939. 1st ed. One of 350 ptd. Signed Christmas 1939 presentation. Frontisport, 5 maps, facs. Teg, untrimmed, partly unopened. Tan/lt blue cl, gilt-lettered crimson leather spine label. (Spine sunned, spotted, label sl chipped.) Plain black bd slipcase (sl worn). *Baltimore*.* $55/£34

DEARMER, MABEL. The Cockyolly Bird. London: Hodder & Stoughton, 1914. 1st ed. 4to. (xiv),221; 10 mtd color plts. Grn pict cl (sl rubbed). Very Clean. *Sotheran.* $477/£298

DEASY, H.H.P. In Tibet and Chinese Turkestan. London, 1901. Teg. Grn buckram (rubbed, sl dampsoiled). *Petersfield.* $160/£100

DEAVER, JOHN B. Surgical Anatomy of the Human Body. Phila: P. Blakiston's Son, (1926-1927). 2nd ed. 3 vols. 481 plts. *Weber.* $100/£63

DeBARTHE, JOE. Life and Adventures of Frank Grouard. Edgar I. Stewart (ed). Norman: Univ of OK, (1958). Dj (lt edgeworn). *Dawson.* $45/£28

DEBO, ANGIE (ed). The Cowman's Southwest, Being the Reminiscences of Oliver Nelson...1878-1893. Glendale, CA: A.H. Clark, 1953. 1st ed. Red cl. VF. *Labordo.* $250/£156

DEBO, ANGIE. Prairie City. NY, 1944. 1st ed. Fine in dj (sl chipped). *Baade.* $37/£23

DEBO, ANGIE. The Rise and Fall of the Choctaw Republic. Norman, 1967. (Edges lt foxed), else Good in dj. *Dumont.* $35/£22

Debrett's Correct Peerage of England, Scotland and Ireland.... London: F. & C. Rivington, 1806. Engr frontis, vi,1011pp; 104pp engrs. Contemp tree calf, gilt. VG (sig, spotted, tp browned; spine ends chipped, upper hinge cracked). *Hollett.* $96/£60

DEBUS, ALLEN G. The English Paracelsians. NY: Franklin Watts, (1966). 1st Amer ed. 6 plts. Fine in dj. *Glaser.* $25/£16

DEBUSSY, CLAUDE. Monsieur Croche the Dilettante Hater. Noel Douglas, 1927. 1st Eng ed. Frontis. VG. *Hollett.* $56/£35

DeCARAVA, ROY. Roy DeCarava: Photographs. James Allinder (ed). Carmel: The Friends of Photography, 1981. Members ed. 82 full-pg b/w plts. (Sm spots of edgewear), else Fine in pict stiff wrappers. *Cahan.* $60/£38

DECKER, PETER. Catalogues of Americana. Austin, 1979. Rpt of 29 cats. 3 vols. (Vol 1 bds spotted), else VG. *Dumont.* $145/£91

DECKER, PETER. A Descriptive Checklist of Western Americana. NY, 1960. Frontis. Good (shelfworn). *Dumont.* $100/£63

DECKER, PETER. The Diaries of.... H.S. Giffen (ed). Georgetown, CA: Talisman, 1966. 1st ed. Fine in dj. *Wantagh.* $65/£41

DECOEN, J. Vemeer-Van Meegeren. Back to the Truth. Two Genuine Vermeers. Rotterdam, 1951. 150plts. *Ars Artis.* $48/£30

Decorative Work of Robert and James Adam. London: Batsford, n.d. c.(1900). 30 plts. (Lib ink stamp tp verso, bkpl; sl rubbed, loss to corners, soiling.) *Edwards.* $120/£75

DEDERA, DON. A Little War of Our Own. Flagstaff, 1988. 2nd ptg. Map. VG in dj (sl worn). *Dumont.* $55/£34

DEE, MINNIE ROOF. From Oxcart to Airplane: A Biography of George H. Hines. Portland: Binfords & Mort, (1939). 1st ed. VG in dj. *Perier.* $30/£19

DEEPING, WARWICK. No Hero—This. NY: Knopf, 1936. 1st US ed. Dec grn cl. (Ep gutters tanned), else Nice in VG dj (sm nicks, tears). *Reese.* $30/£19

DEEPING, WARWICK. Seven Men Came Back. NY: Knopf, 1934. 1st US ed. Grn cl. (Top edges sl sunned), o/w Fine in dj. *Reese.* $45/£28

DEFOE, DANIEL. The Fortunes and Misfortunes of the Famous Moll Flanders. London: John Lane, Bodley Head, 1929. 16 b/w plts by John Austen. Pict eps. VG (eps partly browned, edges sl spotted; spine ends sl bumped) in dj (sl rubbed, nicked, creased). *Ulysses.* $120/£75

DEFOE, DANIEL. The Fortunes and Misfortunes of the Famous Moll Flanders. LEC, 1954. Ltd to 1500 numbered, signed by Reginald Marsh (illus). Fine in slipcase. *Swann*.* $201/£126

DEFOE, DANIEL. A Journal of the Plague Year. Bloomfield, CT: LEC, 1968. One of 1500. Signed by Domenico Gnoli (illus). Dec burlap, leather spine label. Fine in glassine, slipcase. *Pacific*.* $46/£29

DEFOE, DANIEL. A Journal of the Plague Year. LEC, 1968. 1st ed thus. One of 1500 signed by Gnoli (illus). Fine in glassine dj, slipcase. *Fine Books.* $70/£44

DEFOE, DANIEL. The Life and Adventures of Robinson Crusoe of York, Mariner. London: John Major, 1831. 1st ed thus. George Cruikshank (illus). 2 vols. (viii),(i),ii-xv,(xvi),(1),2-434, 1-6; (iv),(1),2-406,(407-408)pp. Teg. NF in 3/4 lt brn morocco, marbled bds by Riviere. *Vandoros.* $400/£250

DEFOE, DANIEL. Robinson Crusoe. NY: Cosmopolitan, 1920. 4to. N.C. Wyeth (illus). Good. *American Booksellers.* $100/£63

DEFOE, DANIEL. Robinson Crusoe. NY: Cosmopolitan Book Corp, 1920. 1st ed. 4to. 13 full-pg color plts by N. C. Wyeth. Teg. Blue cl, color paste label (lt rubbed). *Reisler.* $200/£125

DEFOE, DANIEL. Robinson Crusoe. NY: Cosmopolitan Book Corp, 1920. 1st ed thus. Sm 4to. 13 full-pg color illus by N. C. Wyeth. Dk blue cl, lg color pict label fr cvr. Fine in tissue, orig box. *Houle.* $650/£406

DEFOE, DANIEL. Robinson Crusoe. LEC, 1930. Ltd to 1500 numbered, signed by Edward A. Wilson (illus). Fine in slipcase. *Swann*.* $103/£64

DEFOE, DANIEL. Robinson Crusoe. London: Raphael Tuck & Sons, n.d. (193?). Sm 8vo. Howard Davie & R.B. Ogle (illus). Color frontis, 152 + 6pp ads; dbl-pg pop-up. Glazed pict bds. VG-. *Bookfinders.* $100/£63

DEGAS, HILAIRE GERMAIN EDGAR. Degas Letters. Marcel Guerin (ed). Oxford: Bruno Cassirer, (1947). 1st ed in English. VG in dj. *Turtle Island.* $35/£22

DeGENLIS, MADAME. New Moral Tales. NY: Wilder & Campbell, 1825. 1st US ed. 233pp. Uncut. Orange paper-cvrd bds, label (chipped). (Lt foxed; lacks some spine.) *Second Life.* $150/£94

DeGOLYER, E. and HAROLD VANCE. Bibliography of the Petroleum Industry. College Station, TX, 1944. (Shelfworn, spine faded), else Good. *Dumont.* $175/£109

DeHASS, FRANK S. Buried Cities Recovered; or, Explorations in Bible Lands.... Phila/Boston: Bradley/Gurnsey, 1883. 5th ed. 525pp. Good (rebound in lib cl, lib # on spine). *Worldwide.* $32/£20

DEHN, ADOLF and LAWRENCE BARRETT. How to Draw and Print Lithographs. NY: Amer Artists Group, (1950). Fine in dj. *Truepenny.* $45/£28

DEHN, PAUL. Quake, Quake, Quake. NY: S&S, 1961. 1st ed. Edward Gorey (illus). 109pp. Fine in dj (1-inch chip top fr). *Price.* $95/£59

DEIGHTON, LEN. Billion Dollar Brain. Cape, 1966. 1st UK ed. NF in VG metallic dj. *Williams.* $51/£32

DEIGHTON, LEN. An Expensive Place to Die. Cape, 1967. 1st UK ed. Complete w/the 'Top Secret' file. Fine in dj (price-clipped). *Williams.* $77/£48

DEIGHTON, LEN. Fighter. Cape, 1977. 1st UK ed. Signed. VG + in dj. *Williams.* $48/£30

DEIGHTON, LEN. Funeral in Berlin. NY: Putnam, (1965). 1st Amer ed. Fine in dj. *Pacific*.* $35/£22

DEIGHTON, LEN. Len Deighton's Action Cook Book. Penguin, 1967. 1st Penguin ed. Signed. VG in wrappers (sl rubbed). *Williams.* $26/£16

DEIGHTON, LEN. Only When I Larf. Privately ptd, 1967. 1st ed. One of 150 signed. NF in ring-binder as issued. *Williams.* $1,520/£950

DEIGHTON, LEN. Spy Story. Cape, 1974. 1st UK ed. Fine in Fine dj. *Martin.* $19/£12

DEIGHTON, LEN. Violent Ward. Scorpion, 1993. One of 130 numbered, signed. Fine in special binding. *Williams.* $88/£55

DEIGHTON, LEN. Yesterday's Spy. Cape, 1975. 1st UK ed. Fine in dj. *Williams.* $26/£16

DEIGHTON, LEN. Yesterday's Spy. Cape, 1975. 1st UK ed. Signed. VG in dj. *Williams.* $56/£35

DEIHL, EDNA GROFF. The Little Kitten That Would Not Wash Its Face. NY: Sam'l Gabriel Sons, (1922). 4to. Color pict bds (edges, spine chipped). *Reisler.* $75/£47

DeKAY, JAMES. Zoology of New-York. Pt. II. Birds. Albany: Carroll and Cook, 1844. 1st ed. Thick 4to. 141 hand-colored plts. Teg. 3/4 old black morocco over marbled bds. Fine. *Appelfeld.* $750/£469

DeKAY, JAMES. Zoology of New-York. Pt. V & VI. Mollusca (Shells) and Crustacea. Albany: Carroll and Cook, 1843. 1st ed. 2 vols in 1. 53 hand-colored plts. Teg. 3/4 black morocco over marbled bds. Fine. *Appelfeld.* $450/£281

DEL BUONO, ORESTE and UMBERTO ECO. The Bond Affair. London: Macdonald, (1966). 1st ed in English. NF in dj. *Pacific*.* $29/£18

DEL FIORENTINO, DANTE. Immortal Bohemian. Gollancz, 1952. VG in dj. *Hollett.* $32/£20

DEL VECCHIO, JOHN M. The 13th Valley. NY: Bantam Books, 1982. 1st ed. Fine in dj. *Associates.* $50/£31

DELACORTA. Diva. NY: Summit, 1983. 1st US ed. Fine in Fine dj. *Pettler.* $20/£13

DELACROIX, EUGENE. Selected Letters 1813-1863. Jean Stewart (trans). NY, 1971. 1st US ed. Frontis port. *Edwards.* $38/£24

DELAFIELD, E. M. Diary of a Provincial Lady. London: Macmillan, 1930. 1st Eng ed. 22 full-pg b/w dwgs. Good (fep sl creased, rep partly browned; top edge dusty, sl pitted; spine ends, corners sl rubbed, cvrs patchily faded, worming to rear joint) in dj (nicked, rubbed, dusty, sl mkd, browned). *Ulysses.* $120/£75

DELAFIELD, JOHN, JR. An Inquiry into the Origin of the Antiquities of America. NY: Colt, Burgess, 1839. 1st ed. Lg fldg frontis (wrinkled, w/added folds) ptd on tissue, 142pp; 10 litho plts (5 w/contemp hand-coloring). Orig blind brn cl, gilt. (Lt foxed, sl dampstain margin of few pp; ex-lib, paper spine label remnants, bkpl; ends frayed, nicked.) Cvrs Good. Howes D226. *Baltimore*.* $210/£131

DELAFIELD, R. Report on the Art of War in Europe in 1854, 1855, and 1856. Washington: Bowman, 1861. 1st ed. Hand-colored tp, xxii,277pp; 24 plts (14 hand-colored, 4 fldg), 52 maps, plans (11 fldg). Orig cl. (Dampstained, foxed; rebacked), o/w VG. *Worldwide.* $200/£125

DELAND, MARGARET. The Kays. NY: Harper, 1926. 1st ed. Fine (bkpl) in dj (sl worn, price-clipped). *Second Life.* $45/£28

DELANEY, JOHN. The Blue Devils in Italy. Washington, 1947. 1st ed. VG. *Clark.* $75/£47

DELANEY, MATILDA J. SAGER. The Whitman Massacre. Spokane, 1920. Wraps. (Ink name; lt soiled), else VG. Laid in fldg case. Howes D22. *Dumont.* $150/£94

DELANO, ALONZO. Across the Plains and Among the Diggings. NY: Wilson-Erickson, 1936. Red cl, gilt. VG. Howes D230. *House.* $55/£34

DELANO, ALONZO. Alonzo Delano's California Correspondence...1849-1852. Irving McKee (ed). Sacramento Book Collectors Club, 1952. One of 310 ptd. Buckram, gilt. Fine. *Pacific*.* $40/£25

DELANO, ALONZO. California Correspondence.... Irving McKee (ed). Sacramento: Sacramento Book Collectors Club, 1952. 1st ed in bk form. One of 310 (298 for sale) ptd. 1 plt, 1 map. Orange-brn cl, gilt. VF. *Argonaut.* $90/£56

DELANO, ALONZO. Life on the Plains and Among the Diggings. Auburn/Buffalo: Miller, Orton & Mulligan, 1854. 1st ed. Frontis, 384pp; 3 full-pg wood-engr illus. Orig brn cl (recently rebacked w/top half of spine laid down; worn, frayed, spotted w/sm stains). Text Good (sl foxed, sm stains, 1 leaf partly torn). Howes D230. *Baltimore*.* $90/£56

DELANO, JUDAH. The Washington Directory. Washington, 1822. Pub's roan-backed letterpress bds. (Browned throughout; fr cvr loose, extrems rubbed.) Howes D234. *Swann*.* $316/£198

DELAUNAY, CHARLES. Hot Discography: 1938 Edition. NY: Commodore Record Co, 1943. Blue buckram (corners sl rubbed), gilt. *Petrilla.* $50/£31

DELAUNAY, SONIA. Alphabet. NY: Thomas Y. Crowell, 1972. 1st Amer ed. Sm folio. Color bds. Good in color dj. *Reisler.* $50/£31

DELAVAN, JAMES. Notes on California and the Placer. Oakland, CA: Biobooks, 1956. Ltd to 700. Sm folio. *Heinoldt.* $30/£19

DeLESPINASSE, MLLE. Letters of.... Katharine Prescott Wormeley (trans). Boston: Hardy, Pratt, 1903. Untrimmed. Red cl, gilt. VG. *Second Life.* $35/£22

DELESSERT, ETIENNE. How the Mouse Was Hit on the Head. NY: Doubleday, 1971. 1st ed. 8.75x11.25. 32pp. Silver cl. Fine in dj. *Cattermole.* $30/£19

DELEVOY, ROBERT L. Dimensions of the 20th Century 1900-1945. London: Skira, 1965. Dj, cl slipcase as issued. *Edwards.* $56/£35

DELIEB, ERIC. The Great Silver Manufactory. Matthew Boulton and the Birmingham Silversmiths, 1760-1790. London, 1971. (Lib ink stamp fep.) Dj. *Edwards.* $40/£25

DeLILLO, DON. End Zone. Boston: Houghton Mifflin, 1972. 1st ed. NF in VG dj. *Pettler.* $50/£31

DeLILLO, DON. End Zone. Boston: HMC, 1972. 1st ed. Fine in NF dj (spine sl creased, nicked). *Unger.* $150/£94

DeLILLO, DON. Great Jones Street. Boston: Houghton Mifflin, 1973. 1st ed. Fine in VG+ dj. *Pettler.* $50/£31

DeLILLO, DON. Great Jones Street. Deutsch, 1974. 1st UK ed. NF in dj. *Williams.* $40/£25

DeLILLO, DON. Mao II. NY, 1991. Advance reading copy. Signed. Fine in glossy wraps. *Warren.* $40/£25

DeLILLO, DON. Running Dog. London, 1978. 1st UK ed. NF in NF dj (sl rubbed). *Warren.* $75/£47

DELISLE, FRANCOISE. Friendship's Odyssey. London: Heinemann, 1946. 1st ed. Frontis port. VG in dj. *Hollett.* $40/£25

DELL, FLOYD. Love in the Machine Age. NY: Farrar, 1930. 1st ed. NF (stamp, sig, bkpl) in Good dj (lg chip fr panel, spine #s). *Beasley.* $75/£47

DELL, FLOYD. Runaway. NY: Doran, 1925. 1st ed. Fine in Fine dj. *Beasley.* $150/£94

DELLENBAUGH, FREDERICK S. A Canyon Voyage. New Haven, 1926. 3 fldg maps. (Extrems lt worn, spotted.) Internally VG. *Dumont.* $65/£41

DELLENBAUGH, FREDERICK S. The Romance of the Colorado River. NY: Knickerbocker, 1903. Frontis. Teg. (Name), o/w VG+. *Five Quail.* $95/£59

DELLENBAUGH, FREDERICK S. The Romance of the Colorado River. NY, 1909. Frontis. (Name), o/w VG+. *Five Quail.* $85/£53

DELLENBAUGH, FREDERICK S. The Romance of the Colorado River. Time-Life, 1982. Rpt of 1st ed. Frontis. Gilt edges, page-mkr ribbon. Full leather. VG+. *Five Quail.* $17/£11

DELLER, J. The Art of Letterpress Machining. Pitman, 1951. VG in dj. *Moss.* $19/£12

DELMONT, J. Catching Wild Beasts Alive. NY: Stokes, 1931. 1st ed. NF. *Mikesh.* $32/£20

DELORIA, VINE. We Talk, You Listen. NY, 1970. 1st ed. Signed. NF in dj. *Dumont.* $45/£28

DELTEIL, JOSEPH. The Poilus: An Epic. Jacques LeClercq (trans). NY: Minton, Balch, 1927. 1st ed in English. Gilt lt blue cl. (Bkpl, ink note, sig), o/w VG in pict dj (top edge sl frayed). *Reese.* $60/£38

DELVAUX, PAUL. The Drawings. (NY, 1968.) Dj (few chips, tears at edges). *Swann*.* $57/£36

DEMARINIS, RICK. Jack and Jill. NY: E.P. Dutton, (1979). 1st ed. As New in dj (sl crease to fr/rear flaps). *Bernard.* $20/£13

DEMARINIS, RICK. Scimitar. NY: E.P. Dutton, (1977). 1st ed. As New in dj. *Bernard.* $40/£25

DEMIDOFF, E. After Wild Sheep in the Altai and Mongolia. London: Rowland Ward, 1900. Lg 8vo. Map, color frontis. (Frontis, tp margins sl soiled; faded, fr cvr damp-mkd.) *Petersfield.* $672/£420

DEMIDOFF, E. Hunting Trips in the Caucasus. London: Rowland Ward, 1898. 8vo. Fldg map inserted into rear pastedown. Blue cl (spine faded, extrems bumped). *Christie's*.* $811/£507

DEMIJOHN, T. (Pseud of Thomas Disch and John Sladek.) Black Alice. NY, 1968. 1st ed. Dj. *Swann*.* $115/£72

DEMIJOHN, T. (Pseud of Thomas Disch and John Sladek.) Black Alice. GC: Doubleday, 1968. True 1st ed. Signed by Thomas Disch. NF (sig; top edge stained) in Fine dj. *Agvent.* $200/£125

DEMING, THERESE O. Little Braves. NY: Frederick A. Stokes, 1929. 1st ed. Obl 4to. 9 full-pg color plts by Edwin Willard Deming. Grn pict cl. Good in pict dj (edgeworn). *Reisler.* $175/£109

DEMORNEX, JACQUELINE. Madeleine Vionnet. (NY, 1991.) Folio. Dj. *Swann*.* $126/£79

DEMPSEY, STANLEY and JAMES E. FELL, JR. Mining the Summit. Norman: Univ of OK, (1986). 1st ed. VG in dj. *Lien.* $20/£13

DEMUS, OTTO. The Mosaics of San Marco in Venice. Chicago, (1984). 4 vols. (Lt worn.) Slipcase. *Oinonen*.* $110/£69

DEMUS, OTTO. The Mosaics of San Marco in Venice. Chicago, 1984. 4 vols. Pict slipcase. *Swann*.* $345/£216

DEMUS, OTTO. Romanesque Mural Painting. London, Thames & Hudson, 1970. 126 tipped-in color illus. VF in color dj. *Europa.* $160/£100

DEMUTH, NORMAN. Cesar Franck. Dennis Dobson, 1949. 1st ed. 9 plts. VG in dj. *Hollett.* $40/£25

DENDY, WALTER COOPER. The Philosophy of Mystery. London: Longman, Orme, Brown et al, 1841. 1st ed. xii,443pp. (Shelfworn, spine head sl frayed), else VG. *Brown.* $100/£63

DENHAM, MAJOR et al. Narrative of Travels and Discoveries in Northern and Central Africa, in the Years 1822, 1823, and 1824. Boston: Cummings, Hillard, 1826. 1st US ed. lxiv,255,104,112pp; 1 plt, 3 fldg maps. Orig bds. (Ex-lib, sl foxed; rebacked in cl), o/w VG. *Worldwide.* $175/£109

DENHAM, MAJOR et al. Narrative of Travels and Discoveries in Northern and Central Africa, in the Years 1822, 1823, and 1824. John Murray, 1826. 2nd ed. 2 vols. 8vo. lxxxviii,321; iv,413,(i)+(viii)ads; 3 fldg maps, 12 engr plts (1 hand-colored). All edges uncut. Orig brn paper bds, paper labels. VG (spines worn, loss to spine ends vol 1, labels cracked). *Sotheran.* $720/£450

DENHARDT, ROBERT MOORMAN. The Horse of the Americas. Norman: Univ of OK, 1947. 1st ed. VG (bkpl, sl faded, chipped). *Dumont.* $75/£47

DENHARDT, ROBERT MOORMAN. The Horse of the Americas. Norman, 1948. 2nd ptg. VG (name) in dj. *Woolson.* $30/£19

DENHARDT, ROBERT MOORMAN. The King Ranch Quarter Horses. Norman: Univ of OK, (1970). 1st ed. Fine in dj (price-clipped). *Glenn.* $45/£28

DENHOLM-YOUNG, N. Handwriting in England and Wales. Cardiff: Univ of Wales, 1954. 31 plts. Red cl (spine sl faded). Dj (defective). *Maggs.* $29/£18

DENHOLM-YOUNG, N. Handwriting in England and Wales. Cardiff: Univ of Wales, 1954. 1st ed. 31 sepia plts. VG in buckram bds. *Michael Taylor.* $38/£24

DENING, C. F. W. The Eighteenth-Century Architecture of Bristol. Bristol/London, 1923. 1st ed. Tipped-in frontis; 69 tipped-in plts. Fore, lower edges uncut. (Lt spotted.) *Edwards.* $120/£75

DENISON, E. S. E. S. Denison's Yosemite Views. (SF: H.S. Crocker, 1881.) 1st ed. 9x6. 50 litho plts, dbl-pg map. Stiff pict wrappers. (Top pg edges w/sm worn patch; fr wrapper reattached, spine neatly reglued; lt soiled, chipped), o/w VG. Howes D252. *Pacific**. $1,150/£719

DENISON, HERBERT. A Treatise on Photogravure in Intaglio by the Talbot-Klic Process. London; Iliffe, n.d. (ca 1892). 1st ed. Frontis, guard, 140pp; intaglio plt, guard. (Cl blistered, lt rubbed, name), o/w VG. *Cahan*. $225/£141

DENMAN, THOMAS. An Introduction to the Practice of Midwifery. NY, 1802. 1st Amer ed. 2 vols. 209; 281pp + indexes. Old tree calf. (Ink names; cvrs rubbed, hinges sl split), else VG set. *King*. $250/£156

DENNETT, JOHN FREDERICK (ed). The Voyages and Travels of Captains Parry, Franklin, Ross, and M. Belzoni.... London: J. Jacques & W. Wright, 1826. 7 lithograph/aquatint plts. Mod cl. VG. *Pacific**. $75/£47

DENNIS, GEORGE. The Cities and Cemeteries of Etruria. London: J.M. Dent, (ca 1910). 2 vols. (Bkpls.) *Archaeologia*. $65/£41

DENON, VIVANT. Travels in Upper and Lower Egypt. London: For T.N. Longman & O. Rees/Richard Phillips, 1803. 1st ed in English. 3 vols. 62 maps, plts. Old calf, red/black leather spine labels. (Sl offsetting, sl aged, foxed; white ink lib spine #s, tp blindstamps, card pockets, due date slips; some cvr panels detached, some joints split, cvrs sl worn, scuffed.) Internally Good. *Baltimore**. $375/£234

DENSLOW, W. W. Barn-Yard Circus. NY: G.W. Dillingham Co, (1904). 1st ed. 4to. Good in stiff paper wrappers (dusting, wear, spine chipped). *Reisler*. $175/£109

DENSLOW, W. W. and DUDLEY A. BRAGDON. Billy Bounce. Chicago: M.A. Donohue, (1913). 2nd ed. 16 VG inserted color plts (1 w/sl abrasion at bottom margin w/sl loss of text on opposing leaf). Orange cl, black lettering, mtd color illus fr cvr (sl rubbed, spine sl dknd). *Baltimore**. $120/£75

DENSLOW, W. W. Denslow's ABC Book. NY: G.W. Dillingham, 1903. 1st ed. 4to. Mtd on linen, full color stiff paper wrappers (edges, spine worn, spine partly split). *Reisler*. $200/£125

DENSLOW, W. W. Denslow's Three Little Kittens. NY: G.W. Dillingham, 1904. 1st ed. 4to. Good in color paper wrappers (worn, margins torn). *Reisler*. $265/£166

DENSLOW, W. W. Johnnie Johnston's Air Ship. Batavia: Johnston Harvester Co, 1909. 1st ed. 12pp; 1 dbl-pg, 4 full-pg color illus. VG (few lt finger smudges, old dampstain bottom spine corners, lt ring stain rear cvr) in stapled wraps. *Baltimore**. $400/£250

DENSLOW, W. W. One Ring Circus and Other Stories. NY: G.W. Dillingham Co, (1903). 1st combined ed. 4to. Red cl (worn, rubbed, lg spot rear cvr), color paste label (chipped). (Fep missing, fr hinge cracked; wear, marginal tears.) *Reisler*. $385/£241

DENSLOW, W. W. When I Grow Up. NY: Century, 1909. 1st ed. 4to. Pict tan cl (lt dusty, mkd) w/orange/dk blue/while pict designs. *Reisler*. $600/£375

DENSMORE, FRANCES. Chippewa Music. BAE Bulletin 45. Washington: GPO, 1910. (Ink inscrips; corners bumped, rubbed.) *King*. $45/£28

DENSMORE, FRANCES. Music of Santo Domingo Pueblo New Mexico. L.A.: Southwest Museum, 1938. VG in wraps (worn, chipped). *Dumont*. $75/£47

DENT, ANTHONY and DAPHNE MACHIN GOODALL. The Foals of Epona. London: Galley, 1962. 1st ed. VG in Good+ dj. *October Farm*. $35/£22

DENT, CLINTON THOMAS. Mountaineering. Longmans, Green, 1892. 1st ed. xvi,(440),(ii)pp. Pict cl. Nice (sl spotted, mainly to edges, sl bumped). *Ash*. $120/£75

DENT, EDWARD J. Mozart's Operas. OUP, 1947. 1st ed. 9 plts. VG in dj. *Hollett*. $32/£20

DENTON, SHERMAN F. As Nature Shows Them. Moths and Butterflies of the United States, East of the Rocky Mountains. Boston: J.B. Millet, (1900). Ltd to 500. 2 vols. 8vo. 56 mtd color plts. Aeg. Contemp olive grn morocco (spines faded), gilt butterfly motif cornerpieces, spines gilt in 6 compartments w/raised bands, gilt butterfly centerpieces, gilt turn-ins. *Christie's**. $1,440/£900

DENTZEL, CARL SCHAEFER. The Drawings of John Woodhouse Audubon, Illustrating His Adventures Through Mexico and California 1849-1850. SF: Book Club of CA, 1957. One of 400 ptd. 34 plts (2 color). Prospectus laid in. Leather spine label. Fine. *Pacific**. $138/£86

DENYS, F. WARD. Our Summer in the Vale of Kashmir. Washington: Bryan, 1915. 1st ed. 54 plts (8 color). (Sl rubbed, soiled), o/w VG. *Worldwide*. $45/£28

DEPEW, CHAUNCEY M. (ed). 1795-1895: One Hundred Years of American Commerce.... NY: D.O. Haynes, 1895. 1st ed. 2 vols in 1. 2 color frontisports, xxxiv,336; xii,(337)-678pp; 98 plts. Purple cl (spine faded). *Karmiole*. $100/£63

DEPONS, F. A Voyage to the Eastern Part of Terra Firma...During the Years 1801, 1802, 1803, and 1804.... NY: I. Riley & Co, 1806. 1st ed thus. 3 vols. Fldg map vol 1, partly colored in outline (repaired w/archival tape along some folds, no loss to image). Later cl. (Text spotted; rebound), else Good set. *Brown*. $150/£94

DEPPE, FERDINAND. Ferdinand Deppe's Travels in California in 1837. Gustave O. Arlt (trans). L.A.: Glen Dawson, 1953. 1st ed in English. One of 190 ptd. Cl-backed red bds, ptd paper spine label. VF. *Argonaut*. $60/£38

DERBY, GEORGE H. Report of the Secretary of War Communicating in Compliance with a Resolution of the Senate.... Washington: U.S. Senate, 1852. 17pp; fldg map. Mod dk blue cl, gilt. Fine in matching cl-cvrd slipcase w/leatherette spine label. *Pacific**. $374/£234

DERLETH, AUGUST (ed). Worlds of Tomorrow. N.p.: Pellegrini & Cudahy, 1953. 1st ed. VG in dj (sm tear dj spine head). *Pacific**. $23/£14

DERLETH, AUGUST. And You, Thoreau! CT: New Directions, 1944. 1st ed. VG in wraps. *Any Amount*. $24/£15

DERLETH, AUGUST. And You, Thoreau! Norfolk, CT: New Directions, 1944. 1st ed. Grn bds. VG in dj. *Lucas*. $40/£25

DERLETH, AUGUST. The Chronicles of Solar Pons. Sauk City, WI: Mycroft & Moran, 1973. 1st ed. One of 4000. Black cl. Fine in Fine dj. *Sumner & Stillman*. $75/£47

DERLETH, AUGUST. Dark of the Moon. Sauk City: Arkham House, 1947. 1st ed. One of 2500. (Dampstain to lower edge of cl.) 1st state dj w/grn lettering designed by Utpatel (1/2-inch piece missing from spine foot). *Glenn*. $130/£81

DERLETH, AUGUST. The Memoirs of Solar Pons. Sauk City, WI: Mycroft & Moran, 1951. 1st ed. Ltd to 2000. Black cl. Fine in NF dj. *Sumner & Stillman*. $130/£81

DERLETH, AUGUST. Mr. Fairlie's Final Journey. Sauk City, 1968. 1st ed. VF in dj (fr lt stained). *Bromer*. $50/£31

DERLETH, AUGUST. Mr. Fairlie's Final Journey. Sauk City: Mycroft & Moran, 1968. 1st ed. Fine in Fine dj. *Other Worlds*. $50/£31

DERLETH, AUGUST. Mr. Fairlie's Final Journey. Sauk City, WI: Mycroft & Moran, 1968. 1st ed. Black cl. Fine in NF dj. *Sumner & Stillman*. $75/£47

DERLETH, AUGUST. Not Long for This World. Sauk City: Arkham House, 1948. 1st ed. (Name), else NF. *Pacific**. $58/£36

DERLETH, AUGUST. Not Long for This World. Sauk City: Arkham House, 1948. 1st ed. Signed, inscribed. Dj (sl dknd). *Kane**. $80/£50

DERLETH, AUGUST. A Praed Street Dossier. Sauk City: Mycroft & Moran, 1968. 1st ed. NF in Fine dj. *Other Worlds.* $40/£25

DERLETH, AUGUST. The Reminiscences of Solar Pons. Sauk City, WI: Mycroft & Moran, 1961. 1st ed. Ltd to 2000. Black cl. Fine in NF dj. *Sumner & Stillman.* $95/£59

DERLETH, AUGUST. The Return of Solar Pons. Sauk City, WI: Mycroft & Moran, 1958. 1st ed. One of 2000. Black cl. Fine in NF dj. *Sumner & Stillman.* $115/£72

DERLETH, AUGUST. The Solar Pons Omnibus. Basil Cooper (ed). (Sauk City): Arkham House, (1982). 1st ed. 2 vols. Black cl, gilt. NF in slipcase (banged-up). *Pacific*.* $58/£36

DERLETH, AUGUST. Something Near. Sauk City: Arkham House, 1945. 1st ed. Pict dj (sl age-toned). *Kane*.* $90/£56

DERRIG, PETER. The Glory of the Green Berets. NY: Paperback Library, 1967. 1st ed. Pb orig. NF. *Associates.* $45/£28

Des Imagistes: An Anthology. NY: Albert & Charles Boni, 1914. 1st Amer ed, ptd from watermarked Eng sheets. (Soiled, spine ends rubbed, extrems dknd), else VG. *Pacific*.* $184/£115

DESCARGUES, PIERRE. Hartung. NY, (1977). (Initial ll sl damp-stained.) Dj. *Swann*.* $57/£36

DESCHARNES, ROBERT. The World of Salvador Dali. NY: Harper & Row, (1962). 1st ed. VG in dj. *Pacific*.* $58/£36

Description and Rules for the Management of the Springfield Rifle, Carbine, and Army Revolvers. Caliber .45. Springfield, MA: Nat'l Armory, 1882. 71pp; 4 fldg plts. Ptd bds. (Bds tape-reinforced around edges), else VG. *Pacific*.* $92/£58

Description of the Collection of Ancient Marbles in the British Museum. Parts 3-11. British Museum, 1818-1861. Lg paper copies. 9 vols. Sm folio. 315 engr plts (1 color). Paper labels. (Bottom margin of plts in 1 vol lt dampstained, foxed, blind-stamps to tps; spine of vol 3 sl chipped), o/w Fine set. *Hollett.* $1,200/£750

Description of Vernon County Missouri. Sedalia, MO: J. West Goodwin, 1877. Pamphlet. Fine in blue wraps. *Metropolitan*.* $143/£89

Descriptive and Priced Catalogue of Books, Pamphlets, and Maps Relating...to...California and the Far West, Formerly the Collection of Thomas Wayne Norris.... Oakland: Holmes Book Co, 1948. One of 500 ptd. Frontis dwg by Remington. Red linen-backed patterned bds, paper spine label. NF (extrems sl worn). *Harrington.* $150/£94

Deseret Second Book. Deseret: Regents of the Deseret Univ, 1868. 1st ed. Cl-backed pict paper-cvrd bds (sl soiled, worn). *Kane*.* $110/£69

Deserter; a New Musical Drama. (By Charles Dibdin.) T. Becket, 1773. 1st ed. vi,(ii),36pp. Mod 1/4 dk brn calf, raised bands, gray bds. VG. *Blackwell's.* $96/£60

DESMOND, FRANK. Everybody's Guide to Conjuring. London: Saxon, n.d. (c. 1895). Dec cl. VG. *Dramatis.* $35/£22

DETHLOFF, HENRY C. and IRVIN M. MAY, JR. (eds). Southwestern Agriculture: Pre-Columbian to Modern. Agricultural Hist Soc, (1982). 1st ed. Yellow cl. VF in pict dj. *Argonaut.* $45/£28

DETMOLD, M. and E. Pictures from Birdland. E.B.S. (rhymes). London: J.M. Dent, 1899. 1st ed, 1st bk. 8vo. (56)pp; 24 full-pg color plts. Grn pict paper-cvrd bds w/an ivory-billed woodpecker to fr cvr. VG (edges, spine sl rubbed, ends sl worn). *Sotheran.* $1,277/£798

DEUCHER, SYBIL. Giotto Tended the Sheep. Dutton, 1938. 1st ed. 8.5x11.3. Dorothy Bayley (illus). 96pp. NF in Good+ dj (1/2-inch chip, corner chips, 2 stains). *Price.* $45/£28

DEULIN, CHARLES. Johnny Nut and the Golden Goose. Andrew Lang (trans). Longmans, 1887. 1st ed. Sm folio. (iv),45 leaves. Yellow eps; teg, rest untrimmed. Pale blue bevel-edged cl. Good (partly erased name, bkpl, lt foxed; edges sl rubbed). *Blackwell's.* $96/£60

DEUTSCH, HERMANN B. The Incredible Yanqui: The Career of Lee Christmas. London: Longmans, Green, 1931. 1st ed. Frontis. Gold-stamped 2-tone cl. (Inscrip effaced 1/2-title.) *Dawson.* $60/£38

DEVANEY, D. M. and L. G. ELDREDGE (eds). Reef and Shore Fauna of Hawaii. Honolulu, 1987. Port, 12 color plts. *Sutton.* $58/£36

DEVEAUX, ALEXIS. Spirits in the Street. GC: Anchor, 1973. 1st ed. VG+ in pict dj. *Petrilla.* $75/£47

DeVERE STACKPOLE, H. Pierrette. London: John Lane, 1900. 1st ed. (Sl uniformly soiled), else NF. *Between The Covers.* $85/£53

DEVEREUX, JAMES. The Story of Wake Island. NY, 1947. VG. *Clark.* $35/£22

DEVILLERS, PHILIPPE. Face of North Vietnam. NY: Holt, Rinehart, Winston, 1970. 1st ed. Fine in dj. *Associates.* $150/£94

DEVOL, GEORGE H. Forty Years a Gambler on the Mississippi. NY: George H. Devol, 1892. 2nd ed. Frontisport, 300pp. Pict grn cl. Good (bkseller ticket fr pastedown, bkpl; sl water damage to cvrs, spine lettering faded). Howes D295. *Chapel Hill.* $125/£78

Devotional Somnium; Or, a Collection of Prayers and Exhortations, Uttered by Miss Rachel Baker...During Her Abstracted and Unconscious State.... (By Samuel L. Mitchell.) NY: Van Winkle & Wiley, 1815. 1st ed, 1st issue. Signed in type by John H. Douglas. 12mo. 298 (i.e. 288)pp (1816 ink sig, bkpl). Orig ptd bds (rubbed, fr cvr detached, spine shot). *M & S.* $750/£469

Dew Drop and the Mist. SPCK, 1847. 1st ed. Sq 12mo. Engr frontis, 115,(i)pp. Blind-stamped cl (sl faded), gilt. *Hollett.* $48/£30

DEWAR, GEORGE A. B. The Book of the Dry Fly. London: Lawrence & Bullen, 1897. 1st ed. 6 plts (4 hand-colored). Teg. Grn cl, gilt. (Bkpl; fr hinge starting, soiled), else VG. *Pacific*.* $63/£39

DEWAR, GEORGE A. B. The South Country Trout Streams. London: Lawrence & Bullen, 1899. 1st ed. Gray cl, gilt. NF. *Pacific*.* $40/£25

DEWHURST, KENNETH. Doctor Thomas Sydenham (1624-1689), His Life and Original Writings. Berkeley, 1966. 1st ed. Fine. *Doctor's Library.* $50/£31

DeWINDT, HARRY. Through the Gold-Fields of Alaska to Bering Straits. NY: Harper & Bros, 1898. ix(3)314pp. Fldg map. Dec cl. VG. *High Latitude.* $125/£78

DEXTER, COLIN. The Jewel That Was Ours. Bristol, England: Scorpion, 1991. 1st ed. One of 150 specially bound, numbered, signed. 1/4 leather w/marbled bds. Fine in acetate dj, as issued. *Murder.* $150/£94

DEXTER, COLIN. Last Bus to Woodstock. London: Macmillan, 1975. 1st ed, 1st bk. Signed. NF (pp sl yellowed) in VG dj (chips, edgewear, internal reinforcement). *Janus.* $300/£188

DEXTER, COLIN. Last Bus to Woodstock. Macmillan, 1975. 1st ed, 1st bk. Crown 8vo. Brn bds. VG (pp browned) in dj (1 sm tear). *Blackwell's.* $560/£350

DEXTER, COLIN. The Way Through the Woods. Bristol, England: Scorpion, 1992. One of 150 specially bound, numbered, signed. 1/4 leather w/marbled bds. Fine in acetate dj, as issued. *Murder.* $150/£94

DEXTER, COLIN. The Wench Is Dead. London: Macmillan, 1989. 1st ed. Signed. NF (spine ends sl bumped) in dj (sl creased). *Ulysses.* $128/£80

DEXTER, COLIN. The Wench Is Dead. London: Macmillan, 1989. 1st ed. Signed. Fine in Fine dj. *Janus.* $150/£94

DEXTER, F. THEODORE. Forty-Two Years' Scrapbook of Rare Ancient Firearms. L.A.: Warren F. Lewis, (1954). 1st ed. One of 2000. Signed. NF in dj, orig shipping box. *Pacific*.* $69/£43

DEXTER, F. THEODORE. Forty-Two Years' Scrapbook of Rare Ancient Firearms. L.A., (1954). One of 2000. Dj, pub's shipping box. *Swann**. $92/£58

DEXTER, PETE. Deadwood. NY: Random House, 1986. 1st ed. Signed. Fine in Fine dj. *Unger*. $75/£47

DEXTER, SAMUEL. Some Serious Thoughts on the Foundation, Rise and Growth of the Settlements in New England. Boston, 1738. Sm 8vo. (2),ii,51pp, stitched. (Lacks 1/2-title, corners turned, sl repair final leaf.) *Swann**. $575/£359

DEYDIER, CHRISTIAN. Chinese Bronzes. NY: Rizzoli, 1980. 1st Amer ed. 152 plts. Mint in dj, box. *Argosy*. $65/£41

DHOTEL, JULES. Magic with Small Apparatus. Berkeley Heights, NJ, 1947. 1st Amer ed. (Stamps; sl worn), else Good. *King*. $75/£47

DI GREGORIO, MARIO. T. H. Huxley's Place in Natural Science. New Haven: Yale UP, 1984. 1st ed. Fine in dj. *Archer*. $25/£16

DI LAMPEDUSA, GIUSEPPE. The Leopard. London: Collins & Harvill, 1960. 1st ed. Grn cl. Fine in wrapper (sl worn). *Appelfeld*. $100/£63

DI LAMPEDUSA, GIUSEPPE. The Leopard. LEC, 1988. One of 750 signed by Piero Guccione (illus). Fine in slipcase. *Swann**. $258/£161

DI PESO, CHARLES C. Casas Grandes, a Fallen Trading Center of the Gran Chichimeca. Flagstaff: Northland, (1974). 1st ed. 3 vols. Fine set. *Book Market*. $60/£38

DI PRIMA, DIANE (ed). War Poems. NY: Poets Press, (1968). 1st ed. One of 2000. Fine in pict wrappers. *Reese*. $20/£13

DI SAN LAZZARO, G. Homage to Max Ernst. NY: Tudor, 1971. 1st ed. 29 color, 130 b/w plts. W/orig color litho by Ernst. VG + in dj. *Any Amount*. $96/£60

Dialogues of the Dead. (By George Lyttelton.) London: W. Sandby, 1760. 3rd ed. xii,320pp. Period calf, morocco spine label. (Joints cracking at ends), else VG. *Pacific**. $86/£54

DIAPER, TOM. Tom Diaper's Log. Robert Ross, 1950. 1st ed. 8 plts. Cl-backed marbled bds (spine faded). *Hollett*. $72/£45

Diary of a Desennuyee. (By Catherine Grace Frances Gore.) Phila: E.L. Carey & A. Hart, 1836. 1st Amer ed. 216pp (eps foxed). Grn patterned cl, tan bds, paper spine label (chipped). *Karmiole*. $85/£53

Diary of a Public Man. Unpublished Passages From the Secret History of the American Civil War and Lincoln's Early Administration. New Brunswick: Rutgers Univ, 1946. 1st ed. Brn cl. VG in dj. *House*. $20/£13

Diary of an Ennuyee. Henry Colburn, 1826. New ed. Sprinkled edges. Contemp 1/2 leather over marbled bds. Good (sig; spine head chipped w/loss, head, hinge bases nicked). *Tiger*. $109/£68

Diary of the Wreck of His Majesty's Ship Challenger...May 1835. by G. A. Rothery?. London: Longman, Rees, 1836. 1st, only ed. 8vo. (iii),(i)blank,160pp; 2 fldg litho plts, 2 plans (1 fldg). Orig grn cl, paper spine label. Good (early ink sig, lt browned, water stain to margin of 1 fldg plt; upper joint split, hinges weak, sl rubbed). *Morrell*. $496/£310

DIAZ, BERNAL DEL CASTILLO. The Discovery and Conquest of Mexico, 1517-1521. Mexico City: LEC, 1942. One of 1500. Signed by Miguel Covarrubias (illus), printer, ed. Box (worn). *Kane**. $120/£75

DIAZ, BERNAL DEL CASTILLO. The Discovery and Conquest of Mexico. LEC, 1942. Ltd to 1500 numbered, signed by the editor, Miguel Covarrubias (illus), and Rafael Loera y Chavez (ptr). Fine in slipcase. *Swann**. $316/£198

DIAZ-CANABATE, A. The Magic World of the Bullfighter. London, (1956). Dj (sl worn). *Woolson*. $20/£13

DIBBLE, SHELDON. A Voice from Abroad, or Thoughts on Missions, from a Missionary to His Classmates. Lahainaluna: Press of the Mission Seminary, 1844. xi,132pp. Marbled paper-cvrd bds (rubbed, fr cvr detached), leather spine. *Zubal**. $200/£125

DIBDIN, CHARLES. Songs, Naval and National, of the Late Charles Dibdin; with a Memoir and Addenda. Collected and Arranged by Thomas Dibdin.... John Murray, 1841. 1st ed. xvi,336pp; 12 plts by George Cruikshank. Marbled eps; inner dentelles, teg. Full polished calf, French fillet border to sides, gilt-dec spine, contrasting morocco lettering-pieces. (Margins sl browned; spine, fr cvr cl bound in at end), o/w VG. *Sotheran*. $317/£198

DIBDIN, JAMES C. The Annals of the Edinburgh Stage. Edinburgh: Richard Cameron, 1888. 1st ed. Ltd to 50 numbered, signed. Frontisport, 6 plts, 2 facs. (New eps.) 1/4 morocco, marbled bds, spine gilt. Fine. *Dramatis*. $300/£188

DIBDIN, MICHAEL. Dirty Tricks. London, 1991. 1st ed. Fine in dj. *Petersfield*. $16/£10

DIBDIN, MICHAEL. The Last Sherlock Holmes Story. Cape, 1978. 1st UK ed. Fine in NF dj (price-clipped, fore-edges sl worn). *Williams*. $384/£240

DIBDIN, THOMAS F. A Bibliographical Antiquarian and Picturesque Tour in France and Germany. London: W. Bulmer for the Author, 1821. 1st ed. 3 vols. 4to. Aeg. Contemp gilt-stamped black morocco, gilt paneled spine, wide raised bands. (Plts sl offset), else Fine. *Appelfeld*. $650/£406

DIBDIN, THOMAS F. The Bibliographical Decameron; or, Ten Days Pleasant Discourse Upon Illuminated Manuscripts.... London, 1817. 1st ed. 3 vols. Lg 8vo. 37 plts. Contemp grn straight-grain morocco, gilt. (Lt foxed.) *Swann**. $517/£323

DIBDIN, THOMAS F. A Bibliographical, Antiquarian and Picturesque Tour in France and Germany. London: Robert Jennings and John Major, 1829. 2nd ed. 3 vols. (ii),xliv,421; (ii),iv,428; (ii),iv,481pp. Orig cl panels w/mod cl spines, mod paper spine labels. Fine. *Oak Knoll*. $165/£103

DIBDIN, THOMAS F. Bibliomania; a Bibliographical Romance. London, 1842. New & improved ed. 2 vols. 618pp. Aeg. Full purple pebble-grained morocco, gilt. Fine set. *Truepenny*. $475/£297

DIBDIN, THOMAS F. Bibliomania; or Book-Madness; A Bibliographical Romance. London: C & W, 1876. New improved ed. xviii,618,xxxiv pp. Teg. Contemp 1/2 grn morocco signed by Riviere over marbled colored cvrd bds, spine gilt. Fine. *Oak Knoll*. $450/£281

DIBDIN, THOMAS F. An Introduction to the Knowledge of Rare and Valuable Editions of the Greek and Roman Classics.... London, 1827. 4th ed. 2 vols. 1/2 polished calf (sl rubbed), red morocco spine labels, gilt. *Kane**. $160/£100

DIBDIN, THOMAS F. The Library Companion. London: Harding, Triphook, Lepard, and J. Major, 1824. 1st ed. One of 2000 ptd. (iv),lii,912pp. Contemp calf (rebacked leather spine laid down on new leather; hinges worn). *Oak Knoll*. $115/£72

DIBDIN, THOMAS F. Typographical Antiquities. London: William Miller, 1810/1812/1816/1819. 1st ed. 4 vols. Later calf. (All vols lack spines, all cvrs detached, sl worn, edges scuffed, few w/smoke damage to edges.) Text VG (lt aged, few ll sl creased). *Baltimore**. $200/£125

DIBDIN, THOMAS F. Typographical Antiquities; or The History of Printing in England, Scotland and Ireland. William Miller, 1810-1819. 4 vols. 4to. 26 plts (sl spotting, offsetting). Orig pub's bds (labels chipped w/some loss). *Sotheby's**. $1,104/£690

DICHTER, HARRY and ELLIOTT SHAPIRO. Early American Sheet Music. NY: Bowker, 1941. (Lt worn.) Dj (frayed). *Oinonen**. $80/£50

Dick Birds ABC. Boston: De Wolfe Fiske, (c.1890s). Cl-backed chromolitho bds. (Shelfworn), else VG. *Pacific**. $52/£33

DICK, EVERETT. The Sod-House Frontier, 1854-1890. NY: D. Appleton-Century, 1937. 1st ed. Fine in dj. *Labordo.* $75/£47

DICK, PHILIP K. and ROGER ZELAZNY. Deus Irae. GC, 1976. 1st ed. VG in dj. *King.* $25/£16

DICK, PHILIP K. The Divine Invasion. NY: Timescape Books, (1981). 1st ed. Fine in dj. *Levin.* $65/£41

DICK, PHILIP K. Humpty Dumpty in Oakland. London: Gollancz, 1986. 1st ed. Fine in dj. *Levin.* $45/£28

DICK, PHILIP K. The Man in the High Castle. NY: Putnam, (1962). 1st ed. VG in dj (1.5-inch tear, crease rear panel, sm tear fr corner, corners sl rubbed, price-clipped). *Pacific*.* $316/£198

DICK, PHILIP K. Martian Time Slip. (London): New English Library, (1964). 1st hb ed. (Pp sl tanned), o/w Fine in dj (spine corner worn, price-clipped). *Levin.* $150/£94

DICK, PHILIP K. Mary and the Giant. NY: Arbor House, (1987). 1st ed. (Sm mk rear cvr), o/w Fine in dj (white rear cvr sl yellowed). *Levin.* $45/£28

DICK, PHILIP K. Now Wait for Last Year. GC: Doubleday, 1966. 1st ed. Fine in dj (1/2-inch closed tear rear cvr, sl worn, dust-soiled). *Levin.* $300/£188

DICK, PHILIP K. Our Friends from Frolix 8. London: Kinnell, 1989. 1st trade hb ed. Fine in dj (sl yellowed). *Levin.* $65/£41

DICK, PHILIP K. A Scanner Darkly. GC: Doubleday, 1977. 1st ed. Rev copy, w/slip laid in. VG (spine foot bumped) in NF dj (spine ends rubbed) *Pacific*.* $86/£54

DICK, PHILIP K. The Simulacra. NY: Ace Books, (1964). 1st ed. Pict wraps. (Ink name, sl worn.) *King.* $35/£22

DICK, PHILIP K. The Unteleported Man. NY: Ace Books, (1964). 1st ed. Pict wraps. (Ink name, sl soil.) *King.* $35/£22

DICK, PHILIP K. The Zap Gun. NY: Pyramid Books, (1967). 1st ed. Pict wraps. (Ink name; cvrs sl soiled, spotted.) *King.* $25/£16

Dickens Memento: Catalogue with Purchasers' Names and Prices Realised of the Pictures...of the Late Charles Dickens Sold by Auction in London...on July 9th, 1870. Field & Tuer, n.d. (1884). Pub's cat. Good (pencil sig, lt spotted; spine bumped, dulled). *Tiger.* $157/£98

DICKENS, CHARLES and W. WILKIE COLLINS. The Lazy Tour of the Two Idle Apprentices and Other Stories. Chapman & Hall, 1890. Good (several ll frayed at leading edge; spine bumped). *Tiger.* $240/£150

DICKENS, CHARLES and WILKIE COLLINS. The Wreck of the Golden Mary: A Saga of the California Gold Rush. Kentfield: Allen Press, 1956. One of 200. Rose/marbled bds. NF in acetate dj. *Pacific*.* $207/£129

DICKENS, CHARLES. American Notes for General Circulation and Pictures from Italy. London: Chapman & Hall, 1874. viii,(2),506pp. Grn cl (sl rubbed). *Mott.* $40/£25

DICKENS, CHARLES. American Notes for General Circulation. London: Chapman & Hall, 1843. 1st ed, 1st state w/prelim pg x misnumbered xvi (this is the only prelim pg which is numbered). 2 vols. 7.75x4.75. x,(2),308; vii,306pp + (6) ads pp. Marbled eps; teg. Full red crushed levant morocco (orig vertically vs. horizontally ribbed cl bound in at rear each vol), gilt. Bound by Riviere. Fine (vol 1 leaf w/1-inch tear expertly repaired, final ad leaf vol 2 torn at corner, sl aged). Bkpls of Margaret Manning Couzens. *Pacific*.* $518/£324

DICKENS, CHARLES. American Notes for General Circulation. Chapman & Hall, 1850. 2nd ed. Frontis. Good (few sl creases, sl browned; lt worn, spine sl dull). *Ash.* $104/£65

DICKENS, CHARLES. American Notes. London, 1850. Frontis, xiii,175pp. Ed of Barnaby Rudge bound in. Orig 1/4 leather. (Hinge repaired), else Good. Howes D325. *Dumont.* $75/£47

DICKENS, CHARLES. Barnaby Rudge. Chapman & Hall, 1841. 1st separate issue. Illus, initials after Hablot K. Browne and George Cattermole. Marbled eps. Variant binding: orig mauve fine-diaper cl, cvrs stamped in blind w/borders, stem-leaf, rococo design, spine lettered in gilt. (Bkpl; fr cvr top, spine sl sunned.) *Sotheby's*.* $2,944/£1,840

DICKENS, CHARLES. The Battle of Life, a Love Story. London: Bradbury & Evans, Whitefriars, 1846. 1st ed. Red cl, emb edging, pict gilt. Fine (edges sl bumped). *Metropolitan*.* $316/£198

DICKENS, CHARLES. The Battle of Life. London: Bradbury & Evans, 1846. 1st ed. (i-viii),(1-3),4-175,(176),(1-2)pp. Pale yellow eps; aeg. Orig crimson vertically ribbed cl, dec/pict stamped in blind/gold. (Spine ends rubbed), else NF. *Vandoros.* $500/£313

DICKENS, CHARLES. The Battle of Life: A Love Story. London: Bradbury & Evans, 1846. 1st ed, 2nd state (of 4) of added tp, w/'A Love Story' etched in viny letters on scroll which is part of plate, imprint in type set in 3 lines. Frontis, added tp, (8),176,(1) + 2 ads pp. Aeg. Orig red blind-stamped cl, gilt. VG (ink name; extrems lt rubbed, worn). *Pacific*.* $288/£180

DICKENS, CHARLES. Bleak House. GC: Doubleday, (1953). Edward Gorey (illus). 1/4 black cl, cream cl. NF (ink sig) in dj (lt soiled). *Heritage.* $250/£156

DICKENS, CHARLES. Bleak House. Bradbury & Evans, 1852-1853. 1st ed in parts, 20 numbers in 19. H. K. Browne (illus). All ads listed by Eckel on p81 present. (Offset, foxed.) Ptd blue wrappers (many torn or chipped on spine). *Sotheby's*.* $699/£437

DICKENS, CHARLES. Bleak House. Bradbury & Evans, 1853. 1st issue w/'eligible' misprinted pg 19. H. K. Browne (illus). Marbled edges. Recent 1/4 leather, cl, raised bands. Good (plts waterstained, spotted, sig). *Tiger.* $192/£120

DICKENS, CHARLES. Bleak House. London, 1853. 1st ed in bk form. 40 plts by H. K. Browne. 1/2 olive calf, gilt, by Zaehnsdorf. (Lt marginal dampstain on frontis and add'l tp, marginal browning other plts; spine, joints worn.) *Swann*.* $201/£126

DICKENS, CHARLES. Bleak House. London: Bradbury & Evans, 1853. 1st ed. Demy 8vo. (i-vii),viii-x,(xi),xii-xiv,(xv),xvi,(1),2-624pp; 40 engr plts by H. K. Browne, incl frontis and vignette tp. W/all internal flaws, incl the scarce 'relieved' for 'received' p620. Bound from the parts in orig olive-grn fine diaper cl primary binding. (Spine bottom lt rubbed), e *Vandoros.* $3,750/£2,344

DICKENS, CHARLES. Bleak House. Bradbury & Evans, 1853. 1st ed in bk form. 8vo. 10 dk plts by H. K. Browne. Lt olive grn fine-diaper cl, gilt. (Bkpl; sl faded, soiled, rear hinge starting.) *Sotheby's*.* $4,232/£2,645

DICKENS, CHARLES. Boots at the Holly Tree Inn. NY: Cassell, 1882. 1st ed. 4to. 16 full-pg color engrs by J. C. Beard. Victorian dec bds (corners, spine lt worn). *Reisler.* $250/£156

DICKENS, CHARLES. Charles Dickens' Complete Works. Phila: Lippincott, 1886. People's ed. 15 vols. Marbled edges. 3/4 dk grn calf, marbled bds, gilt. (1 vol w/upper fr joint cracked through, fr cvr sl bent forward), else VG set. *Pacific*.* $173/£108

DICKENS, CHARLES. A Child's History of England. London, 1852-1854. 1st ed, w/most 1st issue points. 3 vols. 12mo. Frontispieces by F.W. Topham. Marbled eps, edges. Gilt-pict reddish-brn cl spines (lt faded; sm spot fr cvr vol 1). *Swann*.* $2,530/£1,581

DICKENS, CHARLES. A Child's History of England. London, 1852-54. 1st ed, earliest state of ad leaves. 3 vols. Frontispieces. Pale reddish-brn cl. *Felcone.* $3,000/£1,875

DICKENS, CHARLES. The Chimes. London: LEC, 1931. One of 1500 numbered, signed by Arthur Rackham (illus). Pict eps. Pict tan buckram (spine sun-dknd, sl rubbed), gilt. *Baltimore*.* $210/£131

DICKENS, CHARLES. The Chimes. London: LEC, 1931. One of 1500 ptd on Japanese vellum paper, signed by Arthur Rackham (illus). Teg. Brn dec linen (dknd around spine). Nice in box. *Appelfeld.* $350/£219

DICKENS, CHARLES. A Christmas Carol. NY: King Features Syndicate, (1946). 12mo. Hal Foster (illus). Color frontis. Cl-backed color pict bds. Good in cardbd slipcase (sides worn, edge detached but present), color paste label. *Reisler.* $225/£141

DICKENS, CHARLES. A Christmas Carol. London: Heinemann, (1948). Arthur Rackham (illus). Aeg. Full blue polished calf by Bayntun (sl worn), gilt. *Oinonen*.* $300/£188

DICKENS, CHARLES. A Christmas Carol. Cleveland: World, (1961). 1st ed. VF in VF dj. *Between The Covers.* $125/£78

DICKENS, CHARLES. A Christmas Carol. Nevada City: Ptd by Harold Berliner, (1976). Ltd to 750. Wolfgang Lederer (illus). 3 piece buckram, gilt. *Truepenny.* $100/£63

DICKENS, CHARLES. A Christmas Carol. Phila: Lippincott, (c. 1915). 12 color plts by Arthur Rackham, guards. Purple cl, gilt. (Spine ends rubbed, spine dull), else VG. *Pacific*.* $58/£36

DICKENS, CHARLES. A Christmas Carol. Phila: J.B. Lippincott, (ca 1910-20). 12 color plts by Arthur Rackham, guards. Red cl, gilt. NF in VG dj (soiled, price-clipped, extrems rubbed), pict cvr label. *Pacific*.* $150/£94

DICKENS, CHARLES. A Christmas Carol. Chapman & Hall, 1843. 1st ed, 3rd state. 8vo. John Leech (engrs), W. J. Linton (woodcuts). Tp ptd in blue/red, dated 1843, 1/2-title, tp verso ptd in blue, reading 'Stave One' on p(1), balance of text uncorrected. Aeg. Orig lt reddish-brn vertically-ribbed cl. (Sl soiled; worn, sl stained.) *Sotheby's*.* $1,195/£747

DICKENS, CHARLES. A Christmas Carol. London: Heinemann, 1915. 1st ed illus by Arthur Rackham. Lg sq 8vo. 12 color plts, guards. Mauve cl, gilt. (Spine gilt dull), o/w Fine. *Sotheran.* $269/£168

DICKENS, CHARLES. A Christmas Carol. LEC, 1934. Ltd to 1500 numbered, signed by Gordon Ross (illus). Fine in slipcase. *Swann*.* $92/£58

DICKENS, CHARLES. Collected Works - 'The Nonesuch Dickens.' Nonesuch, 1937-1938. One of 877 sets. Orig steel plt (this 'The Election at Eatanswill'), incl, specially boxed uniform w/rest of the set, w/signed letter of authenticity from Arthur Waugh. This set's plate engraved by H.K. Browne (Phiz). 23 vols + the boxed orig plt, the 'Nonesuch Dickensiana' vol and the wrappered 'A Note on the Format of the Nonesuch Dickens' by Francis Meynell. NF set in orig linen buckram binding, various colors, w/black leather spine labels lettered in gold. *Williams.* $9,600/£6,000

DICKENS, CHARLES. The Cricket on the Hearth. Bradbury & Evans, 1846. 1st ed, 2nd issue. Frontis, 174,(ii)pp (bkpl). Aeg. Orig red cl (spine ends sl worn), gilt. *Hollett.* $224/£140

DICKENS, CHARLES. The Cricket on the Hearth. Chapman & Hall, 1846. 1st UK ed. VG (spine sl faded, worn) in orig cl. *Williams.* $400/£250

DICKENS, CHARLES. The Cricket on the Hearth. Great Britain: LEC, 1933. Ltd to 1500. Tall 4to. 7 watercolors by Hugh Thomson. Yellow cl. VG in maroon slipcase (edgeworn). *Reisler.* $250/£156

DICKENS, CHARLES. Dame Durden, Little Woman. NY: Redfield, (1855). 1st ed. Blue cl, gilt. (Sl worn), else VG. *Macdonnell.* $275/£172

DICKENS, CHARLES. David Copperfield. NY: Grosset & Dunlap, (n.d. 1935). 1st ed. (Fep clipped), else VF in VF dj (sl shortened). *Between The Covers.* $200/£125

DICKENS, CHARLES. David Copperfield. Boston: Lea & Shepard, 1884. Contents Fine (bookseller label over imprint on cvr) in orange pict wraps (spine ends sl rubbed). *Dramatis.* $30/£19

DICKENS, CHARLES. Dickens's Children. NY: Scribner, 1912. 1st ed. 8vo. Unpaginated. 10 full-pg color illus by Jessie W. Smith. Grn cl bds, gilt, round paper pict onlay. (Corners bumped, spine ends lack sm pieces), o/w VG. *Davidson.* $125/£78

DICKENS, CHARLES. Dombey and Son. London: Bradbury & Evans, 1848. 1st bk ed, later issue. Extra engr tp, 39 Good engr plts by H. K. Browne. W/o inserted errata slip; errata pg incls only 2 lines of corrections. Marbled eps, edges. Later scarlet calf, marbled bds, raised bands, gilt, black leather spine label. (Plts sl foxed, browned, several w/noticeable margin stains; 2 leaves missing section at top corner w/sl text loss; sl scuffed, worn.) *Baltimore*.* $100/£63

DICKENS, CHARLES. Dombey and Son. London, 1848. 1st bk ed. H.K. Browne (illus). (Few ll washed.) Mod 3/4 morocco (sl rubbed, browned, stains, soiled). *Oinonen*.* $130/£81

DICKENS, CHARLES. Dombey and Son. London, 1848. 1st ed in bk form. 1/2 title; 40 plts (lt offsetting) by H. K. Browne. Mod 1/2 teal calf, gilt. *Swann*.* $172/£108

DICKENS, CHARLES. Dombey and Son. London: Bradbury & Evans, 1848. 1st bk ed. In this copy, errata slip contains 8 lines of corrections; there are no typo errors on pg324 or pg426; date 1848 is lettered in gilt at spine foot. H.K. Browne (illus). (Plts heavily foxed.) Pub's cl (Shelfworn, shaken, inner joints broken). 3/4 morocco box (rubbed). *Oinonen*.* $300/£188

DICKENS, CHARLES. Dombey and Son. Bradbury & Evans, 1848. 1st ed in bk form. 8vo. H. K. Browne (illus). Frontis, tp vignette, errata leaf, errata slip. Pale yellow eps. Variant binding: orig olive grn fine-diaper cl, gilt. (Bkpl; sl sunned.) *Sotheby's*.* $6,256/£3,910

DICKENS, CHARLES. Dombey and Son. NY: Peter Beilenson, 1957. Signed by Henry C. Pitz (illus). 2 vols. Full rose red buckram, ptd paper labels. Boxed. *Appelfeld.* $125/£78

DICKENS, CHARLES. Full and Faithful Report of the Memorable Trial of Bardell against Pickwick. Nevada City, CA: Ptd by Harold Berliner, (1974). Ltd to 750 ptd. Wolfgang Lederer (illus). *Truepenny.* $75/£47

DICKENS, CHARLES. The Gadshill Edition of the Works of Charles Dickens, Reprinted in 38 Volumes: 1907-1908. Scribner, 1907-1908. Demy 8vo. Teg. Fine set in orig grn dec cl, gilt. *Vandoros.* $1,750/£1,094

DICKENS, CHARLES. Great Expectations. London: Chapman & Hall, 1861. 1st ed. 3 vols. 8vo. Teg. 3/4 19th-cent red morocco, gilt-paneled spines, raised bands, by Riviere. Full morocco slipcase. *Appelfeld.* $7,500/£4,688

DICKENS, CHARLES. Great Expectations. London, 1861. 1st eds, 1st issues. 3 vols. No ads. Bottom, fore-edges untrimmed. Full crushed levant, gilt. *Felcone.* $8,500/£5,313

DICKENS, CHARLES. Great Expectations. LEC, 1937. Ltd to 1500 numbered, signed by Gordon Ross (illus). Fine in slipcase. *Swann*.* $57/£36

DICKENS, CHARLES. Hard Times. 1854. 1st ed. 8vo. Yellow-coated eps. lt olive grn moire horizontally-ribbed cl, gilt. (Bkpl; sl worn.) *Sotheby's*.* $1,379/£862

DICKENS, CHARLES. Hard Times. NY: Spiral, 1966. Signed by Charles Raymond (illus). 1/4 beige English buckram, Italian blue mould-made paper sides, gilt-stamped. Fine in box. *Appelfeld.* $100/£63

DICKENS, CHARLES. The Haunted Man and the Ghost's Bargain. Chapman & Hall, 1848. 1st UK ed. VG (spine sl worn, faded) in orig cl. *Williams.* $400/£250

DICKENS, CHARLES. Letters of Charles Dickens. Chapman & Hall, 1880. 2 vols. Errata slip vol 1. Good (spines bumped, chipped, sunned, corners rubbed). *Tiger.* $128/£80

DICKENS, CHARLES. The Life and Adventures of Nicholas Nickleby. Phila: Lea & Blanchard, 1839. 1st US bk ed. 39 engr plts by Phiz. Later dk brn morocco, marbled bds, raised bands, gilt. Good (browned, lt foxed, few pp partly torn, few plts chipped, 1 w/sm repaired tear on verso; sl edgeworn, spines rubbed). *Baltimore**. $110/£69

DICKENS, CHARLES. The Life and Adventures of Nicholas Nickleby. London, 1839. 1st ed in bk form. 1st state of p123, w/'visiter' instead of 'sister' on line 17. Frontis port, 1/2 title; 39 plts by H. K. Browne (some heavily browned). Mod 1/2 red calf, gilt. *Swann**. $115/£72

DICKENS, CHARLES. The Life and Adventures of Nicholas Nickleby. London: Chapman & Hall, 1839. 1st ed in bk form, later issue. 1/2-title, orig 2-pg al by Macready tipped in, steel-engr frontis, 39 etched plts by H. K. Browne. Extra-illus w/further 32 etched plts. Teg, partly uncut. Early 20th-cent grn morocco. (Lacks pub's cat, sm repair to outer margin of frontis, clean tear to L5 just affecting text, some plts browned, spotted; lower joints cracked, spine faded.) *Christie's**. $165/£103

DICKENS, CHARLES. The Life and Adventures of Nicholas Nickleby. London, 1839. 1st bk ed, in Smith's 1st issue binding. In this copy the eps are yellow. W/'Sister' reading on pg123. Phiz (illus). (Last leaf gutter torn, affixed at gutter to rep recto). Uncut. Orig cl (shelfworn, browned, soiled, sl stained, inner joints broken). *Oinonen**. $350/£219

DICKENS, CHARLES. The Life and Adventures of Nicholas Nickleby. London: Chapman & Hall, 1839. 1st ed. Bound from the parts. Frontisport by Phiz. W/extra illus: 2 Series, 1 by Peter Palette; ports also by Onwhyn. Marbled eps. Period-style 3/4 polished calf, marbled bds, red/black labels. Nice (sl worn). *Hartfield*. $595/£372

DICKENS, CHARLES. Little Dorrit. London, 1857. 1st ed in bk form. H. K. Browne (illus). Early 1/2 calf (needs rebinding). *Swann**. $69/£43

DICKENS, CHARLES. Little Dorrit. London: Bradburn & Evans, 1857. 1st bk ed. Extra engr tp, 39 engr plts (incl 8 dk plts) by H. K. Browne. Marbled eps; aeg. Later red-brn calf by Riviere, raised bands, dk crimson/black leather spine labels, gilt. (Sl aged; sl scuffed, spine top crackled, chipped.) Text Good. *Baltimore**. $80/£50

DICKENS, CHARLES. Little Dorrit. London: Bradbury & Evans, 1857. 1st bk ed. Engr extra tp, 39 engr plts by H. K. Browne. Early calf, marbled bds, leather spine label. (Browned, foxing to text and plts; spine scuffed, label lacks chunk, spine top scraped, chipped; cvrs lt worn, scuffed.) *Baltimore**. $90/£56

DICKENS, CHARLES. Little Dorrit. London: Bradbury & Evans, 1857. 1st ed in bk form. Marbled edges. 3/4 grn calf, marbled bds, morocco spine labels, raised spine bands. (Foxed, fr hinge cracked), else VG. *Pacific**. $138/£86

DICKENS, CHARLES. Little Dorrit. London: Bradbury & Evans, 1857. 1st ed. 40 engr plts by Phiz. Aeg. Fine 3/4 brn levant morocco, gilt-paneled spine, raised bands. *Appelfeld*. $500/£313

DICKENS, CHARLES. Little Dorrit. Bradbury & Evans, 1857. 1st ed in bk form. 8vo. 8 dk plts by H. K. Browne. Pale yellow eps. Olive grn fine-diaper cl, gilt. (Bkpl, lacks 9-line errata slip; sunned.) *Sotheby's**. $3,680/£2,300

DICKENS, CHARLES. Love Romance of Charles Dickens Told in His Letters to Maria Beadnell (Mrs. Winter). Argonaut, 1936. VG (spine bumped; lacks dj). *Tiger*. $19/£12

DICKENS, CHARLES. Martin Chuzzlewit. London, 1844. 1st ed in bk form. Phiz (illus). Thick 8vo. Later full polished tan calf, gilt extra, red/grn labels by Wallis. *Swann**. $373/£233

DICKENS, CHARLES. Martin Chuzzlewit. London: Chapman & Hall, 1844. 1st ed, 2nd issue (w/'#' corrected on the engr tp). Frontis by Phiz. Aeg; silk ribbon marker. 3/4 crushed grn morocco, linen, gilt. VG (lt foxed; sl rubbed, spine uniformly faded). *Hartfield*. $395/£247

DICKENS, CHARLES. Martin Chuzzlewit. Chapman & Hall, 1844. 1st ed in bk form. 8vo. H. K. Browne (illus). Frontis, 14-line errata slip. Tp vignette in Hatton & Cleaver's state 3 ('no 1st state or priority': Smith), signed 'Phiz' w/100 pounds on the signpost, the 1st figure sharply defined, and 5 studs in the trunk. Pale yellow eps. Variant binding in orig brn horizontally-ribbed cl, gilt. (Bkpl.) *Sotheby's**. $7,728/£4,830

DICKENS, CHARLES. Master Humphrey's Clock. London, 1840-1. 1st bk ed. George Cattermole & Hablot Browne (illus). 3 vols. Pub's cl (shelfworn, vol 1 loose in casing; foxed, sl stained, soiled). *Oinonen**. $70/£44

DICKENS, CHARLES. Master Humphrey's Clock. London, 1840-1. 1st bk ed. George Cattermole & Hablot Browne (illus). 3 vols. Contemp 3/4 black morocco (rubbed, foxed, sl soiled, shelfworn), gilt. *Oinonen**. $180/£113

DICKENS, CHARLES. Master Humphrey's Clock. London, 1840-1. 1st bk ed. 3 vols in 2. George Catermole & Hablot Browne (illus). Frontis, tp, list of Sibson's illus bound in vol 1; 70 plts by Thomas Sibson. 1/2 morocco, marbled bds (lt rubbed, worn, spine gilt lettering mostly gone). *Kane**. $180/£113

DICKENS, CHARLES. Master Humphrey's Clock. London: Chapman & Hall, 1840-41. 1st ed in bk form. 3 vols. (4, incl frontis),iv,306; vi (incl frontis),306; vi (incl frontis),426pp. Marbled eps; teg. Full red crushed levant morocco (orig cl bound in at rear each vol), gilt. Bound by Riviere. (Sl soiled; rear corners vol 3 sl bumped), else Fine. *Pacific**. $431/£269

DICKENS, CHARLES. Master Humphrey's Clock. Chapman & Hall, 1840/41. 1st ed. 3 vols. George Cattermole & Hablot Browne (illus). 3 wood-engr frontispieces, iv,306; vi,306; vi,426pp. Marbled eps; polished red sprinkled edges. Later 19th-cent dk grn morocco, gilt raised bands, morocco-grain dk grn cl sides. Good (pp browned, sl soiled). *Blackwell's*. $240/£150

DICKENS, CHARLES. Miscellaneous Papers from 'The Morning Chronicle,' .... Chapman & Hall, 1914. 2nd ed, issued as part of the Universal Edition. 1/2-tone frontis, 14 plts; (xx),736pp. Beveled cerise coarse buckram, gilt. (Rear corner chewed), o/w Good. *Temple*. $43/£27

DICKENS, CHARLES. Mr. Pickwick's Christmas, Being an Account of the Pickwickians' Christmas at Manor Farm.... NY: Baker & Taylor, (1906). 1st ed. Teg. Olive grn cl, color pastedown on cvr, gilt. Fine. *Glenn*. $220/£138

DICKENS, CHARLES. Mrs. Gamp. NY Public Library, 1956. Ltd to 500. Frontis. NF (name, spine sunned). *Polyanthos*. $60/£38

DICKENS, CHARLES. The Mudfog Papers. London: Richard Bentley, 1880. 1st ed. Red cl. (Tp top sl creased), else VG. *Pacific**. $109/£68

DICKENS, CHARLES. The Mystery of Edwin Drood. London: Chapman & Hall, 1870. 1st ed. 6 orig parts. Steel-engr tp, frontis. Each part in pict blue wrappers, later chemise, 1/2 leather slipcase. (No. I back ads (I) & (5) not present; Nos. II, V & VI back ads not present; spines worn; lt foxed), else VG. *Pacific**. $184/£115

DICKENS, CHARLES. The Mystery of Edwin Drood. London: Chapman & Hall, 1870. 6 orig parts in blue paper wraps. Port engr in part 6, 12 engr plts. VG complete set (1/2 of p5 part 2 torn off; foxed, soiled; all parts w/chips, tears; part 1 rear cvr detached; part 2 lacks rear cvr) in leatherbound folder (rubbed). *Metropolitan**. $230/£144

DICKENS, CHARLES. The Mystery of Edwin Drood. London: Chapman & Hall, 1870. 1st ed in bk form. Steel-engr tp, frontis. Period 3/4 calf, cl, morocco spine label, gilt, raised bands. VG. *Pacific**. $230/£144

DICKENS, CHARLES. The Old Curiosity Shop. Chapman & Hall, 1841. 1st separate issue. George Cattermole & Hablot K. Browne et al (illus). Marbled eps, edges. Variant binding: orig mauve fine-diaper cl, cvrs stamped in blind w/borders, stem-leaf, rococo design, spine lettered in gilt. (Bkpl.) Sotheby's*. $4,048/£2,530

DICKENS, CHARLES. Oliver Twist. Bradbury & Evans, 1846. New ed. 8vo. George Cruikshank (illus). Orig blue cl, gilt. (Bkpl.) Sotheby's*. $2,392/£1,495

DICKENS, CHARLES. Our Mutual Friend. London: Chapman & Hall, 1865. 1st ed in bk form. 2 vols. Period 3/4 calf, marbled bds, morocco spine labels, gilt, raised bands. (Foxed; extrems rubbed, spine leather sl crackling), o/w VG. Pacific*. $173/£108

DICKENS, CHARLES. Our Mutual Friend. Chapman & Hall, 1865. 1st ed in bk form. 2 vols. 8vo. Marcus Stone (illus). 36-pg cat at end of vol 1, w/o the slip tipped in to p(1) of vol 1 of some copies; 4pg cat inserted at end of vol 2. Pale yellow eps. Dk reddish-brn sand-grain cl, gilt. (Bkpls.) Sotheby's*. $3,128/£1,955

DICKENS, CHARLES. The Personal History of David Copperfield. Bradbury & Evans, 1850. 1st issue w/vignette tp dated. H. K. Browne (illus). Aeg. Mod 1/4 leather, marbled bds. Good (plts spotted, blind-stamp). Tiger. $320/£200

DICKENS, CHARLES. The Personal History of David Copperfield. London, 1850. 1st ed, 1st issue, w/engr tp dated 1850. H.K. Browne (illus). Contemp 3/4 calf (rubbed, sl foxed). Oinonen*. $475/£297

DICKENS, CHARLES. The Personal History of David Copperfield. London: Bradbury & Evans, 1850. 1st ed. 8vo. H.K. Browne (illus). Full 19th-cent blue polished calf, richly gilt paneled spine, raised bands, marbled edges. Sound (plts foxed). Appelfeld. $750/£469

DICKENS, CHARLES. The Personal History of David Copperfield. London: Bradbury & Evans, 1850. 1st bk ed. 8vo. Aeg; closely trimmed. Full red crushed morocco, gilt. (Recently re-cased, rebacked, orig morocco spine laid down.) Glenn. $750/£469

DICKENS, CHARLES. The Personal History of David Copperfield. London: Bradbury & Evans, 1850. 1st ed. Demy 8vo. (i-vii),viii-xiv,(xv-xvi),(1),2-624pp; 40 illus by Phiz, incl frontis and vignette tp. Rebound in black 1/2 calf, marbled bds, raised bands, gilt. (Foxed, mostly marginal on some plts), else Very Nice. Vandoros. $795/£497

DICKENS, CHARLES. The Personal History of David Copperfield. London: Bradbury & Evans, 1850. 1st ed. Demy 8vo. (i-vii),viii,(ix),x-xii,(xiii),xiv,(xv-xvi),(1),2-624pp; 40 illus by Phiz, incl frontis and engr tp. Orig olive-grn fine diaper cl in variant pub's binding w/more elaborate dec blind-stamping than primary binding. (Expertly rebacked w/orig spine neatly mtd, preserving orig eps; Bradbury & Evans ad bound in at end.) Overall Very Nice in grn cl slipcase. Vandoros. $1,850/£1,156

DICKENS, CHARLES. The Personal History of David Copperfield. Bradbury & Evans, 1850. 1st ed in bk form. 8vo. Frontis, tp vignette dated 1850, 1 dk plt by H. K. Browne. Pale yellow eps. Olive grn fine-diaper cl, gilt. (Bkpl; sunned.) Sotheby's*. $5,888/£3,680

DICKENS, CHARLES. The Personal History of David Copperfield. Westminster, n.d. Tipped-in color frontis, 19 tipped-in color plts by Frank Reynolds. Edwards. $77/£48

DICKENS, CHARLES. The Personal History, Adventures, Experience, and Observation of David Copperfield the Younger of Blundestone Rookery. Leipzig: Bernard Tauchnitz, 1849/50. Copyright ed. 3 vols. Contemp French 1/4 grn morocco, marbled sides, gilt. Young. $104/£65

DICKENS, CHARLES. Pictures from Italy. Leipzig: Tauchnitz, 1846. (viii),263pp. Marbled edges. 3/4 calf, marbled bds, gilt. Good (pg corner creased; bumped, rubbed, piece out spine, joint tops split). Blue Mountain. $35/£22

DICKENS, CHARLES. Pictures from Italy. Bradbury & Evans, 1846. 2nd ed. Orig cl. Good (old tape mk to margin of last leaf, new eps; rebacked w/orig backstrip relaid, corners rubbed, cvrs sl mkd). Tiger. $48/£30

DICKENS, CHARLES. Pictures from Italy. London: Bradbury & Evans, 1846. 1st ed. 3/4 19th-cent polished calf, richly gilt paneled spine, raised bands, marbled edges. Fine. Appelfeld. $250/£156

DICKENS, CHARLES. Pictures from Italy. Bradbury & Evans, 1846. Orig cl. Good (spine bumped, chipped, sl dull). Tiger. $480/£300

DICKENS, CHARLES. Pictures from Italy. London: For the Author by Bradbury & Evans, 1846. 1st ed. Samuel Palmer (illus). 2pp undated prelim ads, + 2pp undated ads. Orig blue blind-stamped vertically-ribbed cl. NF (1846 sig; few sm cvr spots) in custom cl slipcase. Sumner & Stillman. $575/£359

DICKENS, CHARLES. The Plays and Poems of Charles Dickens. Richard Herne Shepherd (ed). London: W.H. Allen, 1882. 1st ed. 2 vols. Blue cl (cvrs lt rubbed, mkd), spines gilt. Internally Fine. Dramatis. $200/£125

DICKENS, CHARLES. The Posthumous Papers of the Pickwick Club. London, 1837. 1st Eng bk ed, 1st issue, w/'Tony Veller' signboard on engr tp. 43 illus by R. Seymour & Phiz. Aeg. Later 3/4 calf (foxed, sl worn, soiled). Oinonen*. $400/£250

DICKENS, CHARLES. The Posthumous Papers of the Pickwick Club. Chapman & Hall, 1837. 1st bk ed w/all but 1 of the 1st issue points. 8vo. Frontis. This copy w/12 duplicate plts by 'Phiz,' a set of the 1837-8 plts by Newman, 1 extra plt by Leslie. Teg. Red morocco, gilt by Baytuns. (Some plts sl foxed; sl rubbed.) Sotheby's*. $589/£368

DICKENS, CHARLES. The Posthumous Papers of the Pickwick Club. London: Chapman & Hall, 1837. 1st ed. 8vo. Engr tp, 41 plts by R. Seymour & Phiz. Teg. 3/4 tan polished calf, gilt paneled spine, raised bands; red, grn leather labels. VG. Appelfeld. $650/£406

DICKENS, CHARLES. The Posthumous Papers of the Pickwick Club. London, 1837. 1st ed in bk form, w/all 1st issue points. R. Seymour & Phiz (illus). Thick 8vo. Untrimmed. Later full straight-grain maroon morocco gilt by Riviere. Fine. Swann*. $977/£611

DICKENS, CHARLES. Scenes from Pickwick. London: Sir Isaac Pitman & Sons, n.d. (1920). Scarlet cl, gilt. Fine. Glenn. $30/£19

DICKENS, CHARLES. The Short Stories of....Walter Allen (ed). NY: LEC, 1971. One of 1500 ptd. Signed by Edward Ardizzone (illus) & Joseph Blumenthal (ptr). 3/4 cl, marbled bds. Fine in glassine, slipcase. Pacific*. $63/£39

DICKENS, CHARLES. Sissy Jupe: from the Hard Times of Charles Dickens. NY: Redfield, (c. 1855). 12mo. Frontis, 185pp. Blue cl, gilt. Good (foxed; bumped, rubbed, spine head chipped). Blue Mountain. $75/£47

DICKENS, CHARLES. Sketches by 'Boz,' Illustrative of Every-Day Life, and Every-Day People. John Macrone, 1836. 1st ed. 2 vols. 12mo. George Cruikshank (illus). 2 etched frontispieces, guards present, viii,348; (iv),342pp; 14 plts (foxed). Umber chalked paper doublures, feps; gilt edges. Late 19th-cent dk grn crushed, polished morocco, by Tout, gilt raised bands. VG. Blackwell's. $2,720/£1,700

DICKENS, CHARLES. Sketches by 'Boz.' London, 1836. 1st ed, 1st ptg (i.e., by Whiting), 1st bk. 2 vols. 8vo in twelves. 16 inserted plts by George Cruikshank. Yellow coated eps are the appropriate stock, but later. Orig dk grn cl. Overall, NF set (occasional foxing; sl rubbed, soiled, sm cl scuff to rear bd of vol 2). Heritage. $10,000/£6,250

DICKENS, CHARLES. Speeches Literary and Social. Richard Herne Shepherd (ed). John Camden Hotten, (1870). Leaf 1 excised, evidently before publication (v. note); (3)-372pp. Eps coated pale yellow. Grn patterned sand-grain cl. (Spine sl dull, cl snagged), o/w VG. Temple. $160/£100

DICKENS, CHARLES. A Tale of Two Cities. London, 1859. 1st bk ed, later issue w/p213 correctly numbered. Frontis, extra engr tp; 14 plts. 1/2 black morocco, gilt. (Lacks plt list; fr cvr professionally reattached, orig red cl cvrs, spine bound in at end.) *Kane**. $375/£234

DICKENS, CHARLES. A Tale of Two Cities. London: Chapman & Hall, 1859. 1st ed in bk form, 1st issue, p213 misnumbered 113. Etched frontis, tp, 14 plts by H. K. Browne. Contemp 1/2 calf. (Frontis, tp, 2 plts dampstained; clean tear to N3 affecting 2 lines of text; spotted, lacks pub's cat; extrems rubbed.) *Christie's**. $478/£299

DICKENS, CHARLES. The Trial of William Tinkering. London: Constable, (1912). 1st ed. Lg sq 8vo. (vii),8-30+(ii)ads pp; 5 color plts by S. Beatrice Pearse. Gray bds, onlaid illus. NF. *Sotheran*. $205/£128

DICKENS, CHARLES. The Uncollected Writings of Charles Dickens. Harry Stone (ed). London: Allen Lane, Penguin Press, 1969. 2 vols. Buckram. NF in djs (sl rubbed, few sm internal repairs), slipcase (sl rubbed). *Ulysses*. $104/£65

DICKENS, CHARLES. The Uncommercial Traveller. London: Chapman & Hall, 1861. 1st ed. 32pp ads dated Dec 1860. Blindstamped violet cl. NF (spine faded, each cvr w/sm dropletmk). *Sumner & Stillman*. $1,850/£1,156

DICKENS, CHARLES. The Uncommercial Traveller. Chapman & Hall, 1866. 1st cheap ed. Wood-engr frontis, (4),204pp. Brn eps w/pub's ads. Grn cl (2 spine nicks), gilt. *Cox*. $104/£65

DICKENS, CHARLES. The Unpublished Letters of Charles Dickens to Mark Lemon. Walter Dexter (ed). London: Halton & Truscott Smith, 1927. One of 525 numbered. 8 plts, 6 inserted facs. Teg, rest uncut; unopened. (Rear cvr cl sl mottled), o/w Fine. *Temple*. $120/£75

DICKENS, CHARLES. Unpublished Letters...to Mark Lemon. Walter Dexter (ed). London: Smith, 1927. 1st ed. One of 525. Teg, uncut. 3/4 leather, gilt. VG (sl soiled). *Hartfield*. $125/£78

DICKENS, CHARLES. Works. Chapman & Hall, (c.1880). Illus Library ed. 30 vols. 8vo. (Reps 1st 2 vols sl affected by silverfish, lt spotted.) Marbled eps, edges. Contemp polished tree calf (sl rubbed), gilt, by Sotheran's, morocco spine labels. *Sotheby's**. $2,392/£1,495

DICKENS, CHARLES. Works. Chapman & Hall, 1863-1866. Illus Library ed, containing the 1st fully illus ed of 'Great Expectations.' 26 vols. 8vo. H. K. Browne, Marcus Stone, George Cruikshank et al (illus). Frontis, 7 illus by Marcus Stone. Marbled edges. Uniformly bound in late 19th-cent 1/2 calf, marbled bds, spine gilt (w/misspelling 'Dicken's Works' throughout), grn/black morocco labels. Fine set. *Sotheby's**. $3,864/£2,415

DICKENS, CHARLES. Works. Boston: Estes & Lauriat, 1892. Roxburgh ed. One of 1000 sets. 48 vols. 8.5x5.5. Teg. 3/4 levant blue morocco, marbled bds, gilt, sl raised bands. (Spines browned; joints, extrems sl rubbed), else VG set. *Pacific**. $1,265/£791

DICKENS, CHARLES. Works. N.p.: Soc of English Fiction, n.d. Westminster ed. One of 750 sets, this set not numbered. 15 vols. 8vo. 3/4 brn morocco (rubbed). *Oinonen**. $600/£375

DICKENS, HENRY F. Memories of My Father. Victor Gollancz, 1928. (Spine bumped), else Good in dj (clipped, chipped, lacks sm pieces). *Tiger*. $58/£36

DICKENS, MAMIE. My Father as I Recall Him. Roxburghe, (1897). Dec bds. VG (spine bumped, corners rubbed). *Tiger*. $58/£36

DICKENS, MAMIE. My Father as I Recall Him. NY: Dutton, 1900. 1st Amer ed. Fine (lt offsetting 1 text pg, 1 pg carelessly opened). *Between The Covers*. $75/£47

DICKERSON, EDWARD N. Joseph Henry and the Magnetic Telegraph. NY: Scribner, 1885. 65pp. VG in orig ptd wrappers, brick-red cl-backed spine. *Weber*. $75/£47

DICKEY, IMOGENE BENTLEY. Early Literary Magazines of Texas. Austin, 1970. Good in dj (worn). *Dumont*. $35/£22

DICKEY, JAMES. Alnilam. GC: Doubleday, 1987. 1st ed. Signed. Fine in Fine dj. *Smith*. $75/£47

DICKEY, JAMES. Deliverance. Hamilton, 1970. 1st UK ed. VG in dj (edges sl worn). *Williams*. $40/£25

DICKEY, JAMES. Deliverance. London: Hamish Hamilton, 1970. 1st ed. Fine in dj (nick to spine foot). *Smith*. $50/£31

DICKEY, JAMES. Deliverance. Boston: Houghton Mifflin, 1970. 1st ed. Cream cl. Good (bkpl, eps browned, 1/2-title rubbed; spine cocked) in dj (sl edgeworn). *Heritage*. $50/£31

DICKEY, JAMES. The Eye-Beaters, Blood, Victory, Madness, Buckhead and Mercy. GC: Doubleday, 1970. One of 250 signed. 2-tone red cl, gilt. Fine in cardboard slipcase w/ptd paper label. *Heritage*. $100/£63

DICKEY, JAMES. Head-Deep in Strange Sounds. Palaemon, (1979). One of 475 signed. Gray cl. Fine. *Dermont*. $25/£16

DICKEY, JAMES. The Suspect in Poetry. (Madison, MN): Sixties Press, 1964. 1st ed. Signed. (Fep corner wrinkled), else Fine in NF dj (spine sl tanned, few sm nicks). *Between The Covers*. $125/£78

DICKEY, JAMES. Tucky the Hunter. NY: Crown Pub Co, 1978. 1st ed. Marie Angel (illus). 12mo. Unpaginated. As New. *Davidson*. $35/£22

DICKEY, ROLAND F. New Mexico Village Arts. Albuquerque: Univ of NM, 1949. 1st ed. NF in VG dj (chipped). *Turtle Island*. $50/£31

DICKINSON, EMILY. Bolts of Melody. Mabel Loomis Todd and Millicent Todd Bingham (eds). NY: Harper, 1945. 1st ed. Grn cl, gilt, blindstamped pub's device on fr cvr. (Spine ends lt rubbed), o/w Fine in dj (top edge lt chipped, lt soiled). BAL 4695. *Heritage*. $100/£63

DICKINSON, EMILY. Letters of Emily Dickinson. Mabel Loomis Todd (ed). Cleveland/NY: World Pub Co, 1951. 1st ed thus. B/w frontis. VG (ep edges sl browned; spine ends sl bumped) in dj (nicked, rubbed, dusty, sl torn, creased, mkd, browned). *Ulysses*. $120/£75

DICKINSON, EMILY. The Letters of.... Thomas H. Johnson (ed). Cambridge: Harvard Univ, 1958. 1st ed. 3 vols. Blue cl, gilt. Fine in VG slipcase (soiled). *Pacific**. $126/£79

DICKINSON, EMILY. The Poems of Emily Dickinson. LEC, 1952. Ltd to 1500 numbered, signed by Helen Sewell (illus). Fine in slipcase. *Swann**. $115/£72

DICKINSON, EMILY. Poems. Mabel Loomis Todd and T.W. Higginson (eds). Boston: Roberts Bros, 1891. 3rd ed. Grey cl stamped in silver, white linen spine. (Lt soiled, sm spot), o/w VG. *Cummins*. $250/£156

DICKINSON, G. LOWES. Appearances: Being Notes of Travel. Dent, 1914. 1st ed. (Fr cvr sl mkd), else NF. *Any Amount*. $35/£22

DICKINSON, H. W. and RHYS JENKINS. James Watt and the Steam Engine. Oxford: Clarendon, 1927. Uncut. (Sl worn, spotted.) *Oinonen**. $170/£106

DICKINSON, H. W. James Watt, Craftsman and Engineer. Cambridge: CUP, 1936. 1st ed, Amer issue w/Macmillan binding. Frontis, 17 plts. NF (rear pastedown w/traces of removed lib card pocket). *Glaser*. $60/£38

DICKINSON, JOHN. Letters from a Farmer in Pennsylvania. NY, 1903. One of 260. Pict frontis. 1/4 vellum, pale blue bds. VG (bkpl, ink name; lt worn). *Truepenny*. $95/£59

DICKSON, ARTHUR JEROME (ed). Covered Wagon Days. Cleveland: A.H. Clark, 1929. 1st ed, 1st issue. Blue cl. NF. *Labordo*. $225/£141

DICKSON, GORDON R. Alien Art. NY: E.P. Dutton, 1973. 1st ed. VG+ (corner of fep cut; sl shelfworn) in dj (sl faded, sl edgeworn). *My Bookhouse*. $27/£17

DICKSON, GORDON R. None But Man. GC: Doubleday, 1969. 1st ed. Inscribed, signed, dated 1969. VG in dj (extrems sl dknd). *Pacific**. $35/£22

DICKSON, H. R. P. The Arab of the Desert. London: Allen & Unwin, 1967. 2nd ed, enlgd, imp of 1967 (constituting the 4th imp). Demy 8vo. 664pp; 55 plts (7 color); 8 fldg maps, 6 fldg genealogical tables, 4 maps. Fine (ink inscrip) in dj. *Ulysses*. $640/£400

DICKSON, H. R. P. Kuwait and Her Neighbours. Clifford Witting (ed). London: George Allen & Unwin, 1968. 1st ed. Demy 8vo. 627pp; 47 plts, 14 genealogical tables (2 in rear pocket), 6 maps (4 in rear pocket). Fine in dj (sl torn). *Ulysses*. $800/£500

Dictionary of Medical Terminology, Dental Surgery and Collateral Sciences. Phila, 1882. 4th ed. 743pp. Full sheep. (Tattered eps; shaken, scuffed, cracked hinges), o/w Fair. *Doctor's Library*. $50/£31

Dictionary of National Biography. London/Oxford: OUP, 1973-90. 22 vols incl suppl, 7 suppl vols for 1912-21, 1931-85 (of 9 published). Blue cl. *Christie's**. $846/£529

Dictionary of the English Language, Compiled from Dr. Johnson; with the Addition of Words Since Familiarized to Us. London: W. Peacock & Sons, 1803. 'The Sixth Edition.' Engr frontisport, xxviiipp,(130)leaves. Marbled eps; aeg. Contemp red straight grain morocco, gilt. (Frontis sl spotted, few sl spots, stains; extrems sl worn, spine sl faded, leather sl soiled.) Internally VG. *Pirages*. $85/£53

DIDAY, P. A Treatise on Syphilis in New-Born Children and Infants at the Breast. New Sydenham Soc, 1859. xii,272pp. Blind-stamped cl. (Sm lib stamps; cl mkd, spine defective), o/w VG. *Whitehart*. $56/£35

DIDAY, P. A Treatise on Syphilis in New-Born Children and Infants at the Breast. G. Whiley (trans). London: The New Sydenham Soc, 1859. 1st ed in English. (Sl bumped, spine lt sunned.) *Edwards*. $104/£65

DIDION, JOAN. Run River. NY, 1963. 1st ed. VG in VG dj. *Warren*. $95/£59

DIEHL, EDITH. Bookbinding, Its Background and Technique. NY: Rinehart, 1946. 1st ed. 2 vols. Black cl. *Appelfeld*. $125/£78

DIEHL, EDITH. Bookbinding. NY, 1946. 1st ed. 2 vols. Dryad Leaflet #105 laid in. (Lt worn.) Slipcase. *Oinonen**. $110/£69

DIENST, ALEX. The Navy of the Republic of Texas, 1835-1845. (Ft. Collins, CO): Old Army, (n.d.). One of 150. Inscribed presentation by Mike Koury (pub). Frontisport. Red linen. Fine. *Pacific**. $81/£51

DIES, MARTIN. The Trojan Horse in America: A Report to the Nation. NY: Dodd Mead, 1940. 1st ed. (Sm bkpl), else VG in VG dj (1.5-inch chip to top edge). *Pettler*. $65/£41

DIETRICH, MARLENE. Marlene Dietrich's ABC. NY: Frederick Ungar, (1984). Ltd rev ed. One of 250 numbered, signed. As New in 2 copies of dj. *Between The Covers*. $300/£188

DIETZ, AUGUST. The Postal Service of the Confederate States of America. Richmond: Dietz Printing Co, 1929. 1st ed. Signed. 2 color plts. Orig crimson calf, gray coated cl (sl rubbed; spine ends scuffed w/sl loss). VG. *Baltimore**. $130/£81

DIETZ, ERNST and OTTO DEMUS. Byzantine Mosaics in Greece: Hosios Lucas and Daphni. Cambridge, MA: Harvard Univ, 1931. 15 mtd color plts. Blue cl. Good (lib ink spine #, removed bkpl). *Karmiole*. $100/£63

DILKE, CHARLES WENTWORTH. Greater Britain: A Record of Travel in English-Speaking Countries. London: Macmillan, 1868. 1st ed. 2 vols. Color litho frotnispieces, x,(2),(errata slip),404pp + (48)pp ads; (8),428pp. Grn cl, gilt spines. (Eps cracking vol I; extrems sl rubbed), else VG. *Pacific**. $104/£65

DILLARD, ANNIE. An American Childhood. NY: Harper & Row, (1987). One of 250. Signed. Grn cl, gilt spine. Fine in slipcase. *Pacific**. $69/£43

DILLARD, ANNIE. Holy the Firm. NY: Harper & Row, (1977). 1st ed. Fine in Fine dj. *Dermont*. $35/£22

DILLARD, ANNIE. The Living. NY: Harper Collins, 1992. One of 300 numbered, signed. Fine in pict slipcase. *Smith*. $100/£63

DILLARD, ANNIE. Pilgrim at Tinker Creek. NY: Harpers, 1974. 1st ed. VG (sl shelfworn) in dj (edgeworn, sl faded). *My Bookhouse*. $42/£26

DILLARD, ANNIE. Tickets for a Prayer Wheel. (Columbia): Univ of MO, (1974). 1st ed, 1st bk. Fine in Fine dj (top edge sl worn). *Agvent*. $650/£406

DILLEY, ARTHUR URBANE. Oriental Rugs and Carpets. London/NY, 1931. 79 plts. (Extrems rubbed, tips bumped.) *Swann**. $69/£43

DILLEY, ARTHUR URBANE. Oriental Rugs and Carpets. NY/London, 1931. Color frontis, 78 plts (13 color, 7 maps). Fore-edge uncut (sl damp-spotted; eps lt spotted; spine sl discolored). *Edwards*. $104/£65

DILLIN, JOHN G. W. The Kentucky Rifle. Washington: National Rifle Assoc of America, 1924. 1st ed. VG. Howes D342. *Labordo*. $275/£172

DILLIN, JOHN G. W. The Kentucky Rifle. York, PA: Trimmer Ptg, 1959. 4th ed. VG in slipcase (repaired). *Labordo*. $115/£72

DILLON, JOHN TALBOT. Travels Through Spain.... Dublin: S. Price et al, 1781. 1st Dublin ed. xx,496pp; 4 plts, lg fldg map. Early calf (worn, spine extrems chipped, outer hinges cracked but holding). *Karmiole*. $300/£188

DILLON, RICHARD. Embarcadero. NY: Coward-McCann, (1959). 1st ed. Inscribed, signed presentation. Brn cl. VF in pict dj. *Argonaut*. $45/£28

DILLON, RICHARD. Fool's Gold. The Decline and Fall of Captain John Sutter of California. NY: Coward-McCann, (1967). Inscribed, signed presentation. Fine in pict dj. *Argonaut*. $45/£28

DILLON, RICHARD. Great Expectations. The Story of Benicia, California. Benicia, CA: Benicia Heritage Book, (1980). 1st ed. Blue cl, gilt. VF in pict dj. *Argonaut*. $75/£47

DILLON, RICHARD. The Legend of Grizzly Adams. NY: Coward-McCann, (1966). 1st ed. Inscribed. 16 plts. Orange cl. Fine in pict dj (sm chip top edge). *Pacific**. $29/£18

DILLON, RICHARD. Shanghaiing Days. NY: Coward-McCann, (1961). 1st ed. Signed. Rust cl, gilt. VF in pict dj. *Argonaut*. $50/£31

DILLON, RICHARD. Siskiyou Trail. The Hudson's Bay Company Route to California. NY: McGraw-Hill Book Co, (1975). 1st ed. VF in pict dj. *Argonaut*. $60/£38

DIMBLEBY, JONATHAN. The Palestinians. NY: Quartet Books, 1980. 1st US ed. 120 b/w photos by Donald McCullin. Fine in dj. *Cahan*. $50/£31

Dimensions of Black. La Jolla: Museum of Art, February 15-March 29, 1970. NF in black velour wrappers. *Turtle Island*. $65/£41

DIMOCK, A. W. The Book of the Tarpon. NY: Outing, 1911. 1st ed. VG+ (few lt cvr spots). *Bowman*. $120/£75

DIMOCK, GEORGE. Caroline Sturgis Tappan and the Grand Tour. Lenox, MA: Lenox Library Assoc, 1982. 1st ed. Frontis, 47 plts. (Dusty, few sl creases), else NF in pict stiff wrappers. *Cahan*. $40/£25

DIMSDALE, THOMAS J. The Vigilantes of Montana. Helena, MT: State Pub, n.d. 4th ed. Grn cl. Fine. *Labordo*. $85/£53

DIMSDALE, THOMAS. J. The Vigilantes of Montana. Norman: Univ of OK, (1955). VG in dj (sl worn). *Lien*. $17/£11

DINESEN, ISAK. Out of Africa. NY, (1938). 1st ed. Dj (edgeworn, chip on rear panel). *Swann**. $80/£50

DINESEN, ISAK. Out of Africa. NY, 1938. 1st ed. Dj (spine lt tanned). *Swann**. $161/£101

DINESEN, ISAK. Seven Gothic Tales. NY, 1934. 1st ed. One of 1010 numbered. Black cl. (Lacks slipcase.) *Swann**. $103/£64

DINGLE, EDWIN J. Across China on Foot. Bristol: J.W. Arrowsmith, n.d. (1911). 1st ed. Frontisport, 34 plts, fldg map. Red cl. (Sl foxed; spine sl faded.) *Morrell*. $88/£55

DINGMAN, REED O. and PAUL NATVIG. Surgery of Facial Fractures. Phila: W.B. Saunders, 1964. 1st ed. Fine. *Weber*. $150/£94

DINKINS, JAMES. Personal Recollections and Experiences in the Confederate Army. By an Old Johnnie. Cincinnati: Robert Clarke, 1897. 1st ed. Inscribed. 8vo. Frontisport, 280pp. Red cl. (Fr hinge sl tender), else VG. Howes D346. *Chapel Hill*. $700/£438

Dinosaurs. A Pop-Up Book. NY: Random House, 1977. Dot & Sy Barlowe (illus). 3 dbl-pg pop-ups. Glazed pict bds. VG-. *Bookfinders*. $40/£25

DIPRIMA, DIANE. Dinners and Nightmares. NY: Corinth, 1961. 1st Amer ed. VG+ in wraps. *Warren*. $30/£19

DIRINGER, D. The Alphabet: A Key to the History of Mankind. London: Hutchinson, (1968). 3rd ed. 2 vols. (Bkpls), else VG in djs, slipcase. *Pacific**. $86/£54

DIRINGER, D. The Hand Produced Book. London: Hutchinson's, 1953. Red cl (sl bumped). Dj (sl worn). *Maggs*. $56/£35

Discipline of the Wesleyan Methodist Connection of America. Boston, 1843. 1st ed. 96pp. Old calf. (Ink inscrip; fr hinges broken, cvrs heavily worn.) *King*. $150/£94

Discovery of Florida. (By Hernando de Soto.) SF: Book Club of CA, (1946). One of 280. Cl-backed dec bds, paper spine label. NF in dj (sl soiled, worn). *Pacific**. $150/£94

DISHER, MAURICE WILLSON. Blood and Thunder. London: Frederick Muller, (1949). Pict cl. VG in pict dj. *Dramatis*. $30/£19

DISMOND, BINGA. We Who Would Die and Other Poems. NY, 1943. 1st ed. (Spine ends rubbed.) Dj (sl worn). *Swann**. $92/£58

DISNEY, WALT. The 'Pop-up' Minnie Mouse. NY: Blue Ribbon Books, (1933). 1st ed. 8.5x6.5. 3 pop-ups. Pict bds. (Pencil name; soiled), else VG. *Pacific**. $196/£123

DISNEY, WALT. The Adventures of Mickey Mouse, Book I. Phila: David McKay, (1931). 1st ed. Pict bds. (Fr hinge cracked; spine, extrems rubbed), else VG. *Pacific**. $115/£72

DISNEY, WALT. Adventures of Mickey Mouse. Book I. Phila: David McKay, (1931). 1st ed. 32pp. Pict bds (cvrs, spine worn; corners bent). Contents VG. *New Hampshire**. $275/£172

DISNEY, WALT. The Adventures of Mickey Mouse. Book I. Phila: David McKay, (1931). 1st ed. 8vo. Wine-red cl, color paste label (scratch). Nice (text sl fingered). *Reisler*. $450/£281

DISNEY, WALT. Adventures of Mickey Mouse. Book I. Phila: McKay, (1931). 1st ed. 8vo. Color pict eps. Color pict bds. VG (sl rubbed, edgeworn). *Baltimore**. $550/£344

DISNEY, WALT. Adventures of Mickey Mouse. Book I. Phila, (1931). 1st ed of 1st Mickey Mouse bk. 8vo. Cl-backed stiff pict bds (lt edgeworn, rubbed). Nice. *Swann**. $747/£467

DISNEY, WALT. Adventures of Mickey Mouse. Book 2. Phila: McKay, (1932). Sm 8vo. Illus eps. Pict bds (spine, edges worn). VG. *Davidson*. $400/£250

DISNEY, WALT. Bambi. NY: G&D, (1942). 8vo. Yellow pict bds w/full color illus. Good in full color pict dj (worn, few chips). *Reisler*. $70/£44

DISNEY, WALT. The Big Bad Wolf and Little Red Riding Hood. NY: Blue Ribbon Books, (1934). 4to. 64pp. Full color pict bds (lower edge lt rubbed). *Reisler*. $450/£281

DISNEY, WALT. The Cold-Blooded Penguin. NY: Simon & Schuster, 1944. 1st ed. 8vo. 24pp. Cl spine (sl worn), color pict bds. Full color dj. *Reisler*. $75/£47

DISNEY, WALT. Dance of the Hours from Walt Disney's Fantasia. NY: Harper, (1940). 1st ed. 8vo. Illus yellow cl-backed bds. Good in full color dj (lt worn). *Reisler*. $200/£125

DISNEY, WALT. Donald Duck and the Haunted House. A Moving Picture Book. US: Franklin Watts, 1980. 5pp tab-operated mechanicals. Glazed pict bds. VG. *Bookfinders*. $40/£25

DISNEY, WALT. Donald Duck's Ghost Town Adventure. A Pop-Up Turn-Around Book. Maidenhead, UK: Purnell Books, 1978. 5 dbl-pg pop-ups. Glazed pict bds. VG. *Bookfinders*. $50/£31

DISNEY, WALT. Donald Duck. Abbeville Press, 1978. 1st ed. Fine. *Fine Books*. $35/£22

DISNEY, WALT. Donald's Lucky Day. Racine: Whitman, 1939. Obl 4to. 18pp. Good in color ptd wrappers w/tape spine as issued. *Reisler*. $335/£209

DISNEY, WALT. Dumbo. NY: Winkler & Ramen, 1941. Obl 4to. 16pp. Good in color pict wrappers (edges lt worn). *Reisler*. $50/£31

DISNEY, WALT. Elmer Elephant. Whitman, 1938. 9x12. Unpaginated. VG in pict wraps (spine very worn). *My Bookhouse*. $77/£48

DISNEY, WALT. Figaro and Cleo. NY: Random House, 1940. 8vo. Cl-bakced color pict bds. Good in full color pict dj (dusty, closed tear fr panel). *Reisler*. $150/£94

DISNEY, WALT. Hiawatha. Racine: Whitman, 1938. Lg 4to. 10pp. Good in linen-like full color pict wrappers (lt dusty). *Reisler*. $175/£109

DISNEY, WALT. The Life of Donald Duck. NY: Random House, (1941). 1st ed. 11x8.25. Cl-backed pict bds. (Worm hole to lower gutter area of last 1/2 of pp; corners, extrems rubbed), else VG. *Pacific**. $75/£47

DISNEY, WALT. The Life of Donald Duck. NY: Random House, (1941). 4to. 72pp. Cl-backed color pict bds (edges rubbed, worn). *Reisler*. $125/£78

DISNEY, WALT. Mickey Mouse and His Horse Tanglefoot. Phila: David McKay, (1936). 1st ed. 8vo. 60pp. Cl-backed color pict bds (edges lt worn, 1/2-inch chip to fr cvr label, spine mk). VG in full color dj (worn). *Reisler*. $1,200/£750

DISNEY, WALT. Mickey Mouse at the Circus. London: Birn Bros, (1936). 1st Eng ed. 4to. Full color illus bds. VG. *Reisler*. $375/£234

DISNEY, WALT. Mickey Mouse in Giantland. Phila: David McKay, (1934). 1st ed. 8vo. 45pp. Wine-red textured cl, full color paste label. Good. *Reisler*. $575/£359

DISNEY, WALT. Mickey Mouse Stories, Book No. 2. Phila: David McKay, 1934. Good in cl-backed pict stiff wrappers. *Pacific**. $63/£39

DISNEY, WALT. Mickey Mouse Stories—Book No 2. Phila: David McKay, 1934. 1st ed. Red cl, pict cvr label. NF. *Pacific**. $196/£123

DISNEY, WALT. Mickey Mouse Story Book. Phila: David McKay, (1931). 8vo. 62pp. Good in illus cl-backed stiff paper wrappers (sl worn). *Reisler*. $385/£241

DISNEY, WALT. Mickey's Dog Pluto. Racine, WI: Whitman, (1943). Pict bds. (Tp w/clean tear; extrems frayed, cvrs sl soiled), else Good. *King*. $22/£14

DISNEY, WALT. Mickey's Wonder Book. London: Collins, (ca 1950s). 4to. Cl-backed color illus bds (sm spot rear cvr). VG in pict dj (spine sl worn). *Reisler*. $285/£178

DISNEY, WALT. A New Adventure of Walt Disney's Snow White and the Seven Dwarfs. N.p.: Walt Disney Productions, 1952. 1st ed. 5 x 7 1/4. Color pict wrappers. Fine. *Pacific**. $46/£29

DISNEY, WALT. The Nutcracker Suite from Fantasia. Boston: Little, Brown, 1940. 1st ed. Lg 4to. Cl-backed color pict bds (edges sl rubbed). Full color dj (edges worn, rear cvr mkd, sm spine chip). *Reisler.* $150/£94

DISNEY, WALT. Pastoral from Walt Disney's Fantasia. NY: Harper, (1940). 1st ed. 8vo. Illus red cl-backed bds. Good in full color dj (lt worn). *Reisler.* $200/£125

DISNEY, WALT. Peculiar Penguins. Phila: David McKay, (1934). 8vo. 45pp. Red textured cl, color paste label. Good. *Reisler.* $175/£109

DISNEY, WALT. Pedro. NY: G&D, 1943. 8vo. Full color illus paper-cvrd bds. Good in full color dj (edgeworn). *Reisler.* $115/£72

DISNEY, WALT. Pinocchio. Racine: Whitman, (1939). 1st pb ed. 12mo. 144pp. Good in full color paper wrappers. *Reisler.* $100/£63

DISNEY, WALT. Pinocchio. Racine: Whitman, (1940). Sq 8vo. Cl-backed spine, full color illus bds. (Rep missing; lt edgeworn.) *Reisler.* $75/£47

DISNEY, WALT. Pinocchio. NY: Grosset & Dunlap, 1939. Obl 4to. Cl-backed yellow pict bds (lower edge lt dknd), full color illus. Color pict dj (margins torn, mkd). *Reisler.* $125/£78

DISNEY, WALT. Pinocchio. Racine: Whitman, 1939/40. 9x13. Unpaginated. (Sl worn.) Wraps. *My Bookhouse.* $150/£94

DISNEY, WALT. Pluto the Pup. Hollywood: Walt Disney Enterprises, 1937. Lg 4to. 10pp. Good in linenized full color pict paper wrappers. *Reisler.* $175/£109

DISNEY, WALT. The Pop-Up Mickey Mouse. NY: Blue Ribbon Books, (1933). 1st ed. 8.5x6.5. 3 color pop-ups. Pict bds. (Joints sl rubbed), else VG. *Pacific*.* $403/£252

DISNEY, WALT. The Pop-Up Minnie Mouse. NY: Blue Ribbon Books, (1933). 1st ed. 8.5x6.5. 3 color pop-ups. Pict bds. (Crayon name, mks), else VG. *Pacific*.* $86/£54

DISNEY, WALT. Pop-Up Minnie Mouse. NY: Blue Ribbon Books, (1933). 1st ed. 3 VG pop-ups. Cl-backed pict bds (edges, corners lt worn). VG. *Davidson.* $775/£484

DISNEY, WALT. Pop-Up Pinocchio. NY: Blue Ribbon Books, (1932). Thick 8vo. 96pp; 4 dbl-pg full color pop-ups by Harold Lentz. Full color pict bds (sl bump, fr hinge cracked). Full-color illus dj (dusty, margins worn). *Reisler.* $600/£375

DISNEY, WALT. Snow White and the Seven Dwarfs. NY: G&D, (1938). Obl 8vo. Cl-backed color pict bds. Good in full color pict dj (margins worn, sl folds along edges). *Reisler.* $150/£94

DISNEY, WALT. Snow White and the Seven Dwarfs. NY: Viking, (1939). 1st trade ed. 10.5x11.75. NF in dj. *Pacific*.* $138/£86

DISNEY, WALT. Snow White and the Seven Dwarfs. Phila: David McKay, 1937. 1st ed. Sq 4to. Cl-backed color pict bds (lt dusty, edges rubbed). Nice. *Reisler.* $100/£63

DISNEY, WALT. The Sorcerer's Apprentice from Fantasia. NY: G&D, (1940). Obl 8vo. 35pp. Cl-backed color pict bds (rubbed). *Reisler.* $75/£47

DISNEY, WALT. Three Little Pigs. NY: Blue Ribbon Books, (1933). 4to. 64pp; 12 full-pg color plts. Color pict bds (corners sl worn). Full color pict dj (margins worn, fr cvr lacks piece). *Reisler.* $300/£188

DISNEY, WALT. The Tortoise and the Hare. Racine: Whitman, (1935). 1st ed. 8 3/4 x 9 3/4. Pict bds. (Lt smudge fr cvr, creasing along joints), else VG in dj. *Pacific*.* $115/£72

DISNEY, WALT. Walt Disney Annual. Racine, WI: Whitman, (1937). 1st ed, 1st annual. Folio. 8 full-pg color plt inserts. (Margins browned.) Full color illus bds (spine sl worn). Full color dj (marginal chips, folds across rear cvr). *Reisler.* $500/£313

DISNEY, WALT. Walt Disney's Animals from Snow White and the Seven Dwarfs. Racine: Whitman, 1938. 1st ed. 12x8.75. (Spine sl rubbed), else VG in pict stiff linen wrappers. *Pacific*.* $92/£58

DISNEY, WALT. Walt Disney's Babes in Toyland. London: Dean & Son, 1962. 3 dbl-pg pop-ups. Glazed pict bds. VG. *Bookfinders.* $65/£41

DISNEY, WALT. Walt Disney's Bambi Saves the Day. A Pop-Up Turn-Around Book. NY: Windmill Books/E.P. Dutton, 1976. 5 dbl-pg pop-ups. Glazed pict bds. VG. *Bookfinders.* $40/£25

DISNEY, WALT. Walt Disney's Circus. NY: S&S, 1944. 1st ed. 8vo. Unpaginated. VG + in VG + dj. *Davidson.* $225/£141

DISNEY, WALT. Walt Disney's Donald Duck the Pop-Up Astronaut. London: Purnell, 1970. 6 dbl-pg pop-ups. Glazed pict bds. VG. *Bookfinders.* $80/£50

DISNEY, WALT. Walt Disney's Donald Duck's Pop-Up Circus. London: Purnell, 1970. 5 dbl-pg pop-ups. Glazed pict bds. VG. *Bookfinders.* $80/£50

DISNEY, WALT. Walt Disney's Mickey Mouse and the Martian Mix-Up. NY: Franklin Watts, 1978. 6 dbl-pg pop-ups. Glazed pict bds. VG. *Bookfinders.* $50/£31

DISNEY, WALT. Walt Disney's Pinocchio. Racine: Whitman, 1940. 1st ed thus. 13 x 9 1/2. Pict wrappers. (Extrems rubbed), else VG. *Pacific*.* $58/£36

DISNEY, WALT. Walt Disney's Pinocchio. Pop-Up Movie-Go-Round Book. NY: Windmill Books/S&S, 1981. 4 pull-down pop-ups that tie back w/ribbon to form circle. Glazed pict bds. VG. *Bookfinders.* $30/£19

DISNEY, WALT. Walt Disney's Snow White and the Seven Dwarfs. N.p.: Walt Disney Productions, (1937). 1st ed. Promo bk incl order form. 14.75x11. VG in pict wrappers (creased, sl soiled). *Pacific*.* $460/£288

DISNEY, WALT. Walt Disney's Snow White and the Seven Dwarfs. NY: Windmill Books/S&S, 1981. 4 pull-down pop-ups that tie back w/ribbon to form circle. Glazed pict bds. VG. *Bookfinders.* $30/£19

DISNEY, WALT. Walt Disney's Snow White Dairy Recipes. Chicago: American Dairy Assoc, 1955. 12mo. 14pp. Good in color pict wrappers. *Reisler.* $60/£38

DISNEY, WALT. Walt Disney's Tiny Movie Stories. NY: S&S, (1950). The Tiny Golden Library. 12 books housed in a box w/sleeve. Each bk is 2.1x3.15 inches. Box designed to look like movie theatre. VG (box, sleeve worn). *Reisler.* $250/£156

DISNEY, WALT. Walt Disney's Version of Pinocchio. NY: G&D, 1939. Obl slim sm 4to. Color pict eps. Black cl, yellow pict bds (edges sl dusty). VG (sl handled) in complete color pict dj (worn, chipped, sm tears, wrinkling). *Baltimore*.* $20/£13

DISNEY, WALT. Who's Afraid of the Big Bad Wolf: Three Little Pigs. Phila: David McKay, (1933). 1st ed. 8.5x6. (Sm tear lower fr corner, extrems rubbed), else VG in cl-backed pict stiff wrappers. *Pacific*.* $58/£36

DISNEY, WALT. The Wise Little Hen. Racine, WI: Whitman, (1935). Obl lg 4to. 6 full-pg color plts, 9 full-pg b/w illus. Color illus bds. Good in pict color dj. *Reisler.* $350/£219

DISOSWAY, GABRIEL P. The Earliest Churches of New York and Its Vicinity. NY: James G. Gregory, 1865. 1st ed. 416pp. Brn cl. Good + (ll sl browned; sl soiled). *House.* $45/£28

DISRAELI, BENJAMIN. The Bradenham Edition of the Novels and Tales of Benjamin Disraeli. London: Peter Davies, 1926-1927. 12 vols. Teg. Dec cl, gilt. VG set (bkpl each vol; corners, some spine ends bumped, 1 spine head nicked, 1 spine head sl chipped) in djs (nicked, chipped, rubbed, sl torn, creased, dusty, browned, some sl damp-stained at spines, 1 lacks sm piece at spine head). *Ulysses.* $1,040/£650

DISRAELI, BENJAMIN. Parliamentary Reform. Montagu Corry (ed). Longmans, Green, 1867. 1st ed. xi,478,(ii)pp (few marginal blind-stamps). Lib 1/2 morocco (rubbed, scraped), gilt. *Hollett.* $104/£65

DISRAELI, BENJAMIN. The Works of.... NY: M. Walter Dunne, (1904). One of 999. Signed by Robert Arnot (ed). 20 vols. Teg. Gilt-tooled morocco of various colors. (Spines sl sunned), else NF. *Pacific**. $546/£341

DITCHFIELD, P. H. London Survivals. London, 1914. Color frontis. Leather spine label. (Prelims spotted; spine sl discolored.) *Edwards*. $64/£40

DITCHFIELD, P. H. The Old English Country Squire. Methuen, 1912. 1st ed. 24 plts (8 color). (Sl spotted; few sm chips to spine ends.) *Hollett*. $72/£45

DITCHFIELD, P. H. Old English Sports, Pastimes and Customs. Methuen, 1891. 1st ed. xii,132,(ii)pp. Pict cl (sl cockled). *Hollett*. $104/£65

DITCHFIELD, P. H. Vanishing England. Methuen, 1911. 2nd ed. (Half-title foxed; spine sl faded), o/w Very Nice. *Hollett*. $104/£65

DITMARS, R. L. A Field Book of North American Snakes. NY, 1939. 1st ed. Color frontis, 48 plts. (Eps browned, name stamps, pp tanned.) Simulated snakeskin cl. Dj (worn). *Sutton*. $30/£19

DIVIDSON, JOHN (ed). Pictures of Rustic Landscape. (By Birket Foster.) NY: Longmans, Green, 1895. 1st Amer ed. 9.5x6.75. 30 engrs. Aeg. Grn cl, gilt. (Fr joint w/sm gouge, spine ends frayed, cvrs insect-damaged), else VG. *Pacific**. $40/£25

DIVINE, A. D. Dunkirk. NY, 1948. 1st ed. VG+ in VG+ dj. *Pratt*. $20/£13

DIVINE, CHARLES. Cognac Hill. NY: Payson & Clarke, (1927). 1st ed. Pict red cl. VG in pict dj (lt worn, nicked). *Reese*. $50/£31

DIXEY, MARMADUKE. Hell's Bells, a Comedy of the Underworld. London, 1936. 1st ed. Fine (lacks dj). *Petersfield*. $16/£10

DIXON, ALEC. Tinned Soldier. London: Jonathan Cape, 1941. 1st ed. Red cl. VG in dj (sl used). *Maggs*. $192/£120

DIXON, ALEC. Tinned Soldier. London: Cape, 1941. 1st ed. Red cl. VG in dj (sl used). *Maggs*. $240/£150

DIXON, FRANKLIN W. While the Clock Ticked. NY: G&D, 1932. Thick brn ed w/white spine dj. Hardy Boys #11; lists 18 titles on dj flap. 5x7.5. J. Clemens Gretta (illus). 213pp + ads. VG (shelfworn) in dj (chipped, rear dingy). *My Bookhouse*. $155/£97

DIXON, GEORGE. A Voyage Round the World; But More Particularly to the North-West Coast of America Performed in 1785, 1786, 1787, and 1788.... London: Geo. Goulding, 1789. 1st ed. 11.75x9. xxix,(3),360,47,(1)pp; lg copper-engr fldg map (facing frontis), 21 other copper-engr plts, charts, maps. Untrimmed. Mod full calf in period style, raised spine bands, morocco labels. NF (extreme pg edges dknd, sl worming to lower margin of frontis chart, sl stains to some lower margins internally). Howes D365. *Pacific**. $2,185/£1,366

DIXON, GEORGE. A Voyage Round the World; but More Particularly to the North-West Coast of America: Performed in 1785, 1786, 1787, and 1788, in the King George and Queen Charlotte. London, 1789. 1st ed. 4to. 5 fldg maps, 16 engr plts, leaf of music. Contemp calf. *Felcone*. $2,800/£1,750

DIXON, JAMES. Personal Narrative of a Tour Through a Part of the United States and Canada. NY: Lane & Scott, 1849. 1st Amer ed. Frontisport, 431pp. Orig grn cl, gilt. (Sl foxed), o/w Nice. *Mott*. $150/£94

DIXON, JAMES. The Songs of the Bells and Other Poems. R. Groombridge & Sons, 1852. 1st ed. x,154pp. Blind-stamped cl, gilt. VG. *Hollett*. $104/£65

DIXON, JOHN H. Pitlochry Past and Present. Pitlochry: L. Mackay, 1925. 1st ed. 100 full-pg illus (3 color). VG. *Hollett*. $72/£45

DIXON, MAYNARD. Rim-Rock and Sage: The Collected Poems of Maynard Dixon. SF: CA Hist Soc, (1977). 1st ed. One of 1300 ptd. Fine in NF dj (sm spot fr panel). *Pacific**. $75/£47

DIXON, PHIL and PATRICK HANNIGAN. The Negro Baseball Leagues. Amereon, 1992. 1st ed. Fine in Fine dj. *Plapinger*. $100/£63

DIXON, THOMAS. The Clansman. NY: Doubleday, 1905. 1st ed. Red cl. VG. *Labordo*. $35/£22

DIXON, W. MACNEILE. Cinderella's Garden. OUP, 1927. 1st ed. 8vo. Color frontis, 136pp; 12 full-pg b/w illus by George Morrow. Gray/grn eps. Pict cl. VG (mks, rubbed). *Bookmark*. $32/£20

DIXON, WILLIAM HEPWORTH. New America.... London: Hurst & Blackett, 1867. 6th ed. 2 vols. Blue cl (sl faded). NF. *Mott*. $100/£63

DIXON, WILLIAM HEPWORTH. White Conquest. London: C&W, 1876. 1st ed. 2 vols. viii,356,36 ads dated Mar 1887; vi,373pp (eps cracked). Grn cl. *Mott*. $150/£94

DIXSON, ZELLA ALLEN. Concerning Book-Plates. Chicago: Wisteria Cottage Press, 1903. 1st ed. Inscribed. 4-pg als tipped in. 29 plts. Brn dec cl (sl soiled; bkpl, browning ep). *Karmiole*. $75/£47

DOBBINS, W. W. History of the Battle of Lake Erie (September 10, 1813) and Reminiscences of the Flagships 'Lawrence' and 'Niagara.' Erie, PA, 1913. 2nd ed. Frontis port, 4 plts. Blue cl. VG. *Bohling*. $45/£28

DOBELL, BERTRAM. Catalogue of Books Printed for Private Circulation. London: The Author, 1906. 1st ed. Uncut. (Lt worn.) Paper spine label (sl dknd, scuffed). *Oinonen**. $50/£31

DOBELL, H. The Medical Aspects of Bournemouth and Its Surroundings. London, 1886. xii,338pp; 4 color plts. (Sl mkd, spine faded, label; spine, corners worn), o/w VG. *Whitehart*. $64/£40

DOBELL, H. On Winter Cough, Catarrh, Bronchitis, Emphysema, Asthma. London, 1875. 3rd, enlgd ed. xxxvi,292pp + 23pp pub's cat; 2 color plts. (Sl rubbed; pg267 onwards sm ink stain to fore-edge intruding sl on margin, bkpl). *Edwards*. $56/£35

DOBELL, SYDNEY. England in the Time of Civil War. Smith Elder, 1856. 1st ed. 16pp cat bound in at rear. Grn blind-dec cl, gilt. (Spine ends sl bumped), else Fine. *Any Amount*. $56/£35

DOBIE, J. FRANK and JEFF DYKES. 44 Range Country Books and 44 More Range Country Books. Austin: Encino, 1972. Signed by Dykes. NF. *Dumont*. $45/£28

DOBIE, J. FRANK and JEFF DYKES. 44 Range Country Books Topped Out by J. Frank Dobie in 1941 and 44 More Range Country Books Topped Out by Jeff Dykes in 1971. Austin: Encino, 1971. One of 1000. Signed by Dykes. Tp sketch. Paper cvr label. Fine. *Pacific**. $46/£29

DOBIE, J. FRANK and MODY BOATRIGHT. Straight Texas. Austin: Steck, 1937. 1st ed. (Rubberstamps), o/w VG in dj. *Labordo*. $60/£38

DOBIE, J. FRANK (ed). Texas and Southwestern Lore. Austin: TX Folk-Lore Soc, 1927. 1st ed. Blue cl, gilt. (Adhesion damage to pastedowns; spine ends, corners rubbed), else VG. *Pacific**. $40/£25

DOBIE, J. FRANK et al. Mustangs and Cow Horses. Austin: TX Folk-Lore Soc, 1940. 1st ed. Tan cl. (Offset to eps, lower edges of cvrs from earlier jacket protector), else VG in dj (soiled, spine sl sunned, price-clipped). *Pacific**. $46/£29

DOBIE, J. FRANK et al. Mustangs and Cow Horses. Austin: Texas Folk-lore Soc, 1940. 1st ed. Inscribed by Dobie. Tan cl. (Eps dknd), else VG in dj (soiled, worn; spine head, top edge chipped). *Pacific**. $104/£65

DOBIE, J. FRANK. Apache Gold and Yaqui Silver. Boston: Little, Brown, 1939. 1st ed. VG in dj. *Labordo*. $100/£63

DOBIE, J. FRANK. Apache Gold and Yaqui Silver. Boston, 1939. 1st Amer ed. Fine in dj (spine sl chipped, edge rubbed). *Polyanthos.* $100/£63

DOBIE, J. FRANK. Apache Gold and Yaqui Silver. Boston, 1939. One of 265 numbered on rag paper, signed by Dobie & Tom Lea (dwgs). 5 color plts in envelope. 1/2 buckram, paper spine label (rubbed). *Swann*.* $460/£288

DOBIE, J. FRANK. Coronado's Children. Dallas: Southwest Press, (1930). 1st ed, 2nd issue, w/dedication to Dobie's father as 'a clean cowman...' Untrimmed; top edge stained red-orange. Black cl, gilt. (Old news clipping mtd to reps; spine gilt faded, sm tear spine head.) Howes D374. *Baltimore*.* $30/£19

DOBIE, J. FRANK. Coronado's Children. Dallas: Southwest Press, 1930. 1st ed, later issue. Inscribed presentation. 6 plts. Black cl, gilt. (Fr corner bumped), else VG in dj (paper tape repairs on verso at spine head and fr corner, which have bled through; sl worn). Howes D374. *Pacific*.* $184/£115

DOBIE, J. FRANK. Coronado's Children: Tales of Lost Mines and Buried Treasures of the Southwest. NY: Literary Guild, 1931. Fine in Fine dj. *Book Market.* $25/£16

DOBIE, J. FRANK. Cow People. Boston: Little, Brown, (1964). 1st ed. Brn cl. Fine in dj. *House.* $35/£22

DOBIE, J. FRANK. The Flavor of Texas. Dallas: Dealey & Lowe, 1936. 1st ed. Dec cl. (Sl shelfworn), else VG. *Pacific*.* $92/£58

DOBIE, J. FRANK. Guide to Life and Literature of the Southwest. Dallas: Southern Methodist Univ, 1943. 1st ed. Fine in orig blue ptd wrappers (sl worn). *House.* $60/£38

DOBIE, J. FRANK. John C. Duval, First Texas Man of Letters. Dallas: Southwest Review, 1939. One of 1000. 2-tone cl. (Lt shelfworn), else NF. *Pacific*.* $63/£39

DOBIE, J. FRANK. The Longhorns. Boston: Little, Brown, 1941. 1st trade ed. NF in dj (few sm edge tears). *Pacific*.* $86/£54

DOBIE, J. FRANK. The Mustangs. Boston: Little, Brown, (1952). 1st ed. Color frontis. Pict eps. Blue/tan cl. VG in color pict dj (seamed tear, edges lt worn). *House.* $75/£47

DOBIE, J. FRANK. The Mustangs. Boston: Little, Brown, (1952). 1st trade ed, 1st issue dj. Color frontis. 2-tone pict cl. Dj (price-clipped, lt worn). *Dawson.* $100/£63

DOBIE, J. FRANK. The Mustangs. Boston: Little, Brown, 1952. 1st trade ed. Fine in dj. *Labordo.* $75/£47

DOBIE, J. FRANK. On the Open Range. Dallas: Southwest, 1931. 1st ed. VG (spine faded, head tender). *Labordo.* $175/£109

DOBIE, J. FRANK. Prefaces. Boston: Little, Brown, (1975). 1st ed. Black/orange bds. VG in dj. *House.* $25/£16

DOBIE, J. FRANK. Prefaces. Boston: Little Brown, 1975. 1st ed. VG + in dj (skinned). *Labordo.* $35/£22

DOBIE, J. FRANK. Rattlesnakes. Boston: Little, Brown, 1965. 1st ed. Fine in dj. *Labordo.* $40/£25

DOBIE, J. FRANK. Some Part of Myself. Boston: Little, Brown, (1967). 1st ed. Grn cl. Fine in pict dj (spine dknd). *Argonaut.* $45/£28

DOBIE, J. FRANK. Tales of Old-Time Texas. Boston, 1955. 1st Amer ed. NF (sl rubbed) in dj (spine sunned, sm chip, few sm nicks). *Polyanthos.* $30/£19

DOBIE, J. FRANK. Tongues of the Monte. GC: Doubleday, Doran, 1935. 1st ed. Dec cl. Fine (spine sl sunned). *Pacific*.* $46/£29

DOBIE, J. FRANK. Tongues of the Monte. GC, 1935. 1st ed. Signed. (Name; sl worn, dirty.) *Woolson.* $125/£78

DOBIE, J. FRANK. A Vaquero of the Brush Country. Dallas: Southwest Press, 1929. 1st ed, 1st issue w/'Rio Grande River' (instead of Rio Grande) on ep maps; 1st bk. 6 plts. 1/2 tan cl, bds w/snakeskin pattern, ptd cvr label. (Corners, lower edges lt rubbed), else NF in dj (rear soiled, spine ends lt chipped, corners sl nicked). Howes D376. *Pacific*.* $403/£252

DOBIE, J. FRANK. The Voice of the Coyote. London: Hammond, Hammond, (1950). 1st British ed. Blue cl. VG in dj (sm scrape fr cvr). *House.* $45/£28

DOBIE, J. FRANK. The Voice of the Coyote. Boston: Little, Brown, 1949. 1st ed. Brn cl. VG in pict dj (edges lt chipped). *House.* $75/£47

DOBIE, J. FRANK. The Voice of the Coyote. Boston: Little, Brown, 1949. 1st ed. Signed. NF in dj (sl shelfworn, price-clipped). *Pacific*.* $109/£68

DOBLE, JOHN. John Doble's Journal and Letters from the Mines. Charles L. Camp (ed). Denver: Old West Pub Co, (1962). One of 1000. 5 plts, 3 fldg maps. Unopened. Pict cl. Fine. *Pacific*.* $98/£61

DOBLE, JOHN. John Doble's Journal and Letters from the Mines: Mokelumne Hill, Jackson, Volcano and San Francisco, 1851-1865. Charles L. Camp (ed). Dencer: Old West Pub, (1962). 1st ed. One of 1000 ptd. 5 plts, 3 fldg maps. Unopened. Pict cl. Fine. *Pacific*.* $46/£29

DOBSON, AUSTIN. At Prior Park and Other Papers. C&W, 1912. Teg. VG (fore-edge lt spotted, bkpls; spine bumped). *Tiger.* $19/£12

DOBSON, AUSTIN. Eighteenth Century Vignettes. C&W, 1892. Fldg frontis. Teg. Good (sl spotted; spine bumped). *Tiger.* $22/£14

DOBSON, AUSTIN. A Paladin of Philanthropy and Other Papers. London: C&W, 1899. Ad leaf before 1/2-title; Frontis, guard, dbl-pg plan; ptr's imprint leaf, pub's inserted 32-pg cat at end dated Mar 1899; (xii),361,(i blank),(ii)pp. Teg, rest uncut. Brick red coarse buckram, gilt. Good (sl foxed; spine sl faded). *Temple.* $29/£18

DOBSON, AUSTIN. Rosalba's Journal and Other Papers. C&W, 1915. Teg. Good (bkpls, top edge of ll tanned; spine bumped, sl chipped). *Tiger.* $16/£10

DOBSON, AUSTIN. Side-Walk Studies. C&W, 1902. Pub's cat dated March 1902. Teg. Good (bkpl, fore-edge sl spotted; spine bumped, chipped, lt sunned). *Tiger.* $16/£10

DOBSON, G. St. Petersburg. A&C Black, 1910. 1st ed. 32 full-pg illus, fldg color plan. Full contemp calf prize binding, gilt, raised bands. VG (ink inscrip). *Sotheran.* $237/£148

DOBSON, WILLIAM T. A Narrative of the Peninsular Campaign 1807-1814, Its Battles and Sieges. Bickers & Son, 1889. vi,(ii),408pp; 10 plts, 1 map. All eps, edges marbled. Full calf (backstrip rubbed, fr hinge weak), gilt. *Hollett.* $72/£45

DOBYNS, STEPHEN. Concurring Beasts. NY: Atheneum, 1972. 1st ed, 1st bk. Erratum slip laid in. (Date on fr pastedown), else Fine in dj. *Captain's Bookshelf.* $75/£47

DOCKSTADER, FREDERICK J. Indian Art in Middle America. Greenwich: NYGS, (1964). 70 tipped-in color plts. Dj (faded). *Archaeologia.* $125/£78

DOCKSTADER, FREDERICK J. Indian Art in South America. Greenwich: NYGS, (1967). Folio. Color frontis, 49 tipped-in color plts. Dj. *Archaeologia.* $125/£78

DOCKSTADER, LEW et al. Minstrel and Black Face Joke Book. Balt: I. & M. Ottenheimer, (1907). 1st ed. (Pencil-size hole in cvr), o/w VG in pict wraps. *Petrilla.* $45/£28

DOCTOROW, E. L. Big as Life. NY: S&S, (1966). 1st ed. NF in VG dj (lt soiled, internal tape reinforcements, quarter-sized chip upper rt corner, cl at that spot sl dknd). *Agvent.* $400/£250

DOCTOROW, E. L. Drinks Before Dinner. NY, (1979). 1st ed. Signed. Dj. *Swann*.* $80/£50

DOCTOROW, E. L. Lives of the Poets. NY: Random House, (1984). One of 350. Signed. Blue cl, gilt. Fine in slipcase. *Pacific*.* $46/£29

DOCTOROW, E. L. Ragtime. NY: Random House, (1975). 1st ed. Signed. (Sl bumped, edges sl sunned), else Fine in NF dj (2 sm tears). *Between The Covers.* $150/£94

DOCTOROW, E. L. Ragtime. NY, (1975). 1st ed. One of 150 numbered, signed. Slipcase. *Swann**. $230/£144

Documents Relating to the War Power of Congress, the President's Authority as Commander-in-Chief and the War in Indochina. Washington: GPO, 1970. 1st ed. *Associates*. $100/£63

DODD, J. S. The Ancient and Modern History of Gibraltar, and the Sieges...by the Spaniards, from February 13, to June 23, 1727. London, 1781. 1/2 calf (needs rebinding). *Swann**. $103/£64

DODD, WILLIAM. Thoughts in Prison. J. Mawman et al, 1815. xviii,212pp + (iv)pp ads. Untrimmed. Mod 1/2 levant morocco, gilt. VG. *Hollett*. $152/£95

DODD, WILLIAM. Thoughts in Prison...with the Life of the Author, His Last Prayer, and Other Miscellaneous Pieces.... London: Ptd by Dean & Munday, 1816? Contemp unlettered tree sheep (joints sl cracked). Nice. *Boswell*. $225/£141

DODD, WILLIAM. Thoughts in Prison: In Five Parts.... London: C. Dilly, 1789. 3rd ed. Engr frontisport, xxxvi,208pp. Contemp tree calf (sl scuffed), red morocco spine label. *Karmiole*. $75/£47

DODD, WILLIAM. Thoughts in Prison: In Five Parts.... London: C. Dilly, 1793. 4th ed. Frontisport, xxxvi,208pp. Period style full polished calf (rebound), gilt, raised bands. VG. *Hartfield*. $295/£184

DODDRIDGE, JOSEPH. Notes on the Settlement and Indian Wars of the Western Parts of Virginia and Pennsylvania, from 1763 to 1783, Inclusive. Alfred Williams (ed). Albany: Joel Munsell, 1876. 2nd ed. 331pp. Dk brn coated eps. Blue cl, gilt. (Sl aged; spine dknd.) Text Clean, cvrs VG. Howes D390. *Baltimore**. $120/£75

DODDRIDGE. The Principles of the Christian Religion. Boston: Lincoln & Edmands, 1810. 24mo. Woodcut frontis; 1st, last ll pasted to cvrs. VG (sm chip bottom edge p13) in blue marble paper wrappers (spine restored, sm hole rear cvr). *Hobbyhorse*. $115/£72

DODDS, BABY. The Baby Dodds Story. Larry Gara (ed). L.A.: Contemporary, 1959. 1st ed. VG in pict stiff wraps. *Petrilla*. $25/£16

DODDS, GORDON B. The Salmon King of Oregon. Chapel Hill: Univ of NC, (1959). 1st ed. Fine in dj. *Perier*. $40/£25

DODGE, MARY MAPES. Along the Way. NY: Scribner, 1879. 1st ed, in variant 'gilt-extra' binding, w/dec eps. Gilt dec olive brn cl. (Sl rubbed), o/w NF. BAL 4773. *Reese*. $50/£31

DODGE, MARY MAPES. Hans Brinker, or the Silver Skates. NY: McLoughlin, ca 1910. Sm 4to. 4 color plts by Mary Audubon Post. Tan pict cl. VG (sm edge tear 1 pg, fr hinge sl cracked; sl rubbed). *Baltimore**. $25/£16

DODGE, RICHARD I. The Hunting Grounds of the Great West. London, 1877. 1st London ed. 20 plts, fldg map. Pict cl, gilt. (Recased retaining orig eps, bottom sl mkd.) Internally Good. *Hallam*. $176/£110

DODGE, RICHARD I. A Living Issue. Washington: Francis B. Mohun, 1882. 1st ed. 37 pg pamphlet. (Lacks wrappers, removed, tp stamp), else Good. Howes D402. *Brown*. $300/£188

DODGE, RICHARD I. Our Wild Indians. Hartford, 1883. 2nd ptg. (Extrems worn, hinges, couple sigs loosening.) Howes D403. *Baade*. $50/£31

DODGE, RICHARD I. Our Wild Indians: Thirty-Three Years' Personal Experience Among the Red Men of the Great West. Hartford, 1883. 6 color plts. *Dumont*. $100/£63

DODGE, THEODORE A. Riders of Many Lands. NY, 1894. 1st ed. Frederic Remington (illus). 486pp + 2pp ads. (Early bksellers pencil note inside fr cvr; sl worn, dirty.) *Woolson*. $70/£44

DODGE, THEODORE A. Riders of Many Lands. NY: Harper, 1894. 1st ed. Frederick Remington (illus). viii,486pp + (2)pp ads. Teg. Pict brn cl, gilt. Fine (cvrs sl soiled). *House*. $120/£75

DODGE, WILLIAM SUMNER. Robert Henry Hendershot; or, The Brave Drummer Boy of the Rappahannock. Chicago: Church & Goodman, 1867. 1st ed. Frontis, 202pp. Blue cl (edges rubbed), gilt. *M & S*. $225/£141

DODGSON, CAMPBELL. A Catalogue of Etchings by Augustus John, 1901-1914. London, 1920. One of 325. 1/4 cl (spine dknd, extrems worn). *Swann**. $258/£161

DODGSON, CAMPBELL. The Etchings of James McNeill Whistler. London, 1922. 1/4 vellum. (Spine dknd.) *Swann**. $201/£126

DODGSON, CAMPBELL. Prints in the Dotted Manner and Other Metal-Cuts of the XV Century in the Department of Prints and Drawings, British Museum. London, 1937. Folio. 44 plts, incl color frontis. *Swann**. $258/£161

DODGSON, CAMPBELL. Woodcuts of the Fifteenth Century. Manchester: University Press, 1915. Folio folder. 10 color plts. Cl-backed bds, linen tie. VG. *Hollett*. $72/£45

DODGSON, CAMPBELL. Woodcuts of the XV Century in the Department of Prints and Drawings, British Museum. London, 1934-35. 2 vols. Folio. (Vol 1 corner damaged.) *Swann**. $115/£72

DODINGTON, GEORGE BUBB. The Diary of the Late...Baron of Melcombe Regis.... Dublin: William Porter, 1784. 1st Dublin ed. 1/2-title bound in at end, xiv,346pp. Old calf (sl worn). *Young*. $72/£45

DODSLEY, ROBERT. The Economy of Human Life. Boston, 1804. Full sheep, morocco spine label. (Ink notes on eps; lt rubbed.) *Argosy*. $50/£31

DODSON, C. and R. GILLESPIE. The Biology of the Orchids. Nashville: Mid-Amer Orchid Congr., 1967. 1st ed. VG. *Archer*. $22/£14

DOERING, HEINRICH UBBELOHDE. The Art of Ancient Peru. NY: Frederick A. Praeger, 1954. 2nd ed. VG in dj (torn). *Metropolitan**. $69/£43

DOHERTY, P. C. The Death of a King. London: Hale, 1985. 1st ed, 1st bk. Fine in dj (rubbed, sm stain to spine foot). *Murder*. $125/£78

DOIG, IVAN. This House of Sky. NY: HBJ, 1978. 1st ed, 1st bk. NF in dj. *Smith*. $150/£94

DOIG, IVAN. This House of Sky. NY: Harcourt, 1978. 1st ed, 1st bk. NF in NF dj. *Unger*. $175/£109

Doings in London; or, Day and Night Scenes of the Frauds, Frolics, Manners, and Depravities of the Metropolis. (By George Smeeton.) London: Orlando Hodgson, (1840). 10th ed. (iv),423pp; 33 engrs. Orig cl (recased; ex-libris). *Young*. $136/£85

DOLE, EDMUND P. Hiwa, a Tale of Ancient Hawaii. NY/London: Harper, 1900. Inscribed. (Binding dknd), else VG + . *Zubal**. $60/£38

DOLE, NATHAN HASKELL. Peace and Progress: Two Symphonic Poems—The Building of the Organ Onward. Boston: Privately ptd, 1904. 1st ed. One of 150. Signed. (Soiled, sl spotted), else VG-. *Pacific**. $75/£47

Doll Book. NY: McLoughlin Bros, 1914. Shapebook. Tall 4to. 14pp. Good in color pict paper wrappers (spine foot chipped, lt wear, sl folds). *Reisler*. $150/£94

DOLL, WILLIAM H. History of the Sixth Regiment. Columbus, IN, 1903. 1st ed. (Bkpl, ink inscrip; cvrs worn, hinges loose.) *King*. $200/£125

Dollie's ABC. London: Dean & Son, ca 1900. 4to. 10pp (marginal tears); 4 full-pg color plts by Florence Hardy. (Spine chipped.) Color pict wrappers (worn, corner replaced). *Reisler*. $175/£109

Dollikin Dutch and How She Helped Piet and Nella. London: Henry Frowde, (c. 1910). 1st ed. E. Aris (illus). 9 1/2 x 7. Cl-backed pict bds. (Corners rubbed), else VG. *Pacific**. $69/£43

DOLLMAN, FRANCIS T. Examples of Ancient Domestic Architecture. London, 1858. Folio. Frontis, xvi,41pp (lt spotted; new eps); 40 plts at rear (lower, sometimes fore-edge sl waterstained). Emb cl (lt rubbed, sl bumped, few sm splits, rebacked in mod cl, much of orig spine laid down). *Edwards*. $77/£48

DOLLMAN, J. G. and J. B. BURLACE (eds). Rowland Ward's Records of Big Game. London, 1922. Dec eps. (Hinges cracking; spine, fr bd faded.) *Edwards*. $152/£95

DOLMAN, ALFRED. In the Footsteps of Livingstone. John Irving (ed). London, 1924. 1st ed. Color frontis, 5 maps (3 fldg). (Margins lt spotted; spine sl rubbed, sl paint spotting.) *Edwards*. $40/£25

DOMENECH, ABBE EMMANUEL. Seven Years' Residence in the Great Deserts of North America. London: Longman, Green et al, 1860. 1st ed. 2 vols. xxiv,445; xii,465pp; fldg map, 58 plts. Orig full calf prize binding (rebacked, rubbed). Howes D410. *Adelson*. $475/£297

DOMESTICA, ACHETA. (Pseud of L. M. Budgen.) Episodes of Insect Life. London: Reeve, Benham et al, 1849-1850-1851. 1st eds. 3 vols. 3/4 contemp grn calf over marbled bds, gilt paneled spines, raised bands; red, maroon labels, marbled edges. *Appelfeld*. $300/£188

DOMINGUEZ, FRANCISCO ATANASIO. The Missions of New Mexico, 1776. Eleanor B. Adams & Angelico Chavex (trans). Albuquerque: Univ of NM, (1956). 1st ed. Tipped-in color frontis. NF in dj (sl dusty, lt edgeworn). *Pacific**. $63/£39

DONAHEY, WILLIAM. Adventures of the Teenie Weenies. Chicago: Reilly & Lee, (1920). 1st ed. 4to. 9 color plts. Dk grn cl (sl worn, lt rubbed), lg color pict label fr cvr. Text VG (fr hinge lt cracked, ink inscrip). *Baltimore**. $180/£113

DONAHEY, WILLIAM. Adventures of the Teenie Weenies. Chicago: Reilly & Lee, (1920). 1st ed. 4to. 6 full-pg color plts. Grn cl (edgeworn), color paste label (edges chipped). *Reisler*. $285/£178

DONAHEY, WILLIAM. Down the River with the Teenie Weenies. Chicago: Reilly & Lee, (1921). 1st ed. 4to. 8 full-pg color plts. Grn cl, color paste label (edges worn). *Reisler*. $275/£172

DONAHEY, WILLIAM. Teenie Weenie Neighbors. NY: Whittlesey House, (1945). 2nd ptg. 8vo. 68pp; 5 full-pg color plts. Full color pict bds (lower edges rubbed). Full color pict dj (spine lt chipped, lt dusty). *Reisler*. $185/£116

DONAHEY, WILLIAM. Teenie Weenie Town. NY: Whittlesey House, (1942). 1st ed. 8vo. 10 full-pg color plts, 30 b/w dwgs. Red cl, color paste labels fr/rear. Good in full color dj (worn, dusty). *Reisler*. $250/£156

DONAHEY, WILLIAM. The Teenie Weenies in the Wildwood. Chicago: Reilly & Lee, (1923). 1st ed. 4to. 8 full-pg color plts (1 b/w plt w/marginal tear). Brn-tan cl, color paste label (scratched, few notes; fr hinge starting). *Reisler*. $225/£141

DONALD, JAY. Outlaws of the Border. Cincinnati: Forsee & McMakin, 1882. 2nd issue. Pict cl. Good + (edges worn). Howes D415. *Labordo*. $150/£94

DONALDSON, LOIS. Uruguay in Story and Picture. Whitman, 1943. 1st ed. 8x5 oblong. Kurt Wiese (illus). Unpaginated. VG (tape pull fep) in Good dj. *Price*. $25/£16

DONALDSON, M. E. E. Wanderings in the Western Highlands and Islands. Paisley: Alexander Gardner, 1923. 2nd ed. Map. Dec blue cl, gilt. (Rear joint cracking.) *Hollett*. $152/£95

DONALDSON, T. L. Pompeii, Illustrated with Picturesque Views.... London: W.B. Cooke, 1827. 2 vols bound in 1. 80 engr plts and plans, incl 3 hand-colored aquatints. (1 plan spotted, 1st few ll incl tp stained at upper margin, lt soiling, sm emb/ink lib stamps, lib bkpl.) Contemp 1/2 calf (rubbed, spine worn, label detached). *Christie's**. $990/£619

DONALDSON, THOMAS. The Public Domain; Its History with Statistics. Washington: GPO, 1884. 1343pp; 15 fldg maps. *Dumont*. $225/£141

DONALDSON, W. Fifty Years of Green-Room Gossip. London: John & Robert Maxwell, (1881). Pict yellow bds (extrems worn, ex-lib, hinges reinforced w/cl tape). Good. *Dramatis*. $40/£25

DONDERS, F. C. Of the Anomalies of Accomodation and Refraction of the Eye. Wiliam Daniel Moore (trans). New Sydenham Soc, 1864. 1st ed. xvii,(iii),635pp; 1 plt. Optician's panel of letters of different sizes folded, tipped into fr of 1/2 title. (Lib stamps, lib # in ink on tp; sm slits at joints.) *Bickersteth*. $296/£185

DONDORE, DOROTHY A. The Prairie and the Making of Middle America. Cedar Rapids, IA: Torch, 1926. 1st ed. *Ginsberg*. $125/£78

DONLEAVY, J. P. The Ginger Man. Paris: Olympia, (1955). 1st ed. Signed. W/price of '9 Francs' affixed to rear cvr. 12mo. NF (3 lt stains fr cvr) in grn ptd wrappers. *Heritage*. $750/£469

DONLEAVY, J. P. The Ginger Man. London: Neville Spearman, (1956). 1st Eng ed. Blue bds, gilts pine. NF (spine sl faded) in dj (lt soiled, few sm edgetears). *Heritage*. $150/£94

DONLEAVY, J. P. The Ginger Man. Paris: Olympia, 1958. 1st hb ed. Fine in dj. *Williams*. $64/£40

DONLEAVY, J. P. Meet My Maker. The Mad Molecule. Boston, 1964. 1st Amer ed. Signed. Fine (lt rubbed, spine sunned) in dj (few nicks, sl soiled). *Polyanthos*. $35/£22

DONLEY, MICHAEL W. et al. Atlas of California. Culver City: Pacific Book Center, (1979). 1st ed. Fine in Fine dj. *Book Market*. $50/£31

DONNE, JOHN. Complete Poetry and Selected Prose. John Hayward (ed). Nonesuch, 1929. One of 675. Teg on the rough. Orig pale blue morocco, gilt, raised bands. VG (backstrip faded) in marbled bd slipcase. *Blackwell's*. $320/£200

DONNE, JOHN. Complete Poetry and Selected Prose. John Hayward (ed). London: Nonesuch, 1930. 2nd imp. NF. *Agvent*. $40/£25

DONNE, JOHN. The Courtier's Library. Evelyn Mary Simpson (ed). London: Nonesuch, 1930. One of 950. Paper bds (spine faded), skiver label. Black slipcase. *Maggs*. $64/£40

DONNE, JOHN. Devotions—Upon Emergent Occasions. John Sparrow (ed). CUP, 1923. B/w frontisport. VG (top edge sl dusty, ep gutters sl browned; spine ends sl bumped) in dj (nicked, chipped, rubbed, mkd, dusty, sl creased, browned, internal cellotape stains that show through on other side). *Ulysses*. $120/£75

DONNE, JOHN. The Holy Sonnets. London, 1938. One of 550 signed. Eric Gill (illus). Black buckram, gilt. (Fep sl tanned; extrems sl rubbed; no dj.) *Clearwater*. $440/£275

DONNE, JOHN. Love Poems. Nonesuch, 1923. One of 1250 numbered. Unopened. Vellum-backed patterned bds (corner tips worn). Good (bkpl). *Clearwater*. $160/£100

DONNE, JOHN. Love Poems. (London): Nonesuch, 1923. One of 1250 numbered. Sm folio. Frontis. Fore/bottom edges untrimmed. VG in 1/4 vellum, red patterned bds. *Maggs*. $360/£225

DONNE, JOHN. The Poems of.... Cambridge: LEC, 1968. One of 1500. Signed by Imre Reiner (illus). 1/2 red morocco, yellow cl, emb port medallion on fr cvr. Fine in glassine, slipcase. *Pacific**. $69/£43

DONNE, JOHN. Poems...with Elegies on the Author's Death. T.N. for Henry Herringham, 1669. 5th ed. 8vo. Contemp 1/2 calf. (Some ll shaved, 1st few ll repaired, sl dampstained; rebacked, lacks cornerpieces.) *Sotheby's**. $515/£322

DONNE, JOHN. The Tolling Bell. (Stamford: Overbrook, 1941.) One of 540 w/a wood engr by Rudolph Ruzicka. Ptd note laid in. NF. *Pharos*. $45/£28

DONOSO, JOSE. The Boom in Spanish American Literature. NY: Columbia Univ, 1972. 1st US ed. Rev copy w/slip laid in. NF in NF dj (sl water stain to spine verso). *Lame Duck*. $175/£109

DONOSO, JOSE. Charleston. Boston: Godine, 1977. 1st US ed. One of 200 deluxe. Signed. NF. *Lame Duck*. $150/£94

DONOSO, JOSE. Coronation. London: Bodley Head, 1965. 1st British ed, 1st ed in English. NF in dj (sm chips to fr flap-fld tips, spine head lt worn). *Lame Duck*. $150/£94

DONOSO, JOSE. A House in the Country. NY: Knopf, 1984. 1st US ed. Signed. (Remainder stroke to top edge), else NF in dj. *Lame Duck*. $75/£47

DONOSO, JOSE. The Obscene Bird of Night. London: Cape, 1974. 1st British ed. NF in dj (price-clipped). *Lame Duck*. $100/£63

DONOSO, JOSE. Sacred Families. NY: Knopf, 1977. 1st US ed. (Rmdr stamp to bottom edge), else Fine in dj (price-clipped). *Lame Duck*. $25/£16

DONOSO, JOSE. This Sunday. NY: Knopf, 1967. 1st US ed. (Sig), else NF in dj (spine sl faded, fr cvr edge torn 2 inches). *Lame Duck*. $75/£47

DOOLEY, JOHN. John Dooley, Confederate Soldier. His War Journal. Joseph T. Durkin (ed). Georgetown, DC: Georgetown Univ, 1945. 1st ed. Frontisport. Blue cl. NF in dj (worn, tape-reinforced, 2 long closed tears fr panel). *Chapel Hill*. $125/£78

DOOLEY, THOMAS A. Deliver Us From Evil. NY, 1956. 1st ed. VG in dj (worn). *Doctor's Library*. $45/£28

DOOLEY, THOMAS A. The Night They Burned the Mountain. NY, (1960). 1st Amer ed. NF (edges browned) in NF dj (edge sl rubbed). *Polyanthos*. $25/£16

DOOLIN, WILLIAM. Wayfarers in Medecine. London, 1949. 2nd ed. VG in dj (sl worn). *Doctor's Library*. $60/£38

DOOLIN, WILLIAM. Wayfarers in Medicine. London: Heinemann, 1945. (Lettering dulled.) *Hollett*. $56/£35

DOOLITTLE, HILDA. Hippolytus Temporizes: A Play in Three Acts. Boston/NY: Houghton Mifflin, 1927. 1st ed. One of 550. Dec bds. (Spine sl flecked), o/w Fine in unptd dj (chipped), slipcase (defective). *Reese*. $175/£109

DOORLY, GERALD S. The Voyages of the 'Morning'. Huntingdon: Bluntisham Books, 1995. Facs of 1st ed. Map. Mint. *Explorer*. $40/£25

DORAN, ADELAIDE LeMERT. Pieces of Eight Channel Islands, a Bibliographical Guide and Source Book. Glendale, A.H. Clark, 1980. 1st ed. Fine. *Book Market*. $100/£63

DORAN, ADELAIDE LeMERT. Pieces of Eight Channel Islands. Glendale: A.H. Clark, 1980. Pict bds. *Dawson*. $50/£31

DORAN, DR. Monarchs Retired from Business. London: Richard Bentley, 1857. 1st ed. 2 vols. viii,416; vi,420pp; 2 steel-engr plts. Blind-stamped cl (extrems rubbed), gilt. *Hollett*. $72/£45

DORAN, DR. Monarchs Retired from Business. London: Richard Bentley, 1857. 2 vols extended to 4. Extra-illus. Teg. Later 3/4 gilt-ruled brn levant morocco, raised bands, bound by Morrell. Fine. *Pacific**. $316/£198

DORAN, JOHN. Annals of the English Stage from Thomas Betterton to Edmund Kean. Robert W. Lowe (ed). London: Nimmo, 1888. One of 300 numbered sets, w/50 plts each in 2 states. 3 vols. Teg. 3/4 black morocco (rubbed), gilt. *Oinonen**. $325/£203

DORAN, JOHN. Their Majesties' Servants. Robert W. Lowe (ed). London: Nimmo, 1888. Lg paper ed. One of 300. 3 vols. 50 copperplt ports, wood engrs (plts in 2 states). Uncut. Maroon spines, linen bds, ptd labels. VG set (worn). *Hartfield*. $295/£184

DORAT, CLAUDE JOSEPH. The Kisses. London: (Vizetelly), n.d. (ca 1900). One of 400 for US, of 1500. Flowered eps; teg. Crushed tan morocco, gilt, raised bands. Fine. *Book Block*. $275/£172

DOREMUS, PHILIP. Reminiscences of Montclair. Montclair, NJ, 1908. 1st ed. Signed presentaton. (Spine ends worn.) *Heinoldt*. $20/£13

DORFMAN, ARIEL. The Last Song of Manuel Sendero. NY: Viking, 1987. 1st US ed. NF in VG + dj (sm tear to top rear flap-fld tip). *Lame Duck*. $35/£22

DORGELES, ROLAND. (Pseud of Roland Lecavele.) The Cabaret Up the Line. London: John Lane, Bodley Head, (1930). 1st ed in English. Blue cl stamped in red. (Spine sl sunned through dj), o/w NF in pict dj (lt dust-mkd). *Reese*. $175/£109

DORMAN, CHARLES G. Delaware Cabinetmakers and Allied Artisans, 1655-1855. Wilmington, 1960. *Argosy*. $75/£47

DORN, EDWARD. The Newly Fallen. NY: Totem Press, (1961). 1st ed. NF (few sl stains) in ptd wraps. *Antic Hay*. $45/£28

DORR, JOHN V. Cyanidation and Concentration of Gold and Silver Ores. NY, 1936. 1st ed. Maroon cl, gilt. VG. *Larry Price*. $50/£31

DORR, RHETA CHILDE. Susan B. Anthony: The Woman Who Changed the Mind of a Nation. NY: Stokes, 1928. 1st ed. Sm plain card signed by Anthony, 1895, laid in (1 corner creased). Teg, untrimmed. Crimson buckram, gilt. Good (spine top bumped w/crimping). *Baltimore**. $60/£38

DORSET, MRS. The Peacock at Home. London: Grant & Griffith, 1854. 24th ed. Harrison Weir (illus). 12mo. Full-pg engr frontis, 32pp + 1pg list on back wrapper; 3 full-pg engrs. Internally Fine (ink name inside fr cvr) in dec buff stiff paper wrappers (edges sl soiled, lower spine chipped). *Hobbyhorse*. $125/£78

DORSET, PHYLLIS FLANDERS. The New Eldorado, the Story of Colorado's Gold and Silver Rushes. (NY): Macmillan, (1970). 1st ed. Brn cl. Fine in pict dj. *Argonaut*. $50/£31

DORSEY, JOHN M. (ed). The Jefferson-Dunglison Letters. Univ of VA, (1970). 2nd ptg. Inscribed presentation copy. VG. *Book Broker*. $35/£22

DOS PASSOS, JOHN. 1919. NY: Harcourt, Brace, (1932). 1st ed. Orange cl stamped in silver. NF in pict dj (lt edgeworn, sm tear 1 corner). *Reese*. $175/£109

DOS PASSOS, JOHN. 1919. NY: Harcourt, Brace, 1932. 1st ed. (Eps lt foxed), else VG in illus dj (edges lt worn). *Cahan*. $185/£116

DOS PASSOS, JOHN. The 42nd Parallel. NY, 1930. 1st ed. Dj (lt rubbed, sm closed tear fr joint). *Swann**. $201/£126

DOS PASSOS, JOHN. Airways Inc. NY, (1928). 1st ed. Dj (sl worn, spine ends rubbed, internal archival tape repair). *Swann**. $172/£108

DOS PASSOS, JOHN. The Fourteenth Chronicle. Townsend Ludington (ed). Deutsch, 1974. 1st UK ed. VG in dj (rubbed, chipped, sm closed tears, spine faded). *Virgo*. $40/£25

DOS PASSOS, JOHN. The Garbage Man. NY, 1926. 1st ed. (Eps foxed.) Dj (chipped). *Swann**. $201/£126

DOS PASSOS, JOHN. Manhattan Transfer. NY, 1925. 1st ed. (Sig.) Dj (spine extrems chipped). *Swann**. $258/£161

DOS PASSOS, JOHN. One Man's Initiation—1917. London: George Allen & Unwin, 1920. 1st ed, 1st issue, 1st bk. (Spine faded), o/w VG in dj (lt used, few sm chips). *Karmiole*. $500/£313

DOS PASSOS, JOHN. Orient Express. NY, 1927. 1st ed. Dj (sl worn). *Swann**. $287/£179

DOS PASSOS, JOHN. A Pushcart at the Curb. NY, (1922). 1st ed. Dj (sl worn). *Swann**. $230/£144

DOS PASSOS, JOHN. Rosinante to the Road Again. NY, (1922). 1st ed. Dj (spine extrems chipped). *Swann**. $126/£79

DOS PASSOS, JOHN. Streets of Night. NY: Doran, 1923. 1st ed. Fine. *Beasley*. $45/£28

DOS PASSOS, JOHN. Three Soldiers. NY: George H. Doran, (1921). 1st ed, 1st state, w/'signing' at 213:31, and all the other features. Dj in earliest form as well. Signed, inscribed at later date. Black cl stamped in orange. NF in dj (spine sl sunned). *Reese*. $500/£313

DOS PASSOS, JOHN. U.S.A. (The 42nd Parallel, 1919, the Big Money). Boston: Houghton Mifflin, 1946. 1st illus ed. One of 365. Signed by Dos Passos and Reginald Marsh (illus). 3 vols. Teg. Buckram, leather spine labels. Fine in djs, VG slipcase. *Pacific**. $518/£324

DOS PASSOS, JOHN. U.S.A.: I. The 42nd Parallel, II. Nineteen Nineteen, III. The Big Money. NY: The Modern Library, (1937). Inscribed, signed. (Inner hinge weak; spine sl faded.) *Argosy*. $60/£38

DOS PASSOS, JOHN. The Villages Are the Heart of Spain. Chicago: Esquire-Coronet, (1937). 1st ed in bk form. One of 1200 numbered. Pict eps. Paper label. (Sl dust soiled), o/w VG. *Reese*. $150/£94

DOSTOEVSKY, FYODOR. The Brothers Karamazov. LEC, 1949. Ltd to 1500 numbered, signed by Fritz Eichenberg (illus). 2 vols. Fine in slipcase. *Swann**. $138/£86

DOSTOEVSKY, FYODOR. The Brothers Karamazov: A Novel in Four Parts and Epilog. NY: LEC, 1949. One of 1500. Signed by Fritz Eichenberg (illus). 2 vols. 1/2 buckram, red cl. Fine in slipcase. *Pacific**. $115/£72

DOSTOEVSKY, FYODOR. Crime and Punishment. NY: LEC, 1948. One of 1500. Signed by Fritz Eichenberg (illus). 2 vols. Black/red cl. Fine in glassine, slipcase. *Pacific**. $127/£79

DOSTOEVSKY, FYODOR. Crime and Punishment. LEC, 1948. Ltd to 1500 numbered. 2 vols. Fine in slipcase. *Swann**. $138/£86

DOSTOEVSKY, FYODOR. A Disgraceful Affair. Nora Gottlieb (trans). London: Merlin, 1959. 1st Eng ed. NF (feps browned; spine ends, corner sl bumped) in dj (sl nicked, sl rubbed). *Ulysses*. $56/£35

DOSTOEVSKY, FYODOR. Dostoevsky Portrayed by His Wife. S. S. Koteliansky (ed). London: Routledge, 1926. 1st Eng ed. VG (inscrip; spine ends, corners sl bumped; edges sl rubbed). *Ulysses*. $72/£45

DOSTOEVSKY, FYODOR. The Gambler and Notes from the Underground. (Bloomfield, CT): LEC, 1967. One of 1500. Signed by Alexandre Alexeieff (illus). 1/2 calf, pict cl, gilt. Fine in glassine, slipcase. *Pacific**. $63/£39

DOSTOEVSKY, FYODOR. The Grand Inquisitor. S. S. Koteliansky (trans). London, 1930. 1st ed. One of 300 numbered. Pigskin, blue/black onlays upper cvr. (Lt rubbed.) *Swann**. $103/£64

DOSTOEVSKY, FYODOR. The House of the Dead. LEC, 1982. One of 2000 signed by Fritz Eichenberg (illus). Fine in slipcase. *Swann**. $80/£50

DOSTOEVSKY, FYODOR. The Idiot. LEC, 1956. Ltd to 1500 numbered, signed by Fritz Eichenberg (illus). Fine in slipcase. *Swann**. $126/£79

DOSTOEVSKY, FYODOR. The Possessed. LEC, 1959. Ltd to 1500 numbered, signed by Fritz Eichenberg (illus). 2 vols. Fine in slipcase. *Swann**. $126/£79

DOSTOEVSKY, FYODOR. A Raw Youth. LEC, 1974. One of 2000 signed by Fritz Eichenberg (illus). 2 vols. Fine in slipcase. *Swann**. $126/£79

DOSTOYEVSKY, FYODOR. The Letters of Dostoyevsky to His Wife. Elizabeth Hill & Doris Mudie (trans). London: Constable, 1930. 1st Eng ed. Frontisport. VG (spine head sl bumped, cvrs partly faded). *Ulysses*. $120/£75

Dot's Visit to the Gnomes. Dundee: Valentine & Sons, ca 1915. 12mo. 12 full-pg color plts by A. E. Jackson. Cl-backed emb bds (rebacked, edges rubbed, spot rear cvr). *Reisler*. $225/£141

DOTEN, ALFRED. The Journals of Alfred Doten, 1849-1903. Walter Van Tilburg (ed). Reno: Univ of NV, 1973. 3 vols. Fine set in VG orig box. *Perier*. $90/£56

DOUCE, FRANCIS. Holbein's Dance of Death (and) Holbein's Bible Cuts. London: Henry G. Bohn, 1858. Orig ed. Frontis, (vii) ads,xii,475pp. Green blind-stamped cl. VG. *Turtle Island*. $100/£63

DOUGALL, JOHN. Angling Songs and Poems, with Miscellaneous Pieces. Glasgow: Kerr & Richardson, 1901. 1st ed. Frontisport. Dk purple cl, gilt. NF. *Pacific**. $69/£43

DOUGHTY, ARTHUR G. and CHESTER MARTIN. The Kelsey Papers. Ottawa: Public Archives of Canada, 1929. 1st ed. Frontis, fldg map. Stiff ptd wrappers. Fine. *Harrington*. $100/£63

DOUGHTY, CHARLES M. The Clouds. Duckworth, 1912. 1st Eng ed. 24pp pub's ads at rear. Teg. Buckram. VG (eps browned, top edge sl dusty; spine ends, corners sl bumped, bottom cvr edges rubbed) in dj (torn, chipped, spotted, rubbed, mkd, dusty, sl creased, browned, spine head lacks sm piece). *Ulysses*. $120/£75

DOUGHTY, CHARLES M. Mansoul or the Riddle of the World. London, 1920. 1st ed. NF (sl bubbled) in dj (spine sunned, torn, sl soiled). *Polyanthos*. $25/£16

DOUGHTY, CHARLES M. Mansoul or the Riddle of the World. London: Jonathan Cape/Medici Soc, 1923. One of 500 signed. Orig vellum, gilt. *Maggs*. $240/£150

DOUGHTY, CHARLES M. Travels in Arabia Deserta. London: Jonathan Cape, (1949). New & definitive ed. 2 vols. Map. VG in djs (spine ends, corners sl chipped, price-clipped). *Pacific**. $98/£61

DOUGHTY, CHARLES M. Travels in Arabia Deserta. LEC, 1953. Ltd to 1500 numbered. Fine in slipcase. *Swann**. $149/£93

DOUGHTY, DOROTHY. The American Birds of Dorothy Doughty. Worcester, (1962). One of 1500 numbered, signed. Folio. Mtd frontisport, 70 tipped-in color plts. Leather. Plain dj, bd slipcase (cracked). *Swann**. $287/£179

DOUGHTY, J. and P. Some Early American Hunters. NY: Derrydale, 1928. Ltd to 375 numbered. Hand-colored engr frontis. Gray paper-cvrd bds. Fine. *Biscotti*. $175/£109

DOUGHTY, MARION. Afoot Through the Kashmir Valleys. London: Sands, 1902. 1st ed. 12 plts. Teg. Blue ribbed cl, gilt. (Sl loose, spine foot torn), o/w VG. *Morrell*. $144/£90

Douglas's Encyclopedia...a Book of Reference for Bacon Curers,.... London: William Douglas, n.d. (ca 1905). 2nd ed. (Ink #; cvrs worn, shaken.) *King*. $95/£59

DOUGLAS, C. L. Famous Texas Feuds. Dallas, 1936. 1st ed (?). (Pin size stain to fr cvr), else VG. *Baade*. $60/£38

DOUGLAS, C. L. The Gentlemen in White Hats; Dramatic Episodes in the History of the Texas Rangers. Dallas: South-West, 1934. 1st ed. VG (spine head sl tender). *Labordo*. $75/£47

DOUGLAS, C. L. Thunder on the Gulf or The Story of the Texas Navy. Dallas, 1936. 1st ed. VG in dj. *Dumont*. $100/£63

DOUGLAS, KEITH. Alamein to Zem Zem. London: Editions Poetry, 1946. 1st Eng ed. Good (crayon price on fep; title-hinge tender, few fore-edges sl ragged; extrems sl rubbed) in Poor dj. *Clearwater*. $56/£35

DOUGLAS, MICHAEL. (Pseud of Michael and Douglas Crichton.) Dealing or the Berkeley-to-Boston Forty-Brick Lost-Bag Blues. NY: Knopf, 1971. 1st ed. Spiral bound advance galleys ptd on rectos only. VG (few spiral holes pulled; wrappers sl worn). *Between The Covers*. $350/£219

DOUGLAS, NORMAN. The Angel of Manfredonia. SF: Windsor, 1929. One of 225. Signed. (Spine sl faded), o/w VG in glassine wrapper in slipcase (rubbed; top, bottom edges split). *Virgo*. $240/£150

DOUGLAS, NORMAN. Birds and Beasts of the Greek Anthology. London: Chapman & Hall, 1928. 1st Eng ed, revised and corrected. Top edges stained, rest uncut. Oatmeal cl, maroon gilt lettering piece. VG in dj (sl dusty). *Maggs*. $104/£65

DOUGLAS, NORMAN. Footnote on Capri. Sidgwick & Jackson, 1952. 1st Eng ed. NF (spine ends sl bumped) in dj (sl rubbed, nicked, creased, few internally repaired tears rear panel). Ulysses. $72/£45

DOUGLAS, NORMAN. How About Europe? Florence: Privately ptd, 1929. One of 550 numbered, signed. Uncut, mostly unopened. White bds. (Eps mkd, 2 leaves badly opened), o/w VG. Temple. $120/£75

DOUGLAS, NORMAN. Late Harvest. London, 1946. 1st ed. VG + in dj. Gretton. $13/£8

DOUGLAS, NORMAN. London Street Games. St. Catherine, 1916. One of 500 ptd. (Cvrs mkd.) Clearwater. $112/£70

DOUGLAS, NORMAN. London Street Games. London: St. Catherine, 1916. 1st ed. Ltd to 500. Uncut. Good (edges dusty; 1st, last pp sl foxed; bds sl scratched, rubbed; lacks dj). Virgo. $240/£150

DOUGLAS, NORMAN. Looking Back. C&W, 1934. 1st 1-vol ed. Good (spine bumped; lacks dj). Tiger. $16/£10

DOUGLAS, NORMAN. South Wind. NY: Pynson Ptrs, (1932). Signed by Carlotta Petrina (illus). Full natural coarse linen, leather label stamped in silver. Fine. Boxed. Appelfeld. $125/£78

DOUGLAS, NORMAN. South Wind. NY: LEC, 1932. One of 1500 signed by C. Petrina (illus). VG in slipcase (broken). Typographeum. $72/£45

DOUGLAS, NORMAN. Summer Islands. London: Desmond Harmsworth, 1931. One of 500 numbered. Spare title label. VG (spine ends, corners sl bumped, cvrs sl spotted, spine sl faded) in dj (nicked, chipped, rubbed, dusty, sl creased, torn, mkd, price-clipped, sl dknd). Ulysses. $136/£85

DOUGLAS, NORMAN. Together. London: Chapman & Hall, 1923. 1st ed. One of 275 lg paper copies, signed. 2 half-tone plts. Teg, unopened. (Spine faded), else Nice in red buckram, gilt. Cady. $60/£38

DOUGLAS, NORMAN. Together. Chapman & Hall, 1923. One of 275 signed. Lg paper issue. Teg. Buckram. NF (spine sl faded, ends sl bumped). Ulysses. $200/£125

DOUGLAS, ROBERT K. Society in China. Ward, Lock, 1901. 2nd ed. Later 1/2 calf, marbled bds, gilt, spine dated at foot. VF (bkpl). Sotheran. $205/£128

DOUGLAS, SYLVESTER. Reports of Cases Argued and Determined in the Court of King's Bench. London, 1786. 2nd ed. 798pp + table. Old calf. (Old ink names; lacks fr cvr, spine label chipped; dry, soiled.) King. $95/£59

DOUGLAS-HOME, HENRY. The Birdman. Collins, 1977. 1st ed. Inscribed presentation. 16 plts. VG in dj. Hollett. $24/£15

DOUGLASS, FREDERICK. The Life and Times of Frederick Douglass Written by Himself. Hartford: Park Publishing Co, 1882. 2nd ed. Frontisport. Pict blindstamped cl. Fine. Swann*. $230/£144

DOUGLASS, WILLIAM. A Summary, Historical and Political of the First Planting...of the British Settlements in North-America. London, 1760. 2 vols. 8vo. Hand-colored engr fldg map. Contemp speckled sheep (1 cvr loose). Howes D436. Swann*. $805/£503

DOUIE, CHARLES. The Weary Road. London: John Murray, (1929). 1st ed. Grn cl-backed bds, ptd labels. NF (w/o dj). Reese. $45/£28

DOURADO, AUTRAN. Pattern for a Tapestry. London: Peter Owen, 1984. 1st British ed. Signed. Fine in dj. Lame Duck. $150/£94

DOUTHIT, MARY OSBORN. The Souvenir of Western Women. Portland, 1905. 2nd ed. Fine. Perier. $125/£78

DOVE, RITA. Grace Notes. NY: Norton, (1989). 1st ed. Fine in Fine dj. Agvent. $45/£28

DOVE, RITA. Through the Ivory Gate. NY, 1992. 1st Amer ed. Signed presentation. Fine in Fine dj. Polyanthos. $30/£19

DOVER, CEDRIC. American Negro Art. Greenwich, CT: NYGS, (1960). Orig ed. 100 b/w, 8 color plts. Fine in dj. Turtle Island. $125/£78

DOW, GEORGE FRANCIS. Slave Ships and Slaving. Salem: Marine Research Soc, 1927. 1st ed. VG + (sl shelfworn) in dj (edgeworn, spine faded). My Bookhouse. $255/£159

DOW, GEORGE FRANCIS. Whale Ships and Whaling. Salem: Marine Research Soc, 1925. VG. High Latitude. $80/£50

DOW, GEORGE FRANCIS. Whale Ships and Whaling...in Colonial New England. Salem: Marine Research Soc, 1925. 1st ed. (Lt worn.) Slipcase. Oinonen*. $110/£69

DOW, H. J. The Art of Alex Colville. Toronto, 1972. 104 plts (48 color full-pg). Good in dj (sl frayed). Ars Artis. $56/£35

DOW, LORENZO. The Life and Travels of Lorenzo Dow. Hartford, (CT): Lincoln & Gleason, 1804. 1st ed. 16mo. 308pp. Full contemp calf (sl warped, spine top chipped), leather label. Howes D441. M & S. $750/£469

DOWDEN, GEORGE. A Bibliography of the Works of Allen Ginsberg, October, 1943 to July 1, 1967. (SF): City Lights Books, (1971). 1st ed. (Ex-lib w/mks, scrapes to fep), else VG- in dj. Pacific*. $35/£22

DOWDEY, CLIFFORD. The Land They Fought For. The Story of the South as the Confederacy 1832-1865. GC: Doubleday, 1955. 1st ed. Grn cl. Fine in VG + dj (lt worn). House. $30/£19

DOWLING, ALFRED. The Flora of the Sacred Nativity. London: Kegan Paul, Trench, Trubner, 1900. Uncut. Buckram. Bkpl of Will Ingwersen. (Eps browned), else VG. Quest. $160/£100

DOWLING, GREGORY. Double Take. St. Martin's, 1985. 1st US ed. Fine in dj. Murder. $27/£17

DOWN, ROBERT H. A History of the Silverton Country. Portland: Berncliff, 1926. 1st ed. VG. Howes D445. Perier. $125/£78

DOWNES, KERRY. English Baroque Architecture. London, 1966. Good. Washton. $125/£78

DOWNES, WILLIAM HOWE. John S. Sargent, His Life and Work. Thornton Butterworth, 1926. 1st Eng ed. 42 plts. (Few sm damp patches to bd edges.) Hollett. $120/£75

DOWNEY, FAIRFAX. Indian-Fighting Army. (Ft. Collins, CO): Old Army, (1971). Rpt of 1941 ed. Inscribed, signed presentation. Fine in dj (spine sl faded). Pacific*. $40/£25

DOWNEY, JOSEPH T. The Cruise of the Portsmouth, 1845-1847. Howard Lamar (ed). New Haven: Yale Univ Library, 1958. 1st ed. Color frontis. Blue bds, gilt, blue cl backstrip. Fine. Harrington. $60/£38

DOWNIE, R. ANGUS. All About Arran. Blackie, 1935. Plt, map. VG. Hollett. $24/£15

DOWNIE, WILLIAM. Hunting for Gold.... Palo Alto: American West, (1971). Facs ptg of orig 1893 ed. Blue cl, gilt. VF in dj (sl chipped). Argonaut. $45/£28

DOWNING, A. J. The Fruits and Fruit Trees of America. NY: Wiley and Putnam, 1847. 7th ed. (Name; shelf-worn, bds sunned.) Fair Meadow. $125/£78

DOWNING, A. J. The Fruits and Fruit Trees of America. Charles Downing (ed). NY: Wiley & Halsted, 1858. Rev ed. Period 3/4 morocco, gilt. (1st 30pp extrems stained), else VG-. Pacific*. $81/£51

DOWNING, A. J. Rural Essays. G.W. Curtis and F. Bremer (eds). NY, 1890. Frontis, lxxi,557pp; 7 engr plts. (Pp tanned, rear inner hinge cracked; lt soiled, corners worn, sm nick to spine, ends frayed.) Sutton. $100/£63

DOWNING, A. J. Rural Essays. George William Curtis (ed). NY: Putnam, 1853. 1st ed. Engr frontisport, lxxi,557pp. Blind grn cl, gilt. (Browned, sl foxed, bkpl, sig; spine sunned, gilt dull, sl edgeworn, lt old splash stain rear cvr.) Baltimore*. $120/£75

DOWNING, A. J. A Treatise on the Theory and Practice of Landscape Gardening, Adapted to North America; with a View of Country Residences. NY: C.M. Saxton, 1856. 5th ed. (Foxing), else VG. *Pacific**. $127/£79

DOWNING, A. J. A Treatise on the Theory and Practice of Landscape Gardening.... NY: A.O. Moore, 1859. 6th ed. 6 steel engrs, 6 lithos, 104 wood engrs. Red blind-stamped cl. *Appelfeld.* $200/£125

DOWNING, ANTOINETTE F. and VINCENT J. SCULLY, JR. The Architectural Heritage of Newport Rhode Island 1640-1915. Cambridge, MA, 1952. 1st ed. 230 plts. (Bkpl; sl rubbed.) *King.* $200/£125

DOWNING, JAMES. A Narrative of the Life of James Downing. NY: Ptd by John C. Totten, 1821. 1st Amer ed. 143pp. Contemp calf. (Text browned, soiled; calf worn, rubbed, cvrs detached), else Good. *Brown.* $25/£16

DOWNS, FREDERICK, JR. Aftermath. NY: W.W. Norton, 1984. 1st ed. Fine in dj. *Associates.* $25/£16

DOWNS, FREDERICK, JR. The Killing Zone. NY: W.W. Norton, 1978. 1st ed. Fine in dj. *Associates.* $85/£53

DOWNS, JOSEPH. American Furniture. NY, 1952. Folio. (Lt worn.) Dj. *Oinonen**. $60/£38

DOWNS, JOSEPH. American Furniture: Queen Anne and Chippendale Periods in the Henry Francis duPont Winterthur Museum. NY: Macmillan, 1952. 1st ed. VG in dj (extrems chipped, torn, flaps clipped, spine ends bumped). *Pacific**. $104/£65

DOWSETT, J. MOREWOOD. Big Game and Big Life. London: John Bale, Sons & Danielson, (1925). 1st ed. (Lacks fep.) Map. Blue cl (sl soiled), gilt. *Karmiole.* $85/£53

DOWSETT, J. MOREWOOD. The Romance of England's Forests. London: J. Gifford, 1943. Rpt. (Inscrip), o/w NF in Good dj (chipped). *Archer.* $22/£14

DOWSON, ERNEST and ARTHUR MOORE. Adrian Rome. Methuen, 1899. 1st ed. 40pp cat dated Feb 1899. Blue dec cl (rubbed, soiled), gilt. Good+ (eps renewed at an early date, contents sl shaken; string mk at edges, worn, rear bd cockled). *Any Amount.* $120/£75

DOWSON, ERNEST. The Complete Poems of Ernest Dowson. NY: Medusa Head, 1928. One of 775 numbered (of 800). Dec gilt purple cl. VG (inscrip, offsetting from illus onto facing pp, fr hinge cracked, top edge sl dusty; spine ends, corners sl bumped; spine, cvr edges faded). *Ulysses.* $120/£75

DOWSON, J. EMERSON. Tramways. London/NY, 1875. 65 + 18pp ads; fldg table. (Lib mks; top inch of backstrip chipped away.) *Bohling.* $20/£13

DOYLE, A. CONAN. The Adventure of the Blue Carbuncle. NY: Baker Street Irregulars, 1948. Sidney Paget (illus). Blue cl. VG (spine ends rubbed, cl sl faded). *Heritage.* $75/£47

DOYLE, A. CONAN. The Adventures of Gerard. NY: McClure, Phillips, 1903. 1st Amer ed. (x),297pp + 12pp ads dated 1903; 16 full-pg plts. VG in dk grn cl, gilt. *Cady.* $50/£31

DOYLE, A. CONAN. Adventures of Gerard. Newnes, 1903. 1st UK ed. VG. *Williams.* $120/£75

DOYLE, A. CONAN. Adventures of Sherlock Holmes. Girard, KS: Haldeman-Julius, (n.d.). Little Blue Books. Good+ (ink names, ll aging) in designed wrappers (faded to gray). *Gravesend.* $30/£19

DOYLE, A. CONAN. Adventures of Sherlock Holmes. NY: Harper, 1892. 1st ed, 2nd issue w/'if he had' on p65, line 4. Blue cl, gilt. (Bkpl; spine, extrems sl dknd), else VG. *Pacific**. $75/£47

DOYLE, A. CONAN. The Adventures of Sherlock Holmes. London: George Newnes, 1898. Blue cl, gilt. VG (award certificate dated 1899-1900 on fr pastedown, eps browned; extrems lt rubbed). *Glenn.* $150/£94

DOYLE, A. CONAN. The Adventures of Sherlock Holmes. LEC, 1950. Ltd to 1500 numbered. 3 vols. Fine in slipcase. *Swann**. $230/£144

DOYLE, A. CONAN. The Blue Carbuncle. NY: Baker Street Irregulars, 1948. 1st ed. Dj (sl edgeworn). *Swann**. $57/£36

DOYLE, A. CONAN. The British Campaign in France and Flanders 1914-1918. London: Hodder & Stoughton, 1916-(1920). 1st eds. 6 vols. Vols 1, 3, 4 in pub's gilt dk blue cl, rest in contemp gilt plum cl. Good set (prelims, endleaves of 2, 5, 6 tanned; ink names, sl soiled). *Reese.* $125/£78

DOYLE, A. CONAN. The Case-Book of Sherlock Holmes. London: John Murray, (1927). 1st ed. Rose cl. VG (spine severely faded). *Sumner & Stillman.* $275/£172

DOYLE, A. CONAN. The Case-Book of Sherlock Holmes. London: John Murray, (1927). 1st ed. 8vo. Pink cl, gilt. VG (eps browned, margins of 1st/last few ll sl foxed; spine sl faded). *Heritage.* $750/£469

DOYLE, A. CONAN. The Complete Adventures and Memoirs of Sherlock Holmes. NY: Bramhall House, (1975). Rpt. Good+ (ink inscrip, ll aging) in Good+ dj (sl worn). *Gravesend.* $20/£13

DOYLE, A. CONAN. The Complete Sherlock Holmes. GC: Doubleday, 1953. One of 147. Signed on limitation. 2 vols. 1/2 morocco, gilt. (Spine ends sl scuffed), else NF. *Pacific**. $1,035/£647   *Not 1st Am: McClure, 1907 w/illust.?*

DOYLE, A. CONAN. The Croxley Master. NY: George H. Doran, n.d. (1925). 1st Amer ed, 2nd issue, in orange cl pict dec in dk grn. Fine in NF dj. *Sumner & Stillman.* $135/£84

DOYLE, A. CONAN. A Desert Drama, Being the Tragedy of the Korosko. Phila: Lippincott, 1898. 1st Amer ed. 32 full-pg illus. Pict cl. VG. *Maggs.* $192/£120

DOYLE, A. CONAN. A Duet. NY: D. Appleton, 1899. 1st Amer ed, 1st issue, w/19 titles on 1/2-title verso, 1st state ads (begin w/list of 5 Doyle works excluding this one). 8pp undated ads. Red cl, silver/gilt. NF. *Sumner & Stillman.* $75/£47

DOYLE, A. CONAN. A Duet. With an Occasional Chorus. NY, 1899. 1st Amer ed. Dec cvrs, gilt. Fine (sl rubbed). *Polyanthos.* $35/£22

DOYLE, A. CONAN. Exploits of Brigadier Gerard. London, 1896. 1st ed. (Spine lt faded.) *Swann**. $80/£50

DOYLE, A. CONAN. The Final Adventures of Sherlock Holmes. LEC, 1952. Ltd to 1500 numbered. 2 vols. Fine in slipcase. *Swann**. $149/£93

DOYLE, A. CONAN. The German War. London: Hodder & Stoughton, 1914. 1st ed. Good+ (half-title, fore-edge soiled, foxed, stamped date; spine faded) in blue ptd wrappers (sm crease fr wrapper, discoloration to rear). *Gravesend.* $600/£375

DOYLE, A. CONAN. The Great Boer War. Smith, Elder, 1902. Complete ed. 5 color fldg maps. 1/2 calf (extrems rubbed), gilt. *Hollett.* $72/£45

DOYLE, A. CONAN. The Green Flag and Other Stories of War and Sport. London: Smith, Elder, 1900. 1st ed. Frontis. Red cl, gilt. (Top fore corners bumped, spine faded.) *Maggs.* $104/£65

DOYLE, A. CONAN. His Last Bow. London: John Murray, 1917. 1st Eng ed. Good (feps browned, top edge dusty, edges sl spotted, fr hinge cracking; spine faded, gilt oxidized, spine ends sl bumped). *Ulysses.* $240/£150

DOYLE, A. CONAN. His Last Bow. London: John Murray, 1917. 1st (English) ed of the 4th collection. Preface includes the error 'agriculture' rather than 'apiculture.' Rose cl. VG (ll sl foxed; spine faded). *Sumner & Stillman.* $275/£172

DOYLE, A. CONAN. The Hound of the Baskervilles. London, 1902. 1st ed. 8vo. Frontis, 15 plts by Sidney Paget. Gilt-pict cl (extrems lt worn; 1 sig loose). *Swann**. $632/£395

DOYLE, A. CONAN. The Hound of the Baskervilles. George Newnes, 1902. 1st ed. 8vo. (viii), 359pp; 16 plts by Sidney Paget. Red cl, gilt design by Alfred Garth Jones. (Blind-stamp, sm label; spine ends sl rubbed), o/w VG in dj. This dj is a forgery. The genuine dj was titled in scarlet on gray paper; this one is black on cream paper ptd in recent times. *Sotheran.* $1,597/£998

DOYLE, A. CONAN. The Hound of the Baskervilles. SF: Arion, 1985. Ltd to 400 signed by Michael Kenna (photos). Full brn cl. Fine in slipcase. *Truepenny.* $350/£219

DOYLE, A. CONAN. The Land of Mist. NY: Doubleday, Doran, 1926. 1st US ed. VG + in dj (sl worn, edges sl chipped, hinges extensively split). *Williams.* $720/£450

DOYLE, A. CONAN. The Last Galley. Smith, Elder, 1911. 1st UK ed. Fine (sm ink name). *Williams.* $240/£150

DOYLE, A. CONAN. The Later Adventures of Sherlock Holmes. LEC, 1952. Ltd to 1500 numbered. 3 vols. Fine in slipcase. *Swann*.* $230/£144

DOYLE, A. CONAN. Memoirs of Sherlock Holmes. NY: Harper, 1894. New, rev Amer ed. 4pp undated ads. Lt blue dec cl. VG (pp bottoms dampstained; extrems sl shelfworn). *Sumner & Stillman.* $95/£59

DOYLE, A. CONAN. The Memoirs of Sherlock Holmes. G. Newnes, 1894. 1st ed. Frontis. Gilt edges. Pict blue cl, gilt. (Spotted, lib stamp tp verso; sl dknd.) *Sotheby's*.* $442/£276

DOYLE, A. CONAN. The Memoirs of Sherlock Holmes. Newnes, 1894. 1st UK ed. VG (ink inscrip, spine ends sl strengthened). *Williams.* $720/£450

DOYLE, A. CONAN. The Memoirs of Sherlock Holmes. Newnes, 1894. 1st ed. Royal 8vo. Sidney Paget (illus). Frontis, (viii),279pp. Yellow/brn peacock feathers patterned eps; gilt edges. Dk blue bevel-edged cl, gilt. Good (bkpl; hinges sl cracked, cvrs rubbed at backstrip ends, corners, street name present in Strand Library device fr cvr). *Blackwell's.* $800/£500

DOYLE, A. CONAN. Memories and Adventures. London: Hodder & Stoughton, (1924). 1st ed, 2nd imp (incorrectly designated 2nd ed by the pub). One of 1000. Signed. Orig blue cl. VG (sl shelfworn). *Sumner & Stillman.* $850/£531

DOYLE, A. CONAN. Memories and Adventures. Boston: Little, Brown, 1924. 1st ed. Good (cvrs spotted). *Gravesend.* $55/£34

DOYLE, A. CONAN. Memories and Adventures. Boston: Little, Brown, 1924. 1st Amer ed. (Stain to lower extrems frontis, tp), else VG. *Pacific*.* $69/£43

DOYLE, A. CONAN. My Friend the Murderer. NY: Lovell, (1893). 1st Amer ed and 1st ed. A piracy. Pict-stamped blue cl (sl skewed, spine rubbed, sm nick). *Swann*.* $69/£43

DOYLE, A. CONAN. The New Revelation. NY: Doran, (1918). 1st Amer ed. Fine in VG dj (lt worn, lt chipped, soiled, lt red pencil along fr panel edge). *Between The Covers.* $100/£63

DOYLE, A. CONAN. The New Revelation. Hodder & Stoughton, 1918. 1st UK ed. Inscribed. VG (spine, pp browned). *Williams.* $632/£395

DOYLE, A. CONAN. Our African Winter. London: John Murray, 1929. 1st ed. 8vo. Photo frontis. Fine in blue cl (sl spotted), gilt. Dj. *Maggs.* $760/£475

DOYLE, A. CONAN. Our American Adventure. London: Hodder & Stoughton, (1923). 1st ed. 1500 ptd. Black cl (spine sl worn). *Mott.* $60/£38

DOYLE, A. CONAN. The Parasite. The Acme Library Volume I. Constable, 1894. 1st ed, dec 3/4 border to tp, cancel stubs st fr/rear of text, as called for. (v),125pp. Teg, rest untrimmed. 1st issue mid blue fine-ribbed cl, gilt. Good (eps lt browned). *Blackwell's.* $208/£130

DOYLE, A. CONAN. The Poison Belt. NY, (1913). 1st Amer ed. 16 full-pg plts. 2 pieces orig promo material laid in. Scarlet cl, gilt. Fine in Good dj (triangular chip across spine head 1/16 to 3/4-inch deep w/loss to a few letters in title, spine foot lacks 1/16-inch strip, nicked). *Mcclintock.* $1,500/£938

DOYLE, A. CONAN. The Poison Belt. London: Hodder & Stoughton, 1913. 1st ed. VG in lt blue cl, gilt. *Maggs.* $160/£100

DOYLE, A. CONAN. The Refugees. Longmans, Green, 1893. 1st ed. 3 vols. Half-titles not called for. (Lacks ads at end of vol 1, foxed, bkpls.) Marbled bds, 1/2 red morocco, gilt. *Sotheby's*.* $478/£299

DOYLE, A. CONAN. The Refugees. London: John Murray, 1920. New imp. VG in red cl, gilt. *Maggs.* $45/£28

DOYLE, A. CONAN. The Return of Sherlock Holmes. NY: McClure, Philips, 1905. 1st Amer ed. Pict black cl. Good (hinges cracking; spine lettering worn off; fr cvr design, lettering rubbed; shelfworn). *Pacific*.* $58/£36

DOYLE, A. CONAN. The Return of Sherlock Holmes. NY: McClure, Phillips, 1905. 1st ed. Black pict dec cl. VG + (spine lettering 75% flaked away, cvrs lt rubbed). *Warren.* $250/£156

DOYLE, A. CONAN. Round the Red Lamp. London: Methuen, 1894. 1st ed. Red cl (edgeworn, spine faded). *Glenn.* $160/£100

DOYLE, A. CONAN. Sherlock Holmes Crime Stories. Girard, KS: Haldeman-Julius, (n.d.). Little Blue Books. Good + (ink names, ll aging) in ptd wrappers (faded to gray). *Gravesend.* $25/£16

DOYLE, A. CONAN. Sherlock Holmes Detective Stories. Girard, KS: Haldeman-Julius, (n.d.). Little Blue Books. Good + (ink names, ll aging) in ptd wrappers (faded to gray). *Gravesend.* $25/£16

DOYLE, A. CONAN. Sherlock Holmes Mystery Stories. Girard, KS: Haldeman-Julius, (n.d.). Little Blue Books. Good + (ink names, ll aging) in ptd wrappers (faded to gray). *Gravesend.* $25/£16

DOYLE, A. CONAN. Sherlock Holmes. NY: LEC, 1950-52. One of 1500. 8 vols. 8vo. Fine in VG slipcases. *Glenn.* $750/£469

DOYLE, A. CONAN. The Sign of Four. London: Thomas Nelson & Sons, (n.d.). Red cl. Good. *Gravesend.* $15/£9

DOYLE, A. CONAN. The Sign of Four. London: Spencer Blackett, 1890. 1st ed, 2nd issue, w/'Griffith, Farran & Cos Standard Library' at the spine foot, and w/the '8' lacking from '138' on Contents pg. This copy w/o the 8pp ads found only in some copies. Maroon dec cl. Good + (eps sl cracked; vol askew, spine head repaired, few sm scuffs). *Sumner & Stillman.* $1,275/£797

DOYLE, A. CONAN. The Sign of Four. London: George Newnes, 1893. 3rd ed. Red pict cl, gilt. (Name, eps dknd; spine sl faded), o/w Fine. *Mordida.* $375/£234

DOYLE, A. CONAN. Sir Nigel. London: Smith Elder, 1906. 1st ed. Poor in red cl (sl stained), gilt. *Maggs.* $96/£60

DOYLE, A. CONAN. Songs of the Road. London: Smith, Elder, 1911. 1st ed. Fore/bottom edges untrimmed. VG in lt blue buckram, gilt. *Maggs.* $72/£45

DOYLE, A. CONAN. The Speckled Band. London/NY: Samuel French, n.d. (1923). 1st ed, 3rd imp (actually issued in 1923). NF (ink stamp) in brn wrappers. *Sumner & Stillman.* $165/£103

DOYLE, A. CONAN. The Stark Munro Letters, Being a Series of Sixteen Letters Written by J. Stark Munro.... London: Longmans, Green, 1895. 1st ed. Frontis; terminal ads dated August 1895. Fine in dk grn cl, gilt. *Maggs.* $72/£45

DOYLE, A. CONAN. A Study in Scarlet. London: Ward, Lock, Bowden, 1892. 2nd ed, 2nd imp, 1st bk. 24pp undated ads. Beige cl, red cl spine. VG (spine sl dknd, stained). *Sumner & Stillman.* $350/£219

DOYLE, A. CONAN. A Study in Scarlet. London: Dr. Watson's Books, 1993. Special 1st bk facs ed of 1993. Ltd to 500 numbered. NF (fr edge sl bumped) in ptd wrappers in stiff scarlet dj laid into scarlet cl slipcase. *Gravesend.* $75/£47

DOYLE, A. CONAN. The Tragedy of the Korosko. London: Smith, Elder, 1898. 1st ed. Sidney Paget (illus). Deep red cl (upper edge fr cvr sl sunned), gilt. *Maggs.* $104/£65

DOYLE, A. CONAN. Uncle Bernac. NY: Appleton, 1897. 1st Amer ed. Red cl, gilt. Fine. *Macdonnell.* $75/£47

DOYLE, A. CONAN. Uncle Bernac. London, 1897. 1st ed. 8pp pub's ads at rear. Gilt-pict red cl (sl skewed). *Swann*.* $80/£50

DOYLE, A. CONAN. The Valley of Fear. London: Smith, Elder, 1915. 1st Eng ed. Frontis. Rose cl. VG (sl soiled, foxed; top edge fr bd sl worn spot). *Sumner & Stillman.* $375/£234

DOYLE, A. CONAN. Waterloo. London: Samuel French, 1907. 1st ed. Orig grn wraps (head rear cvr dknd). Internally VG. *Dramatis.* $100/£63

DOYLE, A. CONAN. The White Company. NY: Cosmopolitan Book Corp, 1922. 1st Wyeth ed. 13 color plts by N. C. Wyeth. Pict cvr label. (Spine ends sl rubbed), else VG. *Pacific*.* $104/£65

DOYLE, RICHARD. In Fairyland, a Series of Pictures from the Elf-World. 1875. 2nd ed. Folio. Gilt edges. *Sotheby's*.* $957/£598

DOYLE, RICHARD. Manners and Customs of Ye Englyshe. London, (1849). 1st ed. 1/2 morocco (worn). *Argosy.* $100/£63

DOYLE, RODDY. Paddy Clarke Ha Ha Ha. London: Secker & Warburg, (1993). 1st ed. Fine in dj. *Pacific*.* $58/£36

DOYLE, RODDY. Paddy Clarke Ha Ha Ha. Secker, 1993. 1st UK ed. Mint in Mint dj. *Martin.* $45/£28

DRABBLE, MARGARET. Hassan's Tower. Hollywood: Sylvester & Orphanos, 1980. Ltd to 330 signed. Fine dec cl. *Truepenny.* $100/£63

DRABBLE, MARGARET. The Waterfall. Weidenfeld & Nicholson, 1969. 1st UK ed. VG + (ink name) in dj. *Williams.* $29/£18

DRAGO, HARRY SINCLAIR. Great American Cattle Trails. NY: Dodd, Mead, 1965. 1st ed. Fine in dj. *Labordo.* $45/£28

DRAGO, HARRY SINCLAIR. The Great Range Wars. NY: Dodd, Mead, 1970. 1st ed. Fine in dj. *Labordo.* $45/£28

DRAGO, HARRY SINCLAIR. The Legend Makers. NY: Dodd, Mead, 1975. 1st ed. NF in dj. *Labordo.* $45/£28

DRAGO, HARRY SINCLAIR. Lost Bonanzas. NY: Dodd, Mead, 1966. 1st ed. Fine in dj. *Labordo.* $45/£28

DRAGO, HARRY SINCLAIR. Outlaws on Horseback. NY: Dodd, Mead, (1964). 1st ed. One of 150. Signed. Map. Teg. Red morocco, gilt. Fine in slipcase. *Pacific*.* $138/£86

DRAGO, HARRY SINCLAIR. Road Agents and Train Robbers. NY: Dodd, Mead, 1973. 1st ed. Fine in dj. *Labordo.* $45/£28

DRAGO, HARRY SINCLAIR. The Steamboaters. NY: Dodd, Mead, 1967. 1st ed. Fine in dj. *Labordo.* $45/£28

DRAKE, B. The Great Indian Chief of the West; or, Life and Adventures of Black Hawk. Cincinnati: Applegate, 1854. Grn cl (1/2-inch loss spine bottom, sm chips at top; foxing). *Metropolitan*.* $57/£36

DRAKE, BURGESS. The Book of Lyonne. London: Falcon, (1952). 1st ed. 12mo. 8 color plts, line dwgs by Mervyn Peake. Blue cl. VG in color dj. *Reisler.* $285/£178

DRAKE, DANIEL. A Systematic Treatise, Historical, Etiological, and Practical, on the Principal Diseases of the Interior Valley of North America.... Cincinnati, 1850. 1st ed. 19 maps and plts. Orig sheep, gilt-lettered black leather spine labels. (Foxed; rubbed, joints broken.) Howes D469. *Oinonen*.* $400/£250

DRAKE, JOSEPH RODMAN. The Culprit Fay. NY: Carleton, 1867. 118pp (tp sl soiled). Orig full calf (sl scuffed, water-stained), gilt. BAL 4839. *M & S.* $100/£63

DRAKE, LEAH BODINE. A Hornbook for Witches: Poems of Fantasy. Sauk City: Arkham House, 1950. 1st ed. One of 553 ptd. Fine in NF dj (spine lt browned). *Other Worlds.* $1,750/£1,094

DRAKE, ST. CLAIR and HORACE R. CAYTON. Black Metropolis, a Study of Negro Life in a Northern City. NY, (1945). 1st ed, 2nd ptg. Dj. *Swann*.* $57/£36

DRANNAN, W. F. Thirty One Years on the Plains and in the Mountains. Chicago: Thos. W. Jackson, (1900). VG. Howes D482. *Perier.* $25/£16

DRAPER, THEODORE. The 84th Infantry Division in the Battle of Germany November 1944-May 1945. NY, 1946. VG. *Clark.* $95/£59

Dreamland (Moveable). NY: Atlantic Book & Art Corp, (ca 1920's). Obl 4to. Gerta Ries (illus). 14 panels of colored scenes w/series of slots into which figures are inserted. Figures (some cut) housed in ptd envelope. Cl-backed bds (fr edge sl rubbed) w/color illus. Clean. *Reisler.* $485/£303

DREANY, E. JOSEPH. Bible Stories from the Old Testament in Pop-Up Action Pictures. (Somerset)/London: Purnell & Sons, 1953. 4 dbl-pg pop-ups. Internally VG in illus wraps (extrems worn). *Bookfinders.* $70/£44

DREANY, E. JOSEPH. Cowboys in Pop-Up Action Pictures. London: Publicity Products, 1951. 5 dbl-pg pop-ups. VG- in illus wraps. *Bookfinders.* $80/£50

DREANY, E. JOSEPH. Indians in Pop-Up Action Pictures. London: Publicity Products, 1951. 5 dbl-pg pop-ups. VG- in illus wraps. *Bookfinders.* $65/£41

DREESMANN, CECILE. Samplers for Today. Van Nostrand, 1972. VG + in dj (torn). *Whittle.* $32/£20

DREISER, THEODORE. An American Tragedy. NY, 1926. 1st ed. One of 795 numbered sets signed. 2 vols. 8vo. Glassine djs (chipped); slipcase. *Swann*.* $690/£431

DREISER, THEODORE. An American Tragedy. LEC, 1954. Ltd to 1500 numbered, signed by Reginald Marsh (illus). Fine in slipcase. *Swann*.* $149/£93

DREISER, THEODORE. Dawn. NY: Horace Liveright, 1931. 1st ed. Black/red cl, gilt. (Top edge lt dust-soiled), o/w Fine in dj (lt browned, torn, chipped, reinforced w/tape on verso). *Heritage.* $125/£78

DREISER, THEODORE. Dawn. A History of Myself. NY, (1931). One of 245 (of 275) signed. Teg, uncut. Fine. *Polyanthos.* $200/£125

DREISER, THEODORE. Epitaph. NY: Heron Press, (1929). 1st ed. One of 400 numbered, signed. Frontis. Gilt-stamped black cl. (Sm dampstain in top gutter of fep.) *Swann*.* $149/£93

DREISER, THEODORE. Epitaph: A Poem. NY: Heron, (1929). One of 1100 ptd. Signed by Dreiser and Robert Fawcett (decs). Black cl, gilt. (Offset or damage to upper eps, purple stains to upper corners of fep versos; upper fr cvr sl faded), else VG in slipcase (rubbed). *Pacific*.* $46/£29

DREISER, THEODORE. A Gallery of Women. NY: Liveright, 1929. 1st ed. Ltd to 560 signed. 2 vols. Uncut. NF. *Second Life.* $150/£94

DREISER, THEODORE. A Gallery of Women. NY: Horace Liveright, 1929. 1st ed. 2 vols. Purple cl, gilt. VG set (fr cvrs, spines lt faded) in djs (spines browned, lt chipped), orig pub's grn cardboard box w/ptd paper label (worn). *Heritage.* $250/£156

DREISER, THEODORE. A Hoosier Holiday.... NY/London: John Lane, 1916. 1st ed, 1st state of p173 and binding. Frontis. Pict eps. Very Nice (sl dknd, rubbed) in dj (spine defective, lg chip spine toe, old paper reinforcement across verso). *Reese.* $125/£78

DREISER, THEODORE. Sister Carrie. NY, 1900. 1st ed, 1st bk. 8vo. Fine (inner hinges sl weak; rubbed, sm punctures on spine). *Kane*.* $1,800/£1,125

DREISER, THEODORE. Sister Carrie. LEC, 1939. Ltd to 1500 numbered, signed by Reginald Marsh (illus). Fine in slipcase. *Swann**. $258/£161

DRESDEN, DONALD. The Marquis de More. Norman: Univ of OK, (1970). 1st ed. VG in dj. *Lien*. $35/£22

DRESDEN, DONALD. The Marquis de Mores, Emperor of the Bad Lands. Norman: Univ of OK, (1970). 1st ed. Inscribed. NF in dj (lt soiled). *Glenn*. $30/£19

DRESSER, ELMER E. Wildflowers for Calliope. Mason, MI: The Author, 1881. 1st ed. 104pp. (Sl shelfworn, extrems rubbed), else Good. *Brown*. $65/£41

DRESSER, HENRY EELES. Eggs of the Birds of Europe. London: The Author, (1905)-10. 2 vols. 106 color half-tone plts. Teg. Orig cl, gilt. (Orig wrappers bound in at end of vol II; bkpl, joints tender; spines faded, ends bumped.) *Christie's**. $467/£292

DRESSLER, ALBERT. California's Pioneer Mountaineer of Rabbit Creek. SF: Albert Dressler, 1930. 1st ed. Ltd to 525 numbered. Color frontis. Grn cl. VF in color pict dj. *Argonaut*. $75/£47

DREWRY, CARLTON. Cloud Above Clocktime. NY, 1937. 1st ed. As New in dj. *Bond*. $20/£13

DREWRY, CARLTON. The Sounding Summer. NY, 1948. 1st ed, 1st bk. (Lacks dj), o/w As New. *Bond*. $35/£22

DREWRY, WILLIAM SIDNEY. The Southampton Insurrection. Washington: Neale, 1900. 1st ed. Frontis, fldg map, 40 plts. Blue cl, gilt. NF (corners sl rubbed). *Chapel Hill*. $325/£203

DREXEL-BIDDLE, A. J. The Froggy Fairy Book. Phila: Drexel-Biddle & Bradley, 1896. 1st ed. 8vo. 50pp; 9 full-pg b/w plts by John R. Skeen. Aeg. Red pict cl, gilt. Good. *Reisler*. $100/£63

DREYFUS, JOHN. A History of the Nonesuch Press. London: Nonesuch, 1981. Ltd to 950. Maroon cl. Fine in pict dj. *Truepenny*. $250/£156

DRIGGS, JOHN B. Short Sketches From Oldest America. Phila: Geo. W. Jacobs, 1905. 5 photo plts. VG (lib white # on spine, few other mks). *High Latitude*. $45/£28

DRINKWATER, G. C. and T. R. B. SANDERS. The University Boat Race. C. Gurdon (ed). London, 1929. 1st ed. Fldg map. Teg. (Sl browned; sl soiled, spine foot chipped.) *Edwards*. $152/£95

DRINKWATER, JOHN and ALBERT RUTHERSTON. Claud Lovat Fraser. London, 1923. One of 450 numbered, signed by both authors. 40 plts. Dj (spine panel defective). *Swann**. $258/£161

DRINKWATER, JOHN. Cotswold Characters. NY: Yale Univ, 1921. 1st US ed. 5 wood engrs by Paul Nash. NF in VG dj. *Any Amount*. $72/£45

DRINKWATER, JOHN. The Gentle Art of Theatre-Going. London: Robert Holden, 1927. 1st ed. Partly unopened. Nice in dj. *Dramatis*. $30/£19

DRINKWATER, JOHN. A History of the Late Siege of Gibraltar. London: J. Johnson et al, 1786. 2nd ed. xxiv,356pp; 10 lg fldg b/w copper plts. Recent dk brn coated pebbled cl, recent cl spine label, new eps and blanks w/orig blanks still retained at fr/rear. (Lt aging, foxing, few pp w/lt old stains; few sm tears, paper repairs on versos of plts, some w/add'l paper reinforcement at verso margins.) *Baltimore**. $180/£113

DRINKWATER, JOHN. A History of the Siege of Gibraltar, with a Description and Account of That Garrison, from the Earliest Periods. London: T. Spilsbury & Son, 1790. 4th ed. xxiv,356pp; 4 fldg maps, plans, 6 fldg views. Calf, gilt, morocco spine label. (Bkpls, 2 maps torn, worming to lower outside corner of all pp, not affecting plts, maps, except lower margin of frontis map), else VG. *Pacific**. $138/£86

DRINKWATER, JOHN. Loyalties. London: Sidgwick & Jackson, (1919). 1st trade ed. Red bds, ptd spine label. (Top edge sl dust-mkd), else NF in dj. *Reese*. $30/£19

DRINKWATER, JOHN. The Pilgrim of Eternity. London: Hodder and Stoughton, 1925. 1st ed. Signed, dated January, 1933. 12 plts. VG w/fr panel of dj laid-in. *Cady*. $25/£16

DRINKWATER, JOHN. Swords and Ploughshares. London: Sidgwick & Jackson, 1915. 1st ed. Red cl, ptd spine label (sl nicked). VG. *Reese*. $22/£14

DRISCOLL, R. E. Seventy Years of Banking in the Black Hills. Rapid City, 1948. 1st ed. Port. Good+ in orig wraps. *Wantagh*. $45/£28

DRIVER, GEORGE H. Cape-Scapes. Boston, 1930. 1st ed. Inscribed. 9 photo plts. Grn cl. VG. *Larry Price*. $30/£19

DROOP, J. P. Archaeological Excavation. London: CUP, 1915. Maroon cl, gilt. VG (lib spine # removed). *Larry Price*. $25/£16

DROWN, WILLIAM. Compendium of Agriculture, or the Farmer's Guide.... Providence, 1824. 1st ed. Uncut. Mod cl, leather spine label. (Foxing, sl stains, lib stamps.) *Oinonen**. $70/£44

DRUITT, R. The Surgeon's Vade Mecum. London, 1843. 3rd ed. xvi,570pp. 3/4 calf (spine, corners very rubbed). *Whitehart*. $80/£50

DRUMHELLER, DANIEL. Uncle Dan Drumheller Tells Thrills of Western Trails in 1854. Spokane: Inland-American Ptg Co, 1925. Frontisport, 1 other port. Blindstamped black fabricoid. (Bkpl removed fep.) *Dawson*. $100/£63

DRUMMOND OF HAWTHORNDEN, WILLIAM. A Cypress Grove. London: Hawthornden Press, 1919. One of 1000 numbered. VG (spine ends, corners bumped) in dj (nicked, sl rubbed, creased, dusty, browned). *Ulysses*. $88/£55

DRUMMOND OF HAWTHORNDEN, WILLIAM. The Poetical Works of William Drummond of Hawthornden. L. E. Kastner (ed). Manchester: The University Press, 1913. 1st Eng ed. 2 vols. Teg. VG (spine ends sl bumped) in dj (nicked, sl creased, rubbed, mkd, spines browned). *Ulysses*. $152/£95

DRUMMOND, HENRY. Baxter's Second Innings Specially Reported for the...School Team. NY: James Pott, 1892. 1st US ed. Gilt dec pict cl. VG (lt foxed). *Reese*. $60/£38

DRUMMOND, HENRY. The Monkey That Would Not Kill. Hodder & Stoughton, 1898. 1st ed. 16 b/w plts. Aeg. Pict cl. Good (inscrip, feps browned, pp sl thumbed; spine ends, corners bumped, rubbed, cvrs sl mkd). *Ulysses*. $120/£75

DRUMMOND, JAMES. Ancient Scottish Weapons.... George Waterston & Sons, 1881. Ltd to 500. Folio. 26pp; 54 full-pg color lithos. Morocco-backed beveled bds (sl mkd, neatly recased), gilt. *Hollett*. $560/£350

DRUMMOND, W. Memoir on the Antiquity of the Zodiacs of Esneh and Dendera. London, 1821. 1st ed. 191pp. Marbled bds. (Lt foxed, lacks 2 plts; hinge reinforced), o/w VG. *Middle Earth*. $175/£109

DRURY, CLIFFORD M. Chief Lawyer of the Nez Perce Indians, 1796-1876. Glendale: A.H. Clark, 1979. 1st ed. Inscribed. Color frontis. Orig prospectus laid in. Blue cl. Fine. *Harrington*. $60/£38

DRURY, CLIFFORD M. Diary of Titian Ramsay Peale, Oregon to California, Overland Journey, September and October, 1841. L.A.: Glen Dawson, 1957. 1st ed. One of 300. Frontisport, tipped-in color illus. Cl-backed ptd bds. (Extreme bd edges sl dknd), else Fine. *Argonaut*. $50/£31

DRURY, CLIFFORD M. Elkanah and Mary Walker, Pioneers Among the Spokanes. Caldwell: Caxton, 1940. 1st ed. VG in Poor dj. *Perier*. $65/£41

DRURY, CLIFFORD M. Marcus and Narcissa Whitman and the Opening of Old Oregon. Glendale: A.H. Clark, 1973. 1st ed. 2 vols. Vol 1 signed. Blue cl, gilt. Fine. *Pacific**. $98/£61

DRURY, CLIFFORD M. A Tepee in His Front Yard. H. T. Crowley and the Founding of Spokane. Portland: Binfords & Mort, 1949. 1st ed. Signed. VG in dj. *Perier*. $35/£22

DRURY, DRU. Illustrations of Natural History. Wherein Are Exhibited Upwards of Two Hundred Figures of Exotic Insects. Volume III only. The Author, 1782. 4to. 50 hand-colored engr plts (pencil notes in lower margins). Aeg. Contemp calf (rebacked preserving orig spine). Sotheby's*. $3,864/£2,415

DRYDEN, CECIL. Up the Columbia for Furs. Caldwell, ID: Caxton, 1949. 1st ed. Fine in pict dj. Argonaut. $75/£47

DRYDEN, JOHN. All for Love: Antony/Cleopatra. Kentfield: Allen, 1976. One of 140. Frontis. Prospectus laid in. Fine. Pacific*. $150/£94

DRYDEN, JOHN. The Dramatic Works. Montague Summers (ed). London: Nonesuch, 1931-1932. One of 750 sets. 6 vols. Untrimmed. Marbled bds w/buckram spine. Fine set. Second Life. $250/£156

DRYDEN, JOHN. Fables Ancient and Modern. London: Tonson, 1700. 1st ed. Folio. 648pp. Nice (sl foxed) in later leather-backed bds (chipped, spine extrems lack 1-inch pieces). Second Life. $350/£219

DRYDEN, JOHN. Fables Ancient and Modern. London: Jacob Tonson, 1734. 4th ed. Engr frontis, (58),348pp. Orig calf (spine scuffed, extrems chipped; fr hinge cracked), spine label. Karmiole. $75/£47

DRYDEN, JOHN. Original Poems and Translations. London: J. & R. Tonson, 1743. 1st ed. 2 vols. (12),336; (12),336pp. Mottled calf, gilt, morocco spine labels. (Old name; spine ends scuffed), else VG. Pacific*. $259/£162

DRYDEN, JOHN. The Works.... Walter Scott (ed). William Miller, 1808. 18 vols. 8vo. Engr frontisport. Contemp 1/2 calf (sl rubbed). Sotheby's*. $846/£529

DRYDEN, JOHN. The Works...Now First Collected...Illustrated with Notes, Historical, Critical, and Explanatory, and a Life of the Author, by Walter Scott. William Miller, 1808. 1st Scott ed. 18 vols. 8vo. Frontis port vol 1, fldg plt vol 6, plt of medals vol 9, all cancels listed in vol 18 in place. Marbled edges. Contemp diaper-grain sprinkled dk brn calf, gilt, narrow arrow-head rolls on cvr edges, turn-ins. VG (bkpls; unobtrusive damage to fore-edge of fr cvr vol 14; sl mkd). Blackwell's. $1,592/£995

DU BOIS, JOHN VAN DEUSEN. Campaigns in the West, 1856-1861. George P. Hammond (ed). Tucson: AZ Pioneers Hist Soc, 1949. 1st ed. One of 300 ptd. Lg fldg map. 1/2 red morocco, patterned bds, black leather spine label. Fine. Howes D521. Harrington. $350/£219

DU BOIS, W. E. B. The Gift of Black Folk. Boston, 1924. 1st ed. (Sig, pencil underlining; rubbed, spine faded.) Swann*. $138/£86

DU BOIS, W. E. B. Mansart Builds a School: The Black Flame. NY: Mainstream, 1959. 1st eds. Fine in dj (sl dust-worn). Second Life. $75/£47

DU BOIS, W. E. B. The Ordeal of Mansart: the Black Flame. NY: Mainstream, 1957. 1st ed. Fine in dj (sl dust-worn). Second Life. $75/£47

DU BOIS, W. E. B. The Quest for the Golden Fleece. Chicago, 1911. 1st ed. Silver-stamped pict cl. Swann*. $201/£126

DU BOIS, W. E. B. The Souls of Black Folk. NY: Blue Heron, 1953. Signed. VG (sm remnant of bk label to fr pastedown; corners worn). W/o dj, as issued. Agvent. $600/£375

DU BOIS, WILLIAM PENE. Call Me Bandicott. NY: Harper & Row, (1970). 1st ed. 8vo. Color pict bds. Good in full color dj. Reisler. $65/£41

DU BOIS, WILLIAM PENE. The Forbidden Forest. NY: Harper & Row, (1978). 1st ed. 4to. White pict cl. VG in full color dj. Reisler. $60/£38

DU BOIS, WILLIAM PENE. Otto at Sea. NY: Viking, 1936. 1st ed, 1st bk. Sq slim 12mo. Color pict bds. (Lt finger mks few pp, Christmas 1936 ink inscrip; sl edgeworn, lt rubbed.) Cvrs VG. Baltimore*. $100/£63

DU CHAILLU, PAUL. Land of the Midnight Sun, Summer and Winter Journeys Through Sweden, Norway, Lapland and Northern Finland. NY, 1882. 2 vols. Color fldg map. (Spines sl soiled), else Fine set in blue pict cl, gilt. Hallam. $192/£120

DU CHAILLU, PAUL. The Viking Age. John Murray, 1889. 1st ed. 2 vols. xx,591; viii,562,(i)pp; map. Dec maroon cl, gilt. VG set (few spots, 1 joint tender; 1 rear bd sl mkd, sl snagged). Hollett. $240/£150

DU GARD, ROGER MARTIN. The Postman. NY: Viking, 1955. 1st Amer ed. VF in VF dj (sm tear rear cvr). Between The Covers. $100/£63

DU HALDE, P. The General History of China, Containing a Geographical, Historical, Chronological, Political and Physical Description.... John Watts, 1736. 1st Eng ed. 4 vols. 8vo. 4 frontispieces, xiv,509; xiv,438; xiv,496; xiv,464pp; 4 fldg maps, 15 engr plts. Full contemp calf, gilt, raised bands, contrasting black/maroon leather labels. VG set (extrems, bds sl worn). Sotheran. $1,592/£995

DU MAURIER, DAPHNE. Frenchman's Creek. London: Gollancz, 1941. 1st ed. Black cl, gilt. VG in dj (spine sl browned). Maggs. $200/£125

DU MAURIER, DAPHNE. Mary Anne. Victor Gollancz, 1954. 1st ed. VG (fep sl creased; top edge dusty, edges spotted) in dj (worn). Ulysses. $40/£25

DU MAURIER, DAPHNE. My Cousin Rachel. NY: Doubleday, 1952. 1st Amer ed. Grn eps; top edge stained lt grn. Beige cl. (Spine sl skewed), o/w Fine in dj (sl soiled, lt edgeworn). Heritage. $200/£125

DU MAURIER, DAPHNE. The Parasites. Victor Gollancz, 1949. 1st ed. VG (spine sl faded, ends, corner sl bumped) in dj (worn). Ulysses. $58/£36

DU MAURIER, DAPHNE. Rebecca. NY: Doubleday, Doran, 1938. 1st ed. Signed. Red cl, silver wrap-around label. (Joints of label rubbed), else VG. Pacific*. $196/£123

DU MAURIER, GEORGE. The Martian: a Novel. NY: Harper, 1897. 1st ed. Frontisport, iv,(ii),477pp + 2pp pub's cat; 48 full-pg illus. Red cl, gilt (bumped, heavily rubbed, stained). Internally Good (foxed, top corner rear 50 pp lt stained; ink name). Fair. Blue Mountain. $45/£28

DU MAURIER, GEORGE. Trilby. Osgood, McIlvaine, 1894. 7th ed. 3 vols. Pub's cat vol 3. Pict cl. Good (spines bumped, sl chipped). Tiger. $48/£30

DU MAURIER, GEORGE. Trilby. London: Osgood, McIlvaine, 1895. 1st ltd ed. One of 250 numbered, signed lg paper copies. Teg, untrimmed. White vellum, lt olive linen, gilt. (Extrems lt rubbed.) Baltimore*. $160/£100

DU PETIT-THOUARS, ABEL. Voyage of the Venus: Sojourn in California. Charles N. Rudkin (trans). L.A.: Glen Dawson, 1956. One of 200 ptd. 10 plts on both sides of 5 plts (8 hand-colored). 1/2 cl, dec bds, paper spine label. NF. Pacific*. $81/£51

DU TOIT, A. L. The Geology of South Africa. Edinburgh: Oliver & Boyd, 1954. 3rd ed. 41 plts, fldg map. (Underlining, marginal mks), o/w VG. Savona. $56/£35

DU-PLAT-TAYLOR, F. M. Docks, Wharves and Piers. London, 1949. 3rd ed. Dj (chipped, spine sl browned). Edwards. $120/£75

DUANE, WILLIAM. A Hand Book for Infantry. Phila, 1812. 65 engr plts. Contemp calf-backed marbled bds, morocco spine label. (Lib bkpl, ink names, foxed, 2 plts defective; worn.) King. $165/£103

DUANE, WILLIAM. A Hand Book for Infantry: Containing the First Principles of Military Discipline.... Phila, 1814. 9th ed. (Browned throughout; bds soiled.) Swann*. $80/£50

DUBOIS, CARDINAL. Memoirs of Cardinal Dubois. Ernest Dowson (trans). Leonard Smithers, 1899. 1st ed. 2 vols. B/w frontisports. 4,282; 257pp. Unopened. VG (bkpls, feps browned; top edges dusty, spine ends, corners sl bumped). *Ulysses.* $280/£175

DUBOIS, CARDINAL. Memoirs. Ernest Dowson (trans). London: Smithers, 1899. 2 vols. 2 ports. Uncut. (Sl rubbed.) *Stewart.* $96/£60

DUBOIS, FELIX. Timbuctoo the Mysterious. Heinemann, 1897. 1st Eng ed. xi,(i),377pp; 11 maps, plans. All edges uncut, some ll uncut. Grn pict cl, gilt. Good (lib ink stamp, lt browned throughout). *Sotheran.* $192/£120

DUBOSE, JOHN WITHERSPOON. General Joseph Wheeler and the Army of Tennessee. NY: Neale, 1912. 1st ed. Frontisport. Teg. Blue cl. VG (inner hinges reinforced; spine ends, extrems lt rubbed). Howes D523. *Chapel Hill.* $350/£219

DUBUISSON, A. Richard Parkes Bonington: His Life and Work. C.E. Hughes (trans). John Lane, Bodley Head, 1924. Ltd to 1000. 17 color plts. Cl-backed paper bds, spine label. (Sl spotted; sl rubbed, spine faded.) *Hollett.* $208/£130

DUBUS, ANDRE. Broken Vessels. London, 1993. 1st UK ed. Fine in Fine dj. *Warren.* $30/£19

DUBUS, ANDRE. Voices from the Moon. Boston: David Godine, (1984). 1st ed. Fine in dj. *Captain's Bookshelf.* $35/£22

DUBY, GEORGES. History of Medieval Art 980-1440. Geneva/NY, 1986. New ed in 1 vol. Good in slipcase. *Washton.* $95/£59

DUCHAMP, MARCEL. From the Green Box. George Heard Hamilton (trans). New Haven, 1957. 1st ed in English. One of 400. Dj (repaired w/cellotape on verso, causing discoloration on recto). *Swann*.* $69/£43

DUCHAMP, MARCEL. Salt Seller. Michel Sanouillet and Elmer Peterson (eds). NY: OUP, 1973. 1st ed. Fine (sm bkpl) in dj. *Turtle Island.* $135/£84

DUCHOCHOIS, P. C. Industrial Photography. NY: Scovil & Adams, 1901. VG in pict stiff wrappers (spine ends chipped). *Cahan.* $150/£94

DUCHOW, JOHN CHARLES. The Duchow Journal: A Voyage from Boston to California in 1852. (Kentfield): Mallette Dean, 1959. One of 200 ptd. Frontisport. 1/2 cl, dec bds, paper spine label. Fine. *Pacific*.* $86/£54

DUCKWORTH, FRANCIS R. G. Chester. A&C Black, 1910. 1st ed. 10 color plts by E. Harrison Compton, fldg map. Teg. (Feps lt browned; lt dampstained, spine sl faded.) *Edwards.* $72/£45

DUCONGE, ADA SMITH with JAMES HASKINS. Bricktop. NY: Atheneum, 1983. 1st ed. (Inscrip.) Dec dj. *Petrilla.* $25/£16

DUDEN, GOTFRIED. Report on a Journey to the Western States...Several Years Along the Missouri (1824, 25, 26, 27). Columbia: State Historical Soc MO, 1980. As New in dj. *Perier.* $20/£13

DUDIN, M. The Art of the Bookbinder and Gilder, 1772. Richard Macintyre Atkinson (trans). Leeds, England: Elmete, 1977. 1st ed in English. Ltd to 490 numbered. Folio. 16 full-pg plts. Calf, gilt, over cl. Fine. *Karmiole.* $225/£141

DUDLEY, CARRIE. My Peek-a-Boo Show Book. Gordon Volland, Buzza Co., (1928). 1st ed. Obl 8vo. Moveable. Die-cut pp. VG (edges worn, sm tears). *Davidson.* $325/£203

DUDLEY, ROBERT. Secret Memoirs of Robert Dudley, Earl of Leicester, Prime Minister and Favourite of Queen Elizabeth.... London: For Sam Briscoe, 1706. 1st ed. (32),218pp (tp, text lt foxed). 19th-cent red morocco over marbled bds (sl worn). *Karmiole.* $100/£63

DUERRENMATT, FRIEDRICH. Oedipus. LEC, 1989. One of 650 signed by Durrenmatt and Marie Cosindas (photos). Fine in slipcase. *Swann*.* $201/£126

DUERRENMATT, FRIEDRICH. Once a Greek.... NY: Knopf, 1965. 1st Amer ed. VF in VF dj (sl rubbed). *Between The Covers.* $100/£63

DUERRENMATT, FRIEDRICH. The Pledge. NY: Knopf, 1959. 1st Amer ed. VF in VF dj (sm tear). *Between The Covers.* $100/£63

DUERRENMATT, FRIEDRICH. The Quarry. Greenwich, CT: NYGS, 1962. 1st Amer ed. VF in Fine dj (price-clipped). *Between The Covers.* $85/£53

DUERRENMATT, FRIEDRICH. The Visit. Maurice Valency (trans). NY: Random House, (1958). 1st Amer ed. VF in Fine dj (sm scrape fr cvr). *Between The Covers.* $125/£78

DUFEK, GEORGE J. Operation Deep Freeze. NY: Harcourt Brace, (1957). 1st ed. VG in dj. *Perier.* $25/£16

DUFF, JAMES GRANT. A History of the Mahrattas. London: Longman, Rees, Orme et al, 1826. 1st ed. 3 vols. Engr frontis, xxxii,572; engr frontis, xx,484; engr frontis, xx,538pp; 2 fldg maps. Ca 1900 calf, brn marbled bds, gilt. (Bkpls; extrems lt scuffed.) *Karmiole.* $400/£250

DUFF, ROGER. The Moa-Hunter Period of Maori Culture. Wellington, 1950. 1st ed. *Edwards.* $48/£30

DUFFIELD, KENNETH GRAHAM. The Four Little Pigs That Didn't Have Any Mother. Phila: Henry Altemus, (1919). 1st ed. 16mo. 61pp; 29 full color, full-pg illus. Cl-backed pict bds (sl shelfworn), color paste label. Full color dj (spine head lt chipped). *Reisler.* $85/£53

DUFFUS, R. L. The Santa Fe Trail. London: Longmans Green, 1930. 1st ed. Pict eps. Blue cl. Fine. *Harrington.* $35/£22

DUFFY, MAUREEN. The Passionate Shepherdess. London: Cape, 1977. 1st Eng ed. VG (sl bumped, rubbed, sl mkd) in dj (mkd, sl rubbed, creased, internally sl blackened). *Ulysses.* $40/£25

DUFRESNE, JOHN. Louisiana Power and Light. NY: W.W. Norton, (1994). 1st ed. As New in dj. *Pacific*.* $40/£25

DUFTY, ARTHUR RICHARD. European Armour in the Tower of London. London, 1968. 167 plts. Good + . *Washton.* $75/£47

DUGAN, MARK and JOHN BOESSENECKER. The Gray Fox. Norman, 1992. NF in dj. *Dumont.* $30/£19

DUGANNE, A. J. H. The Fighting Quakers, a True Story of the War for Our Union. NY: J.P. Robens, 1866. 2nd ed. Frontis, 116pp. Inserted notice. BAL 4904. *M & S.* $125/£78

DUGDALE, FLORENCE E. The Book of Baby Pets. London: Henry Frowde/Hodder & Stoughton, (1915). 1st ed. 4to. viii,119pp; 19 mtd color plts by E. J. Detmold. Cl-backed bds w/onlaid circular label to fr cvr. Nice (corner tips worn, bds sl rubbed, fore-edge of rear bd lt stained). *Sotheran.* $269/£168

DUGDALE, GILES. William Barnes of Dorset. Cassell, 1953. 1st ed. 8 woodcuts, 2 maps. VG in dj. *Hollett.* $72/£45

DUGDALE, THOMAS and WILLIAM BURNETT. Curiosities of Great Britain. England and Wales Delineated. Volumes I-X (of 11). London: Talluis, n.d. (ca 1845). 10 vols. Pub's cl (shelfworn; foxed). *Oinonen*.* $500/£313

DUGDALE, WILLIAM. The Antient Usage in Bearing of Such Ensigns of Honour as Are Commonly Call'd Arms, with a Catalogue of the Present Nobility of England...Scotland and Ireland. Oxford: Moses Pitt, 1682. 2nd ed. (1),(4),210pp; fldg plt. Dk calf, morocco spine label. (Bkpls, mold spotting, plt torn, backed on later paper; glue to fr joint), else VG. *Pacific*.* $161/£101

DUGDALE, WILLIAM. The Baronage of England. London, 1675-6. 2 vols. 5 fldg plts. Full polished calf. (Bkpl, piece missing blank corner of vol 1 tp, stains on 1st ll both vols, repaired tear vol 2; worn, rubbed, cvr detached, others nearly detached.) *Kane*.* $225/£141

DUGGAN, ALFRED. Count Bohemond. London: Faber & Faber, 1964. 1st ed. Fine in salmon-red cl, gilt. Dj. *Maggs.* $56/£35

DUGGAN, ALFRED. Elephants and Castles. Faber, 1963. 1st ed. (Bkpl; edges sl browned, spotted), o/w VG in VG dj (sl rubbed). *Virgo.* $72/£45

DUGGAR, B. M. (ed). Proceedings of the International Congress of Plant Sciences. Ithaca, NY, 1929. 2 vols. Grn cl, gilt. (Ex-lib), else VG. *Larry Price.* $50/£31

DUGGER, CHRISTINA. Three Cheers for the Pioneers. N.p., 1954. 1st ed? Inscribed. VG (stamp). *Baade.* $45/£28

DUGMORE, A. RADCLYFFE. The Wonderland of Big Game. London, 1925. 1st ed. Map. (Feps lt browned; spine sl faded.) *Edwards.* $56/£35

DUGUID, J. Green Hell. London, 1931. 1st ed. Nice. *Grayling.* $48/£30

DUGUID, J. Tiger-Man. London: Gollancz, 1932. 1st ed. VG + in Good dj. *Mikesh.* $35/£22

DUHAMEL, GEORGES. The Fortunes of the Pasquiers. NY/London: Harper, 1935. 1st US ed. Tan cl. Fine in dj. *Reese.* $50/£31

DUHRING, HENRY. Remarks on the United States of America, with Regard to the Actual State of Europe. London/Amsterdam/NY: Simpkin & Marshall/C.G. Sulpke/W. Jackson, 1833. 1st ed. vi,209pp. Contemp cl (crudely rebacked; worn). Internally NF. *Mott.* $50/£31

DUKE, ALTON. When the Colorado River Quit the Ocean. Yuma, 1974. 1st ed. Grn paper over bds. VG + in dj. *Five Quail.* $35/£22

DUKE, BASIL W. Morgan's Cavalry. NY/Washington: Neale, 1906. 1st ed. 8vo. Frontisport. Teg. Grn cl. Fine. Howes D548. *Chapel Hill.* $550/£344

DUKE, BASIL W. Morgan's Cavalry. NY/Washington: Neale, 1909. 2nd ed. 8vo. Frontisport. Grn cl. (Spine sl faded), else NF in dj (tape at edges on verso). Howes D548. *Chapel Hill.* $650/£406

DULAC, EDMUND. Edmund Dulac's Picture Book for the French Red Cross. London: Hodder & Stoughton, (1915). 1st ed. 4to. Frontis (sl rippled), 19 mtd color plts, b/w port. Olive-tan pict cl. Very Nice. *Reisler.* $175/£109

DULAC, EDMUND. Edmund Dulac's Picture-Book. London: For the Daily Telegraph by Hodder & Stoughton, (1915). 1st ed. 4to. (viii),134,(i)pp; 19 mtd color plts, port photo. Yellow pict cl. (Fore-edge sl speckled), o/w Fine. *Sotheran.* $157/£98

DULAC, EDMUND. Fairy-Book. Fairy Tales of the Allied Nations. London: Hodder & Stoughton, (1916). 1st ed. 4to. 15 full-pg mtd color plts. Tan dec cl. VG in full color pict dj (spine, rear cvr lt mkd), pict cardbd box (browned, 2 sides broken). *Reisler.* $750/£469

DULLES, ALLEN. The Craft of Intelligence. NY: Harper, (1963). 1st ed. Inscribed, dated Oct 24, 1963. Fine (lacks dj). *Between The Covers.* $150/£94

DUMAS, ALEXANDRE. The Black Tulip. Haarlem: LEC, 1951. One of 1500. Signed by Frans Lammers (illus) & Jan Van Krimpen (designer). Teg. Full natural niger morocco, gilt/black leather tulip design, leather spine label. Fine in glassine, slipcase. *Pacific*.* $52/£33

DUMAS, ALEXANDRE. The Count of Monte Cristo. LEC, 1941. Ltd to 1500 numbered, signed by Lynd Ward (illus). 4 vols. Fine in slipcase. *Swann*.* $161/£101

DUMAS, ALEXANDRE. The Man in the Iron Mask. LEC, 1965. Ltd to 1500 numbered, signed by Edy Legrand (illus). Fine in slipcase. *Swann*.* $103/£64

DUMAS, ALEXANDRE. Twenty Years After. LEC, 1958. Ltd to 1500 numbered, signed by Edy Legrand (illus). Fine in slipcase. *Swann*.* $57/£36

DUMAS, FILS ALEXANDRE. Camille. LEC, 1937. Ltd to 1500 numbered, signed by Marie Laurencin (illus). Fine in slipcase. *Swann*.* $488/£305

DUMAS, FILS ALEXANDRE. Camille. LEC, 1955. Ltd to 1500 numbered, signed by Bernard Lamotte (illus). Fine in slipcase. *Swann*.* $46/£29

DUMAS, HENRY. Play Ebony, Play Ivory. Eugene B. Redmond (ed). NY: Random House, (1974). 1st ed. Notes of Julius Lester. VG in ptd dj. *Petrilla.* $150/£94

DUMKE, GLENN S. The Boom of the Eighties in Southern California. San Marino: Huntington Library, 1944. 1st ed. 9 plts. Fine. *Pacific*.* $40/£25

DUMONT, HENRIETTA. Floral Offering...Comprising the Language and Poetry of Flowers. Phila: H.C. Peck, 1851. 6 hand-colored plts. Brn cl. Good. *Appelfeld.* $110/£69

DUMONT-WILDEN, L. The Wandering Prince. G. Bell, 1934. 1st Eng ed. 4 plts. VG in dj (sl rubbed, repaired, price-clipped). *Hollett.* $40/£25

DUN, T. I. From Cairo to Siwa. Cairo, 1933. 1st ed. Ltd to 1000. 1 gold, 1 silver plt (sl surface loss due to adhesion to guards), map. (Bkpl; sl worn.) *Edwards.* $56/£35

DUNAWAY, WAYLAND FULLER. Reminiscences of a Rebel. NY: Neale, 1913. 1st ed. Blue-gray cl. VG (lib bkpl, blindstamp; cvrs lt soiled). *Chapel Hill.* $200/£125

DUNAWAY, WAYLAND FULLER. Reminiscences of a Rebel. NY: Neale, 1913. 1st ed. Blue-gray cl. (Lt offsetting to eps from dj flaps), else Fine in dj (chipped, spine top lacks 1/4-inch, bottom lacks 1.5-inches). *Chapel Hill.* $400/£250

DUNBAR, LIN. Ferns of the Coastal Plain. Columbia: USC Press, 1989. 1st ed. Fine in dj. *Archer.* $15/£9

DUNBAR, PAUL LAURENCE. Candle-Lightin' Time. NY: Dodd, Mead, 1901. 1st ed. Teg. Gilt-dec cl. Fine. *Pacific*.* $138/£86

DUNBAR, PAUL LAURENCE. Candle-Lightin' Time. NY: Dodd Mead, 1901. 1st ed. 50 photos. (Ink inscrip), else Fine in illus cl. Ptd dj (1/2-inch chips, closed tears). *Bromer.* $750/£469

DUNBAR, PAUL LAURENCE. Folks from Dixie. NY, 1898. 1st ed. Pict cl, pict label. (Lt rubbed.) BAL 4921. *Swann*.* $149/£93

DUNBAR, PAUL LAURENCE. Howdy Honey Howdy. NY, 1905. 1st ed. Leigh Richmond Miner (photos). (Hinges starting, sig loose, eps foxed; soiled, spine end frayed.) *Swann*.* $57/£36

DUNBAR, PAUL LAURENCE. Howdy Honey Howdy. NY: Dodd, Mead, 1905. 1st ed. Leigh Richmond Miner (photos). Teg. (1 splatter stain), else Fine. BAL 4955. *Cahan.* $300/£188

DUNBAR, PAUL LAURENCE. Lyrics of Love and Laughter. NY, 1903. 1st ed. Photo frontis. (Lt faded, extrems sl rubbed.) BAL 4945. *Swann*.* $69/£43

DUNBAR, PAUL LAURENCE. Lyrics of Lowly Life. NY, 1896. 1st ed. Frontisport. (Cvrs stained.) BAL 4918. *Swann*.* $149/£93

DUNBAR, PAUL LAURENCE. Speakin O' Christmas. NY, 1914. 1st ed, 1st binding. Pict cl; sm bkseller's ticket fr pastedown. Fine. BAL 4962. *Swann*.* $258/£161

DUNBAR, PAUL LAURENCE. The Uncalled. NY, 1898. 1st ed, 2nd issue binding. Dec stamped cl. (Fr hinge partly cracked.) *Swann*.* $115/£72

DUNBAR, PAUL LAURENCE. When Malindy Sings. NY, 1903. 1st ed. Pict cl. BAL 4948. *Swann*.* $172/£108

DUNCAN, BOB. Buffalo Country. NY: E.P. Dutton, 1959. 1st ed. Black cl. VG in pict dj. *House.* $25/£16

DUNCAN, DAVID DOUGLAS. This is War! Harper, (1951). Good in dj (lacks piece, worn). *Rybski.* $100/£63

DUNCAN, DAVID DOUGLAS. Viva Picasso. NY, (1980). 1st ed. VG in dj (price-clipped). *King.* $40/£25

DUNCAN, DAVID DOUGLAS. Viva Picasso: A Centennial Celebration, 1881-1981. Viking, 1980. 1st ed. Nice in dj. *Rybski.* $50/£31

DUNCAN, GEORGE and BERNARD DARWIN. Present-Day Golf. NY: Doran, (1921). 1st Amer ed. Grn cl, gilt. (Emb stamp, sig; spine ends sl worn), else NF. *Pacific*. $86/£54

DUNCAN, H. O. The World on Wheels. Paris: H.O. Duncan, n.d. (ca 1926). 1st ed. 2 vols. Blue cl, gilt. Good. *Karmiole*. $500/£313

DUNCAN, JANE E. A Summer Ride Through Western Tibet. London: Smith, Elder, 1906. 1st ed. Fldg map, 40 half-tone plts. Grn cl. Good (sl foxed; recased w/new eps, sl rubbed, damp-spotted). *Morrell*. $304/£190

DUNCAN, ROBERT. Derivations. London: Fulcrum, (1968). 1st ed. Red cl. Fine in dj (lt used). *Dermont*. $40/£25

DUNCAN, ROBERT. The First Decade. London: Fulcrum, (1968). One of 150 numbered, signed. Fine in Fine dj. *Dermont*. $150/£94

DUNCAN, ROBERT. Letters. Highlands, NC: Jonathan Williams, 1958. One of 510. NF in marbled wrappers. *Pacific*. $46/£29

DUNCAN, ROBERT. My Mother Would Be a Falconress. N.p.: Oyez, 1968. Signed, dated 1982. Broadside. Fine. *Pacific*. $150/£94

DUNCAN, ROBERT. The Opening of the Field. NY: Grove, (1960). Pb orig. Fine. *Dermont*. $20/£13

DUNCAN, RONALD. Saint Spiv. Dobson, 1961. 1st ed. VG + in VG + dj (sl rubbed). *Any Amount*. $19/£12

DUNCAN, THOMAS D. Recollections of Thomas D. Duncan, a Confederate Soldier. Nashville: McQuiddy Ptg, 1922. Only ed. (Edges sl bumped), else Fine in stiff ptd wraps. *Chapel Hill*. $275/£172

DUNDONALD, THOMAS. The Autobiography of a Seaman. London: Richard Bentley, 1860. 2nd ed. 2 vols. xxiii,428; xv,488pp; 4 fldg charts. Mod 1/2 red calf, gilt. *Hollett*. $352/£220

DUNGLISON, ROBLEY. Human Physiology. Phila, 1832. 1st ed. Vol 1 only. Full leather (hinges, spine chipped). Good (extrems sl worn). *Doctor's Library*. $50/£31

DUNHAM, CURTIS and OLIVER HERFORD. Two in a Zoo. Indianapolis: Bobbs-Merrill, (1904). 1st ed. Pict cl. (Extrems rubbed), else VG. *Pacific*. $46/£29

DUNHAM, EDITH. The Diary of a Mouse. NY: Dodge, (1907). 1st ed. 8vo. Bessie Pease Gutmann (illus). Red cl (spotted), color paste label. *Reisler*. $250/£156

DUNHAM, KATHERINE. Island Possessed. NY, 1969. 1st Amer ed. NF in NF dj. *Polyanthos*. $35/£22

DUNHILL, THOMAS F. Sir Edward Elgar. Blackie, 1938. 1st ed. 8 plts. VG in dj (top edge sl rubbed). *Hollett*. $40/£25

DUNKERLEY, S. Robert Bakewell. Artist—Blacksmith. Cromford, 1988. One of 750. 32 color plts. *Edwards*. $72/£45

DUNKIN, EDWIN. The Midnight Sky: Familiar Notes on the Stars and Planets. (London): Religious Tract Soc, 1891. Teg. Pict cl, gilt. (Lower fr joint cracked through; spine sunned, ends frayed), else VG. *Pacific*. $46/£29

DUNLAP, KNIGHT. Mysticism, Freudianism, and Scientific Psychology. St. Louis: C.V. Mosby, 1920. Ptd grn cl. Good + (bklabel pasted over pub's imprint on tp; edges bumped, crown lt shelfworn). *Gach*. $35/£22

DUNLAP, WILLIAM. A History of the American Theatre. NY: J. & J. Harper, 1832. 1st ed. Orig pink cl-cvrd bds. Good (spine perished). *Pacific*. $58/£36

DUNLAP, WILLIAM. Peter the Great; Or, The Russian Mother. NY: D. Longworth, March 1814. 1st ed. 56pp (foxed). Recent plain wraps. BAL 5014. *M & S*. $150/£94

DUNLAP, WILLIAM. A Trip to Niagara. NY: E.B. Clayton, 1830. 1st ed. Contemp leather-backed limp bds. (Title trimmed from tp, used as a label to backstrip; foxed, inscrips, holograph notes, cues.) *Dramatis*. $85/£53

DUNLOP, JOHN CHARLES and ALISON HAY. The Book of Old Edinburgh. Edinburgh: T. & A. Constable, 1886. xiv,160pp. (Sl string-mks to fr bd, rear bd stained, spine sl dknd.) *Hollett*. $56/£35

DUNLOP, O. JOCELYN. English Apprenticeship and Child Labour. London, 1912. *Petersfield*. $29/£18

DUNLOP, R. H. W. Hunting in the Himalaya. London, 1860. 1st ed. 4 tinted litho plts, 1 plain plt, fldg map. Gilt-pict cl (spine tips sl rubbed; lt foxed, fep mkd). *Oinonen*. $400/£250

DUNLOP, R. H. W. Service and Adventure with the Khakee Ressalah. London, 1858. 8 plts. (Fep loose, bkpl.) *Swann*. $230/£144

DUNN, DOROTHY. American Indian Painting of the Southwest and Plains Areas. Univ of NM, 1968. 1st ed. Fine in dj. *Truepenny*. $250/£156

DUNN, E. R. The Salamanders of the Family Plethodontidae. Northampton, 1926. Frontis, 2 plts, 86 maps. (Pp yellowed, bkpl; varnished.) *Sutton*. $75/£47

DUNN, ESTHER C. Shakespeare in America. NY: Macmillan, 1939. 1st ed. VG. *Dramatis*. $30/£19

DUNN, J. B. The History of Nansemond County Virginia. N.p., (ca 1903). Map. Paper cvr. VG (lt pencil checks; postage stamps fr cvr). *Book Broker*. $40/£25

DUNN, J. P. Massacres of the Mountains: A History of the Indian Wars of the Far West, 1815-1875. NY: Archer House, (1965). Rpt ed. Brn cl. Fine in NF dj (spine faded). Howes D575. *Harrington*. $35/£22

DUNN, JAMES. From Coal Mine Upwards. W. Green, 1910. 1st ed. 20 plts. (Feps sl spotted; spine sl dknd.) *Hollett*. $72/£45

DUNN, JOHN DUNCAN and ELON JESSUP. Intimate Golf Talks. NY: Putnam, 1920. 1st ed. Blue cl, gilt, pict cvr label. (Inscrip; spine ends rubbed, label sl scratched), else VG. *Pacific*. $69/£43

DUNN, JOHN DUNCAN. ABC of Golf. NY: Harper, (1916, but 1919). (Emb stamp, rubberstamp), else VG in Fair dj (lacks lg piece). *Pacific*. $92/£58

DUNN, KATHERINE. Attic. NY: Harper & Row, (1970). 1st ed. NF in dj (spine ends, extrems sl rubbed). *Pacific*. $104/£65

DUNN, KATHERINE. Geek Love. NY, 1989. 1st ed. Fine in Fine dj. *Warren*. $40/£25

DUNN, NELL. The Incurable. London: Jonathan Cape, 1971. 1st ed. Top edge orange. Brownish gray cl-textured bds. Fine in dj. *Temple*. $26/£16

DUNN, NELL. Talking to Women. London: Macgibbon & Kee, 1965. 1st ed. 4 dbl-sided plts. Dk dull blue bds. (Sm label removed fr pastedown), o/w Fine in dj. *Temple*. $26/£16

DUNN, SEYMOUR. Golf Fundamentals. Saratoga Springs: Saratogian Ptg Service, (c.1922). 1st ed. Fldg chart. Dk blue cl, gilt. (Name, stamp, hinges cracking; spotted, spine head frayed, corners rubbed), else Good. *Pacific*. $138/£86

DUNN, WILLIAM EDWARD. Spanish and French Rivalry in the Gulf Region...1678-1702. Austin, 1917. 5 maps (1 fldg). Wraps. (Spine taped), else Good. *Dumont*. $100/£63

DUNN-PATTISON, R. P. Napoleon's Marshalls. London: Methuen, (1909). 20 plts. Good. *Stewart*. $80/£50

DUNNE, J. W. An Experiment with Time. A&C Black, 1927. 1st ed. (Extrems sl rubbed.) *Hollett*. $72/£45

DUNNE, JOHN GREGORY. Delano: The Story of the California Grape Strike. NY: FSG, (1967). 1st ed, 1st bk. Fine in NF dj (lt rubbed, sl soiled). *Between The Covers*. $85/£53

DUNNE, JOHN GREGORY. Vegas. NY: Random House, 1974. 1st ed. Fine in Fine dj (price-clipped). *Pettler*. $25/£16

DUNNE, JOHN GREGORY. Vegas. Quartet, 1974. 1st UK ed. VG + in dj. *Williams*. $77/£48

DUNNE, PETER M. Black Robes in Lower California. Berkeley: Univ of CA, 1952. 1st ed. Fldg map. Maroon cl. Fine in NF dj (spine dknd). *Harrington*. $65/£41

DUNNE, PETER M. Early Jesuit Missions in Tarahumara. Berkeley/L.A.: Univ of CA, 1948. 1st ed. Fldg map. Fine. *Argonaut*. $60/£38

DUNNE, PETER M. Early Jesuit Missions in Taramuhara. Berkeley: Univ of CA, 1948. 1st ed. Fldg map. Maroon cl. Fine in NF dj (spine sl dknd). *Harrington*. $50/£31

DUNNE, PETER M. Pioneer Jesuits in Northern Mexico. Berkeley: Univ of CA, 1944. 1st ed. Fldg map. Maroon cl. Fine in NF dj (spine dknd). *Harrington*. $50/£31

DUNNE, PETER M. (trans). Jacobo Sedelmayr: Missionary Frontiersman Explorer in Arizona and Sonora. Tucson: AZ Pioneers' Hist Soc, 1955. One of 600. Tipped-in frontis, fldg map, facs. Unopened. Fine in dj (sl edgeworn). *Pacific**. $35/£22

DUNNING, JOHN. The Bookman's Wake. NY, 1995. 1st ed. Signed. Fine in Fine dj. *Warren*. $40/£25

DUNNING, JOHN. Deadline. Huntington Beach: James Cahill, 1995. 1st Amer hb ed. One of 200 numbered, signed. Signed chapbook laid in. VF in slipcase. *Mordida*. $150/£94

DUNNING, JOHN. Denver. NY, 1980. 1st ed. NF in NF dj (sm hole rear flap). *Warren*. $45/£28

DUNNING, JOHN. The Holland Suggestions. NY, 1975. Bk club ed. Signed. NF in VG dj. *Warren*. $30/£19

DUNNING, JOHN. Looking for Ginger North. Fawcett, 1980. 1st ed, pb orig. (Reading crease; sm tear at foot, cvr lt creased.) Wraps. *Murder*. $20/£13

DUNNING, JOHN. The Torch Passes. (Huntington Beach: James Cahill, 1995.) 1st ed. Signed. As New in ptd wrappers, loose in cl cvr for Deadline. *Pacific**. $40/£25

DUNNING, JOHN. Tune in Yesterday: The Ultimate Encyclopedia of Old-Time Radio, 1925-1976. Englewood Cliffs: Prentice-Hall, (1976). 1st ed. Fine in dj. *Pacific**. $184/£115

DUNRAVEN, EARL OF. The Great Divide. C&W, 1876. 1st ed. xvi,(4),377pp; 2 lg fldg maps, 15 full-pg wood engrs. Marbled edges. VG (bkpl) in contemp rose calf, morocco label, marbled sides. *Cox*. $144/£90

DUNSANY, LORD. The Chronicles of Rodriguez. London: Putnam, (1922). 1st ed. One of 500. Signed by Dunsany & S. H. Sime (frontis). 1/2 vellum, leather spine label. Fine in dj (extrems chipped, sm tears). *Pacific**. $184/£115

DUNSANY, LORD. The Curse of the Wise Woman. London: Heinemann, (1933). 1st ed. (Eps offsetting, lt foxed; edges lt foxed), o/w NF in dj (spine ends, corners worn, rear cvr dust-soiled, fr flap creased, foxed). *Levin*. $125/£78

DUNSANY, LORD. The Donnellan Lectures 1943. London: Heinemann, 1945. 1st ed. (Pp yellowed; spine ends sl faded), o/w VG in dj (chipped, browned; internally repaired at spine). *Virgo*. $24/£15

DUNSANY, LORD. Fifty-One Tales. London, 1915. 1st ed. Photogravure frontis. Cl-backed bds (tips lt rubbed, edges browned). *Swann**. $115/£72

DUNSANY, LORD. The Fourth Book of Jorkens. Sauk City, 1948. 1st ed. Fine in VG dj (lt soiled). *Mcclintock*. $75/£47

DUNSANY, LORD. Jorkens Remembers Africa. NY: Longmans, Green, 1934. 1st ed. VG in dj (ink initials fr panel). *Pacific**. $138/£86

DUNSANY, LORD. Plays of Near and Far. NY/London, 1923. 1st Amer ed. One of 500 ptd. Good (cvr edges worn). *Mcclintock*. $35/£22

DUNSANY, LORD. Rory and Bran. NY: Putnam, (1937). 1st US ed. (Spine head nicked), else NF in VG + dj (spine foot frayed). Bkpl of Oswald Train. *Other Worlds*. $45/£28

DUNSANY, LORD. Selections from the Writings of Lord Dunsany. Churchtown Dundrum: Cuala, 1912. Ltd to 250. Unopened. (Spine dknd, extrems sl worn.) *Metropolitan**. $115/£72

DUNSANY, LORD. The Strange Journey of Colonel Polders. London: Jarrolds, (1950). 1st ed. Signed. (Eps badly offset) o/w NF in dj (extrems worn). *Levin*. $185/£116

DUNSANY, LORD. Tales of War. Dublin: Talbot, (1918). 1st ed. Cl, gray bds stamped in red/black. (Ink name dated 1919), o/w NF in VG dj (sm chips, tears spine crown, top rear panel). *Reese*. $125/£78

DUNSANY, LORD. Tales of War. Boston: Little, Brown, 1918. 1st Amer ed. VG (bkpl). *Cady*. $35/£22

DUNSANY, LORD. Unhappy Far-Off Things. Boston: Little, Brown, 1919. 1st Amer ed. NF in VG dj (spine ends sl chipped, lt spots fr panel). *Pacific**. $75/£47

DUNSHEE, KENNETH HOLCOMB. Enjine! Enjine! A Story of Fire Protection. NY: Home Insurance, 1939. 1st ed. Fine in wrappers (2 sm spine tears), gilt, color pict paper label. *Argonaut*. $75/£47

DUPIN, JACQUES. Joan Miro. NY: Abrams, (1962). 38 tipped-in color plts. Nice. *Turtle Island*. $375/£234

DUPLAIX, GEORGES. Gaston and Josephine. NY: S&S, (1948). 1st ed thus. F. Rojankovsky (illus). 'A' at rear. VG. *Davidson*. $37/£23

DUPLAIX, GEORGES. Gaston and Josephine. NY: Harper, 1936. 1st ed. 4to. 48pp. Pict bds. (Fep, tp, rep damp-stained), o/w Good. *Davidson*. $85/£53

DUPLAIX, GEORGES. Pee-Gloo. NY: Harper, 1935. 1st ed. VG (spine professionally repaired, edges lt worn). *Davidson*. $200/£125

DUPONT, MARCEL. In the Field (1914-1915): The Impressions of an Officer of Light Cavalry. H. W. Hill (trans). Phila/London: Lippincott/Heinemann, 1916. 1st ed in English, US issue. Red cl stamped in black. Fine in pict dj (3 sm closed edge tears). *Reese*. $75/£47

DuPUY, WILLIAM ATHERTON. The Baron of the Colorados. San Antonio, 1940. Frontis. VG. *Dumont*. $25/£16

DURAND, JEAN B. L. A Voyage to Senegal. London: Richard Phillips, 1806. 184pp; fldg map (lt foxed), 7 plts. Mod cl. *Adelson*. $325/£203

DURAND, RALPH. Guernsey; Past and Present. Guernsey, 1933. 1st ed. Good. *Cox*. $24/£15

DURAND, RALPH. Oxford, Its Buildings and Gardens. London, 1909. 1st ed. 32 color plts. Illus eps; teg. *Edwards*. $120/£75

DURANT, JOHN. The Dodgers. Hastings House, 1948. 1st ed. VG. *Plapinger*. $65/£41

DURAS, MARGUERITE. 10:30 on a Summer Night. NY: Grove, (1962). 1st Amer ed. VF in VF dj. *Between The Covers*. $85/£53

DURET, THEODORE. Manet and the French Impressionists. Phila, 1910. 4to. 2 etchings by Renoir, 1 by Manet, 1 by Morisot. (Joints rubbed, backstrip faded.) *Swann**. $2,300/£1,438

DURKAN, J. and A. ROSS. Early Scottish Libraries. Glasgow: John S. Burns, 1961. Frontis, 48 plts. Maroon cl. Dj (sm tears). *Maggs*. $56/£35

DURNFORD, H. G. The Tunnellers of Holzminden. CUP, 1920. 1st ed. Frontis. Gilt cl-backed bds, pict label. (Ink name; edges worn), else Good. *Reese*. $50/£31

DURRANT, S. D. Mammals of Utah. Lawrence, 1952. (Tp browned, few pp lt foxed, last few pp margins sl wormed, pp tanned.) 91 maps, 30 tables. Aeg. Recent gilt-dec full calf. *Sutton*. $60/£38

DURRELL, LAWRENCE. Acte. Faber, 1965. 1st UK ed. VG + in VG dj (sl rubbed). *Williams*. $35/£22

DURRELL, LAWRENCE. The Alexandria Quartet. NY: Dutton, (1962). 1st Amer ed of 1st one-vol ed. Fine in Fine dj (internally repaired short tear). *Between The Covers.* $150/£94

DURRELL, LAWRENCE. The Alexandria Quartet. Faber & Faber, 1962. 1st collected ed of Justine, Balthazar, Mountolive and Clea. Ltd to 500 numbered, signed. 8vo. 884pp. Teg. Orange buckram w/black handprint motif on fr cvr, spine blocked in black/gilt. Fine in clear plastic wrapper, slipcase as issued. *Sotheran.* $797/£498

DURRELL, LAWRENCE. Balthazar, a Novel. London, 1958. 1st ed. Fine in dj (sl torn). *Petersfield.* $90/£56

DURRELL, LAWRENCE. Beccafico. Montpellier: La Licorne, 1963. One of 200 signed. This copy unnumbered. Fine in wrappers. *Clearwater.* $192/£120

DURRELL, LAWRENCE. Bitter Lemons. London, (1957). 1st ed. (Ink name; top of cvrs sl bumped, sunned), else Good in dj (edges chipped). *King.* $35/£22

DURRELL, LAWRENCE. Bitter Lemons. London, 1957. 1st ed. Fine in dj (torn w/piece missing from back). *Petersfield.* $40/£25

DURRELL, LAWRENCE. The Black Book. Paris: Obelisk, (1938). 1st ed. 8vo. Excellent (ink name fr cvr; cvrs soiled, edges sl rubbed) in wrappers. *Heritage.* $750/£469

DURRELL, LAWRENCE. The Black Book. Paris: Obelisk, 1938. 1st ed. VG (spine tanned, head sl torn) in self-wraps. *Lame Duck.* $500/£313

DURRELL, LAWRENCE. The Black Book. Paris: Obelisk Press, 1938. Wrappers. VG (pg edges sl browned, some pg edges nicked; spine ends nicked, sl bumped, cvrs sl mkd, edges sl creased, nicked). *Ulysses.* $920/£575

DURRELL, LAWRENCE. The Black Book. Paris: Olympia, 1959. VG in VG dj. *Warren.* $50/£31

DURRELL, LAWRENCE. The Black Book. NY: E.P. Dutton, 1960. 1st Amer ed. Black cl, gilt spine. (Spine ends sl rubbed), o/w Fine in dj (lt chipped, soiled). *Heritage.* $75/£47

DURRELL, LAWRENCE. Cities Plains and People, Poems. London, 1946. 1st ed. Fine in dj (faded, sl scratched). *Petersfield.* $80/£50

DURRELL, LAWRENCE. Cities, Plains and People. London, 1946. 1st Eng ed. (Cvr edges sl tanned.) Dj (sl dusty, foxed, tanned). *Clearwater.* $88/£55

DURRELL, LAWRENCE. Clea, a Novel. London, 1960. 1st ed. (Eps sl spotted.) Dj. *Petersfield.* $64/£40

DURRELL, LAWRENCE. Clea. Faber & Faber, 1960. 1st ed. VG (edges sl spotted, dusty, spine foot sl bumped) in dj (nicked, dusty, sl rubbed, mkd, creased, browned). *Ulysses.* $72/£45

DURRELL, LAWRENCE. Collected Poems. London, 1960. 1st ed. Fine in dj. *Petersfield.* $40/£25

DURRELL, LAWRENCE. Deus Loci. Ischia: Privately ptd, 1950. One of 200 signed. This copy unnumbered. Fine in red card wrappers. *Clearwater.* $240/£150

DURRELL, LAWRENCE. Deus Loci. Ischia: Privately ptd, 1950. Ltd to 200, this copy unnumbered. Signed. 8pp. VG in red wrappers (spine sl faded). *Virgo.* $400/£250

DURRELL, LAWRENCE. Deus Loci. Ischia: (Privately ptd), 1950. 1st ed. One of 200 numbered, signed. Uncut. Fine (edges sl faded) in ptd paper wrappers, stapled. *Black Sun.* $500/£313

DURRELL, LAWRENCE. The Ikons and Other Poems. London, 1966. 1st ed. Fine in dj (sl faded). *Petersfield.* $40/£25

DURRELL, LAWRENCE. An Irish Faustus, a Morality in Nine Scenes. London, 1963. 1st ed. Fine in dj. *Petersfield.* $40/£25

DURRELL, LAWRENCE. An Irish Faustus. London: Faber, (1963). 1st Eng ed. Fine in dj (sl soiled, lt edgeworn). *Agvent.* $45/£28

DURRELL, LAWRENCE. Lawrence Durrell and Henry Miller. A Private Correspondence. NY, 1963. 1st Amer ed. Fine in dj (few nicks). *Polyanthos.* $25/£16

DURRELL, LAWRENCE. Monsieur. NY: Viking, (1975). 1st Amer ed. Signed. Top edge stained blue. 1/4 blue cl, gilt, black bds. NF (tape residue fr ep; spine ends sl rubbed) in dj (lt edgeworn, lt soiled). *Heritage.* $85/£53

DURRELL, LAWRENCE. Mountolive. Faber & Faber, 1958. 1st ed. NF (edges sl spotted, spine ends, corner sl bumped) in dj (sl nicked, corners of both flaps clipped, sm worn patch at spine). *Ulysses.* $120/£75

DURRELL, LAWRENCE. Nothing Is Lost, Sweet Self. (London: Turrett Books, 1967.) One of 100 signed by Durrell & Wallace Southam (music). Folio. (4)pp, w/insert of (4)pp of poem set to music. Grn wrappers. Fine (spine extrems sl worn). *Heritage.* $200/£125

DURRELL, LAWRENCE. A Private Country. London, 1943. 1st ed. Uncut except top. (Corners sl bumped.) Dj (sl faded). *Petersfield.* $115/£72

DURRELL, LAWRENCE. Quinx. Faber, 1985. 1st UK ed. Signed, dated 1985. Fine in dj. *Williams.* $48/£30

DURRELL, LAWRENCE. The Red Limbo Lingo. NY: Dutton, 1971. 1st ed. Ltd to 200 signed. Fine in red cl, gilt. Black slipcase. *Bromer.* $175/£109

DURRELL, LAWRENCE. Reflections on a Marine Venus. London, 1953. 1st ed. (Eps faded by dj flap.) Dj (sl chipped). *Petersfield.* $80/£50

DURRELL, LAWRENCE. The Tree of Idleness, and Other Poems. London, 1955. 1st ed. Fine in dj (sl crease, tear). *Petersfield.* $51/£32

DURRELL, LAWRENCE. Two Excursions into Reality. Berkeley, 1947. Circle ed. 1st Amer, 1st trade ed. Lettered bds. Fine in dj (sl mkd). *Clearwater.* $120/£75

DURRELL, LAWRENCE. Vega and Other Poems. London, 1973. 1st ed. Fine in dj. *Petersfield.* $40/£25

DURRELL, LAWRENCE. White Eagles Over Serbia. London: Faber & Faber, 1957. 1st ed. Mottled lt brn cl. Fine in dj. *Temple.* $160/£100

DURRETT, REUBEN T. Traditions of the Earliest Visits of Foreigners to North America. Louisville, KY: John P. Morton, 1908. 1st ed. Frontisport, map. Unopened. NF in orig ptd stiff wraps. *Chapel Hill.* $100/£63

DUSARD, JAY. The North American Cowboy: A Portrait. Prescott: Consortium, 1983. NF in dj. *Dumont.* $250/£156

DUSTMAN, U. M. Construction of Dwelling Houses and Bungalows. Chicago: Charles C. Thompson, 1911. 1st ed. Red cl, gilt. (Sl worn, sm stain fr cvr edge.) Text Good (lt aged). *Baltimore*.* $90/£56

Dutch Cruelty Exemplified. London: J. Fuller & J. Dixwell, 1762. (2),310pp (marginal dampstaining towards end, possibly lacks 1/2-title). 19th-cent sheep (spine dknd, rubbed, joints weak). *Swann*.* $126/£79

DUTTON, A. A. A. A. Dutton's Compendium.... Phoenix: Dutton/Buse, 1977. 1st ed. VG in illus stiff wrappers. *Cahan.* $185/£116

DUTTON, A. A. The Great Stone Tit. Tempe, AZ: Richard Dixon, 1974. 1st ed. (Spine lt worn), else NF in pict wrapper around spiral binding. *Cahan.* $165/£103

DUTTON, BERTHA P. Sun Father's Way. Albuquerque: Univ of NM, 1963. VG in dj. *Dumont.* $85/£53

DUTTON, CLARENCE. Geology of the High Plateaus of Utah. Washington, 1880. xxxii,307pp; 11 heliotype plts, guards, 2 other plts, 2 lg foldouts (1 separated at fold). Good+ (lib emb stamps; inner fr hinge reinforced; corners lt bumped, new spine). *Five Quail.* $275/£172

DUTTON, CLARENCE. Tertiary History of the Grand Canyon District. Washington, 1882. Folio atlas. 23 sheets. Good+. *Five Quail.* $1,495/£934

DUTTON, JOAN PARRY. Exploring America's Gardens. London: Secker & Warburg, 1959. 1st ed. (Browned), else VG in dj (chipped, foxed). *Fair Meadow*. $16/£10

DUTTON, RALPH. The English Country House. NY, 1936. 8vo. 131 b/w plts. Dj (few sm tears, edges rubbed). *Swann**. $546/£341

DUVAL, ELIZABETH. T. E. Lawrence, a Bibliography. NY: Arrow Editions, 1938. 1st ed. Uncut. Black bds, canvas spine. Fine in slipcase. *Maggs*. $240/£150

DUVAL, PAUL. Ken Danby: The New Decade. Ontario: Stoddart, 1984. 1st ed. Pict card. NF. *Whittle*. $24/£15

DUVOISIN, ROGER. Petunia Takes a Trip. NY: Knopf, (1953). 1st ed. Blue cl (edges faded). Full color dj (lt edgeworn). *Reisler*. $65/£41

DUYCKINCK, EVERT. History of the War for the Union. NY: Johnson, Fry, 1862-1865. 3 vols. Engr frontis, tp each vol, 620; 660; 642pp; 75 engr plts. 3/4 brn morocco, marbled bds, gilt. VG + . *House*. $450/£281

DUYCKINCK, EVERT. National Portrait Gallery of Eminent Americans. NY, 1860s. 2 vols. Pub's blind/gilt-stamped morocco. (Lt foxed.) *Swann**. $258/£161

DWIGHT, MARGARET VAN HORN. A Journey to Ohio in 1810. New Haven: Yale Univ, 1912. (Ex-lib), else Good. *Dumont*. $35/£22

DWIGHT, TIMOTHY. Travels in New-England and New-York. New Haven: The Author, 1821-22. 1st ed. 4 vols. Errata slip tipped in to vol 4. 3 fldg maps. Vols 1, 3, 4 full mottled calf (sl worn); vol 2 supplied from another set in red 1/2 leather (spine head chipped), marbled bds (worn). (Sm blindstamp tp vol 2; lt foxed; sm tear vol 1 map; folds of vol 2 map reinforced w/clear tape; inscrip.) *New Hampshire**. $200/£125

DWINELLE, JOHN W. The Colonial History of the City of San Francisco. Towne & Bacon, 1866. 3rd ed. 3 plts, 2 maps. 3/4 leather. (Hinges weak, tp repaired.) *Metropolitan**. $345/£216

DWINELLE, JOHN W. The Colonial History of the City of San Francisco. SF: Towne & Bacon, 1866. 3rd ed. 8.75x5.75. (3),iv-xlv,(4),4-391pp; 2 maps, 3 litho plts. Marbled eps. 3/4 morocco, marbled bds, raised bands, gilt. (Ink inscrip, pencil lib #s; rear cvr sl rubbed), o/w NF. *Pacific**. $575/£359

DWINGER, EDWIN ERICH. Prisoner of War: A Siberian Diary. Ian F.D. Morrow (trans). NY: Knopf, 1930. 1st US ed. Yellow cl. Fine in pict dj (rear sl dust-soiled). *Reese*. $50/£31

DWINGER, ERICH. Between White and Red. Marion Saunders (trans). NY: Scribner, 1932. 1st US ed. Red cl. (Spine faded, crown sl frayed), else Good. *Reese*. $20/£13

DYER, ANTHONY. Classic African Animals. NY: Winchester, (1973). One of 375 numbered, signed by Dyer and Bob Kuhn (illus). Folio. Leatherette-backed bd portfolio w/6 extra color plts in fr cvr pocket. (Sl worn.) Slipcase (sl scuffed). *Oinonen**. $700/£438

DYER, FRANK LEWIS et al. Edison, His Life and Inventions. NY: Harper, 1928. 2nd, rev ed. 2 vols. Fine in djs, slipcase. *Glaser*. $100/£63

DYER, GEORGE. History of the University and Colleges of Cambridge. Longman, Hurst, Rees, Orme, & Brown, 1814. 2 vols. Engr add'l tp, 31 engr plts; extra-illus w/61 engr ports, views, etc. Gilt edges. Contemp straight-grained full morocco (spines rubbed), gilt. *Sotheby's**. $368/£230

DYER, GERTRUDE P. Elsie's Adventures in Insect Land. London: Marcus Ward, 1882. 1st ed. 8vo. C. O. Murray (illus). Aeg. Blue pict cl (spine lt shelfworn; few pp loose), gilt. *Reisler*. $250/£156

DYER, ISAAC WATSON. A Bibliography of Thomas Carlyle's Writings and Ana. Portland, 1928. One of 600. Frontis port. Uncut, unopened. Orig prospective, 2 extra copies of frontis laid in. (Lt worn, sl cvr stain.) *Oinonen**. $70/£44

DYER, JOHN P. The Gallant Hood. Indianapolis: Bobbs-Merrill, (1950). 1st ed. Red cl. VG. *Chapel Hill*. $50/£31

DYHRENFURTH, G. O. To the Third Pole. Hugh Merrick (trans). London: Werner Laurie, (1955). 1st ed in English. Blue cl. NF (ink inscrip; corners sl bumped) in dj (chipped). *Argonaut*. $125/£78

DYKES, JEFF. Billy the Kid. Albuquerque, 1952. 1st ed, 2nd ptg w/minor corrections. Signed, inscribed presentation. Frontis. (Shelfworn, cvrs sunned.) *Oinonen**. $70/£44

DYKES, JEFF. Billy the Kid. Albuquerque: Univ of NM, 1952. 1st ed, 2nd ptg. VG in wrappers (spine worn, faded, rough erasure fr cvr). *Labordo*. $125/£78

DYKES, JEFF. Billy the Kid; The Bibliography of a Legend. Albuquerque, 1952. 2nd ptg. Frontis. (Sl worn), else NF in wraps. *Dumont*. $95/£59

DYKES, JEFF. Collecting Range Life Literature. Bryan, TX, 1982. One of 535 signed. Fine. *Dumont*. $25/£16

DYKES, JEFF. Fifty Great Western Illustrators. Flagstaff, 1975. One of 200 signed, numbered. Fine in slipcase. *Dumont*. $200/£125

DYKES, JEFF. Russell Roundup. College Park, MD, 1972. One of 100 numbered, signed. VG in plain paper dj (soiled). *Dumont*. $75/£47

DYKES, JEFF. Western High Spots. Flagstaff, 1977. VG in dj (sl worn). *Dumont*. $65/£41

DYKES, WILLIAM RICKATSON and E. KATHERINE. Notes on Tulip Species. London: Herbert Jenkins, 1930. 1st ed. 54 color plts. (Text lt spotted.) Orig cl (spine detached). *Christie's**. $163/£102

DYKSTRA, ROBERT R. The Cattle Towns. NY: Knopf, (1968). 1st ed. Good in dj. *Lien*. $30/£19

DYKSTRA, ROBERT R. The Cattle Towns. NY: Knopf, 1968. 1st ed. Fine in dj. *Labordo*. $55/£34

DYLAN, BOB. Tarantula. MacGibbon & Kee, 1971. 1st UK ed. NF in NF dj (price-clipped, 2 top corners sl stained). *Sclanders*. $16/£10

DYMOND, JONATHAN. Essays on the Principles of Morality, and of the Private and Political Rights and Obligations of Mankind. NY: Collins, 1845. Later ptg. Inscribed presentation from pubs. 576pp. Black cl. Good (foxed; extrems worn). *Lucas*. $45/£28

DYRENFORTH, JAMES and MAX KESTER. Adolf in Blunderland. London: Frederick Muller, (1939). 3rd ed. Signed by both. 8vo. Red/black illus bds. Good in pict dj (tape to rear cvr, spine lt worn). *Reisler*. $175/£109

DYSON, WILL. Kultur Cartoons. London/Boston: Stanley Paul/Page Co, (1915). 1st ed. Folio. Blank + 3 letter press ll, 20 tipped-in plts on stiff card, mtd rectos only. Dk brn wrappers, string-tied at spine. (Pencil name, sm tape stain tp, ll dust-soiled; fr wrapper soiled, sm chips, nicks), else Good. *Reese*. $65/£41

E

EAGAN, EDDIE. Fighting for Fun: The Scrap Book of Eddie Eagan. London: Lovat Dickson, 1932. 1st ed. Frontis. (Spine sl sunned), else VG. *Pacific**. $29/£18

EAMES, WILBERFORCE. A Bibliography of Captain John Smith. NY, 1927. Unopened. VG in ptd cvrs. *Moss*. $48/£30

EARDLEY-WILMOT, S. The Life of an Elephant. NY: Longmans, 1912. 1st ed. Photogravure frontis. Teg. Pict, gilt cl. *Mikesh*. $60/£38

EARHART, AMELIA. The Fun of It. Random Records of My Own Flying and of Women in Aviation. NY: Harcourt, Brace, (1932). Signed, dated on fep 1935. Recording enclosed in rear pocket. Brn cl. Appelfeld. $350/£219

EARL, L. Crocodile Fever. London: Collins, 1954. 1st ed. Fine in Good+ dj. Mikesh. $25/£16

EARLE, ALICE MORSE. Old Time Gardens Newly Set Forth. NY: Macmillan, 1901. 1st ed. Pict cl, gilt. (Fep, 1st few pp damaged rear rt corner, browned), o/w Good. Fair Meadow. $50/£31

EARLE, ALICE MORSE. Sun Dials and Roses of Yesterday. NY: Macmillan, 1902. 1st ed. Teg, some pp uncut. Dec cl, gilt. (Inscrip, inner hinge cracked), else VG. Fair Meadow. $60/£38

EARLE, MRS. C. W. Memoirs and Memories. London: Smith Elder, 1911. 2nd imp. 4 ports. (Extrems sl rubbed.) Hollett. $40/£25

EARLE, MRS. C. W. More Potpourri from a Surrey Garden. NY: Macmillan, 1899. 1st Amer ed. vii-ix,463,3pp ads. Teg. (Shelfworn, spine, bds stained), else VG. Fair Meadow. $35/£22

EARLE, MRS. C. W. Potpourri from a Surrey Garden. London: Smith, Elder, 1897. 8th ed. x-xii,2-381pp. Teg. 3/4 leather, pale grn cl w/Florentine spine designs. Good (scattered color pencil lines, faded outlines of newspaper clippings fep, browned; base of leather discolored). Fair Meadow. $50/£31

Early American Turf Stock 1730-1830. (By Fairfax Harrison.) Richmond: Privately ptd at Old Dominion Press, 1934-35. 2 vols. Paper spine labels. (Sl worn.) Oinonen*. $225/£141

Early Children's Books and Their Illustration. (By Gerald Gottlieb.) NY/Boston: Morgan Library/Godine, (1975). 1st ed. Frontis. VG in dj (shelfworn, long tears, nicks, spine soiled). Reese. $150/£94

Early Children's Books and Their Illustration. (By Gerald Gottleib.) NY: Pierpoint Morgan Library, 1975. Folio. Red cl, gilt. Fine in pict dj (edges chipped, lg chip lower rt corner). Hobbyhorse. $150/£94

Early Chinese Art. A Catalogue of Early bronzes, Jades and Allied Decorative Works of Art from the Cunliffe Collection.... Bluett & Sons, 1973. Folio. 4 tipped-in color plts. 8pp cat rear pocket. VG. Hollett. $72/£45

Early Milwaukee: Papers from the Archives of the Old Settler's Club of Milwaukee County. Milwaukee: The Club, 1916. 1st ed. Frontis. (Extrems lt rubbed.) Sadlon. $75/£47

EARLY, ALICE K. English Dolls, Effigies and Puppets. Batsford, 1955. 1st ed. Color frontis. Dj (sl chipped). Edwards. $40/£25

EARLY, JUBAL A. Lieutenant General Jubal Anderson Early, C.S.A. Phila/London: Lippincott, 1912. 1st ed. Frontisport. Teg. Red cl. NF. Chapel Hill. $350/£219

EARLY, JUBAL A. A Memoir of the Last Year of the War for Independence. Lynchburg: Charles W. Button, 1867. 1st US ed. 136pp (sl aging). Orig ptd salmon wraps (dusty, sl soiled, worn, chipped). Howes E14. Baltimore*. $90/£56

East of the Sun and West of the Moon. Old Tales from the North. (By Peter Asbjoornsen.) London: Hodder & Stoughton, (n.d.). 4to. 24 mtd color plts by Kay Nielsen. Orig blue cl w/blindstamped borders. Fine in dj w/color illus by Nielsen mtd to fr cvr. Rear cvr of dj carries ads for 'Hodder & Stoughton's Art Colour Presentation Books' incl 1 for Edmund Dulac's 'Fairy Book' (1916). Christie's*. $939/£587

EASTLAKE, WILLIAM. Castle Keep. NY: S&S, (1965). 1st ed. VF in VF dj. Between The Covers. $125/£78

EASTLAKE, WILLIAM. Castle Keep. S&S, 1965. 1st US ed. Fine in VG dj (spine sl faded) Williams. $88/£55

EASTMAN, CHARLES A. From the Deep Woods to Civilization. Boston, 1916. 1st ed. Good (extrems worn). Dumont. $45/£28

EASTMAN, CHARLES A. Indian Boyhood. Boston: Little, Brown, 1919. Good in pict cl (cvrs worn, spine lettering faded). Lien. $25/£16

EASTMAN, ELAINE GOODALE. Pratt: The Red Man's Moses. Norman: Univ of OK, 1935. 1st ed. Good (spine ends sl worn). Lien. $50/£31

EASTMAN, MAX and 'WILLIAMS'. The Ballad of Joseph the Nazarene [and] A Sermon on Reverence. N.p., n.d. 1st ed. Fine (sticker) in wraps. Beasley. $85/£53

EASTON, JOHN. British Postage Stamp Design. Faber, 1946. 42 plts. (Cl faded.) Hollett. $40/£25

EASTON, JOHN. An Unfrequented Highway, Through Sikkim and Tibet to Chumolaori. London: Scholartis, 1928. Ltd to 960. 16 plts. Red cl (spine sl faded). VG (bkpl). Karmiole. $150/£94

EASTON, MALCOLM and MICHAEL HOLROYD. The Art of Augustus John. London, 1974. 1st UK ed. 25 color plts. Dj. Edwards. $40/£25

EATES, MARGOT. Paul Nash...1889-1946. (London, 1973.) Dj. Swann*. $57/£36

EATON, ALLEN H. Handicrafts of New England. NY, 1949. 1st Amer ed. NF. Polyanthos. $35/£22

EATON, CLEMENT. A History of the Southern Confederacy. NY: Macmillan, 1954. 1st ed. Inscribed. Navy cl. (Bkpl), else NF in dj (lt chipped). Chapel Hill. $50/£31

EATON, D. C. Beautiful Ferns. Boston, (1881). 158pp (inscrip, pp, plts tanned); 14 chromolitho plts, guards. Aeg. Pict cl (soiled, sm tear spine head, rubbed), gilt. Sutton. $250/£156

EATON, D. CADY. A Handbook of Modern French Painting. NY, 1911. 1st Amer ed. Fine. Polyanthos. $35/£22

EATON, ELON HOWARD. Birds of New York. Albany, 1910-14. 2 vols. 106 color plts by Louis Agassiz Fuertes. Grn cl, gilt. Fine set. Kane*. $100/£63

EATON, ELON HOWARD. Birds of New York. Albany, 1910-1914. 2 vols. 106 color plts. Good. Rybski. $125/£78

EATON, FRANK. Pistol Pete. London: Arco, 1953. 1st British ed. Blue cl. VG+ in color pict dj (sl rubbed). House. $25/£16

EATON, JOHN MATTHEWS. A Treatise on the Art of Breeding and Managing Tame, Domesticated, Foreign, and Fancy Pigeons.... The Author, 1858. 1st, only ed. 8vo. 17 hand-colored aquatint plts by Dean Wolstenholme. Aeg. Recent burgundy 1/2 morocco, w/matching washed silk bds, gilt. (Lt internal spotting.) Externally Fine. Sotheran. $637/£398

EATON, SEYMOUR. More About Teddy B and Teddy G, the Roosevelt Bears. Phila: Edward Stern, 1907. 1st ed. 4to. 186pp (sm marginal tear); 15 full-pg color plts by R. K. Culver. Color paste label. (Corners, lower edge sl shelfworn.) Reisler. $450/£281

EATON, SEYMOUR. The Roosevelt Bears Abroad. Phila: Edward Stern, 1908. 1st ed. 4to. 178pp; 15 full-pg color plts by R. K. Culver. Color paste label. (Corner worn, lettering rubbed.) Reisler. $400/£250

EATON, SEYMOUR. The Roosevelt Bears. Phila: Edward Stern, 1906. 1st ed. 4to. 180pp; 16 color plts by V. Floyd Campbell. Grn cl, pict label. VG+. Davidson. $325/£203

EATON, SEYMOUR. The Roosevelt Bears. Phila: Edward Stern, 1906. 1st ed. 4to. 16 full-pg color plts by V. Floyd Campbell. Dk grn cl-backed bds (edges rubbed), color paste label. Nice. Reisler. $475/£297

EBELING, WALTER. Handbook of Indian Foods and Fibers of Arid America. Berkeley: Univ of CA, 1986. 1st ed. Fine in Fine dj. Book Market. $250/£156

EBER, DORTHY HARLEY. When the Whalers Were up North. Boston: David Godone, (1989). 1st US ed. VF in dj. Perier. $35/£22

EBERHART, MIGNON G. Five Passengers from Lisbon. Random, 1946. 1st ed. (Spine sl slanted), else Fine in dj (rear lt soiled). Murder. $55/£34

EBERHART, MIGNON G. With This Ring. NY: Random House, (1941). 1st ed. Gray cl. VG (bkpl; spine sl cocked; spine, top cvr edges lt browned) in dj (price-clipped, lt chipped, soiled). *Heritage.* $75/£47

EBERHART, MIGNON G. Wolf in Man's Clothing. NY: Random House, (1942). 1st ed. Beige cl. VG (pastedowns lt browned; spine ends sl rubbed) in dj (lt edgeworn, spine lt browned). *Heritage.* $100/£63

EBERHART, RICHARD. Burr Oaks. NY: OUP, 1947. 1st ed, Amer issue. Fine in VG dj (spine tanned). *Reese.* $50/£31

EBERLEIN, H. D. and CORTLANDT VAN DYKE HUBBARD. Glass in Modern Construction. NY/London, 1937. 62 b/w plts at rear. (Margins lt browned, few margins sl thumbed; lib ink stamps, label remains; worn, spine bumped, #s.) *Edwards.* $64/£40

EBERLEIN, H. D. Interiors, Fireplaces and Furniture of the Italian Renaissance. NY, 1916. 82 plts. (Sl soiled.) *Washton.* $45/£28

EBERLEIN, H. D. Manor Houses and Historic Homes of Long Island and Staten Island. Phila, 1928. 1st ed. Photogravure frontis. (Stamps.) *Heinoldt.* $50/£31

EBERLEIN, H. D. Villas of Florence and Tuscany. Phila, 1922. Inscribed, signed. 300 plts. (Cocked, 1st gathering becoming loose.) *Swann*.* $161/£101

EBERSTADT. The Annotated Eberstadt Catalogs of Americana. NY, 1965. 4 vols. VG. *Dumont.* $175/£109

EBERT, FREDERIC ADOLPHUS. A General Bibliographical Dictionary. Arthur Browne (trans). Oxford, 1837. 1st ed in English. 4 vols. Uncut. Paper labels. (Foxed, shelfworn, 1 spine torn.) *Oinonen*.* $160/£100

EBIN, DAVID (ed). The Drug Experience: First-Person Accounts of Addicts, Writers, Scientists and Others. NY: Orion, 1960. 1st ed. VG + (lacks dj). *Sclanders.* $22/£14

EBY, KERR. War. New Haven, 1936. Inscribed, signed. 28 repros of etchings. Dj. *Swann*.* $161/£101

ECCLESTON, ROBERT. The Mariposa Indian War, 1850-1851. C. Gregory Crampton (ed). Salt Lake City: Univ of UT, 1957. 1st ed. One of 500 ptd. Tipped-in frontisport, fldg map. Brn cl. Fine. *Harrington.* $90/£56

ECCLESTON, ROBERT. The Mariposa Indian War, 1850-1851. Gregory Crampton (ed). Salt Lake City: Univ of UT, 1957. 1st ed. Frontisport, fldg map. Orange cl, gilt. Fine. *Pacific*.* $98/£61

ECKARDT, ANDREAS. A History of Korean Art. J.M. Kindersley (trans). London: Edward Goldston, 1929. 1st ed. 168 plts, 4 color plts, 8 inset-plts, map. Gilt dec red linen, blue/black morocco spine labels. Good. *Karmiole.* $175/£109

ECKEL, JOHN C. The First Editions of the Writings of Charles Dickens and Their Values. London, 1913. Large paper copy. One of 250 numbered, signed by Eckel & pub. Teg. Uncut. 1/2 vellum (shelfworn, spine soiled). *Oinonen*.* $160/£100

ECKEL, JOHN C. The First Editions of the Writings of Charles Dickens and Their Values. London: Chapman & Hall, 1913. 1st ed. Ltd to 750. Port, 33 plts. Brn cl (sl rubbed). *Maggs.* $160/£100

ECKENHOFF, JAMES E. Anasthesia from Colonial Times. Phila, 1966. 1st ed. VG (fr flysheet removed; extrems sl worn). *Doctor's Library.* $40/£25

ECKENRODE, H. J. and BRYAN CONRAD. James Longstreet, Lee's War Horse. Chapel Hill: Univ of NC, 1936. 1st ed. Frontispiece. Red cl. (Bkpl), else NF in dj (price-clipped, few tape repairs on verso). *Chapel Hill.* $200/£125

ECKER, A. The Anatomy of the Frog. G. Haslam (trans). Oxford: Clarendon, 1889. 1st ed. 449pp; 2 fldg color plts. VG + . *Mikesh.* $75/£47

ECKERT, A. W. The Owls of North America. NY: Weathervane, (1987). 59 full-pg color repros, b/w dwgs, maps. Fine in NF dj. *Mikesh.* $45/£28

ECKERT, ROBERT P. Edward Thomas: A Biography and a Bibliography. London: J.M. Dent, (1937). 1st ed. Port. Grn cl stamped in gilt/black. VG (ink name, lt foxed). *Reese.* $55/£34

ECKSTORM, FANNIE HARDY. The Penobscot Man. Boston/NY: Houghton Mifflin, 1904. 1st ed. Frontis. Red cl. VG. *Lucas.* $80/£50

ECO, UMBERTO. The Name of the Rose. NY, 1983. 1st Amer ed. Signed. NF in NF dj. *Warren.* $95/£59

ECO, UMBERTO. Postscript to the Name of the Rose. NY, 1983. 1st Amer ed. Signed. NF in NF dj (sl worn). *Warren.* $60/£38

ECO, UMBERTO. A Theory of Semiotics. Bloomington: IN Univ, (1976). 1st ed. Signed. Fine in NF dj (lt rubbed, spine lettering sl faded). *Between The Covers.* $175/£109

ECO, UMBERTO. The Three Astronauts. London: Secker & Warburg, 1989. 1st ed. 8x11. Eugenio Carmi (illus). Unpaginated. NF in VG dj (1-inch tear, fld to rear). *Price.* $25/£16

ECTON, JOHN. Liber Valorum and Decimarum. London: R. Gosling, 1728. 3rd ed. xiv,(xxxii),475,(13)pp. Contemp paneled calf (neatly rebacked), raised bands, red morocco label. *Young.* $80/£50

EDDINGTON, ARTHUR. The Expanding Universe. Cambridge, 1933. 1st Eng ed. VG (spine sl sunned) in dj. *Clearwater.* $40/£25

EDDISON, E. R. Mistress of Mistresses. NY, 1935. 1st ed. Dj (lt soiled, sm closed tears). *Swann*.* $69/£43

EDDISON, E. R. Mistress of Mistresses: A Vision of Zimiamvia. NY: E.P. Dutton, (1935). 1st Amer ed. (Name, bkpl), else VG in dj (soiled). *Pacific*.* $104/£65

EDDISON, E. R. The Worm Ouroboros. London, (1922). 1st ed. *Swann*.* $69/£43

EDDISON, E. R. The Worm Ouroboros. London: Jonathan Cape, (1922). 1st ed, 1st bk. (Bkpl), else VG in dj (spine ends chipped, extrems rubbed). *Pacific*.* $230/£144

EDDY, MARY BAKER. Science and Health. Boston, 1875. 1st ed, 1st issue, w/o index. One of 1000. 12mo. Errata leaf tipped in at end. Mod crimson morocco, gilt. Cl fldg case. *Swann*.* $1,955/£1,222

EDELSTEIN, LUDWIG. Ancient Medicine. Selected Papers of Ludwig Edelstein. Owsei Temkin and C. Lilian (eds). Balt: Johns Hopkins, (1967). 1st ed. Frontisport. Linen, cl spine. VG (lib bkpl, stamp; faint spine #s). *Glaser.* $45/£28

EDEN, EMILY. The Semi-Detached House. London: Elkin Mathews & Marrot, 1928. VG. *Cady.* $20/£13

Edgar Rice Burroughs Library of Illustration. White Plains, MO: Russ Cochran, (1976). One of 2000. 3 vols. Linen, gilt, leather cvr title labels, gilt, color pict cvr labels. (Gilt at spine bottoms sl rubbed), else NF in slipcase. *Pacific*.* $374/£234

EDGAR, J. DOUGLAS. The Gate to Golf. St. Albans: Edgar, 1920. 1st UK ed. Reddish cl, gilt. (Emb stamp; soiled), else VG. *Pacific*.* $259/£162

EDGAR, MORTON. The Great Pyramid. Glasgow, 1924. 3 vols. VG set. *Middle Earth.* $275/£172

EDGAR, RANDOLPH. A Record of Old Boats. Ward C. Burton (ed). (Minneapolis: Privately ptd, 1933.) Memorial ed. Ptd paper label. VG. *Wantagh.* $35/£22

EDGELL, G. H. The American Architecture of To-Day. NY/London: Scribner, 1928. 1st ed. Untrimmed. Dk grn cl, gilt. Good (fr hinge split, sl aging, finger mks, lacks fep; spine dknd, lettering dull, ends frayed). *Baltimore*.* $20/£13

EDGERTON, CLYDE. The Floatplane Notebooks. Chapel Hill: Algonquin, 1988. 1st ed. Signed. Fine in Fine dj. *Unger.* $75/£47

EDGERTON, CLYDE. The Floatplane Notebooks. London: Viking, 1989. 1st Eng ed. Signed. Fine in Fine dj. *Unger.* $50/£31

EDGERTON, CLYDE. Walking Across Egypt. NC: Algonquin, 1987. 1st ed. Fine in NF dj. *Warren.* $35/£22

EDGERTON, FRANKLIN. The Elephant-Lore of the Hindus: The Elephant-Sport (Matanga-Lila) of Nilakantha. New Haven: Yale Univ, 1931. 1st ed. (Ink notes pg xiv; sl rubbed), o/w VG. *Worldwide.* $65/£41

EDGEWORTH, MARIA. Helen, a Tale. Richard Bentley, 1838. Frontis. Marbled edges. Contemp 1/2 leather, marbled bds, raised bands, gilt. VG. *Tiger.* $90/£56

EDGEWORTH, MARIA. The Little Merchants, or Honesty and Knavery Contrasted. New Haven: Sidney's, 1808. Sq slim 16mo. Orig unptd marbled wraps and blanks prepared from scraps of excess ll from other publications (lt rubbed). Text NF (lt browned). *Baltimore*.* $25/£16

EDGEWORTH, MARIA. Patronage. London, 1814. 1st ed. 4 vols. (Vol 1 marginal pencil doodles, lacks 1/2 title.) Contemp 3/4 calf (rubbed, sl stained, browned, soiled). *Oinonen*.* $130/£81

EDGEWORTH, MARIA. Tales and Novels. NY: Harper, 1852. 20 vols in 10. Steel-engr frontispieces, added tps. Blindstamped cl, gilt. (Foxed, bkpls; cvrs faded, worn), else Good+. *Pacific*.* $58/£36

EDGEWORTH, RICHARD LOVELL and MARIA. Essay on Irish Bulls. London: J. Johnson, 1802. 1st ed. 316pp. 3/4 tan calf, marbled bds, gilt. VG (spine head chipped, lacks sm piece, extrems worn). Internally Fine. Bkpl Yale Lib Edgeworth Coll (dup). *Argonaut.* $300/£188

EDIE, GEORGE. The Art of English Shooting, (1775). SF: Arion, 1993. One of 250. Frontis. 1/4 brn morocco, marbled bds. Fine in Fine cl/marbled bds slipcase. *Harrington.* $100/£63

EDLIN, H. L. British Woodland Trees. London: Batsford, 1949. 3rd ed. Fine in NF dj. *Archer.* $20/£13

EDLIN, H. L. England's Forests. Faber, 1958. 1st ed. 7 maps. Dj (chipped, sl loss). *Edwards.* $24/£15

EDMONDS, HARFIELD H. and NORMAN N. LEE. Brook and River Trouting. A Manual of Modern North Country Methods. Bradford: The Authors, (1916). 1st ed. Henry A. Siegel's bkpl. (Shelfworn, sl shaken.) *Oinonen*.* $110/£69

EDMONDS, WALTER D. Drums Along the Mohawk. Boston: Little, Brown, 1936. 1st ed. (Spine ends sl sunned), else VG in dj (spine ends sl worn). *Pacific*.* $29/£18

EDMONDS, WALTER D. Wilderness Clearing. Dodd, 1944. 1st ed. John De Martelly (illus). 156pp. VG (name) in Good dj (spine ends, corners chipped). *Price.* $40/£25

EDMONDSON, JAMES K. My Dear Emma (War Letters of Col. James K. Edmondson, 1861-1865). Charles W. Turner (ed). Verona, (1978). 1st ed. Fine. *Pratt.* $30/£19

EDMUNDS, JOHN (comp.) A Williamsburg Songbook. Holt, Rinehart & Winston, (c1964). 1st ed. VG in Good dj. *Book Broker.* $50/£31

EDMUNDSON, WILLIAM. A Journal of the Life, Travels, Sufferings, and Labour of Love in the Work of the Ministry.... Dublin: Ptd by Christopher Bentham, 1820. 3rd ed. 320pp. Contemp calf, red morocco label. *Young.* $112/£70

EDWARD, DAVID B. The History of Texas, or, the Emigrant's, Farmer's, and Politician's Guide.... Cincinnati: J.A. James, 1836. 1st ed. 336pp + (1)ad pg. Mod leather, gilt. (Lacks orig map, but facs supplied; lib blindstamps, old ink names), else VG. Howes E48. *Pacific*.* $489/£306

EDWARDES, CHARLES. Rides and Studies in the Canary Islands. London, 1888. 1st ed. Frontis, xx,365pp; 19 plts. Uncut. Pict cl, gilt. *Maggs.* $280/£175

EDWARDES, ERNEST L. The Grandfather Clock. Altrincham, 1952. New ed. Frontis, 54 plts. (Eps lt spotted.) Dj (lt soiled, sm tear lower edge). *Edwards.* $48/£30

EDWARDS, A. Rock Gardens.... Ward, Lock, 1929. 1st ed. 8 color plts. Good. *Cox.* $24/£15

EDWARDS, AMELIA B. A Midsummer Ramble in the Dolomites. Routledge & Sons, (1889). 2nd ed. 389pp; fldg color map. Uncut. Blue pict cl, gilt. Very Bright (extrems sl bumped). *Sotheran.* $157/£98

EDWARDS, AMELIA B. Pharaohs, Fellahs, and Explorers. NY, 1891. 1st ed. Frontisport, 325pp. Teg. *Edwards.* $80/£50

EDWARDS, AMELIA B. Untrodden Peaks and Unfrequented Valleys. Leipzig: Tauchnitz, 1873. 11 mtd albumen prints (sl foxed). Marbled eps. (Sl yellowed.) Later blue morocco, marbled bds (sl worn, rubbed; corner fr cvr scraped, obliterating most of owner initials), gilt. *Baltimore*.* $90/£56

EDWARDS, AMELIA B. Untrodden Peaks and Unfrequented Valleys. A Midsummer Ramble in the Dolomites. Routledge & Sons, (c. 1893). 3rd ed. 389pp. Pict cl (Spines sl faded), o/w Good. *Sotheran.* $128/£80

EDWARDS, B. B. The Missionary Gazetteer. Boston, 1832. Orig cl (partly faded, discolored; lt foxed). *Swann*.* $69/£43

EDWARDS, BRYAN. The History, Civil and Commercial, of the British Colonies in the West Indies. London: John Stockdale, 1801. 3rd ed, w/'considerable additions.' 3 vols. Frontisport, xxiv,xxiii,576; vii,617,(1); xxxii,477pp; complete w/10 fldg plts, 11 fldg maps. Contemp full calf (scuffed, corner worn, rebacked w/new leather labels). Clean (sl foxed, offsetting, primarily to plts). *Argonaut.* $750/£469

EDWARDS, C. The History and Poetry of Finger-Rings. NY: John W. Lovell, c1874. vii,239pp. VG. *Blake.* $150/£94

EDWARDS, E. I. Desert Harvest. L.A.: Westernlore, 1962. Good in dj. *Dumont.* $85/£53

EDWARDS, E. I. The Valley Whose Name Is Death. Pasadena: San Pasqual Press, 1940. One of 500. Fine. *Book Market.* $125/£78

EDWARDS, E. I. The Valley Whose Name Is Death. Pasadena: San Pasqual, 1940. 1st ed. Ltd to 500 (tp verso states limitation as 1000). Map. Brn linen, paper spine label. (Label sl dknd), else Fine. *Pacific*.* $127/£79

EDWARDS, EDWARD. A Practical Treatise of Perspective, on the Principles of Dr. Brook Taylor. London: Leigh, Sotheby, 1803. Engr frontis, xii,316pp; errata leaf,40 engr plts. 1/2-leather, marbled bds (sl worn, spine torn). *Ars Artis.* $400/£250

EDWARDS, ELZA IVAN. Desert Harvest. L.A.: Westernlore, 1962. One of 600. Uncut. (Lt worn.) Dj (frayed). *Oinonen*.* $50/£31

EDWARDS, G. W. and H. W. MABIE. A Book of Old English Ballads. Macmillan, 1896. 1st ed. VG+. *Fine Books.* $30/£19

EDWARDS, H. L. R. Skelton: The Life and Times of an Early Tudor Poet. London: Cape, 1949. 1st Eng ed. VG (top edge sl faded; spine ends, corners sl bumped; cvrs sl bowed, sl mkd) in dj (nicked, torn, creased, sl rubbed, dusty, internally repaired, dknd). *Ulysses.* $48/£30

EDWARDS, HARRY STILLWELL. Eneas Africanus. Macon, GA: J.W. Burke, (1920). 1st ed. Frontisport; 4 plts, dbl-pg map. Gilt stamped brown suede. Fine. *House.* $50/£31

EDWARDS, J. B. Early Days in Abilene. Abilene, TX: Abilene Daily Chronicle, 1938. 1st ed thus. VG in wrappers. *Labordo.* $250/£156

EDWARDS, JONATHAN. A Careful and Strict Inquiry into the Modern Prevailing Notions of That Freedom of Will. Boston, 1754. 1st ed. Contemp sheep. *Felcone.* $4,000/£2,500

EDWARDS, JONATHAN. Memoirs of the Rev. David Brainerd; Missionary to the Indians.... New-Haven: S. Convrse, 1822. 507pp (browned, lt age-spotted). Old leather (rubbed, joints splitting). *Zubal*.* $80/£50

EDWARDS, JONATHAN. Some Thoughts Concerning the Present Revival of Religion in New-England. Lexington: Joseph Charless, 1803. Contemp sheep (extrems rubbed, spine top chipped). Swann*. $258/£161

EDWARDS, LEO. Jerry Todd and the Oak Island Treasure. NY: G&D, 1925. Lists Jerry Todd and The Buffalo Bill Bathtub. 5x7.5. Bert Salg (illus). 233pp + ads. VG + (corners bumped) in VG dj (extrems worn). My Bookhouse. $57/£36

EDWARDS, LIONEL. Horses and Ponies. London: Country Life, (1938). 1st ed. 4to. (viii),111pp. Grn cl (rubbed, mkd). Internally Very Clean. Sotheran. $93/£58

EDWARDS, LIONEL. My Hunting Sketch Book. London/NY, 1928. Vol 1 (of 2). 15 mtd color plts. (Lt foxing.) Dj (corners worn). Swann*. $149/£93

EDWARDS, LIONEL. My Scottish Sketch Book. London, 1929. One of 250 numbered, signed. 4to. 16 mtd color plts. Cl, vellum back. (Sl worn, spine lettering faded.) Oinonen*. $550/£344

EDWARDS, PAUL. English Garden Ornament. Bell, 1965. VG in dj. Hadley. $24/£15

EDWARDS, PHILIP L. California in 1837. Sacramento: A.J. Johnston, 1890. 1st ed. 47pp. Orig ptd wrappers. VG + . Howes E66. Parmer. $325/£203

EDWARDS, PHILIP L. The Diary of Philip Leget Edwards. The Great Cattle Drive from California to Oregon in 1837. SF: Grabhorn, 1932. One of 500 ptd. Color facs of 1837 litho. Cl-backed marbled bds, paper cvr/spine labels. Fine (eps dknd by binder's glue; spine faded). Argonaut. $75/£47

EDWARDS, RALPH. The Shorter Dictionary of English Furniture. London, (1964). Dj. Swann*. $69/£43

EDWARDS, S. J. CELESTINE. From Slavery to a Bishopric. London: John Kensit, 1891. 1st ed. Frontisport. (Hinges cracked, pencil scrawls on eps; waterstains on fr cvr.) Swann*. $115/£72

EDWARDS, SAMUEL E. The Ohio Hunter. Battle Creek: Review & Herald Steam Press Print, 1866. 1st ed. Wood-engr frontis port, 240pp. Blind brn cl, gilt. Text Good (lt aged, sl foxed, few sm stains; extrems fraying, lt rippling, faint discoloration). Howes E70. Baltimore*. $375/£234

EDWARDS, SAMUEL. Rebel! NY, (1974). 1st ed. (Rep cut out), o/w Fine in dj (sl worn). Pratt. $25/£16

EDWARDS, SYDENHAM TEAK. Edwards's Botanical Register: Or, Ornamental Flower-Garden and Shrubbery. John Lindley (ed). London: Ridgway, 1842. New Series, Vol V. 8vo. 64 (of 69?) Fine hand-colored plts. 3/4 morocco (worn). Oinonen*. $650/£406

EDWARDS, SYDENHAM TEAK. Edwards's Botanical Register: Or, Ornamental Flower-Garden and Shrubbery. John Lindley (ed). London: Ridgway, 1845. New Series, Vol VIII. 8vo. 65 (of 69) Fine hand-colored plts. 3/4 morocco (worn). Oinonen*. $700/£438

EDWARDS, WILLIAM H. Football Days. NY: Moffat, Yard, 1916. 1st ed. Blue cl, gilt. (Bkpl; hinges cracked), else VG. Pacific*. $40/£25

Edwin Davis French, a Memorial. (By Ira Hutchinson Brainerd.) NY: Privately ptd, 1908. One of 425 (of 475) numbered. 2 photogravure plts, 10 mtd bkpls, mtd engr. Olive cl (extrems lt rubbed), gray bds. Karmiole. $100/£63

EGAN, HOWARD R. Pioneering the West 1846 to 1878. Richmond, UT: Howard R. Egan estate, 1917. (Lt shelfworn), else Good. Howes E76. Dumont. $100/£63

EGAN, PIERCE. Life in London; or, The Day and Night Scenes of Jerry Hawthorn.... London, 1821. 1st ed. W/half-title and inserted ads, w/o leaf 'To the Subscribers.' 36 color aquatint plts by Isaac, Robert & George Cruikshank; 3 fldg sheets of engr music. Later 19th-cent red straight-grain morocco (crudely rebacked retaining most of orig backstrip), gilt. Swann*. $126/£79

EGAN, PIERCE. The Life of an Actor. London: C.S. Arnold, 1825. 1st ed. Tall 8vo. xvi,272pp; 27 aquatint plts, guards. Marbled eps; teg, uncut, gilt inner dentelles. Full crushed red morocco, gilt. Fine (lt foxed). Hartfield. $895/£559

EGE, ROBERT J. Settling the Dust. (Chinook, MT: R.J. Ege, 1968.) (1st ed.) Ltd, signed ed. Soft cvrs. VG. Lien. $20/£13

EGEDE, HANS. A Description of Greenland. London: T. & J. Allman, 1818. 2nd ed. Fldg frontis map, cxvii,225pp. Orig paper bds, uncut. VG (rebacked to match w/new paper label). High Latitude. $375/£234

EGENHOFF, ELISABETH L. (comp). Fabricas: A Collection of Pictures and Statements on the Mineral Materials Used in Building in California Prior to 1850. SF: CA Division of Mines, 1952. 1st ed. Gray wrappers. Fine. Harrington. $45/£28

EGERTON, JUDY. George Stubbs, 1724-1806. (London): Tate Gallery/Yale Center for British Art, (1984). 1st ed. Sm folio. Lt brn cl, gilt. Fine in dj (sl rubbed). Baltimore*. $40/£25

EGGENHOFER, NICK. Wagons, Mules and Men. NY, (1961). 1st ed. Frontis. Ptd eps. ('O.P./1st Edition [&] Out of Print' inked on fep, 1/2-title), o/w VG in VG dj. Sagebrush. $150/£94

EGGENHOFER, NICK. Wagons, Mules and Men. NY: Hastings House, 1961. 1st trade ed. Fine in dj. Labordo. $175/£109

EGGLESTON, EDWARD. The Hoosier School-Boy. NY: Scribner, 1883. 1st ed, state B. 8vo. 181pp + 6pp pub's cat; 5 plts. Pict grn cl. Good (fr hinge cracked, name; bumped, rubbed, sm stain). Blue Mountain. $85/£53

EGGLESTON, GEORGE CARY. The History of the Confederate War. NY: Sturgis & Walton, 1910. 1st ed. 2 vols. Blue cl. (Bkpls, inner hinges cracked, repaired vol 1; extrems lt rubbed), else VG. Chapel Hill. $200/£125

EGLESTON, THOMAS. The Metallurgy of Silver, Gold, and Mercury in the United States. NY, 1890. 1st ed. Vol 2 only. 920pp. Brn cl, gilt. VG. Larry Price. $195/£122

EGLINTON, JOHN. A Memoir of A E—George William Russell. London: Macmillan, 1937. 1st Eng ed. Cl-backed marbled paper bds. VG (name label, pp edges browned; spine head, 2 corners sl bumped) in dj (rubbed, dusty, sl frayed, spine/edges dknd). Ulysses. $72/£45

EHRENTHEIL, OTTO and WALTER MARCHAND. Clinical Medicine and the Psychotic Patient. Springfield: Charles C. Thomas, (1960). 1st ed. Brn cl. Fine in dj. House. $25/£16

EHRLICH, GEORGE. Kansas City, Missouri, an Architectural History, 1826-1976. Kansas City: Historic Kansas City Corp, (1979). 1st ed. NF in NF dj. Glenn. $45/£28

EHRLICH, GRETEL. The Solace of Open Spaces. (NY): Viking, (1985). 1st ed. VF in dj. Captain's Bookshelf. $75/£47

EICHELBERGER, R. Our Jungle Road to Tokyo. NY, 1950. VG in Good dj. Clark. $45/£28

EICHENBERG, FRITZ. Dick Whittington and His Cat. NY: Holiday House, 1937. 1st ed. Illus stiff bds, cl tape spine as issued. VG. Turtle Island. $75/£47

EICHENBERG, FRITZ. The Wood and the Graver: The Work of Fritz Eichenberg. NY, (1977). One of 150 w/signed wood engr laid in. Dj, slipcase. Swann*. $172/£108

EICHENBERG, FRITZ. The Wood and the Graver: The Work of Fritz Eichenberg. Barre, 1977. One of 500 numbered, signed, w/signed engr laid into rear pocket. Slipcase. Swann*. $126/£79

EICHLER, FR. A. A Treatise on the Manufacture of Liquors, Syrups, Cordials and Bitters.... Phila: F. A. Eichler, 1874. 5th ed. Cl-backed ptd bds. VG- (soiled, cvrs stained, cl piece along spine eaten away). Pacific*. $58/£36

EIDE, ARTHUR HANSIN. Drums of Diomede: the Transformation of the Alaska Eskimo. Hollywood: House-Warren, c. 1952. VG in dj (tape repaired). High Latitude. $30/£19

EIDSON, TOM. St. Agnes' Stand. NY: Putnam, 1994. 1st ed, 1st bk. Rev copy. Fine in Fine dj. *Unger.* $65/£41

EILAND, MURRAY L. Chinese and Exotic Rugs. London, 1979. 1st ed. 52 color plts. (Lib ink stamp, label.) Dj (spine faded). *Edwards.* $58/£36

EINARSEN, A. S. The Pronghorn Antelope. Washington, (1948). Color frontis, color plt. (Spine lt faded.) *Sutton.* $50/£31

EINSTEIN, ALBERT. About Zionism: Speeches and Letters. Leon Simon (trans). NY: Macmillan, 1931. 1st Amer ed. (Name), else VG in Good dj (extrems chipped, lacks spine piece, tear, crease). *Pacific*.* $127/£79

EINSTEIN, ALBERT. The Fight Against War. Alfred Lief (ed). NY, (1933). John Day Pamphlets No. 20. NF in ptd wraps (price-clipped). *Polyanthos.* $20/£13

EINSTEIN, ALBERT. Relativity. The Special and General Theory. A Popular Exposition. NY: Crown, (1961). Fine in dj. *Glaser.* $25/£16

EINSTEIN, CHARLES. Willie Mays: Coast to Coast Giant. Putnam, 1963. 1st ed. VG. *Plapinger.* $25/£16

EISELEY, L. Man, Time and Prophecy. NY: HB&W, 1966. 1st ed. Fine in Good dj. *Mikesh.* $30/£19

EISEN, GUSTAVUS A. and FAHIM KOUCHAKJI. Glass: Its Origin, History, Chronology, Technic, and Classification to the Sixteenth Century. NY: William Edwin Rudge, 1927. One of 525 numbered set. 2 vols. 188 plts. Cl-backed bds (lt soiled, tips bumped). Slipcase (worn, cellotape repairs). *Swann*.* $258/£161

EISENSTAEDT, ALFRED. Witness to Our Time. NY, (1967). Folio. Dj (3 sm tears). *Swann*.* $230/£144

EKINS, CHARLES. Naval Battles, from 1744 to the Peace in 1814, Critically Reviewed and Illustrated. London: Baldwin, Cradock & Joy, 1824. xxviii,425pp + 2 subs; 79 plts. Contemp 1/2 calf (rubbed, hinges, spine worn). *Adelson.* $425/£266

Elaboratory Laid Open, or, the Secrets of Modern Chemistry and Pharmacy Revealed.... (By Robert Dossie.) London: J. Nourse, 1758. 1st ed. 8vo. (2),xi,(3),375,(9)pp. Later antique style calf, red morocco spine label. VG (lib stamp, few brn spots). *Glaser.* $650/£406

ELDER, LONNE III. Ceremonies in Dark Old Men. NY: FSG, (1969). 1st ed. Textured bds. VG + in pict dj. *Petrilla.* $75/£47

ELDER, PAUL (comp). California the Beautiful: Camera Studies.... SF: Paul Elder, (1911). 1/2 burlap, bds, gilt, photo pict cvr label. VF in 2-part box (seams splitting, worn). *Pacific*.* $81/£51

ELDER, WILLIAM. Biography of Elisha Kent Kane. Phila/NY: Childs & Peterson/Sheldon, Blakeman, 1858. Frontis port, extra engr tp, 416pp. Blindstamped cl. VG (prelims sl foxed, ex-lib). *High Latitude.* $40/£25

ELDERFIELD, JOHN. The Cut-Outs of Henri Matisse. NY: George Braziller, (1978). 45 color plts. Fine in dj. *Turtle Island.* $45/£28

ELDERFIELD, JOHN. Frankenthaler. NY (1989). Sm sq folio. Plastic dj. *Swann*.* $103/£64

ELDREDGE, ZOETH SKINNER. The Beginnings of San Francisco from the Expedition of Anza, 1774 to the City Charter of April 15, 1850. SF: The Author, 1912. 2 vols. 15 maps (8 fldg), 29 plts. Teg. Grn cl, gilt spines. (Bkpl, spines faded), o/w NF. *Pacific*.* $69/£43

ELDRIDGE, FRED. Wrath in Burma. GC, 1946. 1st ed. Good in dj (chipped, torn, price-clipped). *King.* $15/£9

ELDRIDGE, GEORGE H. A Geological Reconnaissance Across Idaho. Washington: GPO, 1895. (Lib stamps; sl soiled), else VG. *Dumont.* $75/£47

Election Law. State of Rhode Island and Providence Plantations. In General Assembly, January Session, A.D. 1844. (Providence, RI: Knowles & Vose, 1844.) 1st ed. 16pp. Sewn, uncut as issued. (Soiled.) *M & S.* $125/£78

Elfin Song, a Book of Verse and Pictures. London: Blackie & Son, (1912). 1st ed. 8vo. (xii),15-142pp; 12 mtd color plts by Florence Harrison. Teg, rest uncut. Gray cl, gilt. (Eps sl browned; sm patch cl bubbled), o/w Very Bright in gray ptd dj (sl stained, browned, 2-inch spine loss). *Sotheran.* $269/£168

ELIAS, HORACE J. Mighty Mouse Prehistoric Animal Book. Magic Punch-Out See-Thru Picture Storybook. NY: Ottenheimer, 1977. 26pp w/flap to be lifted on each illus, seeing through to next pg. Glazed pict bds. VG. *Bookfinders.* $35/£22

ELIOT, GEORGE. (Pseud of Mary Anne Evans.) Adam Bede. NY: Harper, 1859. 1st Amer ed. Brn cl, gilt. (Foxed; spine ends rubbed), else VG. *Pacific*.* $29/£18

ELIOT, GEORGE. (Pseud of Mary Anne Evans.) How Lisa Loved the King. Boston: Fields, Osgood, 1869. 1st ed. 48pp. NF (inscrip) in grn cl, gilt. *Second Life.* $200/£125

ELIOT, GEORGE. (Pseud of Mary Anne Evans.) The Legend of Jubal and Other Poems. William Blackwood & Sons, 1874. 1st ed. (vi),242pp + 16 ads. (Extrems rubbed.) *Young.* $40/£25

ELIOT, GEORGE. (Pseud of Mary Anne Evans.) The Novels. Edinburgh: William Blackwood, (c.1901). 10 vols. Marbled edges. 3/4 dk brn morocco, marbled bds, gilt. (Bkpls), else NF. *Pacific*.* $259/£162

ELIOT, GEORGE. (Pseud of Mary Anne Evans.) Silas Marner. NY: Harper, 1861. 1st Amer ed. Black cl, gilt. VG (spine snags). *Macdonnell.* $150/£94

ELIOT, GEORGE. (Pseud of Mary Anne Evans.) Silas Marner. Blackwood, 1861. 1st UK ed. Brn cl. VG (cvrs sl worn, spine foot split). *Williams.* $560/£350

ELIOT, GEORGE. (Pseud of Mary Anne Evans.) Silas Marner. LEC, 1953. Ltd to 1500 numbered, signed by Lynton Lamb (illus). Fine in slipcase. *Swann*.* $80/£50

ELIOT, GEORGE. (Pseud of Mary Anne Evans.) The Works. Edinburgh: William Blackwood, 1878. 20 vols. 8vo. Teg. 3/4 red polished calf, gilt paneled spines, raised bands, maroon/green leather labels. Fine. *Appelfeld.* $1,500/£938

ELIOT, GEORGE. (Pseud of Mary Anne Evans.) The Works. NY: Merrill & Baker, 1895. Illus Cabinet ed. 24 vols. 8vo. Teg. 3/4 grn morocco, onlaid crimson morocco on spines, gilt. (Some spines faded), o/w Fine. *Cummins.* $2,000/£1,250

ELIOT, T. S. Animula. London: Faber & Faber, 1929. 1st ed. One of 400 signed. (Bds sl dusty, sm defect spine head.) *Maggs.* $176/£110

ELIOT, T. S. Animula. London, 1929. 1st ed. One of 400 lg paper copies signed. Yellow bds. *Swann*.* $345/£216

ELIOT, T. S. Ara Vus Prec. Ovid, 1920. 1st ed, 2nd issue in orig black cl bds, yellow cl spine. One of 264 (this unnumbered), initials, colophon by E. A. Wadsworth. 4to. *Sotheby's*.* $1,379/£862

ELIOT, T. S. Ash Wednesday. London, 1930. 1st ed. One of 600 numbered, signed. Sq 8vo. Gilt-stamped blue cl (spine sl dknd). Slipcase. *Swann*.* $632/£395

ELIOT, T. S. Charles Whibley. London, 1931. VG in orig wraps. *Edrich.* $26/£16

ELIOT, T. S. The Classics and the Man of Letters. London: OUP, 1942. 1st ed. Orig pale blue wrappers. VG (inscrip, sig; sl browned, few edge tears). *Heritage.* $200/£125

ELIOT, T. S. The Cocktail Party. London: Faber & Faber, 1950. 1st ed. W/error at p29, line 1 'here' for 'her.' Grn cl, gilt. Fine in dj (sl torn). *Cummins.* $75/£47

ELIOT, T. S. Dante. London, (1929). 1st ed. Pict bds. (Bkpl, ink name; rear outer hinge cracked, spine ends sl frayed), else Good in dj (incomplete). *King.* $75/£47

ELIOT, T. S. Dante. London, (1929). 1st ed. Pub's prospectus laid in. Pict bds. Dj. *Swann*.* $126/£79

ELIOT, T. S. The Dry Salvages. London: Faber & Faber, 1941. 1st ed. One of the 'early' copies w/the 'Adelphi' watermark. Pale blue wrappers (edges browned), stapled as issued. *Maggs.* $40/£25

ELIOT, T. S. Essays Ancient and Modern. Faber & Faber, 1936. 1st Eng ed. VG (prelims, edges spotted, inscrip, top edge dusty; bottom cvr edges shelf shoddy) in dj (nicked, rubbed, mkd, faded, torn, dusty, sl chipped, creased, browned). *Ulysses.* $264/£165

ELIOT, T. S. For Lancelot Andrewes. Faber & Faber, 1929. 1st UK ed, 2nd imp. Inscribed. VG. *Williams.* $240/£150

ELIOT, T. S. Four Quartets. NY: Harcourt, Brace, (1943). W/'First American Edition' on c. pg, but this is true 1st ed. Black cl (rubbed), gilt spine (flaking). Text VG (eps, edges sl aged). *Baltimore*.* $210/£131

ELIOT, T. S. Four Quartets. London, (1960). One of 290 signed. Tall 4to. Vellum-backed marbled bds. VF in pub's marbled slipcase. *Felcone.* $2,800/£1,750

ELIOT, T. S. Four Quartets. Faber, 1944. 1st ed. Tan cl. NF (few pp sl cockled at top edges; sl dusty, 2 sm mks, spine sl creased). *Any Amount.* $32/£20

ELIOT, T. S. Marina. London, 1930. 1st ed. One of 400 lg paper copies signed. Blue bds. *Swann*.* $345/£216

ELIOT, T. S. Notes Toward the Definition of Culture. London: Faber & Faber, 1948. 1st ed. VG + (fore-edges of pp, bds sl foxed; spine faded) in dj. *Lame Duck.* $150/£94

ELIOT, T. S. Old Possum's Book of Practical Cats. NY: HB, (1939). 1st Amer ed. One of 2000 ptd. VG (sig; lt soiled; lacks dj). *Agvent.* $75/£47

ELIOT, T. S. Poems. Richmond: Hogarth, 1919. 1st ed, 1st state w/the misprints on p(13). One of fewer than 250. 8vo. Batik wrappers (separated along hinge, upper corners sl defective), label ptd in black, black 1/4 morocco box. *Sotheby's*.* $6,992/£4,370

ELIOT, T. S. Poems. NY, 1920. 1st Amer ed. 8vo. Dj (sl faded, chipped). *Sotheby's*.* $1,379/£862

ELIOT, T. S. Prufrock and Other Observations. Egoist, 1917. 1st ed, 1st bk. One of 500. 8vo. VF in wrappers, black 1/4 morocco box. *Sotheby's*.* $10,120/£6,325

ELIOT, T. S. Religious Drama: Mediaeval and Modern. NY: House of Books, 1954. 1st ed. Ltd to 300 signed, numbered. 8vo. VF in tissue dj. *Black Sun.* $550/£344

ELIOT, T. S. Reunion by Destruction. (London: Westminster, The Pax House, 1943.) 1st ed. (Loose, staples gone.) Brn ptd wrappers (sl soiled). *Maggs.* $88/£55

ELIOT, T. S. The Rock. NY: Harcourt, Brace, (1934). 1st ed. Tan cl, red paper spine label. (Ink stamp; spine sl dknd), o/w NF in dj (lt chipped, soiled, spine browned). *Heritage.* $150/£94

ELIOT, T. S. Selected Essays, 1917-1932. NY: Harcourt, Brace, 1932. 1st US ed. VG (ep edges sl browned; top edge spotted, dusty; fore-edge sl browned, sl spotted; spine sl faded; spine foot, 2 corners sl bumped) in dj (nicked, sl creased, rubbed, mkd, dusty, sl dknd). *Ulysses.* $400/£250

ELIOT, T. S. Sweeney Agonistes. London, (1932). 1st ed. Dj (nick spine base, rear panel edge). *Swann*.* $69/£43

ELIOT, T. S. The Undergraduate Poems. (Cambridge, 1949.) 1st ed, pub w/o authorization. Stapled gray paper wrappers. *Black Sun.* $100/£63

ELIOT, T. S. The Use of Poetry and the Use of Criticism. Harvard Univ, 1933. Teg. VG (inscrip, ep edges sl browned, offsetting to fep from fr dj flap; spine, cvr edges sl faded) in dj (nicked, chipped, rubbed, dusty, sl torn, creased, browned). *Ulysses.* $248/£155

ELIOT, T. S. The Waste Land. London, (1961). One of 300 ptd, signed. 4to. Parchment-backed marbled bds. Fine in slipcase. *Heritage.* $2,500/£1,563

ELIOT, T. S. The Waste Land. NY: Harcourt, Brace, Jovanovich, (1971). One of 250. Frontisport. Gray cl, gilt. Fine in VG slipcase. *Pacific*.* $92/£58

ELIOT, T. S. The Waste Land. NY, 1922. 1st ed. One of 1000 numbered. 8vo. Flexible cl bds. The flexible bds and the larger size of type in which the number is stamped denote, according to Gallup, an early copy; however this also has the letter 'a' dropped from line 339, signifying the 2nd state. Dj (chipped, crudely repaired internally). *Sotheby's*.* $3,496/£2,185

ELIOT, T. S. The Waste Land. Richmond: Hogarth, 1923. 1st Eng ed. One of about 460. 8vo. (Foxed.) Blue marbled paper bds (rubbed, backstrip torn), white paper label fr cvr (2nd state w/heavy single-line rule above and below title). *Sotheby's*.* $1,379/£862

ELIOT, T. S. The Waste Land. Hogarth, 1923. 1st Eng ed. One of about 460. 8vo. Marbled bds, ptd label on fr cvr w/border of asterisks. (Foxed; backstrip faded, extrems sl rubbed.) *Sotheby's*.* $1,656/£1,035

ELIOT, T. S. The Waste Land. Faber & Faber, 1940. 1st ed. VG (eps sl spotted, 2 sm holes in fr hinge; top edges sl dusty, edges spotted, spine ends, corners sl bumped) in dj (sl rubbed, creased, dusty, spine, edges faded). *Ulysses.* $88/£55

ELIOT, WILLARD A. Forest Trees of the Pacific Coast. NY, 1948. Rev ed. Grn cl, gilt. VG in dj (worn). *Larry Price.* $28/£18

ELKIN, R. H. The Children's Corner. London: Augener, (1914). 1st ed. Obl 4to. Henriette Willebeek Le Mair (illus). 15 full-pg mtd color plts. (New eps.) Tan cl, gilt, color oval paste label. *Reisler.* $290/£181

ELKIN, STANLEY. A Bad Man. NY: Random House, 1967. 1st ed. Fine in NF dj (lt worn, sm tears at top edge). *Beasley.* $60/£38

ELKIN, STANLEY. Boswell. NY: Random House, 1964. 1st ed, 1st bk. NF in dj (lt used, internal mends). *Beasley.* $125/£78

ELKIN, STANLEY. The Dick Gibson Show. NY: Random House, 1971. 1st ed. Fine (sticker stain fep) in NF dj. *Beasley.* $40/£25

ELKINGTON, J. The Doukhobors. Phila: Ferris & Leach, 1903. 1st ed. Signed. Orig cl (rebacked w/old spine relaid). Good. *Walcot.* $32/£20

ELKUS, RICHARD J. Alamos: A Philosophy in Living. SF: Grabhorn, 1965. Ltd to 487 signed by Elkus and Edwin & Robert Grabhorn. Folio. 24 mtd photo plts. Leather-backed dec cl. VF. *Argonaut.* $300/£188

ELLACOMBE, H. N. Shakespeare as an Angler. London: Elliot Stock, 1883. 1st ed. Frontis woodcut. Teg. Vellum, gilt. (Soiling), else NF. *Pacific*.* $63/£39

ELLER, IRWIN. The History of Belvoir Castle. London, 1861. Engr frontis, add'l engr tp, viii,410pp; fldg table. (Plts foxed; spine sl chipped.) *Edwards.* $61/£38

ELLET. The Characters of Schiller. Boston: Otis, Broaders, 1839. 1st ed. Orig blind-dec cl (sl soiled, spine sunned, ends worn; foxed, prelim blank removed). *Dramatis.* $30/£19

ELLICE, EDWARD C. Place-Names in Glengarry and Glenquoich. Swan Sonnenschein, 1898. 1st ed. Frontis, viii,127pp; lg fldg map. Uncut. (Bkpl; extrems sl rubbed.) *Hollett.* $96/£60

ELLIGEN, J. The Terrible Deeds of George L. Shaftesbury.... St. Louis, MO: Barclay & Rulison, 1851. 1st ed. 36pp. Orig ptd fr wrapper. VG (frayed). *M & S.* $350/£219

ELLINGTON, CHARLES G. The Trial of U.S. Grant: The Pacific Coast Years, 1852-1854. Glendale: A.H. Clark, 1987. 1st ed. Full leather. Fine in Fine dj. *Book Market.* $45/£28

ELLIOT, D. G. The Birds of Daniel Giraud Elliot. Adrian Thorpe (ed). London: Ariel, 1979. One of 1000. Folio. 12 Fine color plts. Grn cl. Mint in dj. *Henly.* $120/£75

ELLIOT, D. G. A Monograph of the Paradiseidae or Birds of Paradise. NY, 1977. One of 250 (of 500) numbered. Folio. 37 plts. 1/2 morocco, gilt, by Zaehnsdorf. *Swann*.* $747/£467

ELLIOT, G. F. SCOTT. The Romance of Plant Life. London, 1907. 34 plts. Blue dec cl, gilt. VG. *Larry Price.* $40/£25

ELLIOT, JAMES. The Poetical and Miscellaneous Works of James Elliot.... Greenfield, MA: Thomas Dickman, for the Author, 1798. 1st ed. 12mo. 271,(5)pp. Contemp sheep, leather label. VG (hinges sl starting, sl warped). Howes E97. *M & S.* $1,850/£1,156

ELLIOT, T. J. A Medieval Bestiary. Boston: Godine, 1971. 1st ed. One of 1000. Gillian Tyler (illus). Red cl bds, gray spine. Fine in Fine dj, slipcase. *Davidson.* $65/£41

ELLIOTT, CHARLES W. Remarkable Characters and Places of the Holy Land. Hartford, CT: Burr, 1867. 1st ed. 640pp; 13 steel engrs, color map. Aeg. (Lt foxed; edges sl rubbed), o/w VG. *Worldwide.* $65/£41

ELLIOTT, D. S. and ED BARTHOLOMEW. The Dalton Gang and the Coffeyville Raid. Ft. Davis, 1968. Ltd to 750 signed, numbered. NF. *Baade.* $75/£47

ELLIOTT, ELLEN COIT. Footholds in Chaos. L.A., 1939. Plain bds, cl spine, paper spine/cvr labels. *Dawson.* $50/£31

ELLIOTT, HENRY W. Report Upon the Condition of Affairs in Territory of Alaska. Washington: GPO, 1875. 277pp. Marbled eps, edges, bds. 3/4 leather (rubbed). *Heinoldt.* $85/£53

ELLIOTT, MARY. The Adventures of Thomas Two-Shoes. London: W. Darton, June 1818. 12mo. Full-pg fldg copper engr frontis, 63pp,1pg bk list+1pg list on lower wrapper; 2 plts. Internally Fine in buff stiff paper wrappers (lt soiled, corner fr cvr creased, spine edges sl chipped). *Hobbyhorse.* $375/£234

ELLIOTT, MARY. Early Seeds, to Produce Spring Flowers. London: William Darton, n.d. (ca 1825). 1st ed. 8vo. Frontis, 24pp+1pg list on lower wrapper; 24 Fine copper engrs, some dated 1st mo. 2nd, 1824. VG (ink dedication at verso of frontis, sl spotted) in buff stiff paper wrappers (spine sl chafed). *Hobbyhorse.* $375/£234

ELLIOTT, MARY. Rural Employments; or A Peep into Village Concerns. London: William Darton, 1820. 1st ed. 12mo. Frontis, 72pp; 17 full-pg copper engrs. Mod 3/4 leather, marbled paper on bds, gilt. Fine (ink sig on frontis). *Hobbyhorse.* $350/£219

ELLIOTT, MARY. Rustic Excursions to Aid Tarry-at-Home Travellers: For the Amusement and Instruction for Young Persons. London: William Darton, ca 1825. 12mo. 96pp, Darton's business card at end; 24 hand-colored copperplts. Leather (backstrip replaced), gilt. VG. *Reisler.* $500/£313

ELLIOTT, RUSSELL. Nevada's Twentieth-Century Mining Boom. Tonopah-Goldfield-Ely. Reno, NV, 1966. 1st ed. (Traces of removed bkpl), o/w VG+ in VG dj. *Sagebrush.* $45/£28

ELLIOTT, WILLIAM. Carolina Sports by Land and Water; Including Incidents of Devil-Fishing, Wild-Cat, Deer and Bear Hunting, etc. NY: Derby & Jackson, 1859. Frontis. (Sl shelfworn), else VG. *Pacific*.* $92/£58

ELLIS, ALBERT F. Ocean Islands and Nauru, Their Story. Sydney, 1936. Frontisport, 3 maps (2 on 1 fold in rear). (Lacks fep, prelims lt spotted; spine lt dknd.) *Edwards.* $88/£55

ELLIS, ALBERT. The Folklore of Sex. NY, 1951. 1st ed. Red cl bds. VG. *Doctor's Library.* $40/£25

ELLIS, EDWARD S. Iron Heart, War Chief of the Iroquois. Cassell, 1900. 1st ed. 8vo. Frontis, 386pp,16pp ads; 4 mono plts by Brinkman & Grant. Pict grn cl, gilt. (Sl worn, lg pink stain rear cvr), else VG. *Bookmark.* $29/£18

ELLIS, EDWIN JOHN and W. B. YEATS. The Works of William Blake, Poetic, Symbolic and Critical. Bernard Quaritch, 1893. Lg paper copy. 3 vols. 8vo. Frontisports. Teg. Orig 1/2 morocco, gilt. (Spotted; vol 3 corners worn.) *Sotheby's*.* $1,509/£943

ELLIS, ELMER. Henry Moore Teller: Defender of the West. Caldwell: Caxton, 1941. 1st ed. Dj. *Ginsberg.* $50/£31

ELLIS, GEORGE and G. H. FORD. Illustrations of Dissections in a Series of Coloured Plates the Size of Life. London: James Walton, 1867. Plt vol only. 58 chromolitho plts (most spotted w/lt soil; emb lib stamps, lib bkpl). Orig 1/2 morocco (worn). *Christie's*.* $397/£248

ELLIS, GEORGE. Illustrations of Dissections, in a Series of Original Colored Plates...Dissection of the Human Body. NY, 1882. 2nd ed. 2 vols. 479pp. Blue lib cl. (Ex-lib; rebound), o/w Good. *Doctor's Library.* $200/£125

ELLIS, GEORGE. Modern Practical Joinery. Volume 2: Constructional Joinery. Batsford, 1921. 4th ed. Good+ (extrems worn). *Whittle.* $40/£25

ELLIS, GEORGE. Modern Practical Stairbuilding and Handrailing. Part 2: Handrailing and Wreathmaking. Batsford, 1932. 1st ed. (Fr opening cracked, cvrs mkd), o/w Good+. *Whittle.* $56/£35

ELLIS, GEORGE. Specimens of Early English Metrical Romances, Chiefly Written During the Early Part of the Fourteenth Century. London/Edinburgh: Longman, Hurst, Rees & Orme/Constable, 1805. 3 vols. 1/2-titles not called for; (viii),387,(i blank); (iv),404; (iv),419,(i ads)pp. Oil-marbled edges, eps. Old 1/2 natural morocco-faced sheep, rose-madder bubble-grain cl sides. (Lib blindstamps; leather rubbed, peeling; gilt shelf mks on spine), o/w Fine. *Temple.* $104/£65

ELLIS, MARTHA DOWNER. Bell Ranch Recollections. Clarendon, TX, 1965. Signed. NF. *Dumont.* $50/£31

ELLIS, RICHARD N. General Pope and U. S. Indian Policy. Albuquerque: Univ of NM, (1970). 1st ed. VG in dj. *Lien.* $25/£16

ELLIS, RICHARD W. Book Illustration. Kingsport, TN: Kingsport Press, 1952. VG+. *Truepenny.* $35/£22

ELLIS, SARAH. Summer and Winter in the Pyrenees. Fisher, Son, (n.d., 1841). 1st ed. Steel-engr frontis, vii,(v),393pp. Speckled edges. Contemp 1/2 calf, raised bands, maroon label, gilt, marbled bds. VG (ink inscrip, frontis, tp sl foxed, bkpl). *Sotheran.* $256/£160

ELLIS, SARAH. The Women of England. Fisher, Son & Co, 1839. Engr frontisport (browned), 343pp. Orig blind-stamped cl (spine head neatly repaired), gilt. *Hollett.* $136/£85

ELLIS, W. T. Memories: My Seventy-Two Years in the Romantic Country of Yuba, California. Eugene: Univ of OR, 1939. 1st ed. 1/2 cl, bds, paper spine label. Fine. *Pacific*.* $63/£39

ELLIS, WILLIAM. History of Madagascar. London: Fisher, Son, 1838. 2 vols. xv,517,2 ads; xii,537pp,2 ads; 10 plts (foxed), 2 maps. Orig cl (vol 1 rebacked; rubbed). *Adelson.* $375/£234

ELLIS, WILLIAM. The Modern Husbandman...Necessary for All Landlords and Tenants of Either Ploughed, Grass, or Wood Grounds. London: For D. Browne, 1750. Later ed. 8 vols. 8vo. Contemp speckled calf. (Lib stamps on tps, lt spotted, joints cracked; rubbed.) *Christie's*.* $883/£552

ELLIS, WILLIAM. A Narrative of a Tour Through Hawaii, or, Owhyhee.... H. Fisher Son/P. Jackson, 1827. 2nd ed. 8vo. 480pp; 8 engr plts, 2 fldg maps. Full contemp calf (rebacked, preserving spine, bds sl bowed, faded), gilt. Very Clean. *Sotheran.* $632/£395

ELLIS, WILLIAM. Polynesian Researches, During a Residence of Nearly Eight Years in the Society and Sandwich Islands. NY, 1833. 4 vols. Engr frontispieces, add'l tps, 3 fldg maps. Orig cl (spines faded; foxed throughout, lib stamp versos each frontis). *Swann*.* $373/£233

ELLISON, HARLAN. Angry Candy. Boston: HMCo, 1988. 1st ed. NF in NF dj. *Dermont.* $20/£13

ELLISON, HARLAN. Memos from Purgatory. CA: Powell, 1969. 1st Amer ed. Pb orig. VG. *Warren.* $50/£31

ELLISON, JOSEPH. California and the Nation, 1850-1869.... Berkeley: Univ of CA, 1927. 1st ed. Unopened. NF in ptd wrappers (edges sl worn, spine sl sunned). *Pacific*.* $35/£22

ELLISON, RALPH. The Invisible Man. NY: Random House, 1952. 1st ed. Top edge stained black. Black/cream cl. NF (fep lt browned; spine lettering sl flaked) in dj (extensive restoration). *Heritage*. $500/£313

ELLISON, RALPH. Shadow and Act. London, (1967). 1st Eng ed. Dj (sl edgeworn, sm closed tear). *Swann**. $46/£29

ELLROY, JAMES. Blood on the Moon. NY: Mysterious, 1984. 1st ed. Fine in NF dj. *Beasley*. $35/£22

ELLROY, JAMES. Clandestine. NY: Avon, 1982. 1st ed. Pb orig. (Top corner creased, edges sl worn.) Wraps. *Murder*. $25/£16

ELLROY, JAMES. Silent Terror. L.A.: Blood & Guts, 1986. 1st hb ed. Ltd ed. One of 350 numbered signed. VF in VF dj. *Murder*. $200/£125

ELLSBERG, EDWARD. The Saga of the 'Jeanette'. NY: Dodd, Mead, 1938. Fine in dj. *Explorer*. $40/£25

ELLSWORTH, HENRY. Washington Irving on the Prairie. NY: American Book Co, 1937. Map. *Dumont*. $45/£28

ELLSWORTH, ROBERT HATFIELD. Chinese Furniture: Hardwood Examples of the Ming and Early Ch'ing Dynasties. NY, (1971). 1st ed. Folio. Slipcase. *Swann**. $690/£431

ELLWANGER, GEORGE H. In Gold and Silver. NY: D. Appleton, 1892. 1st ed. One of 200 lg paper copies. Grn cl, paper spine label. (Label chipped), else VG. *Pacific**. $69/£43

ELLWANGER, GEORGE H. The Pleasures of the Table. NY: Doubleday, Page, 1902. 1st ed. Teg. NF. *Pacific**. $109/£68

ELMAN, ROBERT. The Great American Shooting Prints. NY, 1972. One of 450 specially bound, signed. Obl folio. 3/4 leather (sl worn). Slipcase. *Oinonen**. $190/£119

ELMAN, ROBERT. The Great American Sporting Prints. NY, 1972. One of 450 specially bound, signed. This copy marked 'H/C.' Obl folio. 72 color plts. Envelope w/4 add'l color plts laid in. 1/2 leather. Cl slipcase. *Swann**. $69/£43

ELMENDORF, DWIGHT L. A Camera Crusade Through the Holy Land. NY: Scribner, 1912. 1st ed. 100 plts. Teg. (Leaf torn, repaired; edges rubbed), o/w VG. *Worldwide*. $45/£28

Elmer Adler in the World of Books. Princeton Univ, 1964. One of 2100. *Dawson*. $15/£9

ELMORE, F. H. Ethnobotany of the Navajo. Albuquerque: Univ of NM, 1944. 1st ed. VG in wraps. *Mikesh*. $45/£28

ELPHINSTONE, MOUNTSTUART. The History of India: The Hindu and Mahometan Periods. London, 1866. 5th ed. xxxii,90pp; fldg map (torn, creased w/o loss). Dec eps. Early leather (sl wormed, corners rubbed w/loss, spine ends torn; sl browned, pencil mks.) *Edwards*. $45/£28

ELSENSOHN, M. ALFREDA. Pioneer Days in Idaho County. Caldwell, ID: Caxton Ptrs, 1947-1951. 1st ed. Vol 1 signed. 2 vols. VG set. *Labordo*. $150/£94

ELSTON, ROY. The Traveller's Handbook for Palestine and Syria. Harry Charles Luke (ed). London: Marshall, 1929. 2nd ed. 10 maps (1 lg fldg in rear pocket). (Lacks frontis map; sl rubbed), o/w VG. *Worldwide*. $35/£22

ELTON, C. I. and M. A. The Great Book Collectors. Kegan Paul, 1893. 1st ed. 10 plts. Unopened. Rose cl. (Bkpl; spine faded.) *Moss*. $48/£30

ELTON, C. I. and M. A. The Great Book-Collectors. London: Kegan Paul, Trench, Trubner, 1893. 1st ed. Frontis, viii,228pp; 9 plts. Red cl (sl faded, rubbed, bumped), gilt. *Maggs*. $38/£24

ELTON, OLIVER. C. E. Montague, a Memoir. London: C&W, 1929. 1st ed. Port. Gilt dk grn cl. VG. *Reese*. $30/£19

ELUARD, PAUL. Misfortunes of the Immortals. Hugh Chisholm (trans). (NY): Black Sun, (1943). New ed. One of 610. Illus bds. (Inscrip, edges browned; spine tip discolored, sm chip), else Nice. *Turtle Island*. $450/£281

ELVILLE, E. M. Paperweights. Country Life, 1957. Color frontis; 16 plts. (Stamp to foot of prelims.) Dj. *Hollett*. $40/£25

ELVIN, LAURENCE. Family Enterprise. Lincoln: Privately ptd, 1986. Ltd to 1000. VG in dj. *Hollett*. $56/£35

ELVIN, LAURENCE. Pipes and Actions. Lincoln: The Author, 1995. 1st ed. Ltd to 900. VG in dj. *Hollett*. $46/£29

ELWES, HENRY JOHN and AUGUSTINE HENRY. The Trees of Great Britain and Ireland. Edinburgh: Privately ptd, 1906-1913. 15 parts in 7 vols. Folio. 419 plts (5 color). (Sl spotted.) Orig wrappers, in cl-backed portfolios as issued, ties. *Sotheby's**. $920/£575

ELWOOD, LOUIE BUTLER. Queen Calafia's Land: An Historical Sketch of California. SF: Grabhorn, 1940. 1st ed. One of 325. Marbled bds, tan sheepskin backstrip. Fine. *Harrington*. $125/£78

ELY, ALFRED et al (eds). North American Big Game. NY: Scribner, 1939. 1st ed. Ltd to 3000. VG (name; sm repair to spine head) in VG dj (sm pieces torn from rear edge, 1/4-inch piece torn from spine). *Backman*. $400/£250

ELY, SIMS. The Lost Dutchman Mine. NY, 1953. Good in dj (chipped). *Dumont*. $35/£22

EMANUEL, F. The Illustrators of Montmartre. A. Single, 1904. Color frontis, 19 plts. Good in dec cl. *Moss*. $14/£9

EMANUEL, HARRY. Diamonds and Precious Stones. London: John Camden Hotten, 1867. 2nd ed. Blue cl, gilt. (Fr hinge starting; spine ends chipped), else VG. *Pacific**. $46/£29

EMANUEL, WALTER. A Dog Day. NY: E.P. Dutton, (1919). 1st ed. Cecil Aldin (illus). Cl-backed pict bds. (Names; corners rubbed), else VG. *Pacific**. $81/£51

EMANUEL, WALTER. A Dog Day. London: Heinemann, 1904. New cheap ed. 28 plts. Ptd bds (backstrip, corners torn). *Petersfield*. $32/£20

EMBREY, ALVIN T. History of Fredericksburg, Virginia. Richmond: Old Dominion, 1937. Signed, inscribed. Good in dj (worn). *Brown*. $30/£19

EMECHETA, BUCHI. Second Class Citizen. Alison & Busby, 1974. 1st ed. Signed. (Lower edges sl bruised), else Fine in dj. *Any Amount*. $40/£25

EMERSON, A. E. and E. FISH. Termite City. Chicago: Rand McNally, 1937. 1st ed. Dec eps. NF in Good+ dj. *Mikesh*. $30/£19

EMERSON, EDWARD WALDO. Emerson in Concord. Boston/NY: Houghton Mifflin, 1889. 1st ed thus. Frontis, 266pp. Teg. Grn cl. VG. *Lucas*. $45/£28

EMERSON, L. W. Cimarron Bend. Macaulay, 1936. 1st ed. VG in pict dj (chipped). *Fine Books*. $35/£22

EMERSON, RALPH WALDO and ARTHUR CLOUGH. Emerson-Clough Letters. Howard F. Lowry and Ralph L. Rusk (eds). Cleveland: Rowfant Club, 1934. 1st ed. One of 165 numbered. Marbled bds, paper label. NF (bkpl, inscrip) in unptd plain wrapper (chipped). BAL 5331. *Reese*. $85/£53

EMERSON, RALPH WALDO. The Complete Works of.... Boston, (1903-1904). Concord ed. 12 vols. 8x5 inches. Teg. 3/4 gilt-stamped burgundy leather. (Extrems sl frayed.) *King*. $695/£434

EMERSON, RALPH WALDO. The Essays. LEC, 1934. Ltd to 1500 numbered, signed by John Henry Nash (designer). Fine in slipcase. *Swann**. $80/£50

EMERSON, RALPH WALDO. Letters and Social Aims. Boston: James R. Osgood, 1876. 1st ed, 1st ptg. Grn cl, gilt. (Sigs; fr cvr lt flecked, sm pinhole to joint), o/w Very Nice. *Reese*. $100/£63

EMERSON, RALPH WALDO. Letters and Social Aims. Boston: James R. Osgood, 1876. 1st ed, 1st ptg, w/the error 'inviolate' on the 5th line of p308. Grn cl, beveled. NF (sl soiled). *Sumner & Stillman*. $125/£78

EMERSON, RALPH WALDO. The Method of Nature. Boston: Samuel G. Simpkins, 1841. 1st ed. Nice (lt aged, 1st pg sl chipped; lacks orig ptd wrappers and spine stitching); laid into marbled paper folder. BAL 5190. *Baltimore**. $40/£25

EMERSON, RALPH WALDO. The Poems of Ralph Waldo Emerson. LEC, 1945. Ltd to 1500 numbered, signed by Richard and Doris Beer (illus). Fine in slipcase. *Swann**. $69/£43

EMERSON, RALPH WALDO. Poems. Boston, 1847. 1st Amer ed. Jan 1, 1847 cat. Orig glazed yellow bds (rebacked w/cl & new ptd label; stained). VG. BAL 5211. *M & S*. $250/£156

EMERSON, RALPH WALDO. Society and Solitude. Boston: Fields, Osgood, 1870. 1st ed, 1st ptg. Terra cotta cl, gilt. NF. BAL 5260. *Macdonnell*. $60/£38

EMERSON, RALPH WALDO. Tantalus. Canton, PA: Kirgate, 1903. 1st Amer ed. Pub's signed presentation inscription. One of 90. Vellum spine. (Lt edgeworn.) BAL 5313. *Dermont*. $75/£47

EMERSON, WILLIAM K. Chevrons: Illustrated History and Catalog of U.S. Army Insignia. Washington: Smithsonian Inst, 1983. 1st ed. Tan cl. Fine in NF dj. *Harrington*. $60/£38

EMERY, WALTER B. Egypt in Nubia. London: Hutchinson, (1965). 33 plts (1 color). (Sig.) Dj. *Archaeologia*. $35/£22

EMERY, WALTER B. Nubian Treasure. London: Methuen, 1948. 48 plts. Emb cl, gilt. (Owner stamp.) *Archaeologia*. $65/£41

EMMETT, CHRIS. In the Path of Events. Waco: Jones & Morrison, 1959. VG in dj (sl worn). *Dumont*. $45/£28

EMMETT, CHRIS. Shanghai Pierce, a Fair Likeness. Norman, 1953. 1st ed. (Sl edgeworn), o/w Fine in dj (sl edgeworn). *Baade*. $75/£47

EMORY, FREDERIC. Queen Anne's County, Maryland: Its Early History and Development. Balt: MD Hist Soc, 1950. 1st ed. Frontis photo. Red cl, gilt. (Ink presentation.) Text Clean, cvrs VG. *Baltimore**. $35/£22

EMORY, WILLIAM H. Notes of a Military Reconnoissance, from Fort Leavenworth, in Missouri, to San Diego, in California, Including Part of the Arkansas, Del Norte, and Gila Rivers. Washington: Wendell & Van Benthuysen, 1848. House Ex Doc No 41. 614pp; 64 litho/engr plts, 3 battle-plans, 2 fldg maps. Lg fldg map of AR Rio del Norte and Rio Gila supplied in this copy, set loose in a specially made (mod) pocket of matching black cl which is attached to the outside of the rear cvr. Orig black cl, paper spine label. (This copy lacks map of the Territory of NM; lg map w/few sm tears, separately sl along 1 paper joint; 1 text leaf loose but present, bkpl, due date sticker affixed to rep, ink # on back of tp bleeding through, lacks fep; new rear pastedown; spine, joints repaired, label chipped, rubbed), else VG +. Howes E145. *Pacific**. $920/£575

EMORY, WILLIAM H. Notes of a Military Reconnoissance, from Fort Leavenworth, in Missouri, to Sand Diego, in California. Washington: Wendell & Van Benthuysen, 1848. 614pp; 64 plts, 6 maps (3 fldg). Orig full leather (worn, hinges repaired). Internally VG (sl foxed, maps sl split). *Dumont*. $750/£469

EMORY, WILLIAM H. Report on the United States and Mexican Boundary Survey.... Washington: A.O.P. Nicholson, 1857-1859. 1st Senate ed. 2 parts in 3 vols. Thick 4to. xvi,258,viii,174; 270,78; (viii),62,33,35,85,iipp; 77 b/w plts, 2 fldg engr charts, 37 hand-colored litho plts, 266 b/w litho plts, 1 full-pg, 2 lg fldg engr maps (1 w/hand-colored highlights). Recent plain soft calf (rather inappropriate new binding), blue cl gilt-lettered spine labels. (Lt scattered aging, sl foxing.) Howes E1436. *Baltimore**. $2,100/£1,313

EMPSON, WILLIAM. Collected Poems. C&W, 1955. 1st ed. Fine (spine foot, corner bumped) in dj (nicked, sl creased, rubbed, dusty, sl torn, spine, edges sl dknd). *Ulysses*. $88/£55

EMPSON, WILLIAM. Letter IV. Cambridge: W. Heffer & Sons, 1929. 1st Eng ed, 1st bk. VG in wrappers (mkd, dusty, rear cvr sl soiled). *Ulysses*. $136/£85

EMPSON, WILLIAM. Seven Types of Ambiguity. London: C&W, 1930. 1st Eng ed. Errata slip tipped in. VG (fep partly browned, edges sl spotted; spine ends, 2 corners sl bumped) in dj (rubbed, nicked, edges creased, spine sl dknd). *Ulysses*. $104/£65

EMPSON, WILLIAM. Using Biography. London: C&W, 1984. 1st ed. VG in dj. *Virgo*. $24/£15

Encyclopaedia Britannica. Cambridge: CUP, 1911. 11th ed. 28 vols. Aeg. Flexible maroon morocco, gilt. (Spines sunned), else VG. *Pacific**. $403/£252

Encyclopaedia Britannica; or, A Dictionary of Arts and Sciences, Compiled Upon a New Plan. London, n.d. Facs rpt of Edinburgh 1771 ed. (Lt foxing.) Orig buckram. *Edwards*. $160/£100

Encyclopedia of World Art. NY: McGraw Hill, 1959-1968. 15 vols. *Metropolitan**. $258/£161

ENDE, MICHAEL. The Neverending Story. NY: Doubleday, 1983. 1st US ed. 5 3/4 x 8 1/2. 396pp. VG in dj. *Cattermole*. $65/£41

ENDICOTT, WENDELL. Adventures with Rod and Harpoon Along the Florida Keys. NY: Stokes, 1925. 1st ed. Teg. Grn cl. VF in VG dj. *Bowman*. $120/£75

Endless Amusement: A Collection of Nearly 400 Entertaining Experiments.... Phila: Lea & Blanchard, 1847. From the 7th London ed. 200pp + ads. Orig cl. (Worn, rubbed, parts of spine gone), else Good. *Brown*. $65/£41

Endymion. (By Benjamin Disraeli.) Dawson Bros, 1880. 1st Canadian ed. Good (notes; spine bumped, chipped). *Tiger*. $56/£35

ENGBECK, JOSEPH H., JR. State Parks of California from 1864 to the Present. (Portlaand: Charles H. Belding, 1980.) Ltd to 1000 signed by Engbeck & Philip Hyde (photos). Brn/black paper-cvrd bds, gilt spine. Fine in pict dj. *Pacific**. $75/£47

ENGEL, CLAIRE ELIANE. Mont Blanc. Allen & Unwin, 1965. 1st Eng ed. VG in dj (spine, edges sl browned). *Hollett*. $56/£35

ENGEL, CLAIRE ELIANE. Mountaineering in the Alps. Allen & Unwin, 1971. Rev, enlgd ed. 24 plts. VG in dj (edges sl worn). *Hollett*. $48/£30

ENGELBACH, WILLIAM. Endocrine Medicine. Springfield: Thomas, 1932. 1st ed. 3 vols + index & bibliography vol. Pebbled cl. Fine set. *Glaser*. $100/£63

ENGLAND, GEORGE ALLAN. The Air Trust. St. Louis: Phil Wagner, (1915). 1st ed. Ptd, typed presentation slip signed in ink tipped to fep. 6 b/w plts by John Sloan. Grn cl, gilt. (Lower hinge cracked, lib stamp fep verso, ink # recto; sl worn, spine sl turned, fr cvr sl spotted.) *Baltimore**. $60/£38

England, as Seen by an American Banker.... (By C. B. Patten.) Boston: Lothrop, 1885. 1st ed. 2ff., 345pp. *Marlborough*. $240/£150

ENGLEFIELD, HENRY C. A Description of the Principal Picturesque Beauties, Antiquities, and Geological Phenomena, of the Isle of Wight. London: Ptd by William Bulmer, 1816. Royal 4to. vi,238pp + (iv) index + (vii-xxvii); 46 engr plts incl 8 dbl-pg, 1 dbl-pg hand-colored aquatint, 3 fldg maps (1 color). (Lacks frontisport, 9 marginal lib ink stamps mainly to prelims, 1 map w/ink stamp towards margin, 4 plts w/marginal ink stamps, sl browned, sm stain fr pastedown.) Contemp morocco (sympathetically rebacked w/much of orig spine laid down, 1 raised band built up; sl worn). *Edwards*. $1,040/£650

ENGLEHARDT, ALEXANDER PLATONOVICH. A Russian Province of the North. Westminster: Archibald Constable, 1899. xix,356pp; 2 fldg maps. Dec cl (soiled). VG. *High Latitude*. $195/£122

ENGLEHARDT, ZEPHYRIN. The Franciscans in California. Harbor Springs, MI: Holy Childhood Indian School, 1897. 1st ed. (4),xvi,516,(1)pp. (Spine repaired, joints, corners worn), else VG. Howes E152. *Pacific**. $115/£72

ENGLEHARDT, ZEPHYRIN. The Missions and Missionaries of California. SF: James H. Barry, 1929, 1912-1916. 5 vols incl index. Vol 1 is 2nd ed, rest are 1st eds. (Sl shelfworn), else NF. Howes E154. *Pacific**. $259/£162

ENGLEHARDT, ZEPHYRIN. The Missions and Missionaries of California. Santa Barbara, CA: Mission Santa Barbara, 1929-1930. 2nd ed. 2 vols. NF set. Howes E154. *Labordo*. $100/£63

English Dance of Death, from the Designs of Thomas Rowlandson, with Metrical Illustrations, by the Author of 'Doctor Syntax.' (By William Combe.) London: R. Ackermann, 1815-1816. 1st ed. 2 vols. 9.25x5.5. Pict engr tp, 72 hand-colored aquatint plts; later tissue guards bound-in. Teg. Gilt-ruled, stamped tan calf (expertly rebacked w/orig panels, morocco spine labels laid on). Bound by Tout, restored by J. Macdonald. (Bkpls; corners professionally repaired), else VG. *Pacific**. $920/£575

English Institute Annual, 1940. NY: Columbia Univ, 1941. 1st US ed. Fine in dj (sl nicked, sl creased, spine sl dknd). *Ulysses.* $88/£55

ENGLISH, G. Getting Acquainted with Minerals. Rochester: Mineralogical Pub, c1934. 1st ed, 1st ptg. VG (spine faded). *Blake.* $75/£47

ENGLISH, ISOBEL. Every Eye. Andre Deutsch, 1956. 1st ed. Inscribed presentation. VG (prelims, edges, eps spotted, feps lt browned; sl cocked, spine ends, corners sl bumped) in dj (worn). *Ulysses.* $40/£25

ENGSTROM, J. ERIC. Coins in Shakespeare. NH: Dartmouth College, 1964. VG in glassine dj. *Hollett.* $56/£35

ENNIS, GEORGE PEARSE. Making a Water Colour. London: The Studio Ltd, 1933. 1st ed. 10 tipped-in b/w photos. Illus woodblock prt bds, cl spine. NF. *Turtle Island.* $60/£38

ENOCK, C. REGINALD. Farthest West: Life and Travel in the United States. London: John Long, 1910. 1st ed. Map. (Sl worn.) *Mott.* $20/£13

ENRIGHT, D. J. Memoirs of a Mendicant Professor. C&W, 1969. 1st Eng ed. NF (spine ends sl bumped) in dj (sl dusty, creased, spine sl dknd). *Ulysses.* $56/£35

ENRIGHT, D. J. Unlawful Assembly. London: C&W/Hogarth, 1968. 1st ed. NF (sig) in NF dj. *Agvent.* $45/£28

ENRIGHT, ELIZABETH. Thimble Summer. Rinehart, 1938. 1st ed. 124pp. Good (ex-lib; cvr worn w/1/4-inch hole in spine, fr hinge partly shaken). *Price.* $22/£14

ENSLOW, ELLA and ALVIN HARLOW. Schoolhouse in the Foothills. NY: S&S, 1937. 5th ptg. VG in dj (edge torn). *Perier.* $15/£9

ENTICK, JOHN. The General History of the Late War. London: For Edward Dilly, 1763. 1st ed. 5 vols. Frontisports, 44 copper plts. Early full gilt-ruled calf. (Feps lt browned; extrems rubbed, loss to spine ends, joints cracked.) *Edwards.* $512/£320

ENTICK, JOHN. A New Naval History; or, Compleat View of the British Marine. London, 1757. Folio. Map, 5 plts. Contemp sheep (worn, fr cvr loose; sl worming lower margin several ll). *Swann**. $258/£161

Eothen. (By A. W. Kinglake.) John Ollivier, 1845. 3rd ed. Half-title present, fldg color litho frontis, xiii,(i),424pp; 1 color litho plt. Yellow chalked eps. Orig vertical ribbed grn cl (sm split head of rear joint, corners sl bumped), gilt. Good (foxed throughout, name; fr hinge split but firm). *Blackwell's.* $152/£95

Eothen. (By A. W. Kinglake.) Longman, Brown, Green & Longmans, 1852. New ed. 256pp. Contemp dk grn 1/2 calf, marbled bds, gilt, maroon leather label. Good. *Sotheran.* $77/£48

EPICTETUS. The Discourses. P. E. Matheson (trans). Berne: LEC, 1966. One of 1500. Signed by Hans Erni (illus). Gilt-dec cl, morocco spine label. Fine in glassine, slipcase. *Pacific**. $75/£47

Epicure in China: Eight Complete Chinese Epicurean Dinners. SF: Colt, (1939). 1st ptg. Orange bds, black cl backstrip. VG (worn, spotted). *Harrington.* $45/£28

Epicure in Mexico. (SF): Colt, 1940. 1st ed. One of 1000 (unstated). Grn bds, yellow cl backstrip. Fine. *Harrington.* $45/£28

EPICURUS. The Extant Works of Epicurus. LEC, 1947. Ltd to 1500 numbered, signed by Bruce Rogers (designer). Fine in slipcase. *Swann**. $230/£144

EPSTEIN, BEN. The Mickey Mantle Story. (As told by Mickey Mantle.) Holt, 1953. Later ptg. VG+ in VG dj. *Plapinger.* $185/£116

EPSTEIN, BEN. Yogi Berra: The Muscle Man. Barnes, 1951. 1st ed. VG. *Plapinger.* $125/£78

EPSTEIN, DANIEL MARK. No Vacancies in Hell: Poems. NY: Liveright, (1973). 1st ed, 1st bk. Presentation copy inscribed. Fine in dj. *Blue Mountain.* $35/£22

EPSTEIN, LESLIE. Goldkorn Tales. NY: E.P. Dutton, (1985). 1st ed. As New in dj. *Bernard.* $15/£9

EPSTEIN, LESLIE. P. D. Kimerakov. Boston/Toronto: Little, Brown, (1975). 1st ed, 1st bk. Advance rev copy w/slip laid in. Fine in dj. *Bernard.* $35/£22

Equality: A History of Lithconia. Phila: Prime, (1947). 1st ed thus. One of 500. Fine in NF dj. *Other Worlds.* $75/£47

Equine F.F.Vs. A Study of the Evidence for the English Horses Imported into Virginia Before the Revolution. (By Fairfax Harrison.) Richmond: Privately ptd at Old Dominion Press, 1928. Uncut. Paper spine label. (Sl worn.) *Oinonen**. $100/£63

ERASMUS, DESIDERIUS. The Colloquies, of Familiar Discourses of.... H. M. Gent (trans). London: H. Brome et al, 1671. 1st ed thus. Frontis port, (8),555+(2)ad pp. Period calf, later morocco spine label. (New eps, bkpl), else VG. *Pacific**. $230/£144

ERASMUS, DESIDERIUS. The Praise of Folly. LEC, 1943. Ltd to 1500 numbered, signed by Lynd Ward (illus). Fine in slipcase. *Swann**. $230/£144

ERASMUS, DESIDERIUS. Witt Against Wisdom, or a Panegyrick upon Folly. Oxford: L. Litchfield, 1683. 1st ed thus. (18),(6),157+(1)ad pg. Calf. (New eps, lacks prelims to tp, contemp notes), else VG. *Pacific**. $196/£123

ERCKER, LAZARUS. Treatise on Ores and Assaying. A. Sisco and C. Smith (trans). Univ of Chicago, c1951. VG. *Blake.* $75/£47

ERDOES, RICHARD. Saloons of the Old West. NY: Knopf, 1979. 1st ed. Fine in dj. *Labordo.* $30/£19

ERDRICH, LOUISE. The Beet Queen. Henry Holt, (1986). 1st ed. Signed. Fine in Fine dj. *Authors Of The West.* $60/£38

ERICHSEN, H. (ed). The London Medical Student and Other Comicalities. Detroit, MI, 1885. 207pp (2 sm ink stamps, sm water stain margin last few pp). Blind stamped cl (spine, corners worn; rear inner hinge cracked). *Whitehart.* $64/£40

ERICHSEN, JOHN ERIC. The Science and Art of Surgery. Phila: Henry C. Lea, 1869. 5th rev ed. xxxi,1228pp. Good (spine, cvr worn, faded). *Bookcell.* $40/£25

ERICKSON, ERIK HOMBURGER. Observations on the Yurok: Childhood and World Image. Berkeley: Univ of CA, 1943. 1st ed. (Inscrip), o/w Fine in wraps. *Beasley.* $75/£47

ERICKSON, RICA. The Drummonds of Hawthornden. Western Australia: Lamb Paterson, 1969. 1st ed. NF in dj. *Archer.* $35/£22

Erie, a Guide to the City and County. Phila, 1938. 1st ed. Good (lacks pocket map) in dj (chipped, stuck to back cvr). *Bohling.* $20/£13

ERNEST, EDWARD. Animated Animals. Akron, OH: Saalfield, 1943. 26x20 cm. Julian Wehr (engineer). 4pp tab-operated mechanicals. Pict bds. VG in Good dj. *Bookfinders.* $200/£125

ERNEST, EDWARD. The Animated Circus Book. NY: G&D, (1943). Sq 8vo. 4 moveables by Julian Wehr. Spiral-bound pict bds. VG in dj (lt torn, frayed). *Davidson.* $300/£188

ERNST, DONNA B. Sundance, My Uncle. College Station, TX: The Early West, (1992). 1st ed. One of 1500. Fine in dj. *Lien.* $22/£14

ERNST, MORRIS L. The Best Is Yet.... NY: Harper, (1945). 1st ed. Fine in NF dj (sm tears). *Between The Covers.* $50/£31

ERRINGTON, P. L. Muskrats and Marsh Management. Harrisburg, 1961. Frontis. Buckram (lt soiled; eps foxed, pp tanned). Dj (worn, torn, lacks pieces). *Sutton*. $32/£20

ERSKINE, FIRTH. Naked Murder. Macaulay, 1933. 1st ed, 1st bk. (Sl worn), else NF in dj (edges sl chipped, writing on rear cvr, rear inside flap). *Murder*. $50/£31

ERSKINE, GLADYS S. Broncho Charlie, a Saga of the Saddle. NY, (1934). 1st ed. *Heinoldt*. $35/£22

ERSKINE, JOHN (ed). Books and Habits from the Lectures of Lafcadio Hearn. London, 1922. 1st ed. NF (name). *Polyanthos*. $35/£22

ERSKINE, JOHN E. Journal of a Cruise Among the Islands of the Western Pacific.... London: John Murray, 1853. 1st ed. vi,2,errata,488pp; fldg map, 7 plts (4 color). 1/2 brn calf, marbled bds (rubbed), gilt, black label. *Adelson*. $475/£297

ERSKINE, MARGARET. The House in Belmont Square. London: Hodder & Stoughton, 1963. 1st ed. (Fore-edge lt stained), o/w Fine in dj. *Mordida*. $65/£41

ERSKINE, MICHAEL. The Diary of Michael Erskine. J. Evetts Haley (ed). Midland, TX: Nita Stewart Haley Memorial Lib, (1979). 1st ed. Signed. VG. *Lien*. $75/£47

ERSKINE, THOMAS. The Speeches of the Hon. Thomas Erskine...on Subjects Connected with the Liberty of the Press.... James Ridgway (ed). NY: Eastburn, Kirk, 1813. 1st ed. 2 vols. 602; 604pp (foxed). Later paper-cvrd bds, cl spines. *M & S*. $250/£156

ERVINE, ST. JOHN G. The Magnanimous Lover. Dublin: Maunsel, 1912. 1st ed. (Orig stitching perished, not present), o/w Fine in ptd wrappers. *Maggs*. $48/£30

ERWIN, ALLEN A. The Southwest of John H. Slaughter, 1841-1922. Glendale: A.H. Clark, 1965. 1st ed. Frontis, fldg map. Red cl. Dj. *Dawson*. $100/£63

ERWIN, BETTY K. Aggie, Maggie, and Tish. Boston: Little Brown, 1965. 1st ed. Paul Kennedy (illus). 154pp. VG in VG dj (edgeworn). *Price*. $25/£16

ESCOFFIER, A. A Guide to Modern Cookery. Heinemann, 1930. Port. Orig cl (rubbed, worn, rebacked retaining orig backstrip). *Cox*. $32/£20

ESDAILE, A. A List of English Tales and Prose Romances Printed before 1740. Bibliographical Soc, 1912. Good in linen-backed bds. *Moss*. $144/£90

ESDAILE, A. A Student's Manual of Bibliography. Allen & Unwin, 1931. 1st ed. 7 leaves of bk paper samples. VG. *Moss*. $48/£30

ESHBACH, LLOYD ARTHUR (ed). Of Worlds Beyond. Reading: Fantasy, 1947. 1st ed. NF in NF dj (2 sm closed tears, sm chip to bottom of rear panel). *Other Worlds*. $100/£63

ESKEW, GARNETT LAIDLAW. The Pageant of the Packets. NY, (1929). 1st ed. VG in dj (worn, torn). *King*. $75/£47

ESPINOSA Y TELLO, JOSE. A Spanish Voyage to Vancouver and the North-West Coast of America. Cecil Jane (trans). London: Argonaut, 1930. One of 525. 6 plts (incl fldg frontis), fldg map. Unopened. 1/2 vellum, gilt. (Lt soiled; 1 corner, lower edge fr cvr bumped), else VG. Internally Fine. *Pacific**. $150/£94

ESPINOSA, CARMEN. Shawls, Crimolines, Filigree. El Paso: TX Western, 1970. 1st ed. Fine in dj. *Labordo*. $30/£19

ESPINOSA, J. MANUEL. First Expedition of Vargas into New Mexico, 1692. Albuquerque: Univ of NM, 1940. Frontis. (Few pp foxed; spine faded), else VG. *Dumont*. $150/£94

ESPINOSA, JOSE E. Saints in the Valleys. Albuquerque: Univ of NM, 1960. Orig ed. Fine in dj. *Turtle Island*. $60/£38

ESPINOSA, JOSE E. Saints in the Valleys. Albuquerque: Univ of NM, 1967. 1st rev ed. VG in dj. *Dumont*. $40/£25

ESQUEMELING, JOHN. The Buccaneers of America. London: Routledge, 1911. Blue/grn cl. NF. *American Booksellers*. $45/£28

ESQUEMELING, JOHN. The Buccaneers of America; or, The Pirates of Panama. NY: Frederick A. Stokes, (1914). 1st ed thus. George Alfred Williams (illus). 8 3/4 x 6. Red cl, pict cvr label. (Spine sl dull, sm bumps lower corners), else VG. *Pacific**. $52/£33

ESQUIVEL, LAURA. Like Water for Chocolate. NY: Doubleday, 1989. Advance reading copy. Fine in dec wrappers. *Smith*. $85/£53

ESQUIVEL, LAURA. Like Water for Chocolate. NY: Doubleday, 1992. 1st Amer ed. Fine in dj. *Pacific**. $81/£51

Essay on the Genius of George Cruikshank. (By William Makepeace Thackeray.) (London): Henry Hooper, 1840. 1st ed. Teg. Gilt-ruled calf, morocco spine labels, raised bands; bound by Worsfold. (Old bits of tape to frontis verso, extrems of few pp, incl 1 plt; fr joint starting), else VG. *Pacific**. $92/£58

Essay on the Natural History of Guiana.... (By Edward Bancroft.) London: T. Becket & P.A. De Hondt, 1769. 1st ed. 402pp, contents leaf, 2 ll pub's ads. Later leather-backed cl. (Ms notes blanks, margins.) *Kane**. $200/£125

ESSE, JAMES. (Pseud of James Stephens.) Hunger. Dublin: Candle Press, 1918. 1st ed. (Lt sunned), else Fine in ptd wrappers. *Reese*. $85/£53

ESSICK, ROBERT N. William Blake, Printmaker. Princeton: Princeton Univ, (1980). 1st ed. 236 b/w plts. Lt blue buckram, gilt. Fine in NF dj. *Baltimore**. $70/£44

ESTABROOK, EMMA FRANKLIN. Givers of Life. Albuquerque: Univ of NM, 1931. Inscribed. (Bkpl; hinges repaired, lib stamp), else VG. *Dumont*. $75/£47

Estelle Doheny Collection. (Sale catalog.) NY: Christie's, 1987-89. 7 vols, incl 'Index and Price Lists.' 3 vols w/price lists laid in. (Lt worn.) *Oinonen**. $180/£113

ESTERGREEN, MARION. The Real Kit Carson. Taos, NM: (Kit Carson Memorial Foundation), 1955. 1st ed. Cvr port. (Lt dampstain to corner of last few ll), else Fine in grn pict wrappers (edges faded). *Argonaut*. $20/£13

ESTES, ELEANOR. The Tunnel of Hugsy Good. HB, 1972. 1st ed. Edward Ardizzone (illus). 244pp. Fine in Fine dj. *Price*. $45/£28

ESTLEMAN, LOREN. Bloody Season. NY: Bantam, (1988). 1st ed. Signed. Fine in Fine dj. *Book Market*. $25/£16

ETCHISON, DENNIS (ed). Lord John Ten: A Celebration. Northridge: Lord John, 1988. 1st ed. One of 250. Signed by all contributors. 1/4 black cl, dec bds. Fine. *Pacific**. $127/£79

ETON, W. A Survey of the Turkish Empire.... London, 1799. 2nd ed. Orig bds (needs rebinding). Cl fldg case. *Swann**. $172/£108

ETS, MARIE HALL. My Dog Rinty. NY: Viking, 1946. 1st ed. 7.5x9.5. A. & A. Alland (illus). 32pp. Good (ex-lib). *Cattermole*. $75/£47

ETTINGHAUSEN, MAURICE L. Rare Books and Royal Collectors: Memoirs of an Antiquarian Bookseller. NY: S&S, 1966. 1st ed. Brn cl. Fine in NF dj. *Harrington*. $60/£38

EURIPIDES. Medea, Hippolytus, The Bacchae. London: LEC, 1967. One of 1500. Signed by Michael Ayrton (illus). 1/2 cl. Fine in glassine, slipcase. *Pacific**. $35/£22

EURIPIDES. Medea, Hippolytus, the Bacchae. Philip Vellacott (trans). London: LEC, 1967. One of 1500 ptd. Signed by Michael Ayrton (illus). 1/2 cl. Fine in glassine, slipcase (sl sunned). *Pacific**. $52/£33

EURIPIDES. Three Plays of Euripides: Medea, Hippolytus and the Bacchae. LEC, 1967. Ltd to 1500 numbered, signed by Michael Ayrton (illus). Fine in slipcase. *Swann**. $46/£29

EUSTIS, CELESTINE. Cooking in Old Creole Days. Derrydale, 1928. Ltd to 500. (Edges worn), else VG. *Perier*. $275/£172

EVANGELISTA, BENNY. The Oldest History of the World. (1926). 1st ed. Port. (Cvrs soiled, rubbed.) Wraps. *King*. $50/£31

EVANS, ARTHUR G. Collectors Guide to Rollei Cameras. Grantsburg, WI: Centennial Photo Service, 1986. Fine in dj. Cahan. $40/£25

EVANS, C. S. Cinderella. London: Heinemann, (1919). 1st ed. 4to. Mtd color frontis by Arthur Rackham. Orange/black bds w/silhouette. (Lt edgeworn.) Gray dj (sl edgeworn). Reisler. $335/£209

EVANS, C. S. Cinderella. London: Heinemann, (1919). 1st Rackham ed. One of 300 ptd on Japanese vellum, signed by Arthur Rackham (illus). 4to. Mtd color plt. Teg. Gilt-stamped bds over vellum spine. Fine. Appelfeld. $850/£531

EVANS, C. S. Cinderella. London: Heinemann, 1919. Ltd to 850 'Edition de Luxe' copies signed by Arthur Rackham (illus), w/add'l color plt. This copy one of 525 on hand-made paper. (Lt spotting.) 1 mtd color plt on white paper. Teg. Cl-backed pict paper-cvrd bds (corners lt rubbed). Christie's*. $829/£518

EVANS, C. S. Cinderella. Heinemann, 1919. Signed ltd ed. One of 300 on vellum. 4to. 110pp. Complete w/mtd color frontis, 4 silhouette dwgs w/color (3 dbl-pg), 13 full-pg silhouette dwgs by Arthur Rackham. Teg. Orig vellum-backed bds (sl fingered, base lt damped), gilt. Hollett. $1,040/£650

EVANS, C. S. The Sleeping Beauty. London: Heinemann, (1920). Ltd to 625 on hand-made paper, signed by Arthur Rackham and w/1 extra plt. 1 mtd color plt on white paper. Teg. Orig vellum-backed pict paper-cvrd bds (lt stained, rubbed), gilt. Christie's*. $442/£276

EVANS, CERINA W. Collis Potter Huntington. Mariner's Museum, 1954. 2 vols. (Sl worn, cvrs sl stained.) Rybski. $65/£41

EVANS, CHARLES W. Biographical and Historical Accounts of the Fox, Ellicott, and Evans Families. Buffalo: Baker, Jones, 1882. 281pp(pencil notes) + 5 full-pg charts. Black bds (recased retaining orig spine), gilt. Cullen. $225/£141

EVANS, CHARLES. Eye on Everest. London, 1955. (Edges lt faded.) Dj (sl foxed, chipped w/sl loss). Edwards. $40/£25

EVANS, CHICK, JR. Chick Evans' Golf Book. Chicago: Thos. E. Wilson, (1921). 1st ed. Grn cl, gilt. (Emb stamp; 3 sm spine spots), else NF. Pacific*. $207/£129

EVANS, DONALD. Sonnets from the Patagonian: The Street of Little Hotels. NY: Claire Marie, 1914. 1st ed. Pale blue drab bds (sunned, rubbed), ptd title label. Any Amount. $58/£36

EVANS, ELWOOD and EDMOND S. MEANY (eds). The State of Washington. (WA: World's Fair Commission, 1893.) 1st ed. Frontis, 224pp. (Spine sl dknd), else VF in orig grn pict ptd wrappers. Argonaut. $125/£78

EVANS, ELWOOD. History of the Pacific Northwest: Oregon and Washington. Portland: North Pacific Hist, 1889. 2 vols. 653; 704pp. Red cl (sl stained). VG leather spines. Perier. $495/£309

EVANS, G. P. Big-Game Shooting in Upper Burma. London: Longmans Green, 1912. Lg fldg color map at rear. Grn cl, gilt. VG+ (prelims lt foxed). Bowman. $125/£78

EVANS, GEORGE BIRD (ed). The Best of Nash Buckingham. NY: Winchester, 1973. 1st ed. Brn buckram. Fine in NF color pict dj. Biscotti. $60/£38

EVANS, GEORGE BIRD. The Upland Shooting Life. NY: Knopf, 1971. 1st ed. Brn cl. Color pict dj. Biscotti. $45/£28

EVANS, GEORGE EWART. Ask the Fellow Who Cut the Hay. London, 1956. Thomas Bewick (illus). Fine in dj (sl worn). Petersfield. $26/£16

EVANS, GLEN L. and T. N. CAMPBELL. Indian Baskets. Austin, TX: TX Memorial Museum, 1952. 1st ed. 6 color photo plts. Fine in orig ptd wrappers. Argonaut. $50/£31

EVANS, GWENDOLEN MARY. Turn Again Lane. London: Frederick Warne, 1929. 1st ed. 8vo. 10 full-pg color plts. Cl-backed red-orange bds. VG in full color dj (margins worn, rear cvr mkd). Reisler. $125/£78

EVANS, H. Falconry. Edinburgh: J. Barth, (1978). NF in NF dj. Mikesh. $30/£19

EVANS, J. Letters Written During a Tour Through North Wales, in the Year 1798.... C. & R. Baldwin, 1804. 3rd ed. xix,415pp (lt spotted, margin of leaf a4 repaired, bkpl). Old 1/2 calf (sl rubbed, neatly recased), gilt. Hollett. $224/£140

EVANS, JAMES W. and A. WENDELL KEITH. Autobiography of Samuel S. Hildebrand, the Renowned Missouri 'Bushwacker' and Inconquerable Rob Roy of America. Jefferson City, MO: State Times Book, 1870. 1st ed. Good+ (rubbed, edges worn, esp spine ends). Labordo. $350/£219

EVANS, JOAN and MARY S. SERJEANTSON. English Mediaeval Lapidaries. Early English Text Soc, 1933. 1st ed. Facs frontis. Brn cl (sl damp-faded), gilt. Cox. $24/£15

EVANS, JOAN. A History of Jewellery, 110-1870. Boston: Boston Book & Art, (1970). 2nd ed. 204 photo plts (12 color). Good in dj. Karmiole. $85/£53

EVANS, JOHN. The Ancient Stone Implements, Weapons and Ornaments, of Great Britain. Longmans, Green, 1897. 2nd ed. xviii,747pp. Fine. Hollett. $152/£95

EVANS, KATHERINE. Raphael's Cat. Bobbs-Merrill, 1961. 1st ed. 8.7x11.2. Unpaginated. VG (sm bump to bds) in Good dj (scuffed, 2-inch fr tear). Price. $30/£19

EVANS, LADY. Lustre Pottery. Methuen, 1920. 1st ed. 24 plts. Fore, lower edges uncut. (Feps browned, lib bkpl, spotted; sl rubbed.) Edwards. $144/£90

EVANS, MARI. Jim Flying High. Doubleday, 1979. 1st ed. 4to. Ashley Bryan (illus). Unpaginated. Fine in VG dj (top edge worn, torn). Price. $30/£19

EVANS, MYFANWY. Frances Hodgkins. (London): Penguin Books, (1948). 1st ed. 32 full-pg plts (16 color). Fine in dj, color illus wrappers. Turtle Island. $30/£19

EVANS, NICHOLAS. The Horse Whisperer. (NY): Delacorte, (1995). Advance reading copy. (Sm rubbed spot), else Fine in wrappers w/wraparound band. Between The Covers. $85/£53

EVANS, OLIVER. The Young Mill-Wright and Miller's Guide. Phila: Carey & Lea, 1826. 5th ed. Mod buckram. (Foxed, few repairs; sl rubbed.) Metropolitan*. $86/£54

EVANS, RUTH. The Jungle of Tonza Mara. Macmillan, 1963. 1st ed. 7x10. Lawrence B. Smith (illus). 69pp. Fine in color dj (long closed spine tear). Price. $25/£16

EVANS, SEBASTIAN (trans). The High History of the Holy Graal. J.M. Dent, (1898). Ltd to 200 numbered for England, 50 numbered for America. 2 vols. 2 b/w frontispieces. Teg. 1/2 vellum. VG (tp, frontispieces, eps browned; spines dknd, ends sl rubbed; cvrs dusty). Ulysses. $288/£180

EVANS, WALKER. American Photographs. (NY): MOMA, (1938). 1st ed w/errata slip. One of 5000. 87 plts. (Ex-lib, mkd, rubbed.) King. $65/£41

EVANS, WALKER. American Photographs. NY: MOMA, 1938. 1st ed. 87 photo plts. Ptd spine label. (Eps sl foxed), else Fine in dj (age-toned, missing few sm chips). Cahan. $400/£250

EVANS, WALKER. American Photographs. NY: MOMA, 1938. Correct 1st ed w/spine label, dj w/o photo. 8vo. Wrap-around band. Fine in dj. Smith. $850/£531

EVANS, WALKER. Many Are Called. NY, 1966. (Fore-edge sl soiled.) Ptd wrappers (sl worn). Swann*. $126/£79

EVANS, WALKER. Message from the Interior. NY: Eakins, 1966. 1st ed. Sq folio. 12 full-pg VG b/w photo plts, guards. Ptd label fr cvr. (Bottom edge 1st few ll sl soiled; edges rubbed, paper label stained.) Cahan. $250/£156

EVELYN, JOHN. Diary. William Bray (ed). London, 1879. New ed. 4 vols. Fldg pedigree. Teg, rest uncut. Japon-backed cl bds. (Tps, bd fore-edges spotted; spines sl soiled.) Edwards. $160/£100

EVELYN, JOHN. Directions for The Gardiner at Says-Court, But Which May Be of Use for Other Gardens. Geoffrey Keynes (ed). Nonesuch, 1932. 1st ed. One of 800. Marbled mid grn eps; teg on the rough, rest untrimmed. Marbled mid grn bds, pale grn leather label. Fine in dj. *Blackwell's.* $296/£185

EVELYN, JOHN. The Life of Mrs. Godolphin.... Samuel (Wilberforce) Bishop of Oxford (ed). William Pickering, 1848. Engr frontis (lt spotted), xviii,292pp. Good in contemp 1/2 vellum, marbled sides (rubbed), morocco label. *Cox.* $40/£25

EVELYN, JOHN. Memoirs for My Grand-Son.... Oxford: Nonesuch, 1926. 1st ed thus. Ltd to 1250 numbered. Vellum. (Bkpl), else VG. *King.* $35/£22

EVELYN, JOHN. Silva: or, a Discourse of Forest-Trees.... London, 1729. 5th ed. (ii),xxviii,329,vi,(iv),235,(v)pp; folio. Contemp calf (rebacked, much of spine laid down). Bkpl of James Bateman. *Henly.* $392/£245

EVELYN, JOHN. Silva: or, a Discourse of Forest-Trees.... London, 1776. 1st Hunter ed, 6th ed of bk. (lvi),649,(ix); port, 40 plts, fldg table. Contemp spinkled calf (rebacked), orig label. (Sl spotted at end, some plts offset, extrems worn), o/w Fine. *Henly.* $440/£275

EVELYN, JOHN. Silva: or, A Discourse of Forest-Trees.... York, 1812. 4th ed. 2 vols. Frontisport; 45 engr plts. 1/2 mod smooth calf, marbled bds, gilt. (Bkpl each vol, foxed.) *Kane*.* $300/£188

Evening in Autumn; or, The Useful Amusement, Intended for Children. London: Harvey & Darton, 1821. 1st ed. Sq 12mo. Frontis, 110pp + 2pp ads; 3 full-pg copper engrs. Orig leather spine, gilt, marbled paper on bd. Internally Sound (ink dedication verso of frontis; cvr worn, rubbed). *Hobbyhorse.* $115/£72

EVERARD, H. S. C. Golf in Theory and Practice: Some Hints to Beginners. London: George Bell & Sons, 1898. 3rd ed. Pict red cl, gilt. (Emb stamp, hinges cracking; soiled), else VG. *Pacific*.* $150/£94

EVERARD, H. S. C. A History of the Royal and Ancient Golf Club: St. Andrews from 1754-1900. Edinburgh: William Blackwood, 1907. 1st ed. 10x7.25. Teg. Grn cl, gilt. (Emb stamp; spine ends sl rubbed), else VG. *Pacific*.* $1,265/£791

EVERETT, G. W. The Letters of Junius. London: Faber & Gwyer, 1927. 1st ed. Uncut. VG. *Hollett.* $32/£20

EVERETT, PERCIVAL L. Sader. NY, 1983. 1st Amer ed. NF in NF dj (lt rubbed, sm closed tear). *Warren.* $35/£22

EVERITT, CHARLES. The Adventures of a Treasure Hunter. Little, Brown, 1951. 1st ed. VG in dj (sl defective). *Moss.* $32/£20

EVERITT, CHARLES. The Adventures of a Treasure Hunter: A Rare Bookman in Search of American History. Boston, 1951. VG in dj. *Truepenny.* $45/£28

EVERITT, GRAHAM. English Caricaturists and Graphic Humorists of the Nineteenth Century. London, 1886. 1st ed. xx,427pp. Uncut. Pub's cl. (Rear inner joint broken; shelfworn, foxed, sl soiled.) *Oinonen*.* $80/£50

EVERITT, GRAHAM. English Caricaturists and Graphic Humorists of the Nineteenth Century. London: Swan Sonnenschein, 1886. 1st ed. Teg. Grn dec cl (recased, worn). Good. *Appelfeld.* $125/£78

EVERSON, WILLIAM. Black Hills. N.p.: Didymus Press, (1973). 1st ed. One of 285. 1/2 cl. Fine. *Pacific*.* $92/£58

EVERSON, WILLIAM. Blame It on the Jet Stream! N.p.: Lime Kiln Press, 1978. One of 150. Signed, inscribed to George Houle. 1/2 morocco. Fine. *Pacific*.* $92/£58

EVERSON, WILLIAM. The Blowing of the Seed. New Haven: Henry W. Wenning, 1966. 1st ed. Ltd to 218 signed. Inscribed presentation. VF in leather-backed dec bds. *Bromer.* $300/£188

EVERSON, WILLIAM. In Medias Res: Canto One of an Autobiographical Epic: Dust Shall Be Serpent's Food. SF: Adrian Wilson, 1984. One of 226. Signed by Everson, Tom Killion (woodcuts), & Adrian Wilson. 1/2 turquoise niger, gilt-dec cvr label. Fine in VG slipcase. *Pacific*.* $184/£115

EVERSON, WILLIAM. In the Fictive Wish. (Berkeley): Oyez, (1967). One of 200. Signed. Purple cl, spine label. Fine in plain dj. *Pacific*.* $98/£61

EVERSON, WILLIAM. Mexican Standoff. Emeryville: Lapis Press, 1989. 1st ed. One of 100. Signed by Everson & Robin Eschner (frontis). Orange cl, paper spine label. Fine in glassine dj. *Pacific*.* $46/£29

EVERSON, WILLIAM. On Printing. Peter Koch (ed). SF: Book Club of CA, 1992. 1st ed. One of 400 ptd. Frontisport. Burgundy cl, paper spine. As New in slipcase. *Pacific*.* $127/£79

EVERSON, WILLIAM. Poems of Nineteen Forty Seven. (Reno): Black Rock Press, (1967). One of 180. Signed. Grn cl. Fine. *Pacific*.* $69/£43

EVERSON, WILLIAM. The Poet Is Dead: A Memorial for Robinson Jeffers. Santa Cruz: Good Book Press, 1987. One of 140. Signed. Full crushed brn morocco. Fine in slipcase. *Pacific*.* $109/£68

EVERSON, WILLIAM. River-Root. (Berkeley): Oyez Press, 1976. One of 250. Signed twice, inscribed. 1/2 calf, dec bds, gilt. Fine. *Pacific*.* $104/£65

EVERSON, WILLIAM. Triptych for the Living. (Oakland): Seraphim, 1951. 1st ed. One of 200. Inscribed. 8vo. Mary Fabilli (illus). 26pp. VF in goat vellum w/red cl ties. *Bromer.* $2,850/£1,781

Evolution. NY: Putnam, 1986. 5 dbl-pg pop-ups. Glazed pict bds. VG. *Bookfinders.* $35/£22

EWAN, JOSEPH. Rocky Mountain Naturalists. (N.p.): Univ of Denver, (1950). 1st ed. 9 ports. Brn cl. VG + in dj. *House.* $35/£22

EWART, GAVIN. The Deceptive Grin of the Gravel Porters. London: London Magazine Editions, 1968. 1st Eng ed. Inscribed presentation. VG (spine sl faded, creased) in wrappers. *Ulysses.* $48/£30

EWART, WILFRID. Scots Guard. John Gawsworth (ed). London, 1934. 1st Eng ed. VG (fore-edges foxed; sl mkd, faded) in dj (sl stained, nicked, torn, spine tanned). *Clearwater.* $152/£95

EWART, WILFRID. Scots Guard. T. Armstrong (ed). London: Rich & Cowan, 1934. 1st ed. Brn cl stamped in white. (Fore-edge lt foxed, edges sunned), else VG in dj (chipped, old inner mends). *Reese.* $135/£84

EWBANK, THOMAS. Life in Brazil. NY: Harper, 1856. xvi,17-469pp. (Lib label ep; cl rubbed, spine ends frayed, few sm stains.) *Adelson.* $185/£116

EWELL, R. S. The Making of a Soldier. Richmond: Whittet & Shepperson, 1935. 1st ed. Frontisport, 2 plts. Fine in NF dj. *Chapel Hill.* $80/£50

EWERS, HANNS HEINZ. Blood. NY, 1930. One of 750 numbered. Full-size pict fr cvr label. (Bkpl; lt wear.) *Swann*.* $69/£43

EWERS, HANNS HEINZ. Rider of the Night. NY: John Day, (1932). 1st Amer ed. Fine in NF pict dj. *Between The Covers.* $225/£141

EWERS, JOHN C. Artists of the Old West. NY, 1965. Dj. *Argosy.* $60/£38

EWERS, JOHN C. The Horse in Blackfoot Indian Culture. Washington, 1955. 1st ed. VG (bkpl). *Baade.* $55/£34

EWERS, JOHN C. (ed). Adventures of Zenas Leonard, Fur Trader. Norman: Univ of OK, (1959). 1st ed. Fine in Fine dj. *Book Market.* $40/£25

EWERT, THEODORE. Private Theodore Ewert's Diary of the Black Hills Expedition of 1874. John M. Carroll and Lawrence A. Frost (eds). (Piscataway, NJ): CRI Books, (1976). 1st ed. Inscribed, signed presentation by Carroll. Frontisport, 2 maps. Fine in dj. *Pacific**. $75/£47

EWING, JAMES. A Treatise on the Office and Duty of a Justice of the Peace, Sheriff, Coroner, Constable. And of Executors, Administrators, and Guardians.... Trenton: D. Fenton, 1832. 2nd ed. Contemp sheep (worn, rubbed; foxed). Sound. *Boswell*. $125/£78

EWING, JOHN. The Royal Scots 1914-1919. Edinburgh: Oliver & Boyd, 1925. 1st ed. 2 vols. 36 plts, 47 maps (11 fldg). VG in djs. *Hollett*. $240/£150

EWING, JULIANA HORATIA. Daddy Darwin's Dovecot. London: SPCK, (1884). 1st ed. 8vo. Randolph Caldecott (illus). Color frontis, 52pp. Pict bds (lt edgeworn, professionally rebacked w/new eps). VG. *House*. $120/£75

EWING, JULIANA HORATIA. Dandelion Clocks and Other Tales. London: SPCK, (1887). Gordon Browne et al (illus). 8vo. Orig yellow pict bds (extrems rubbed, hinges starting). Good. *Houle*. $125/£78

EWING, JULIANA HORATIA. Mary's Meadow. SPCK, 1886. 1st separate ed. Gordon Browne (illus). 96pp (half-title sl browned). Pict bds (corners, spine worn). *Hollett*. $40/£25

EWING, JULIANA HORATIA. Three Christmas Trees. NY: Macmillan, 1930. 1st ed. 8vo. Color frontis, 8 full-pg b/w plts by Pamela Bianco. Grn cl, gilt. Good. *Reisler*. $50/£31

EWING, JULIANA HORATIA. A Week Spent in a Glass-Pond. NY: A. Worthington, (ca 1890). 8vo. (16)ff. Fine in pict bds; orig pict dj (losses to edge). *Bromer*. $600/£375

Examination of the Conduct of Great Britain Respecting Neutrals. (By Tench Coxe.) Phila: B. Graves, 1807. 1st ed. 72pp (tp, foremargin p59 sl soiled). Mod purple linen, black morocco spine label. Howes C836. *Karmiole*. $200/£125

Excursion Through the United States and Canada During the Years 1822-23. (By William Newnham Blane.) London, 1824. 1st ed. 2 fldg maps, fldg table, all linen-backed. Later 1/2 calf. (Bkpl, lt browned, foxed, lacks errata leaf; extrems worn.) Howes B521. *Swann**. $258/£161

Excursion Through the United States and Canada. (By William N. Blane.) Baldwin, Craddock, & Joy, 1824. 2 fldg maps, 1 hand-colored (1 sl torn at inner, lower margins; tp neatly repaired at corner; contents pg w/inner corner torn away). 19th-cent 1/2 calf (spine sl rubbed). *Sotheby's**. $294/£184

EXLEY, FREDERICK. A Fan's Notes. NY/Evanston/London: Harper & Row, (1968). 1st ed, 1st bk. Fine in dj. *Bernard*. $150/£94

EXLEY, FREDERICK. A Fan's Notes. NY, 1968. 1st ed. NF in VG dj (repaired 2/3-inch spine tear). *Warren*. $50/£31

EXLEY, FREDERICK. Pages from a Cold Island. NY, (1975). 1st ed. VG in dj. *King*. $20/£13

Exploits, Curious Anecdotes, and Sketches of the Most Remarkable Scottish Gypsies. Galashiels: Ronald C. Hodges, 1983. One of 200. Frontis. VG in orig ptd wrappers. *Hollett*. $32/£20

Extra Binding at the Lakeside Press, Chicago. (Chicago): R.R. Donnelley, 1925. 1st ed. Color frontis, 28 b/w photo plts. Patterned black bds (worn, partly scuffed, lacks spine), ptd paper label fr cvr. Text Good. *Baltimore**. $30/£19

EYRE, ALAN MONTGOMERY. Saint John's Wood. London: Chapman & Hall, 1913. Presentation copy. Grn cl. *Marlborough*. $80/£50

EYRE, ELIZABETH. Death of a Duchess. London: Headline, 1991. 1st ed. Fine in dj. *Murder*. $60/£38

EYRE-TODD, GEORGE. Scotland Picturesque and Traditional. Gowans & Gray, 1921. 2nd ed. Dec cl, gilt. (Feps sl spotted, joints strained; extrems sl rubbed.) *Hollett*. $32/£20

Ezra Pound His Metric and Poetry. (By T. S. Eliot.) NY, 1917 (i.e. 1918). 1st ed. 8vo. Frontis. Rose-pink bds (backstrip faded). *Sotheby's**. $589/£368

F

F., H. H. (ed). Records of a Lifelong Friendship 1807-1882: Ralph Waldo Emerson and William Henry Furness. Boston/NY: Houghton Mifflin, 1910. 1st ed. One of 750. Frontis. Some pp unopened. Brn cl. VG. *Lucas*. $65/£41

F., M. T. (Pseud of Katherine Anne Porter.) My Chinese Marriage. NY: Duffield, 1921. 1st ed. Teg, untrimmed. Grn cl, lt yellow-grn bds, ptd paper spine label, gilt. VG (sig; sl rubbed, hinges sl cracked, rear pastedown lt foxed). *Baltimore**. $80/£50

F., M. T. (Pseud of Katherine Anne Porter.) My Chinese Marriage. NY: Duffield, 1921. 1st ed, 1st bk. (Sl smudged.) *Kane**. $100/£63

FABER, GEOFFREY. Twelve Years. London: Privately ptd, 1962. 1st Eng ed. Fine in dj, stiff card wrappers. *Clearwater*. $48/£30

FABES, GILBERT. Modern First Editions: Points and Values. London: W. & G. Foyle, 1929. One of 750 ptd. VG + in dj. *Zubal**. $40/£25

FABES, GILBERT. The Romance of a Bookshop 1904-1929. Privately ptd, 1929. 1st ed. Author's copy. (Sl worn.) *Moss*. $32/£20

Fable Nook and Story Book: A Collection of Catchy Rhymes and Amusing Stories for the Little Ones. (N.p.: W.E. Scull, 1901.) Walter Crane et al (illus). Cl-backed chromolitho bds. (Cvrs scratched, extrems rubbed), else VG. *Pacific**. $58/£36

Fables of Aesop and Others Translated into Human Nature. (By Charles H. Bennett.) London: Kent, (1857). 1st ed. 4to. Cl-backed color pict bds (spotted, edges rubbed, rebacked w/some separations within). *Reisler*. $600/£375

Fabre's Book of Insects. London: Hodder & Stoughton, (1921). 1st ed. 4to. 12 mtd color plts by E. Detmold. White cl, gilt. Nice in dec dj (worn, dusty), color paste label. *Reisler*. $485/£303

FABYAN, ROBERT. The New Chronicles of England and France, in Two Parts; by Robert Fabyan. Named by Himself the Concordance of Histories. Reprinted from Pynson's Edition of 1516.... London: F.C. & J. Rivington et al, 1811. Rpt. (2),xxi,(2),723,(72)pp. Marbled edges. 19th-cent 3/4 morocco, gilt, raised bands. (Apparently lacks leaf, sl foxed, bkpl; rubbed, sl worn, spine scuffed), else VG. *Pacific**. $115/£72

FADIMAN, CLIFTON. Wally the Wordworm. NY: Macmillan, 1964. 1st ed. 6x7. Arnold Roth (illus). 88pp. Cl spine, pict bds. VG. *Cattermole*. $30/£19

Faeries Pop-Up Book. London: Kestrel/Penguin, 1980. Brian Froud & Alan Lee (illus). 6 dbl-pg pop-ups. Glazed pict bds. VG. *Bookfinders*. $40/£25

FAGAN, W. L. (ed). Southern War Songs. NY, 1890. Color frontis. Pub's pict cl (extrems rubbed, spine ends frayed; fr hinge starting). *Swann**. $69/£43

FAGG, WILLIAM. The Sculpture of Africa. NY: Praeger, (1958). 1st US ed. Folio. Black/brn cl, gilt. Very Clean in VG dj (price-clipped). *Baltimore**. $35/£22

FAGG, WILLIAM. Tribes and Forms in African Art. NY: Tudor, (ca 1965). 1st US ed. 122 full-pg b/w photos. Yellow cl (sl shelfworn). Text Fine, cvrs Clean in dj (sl worn, chipped, sm edge tears). *Baltimore**. $20/£13

FAHEY, HERBERT. Early Printing in California.... SF: Book Club of CA, 1956. 1st ed. Ltd to 400 ptd. Folio. Frontisport. Morocco label. (Spine foot, corners sl rubbed), else Fine. *Argonaut*. $250/£156

FAINLIGHT, RUTH et al. Poems. London: Rainbow Press, 1971. 1st ed. One of 300. Signed by all 3 authors. Grn calf, gilt. Fine in VG leather slipcase. *Pacific**. $46/£29

Fair France: Impressions of a Traveller. (By Dinah Maria Craik.) Hurst & Blackett, 1871. Marbled edges. Contemp full-leather, raised bands, leather spine label (lt rubbed). VG. *Tiger.* $152/£95

FAIR, A. A. (Pseud of Erle Stanley Gardner.) Pass the Gravy. Heinemann, 1960. 1st Eng ed. VG (spine tail sl bumped) in dj (rubbed, spine sl faded). *Ulysses.* $40/£25

FAIRCHILD, DAVID. Garden Islands of the Great East. NY: Scribner, 1943. 1st ed. VG in dj (worn). *Quest.* $45/£28

FAIRCHILD, DAVID. The World Grows Round My Door. NY/London, 1947. *Edwards.* $61/£38

FAIRFIELD, ASA. Fairfield's Pioneer History of Lassen County, California; Containing Everything That Can Be Learned About It from the Beginning to 1870. SF: The Author, (1916). 1st ed. xxii,506pp; 4 plts, fldg map. Teg. Pict cl. Fine. Howes F11. *Argonaut.* $250/£156

FAIRLESS, MICHAEL. Stories Told to Children. London: Duckworth, 1914. 1st ed. Lg 8vo. Flora White (illus). (iv),5-201pp. Grn cl, gilt. Fine. *Sotheran.* $141/£88

Fairy Footsteps, Lessons from Legends. London: Henry Lea, (1861). 1st ed. 8vo. (iv),188; 8 monochrome plts by Alfred Crowquill. Aeg. Dk grn blind-stamped cl. *Sotheran.* $157/£98

Fairy Garland, Being Fairy Tales from the Old French. London/NY: Cassell, (1928). One of 1000 signed by Edmund Dulac (illus). 4to. 12 color illus. Teg. Blue linen bds over vellum spine. Fine. *Appelfeld.* $600/£375

Fairy Tales Pop-Up Book. London: Dean Intl, 1974. 3 dbl-pg pop-ups. Glazed pict bds. VG. *Bookfinders.* $15/£9

FAITHFULL, EMILY. Three Visits to America. NY: Fowler & Wells, 1884. 1st Amer ed. pp xvi,400,(16) ads. Pict cl (sl dull). *Mott.* $150/£94

FALCONER, RICHARD. The Voyages, Dangerous Adventures and Imminent Escapes of Captain Richard Falconer.... London: W. Chetwood, 1720. 1st ed. 8vo. Frontis, viii,179,(180)ads. Full contemp calf (endcaps, joints professionally repaired), gilt. Internally Clean. Howes C356. *House.* $750/£469

FALCONER, WILLIAM. Universal Dictionary of the Marine.... London, 1784. New ed. 12 fldg engr plts. Contemp sheep. (Lt foxed, affecting plts; clean tear plt 2 repaired w/cellotape on verso; worn, fr cvr detached.) *Swann**. $230/£144

FALK, BERNARD. Thomas Rowlandson: His Life and Art. NY: Beechurst, (1952). 1st ed. Supp at rear. Red cl, gilt. Good in dj (lt chipped). *Karmiole.* $75/£47

FALK-RONNE, ARNE. Back to Tristan. Allen & Unwin, 1967. 1st Eng ed. VG in dj. *Walcot.* $26/£16

FALKNER, J. MEADE. The Lost Stradivarius. NY, 1896. Probably 1st Amer ptg. Good in ptd card wrappers (skillfully restored w/spine laid down, sm tear in bottom edge of fr cvr). *Clearwater.* $120/£75

FALLACI, ORIANA. A Man. NY, 1980. 1st Amer ed. Fine (sl rubbed) in NF dj (price-clipped). *Polyanthos.* $25/£16

FALLADA, HANS. (Pseud of Rudolf Ditzen.) Iron Gustav. Philip Owens (trans). London: Putnam, (1940). 1st British ed. Gilt black cl. Fine in NF dj (trimmed sl too short). *Reese.* $45/£28

FALLADA, HANS. (Pseud of Rudolf Ditzen.) Wolf Among Wolves. NY: Putnam, 1938. 1st US ed. Tan cl. (Few spots top edge), else Fine in NF dj (price-clipped). *Reese.* $40/£25

FALLAS, CARL. Saint Mary's Village Through the Eyes of an Unknown Soldier Who Lived On. London: Hodder & Stoughton, (1954). 1st ed. Blue cl. (Ink name, date), o/w Nice in VG dj (sm chip). *Reese.* $35/£22

FALLODON, VISCOUNT GREY OF. Fallodon Papers. London: Constable, 1926. Black cl, gilt. Fine. *Pacific**. $29/£18

FALLS, C. B. The Modern ABC Book. NY: John Day, 1930. 1st ed. Lg 4to. Dk blue cl (fr hinge weak, sm ripple rear cvr). *Reisler.* $200/£125

FALLS, DE WITT C. The Comic Military Alphabet. NY: Stokes, 1894. 1st ed. 26 VF color plts. Red/white/blue cl, sm mtd color illus fr cvr. (Cvr fore-edges discolored.) *Baltimore**. $85/£53

FALSTAFF, JAKE. Alice in Justice-Land. NY: ACLU, 1935. Rpt from New York World, 1929. 8vo. 11pp (dkng), ptd self-wrappers. *Reisler.* $85/£53

Family Coach. London: Castell Bros, (ca 1890). Obl 8vo (shapebook). 8pp. Chromolitho stiff paper wrappers (edges sl worn). *Reisler.* $300/£188

Famous Parks and Gardens of the World. London, 1880. 230pp. Aeg. (Sl foxed affecting prelims, hinges sl cracked; rubbed.) *Edwards.* $120/£75

FANE, JULIAN. A Letter. London: John Murray, 1960. 1st ed. Blue bds. Fine in dj (sl mkd). *Temple.* $11/£7

FANNING, EDMUND. Voyages and Discoveries in the South Seas 1792-1832. Salem, MA: Marine Research Soc, 1924. 32 plts. Dec eps. Blue cl. VG (corners lt worn, foxed). *Parmer.* $115/£72

FANNING, PETER. Great Crimes of the West. SF: Ed Barry, 1929. 1st ed. Grn cl. VG. *Labordo.* $75/£47

FANTE, JOHN. Dago Red. NY: Viking, 1940. 1st ed. VG in dj (soiled, sm chips). *Smith.* $350/£219

FAR, ISABELLA. De Chirico. NY, n.d. 172 plts (80 color). Dj. *Edwards.* $40/£25

FARADAY, MICHAEL. A Course of Six Lectures on the Chemical History of a Candle. William Crookes (ed). Griffin, Bohn, 1861. 1st ed. viii,208pp + 8pp ads. (2 sections sl loose; sl mkd, bumped.) *Hollett.* $120/£75

FARADAY, MICHAEL. Experimental Researches in Chemistry and Physics. London: Richard Taylor & William Francis, 1859. 1st collected ed. 8vo. viii,496pp; 3 plts (1 fldg). Complete w/errata slip at p445. Partly unopened. Emb cl (spine lt sunned, ends sl worn). VG (bkpl, fr hinge starting). *Glaser.* $600/£375

FARADAY, MICHAEL. Experimental Researches in Chemistry and Physics. Richard Taylor & William Francis, 1859. 1st ed. 8vo. viii,496pp; 3 engr plts. Errata slip p445. Orig cl (recently expertly rebacked w/orig spine laid down). VG (ex-lib, bkpl, blind-stamps). *Sotheran.* $797/£498

FARADAY, MICHAEL. Experimental Researches in Electricity. Reprinted from the Philosophical Transactions, with other Electrical Papers. London: Bernard Quaritch/Richard & John Edward Taylor, 1839, 1855/1844. Reissue of vols 2, 3; 1st bk ed of vol 2. 3 vols. 8vo. viii,574; viii,302; viii,588pp; 17 engr plts (13 fldg). Orig full dk-grn cl. Fine set. *Weber.* $875/£547

FARBER, EDUARD (ed). Great Chemists. NY: Interscience Pubs, 1961. 1st ed. 1/4 white cl, red bds. (Inscrip), else Fine. *Weber.* $80/£50

FARBER, JAMES. Texas, C.S.A. A Spotlight on Disaster. NY: Jackson, (1947). 1st ed. One of 1000, this copy not signed or numbered as called for. Blue cl. (Few pp creased at upper corners, pencil marginalia, underlining), else VG in dj (sl worn). *Chapel Hill.* $50/£31

FARBER, NORMA. How the Left-Behind Beasts Built Ararat. NY: Walker, 1978. 1st ed. 8x10.5. Antonio Frasconi (illus). Unpaginated. NF in VG- dj (1.5-inch tear, top rear edgeworn). *Price.* $25/£16

FARBMAN, MICHAEL (ed). Masterpieces of Russian Painting. London, 1930. 20 color plts, 43 monochrome repros. (Cl discolored.) Internally VG. *Washton.* $50/£31

Farewell American Tour of Mme. Sarah Bernhardt and Mons. Coquelin...La Tosca. NY: Rullman, (1891). Ptd wrappers (chipped). *Rostenberg & Stern.* $85/£53

FARINA, RICHARD. Been Down So Long It Looks Like Up to Me. NY: Random House, 1966. 1st ed, 1st bk. VG in VG dj (price-clipped; clear-tape repair). *Pettler.* $45/£28

FARINA, RICHARD. Been Down So Long It Looks Like Up to Me. NY: Random House, 1966. 1st ed, 1st bk. VG in dj (sig fr flap). *Smith.* $75/£47

FARISH, THOMAS EDWIN. History of Arizona. Phoenix, 1915. 1st ed. 1st 2 vols only. NF. Howes F37. *Baade.* $65/£41

FARJEON, ELEANOR. Ameliaranne's Washing-Day. Harrap, 1934. 1st ed. 8vo. S.B. Pearse (illus). (60)pp. Cl w/pict onlay. NF. *Bookmark.* $77/£48

FARJEON, ELEANOR. Elizabeth Myers. Aylesford: St. Albert's, 1957. One of 100 lg paper copies signed by Farjeon, Sara Jackson (sonnet writer), and Edward Walters (designer). This copy add'ly inscribed by Farjeon. Fine in card wrappers. *Clearwater.* $88/£55

FARJEON, ELEANOR. The Glass Slipper. London: Oxford Children, 1962. 5.5x8. Ernest Shepard (illus). 176pp. VG in dj. *Cattermole.* $28/£18

FARJEON, ELEANOR. Grannie Gray. J.M. Dent, 1939. 1st ed. 8vo. Joan Jefferson Farjeon (illus). 148pp. VG + in pict dj (mended). *Bookmark.* $40/£25

FARJEON, ELEANOR. Humming-Bird. Plymouth, UK: Michael Joseph, 1936. 1st ed. 320pp. VG in dj (edges heavily chipped, 1/2-inch spot top edge). *Price.* $30/£19

FARJEON, ELEANOR. Martin Pippin in the Apple Orchard. OUP, 1952. 1st illus ed. 8vo. Richard Kennedy (illus). 305pp. NF (edges faded) in VG pict dj. *Bookmark.* $40/£25

FARJEON, ELEANOR. Ten Saints. NY: OUP, 1936. 1st ed. Helen Sewell (illus). (Name; lt worn), o/w NF in dj (extrems lt chipped). *Hermitage.* $50/£31

FARLEY, JOSEPH PEARSON. Three Rivers: The James, the Potomac, the Hudson. A Retrospect of Peace and War. NY/Washington: Neale, 1910. 1st ed. Color frontis, 9 add'l color plts. Teg. Blue cl. VG + (bkpl; cvrs lt rubbed). *Chapel Hill.* $150/£94

FARLEY, RALPH MILNE. An Earthman on Venus. Avon Pub Co, (1950). Wraps. (Sl worn, sm spine tear), else VG. *King.* $37/£23

FARLEY, WALTER. The Black Stallion and Flame. Random House, 1960. 1st ptg. VG (bkpl) in VG dj (spine tips sl worn). *Price.* $25/£16

FARLEY, WALTER. Black Stallion and Satan. Chicago: Random, 1949. 1st ed. 5.5x8.25. 208pp. Good in dj. *Cattermole.* $35/£22

FARLEY, WALTER. The Black Stallion Revolts. Chicago: Random, 1953. 1st ed. 5.5x8.25. 305pp. VG in dj. *Cattermole.* $35/£22

FARMAN, ELBERT E. Egypt and Its Betrayal. NY: Grafton, 1908. 1st ed. 25 plts. Teg, untrimmed, unopened, as issued. Dj protective cardbd slipcase. *Worldwide.* $25/£16

Farmer's Instructor; or Every Man His Own Lawyer. Buffalo: Oliver Spafford, 1824. 2nd ed. Contemp calf (worn, stained). Usable. *Boswell.* $150/£94

FARMER, HENRY GEORGE. A History of Music in Scotland. London, (c. 1949). Henrichsen ed. 15 plts. VG in dj (torn, chipped). *Hollett.* $40/£25

FARMER, HENRY GEORGE. Music Making in the Olden Days. London, 1950. Peters-Henrichsen ed. 6 plts. VG in dj (sl creased, torn). *Hollett.* $104/£65

FARMER, PENELOPE. The China People. London: Hutchinson, 1960. 1st ed. 5.25x8. 96pp. VG (inscrip) in dj. *Cattermole.* $45/£28

FARMER, PENELOPE. The Summer Birds. C&W, 1962. 1st ed, 1st bk. Signed. VG in dj. *Green Meadow.* $72/£45

FARMER, PHILIP JOSE. Blown or Sketches Among the Ruins of My Mind: An Exorcism (Ritual 2). L.A.: Essex House, (1969). Pb orig. (Sm scrape from sticker removal fr wrap, sl rubbed), else NF in wrappers. *Between The Covers.* $200/£125

FARMER, PHILIP JOSE. Doc Savage: His Apocalyptic Life. GC: Doubleday, 1973. 1st ed. Pub's file copy stamp fep. Fine in VG + dj (rear panel lt soiled, spine sl creased, nicked). *Any Amount.* $77/£48

FARMER, PHILIP JOSE. Flesh. (NY): Beacon/Galaxy, (1960). 1st ed. VG- in pict wrappers. *Other Worlds.* $25/£16

FARMER, PHILIP JOSE. Gods of River World. NY: Putnam, (1983). 1st ed. NF in dj. *Antic Hay.* $25/£16

FARMER, PHILIP JOSE. The Grand Adventure: Masterworks of Science Fiction. NY: Berkeley Books, (1984). One of 325. Signed. Dec burgundy cl. Fine in slipcase. *Pacific*.* $63/£39

FARMER, PHILIP JOSE. The Image of the Beast: An Exorcism (Ritual 1). L.A.: Essex House, (1968). 1st ed. Pb orig. (Bump upper rt corner, lt spine creases), else NF. *Between The Covers.* $200/£125

FARMER, PHILIP JOSE. Love Song. NY: Brandon House, (1970). 1st ed. Signed. (Pp sl browned, rubbed, few sm scrapes), else NF in wrappers. *Between The Covers.* $275/£172

FARMER, PHILIP JOSE. Love Song. San Antonio: Dennis McMillan, 1983. One of 500 numbered, signed. Fine in dj. *Smith.* $75/£47

FARMER, PHILIP JOSE. The Unreasoning Mask. NY: Putnam, (1981). One of 500 numbered, signed. Black cl. Fine in slipcase. *Antic Hay.* $100/£63

Farmyard Friends with Pop-Up Pictures. (Somerset)/London: Purnell & Sons, n.d. (195?). 4 dbl-pg pop-ups. Glazed pict bds. VG. *Bookfinders.* $35/£22

Farmyard Friends. Come to Life Stories. London: Sandle Bros, n.d. (195?). 2 dbl-pg pop-ups (sm tape repair to 2nd pop-up). Illus bds. *Bookfinders.* $75/£47

FARNHAM, CHARLES HAIGHT. A Life of Francis Parkman. Boston: Little, Brown, 1901. 2 photogravure ports. Teg. Grn ribbed cl, gilt. VG. *House.* $20/£13

FARNHAM, ELIZABETH. Life in Prairie Land. NY, 1846. 1st ed. 408pp. 3/4 leather (rebound; stamp, ink #). *Heinoldt.* $45/£28

FAROVA, ANNA. Andre Kertesz. Prague: Odeon, (1966). (Sm bklabel rear pastedown.) Pict wrappers. *Swann*.* $138/£86

FAROVA, ANNA. Robert Capa. Prague: Odeon, (1973). Pict wrappers (sl worn). *Swann*.* $126/£79

FARQUHAR, FRANCIS P. History of the Sierra Nevada. Berkeley/L.A.: Univ of CA, 1965. 1st ed. Color frontis, 5 maps. Blue cl, gilt. Fine in pict dj (price-clipped). *Pacific*.* $75/£47

FARQUHAR, FRANCIS P. History of the Sierra Nevada. Berkeley/L.A.: Univ of CA w/Sierra Club, 1965. 1st ed. Frontis. Errata slip laid-in. Pict cl. (Eps browned from dj.) Dj (lt edgeworn). *Dawson.* $100/£63

FARQUHAR, FRANCIS P. History of the Sierra Nevada. Berkeley: Univ of CA, 1965. 1st ed. Signed. Frontis. Orig errata slip laid in. Silver-dec blue cl, gilt. (Eps sl offset), else VF in pict dj (spine dknd). *Argonaut.* $150/£94

FARQUHAR, FRANCIS P. Place Names of the High Sierra. SF: Sierra Club, 1926. 1st ed. Ltd to 750 bound in wrappers (but not indicated). NF in gray wrappers (spine dknd, ends lt chipped). *Argonaut.* $190/£119

FARQUHAR, GEORGE. The Recruiting Officer: A Comedy. London: Peter Davies, 1926. One of 550 numbered. 12 color plts. Parchment-backed patterned bds (sl faded). *Argosy.* $100/£63

FARRAN, RICHARD M. (Pseud of John Betjeman.) Ground Plan to Skyline. Newman Neame Take Home Books, 1960. 1st Eng ed. Card wrappers (1 corner sl creased). *Clearwater.* $120/£75

FARRAR, CHARLES A. J. Through the Wilds. A Record of Sport and Adventure in the Forests of New Hampshire and Maine. Boston: Estes & Lauriat, (1892). 1st ed. xiv,415pp. Black, gilt pict grn cl. Good+ (extrems lt worn, fr hinge tape repaired). *House.* $55/£34

FARRAR, F. W. Great Books: Bunyan, Shakespeare, Dante, Milton. Isbister, 1898. 4pp integral ads at end dated Autumn 1898. Teg, rest uncut; eps coated dk grn. Ribbed olive grn cl, gilt. NF. *Temple.* $21/£13

FARRAR, R. Johnny Reb, the Confederate; and Rip Van Winkle, or the Virginian that Slept Ten Years: Two Lectures. By J. [sic] R. Farrar. Richmond: Ptd by W.A.R. Nye, 1869. 1st ed thus. 22,19pp + errata slip. Fine in ptd orange wraps (rear wrap sl chipped at bottom). *Chapel Hill.* $250/£156

FARRELL, J. G. Troubles. London, 1970. 1st Eng ed. Very Nice (inscrip, fep shelf-mkd) in dj (sl chafed). *Clearwater.* $152/£95

FARRELL, JAMES T. Lonely for the Future. NY, 1966. 1st ed. Fine in NF dj. *Warren.* $40/£25

FARRELL, JAMES T. My Days of Anger. London: Routledge, 1945. 1st ed. Black buckram. Fine in dj (sl frayed, verso strengthened). *Temple.* $26/£16

FARRELL, JAMES T. No Star Is Lost. London: Constable, 1939. 1st Eng ed. Black buckram. VG in dj (frayed, sl chipped, verso strengthened). *Temple.* $50/£31

FARRELL, JAMES T. The Silence of History. GC: Doubleday, 1963. 1st ed. VF in VF dj. *Between The Covers.* $100/£63

FARREN, ROBERT. Cambridge and Its Neighborhood. Cambridge: Macmillan, 1881. 1st ed. Tall folio. 6pp text + etched tp, dedication, contents pp; 25 full-pg etchings, each preceded by etched pict caption pg, + 3 other full-pg etchings, all signed in the plts. Teg, untrimmed. Navy cl, gilt. (Sl aged, sl offsetting to some plts from guards; sl handled, rubbed.) *Baltimore*.* $140/£88

FARRER, J. A. Books Condemned to Be Burnt. London: Elliot Stock, 1892. xii,206pp. Uncut. (Headcaps sl bumped.) *Maggs.* $29/£18

FARRER, R. The Rainbow Bridge. London, 1921. 1st ed. 16 plts, 1 map. (Pp yellowed, bkpl, foxed, sm stain rep; inner fr hinge, joint reinforced w/cl tape; soiled, worn, sm tears to spine ends.) *Sutton.* $85/£53

FARRER, REGINALD. The Dolomites. A&C Black, 1913. 1st ed. Fldg map. Blue pict cl, gilt. VG. *Sotheran.* $157/£98

FARRER, REGINALD. The English Rock-Garden. London, 1928. 4th imp. 2 vols. 102 plts. (Lt browning; spines, joints sl chipped, surface mks.) *Edwards.* $64/£40

FARRER, REGINALD. The Garden of Asia. London, 1904. 1st ed. Red cl, gilt. VG. *Larry Price.* $95/£59

FARRER, REGINALD. The Garden of Asia; Impressions from Japan. Methuen, 1904. 1st ed, 1st bk. Marbled eps. Later 1/2 calf, marbled bds, raised bands, black leather label, gilt. Fine (bkpl). *Sotheran.* $320/£200

FARRER, REGINALD. In a Yorkshire Garden. London, 1909. 1st ed. 16 photo plts. Marbled eps; teg. Grn 1/2 calf (orig cl cvr, spine title bound in), raised bands, gilt. VG. *Larry Price.* $195/£122

FARRER, REGINALD. My Rock-Garden. Edward Arnold, 1907. 1st ed. 16 half-tone plts. Teg, rest uncut. Good (bkpl) in dec cl. *Cox.* $24/£15

FARRINGTON, S. KIP. Atlantic Game Fishing. NY: GC Publishing, (1939). Deluxe ed. Lynn Bogue Hunt (illus). Dk blue cl, gilt spine. (Sl adhesion residue fr cvr), else NF. *Pacific*.* $40/£25

FARRINGTON, S. KIP. Railroading from the Rear End. NY: Coward, McCann, 1946. Good in dj (chipped). *Dumont.* $35/£22

FARROW, G. E. The Escape of the Mullingong. Blackie, 1907. 1st ed. 8vo. 148pp,32pp; 58 illus by Gordon Brown. Aeg. Pict navy-blue cl, gilt. VG (sl fingermks; sl rubbed). *Bookmark.* $72/£45

FARROW, G. E. Pixie Pickles. London: Skeffington & Son, (1904). 1st ed. Lg 4to. 20 full-pg illus by Harry B. Neilson. Cl-backed pict bds (worn, mks to rear cvr, hinges cracked). *Reisler.* $175/£109

FARSON, NEGLEY. Going Fishing. London, (1942). 1st ed. 16 plts. (Eps foxed.) Color map as dj. *Petersfield.* $77/£48

FASSBENDER, ADOLF. Pictorial Artistry: The Dramatization of the Beautiful in Photography. NY, (1937). One of 1000 signed, numbered. Folio. Spiral bound. (Offsetting; lt soiled, corners bumped.) *Swann*.* $345/£216

FAST, HOWARD. Citizen Tom Paine. NY: Duell, Sloan, 1943. 1st ed. NF (bkpl) in VG+ dj (spine faded, sl chipped). *Unger.* $50/£31

FAST, JULIUS. The Beatles. The Real Story. NY: Putnam, 1968. 1st ed. Fine in dj (lt used). *Beasley.* $40/£25

FATEMI, NASROLLAH SAIFPOUR. Diplomatic History of Persia, 1917-1923. NY: Moore, 1952. 1st ed. (Sl rubbed, lib spine #), o/w VG. *Worldwide.* $35/£22

FATH, CREEKMORE. The Lithographs of Thomas hart Benton. Austin, (1969). Frontis signed, inscribed by Benton. Obl sm folio. Dj. *Swann*.* $161/£101

Father Tuck's Fidgety Phil and Other Tales. London: Raphael Tuck & Sons, (ca 1905). Louis Wain (illus). 8vo. 14pp; 4 of the pp + cvrs are in full color, rest are in black/orange. Good in stiff pict wrappers (lt marginal stain inside fr cvr). *Reisler.* $1,600/£1,000

FAUCON, BERNARD. Summer Camp. NY: Xavier Moreau, (1980). 1st US(?) ed. 40 full-pg color photos. Fine in illus dj. *Cahan.* $125/£78

FAULK, ODIE B. Destiny Road. NY: OUP, (1973). VG in dj. *Lien.* $15/£9

FAULK, ODIE B. (ed). Derby's Report on Opening the Colorado 1850-1851. Univ of NM, 1969. 1st ed. Fldg map. Brn cl. VG+ in pict dj. *Five Quail.* $35/£22

FAULKNER, WILLIAM. Absalom, Absalom! NY, 1936. 1st ed. 8vo. *Swann*.* $517/£323

FAULKNER, WILLIAM. Absalom, Absalom! NY: Random House, 1936. One of 300 signed. VG (ink date; tips worn through, spine sl sunned). *Metropolitan*.* $690/£431

FAULKNER, WILLIAM. As I Lay Dying. NY: Cape/Smith, (1930). 1st ed, 1st issue, w/initial 'I' on p11 out of alignment. One of 750. Fine in tan cl. Tan dj (few sm chips, spine lt toned). *Bromer.* $1,250/£781

FAULKNER, WILLIAM. Big Woods. NY: Random House, (1955). 1st ed, 1st ptg. Grn cl. VF in VF dj. *Macdonnell.* $200/£125

FAULKNER, WILLIAM. Doctor Martino and Other Stories. NY: Harrison Smith/Robert Haas, 1934. 1st ed. VG (sl shelfworn, spine discolored at lower edge) in dj (torn, 1.5-inch chip out of lower spine, edgeworn, spotted). *My Bookhouse.* $205/£128

FAULKNER, WILLIAM. Doctor Martino and Other Stories. NY: Harrison Smith & Robert Haas, 1934. 1st ed. One of 360. Signed. Black/red cl, gilt. (Sl shaken; spine chipped, sl sunned; extrems rubbed), else VG-. *Pacific*.* $489/£306

FAULKNER, WILLIAM. Doctor Martino and Other Stories. NY: Harrison Smith, Robert Haas, 1934. 1st ed. (Sl offset from wrapper to spine), o/w VF in blue cl, gilt. Dj (extrems chipped, 2.5-inch closed tear). *Bromer.* $500/£313

FAULKNER, WILLIAM. A Fable. (NY): Random House, (1954). 1st trade ed. Maroon cl. (Cvr edges lt faded), o/w Fine in dj (lt chipped, browned). *Heritage.* $75/£47

FAULKNER, WILLIAM. A Fable. NY: Random House, (1954). 1st ed, trade issue. Plum cl. Fine in dj (price-clipped). *Reese.* $100/£63

FAULKNER, WILLIAM. A Fable. NY: Random House, (1954). 1st ed. Fine in dj. *Pacific*.* $138/£86

FAULKNER, WILLIAM. A Fable. (NY): Random House, (1954). 1st ed. One of 1000 signed. 8vo. Top edge stained blue. Blue cl. Fine in glassine wrapper (chipped, browned), pub's cardboard slipcase (lt soiled). *Heritage.* $750/£469

FAULKNER, WILLIAM. A Fable. NY: Random House, (1954). 1st ed. One of 1000 numbered, signed. Pict blue cl stamped in gold/white/dk blue. VF complete w/glassine wrapper, slipcase. *Argonaut.* $900/£563

FAULKNER, WILLIAM. A Green Bough. NY: Smith & Haas, (1933). One of 360 numbered, signed. NF (bottom corner sl bumped, spine sl tanned), w/o dj as issued. *Between The Covers.* $950/£594

FAULKNER, WILLIAM. A Green Bough. NY: Harrison Smith & Robert Haas, 1933. 1st trade ed. Lynd Ward (illus). Grn cl. NF (eps, cvr edges lt browned) in dj (browned, chipped, reinforced w/tape on verso). *Heritage.* $250/£156

FAULKNER, WILLIAM. Hunting Stories. LEC, 1988. One of 850 signed by Neil Welliver (illus). Fine in slipcase. *Swann*.* $201/£126

FAULKNER, WILLIAM. Idyll in the Desert. NY: Random House, 1931. 1st ed. Ltd to 400 signed. VF in marbled paper bds, ptd label. Glassine dj (chipped). *Bromer.* $1,250/£781

FAULKNER, WILLIAM. Intruder in the Dust. NY: Random House, (1948). 1st ed. Fine in dj (sl worn). *Lenz.* $200/£125

FAULKNER, WILLIAM. Intruder in the Dust. Chatto, 1949. 1st UK ed. VG (sl bumped) in dj (short closed tear, spine head sl creased). *Williams.* $144/£90

FAULKNER, WILLIAM. Jealousy and Episode. Minneapolis: Faulkner Studies, 1955. 1st ed in bk form. One of 500. Peach cl. NF (cl sl faded). *Heritage.* $350/£219

FAULKNER, WILLIAM. Knight's Gambit. NY: Random House, (1949). 1st ed. Top edge stained gray-blue. Brick-red cl. VG dj (sl chipped, few sm edge tears). *Baltimore*.* $250/£156

FAULKNER, WILLIAM. Knight's Gambit. NY: Random House, 1949. 1st ed. Fine in VG dj (extrems sl creased, frayed, sm loss top of 1 joint, panels sl soiled, mkd). *Pirages.* $125/£78

FAULKNER, WILLIAM. Knight's Gambit. Chatto, 1951. 1st UK ed. VG in dj (sl loss to spine extrems, edges sl worn). *Williams.* $120/£75

FAULKNER, WILLIAM. Light in August. (NY): Harrison Smith & Robert Haas, (1932). 1st ed, 1st ptg w/'Jefferson' for 'Mottstown' on p340, line 1. 1st binding in rough tan cl stamped in orange on fr, blue/orange on spine. Fine in dj (spine head sl chipped, spine sunned, lt spotted; fr panel sl scratched; soiled, corners rubbed), else Fine in VG dj. *Pacific*.* $431/£269

FAULKNER, WILLIAM. Light in August. NY, (1932). 1st ed. 8vo. Rough linen. Dj (top edges lt worn). *Swann*.* $632/£395

FAULKNER, WILLIAM. Light in August. (Rahway, NJ): Smith & Haas, (1932). 1st ed. 1st binding, rough tan cl stamped in orange on fr, blue/orange on spine. VF in orange/blue dj (sl soiled, extrems worn). *Bromer.* $650/£406

FAULKNER, WILLIAM. The Mansion. NY: Random House, (1959). 1st trade ed. Blue cl. VF in NF color pict dj (1-inch tear to crease). *Argonaut.* $150/£94

FAULKNER, WILLIAM. The Mansion. NY: Random House, 1959. 1st ed. Fine in dj (used). *Beasley.* $75/£47

FAULKNER, WILLIAM. Mirrors of Chartres Street. (Minneapolis: Faulkner Studies, 1953.) 1st ed, 1st issue. Ltd to 1000 numbered. Fine in illus dj. *Cahan.* $250/£156

FAULKNER, WILLIAM. Mosquitoes. NY, 1927. 1st ed. 8vo. Blue cl. NF in VG dj (backstrip dknd, 1 tape repair to verso), 1/4 morocco clamshell case. *Heritage.* $2,500/£1,563

FAULKNER, WILLIAM. Notes on a Horsethief. Greenville, MS: Levee, (1950). 1st ed. Ltd to 975 numbered, signed. 8vo. Grn cl w/silver design on fr cvr. NF (cvrs lt rubbed at tips). *Black Sun.* $650/£406

FAULKNER, WILLIAM. Notes on a Horsethief. Greenville, 1950. 1st ed. One of 950 numbered, signed. (Lt rubbed.) *Swann*.* $431/£269

FAULKNER, WILLIAM. Pylon. London: Chatto & Windus, 1935. 1st Eng ed, 1st issue bound in rose-brn cl w/top edge stained rose, bottom edge untrimmed, 4 pp ads at rear. VG (feps partly browned; spine foot sl bumped, spine lettering flaking) in dj (nicked, sl rubbed, creased, dusty; spine, edges browned). *Ulysses.* $560/£350

FAULKNER, WILLIAM. Pylon. NY: Harrison Smith & Robert Haas, 1935. 1st ed. 8vo. Blue/black cl, gilt. NF (spine sl faded, extrems sl rubbed) in dj (chipped, folds worn, sm scrape to spine, rear panel browned). *Heritage.* $750/£469

FAULKNER, WILLIAM. Requiem for a Nun. NY, (1951). 1st ed. Two-tone cl. VG in dj (sl dknd, top edge sl frayed). *King.* $125/£78

FAULKNER, WILLIAM. Requiem for a Nun. NY: Random House, (1951). One of 750 signed. 1/2 black cl, marbled bds. Good (eps faded; spine faded, bds scratched). *Heritage.* $450/£281

FAULKNER, WILLIAM. Requiem for a Nun. NY, (1951). 1st ed. One of 750 numbered, signed. 1/2 cl, bds. (Signs of bkpl removal.) Mylar dj. *Swann*.* $488/£305

FAULKNER, WILLIAM. Requiem for a Nun. NY: Random House, (1951). 1st ed. One of 750 signed. 3/4 cl, marbled bds. VG. *Holmes.* $500/£313

FAULKNER, WILLIAM. Requium for a Nun. NY: Random House, (1951). 1st Trade ed. NF in dj (sm chip fr panel, spine head rubbed, foot lt chipped). *Pacific*.* $58/£36

FAULKNER, WILLIAM. Sanctuary. NY: Jonathan Cape & Harrison Smith, (1931). 1st ed, 1st ptg. 8vo. Magenta bds, gray cl spine. NF (bkpl; spine ends lt rubbed) in dj (spine faded, rear panel sl browned, lt edgeworn). *Heritage.* $2,750/£1,719

FAULKNER, WILLIAM. Sanctuary. London: C&W, 1931. 1st Eng ed. 8vo. Maroon cl, gilt. NF (bkpl; spine ends, corner lt rubbed) in dj (browned). *Heritage.* $1,000/£625

FAULKNER, WILLIAM. Sartoris. NY, (1929). 1st ed, 1st ptg, w/'Bendow' on p179, top edge stained red. *Kane*.* $120/£75

FAULKNER, WILLIAM. Selected Letters of William Faulkner. Joseph Blotner (ed). Scolar Press, 1977. 1st Eng ed. NF (spine ends sl bumped) in dj (sl nicked, creased). *Ulysses.* $56/£35

FAULKNER, WILLIAM. Soldier's Pay. London: C&W, 1930. 1st Eng ed. 8vo. Top edge stained grn. Grn cl, gilt spine. NF (eps lt browned, edges foxed) in dj (lt soiled, browned). *Heritage.* $1,500/£938

FAULKNER, WILLIAM. The Sound and the Fury. C&W, 1931. 1st Eng ed. 2nd issue yellow cl. VG (feps partly browned) in dj (backstrip panel browned). *Blackwell's.* $216/£135

FAULKNER, WILLIAM. These 13, Stories. NY: Cape & Smith, (1931). 1st ed. 1st ptg, w/error on contents pg, reversing 2 numerals in pg listed for 'Hair.' Fine in blue/gray cl (sl offset from dj). Dj (spine faded, ends rubbed) w/title spelled out 'These Thirteen.' *Bromer.* $750/£469

FAULKNER, WILLIAM. These 13, Stories. NY: Cape & Smith, (1931). 1st ed. Ltd to 299 numbered, signed. Fine in gray/rust cl. Red morocco, cl slipcase w/chemise. *Bromer.* $1,650/£1,031

FAULKNER, WILLIAM. These 13. NY: Jonathan Cape & Harrison Smith, 1931. 1st ed, 1st ptg. 1/4 linen, blue bds. (Spine sl aged), else Fine in dj (spine sunned). *Macdonnell.* $600/£375

FAULKNER, WILLIAM. This Earth. NY, 1932. 1st ed. Pict 2-tone stiff brn wrappers (sm crease base of fr/rear cvrs). *Swann**. $149/£93

FAULKNER, WILLIAM. The Town. NY, (1957). 1st ed. VG in dj (sl used). *King*. $75/£47

FAULKNER, WILLIAM. The Town. NY: Random House, (1957). 1st ed. Red cl. Fine in dj. *Appelfeld*. $125/£78

FAULKNER, WILLIAM. The Town. NY, (1957). 1st ed. Dj (lt rubbed). *Swann**. $138/£86

FAULKNER, WILLIAM. The Town. NY, (1957). 1st ed. One of 450 numbered, signed. Mylar dj. *Swann**. $575/£359

FAULKNER, WILLIAM. The Unvanquished. NY: Random House, (1938). 1st ed. Fine in gray cl. Dj (spine dknd). *Bromer*. $525/£328

FAULKNER, WILLIAM. The Unvanquished. NY: Random House, (1938). One of 250 numbered, signed. Fine (bd bottoms sl rubbed), w/o dj or slipcase as issued. *Between The Covers*. $2,500/£1,563

FAULKNER, WILLIAM. The Unvanquished. NY: Random House, (1938). 1st ed. One of 250 specially bound, signed. 8vo. Edward Shenton (illus). 293pp. Teg. Patterned bds, red cl spine. NF (inner gutters sl browned), issued w/o dj or slipcase. *Chapel Hill*. $2,500/£1,563

FAULKNER, WILLIAM. The Wild Palms. NY, (1939). 1st ed, 1st ptg. Advance copy. Ptd wraps made from dj. (Sl cocked, worn; rear flap of dj detached but present.) Cl slipcase. *Kane**. . $350/£219

FAULKNER, WILLIAM. The Wild Palms. London, 1939. 1st Eng ed. VG (feps partly browned, edges spotted; spine tail, bottom corners sl bumped) in dj (internally browned at flaps, sl nicked, rubbed, dusty). *Ulysses*. $720/£450

FAULKNER, WILLIAM. William Faulkner's Speech of Acceptance upon the Award of the Nobel Prize...on the Tenth of December, Nineteen Hundred Fifty. NY: Spiral, 1951. One of 3500. (Lt soiled, worn), o/w VG in orig ptd wrappers. *Cummins*. $75/£47

FAULKNER, WILLIAM. The Wishing Tree. NY: Random House, (1964). 1st ed. Blue cl. NF (bkpl; eps, spine lt browned) in dj (price-clipped, sl browned, chip). *Heritage*. $125/£78

FAULKS, SEBASTIAN. Birdsong. London: Hutchinson, 1993. 1st Eng ed. Signed. Fine in dj. *Ulysses*. $152/£95

FAULKS, SEBASTIAN. The Girl at the Lion d'Or. London, 1989. 1st Eng ed. Fine in dj (sl torn). *Clearwater*. $88/£55

FAUST, ERNEST C. Animal Agents and Vectors of Human Disease. Phila, 1955. 1st ed. Red cl. VG. *Larry Price*. $35/£22

FAUX, WILLIAM. Memorable Days in America: Being a Journal of a Tour to the United States. London, 1823. May or may not have been issued w/half-title. Frontis. Early 1/2 calf. (Lt browned; cvrs loose.) Howes F60. *Swann**. $230/£144

FAVENC, ERNEST. The History of Australian Exploration from 1788 to 1888. Sydney: Turner & Henderson, 1888. 1st ed. (xvi),474,(vi)pp. Aeg. Contemp morocco, banded, extra gilt. Good (lib label, accession mks on prelims, 1 map sl torn, sm tear inner tp margin, few mks, ad leaf chipped; sm spine shelf mk, sl dknd, worn). *Ash*. $400/£250

Favourite Fables for Tiny Tots. London: Wells Gardner Darton, (1899). 1st ed. 3x2.5. 132pp; 30 full-pg line dwgs, vignettes. Aeg. Color pict cl (1/2-inch spine tear). VG in pub's slipcase (fragment of ptd label, sides broken, missing). *Reisler*. $175/£109

FAXON, ALICIA CRAIG. Dante Gabriel Rossetti. London: Phaidon, 1989. 1st ed. Dj. *Edwards*. $72/£45

FAY, C. R. Palace of Industry. Cambridge: CUP, 1951. 1st ed. 16 plts. Pict eps. VG in dj (sl edgeworn). *Hollett*. $48/£30

FAY, THEODORE S. Views in New-York and Its Environs, from Accurate, Characteristic and Picturesque Drawings.... NY: Peabody, 1831-(1834). 1st ed. 4to. 58pp (foxed); all 15 plts (dup plt in part 5); color map, engr tp present. 2-pg ad leaf noted by BAL in part 2, smaller 'Notice' indicating that part 3 was delayed. 7 of 8 parts complete (plt from part 8 present, but not text), o/w complete set. Orig ptd wrappers (mostly loose, chipped). (Part 4 lacks back wrap, part 6 lacks fr wrap, repairs to both plts part 7.) Howes F64. *M & S*. $2,250/£1,406

FEA, ALLAN. Old World Places. London, 1912. Teg, rest uncut. (Feps browned; nick lower joint.) *Edwards*. $32/£20

FEA, ALLAN. Picturesque Old Houses. London, n.d. xii,224pp. Teg, rest uncut. Illus mtd upper bd. (Spotting, heavy in parts; marginal pencil notes, upper hinge cracked, bkpl, feps sl browned; rubbed, spine lt faded.) *Edwards*. $32/£20

FEARING, DANIEL B. A Catalogue of an Exhibition of Angling Bookplates, Forming the Collection of Daniel B. Fearing, Newport, R.I. NY: Privately ptd, 1918. 1st ed. One of 500 ptd. Tinted etched frontis. Unopened. Dec bds. (Spine ends sl bumped), else VG. *Pacific**. $92/£58

FEARING, KENNETH. Afternoon of a Pawnbroker and Other Poems. NY: HB & Co, (1943). 1st ed. (Fep top corner clipped), else VF in VF dj. *Between The Covers*. $200/£125

FEARING, KENNETH. The Big Clock. Bodley Head, 1947. 1st UK ed. VG in dj (edges sl torn). *Williams*. $64/£40

FEARING, KENNETH. The Crozart Story. GC: Doubleday, 1960. 1st ed. VF in VF dj. *Between The Covers*. $85/£53

FEARING, KENNETH. New and Selected Poems. Bloomington: IN Univ, (1956). 1st ed. VF in VF dj. *Between The Covers*. $150/£94

FEARING, KENNETH. Stranger at Coney Island and Other Poems. NY: HB & Co, (1948). 1st ed. (Sm spot fep), else VF in NF dj (rubbed; 2 internal brn paper repairs). *Between The Covers*. $85/£53

FEARON, HENRY B. A Narrative of a Journey of Five Thousand Miles Through the Eastern and Western States of America. London: Longman, Hurst et al, 1818. 2nd ed. ix,454pp (lacks 1/2-title). New 1/2 black morocco, gilt. Howes F65. *Adelson*. $150/£94

FEARON, HENRY B. Sketches of America. London: Longman, 1818. 2nd ed. (x),454pp. Orig 1/2 calf (neatly rebacked), red morocco label. *Young*. $208/£130

FEATHER, LEONARD. The Book of Jazz: A Guide to the Entire Field. NY: Horizon, (1957). 1st ed. Discography. VG in ptd dj. *Petrilla*. $30/£19

FEATHERSTONE, DAVID. The Diana Show: Pictures Through a Plastic Lens. Untitled 21. Carmel, CA: The Friends of Photography, 1980. 3 full-pg b/w photos. Fine in illus stiff wrappers. *Cahan*. $50/£31

FEATHERSTONE, DAVID. Doris Ulmann, American Portraits. Albuquerque: Univ of NM, 1985. 1st ed. 74 full-pg b/w photo plts. VG in pict stiff wrappers. *Cahan*. $40/£25

FEATHERSTONHAUGH, G. W. Geological Report of an Examination Made in 1834 of the Elevated Country Between the Missouri and Red Rivers. Ptd by Gales & Seaton, 1835. 1st ed. 97pp; lg fldg hand-colored plan. Mod 1/2 levant morocco, gilt. Excellent (faint spotting, browning). *Hollett*. $352/£220

FEDDEN, ROMILLY (ed). The Basque Country. A&C Black, 1921. 1st ed. 24 color plts. Dec cl. (Edges sl foxed; extrems sl rubbed.) *Edwards*. $56/£35

FEDDEN, ROMILLY. Golden Days. London: Black, 1919. 1st ed. Frontis. Blue cl, gilt. NF. *Bowman*. $75/£47

Federal Theatre. Volumes 1-2. NY: Bureau of Research and Publication, 1935-36. Paper cvr label. VG (several orig wraps bound in w/few lib stamps). *Dramatis*. $250/£156

FEDERN, KARL. Baron Fritz. Donald Douglas (trans). NY: Farrar & Rinehart, (1930). 1st US ed. Tan cl. Nice in pict dj (chips, spine tanned). *Reese.* $35/£22

FEDERSPIEL, MATTHEW N. Harelip and Cleft Palate: Cheiloschisis.... St. Louis: C.V. Mosby, 1927. (Lacks fr fep, ex-lib, stamp), else Good. *Weber.* $45/£28

FEE, CHESTER ANDERS. Chief Joseph: The Biography of a Great Indian. NY: Wilson-Erickson, 1936. 1st ed. (Ink name), else VG in dj. *Perier.* $150/£94

FEJES, CLAIRE. Villagers. NY: Random House, 1981. 1st ed. Inscribed in 1985. Fine in dj. *Smith.* $30/£19

FELD, CHARLES. Picasso. NY: Abrams, (1969). 405 plts. Silk-screened cl. (Lt soiled), else Nice. *Turtle Island.* $100/£63

FELDMAN, ANNETTE. Handmade Lace and Patterns. NY: Harper & Row, 1975. 1st ed. VG (sl cocked, sl worn) in dj (taped). *My Bookhouse.* $24/£15

FELKER, CLAY. Casey Stengel's Secret. Walker, 1961. 1st ed. VG in Good+ dj. *Plapinger.* $50/£31

FELLOWES, EDMUND H. Orlando Gibbons. Oxford: Clarendon, 1925. 1st ed. 3 plts, fldg genealogy. VG. *Hollett.* $48/£30

FELLOWES, WILLIAM DORSET. A Visit to the Monastery of La Trappe, in 1817. London: William Stockdale, 1818. 1st ed. 12 color plts, 1 etching, 1 plt in outline. 1/2 cl, leather spine, tips. Very Nice (bkpl; cvrs sl worn). *Black Sun.* $450/£281

FELLOWS, CHARLES. A Journal Written During an Excursion in Asia Minor. London: John Murray, 1839. 1st ed. x,(i),347pp; dbl-pg map, 19 (of 20) plts, incl 1 dbl-pg, 1 etched plt. (Lt browned, lib blindstamps.) Mod 1/2 calf (rebound), marbled bds, gilt, raised bands, leather spine label. *Edwards.* $320/£200

FELS, FLORENT. Henri Matisse. Paris, 1929. One of 500 numbered. 4 color pochoir plts. Cl; orig wrappers bound in. *Swann*.* $373/£233

FELT, JOSEPH B. The Customs of New England. Boston: T.R. Marvin, 1853. 1st ed. (2),208pp. Orig ptd wrappers (sl chipped, soiled). Custom brn linen folder and slipcase. Howes F73. *Karmiole.* $125/£78

FELTON, MRS. Life in America. A Narrative of Two Years City and Country Residence in the United States. Hull: John Hutchinson, 1838. 1st ed. Dbl-pg frontis, 120pp. Aeg. Orig emb cl, gilt. *Mott.* $175/£109

Female Jockey Club, or, A Sketch of the Manners of the Age. (By Charles Pigott.) NY, 1794. 1st Amer ed. Contemp sheep (lacks spine ends; browned throughout). *Swann*.* $149/£93

FENICHEL, OTTO. The Psychoanalytic Theory of the Neurosis. NY: Norton, 1945. 1st ptg. VG (shaken). *Beasley.* $45/£28

FENN, ELEANOR. Cobwebs to Catch Flies; or, Dialogues in Short Sentences Adapted to Children. Volume II. Containing Instructive Lessons in Words of One Syllable, Two.... London: John Marshall, (ca 1809). Tall 12mo. 72pp (worn; some coloring). Paper-cvrd bds (bds rubbed, spine taped), paste label. *Reisler.* $250/£156

FENN, ELEANOR. Fables in Monosyllables by Mrs. Teachwell to Which Are Added Morals in Dialogues Between a Mother and Children. Phila: Thomas Dobson, 1798. 1st Amer ed. 2 titles bound together, each dated 1798 and retaining their own pagination. 12mo. Leather-backed Dutch floral bds (fr cvr detached, edgeworn). Overall VG (few pp lt browned). *Reisler.* $900/£563

FENN, G. MANVILLE. Menhardoc. London: Blackie & Son, 1885. 1st Eng ed. 32 pp pub's cat at rear. 8 full-pg illus by C.J. Staniland. Color pict cl. VG (edges spotted; cvrs sl rubbed, spine ends sl bumped). *Ulysses.* $104/£65

FENNELL, JAMES H. A Natural History of British and Foreign Quadrupeds. London, 1843. 556pp; 200 woodcuts. Marbled eps; teg. Full brn calf, raised bands, gilt. VG. *Larry Price.* $495/£309

FENNEMAN, NEVIN M. Physiography of Western United States. NY, 1931. 1st ed, 4th imp. Lg color fldg map in pocket. Olive cl, gilt. VG. *Larry Price.* $49/£31

FENNING, DANIEL. The Young Algebraist's Companion; or, A New and Easy Guide to Algebra.... London: G. Keith & J. Robinson, 1751. 2nd ed. xvi,238pp + 1 leaf ads. Contemp calf (rubbed). *Karmiole.* $150/£94

FENOLLOSA, ERNEST. Epochs of Chinese and Japanese Art. London, (1921). New, rev ed. 2 vols. 1/4 cl (sm wormholes on spine of vol 1). *Swann*.* $201/£126

FENTON, ALFRED H. Dana of the Sun. NY/Toronto: Farrar & Rinehart, (1941). 1st ed. Signed, inscribed presentation. Grn cl. VG in dj (sl worn). *Lucas.* $40/£25

FENTON, EDWARD. The Troublesome Voyage of Captain Edward Fenton 1582-83. E. G. R. Taylor (ed). Cambridge: Hakluyt Soc, 1959. Blue cl, gilt. (Sm spine spots), else VG. *Parmer.* $45/£28

FENTON, JAMES. The Memory of War, Poems 1968-1982. Edinburgh: Salamander, 1982. 1st ed. Fine in dj. *Reese.* $25/£16

FENTON, JAMES. Our Western Furniture. Oxford: Sycamore, 1968. One of 200 ptd. 1st bk. NF (nameplt; rear cvr sl soiled). *Ulysses.* $264/£165

FENTON, JAMES. You Were Marvellous. Theatre Reviews. London, 1983. 1st Eng ed. VG in dj (sl faded, dusty). *Clearwater.* $56/£35

FENWICK, K. (ed). The Third Crusade. London: Folio Soc, 1958. Vellum-look bds, gilt. Slipcase (sl worn). *Maggs.* $32/£20

FERBER, EDNA. American Beauty. GC: Doubleday, Doran, 1931. 1st ed. One of 150 numbered, signed. Fine in VG slipcase. *Smith.* $125/£78

FERBER, EDNA. A Peculiar Treasure. NY: Doubleday, Doran, 1939. 1st ed. One of 351 signed. Teg. 1/4 black cl, dec bds, ptd paper spine label. VG (eps, spine, label lt browned). *Heritage.* $150/£94

FERBER, EDNA. Saratoga Trunk. GC: Doubleday, Doran, 1941. 1st ed. One of 462. Signed. Teg. Blue cl, gilt. (Lacks slipcase), else Fine. *Pacific*.* $46/£29

FERGUSON, ALEXANDER HUGH. The Technic of Modern Operations for Hernia. Chicago, 1907. 1st ed. Red cl bds. VG (extrems sl worn). *Doctor's Library.* $100/£63

FERGUSON, CHARLES D. The Experiences of a Forty-Niner During a Third of a Century in the Gold Fields. Chico, 1924. 1st ed thus. VG in pict wraps. *Baade.* $50/£31

FERGUSON, CHARLES D. The Experiences of a Forty-Niner During Thirty-Four Years' Residence in California and Australia. Cleveland, 1888. *Swann*.* $115/£72

FERGUSON, F. O. Architectural Perspective. London: Crosby, Lockwood & Son, 1891. 1st ed. 41pp; 39 fldg plts. Orig bds (strongly rebacked). *Young.* $120/£75

FERGUSON, JAMES (ed). The British Essayists. London: Thomas Tegg & William Blair, 1819. 20 (of 45) vols. Period blind-ruled dk brn calf, gilt, morocco spine labels. (Lacks many spine labels), else VG set. *Pacific*.* $150/£94

FERGUSON, JAMES. The Art of Drawing in Perspective Made Easy. London: W. Strahan & T. Cadell, 1775. 1st ed. xii,124pp; 9 engr fldg plts. Orig calf (scuffed, rebacked, spine top rubbed; rear hinge starting; old red morocco spine label. *Karmiole.* $300/£188

FERGUSON, JAMES. The Art of Drawing in Perspective.... London: W. Strahan, 1777. 2nd ed. 8vo. xii,123,(1), 9 engr fldg plts. Calf (expertly rebacked). *Marlborough.* $440/£275

FERGUSON, JAMES. Astronomy Explained upon Sir Isaac Newton's Principles, and Made Easy to Those Who Have Not Studied Mathematics.... London: J. Johnson et al, 1803. 11th ed (so stated). (8),503,(16)pp; 18 fldg copper-engr plts (incl frontis). Period tree sheep, morocco spine label. (Ink name, corner of 1 plt chipped, another w/sm hole; cvrs worn, fr detached, rear joint cracked), else VG- internally. *Pacific**. $69/£43

FERGUSON, JAMES. An Easy Introduction to Astronomy, for Young Gentlemen and Ladies.... London: T. Cadell, 1779. (4)ff,247,(1)pp (soiled, pastedowns lifted); 7 engr plts. Orig full calf (corners showing, rubbed, fr hinge starting, spine ends worn). *Weber*. $225/£141

FERGUSON, JAMES. Lectures on Select Subjects in Mechanics, Hydrostaticks, Penumaticks, and Optics. A. Millar, 1760. 1st ed. (viii),417pp + (vi, index, ad)pp; complete w/23 plts. Old polished calf, gilt, raised bands, spine label. (Bkpl; sl rubbed, scraped at edges, upper hinge tender.) *Hollett*. $352/£220

FERGUSON, JAMES. Lectures on Select Subjects in Mechanics, Hydrostatics, Pneumatics, and Optics. London: A Millar, 1764. 2nd ed. (viii),252,(4)pp; 23 fldg engr copperplts. Orig full calf (worn, restored, corners renewed, bumped), 2 black leather spine labels. Internally Very Clean. *Weber*. $425/£266

FERGUSON, JOHN ALEXANDER. A Bibliography of Australia, 1784-1900. Canberra, 1976-86. 7 vols. (Lt worn.) Djs (except vol 4). *Oinonen**. $350/£219

FERGUSON, JOHN. Bibliotheca Chemica; a Catalogue of the Alchemical, Chemical and Pharmaceutical Books in the Collection of the Late James Young of Kelly and Durris. London: Holland, (1954). Rpt of 1906 ed. 2 vols. VG set (spine vol 2 blistered). *Glaser*. $225/£141

FERGUSON, WILLIAM. America by River and Rail. London: James Nisbet, 1856. 1st ed. viii,511pp; 2 plts. Grn cl (rebacked, old back laid down; corners rubbed). Internally Fine. Howes F85. *Mott*. $125/£78

FERGUSSON, BERNARD. Eton Portrait. London: John Milles, 1937. 1st ed. Laszlo Moholy-Nagy (photos). (Cl faded, sl spotted), else NF. *Cahan*. $200/£125

FERGUSSON, EMA. Murder and Mystery in New Mexico. Albuquerque, 1948. 1st ed. Fine (owner ink info) in dj (chipped). *Baade*. $40/£25

FERGUSSON, HARVEY. Rio Grande. NY: Knopf, 1933. 1st ed. NF in dj (chipped, lt stained). *Labordo*. $75/£47

FERGUSSON, HARVEY. Wolf Song. Knopf, 1927. 1st ltd ed of 100, numbered, signed. Fine in glassine dj. (Lacks slipcase.) *Authors Of The West*. $300/£188

FERLINGHETTI, LAWRENCE and NANCY J. PETERS. Literary San Francisco: A Pictorial History from Its Beginnings to the Present Day. Harper & Row, (1980). 1st ed. Fine in dj. *Authors Of The West*. $35/£22

FERLINGHETTI, LAWRENCE. The Canticle of Jack Kerouac. Lowell: Spotlight Press, 1987. One of 350. Signed. Sewn in wraps. Fine. *Beasley*. $60/£38

FERLINGHETTI, LAWRENCE. Fuclock. London: Fire, 1968. 1st ed. Signed. Folded broadside. Fine. *Beasley*. $60/£38

FERLINGHETTI, LAWRENCE. Moscow in the Wilderness, Segovia in the Snow. SF: Beach Books, 1967. 1st ed. Fldg broadside. Fine. *Beasley*. $40/£25

FERLINGHETTI, LAWRENCE. One Thousand Fearful Words for Fidel Castro. SF: City Lights, 1961. 1st ed. Signed. Fldg broadside. Fine. *Beasley*. $40/£25

FERLINGHETTI, LAWRENCE. The Sea and Ourselves at Cape Ann. Madison: Red Ozier, 1979. 1st ed. Signed. One of 200. Fine in wraps. *Beasley*. $85/£53

FERLINGHETTI, LAWRENCE. Starting from San Francisco. (NY): New Directions, (1961). 1st ed. Pict bds w/record in rear sleeve. Fine (sl bumped, rubbed). *Between The Covers*. $150/£94

FERLINGHETTI, LAWRENCE. Tentative Description of a Dinner Given to Promote the Impeachment.... SF: Golden Mountain, 1958. 1st ed, 2nd state wraps in black instead of gold. Signed. Fine. *Beasley*. $30/£19

FERLINGHETTI, LAWRENCE. A Trip to Italy and France. New Directions, (1981). 1st ed. Ltd to 250 numbered, signed. VG. *King*. $75/£47

FERLINGHETTI, LAWRENCE. White on White. SF: Committee on Breytenbach Case, 1977? 1st ed. Fldg broadside. Fine. *Beasley*. $50/£31

FERLINGHETTI, LAWRENCE. A World Awash with Fascism and Fear. SF: Cranium, 1971. 1st ed. Signed. Folded broadside. NF. *Beasley*. $40/£25

FERM, VERGILIUS. Forgotten Religions. NY: Philosophical Library, (1950). (Blind-emb stamp.) *Archaeologia*. $35/£22

FERMOR, PATRICK LEIGH. Three Letters from the Andes. Murray, 1991. 1st ed. Signed. Fine in dj. *Any Amount*. $38/£24

FERMOR, PATRICK LEIGH. A Time to Keep Silence. London: John Murray, 1957. 1st Eng ed. VG (feps partly browned; cvrs sl mkd, bowed; spine ends, corners sl bumped) in dj (nicked, sl rubbed, sl creased, edges sl browned). *Ulysses*. $96/£60

FERRALL, S. A. A Ramble of Six Thousand Miles Through the United States of America. London: Effingham Wilson, 1832. Only ed. Facs frontis, xii,360pp (sig tp). Half-title present. Uncut. Orig bds (worn), paper label (worn). Internally Fine. Howes F93. *Mott*. $200/£125

FERRARS, MAX and BERTHA. Burma. Sampson Low, Marston, 1900. 1st ed. Fldg map. Teg. Dec cl, gilt. VG (sl shaken, few sm mks). *Ash*. $200/£125

FERRIER, J. P. Caravan Journeys and Wanderings in Persia, Afghanistan, Turkistan and Beloochistan.... London: Murray, 1856. Thick 8vo. Map. Recent 1/2 calf, red label, raised bands, gilt. *Petersfield*. $720/£450

FERRIER, J. P. History of the Afghans. William Jesse (trans). London: John Murray, 1858. 1st ed. Demy 8vo. xxi,491pp; 2 maps (1 fldg), pub's list dated January 1858. VG (bkpl) in blind-emb cl (spine head sl chipped). *Ulysses*. $960/£600

FERRIGINO, ROBERT. The Horse Latitudes. Hamish Hamilton, 1990. 1st ed. Fine in dj. *Any Amount*. $32/£20

FERRIS, JAMES CODY. The X-Bar-X Boys at Copperhead Gulch. NY: G&D, 1933. X-Bar-X Boys #12; lists 16 titles on dj flap. 5x7.5. 219pp + ads. VG + (sl shelfworn) in dj (edgeworn). *My Bookhouse*. $42/£26

FERRIS, JAMES CODY. The X-Bar-X Boys on Big Bison Trail. NY: G&D, 1927. X-Bar-X Boys #4; lists to #16 on dj flap. 5x7.5. Walter S. Rogers (illus). 216pp + ads. VG + in dj (sl worn). *My Bookhouse*. $42/£26

FERRIS, JAMES CODY. The X-Bar-X Boys Seeking the Lost Troopers. NY: G&D, 1941. 1st ed. X-Bar-X Boys #20; lists only 19 titles on dj flap. 5x7.5. 213pp + ads. VG (shelfworn) in dj (chipped, worn). *My Bookhouse*. $37/£23

FERRIS, ROBERT G. (ed). Lewis and Clark—Historic Places Associated with Their Transcontinental Exploration 1804-06. Washington: USDI National Park Service, 1975. Fine. *Perier*. $30/£19

FERRIS, ROBERT G. (ed). Prospector, Cowhand, and Sodbuster. Washington: US Dept of Interior, Nat'l Park Service, 1967. 1st ed. Fine. *Book Market*. $10/£6

FERRIS, W. A. Life in the Rocky Mountains. Paul C. Phillips (ed). Denver: Old West, 1940. 1st bk ed. Frontis, 2 maps (1 fldg), 3 facs plts. Red cl. Fine (spine gilt sl worn) in VG + dj (sl chipped, soiled). Howes F100. *Harrington*. $250/£156

FERRIS, WILLIAM. Blues from the Delta. GC: Anchor Press/Doubleday, 1978. 1st ed. VG in pict dj. *Petrilla*. $25/£16

FERRO, ROBERT. The Family of Max Desir. NY, 1983. 1st ed. Signed. (Name, date), o/w Fine in Fine dj. *Warren*. $40/£25

FESTING, GABRIELLE. Strangers Within the Gates. William Blackwood & Sons, 1914. 1st ed. Color-ptd frontis. Red pict cl, gilt. (Spine ends bumped), o/w VG. *Sotheran*. $96/£60

Festivals in San Francisco. Stanford Univ, James Ladd Delkin, 1939. 1st ed. One of 1000 ptd. Frontis, 3 full-pg illus. Linen-backed dec bds, paper spine label. Fine. *Harrington*. $85/£53

FETHERSTON, F. M. Yarns Round a Prairie Camp Fire. London, (1860?). 61pp. Orig ptd wraps (skillfully re-attached). *Kane**. $70/£44

FEWKES, JESSE WALTER. Antiquities of the Mesa Verde National Park: Cliff Palace. BAE Bulletin 51. Washington: GPO, 1911. 1st ed. Fldg plan. Grn cl. VG + (spine dknd, 2 corners sl bumped). *Harrington*. $45/£28

FEWKES, JESSE WALTER. Hopi Katcinas Drawn by Native Artists. Chicago: Rio Grande, (1962). Rpt. 63 color plts. Full black leather, gilt. Fine. *Argonaut*. $100/£63

FEWKES, JESSE WALTER. Hopi Katcinas Drawn by Native Artists. NM: Rio Grande, (1969). Facs rpt. Fine. *Book Market*. $40/£25

FIALA, ANTHONY. Fighting the Polar Ice. NY: Doubleday, Doran, 1907. 2nd ed. Fldg map. Teg. VG (ex-lib). *High Latitude*. $100/£63

FIDLER, ISAAC. Observations on Professions, Literature, Manners, and Emigration, in the United States and Canada...in 1832. NY: J. & J. Harper, 1833. 1st Amer ed. 247pp (sl foxed, eps stained). Orig cl (faded, spine sl worn), paper label. Howes F110. *Mott*. $50/£31

Field Book. (By W. H. Maxwell.) London, 1936. Contemp 1/2 calf (rubbed; tp grubby). *Grayling*. $112/£70

FIELD, EUGENE. Lullaby-Land; Songs of Childhood Selected by Kenneth Grahame. Toronto: George N. Morang, (1900). 1st Canadian ed. 8vo. Charles Robinson (illus). (vi),229pp. Teg. 1/2 dk blue calf over blue cl sides, 5 raised spine bands, gilt. Fine (orig cl cvr bound in at rear). *Sotheran*. $237/£148

FIELD, EUGENE. Poems of Childhood. NY: Scribner, 1904. 1st ed w/illus by Maxfield Parrish. Sm 4to. 8 color plts. Pict eps; untrimmed. Black cl, gilt, mtd color illus on fr cvr. Cvrs Good (sl worn, lt scuffed; eps sl aged). *Baltimore**. $110/£69

FIELD, EUGENE. Poems of Childhood. NY: Scribner, 1904. Initial ed w/these illus. 8 Fine color plts by Maxfield Parrish, guards. Pict eps; untrimmed. Black cl, gilt, lt mtd color pict label fr cvr. (Cvrs sl dusty, edges sl spotted, sl wear.) Text Clean. *Baltimore**. $160/£100

FIELD, EUGENE. Verse and Prose. Boston: Bibliophile Soc, 1917. 1st Amer ed. Teg, uncut. 1/2 vellum, gilt. NF (bkpl; traces of removed bkpl rep). *Polyanthos*. $35/£22

FIELD, EUGENE. With Trumpet and Drum. NY, 1892. 1st Amer ed. Teg. Pict cvrs. NF (inscrip; sl rubbed, spine sunned). *Polyanthos*. $25/£16

FIELD, EUGENE. The Writings in Prose and Verse of Eugene Field. NY: Scribner, 1920. 12 vols. Frontispieces. Teg; unopened. 3/4 crushed dk grn morocco, marbled bds, gilt. (Internal dampstaining vol 6), else NF. *Pacific**. $196/£123

FIELD, G. A Grammar of Colouring. London, 1882. 3rd ed. Rev, enlgd. xvi,224pp. *Ars Artis*. $56/£35

FIELD, MICHAEL. (Pseud of Katherine Bradley & Edith Cooper.) Underneath the Bough: A Book of Verses. Portland, ME: Thomas B. Mosher, 1898. 1st ed thus. Ltd to 925. 93pp. Pale blue silk ribbon marker present. Unopened. VG + in cream wrappers w/overlapping fore-edges. *Truepenny*. $35/£22

FIELD, RACHEL. Calico Bush. Macmillan, 1931. 1st ed. Inscribed, signed. Allen Lewis (illus). 213pp. Lt blue, yellow cl w/3-inch paper plt set in w/title. NF (spine foot sl rubbed, corners bumped 1/8-inch). *Price*. $150/£94

FIELD, RACHEL. Just Across the Street. Macmillan, 1933. 1st ed. 109pp. VG (spine faded, bumped w/wrinkle across title; bottom corners bumped). *Price*. $30/£19

FIELD, RICHARD M. The Principles of Historical Geology from the Regional Point of View. Princeton Univ, 1933. 1st ed. 10 fldg maps in pocket. Blue cl, gilt. VG (ex-lib). *Larry Price*. $49/£31

FIELD, ROBERT D. The Art of Walt Disney. NY: Macmillan, 1942. 1st ed. 59 plts. Tan cl. Good (sl handled; sl rubbed, lt dusty). *Baltimore**. $70/£44

FIELD, ROSWELL M. The Passing of Mother's Portrait. Herrin, IL: Trovillion Private Press, 1948. One of 989 signed. Good (faded, spotted). *Bohling*. $20/£13

FIELD, SARA BARD. Vintage Festival. A Play Pageant. Festivities Celebrating the Vine.... SF: The Book Club of CA, 1920. One of 500. Full-pg signed presentation dated April 1926. VG. *Perier*. $97/£61

FIELD, STEPHEN J. California Alcade. Oakland: Biobooks, 1950. One of 600. Frontisport, lg color fldg map. Red buckram. VG. *House*. $25/£16

FIELDER, MILDRED. Railroads of the Black Hills. Seattle: Superior Pub, (1964). (1st ed.) VG + in dj (edgeworn, price-clipped). *Bohling*. $35/£22

FIELDING, DAPHNE. The Duchess of Jermyn Street. Boston: Little, Brown, 1964. 1st US ed. VG in dj (sl soiled, faded, spine ends sl chipped, price-clipped). *Virgo*. $19/£12

FIELDING, HENRY. A Clear State of the Case of Elizabeth Canning, Who Hath Sworn That She Was Robbed...for Which One Mary Squires Now Lies Under Sentence of Death. London: A. Millar, 1753. 2nd ed. 62pp. Calf-backed bds. Good. *Young*. $120/£75

FIELDING, HENRY. The History of the Adventures of Joseph Andrews, and his Friend Mr. Abraham Adams. A. Millar, 1743. 3rd ed. 2 vols. Contemp full leather (respined), raised bands. Good (ex-lib, stamp, contemp sigs, lt spotted; corners rubbed, spine shelf #). *Tiger*. $152/£95

FIELDING, HENRY. The History of the Adventures of Joseph Andrews, and of His Friend Mr. Abraham Adams. London: A. Millar, 1742. 1st ed. Ltd to 1500. 2 vols. Small 8vo. 6pp pub's ads present. Full 19th-cent speckled calf (expertly rebacked), gilt paneled spines, raised bands, edges gilt, by Riviere. Fine. *Appelfeld*. $1,650/£1,031

FIELDING, HENRY. The History of the Life of the Late Mr. Jonathan Wild, the Great. LEC, 1943. Ltd to 1500 numbered, signed by T. M. Cleland (illus). Fine in slipcase. *Swann**. $115/£72

FIELDING, HENRY. The History of Tom Jones, a Foundling. London: A. Millar, 1759. 1st ed. Errata leaf in vol 1, called-for cancels throughout. 6 vols. 8vo. Full contemp calf, red morocco spine labels, gilt. (Foxed, at least 3 ll torn, fep of vol 1 loose; worn, rubbed.) Fldg case (worn) w/imitation leather backstrips. *Kane**. $1,600/£1,000

FIELDING, HENRY. The History of Tom Jones, a Foundling. Paris: Fr. Amb. Didot, 1780. 4 vols. Extra-illus w/complete set of 12 hand-colored copperplt engrs by Moreau le Jeune. Aeg. Contemp full grn levant morocco, gilt. VG set (extrems worn, vol 2 and 3 headcaps chipped). *House*. $500/£313

FIELDING, HENRY. The History of Tom Jones: A Foundling. NY: LEC, 1952. One of 1500. Signed by T. M. Cleland (illus). 2 vols. Buckram, paper spine labels. Fine in glassine, slipcase. *Pacific**. $69/£43

FIELDING, HENRY. The Works.... Gay & Bird, (1905). 12 vols. Frontispieces. Teg. Contemp 1/2 calf by Bumpus (spines faded, sl rubbed). *Sotheby's**. $478/£299

FIELDING, MANTLE. Dictionary of American Painters, Sculptors and Engravers. Phila, (1945). One of 700. (Extrems rubbed.) *Swann**. $103/£64

FIELDING, T. H. and J. WALTON. A Picturesque Tour of the English Lakes. R. Ackerman, 1821. Half-title, hand-colored tp vignette, 48 hand-colored plts (some faint discoloration). 19th-cent 1/2 morocco (sides sl rubbed). *Sotheby's**. $1,563/£977

FIELDING, T. H. Synopsis of Practical Perspective, Lineal and Aerial. London, 1829. 1st ed. 136pp; 17 engr plts. 1/2-leather (neatly rebacked). *Ars Artis*. $120/£75

FIERSTEIN, HARVEY. Torch Song Trilogy. NY: Villard, 1983. 1st ed. VF in VF dj (sl rubbed). *Between The Covers*. $175/£109

Fifteenth Century Woodcuts and Metalcuts from the National Gallery of Art. Washington: Nat'l Gallery of Art, n.d. (1965). Good in wrappers (backstrip sl rubbed). *Washton*. $75/£47

Fifty Fish from American Waters. Richmond: Allen & Ginter, (c. 1880s). 1st ed. 10 ll. String-bound chromolitho wrappers. (Cvrs soiled), else VG. *Pacific**. $115/£72

Fifty Years of Fettes. Edinburgh: T. & A. Constable, 1931. 1st ed. 18 plts. Buckram (spine sl dknd), gilt. *Hollett*. $48/£30

FILBY, F. A. A History of Food Adulteration and Analysis. London: Allen & Unwin, 1934. Good + (new eps; spine sl damaged). *Savona*. $32/£20

FILLIS, JAMES. Breaking and Riding with Military Commentaries. (London), Nd. 4th ed. (Name; binding sl spotted, cockeyed.) *Woolson*. $50/£31

FINBERG, A. J. Early English Water-Colour Drawings by the Great Masters. Geoffrey Holme (ed). London: The Studio, 1919. 44 plts. Teg. (1/2-title, last leaf browned; upper bd, spine sl faded.) *Edwards*. $48/£30

FINBERG, A. J. The History of Turner's Liber Studiorum. London, 1924. One of 650 signed. 91 plts. (Bkpl, lt spotted; cl lt soiled, nick.) *Edwards*. $320/£200

FINCH, CHRISTOPHER. The Art of Walt Disney. NY: Harry N. Abrams, (1973). White linen w/cut-out Mickey on cvr. Fine. *Appelfeld*. $125/£78

FINCH, EDWIN W. The Frontier, Army and Professional Life of Edwin W. Finch, M.D. (New Rochelle, NY, 1909.) 1st ed. Photo frontisport. Red cl. VG. *Chapel Hill*. $125/£78

FINCH, GEORGE INGLE. The Making of a Mountaineer. London: Arrowsmith, (1927). 3rd imp. Blue cl, spine gilt. Good (bumped, rubbed, spine dknd). *Blue Mountain*. $25/£16

FINCH, ROBERT (ed). The Story of Minor League Baseball. National Assoc of Prof BB Leagues, 1953. 1st ed. VG (fr hinge repaired, spine faded). *Plapinger*. $200/£125

FINCH, ROBERT. The Strength of the Hills. Toronto: McClelland & Stewart, 1948. 1st ed. Inscribed 1950. Fine in VG dj (lt chipped). *Reese*. $55/£34

FINDEN, EDWARD (ed). The Beauties of Moore: A Series of Portraits of His Principal Female Characters. London: Chapman & Hall, 1847. 1st ed. 25 engr plts. Aeg. Red morocco, gilt. (Foxed; spine ends worn, spine dknd, extrems sl rubbed), else VG. *Pacific**. $109/£68

FINDEN, EDWARD FRANCIS and WILLIAM. The Ports, Harbours and Watering-Places, and Picturesque Scenery of Great Britain. Virtue, n.d. 6 vols. 4to. 2 engr tps, 142 engr plts. Gilt edges. Orig pub's cl, gilt. (Sl spotting.) *Sotheby's**. $1,251/£782

Fine Books Published by the Limited Editions Club, 1929-1985. LEC, 1985. One of 800. Fine in slipcase. *Swann**. $201/£126

FINER, ANN and GEORGE SAVAGE (eds). The Selected Letters of Josiah Wedgwood. Cory, Adams & Mackay, 1965. 1st ed. 15 plts (2 color). (Sl marginal pencil lining.) Dj (sl soiled). *Hollett*. $56/£35

FINERTY, JOHN F. War-Path and Bivouac, or the Conquest of the Sioux. Chicago: Publication Office, 1890. 1st ed. (22),25-460pp. Gilt-dec blue cl. (Corners, spine ends worn, rubbed, shelfwear), else VG. Ink sig of W.A. Menio, May 1890. Howes F126. *Pacific**. $115/£72

FINK, DANIEL. Barns of the Genesee Country 1790-1915. Geneseo, NY, (1987). 1st ed. Signed. VG in dj (price-clipped). *King*. $45/£28

FINKELSTEIN, SAMUEL (ed). Regiment of the Century: The Story of the 397th Infantry Regiment. Stuttgart, 1945. VG. *Clark*. $75/£47

FINKELSTEIN, SIDNEY. Jazz: A People's Music. NY: Citadel, (1948). 1st ed. Black bds (corners bumped). *Petrilla*. $25/£16

FINKELSTEIN, SIDNEY. Jazz: A People's Music. NY: Citadel, 1948. 1st ed, 1st issue. Black bd w/yellow stamping. Fine in NF blue/black/tan dj. *Beasley*. $50/£31

FINLAY, IAN HAMILTON. The Dancers Inherit the Party. London: Fulcrum, (1969). 1st ed. Black cl. Fine in Fine dj. *Dermont*. $100/£63

FINLAY, IAN HAMILTON. Rhymes for Lemons. Lanark, Scotland: Wild Hawthorn Press, (1970). One of 300. Signed, numbered. Illus fldg bk. Fine. *Turtle Island*. $60/£38

FINLAY, IAN. Scottish Gold and Silver Work. C&W, 1956. Dj (chipped, sl rubbed). *Edwards*. $56/£35

FINLAY, ROSS. The Unknown Highlands. Foulis, 1970. 1st ed. 16 maps. VG in dj. *Hollett*. $32/£20

FINLEY, ERNEST LATIMER (ed). History of Sonoma County, California: Its People and Resources. Santa Rosa: Press Democrat Pub Co, 1937. Marbled eps, edges. Orig gilt-lettered morocco. (Scuffed), else VG. *Pacific**. $75/£47

FINLEY, JAMES B. History of the Wyandott Mission, at Upper Sandusky, Ohio.... Cincinnati, 1840. 1st ed. 432pp (foxed, soiled, lib mks). Contemp calf (rubbed, upper joint broken). Howes F144. *Oinonen**. $50/£31

FINLEY, JAMES B. Life Among the Indians; or, Personal Reminiscences and Historical Incidents.... Cincinnati: Cranston & Curts, (c. 1868). 548pp + 4pp ads. Blue cl. VG (text sl toned; edges lt worn). Howes F145. *House*. $65/£41

FINLEY, JAMES B. Sketches of Western Methodism. Cincinnati, 1855. 551pp; port. (Foxed, sl worn.) *King*. $25/£16

FINLEY, JOHN. The French in the Heart of America. NY, 1915. 1st ed. (Hinges repaired), else Good. *Dumont*. $50/£31

FINN, DAVID. Henry Moore: Sculpture and Environment. NY: Abrams, 1970. Dj. *Argosy*. $85/£53

FINNEY, CHARLES G. The Circus of Doctor Lao. London: Grey Walls, 1948. 1st Eng ed. 8 full-pg color illus. (Spine sl faded, foot worn, head bumped; cvrs sl mkd, handled; lacks dj.) *Clearwater*. $48/£30

FINNEY, CHARLES G. The Circus of Doctor Lao. London: Grey Walls, 1948. 1st UK ed. VG in dj. *Smith*. $100/£63

FINNEY, CHARLES G. The Circus of Doctor Lao. LEC, 1982. One of 2000 signed by Claire Van Vliet (illus). Fine in slipcase. *Swann**. $92/£58

FINNEY, CHARLES G. The Circus of Doctor Lao. (To Which Boris Artzybasheff Has Added Seven Interpretations of His Own). NY: Viking, 1935. 1st ed, 1st bk. VG + in Nice dj (sl rubbed, price-clipped). *Smith*. $150/£94

FINNEY, JACK. The House of Numbers. (NY): Dell First Edition, (1957). Pb orig. VG (sm crease corner, pp sl browned, spine edge sl rubbed). *Between The Covers*. $85/£53

FINNEY, JACK. Time and Again. NY: S&S, (1970). 1st ed. Signed, inscribed. (Dampstaining to top edges of cvrs, pp), else Good in VG dj. *Pacific**. $150/£94

FIRBANK, RONALD. Caprice. London: Grant Richards, 1917. 1st ed. Frontis. VG + in VG- dj (extrems chipped, few brn fr cvr stains). *Lame Duck*. $300/£188

FIRBANK, RONALD. The Flower Beneath the Foot. NY: Brentano's, 1924. 1st US ed. Good + (spine worn) in dj (chipped, worn). *Beasley*. $40/£25

FIRBANK, RONALD. The New Rythum and Other Pieces. London: Gerald Duckworth, 1962. 1st Eng ed. B/w frontis photo, 10 b/w plts, dbl-pg spread repro. NF (spine ends, corner sl bumped) in dj (nicked, sl creased, price-clipped). *Ulysses.* $58/£36

FIRBANK, RONALD. Odette: A Fairy Tale for Weary People. London: Grant Richards, 1916. 1st ed. 4 plts. Ptd paper wrappers. VG (sl browned, lt chipped). *Heritage.* $200/£125

FIRBANK, RONALD. Odette: A Fairy Tale for Weary People. Grant Richards, 1916. 1st UK ed. VG in pict wrappers (sl browned). *Williams.* $232/£145

FIRBANK, RONALD. The Princess Zoubaroff. London: Grant Richards, 1920. 1st ed. Fine. *Beasley.* $125/£78

FIRBANK, RONALD. Vainglory. NY: Brentanos, (1925). 1st Amer ed. VG+ (fep sl offset; sl bumped) in VG dj (crown lt nicked). *Between The Covers.* $150/£94

FIRBANK, RONALD. When Widows Love and Tragedy in Green. Edward Potoker (ed). London: Enitharmon, 1980. One of 300. Inscribed by Potoker. Fine in dj (fr edge sl torn). *Lame Duck.* $35/£22

FIREBAUGH, W. C. The Inns of the Middle Ages. Chicago: Pascal Covici, 1924. 1st ed. One of 900. 1/2 cl. (Extrems rubbed), else VG. *Pacific*.* $52/£33

First Impressions of America. (By John Walter.) London: Privately ptd, 1867. Only ed. 2 prelim ll, 131pp. Aeg. Red cl, gilt. NF. *Mott.* $175/£109

First Night Gilbert and Sullivan. LEC, 1958. Ltd to 1500 numbered. Fine in slipcase. *Swann*.* $138/£86

First Steamship Pioneers. SF: First Steamship Pioneers Assoc, (1874). 1st ed. Ltd to 100. 10.25x7.75. (11),ii-viii,(3),2-393pp. Marbled eps. Full morocco, gilt, raised bands. Lot includes June 23, 1849, issue of New York Weekly Herald. (Bkpl, 1849 newspaper lt foxed, worn; leather sl scuffed), o/w VG. *Pacific*.* $690/£431

First Through the Grand Canyon. Doubleday, 1915. Pict eps. Blue cl. (Lt worn, soiled), else VG. *Five Quail.* $22/£14

FISCHEL, O. Raphael. London: Kegan Paul, 1948. 2 vols. 302 plts. Good in dj (torn). *Ars Artis.* $168/£105

FISCHER, BRUNO. The Dead Men Grin. Phila: David McKay, 1945. 1st ed. (Cvrs lt soiled), else VG in dj (lt worn). *Murder.* $75/£47

FISCHER, LE ROY H. Lincoln's Gadfly. Norman, (1964). 1st ed. VG in dj (price-clipped). *King.* $25/£16

FISH, DONALD. Airline Detective. London: Collins, 1962. 1st ed. Fine in dj (few sm tears). *Mordida.* $100/£63

FISH, MARGERY. We Made a Garden. Newton Abbot: David & Charles, 1970. 4th imp. VG in dj. *Fair Meadow.* $45/£28

FISHBEIN, MORRIS. A Bibliography of Infantile Paralysis 1789-1944, with Selected Abstracts and Annotations. Phila, 1946. 1st ed. Red cl bds. VG. *Doctor's Library.* $200/£125

FISHER, A. K. The Hawks and Owls of the United States in Their Relation to Agriculture. WA, 1893. 26 color litho plts. (Shelfworn, sl spotted, foxed.) *Oinonen*.* $160/£100

FISHER, A. RIGBY (ed). Compendium for Printers. Hutchinson Ptg Trust, (1937). Orig 1/4 blue morocco, gilt. VG. *Hollett.* $72/£45

FISHER, ALEXANDER. A Journal of a Voyage of Discovery to the Arctic Regions...1819 and 1820. London: Longman, Hurst, et al, 1821. 4th ed. xi,320pp. 2 maps (one fldg). Old 1/2 calf (rubbed). VG. *High Latitude.* $250/£156

FISHER, DOROTHY CANFIELD. And Long Remember. Whittlesey, 1959. 1st ed. 7x10. Ezra Jack Keats (illus). 118pp. VG (bkpl) in VG dj (sm chips, edgeworn). *Price.* $18/£11

FISHER, E. M. The Osteology and Myology of the California River Otter. Stanford Univ, 1942. (Pp tanned.) Wrappers (soiled). *Sutton.* $25/£16

FISHER, H. D. The Gun and the Gospel. Chicago: Kenwood Press, 1896. 1st ed. Frontisport. Navy cl. (Pp browned; sl worn), else VG. *Glenn.* $95/£59

FISHER, H. I. Adaptations and Comparative Anatomy of the Locomotor Apparatus of New World Vultures. Notre Dame, 1946. 13 plts. (Lt worn.) Wrappers (name stamp). *Sutton.* $30/£19

FISHER, HARRISON. American Girls in Miniature. NY: Scribner, 1912. 1st ed. 12mo. 32 full-pg illus. Cl-backed bds, color paste label. VG. *Reisler.* $400/£250

FISHER, HARRISON. Bachelor Belles. NY: G&D, (1908). 8vo. Theodore B. Hapgood (decs). Lt gray cl, color paste label. Good in glassine dj, color pict box (dusty, corners taped). *Reisler.* $250/£156

FISHER, HARRISON. The Little Gift Book. NY: Scribner, 1913. 1st ed. 8vo. 32 full-pg color plts. Color illus bds. Good in glassine dj (worn), pub's pict box (sides broken, cvrs dusty). *Reisler.* $625/£391

FISHER, JAMES. The Fulmar. Collins, 1952. 1st ed. 4 color, 78 b/w plts, 70 maps, diags & line dwgs. (Cl lettering sl dull.) *Hollett.* $136/£85

FISHER, L. E. The Death of the Evening Star. NY: Doubleday, 1972. 1st ed. Fine in dj. *Walcot.* $16/£10

FISHER, LOUISE B. An Eighteenth Century Garland. Williamsburg: Colonial Williamsburg, 1951. 1st ed. (Browned; corners bumped), else VG. *Fair Meadow.* $15/£9

FISHER, M. F. K. Answer in the Affirmative and The Oldest Man. (Vineburg, CA), 1989. Ltd to 200. Gray cl. Mint in dj. *Truepenny.* $75/£47

FISHER, M. F. K. Boss Dog: A Fable in Six Parts. (Covelo): Yolla Bolly, (1990). Ltd to 255. Block-ptd stiff wrappers of Indian straw paper, slipcase. *Truepenny.* $155/£97

FISHER, M. F. K. Here Let Us Feast. NY: Viking, 1946. 1st ed. NF in dj (rear panel browned). *Smith.* $100/£63

FISHER, M. F. K. How to Cook a Wolf. NY: Duell, Sloan & Pearce, (1942). 1st ed. Fair (shelfworn) in dj (heavily chipped, torn, flaps clipped). *Pacific*.* $40/£25

FISHER, M. F. K. How to Cook a Wolf. NY: Duell, Sloan & Pearce, 1942. 1st ed. VG+ in dj (rubbed, few chips). *Smith.* $225/£141

FISHER, M. F. K. Spirits of the Valley. (NY): Targ Editions, 1985. 1st ed. One of 250, signed. Fine in glassine wrapper. *Reese.* $125/£78

FISHER, M. F. K. The Story of Wine in California. Berkeley: Univ of CA, 1962. 1st ed. NF in dj. *Pacific*.* $46/£29

FISHER, MARGERY. Who's Who in Children's Books. Weidenfeld & Nicolson, 1978. Dj. *Forest.* $32/£20

FISHER, MURRAY. The Golliwog's Dream and Other Stories for Little Folk. London: Cassell, (1910). 4to. Frank Hart (illus). Cl-backed color pict bds (corners, fr hinge sl worn; sig on cvr). Nice. *Reisler.* $375/£234

FISHER, O. C. and J. C. DYKES. King Fisher. Norman: Univ of OK, (1967). VG in dj (sl worn). *Lien.* $17/£11

FISHER, RALPH E. Vanishing Markers: Memories of Boston and Maine Railroading, 1946-1952. Stephen Greene, (1976). 1st ed. Good in dj. *Rybski.* $30/£19

FISHER, RAYMOND H. Bering's Voyages, Whither and Why. Seattle: Univ of WA, (1977). 1st ed. Red cl. Fine in dj (sm spine tear). *Argonaut.* $45/£28

FISHER, RICHARD. Introduction to a Catalogue of the Early Italian Prints in the British Museum. Chiswick, 1886. viii,470pp. (Lib label, cardholder, tp sl soiled; fr hinge cracked, tender, lib label, worn.) *Edwards.* $48/£30

FISHER, RUTH B. On the Borders of Pigmy-Land. Marshall Bros, (n.d. c. 1910). 4th ed. Frontisport. Grn pict cl, gilt. Good (lt foxed; sm worm-hole mid upper joint). *Sotheran.* $96/£60

FISHER, STEVE. The Big Dream. GC: Doubleday, 1970. 1st ed. Fine in Fine dj. *Between The Covers.* $125/£78

FISHER, STEVE. Destination Tokyo. NY: Appleton Century, 1943. 1st ed. Fine in NF dj (sl spine loss). *Between The Covers.* $300/£188

FISHER, SYDNEY GEORGE. The Struggle for American Independence. Phila: Lippincott, (1908). 1st ed. 2 vols. *Ginsberg.* $125/£78

FISHER, VARDIS and OPAL LAUREL HOLMES. Gold Rushes and Mining Camps of the Early American West. Caldwell: Caxton Ptrs, 1968. 1st ed. Fine in dj. *Labordo.* $95/£59

FISHER, VARDIS and OPAL LAUREL HOLMES. Gold Rushes and Mining Camps of the Early American West. Caldwell: Caxton Ptrs, 1979. 4th ed. Fine in dj. *Pacific*.* $29/£18

FISHER, VARDIS and OPAL LAUREL HOLMES. Gold Rushes and Mining Camps of the Early American West. Caldwell, ID: Caxton, 1979. 4th ptg. Buckram. VF in dj. *Argonaut.* $75/£47

FISHER, VARDIS. Children of God. NY: Harper, 1939. 1st ed. VG in dj (worn). *Labordo.* $85/£53

FISHER, VARDIS. City of Illusion. NY: Harper, (1941). 1st ed. Fine in VG dj (chipped). *Between The Covers.* $100/£63

FISHER, VARDIS. City of Illusion. Caldwell: Caxton, 1941. 1st ed. One of 100. Signed. Teg. Black morocco, gilt. Fine. *Pacific*.* $81/£51

FISHER, W. B. (ed). The Cambridge History of Iran. Cambridge: CUP, 1968. 1st ed. 8 vols. Fine set. *Pacific*.* $288/£180

FISHER, W. K. Asteroidea of the North Pacific and Adjacent Waters. Washington, 1911-30. 3 vols. 120 (of 122); 81; 94 plts. Buckram, wraps bound in. (Lib stamps.) *Henly.* $237/£148

FISHER, W. K. Four New Genera and Fifty-Eight New Species of Starfishes from the Philippine Islands, Celebes, and the Moluccas. Washington: GPO, 1913. Mostly unopened. Fine in ptd wraps. *Parmer.* $25/£16

Fisherman's Daughter; or, Sebie's Lessons, and the Way She Learned Them. Boston/NY: Amer Tract Soc, n.d. (ca 1865). 12mo. Full-pg engr color frontis, plt guard, 143pp; 2 full-pg engrs. Blind-tooled grn cl on bds, gilt. Good (ink dedication fep, foxed, spotted; cvrs faded, spine sl chipped). *Hobbyhorse.* $70/£44

Fishermen's Own Book. (By George H. Proctor.) Gloucester: Procter Bros, (1882). 1st ed. (i),274pp + 38pp display ads at fr/rear; 3 plts. Brn coated eps. Dk brn cl, gilt. (Sl foxed, sl browned, esp eps, blanks; extrems sl worn.) Howes P627. *Baltimore*.* $70/£44

FISK, J. H. Miners' and Assayers' Text-Book...of all the Principal Metal-Bearing Rocks Including Gold and Silver Bullion. Portland, OR, 1898. 1st ed. 267pp + 24pp pamphlet bound in. Black cl, gilt. (Worn, loose), else Good-. *Larry Price.* $95/£59

FISK, NICHOLAS. Lindbergh the Lone Flyer. Hamilton, 1968. 1st ed. Sq lg 8vo. Raymond Briggs (illus). (40)pp. Pict bds. VG. *Bookmark.* $35/£22

FISKE, JOHN. The American Revolution. Boston, 1897. Illus ed. 2 vols. Teg. Fine (bkpls). *Polyanthos.* $50/£31

FISKE, JOHN. Darwinism and Other Essays. London, 1879. 1st ed. viii,283pp + 32pp pub's cat. (Prelims sl spotted, ex-lib, bkpl, blindstamp tp, upper hinge cracked, lower joint splitting, extrems nicked.) *Edwards.* $72/£45

FITCH, CLYDE. Pamela's Prodigy. A Lively Comedy. NY: George M. Allen, 1893. 1st ed in bk form. Olive cl, color illus mtd fr cvr. Fine. *Cummins.* $75/£47

FITCH, ELIJAH. A Discourse, the Substance of Which Was Delivered at Hopkinton, on the Lord's-Day, March 24th, 1776.... Boston: John Boyle, 1776. In this copy, owing to a piece of dropped type in imprint, date on tp reads 'MDCCLXXV.' 30pp. Contemp plain wrappers, stitched (worn, frayed, sm tears; stains, soiled). *Oinonen*.* $275/£172

FITCH, SAMUEL SHELDON. Six Lectures on the Uses of the Lungs. NY, 1852. New ed. 368pp. Tooled cl bds (extrems sl worn). VG. *Doctor's Library.* $75/£47

FITCH, STEVE. Diesels and Dinosaurs. Berkeley: Long Run, 1976. 1st ed. Ltd to 2000. 50 full-pg b/w photos. NF in pict stiff wrappers. *Cahan.* $45/£28

FITCH, STEVE. Diesels and Dinosaurs. Berkeley: Long Run, 1976. 1st ed. Signed. Fine in dj. *Smith.* $125/£78

FITCHETT, LAURA S. Beverages and Sauces of Colonial Virginia. Neale, 1906. 1st ed. (Cvr worn.) *Book Broker.* $150/£94

FITE, EMERSON D. and ARCHIBALD FREEMAN. A Book of Old Maps. NY, 1969. Rpt of 1929 ed. Sm folio. VG in dj. *Dumont.* $100/£63

FITHIAN, PHILIP VICKERS. Journal and Letters of Philip Vickers Fithian, 1773-1774. Hunter Dickinson Farish (ed). Col. Williamsburg, 1943. Frontis. VG. Howes F163. *Book Broker.* $25/£16

FITKIN, GRETCHEN M. The Great River. Shanghai, 1922. 1st ed. 19 photo plts. Brn dec cl. (Edgeworn), else VG. *Larry Price.* $49/£31

FITTIPALDI, EMERSON and ELIZABETH LAYWARD. Flying on the Ground. William Kimber, 1973. 1st ed. VG in dj. *Hollett.* $48/£30

FITTIS, ROBERT SCOTT. Sports and Pastimes of Scotland. London, 1891. 2112pp. (Ex-lib, mks, sl worn, inner hinges weak.) *King.* $45/£28

FITZ GIBBON, CONSTANTINE. Going to the River. London: Cassell, (1963). 1st ed. Gilt tan cl bds. NF in dj (price-clipped). *Reese.* $35/£22

FITZ GIBBON, CONSTANTINE. The Holiday. London: Cassell, 1953. 1st ed. Lt blue cl. (2 or 3 fox spots on edges), o/w Fine in dj (frayed). *Temple.* $42/£26

FITZ, GRANCEL. North American Head Hunting. NY: OUP, 1957. 1st ed. Color frontis. Grn cl. NF in color, pict dj. *House.* $20/£13

FITZGERALD, EDWARD. Letters and Literary Remains.... W.A. Wright (ed). London: Macmillan, 1889. 1st ed. 3 vols. Frontispieces. VG (spines sunned). *Agvent.* $100/£63

FITZGERALD, EDWARD. Letters of.... London: Macmillan, 1894. 1st ed. 2 vols. Frontis. VG (spines sl soiled). *Agvent.* $50/£31

FITZGERALD, F. SCOTT. All the Sad Young Men. Scribner, 1926. 1st ed. VG + in Attractive dj (sl inner reinforcement, lt chipped, 1-inch x 1/4-inch chip rear panel). *Fine Books.* $1,250/£781

FITZGERALD, F. SCOTT. All the Sad Young Men. NY: Scribner, 1926. 1st ed. 8vo. Grn cl. NF (ink name, sl offset to eps from dj flaps; spine extrems sl rubbed) in dj (folds expertly restored, sl browned, esp spine). *Heritage.* $1,650/£1,031

FITZGERALD, F. SCOTT. The Beautiful and Damned. NY: Scribner, 1922. 1st ed, 2nd issue w/ads at rear. Dk grn cl, gilt. (Sl flecks to fr cvr), else NF. *Pacific*.* $40/£25

FITZGERALD, F. SCOTT. The Beautiful and Damned. NY: Scribner, 1922. 1st ed, 1st ptg. Grn cl. VG (eps browned, lt foxed; spine ends sl rubbed, spine lettering faded). *Heritage.* $200/£125

FITZGERALD, F. SCOTT. The Beautiful and Damned. NY, 1922. 1st ed. 8vo. Dj (3 inner tape repairs). *Swann*.* $2,990/£1,869

FITZGERALD, F. SCOTT. The Beautiful and Damned. NY: Scribner, 1922. 1st ed, 1st ptg. 8vo. Dk grn cl. Fine (sl soiled) in 1st issue pict dj (restoration) w/fr panel title lettering in white outlined in black; 1/4 morocco clamshell case. *Heritage.* $3,000/£1,875

FITZGERALD, F. SCOTT. F. Scott Fitzgerald's Ledger: A Facsimile. Washington: NCR/Microcard Editions, (1972). One of 1000. Fine in slipcase. *Pacific*.* $29/£18

FITZGERALD, F. SCOTT. Flappers and Philosophers. NY: Scribner, 1920. 1st ed, 1st ptg. Grn cl. Fine. *Cummins.* $250/£156

FITZGERALD, F. SCOTT. The Great Gatsby. NY: Scribner, 1925. 1st ed, 2nd ptg. Fine (lacks dj). *Captain's Bookshelf.* $125/£78

FITZGERALD, F. SCOTT. The Great Gatsby. NY: Scribner, 1925. 1st ed, 1st issue w/'sick in tired' on p205. Dk grn cl. (Newspaper article mtd to fr pastedown, w/offset to eps and 1/2-title; spine ends rubbed, shelfworn), else VG-. *Pacific*.* $150/£94

FITZGERALD, F. SCOTT. The Great Gatsby. NY: Scribner, 1925. 1st ed, 1st ptg. Untrimmed. Dk grn cl, ilt. (Lt aged, partial tear 1 leaf, top edge dusty, sl pencil notes eps; spine sl turned, sl edgeworn.) Internally Good. *Baltimore*.* $260/£163

FITZGERALD, F. SCOTT. The Great Gatsby. NY: Scribner, 1925. 1st ed, 1st state, w/'chatter' on p60, 'northern' on p205, 'sick in tired' on p205, 'Union Street Station' on p211, and Scribner's seal on c. pg. (Rear inner hinge sl cracked; extrems sl worn, ring on rear cvr.) *New Hampshire*.* $300/£188

FITZGERALD, F. SCOTT. The Great Gatsby. NY: Scribner, 1925. 1st ed, 1st issue. Fine (sig). *Bromer.* $700/£438

FITZGERALD, F. SCOTT. The Great Gatsby. NY: Scribner, 1925. 1st issue. 8vo. Grn cl (extrems sl worn). Dj (worn; lacks fr flap, 1/2-inch along bottom fr, 2 lg losses on spine). *Metropolitan*.* $5,750/£3,594

FITZGERALD, F. SCOTT. The Great Gatsby. LEC, 1980. One of 2000 signed by Fred Meyer (illus). Fine in slipcase. *Swann*.* $103/£64

FITZGERALD, F. SCOTT. The Last Tycoon. Scribner, 1941. VG +. *Fine Books.* $15/£9

FITZGERALD, F. SCOTT. Taps at Reville. NY: Scribner, 1935. 1st ed. 8vo. Dk grn cl. Fine in dj (repaired). *Appelfeld.* $650/£406

FITZGERALD, F. SCOTT. Tender Is the Night. NY: LEC, (1982). One of 2000. Signed by Fred Meyer (illus) & Charles Scribner III (intro). Prospectus laid in. Fine in Fine box. *Polyanthos.* $75/£47

FITZGERALD, F. SCOTT. Tender Is the Night. LEC, 1982. Ltd to 1500 numbered, signed by Fred Meyer (illus). Fine in slipcase. *Swann*.* $126/£79

FITZGERALD, F. SCOTT. This Side of Paradise. NY, 1920. 1st ed, 3rd ptg. Signed. One of approx 500 w/'Author's Apology' leaf tipped-in. 8vo. (Sm closed tear spine head.) *Swann*.* $1,150/£719

FITZGERALD, F. SCOTT. The Vegetable. Scribner, 1923. 1st ed. Grn cl. (Spine dull), else Good. *Whiteson.* $200/£125

FITZGERALD, F. SCOTT. The Vegetable. NY: Scribner, 1923. 1st ed. Dk grn cl, gilt. Overall NF (lt offsetting to eps from dj flaps; spine ends sl rubbed) in dj (edges chipped, sl soiled). *Heritage.* $1,500/£938

FITZGERALD, JOHN D. Me and My Little Brain. Dial, 1971. 1st ed. Mercer Mayer (illus). 150pp. NF in VG- dj (lg wrinkles top edge, sm chips). *Price.* $25/£16

FITZGERALD, O. P. California Sketches. Nashville: Southern Methodist Pub House, 1879. 2nd ed. 208pp. (Shelfworn, rubbed, sl spotted), else Good. *Brown.* $50/£31

FITZGERALD, PENELOPE. The Golden Child. Duckworth, 1977. 1st ed. VG in dj (rubbed, creased). *Ulysses.* $72/£45

FITZGERALD, PENELOPE. Human Voices. London: Collins, 1980. 1st ed. Charcoal bds. Fine in dj. *Temple.* $16/£10

FITZGERALD, PENELOPE. Offshore. Collins, 1979. 1st UK ed. NF in dj. *Williams.* $35/£22

FITZGERALD, PERCY. Chronicles of a Bow Street Police-Office. London, 1888. 1st ed. 2 vols. (Spine heads lt worn.) *Swann*.* $258/£161

FITZGERALD, PERCY. The Garrick Club. London: Elliot Stock, 1904. 1st ed. (Joints strengthened; sl soiled.) *Hollett.* $96/£60

FITZGERALD, PERCY. The Life of Charles Dickens as Revealed in His Writings. London: C&W, 1905. 1st ed. 2 vols. 2 ports, 2 facs. (Lib label pastedown, label removed from other pastedown, few pencilled marginalia; sl bumped.) *Hollett.* $72/£45

FITZGERALD, PERCY. Life of James Boswell with an Account of His Sayings, Doings, and Writings. NY, 1891. 1st US ed. 2 vols. Clean set (few lt lib stamps; neat old paper labels at spine feet, heads sl chafed). *Gretton.* $96/£60

FITZGERALD, PERCY. The Life of Laurence Sterne. London: Downey, 1896. 1st Eng ed. 2 vols. Teg. Dec cl, gilt. VG set (eps browned; spine ends, corners sl bumped; spines faded, rubbed; vol 2 cvr edges faded, mkd). *Ulysses.* $88/£55

FITZGERALD, S. J. ADAIR. The Zankiwank and the Bletherwitch. An Original Fantastic Fairy Extravaganza. London: J.M. Dent, 1896. 1st ed. 8vo. 41 illus by Arthur Rackham, 17 full-pg (sl spotted). Teg. Grn pict cl, gilt. *Christie's*.* $515/£322

FITZGERALD, WILLIAM WALTER AUGUSTINE. Travels in the Coastlands of British East Africa. London: Chapman and Hall, 1898. 1st ed. Inscribed. Thick 8vo. Frontisport, xxiv,774pp; 5 maps (2 fldg). Teg. Maroon dec cl, gilt. Good (sl foxed, ink stamps; extrems sl rubbed, upper hinge cracked). *Morrell.* $576/£360

FITZGERALD, ZELDA. Save Me the Waltz. Grey Walls, 1953. 1st ed. VG (feps lt browned; top edge sl dusty, spine ends sl bumped) in dj (nicked, sl torn, rubbed, dusty, spine faded). *Ulysses.* $88/£55

FITZGIBBON, MARY. Trip to Manitoba; or, Roughing It on the Line. Toronto: Rose, 1880. 1st ed. (16),14-167pp. Dec wrappers (lt stained). *Ginsberg.* $300/£188

FITZHUGH, LOUISE. Bang Bang You're Dead. NY: Harper & Row, 1969. 1st ed. 11.75x10.75. Sandra Scoppettone (illus). 32pp. Cl spine, pict bds. VG. *Cattermole.* $40/£25

FITZHUGH, PERCY KEESE. The Parachute Jumper. NY: G&D, 1930. Tom Slade #19; final bk in the series. 5x7.5. E. N. Townsend (illus). 197pp + ads. VG (top edge soiled, sl cocked) in dj (chipped, dingy). *My Bookhouse.* $155/£97

FITZHUGH, PERCY KEESE. Pee-Wee Harris: Mayor for a Day. NY: G&D, 1926. 1st ed. Pee-Wee Harris #9; lists 8 titles on dj. 5x7.5. H. S. Barbour (illus). 246pp + ads. VG (shelfworn) in dj (edgeworn, few chips). *My Bookhouse.* $27/£17

FITZHUGH, PERCY KEESE. Westy Martin. NY: G&D, 1924. Westy Martin #1; lists 5 titles on dj. 5x7.5. 196pp + ads. VG (shelfworn, soiled) in dj (ragged). *My Bookhouse.* $22/£14

FITZMAURICE, R. Principles of Modern Building. Volume 1. HMSO, 1938. 1st ed. 19 plts. VG. *Hollett.* $64/£40

FITZPATRICK, GEORGE and JOHN L. SINCLAIR. Profile of a State—New Mexico. Albuquerque: Horn & Wallace, 1965. Good in dj. *Dumont.* $20/£13

FITZPATRICK, PERCY. Jock of the Bushveld. Longmans, Green, 1907. 1st ed, 1st issue. Color frontis, 22 plts. Blue pict cl, gilt. (Fr bd sl bowed, extrems sl rubbed), o/w VG. *Sotheran.* $448/£280

FITZSIMMONS, CORTLAND. The Evil Men Do. NY: Stokes, 1941. 1st ed. Inscribed. NF (few sm bumps) in VG + dj (lt edgeworn, spine sl sunned). *Janus.* $85/£53

FITZSIMONS, CECILIA. My First Birds. A Pop-Up Nature Guide. NY: Harper & Row, 1985. 6 pop-ups. Glazed pict bds. VG. *Bookfinders.* $20/£13

FITZSIMONS, RAYMUND. The Baron of Piccadilly. London: Geoffrey Bles, 1967. 1st ed. 38 plts. VG in dj. *Hollett.* $32/£20

FITZSIMONS, RAYMUND. The Charles Dickens Show. Geoffrey Bles, 1970. 1st Eng ed. Fine (spine ends sl bumped) in dj (edges sl rubbed). *Ulysses.* $32/£20

FITZSIMONS, V. F. M. Snakes of Southern Africa. Cape Town, 1962. 78 maps (1 fldg). (Name stamps, few pp lt foxed; lt stained, mottled.) Dj (edges chipped). *Sutton.* $185/£116

Five Black Arts. Columbus: Follet, Foster, 1861. viii,392pp. 15 plts. (Cl soiled, spotted; hinges sl split.) *Oak Knoll*. $55/£34

Five Little Pigs. London: Bancroft, 1964. 5 dbl-pg pop-ups by V. Kubasta. VG in pict wraps. *Bookfinders*. $70/£44

Five Little Pigs. (NY): McLoughlin Bros, n.d. (ca 1856). Aunt Mary's Little Series. Sq 12mo. 4 leaves, 1pg bk list on lower wrapper. Pict paper wrappers. VG (vignettes colored by child; spine reinforced, sm spots fore-edge fr wrapper). *Hobbyhorse*. $130/£81

Five Young American Poets. Norfolk: New Directions, 1944. 1st ed. VG in dj (spine, extrems dknd, sm spot rear panel). *Pacific**. $46/£29

FLACCUS. Passaic, a Group of Poems Touching That River: With Other Musings. NY: Wiley & Putnam, 1842. 1st ed. Period 3/4 calf, marbled bds, gilt, morocco spine label. NF. *Pacific**. $63/£39

FLAHERTY, ROBERT and FRANCES H. My Eskimo Friends 'Nanook of the North'. NY: Doubleday, Page, 1924. 9 photogravure plts (3 color), 6 maps. (Corners worn), else VG. *High Latitude*. $150/£94

FLAHERTY, ROBERT. The Captain's Chair. NY: Scribner, 1938. VG in dj. *High Latitude*. $35/£22

FLAKE, CHAD. A Mormon Bibliography 1830-1930. SLC, 1978. Internally Clean (shelfworn, fr hinge broken). *Dumont*. $100/£63

FLANAGAN, EDWARD, JR. The Angels: A History of the 11th Airborne Division 1943-1946. Washington, 1948. 1st ed. VG. *Clark*. $125/£78

FLANAGAN, H. What Was Federal Theatre? Washington: American Council for Public Affairs, n.d. 1st ed. Fine in self-wraps. *Beasley*. $45/£28

FLANAGAN, HALLIE. Arena. NY, 1940. 1st Amer ed. Dec cvrs. Fine (spine sl rubbed). *Polyanthos*. $35/£22

FLANAGAN, SUE. Trailing the Longhorns. Austin: Madrona, 1974. 1st ed. Fine in dj. *Labordo*. $45/£28

FLANAGAN, SUE. Trailing the Longhorns: A Century Later. Austin: Madrona, (1974). 1st ed. One of 250. Signed by Flanagan and L. W. Bennett of Madrona Press. 1/2 leather, pict cvr label, gilt. Fine in slipcase. *Pacific**. $138/£86

FLANDRAU, GRACE. The Verendrye Overland Quest of the Pacific. Great Northern Railway, 1925. Rpt. Fine in wraps. *Perier*. $12/£8

FLANNER, JANET. The Stronger Sex. NY, (1941). One of 1750 numbered. Folio. Mtd repros. Pict cl (sl soiled, edges lt browned). Slipcase. *Swann**. $57/£36

FLANNER, JANET. The Stronger Sex.... NY, (1941). One of 1750. Folio. 24 tipped-in plts (21 color) by Marcel Vertes. Color-pict cl. *Swann**. $230/£144

FLATT, ADRIAN E. The Care of Minor Hand Injuries. St. Louis: C.V. Mosby, 1959. 1st ed. Fine. *Weber*. $100/£63

FLATTAU, JOHN et al (eds). Contact: Theory. NY: Lustrum, 1980. 1st ed. Fine in NF dj. *Cahan*. $75/£47

FLAUBERT, GUSTAVE. Bouvard and Pecuchet. London: H.S. Nichols, 1896. 1st ed in English. (Feps offset; extrems sl shelf worn), else VG + in blue cl, gilt. *Lame Duck*. $275/£172

FLAUBERT, GUSTAVE. Bouvard and Pecuchet. London: H.S. Nichols, 1896. 1st Eng ed. Frontis, tp, 7 plts. Teg, rest uncut. Blue cl, gilt. Fine (gilt on fr panel sl dull). *Maggs*. $400/£250

FLAUBERT, GUSTAVE. Madame Bovary. LEC, 1938. Ltd to 1500 numbered, signed by Gunter Bohmer (illus). Fine in slipcase. *Swann**. $161/£101

FLAUBERT, GUSTAVE. Salammbo. M. French Sheldon (trans). London: Saxon, 1886. 1st ed in English, trade issue. Blue cl, gilt. (Sl string indents at beveled edges, sl rubbed, fore-edge spotted), o/w Very Nice. *Reese*. $225/£141

FLAUBERT, GUSTAVE. Salammbo. E. P. Mathers (trans). Waltham, St. Lawrence: Golden Cockerel, 1931. 1st ed. One of 500. (Ad pasted to ep; corners worn; no dj.) *Typographeum*. $125/£78

FLAUBERT, GUSTAVE. Salammbo. LEC, 1960. Ltd to 1500 numbered, signed by Edward Bawden (illus). Fine in slipcase. *Swann**. $34/£21

FLAUBERT, GUSTAVE. Sentimental Education. London: H.S. Nichols, 1898. 1st ed in English. 2 vols. VG + (inscrip vol 1, eps, pg edges lt foxed; extrems shelf-worn) in blue cl, gilt. *Lame Duck*. $450/£281

FLAUBERT, GUSTAVE. The Temptation of Saint Anthony. D. F. Hannigan (trans). H.S. Nichols, 1895. 1st Eng ed. 9 b/w plts. Teg. Dec cl, gilt. Good (prelims, edges, eps browned, protruding pg edges nicked; hinges cracked, cvrs mkd, edges rubbed, spine faded, ends, corners bumped, rubbed). *Ulysses*. $120/£75

FLAUBERT, GUSTAVE. The Temptation of St. Anthony. LEC, 1943. Ltd to 1500 numbered, signed by Warren Chappell (illus). Fine in slipcase. *Swann**. $69/£43

FLAUBERT, GUSTAVE. Three Tales. LEC, 1978. One of 1600 signed by Mary Neama (illus). Fine in slipcase. *Swann**. $34/£21

FLAXMAN, JOHN. Anatomical Studies of the Bones and Muscles, for the Use of Artists.... London: M.A. Nattali, 1833. Thin folio. Frontis port (sl offset), 13pp (margins lt browned, sl thumbed, spotting); 21 plts (ink blot plt 7, not on illus). Uncut. Cl-backed bds, paper label fr bd. *Edwards*. $240/£150

FLEAY, D. Nightwatchmen of Bush and Plain. Melbourne: Jacaranda, 1968. 1st ed. NF. *Mikesh*. $25/£16

FLECKER, JAMES ELROY. The King of Alsander. Max Goschen, 1914. 1st ed, 1st issue. Red dec cl, gilt. (Faint cup mk fr cvr, spine head sl bumped), else VG. *Any Amount*. $88/£55

FLECKER, JAMES ELROY. The Old Ships. London: Poetry Bookshop, n.d. (1915). 1st ed. Uncut. Pict wrappers (overlapping edges sl worn). *Maggs*. $32/£20

FLECKER, JAMES ELROY. Some Letters from Abroad. Heinemann, 1930. 1st ed. VG + in VG dj. *Any Amount*. $45/£28

FLEMING, ALEXANDER. Penicillin. Its Practical Application. London: Butterworth, 1946. 1st ed. Blue-grn cl (lt edgeworn). *Glenn*. $300/£188

FLEMING, ANDREW. Blood Stains in Criminal Trials. Pittsburgh, 1861. 1st separate ed. 69pp. (Ink inscrip; lacks fep, spine cvr.) *King*. $35/£22

FLEMING, BERRY (comp). Autobiography of a Colony. The First Half Century of Augusta, Georgia. Athens: Univ of GA, 1957. 1st ed. One of 750. VG in dj. *Brown*. $20/£13

FLEMING, G. H. Murderer's Row. Morrow, 1985. 1st ed. Fine in VG + dj. *Plapinger*. $100/£63

FLEMING, G. H. (ed). The Dizziest Season. Morrow, 1984. 1st ed. Fine in VG + dj. *Plapinger*. $50/£31

FLEMING, HOWARD A. Canada's Arctic Outlet. L.A.: Univ of CA, 1957. 1st ed. Frontis map. Blue cl. VF. *Argonaut*. $125/£78

FLEMING, IAN. Casino Royale. Cape, 1953. 1st UK ed. One of 4750 ptd. NF in VG dj (sl professional restoration to the word 'Ian' at spine head). *Williams*. $5,760/£3,600

FLEMING, IAN. Chitty Chitty Bang Bang. A Pop-Up Book. Albert G. Miller (ed). NY: Random House, 1968. Gwen Gordon & Dave Chambers (illus). 3 dbl-pg pop-ups. Glazed pict bds. (Sl edgeworn), else VG. *Bookfinders*. $150/£94

FLEMING, IAN. The Diamond Smugglers. Pan, 1960. 1st pb ed. VG. *Williams*. $19/£12

FLEMING, IAN. Diamonds Are Forever. London: Jonathan Cape, (1956). 1st ed. NF in VG dj (upper fr panel lacks sm piece, spine ends rubbed, head sl creased, flap tips clipped). *Pacific**. $404/£253

FLEMING, IAN. Diamonds Are Forever. London: Jonathan Cape, 1956. 1st ed. 8vo. Black cl. NF (eps, fore-edge lt foxed; spine sl cocked) in dj (price-clipped, lt faded, soiled, spine top sl chipped). *Heritage.* $600/£375

FLEMING, IAN. Diamonds Are Forever. Cape, 1956. 1st UK ed. Fine in NF dj (spine head sl worn). *Williams.* $680/£425

FLEMING, IAN. Dr. No. Cape, 1958. 1st UK ed. Issue w/blind-stamped woman's figure on fr bd. VG (fep stained) in VG dj (spine head sl worn, rear panel sl dusty). *Williams.* $216/£135

FLEMING, IAN. For Your Eyes Only. Pan, 1962. 1st pb ed. VG + . *Williams.* $22/£14

FLEMING, IAN. Goldfinger. Cape, 1959. 1st UK ed. VG + in dj (edges lt worn). *Williams.* $160/£100

FLEMING, IAN. Live and Let Die. Cape, 1954. 1st UK ed. VG (ink inscrip) in 1st issue dj (edges worn, few short closed tears, chips; rear panel browned). *Williams.* $1,200/£750

FLEMING, IAN. The Man with the Golden Gun. (NY): NAL, (1965). 1st Amer ed. Black cl, gilt. (Ink inscrip), o/w Fine in dj (lt soiled, creased, sl tears). *Heritage.* $50/£31

FLEMING, IAN. The Man with the Golden Gun. London: Jonathan Cape, (1965). 1st ed. Black cl, gilt. Fine in dj. *Heritage.* $100/£63

FLEMING, IAN. The Man with the Golden Gun. NY: NAL, 1965. 1st US ed. Fine in Fine dj. *Beasley.* $45/£28

FLEMING, IAN. The Man with the Golden Gun. Cape, 1965. 1st UK ed. Variant, w/plain white rather than grn eps. NF in dj. *Williams.* $112/£70

FLEMING, IAN. The Man with the Golden Gun. Jonathan Cape, 1965. 1st ed. 8vo. Variant binding in black cl w/gun design blocked in gilt on fr cvr. Dj. *Sotheby's*.* $1,747/£1,092

FLEMING, IAN. Moonraker. Cape, 1955. 1st UK ed. VG in dj (spine, rear panel sl browned). *Williams.* $1,592/£995

FLEMING, IAN. Octopussy and the Living Daylights. London: Jonathan Cape, (1966). 1st ed. Gray cl. Fine in dj. *Heritage.* $75/£47

FLEMING, IAN. Octopussy and the Living Daylights. London: Jonathan Cape, 1966. 1st ed. NF (sl shelfworn) in NF dj. *My Bookhouse.* $72/£45

FLEMING, IAN. On Her Majesty's Secret Service. London: Cape, (1963). 1st ed. (Sl torn, soiled), o/w VG in dj. *Petersfield.* $42/£26

FLEMING, IAN. On Her Majesty's Secret Service. London: Jonathan Cape, (1963). 1st ed. Dk brn cl. Fine in dj (rear panel sl soiled). *Heritage.* $200/£125

FLEMING, IAN. On Her Majesty's Secret Service. Jonathan Cape, 1963. One of 250 numbered, signed. The only bk by Fleming issued in a signed ltd ed. Color frontisport. Teg. 1/4 vellum. NF (tp sl browned around an unaffected patch the size of a business card) in glassine dj. *Ulysses.* $4,000/£2,500

FLEMING, IAN. On Her Majesty's Secret Service. Cape, 1963. One of 250 signed. Fine in orig clear plastic dj (sm chip fr panel). *Williams.* $4,720/£2,950

FLEMING, IAN. The Spy Who Loved Me. Pan, 1967. 1st pb ed. VG + . *Williams.* $22/£14

FLEMING, IAN. Thunderball. London, 1961. 1st Eng ed. Fine in dj (sl rubbed). *Clearwater.* $112/£70

FLEMING, IAN. Thunderball. Cape, 1961. 1st UK ed. NF in dj. *Williams.* $120/£75

FLEMING, IAN. You Only Live Twice. London: Cape, (1964). 1st ed. (Sl spine slant), else Fine in NF dj (spine sl tanned). *Between The Covers.* $125/£78

FLEMING, IAN. You Only Live Twice. London, (1964). 1st ed. Uncorrected proof. Fine in ptd wrappers (lt rubbed). *Swann*.* $230/£144

FLEMING, IAN. You Only Live Twice. Cape, 1964. 1st UK ed. NF (stamp to fep verso) in VG dj (sm closed tears). *Williams.* $32/£20

FLEMING, IAN. You Only Live Twice. NY: NAL, 1964. 1st US ed. Fine in Fine dj (spine sl sunned). *Beasley.* $40/£25

FLEMING, JANE A. Garment Making. Arnold, n.d. (c. 1910). Pict cl. VG (lt worn). *Whittle.* $32/£20

FLEMING, JOHN A. (ed). The Ziegler Polar Expedition 1903-1905. Washington: Nat'l Geographic Soc, 1907. 3 fldg maps in pocket. Good (lower cvr spotted, abraded). *High Latitude.* $110/£69

FLEMING, JOHN. Robert Adam and His Circle in Edinburgh and Rome. London, 1962. Good + . *Washton.* $45/£28

FLEMING, LINDSAY. History of Pagham in Sussex. Privately ptd at Ditchling Press, 1949. One of 300. 3 vols. 18 plts, 3 fldg maps. Djs. *Marlborough.* $480/£300

FLEMING, PETER. Invasion 1940. Rupert Hart-Davis, 1957. 1st ed. Frontis map. Buckram. NF (spine ends sl bumped) in dj (nicked, sl rubbed, sl creased). *Ulysses.* $58/£36

FLEMING, R. HARVEY (ed). Minutes of Council, Northern Department of Ruperts Land, 1821-31. London: Hudson's Bay Record Soc, 1940. 1st ltd ed. Fine. *Perier.* $85/£53

FLEMING, SANDFORD. Report Canadian Pacific Railway. Ottawa, 1880. 373pp; 7 fldg maps. Grn cl (new calf spine, ep), gilt. Good + (ex-lib, perf tp). *Larry Price.* $295/£184

FLEMING, VIVIAN MINOR. The Wilderness Campaign. Richmond: W.C. Hill Ptg, 1922. 1st ed. Inscribed. (Fore-edge sl browned), else VG + in ptd tan wraps. *Chapel Hill.* $175/£109

FLEMING, WALTER L. Documentary History of Reconstruction. Cleveland: A.H. Clark, 1906. 1st ed. 2 vols. 9 facs. Teg. Olive cl. VG set (sig; lt rubbed). Howes F182. *Chapel Hill.* $350/£219

FLEMING, ALEXANDER. Penicillin. Its Practical Application. Phila: Blakiston, 1946. 1st Amer ed. (Worn.) Dj (chips, frayed). *Oinonen*.* $160/£100

FLETCHER, C. R. L. Gustavus Adolphus and the Struggle of Protestants for Existence. Putnam, 1890. xviii,316pp. Contemp full tree calf, gilt. VG. *Hollett.* $56/£35

FLETCHER, COLIN. The Man Who Walked Through Time. NY, 1967. 1st ed. Fldg map. VG + in dj. *Five Quail.* $25/£16

FLETCHER, HANSLIP. Changing London. London, 1933. Etched frontis signed by author, 49 plts. Teg. Maroon cl (rebound; textual browning). *Edwards.* $80/£50

FLETCHER, HAROLD. Antarctic Days with Mawson. (Sydney): Angus & Robertson, 1984. Map. VG in dj. *High Latitude.* $30/£19

FLETCHER, IFAN KYRLE. Ronald Firbank, a Memoir. Duckworth, 1930. 1st Eng ed. B/w frontis photo. Cutting from issue of the Sphere for 8th November 1930 loosely inserted. VG (top edge sl dusty, edges sl spotted; spine ends, corner sl bumped) in dj (nicked, torn, creased, dusty, sl mkd, rubbed, sl dknd, 2 sellotape mks). *Ulysses.* $200/£125

FLETCHER, J. S. Picturesque History of Yorkshire. Caxton, n.d. 6 vols. Fldg map, 56 plts incl 18 photogravure plts, 13 color plts. Aeg. (Feps lt browned; several spines lt faded.) *Edwards.* $280/£175

FLETCHER, J. W. A Condensed Life of the Right Honourable Winston Leonard Spencer Churchill.... London/Sydney: Privately ptd/New Century, 1941. 1st Eng ed. VG (edges, eps spotted; spine foot bumped) in dj (dusty, sl rubbed). *Ulysses.* $72/£45

FLETCHER, L. The Optical Indicatrix and the Transmission of Light in Crystals. Henry Frowde, 1892. xii,112pp. Bkpl of Arthur Raistrick. VG. *Hollett.* $72/£45

FLETCHER, PETER. The Long Sunday. London, 1958. 1st ed. Edward Ardizzone dj (sm tears). *Petersfield.* $24/£15

FLETCHER, ROBERT H. (ed). The Annals of the Bohemian Club. (SF: Bohemian Club, 1900-1972.) Vols I, II 2nd ed. One of 600 complete sets. 5 vols. Blue cl. Good. *Karmiole.* $125/£78

FLETCHER, ROBERT. Free Grass to Fences. NY: University, 1960. 1st ed. Fine in dj. *Labordo.* $75/£47

FLETCHER, SYDNEY. The Cowboy and His Horse. NY: G&D, 1951. 1st ed. NF in VG dj (worn). *Labordo.* $55/£34

FLETCHER, WILLIAM YOUNGER et al. Some Minor Arts as Practised in England.... Seeley, 1894. 1st ed. Folio. viii,82pp, ad leaf; 16 plts (12 color). Grn cl (spine lt rubbed, faded), gilt. Good. *Cox.* $64/£40

FLETCHER, WILLIAM YOUNGER. English Book Collectors. Alfred Pollard (ed). London: Kegan, Paul, Trench, Trubner, 1902. 1st ed. Gilt-stamped cl. *Dawson.* $50/£31

FLEXNER, ABRAHAM. I Remember. NY, 1940. VG (extrems sl worn). *Doctor's Library.* $35/£22

FLINDERS, MATTHEW. Matthew Flinders' Narrative of His Voyage in the Schooner Francis: 1798. Golden Cockerel, 1946. One of 750 numbered. Sm folio. 9 wood-engrs. Teg, rest uncut. Grn cl, gilt. Fine in slipcase. *Sotheran.* $749/£468

FLINT, MARK. Grig the Greyhound. Country Life, 1938. 1st ed. iii,108pp; 10 full-pg dwgs by Lionel Edwards. Dj (sl dusty). *Hollett.* $48/£30

FLINT, RALPH. Contemporary American Etching. NY, (1930). Etched frontis by Frank Benson. 1/4 cl. *Swann*.* $126/£79

FLINT, THOMAS. Diary of Thomas Flint: California to Maine and Return, 1851-1855. L.A., 1923. 1st ed. 78pp; 1 plt; fldg map. VG (bkpls) in ptd wrappers. *Pacific*.* $63/£39

FLINT, TIMOTHY. The History and Geography of the Mississippi Valley. Cincinnati: E.H. Flint, 1833. 3rd ed. 2 vols in 1. Contemp calf, morocco spine label. (Foxed throughout), else VG. *Pacific*.* $58/£36

FLINT, TIMOTHY. Recollections of the Last Ten Years in the Valley of the Mississippi. Carbondale: Southern IL Univ, (1968). Fine in NF dj. Howes F204. *Harrington.* $40/£25

FLINT, TIMOTHY. Recollections of the Last Ten Years, Passed in Occasional Residences and Journeyings in the Valley of the Mississippi.... Boston: Cummings, Hilliard, 1826. 1st ed. (2),395pp. Uncut. Old calf-backed cl. VG (browned, stained). BAL 6113. Howes F204. *M & S.* $475/£297

FLINT, TIMOTHY. Recollections of the Last Ten Years. Boston, 1826. 1st ed. (ii),395pp. Contemp 1/2 calf. (Browned, tp lt dampstained; edgeworn.) *Maggs.* $192/£120

FLINT, W. RUSSELL. Drawings. London, (1950). Sm folio. (Sl foxed throughout.) Dj (few sm chips, tears at edges). *Swann*.* $172/£108

FLINT, W. RUSSELL. In Pursuit: An Autobiography. London: Medici Society, (1970). One of 150 numbered in full leather, signed by Flint's son, Francis. Sm folio. Blue morocco, gilt. Slipcase. *Swann*.* $345/£216

FLINT, W. RUSSELL. Models of Propriety: Occasional Caprices for the Edification of Ladies and the Delight of Gentlemen. London: Michael Joseph, (1951). One of 500. Signed. Teg. Blue/yellow cl, gilt. Fine. *Pacific*.* $161/£101

FLOOD, WILLIAM H. GRATTAN. Early Tudor Composers. OUP, 1925. 1st ed. Unopened. Cl-backed marbled bds. VG. *Hollett.* $48/£30

FLOOD, WILLIAM H. GRATTAN. The Story of the Bagpipe. Frederick J. Crowest (ed). Walter Scott Pub, 1911. 26 plts. Teg, uncut. Dec cl (spine sl faded, stained), gilt. *Hollett.* $56/£35

FLORES, DAN L. Jefferson and Southwestern Exploration. Norman: Univ of OK, 1985. VG in dj. *Dumont.* $35/£22

FLORIAN. William Tell, or the Patriot of Switzerland. And Hofer, the Tyrolese. London: J. Harris, n.d. (1830). New Edition. 12mo. 2 half-titles, 252pp + 24pg list; each story w/6 full-pg by 2 VF copper engrs dated respectively Nov 20, 1823 and March 1st, 1824. Marbled paper on bds, red roan spine, gilt. VG (edges, corners rubbed). *Hobbyhorse.* $215/£134

FLORIN, LAMBERT. Historic Glimpses of Trees of the West. Seattle: Superior, 1977. 1st ed. Fine in dj (price-clipped, 4-inch tear). *Archer.* $30/£19

FLORIN, LAMBERT. Western Ghost Towns—Shadows. Seattle: Superior, (1964). 1st ed. Fine in dj. *Perier.* $30/£19

FLOURNOY, MARY H. Side Lights on Southern History. Richmond: Dietz, 1939. 1st ed. Inscribed. Frontis. Red cl. NF in VG dj (lt edgeworn, soiled). *Chapel Hill.* $85/£53

FLOWER, DESMOND. A Thousand Years of French Books. CUP, 1948. VG in ptd cvrs. *Moss.* $8/£5

FLOWER, JESSIE GRAHAM. Grace Harlowe's Golden Summer. Phila: Altemus, 1917. 5x7.5. 256pp + ads. VG + (sl shelfworn) in dj (sl edgeworn). *My Bookhouse.* $27/£17

FLOWER, JESSIE GRAHAM. Grace Harlowe's Overland Riders and the Kentucky Mountaineers. Phila: Altemus, 1921. 5x7.5. 253pp + ads. VG + (sl shelfworn) in dj (sl edgeworn). *My Bookhouse.* $27/£17

FLOWER, JESSIE GRAHAM. Grace Harlowe's Problem. Phila: Altemus, 1916. 5x7.5. 256pp + ads. VG + (sl shelfworn) in dj (sl edgeworn). *My Bookhouse.* $22/£14

FLOWER, JESSIE GRAHAM. Grace Harlowe's Return to Overtow College. Phila: Altemus, 1915. 5x7.5. 256pp + ads. VG + (sl shelfworn) in dj (edgeworn). *My Bookhouse.* $27/£17

FLOWER, JOHN. Views of Ancient Buildings in the Town and Country of Leicester. London, (1930). Folio. Litho tp, 24 plts. Contemp 1/2 calf. (Foxed; worn, rubbed, cvrs loose.) *Swann*.* $115/£72

FLOWER, MARGARET. Victorian Jewellery. Cassell, 1951. 1st ed. 10 color plts. Buckram (sl stained, faded), gilt. *Hollett.* $48/£30

FLOWERDEW, HENRY. The Parr, Salmon, Whitling and Yellowfin Controversy.... Manchester/London: Abel Heywood/Simpkin, Marshall, 1883. 2nd ed. Grn cl, gilt. (Spine ends rubbed), else VG. *Pacific*.* $115/£72

Flowering Plants from Cuban Gardens. Havana: Garden Section of the Woman's Club of Havana, 1952. 1st ed. (Sl rubbed), o/w Fine. *Archer.* $25/£16

FLOWERS, CHARLES. It Never Rains in Los Angeles. NY: Coward-McCann, 1970. 1st ed. Fine in Fine dj. *Beasley.* $35/£22

FLOYD, DALE E. (ed). Chronological List of Actions, etc, with Indians, from January 15, 1837 to January, 1891. (Fort Collins, Co): Old Army, (1979). 1st ed thus. Brn leatherette, gilt. (Notes in list), o/w Fine. *Harrington.* $50/£31

FLOYD, GRACE C. Busy Bees. London: Raphael Tuck & Sons, (ca 1910). 8vo. Mabel Lucie Attwell (illus). 5 cl-backed color pict bds (incl cvrs). Nice (bds rubbed). *Reisler.* $685/£428

FLOYD, GRACE C. Three Little Kittens (Father Tuck's Nursery Tales Series). London: Raphael Tuck & Son, (ca 1900). 4to. 4 full-pg color plts. Good in stiff paper wrappers (lt worn). *Reisler.* $100/£63

FLOYER, JOHN. Psychrolousia: or, The History of Cold-Bathing, Both Ancient and Modern...To Which Is Added, an Appendix by Dr. Edward Baynard. London: William & John Innys, 1722. 5th ed. 8vo. (21),491,(30),(1 ad)pp. Mod 1/2 calf over marbled bds. Sigs of Philip Sydenham & Guy Grippy. VG (marginal browning). *Glaser.* $500/£313

Fly-Fishing in Salt and Fresh Water. London: John Van Voorst, 1851. 1st ed. Slim 8vo. Gray-grn blind-stamped cl. 6 illus (5 hand-colored). (Eps lt foxed, sl tape residue rear pastedown; sm tear spine cl.) *Glenn.* $550/£344

Flying for 1937: The Junior Aircraft Year Book. Volume Four. NY: Aeronautical Chamber of Commerce, 1937. Good. *Zubal**. $20/£13

FLYNT, JOSIAH. Notes of an Itinerant Policeman. Boston, 1900. 1st ed. Port. Teg. Dec cl. (Bkpl removed; cvrs rubbed.) *King*. $25/£16

FOA, EDOUARD. After Big Game in Central Africa. Frederic Lees (trans). London: A&C Black, 1899. 1st Eng ed. 1/2-title, frontis, xxvii,(i)blank,330,10 ads; map, 29 plts. Blue cl, gilt. VG (sl foxed, lib stamp, 1 plt trimmed w/out loss; spine head mkd). *Morrell*. $304/£190

FOAN, GILBERT A. The Art and Craft of Hairdressing. New Era, n.d. c.(1931). 10 plts. 1/2 morocco, cl bds. (Tp, frontis lt spotted; cl sl damp-spotted.) *Edwards*. $48/£30

FOAN, GILBERT A. The Art and Craft of Hairdressing. N. E. B. Wolters (ed). London: New Era Pub, (1958). 4th ed. 3/4 grn morocco, gilt. NF. *Pacific**. $92/£58

FOCH, FERDINAND. The Memoirs of Marshall Foch. T. Bentley Mott (trans). London: Heinemann, (1931). 1st British ed. Frontis. Gilt-dec black cl. (Inscrip), else VG. *Reese*. $35/£22

FOGDALL, ALBERTA BROOKS. Royal Family of the Columbia: Dr. John McLoughlin and His Family. Fairfield, WA: Ye Galleon, 1978. 1st ed. Signed. Fine in VG dj. *Perier*. $35/£22

FOGEL, LAWRENCE J. Biotechnology: Concepts and Applications. Englewood-Cliffs: Prentice Hall, 1963. 1st ed. Grn cl. VG + in dj (rubbed). *House*. $65/£41

FOGG, WILLIAM PERRY. Arabistan. London: Sampson Low, 1875. xxii,350pp; 13 full-pg illus. (1st/last leaf browned, sl loss fep, feps sl stained; corners rubbed w/sl cl loss, spine chipped.) *Edwards*. $400/£250

FOGHT, H. W. The Trail of the Loup. 1976. Facs rpt. 2 fldg panorama photos. (Sig, address, ink notes; cvrs lower edges bumped), else Fine. *Baade*. $85/£53

FOLEY, HENRY. Records of the English Province of the Society of Jesus. London: Burns & Oates, 1877-83. 5 vols + 3 supp vols. Thick 8vo. 45 photo ports. Mod 1/2 grn levant morocco, gilt. VG set (few edges sl dusty, marginal blind stamps). *Hollett*. $1,040/£650

FOLEY, JOHN P. (ed). The Jefferson Cyclopedia.... Funk & Wagnalls, 1900. Patrons' Centennial Edition. VG. *Book Broker*. $175/£109

Folk-Lore and Legends Oriental. London: W.W. Gibbings, 1889. 1st ed. Maroon cl, floral-patterned bds. VG. *Glenn*. $30/£19

FOLKES, JOHN GREGG. Nevada's Newspapers: A Bibliography...1854-1964. Reno: Univ of NV, 1964. 1st ed. VG in orig red ptd wrappers. *House*. $25/£16

FOLLANSBEE, ROBERT. Upper Colorado River and Its Utilization. Washington: USGS, 1929. 13 plts, incl lg fldg map. Orange wraps. Externally Poor; internally VG + . *Five Quail*. $50/£31

FOLLETT, KEN. Pillars of the Earth. NY: Morrow, 1989. 1st ed. Signed. Fine in Fine dj. *Beasley*. $45/£28

FON, WENG (ed). The Great Bronze Age of China. NY: MMA/Knopf, 1980. 1st ed. VG in dj (frayed). *Worldwide*. $30/£19

FONER, PHILIP S. The Life and Writings of Frederick Douglass. NY, (1950-1955). 1st ed. 4 vols. Frontispieces. Djs (lt edge-worn, spines dknd). *Swann**. $57/£36

FONG, WEN. Summer Mountains. NY: MMA, 1975. Sm folio. Fine in slipcase. *Turtle Island*. $40/£25

FONTAINE, FELIX. The Golden Wheel Dream-Book, and Fortune-Teller.... NY: Dick & Fitzgerald, (1890). Frontis color fldg plt. Cl-backed chromolitho bds. (Tear, tape repair to frontis; corners rubbed), else VG. *Pacific**. $35/£22

FONTANA, FELIX. Treatise on the Venom of the Viper. J. Skinner (trans). London, 1787. 1st Eng ed. 2 vols. 8vo. xix,409,xiv; ii,(1),395,xi,xxiipp (foxed, 1st 1/2-title repaired, mtd; lib stamps to tps, professionally repaired tears to 1 pg, eps renewed, pp tanned); 10 engr fldg plts (split at fold, 1-inch tear to 1 plt, lib stamps). Mod 1/2 calf, marbled bds. *Sutton*. $1,000/£625

Fool's Errand. NY, 1879. 361pp + ads. Red cl. (Bkpl; inner hinges cracked), o/w VG. *Truepenny*. $125/£78

FOOTE, JOHN TAINTOR. Jing. NY: Derrydale, 1936. Ltd to 950 numbered. Fine. *Biscotti*. $100/£63

FOOTE, SAMUEL. The Dramatic Works.... London: Lowndes & Bladon, n.d. Plays dated 1781-1795. 2 vols. Full mottled calf, gilt, raised bands, black leather title labels. Nice set (nicely rebacked). *Hartfield*. $325/£203

FOOTE, SHELBY. The Civil War. NY: RH, (1963). 1st ed. NF in VG dj (price-clipped, few sm tears). *Agvent*. $150/£94

FOOTE, SHELBY. Tournament. NY, 1949. 1st ed. VG + (name remnants erased) in VG + dj (spine dknd). *Warren*. $150/£94

FOOTE, W. Complete Mineral Catalog. Phila: Foote Mineral, 1909. 12th ed. (Top margin pp, rear cvr stained), else Good. *Blake*. $60/£38

FOOTNER, HULBERT. Maryland Main and the Eastern Shore. NY: D. Appleton Century, 1942. 1st ed. Signed. Good in dj (rubbed, chipped). *Brown*. $20/£13

FORBES, A. Chinese Gordon. Routledge, 1884. 1st ed. Photo frontisport, 252pp. Dec cl (mkd, faded), gilt. *Hollett*. $104/£65

FORBES, A. The Life of Napoleon III. London: C&W, 1898. Frontis, 36 plts. Teg. Good. *Stewart*. $32/£20

FORBES, ALEXANDER. California: A History of Upper and Lower California. SF: John Henry Nash, 1937. Rpt of orig 1839 ed. Ltd to 650. Lg fldg map. Cl-backed marbled bds, paper spine label. (Bkpl; corners lt worn, spine top sl jammed), else Fine. *Argonaut*. $175/£109

FORBES, ALEXANDER. California: a History of Upper and Lower California. SF: John Henry Nash, 1937. 3rd ed. One of 650. Fldg map, 10 full-pg engr illus, facs letter. Dec bds w/cl spine, paper label. Dj (sm nick). *Dawson*. $200/£125

FORBES, ALEXANDER. Quest for a Northern Air Route. Cambridge: Harvard Univ, 1953. 1st ptg. VG in dj. *High Latitude*. $40/£25

FORBES, ANNA. Insulinde. Edinburgh: William Blackwood, 1887. 1st ed. xii,305,(1)blank,(2) ads; fldg color map (foxed). Blue cl, gilt. Good (mkd, lacks 1/2-title, rep corner torn; sl rubbed). *Morrell*. $248/£155

FORBES, CHARLES. Iceland; Its Volcanoes, Geysers, and Glaciers. London, 1860. Pub's gilt-pict cl (faded, hinges weak; lib ink #s on backstrip, bkpls). *Swann**. $103/£64

FORBES, FREDERICK E. Dahomey and the Dahomans: Being the Journals...in the Years 1849 and 1850. London, 1851. 2 vols. Early 1/2 calf. (Ex-lib, emb stamps on each plt, tp; needs rebinding.) *Swann**. $115/£72

FORBES, H. O. A Handbook to the Primates. Allen's Naturalists Library, 1894. 2 vols. 29 color plts, 8 maps. *Hallam*. $48/£30

FORBES, JACK D. Warriors of the Colorado: The Yumas of the Quechan Nation.... Norman: Univ of OK, (1965). 1st ed. Fine in VG dj. *Book Market*. $35/£22

FORBES, JAMES. Letters from France Written in the Years 1803 and 1804 Including a Particular Account of Verdun and the Situation of the British Captives in that City. London: J. White, 1806. 2 vols. Frontispieces. Contemp, speckled calf (sl rubbed, corners vol 1 damaged). *Stewart*. $240/£150

FORBES, JAMES. Letters from France, Written in the Years 1803 and 1804. London: J. White, 1806. 2 vols. viii,428; 453pp; aquatint frontispieces (offset). Early 1/2 calf, marbled bds, gilt, morocco spine labels. (Pp407-8 lacks corner, sl foxing to 1st/last ll, bkpl; corners rubbed w/sl loss, spines worn.) *Edwards.* $280/£175

FORBES, MRS. A. S. C. Mission Tales in the Days of the Dons. Chicago: McClung, 1909. 1st ed. VG. *Book Market.* $30/£19

FORBES-LEITH, F. A. C. Checkmate. NY: McBride, 1927. 1st ed. Signed presentation. Frontis, 14 plts. (Sl rubbed), o/w VG. *Worldwide.* $55/£34

FORBES-MITCHELL, WILLIAM. Reminiscences of the Great Mutiny 1857-59.... Macmillan, 1897. 4th ed. xii,291pp; 2 fldg plans. Marbled eps. Full contemp grn calf prize binding, raised bands, gilt, red leather label. VG. *Sotheran.* $136/£85

FORBUSH, EDWARD HOWE. Birds of Massachusetts and Other New England States. Norwood, MA: Norwood, 1929. 3rd ed. 3 vols. 4to. 93 Fine color plts by Louis Agassiz Fuertes. Uncut. Dk grn cl, gilt. Fine. *Sotheran.* $637/£398

Ford Model 'A' Instruction Book. Ford Motor, 1930. Wraps. (Ink inscrip; dealer stamp; sl faded w/ink spot.) *King.* $25/£16

FORD, ALLA T. (ed). The High-Jinks of L. Frank Baum. Hong Kong: Ford, 1969. 1st ed. Inscribed, signed. One of 500. 2.5x2. Fine in pict wrappers, hand-painted rear cvr. *Pacific*.* $104/£65

FORD, C. Where the Sea Breaks Its Back. London: Gollancz, 1967. 1st ed. Fine in VG dj. *Mikesh.* $30/£19

FORD, CHARLES HENRI. Secret Haiku. (NY): Red Ozier, (1982). 1st ed. One of 155 numbered, signed by Ford & Isamu Noguchi (illus). Silk over bds, gilt. Fine. *Reese.* $75/£47

FORD, CHARLES HENRI. Spare Parts. (Athens, 1966.) One of 850 numbered. Pict bds (extrems rubbed). *Swann*.* $57/£36

FORD, FORD MADOX. The English Novel from the Earliest Days to the Death of Joseph Conrad. London: Constable, 1930. 1st ed. Blue buckram, gilt. VG. *Maggs.* $72/£45

FORD, FORD MADOX. Henry for Hugh. Phila/London: Lippincott, 1934. 1st ed. VG (reps sl spotted; cvrs sl rubbed, mkd, dusty; spine ends sl bumped, corner bruised) in dj (chipped, rubbed, mkd, dusty, sl torn, creased, internally repaired). *Ulysses.* $232/£145

FORD, FORD MADOX. Last Post. London: Duckworth, (1928). 1st British ed. Grn cl, gilt. VG in dj (few minute edge nicks). *Reese.* $450/£281

FORD, FORD MADOX. A Man Could Stand Up. London: Duckworth, (1926). 1st ed. Inscribed in 1931. Olive grn cl, gilt. VG in dj (sm dent, sm closed edge tear). *Reese.* $650/£406

FORD, FORD MADOX. Mister Bosphorus and the Muses or a Short History of Poetry in Britain. London: Duckworth, 1923. 1st ed. One of 1000 ptd. 11 wood engrs by Paul Nash. Black cl-backed illus gray paper bds. Good (eps, prelims, fore-edges lt spotted; fep crease; bds sl shelfworn, sl bowed). *Maggs.* $400/£250

FORD, FORD MADOX. No More Parades. London: Duckworth, (1925). 1st ed. Grn cl, gilt. (Faint offset eps from dj flaps), o/w Fine in dj. *Reese.* $600/£375

FORD, FORD MADOX. Parade's End. NY: Knopf, 1961. Omnibus ed, later ptg. Gilt cl, bds. Fine in dj (price-clipped). *Reese.* $15/£9

FORD, FORD MADOX. Provence. From Minstrels to the Machine. Phila: Lippincott, 1935. 1st ed. (Cvr edges sl dknd), o/w Fine in dj (sl chipped, torn, spine creased). *Jaffe.* $225/£141

FORD, FORD MADOX. The Rash Act. NY, 1933. 1st Amer ed. NF (sl rubbed) in dj (spine sunned, chipped). *Polyanthos.* $45/£28

FORD, FORD MADOX. Some Do Not.... NY: Thomas Seltzer, 1924. 1st Amer ed. Yellow cl, black bds. VG in dj (few sm old inner mends, tanned, sm spine chips, clean split fr flap fold). *Reese.* $125/£78

FORD, GERALD. A Time to Heal. NY: Harper & Reader's Digest, 1979. 1st ed. Signed on tipped-in leaf. Fine in Fine dj. *Beasley.* $125/£78

FORD, GORDON ONSLOW. Painting in the Instant. London: Thames & Hudson, (1964). Fine in dj. *Turtle Island.* $55/£34

FORD, GUS. Texas Cattle Brands. Dallas: Clyde C. Cockrell, 1936. 1st ed. VG. *Labordo.* $125/£78

FORD, HENRY A. The History of Putnam and Marshall Counties. Lacon, IL, 1860. 16mo. Lib buckram. (Ink lib stamp tp.) Howes F249. *Swann*.* $546/£341

FORD, HENRY CHAPMAN. An Artist Records the California Missions. Norman Neuerburg (ed). SF: Book Club of CA, 1989. One of 450 ptd. Prospectus laid in. 1/4 cl, dec bds. Fine. *Pacific*.* $40/£25

FORD, JESSE HILL. The Conversion of Buster Drumwright. Nashville: Vanderbilt, 1964. 1st ed. Fine in NF dj. *Pettler.* $30/£19

FORD, JESSE HILL. The Liberation of Lord Byron Jones. Boston: Atlantic-Little Brown, 1965. 1st ed. NF in VG + dj (price-clipped). *Pettler.* $20/£13

FORD, JULIA ELLSWORTH. Snickerty Nick...Rhymes by Witter Bynner. NY: Moffat, Yard, 1919. 1st ed. 4to. 3 color plts by Arthur Rackham. Blue pict cl (lt spotted). Dj (rear cvr w/sm piece of margin torn away, few other tears). *Christie's*.* $478/£299

FORD, P. R. J. The Oriental Carpet. NY: Abrams, (1981). 1st US ed. Folio. 400 color plts, 14 maps. Scarlet cl, gilt spine. (Edges sl dusty.) Text VG in dj (sl rubbed, worn). *Baltimore*.* $80/£50

FORD, PAUL LEICESTER et al. Mason Locke Weems: His Works and Ways. NY, 1929. One of 200 numbered sets. 3 vols. 1/4 cl. Slipcases. *Swann*.* $149/£93

FORD, PAUL LEICESTER. The New-England Primer. NY, 1897. One of 425 numbered. Uncut. Leather-backed bds (rubbed, soiled, spine ends worn). *Oinonen*.* $60/£38

FORD, RICHARD. The Sportswriter. NY, 1986. 1st ed. Pb orig. NF in wraps. *Warren.* $75/£47

FORD, RICHARD. Wildlife. NY: Atlantic Monthly, (1990). One of 200 numbered, signed. Fine in Fine slipcase. *Lenz.* $150/£94

FORD, RICHARD. Wildlife. London: Collins Harvill, 1990. 1st ed. Signed. Fine in dj. *Smith.* $100/£63

FORD, ROBERT. Thistledown. Paisley: Alexander Gardner, 1913. 16 plts by John Duncan. Teg, uncut. Buckram, gilt. (Fep removed; lt string-mks to fr bd.) *Hollett.* $40/£25

FORD, WORTHINGTON CHAUNCEY. George Washington. NY, 1900. One of 1250 numbered sets. 2 vols. 4 tls laid in. 3/4 morocco (extrems rubbed), gilt. *Swann*.* $201/£126

FORDHAM, ELIAS PYM. Personal Narrative of Travels in Virginia, Maryland, Pennsylvania,...and...Residence in the Illinois Territory: 1817-1818. Frederick Austin Ogg (ed). Cleveland: A.H. Clark, 1906. 1st ed. Grn cl. Roderick Terry bkpl. Howes F257. *Mott.* $125/£78

FORDYCE, JAMES. Addresses to Young Men. Boston: William Green, (1782). 1st Amer ed. 2 vols in 1. 174; (174)-352pp (foxed, feps torn). Contemp calf, grn morocco spine label. *Karmiole.* $150/£94

Foreign Journalists Under Franco's Terror. By a Journalist. London: United Editorial Ltd, (1938?). 1st ed. Ptd wrappers. (Wrappers sl tanned), o/w NF. *Reese.* $85/£53

FOREMAN, CAROLYN THOMAS. Oklahoma Imprints 1835-1907. Norman, OK: Univ of OK, 1936. 1st ed. Fine in VG dj. *Wantagh.* $85/£53

FOREMAN, GRANT. Fort Gibson. Muskogee, OK: Hoffman Speed, n.d. 1st ed. VG in wrappers. *Labordo.* $15/£9

FOREMAN, GRANT. Sequoyah. Norman: Univ of OK, 1938. 1st ed. Orange cl, paper spine label. NF (extrems sl worn, spine dknd). *Harrington.* $45/£28

FORESTER, C. S. The African Queen. Boston: Little, Brown, 1935. 1st US ed. One of 2500 ptd. Tan cl stamped in blind/grn. (Pencil name erased ep, top edge sl dust-soiled), o/w Nice in dj (lt soiled, 2 short tears spine crown), fldg cl case. *Reese.* $650/£406

FORESTER, C. S. The Annie Marble in Germany. London, 1930. 1st Eng ed. Good (cvrs sl mkd, spotted; lacks dj). *Clearwater.* $104/£65

FORESTER, C. S. Brown on Resolution. London: John Lane, Bodley Head, (1929). 1st ed. Blue cl. (Eps foxed, inscrip on slip affixed to tp; spine faded), o/w Good. *Reese.* $85/£53

FORESTER, C. S. Captain Hornblower R.N. Michael Joseph, 1965. 1st UK ed, 1st ptg thus, containing 'Hornblower and the Hotspur,' 'The Happy Return,' 'A Ship of the Line.' NF in dj (few sm abraded patches). *Williams.* $51/£32

FORESTER, C. S. The General. London: Michael Joseph, (1936). 1st ed. Red-brn cl stamped in silver. (Sl dusty), o/w VG + in dj (sm closed edge tear). *Reese.* $250/£156

FORESTER, C. S. Gold from Crete. Boston, (1970). 1st Amer ed. Very Nice (corner sl bumped) in dj (price-clipped). *Clearwater.* $40/£25

FORESTER, C. S. The Happy Return. London: Michael Joseph, 1937. 1st ed. Grn coarse linen. Nice (few ll lt foxed). *Temple.* $26/£16

FORESTER, C. S. The Happy Return. Michael Joseph, 1937. 1st UK ed. Fine (bkpl) in NF dj (few sm closed tears). Complete w/wrap-around band. *Williams.* $720/£450

FORESTER, C. S. Hornblower and the Crisis. London, 1967. 1st Eng ed. Fine in dj (sl torn, nicked). *Clearwater.* $48/£30

FORESTER, C. S. Hornblower and the Hotspur. Boston: Little, Brown, (1962). 1st US ed. Nice in dj. *Second Life.* $45/£28

FORESTER, C. S. Hornblower and the Hotspur. London: Michael Joseph, 1962. 1st ed. VG in dj (sl chipped, sm closed edge tears). *Virgo.* $24/£15

FORESTER, C. S. The Hornblower Companion. Michael Joseph, 1964. 1st UK ed. NF in VG dj (few sm closed tears, sl rubbed). *Williams.* $176/£110

FORESTER, C. S. Lieutenant Hornblower. London: Michael Joseph, 1952. 1st ed. (Spine sl rubbed), o/w VG in Good dj (sl rubbed; spine sl chipped). *Virgo.* $24/£15

FORESTER, C. S. Lieutenant Hornblower. Boston: Little, Brown, 1952. 1st US ed. VG in dj. *Second Life.* $45/£28

FORESTER, C. S. Long Before Forty. London, 1967. 1st Eng ed. Nice (inscrip; extrems sl bumped) in dj (price-clipped). *Clearwater.* $40/£25

FORESTER, C. S. Louis XIV, King of France and Navarre. London, 1928. 1st Eng ed. (Foxed; 1 edge sl knocked, cvrs sl faded, mkd; lacks dj.) *Clearwater.* $80/£50

FORESTER, C. S. Love Lies Dreaming. London, 1927. 1st Eng ed. Good (spine creased, handled; hinges tender, lacks dj). *Clearwater.* $160/£100

FORESTER, C. S. The Man in the Yellow Raft. London, 1969. 1st Eng ed. Fine in dj (sl torn). *Clearwater.* $40/£25

FORESTER, C. S. Marionettes at Home. London, 1936. 1st Eng ed. *Clearwater.* $32/£20

FORESTER, C. S. Mr. Midshipman Hornblower. Boston: Little, Brown, 1950. 1st US ed. VG (ex-lib; remnants from tape removal eps, cvr) in dj. *Second Life.* $35/£22

FORESTER, C. S. The Naval War of 1812. London, 1957. 1st Eng ed. Very Nice in dj (sl nicked). *Clearwater.* $48/£30

FORESTER, C. S. The Paid Piper. Methuen, 1924. 1st ed, 1st issue, w/cat dated Sept 1923. Fine. *Williams.* $440/£275

FORESTER, C. S. The Peacemaker. London, 1934. 1st Eng ed. Good (cvr edges sl bumped; lacks dj). *Clearwater.* $88/£55

FORESTER, C. S. Randall and the River of Time. London: Michael Joseph, (1951). 1st British ed. Black cl stamped in silver. Fine in dj. *Reese.* $60/£38

FORESTER, C. S. Randall and the River of Time. London, 1951. 1st Eng ed. Nice (spine sl creased, mkd) in dj (sl nicked). *Clearwater.* $48/£30

FORESTER, C. S. The Sky and the Forest. Michael Joseph, 1948. 1st UK ed. VG + in dj. *Williams.* $45/£28

FORESTER, C. S. U 97. London: John Lane, 1931. 1st ed. (Spine, top cvr edges sl faded), o/w NF in dj (sl chipped). *Else Fine.* $750/£469

FORESTER, FRANK (Pseud of Henry William Herbert.) (ed). Sporting Scenes and Sundry Sketches: Being the Miscellaneous Writings of J. Cypress, Jr. NY, 1842. 1st ed. 2 vols. Pub's cl (lt worn; foxed). BAL 8068. *Oinonen*.* $150/£94

FORESTER, FRANK. (Pseud of Henry William Herbert.) Frank Forester's Fish and Fishing of the United States, and British Provinces of North America. London: Richard Bentley, 1849. 1st ed. Grn cl, gilt. (Bkpl; spine head cl torn, needs repairing, spine dknd, sl shelfworn), else VG-. *Pacific*.* $109/£68

FORESTER, FRANK. (Pseud of Henry William Herbert.) Frank Forester's Fish and Fishing of the United States, and British Provinces of North America.... NY: American News Co, (1859). New ed. Grn cl, gilt. VG. *Pacific*.* $69/£43

FORESTER, FRANK. (Pseud of Henry William Herbert.) Frank Forester's Fugitive Sporting Sketches. Will Wildwood (ed). Westfield, WI, 1879. 1st ed. Grn cl, gilt. (Sl insect damage cvrs), else VG. *Pacific*.* $92/£58

FORESTER, FRANK. (Pseud of Henry William Herbert.) Hitchcock Edition of Frank Forester. NY, (1930). One of 750 numbered sets. 4 vols. (Sl worn, spine gilt partly worn away.) *Oinonen*.* $160/£100

FORESTER, FRANK. (Pseud of Henry William Herbert.) Trouting Along the Catasauqua. NY: Angler's Club, 1927. One of 423 numbered. Frontis. Uncut, unopened. Batik bds (lt worn), buckram back, paper labels. *Oinonen*.* $225/£141

FORESTER, FRANK. (Pseud of Henry William Herbert.) The Warwick Woodlands, My Shooting Box, The Quorndon Hounds, The Deerstalkers. NY: Derrydale, 1930. Hitchcock ed. Ltd to 750 numbered sets. 4 vols. Blue cl. Fine set in VG slipcase. *Biscotti.* $450/£281

FORESTIER, J. C. N. Garden: A Note Book of Plans and Sketches. Helen M. Fox (trans). NY: Scribner, 1924. 1st ed. Grn cl, gilt. (Old name), else VG. *Pacific*.* $92/£58

FORKEL, J. N. Life of John Sebastian Bach; with a Critical Review of His Compositions. London: T. Boosey, 1820. 1st Eng ed. xi,116pp; 3 fldg plts. Untrimmed. Orig cl-backed bds, handwritten paper spine label. (Ink notes, lacks rep; cvrs rubbed, worn), else VG. *Pacific*.* $173/£108

FORMAN, H. BUXTON and THOMAS J. WISE. Between the Lines. Letters and Memoranda Interchanged.... Austin: Univ of TX, 1945. 1st ed. One of 525. This copy inscribed by Fannie Ratchford to Bert Toggweiler. 126 facs plts in collotype. Fine in Fine slipcase. *Vandoros.* $195/£122

FORMAN, H. BUXTON. The Shelley Library: An Essay in Bibliography. London: Reeves & Turner, 1886. Orig wrappers (detached). *Maggs.* $13/£8

FORMAN, SAMUEL. Narrative of a Journey Down the Ohio and Mississippi in 1789-90. Cincinnati, 1888. Orig letterpress wrappers. Howes F263. *Swann*.* $161/£101

FORNELL, EARL WESLEY. The Galveston Era: The Texas Crescent on the Eve of Secession. Austin: Univ of TX, (1961). 1st ed. Fine in dj. *Sadlon.* $40/£25

FORREST, EARLE R. Arizona's Dark and Bloody Ground. Caldwell, 1959. 4th ptg, rev, enlgd. VG. Howes F265. *Baade.* $25/£16

FORREST, EARLE R. Missions and Pueblos of the Old Southwest. Cleveland: A.H. Clark, 1929. 1st ed. 32 photo plts. Teg. Blue cl. Fine. *Karmiole.* $125/£78

FORREST, THOMAS. A Voyage to New Guinea and the Moluccas, from Balambangan...in the Tartar Galley...During the Years, 1774, 1775, and 1776. Dublin: Messrs. Price et al, 1779. Dublin ed. 4 engr maps, plts (discoloring). Contemp mottled calf (rebacked). *Sotheby's*.* $478/£299

FORSTER, E. M. Alexandria. A History and Guide. NY: Doubleday, 1961. 1st Amer ed. VF in illus wrappers. *Blackwell's.* $40/£25

FORSTER, E. M. Alexandria: A History and a Guide. Alexandria: Whitehead Morris, 1922. 1st ed. 3 fldg maps, 1 in rear pocket. Buff bds. (Pencil inscrip, inscrip on cvr; fr cvr sl scuffed, soiled.) *Christie's*.* $368/£230

FORSTER, E. M. Aspects of the Novel. Arnold, 1927. 1st ed. Maroon cl, gilt. VG (name). *Blackwell's.* $96/£60

FORSTER, E. M. Battersea Rise. NY: Harcourt, Brace, (1955). 1st ed. Signed. Untrimmed. Patterned white bds. VG (inscrip) in gray morocco, marbled bd solander case, gilt. *Baltimore*.* $280/£175

FORSTER, E. M. The Celestial Omnibus and Other Stories. Sidgwick & Jackson, 1911. 1st ed. One of 1000 ptd. Pict eps; teg. Dec cl, gilt. Good (sl shaken, sl mks; sl rubbed, faded). *Ash.* $80/£50

FORSTER, E. M. The Celestial Omnibus and Other Stories. Sidgwick, 1911. 1st ed. Teg. Pale brn cl, gilt. Fine. *Blackwell's.* $224/£140

FORSTER, E. M. England's Pleasant Land. Hogarth, 1940. 1st ed. Orange cl. Fine in dj. *Blackwell's.* $48/£30

FORSTER, E. M. England's Pleasant Land. Hogarth, 1940. 1st ed. Fine in dj (sl dusty, spine, edges sl faded, later price sticker pasted over orig price on fr flap). *Ulysses.* $104/£65

FORSTER, E. M. England's Pleasant Land. A Pageant Play. London: Hogarth, 1940. 1st ed. VG in variant dk orange cl. *Cady.* $25/£16

FORSTER, E. M. The Eternal Moment and Other Stories. Sidgwick & Jackson, 1928. 1st ed. Maroon cl, gilt. VG (spine faded). *Blackwell's.* $112/£70

FORSTER, E. M. Goldsworthy Lowes Dickinson. Arnold, 1934. 1st ed. 9 plts. Tail edges untrimmed. Dk blue cl, gilt. Good (eps lt foxed) in dj (soiled, rubbed, sl defective). *Blackwell's.* $216/£135

FORSTER, E. M. The Hill of Devi, Letters from Dewas State Senior. London, 1953. 1st ed. VG in dj. *Gretton.* $19/£12

FORSTER, E. M. Howard's End. NY: Knopf, 1921. 1st Amer ed. VG (name, note) in dj (spine ends chipped, flaps detached, reattached w/tape to verso). *Pacific*.* $259/£162

FORSTER, E. M. The Life to Come and Other Stories. London, 1972. VG in dj. *Typographeum.* $35/£22

FORSTER, E. M. The Life to Come and Other Stories. Oliver Stallybrass (ed). Edward Arnold, 1972. 1st Eng ed. NF (spine head sl bumped) in dj (sl creased, internally reinforced, price-clipped). *Ulysses.* $56/£35

FORSTER, E. M. Maurice. Arnold, 1971. 1st UK ed. Fine in NF dj (price-clipped). *Williams.* $40/£25

FORSTER, E. M. Maurice. NY: Norton, 1971. 1st ed. Fine in NF dj (spine lt worn). *Beasley.* $45/£28

FORSTER, E. M. A Passage to India. NY: Harcourt, Brace, (1924). 1st Amer ed. VG. *Pacific*.* $58/£36

FORSTER, E. M. A Passage to India. London, 1924. 1st ed. (Extrems lt rubbed.) *Swann*.* $172/£108

FORSTER, E. M. A Passage to India. Edward Arnold, 1924. 1st Eng ed. VG (inscrip, feps lt browned; cvr edges sl rubbed, spine sl faded, spine ends, corners sl bumped). *Ulysses.* $248/£155

FORSTER, E. M. A Passage to India. London: Arnold, 1924. 1st ed. NF (eps sl offset; sl dusty, top edge sl bumped; lacks dj). *Between The Covers.* $350/£219

FORSTER, E. M. A Passage to India. London: Edward Arnold, 1924. 1st UK ed. VG (ink inscrip fep; bds sl dknd). *Williams.* $360/£225

FORSTER, E. M. A Passage to India. London: Edward Arnold, 1924. 1st ed. 8vo. Red cl, lettered in black. VG. *Maggs.* $640/£400

FORSTER, FREDERICK J. Tippytoes Comes to Town. Chicago: Rand McNally, (1926). 1st ed. 10x8. Uldene Trippe (illus). Pict cvr label. (Old spine label), else NF. *Pacific*.* $58/£36

FORSTER, GEORGE. A Voyage Round the World, in His Britannic Majesty's Sloop, Resolution...during the Years 1772, 3, 4, and 5. London: B. White, 1777. 1st ed. 2 vols. 4to. xviii,(2),602,(1); (4),607pp; lg fldg copper-engr chart. Period tree calf (rebacked w/mod calf), gilt, raised bands, morocco lettering pieces. (Offset, neat repair to short stub tear on frontis chart; private lib bkpls, blindstamps, ink #, few other mks; discoloration to eps; 1st tp w/offset, soiled patch; bkseller's note tipped to fep), else NF set. Bkpls George Manners. *Pacific*.* $1,840/£1,150

FORSTER, JOHN REINOLD. Observations Made During a Voyage Round the World, on Physical Geography, Natural History, and Ethic Philosophy. London: G. Robinson, 1778. 1st ed. 4to. (4),iii,(1),iv,(9)-16,(9)-649,(2)pp; fldg copper-engr chart, 2 tables (1 fldg). Period tree calf (rebacked w/mod calf), gilt, raised bands, morocco lettering pieces. (Private lib bkpls, blindstamps, few other mks; discoloration to eps; fldg chart lt foxed), else NF. Bkpl of George Manners. *Pacific*.* $1,150/£719

FORSTER, JOHN. The Life and Times of Oliver Goldsmith. London: Chapman & Hall, 1863. 4th ed. xl,472pp. 1/2 calf (edges sl rubbed), gilt. *Hollett.* $56/£35

FORSTER, JOHN. The Life and Times of Oliver Goldsmith. London: Chapman & Hall, 1871. 2 vols. Extra-illus by the insertion of 93 Fine engr plts (some inlaid to size of pg). Teg. Full navy blue levant morocco, gilt paneled spiens, raised bands, inner gilt dentelles. Fine set. *Appelfeld.* $400/£250

FORSTER, JOHN. The Life of Charles Dickens. London: Chapman & Hall, 1874. 12th thousand. 3 vols. xviii,398; xx,462; xv,552pp. VG set (some joints sl tender; extrems sl rubbed). *Hollett.* $192/£120

FORSTER, MARGARET. The Battle for Christabel. C&W, 1991. 1st ed. Signed. Fine in dj. *Virgo.* $32/£20

FORSTER, WILLIAM. Memoirs of William Forster. Benjamin Seebohm (ed). London: Alfred W. Bennett, 1865. 1st ed. 2 vols. viii,394; (vi),400pp. (Spines sl faded), o/w Fine set. *Young.* $120/£75

FORSYTE, CHARLES. The Decoding of Edwin Drood. Victor Gollancz, 1980. 1st ed. Fine in dj. *Ulysses.* $32/£20

FORSYTH, FREDERICK. The Biafra Story. Penguin, 1969. 1st UK ed, 1st bk. Orig pb. VG (ink name; spine faded). *Williams.* $35/£22

FORSYTH, FREDERICK. The Fourth Protocol. Hutchinson, 1984. 1st UK ed. Signed. VG + in dj. *Williams.* $40/£25

FORSYTH, FREDERICK. The Odessa File. Hutchinson, 1972. 1st UK ed. Fine in dj. *Williams.* $40/£25

FORSYTH, GEORGE A. The Story of the Soldier. NY: D. Appleton, 1900. 1st ed. 6 plts. Dec cl. (Bold sig, few sm unobtrusive rubber/blindstamps; spine sunned, ends rubbed), else VG. Howes F270. *Pacific*.* $98/£61

Fort-La-Fayette Life. 1863-64. In Extracts from the 'Right Flanker,' a Manuscript Sheet Circulating Among the Southern Prisoners in Fort-La-Fayette, in 1863-64. London: Simpkin, Marshall, 1865. 1st ed. 102pp; dbl-pg facs. Grn cl. (Bkpl; sm spine stain), else NF. *Chapel Hill.* $350/£219

FORTESCUE, J. A History of the British Army. London, 1910-17. Vols 1-8 (of 13) bound in 9 vols plus 3 vols of maps. 12 vols. *Petersfield.* $288/£180

FORTESCUE, J. A Short Account of Canteens in the British Army. CUP, 1928. 1st ed. VG (spine ends, corner bumped, spine sl faded; lacks dj). *Ulysses.* $56/£35

FORTNUM, C. DRURY E. A Descriptive Catalogue of the Maiolica Hispano-Moresco, Persian, Damascus, and Rhodian Wares, in the South Kensington Museum. London, 1873. 12 mtd color plts. 1/2 morocco (rubbed). Internally VG. *Washton.* $350/£219

FORTUNE, ROBERT. A Residence Among the Chinese. John Murray, 1857. 1st ed. Frontis, (xvi),440pp; 5 plts. Contemp 1/2 calf (rebacked). *Bickersteth.* $232/£145

FOSBROKE, THOMAS DUDLEY. Encyclopedia of Antiquities, and Elements of Archaeology, Classical and Medieval. London, 1825. 2 vols. 57 engr plts. Contemp diced calf, gilt. (Lt foxed, affecting some plts; hinge cracked; cvrs worn.) *King.* $250/£156

FOSKETT, DAPHNE. British Portrait Miniatures. Spring Books, 1968. 24 color, 191 monochrome plts. VG in dj. *Hollett.* $48/£30

FOSKETT, DAPHNE. A Dictionary of British Miniature Painters. NY/Washington: Praeger, (1972). 1st US ed. 2 vols. 31 color plts vol 1, 400 b/w plts vol 2. Royal blue cl, gilt. (Sl shelfworn.) Internally NF in djs (sl sunned, edgeworn). *Baltimore*.* $50/£31

FOSKETT, REGINALD (ed). The Zambesi Journal and Letters of Dr. John Kirk 1858-63. London, 1965. 1st ed. 2 vols. 19 plts. Dj (chipped). *Edwards.* $64/£40

FOSSETT, FRANK. Colorado: Its Gold and Silver Mines, Farms and Stock Ranges, and Health and Pleasure Resorts. Tourist's Guide to the Rocky Mountains. NY: C.G. Crawford, 1879. 1st ed. vii,540pp. (Contents dknd, new eps; rebacked w/orig spine strip laid on, cvrs worn), else VG. Howes F281. *Pacific*.* $92/£58

FOSTER, B. G. Abraham Lincoln Inventor. N.p.: Privately ptd, 1928. Port. Good + in ptd wraps. *Wantagh.* $20/£13

FOSTER, BIRKET. Pictures of English Landscape. London, 1863. 30 engr plts. Dec eps, marbled eps; aeg. (Some ll detached, some cellotaped.) Gilt-tooled morocco (spine faded, intruding sl onto bds). *Edwards.* $77/£48

FOSTER, CLEMENT LE NEVE. The Elements of Mining and Quarrying. London: Charles Griffin, 1917. 3rd ed. Frontis. (Spine sl faded, few pinholes, rear hinge worn, label partly removed.) *Hollett.* $72/£45

FOSTER, CLEMENT LE NEVE. A Treatise on Ore and Stone Mining. London: Charles Griffin, 1905. 6th ed. Frontis. (Extrems sl rubbed, mkd.) *Hollett.* $224/£140

FOSTER, ELIZABETH ANDROS. Motolinia's History of the Indians of New Spain. (Albuquerque): Cortes Soc, 1950. One of 500 ptd. (Shelfworn), else VG. *Dumont.* $95/£59

FOSTER, FRANK P. An Illustrated Encyclopaedic Medical Dictionary. NY: Appleton, 1890-93. 4 vols in 12, as issued. Pub's cl (worn). VG set. *Oinonen*.* $100/£63

FOSTER, GEORGE C. The Oldest Profession. London: Selwyn & Blount, (1925). 1st ed. Black cl. Fine in NF pict dj (spine sunned, sm closed tear). *Reese.* $35/£22

FOSTER, H. LINCOLN. Rock Gardening: a Guide to Growing Alpines and Other Wildflowers.... Boston: Houghton Mifflin, 1968. 1st ed. VG in dj (chipped). *Fair Meadow.* $40/£25

FOSTER, J. J. Miniature Painters, British and Foreign. London/NY, 1903. Author's ed. 2 vols. Folio. Frontis ports, 123 plts. Marbled eps; teg, rest uncut. (Margins sl browned; fore-edge of bds sl soiled, corners sl bumped, vol 2 spine head sl bumped, chipped.) *Edwards.* $216/£135

FOSTER, JOHN. An Appeal to the Young, on the Importance of Religion. NY: Amer Tract Soc, n.d. (ca 1860). 12mo. 69pp. Leather back, marbled paper on bds, gilt. Internally Fine. Good (ink sig inside upper cvr; spine rubbed, cracked, w/trace of orig gilt title, bd edges rubbed). *Hobbyhorse.* $55/£34

FOSTER, JOSEPH K. Raphael Soyer: Drawings and Watercolors. NY, (1968). Dj (bottom of spine missing). *Swann*.* $46/£29

FOSTER, M. Lectures on the History of Physiology During the 16th, 17th and 18th Centuries. Cambridge, 1901. Frontisport. New binders cl. (Lt pencil notes margins few text pp), o/w VG. *Whitehart.* $56/£35

FOSTER, MARK. The Denver Bears. Pruett, 1983. 1st ed. Fine in VG + dj. *Plapinger.* $75/£47

FOSTER, POPS. Pops Foster, New Orleans Jazzman. An Autobiography. As told to Tom Stoddard. Berkeley: Univ of CA, 1971. 1st ed. Fine in Fine dj (spine sunned). *Beasley.* $30/£19

FOSTER, R. F. Whist Tactics. London: Mudie & Sons, 1895. 1st ed. (iv),iii,141,viipp + 12 ads; 26 full-pg illus. Aeg. Mid-grn cl, gilt. Good. *Young.* $32/£20

FOSTER, SAMUEL T. One of Cleburne's Command. Norman D. Brown (ed). Austin, (1980). 1st ed. VG + in VG + dj. *Pratt.* $50/£31

FOSTER, STEPHEN CLARK. El Quacheno: How I Want to Help Make the Constitution of California.... L.A.: Dawson's Book Shop, 1949. One of 100. *Dawson.* $50/£31

FOSTER, STEPHEN S. The Brotherhood of Thieves, or a True Picture of the American Church and Clergy. New London, (CT): William Bolles, 1843. 1st ed. 68pp. Orig ptd fr wrapper (sl soiled). *M & S.* $275/£172

FOSTER, WILLIAM (ed). Travels of John Sanderson in the Levant 1584-1602. London: CUP, 1931. Blue cl. Fine. *Appelfeld.* $60/£38

FOSTER, WILLIAM HARNDEN. New England Grouse Shooting. NY: Scribner, 1942. 1st ed. Folio. Color frontis. VF in NF dj (lt chipped). *Bowman.* $225/£141

FOSTER-HARRIS. The Look of the Old West. NY: Viking, 1955. 1st ed. *Book Market.* $22/£14

FOTHERGILL, JOHN. Chain of Friendship, Selected Letters of Dr. John Fothergill, 1735-1780. Cambridge, 1971. 1st ed. VG. *Doctor's Library.* $45/£28

FOTHERGILL, JOHN. My Three Inns. London, 1949. VG in dj (sl torn). *Gretton.* $10/£6

FOUGERA, KATHERINE GIBSON. With Custer's Cavalry. Caldwell: Caxton Ptrs, 1942. 2nd ptg. Blue cl, gilt. VG (bkpl). *Pacific*.* $46/£29

FOUGUERA, KATHERINE GIBSON. With Custer's Cavalry. Caldwell, ID: Caxton Ptrs, 1940. 1st ed. Signed. VG in dj. *Labordo.* $185/£116

FOULKS, EDWARD F. The Arctic Hysterias of the North Alaskan Eskimo. Washington: American Anthropological Assn. No. 10, c. 1972. VG. *High Latitude.* $30/£19

FOUNTAIN, N. Underground—the London Alternative Press 1966-74. Routledge, 1988. Fine in dj. *Moss.* $26/£16

FOUQUE, VICTOR. The Truth Concerning the Invention of Photography, Nicephore Niepce, His Life, Letters and Works. NY, 1935. (Eps dampstained, ll w/ptr's creases.) *Swann*.* $258/£161

Four Gospels of the Lord Jesus Christ. According to the Authorized Version of King James I. Waltham St. Lawrence: Golden Cockerel, 1931. One of 482 (of 500). Folio. Eric Gill (illus). Teg, rest uncut. Orig 1/2 white pigskin, cl sides. VG (corners sl worn from slipcase, spine dknd, few spine bands lt worn, sl spotted) in slipcase. *Maggs*. $3,840/£2,400

Four Gospels. Leipzig: LEC, 1932. One of 1500 ptd. Signed by Emil Rudolf Weiss (decs). 1/2 vellum, gilt. (Spine gilt wearing off), else NF in Fine slipcase. *Pacific**. $40/£25

FOURCADE, FRANCOISE. Art Treasures of the Peking Museum. NY: Harry Abrams, (1965). Folio. 87 tipped-in color plts. Fine in dj. *Turtle Island*. $35/£22

FOURGEAUD, VICTOR H. The First Californiac. SF: Press of Lewis & Dorothy Allen, 1942. 1st bk ed. One of 225. Frontis, 2 ports. Blue pict bds, calf spine. Fine. *Harrington*. $225/£141

FOWLER, GENE. Schnozzola, the Story of Jimmy Durante. NY, 1951. 1st ed. Good in dj (edges frayed). *King*. $22/£14

FOWLER, HARLAN D. Three Caravans to Yuma. Glendale: A.H. Clark, 1980. 1st ed. One of 750. Fine. *Pacific**. $58/£36

FOWLER, JOHN. Journal of a Tour in the State of New York, in the Year 1830. London: Whittaker, Treacher, & Arnot, 1831. Only ed. 333pp. Orig cl (faded, spine sl worn), paper label. Howes F299. *Mott*. $100/£63

FOWLER, JOHN. Journal of a Tour in the State of New York, in the Year 1830. NY, 1970. Facs rpt of 1831 ed. *Edwards*. $24/£15

FOWLER, LAURENCE HALL and ELIZABETH BAER. The Fowler Architectural Collection of the John Hopkins University. SF: Alan Wofsy Fine Arts, 1991. Rpt of 1961 orig ed. 30 plts. Grn linen. Fine in pict dj. *Karmiole*. $150/£94

FOWLER, LAURENCE HALL and ELIZABETH BAER. The Fowler Architectural Collection of the Johns Hopkins University. Balt: Evergreen House Foundation, 1961. 1st ed, 1st state, w/Fowler's first name incorrectly spelled on tp; corrected tp tipped in. 20 b/w plts. Grn buckram, gilt. (Sl handled.) *Baltimore**. $100/£63

FOWLER, MELVIN L. (ed). Explorations into Cahokia Archaeology. Urbana: Univ of IL, 1977. 2nd ed. Heavy pict wrappers (crease, spot on rear cvr). NF. *Connolly*. $20/£13

FOWLER, SYDNEY. Four Callers in Razor Street. Temple, 1946. 1st UK ed. Fine in VG dj (sl dusty). *Williams*. $40/£25

FOWLES, JOHN. A Brief History of Lyme. Lyme Regis, 1981. Signed. VG in wraps. *King*. $35/£22

FOWLES, JOHN. The Collector. London: Jonathan Cape, (1963). 1st ed, 1st bk. (Few spots bottom pg edges), else NF in dj. *Pacific**. $374/£234

FOWLES, JOHN. The Collector. London: Jonathan Cape, (1963). 1st ed, 1st bk, 1st issue dj w/quote from bk on rear panel & no critic's blurbs. Fine in NF dj (spine ends sl rubbed). *Pacific**. $403/£252

FOWLES, JOHN. The Collector. London: Cape, (1963). 1st ed, 1st bk. Fine in 1st state dj. *Reese*. $500/£313

FOWLES, JOHN. The Collector. Boston, 1963. 1st Amer ed, 1st bk. Dj (lt rubbed). *Swann**. $115/£72

FOWLES, JOHN. The Collector. Boston: Little, Brown, 1963. 1st US ed, 1st bk. Fine in Fine dj (rear panel sl soiled). *Unger*. $150/£94

FOWLES, JOHN. Daniel Martin. Cape, 1977. 1st UK ed. Fine in dj. *Williams*. $29/£18

FOWLES, JOHN. The French Lieutenant's Woman. London: Cape, (1969). 1st ed. (Fore-edge sl smudged), o/w Fine in dj. *Reese*. $100/£63

FOWLES, JOHN. The French Lieutenant's Woman. Boston: Little, Brown, (1969). 1st Amer ed. Signed. (Cvrs, spine lettering faded), else VG in dj (price-clipped). *Pacific**. $127/£79

FOWLES, JOHN. The French Lieutenant's Woman. Boston: Little, Brown, 1969. 1st ed. NF in dj. *Smith*. $30/£19

FOWLES, JOHN. The French Lieutenant's Woman. Cape, 1969. 1st ed. Pict eps. Brn bds, gilt. VG in dj (sl rubbed). *Blackwell's*. $128/£80

FOWLES, JOHN. Lyme Regis Camera. Dovecote, 1990. 1st UK ed. Fine in wrappers. *Martin*. $19/£12

FOWLES, JOHN. A Maggot. London: Jonathan Cape, (1985). 1st ed. One of 500 signed. Beige cl, gilt, marbled bds. Fine in glassine wrapper. *Heritage*. $150/£94

FOWLES, JOHN. The Magus. London: Cape, (1966). 1st British ed. Fine in dj. *Reese*. $150/£94

FOWLES, JOHN. Mantissa. Boston: Little, Brown, 1982. 1st ed. One of 510 signed. Red buckram, gilt. Fine in pub's blue cl slipcase, paper label. *Cady*. $75/£47

FOWLIE, WALLACE. Rimbaud. The Myth of Childhood. London: Dennis Dobson, 1946. 1st ed. NF (name) in VG dj (tears, sm chip). *Beasley*. $30/£19

FOX, CARL. The Doll. NY: Abrams, (1977). 1st ed. 70 color plts (many tipped-in). Full red velvet, gilt. NF in illus dj. *Cahan*. $100/£63

FOX, CHARLES JAMES. A History of the Early Part of the Reign of James the Second. London: William Miller, 1808. 1st ed. Engr frontis, (4),lii,280,clviiipp + 8pp ads. Orig mottled calf (spine, extrems rubbed), gilt, red morocco label. *Karmiole*. $150/£94

FOX, CHARLES K. Rising Trout. Carlisle: Privately ptd, (1967). Ltd ed. Signed. Pict cl (lt worn). Dj. *Oinonen**. $90/£56

FOX, CHARLES K. The Wonderful World of Trout. Rockville Centre: Freshet, (1971). Rev ed. One of 350 numbered, signed. Gilt-stamped leatherette (lt worn). Slipcase. *Oinonen**. $100/£63

FOX, CYRIL. Pattern and Purpose. Cardiff: Nat'l Museum of Wales, 1958. 1st ed. Frontis, 80 plts, fldg map. (Bkpl; spine sl soiled, fr bd sl warped.) *Edwards*. $56/£35

FOX, D. L. Animal Biochromes and Structural Colours. Cambridge: Cambridge Univ, 1953. 1st ed. 3 color plts. NF in VG+ dj. *Mikesh*. $37/£23

FOX, EDITH. Roller Bears and the Safeway Tribe. Macmillan, 1928. 1st ed. Marguerite de Armond (illus). 259pp. Tan cl. VG (ex-lib; sl loose). *Price*. $40/£25

FOX, FRANK. Switzerland. A&C Black, 1917. 2nd ed. Map. Dec cl, gilt. (Extrems sl rubbed), o/w VG. *Sotheran*. $96/£60

FOX, GEORGE. The Autobiography of George Fox, from His Journal. Henry Stanley Newman (ed). London/Leominster: S.W. Partridge/Orphans' Printing Press, 1886. xxxi,(i),422,(ii)pp (prelims, final leaf spotted, joints tender); engr port. Blind-stamped cl (backstrip faded), gilt, beveled bds, leather spine label. *Hollett*. $72/£45

FOX, GUSTAVUS VASA. Confidential Correspondence of Gustavus Vasa Fox. Robert Means Thompson and Richard Wainwright (eds). NY: Naval Hist Soc, 1918-1919. 1st ed. One of 1200 ptd, w/note to subscribers laid in. 2 vols. Engr frontisports. Teg, rest untrimmed, partly unopened. Orig vellum-backed bds, gilt. Fine in glassine djs (lt used), pub's slipcases. *Chapel Hill*. $110/£69

FOX, HELEN M. Garden Cinderellas. NY, 1928. 1st ed. Color frontis. Grn cl, gilt. VG (ex-lib). *Larry Price*. $30/£19

FOX, HELEN M. Garden Cinderellas. NY: Macmillan, 1928. 1st ed. VG in dj (chipped). *Fair Meadow*. $45/£28

FOX, HELEN M. Patio Gardens. NY: Macmillan, 1929. 1st ed. 2 fldg plans. Fine. *Quest*. $85/£53

FOX, IRVING. Fleas of Eastern United States. Ames: IA State College, 1940. 1st ed. VG. *Archer*. $35/£22

FOX, JOHN, JR. Little Shepherd of Kingdom Come. NY: Scribner, 1931. 1st ed. 4to. 14 full-pg color plts by N. C. Wyeth. Tinted top. Black cl, gilt, color pict paste label. Good in pub's box (edges, corners sl rubbed) w/color paste label. *Reisler.* $375/£234

FOX, JOHN, JR. The Little Shepherd of Kingdom Come. NY, 1931. Ltd to 512 numbered, signed by N. C. Wyeth (illus). 16 full-pg tipped-in color plts. Teg. Vellum backed cl. (Spine head torn 1 inch at center; vellum sl dknd.) *King.* $495/£309

FOX, JOHN. The Book of Martyrs.... Liverpool: Nuttall, Fisher & Dixon, 1807. 2 vols. x,11-612; (ii),530pp; 22 engr plts. Contemp full tree calf, gilt, spine labels. VG set (browned, offsetting, label). *Hollett.* $192/£120

FOX, JOSEPH. The Natural History of the Human Teeth. AL, 1981. Facs rpt of 1803 ed. 13 plts. Marbled eps, aeg. Full dec gilt cowhide. *Edwards.* $72/£45

FOX, MARGARET. The Life of Margaret Fox, Wife of George Fox. Phila, 1859. 112pp. (Bkpl) else VG + . *Bohling.* $15/£9

FOX, MARY ANNA. The Discontented Robins, and Other Stories, for the Young. Boston: Charles Fox, n.d. (1847). 12mo. Frontis, 131pp; 5 full-pg round wood engrs. Frontis, 2 engrs signed F. E. Fox. Blind-tooled cl, gilt. Fine (shelfworn, sm chip at spine crown). *Hobbyhorse.* $100/£63

FOX, MAUDE A. Both Sides of the Mountain. Palm Desert: Desert Magazine Press, 1954. 1st ed. Signed. Fine in Fine dj. *Book Market.* $50/£31

FOX, PAUL. Four Men. NY: Scribner, 1946. 1st ed. White cl. Fine in NF pict dj (few sm fox mks, smudges). *Reese.* $40/£25

FOX, PAULA. The Little Swineherd and Other Tales. Dutton, 1978. 1st ed. 7.4x9.2. Leonard Lubin (illus). 112pp. Fine in VG dj. *Price.* $35/£22

FOX, SANFORD J. Science and Justice. The Massachusetts Witchcraft Trials. Balt: Johns Hopkins, (1968). 1st ed. Dbl-pg frontis. Black cl. Fine in VG dj (edges worn). *House.* $20/£13

FRADKIN, PHILIP L. A River No More. NY, 1981. 1st ed. Map. Blue/black cl. VG + in dj. *Five Quail.* $35/£22

FRAENKEL, MICHAEL. Bastard Death. Paris: Carrefour, 1946. 2nd ptg. NF in ptd dj. *Polyanthos.* $25/£16

FRAENKEL, MICHAEL. The Genesis of the Tropic of Cancer. (Berkeley): Bern Porter, 1946. 1st ed. Fine (short tear, upper edge sl soiled) in stapled wrappers in stiff card dj. *Between The Covers.* $85/£53

FRAIKIN, GLENN L. Inside Nevada Gambling. Adventures of a Winning System Player. NY: Exposition, (1965). VG in dj. *Perier.* $20/£13

FRANC, MIRIAM ALICE. Isben in England. Boston: Four Seas, 1919. 1st Amer ed. VG. *Dramatis.* $25/£16

FRANCATELLI, CHARLES ELME. The Modern Cook. Richard Bentley, 1855. 9th ed. Engr frontis, xvi,552pp. VG (sl spotted) in contemp 1/2 calf (rubbed). *Cox.* $104/£65

FRANCE, ANATOLE. The Crime of Sylvestre Bonnard. Lafcadio Hearn (trans). NY: Harper, 1890. 1st ed, 2nd state. Teg. Brn cl, ptd paper spine label. (Clippings pasted to feps; sl rubbed, label lt scuffed), o/w VG in 1/4 brn morocco slipcase. BAL 7919. *Cummins.* $200/£125

FRANCE, ANATOLE. The Crime of Sylvestre Bonnard. LEC, 1937. Ltd to 1500 numbered, signed by Sylvain Sauvage (illus). Fine in slipcase. *Swann*.* $57/£36

FRANCE, ANATOLE. The Crime of Sylvestre Bonnard. Lafcadio Hearn (trans). NY: Marchbanks, 1937. Sylvain Sauvage (illus). Full grn linen, stamped in gilt/grn. Box (worn). *Appelfeld.* $125/£78

FRANCE, ANATOLE. Penguin Island. LEC, 1947. Ltd to 1500 numbered, signed by Malcolm Cameron (illus). Fine in slipcase. *Swann*.* $69/£43

FRANCHERE, GABRIEL. Adventure at Astoria 1810-1814. Norman: Univ of OK, 1967. 1st ed thus. Fine in dj. *Labordo.* $35/£22

FRANCHERE, GABRIEL. Narrative of a Voyage to the Northwest Coast of America in the Years 1811, 1812, 1813, and 1814.... J. V. Huntington (ed). NY: Redfield, 1854. 1st ed in English. 376pp + 8pp pub's ads; 3 wood-engr plts. Dk grn cl, gilt. (2 leaves detached w/long tear; spine head frayed), else VG. Howes F310. *Baltimore*.* $160/£100

FRANCIS, AUSTIN M. Catskill Rivers. Birthplace of American Fly Fishing. NY: Beaverkill, 1983. One of 300, this copy not numbered or signed. Aeg. Full brn morocco (lt worn). Slipcase. *Oinonen*.* $300/£188

FRANCIS, DICK. Blood Sport. NY: Harper & Row, (1968). 1st ed. Fine in Fine dj. *Lenz.* $125/£78

FRANCIS, DICK. Blood Sport. Michael Joseph, 1967. 1st UK ed. VG in dj (sl rubbed, edges worn). *Williams.* $136/£85

FRANCIS, DICK. Bolt. London: Michael Joseph, 1986. 1st ed. Fine in Fine dj. *Unger.* $75/£47

FRANCIS, DICK. Bonecrack. NY: Harper & Row, (1972). 1st ed. Fine in Fine dj. *Lenz.* $85/£53

FRANCIS, DICK. Bonecrack. London: Michael Joseph, 1971. 1st Eng ed. Signed. NF (spine foot sl bumped) in dj (spine head sl rubbed). *Ulysses.* $104/£65

FRANCIS, DICK. Comeback. Michael Joseph, 1991. 1st UK ed. NF in dj. *Williams.* $16/£10

FRANCIS, DICK. The Edge. London: Michael Joseph, 1988. 1st Eng ed. Signed. VG (cvrs sl cocked, spine ends sl bumped) in dj (sl creased). *Ulysses.* $56/£35

FRANCIS, DICK. The Edge. NY, 1989. 1st US ed. As New in dj. *Bond.* $15/£9

FRANCIS, DICK. Flying Finish. Michael Joseph, 1966. 1st UK ed. Signed. Fine in VG + dj. *Williams.* $280/£175

FRANCIS, DICK. High Stakes. NY: Harper & Row, 1975. 1st US ed. (Spine slant), else VG in VG dj (price-clipped). *Pettler.* $20/£13

FRANCIS, DICK. Hot Money. Michael Joseph, 1987. 1st UK ed. Inscribed. NF in dj. *Williams.* $32/£20

FRANCIS, DICK. Hot Money. Putnam, 1988. 1st US ed. Signed. NF in dj. *Williams.* $24/£15

FRANCIS, DICK. Knockdown. London, 1974. 1st ed. NF in NF dj. *Warren.* $50/£31

FRANCIS, DICK. Nerve. Michael Joseph, 1964. 1st UK ed. NF in VG dj (spine lt browned, couple sm closed tears). *Williams.* $560/£350

FRANCIS, DICK. Nerve. Joseph, 1964. 1st ed. Crown 8vo. Mid grn bds, gilt. Fine in dj. *Blackwell's.* $776/£485

FRANCIS, DICK. Proof. Michael Joseph, 1984. 1st UK ed. VG in dj. *Williams.* $16/£10

FRANCIS, DICK. Rat Race. NY: Harper & Row, (1971). 1st ed. Fine in Fine dj. *Lenz.* $100/£63

FRANCIS, DICK. Reflex. Michael Joseph, 1980. 1st UK ed. VG in dj. *Williams.* $16/£10

FRANCIS, DICK. Risk. Michael Joseph, 1977. 1st UK ed. Presentation copy. Inscribed 1977. NF (fep sl stained) in dj (price-clipped, sl mkd). *Williams.* $88/£55

FRANCIS, DICK. Slay-Ride. London: Michael Joseph, 1973. 1st ed. Gray-fawn bds. Fine in dj. *Temple.* $48/£30

FRANCIS, DICK. Slay-Ride. Michael Joseph, 1973. 1st UK ed. Inscribed 1973. VG in dj (spine sl bumped). *Williams.* $120/£75

FRANCIS, DICK. Smokescreen. Joseph, 1972. 1st ed. VG in dj w/wraparound band. *Any Amount.* $26/£16

FRANCIS, DICK. The Sport of Queens. NY: Harper, (1969). 1st Amer ed, 1st bk. Fine in NF dj (sl worn). *Between The Covers.* $200/£125

FRANCIS, DICK. The Sport of Queens. Michael Joseph, 1957. 1st UK ed, 1st bk. Fine (bkpl) in VG + dj (sm closed tear to fr panel edge). *Williams*. $320/£200

FRANCIS, DICK. Trial Run. Michael Joseph, 1978. 1st UK ed. VG in dj. *Williams*. $22/£14

FRANCIS, FRANCIS. Angling Reminiscences. London: Cox, 1887. 248pp + 32pp ads. Grn cl, gilt. Fine. *Bowman*. $50/£31

FRANCIS, FRANCIS. A Book on Angling, Being a Complete Treatise on the Art of Angling in Every Branch. London: Longmans, Green, 1880. 5th ed. Frontis, 17 plts (6 hand-colored). Purple cl, gilt. (Bkpl; sig detached, fr hinge starting), else VG. *Pacific**. $230/£144

FRANCIS, FRANCIS. A Book on Angling: Being a Complete Treatise of the Art of Angling in Every Branch. London, 1867. 2nd ed. 15 plts (5 hand-colored). (Fep missing, sl foxed, soiled; shelfworn, shaken.) *Oinonen**. $110/£69

FRANCIS, FRANCIS. A Book on Angling: Being a Complete Treatise on the Art of Angling in Every Branch. London, 1867. 1st ed. 15 plts (5 hand-colored). (Shelfworn, loose in casing.) *Oinonen**. $450/£281

FRANCIS, FRANCIS. Fish-Culture: A Practical Guide to the Modern System of Breeding and Rearing Fish. London: Routledge, Warne, Routledge, 1863. 1st ed. Frontis. Blindstamped grn cl, gilt. NF. *Pacific**. $86/£54

FRANCIS, FRANCIS. The Practical Management of Fisheries. London: Horace Cox, 1883. 1st ed. Fldg plt. Blue cl, gilt. NF. *Pacific**. $58/£36

FRANCIS, GRANT R. Old English Drinking Glasses, Their Chronology and Sequence. London, 1926. Folio. 82 plts. *Swann**. $172/£108

FRANCIS, J. G. A Book of Cheerful Cats and Other Animated Animals. NY: Century, 1892. 1st ed. Obl 8vo. ix,37pp. Olive paper over bds (edges lt rubbed, spine ends lt chipped). VG. *House*. $110/£69

FRANCIS, JOHN. Annals, Anecdotes and Legends: A Chronicle of Life Assurance. Longman, Brown, Green & Longmans, 1853. 1st ed. Half-title, 32-pg pub's cat at end. *Sotheby's**. $238/£149

FRANCIS, RELL G. The Utah Photographs of George Edward Anderson. Lincoln, 1979. VG in dj. *Dumont*. $50/£31

FRANCIS, RICHARD S. Golf: Its Rules and Decisions. NY: Macmillan, 1937. 1st ed. Inscribed, signed by John H. Beers. Grn cl, gilt. Fine (emb stamp). *Pacific**. $40/£25

FRANCK, CARL L. The Villas of Frascati 1550-1750. NY, 1966. Color frontis. Good + . *Washton*. $35/£22

FRANCKE, A. H. A History of Western Tibet. London: S.W. Partridge, n.d. (1907). 1st ed. 1/2-title, xiv,191,(1)blank,32 pub's list; 23 plts, 4 maps. Grn dec cl, gilt. VG (lt foxed). *Morrell*. $192/£120

FRANK, ANNE. Diary of a Young Girl. (Northampton): Pennyroyal, 1985. Ltd to 350 w/10 full-pg etchings signed by Joseph Goldyne (illus). Signed by Barry Moser (designer) and Goldyne. Folio. Full gray blind-stamped morocco. VG + . *Truepenny*. $750/£469

FRANK, ROBERT. The Americans. NY, (1978). (Fep, 1/2-title creased, pencil notes.) Dj (soiled). *Swann**. $115/£72

FRANK, ROBERT. The Americans. NY: Grove, 1959. 1st US ed. (Spine lettering, extrems rubbed; old tape mks between 2 ll), else VG. *Cahan*. $400/£250

FRANK, ROBERT. The Americans. (NY): Aperture/MOMA, 1969. Rev, enlgd ed. (Lt foxed, thumbed, sl ptg defect to 1 plt.) Photo-pict stiff wrappers (rubbed, sl soiled, backstrip age-dknd). *Swann**. $92/£58

FRANK, ROBERT. The Lines of My Hand. N.p.: Lustrum, (1972). 1st ed. (Margins sl yellowed.) Pict wrappers (extrems sl worn). *Swann**. $287/£179

FRANK, WALDO et al (eds). America and Alfred Stieglitz. NY: Literary Guild, (1934). 1st ed. Black cl. Good. *Appelfeld*. $100/£63

FRANKAU, GILBERT. The Guns. London: C&W, 1916. 1st ed. Blue wrapper. (Spine chipped, lg tape mends at ends, edges sunnejd), else Good. *Reese*. $25/£16

FRANKAU, JULIA. An Eighteenth Century Artist and Engraver, John Raphael Smith, His Life and Works. Macmillan, 1902. 2 vols, incl folio of plts. 8vo, folio. 79 plts. Teg. Contemp full crimson morocco, gilt. (Plts sl spotted.) *Sotheby's**. $2,024/£1,265

FRANKE, PAUL. They Plowed up Hell in Old Cochise! Douglas, AZ: Douglas Climate Club, 1950. 1st ed. VG in stiff wrappers. *Lien*. $20/£13

FRANKENSTEIN, ALFRED. After the Hunt. Berkeley: Univ of CA, 1953. Orig ed. NF in dj. *Turtle Island*. $100/£63

FRANKENSTEIN, ALFRED. After the Hunt: William Harnett and Other American Still Life Painters. Univ of CA, (1975). New rev ed. Good in dj. *Rybski*. $85/£53

Frankenstein; or, The Modern Prometheus. (By Mary Wollstonecraft Shelley.) Lackington, Hughes, Mavor, & Jones, 1818. 1st ed. Vols 2 and 3 only. 12mo. Vol 2 p21 misnumbered 12, p25 correctly numbered; half-titles and ads present in both vols. (Sl browned.) 19th-cent calf (worn, lacks spines, vol 2 lacks fr cvr, vol 3 fr cvr detached). *Sotheby's**. $1,840/£1,150

FRANKFURTER, FELIX. The Case of Sacco and Vanzetti. Boston, 1927. 1st ed. Dj (sm archival tape mends, sm dampstain). *Swann**. $161/£101

Frankie in Wonderland. NY: Dutton, 1934. 1st ed. Stapled as issued in orig grained brn wrappers. *Maggs*. $40/£25

FRANKL, PAUL. Form and Re-Form. NY, (1930). (Shaken, spine faded, rubbed.) *Swann**. $172/£108

Franklin Primer, or Lessons in Spelling and Reading, Adapted to the Understanding of Children. Greenfield, MA/Boston/NY: A. Phelps/Crocker & Brewster/Mahlon Day, 1841. 28th ed. 12mo. 54pp + 1pg ad on lower wrapper. Four 1/3pg wood engrs. Pict alphabet composed of 25 (no X) wood engr figs. Pict pink paper wrappers. Fine (pencil dedication, lt foxing). *Hobbyhorse*. $125/£78

FRANKLIN, BENJAMIN. The Autobiography of.... SF: LEC, 1931. One of 1500. Signed by John Henry Nash (ptr). Frontis port. Vellum-backed marbled bds, gilt. NF in slipcase (broken). *Pacific**. $62/£39

FRANKLIN, BENJAMIN. Benjamin Franklin's Memoirs. Max Farrand (ed). Berkeley: Univ of CA, 1949. Parallel text ed. Red cl, gilt. Good in dj (sl soiled). *Karmiole*. $85/£53

FRANKLIN, BENJAMIN. Poor Richard's Almanack. Being the Almanacks of 1733, 1749, 1756, 1757, 1758, First Written Under the Name Richard Saunders. NY: Rimington & Hooper, 1928. Ltd to 350. NF in cl-cvrd slipcase (sm split 1 edge). *Zubal**. $35/£22

FRANKLIN, BENJAMIN. Poor Richard's Almanacks for the Years 1733-1758. LEC, 1964. Ltd to 1500 numbered, signed by Norman Rockwell (illus). Fine in slipcase. *Swann**. $172/£108

FRANKLIN, BENJAMIN. Works of the Late Doctor Benjamin Franklin, Consisting of His Life Written by Himself; Together with Essays, ...Chiefly in the Manner of the Spectator. London: A. Millar, 1799. 2 vols. Frontis. Mod 3/4 levant red morocco, gilt, raised bands, bound by Sangorski & Sutcliffe. (Names dated 1807, bkpls; spines sunned), else VG. *Pacific**. $230/£144

FRANKLIN, BENJAMIN. Works of.... London: G.G.J. & J. Robinson, 1793. 2nd ed. 2 vols. Engr tps, (x),317; (iii),290pp. Contemp calf (neatly rebacked, re-labeled). Nice set. *Young*. $256/£160

FRANKLIN, COLIN. Fond of Printing. Bk Club of CA, 1980. One of 950. *Dawson*. $25/£16

FRANKLIN, COLIN. Themes in Aquatint. SF: Book Club of CA, 1978. 1st ed. One of 500. 1/4 cl, marbled bds. Prospectus, ptr's notice card laid in. NF. *Pacific**. $81/£51

FRANKLIN, JOHN HOPE. The Free Negro in North Carolina 1790-1860. Chapel Hill, 1943. 1st ed. (Cvrs sl discolored), else Good in dj (soiled, worn). *King*. $50/£31

FRANKLIN, JOHN. Journey to the Shores of the Polar Seas in 1819-20-21-22. John Murray, 1829. 4 vols. 4 engr frontisports, 19 engr plts, fldg engr map. Contemp calf. (Spotting.) *Sotheby's**. $221/£138

FRANKLIN, JOHN. Narrative of a Journey to the Shores of the Polar Sea, in the Years 1819, 20, 21 and 22. John Murray, 1823. 1st ed. 4to. 30 engr plts (incl 11 hand-colored aquatints), 4 fldg engr maps. Contemp red 1/2 morocco, gilt spine. (Spotted; sl rubbed.) *Sotheby's**. $1,251/£782

FRANKLIN, JOHN. Narrative of a Second Expedition to the Shores of the Polar Sea, in the Years 1825, 1826, and 1827.... London: John Murray, 1824. xxiv,320,clviipp; errata slip; 31 plts, 6 fldg maps. Old 1/2 blue morocco, gilt. VG (extrems sl rubbed). Bkpl of George John. *High Latitude*. $990/£619

FRANKLIN, MORRIS JULIUS. Conversion of Morris Julius Franklin; or Proofs of the Messiahship of Jesus of Nazareth. NY: John A. Gray, 1855. 52pp (foxed). Orig ptd wrappers. *M & S*. $150/£94

FRANKLIN. The Art of Making Money Plenty, in Every Man's Pocket. London/York: Darton, Harvey & Darton/Wm. Alexander, 1817. Eng ed of Amer ed. Sq 12mo. Full-pg engr tp, 8pp+1pg list on lower wrapper, paper watermkd 1815. Fine (sl spotted) in red stiff paper wrappers, fitted in custom-made box (corners bumped) w/red roan spine, gilt. *Hobbyhorse*. $1,200/£750

FRANQUI, CARLOS. Diary of the Cuban Revolution. NY: Viking, (1980). 1st US ed. Fine in dj. *Bernard*. $30/£19

FRANTZ, JOE B. and JULIAN E. CHOATE, JR. The American Cowboy. Norman, (1955). 1st ed. VG in VG dj. *Woolson*. $45/£28

FRANZKE, ANDREAS. Dubuffet. NY, (1981). Dj. *Swann**. $115/£72

FRASCASTORII, HIERONYMI. De Contagiosis Morbis et Eorum Curatione. Wilmer Cave Wright (trans). NY: Putnam, 1930. 1st ed in English. 2 ports. Red cl. VG. *House*. $100/£63

FRASER, GEORGE MacDONALD. The Candlemass Road. Harvill/Harper Collins, 1993. 1st UK ed. Fine in dj. *Williams*. $38/£24

FRASER, GEORGE MacDONALD. Flash for Freedom! London: Barrie & Jenkins, (1971). 1st ed. Paper-cvrd bds. VG (top, fore-edge foxed) in dj (price-clipped). *Antic Hay*. $85/£53

FRASER, GEORGE MacDONALD. Flashman and the Dragon. London: Collins Harvill, 1985. 1st Eng ed. NF in dj. *Antic Hay*. $50/£31

FRASER, GEORGE MacDONALD. Flashman and the Mountain of Light. Collins Harvill, 1990. 1st UK ed. Fine in dj (price-clipped). *Williams*. $48/£30

FRASER, GEORGE MacDONALD. Flashman and the Mountain of Light. London: Collins Harvill, 1990. 1st Eng ed. Paper-cvrd bds. NF (corner sl bumped) in dj. *Antic Hay*. $50/£31

FRASER, GEORGE MacDONALD. Flashman and the Redskins. Collins, 1982. 1st Eng ed. Fine (spine ends sl bumped) in dj (spine sl faded). *Ulysses*. $72/£45

FRASER, GEORGE MacDONALD. Flashman and the Redskins. London: Collins, 1982. 1st ed. NF in dj (lt foxed, mainly interior). *Antic Hay*. $75/£47

FRASER, GEORGE MacDONALD. Flashman at the Charge. London: Barrie & Jenkins, (1973). 1st Eng ed. Paper-cvrd bds. NF (edges foxed) in dj (price-clipped). *Antic Hay*. $85/£53

FRASER, GEORGE MacDONALD. Flashman at the Charge. Barrie & Jenkins, 1973. 1st UK ed. VG in dj. *Williams*. $61/£38

FRASER, GEORGE MacDONALD. Flashman in the Great Game. London: Barrie & Jenkins, (1975). 1st ed. NF in dj (sl worn, sm tear). *Antic Hay*. $85/£53

FRASER, GEORGE MacDONALD. Flashman's Lady. (London): Barrie & Jenkins, (1977). 1st Eng ed. Fine in dj (price-clipped). *Antic Hay*. $85/£53

FRASER, GEORGE MacDONALD. Flashman. London: Herbert Jenkins, (1969). 1st Eng ed. Paper-cvrd bds. VG (edges sl foxed, sm stain 1st few pp) in dj (few sm tears, sm chip, price-clipped). *Antic Hay*. $175/£109

FRASER, GEORGE MacDONALD. Flashman. NY: World, 1969. 1st US ed. NF in NF dj (inner flaps offset). *Unger*. $125/£78

FRASER, GEORGE MacDONALD. Flashman. Jenkins, 1969. 1st UK ed. NF (edges sl spotted) in dj. *Williams*. $152/£95

FRASER, GEORGE MacDONALD. McAuglan in the Rough. London, 1974. 1st ed. VG in VG+ dj. *Warren*. $35/£22

FRASER, GEORGE MacDONALD. Mr. American. Collins, 1980. 1st UK ed. NF in dj. *Williams*. $48/£30

FRASER, GEORGE MacDONALD. The Pyrates. NY: Knopf, 1984. 1st US ed. Fine in Fine dj. *Beasley*. $30/£19

FRASER, GEORGE MacDONALD. Royal Flash. Barrie & Jenkins, 1970. 1st UK ed. VG+ in dj (sl mk rear panel). *Williams*. $104/£65

FRASER, GEORGE MacDONALD. The Sheikh and the Dustbin. Collins Harvill, 1988. 1st UK ed. Fine in dj. *Williams*. $40/£25

FRASER, HUGH. Amid the High Hills. London, 1934. 2nd ed. Very Nice. *Grayling*. $56/£35

FRASER, JAMES BAILLIE. The Dark Falcon. London, 1844. 1st ed. 4 vols. 8vo. Contemp 1/4 sheep (needs rebacking). *Swann**. $690/£431

FRASER, JAMES. Cattle Brands in Arizona. Flagstaff, 1968. Ltd to 1000. Pict labels. Fine (ink stamp, fep clipped). *Baade*. $50/£31

FRASER, JAMES. The History of Nadir Shah, Formerly Called Thamas Kuli Khan, the Present Emperor of Persia. London, 1742. Engr map, plt (trimmed). Contemp calf. (Ink lib stamp; fr cvr loose.) *Swann**. $126/£79

FRASER, MRS. ALEXANDER. A Maddening Blow. London: Hurst & Blackett, 1878. 1st ed. 3 vols. Grn cl (spine ends worn, inner joints cracked, broken), gilt. Slipcase. *Young*. $280/£175

FRASER, MRS. H. A Diplomatist's Wife in Japan; Letters from Home to Home. Hutchinson, 1899. 1st ed. 2 vols. xviii,446; x,439pp. All edge uncut. Purple cl, gilt. Good set (lt browned throughout; spines sl faded). *Sotheran*. $352/£220

FRASER, SAMUEL. American Fruits. NY: OJ, 1924. 1st ed. Blue lib cl, gilt. (T stamp; rebound, lib spine # removed), else VG. *Larry Price*. $30/£19

FRAY, I. T. Early Homes of Ohio. Richmond, (1936). 1st ed. (Sl stained), else Good in dj (chipped). *King*. $65/£41

FRAYN, MICHAEL. Alphabetical Order and Donkeys' Years. Eyre Methuen, 1977. 1st UK ed. Fine in dj. *Williams*. $29/£18

FRAZER, JAMES. The Golden Bough. London: Macmillan, (1959). Abridged ed. Full tan polished calf, gilt mitre lines on cvrs, gilt paneled spine, raised bands, blue/grn spine labels, inner gilt dentelles, edges gilt, by Bayntun. Fine. *Appelfeld*. $250/£156

FRAZER, JAMES. The Golden Bough. London: Macmillan, 1922. 3rd ed. 12 vols. 8.5x5.5. Teg, gilt inner dentelles. Gilt-tooled levant grn morocco, raised bands, bound by the Harcourt Bindery. (Spines dknd, 1 raised band broken), else VG set. *Pacific**. $633/£396

FRAZER, JAMES. The Golden Bough. Macmillan, 1936. 3rd ed. 13 vols. Frontis. Teg, rest uncut. (Feps lt browned.) Djs (sl spotted, chipped). *Edwards*. $720/£450

FRAZER, JAMES. The Golden Bough. LEC, 1970. Ltd to 1500 numbered, signed by James Lewicki (illus). 2 vols. Fine in slip-case. *Swann*.* $92/£58

FRAZER, LADY. Leaves from the Golden Bough. NY: Macmillan, 1924. 1st ed. 239pp; 16 b/w plts by H. M. Brock. Navy cl. VG (name). *Price.* $40/£25

FRAZER, ROBERT W. Forts of the West. Norman: Univ of OK, (1965). 1st ed. Dj. *Dawson.* $40/£25

FRAZIER, E. FRANKLIN. The Negro Family in Chicago. Chicago, (1932). 1st ed. (Fr cvr heavily spotted.) *King.* $25/£16

FREAR, W. F. Mark Twain and Hawaii. Chicago: Lakeside, 1947. 1st ed. One of 1000 numbered, signed. Brn cl, gilt. Fine. BAL 3576. *Macdonnell.* $100/£63

FREDDI, CHRIS. Pork. London: Routledge & Kegan Paul, (1982). 1st Eng ed, 1st bk. VF in dj. *Captain's Bookshelf.* $60/£38

FREDERIC, LOUIS. Japan. NY: Abrams, n.d. (ca 1977). Folio. 49 maps, line dwgs. NF in dj. *Worldwide.* $75/£47

FREDERICK II OF HOHENSTAUFEN. The Art of Falconry. C. A. Wood and F. M. Fyfe (eds). Boston: Branford, (1955). 186 color, b/w plts. (Rear cvr dampstained.) Internally NF. *Mikesh.* $45/£28

FREDERICK, CHARLES et al. Fox-Hunting. Seeley, Service, (1947). 4 color, 45 half-tone plts. Fine in buckram-backed bds. Dj (sl rubbed) w/mtd color plts. *Cox.* $29/£18

FREDERICK, CHARLES et al. Fox-Hunting. The Lonsdale Library Volume VII. London, 1930. One of 375 numbered, signed, w/signed frontis by Lionel Edwards. 5 mtd color plts. Uncut, teg. Full leather (lt rubbed), gilt. *Oinonen*.* $150/£94

FREDERICK, J. V. Ben Holladay: The Stagecoach King. Lincoln: Univ of NE, (1989). VG. *Lien.* $20/£13

FREEDBERG, SYDNEY J. Parmigianino. Westport, 1971. Rpt ed. Good+. *Washton.* $125/£78

FREEDMAN, JILL. Street Cops. NY: Harper & Row, 1981. 1st ed. NF in pict stiff wrappers. *Cahan.* $30/£19

FREELING, NICOLAS. Flanders Sky. NY, 1992. 1st Amer ed. Fine in Fine dj. *Polyanthos.* $20/£13

FREEMAN, BRAD. Joe. (N.p.: Brad Freeman, 1984.) 1st ed. Fine in color-illus stiff wrappers. *Cahan.* $45/£28

FREEMAN, DOUGLAS SOUTHALL. A Calendar of Confederate Papers. With a Bibliography of Some Confederate Publications. Richmond: Confederate Museum, 1908. 1st ed. Grn cl. NF (bkseller's ticket rear pastedown; extrems sl worn). *Chapel Hill.* $200/£125

FREEMAN, DOUGLAS SOUTHALL. Lee's Lieutenants: A Study in Command. NY: Scribner, 1942-44. 1st ed of vols 1, 3. Vol 1 signed. 3 vols. (Lt aging.) Untrimmed. Black cl (sl worn, spotted; shelf streaks vol 1). Howes F349. *Baltimore*.* $150/£94

FREEMAN, DOUGLAS SOUTHALL. Lee's Lieutenants: A Study in Command. Scribner, 1942-45. 3 vols. VG. *Book Broker.* $200/£125

FREEMAN, DOUGLAS SOUTHALL. R. E. Lee. NY: Scribner, (1936). Pulitzer Prize ed. 4 vols. Pebbled blue cl, gilt. (Ink underlining between pp416-29 vol 1), else Fine set. *Chapel Hill.* $250/£156

FREEMAN, DOUGLAS SOUTHALL. R. E. Lee. NY: Scribner, 1934-35. 1st eds of vols 3 & 4, early ptgs of vols 1 & 2. 1952 Tls laid in. 4 vols. Red cl. NF (bkpls; spines sl faded). *Chapel Hill.* $300/£188

FREEMAN, DOUGLAS SOUTHALL. R. E. Lee. NY, 1934-35. 4 vols. 1/2 morocco, gilt, by Frost of Bath. *Swann*.* $316/£198

FREEMAN, DOUGLAS SOUTHALL. R. E. Lee. NY, 1936. Pulitzer Prize ed. 4 vols. (Sl spotted, worn.) *King.* $250/£156

FREEMAN, DOUGLAS SOUTHALL. The South to Posterity. NY: Scribner, 1939. 1st ed. Grn cl. NF in dj (folds rubbed). *Chapel Hill.* $150/£94

FREEMAN, E. A. Some Impressions of the United States. London: Longmans et al, 1883. 1st ed. pp xi,289,12 ads. (Eps cracked; faded.) *Mott.* $45/£28

FREEMAN, EDWARD A. An Essay on the Origin and Development of Window Tracery in England. Oxford, 1851. 74 litho plts. *Swann*.* $69/£43

FREEMAN, GEORGE D. Midnight and Noonday; Or the Incidental History of Southern Kansas and the Indian Territory.... Caldwell, KS: G.D. Freeman, 1892. 2nd ed. VG (cvrs lt worn, spine faded, fr hinge starting). Howes F353. *Labordo.* $475/£297

FREEMAN, HARRY C. A Brief History of Butte, Montana. Chicago, 1900. 1st ed. Color frontis. Brn dec cl. VG. *Larry Price.* $125/£78

FREEMAN, J. J. and D. JOHNS. A Narrative of the Persecution of the Christians in Madagascar. London, 1840. viii,298pp + 6pp pub's ads; hand-colored frontis, tp vignette (both foxed; tp hinge sl torn, lacks tissue guard). Orig emb cl (spine head sl chipped). *Edwards.* $152/£95

FREEMAN, JIM. Practical Steelhead Fishing. NY: Barnes, 1966. 1st ed. 2 color plts. VF in dj. *Bowman.* $50/£31

FREEMAN, LEILA CROCHERON. Nip and Tuck. NY: J.H. Sears, (1926). 1st ed. Lg 4to. 8 full-pg color plts. Orange cl (rear hinge weak), color paste label. Black dj (worn). *Reisler.* $250/£156

FREEMAN, LEWIS R. The Colorado River; Yesterday, To-Day and Tomorrow. NY, 1923. (Bkpl; extrems sl worn), else Good. *Dumont.* $75/£47

FREEMAN, LEWIS R. Down the Columbia. NY: Dodd, Mead, 1921. 1st ed. VG. *Perier.* $50/£31

FREEMAN, MARGARET B. Herbs for the Medieval Household. NY: MMA, 1956. 2nd ed. One of 3000. Frontis. Dec paper-cvrd bds. Fine in dj. *Quest.* $40/£25

FREEMAN, MARGARET B. The St. Martin Embroideries: A 15th Century Series.... MMA, 1968. 1st ed. 2 color plts. (Sm label mk), o/w VG+ in dj (chipped). *Whittle.* $32/£20

FREEMAN, R. AUSTIN. Death at the Inn. NY, 1937. 1st Amer ed. Dj (spine extrems, tips lt rubbed). *Swann*.* $172/£108

FREEMAN, R. AUSTIN. Dr. Thorndyke Intervenes. Hodder & Stoughton, 1933. 1st UK ed. VG+ in dj. *Williams.* $1,200/£750

FREEMAN, R. AUSTIN. Mr. Polton Explains. Hodder & Stoughton, 1940. 1st UK ed. VG in dj (sl edgeworn). *Williams.* $520/£325

FREEMAN, R. AUSTIN. The Mystery of 31, New Inn. NY, 1937. 1st Amer ed. Dj (spine base lt worn). *Swann*.* $126/£79

FREEMAN, R. AUSTIN. The Penrose Mystery. Hodder & Stoughton, 1936. 1st UK ed. VG (spine sl rubbed). *Williams.* $96/£60

FREEMAN, R. AUSTIN. The Stoneware Monkey. Hodder & Stoughton, 1938. 1st UK ed. VG+ (spine foot sl bumped). *Williams.* $96/£60

FREEMAN, SARAH ELIZABETH. Medals Relating to Medicine and Allied Sciences in the Numismatic Collection of the Johns Hopkins University. Balt, 1964. 1st ed. NF. *Doctor's Library.* $200/£125

FREEMAN, STRICKLAND. The Art of Horsemanship Altered and Abbreviated. The Author, 1806. 1st ed. Half-title, 16 engr plts. 19th-cent 1/2 calf. *Sotheby's*.* $442/£276

FREESE, STANLEY. Windmills and Mill Wrighting. Cambridge: CUP, 1957. 1st ed. Fldg plan, 35 plts. Fine in dj. *Hollett.* $104/£65

FREIDMANN, HERBERT. The Cowbirds, a Study in the Biology of Social Parasitism. Springfield, IL, 1929. Dec cl. *Petersfield.* $56/£35

FREIRE DE ANDRADA, JACINTO. The Life of Dom John de Castro, the Fourth Vice-Roy of India. London, 1664. 1st ed. 2 plts (dbl-pg plt chipped at edges; lacks frontisport). Early 1/4 sheep (needs rebinding; repairable tears on several ll, incl tp; ink lib stamps). *Swann**. $287/£179

FREMANTLE, ARTHUR and FRANK A. HASKELL. Two Views of Gettysburg. Richard Harwell (ed). Chicago: Lakeside, 1964. *Mott.* $25/£16

FREMANTLE, ARTHUR. The Fremantle Diary. Walter Lord (ed). London: Andre Deutsch, (1956). Dj. *Mott.* $25/£16

FREMANTLE, ARTHUR. Three Months in the Southern States April-June 1863. Edinburgh/London: William Blackwood, 1863. 1st ed. Frontisport, pp vli,316,(20) ads; 5 ports. Blue cl. (Sl foxed; binder's ticket; spine sl worn.) Howes F361. *Mott.* $350/£219

FREMANTLE, ARTHUR. Three Months in the Southern States, April-June 1863. William Blackwood & Sons, 1863. 1st Eng ed. ix,316,20 ads pp; 6 engr ports. Blue cl, gilt. VG (inscrip; extrems sl rubbed). *Sotheran.* $237/£148

FREMANTLE, ARTHUR. Three Months in the Southern States. London, 1863. 1984 Time-Life Collector's Library of the Civil War Edition. Leather. Fine. *Pratt.* $30/£19

FREMONT, JESSIE BENTON. Mother Lode Narratives. Shirley Sargent (ed). Ashland: Lewis Osborn, 1970. Ltd to 650. Signed, typed inscription tipped in. Prospectus laid in. Dk blue cl, white bds, gilt. Fine in ptd dj. *Pacific**. $104/£65

FREMONT, JESSIE BENTON. A Year of American Travel. SF: Book Club of CA, 1960. One of 450. Pub's announcement laid in. (Bkpl; shelfworn), else VG. *Dumont.* $100/£63

FREMONT, JOHN C. Memoirs of My Life. Volume I (all published). Chicago/NY: Belford, Clarke & Co, 1887. 1st ed. Frontis, xx,655pp; 81 full-pg illus, 7 maps (4 fldg). Dec-stamped brn cl. (Map to face p120 moved to end of bk; extrems lt worn.) *Dawson.* $400/£250

FREMONT, JOHN C. Narratives of Exploration and Adventure. Allan Nevins (ed). NY: Longmans, Green, 1956. 1st ed. Black cl. Fine in dj. *House.* $30/£19

FREMONT, JOHN C. and MAJOR EMORY. Notes of Travel in California. NY: D. Appleton, 1849. 186,(6)pp; 2 maps (1 fldg). Orig leather (1/2-inch loss at spine head; browned, pencil notes, 4-inch tear to fldg map w/no loss). *Dumont.* $275/£172

FREMONT, JOHN C. Report of the Exploring Expedition to the Rocky Mountains in the Year 1842, and to Oregon and North California...1843-'44. Washington, 1845. 1st ed, Senate issue. 22 stone lithos, 5 maps (2 facs, 1 lg fldg map in rear pocket). Black lib buckram, gilt spine. (Soiled, foxed, old ink stain on fore-edge, affecting few words; dampstained throughout; recently rebound.) Howes F370. *Glenn.* $325/£203

FREMONT, JOHN C. Report of the Exploring Expedition to the Rocky Mountains in the Year 1842. Washington: Gales & Seaton, 1845. Orig cl. (Lacks map in rear pocket; extrems worn.) Howes F370. *Swann**. $230/£144

FREMONT, JOHN C. Report of the Exploring Expedition to the Rocky Mountains in the Year 1842.... Washington: Blair & Rives, 1845. 1st ed, House issue. 583pp; 21 (of 22) litho plts, 4 maps (2 fldg). Marbled eps, aeg. Orig full presentation morocco, gilt. W/o lg fldg map, which is generally not present in presentation copies. (Lacks 1 plt, another detached but present; foxing, lacks fep; extrems sl scuffed), else VG. Howes F370. *Pacific**. $288/£180

French Cabinetmakers of the Eighteenth Century. (By Jean Meuvret & Claude Fregnac.) (NY): Hachette, (1965). 1st ed. White cl (sl soiled). Dj (chipped). *Karmiole.* $85/£53

French in Indo-China. (By Francois Garnier.) London: T. Nelson, 1884. 1st ed. Frontis, 263pp; map. Blue pict cl, gilt. (Sl soiled, foxed, fep torn away; fr cvr damp-stained, rubbed.) *Morrell.* $56/£35

FRENCH, ALLEN. Historic Concord: A Handbook of Its Story and Its Memorials.... Concord: (Riverside), 1942. 1st ed. Signed, dated presentation. VG in wrappers. *Lucas.* $20/£13

FRENCH, FRANK. Home Fairies and Heart Flowers: Twenty Studies of Children's Heads with Floral Embellishments.... Poems by Margaret Sangster. NY: Harper, 1887. 1st ed. 13x10.25. Aeg. Pict mustard cl, gilt. (Name dated 1886; upper corners, spine ends sl worn), else NF. *Pacific**. $98/£61

FRENCH, LEIGH, JR. and EDITH TUNIS SALE. Colonial Interiors. First and Second Series. NY: William Helburn, 1923/1930. 1st eds. 2 vols. Folio. 125 plts; 159 plts. Blue cl, gilt. VG (lt soiled, extrems worn). *House.* $195/£122

FRENCH, WILLIAM. Some Recollections of a Western Ranchman, New Mexico 1883-1889. London: Methuen, 1927. 1st ed. (Edges lt worn, browned), else NF. Howes 375. *Dumont.* $350/£219

FRENCH, WILLIAM. Some Recollections of a Western Ranchman.... [with] Further Recollections of a Western Ranchman, New Mexico, 1883-1899. Jeff C. Dykes (ed). NY: Argosy-Antiquarian, 1965. 1st ed thus. One of 750. 2 vols. Grn cl. Fine in Fine slipcase. Howes F375. *Harrington.* $150/£94

FRENCH-SHELDON, MARY. Sultan to Sultan. Boston: Arena, 1892. Inscribed. 10,435pp; 26 plts, map. Orig cl (rebacked, ex-lib). *Adelson.* $225/£141

FRENEAU, PHILIP. Poems Written Between the Years 1768 and 1794. Monmouth, NJ: The Author, 1795. 1st ed. 456pp (foxed); 5 engr plts. Complete w/half-title. 19th-cent grn morocco, marbled bds. *Karmiole.* $275/£172

FRENSSEN, GUSTAV. The Anvil. Huntley Paterson (trans). Boston/NY: Houghton Mifflin, 1930. 1st US ed. Black cl. (Top corner fep clipped, lower edge worn), o/w Fine in dj. *Reese.* $30/£19

FRERE-COOK, CERVIS (ed). The Decorative Arts of the Mariner. London: Cassell, 1966. 1st ed. Lg dec brn cl, gilt. VG in dj. *Parmer.* $75/£47

FRESENIUS, C. R. and H. WILL. New Methods of Alkimetry. J. Lloyd Bullock (ed). London: Taylor & Walton, 1843. 1st ed. Paper label on fr bd. VG. *Hollett.* $104/£65

FRESHFIELD, DOUGLAS W. Below the Snow Line. Constable, 1923. 1st ed. 9 maps. Grn ribbed cl, gilt. (Few spots.) *Hollett.* $72/£45

FRESHFIELD, DOUGLAS W. The Exploration of the Caucasus. Edward Arnold, 1896. 1st ed. 2 vols. Sm 4to. xxiii,278; x,296pp; 76 gravure plts, 4 maps (1 in rear pocket), 3 panoramas by Vittorio Sella. 2-tone cl, gilt. VG set (few edges, margins sl dknd, few sm smoke stains; 2 bds dknd, sl stained, 1 bd lettering dull, spines evenly dknd). *Hollett.* $1,200/£750

FRESHFIELD, DOUGLAS W. Italian Alps. Longmans, Green, 1875. 1st ed. xvi,385pp; 10 wood-engrs, 5 fldg maps (2 partly colored). Grn dec cl (neatly recased), gilt. *Hollett.* $256/£160

FRESHFIELD, DOUGLAS W. Italian Alps. Oxford: Basil Blackwell, 1937. 16 plts. VG in dj (sl soiled, few edge chips). *Hollett.* $48/£30

FRESHFIELD, DOUGLAS W. Travels in the Central Caucasus and Bashan. London: Longmans, Green, 1869. 1st ed. Crown 8vo. xv,509pp + 1 leaf pub's ads; 3 fldg maps, 5 plts (incl 2 panoramas on 1 plt). VG. *Ulysses.* $1,120/£700

FRESHMAN, CHARLES. The Autobiography of the Rev. Charles Freshman. Toronto: Samuel Rose, Wesleyan Book Room, 1868. 1st ed. Frontis, 16,316,(1)pp. *M & S.* $175/£109

FREUCHEN, PETER. Arctic Adventure. Heinemann, 1936. 1st ed. VG in dj. *Walcot.* $51/£32

FREUD, ERNST L. et al (eds). Sigmund Freud: His Life in Pictures and Words. Christine Trollope (trans). NY: Harcourt, Brace, Jovanovich, (1976). 1st Amer ed, 1st ptg. Folio. Beige linen. VG in dj. *Gach.* $85/£53

FREUD, MARTIN. Parole d'Honneur. Phyllis & Trevor Blewitt (trans). London: Gollancz, 1939. 1st British ed. Pale blue cl stamped in dk blue. (Spine, edges sunned through dj), else NF in dj. *Reese*. $75/£47

FREUD, SIGMUND and JOSEF BREUER. Studies on Hysteria. James Strachey (trans). NY: Basic Books, (1957). 1st ptg. Black cl. VG+ in dj. *House*. $30/£19

FREUD, SIGMUND. Civilization and Its Discontents. Joan Riviere (trans). NY: Jonathan Cape & Harrison Smith, (1930). 1st Amer ed. VG in Fair dj (lacks spine top, fr panel detached, extrems chipped, stained). *Pacific**. $52/£33

FREUD, SIGMUND. The Future of an Illusion. London: Hogarth, 1934. 2nd imp. (Eps spotted.) *Hollett*. $40/£25

FREUD, SIGMUND. Inhibitions, Symptoms, and Anxiety. London: Hogarth, 1936. 1st Eng ed. (Name, label), else VG in dj (spine faded, ends chipped). *Pacific**. $69/£43

FREUD, SIGMUND. The Interpretation of Dreams. A.A. Brill (trans). NY: Macmillan, 1913. 1st Amer ed. Amer issue exists in at least 2 states: w/tp integral and w/tp a cancellandum. Tp this copy is integral. 8vo. xiii,510pp. Errata tipped in. Blue streaked cl, gilt. (Sig; sm discoloration rear cvr), o/w VG. *Weber*. $675/£422

FREUD, SIGMUND. On Aphasia. NY: IUP, 1953. 1st ed in English. Fine in dj (lt worn). *Beasley*. $65/£41

FREUD, SIGMUND. An Outline of Psycho-Analysis. J. Strachey (trans). NY: W.W. Norton, (1949). 1st ptg. Black cl (spine gilt flaked). VG. *House*. $35/£22

FREUD, SIGMUND. The Question of Lay Analysis. London, (1947). 1st Eng ed. VG in dj (rubbed). *King*. $35/£22

FREUD, SIGMUND. Three Essays on the Theory of Sexuality. London: Imago, 1949. 1st UK ed. (Few scribbles), else Fine in NF dj. *Beasley*. $80/£50

FREUD, SIGMUND. Totem and Taboo. James Strachey (trans). NY: W.W. Norton, (1952). 1st Amer ed. Fine. *Pacific**. $35/£22

FREUNDLICH, AUGUST L. William Gropper: Retrospective. L.A., 1968. Signed, inscribed by Gropper, w/ink sketch of man's head. Slipcase. *Swann**. $172/£108

FREUNDLICH, HERBERT. Colloid and Capillary Chemistry. H. Stafford Hatfield (trans). London: Methuen, (1926). 1st ed in English. 7 plts. Grn cl. VG. *House*. $100/£63

FREWEN, MORETON. Melton Mowbray, and Other Memories. London: Herbert Jenkins, 1924. 1st ed. VG. Howes F380. *Labordo*. $325/£203

FREY, A. M. The Cross Bearers. London/NY: Putnam, (1931). 1st ed in English. 4pp promo leaflet laid in. Brn/white cl stamped in red. Fine in dj (lt nicked, flaps foxed). *Reese*. $125/£78

FREYRE, GILBERTO. Mother and Son. NY: Knopf, 1967. 1st US ed. VG+ in dj. *Lame Duck*. $45/£28

FREZIER, AMEDEE FRANCOIS. A Voyage to the South-Sea, and Along the Coasts of Chili and Peru, in the Years 1712, 1713, and 1714. London, 1717. 4to. 37 maps, plts. Contemp paneled calf. (Scattered foxing, offsetting from tp to frontis map; expertly rebacked, retipped.) *Swann**. $1,035/£647

FREZIER, AMEDEE FRANCOIS. A Voyage to the South-Sea, and Along the Coasts of Chili and Peru, in the Years 1712, 1713, and 1714. London, 1717. 1st ed in English. 4to. 37 maps, plts. Mod bds. *Felcone*. $1,200/£750

FREZIER, AMEDEE FRANCOIS. A Voyage to the South-Sea, and Along the Coasts of Chili and Peru, in the Years 1712, 1713, and 1714. London: Jonah Bowyer, 1717. 1st ed in English. 4to. (14),335,(9)pp; 37 copper-engr maps, charts, views. Mod blind-stamped sheep, gilt, raised bands. There is no plt numbered XXX, as issued, and a plate numbered 36 follows plt XXXVI. (Margins sl foxed, 1/2x2-inch piece missing from lower margin pp333-4, not affecting text), else Fine. *Pacific**. $2,875/£1,797

FRIDGE, IKE. History of the Chisum War; Or, Life of Ike Fridge. Electra, TX: Jodie B. Smith, 1927. 1st ed. NF in stiff pict wrappers (clear tape on inner hinges to seal staples which are starting to rust). Howes F384. *Labordo*. $800/£500

FRIED, MICHAEL. Morris Louis. NY, (1980?). Dj. *Swann**. $80/£50

FRIEDAN, BETTY. The Feminine Mystique. NY: Norton, 1963. 1st ed. (Stamp top edge), else Fine in NF dj. *Beasley*. $100/£63

FRIEDLANDER, JOHNNY. Oeuvre, 1961-1965. (NY/Stuttgart, 1967.) Sm folio. Mtd color plts. Color litho laid in. Bd slipcase. *Swann**. $92/£58

FRIEDLANDER, LEE. The American Monument. NY: Eakins Press Foundation, (1976). 1st ed. Signed. Obl folio. *Swann**. $460/£288

FRIEDLANDER, LEE. Factory Valleys. NY, (1982). One of 1000 signed. Dj (sl worn). *Swann**. $258/£161

FRIEDLANDER, LEE. Flowers and Trees. NY: Haywire, 1981. 1st ed. Folio. 40 plts. Spiral bound. Fine. *Cahan*. $175/£109

FRIEDLANDER, LEE. Fourteen American Monuments. NY/Boston: Eakins Press Foundation/Institute of Contemporary Art, 1977. 14 b/w photos. Fine in stiff wrappers. *Cahan*. $30/£19

FRIEDLANDER, LEE. Self Portrait. NY: Haywire, 1970. 1st ed. (Sl rubbed), else Fine in pict stiff wrappers. *Cahan*. $150/£94

FRIEDLANDER, MAX J. Early Netherlandish Painting. NY, (1967)-1973. Vols 1-10 in 12. 4to. Djs. *Swann**. $1,265/£791

FRIEDMAN, BRUCE JAY. Steambath. NY: Knopf, 1971. 1st ed. VF in VF dj. *Between The Covers*. $200/£125

FRIEDMAN, BRUCE JAY. Stern. NY: S&S, 1962. 1st ed, 1st bk. VG in dj (lt soiled, tape mends). *Bromer*. $75/£47

FRIEDMAN, I. K. The Autobiography of a Beggar. Boston, 1903. 1st Amer ed. NF (sl rubbed, spine sl sunned). *Polyanthos*. $30/£19

FRIEDMAN, I. K. The Radical. NY: Appleton, 1907. 1st ed. Fine. *Beasley*. $150/£94

FRIEDMAN, KINKY. Greenwich Killing Time. NY: Morrow, (1986). 1st ed, 1st bk. Signed. Fine in Fine dj. *Between The Covers*. $85/£53

FRIEDMAN, MARTIN. The Frozen Image: Scandinavian Photography. Minneapolis/NY: Walker Art Center/Abbeville, 1982. 1st ed. Fine in dj. *Cahan*. $75/£47

FRIEDMANN, H. The Cowbirds. Springfield: Thomas, 1929. 1st ed. 28 plts. Pict cl, gilt. NF in VG dj. *Mikesh*. $45/£28

FRIEL, BRIAN. Philadelphia, Here I Come! Faber & Faber, 1965. 1st ed. VG (prelims, edges, eps sl spotted; top edge sl dusty, bottom edges discolored) in dj (sl creased, spotted). *Ulysses*. $72/£45

FRINK, MAURICE. Cow Country Cavalcade. Denver: Old West Pub, 1954. VG in dj. *Dumont*. $40/£25

FRINK, MAURICE. When Grass Was King. Boulder, CO: Univ of CO, 1956. 1st ed. One of 1500. Signed by Frink. VG+ in dj. *Labordo*. $95/£59

FRINK, MAURICE. When Grass Was King. Boulder: Univ of CO, 1956. Good in dj (worn). *Dumont*. $95/£59

FRISCH, MAX. Bluebeard. Methuen, 1983. 1st Eng ed. Signed, dated. NF in dj (sl mkd). *Ulysses*. $56/£35

FRISWELL, HAIN. Marcus Ward's Fable Picture Book of Animals and Their Masters. London: Marcus Ward, (ca 1875). Obl 4to. 24 full-pg color plts. Brn emb cl (spine worn). *Reisler*. $385/£241

FRISWELL, J. HAIN. Life Portraits of William Shakespeare. Sampson Low et al, 1864. 1st ed. 128pp; 8 photo plts. Aeg. Beveled bds (sl mkd, fore-edges dampstained, gutta-percha binding sl shaken, refixed). *Hollett*. $104/£65

FRITH, FRANCIS. Egypt and Palestine. London: James S. Virtue, n.d. c.(1857). 2 vols. Folio. Tp + intro(ii) + contents(ii) + subs list(ii); 76 mtd photos. (Several photos w/sl staining, discoloring, 1 w/minor loss to image; some mounts w/sl marginal staining not affecting photos; feps lt browned.) Marbled eps; aeg. Contemp gilt-ruled morocco (extrems worn, surface loss, sympathetically rebacked) w/gilt-ruled raised bands. *Edwards.* $6,720/£4,200

FRITH, FRANCIS. The Gossiping Photographer on the Rhine. Reigate: Frith, (1864). 1st ed. Crown 4to. 32pp; 16 mtd albumen photos (incl vignette tp). Aeg. Good in grn cl (few sm mks rear cvr), gilt, spine plain. *Ulysses.* $1,200/£750

FRITH, W. P. My Autobiography and Reminiscences. London, 1887. 2nd ed. 2 vols. Frontisports, viii,389; vi,352,(ii)pp. (Prelims lt browned; spines sl rubbed.) *Edwards.* $72/£45

Frog He Would A Woo-ing Go. NY: McLoughlin Bros, (ca 1880). Lg 4to. (Spine chipped, sm split, lt dusty, margins worn.) *Reisler.* $375/£234

Frog Who Would a Wooing Go. Boston: Brown, Taggard & Chase, (ca 1857). 12mo. 32pp. Good in color pict wrappers (rebacked). *Reisler.* $125/£78

Froggy Would A-Wooing Go [Father Tuck's Nursery Series]. London: Raphael Tuck & Sons, (ca 1890). 4to. 4 full-pg color plts by G. H. Thompson. Very Nice in color pict wrappers. *Reisler.* $250/£156

FROHNE, HENRY W. et al. Color Schemes for the Home and Model Interiors. Phila/London, 1919. 40 plts. (Tp lt spotted, margins sl browned; lt soiled.) *Edwards.* $64/£40

FROISETH, JENNIE A. The Women of Mormonism, or the Story of Polygamy. Detroit: Paine, 1887. 416pp. Gilt edges. Full blind-stamped morocco. *Cullen.* $35/£22

FROISSART, J. The Chronicles of England, France, Spain and Other Places Adjoining. NY: LEC, 1959. One of 1500. Signed by Henry C. Pitz (illus). Blue dec cl. Fine in slipcase. *Pacific*.* $58/£36

FROISSART, J. Chronicles of England, France, Spain, and the Adjoining Countries, from the Latter Part of the Reign of Edward II to the Coronation of Henry IV. London: William Smith, 1844. 2 vols. 3/4 drab olive calf, marbled bds, gilt, raised bands, morocco spine labels. (Bkpls), else VG. *Pacific*.* $127/£79

FROLICH, LORENZ. Little Rosy's Picture-Book. NY: D. Appleton, 1870. 1st ed. 10.25x7. Blue cl, gilt. VG. *Pacific*.* $58/£36

From Incas to Indios. Paris/NY, (1956). (Feps sl damaged by dj, initials fr pastedown.) Dj (worn, extrems age-dknd.) *Swann*.* $115/£72

FROST, A. B. Shooting Pictures [cover title]. NY: Winchester, (1972). One of 750 numbered. Folio. 12 color facs prints. Loose in cl portfolio w/accompanying text bound in, as issued. (Lt worn, stained, spotted.) *Oinonen*.* $225/£141

FROST, H. GORDON. Blades and Barrels: Six Centuries of Combination Weapons. El Paso, (1972). One of 300 numbered, signed. This add'lly signed, inscribed. Leatherette. *Swann*.* $172/£108

FROST, JENNETT BLAKESLEE. California's Greatest Curse. SF: Joseph Winterburn, 1879. 1st ed. 83pp. Grn cl, gilt. (Ink name dated SF Jan 12, 1883; extrems, edges rubbed), else VG. *Pacific*.* $52/£33

FROST, JOHN. Pictorial History of Mexico and the Mexican War. Phila: Thomas, Copperthwait, 1849. Emb calf, gilt, leather spine label. (Spine sl sunned), else VG. *Pacific*.* $98/£61

FROST, LAWRENCE A. The Court-Martial of General George Armstrong Custer. Norman, (1968). 1st ed. (Top edge spotted), else Good in dj (worn). *King.* $35/£22

FROST, LAWRENCE A. The Custer Album. Seattle: Superior, 1964. 1st ed. VG in dj. *Labordo.* $60/£38

FROST, LAWRENCE A. Custer's 7th Cav and the Campaign of 1873. El Segundo: Upton & Sons, 1986. Inscribed, signed presentation. Fine in dj. *Pacific*.* $58/£36

FROST, LAWRENCE A. General Custer's Libbie. Seattle: Superior, (1976). 1st ed. Fine in dj. *Perier.* $50/£31

FROST, LAWRENCE A. (ed). Some Observations on the Yellowstone Expedition of 1873. Glendale: A.H. Clark, 1981. 1st ed. One of 350. Frontis, fldg map. Buckram, gilt. *Dawson.* $100/£63

FROST, LAWRENCE A. (ed). With Custer in '74: James Calhoun's Diary of the Black Hills Expedition. (Provo, UT): BYU Press, (1979). 1st ed. Brn cl. Fine. *Harrington.* $65/£41

FROST, ROBERT. Collected Poems of Robert Frost. NY, (1939). 1st ed. Signed. Gilt-pict cl (spine dknd). *Swann*.* $201/£126

FROST, ROBERT. The Complete Poems of Robert Frost. LEC, 1950. Ltd to 1500 numbered, signed by Frost, Thomas W. Nason (illus) and Bruce Rogers (designer). 2 vols. Fine in slipcase. *Swann*.* $488/£305

FROST, ROBERT. In the Clearing. NY: Holt, Rinehart & Winston, (1962). 1st trade ed. Signed presentation. Gray cl, white spine lettering. Dj (price-clipped, sl worn). *Baltimore*.* $150/£94

FROST, ROBERT. In the Clearing. NY: Rinehart & Winston, (1962). 1st ed. Ltd to 1500 signed. VF in slipcase. *Bromer.* $325/£203

FROST, ROBERT. In the Clearing. NY, 1962. 1st Amer ed. NF (name, sl rubbed) in NF dj (sl rubbed). *Polyanthos.* $30/£19

FROST, ROBERT. In the Clearing. NY: Holt, Rinehart & Wilson, 1962. 1st ed, 1st issue. Slate-gray cl, silver spine lettering. Fine in NF coated paper dj w/photo port on fr cvr. *Vandoros.* $50/£31

FROST, ROBERT. A Masque of Mercy. NY: Henry Holt, (1947). 1st trade ed. Blue cl, gilt. Fine in dj (edges, spine sl faded). *Heritage.* $60/£38

FROST, ROBERT. A Masque of Mercy. NY, (1947). 1st ed. One of 751 signed. Orig photo of Frost tipped to fr pastedown. Slipcase (defective). *Swann*.* $258/£161

FROST, ROBERT. New Hampshire. NY: Henry Holt, 1923. 1st ed. 1/2 cl, gilt, paper cvr label. Fine. *Pacific*.* $75/£47

FROST, ROBERT. The Poetry of Robert Frost. Edward Connery Lathem (ed). Barre: Imprint Society, 1971. 1st ed. One of 1950. Signed by Rudolph Ruzicka (designer). 2 vols. Mtd frontisport. Fine. *Pacific*.* $63/£39

Frosty the Snowman and the Snow Ghost. Kansas City: Hallmark, 1979. Judi K. Howen (designed by). Dick Dudley (engineer). 5 dbl-pg pop-ups. Glazed pict bds. VG-. *Bookfinders.* $45/£28

FROTHINGHAM, ALICE WILSON. Talavera Pottery. With a Catalogue of the Collection in the Hispanic Society of America. NY, 1944. Good in wrappers. *Washton.* $45/£28

Fruits of Enterprize Exhibited in the Travels of Belzoni in Egypt and Nubia...by the Author of 'The India Cabinet.' (By Sarah Atkins.) John Harris, 1824. 4th ed. 12mo in 6's. Frontis, xii,238,(2)pp, ad leaf present; 11 plts (24 views). Orig 1/4 red roan, gilt, buff ptd bds. Good (inscrips; lacks fep; rubbed, edges worn). *Blackwell's.* $104/£65

FRY, CHRISTOPHER. The Boy with a Cart. NY: Oxford, 1950. 1st Amer ed. As New in dj. *Between The Covers.* $125/£78

FRY, CHRISTOPHER. Curtmantle. NY: Oxford, 1961. 1st Amer ed. VF in VF dj (sm mk on spine). *Between The Covers.* $125/£78

FRY, CHRISTOPHER. The Dark Is Light Enough. London: Oxford, 1954. 1st ed. VF in VF dj (thin dknd line top of rear cvr). *Between The Covers.* $150/£94

FRY, CHRISTOPHER. An Experience of Critics and the Approach to Dramatic Criticism. Kaye Webb (ed). (By Ivor Brown, W. A. Darlington, Alan Dent, et al.) NY: Oxford, 1953. 1st Amer ed. VF in VF dj (rear cvr sm stain). *Between The Covers.* $100/£63

FRY, CHRISTOPHER. A Phoenix Too Frequently. London: Oxford, 1959. 1st ed. VF in dj (price-clipped, 2 sm internal tears), else Fine. *Between The Covers*. $150/£94

FRY, CHRISTOPHER. A Sleep of Prisoners. NY: Oxford, 1951. 1st Amer ed. VF in VF dj (sl rubbed). *Between The Covers*. $100/£63

FRY, CHRISTOPHER. A Sleep of Prisoners. London: Oxford, 1951. 1st ed. VF in VF dj (sm wrinkle at spine foot). *Between The Covers*. $150/£94

FRY, CHRISTOPHER. Venus Observed. London: Oxford, 1950. 1st ed. VF in VF dj (sl rubbed). *Between The Covers*. $200/£125

FRY, EDITH. Short Poems. The Author, 1923. 1st ed. Good in brn dec wraps (soiled, creased, top edges nicked). *Any Amount*. $19/£12

FRY, EDMUND. Pantographia; Containing Accurate Copies of All the Known Alphabets in the World. Cooper & Wilson, 1799. 1st ed. Contemp blind-stamped calf. (Sl spotted, rubbed; spine ends sl chipped.) *Sotheby's**. $405/£253

FRY, ELIZABETH. Memoir of the Life of Elizabeth Fry, with Extracts from Her Journal and Letters. London: Charles Gilpin/John Hatchard & Son, 1847. 1st ed. 2 vols. xii,495,(iv); viii,524,(iv)pp; 2 engr ports. Orig blind-stamped cl (sl damped, joints stiff), gilt. *Hollett*. $224/£140

FRY, GLADYS WINDSOR. Embroidery and Needlework. Pitman, 1950. 4th ed. 20 tipped-in color plts. Dec cl. VG. *Whittle*. $40/£25

FRY, JOSEPH STORRS. An Essay on the Construction of Wheel-Carriages. London: J. & A. Arch et al, 1820. 1st ed. viii,138pp. Orig bds, lg paper label. (Spotting, esp eps, tp, and fore-edges; bkpl; hinges sl worn.) *Hollett*. $440/£275

FRY, ROGER et al. Chinese Art. London: Batsford, 1949. 3rd ptg. 85 plts. VG. *Turtle Island*. $30/£19

FRY, ROGER. Architectural Heresies of a Painter. London: C&W, 1921. 1st ptg. Pamphlet. (Extrems browned), else VG in ptd wrappers. *Turtle Island*. $65/£41

FRY, ROGER. Architectural Heresies of a Painter. London: C&W, 1921. 1st ed. Uncut. Sewn as single gathering into gray-fawn wrappers. (Wrapper edges sl dknd), o/w Nice. *Temple*. $96/£60

FRY, ROGER. Cezanne. Hogarth, 1927. 40 b/w plts. Cl-backed pict bds. (Bkpl, tp, few ll sl spotted; feps, bds browned.) *Edwards*. $64/£40

FRY, ROGER. Flemish Art. C&W, 1927. 1st ed. 32 plts. Cl-backed dec bds. (Sl spotted.) *Hollett*. $48/£30

FRY, ROGER. Flemish Art; A Critical Survey. London: C&W, 1927. 1st ed. Dec cl. Fine in dj (torn, repaired). *Europa*. $38/£24

FRY, ROGER. Letters of Roger Fry. Denys Sutton (ed). London: C&W, 1972. 1st ed. 2 vols. (Name vol 2), o/w Very Nice set in djs. *Virgo*. $72/£45

FRY, ROGER. A Sampler of Castile. Richmond: Hogarth, 1923. 1st ed. Ltd to 550 numbered. 16 plts. Cl-backed dec bds. Good (sl worn, mkd). *Ash*. $200/£125

FRY, ROSALIE. Pipkin Sees the World. NY: Dutton, 1951. 1st ed. 96pp. Brn cl, stamped. Good (corners bumped, lt soiled). *Price*. $18/£11

FRY, W. H. (ed). A Complete Treatise on Artificial Fish-Breeding. NY: D. Appleton, 1854. 1st ed. 3 wood engrs. (Names; cvrs stained, spine head perished), else VG-. *Pacific**. $40/£25

FRYE, T. and G. RIGG. Elementary Flora of the Northwest. NY: Amer Book Co, 1914. 1st ed. Brn cl. VG. *Archer*. $25/£16

FRYER, JANE EAYRE. The Mary Frances Cook Book. Phila: John C. Winston, (1912). 1st ed. Margaret G. Hays (illus), Jane Allen Boyer (decs). 8vo. Blue cl, color paste label, spine gilt (sl dknd). VG in full color dj (dusty, chipped). *Reisler*. $225/£141

FRYER, JANE EAYRE. The Mary Frances Cook Book. Phila: John C. Winston Co, 1912. M. Hays & J. A. Boyer (illus). 175pp. Blue cl, paper pict onlay. VG (ink name). *Davidson*. $160/£100

FRYER, JANE EAYRE. The Mary Frances First Aid Book. Phila: John C. Winston, (1916). Jane Allen Boyer (illus). 12mo. 144pp. Pict onlay. VG (p113 discolored; edges bumped). *Davidson*. $150/£94

FRYER, JOHN. A New Account of East India and Persia Being Nine Years' Travels. 1672-1681. William Crooke (ed). London: Hakluyt Soc, 1909,12,15. 3 vols. Unopened. Blue cl. (Paper aged; sl shelfworn), else VG set. *Parmer*. $350/£219

FRYNTA, EMANUEL. Hasek: The Creator of Schweik. Artia, 1965. 1st ed. White cl. NF in dj (chipped). *Whittle*. $24/£15

FRYXELL, F. M. The Physiography of the Region of Chicago. Chicago: Univ of Chicago, 1927. 1st ed. 5 color fldg maps. VG (exlib) in brn wraps. *Larry Price*. $30/£19

FUCHS, VIVIAN. Antarctic Adventure. London: Cassell, 1959. Fine in dj. *Explorer*. $14/£9

FUCHS, VIVIAN. Of Ice and Men. Shropshire: Anthony Nelson, 1982. Mint in dj. *Explorer*. $29/£18

FUELL, MELISSA. Blind Boone, His Early Life and His Achievements. Kansas City, 1915. 1st ed. 1/2 leather. (Fr hinge partly cracked; spine faded, rubbed.) *Swann**. $201/£126

FUENTES, CARLOS. The Buried Mirror, Reflections on Spain and the New World. Boston: Houghton Mifflin, 1992. 1st ed. NF in dj. *Dumont*. $35/£22

FUENTES, CARLOS. A Change of Skin. Sam Hileman (trans). London: Jonathan Cape, (1968). 1st Eng ed. Top edge stained black. Purple bds, gilt. Fine in dj (lt soiled). *Heritage*. $60/£38

FUENTES, CARLOS. Christopher Unborn. NY: FSG, 1989. 1st US ed. Fine in Fine dj. *Lame Duck*. $35/£22

FUENTES, CARLOS. The Death of Artemio Cruz. Sam Hileman (trans). NY: Farrar, Straus, (1964). 1st Amer ed. Signed. 1/4 black cl, gilt, black bds. NF (bds lt spotted) in dj (lt edgeworn). *Heritage*. $100/£63

FUENTES, CARLOS. The Death of Artemio Cruz. London, 1964. 1st ed. Fine in NF dj. *Polyanthos*. $30/£19

FUENTES, CARLOS. The Death of Artemio Cruz. London: Collins, 1964. 1st British ed. Signed. NF in dj (1-inch tear to fr cvr bottom edge, tape-repaired on verso). *Lame Duck*. $175/£109

FUENTES, CARLOS. Distant Relations. NY: FSG, 1982. 1st US ed. Fine in dj. *Lame Duck*. $50/£31

FUENTES, CARLOS. The Hydra Head. Margaret Sayers Peden (trans). NY: FSG, (1978). 1st US ed. Black cl, gilt. Fine in dj. *Heritage*. $50/£31

FUENTES, CARLOS. The Hydra Head. NY: FSG, 1978. 1st US ed. (Pg tops, fore-edges lt foxed), else NF in dj. *Lame Duck*. $35/£22

FUENTES, CARLOS. The Old Gringo. London: Andre Deutsch, 1985. 1st British ed. Fine in dj. *Lame Duck*. $65/£41

FUENTES, NORBERTO. Hemingway in Cuba. Lyle Stuart, 1984. 1st ed. (Rmdr stripe to bottom edge), else Fine in dj. *Lame Duck*. $35/£22

FUGARD, ATHOL. The Blood Knot. NY: Odyssey, (1964). 1st US ed, 1st bk. Tls of pub's associate laid in. Fine in dj (sl dust soiled). *Reese*. $125/£78

FUGINA, FRANK J. Lore and Lure of the Scenic Upper Mississippi River. Winona, MN: The Author, (1945). 2nd ptg. Signed. Promo letters laid in. Fine in dj. *Perier*. $65/£41

FUJIOKA, RYOCHI et al. Tea Ceremony Utensils. NY/Tokyo: Weatherhill/Shibundo, (1973). 1st ed. Laminated bds. Fine in dj. *Turtle Island*. $40/£25

Fukaku Hyakkei (100 Views of Fuji). (Nagoya/Kyoto: Eirakuya Toshiro/Unsodo, ca 1900/ca 1920). 3 vols. 8vo. Oriental fold. Vol 1: 31 views, vol 2: 30 views, vol 3: 40 views. Images Fine. Stitched Oriental-style in plain wrappers (lt soil, rubbing). *Bromer*. $750/£469

FULFORD, HARRY. Potted Golf. Glasgow: Dalross, 1910. 1st ed. Grn cl. NF (emb stamp). *Pacific**. $46/£29

FULLER, ANDREW. The Grape Culturist. NY: D&K, 1864. 1st ed. 263pp. Dk blue cl (corners chewed, bds soiled). Good. *Archer*. $25/£16

FULLER, ANNA. Peak and Prairie. NY, 1894. 1st ed. Frontis, v,391pp. Good (bds soiled). *Dumont*. $35/£22

FULLER, CLARK. Pioneer Paths. Broken Bow, NE: Purcells Inc, (1974?). 1st ed. Fine in VG dj. *Perier*. $17/£11

FULLER, CLAUD E. The Breech-Loader in the Service. Topeka, (1933). (Extrems rubbed, rear hinge starting.) *Swann**. $46/£29

FULLER, HENRY B. From the Other Side: Stories of Transatlantic Travel. Boston: Houghton, 1898. 1st ed. Signed, dated 1923. Grn linen, gilt. VG (edges rubbed, spine sl sunned). BAL 6468. *Reese*. $100/£63

FULLER, JOHN. Flying to Nowhere. Salamander, 1983. 1st UK ed. Fine in dj w/orig wrap-around band. *Williams*. $40/£25

FULLER, MARGARET. A New England Childhood. Boston: Little, Brown, 1916. 1st ed. Pict eps. Teg. Pict blue cl. Fine (lt soil). *House*. $35/£22

FULLER, PETER. Robert Natkin. NY, (1981). Dj. *Swann**. $103/£64

FULLER, R. BUCKMINSTER. Critical Path. NY, (1981). 1st ed. Signed, dated. VG in dj (spine sunned, sm tear). *King*. $75/£47

FULLER, R. BUCKMINSTER. Operating Manual for Spaceship Earth. Carbondale: Southern IL Univ, 1970. 1st ed, 2nd ptg. Signed, inscribed presentation. Fine in NF dj (lt shelfworn). *Any Amount*. $58/£36

FULLER, R. BUCKMINSTER. Tetrascroll Goldilocks and the Three Bears. ULAE/St. Martins, 1982. 1st ed. 8.6x11.3. 129pp; 21 plts. Fine (sl edgeworn) in VG dj. *Price*. $45/£28

FULLER, R. BUCKMINSTER. Untitled Epic Poem on the History of Industrialization. Highlands, NC: Jonathan Williams, 1962. Rev copy w/ptd slip. NF in illus wrappers, NF ptd acetate dj. *Dermont*. $50/£31

FULLER, RICHARD E. The Geomorphology and Volcanic Sequences of Steens Mountain in Southeastern Oregon. Seattle: Univ of WA, 1931. (Ex-lib, labels, stamps, spine labels.) *Hollett*. $48/£30

FULLER, ROY. The Carnal Island. Andre Deutsch, 1970. 1st ed. NF (top edge sl dusty, spine foot sl bumped) in dj (spine sl faded). *Ulysses*. $48/£30

FULLER, ROY. The Father's Comedy. Andre Deutsch, 1961. 1st ed. VG (traces of bkpl; top edge sl dusty, cvrs sl bowed) in dj (worn, internally repaired). *Ulysses*. $51/£32

FULLER, ROY. Image of a Society. NY, 1957. 1st Amer ed. NF (name) in NF dj (sl rubbed). *Polyanthos*. $25/£16

FULLER, ROY. My Child, My Sister. Andre Deutsch, 1965. 1st ed. VG (top edge dusty, cvrs sl bowed) in dj (worn). *Ulysses*. $58/£36

FULLER, ROY. Off Course—Poems. London: Turret Books, 1969. One of 250 numbered, signed. VG (spine ends, corners sl bumped, rubbed); no dj as issued. *Ulysses*. $58/£36

FULLER, ROY. The Perfect Fool. Andre Deutsch, 1963. 1st ed. NF (top edge sl dusty, spine foot sl bumped) in dj (worn). *Ulysses*. $58/£36

FULLER, ROY. The Ruined Boys. Andre Deutsch, 1959. 1st ed. VG (feps lt browned, bkpl traces; sl mkd, top edge mkd, dusty, bottom edge sl soiled, spine gilt oxidised) in dj (worn). *Ulysses*. $58/£36

FULLER, ROY. The Second Curtain. Derek Verschoyle, 1953. 1st ed. VG (bkpl remains, fep lt browned; spine ends sl bumped) in dj (nicked, sl rubbed, dusty, spine, edges browned). *Ulysses*. $72/£45

FULLER, ROY. With My Little Eye. John Lehmann, 1948. 1st Eng ed. VG (top edge dusty; spine ends, corners bumped) in dj (nicked, torn, chipped, mkd, dusty, sl rubbed, creased, sl browned). *Ulysses*. $88/£55

FULLER, T. An Essay on Wheel Carriages. London: Longman, Rees, Orme et al, 1828. 7 full-pg plts incl frontis. (Foxed, damp-stained, edges brittle; shaken, soiled, chipped, edgeworn, spine split, chipped.) *Metropolitan**. $86/£54

FULLER, THOMAS O. Pictorial History of the American Negro. Memphis, TN, 1933. 1st ed. (2pp w/tape mks, underlining; cvrs worn w/paint spots.) *King*. $95/£59

FULLER, THOMAS. The Church-History of Britain. London, 1655. 1st ed. Folio. 3 plts (of 5). Mod 3/4 morocco (worn). *Oinonen**. $100/£63

FULLERTON, B. M. Selective Bibliography of American Literature. NY, 1936. Good in dj (chipped). *Dumont*. $65/£41

FULLERTON, HUGH S. Jimmy Kirkland of the Cascade College Team. Phila: Winston, 1915. 5.5x7.5. Charles Paxson Gray (illus). 265pp. VG+ (corners bumped) in dj (few spots). *My Bookhouse*. $87/£54

FULLERTON, HUGH S. Jimmy Kirkland of the Shasta Boys Team. Phila: Winston, 1915. Lists 3 titles. 5.5x7.5. Charles Paxson Gray (illus). 270pp. VG (shelfworn) in dj (lacks 1/3 of spine). *My Bookhouse*. $82/£51

FULOP-MILLER, RENE. The Russian Theatre. London: George G. Harrap, 1930. 1st ed. One of 300 (of 650) for England. 4to. 48 color plts, 557 half-tones. Teg. Maroon cl, gilt. (Prelim ll, sl foxed; spine faded), o/w Fine. *Maggs*. $600/£375

FULTON, E. G. Vegetarian Cook Book. Mountain View, CA: Pacific Press Pub Assoc, 1914. 1st ed thus. (Browned; extrems rubbed, spine lettering dknd), else Good. *Brown*. $25/£16

FULTON, ROBERT. The Illustrated Book of Pigeons, with Standards for Judging. Lewis Wright (ed). London: Cassell, Petter & Galpin, (c. 1886). 1st ed. 50 chromolitho plts. Period 3/4 morocco, mottled bds, gilt. Some plts bound in at places different from contents listing, but all present. VG. *Pacific**. $288/£180

FULTON, ROBERT. Torpedo War, and Submarine Explosions. NY, 1810. 1st ed. Obl 4to. 57,(3)pp; 5 woodcut plts. Loose in orig wrappers (stitching removed, lacks backstrip; lt offsetting from plts, old sig). Cl folder. *Swann**. $9,775/£6,109

FUNAROFF, S. Exile from a Future Time. NY: Dynamo, 1943. 1st ed. VG in wraps (worn). *Beasley*. $60/£38

FUNKHOUSER, WILLIAM DELBERT. Wild Life in Kentucky. Frankfort, KY: Kentucky Geological Surv, 1925. 1st ed. (Sl dingy, corners bumped), else VG. *My Bookhouse*. $47/£29

FUNNELL, K. Snodland Paper Mill. C. Townsend Hook, (1980). Fine in dj. *Moss*. $26/£16

FURBER, GEORGE C. The Twelve Months Volunteer. Cincinnati: J.A. & U.P. James, 1850. Fldg map. Orig full leather. (Foxed; hinges strengthened w/new eps, one sig starting.) Howes 420. *Dumont*. $250/£156

FUREY, MICHAEL. (Pseud of Sax Rohmer.) Wulfheim. London: Jarrolds, n.d. (1950). 1st Eng ed. VG (feps partly browned; spine ends bumped, cvrs sl spotted) in dj (sl creased, rubbed, dusty). *Ulysses*. $440/£275

FURLONG, C. W. The Gateway to the Sahara, Adventures and Observations in Tripoli. NY, 1914. New, enlgd ed. Signed presentation. 3 maps. (Headband split, tape-repaired.) *Hallam*. $64/£40

FURLONG, C. W. The Gateway to the Sahara. NY: Scribner, 1914. 2nd ed. 36 plts (4 color), 3 maps. (Ex-lib; edges rubbed, lib spine #), o/w VG. *Worldwide*. $18/£11

FURLONG, C. W. Let'er Buck. NY: Putnam, 1927. Inscribed, w/sketch. Good (dusty; bkpl) in dj (chipped). *Dumont*. $175/£109

FURNAS, J. C. The Road to Harper's Ferry. London: Faber & Faber, (1961). 1st ed. Blue cl. (Bkpl), else Fine in NF dj. *Chapel Hill*. $40/£25

FURNAS, J. C. The Road to Harper's Ferry. NY, 1959. 1st ed. VG + in VG + dj. *Pratt*. $22/£14

FURNAS, ROBERT W. (ed). Arbor Day. Lincoln: State Journal, 1888. 1st ed. Frontisport. White bds, gilt. (Sl soiled), else VG. *Pacific**. $46/£29

FURNEAUX, RUPERT. Tried by Their Peers. London: Cassell, 1959. Sound (worn). *Boswell*. $45/£28

FURNEAUX, WILLIAM S. Philips' Anatomical Model. London: George Philip & Son, n.d. (ca 1910). Fldg moveable color plt. Pict bds (soiled, chipped). *Hollett*. $48/£30

FURNESS, WILLIAM HENRY. The Home-Life of Borneo Head-Hunters. Its Festivals and Folk-Lore. Phila: Lippincott, 1902. 1st ed. Ltd to 500. Inscribed presentation. Pub's red cl (mkd), gilt. *Sotheby's**. $810/£506

FURNISS, HARRY. Paradise in Piccadilly, the Story of Albany. London: Bodley Head, 1925. 1st ed. Frontis, 50 plts. Pale blue cl (sl dusty, worn). *Marlborough*. $120/£75

FURST, HERBERT. The Decorative Art of Frank Brangwyn. London, (1924). One of 120 numbered, w/signed woodcut self-port by Brangwyn. Folio. 33 color plts. White cl (lt soiled). *Swann**. $287/£179

FURST, JILL LESLIE and PETER T. Pre-Columbian Art of Mexico. NY: Abbeville, (1980). 1st ed. Folio. 4 fldg full color photos, map. Red cl. VF in dj. *Argonaut*. $175/£109

FUSELI, HENRY. Lectures on Painting. London/Edinburgh: T. Cadell & W. Davies/W. Blackwood, 1820. 1st ed. Engr frontisport, tp engr vignette, 257pp; port, errata slip tipped-in. Full calf. (Prelims sl foxed; lt worn), else Nice. *Turtle Island*. $175/£109

FUSELI, HENRY. The Mind of Henry Fuseli. London: Routledge & Kegan Paul, (1951). NF in dj. *Turtle Island*. $55/£34

FUSSELL, G. E. Old English Farming Books 1523-1793. Aberdeen, 1978. 1-vol rpt. One of 500 numbered. Fine in dj. *Moss*. $72/£45

FUTRELLE, JACQUES. My Lady's Garter. Chicago/NY, (1912). 1st ed. Frontisport. VG. *Mcclintock*. $17/£11

FYFE, H. HAMILTON. South Africa To-Day. London, 1911. 1st ed. 35 plts. (Sl browned, bkpl removed; sm perf, crease spine head.) *Edwards*. $96/£60

FYFIELD, FRANCES. Deep Sleep. Heinemann, 1991. 1st UK ed. Signed. Fine in dj. *Williams*. $29/£18

FYFIELD, FRANCES. A Question of Guilt. Heinemann, 1988. 1st UK ed, 1st bk. Fine in dj. *Williams*. $32/£20

FYFIELD, FRANCES. A Question of Guilt. London: Heinemann, 1988. 1st ed. Signed. Fine in dj. *Murder*. $75/£47

FYFIELD, FRANCES. Shadow Play. Bantam, 1993. 1st UK ed. Signed. Fine in dj. *Williams*. $24/£15

FYFIELD, FRANCES. Shadows on the Mirror. Heinemann, 1989. 1st UK ed. Fine in dj. *Williams*. $32/£20

FYLEMAN, ROSE. Fifty-One New Nursery Rhymes. Methuen, 1931. 1st ed. Obl 4to. Dorothy Burroughes (illus). viii,99pp. Cl-backed pict bds (corners sl bumped). *Hollett*. $64/£40

FYSON, P. F. The Flora of the South Indian Hill Stations. Madras, 1932. 2 vols. 611 plts, w/133 hand-colored (by former owner?). (Spines chipped, joints sl rubbed, lower joint vol 2 split.) *Edwards*. $360/£225

G

G'AG, WANDA. Growing Pains. Diaries and Drawings for the Years 1908-1917. NY: Coward-McCann, (1940). 1st ed. Thick 8vo. Beige textured cl w/brn signature imprint on cvr. Good. *Reisler*. $75/£47

G'AG, WANDA. Snippy and Snappy. NY: Coward-McCann, 1931. 1st ed. Obl 4to. Yellow bds. Very Nice in matching dj (lt dusty, sm marginal tear). *Reisler*. $450/£281

G'AG, WANDA. Snow White and the Seven Dwarfs. NY: Coward-McCann, (1938). 1st ed. 8vo. Color illus bds (sl edgeworn). Color dj (worn, top edge lacks piece). *Reisler*. $200/£125

G'AG, WANDA. Snow White. NY: Coward McCann, 1938. 1st ed. 6 1/4 x 8 1/4. 43pp. Pict bds (spine ends worn). Good. *Cattermole*. $100/£63

GA'G, WANDA. Growing Pains. NY: Coward-McCann, 1940. 1st ed. 8vo. 179pp. Beige cl bds. VG (sig loose) in VG dj. *Davidson*. $150/£94

GABLIK, SUZI. Magritte. Greenwich: NYGS, (1970). 21 color plts. Mint in dj. *Argosy*. $60/£38

GADBURY, JOHN. Ephemerides of the Celestial Motions and Aspects, Eclipses of the Luminaries...for XX Years. Beginning Anno 1682. London: Macock, 1680. 1st ed. (292)ll. Newer calf (rubbed). *Oinonen**. $180/£113

GADD, C. J. The Stones of Assyria. London: C&W, 1936. 1st ed. 47 plts. 1/2 calf, marbled bds. (Copyright info inked out on tp verso.) *Archaeologia*. $275/£172

GADDIS, THOMAS E. Birdman of Alcatraz. Random House, 1955. 1st US ed. NF in VG dj (sl dusty, creased, sl chipped). *Williams*. $96/£60

GADDIS, WILLIAM. Carpenter's Gothic. (NY, 1985.) 1st ed. VG in dj. *King*. $20/£13

GADDIS, WILLIAM. JR. NY, 1975. 1st ed. Fine in NF dj. *Warren*. $150/£94

GADE, JOHN ALLYNE. The Life and Times of Tycho Brahe. NY: American-Scandinavian Foundation, 1947. Map. VG in dj (corners worn). *Weber*. $75/£47

GADOW, HANS. Through Southern Mexico. London, 1908. 1st ed. Fldg map. Teg. (Feps lt browned, fr hinge cracked.) *Edwards*. $120/£75

GAEDE, M. and MARNIE. Camera, Spade and Pen. Tuscon: Univ of AZ, 1980. VG in dj. *Dumont*. $50/£31

GAEDE, M. Images from the Great West. La Canada, CA: Chaco Press, 1990. (Rmdr stamp top edge), else Fine in dj. *Dumont*. $35/£22

GAER, JOSEPH (ed). Bibliography of California Literature. NY, 1970. VG. *Dumont*. $25/£16

GAGE, JOHN. J. M. W. Turner. A Wonderful Range of Mind. Yale Univ, 1987. 1st ed. Dj. *Edwards*. $56/£35

GAGE, SIMON HENRY. The Microscope: An Introduction to Microscopic Methods and To Histology. Ithaca, 1904. 9th ed. Good (inner hinges starting; extrems worn). *Doctor's Library*. $80/£50

GAINES, ERNEST J. The Autobiography of Miss Jane Pittman. NY: Dial, 1971. 1st ed. Inscribed, dated 1971. Fine in VG + dj (extrems worn). *Smith*. $300/£188

GAINES, PIERCE W. William Cobbett and the United States. A Bibliography.... Worcester, MA: American Antiquarian Soc, 1971. Fine in dj. *Mott*. $50/£31

GAINSBOROUGH, THOMAS. The Letters of Thomas Gainsborough. Mary Woodall (ed). Cupid, 1963. Rev ed. Ltd to 1200. Als from John Hayes loosely inserted. Frontis, 26 b/w plts, 4 b/w inserted photos. Cl-backed marbled bds. (Bkpl; upper edge sl browned.) *Edwards*. $88/£55

GAITE, CARMEN MARTIN. The Back Room. NY: Columbia, 1983. 1st US ed. (Dj affixed to fr bd w/tape), else Fine in VG + dj. *Lame Duck.* $45/£28

GALE, NORMAN. Cricket Songs. Constable, 1894. 1st ed. xii,67,24pp. VG. *Hollett.* $104/£65

GALEANO, EDUARDO. Faces and Masks. NY: Pantheon, 1987. 1st US ed. Signed. Fine in dj. *Lame Duck.* $150/£94

GALILEI, GALILEO. Galileo's Letter About the Libration of the Moon. Sesto Prete (trans). NY: John F. Fleming, 1965. 1st ed. Folio. Calf spine. Fine. *Glaser.* $95/£59

GALILEI, GALILEO. Operations of the Geometric and Military Compass, 1606. Stillman Drake (trans). Washington: Smithsonian Inst, 1978. 1st ed this trans. Frontisport. Fine in ptd pict wrappers. *Glaser.* $25/£16

GALIZZI, G. B. The Life and Death of Sir John Falstaff. J.M. Dent, 1923. (Prelims, tp lt spotted, ex-lib; fr hinge cracked, edges lt soiled, rubbed.) *Edwards.* $45/£28

GALL, ALICE CREW. Mother McGrew and Gerald Giraffe. NY: Cupples & Leon, (1917). 1st ed. Lee Wright Stanley (illus). 8 x 6 1/4. Cl-backed pict bds. (Soiled, extrems rubbed), else VG. *Pacific*.* $69/£43

GALLAGHER, GARY W. Stephen Dodson Ramseur, Lee's Gallant General. Chapel Hill: Univ of NC, (1986). 3rd ptg. Gray cl. Fine. *Chapel Hill.* $25/£16

GALLAGHER, MARK. Explosion!. Arbor House, 1987. 1st ed. Fine in VG + dj. *Plapinger.* $85/£53

GALLAGHER, SHARON. Inside the Personal Computer. Cross River, 1984. Glazed pict bds. Fine. *Bookfinders.* $60/£38

GALLAHER, DeWITT CLINTON. A Diary Depicting the Experiences of DeWitt Clinton Gallaher in the War Between the States.... (Charleston, WV?, ca 1961.) 1st ptg. Fine in stiff gray ptd wraps. *Chapel Hill.* $75/£47

GALLATIN, A. E. Art and the Great War. NY: E.P. Dutton, 1919. 1st ed. 100 plts. Grn cl-backed bds, gilt. (Spine ends rubbed), else VG. *Pacific*.* $46/£29

GALLATIN, A. E. Notes on Some Rare Portraits of Whistler. NY/London: John Lane Co/John Lane, The Bodley Head, 1916. One of 100 initialled. 6 port repros, guards. Good (fr hinge cracked; spine ends, corners bumped, bruised; cvrs mkd, sl soiled). *Ulysses.* $248/£155

GALLATIN, ALBERT. A Memoir on the North-Eastern Boundary. NY, 1843. Fldg copy of 'Jay' map. Orig wrappers. *Swann*.* $138/£86

GALLICHAN, WALTER M. Fishing and Travel in Spain; An Angler's Guide. F. E. Robinson, 1904. 1st ed. Red pict cl, gilt. Very Bright (ink inscrip). *Sotheran.* $88/£55

GALLICO, PAUL. The Poseidon Adventure. Heinemann, 1969. 1st UK ed. NF in VG dj. *Williams.* $29/£18

GALLICO, PAUL. The Small Miracle. DD, 1952. 1st ed. 4.5x7.8. Reisie Lonette (illus). 58pp. NF in VG dj (edgeworn, nick rear flap fold). *Price.* $38/£24

GALLUP, DONALD. (ed). The Flowers of Friendship: Letters Written to Gertrude Stein. NY: Knopf, 1953. 1st ed. Fine in Fine dj (1/16 inch short). *Between The Covers.* $75/£47

GALPIN, FRANCIS W. Old English Instruments of Music. Methuen, 1911. 2nd ed. Red cl, gilt. (Feps lt browned; fore-edge sl spotted.) *Hollett.* $88/£55

GALPIN, FRANCIS W. A Text Book of European Musical Instruments. Williams & Norgate, 1937. 10 plts. VG. *Hollett.* $72/£45

GALSWORTHY, JOHN. Another Sheaf. London: Heinemann, (1919). 1st collective ed. Gray bds, gilt. Fine in dj. *Reese.* $50/£31

GALSWORTHY, JOHN. Awakening. NY, (1920). 1st ed. Ptd paper over bds. (Name, birthday card mtd on fep, bkpl, lt damp-stained, hinges cracking; extrems worn, spine faded.) *Woolson.* $35/£22

GALSWORTHY, JOHN. The Forsyte Saga. London: Heinemann, 1922. 1st ed. One of 275. Signed. Frontisport, guard. Grn leather, gilt. (Extrems sl scuffed), else NF in slipcase. *Pacific*.* $104/£65

GALSWORTHY, JOHN. The Foundations. London: Duckworth, (1920). 1st ed. Grn cl. (Sl faded in spots), else VG in dj (chipped). *Reese.* $20/£13

GALSWORTHY, JOHN. Fraternity. Heinemann, 1909. 1st ed. VG (feps browned; sl mkd, edges sl rubbed, top edge sl dusty, spine ends, corners bumped). *Ulysses.* $104/£65

GALSWORTHY, JOHN. The Inn of Tranquility. Heinemann, 1912. 1st ed. Good (blank mtd nameplate, eps lt browned; sl mkd, spine ends, corners sl bumped, rubbed, edges spotted). *Ulysses.* $88/£55

GALSWORTHY, JOHN. Maid in Waiting. London: Heinemann, 1931. 1st ed. VG (eps sl yellowed) in dj (sl yellowed, soiled; edges sl chipped). *Virgo.* $24/£15

GALSWORTHY, JOHN. The Man of Property. NY/London: Putnam, 1906. 1st Amer ed. Tan dec cl. NF (sl shelfworn). *Sumner & Stillman.* $160/£100

GALSWORTHY, JOHN. The Man of Property. LEC, 1964. Ltd to 1500 numbered, signed by Charles Mozley (illus). Fine in slipcase. *Swann*.* $92/£58

GALSWORTHY, JOHN. A Modern Comedy. London: Heinemann, 1929. 1st ed, ltd issue. One of 1030 signed. W/add'l autograph quotation in Galsworthy's hand. Full vellum, gilt. NF. *Vandoros.* $175/£109

GALSWORTHY, JOHN. Saint's Progress. Heinemann, 1919. 1st ed. VG (feps browned; sl mkd, top edge dusty, spine sl faded, spine foot, corner sl bumped). *Ulysses.* $72/£45

GALSWORTHY, JOHN. The Silver Spoon. London: Heinemann, (1926). 1st ed. One of 265 numbered, signed. Uncut. Fine in pub's dj. *Second Life.* $150/£94

GALSWORTHY, JOHN. The Slaughter of Animals for Food. London, 1912. NF in ptd wraps (sl dust-soiled). *Polyanthos.* $25/£16

GALSWORTHY, JOHN. Soames and the Flag. London: Heinemann, 1930. 1st ed. One of 1025 numbered, specially bound, signed. Teg. Full gilt vellum over bds. (Eps lt foxed), o/w NF in acetate wrapper (sl dknd, offset) w/unptd flaps, in slipcase. *Reese.* $50/£31

GALSWORTHY, JOHN. Swan Song. NY: Scribner, 1928. 1st Amer ed. Purple cl. Fine in dj (sl worn, esp rear fold). *Glenn.* $45/£28

GALT, JOHN. Lawrie Todd; or, the Settlers in the Woods. Richard Bentley, 1832. Frontis. Marbled edges. Orig 1/2 leather, marbled bds, pub's presentation binding (sl rubbed). VG. *Tiger.* $40/£25

GALTON, FRANCIS. Finger Prints. London/NY: Macmillan, 1892. 1st ed. 23 cm. xvi,216pp; 16 plts. Orig plum cl. Fine (sm gilt lib # spine foot, lib lending label pasted to rear cvr). *Weber.* $675/£422

GALTSOFF, P. S. et al. Culture Methods for Invertebrate Animals. Ithaca: Comstock, 1937. 1st ed. Fine in VG dj. *Mikesh.* $30/£19

GALVIN, JOHN (ed). The Coming of Justice to California: Three Documents. (SF): John Howell-Books, 1963. 1st collected ed. One of 750. Inscribed. 2 maps (1 fldg). Unopened. Red cl. Fine. *Harrington.* $75/£47

GALVIN, JOHN (ed). The First Spanish Entry into San Francisco Bay 1775. SF: John Howell Books, 1971. Fldg map. NF in dj (faded). *Dumont.* $55/£34

GALVIN, JOHN. The Etchings of Edward Borein. SF, 1971. Folio. Dj (chipped). *Argosy.* $125/£78

GAMBLE, JAY MACK. Steamboats on the Muskingum. Staten Island: Steamship His. Soc. of Am., 1971. VG in dj. *American Booksellers.* $30/£19

GAMBRELL, HERBERT PICKENS. Mirabeau Buonaparte Lamar. Dallas: Southwest, 1934. Good in dj (chipped, stained). *Dumont.* $125/£78

GAMBRELL, HERBERT. Anson Jones, the Last President of Texas. GC, 1948. 1st ed. (Sl bumped), o/w VG in dj (edgeworn, chipped, price-clipped). *Baade.* $30/£19

GAMBRILL, RICHARD V. N. and JAMES C. MacKENZIE. Sporting Stables and Kennels. NY: Derrydale, 1935. Ltd to 950 numbered. Second state w/corrected p79. Folio. Color frontis. Red cl. VG. *Biscotti.* $200/£125

GANDHI, MOHANADASA KARAMCHAND. Christian Missions, Their Place in India. Ahmedabad: Navajivan, (1941). 1st ed. Ltd to 2000. Gray linen, blue bds. Good in dj. *Karmiole.* $85/£53

GANNETT, HENRY. A Gazetteer of Colorado. Washington: GPO, 1906. Wraps (fr, rear strengthened, spine repaired). Internally Good. *Dumont.* $30/£19

GANNETT, HENRY. A Gazetteer of Texas. Washington, 1904. 2nd ed. 14 half-pg maps. (Wraps browned), else VG. *Dumont.* $65/£41

GANTSCHEV, IVAN. The Volcano. London: Neugebauer, 1981. 4to. Unpaginated. NF in NF dj (flap corner clipped). *Price.* $45/£28

GANTT, PAUL H. The Case of Alfred Packer. Denver, 1952. *Dumont.* $45/£28

GANZ, A. W. Berlioz in London. Quality, 1950. 1st ed. 13 plts. VG in dj. *Hollett.* $32/£20

GANZHORN, JACK. I've Killed Men. NY: Devin-Adair, 1959. 1st Amer ed. Fine in dj. *Labordo.* $75/£47

GAPP, S. H. Where Polar Ice Begins. Bethlehem, PA: Religious Education Board of the Moravian Church in America, 1928. Sm map. VG in ptd wrapper. *High Latitude.* $45/£28

GARBEDIAN, H. GORDON. Albert Einstein: Maker of Universes. NY, 1939. 1st ed. 16 photo plts. Brn cl, gilt. VG. *Larry Price.* $30/£19

GARBERI, MERCEDES PRECERUTTI. Frescoes from Venetian Villas. London, 1971. 40 color plts. Good in dj. *Washton.* $145/£91

GARCES, FRANCISCO. On the Trail of a Spanish Pioneer: The Diary and Itinerary of Francisco Garces (Missionary Priest).... Elliot Coues (ed). NY: Harper, 1900. One of 950. 2 vols. Blue cl, gilt. (Rubberstamps, extreme pg edges sl dknd; sl shelfworn), else NF. Howes C801. *Pacific*.* $259/£162

GARCES, FRANCISCO. A Record of Travels in Arizona and California 1775-1776. SF: John Howell-Books, 1967. 2nd ed in English. Ltd to 1250. 6 full-color plts (2 dbl-pg), 3 maps (1 lg fldg laid in at end). VG + . *Five Quail.* $75/£47

GARCES, FRANCISCO. A Record of Travels in Arizona and California, 1775-1776. SF: John Howell, 1965. 1st ed. Ltd to 1250. Fldg map. Fine. *Book Market.* $85/£53

GARCIA LORCA, FEDERICO. From Lorca's Theatre. Five Plays. Richard O'Connell and James Graham (trans). NY: Scribner, 1941. 1st ed. VG (glue remnants) in VG dj (chipped, spine dknd). *Warren.* $35/£22

GARCIA LORCA, FEDERICO. Lament for the Death of a Bullfighter and Other Poems. London: Heinemann, 1937. 1st British ed. NF in VG + dj (fragile, few sm edge-tears, upper borders tanned). *Lame Duck.* $150/£94

GARCIA LORCA, FEDERICO. Poems of F. Garcia Lorca. NY: Oxford, 1939. 1st US ed. NF in VG + dj (price-clipped). *Lame Duck.* $250/£156

GARCIA LORCA, FEDERICO. Poems. R. M. Nadal (ed). London: Dolphin, 1939. 1st British ed. (Feps offset), else NF in VG + dj (spine tanned). *Lame Duck.* $150/£94

GARCIA LORCA, FEDERICO. The Poet in New York and Other Poems. Rolfe Humphries (trans). NY: Norton, (1940). 1st ed. Fine in VG dj (spine tanned, sm edge nicks). *Reese.* $125/£78

GARCIA LORCA, FEDERICO. Selected Poems of Federico Garcia Lorca. NY: Transatlantic Arts, 1947. 1st US ed. (Name, edges sunned), else Fine in dj (lt used). *Beasley.* $45/£28

GARCIA LORCA, FEDERICO. Selected Poems. London: Hogarth, 1943. 1st ed. VG in dj. *Lame Duck.* $150/£94

GARCIA MARQUEZ, GABRIEL. The Autumn of the Patriarch. London: Cape, 1977. 1st British ed. NF in dj. *Lame Duck.* $100/£63

GARCIA MARQUEZ, GABRIEL. Chronicle of a Death Foretold. London: Cape, 1982. 1st British ed, 1st ed in English. Fine in dj. *Lame Duck.* $125/£78

GARCIA MARQUEZ, GABRIEL. Chronicle of a Death Foretold. NY, 1983. 1st Amer ed. (Edges sl soiled), else Good in dj. *King.* $35/£22

GARCIA MARQUEZ, GABRIEL. Chronicle of a Death Foretold. NY: Knopf, 1983. 1st US ed, 1st issue w/One Hundred Days of Solitude mistakenly cited on front dj flap. Fine in dj. *Lame Duck.* $45/£28

GARCIA MARQUEZ, GABRIEL. Clandestine in Chile. Asa Zatz (trans). NY: Henry Holt, (1987). 1st Amer ed. 1/4 tan cl, cream bds. Fine in dj (spine faded). *Heritage.* $75/£47

GARCIA MARQUEZ, GABRIEL. Clandestine in Chile. Cambridge: Granta Books, (1987). 1st Eng ed. Inscribed. Fine in Fine dj. *Between The Covers.* $500/£313

GARCIA MARQUEZ, GABRIEL. Clandestine in Chile. Cambridge: Granta, 1989. 1st British ed. Fine in Fine dj. *Lame Duck.* $45/£28

GARCIA MARQUEZ, GABRIEL. Collected Stories. Gregory Rabassa and S.J. Bernstein (trans). NY: Harper & Row, 1984. 1st US ed. Fine (spine head sl bumped) in dj. *Ulysses.* $88/£55

GARCIA MARQUEZ, GABRIEL. The General in His Labyrinth. NY, 1990. 1st Amer ed. VG in dj. *King.* $22/£14

GARCIA MARQUEZ, GABRIEL. The General in His Labyrinth. NY: Knopf, 1990. 1st Amer ed. Grn cl, gilt. (Cvrs sl spotted), o/w Fine in dj. *Heritage.* $50/£31

GARCIA MARQUEZ, GABRIEL. The General in His Labyrinth. NY: Knopf, 1990. 1st ed. One of 350 signed. Fine in leather, pict slipcase. *Smith.* $325/£203

GARCIA MARQUEZ, GABRIEL. The General in His Labyrinth. NY: Knopf, 1990. 1st US ed. One of 350 signed, numbered. Fine in pub's full leather. Slipcase. *Lame Duck.* $375/£234

GARCIA MARQUEZ, GABRIEL. The General in His Labyrinth. London: Cape, 1991. 1st British ed. Fine in dj. *Lame Duck.* $65/£41

GARCIA MARQUEZ, GABRIEL. In Evil Hour. NY: Harper & Row, 1979. 1st US ed, 1st issue in dj reading 'Marquez' instead of 'Garcia Marquez' on the spine. NF in variant dj. *Lame Duck.* $500/£313

GARCIA MARQUEZ, GABRIEL. In Evil Hour. London: Cape, 1980. 1st British ed. Fine in dj (price-clipped). *Lame Duck.* $50/£31

GARCIA MARQUEZ, GABRIEL. Innocent Erendira. NY: Harper & Row, 1978. 1st US ed. Fine in dj. *Lame Duck.* $65/£41

GARCIA MARQUEZ, GABRIEL. Innocent Erendira. London: Cape, 1979. 1st British ed. Fine in dj (price-clipped). *Lame Duck.* $55/£34

GARCIA MARQUEZ, GABRIEL. Leaf Storm and Other Stories. Gregory Rabassa (trans). London, 1972. 1st Eng ed. Fine in dj. *Clearwater.* $80/£50

GARCIA MARQUEZ, GABRIEL. Leaf Storm and Other Stories. NY: Harper & Row, 1972. 1st US ed. NF in VG + dj (1-inch tear rear cvr, few sm edge-tears). *Lame Duck.* $100/£63

GARCIA MARQUEZ, GABRIEL. Leaf Storm and Other Stories. NY: Harper & Row, 1972. 1st US ed. Inscribed in 1991. NF in VG + dj (sm edge tear rear panel, extrems worn). *Lame Duck.* $1,250/£781

GARCIA MARQUEZ, GABRIEL. Love in the Time of Cholera. NY: Knopf, 1988. 1st US trade ed. Fine in dj. *Lame Duck.* $65/£41

GARCIA MARQUEZ, GABRIEL. Love in the Time of Cholera. Edith Grossman (trans). NY: Knopf, 1988. One of 350 signed. (Few pp poorly inked), else VF in acetate, slipcase. *Pharos.* $350/£219

GARCIA MARQUEZ, GABRIEL. Love in the Time of Cholera. NY, 1988. One of 350 signed. Fine in Fine dec acetate dj, Fine pub's slipcase. *Warren.* $400/£250

GARCIA MARQUEZ, GABRIEL. No One Writes to the Colonel and Other Stories. J.S. Bernstein (trans). NY: Harper & Row, (1968). 1st ed, 1st ptg. Fine in NF 1st ptg dj (rear white panel sl smudged). *Reese.* $500/£313

GARCIA MARQUEZ, GABRIEL. No One Writes to the Colonel. NY: Harper & Row, 1968. 1st ed, 1st issue w/photo on rear panel attributed to Jerry Bauer. (Bd edges lt shelfworn), else NF in VG + dj (sm edge-tears, 2 tape-repaired on verso). *Lame Duck.* $650/£406

GARCIA MARQUEZ, GABRIEL. No One Writes to the Colonel. London: Cape, 1971. 1st British ed. Fine in NF dj (spine head sl worn). *Lame Duck.* $350/£219

GARCIA MARQUEZ, GABRIEL. One Hundred Years of Solitude. NY: Harper & Row, (1970). 1st Amer ed. VG in later state dj w/o exclamation point at end of 1st paragraph of fr dj flap (spine head chipped, fr joint head lacks sm piece). *Pacific*.* $196/£123

GARCIA MARQUEZ, GABRIEL. One Hundred Years of Solitude. NY: Harper & Row, (1970). 1st Amer ed, 1st issue w/exclamation point at end of 'Latin America' on fr flap. (Spine sl leaning), else NF in dj (spine head, corners sl rubbed, sm closed tear fr panel). *Pacific*.* $546/£341

GARCIA MARQUEZ, GABRIEL. One Hundred Years of Solitude. NY: Harper & Row, 1970. 1st US ed, issue w/the period at the end of the 1st paragraph of dj flap text. (Pg top edges foxed, price circled in ink on fep, eps lt tanned), else VG + in dj (spine sl faded, extrems worn, sl nicked). *Lame Duck.* $375/£234

GARCIA MARQUEZ, GABRIEL. One Hundred Years of Solitude. London: Cape, 1970. 1st British ed. NF in dj (spine base lt worn). *Lame Duck.* $500/£313

GARCIA MARQUEZ, GABRIEL. One Hundred Years of Solitude. NY: Harper & Row, 1970. 1st US ed, issue w/the exclamation point at the end of the 1st paragraph of front-flap text on dj. Inscribed in 1991. NF in NF dj (rear cvr scratch). *Lame Duck.* $3,500/£2,188

GARCIA MARQUEZ, GABRIEL. One Hundred Years of Solitude. LEC, 1983. One of 2000 signed by Rafael Ferer (illus). Fine in slipcase. *Swann*.* $230/£144

GARCIA MARQUEZ, GABRIEL. Strange Pilgrims. NY: Knopf, 1993. 1st US ed. Fine in dj. *Lame Duck.* $25/£16

GARCIA, CRISTINA. Dreaming in Cuban. NY, 1992. 1st Amer ed, 1st bk. Fine in Fine dj. *Polyanthos.* $25/£16

GARD, WAYNE et al. Along the Early Trails of the Southwest. Austin: Pemberton, 1969. 1st ed. Fine in dj. *Labordo.* $45/£28

GARD, WAYNE. The Chisholm Trail. Norman, 1965. VG in dj (spine faded). *Dumont.* $35/£22

GARD, WAYNE. Fabulous Quarter Horse; Steel Dust. NY: Duell, Sloan & Pearce, 1958. 1st ed. VG in dj. *Labordo.* $55/£34

GARD, WAYNE. Frontier Justice. Norman: Univ of OK, 1949. 1st ed. (Offsetting from news clipping to rep), o/w Fine in dj. *Labordo.* $75/£47

GARD, WAYNE. Rawhide Texas. Norman: Univ of OK, 1965. 1st ed. Fine in dj. *Labordo.* $55/£34

GARDEN CLUB OF VIRGINIA. Homes and Gardens in Old Virginia. Frances Archer Christian and Susanne Williams Massie (eds). Richmond: Garrett & Massie, n.d. (1931). 4th ed. (Sl shelfworn), else VG. *Fair Meadow.* $50/£31

GARDENER, ROBERT W. The Parthenon: Its Science of Forms. NY, 1925. One of 700. Folio. 11 plans. Cl-backed bds (lt soiled, corners worn). *Swann*.* $57/£36

Gardening with the Experts. NY: Macmillan, 1941. 1st ed. VG in dj (chipped). *Fair Meadow.* $30/£19

GARDINER, ALAN H. Ancient Egyptian Onomestica. London: OUP, (1968). 3 vols. Folio, 8vo. *Archaeologia.* $475/£297

GARDINER, ALAN H. Egypt of the Pharaohs: An Introduction. Oxford: Clarendon, 1961. 1st ed. 22 plts, 3 maps. VG in dj (sl torn). *Worldwide.* $50/£31

GARDINER, ALAN H. Egyptian Grammar: Being an Introduction to the Study of Hieroglyphics. Oxford: Clarendon, 1927. 1st ed. Blue cl, gilt spine. NF. *Pacific*.* $92/£58

GARDINER, DOROTHY. West of the River. NY: Thomas Y. Crowell, 1941. VG in dj (worn). *Dumont.* $30/£19

GARDINER, HOWARD C. In Pursuit of the Golden Dream: Reminiscences of San Francisco and the Northern and Southern mines, 1849-1857. Dale E. Morgan (ed). Stoughton, MA: Western Hemisphere, 1970. 1st ed. 8 plts, 2 maps (1 fldg). Red cl, gilt. Fine. *Pacific*.* $29/£18

GARDINER, J. STANLEY (ed). The Fauna and Geography of the Maldive and Laccadive Archipelagos. Cambridge, 1903-06. 2 vols, incl Supplements I and II. 100 plts. (1/2-inch tear to half-title; spines, edges faded, corners bumped.) *Sutton.* $485/£303

GARDINER, LESLIE E. Faces, Figures, and Feelings. London: Robert Hale, (1959). 21 plts. Dj. *Weber.* $37/£23

GARDINER, SAMUEL RAWSON. Oliver Cromwell. London: Goupil, 1899. 1st ed. One of 1475. Hand-tinted frontis, guards. Teg. 3/4 red morocco, gilt, morocco spine label. (Bkpl; spine, extrems sl sunned), else VG. *Pacific*.* $161/£101

GARDINER, WREY. The Dark Thorn. London: Grey Walls Press, 1946. 1st ed. Frontis port. Dk blue cl. (Edges lt foxed), o/w Fine in dj (sl creased, frayed). *Temple.* $19/£12

GARDNER, ARTHUR. English Medieval Sculpture. Cambridge, 1951. (Spine sl sunned.) *Washton.* $90/£56

GARDNER, ARTHUR. A Handbook of English Medieval Sculpture. CUP, 1937. Frontis. Pub's gray buckram. VG. *Peter Taylor.* $42/£26

GARDNER, C. HARVEY (ed). The Literary Memoranda of William Hickling Prescott. Norman, 1961. 2 vols. VG in slipcase. *Dumont.* $50/£31

GARDNER, CHARLES M. The Grange. Washington, 1949. 1st ed. Good. *Rybski.* $45/£28

GARDNER, ERLE STANLEY. The Case of the Gold-Digger's Purse. London: Cassell, (1948). 1st UK ed. (Edges lt faded.) Dj. *Glenn.* $50/£31

GARDNER, ERLE STANLEY. The Case of the Troubled Trustee. NY, (1965). 1st ed. VG in dj (edges frayed). *King.* $20/£13

GARDNER, ERLE STANLEY. Hunting the Desert Whale. Jarrolds, 1963. 1st UK ed. Fine in VG dj (price-clipped). *Williams.* $24/£15

GARDNER, JAMES. Role of Honor. Putnam, 1984. 1st Amer ed. Inscribed. VF in dj. *Murder.* $37/£23

GARDNER, JOHN STARKIE. A Monograph of the British Eocene Flora. Volume II, Part I—Gymnospermae. London: Palaeontographical Soc, 1883. 60pp; 9 tinted litho plts. VG in mod grn wrappers. *Hollett.* $88/£55

GARDNER, JOHN STARKIE. A Monograph of the British Eocene Flora. Volume II, Part II—Gymnospermae. London: Palaeontographical Soc, 1884. 61-91pp; 10 tinted litho plts. VG in mod grn wrappers. *Hollett.* $104/£65

GARDNER, JOHN. Building Classic Small Craft. Camden: Intl. Marine, 1977. VG in dj (chipped). *American Booksellers.* $45/£28

GARDNER, JOHN. The Gawain-Poet. Lincoln, NE: Cliff's Notes, (1967). 1st ed. Fine in wraps. *Agvent.* $60/£38

GARDNER, JOHN. Grendel. NY, 1971. 1st ed. VG+ in VG+ dj (spine faded). *Warren.* $85/£53

GARDNER, JOHN. Grendel. NY: Knopf, 1971. 1st ed. VG in dj (spine sunned). *Pacific*.* $98/£61

GARDNER, JOHN. Household Medicine. London: Smith, Elder, 1863. 2nd ed. viii,542pp (spotting). 1/2 morocco (sl rubbed), gilt. *Hollett.* $104/£65

GARDNER, JOHN. In the Suicide Mountains. NY: Knopf, 1977. 1st ed. Pict eps; top edge stained purple. 1/4 cream cl, pale blue blindstamped bds, gilt. (Heavy pencil inscrip), o/w Fine in pict dj (price-clipped, lt edgeworn). *Heritage.* $75/£47

GARDNER, JOHN. The King's Indian. NY, 1974. 1st ed. Fine in NF dj. *Warren.* $40/£25

GARDNER, JOHN. Licence Renewed. (London): Jonathan Cape/Hodder & Stoughton, (1981). 1st ed. Black cl, gilt. Fine in dj. *Heritage.* $100/£63

GARDNER, JOHN. Nickel Mountain. NY: Knopf, 1983. 1st ed. 9 plts. Cream cl, gilt spine. Fine in dj (spine sl faded). *Heritage.* $125/£78

GARDNER, JOHN. Spin the Bottle. The Autobiography of an Alcoholic. Muller, 1964. 1st UK ed, 1st bk. Inscribed. VG in dj (edges sl worn, browned). *Williams.* $120/£75

GARDNER, JOHN. Stillness and Shadows. NY, 1986. 1st ed. (Ink name, date; removal mk on fep), else VG in dj (sl worn). *King.* $25/£16

GARDNER, RAYMOND HATFIELD. The Old Wild West. San Antonio: Naylor, 1944. Frontis. VG in dj (lt soiled). *Dumont.* $75/£47

GARDNER, ROBERT E. Arms Fabricators, Ancient and Modern. Columbus, OH: F.J. Heer Ptg, 1934. Red cl (spine faded). *Cullen.* $175/£109

GARDNER, ROBERT E. Five Centuries of Gunsmiths, Swordsmiths and Armourers 1400-1900. (Columbus, OH: Walter Heer), 1948. 1st ed. Blue cl. (Sm spine tear), else VG. *Glenn.* $40/£25

GARFIELD, VIOLA E. Meet the Totem. Sitka: Sitka Pub Co, (1951). VG in wraps. *Perier.* $12/£8

GARIS, HOWARD R. Uncle Wiggily's Friends. (NY): Platt & Munk, 1939. 8vo. George Carlson (illus). Color pict boxed set of 4 vols. 10pp each vol. (Corner of 1pg clipped), o/w VG set. *Reisler.* $175/£109

GARLAND, HAMLIN et al. Native Folk Spirit in Literature, Three Essays.... Cedar Rapids: Friends of the Torch Press, 1957. 1st this ed. One of 350. Paper spine label. NF. *Reese.* $35/£22

GARLAND, HAMLIN. Back-Trailers from the Middle Border. NY: Macmillan, 1928. 1st ed. Black dec cl. Mint in Mint dj. *Sumner & Stillman.* $125/£78

GARLAND, HAMLIN. The Light of the Star. NY: Harper, 1904. 1st ed. Signed, inscribed. Frontis. Pict gilt-lettered cl. (Cuts to fr pastedown where photo was inserted), else VG. *Pacific*.* $23/£14

GARLAND, HAMLIN. Trail-Makers of the Middle Border. NY: Macmillan, 1924. 1st ed. Fine in dj (sm chip spine head). *Captain's Bookshelf.* $125/£78

GARLAND, JAMES A. The Private Stable. Its Establishment, Management and Appointments. Boston, 1903. New ed. Gilt-pict cl (shelfworn, cvr spotted). *Oinonen*.* $200/£125

GARLAND, PATRICK. Brief Lives. Adapted for the Stage. London, 1967. 1st Eng ed. Fine in dj (sl torn). *Clearwater.* $40/£25

GARLICK, THEODATUS. A Treatise on the Artificial Propagation of Fish. NY, 1858. 2nd ed, apparently consisting of the orig sheets of the 1st, w/new title leaf. 142pp + ad leaf. Blindstamped cl (lt worn, sl foxed, soiled; eps removed). *Oinonen*.* $50/£31

GARMAN, CHARLES EDWARD. Letters and Addresses of Charles Edward Garman. Boston: Houghton Mifflin, 1909. 2 photogravure ports. Ruled crimson cl, gilt. (Rubbed), else VG. *Gach.* $50/£31

GARMAN, R. H. Moving Picture Animals. Chicago: Ideal Book Builders, 1907. #4 in Children's Favorite Series. Tall 4to shape bk. 3 sets of leaves, each set w/6 overlay slips for transformations. Color pict wraps. NF (edges sl dusty). *Baltimore*.* $60/£38

GARNER, ALAN. The Guizer. Hamish Hamilton, 1985. 1st ed. (Sm stain fep), o/w Fine in dj. *Any Amount.* $26/£16

GARNER, ALAN. The Owl Service. London: Collins, 1967. 1st ed. 8vo. (viii),9-156pp. Orange flecked cl. Very Nice (sm scribble, rubbing to fep) in dj (sm nick w/sl loss). *Sotheran.* $141/£88

GARNER, BESS ADAMS. Windows in an Old Adobe. Pomona: Saunders, 1939. 1st ed. Ltd to 2000. Fine. *Book Market.* $30/£19

GARNER, GRETCHEN. An Art History of Ephemera...Photographs, 1976-1978. Chicago: Tulip, 1982. 1st ed. Fine in spiral bound ptd stiff wrappers. *Cahan.* $65/£41

GARNER, HARRY. Chinese Lacquer. Faber, 1979. 1st ed. 9 color, 214 monochrome plts. VG in dj. *Hollett.* $96/£60

GARNER, R. J. The Grafter's Handbook. Faber, 1947. 1st ed. 95 diags, 24 plts. Dj (sl chipped). *Edwards.* $24/£15

GARNER, R. L. Gorillas and Chimpanzees. London, 1896. (Cl lt mkd.) *Grayling.* $80/£50

GARNETT, DAVID. Beaney-Eye. London: C&W, 1935. 1st ed. NF in pict dj. *Cady.* $35/£22

GARNETT, DAVID. No Love. London: C&W, 1929. 1st ed. Mottled plum, black cl, gilt. VG w/fr panel, ptd turn-in of dj laid in. *Cady.* $25/£16

GARNETT, DAVID. No Love. London: C&W, 1929. 1st ed. One of 160 signed. Uncut. Yellow cl. (Spine sl grubby), o/w NF. *Maggs.* $120/£75

GARNETT, DAVID. The Old Dovecote and Other Stories. London: Elkin Mathews & Marrott, 1928. 1st ed. One of 530 signed. Nice. *Cady.* $25/£16

GARNETT, DAVID. Plough Over the Bones. (London): Macmillan, (1973). 1st ed. Fine in dj. *Reese.* $30/£19

GARNETT, DAVID. War in the Air. September 1939 to May 1941. London: C&W, 1941. 1st ed. 8 plts. (Spine sl dull), else Nice. *Cady.* $30/£19

GARNETT, EDWARD. The Trial of Jeanne D'Arc and Other Plays. London: Cape, 1931. One of 100 signed. Teg. VG in vellum-backed marbled bds. *Cady.* $75/£47

GARNETT, EVE. The Family from One End Street. London: Muller, 1938. 9th ed. 5.5x8.75. 212pp. VG in dj. *Cattermole.* $35/£22

GARNETT, RICHARD (ed). Relics of Shelley. London: Edward Moxon, 1862. Text-paper ad leaf at end, probably ptd as [A1]; (iii)-xvi,191,(i blank),(ii)pp, pub's 8-pg cat dated July 1862 bound between feps. Edges uncut, eps coated pale yellow. Purple coarse morocco cl, gilt. (Spine dull, dknd, gilt sl rubbed), o/w Good. *Temple.* $224/£140

GARON, PAUL. The Devil's Son-in-Law. The Story of Peetie Wheatstraw and His Songs. London: Studio Vista, 1971. 1st ed. Fine in Fine dj. *Beasley.* $35/£22

GARRAN, ANDREW (ed). Picturesque Atlas of Australasia. Sydney: Picturesque Atlas Publishing, 1886. 3 vols. Frontis ports each vol, add'l tp vol I. Aeg. Contemp black morocco (vols 2, 3 worn), gilt. *Christie's*.* $360/£225

GARRARD, LEWIS H. Wah-To-Yah and the Taos Trail. Ralph P. Bieber (ed). Glendale: A.H. Clark, 1938. 1st ed thus. Red cl. VF. Howes G70. *Labordo.* $150/£94

GARRETSON, MARTIN S. The American Bison. NY: NY Zoological Soc, 1938. 1st ed. Fine in dj. *Labordo.* $85/£53

GARRETSON, MARTIN S. The American Bison. NY: NY Zoological Soc, 1938. VG in dj (sl chipped). *Dumont.* $150/£94

GARRETT, GARET. The Wild Wheel. The World of Henry Ford. London: Cresset, 1952. 13 plts. VG in dj (price-clipped). *Hollett.* $24/£15

GARRETT, PATRICK F. The Authentic Life of Billy the Kid. NY, 1927. 1st ed thus. VG- (sig, date; cvrs lt worn, top backstrip starting to fray). *Baade.* $60/£38

GARRETT, PATRICK F. The Authentic Life of Billy the Kid. Albuquerque: Horn & Wallace, 1964. 1st ed. Fine in dj. *Labordo.* $175/£109

GARRETT, PATRICK F. Pat F. Garrett's Authentic Life of Billy the Kid. NY: Macmillan, 1927. 1st ed. Paper label pasted on, paper title on backstrip. VG in dj (worn, chipped). Howes G73. *Labordo.* $225/£141

GARRICK, DAVID. The Diary of David Garrick. Ryllis Clair Alexander (ed). NY: OUP, 1928. One of 575 numbered. Parchment-backed patterned bds (corner tips sl chafed). Good (sl grubby; no slipcase). *Clearwater.* $80/£50

GARRICK, DAVID. The Letters of David Garrick. David M. Little and George M. Kahrl (eds). Cambridge: Belknap, 1963. 3 vols. Fine in slipcase. *Dramatis.* $50/£31

GARRICK, DAVID. Some Unpublished Correspondence. George Pierce Baker (ed). Boston, 1907. One of 430 numbered. (Inscrip; fr hinge cracked, cvrs sl mkd, handled in places, spine tanned.) *Clearwater.* $104/£65

GARRITY, JOHN. The George Brett Story. Coward McCann & Geoghegan, 1981. 1st ed. Fine in Fine dj. *Plapinger.* $50/£31

GARSTANG, JOHN. The Burial Customs of Ancient Egypt. London: Archibald Constable, 1907. Frontis, 15 plts. *Archaeologia.* $650/£406

GARSTIN, CROSBIE. Samuel Kelly: An Eighteenth Century Seaman. NY: Stokes, 1925. Grn cl. VG. *American Booksellers.* $75/£47

GARTHWAITE, MARION. Tomas and the Red Headed Angel. Messner, 1950. 1st ed. Lorence Bjorklund (illus). 190pp. VG in dj (chipped). *Price.* $30/£19

GARTON, RAY. Crucifax Autumn. Arlington Heights: Dark Harvest, 1988. One of 300 numbered, signed by Garton and Bob Eggleton (illus). (Lt worn.) Dj, slipcase. *Oinonen*.* $30/£19

GARTRELL, MARJORIE. Dear Primitive: A Nurse Among the Aborigines. Sydney: Angus & Robertson, (1957). 1st ed. (Corner bumped; lt worn), else Fine in dj. *Hermitage.* $20/£13

GARVIN, RICHARD M. and EDMOND G. ADDEO. The Midnight Special: The Legend of Leadbelly. NY: Bernard Geis, (1971). 1st ed. VG in dj (lt chipped). *Petrilla.* $30/£19

GARY, ROMAIN. Hissing Tales. NY, (1964). 1st Amer ed. Two-tone cl. VG in dj (sl rubbed). *King.* $17/£11

GASCOYNE, DAVID. Holderlin's Madness. London, (1938). 1st Eng ed. Nice (sticker; spine, edges sl tanned) in dj (tanned, sl mkd, torn, nicked, lacks head of spine panel). *Clearwater.* $136/£85

GASCOYNE, DAVID. Night Thoughts. Andre Deutsch, 1956. Inscribed presentation. VG (prelims sl spotted; cvrs sl bowed, spine ends sl bumped) in dj (rubbed, torn, chipped, internally repaired). *Ulysses.* $120/£75

GASCOYNE, DAVID. A Short Survey of Surrealism. Cobden-Sanderson, 1935. 1st Eng ed. Good (cvrs sl mkd, spine sl faded; no dj). *Clearwater.* $88/£55

GASH, JONATHAN. Gold from Gemini. Collins, 1978. 1st UK ed. Fine in dj (spine sl faded). *Williams.* $360/£225

GASH, JONATHAN. The Gondola Scam. Collins, 1984. 1st UK ed. Fine in NF dj. *Williams.* $152/£95

GASH, JONATHAN. The Grail Tree. London: William Collins, 1979. 1st Eng ed. VG (fore-edge sl mkd; spine tail bumped) in dj (sl creased). *Ulysses.* $400/£250

GASH, JONATHAN. The Judas Pair. NY: Harper & Row, 1977. 1st Amer ed, 1st bk. (Edges sl browned), o/w VG in dj (chipped, rubbed, sl browned). *Virgo.* $104/£65

GASH, JONATHAN. The Tartan Ringers. Collins, 1986. 1st UK ed. Fine in dj. *Williams.* $104/£65

GASKELL, MRS. Cranford. London: Macmillan, 1898. 1st ed w/color plts. 8vo. Hugh Thomson (illus). Teg. 1/2 leather w/raised bands, gilt, floral bds. Good. *Reisler.* $150/£94

GASKELL, P. A Bibliography of the Foulis Press. London: Soho Bibliographies, 1964. Maroon cl. Dj. *Maggs.* $35/£22

GASKELL, P. The First Editions of William Mason. Cambridge: Bowes & Bowes, 1951. Orig wrappers. *Maggs.* $16/£10

GASQUET, ABBOT. English Monastic Life. London: Methuen, 1905. 3rd ed. Frontisport, 18 plts, 3 fldg plans, 5 maps. Red cl (sl bumped), gilt. *Maggs.* $29/£18

GASS, PATRICK. A Journal of the Voyages and Travels of a Corps of Discovery Under the Command of Capt. Lewis and Capt. Clarke.... Pittsburgh: David M'Keehan, 1807. 1st ed. viii,(2),(11)-262pp. Period leather-backed marbled bds, gilt spine. (Few pp shaved close to text affecting at least 1 sig mk, several pp w/old horizontal creases, 1-inch tear to pp13-14; bds worn, portions of paper covering them worn), o/w VG. Howes G77. *Pacific*.* $2,070/£1,294

GASS, ROSS. Don Francisco de Paula Martin. Honolulu: Univ of HI, 1973. 1st ed. VG (ex-lib) in Fine dj. *Archer.* $20/£13

GASS, WILLIAM H. In the Heart of the Heart of the Country and Other Stories. NY: Harper & Row, (1968). 1st ed. As New in As New dj. *Dermont.* $100/£63

GASS, WILLIAM H. Mad Meg in the Maelstrom. Chicago: Ravine, 1976. One of 150. Broadside. Fine. *Smith.* $150/£94

GASS, WILLIAM H. Omensetter's Luck. NY, 1966. 1st ed, 1st bk. Fine in VG + dj. *Warren.* $95/£59

GASS, WILLIAM H. Omensetter's Luck. NY: NAL, 1966. 1st ed, 1st bk. (Prelims lt creased), o/w Fine in dj (lt used). *Beasley.* $150/£94

GASS, WILLIAM H. Omensetter's Luck. NY: NAL, 1966. Rev copy, 1st bk. Fine in VG + dj (spine head chipped, 1-inch tear). *Lame Duck.* $250/£156

GASS, WILLIAM H. Omensetter's Luck. London: Collins, 1967. 1st ed, 1st bk. NF in dj (spine head bumped, rear panel lt soiled). *Smith.* $200/£125

GASS, WILLIAM H. On Being Blue. David R. Godine, (1977). One of 225 numbered, signed. Blue cl. Fine in dj, pub's slipcase. *Dermont.* $125/£78

GASS, WILLIAM H. The Tunnel. NY, 1995. 1st ed. Advance rev copy w/slip laid in. Fine in Fine dj. *Warren.* $30/£19

GASS, WILLIAM H. Willie Masters' Lonesome Wife. NY: Knopf, 1971. 1st trade ed. Fine in Fine dj. *Beasley.* $40/£25

GASS, WILLIAM H. The World Within the Word. NY: Knopf, 1978. 1st ed. Fine in Fine dj. *Pettler.* $40/£25

GASS, WILLIAM H. (ed). A Temple of Texts: Fifty Literary Pillars. St. Louis: Olin Library, 1991. 1st ed. Fine. *Beasley.* $35/£22

GASTON, EDWIN W. The Early Novel of the Southwest. (Albuquerque): Univ of NM, (1961). 1st ed. Blue cl. Fine in NF dj (sl worn; spine, edges dknd). *Harrington.* $40/£25

GATES, BARRINGTON. Poems. Hogarth, 1925. 1st ed. Marbled paper bds. Good (spotted; sl mkd, top edge dusty, spine ends chipped, sl rubbed, foot sl split, corners sl bumped). *Ulysses.* $120/£75

GATES, DORIS. Sensible Kate. Viking, 1949. 4th ed. Marjorie Torrey (illus). 189pp. NF in Good+ dj (corner, edges bumped, chipped; spine faded, chipped). *Price.* $22/£14

GATES, ELEANOR. Good-Night (Buenas Noches). NY: Y. Crowell, 1907. 1st ed in bk form. 8vo. 5 color plts by Arthur Rackham. (Lt staining). Pict cl. *Christie's*.* $552/£345

GATES, JOSEPHINE S. More About Live Dolls. Ohio: Franklin Ptg Co, (1903). 1st ed. V. Keep (illus). Red cl, black spine, pict Christmas label. VG (lt soil). *Davidson.* $100/£63

GATHORNE-HARDY, ROBERT. The Native Garden. Thomas Nelson, 1961. 1st Eng ed. 6 color plts. VG (edges, eps sl spotted; spine ends, 2 corners sl bumped; bottom edge fr cvr sl dented) in dj (sl creased, rubbed). *Ulysses.* $56/£35

GATHORNE-HARDY, ROBERT. Traveller's Trio. London: Thos. Nelson, 1963. 1st ed. Fine in VG- dj. *Archer.* $25/£16

GATSCHET, A. S. The Klamath Indians of S. W. Oregon. Washington, 1890. 1st ed. Map, 711pp. (Ex-lib; lt shaken), else VG. *Mikesh.* $75/£47

GATTI, A. Tom-Toms in the Night. London, 1932. 3rd imp. Fine. *Grayling.* $48/£30

GATTY, HORATIA. Juliana Horatia Ewing and Her Books.... SPCK, 1885. 1st ed. 88pp; port. Orig bds (lt soiled, worn). *Cox.* $24/£15

GATTY, MRS. ALFRED. The Fairy Godmothers and Other Tales. George Bell, 1851. 1st bk. Frontis. Good (spine bumped, chipped). *Tiger.* $80/£50

GAUBA, K. L. Uncle Sham: The Strange Tale of a Civilization Run Amok. C. Kendall, 1929. 1st Amer ed. Fine in NF dj (spine sl rubbed). *Fine Books.* $85/£53

GAUGUIN, PAUL. The Intimate Journals of Paul Gauguin. Van Wyck Brooks (trans). London: Heinemann, 1922. One of 530. 24 tissue-guarded b/w plts. Teg. Buckram (sl dusty, spine tail sl bumped). VG. *Ulysses.* $152/£95

GAUGUIN, PAUL. Noa Noa: Voyage to Tahiti. Jonathan Griffin (trans). NY: Reynal, (c.1954). Dec cl. NF. *Pacific*.* $46/£29

GAUNT, MARY. Alone in West Africa. Scribner, (c. 1912). 1st ed. Blue pict emb cl, gilt. (Faint chalk [?] mk fr bd), o/w VG. *Sotheran.* $205/£128

GAUNT, WILLIAM. The Great Century of British Painting: Hogarth to Turner. London: Phaidon, 1971. 1st ed. 180 plts (23 color). Dj. *Edwards.* $32/£20

GAUNT, WILLIAM. The Restless Century. Painting in Britain 1800-1900. London: Phaidon, 1972. 1st ed. Dj. *Edwards.* $40/£25

GAUTIER, THEOPHILE. Constantinople of Today. David Bogue, 1854. 1st Eng ed. Wood-engr frontis, (i),368pp; 6 sepia tinted wood-engr plts. Aeg. Full contemp calf (neatly rebacked), gilt, raised bands, dec tooled borders. (Corners sl rubbed), o/w VG. *Sotheran.* $205/£128

GAUTIER, THEOPHILE. Mademoiselle de Maupin. LEC, 1943. One of 1100 signed by Andre Dugo (illus). Fine in slipcase. *Swann*.* $34/£21

GAVIN, D. ANTONIO. A Master-Key to Popery. Hagerstown, MD: Published for Subscribers, 1822. 1st MD ed. 297pp. Orig full sheep. (Lt foxed, fr hinge tender, rubbed), o/w VG. *Chapel Hill.* $200/£125

GAWSWORTH, JOHN. Apes, Japes and Hitlerism. Unicorn, 1932. 1st Eng ed. Good (foxed; sl spotted) in dj. *Clearwater.* $152/£95

GAWSWORTH, JOHN. Epithalamium for He Bates.... Blue Moon/Friern Barnet, 1931. One of 40 signed. NF in wraps. *Any Amount.* $72/£45

Gay Dog. The Story of a Foolish Year. London: Heinemann, 1905. 1st ed. 4to. (52)pp; 24 full-pg pastel plts by Cecil Aldin. Beige pict bds. (Tp, last 2 leaves browned; sm spine snag, edges sl rubbed), o/w Internally Fine. *Sotheran.* $360/£225

GAY, FRANK B. Descendants of John Drake of Windsor, Connecticut. Tuttle, 1933. Good. *Rybski.* $65/£41

GAY, JOHN. The Beggar's Opera. Paris: LEC, 1937. One of 1500. Signed by Mariette Lydis (lithos). Teg, uncut. Dec cvrs, gilt. Fine (spine sl sunned). *Polyanthos.* $45/£28

GAY, JOHN. The Beggar's Opera. LEC, 1937. Ltd to 1500 numbered, signed by Mariette Lydis (illus). Fine in slipcase. *Swann*.* $115/£72

GAY, JOHN. Fables by the Late Mr. Gay. London: J.F. & C. Rivington et al, 1792. 1st Bewick ed. Wood-engr frontis, vii,232pp (sm piece torn from margin of C2, not affecting text); 66 wood engr vignettes by John Bewick. Old calf (rebacked). *Young.* $240/£150

GAY, JOHN. Fables. London, 1703. 2 vols. 9.5x5.5. 225; 176pp; 10 copper-engr plts. Period mottled calf, gilt spines, morocco labels. (Bkpls, ink inscrips, hinges cracked, vol 1 cvrs detached, sl foxed, offsetting from plts, tps sl shaved affecting dates), else Nice set. *King.* $300/£188

GAY, JOHN. Fables. Alnwick: W. Davison, 1842. Frontis, xii,216pp. (Mod rebacking.) *Marlborough.* $72/£45

GAY, JOHN. Poems on Several Occasions. London: H. Lintot/J.&R. Tonson, 1737. 2 vols. Engr frontis, (vi),260; 260pp; 2 engr plts. Old calf (rebacked), raised bands, gilt. (Bkpl, sigs.) *Young.* $176/£110

GAY, JOHN. The Poetical Works of John Gay. G. C. Faber (ed). Humphrey Milford/OUP, 1926. VG (spine ends sl bumped) in dj (nicked, chipped, rubbed, dusty, sl mkd, internally repaired, browned, 1-inch snag spine). *Ulysses.* $64/£40

GAY, JOHN. Polly. London: Heinemann, (1923). 1st ed. Ltd to 380 numbered, signed by William Nicholson (illus). 4to. (xvi),106pp; 9 mtd color plts, guards. Teg, rest uncut. Blue cl. (Spine cl discolored), o/w Nice. *Sotheran.* $301/£188

GAY, JOHN. Polly. London: The Author, 1729. 1st ed, 1st issue. (Closely trimmed, affecting 1 leaf of music.) Mod wraps, in cl case. *Kane*.* $170/£106

GAY, JOHN. Rural Sports, Together with The Birth of the Squire and the Hound and the Huntsman. NY: William Edwin Rudge, 1930. One of 225. Signed. Teg. Blind-ruled calf, gilt. (Spine, extrems sunned), else NF. *Pacific*.* $98/£61

GAY, ROMNEY. Tommy Grows Wise. NY: G&D, 1939. 7.25 sq. VG. *American Booksellers.* $25/£16

GAY, ZHENYA. Town Cats. Text by Jan Gay. NY: Knopf, 1932. 1st ed. Nice in dj. *Turtle Island.* $35/£22

GAYLE, NEWTON. Death in the Glass. NY, 1937. 1st ed. VG in dj (frayed). *King.* $25/£16

GAZE, HAROLD. The Merry Piper or the Magical Trip of the Sugar Bowl Ship. London: Longmans, Green, 1925. 1st ed. 4to. 8 full-pg color plts. Gray cl. Good in pict dj w/color paste label. *Reisler.* $285/£178

GAZELEY, W. J. Clock and Watch Escapements. London, 1956. 1st ed. Dj (lt soiled, sl chipped). *Edwards.* $32/£20

GEDDES, NORMAN BEL. Horizons. Boston: Little, Brown, 1932. 1st ed. Fine in dj, glassine. *Pacific**. $207/£129

GEDDES, R. STANLEY. Burlington Blue-Grey, a History of the Slate Quarries.... Kirkby-in-Furness: Privately pub, 1975. 1st ltd ed. 2 maps, 4 fldg sections, 19 diags. VG in dj. *Hollett*. $64/£40

GEDDIE, JOHN. The Lake Regions of Central Africa. London: T. Nelson, 1883. 2nd ed. Engr frontis, vi,(i)list,(i)blank,(9)-275pp; 31 engr plts, dbl-pg map. Edges gilt. Contemp blue prize calf (fr cvr sl rubbed), gilt, red labels. VG. *Morrell*. $56/£35

GEDDINGS, E. (ed). North American Archives of Medical and Surgical Science. Balt, 1835. 1st ed. 2 vols in 1. 900pp. Orig marble-cvrd bds w/leather spine,tips. (Foxed; worn, hinges cracked), o/w Good. *Doctor's Library*. $250/£156

GEE, ERNEST R. Early American Sporting Books. NY: Derrydale, 1928. One of 400. Beige cl backed over mottled paper-cvrd bds. Fine. *Biscotti*. $225/£141

GEE, ERNEST R. The Sportsman's Library. NY: R.R. Bowker, 1940. 1st ed. Ltd to 600. Grn buckram (spine sl dknd). NF. *Biscotti*. $150/£94

GEE, JOHN. Bunnie Bear. Minneapolis: Gordon Volland, (1928). 1st ptg. 12mo. Full color pict bds (corners lt worn). Clean in color pict box (edgeworn). *Reisler*. $250/£156

GEERLINGS, GERALD. Wrought Iron in Architecture. NY, 1929. (Lt worn.) *Oinonen**. $70/£44

GEIGER, HERMANN. Alpine Pilot. Alan Tuppen (trans). Cassell, 1956. 1st ed. Color frontis. VG in dj. *Hollett*. $32/£20

GEIGER, MAYNARD J. The Life and Times of Fray Junipero Serra, O.F.M., or the Man Who Never Turned Back (1713-1784). Washington: Academy of American Franciscan Hist, 1959. 1st ed. 2 vols. Frontisport each vol, 11 plts, 6 maps. Blue cl, gilt. VF set. *Argonaut*. $200/£125

GEIGER, MAYNARD J. The Serra Trail in Picture and Story. Santa Barbara: Franciscan Fathers of CA, (1960). 1st ed. Ltd to 500. Signed. Blue cl, gilt. (Spine sl faded) else Fine. *Argonaut*. $125/£78

GEIGER, VINCENT and WAKEMAN BRYARLY. Trail to California. David M. Potter (ed). New Haven: Yale Univ, 1945. 1st ed. Frontis, fldg map. Fine in Good dj (chipped, sl losses spine ends). *Harrington*. $40/£25

GEIKIE, ARCHIBALD. The Scenery of Scotland. Macmillan, 1901. 3rd ed. 4 color fldg maps. VG. *Hollett*. $72/£45

GEIKIE, ARCHIBALD. The Story of a Boulder. Edinburgh: Thomas Constable, 1858. 1st ed. xvi,263pp. Blind-stamped grn cl, gilt. (Spine faded.) *Hollett*. $192/£120

GEIKIE, JAMES. Prehistoric Europe. Edward Stanford, 1881. (1st ed.) xviii,592,(vi)pp; 5 colored plts, maps. Gilt (extrems rubbed; marginal, textual underlining), o/w VG. *Hollett*. $96/£60

GEIRINGER, KARL. Musical Instruments. Bernard Miall (trans). Allen & Unwin, 1943. 1st ed. 66 plts (2 color). VG in dj (worn, chipped). *Hollett*. $96/£60

GELERT. (Pseud of Greville.) A Guide to the Foxhounds and Staghounds of England; to Which Are Added, the Otterhounds and Harriers of Several Counties. London: Whittaker, 1849. 1st ed. Top edges uncut. Orig scarlet cl (spine ends sl worn, corners bumped), gilt. *Maggs*. $320/£200

GELL, E. M. John Franklin's Bride. London: John Murray, 1930. VG. *Explorer*. $58/£36

GELLHORN, MARTHA. The Wine of Astonishment. NY, 1948. 1st ed. VG in VG dj. *Warren*. $35/£22

Gems from Mother Goose: Little Jack Horner. NY: McLoughlin Bros, 1899. Toybook. 4to. 14pp incl cvrs. Good in color pict paper wrappers (lt mkd, spine chipped). *Reisler*. $90/£56

GENAUER, EMILY. Chagall at the 'Met.' NY: Metropolitan Opera, (1971). 1st Amer ed. NF in dj (spine ends, corners sl rubbed), slipcase. *Pacific**. $52/£33

GENAUR, EMILY. Chagall at the 'Met.' NY, (1971). Folio. (Lt worn.) Dj. *Oinonen**. $60/£38

GENDERS, ROY. The Cottage Garden: and the Old Fashioned Flowers. London: Pelham Bks, 1983. New ed. 16 color, 58 b/w plts. VG in dj. *Fair Meadow*. $30/£19

Geneologies of Pennsylvania Families. Balt: Geneological Pub, 1982-83. 4 vols. VG set. *Brown*. $125/£78

General History of the Turks, Moguls, and Tatars, Vulgarly Called Tartars, Together, with a Description of the Countries They Inhabit. London: J. & K. Knapton et al, 1739-30. 1st ed in English. 2 vols. 2 maps. Period paneled calf, gilt, morocco spine labels. (Vol 1 map w/sm edge tear; pp, cvrs sl stained), else VG. *Pacific**. $230/£144

General Laws Passed by the Legislature of Wisconsin in the Year Eighteen Hundred and Fifty-Eight. Together with Joint Resolutions and Memorials. Madison: Calkins & Webb, 1858. (1st, last ll foxed.) Later simulated leather-backed marbled bds. *Sadlon*. $15/£9

Genesis. LEC, 1989. One of 400 signed by Jacob Lawrence (illus). Fine in slipcase. *Swann**. $1,495/£934

GENET, JEAN. Funeral Rites. NY: Grove, (1969). 1st Amer ed. VF in VF dj. *Between The Covers*. $100/£63

GENET, JEAN. May Day Speech. SF: City Lights, 1970. 1st ed. Fine in wraps. *Beasley*. $30/£19

GENET, JEAN. Miracle of the Rose. NY, (1966). 1st Amer ed. VG in dj. *King*. $25/£16

GENET, JEAN. Poems. Onan City, n.d. Pirate ed by Lola Pozo, distributed by City Lights. Fine in wraps. *Beasley*. $25/£16

GENET, JEAN. The Thief's Journal. NY: Grove, (1964). 1st Amer ed. VF in VF dj. *Between The Covers*. $100/£63

GENINI, R. and R. HITCHMAN. Romualdo Pacheco. Pat Reagh, 1985. One of 500. *Dawson*. $45/£28

GENTHE, ARNOLD. As I Remember. NY, (1936). 112 repros. (Eps age-dknd, pencil notes, ink inscrip; sl worn, corners bumped, rear hinge cracked.) *Swann**. $80/£50

GENTHE, ARNOLD. Highlights and Shadows. NY: Greenberg, (1937). 1st ed. Opaque plastic fr cvr (lt rubbed, worn), black plastic spiral spine. Internally VG (sl worn). *Baltimore**. $60/£38

GENTHE, ARNOLD. Impressions of Old New Orleans. NY, (1926). 1st ed. 101 repros. (Bkpl, eps age-dknd, tp sl soiled; worn.) *Swann**. $103/£64

GENTHE, ARNOLD. Impressions of Old New Orleans. NY: Doran, (1926). 1st ed. 101 full-pg repros. Dk grn cl, lt grn bds, gilt. VG (bkpl mostly removed fep; sl worn, rubbed) in dj (worn, chipped). *Baltimore**. $110/£69

GENTHE, ARNOLD. Isadora Duncan. NY, 1929. 1st ed. Teg. (Loose in binding; thumb mks.) *King*. $100/£63

GENTHE, ARNOLD. Old Chinatown. NY, 1913. (Prelims foxed; rubbed.) *Swann**. $149/£93

Gentleman Angler: Containing Short, Plain, and Easy Instructions...Angling for Salmon, Salmon-Peal, Trout.... London: A. Buttersworth, 1726. 1st ed. (12),184,(8)pp. 19th-cent calf. (Lacks feps, internal stains), else VG. *Pacific**. $374/£234

Gentleman's Recreation: In Four Parts, Viz. Hunting, Hawking, Fowling, Fishing.... (By Nicholas Cox.) London: Collins for Cox, 1686. 3rd ed. Frontis, 4 fldg plts (sl soiled, stained, strengthened on versos, few tears repaired, sl loss, most of pg91/92 from the final section torn away, paper flaws). Old calf (rebacked, worn, soiled). *Oinonen**. $225/£141

GENTRY, CURT. The Killer Mountains. (NY, 1968.) NF in NF dj. *Sagebrush*. $30/£19

GENTRY, CURT. The Madams of San Francisco. GC, 1964. 1st ed. VG in VG dj. *Woolson*. $15/£9

GENTRY, HOWARD S. Rio Mayo Plants. A Study of Flora and Vegetation of the Valley of the Rio Mayo, Sonara. Washington, 1942. Fldg 2 color map. Gilt-emb cl. Fine. *Brooks.* $125/£78

GENTRY, THOMAS G. Nests and Eggs of Birds of the United States. Phila: J.A. Wagenseller, 1882. Frontisport, 54 full-pg chromolitho plts. Pub's cl (worn; 1st few ll detached). *Kane*.* $400/£250

Geographic Names of Antarctica. Washington: GPO, 1956. Gazetteer No.14, rev ed. VG in ptd wrapper. *High Latitude.* $30/£19

Geological Survey of Michigan. As follows: Vol I, NY, 1873; 3 color plts. Vol II, NY, 1873. Vol III, NY, 1876; 4 color plts, 55 plts of coral, fldg map. Vol IV, NY, 1881. Vol V, Lansing, 1895. Vol VI, Lansing, 1898. Vol VII, Lansing, 1900. Vol VIII. Vol IX, Lansing, 1903; color chart. (Lt foxed, stained, ink stamps; cvrs worn, inner hinges cracked, spines dull, ends frayed, corners bumped, vol IX cvrs water stained.) *King.* $495/£309

GEORGE, ELIOT. The Leather Boys. Washington: Guild, 1965. 1st ed. VF in Fine black dj (lt rubbed). *Between The Covers.* $75/£47

GEORGE, ERNEST. Etchings in Belgium. Seeley, Jackson & Halliday, 1883. 2nd ed. Sm folio. 30pp; 30 etched plts. Uncut. (Cl sl stained.) *Hollett.* $352/£220

GEORGE, ERNEST. Etchings of Old London. London: Fine Art Soc, 1884. Folio. vipp; 20 etchings w/letterpress. Pict cl (sl soiled). *Marlborough.* $320/£200

GEORGE, J. N. English Guns and Rifles. Harrisburg, 1947. Frontis, 24 plts. Fine in dj. *Hallam.* $72/£45

GEORGE, JEAN CRAIGHEAD. Julie of the Wolves. NY: Harper & Row, (1972). 1st ed. 8vo. John Schoenherr (illus). Color illus bds. Fine in color dj. *Reisler.* $125/£78

GEORGE, LLEWELLYN. A to Z Horoscope Maker and Delineator. Llewellyn, 1928. 1st ed. VG (rebound). *Middle Earth.* $75/£47

GEORGE, WILMA. Animals and Maps. Berkeley, 1969. VG in dj (sl worn). *Dumont.* $45/£28

Georgia and the General Government. Milledgeville: Ptd by Camak & Ragland, 1826. 79pp. (Browned), else Good. *Brown.* $75/£47

Georgia O'Keeffe, a Portrait by Alfred Stieglitz. NY, (1978). 1st ed. Folio. Slipcase (faded). *Swann*.* $201/£126

Georgia Scenes, Characters, Incidents, &c. in the First Half of the Republic. By a Native Georgian. (By Augustus Baldwin Longstreet.) NY: Harper, (1840). 2nd ed. 214,(2)pp; 12 plts. Orig cl. VG. *Petrilla.* $45/£28

GERARD, FRANCIS. Concrete Castle. London: Rich & Cowan, 1936. 1st ed. VG in dj (fr panel creased, corners, spine worn, torn). *Mordida.* $100/£63

GERARD, J. W. London and New York: Their Crime and Police. NY: William C. Bryant, 1853. 1st separate ed. 24pp. Orig ptd wraps. (Sm closed tear fore-edge fr wrap, spine sl worn, wraps soiled), o/w VG. *Chapel Hill.* $150/£94

GERARD, L. A Son of the Sahara. Macaulay, 1922. 1st ed. VG + in dj. *Fine Books.* $45/£28

GERARD, MAX (ed). Dali. NY, (1968). Pict cl. Good in dj (used). *King.* $95/£59

GERARD, MONTAGU GILBERT. Leaves from the Diaries of a Soldier and Sportsman During Twenty Years' Service in India and Other Countries, 1865-1885. London, 1903. *Petersfield.* $115/£72

GERE, C. American and European Jewelry 1830-1914. NY: Crown, c1975. Fine in dj. *Blake.* $150/£94

GERHARD, PETER and HOWARD E. GULICK. Lower California Guidebook, a Descriptive Traveler's Guide. Glendale: A.H. Clark, 1962. 3rd ed. Frontis, fldg color map. Fine in dj. *Argonaut.* $40/£25

GERHARD, PETER. The North Frontier of New Spain. Princeton: Princeton Univ, (1982). Red cl. Dj. *Dawson.* $45/£28

GERHARD, PETER. Pirates on the West Coast of New Spain 1575-1742. Glendale: A.H. Clark, 1960. 1st ed. Fine. *Book Market.* $50/£31

GERHARDI, WILLIAM. Jazz and Jasper: The Story of Adams and Eva. London: Duckworth, 1928. 1st ed. Lower edges uncut. Magenta rough cl. (Spine faded), o/w Nice. *Temple.* $29/£18

GERHARDI, WILLIAM. Resurrection. London/Toronto/Melbourne/Sydney: Cassell, 1934. 1st ed. Dk grn fine diaper cl. (Sm restoration to cl at head of rear joint), o/w Fine. *Temple.* $26/£16

GERHARDI, WILLIAM. The Romanovs. London: Rich & Cowan, 1940. 1st ed. 10 plts. Uncut. Orig buckram, gilt. (Few marginal blind stamps, stamp verso tp; sm lib #s at spine foot.) *Hollett.* $48/£30

GERMAN-REED, T. Bibliographical Notes on T. E. Lawrence's Seven Pillars of Wisdom and Revolt in the Desert. London: W. & G. Foyle Ltd, 1928. 1st ed. One of 350 numbered (of 375). Brn cl, gilt. Fine in dj. *Maggs.* $136/£85

GERNSBACK, HUGO. Ralph 124C 41 + : A Romance of the Year 2660. Boston, 1925. 1st ed. Gilt-stamped blue cl. *Swann*.* $345/£216

GERNSHEIM, HELMUT and ALISON. The History of Photography from the Camera Obscura to the Beginning of the Modern Era. NY/St. Louis/SF, (1969). (Extrems worn.) Dj (worn, torn). *Swann*.* $172/£108

GERNSHEIM, HELMUT and ALISON. L. J. M. Daguerre. The History of the Diorama and the Daguerrotype. London: Secker & Warburg, 1956. 1st ed. Frontis port. VG in dj (sl worn). *Hollett.* $136/£85

GERNSHEIM, HELMUT. The History of Photography. London, 1969. Rev, enlgd ed. Dj (sm cut). *Edwards.* $240/£150

GERNSHEIM, HELMUT. Julia Margaret Cameron, Her Life and Photographic Work. London/NY, 1948. 1st ed. 54 plts. Associated material loosely inserted. Dj (lt soiled, ragged). *Edwards.* $96/£60

GERNSHEIM, HELMUT. Julia Margaret Cameron. London: Fountain, 1948. 1st ed. VG in VG dj (few chips). *Smith.* $125/£78

GERNSHEIM, HELMUT. Lewis Carroll, Photographer. NY, 1949. 1st ed. 64 photgravures. (Glue remains fr pastedown; extrems lt worn.) Dj (worn, price-clipped). *Swann*.* $138/£86

GERNSHEIM, HELMUT. Lewis Carroll, Photographer. NY: Chanticleer, 1950. 2nd ed. 64 photogravure plts. (Bds lt damp-spotted.) Dj (lt soiled, chipped, sl loss to corners, spine head). *Edwards.* $144/£90

GERRARD, ROY. Sir Cedric. FSG, 1984. 1st Amer ed. 9.3x10.3. Unpaginated. NF in VG + dj (upper spine sl bumped). *Price.* $22/£14

GERRARE, WIRT. (Pseud of William Oliver Greener.) A Bibliography of Guns and Shooting. Westminster: Roxburghe, n.d. (1894). 1st ed. vii,216pp, ads. Dec blue buckram, gilt. VG. *Biscotti.* $195/£122

GERRING, CHARLES. Notes on Printers and Booksellers with a Chapter on Chap Books. Nottingham: Frank Murray, 1900. 1st ed. Frontis, subs list, 54 plts. Uncut. Mod cl, ptd paper spine/cvr label. *Forest.* $72/£45

GERRING, CHARLES. Notes on Printers and Booksellers with a Chapter on Chap Books. Simpkin Marshall, 1900. 43 plts. Uncut. Paper-cvrd bds. Good. *Moss.* $112/£70

GERRITSZ, HESSELL. The Arctic North-East and West Passage. Amsterdam: Frederick Muller, 1878. (4)xxvii(84)47pp. 4 maps (2 fldg). VG (sl soiled, spine repaired). *High Latitude.* $135/£84

GERSHWIN, GEORGE. George Gershwin's Song Book. NY: Harms, (1932). 1st trade ed. Frontisport, 18 full/dbl-pg color illus. Red-brn suede cl, lt brn buckram stamped in dk blue. (Binding adhesive stains at joints and pastedown edges; spine ends sl frayed, cvrs sl worn, dusty, few corners lt bumped.) Color pict dj (heavily chipped, several long tears, later ink note on fr flap margin). *Baltimore**. $100/£63

GERSTACKER, FREDERICK. Western Lands and Western Waters. London, 1864. 1st ed in English. 12,388pp. (Rebound.) *Heinoldt*. $45/£28

GERSTELL, RICHARD. The Steel Trap in North America.... (Harrisburg, PA): Stackpole Books, (1985). 1st ed. Frontis. Tan cl. VF in dj. *Argonaut*. $125/£78

GERSTLEY, JAMES M. Borax Years, 1933-1961. L.A.: U.S. Borax Co, 1979. 1st ed. Fine in Fine dj. *Book Market*. $22/£14

GERTLER, MARK. Selected Letters. Noel Carrington (ed). London: Rupert Hart-Davis, 1965. 1st ed. VG in dj. *Turtle Island*. $45/£28

GERTSCH, W. J. American Spiders. NY: Van Nostrand, 1949. 1st ed. 32 color plts. VG + (ex-lib) in NF dj. *Mikesh*. $37/£23

GESCHICKTER, CHARLES F. and MURRAY MARCUS COPELAND. Tumors of Bone. NY, 1931. 1st ed. Inscribed by Dean Lewis. NF (ex-lib, stamps, bkpl removed). *Weber*. $300/£188

GESSI PASHA, ROMOLO. Seven Years in the Soudan. London, 1892. 1st ed. Frontisport, xxiv,467pp; 22 plts (2 dbl-pg). Gilt-ruled leather-backed cl, raised bands. (Ink stamp; rebound.) *Edwards*. $360/£225

GETLEIN, FRANK and DOROTHY. The Bite of the Print. London, 1964. (Margins sl browned, bkpl.) Dj (sl chipped, spine faded). *Edwards*. $40/£25

GETTINGS, FRED. Ghosts in Photographs. NY: Harmony Bks, 1978. 1st ed. (Bkpl), else NF in illus dj. *Cahan*. $60/£38

GHENT, W. J. The Early Far West. NY: Tudor Pub, 1936. (Bkpl; spine faded), else VG. *Dumont*. $30/£19

GHENT, W. J. The Road to Oregon. London/NY/Toronto: Longmans, Green, 1929. 1st ed. Map. Dk grn cl, gilt. VF in pict dj (spine sunned). *Argonaut*. $150/£94

GHOSE, SUDHIN. (ed). Folk Tales and Fairy Stories from India. Golden Cockerel, 1961. One of 400 (of 500). Sm folio. 6 plts. Untrimmed. Mid brn cl, gilt. Good (sm area of damp-spotting on fr cvr). *Blackwell's*. $80/£50

GHOSE, ZULFIKAR. The Contradictions. London/Melbourne/Toronto: Macmillan, 1966. 1st ed. Fine in dj (spine faded). *Temple*. $19/£12

Ghost Corps Thru Hell and High Water. N.p., 1945. Fldg color map. VG in pict wraps. *Clark*. $65/£41

GIARDINE, CESARE. Varennes. Una, Lady Troubridge (trans). London: Butterworth, 1937. Frontis; 16 plts. Good. *Stewart*. $32/£20

GIBB, GEORGE SWEET. The Whitesmiths of Tauton. Cambridge, MA, 1946. 2nd ptg. W/orig Reed & Barton trade card, ca 1876. 419pp. (Bkpl, ink name; cvrs worn.) *King*. $35/£22

GIBBES, JAMES G. Who Burnt Columbia? Newberry, SC: Aull, 1902. 1st ed. Maroon cl. (Fr inner hinge cracked; spotted, extrems rubbed), else Good. *Chapel Hill*. $200/£125

GIBBES, R. W. Cuba for Invalids. NY: W.A. Townsend, 1860. 1st ed. xii,214pp. (Sl shelfworn, spine ends worn), o/w VG. *Brown*. $100/£63

GIBBINGS, ROBERT. Iorana! A Tahitian Journal. Boston, 1932. 1st Amer ed, 1st bk. NF. *Polyanthos*. $95/£59

GIBBINGS, ROBERT. Till I End My Song. Dent, 1957. 1st ed. Watercolor frontis. VG in dj (torn). *Whittle*. $19/£12

GIBBINGS, ROBERT. A True Tale of Love in Tonga. London, 1936. 1st ed. 23 engrs. (Eps soiled by dj.) Dj (sl torn). *Petersfield*. $67/£42

GIBBINGS, ROBERT. The Wood Engravings of Robert Gibbings. Patience Empson (ed). J.M. Dent, 1959. 1st ed. Color frontis. Buckram, gilt. VG in plastic wrapper. *Hollett*. $192/£120

GIBBON, EDWARD. The Decline and Fall of the Roman Empire. J. B. Bury (ed). London: Methuen, 1900. 7 vols. Red cl, gilt spines. (Foxed), else VG. *Pacific**. $115/£72

GIBBON, EDWARD. The History of the Decline and Fall of the Roman Empire. London: A. Strahan & T. Cadell, 1777-88. New ed vols 1-3, 1st of the rest. 6 vols. 4to. Engr port vol 1, 3 fldg maps, 1/2 titles in vols 2-6. Contemp full calf (rebacked; spines, extrems worn; vol 1 fr joint started; bkpls). *Swann**. $747/£467

GIBBON, EDWARD. The History of the Decline and Fall of the Roman Empire. W. Strahan & T. Cadell, 1781-1788. 6 vols. 4to. Vol 1 new ed, 1782; vol 2-3 2nd ed, 1781; vols 4-6 1st ed, 1788. Frontisport, 2 fldg maps. (Sl spotted, vol 3 O2 sl torn.) Contemp calf, gilt (rubbed, chipped, fr cvr vol 1 detached, joints cracked), gilt. *Sotheby's**. $699/£437

GIBBON, EDWARD. The History of the Decline and Fall of the Roman Empire. Dublin: Luke White, 1789. 6 vols. Frontisport. Period mottled calf, morocco spine labels, gilt. (Stenciled names; joints sl weak), else VG. *Pacific**. $489/£306

GIBBON, EDWARD. The History of the Decline and Fall of the Roman Empire. London: T. Cadell & W. Davies et al, 1820. New ed. 12 vols. B/w frontis. Marbled edges. 3/4 brn leather, marbled bds, gilt. VG set (vol 1 spine head sl chipped). *Turtle Island*. $250/£156

GIBBON, EDWARD. The History of the Decline and Fall of the Roman Empire. Edinburgh: Thomas Nelson & Peter Brown, 1831. 12 vols. Engr frontis, 2 lg fldg maps. Orig buckram, paper labels. Very Nice set. *Young*. $216/£135

GIBBON, EDWARD. The History of the Decline and Fall of the Roman Empire. London: John Murray, 1838. Ed ptd in lg type. 13 vols. Tall 8vo. Teg. 3/4 maroon polished calf, gilt paneled spines, raised bands, black leather spine labels. Fine set. *Appelfeld*. $1,600/£1,000

GIBBON, EDWARD. The History of the Decline and Fall of the Roman Empire. London: John Murray, 1854. 8 vols. Teg. Period gilt-ruled tree calf, morocco spine labels. (Spines sl worn, top spine panel of vol 1 replaced w/later calf), else VG set. *Pacific**. $259/£162

GIBBON, EDWARD. The History of the Decline and Fall of the Roman Empire. J. B. Bury (ed). London: Methuen, 1896-1900. 1st ed. 7 vols. Red cl. VG (vol 1 spine faded; sl worn). *Agvent*. $250/£156

GIBBON, EDWARD. The History of the Decline and Fall of the Roman Empire. J. B. Bury (ed). (NY): LEC, 1946. One of 1500. 7 vols. 1/4 morocco, marbled bds. Fine in glassine, slipcase. *Pacific**. $230/£144

GIBBON, EDWARD. The Miscellaneous Works of Edward Gibbon, Esq., with Memoirs.... London: John Murray, 1814. 5 vols. 5 copper-engr plts vol 1, fldg table vol 3. Marbled eps; aeg. Later 3/4 calf, gilt, morocco labels. (Spine ends worn), else VG. *Pacific**. $138/£86

GIBBON, EDWARD. Miscellaneous Works with Memoirs of His Life and Writings, Composed by Himself: Illustrated from His Letters...by John Lord Sheffield. London: A. Strahan, 1796-1815. 1st ed. 3 vols. 4to. Frontisport, frontis silhouette, (xxvi),703pp; viii,726,(2)pp; x,691pp + (2)ads. Rebound in contemp-style 1/2 calf, raised bands, twin morocco labels, dates at each spine foot. VG set (lib stamps). *Young*. $480/£300

GIBBON, EDWARD. Miscellaneous Works...with Memoirs of His Life and Writings. John Sheffield (ed). London: A. Strahan/T. Cadell Jun/W. Davies, 1796. 1st ed. 2 vols. Frontisport vol 1. Contemp marbled calf (rubbed; joints sl flaked), raised bands, gilt, red/dk grn morocco spine labels (faded). Internally Fine (few ll sl foxed, spots, smudged; lg mod bkpls; 1830 inscrips, one partly scratched out; sig; tipped-in sheet vol 1). *Pirages*. $450/£281

GIBBON, EDWARD. Private Letters of Edward Gibbon 1753-1794. R. E. Prothero (ed). London, 1896. 1st ed. 2 vols. 400; 430pp. VG. *Gretton.* $48/£30

GIBBON, MONK. The Climate of Love. Gollancz, 1961. 1st ed. Inscribed presentation. VG (feps lt browned; edges spotted, spine ends, corner sl bumped) in dj (worn). *Ulysses.* $45/£28

GIBBONS, ALFRED. Exploration and Hunting in Central Africa. London, 1898. 8vo. Gilt-pict cl (inner joint cracked, edges rubbed). Generally Nice. *Oinonen*.* $650/£406

GIBBONS, JOHN. Is This America? NY: E.P. Dutton, 1935. Fine in dj (used). *Mott.* $20/£13

GIBBONS, STELLA. Ticky. London/NY/Toronto: Longmans, Green, 1943. 1st ed. Blue cl. Fine. *Temple.* $22/£14

GIBBONS, STELLA. Westwood; or, The Gentle Powers. London: Longmans, Green, 1946. 1st ed. Mottled lt violet cl, thin bds. (Top edges sl foxed, spine sl faded), o/w Fine in dj (spine faded). *Temple.* $26/£16

GIBBS, JAMES. Rules for Drawing the Several Parts of Architecture, in a More Exact and Easy Manner Than Has Been Heretofore Practised. London, 1732. 1st ed. Lg folio. (Lacks privilege leaf.) 64 engr plts. Calf. *Felcone.* $1,800/£1,125

GIBBS, MAY. The Complete Adventures of Snugglepot and Cuddlepie. Sydney: Angus & Robertson, 1949. Early ed. Royal 8vo. vi,218pp; 5 color plts. Mid-blue cl-backed buff pict bds. (Upper cvr sl rubbed), o/w VG. *Sotheran.* $157/£98

GIBBS, PHILIP. From Bapaume to Passchendale 1917. London, 1918. 1st Eng ed. VG (fore-edges sl foxed). *Clearwater.* $80/£50

GIBBS, W. M. Spices and How to Know Them. Buffalo: Matthews-Northrup, 1909. 1st ed. Fldg map. Grn cl. NF. *Archer.* $30/£19

GIBBS, WILLIAM. Decorative Alphabets for the Chisel, the Brush, the Pen, and the Needle with Cypers, Monograms, and Initial Letters. London: Houlston & Wright, n.d. (ca 1865). 47 color plts (few ll loose, sl frayed). Pub's cl (shelfworn, soiled). *Oinonen*.* $130/£81

GIBBS-SMITH, CHARLES H. The Fashionable Lady in the 19th Century. London: HMSO, 1969. 2nd imp. Protected orig bds (accession # spine; ex-lib, ink stamp fep). *Edwards.* $24/£15

Gibraltar and Its Sieges, with a Description of Its Natural Features. Thomas Nelson & Sons, 1882. Frontis, 158,(x) ads pp. Pict grn cl, gilt. Good (ink inscrip frontis verso; fr bd sl worn). *Sotheran.* $77/£48

GIBRAN, KAHLIL. Sand and Foam. London: Heinemann, 1927. 1st ed. Frontis, 6 plts. Top edge dk cerise. Cerise cl. Fine in dj (frayed, chipped). *Temple.* $26/£16

GIBSON, A. M. The Life and Death of Colonel Albert Jennings Fountain. Norman: Univ of OK, (1965). 1st ed. Fine in VG dj. *Perier.* $45/£28

GIBSON, ALEXANDER GEORGE. The Physician's Art. OUP, 1933. 1st ed. (Cl lt soiled.) *Edwards.* $32/£20

GIBSON, C. Shoot If You Must. NY: Dillon, 1950. One of 250 numbered. Inscribed. (Lt worn.) *Oinonen*.* $90/£56

GIBSON, CHARLES DANA. London as Seen by Charles Dana Gibson. Scribner, 1897. 1st ed. (Corners worn), else VG in pict bds, pub's orig box (worn). *Fine Books.* $175/£109

GIBSON, CHARLES DANA. Sketches in Egypt. NY: Doubleday & McClure, 1899. 1st ed. Dec cl. (Cvrs soiled), else VG. *Pacific*.* $63/£39

GIBSON, COLIN. Highland Deer Stalker. London: Seeley & Service, 1958. 1st ed. Dj (price-clipped, chipped, lt soiled). *Christie's*.* $136/£85

GIBSON, HORATIO GATES (ed). Memoir of David Jameson.... Washington: Washington Barracks, 1887. 178pp (not consecutive pagination). Orig wraps. (Edges chipped, sl stained), else Good. *Brown.* $150/£94

GIBSON, J. W. Recollections of a Pioneer. St. Joseph, MO: Nelson-Hanne Ptg, 1912. 1st ed. Red cl (edges worn, cvrs faded). VG. Howes G154. *Labordo.* $800/£500

GIBSON, JAMES R. Feeding the Russian Fur Trade. Madison: Univ of WI, 1969. 1st ed. 10 plts, 10 maps. Blue cl. Fine in pict dj. *Argonaut.* $50/£31

GIBSON, STRICKLAND. Some Oxford Libraries. Oxford: Humphrey Milford, 1914. 12 plts. Grn cl (spine faded; inscrip). *Maggs.* $29/£18

GIBSON, W. The Farrier's New Guide. Containing, First, The Anatomy of a Horse...Secondly, An Account of All the Diseases.... London: Osborn & Longman, 1731. 7th ed. 2 parts in 1 vol, w/separate titles and pagination. Fldg frontis, 6 engr plts. Old calf. (Broken; foxing, soiling.) *Oinonen*.* $110/£69

GIBSON, W. A New Treatise on the Diseases of Horses. London, 1754. 2nd ed. 2 vols. 32 engr plts. Contemp calf (rubbed; sl foxed, soiled). Sound. *Oinonen*.* $225/£141

GIBSON, W. B. The New Magician's Manual. Kemp, 1936. 1st ed. NF in VG dj (worn, torn, chipped). *Fine Books.* $150/£94

GIBSON, W. HAMILTON. Our Edible Toadstools and Mushrooms and How to Distinguish Them. Harper, 1895. 1st ed. 337pp; 30 color plts. Brn cl dec w/mushrooms, gilt. (Foxed; spine bottom weak), else Good. *Fair Meadow.* $75/£47

GIBSON, WALTER B. Popular Card Tricks. NY, n.d. (c. 1928). Pict stapled wraps. (Paper browned; spine failing, cvrs creased, edges chipped.) *King.* $25/£16

GIBSON, WALTER M. The Prison of Weltevreden; and a Glance at the East Indian Archipelago. NY: J.C. Riker, 1856. 1st ed. Frontis, xiv,496pp; 9 plts. Patterned brn cl (spine faded). *Karmiole.* $125/£78

GIBSON, WILFRID W. The Early Whistler. London: Ariel Poems, (1927). 1st Eng ed. Fine in pict card wrappers. *Clearwater.* $40/£25

GIBSON, WILFRID W. Friends. London: Elkin Mathews, 1916. 1st ed. Ptd buff wrappers. (Overlap edges lt used), else NF. *Reese.* $45/£28

GIBSON, WILFRID W. Whin. London: Macmillan, 1918. 1st ed. Gilt dk blue cl. (Backstrip rubbed), else Good. *Reese.* $15/£9

GIBSON, WILLIAM C. (ed). British Contributions to Medical Science. London: Wellcome Inst, 1971. 1st ed. Fine in dj. *Glaser.* $45/£28

GIBSON, WILLIAM. Burning Chrome. NY: Arbor House, (1986). 1st ed. Signed. Fine in dj. *Levin.* $75/£47

GIBSON, WILLIAM. The Seesaw Log. NY: Knopf, 1959. 1st ed. VF in VF black dj. *Between The Covers.* $125/£78

GIBSON, WILLIAM. Virtual Light. NY, 1993. Ltd to 150 signed. Fine in NF slipcase. *Warren.* $125/£78

GIBSON-HILL, C. A. British Sea Birds. London: Witherby, 1947. 1st ed. Teg. 1/2 leather, pict cl, gilt. VG + . *Mikesh.* $35/£22

GIDE, ANDRE. If It Die.... NY, (1935). One of 1600 numbered. (Spine ends sl discolored), else Good in dj (defective). *King.* $25/£16

GIDION-WELCKER, CAROLA. Contemporary Sculpture. NY, 1960. 3rd imp. (Lib ink stamp fep.) Dj (sl rubbed). *Edwards.* $40/£25

GIFFEN, GEORGE. With Bat and Ball. Ward Lock, 1898. xv,240pp; 80 ports (some sl dusty, edges chipped). Pict stiff wrappers (sl rubbed, creased). *Hollett.* $104/£65

GIFFEN, GUY J. California Expedition. Oakland: Biobooks, (1951). 1st CA ed. Ltd to 650. Fine. *Book Market.* $45/£28

GIFFORD, EDWARD S., JR. The Evil Eye. Studies in the Folklore of Vision. NY: Macmillan, 1958. 1st ed. Fine in Fine dj. *Beasley.* $50/£31

Gift: A Christmas, New Year, and Birthday Present. Phila: Carey & Hart, 1845 (1844). 1st ed, 1st issue, w/date on spine and on extra engr tp. Contains 1st ptg of 'The Purloined Letter' by Edgar Allan Poe. 7 (of 8) b/w steel-engr plts. Aeg. Orig dk grn morocco, gilt. Text Good (sl foxed, few sigs lt sprung, sm chunk missing from bottom of fep, plts heavily foxed; edges, joints scuffed, cvrs sl worn, spine top sl chipped). BAL 16143. *Baltimore**. $400/£250

GILBERT, G. K. et al. Department of the Interior, United States Geological Survey.... Washington: GPO, 1907. 1st ed. 55 plts, 2 fldg maps. Gray ptd wrappers. (Spine sl chipped, frayed), o/w VG. *Pacific**. $58/£36

GILBERT, G. K. et al. The San Francisco Earthquake and Fire of April 18, 1906. US Geol Surv Bull, 1907. 55 photo plts, 2 fldg maps. Good+ in orig gray wraps in tan wraps (ex-lib). *Larry Price*. $49/£31

GILBERT, J. WARREN. The Blue and the Gray. N.p., (1922). 'People's pictorial ed.' Fldg color map. VG+ in pict wraps. *Pratt*. $30/£19

GILBERT, JOSEPH HENRY. Agricultural Investigations at Rothamsted, England, During a Period of Fifty Years. Washington: GPO, 1895. Frontis port, 316pp; 2 fldg tables (1 color). Orig 1/2 calf, gilt. Bkpl of Arthur Raistrick. (Eps browned at edges from turn-ins; rubbed, spine flaked.) *Hollett*. $120/£75

GILBERT, LIONEL. The Royal Botanic Gardens, Sydney...1816-1985. Melbourne: Oxford, 1986. 1st ed. Fine in dj. *Archer*. $30/£19

GILBERT, MICHAEL. Overdrive. Harper, 1967. 1st Amer ed. Fine in dj. *Murder*. $45/£28

GILBERT, PERRY W. (ed). Sharks and Survival. Boston, 1963. Gray-grn dec cl. VG. *Larry Price*. $35/£22

GILBERT, VIVIAN. The Romance of the Last Crusade. NY/London: Appleton, 1925. Frontis. (Tp foxed; sl rubbed), o/w VG. *Worldwide*. $16/£10

GILBERT, W. S. The Bab Ballads and Songs of a Savoyard. London: Macmillan, 1926. 350 illus. Full red polished calf, gilt paneled spine, raised bands, leather spine labels, inner gilt dentelles, edges gilt, by Riviere. Fine in linen slipcase. *Appelfeld*. $200/£125

GILBERT, W. S. Her Majesty's Ship 'Pinafore.' Boston: Alfred Mudge, 1878. (Text thumbed, soiled.) Pict wraps (browned, edges frayed, backstrip worn). *Dramatis*. $35/£22

GILBERT, W. S. Selected Bab Ballads. London, Christmas 1955. Ltd to 1500. Good (lt mkd). *Cox*. $32/£20

GILBERT, W. S. Songs of a Savoyard. Routledge, 1891. xi,142,(ii)pp (feps sl spotted). Pict cl (sl fingered), gilt. *Hollett*. $72/£45

GILBERT, W. S. The Story of the Mikado. Chiswick for Daniel O'Connor, 1921. 1st ed. 4to. 115pp; 6 color plts by Alice B. Woodward, guards. Dbl-spread pict eps in white/orange; orange pg edges. Illus bds. (Edges lt worn), else VG. *Bookmark*. $56/£35

GILBERT, WALTER E. Arctic Pilot. Kathleen Shackleton (as told to). London: T. Nelson, (1941, 2nd ptg). Map. VG in dj. *High Latitude*. $40/£25

GILBERT, WILLIAM. On the Magnet. NY: Basic Books, (1958). Facs rpt. Marbled bds, cl spine. Fine in pict slipcase. *Glaser*. $95/£59

GILBEY, WALTER and E. D. CUMING. George Morland. A&C Black, 1907. One of 250 signed. (Half-title sl spotted.) 50 color plts. Teg, untrimmed. Dec cream cl, gilt, beveled bds. *Hollett*. $440/£275

GILBEY, WALTER (comp). Animal Painters of England from the Year 1650. London, 1900. 2 vols. Teg, rest uncut. Gilt/black lion illus upper bds. (Upper hinge cracked vol 1, eps lt spotted; cl soiled, spines sl bumped.) *Edwards*. $216/£135

GILBEY, WALTER. George Morland. London: A&C Black, 1907. One of 250. 50 plts, guards. Teg. Pict cl, gilt. (Sl soiled, spine sl dknd), else VG. *Pacific**. $109/£68

GILBRETH, FRANK B. Motion Study; a Method for Increasing the Efficiency of the Workman. NY: D. Van Nostrand, 1911. 1st ed. Dk grn cl, gilt. VG (sm edge stains, outer corner showing). *Weber*. $250/£156

GILCHRIST, ALEXANDER. Life of William Blake.... London, 1880. 2nd ed. 2 vols. Mtd India paper frontispieces. Later 1/2 red morocco, gilt extra. (Vol 1 fr joint top started.) *Swann**. $345/£216

GILCHRIST, ELLEN. In the Land of Dreamy Dreams. Fayetteville: Univ of AR, 1981. 1st ed, cl-bound issue. Signed. VF in dj. *Reese*. $1,000/£625

GILCHRIST, H. H. Anne Gilchrist: Her Life and Writings. London: T. Fisher Unwin, 1887. 2nd ed. Frontis, xxi,(iii),368pp; 10 plts. Fair; internally Good. *Blue Mountain*. $35/£22

GILCHRIST, H. H. Anne Gilchrist: Her Life and Writings. T. Fisher Unwin, 1887. Dec cl. Good (sig, sl spotted; spine bumped, dull, fr hinge nicked, corners rubbed, fr cvr lacks sm piece). *Tiger*. $58/£36

GILCHRIST, JAMES. Anglican Church Plate. London, 1967. Good+ in dj. *Washton*. $40/£25

GILDER, RODMAN. The Battery. Boston, 1931. VG in dj (frayed). *Heinoldt*. $15/£9

GILES, F. KENWOOD. Hide and Seek in Fairyland. London: Raphael Tuck & Sons, (ca 1950). Sq 4to. 16pp. Cl-backed color pict bds (rebacked, worn). *Reisler*. $100/£63

GILES, G. M. A Handbook of the Gnats or Mosquitoes Giving the Anatomy and Life History of the Culicidae. London: Bale/Danielsson, 1900. Frontis, 7 plts. (Bkpl; sl worn), o/w VG. *Savona*. $45/£28

GILES, VAL C. Rags and Hope, the Memoirs of Val C. Giles.... Mary Lasswell (ed). NY, (1961). 1st ed. Fine in dj (sl worn). *Pratt*. $40/£25

GILETTE, WILLIAM. The Painful Predicament of Sherlock Holmes. Chicago: Ben Abramson, 1955. 1st ed, 1st ptg. Batik-cvrd bds, paper cvr label. VG. *Dramatis*. $40/£25

GILFILLAN, ARCHER. Sheep. Boston: Little, Brown, 1929. 1st ed. Inscribed, signed. VG+ in dj (worn, chipped). *Labordo*. $85/£53

GILFILLAN, ARCHER. A Shepherd's Holiday. Custer, SD: Chronicle Shop, 1936. 1st ed. Sm folio. Good in pict wrappers. *Lien*. $40/£25

Gilgamesh. LEC, 1974. One of 2000 signed by Irving Amen (illus). Fine in slipcase. *Swann**. $34/£21

GILL, EMLYN. Practical Dry-Fly Fishing. London: George Newnes, (1912). 1st British ed. Gilt-lettered grn cl. NF. *Pacific**. $63/£39

GILL, ERIC. Autobiography. London: Cape, 1940. 1st ed. Variant blue cl. (Eps offset), o/w VG in dj (soiled; spine chipped, browned). *Virgo*. $56/£35

GILL, ERIC. Clothes: An Essay upon the Nature and Significance of the Natural and Artificial Integuments Worn by Men and Women. London, 1931. One of 165 numbered. Signed. 10 wood-engr illus. 1/4 pigskin. *Swann**. $287/£179

GILL, ERIC. The Engravings of Eric Gill. Wellingborough: Christopher Skelton, 1983. One of 1350. Cream cl-backed, black cl bds, gilt. VG in black cl, grn paper slipcase. *Maggs*. $296/£185

GILL, ERIC. Last Essays. Cape, 1942. 2nd imp. Uncut. VG+ in plastic-cvrd dj. *Whittle*. $24/£15

GILL, ERIC. Last Essays. Cape, 1942. 1st UK ed. Fine in VG dj. *Williams*. $72/£45

GILL, ERIC. The Lord's Song, a Sermon. Golden Cockerel, 1934. 1st ed. One of 500. Full-pg wood engr. Untrimmed. White canvas, gilt. VG (bkpl). *Blackwell's*. $320/£200

GILL, ERIC. The Lord's Song, a Sermon. Golden Cockerel, 1934. One of 500 numbered. Narrow 8vo. Full-pg engr. Uncut, partly unopened. Cream buckram, gilt. Fine. *Sotheran*. $520/£325

GILL, ERIC. Trousers and the Most Precious Ornament. London: Faber, 1937. 1st ed. (Few pp sl foxed; cvrs sl soiled), o/w VG in wrappers. *Virgo*. $56/£35

GILL, ERIC. Work and Leisure. London: Faber & Faber, 1935. 1st ed. (Eps sl spotted), else VG. *Michael Taylor*. $19/£12

GILL, MRS. Six Months in Ascension. London: John Murray, 1878. 1st ed. 1/2-title, liv,(ii),285,(1)blank,24 pub's list; map. Brn dec cl. Sound (ink inscrip; sl stained, rubbed, spine foot crumpled, hinges cracked). *Morrell*. $112/£70

GILL, N. J. The Flyer's Guide: An Elementary Handbook for Aviators. NY: E.P. Dutton, (1917). 1st ed. Red cl, gilt. NF. *Pacific**. $52/£33

GILL, THEODORE. Notes on the Structure and Habits of the Wolffishes. Washington: GPO, 1911. Unopened. Fine in wraps (sl dknd). *Parmer*. $30/£19

GILL, THOMAS. The Technical Repository, Containing Practical Information.... London: T. Cadell, Strand, 1832. 432+pp; xiv plts. Good+ (ex-lib, in lib binding, worn). *Bookcell*. $27/£17

GILLAM, JOHN GRAHAM. Gallipoli Diary. London: George Allen & Unwin, (1918). 1st ed. Red cl stamped in black. (Lower edges sl spotted; sl foxed, ink name), else VG. *Reese*. $65/£41

GILLELAN, G. HOWARD. Complete Book of the Bow and Arrow. Harrisburg: Stackpole Books, 1971. 1st ed. VG+ (inscrip) in VG dj (scuffed, few sm edge tears). *Backman*. $22/£14

GILLER, J. U. Rhymes of Boyhood. Phila: Ptd by William Brown, 1836. iv,67pp (eps lt foxed). Orig patterned cl (neatly rebacked in matching cl). *Hollett*. $136/£85

GILLESPIE, W. M. A Treatise on Land-Surveying. NY: D. Appleton, 1869. 8th ed. vi,428pp. Good+ (water stains 1/2-inch on pg bottoms; rebacked). *Bookcell*. $30/£19

GILLETT, JAMES B. Six Years with the Texas Rangers 1875-1881. New Haven, 1925. 2nd ed. NF (label) in dj (chipped, soiled, back-stained, price-clipped). Howes G177. *Baade*. $65/£41

GILLHAM, CHARLES E. Sled Dog and Other Poems of the North. Huntington, WV: Standard, (1950). Fine. *Perier*. $25/£16

GILLIAM, HAROLD and PHILIP HYDE. Island in Time: The Point Reyes Peninsula. SF: Sierra Club, (1962). 32 plts, 2 maps. Grn cl, gilt. Fine in pict dj (spine chip). *Pacific**. $29/£18

GILLILAND, MAUDE T. Rincon. Brownsville: Privately pub, 1964. 1st ed. Signed. Fine (inscrip) in dj (sl worn). *Baade*. $100/£63

GILLIS, J. M. The U.S. Astronomical Expedition to the Southern Hemisphere, During the Years 1849-'50-'51-'52. Volumes I and II (of 4) only. Washington: A.O.P. Nicholson, 1855. 1st ed. xiii,(2),556; ix,(3),300pp; lg fldg panorama w/hand-tinting; 9 engr maps (4 fldg), 19 color lithos, 5 duotone lithos, 17 steel-engr plts. (Repairs to ep hinges, some offset from plts; sl cvr wear, esp extrems), else VG. *Pacific**. $288/£180

GILLMOR, FRANCES and LOUISA WADE WETHERILL. Traders to the Navajos. Boston/NY: Houghton Mifflin, 1934. 1st ed. 9 plts. Orange cl. (Spine sl dknd), else Fine. *Argonaut*. $75/£47

GILLMOR, FRANCES and LOUISA WADE WETHERILL. Traders to the Navajos. Boston, 1934. 1st ed. Clean in dj (chipped). *Dumont*. $85/£53

GILLMORE, PARKER. The Hunter's Arcadia. London, 1886. Pict gilt cl. (Lt rubbed, browned.) *Grayling*. $104/£65

GILLMORE, PARKER. Prairie and Forest. London: Chapman & Hall, 1874. 1st ed. Frontis, x,383pp; 12 plts. Black/gilt-stamped pict cl. *Mott*. $100/£63

GILLMORE, PARKER. Prairie and Forest. London, 1881. viii,396pp. Marbled eps; aeg. Full calf. (Bkpl; spine sl faded.) *Edwards*. $61/£38

GILLRAY, JAMES. Fashionable Contrasts. (London): Phaidon, (1966). 1st ed. Color frontis. Blue linen. Fine in dj. *Karmiole*. $75/£47

Gillyflower Garden Book. Thomas Nelson, n.d. ca 1918. Lg 8vo. 12 color plts by Anne Anderson. Oatmeal cl, pict onlay. VG (sl creased; lt dusty). *Bookmark*. $120/£75

GILMAN, CHARLOTTE PERKINS. The Crux. NY: Charlton, 1911. 1st ed. (Bottom of 1st 16pp waterstained), o/w Fine in ptd wraps. *Second Life*. $250/£156

GILMAN, CHARLOTTE PERKINS. The Home. NY: McClure, Phillips, 1903. 1st ed. VG (fr hinge tender, sl rubbed, faded). *Second Life*. $350/£219

GILMAN, CHARLOTTE PERKINS. The Living of.... NY: Appleton, 1935. 1st ed. Frontisport, 7 plts. Fine in dj (sl chipped). *Second Life*. $325/£203

GILMAN, CHARLOTTE PERKINS. Moving the Mountain. NY: Charlton, 1911. 1st ed. Fine in plain brn paper dj (worn). *Second Life*. $350/£219

GILMAN, D. The Life of James Dwight Dana. NY: Harper, c1899. xii,409pp. VG. *Blake*. $150/£94

GILMAN, J. J. (ed). The Art and Science of Growing Crystals. NY, 1963. Fine in dj. *Henly*. $45/£28

GILMOR, HARRY. Four Years in the Saddle. NY: Harper, 1866. 1st ed. Wood-engr frontis, (ix),291pp. Brick-red cl over beveled bds, gilt. (Shaken, sigs; pp loose; lacks feps, blanks; lt worn, spine ends frayed.) Howes G187. *Baltimore**. $45/£28

GILMOUR, DAVID. Paisley Weavers of Other Days. Edinburgh: David Douglas, 1898. 1st ed. Frontis, xviii,297,(ii)pp (lib label on ep). Ribbed cl (spine sl dull), gilt. *Hollett*. $56/£35

GILMOUR, JOHN and MAX WALTERS. Wild Flowers. Collins, 1954. 1st ed. VG in dj (extrems sl frayed, rear panel sl mkd). *Hollett*. $64/£40

GILMOUR, MARGARET. Ameliaranne at the Circus. Phila: David McKay, (1931). 1st ed. 8vo. Unpaginated. 30 full-pg color illus by S. B. Pearse. Illus eps. VG in dj (lt soiled). *Davidson*. $80/£50

GILMOUR, MARGARET. Ameliaranne Gives a Concert. London: George G. Harrap, (1944). 1st ed. 8vo. 32 full-pg color illus by Susan B. Pearse. Cl-backed color pict bds (sl shelfworn). VG full color pict dj. *Reisler*. $110/£69

GILMOUR, MARGARET. Trying Toby. George Harrap, 1925. 1st ed. 12mo. (61)pp; 30 color plts by Jack Orr. Paper-cvrd bds, pict onlay to fr bd. *Hollett*. $48/£30

GILPIN, LAURA. The Enduring Navaho. Austin: Univ of TX, 1968. 1st ed. Fine (inscrip) in illus dj. *Cahan*. $150/£94

GILPIN, LAURA. The Mesa Verde National Park: Reproductions from a Series of Photographs by Laura Gilpin. Colorado Springs: Gilpin Pub, 1927. 1st ed. NF+ (sl worn) in pict wrappers. *Pacific**. $316/£198

GILPIN, LAURA. The Pueblos: A Camera Chronicle. NY: Hastings House, 1941. 1st ed. Frontis. (Eps sl dknd; faded, spine sl soiled), else NF. *Cahan*. $150/£94

GILPIN, WILLIAM. Remarks on Forest Scenery. R. Blamire, 1791. 1st ed. 2 vols. (4),viii,328,iv,7; (2),308,iv,xxpp; dbl-pg map, 31 etchings, tinted aquatints. Uncut. Contemp 1/2 crimson roan, marbled sides, morocco labels. Good set (strip torn from tp tail margin vol 1; sl rubbed, worn, backstrip tails chipped). *Cox*. $176/£110

GILPIN, WILLIAM. Remarks on Forest Scenery. London: Blamire, 1794. 2nd ed. 3 bks in 2 vols. Half-titles; 17 aquatint plts vol I; 14 aquatint plts vol 2; dbl-pg map. Uniform diced russia, tp w/dbl gilt line framing, dbl head-bands. (Gilt titling sl faded, sl internal browning; vol II spine repaired), o/w Fine set. *Europa*. $272/£170

GILROY, FRANK D. Private. NY: HBJ, (1970). 1st ed. VF in VF dj (sl rubbed). *Between The Covers*. $100/£63

GIMBEL, R. Charles Dickens' A Christmas Carol. Yale Univ, 1956. Mint. *Moss.* $22/£14

GIMLETT, F. E. Over Trails of Yesterday. Arbor-Villa via Salida, CO: The Hermit (of Arbor-Villa), 1943. 1st ed. Frontis. VG (lt foxing to pp facing cvrs) in textured ptd wrappers. *Connolly.* $35/£22

GIMLETTE, G. H. D. A Postscript to the Records of the Indian Mutiny. London, 1927. 1st ed. (Lt browned.) *Edwards.* $77/£48

GINGRICH, ARNOLD (ed). The Gordon Garland. NY: Theodore Gordon Flyfishers, 1965. 1st ed. Ltd to 1500 numbered. 1/2 navy leather, gilt, over emb grn paper-cvrd bds. Fine in NF slipcase. *Biscotti.* $145/£91

GINGRICH, ARNOLD (ed). The Gordon Garland. A Round of Devotions by His Followers. NY: Theodore Gordon Flyfishers, 1965. One of 1500 numbered. Uncut, unopened. 1/2 leather (spine tips rubbed). Slipcase. *Oinonen*.* $110/£69

GINGRICH, ARNOLD (ed). The Gordon Garland: A Round of Devotions by His Followers. NY: Theodore Gordon Flyfishers, 1965. 1st ed. One of 1500. Frontisport. 1/4 levant morocco, bds, gilt. Fine in slipcase. *Pacific*.* $219/£137

GINGRICH, ARNOLD. The Fishing in Print. A Guided Tour Through Five Centuries of Angling Literature. NY: Winchester, (1974). (Lt worn.) Dj. *Oinonen*.* $30/£19

GINSBERG, ALLEN. Bixby Canyon Ocean Path Word Breeze. NY: Gotham Book Mart, 1972. 1st ed. Signed. Fine in wrappers, pict cvr label. *Pacific*.* $35/£22

GINSBERG, ALLEN. Careless Love. Madison: Red Ozier, (1978). 1st separate ed. One of 280. Signed. Fine in marbled wrappers. *Pacific*.* $40/£25

GINSBERG, ALLEN. Collected Poems, 1947-1980. NY: Harper, 1984. 1st ed. Fine in NF dj. *Beasley.* $40/£25

GINSBERG, ALLEN. Howl. Barry Miles (ed). NY: Harper, 1986. 1st ed. Fine in NF dj. *Beasley.* $25/£16

GINSBERG, ALLEN. Improvised Poetics. NY: Anonym, 1972. 1st ed. Fine in wraps. *Beasley.* $35/£22

GINSBERG, ALLEN. Iron Horse. Toronto: Coach House, 1973. 1st ed. One of 1000. Fine in wraps. *Beasley.* $35/£22

GINSBERG, ALLEN. Kaddish and Other Poems 1958-1960. SF: City Lights, 1961. Correct 1st ed w/Villiers imprint at foot of p100. Fine in wraps (lt soiled). *Beasley.* $100/£63

GINSBERG, ALLEN. Planet News, 1961-1967. (SF): City Lights Books, (1968). 1st ed. One of 500. Signed. Black cl, gilt. Fine in slipcase. *Pacific*.* $98/£61

GINSBERG, ALLEN. T.V. Baby Poem. SF: Beach Texts, 1968. 1st ed. Fine in wraps. *Beasley.* $40/£25

GINSBERG, ALLEN. Wichita Vortex Sutra. Coyote, 1966. 1st ed. Fine in wraps. *Beasley.* $60/£38

GINZBERG, ELI et al. The Ineffective Soldier; Lessons for Management and the Nation. NY: Columbia Univ, 1959. 1st ed. 3 vols. Fine in djs. *Weber.* $75/£47

GINZBURG, RALPH. Castrated. My Eight Months in Prison. NY, (1973). 1st Amer ed. Fine in NF dj. *Polyanthos.* $25/£16

GIORNO, JOHN. Cancer in My Left Ball: Poems 1970-1972. (West Glover, VT): Something Else, (1973). 1st ed. VF in Fine dj. *Between The Covers.* $125/£78

GIPSON, FRED. Fabulous Empire; Colonel Zack Miller's Story. Boston: Houghton Mifflin, 1946. 1st ed. VG in dj. *Labordo.* $50/£31

GIPSON, FRED. Hound-Dog Man. NY: Harper, 1949. 1st ed. NF in dj. *Labordo.* $60/£38

GIPSON, LAWRENCE HENRY. The British Isles and the American Colonies: The Southern Plantations, 1748-1754. Knopf, (1967). Nice in dj. *Rybski.* $45/£28

GIPSON, LAWRENCE HENRY. Lewis Evans. To Which is Added, Evan's A Brief Account of Pennsylvania. Phila: Historical Soc of PA, 1939. 1st ed. 6 maps (5 lg fldg). Beige cl (sl soiled). *Karmiole.* $85/£53

GIPSON, LAWRENCE HENRY. The Moravian Indian Mission on White River. Indianapolis: IN Hist Bureau, 1938. 1st ed. Frontis, 2 plts. Blue cl. NF. *Chapel Hill.* $125/£78

GIRAUD, S. LOUIS (ed). Bookano Stories with Pictures That Spring Up in Model Form. London: Strand Publications, (1941). 4to. 5 dbl-pg pop-ups. Full color illus bds (sl worn). *Reisler.* $185/£116

GIRAUD, S. LOUIS (ed). Bookano Stories with Pictures That Spring Up in Model Form: No. 4. London: Strand, (1937). 4to. 5 Fine dbl-pg pop-ups. Full color illus bds. (Sl spine crease), o/w VG in pub's box (lt worn). *Reisler.* $450/£281

GIRAUD, S. LOUIS (ed). Bookano Stories. London: Daily Sketch & Sunday Graphic, (1947). No. 14 of Bookano Stories. 4to. 5 dbl-pg pop-ups. (Spine sl worn), o/w Nice. *Reisler.* $225/£141

GIRAUDOUX, JEAN. Duel of Angels. Christopher Fry (trans). NY: Oxford, 1959. 1st Amer ed. VF in VF dj (spine foot sl rubbed). *Between The Covers.* $85/£53

GIRAUDOUX, JEAN. Tigers at the Gate. Christopher Fry (trans). NY: Oxford, 1955. 1st Amer ed. VF in VF dj (sl rubbed). *Between The Covers.* $85/£53

GIRDLESTONE, C. M. Mozart's Piano Concertos. Cassell, 1948. 1st ed. (Spine sl faded.) Dj. *Hollett.* $56/£35

GIRNAU, FREDERIC H. Clara's Secret Love Life. L.A., (1931). Wraps (worn). *King.* $25/£16

GIROUARD, MARK. Robert Smythson and the Architecture of the Elizabethan Era. Country Life, 1966. 1st ed, 1st bk. VG in dj. *Hadley.* $51/£32

GIROUARD, MARK. Robert Smythson and the Elizabethan Country House. Yale Univ, 1983. Dj. *Edwards.* $48/£30

GIRTIN, TOM. In Love and Unity. London: Hutchinson, 1961. 1st ed. Dj (sl soiled). *Edwards.* $24/£15

GISBORNE, THOMAS. An Enquiry into the Duties of the Female Sex. London: T. Cadell, Jun. & W. Davies, 1797. 1st ed. viii,426pp + pub's ad leaf. Old calf, marbled bds, gilt. (Lt browned, foxed; fr joint splitting; edges worn, scuffed, spine rubbed.) *Baltimore*.* $120/£75

GISH, ANTHONY. American Bandits. Girard, KS: Haldeman-Julius, 1938. 1st ed. VG in wrappers (sm closed tear fr cvr). *Labordo.* $20/£13

GISSING, GEORGE. The Crown of Life. NY: Frederick A. Stokes, 1899. 1st Amer ed. Grn dec cl, gilt. VG (fep sl cracked; corners sl shelfworn). *Sumner & Stillman.* $85/£53

GISSING, GEORGE. The House of Cobwebs and Other Stories. Archibald Constable, 1906. New eps. Good (lt spotted; spine bumped, cvrs sl mkd). *Tiger.* $58/£36

GISSING, GEORGE. Human Odds and Ends. Lawrence & Bullen, 1898. Good (sig, occasional thumbmk; spine bumped, cvrs sl mkd). *Tiger.* $96/£60

GISSING, GEORGE. Notes on a Social Democracy. Enitharmon, 1968. One of 400 numbered. Tp design by Walter Crane. NF in dj (sl dusty), wrappers. *Ulysses.* $88/£55

GISSING, GEORGE. The Paying Guest. London: Cassell, 1895. 1st ed. Mustard cl. VG (spine sl faded). *Maggs.* $136/£85

GISSING, GEORGE. Short Stories of To-Day and Yesterday. London/Bombay/Sydney, George C. Harrap, (1929). 1st ed. Fine in NF dj. *Sumner & Stillman.* $85/£53

GISSING, GEORGE. The Town Traveller. Methuen, 1898. Pub's cat dated April 1898. Good (Bkpl; fore-edge lt spotted; spine bumped, sunned, sl chipped, fr cvr label removed, water mk rear cvr). *Tiger.* $74/£46

GISSING, GEORGE. A Yorkshire Lass. NY: Privately ptd, 1928. One of 93 numbered. Patterned paper bds. VG (top edge dusty; spine ends sl bumped). *Ulysses*. $400/£250

GITTINGS, JOHN G. Personal Recollections of Stonewall Jackson. Cincinnati: Editor Pub, 1899. 1st ed. 8vo. Frontisport, 311pp; add'l port, plt. Red cl. VG (lt soiled, spine faded). *Chapel Hill*. $750/£469

GLADSTONE, WILLIAM EWART. The Vatican Decrees in Their Bearing on Civil Allegiance: A Political Expostulation. London: John Murray, 1874. 1st ed. 32pp. New bds. Good. *Young*. $64/£40

GLAESER, ERNST. Class 1902. London: Martin Secker, 1929. 1st British ed. Blue cl stamped in red/gilt. (Lt foxed), o/w VG in dj. *Reese*. $75/£47

GLAISTER, GEOFFREY ASHALL. Glossary of the Book. London, (1960). VG in dj. *Truepenny*. $75/£47

GLANVILLE, PHILLIPA. London in Maps. London: The Connoisseur, 1972. Dj, slipcase. *Marlborough*. $64/£40

GLANVILLE, S. R. K. The Egyptians. London: A&C Black, 1933. Frontis. (Sig.) Dj (tattered). *Archaeologia*. $25/£16

GLASGOW, ELLEN. The Builders. GC: Doubleday, Page, 1919. 1st ed. Red cl stamped in black/red. VG in pict dj (old inner mends on verso). *Reese*. $125/£78

GLASGOW, ELLEN. Phases of an Inferior Planet. NY/London: Harper, 1898. 1st ed. (Name; few lt spots to fr cvr), o/w VG. *Bernard*. $150/£94

GLASIER, P. As the Falcon Her Bells. London: Heinemann, 1963. 1st ed. Color frontis. (Fr cvr mottled), else VG in Good+ dj. *Mikesh*. $30/£19

GLASS, DUDLEY. Round the World with the Redhead Twins. Methuen, 1933. 1st ed. Tall wide 8vo. 49pp; 24 full-pg illus by George Sherringham. Pict bds. VG+ in orig glassine dj (torn). *Bookmark*. $96/£60

GLASSCOCK, C. B. Here's Death Valley. NY: G&D, (1940). Tan cl. VG in color pict dj (edge chipped). *House*. $20/£13

GLASSCOCK, C. B. Then Came Oil. NY: G&D, 1938. Unopened. VG in dj (sl worn). *Dumont*. $40/£25

GLASSER, RONALD J. 365 Days. NY, 1971. 1st ed. NF in NF dj. *Warren*. $50/£31

GLAZIER, WILLARD. Down the Great River. Phila: Hubbard, 1891. 1st ed. (i)ad,xxvi,(27)-443,(1)blank,lxiiipp; fldg map. Beveled edges. Maroon dec cl (sl damp-stained, rubbed), gilt. Internally VG. *Morrell*. $48/£30

GLEASON, F. Gleason's Pictorial, Volume V. Boston, 1853. 1st ed. Period calf, gilt. (Sl dampstained throughout, esp tp; extrems rubbed, scuffed), else VG. *Pacific**. $69/£43

GLEASON, H. and A. CRONQUIST. Manual of Vascular Plants of Northeastern United States and Adjacent Canada. NY: Van Nostrand Reinhold, 1963. Ltr ptg. VG. *Archer*. $35/£22

GLEASON, HERBERT W. Through the Year with Thoreau. Boston/NY: Houghton Mifflin, 1917. 1st ed. Pict blue cl (sl worn, spine lettering dull). Good. *Lucas*. $90/£56

GLEASON, HERBERT W. Through the Year With Thoreau. Sketches of Nature From the Writings of Henry D. Thoreau. Boston: Houghton Mifflin, 1917. 1st ed. Color, pict blue-gray cl, gilt. Clean. *House*. $50/£31

GLEASON, R. B. Talks to My Patients; Hints on Getting Well and Keeping Well. NY, 1871. 1st ed. 228pp. Grn cl bds. VG. *Doctor's Library*. $45/£28

GLEIG, G. R. The Life of Arthur Duke of Wellington. London: Longmans, Green, 1878. Engr frontisport, (viii),500pp (bkpl). Contemp 1/2 calf (extrems rubbed), gilt. *Hollett*. $56/£35

GLEIZES, ALBERT and JEAN METZINGER. Cubism. London, (1913). 1st Eng ed. *Swann**. $201/£126

Glendale City Directory, 1922. Long Beach: Western Directory, 1922. Clean in ptd cl. *Dawson*. $75/£47

GLENN, SHIRLEY. West of Hell's Fringe. Norman, 1978. 1st ed. NF in dj. *Baade*. $60/£38

GLIMCHER, ARNOLD B. Louise Nevelson. NY/Washington, (1972). Signed by Glimcher and Nevelson. Frontis. Dj (sl chipped). *Argosy*. $100/£63

GLOAG, JOHN. Men and Buildings. Chantry Publications, 1950. 2nd ed. VG. *Hadley*. $24/£15

GLOVER, W. J. (ed). British Fairy and Folk Tales. London: A&C Black, 1928. 8vo. vi,281pp; 4 color plts by Charles Folkard. Pict blue cl. VG. *House*. $50/£31

GLOYD, H. K. The Rattlesnakes. Chicago, 1940. 31 plts, 22 maps. Stiff wrappers (spine faded, name to tp, wrapper). *Sutton*. $110/£69

GLOZER, LISELOTTE and WILLIAM. California in the Kitchen. Privately ptd, 1960. Ltd to 500. VG. *Perier*. $75/£47

GLUCK, JAY and SUMI HIRAMOTO GLUCK (eds). A Survey of Persian Handicraft. Tehran: Bank Melli Iran, 1977. 1st ed. Lg fldg map laid in. Blue linen. Good in dj. *Karmiole*. $100/£63

GLUCKMAN, ARCADI. United States Muskets, Rifles and Carbines. Buffalo, 1948. (Ink name; cvrs rubbed.) *King*. $40/£25

GNUDI, MARTHA TEACH and JEROME PIERCE WEBSTER. The Life and Times of Gaspare Tagliacozzi Surgeon of Bologna 1545-1599. NY: Herbert Reichner, (1950). 1st ltd ed. Frontis, 76 plts. Buckram. *Forest*. $72/£45

GOBAT, SAMUEL. Journal of a Three Years' Residence in Abyssinia. London: Hatchard, 1834. 1st ed. (ii) 1/2-title, xxi,(i)blank,371,(1)blank,(15)index,(1)imprint; fldg engr map. Orig plum patterned cl (faded), paper label. Fine (bkpl, ink inscrip). *Morrell*. $424/£265

GODDEN, GEOFFREY A. An Illustrated Encyclopaedia of British Pottery and Porcelain. London, (1968). 2nd imp. 16 full-color plts. Fine in dj. *Argosy*. $60/£38

GODDEN, GEOFFREY A. Stevengraphs and Other Victorian Silk Pictures. Rutherford, NJ: Fairleigh Dickinson Univ, (1971). 1st Amer ed. 321 plts (12 color). Orig Stevens silk bookmark laid in. Tan linen. Fine in pict dj. *Karmiole*. $85/£53

GODDEN, RUMER. A Candle for St. Jude. NY: Viking, (1948). 1st ed. VF in VF dj. *Between The Covers*. $150/£94

GODDEN, RUMER. In Noah's Ark. NY: Viking, 1949. 1st ed. VF in VF dj (spine foot sl rubbed). *Between The Covers*. $150/£94

GODDEN, RUMER. The Tale of the Tales. Frederick Warne, 1971. 1st ed. VG in dj. *Hollett*. $72/£45

GODEFROY, LOUIS. Albert Besnard. NY, 1969. *Swann**. $46/£29

Godey's Ladies' Book 1846. Sarah Hale (ed). Phila: Godey's Ladies' Book, 1849. Full calf. (Joints cracked through), else VG, though not collated. *Pacific**. $150/£94

Godey's Ladies' Book 1849. Phila: Godey's Ladies' Book, 1849. Aeg. Black morocco (rebacked in later morocco), gilt, gilt owner name fr cvr. VG, though not collated. *Pacific**. $184/£115

GODEY, L. and S. HALE. Lady's Book. Phila: Louis A. Godey, 1869. 8vo. 552pp; 3 fldg plts (1 loose). Black leather spine, raised band. Good. *Davidson*. $150/£94

GODFREY, A. S. T. The Cradle of the North Wind. Methuen, 1938. 1st ed. VG in dj (torn). *Walcot*. $27/£17

GODFREY, EDWARD S. Field Diary of Lt. Edward Settle Godfrey...Covering the Period from May 17, 1876...a Few Days After September 24, 1876.... Edgar I. and Jane R. Stewart ((By Edward Settle Godfrey.) (Portland): Champoeg, 1957. 1st ed. One of 1000 ptd. Fldg pictograph, 2 fldg maps. Pict cl. Fine. *Pacific**. $98/£61

GODFREY, M. J. Monograph and Iconograph of Native British Orchidaceae. London: CUP, 1933. 1st ed. 58 color plts by Hilda M. Godfrey, 9 b/w plts, port. Teg. (Feps lt browned; cl edges sl discolored.) Dj (soiled, chipped w/loss). *Edwards.* $360/£225

GODFREY, W. H. Gardens in the Making. London: Batsford, 1914. 1st ed. 8 dbl-pg plans. *Quest.* $75/£47

GODMAN, J. D. Rambles of a Naturalist. Phila: T. Ash, 1833. 1st ed. 151pp. (Heavily foxed), else VG + . *Mikesh.* $125/£78

GODSELL, P. H. Arctic Trader. Toronto, 1943. *Grayling.* $32/£20

GODWIN, PETER. Mukiwa: A White Boy in Africa. Picador, 1996. 1st ed. Fine in dj. *Virgo.* $32/£20

GODWIN, TOM. The Survivors. Hicksville: Gnome, (1958). 1st ed. Probable 1st state binding (pale blue bds lettered in dk blue). VG + in VG + dj. *Other Worlds.* $35/£22

GODWIN, WILLIAM. Essay on Sepulchres. W. Millar, 1809. 1st ed. 8vo. Engr frontis. Orig cl-backed bds. (Sl foxed.) *Sotheby's*.* $699/£437

GOETHE, C. M. Geogardening. Sacramento, 1948. 1st ed. Brn cl. VG. *Larry Price.* $40/£25

GOETHE. The Sorrows of Werter. F. Gotzberg (trans). T. Hurst et al, 1802. 1st ed thus. Frontis, iv,194pp(bkpl),(2) ad leaf; 4 copperplts. Contemp tree calf, gilt. *Cox.* $72/£45

GOETHE. The Story of Reynard the Fox. LEC, 1954. Ltd to 1500 numbered, signed by Fritz Eichenberg (illus). Fine in slipcase. *Swann*.* $92/£58

GOETHE. Wilhelm Meister's Apprenticeship. LEC, 1959. Ltd to 1500 numbered, signed by William Sharp (illus). Fine in slipcase. *Swann*.* $69/£43

GOETHE. See also VON GOETHE

GOETTE, J. Jade Lore. NY: Reynal & Hitchcock, n.d. (ca 1936). Good. *Blake.* $175/£109

GOETZ, RUTH and AUGUSTUS. The Immoralist. NY: Dramatists Play Service, (1954). 1st ed. VF in VF dj. *Between The Covers.* $175/£109

GOETZMANN, WILLIAM H. Army Exploration in the American West, 1803-1863. New Haven: Yale Univ, (1960). 2nd ptg. (Sm stain to rep, hinge cracking before tp; corners lt bumped), else VG in dj (extrems worn, price-clipped). *Pacific*.* $92/£58

GOETZMANN, WILLIAM H. Exploration and Empire. NY: Knopf, 1966. 1st ed. Errata slip laid in. Fine in NF dj. *Pacific*.* $138/£86

GOFF, FREDERICK R. Incunabula in American Libraries. A Third Census. NY, 1964-72. 2 vols, incl supplement. Prospectus to each vol laid in. (Lt worn, spines faded.) *Oinonen*.* $190/£119

GOFFIN, ROBERT. Horn of Plenty. NY: Allen, Towne & Heath, 1947. 1st ed in English. Port. VG in pict dj. *Petrilla.* $50/£31

GOFFIN, ROBERT. Horn of Plenty. The Story of Louis Armstrong. NY: Allen, Towne & Heath, 1947. 1st ed. (Name, rear bd sl soiled), else Fine in dj (lt used, 1-inch tear spine fold). *Beasley.* $65/£41

GOFFIN, ROBERT. Jazz: From the Congo to the Metropolitan. GC: Doubleday, 1944. 1st ed. NF in dj (lt used). *Beasley.* $60/£38

GOFFIN, ROBERT. Jazz: From the Congo to the Metropolitan. GC: Doubleday, 1944. 1st ed, 1st bk. (Eps sl foxed.) Pict dj. *Petrilla.* $60/£38

GOGARTY, OLIVER ST. JOHN. Intimations. NY: Abelard, (1950). 1st Amer ed. NF in VG dj. *Agvent.* $30/£19

GOGOL, NIKOLAI. Chichikov's Journeys (Dead Souls). LEC, 1944. One of 2000 sets signed by Lucille Corcos (illus). 2 vols. Fine in slipcase. *Swann*.* $57/£36

GOGOL, NIKOLAI. The Overcoat and The Government Inspector. LEC, 1976. One of 2000 signed by Saul Field (illus). Fine in slipcase. *Swann*.* $46/£29

GOGOL, NIKOLAI. Taras Bulba. Hutchins Hapgood (trans). NY: Knopf, 1931. 1st ed illus thus. Fine in NF dj (spine sl faded). *Between The Covers.* $85/£53

GOHM, DOUGLAS. Antique Maps. London, 1972. (Shelfworn), else Good. *Dumont.* $30/£19

Gold Stories of '49 by a Californian. (By Nuima Smith.) Boston: Copeland & Day, 1896. 1st ed. Dec orange cl. Good (sm stamp; soiled). *Reese.* $50/£31

GOLD, H. L. The Old Die Rich and Other Science Fiction Stories. NY, (1955). 1st ed. VG + in dj (worn). *Mcclintock.* $20/£13

GOLD, MICHAEL. Charlie Chaplin's Parade. NY: Harcourt, Brace, (1930). Sq 4to. 64pp. Cl-backed orange bds. (Ex-lib; edgeworn, edges of rear cvr damaged). *Reisler.* $100/£63

GOLD, THOMAS D. History of Clarke County Virginia and Its Connection with the War Between the States. (Berryville, VA, 1914.) 1st ed. 8vo. Blue cl. VG (rear inner hinge cracked; lt spotting along bottom of cvrs). *Chapel Hill.* $750/£469

GOLDBERG, EDWARD L. Patterns in Late Medici Art Patronage. Princeton, 1983. Good + in dj. *Washton.* $50/£31

GOLDBERG, ISAAC. Tin Pan Alley: A Chronicle of the American Popular Music Racket. NY: John Day, 1930. 1st ed. 8 plts. Pict cl (spine ends lt worn). *Petrilla.* $65/£41

GOLDBERG, N. L. John Crome the Elder. Oxford: Phaidon, 1978. 2 vols. 16 color plts, 243 plt illus. Good in dj. *Ars Artis.* $96/£60

GOLDBERG, ROSELEE. Performance. NY: Abrams, (1979). 1st ed. Photo illus wrappers. (Ink mks 4pp), else Nice. *Turtle Island.* $45/£28

Golden Book of Famous Women. Hodder & Stoughton, (1919). 1st ed. Lg 4to. 200pp; 16 mtd color plts by Eleanor Fortescue Brickdale, guards. Pict sky-blue cl, gilt. VG (foxed, esp eps; lt spotted). *Bookmark.* $104/£65

Golden Staircase: Selected Verses and Poems for Children. Buffalo: Berger Pub, 1907. 1st ed. Chromolitho bds. (Cvrs sl warped), else VG. *Pacific*.* $35/£22

GOLDENBERG, ISAAC. The Fragmented Life of Don Jacobo Lerner. NY: Persea, 1976. Fine in dj. *Lame Duck.* $45/£28

GOLDER, F. A. Bering's Voyages: An Account of the Efforts of the Russians to Determine the Relation of Asia and America. NY: American Geographical Soc, 1922/1935. 1st ed. 2 vols. (Cvr lettering rubbed), else VG. *Pacific*.* $138/£86

GOLDFRANK, ESTHER S. The Artist of 'Isleta Paintings' in Pueblo Society. Washington: Smithsonian, 1967. (Name.) *Turtle Island.* $60/£38

Goldilocks and the Three Bears. An All-Action Treasure Hour Pop-Up Book. London: Murray's Children's Books, 1978. 6 dbl-pg pop-ups by V. Kubasta. Glazed pict bds. VG. *Bookfinders.* $45/£28

GOLDING, LOUIS. Good-Bye to Ithaca. NY/London: Yoseloff, 1958. 1st US ed. 31 plts, 2 maps. VG in dj (tattered). *Worldwide.* $20/£13

GOLDING, LOUIS. In the Steps of Moses the Conqueror. London: Rich & Cowan, 1938. 1st ed. Black cl. VG in dj (edges sl frayed). *Maggs.* $104/£65

GOLDING, LOUIS. Sorrow of War Poems. London: Methuen, (1919). 1st ed, 1st bk. Gray bds, ptd spine label. NF in dj. *Reese.* $85/£53

GOLDING, WILLIAM. Darkness Visible. London: Faber, 1979. 1st ed. (Edges sl browned), o/w VG in dj. *Virgo.* $40/£25

GOLDING, WILLIAM. Darkness Visible. Faber & Faber, 1979. 1st Eng ed. NF (paper browning; spine head bumped) in dj (spine head sl creased). *Ulysses.* $45/£28

GOLDING, WILLIAM. An Egyptian Journal. Faber & Faber, 1985. 1st Eng ed. Fine in dj (sl creased). *Ulysses.* $40/£25

GOLDING, WILLIAM. Fire Down Below. Faber, 1989. 1st UK ed. Signed. Fine in dj. *Williams*. $61/£38

GOLDING, WILLIAM. Lord of the Flies. London: Faber & Faber, (1954). 1st ed. (Spine sunned), else VG in dj (spine ends sl rubbed, price and flap tips clipped). *Pacific**. $1,610/£1,006

GOLDING, WILLIAM. Lord of the Flies. London: Faber, (1954). 1st ed, 1st bk. Fine in dj (sl worn). *Lenz*. $2,500/£1,563

GOLDING, WILLIAM. Lord of the Flies. NY: Coward-McCann, (1955). Fine (sm sticker) in dj (sl worn). *Lenz*. $750/£469

GOLDING, WILLIAM. A Moving Target. London: Faber, 1982. 1st ed. Fine in dj. *Virgo*. $35/£22

GOLDING, WILLIAM. Nobel Lecture. London: Sixth Chamber Press, 1984. Ltd to 500 bound in limp wrappers. Fine. *Virgo*. $40/£25

GOLDING, WILLIAM. The Paper Men. Faber, 1984. 1st UK ed. Fine in dj. *Williams*. $32/£20

GOLDING, WILLIAM. The Pyramid. London: Faber & Faber, 1967. 1st Eng ed. Fine in dj (edges sl rubbed). *Ulysses*. $136/£85

GOLDING, WILLIAM. The Pyramid. Faber, 1967. 1st UK ed. Signed. NF in VG dj (sl browned). *Williams*. $280/£175

GOLDING, WILLIAM. Rites of Passage. Faber, 1980. 1st UK ed. NF in NF dj. *Martin*. $19/£12

GOLDING, WILLIAM. The Spire. London: Faber & Faber, 1964. 1st ed. Mottled pinkish-purple cl. Fine in dj. *Temple*. $77/£48

GOLDING, WILLIAM. The Spire. London: Faber & Faber, 1964. 1st ed. Purple cl, gilt. VG in dj (edges browned). *Maggs*. $96/£60

GOLDMAN, MARCUS SELDEN. In Praise of Little Fishes. Boston: David Godine, (1977). 1st ed. One of 300 ptd. Signed. Cl-backed dec bds. NF in glassine. *Pacific**. $92/£58

GOLDMAN, WILLIAM. Boys and Girls Together. NY: Atheneum, 1964. 1st ed. VF in VF dj. *Between The Covers*. $175/£109

GOLDMAN, WILLIAM. The Princess Bride. NY, 1973. 1st Amer ed. NF in NF dj. *Warren*. $250/£156

GOLDMAN, WILLIAM. The Princess Bride. (London: Macmillan, 1975.) 1st British ed. (Warping to middle pp), else VG in dj (extrems sl rubbed). *Pacific**. $81/£51

GOLDMAN, WILLIAM. The Temple of Gold. NY: Knopf, 1957. 1st ed, 1st bk. 1/4 black cl, gilt, blindstamped red bds. (Ink name), o/w Fine in dj (spine sl browned, lower extrem chipped). *Heritage*. $200/£125

GOLDRING, DOUGLAS. Regency Portrait Painter. London: MacDonald, 1951. 46 plts. VG in dj (edges sl frayed, chipped). *Hollett*. $32/£20

GOLDRING, DOUGLAS. Reputations: Essays in Criticism. London: Chapman & Hall, 1920. 1st ed. Gilt blue cl. VG. *Reese*. $22/£14

GOLDRING, WILLIAM. The Book of the Lily. London: John Lane, 1905. 1st ed. 17 b/w photo plts. Grn dec cl. (Lt foxed), else VG. *Larry Price*. $25/£16

GOLDSBOROUGH, CHARLES W. The United States Naval Chronicle. Volume I (all published). Washington, 1824. 1st ed. 393,(xii)pp. Errata slip. Orig bds (backstrip badly chipped). Howes G225. *Cullen*. $300/£188

GOLDSBOROUGH, W. W. The Maryland Line in the Confederate States Army. Balt: Kelly, Piet, 1869. 1st ed. Frontis (top torn off, not affecting image), 357pp + (3)pp ads. Rose cl. VG (lt dampstain to last 50pp; spine sunned). Howes G226. *Chapel Hill*. $400/£250

GOLDSCHMIDT, LUCIEN and WESTON J. NAEF. The Truthful Lens, A Survey of the Photographically Illustrated Book 1844-1914. NY: Grolier Club, (1980). 1st ed. One of 1000. (Sl worn.) Slipcase (sl rubbed). *Swann**. $460/£288

GOLDSMID, EDMUND. Bibliotheca Curiosa. A Complete Catalogue of All the Publications of the Elzevier Presses.... Edinburgh: Privately ptd, 1888. 1st ed. One of 200. 3 vols. Ptd bds (rebacked in later cl; loose). *Forest*. $136/£85

GOLDSMITH, LEWIS. An Exposition of the Conduct of France Towards America. London, 1810. Contemp 1/2 calf (worn; hinges reinforced). *Swann**. $57/£36

GOLDSMITH, OLIVER. The Beauties of English Poesy. London, 1767. 1st ed. 2 vols. Contemp calf (skillfully rebacked, orig spine and labels; lacks 1/2-titles). Individually boxed in morocco-backed slipcase. *Metropolitan**. $373/£233

GOLDSMITH, OLIVER. The Citizen of the World: Or, Letters from a Chinese Philosopher. London: Taylor & Hessey et al, 1809. 2 vols. Period diced russia, gilt. VG. *Pacific**. $46/£29

GOLDSMITH, OLIVER. The Deserted Village. London, 1770. 6th ed. 23pp. Mod 3/4 calf. *Argosy*. $150/£94

GOLDSMITH, OLIVER. The Deserted Village. East Aurora: Roycroft Shop, 1898. One of 470 signed by Elbert Hubbard. 18 hand-illuminated initials. Teg. Gray bds (corners worn), grn linen spine. *Appelfeld*. $150/£94

GOLDSMITH, OLIVER. The Deserted Village. London: Gowans & Gray, 1907. 1st ed illus by Stephen Reid. Dbl-spread color frontis, 13 full-pg plts. Deluxe white cl. (Sm ink mk fr bd.) *Sotheran*. $221/£138

GOLDSMITH, OLIVER. The Miscellaneous Works...Containing All His Essays and Poems. London: W. Griffin, 1775. 1st ed. Half-title, (viii),iv,9-200pp. Contemp calf, raised bands, red morocco label. VG. *Young*. $448/£280

GOLDSMITH, OLIVER. Mrs. Mary Blaize. Routledge, n.d. c1885. Obl 4to. 24pp; 6 color plts by Randolph Caldecott. (Spine foot sl worn), else VG + in pict wraps. *Bookmark*. $35/£22

GOLDSMITH, OLIVER. The Roman History, from the Foundation of the City of Rome to the Destruction of the Western Empire. London: S. Baker & G. Leigh et al, 1769. 1st ed. 2 vols. Period calf, gilt, vol II w/morocco spine labels. (Vol I lacks spine labels, glue to spine ends, joints), else VG. *Pacific**. $138/£86

GOLDSMITH, OLIVER. The Vicar of Wakefield. George G. Harrap, (1929) 1st Arthur Rackham illus ed. Teg. Dec cl, gilt. VG. *Ash*. $152/£95

GOLDSMITH, OLIVER. The Vicar of Wakefield. London: Harrap, (1929). 1st ed. 12 color plts by Arthur Rackham. Blue cl, gilt. VG (1/2-title, rear pg yellowed, ink inscrip; corners very bumped, spine worn). *My Bookhouse*. $165/£103

GOLDSMITH, OLIVER. The Vicar of Wakefield. Phila: David McKay, (1929). One of 775 numbered, signed by Arthur Rackham (illus). One of 200 Amer copies. 12 tipped-in color plts. Deckle edges. Full gilt-dec vellum. Fine in box (broken, taped). *Cullen*. $725/£453

GOLDSMITH, OLIVER. The Vicar of Wakefield. Phila: David McKay, (1929). 1st Rackham ed. One of 775 ptd on special paper, signed by Arthur Rackham (illus). 4to. 12 color plts. Teg. Full white vellum gilt. Fine. *Appelfeld*. $850/£531

GOLDSMITH, OLIVER. The Vicar of Wakefield. London: Sammells & Finch, 1792. 2 vols in 1. Period tree, mottled calf, gilt, morocco spine bands. NF. *Pacific**. $207/£129

GOLDSMITH, OLIVER. The Vicar of Wakefield. London: Macmillan, 1890. 1st ed illus by Hugh Thomson. Deluxe ed in lg paper issue. (xxxvi),305pp. Teg, rest uncut. Full red morocco (finely rebound), gilt extra, raised spine bands. VF. *Sotheran*. $237/£148

GOLDSMITH, OLIVER. The Vicar of Wakefield. London: Methuen, 1904. 24 color plts by Thomas Rowlandson. Teg. 1/4 vellum, paper spine labels. (Eps foxed; labels chipped), else VG. *Pacific**. $35/£22

GOLDSMITH, OLIVER. The Works. Peter Cunningham (ed). London: John Murray, 1854. 4 vols. Extra engr frontispieces, 1 frontis port. Teg, untrimmed. Later dk grn-brn morocco, grn cl by Riviere, raised bands, gilt. Very Nice set (bkpls, spines sl dknd, cvrs sl rubbed). *Baltimore**. $190/£119

GOLDSTEIN, MILTON. The Magnificent West: Yosemite. GC: Doubleday, n.d. 60 color plts. Tan cl. Fine in pict dj. *Pacific**. $23/£14

GOLDSTON, WILL. Great Magician's Tricks. London: Will Goldston, (1931). Ltd ed. (Spine sunned), else NF. *Pacific**. $374/£234

GOLDSTON, WILL. Will Goldston's Exclusive Magical Secrets. London: The Magician, (1912). Ltd ed. Gilt-lettered morocco, locking metal clasp w/key. (Joints worn, cracked; gilt-stamped name fr cvr), else VG. *Pacific**. $259/£162

GOLDWATER, BARRY. Delightful Journey Down the Green and Colorado Rivers. Tempe, 1970. Fine. *Five Quail.* $75/£47

GOLDWATER, ROBERT and MARCO TREVES. Artists on Art. From the XIV to the XX Century. London: Pantheon, 1947. 2nd rev ed. Dj (chipped, sl torn). *Edwards.* $32/£20

Golfer's Manual, Being an Historical and Descriptive Account of the National Game of Scotland by 'A Keen Hand' and Originally Published in 1857. (By H. B. Farnie.) London: Dropmore, 1947. One of 750. 1/2 cl, golf-dec bds, gilt. (Emb stamp), else Fine in VG dj (spine, fr joint sl browned, head rubbed), slipcase. *Pacific**. $489/£306

GOLL, YVAN. Four Poems of the Occult. Francis Carmody (ed). Kentfield: Allen Press, (1962). One of 130. 15 1/2 x 11. Loose sigs in paper portfolios. Fine in cl chemise, slipcase. *Pacific**. $1,610/£1,006

GOLLEY, F. B. et al (eds). Small Mammals. Cambridge, 1975. Dj. *Sutton.* $90/£56

GOLOVIN, P. N. The End of Russian America, Captain P. N. Golovin's Last Report, 1862. Basil Dmytryshyn & E. A. P. Crownhart-Vaughan (trans). Portland: OR Hist Soc, 1979. 1st ed in English. 8 maps. Gray cl. Fine in pict dj (spine faded). *Argonaut.* $125/£78

GOMBRICH, E. H. Norm and Form. London: Phaidon, (1971). 2nd ed. Fine in dj. *Turtle Island.* $55/£34

GOMEZ, MORENO MANUEL. The Golden Age of Spanish Sculpture. Greenwich: NYGS, (1964). Fine in dj. *Truepenny.* $75/£47

GOMME, ALICE B. Children's Singing Games. London: David Nutt in the Strand, (1893). 1st ed. Lg sq 8vo. Winifred Smith (illus). (vi),7-70pp, tipped-in ad. Buff pict cl. (Sm spot upper cvr), o/w Very Clean. *Sotheran.* $141/£88

GOMME, ALICE B. Children's Singing Games. Second Series. London: David Nutt in the Strand, (1894). 1st ed. Sm 4to. Winifred Smith (illus). (viii),9-70pp. Buff cl. Very Nice (3 closed tears neatly repaired w/archival tissue). *Sotheran.* $109/£68

GOMME, GEORGE LAURENCE (ed). The Gentleman's Magazine Library. London: Elliot Stock, 1888. 1st Eng ed thus. viii,349,(3)pp. (Cvrs yellowed, spine chipped.) *Oak Knoll.* $50/£31

GOMME, GEORGE LAURENCE (ed). The Gentleman's Magazine Library. London: Elliot Stock, 1888. 349pp + ads. Teg, uncut. Leather-backed cl. *Argosy.* $60/£38

GOMPERTZ, BENJAMIN. The Principles and Application of Imaginary Quantities.... London: Scientific Press, 1817-18. 1st ed. 2 vols. 35; 44pp (few ll lt soiled, marginal dampstaining vol 2). Good in early paper wrappers (spine eroded). *Glaser.* $275/£172

GONCHAROV, IVAN. Oblomov. C. J. Hogarth (trans). Allen & Unwin, 1915. 1st ed in English. (Sl stain to 1 pg; spine sunned, sl bumped), o/w Sharp. *Any Amount.* $38/£24

GONZALES, BABS. I Paid My Dues. Hard Times—No Bread. NJ: Expubidence, 1967. 1st Amer ed. NF in orig pict wrappers. *Warren.* $20/£13

GOOCH, FANNY CHAMBERS. Face to Face with the Mexicans. NY, 1887. Color frontis, 584,(iv)pp; 2 ports. Aeg. Illus cl. (Fr hinge cracked; cl discolored, spine chipped, lt marginal browning, sm chips rear joint.) *Edwards.* $136/£85

Good Genius That Turned Everything into Gold; or, The Queen Bee and the Magic Dress. London: David Bogue, 1847. 1st ed. 4 engr plts by George Cruikshank. Aeg. Caramel calf(orig cl bound in at rear), gilt, morocco spine labels, raised bands; bound by Root & Son. Fine. *Pacific**. $92/£58

GOOD, PETER P. The Family Flora and Materia Medica Botanica, Containing the Botanical Analysis, Natural History and Chemical and Medical Properties of Plants. Elizabethtown, NJ: The Author, (1851?). 1st complete ed. Vol II described on tp as 'A New Edition, Revised and Enlarged.' Vols I-(II) (all). 8vo. Prospectus. 98 Fine color plts. Orig cl. Fine (foxed; few spots to cl). *M & S.* $2,500/£1,563

GOODALL, A. The Wandering Gorillas. London: Collins, 1979. 1st ed. Fine in Fine dj. *Mikesh.* $30/£19

GOODALL, JOHN S. Creepy Castle. Atheneum, 1975. VG- (name; corners sl rubbed). *Price.* $30/£19

GOODALL, JOHN S. Creepy Castle. NY: Athaneum, 1975. 32pp. Glazed pict bds. VG in VG dj. *Bookfinders.* $40/£25

GOODALL, JOHN S. Paddy Finds a Job. London: Macmillan Children's Books, 1981. 6 dbl-pg pop-ups. Glazed pict bds. VG. *Bookfinders.* $45/£28

GOODCHILD, W. Precious Stones. NY: D. Van Nostrand, 1908. (Stamp), else Good. *Blake.* $65/£41

GOODE, G. B. The Fisheries and Fishery Industries of the United States. Washington, 1884. 2 vols. xxxiv,895,xxpp (name, pp tanned, upper margin few pp dampstained; lt foxed); atlas of 292 plts (tanned, upper corners of many plts sl creased, sm marginal tears to 2 plts). Recent binder's cl. *Sutton.* $250/£156

GOODE, JOHN. Recollections of a Lifetime. NY/Washington: Neale, 1906. 1st ed. Frontisport. Gray buckram (soiled). Internally Clean (bkpl, blindstamp). *Chapel Hill.* $75/£47

GOODELL, WILLIAM. The American Slave Code in Theory and Practice. NY: American & Foreign Anti-Slavery Soc, 1853. 2nd ed. (Name, dated 1853; spine ends chipped, lower spine repaired, extrems sunned), else VG-. *Pacific**. $46/£29

GOODENOUGH, ERWIN R. Jewish Symbols in the Greco-Roman Period. Volumes I-III only. NY: Pantheon Books, 1953. *Christie's**. $110/£69

GOODHUE, BERTRAM GROSVENOR. A Book of Architectural and Decorative Drawings. NY, 1924. 2nd ptg. Folio. 1/2 cl (ex-lib; artlessly rebacked retaining orig backstrip). *Swann**. $103/£64

GOODIS, DAVID. Night Squad. Greenwich: Gold Medal, 1961. 1st ed. NF (sl worn) in wraps. *Beasley.* $35/£22

GOODIS, DAVID. Somebody's Done For. NY: Banner, 1967. 1st ed. Pb orig. Good+ (reading crease, spine edge rubbed, edges worn) in wraps. *Murder.* $65/£41

GOODISON, NICHOLAS. English Barometers 1680-1860. London, 1969. 1st UK ed. Dj (sl torn, chipped). *Edwards.* $56/£35

GOODMAN, DAVID MICHAEL. A Western Panorama, 1849-1875. Glendale: A.H. Clark, 1966. 1st ed. Fldg map. Red cl. Fine (sl edgeworn). *Harrington.* $45/£28

GOODMAN, MICHAEL and TONY VISCARDI. Space Probes: Collaborative Research. Atlanta: Nexus, 1981. 1st ed. Pop-up on tp. Fine in stiff wrappers. *Cahan.* $45/£28

GOODMAN, PAUL. Growing Up Absurd. NY, 1965. 1st ed. VG in dj. *Typographeum.* $32/£20

GOODMAN, PAUL. Hawkweed. NY: Random House, (1967). 1st ed. Fine in NF dj (2 sm edge tears). *Reese.* $30/£19

GOODMAN, PAUL. Making Do. NY, 1963. 1st Amer ed. Fine in NF dj (sm edge nick). *Polyanthos*. $25/£16

GOODMAN, PHILIP. Franklin Street. NY, 1942. 1st Amer ed. NF in dj (sl rubbed). *Polyanthos*. $25/£16

GOODMAN, RICHARD M. and ROBERT J. GORLIN. The Face in Genetic Disorders. St. Louis: C.V. Mosby, 1970. (Sig.) *Weber*. $55/£34

GOODNIGHT, CHARLES et al. Pioneer Days in the Southwest from 1850 to 1879. Guthrie, OK: State Capital, 1909. 1st ed. Pict cl. VG + . *Labordo*. $125/£78

GOODRICH, FRANK B. Flirtation, and What Comes of It. NY: Rudd & Charleston, 1861. 1st ed. Inscribed presentation. Unptd wraps. (Foxed; spine worn, cvr edges chipped.) *Dramatis*. $50/£31

GOODRICH, LLOYD. Raphael Soyer. NY, ca 1972. Bkpl signed by Soyer mtd to tp. Dj. *Swann**. $230/£144

GOODRICH, LLOYD. Reginald Marsh. NY: Abrams, (1972). Obl folio. Dj (tears reinforced w/cellotape). *Swann**. $230/£144

GOODRICH, LLOYD. Reginald Marsh. NY: Abrams, 1972. Obl folio. Dj. *Argosy*. $300/£188

GOODRICH, LLOYD. Thomas Eakins. Washington/Cambridge: National Gallery by Harvard Univ, 1982. 2 vols. Fine in slipcase. *Turtle Island*. $90/£56

GOODRICH, LLOYD. Thomas Eakins: His Life and Work. NY, 1933. *Swann**. $126/£79

GOODRICH, S. G. Peter Parley's Geography for Beginners. NY: Huntington & Savage, 1849. Stereotyped ed. Sq 8vo. Full-pg engr frontis, 1/2-title, 160pp + 1 ad lower cvr. Pict paper on bds, black leather spine. Internally Fine. VG (pencil dedication fep; cvr rubbed at edges, chipped along fldg, soiled, sm chip at spine crown). *Hobbyhorse*. $200/£125

GOODRICH, S. G. (ed). The Token. Boston, 1830. 1st ed. Orig pub's purple silk (spine corners sl worn). Leather slipcase w/contrasting labels. BAL 7571. *Swann**. $287/£179

GOODRICH-FREER, A. Arabs in Tent and Town. London, 1924. 1st ed. (1 plt detached; sm split to fr joint head, spine sl chipped, joints sl rubbed.) *Edwards*. $120/£75

GOODRIDGE, CHARLES M. Narrative of a Voyage to the South Seas, and the Shipwreck of the Princess of Wales Cutter, with an Accout of Two Years Residence on an Uninhabited Island. Exeter: W. C. Featherstone, 1841. 4th ed. Frontis, (xxix)(11)-170pp; 2 plts. Errata slip present. VG. *High Latitude*. $195/£122

GOODRIDGE, CHARLES M. Narrative of a Voyage to the South Seas.... Exeter: W.C. Featherstone, 1841. 3 litho plts, incl frontis. (Foxed, dampstained; hinges weak, dampstained, worn, bumped.) *Metropolitan**. $356/£223

GOODSALL, ROBERT H. Palestine Memories, 1917-1918-1925. Canterbury, 1925. One of 300. Good (sl mkd, faded, back cvr edges string-dented). *Clearwater*. $120/£75

GOODSPEED, CHARLES ELIOT. Angling in America. Boston, 1939. 1st ed. One of 795 signed. Prospectus tipped in at rear. Blue cl, leather labels. (Spine label sl faded, rubbed.) *Kane**. $225/£141

GOODSPEED, H. et al. The Genus Nicotiana. Waltham: Chron. Botanica, 1954. 1st ed. Fine in VG + dj. *Mikesh*. $95/£59

GOODWIN, C. C. As I Remember Them. Salt Lake City: Salt Lake Commercial Club, 1913. 1st ed. Frontisport. Red cl, gilt. Fine (eps renewed; spine ends, corner lt rubbed, fr cvr sl spotted). *Argonaut*. $100/£63

GOODWIN, C. C. The Comstock Club. Salt Lake City, 1891. 1st ed. 288pp. (Cvrs lt rubbed, bk loose.) *King*. $35/£22

GOODWIN, FRANCIS. Rural Architecture: First (and Second) Series of Designs.... London: The Author and John Weale, 1835. 2nd ed. 2 vols, each w/supplement bound in at rear. 99 engr and aquatint plts, guards. Orig blind grn cl, gilt. (Sl aging, offsetting, lt foxed; sl worn, rubbed, 1 vol retightened w/lt rippling to spine, sl fraying, nicks.) *Baltimore**. $400/£250

GOODWIN, GORDON. Thomas Watson, James Watson, Elizabeth Judkins. London, 1904. One of 520. Frontisport, 5 plts. Teg, rest uncut. (Spine lt faded.) *Edwards*. $72/£45

GOODYKOONTZ, COLIN B. Home Missions on the American Frontier. Caldwell: Caxton, 1939. 1st ed. VG in dj. *Lien*. $40/£25

Goosey Gander Stories. London: Henry Frowde/Hodder & Stoughton, ca 1925. Thick 16mo. MvR and Lilian Govey (illus). All edges tinted. Red cl, gilt, color paste label. Clean (sl separation within). *Reisler*. $275/£172

GORDIMER, NADINE. The Conservationist. London: Cape, (1974). 1st UK ed. Fine in dj. *Hermitage*. $65/£41

GORDIMER, NADINE. Face to Face. Johannisberg: Silver Leaf Books, 1949. 1st UK ed, 1st bk. Signed. VG (ink inscrip; spine sl faded, extrems worn) in dj (amateurish restoration). *Williams*. $720/£450

GORDIMER, NADINE. The Lying Days. Gollancz, 1953. 1st ed. VG (bkpl taped to fep, lt browned, fr pastedown sl tape-mkd; sl bumped, top edge dusty) in dj (nicked, rubbed, mkd, dusty, sl torn, chipped, creased, spine, edges browned). *Ulysses*. $120/£75

GORDIMER, NADINE. Town and Country Lovers. Hollywood: Sylvester & Orphanos, 1980. Ltd to 330 signed. Fine dec cl. *Truepenny*. $100/£63

GORDIMER, NADINE. A World of Strangers. NY: S&S, 1958. 1st ed. NF in dj (flap tips clipped). *Pacific**. $40/£25

GORDIMER, NADINE. A World of Strangers. London: Victor Gollancz, 1958. 1st UK ed. Fine in dj (lt chipped, dknd). *Hermitage*. $45/£28

GORDON, A. C. and THOMAS NELSON PAGE. Befo' De War, Echoes in Negro Dialect. NY: Scribner, 1888. vi,131pp. VG. *Cullen*. $75/£47

GORDON, A. L. Bush Ballads and Galloping Rhymes. Melbourne: Clarson, Massina, 1876. (2nd ed.) (iv),108pp. Black chalked eps. Sand-grain limp grn cl (loss of surface color, spine ends rubbed), gilt. Good (bkpl). *Blackwell's*. $128/£80

GORDON, A. L. Poems: Sea Spray and Smoke Drift; Bush Ballads and Galloping Rhymes; Ashtaroth: A Dramatic Lyric. Melbourne: A.H. Massina, 1880. Aeg. Period gilt-tooled red morocco, raised bands. (Foxed, inscrip; spine sl sunned), else VG. *Pacific**. $69/£43

GORDON, C. G. The Journals of Major Gen. C. G. Gordon at Kartoum. London: Keegan Paul, 1885. 1st ed. 2 vols. Frontis, port, map. Teg. 3/4 brn morocco, gilt paneled spines, raised bands. Fine. *Appelfeld*. $250/£156

GORDON, CAROLINE. Penhally. NY: Scribner, 1931. 1st ed, 1st bk. VG + in dj (spine sl faded). *Lame Duck*. $2,000/£1,250

GORDON, CAROLINE. The Strange Children. NY: Scribner, 1951. 1st ed. NF (bk label fr flap) in dj (chipped, 1/4-inch chip fr panel). *Hermitage*. $75/£47

GORDON, CAROLINE. The Women on the Porch. NY: Scribner, 1944. 1st ed. Black cl. VG (top edge, eps sl soiled; cvr edges lt spotted) in dj (chipped, soiled). *Heritage*. $125/£78

GORDON, DONALD E. Ernst Ludwig Kirchner. Cambridge, MA: Harvard Univ, 1968. 140 full-pg repros. Fine in dj. *Turtle Island*. $325/£203

GORDON, DUDLEY. Crusader in Corduroy. L.A., 1972. NF in dj. *Dumont*. $45/£28

GORDON, E. O. Prehistoric London. London, 1946. 4th ed. 21 plts. Blue cl. VG in dj (worn). *Larry Price*. $25/£16

GORDON, E. V. (ed). The Battle of Maldon. London: Methuen, 1937. Frontis, map. Wrappers. *Maggs*. $45/£28

GORDON, ELIZABETH. The Mighty Hunter in Toyland. NY: Dodd, Mead, 1908. 1st ed. 8x10. Charles Wylie (illus). Cl-backed pict bds. (Fep askew, few pp spotted; sl stained, extrems rubbed), else VG-. *Pacific**. $81/£51

GORDON, ELIZABETH. Really So Stories. Joliet: P.F. Volland, (1924). 1st ed. 8vo. John Rae (illus). Cl-backed full color illus bds. Clean in matching pub's box. *Reisler*. $125/£78

GORDON, ISRAEL et al. Medical Jurisprudence. Edinburgh: E.& S. Livingstone, 1953. 3rd ed. (Rear hinge sl cracked), else VG. *Weber*. $45/£28

GORDON, JAN and CORA J. Two Vagabonds in Sweden and Lapland. London, 1926. 1st ed. 4 color plts. (Lt marginal browning, feps lt browned; spine sl discolored, chipped.) Dj (ragged w/loss). *Edwards*. $26/£16

GORDON, JOHN B. Reminiscences of the Civil War. NY: Scribner, 1911. Later ed. 3 ports. Blue cl. VG (bkpl). *Chapel Hill*. $50/£31

GORDON, LADY DUFF. Last Letters from Egypt. London: Macmillan, 1875. 1st ed. Frontis, xl,346pp. (Bkpl; sl rubbed, spine torn), o/w VG. *Worldwide*. $65/£41

GORDON, MARGARET MARIA. The Home Life of Sir David Brewster, by His Daughter. Edinburgh: Edmonston & Douglas, 1869. Frontis photo, (xii),440pp. Contemp 1/2 calf. Fine. *Weber*. $275/£172

GORDON, PETER. Diamonds Are Forever. Chronicle, 1987. 1st ed. Fine in Fine dj. *Plapinger*. $65/£41

GORDON, S. ANNA. Camping in Colorado. NY: W.B. Smith, 1882. 2nd ed. Red cl (edges worn, spine frayed, lt soiled), gilt. VG. *Hermitage*. $150/£94

GORDON, SETON. The Charm of the Hills. Cassell, 1931. 42 plts. VG. *Hollett*. $56/£35

GORDON, SETON. The Charm of the Skye. Cassell, 1931. 2nd ed. Map. (Fr hinge sl worn.) *Hollett*. $56/£35

GORDON, SETON. Highways and Byways in the West Highlands. Macmillan, 1935. 1st ed. (Fore-edge sl spotted), o/w Fine. *Hollett*. $48/£30

GORDON, SETON. The Immortal Isles. Williams & Norgate, 1926. 1st ed. 6 color plts. VG. *Hollett*. $72/£45

GORDON, THEODORE. The Complete Fly Fisherman: The Notes and Letters of Theodore Gordon. John McDonald (ed). NY: Scribner, 1947. 1st ed. VG. *Pacific**. $81/£51

GORDON, W. J. Our Home Railways. How They Began and How They Worked. London/NY, n.d. 36 color plts. (Hinges cracked, sl shaken, spine faded.) *Edwards*. $56/£35

GORDON, W. J. Perseus the Gorgon Slayer. London: Sampson Low et al, n.d. (1883). T. R. Spence (illus). 4to. Frontis, 1/2-title, 16 leaves. Yellow eps. Red edges. Full color pict chromolitho paper on bds, grn cl spine. Fine (edges lt rubbed). *Hobbyhorse*. $175/£109

GORDON, WILLIAM. The History of the Rise, Progress, and Establishment, of the Independence of the United States of America. The Author, 1788. 1st ed. 4 vols. 8vo. 9 fldg engr plts, subs list. Contemp 1/2 calf. (Spotted; rubbed.) *Sotheby's**. $920/£575

GORDON-CUMMING, CONSTANCE FREDERICA. Granite Crags of California. Edinburgh: William Blackwood, 1896. 2nd ptg. x,384pp; map. Pict cl, earlier binding w/spine gilt. (Fr inner hinge weak, ms index rep.) *Dawson*. $150/£94

GORDON-TAYLOR, GORDON. The Abdominal Injuries of Warfare. Bristol/London: John Wright/Simpkin Marshall, 1939. 3 color plts. (2 sm defects fr cvr), else Fine. *Weber*. $35/£22

GORER, EDGAR and J. F. BLACKER. Chinese Porcelain and Hard Stones. London: Bernard Quaritch, 1911. 1st ed. One of 1000 numbered sets. 2 vols. Folio. xxxviii,254pp; 254 color plts (some fldg). Teg. Fine set in buckram, gilt. *Ulysses*. $1,920/£1,200

GORER, GEOFFREY. The Revolutionary Ideas of the Marquis de Sade. Wishart, 1934. 1st Eng ed. Fine in dj. *Clearwater*. $48/£30

GORER, RICHARD. The Flower Garden in England. Batsford, 1975. VG in dj. *Hadley*. $24/£15

GOREY, EDWARD and PETER NEUMEYER. Donald Has a Difficulty. Santa Barbara: Capra, 1970. 1st ed. 7.5x5.75. 44pp. VG in wraps. *Cattermole*. $40/£25

GOREY, EDWARD. Amphigorey Also. NY: Congden & Weed, (1983). 1st ed. One of 250 numbered, signed. Dj, slipcase. *Swann**. $92/£58

GOREY, EDWARD. The Dwindling Party. NY: Random House, 1982. 6 dbl-pg pop-ups. Glazed pict bds. VG. *Bookfinders*. $50/£31

GOREY, EDWARD. Edward Gorey's Haunted Looking Glass. NY, 1984. 1st ed thus. NF in NF dj. *Warren*. $35/£22

GOREY, EDWARD. The Glorious Nosebleed. NY: Dodd, Mead, (1974). One of 250 signed (of 276). Orange pict bds. Fine in dj (price-clipped, spine sl faded), cardboard open-end slipcase. *Heritage*. $125/£78

GOREY, EDWARD. The Listing Attic. Boston: Little, Brown, (1954). 1st ed. 8vo. Color pict bds (lower edge lt shelfworn). Color pict dj (sl marginal wear, tears). *Reisler*. $225/£141

GOREY, EDWARD. The Loathesome Couple. NY: Dodd, Mead, (1977). 1st ltd ed. One of 250 numbered, signed. Pict white bds. Near Mint in VG matching dj (price-clipped, spine browned), plain black paper-cvrd board slipcase (sl rubbed). *Baltimore**. $110/£69

GOREY, EDWARD. The Pointless Book; or, Nature and Art. N.p.: Fantod Press, 1993. 1st ed. Signed on fr cr (as Garrod Weedy). 2 vols bound together as issued. Fine. *Pacific**. $58/£36

GOREY, EDWARD. The Prune People. NY: Albondocani, 1983. 1st ed. One of 426 signed. 14 full-pg illus. Fine in orange pict wrappers. *Heritage*. $60/£38

GOREY, EDWARD. The Remembered Visit. NY: S&S, 1965. 1st ed. 7.25x5.25. 64pp. Pict bds. VG (ex-lib) in dj. *Cattermole*. $25/£16

GOREY, EDWARD. The Sinking Spell. NY: Ivan Obolensky, 1964. 1st ed. Pb orig. Fine in stiff wrappers. *Janus*. $30/£19

GOREY, EDWARD. The Unstrung Harp. NY, 1953. 1st ed, 1st bk. VG + (lacks dj). *Warren*. $95/£59

GOREY, EDWARD. The Utter Zoo. NY: Meredith, 1967. 1st ed. 7x6.75. 28pp. Pict bds. Fine in dj. *Cattermole*. $35/£22

GOREY, EDWARD. The Vinegar Works. NY, (1963). 1st ed. 3 vols. Pict bds. Slipcase. *Swann**. $172/£108

GOREY, EDWARD. The Vinegar Works. NY: S&S, 1963. 1st eds. 3 vols. Each w/1963 signed ink presentation. Pict bds. Fine set in VG pict bd slipcase (sl worn). *Baltimore**. $160/£100

GORGAS, FERDINAND J. S. Dental Medicine: A Manual of Dental Materia Medica and Therapeutics. Phila, 1909. 8th ed. Full leather. VG. *Doctor's Library*. $50/£31

GORHAM, MAURICE. Back to the Local. Marshall, 1949. 1st ed. Edward Ardizzone (illus). (Spine end sl worn), else VG + in VG dj (sl chipped). *Any Amount*. $45/£28

GORKI, MAXIM. Bystander. Bernard Guilbert Guerney (trans). NY: Jonathan Cape & Harrison Smith, 1930. VG (feps spotted, partly browned; spine foot sl bumped) in dj (rubbed, chipped, torn, defective rear panel). *Ulysses*. $104/£65

GORKI, MAXIM. Reminiscences of Leonid Andreyev. Katherine Mansfield & S. S. Koteliansky (trans). NY: Crosby Gaige, 1928. 1st Amer ltd ed. One of 400. (Edges sl faded), o/w VG. *Virgo.* $40/£25

GORKY, MAXIM. Bystander. Cape, 1930. 1st ed in English. VG + in dj (price-clipped, sl dusty, couple closed tears to spine head). *Williams.* $152/£95

GORKY, MAXIM. Reminiscences of Leo Nicolayevitch Tolstoi. Richmond: Leonard & Virginia Woolf, 1920. 1st ed. Cut flush at top, lower edges. Lime grn/white marbled self-wrappers over thin plain white bds. (Spine faded, tail chipped; wrappers sl creased, frayed), o/w Fine. *Temple.* $120/£75

GORMAN, HERBERT. Suzy. NY: Farrar & Rinehart, (1934). 1st ed. Gilt black cl. VG (bkpl; cl sl dusty) in pict dj (chipped). *Reese.* $35/£22

GORMAN, J. T. With Lawrence to Damascus. London: OUP, 1940. 1st ed. Frontis. VG in orange/blue illus stiff paper wrappers. *Maggs.* $160/£100

GORSKI, ROGER A. and RICHARD E. WHALEN (eds). Brain and Behavior. Berkeley: Univ of CA, 1966. 1st ed. Tan/brick cl. Fine in dj. *House.* $75/£47

GOSLING, W. G. Labrador: Its Discovery, Exploration, and Development. London: Alston Rivers, 1910. Fldg map. VG (spine sl dull). *High Latitude.* $200/£125

GOSNELL, H. A. Before the Mast in Clippers. NY: Derrydale, 1937. Ltd to 950 numbered. Color frontis; 6 fldg maps. 3/4 red cl over beige paper-cvrd bds. Fine. *Biscotti.* $175/£109

Gospels of Saint Matthew, Saint Mark, Saint Luke and Saint John Together with the Acts of the Apostles. NY: Kress Foundation, 1959. 1st Amer ed. Fine in VG glassine dj, Fine box. *Polyanthos.* $95/£59

Goss-Udderzook Tragedy: Being a History of a Strange Case of Deception and Murder.... Balt: Balt Gazette, 1873. Pamphlet. 59pp; port. Good in wrappers (dust soiled, lt stained). *Brown.* $50/£31

GOSSE, EDMUND. Eliza Brightwen. The Life and Thoughts of a Naturalist. W. H. Chesson (ed). London/Leipsic, 1909. Frontis port (fore-edge sl water-stained), 1 other port. Fore/lower edges uncut. (Bkpl; sl rubbed, edges water-stained, spine lt faded.) *Edwards.* $26/£16

GOSSE, EDMUND. Inter Arma. London: Heinemann, 1916. 1st ed. Brn cl stamped in gilt/blind. Fine in Fine dj (sm edge tear) w/pub's price increase sticker. *Reese.* $40/£25

GOSSE, EDMUND. Silhouettes. Heinemann, 1925. 1st Eng ed. VG (spotting to edges, some internally; feps partly browned; spine ends, cvr edges sl bumped) in dj (nicked, rubbed, dusty, browned). *Ulysses.* $104/£65

GOSSE, EDMUND. Three French Moralists and the Gallantry of France. London: Heinemann, 1918. 1st Eng ed. VG (2 inscrips, feps partly browned, edges sl spotted; spine ends, corners bumped, cvrs sl mkd in dj (nicked, rubbed, sl torn, mkd, creased, browned). *Ulysses.* $120/£75

GOSSE, P. H. Actinologia Brittanica. A History of the British Sea-Anemones and Corals. John Van Voorst, 1860. 1st ed. 2 Fine als (1 is 3pp; other is 2pp) tipped-in to fr pastedown. xl,362pp + (ii)pp ads; 12 chromolitho plts, guards. Blind-stamped cl, gilt. (Margins of 1/2-title sl browned), o/w Fine. *Hollett.* $384/£240

GOSSE, P. H. The Aquarium. John Van Voorst, 1854. 1st ed. xiii,(i),278,(ii)pp; 6 chromolithos laid on to card, 6 woodcut plts. Aeg. Blind-stamped blue cl (fr joint sl strained), gilt. *Hollett.* $256/£160

GOSSE, P. H. The Birds of Jamaica. John Van Voorst, 1847. 1st ed. x,448,(ii)pp. Complete w/half-title, errata leaf. Teg. Orig cl (bds sl damp-mkd, mainly at foot), gilt. *Hollett.* $280/£175

GOSSE, P. H. The Canadian Naturalist. John Van Voorst, 1840. 1st ed. xii,372pp. Orig blind-stamped cl (spine ends sl chipped, bd corners sl bumped, fr hinge cracking at top), gilt. *Hollett.* $224/£140

GOSSE, P. H. Evenings at the Microscope. SPCK, n.d. (1859). 1st ed. xii,506pp + 4pp ads. Gray-mauve beaded/blind-stamped cl (extrems sl rubbed), gilt. Very Nice (joints sl cracked). *Hollett.* $352/£220

GOSSE, P. H. A Handbook to the Marine Aquarium. John Van Voorst, 1856. 2nd ed. Woodcut frontis, viii,48,(xii)pp. Ribbed/blind-stamped blue-grn cl (spine faded), gilt. *Hollett.* $104/£65

GOSSE, P. H. A History of the British Sea-Anemones and Corals; With Coloured Figures of the Species and Principal Varieties. Van Voorst, 1860. 1st ed thus. xl,361pp; 11 Fine chromolithos by W. Dickes, 1 uncolored litho. Dk grn cl, gilt. VG (bkpl; spine ends lt rubbed). *Sotheran.* $477/£298

GOSSE, P. H. Life in Its Lower, Intermediate, and Higher Forms. James Nisbet, 1857. 2nd ed. viii,363pp; 2 plts. (Neatly recased.) *Hollett.* $136/£85

GOSSE, P. H. A Naturalist's Rambles on the Devonshire Coast. John Van Voorst, 1853. 1st ed, 1st issue. xvi,451,(vi)pp, ads dated Jan 1853; 28 litho plts (12 color). Blind-stamped cl (sl faded, lt crease in backstrip), gilt. VG (spotted, joints sl cracked). *Hollett.* $224/£140

GOSSE, P. H. Omphalos. London: John van Voorst, 1857. 1st ed. xiii,(i),376,(vi)pp. Blind-stamped cl, gilt. VG. *Hollett.* $288/£180

GOSSE, P. H. Omphalos: An Attempt to Untie the Geological Knot.... John Van Voorst, 1857. 1st ed. xiii,(i),376,(6)pp. Cream chalked eps. Orig morocco-grain lt grn cl, gilt. Good (unobtrusive foxing, name; hinges split but firm, spine ends sl worn). *Blackwell's.* $320/£200

GOSSE, P. H. Tenby: A Sea-Side Holiday. London, 1856. Frontis, tp (both sl foxed); 24 plts. (Sl damp-mkd.) *Petersfield.* $56/£35

GOSSE, P. H. A Year at the Shore. Alexander Strahan, 1865. 1st ed. Frontis, xii,330,(ii)pp; 36 chromolitho plts. Teg. Grn cl, gilt, beveled bds. VG (frontis, fore-edge sl spotted, some plts offset on tissues, rear joint sl strained). *Hollett.* $224/£140

GOSSE, PHILIP. Memoirs of a Camp Follower. London/NY/Toronto: Longmans, Green, 1934. 1st ed. Etched frontisport. Gilt tan cl. (Edges foxed, eps smudged; cl faded through dj), o/w VG in dj (lt dust-soiled, sl chipped). *Reese.* $75/£47

GOSSE, PHILIP. The Pirate's Who's Who. London: Dulau, 1924. 1st Eng ed. 6 b/w plts. Teg. Good (spotted; spine ends, corners sl bumped, rubbed, rear hinge cracked). *Ulysses.* $200/£125

GOSSE, PHILIP. Rest Billets. (London): Dulau, 1927. 1st ed. One of 175. Frontis. Unopened. Gilt cl, marbled bds. (Few sl bumps, lt edgewear), else NF in glassine dj. *Reese.* $85/£53

GOSSE, PHILIP. St. Helena 1502-1938. London et al: Cassell, 1938. Color frontis, map. Fine in dj (1-inch chip at spine foot). *Explorer.* $72/£45

GOTCH, J. ALFRED. The Growth of the English House. Batsford, 1928. Rev, enlgd ed. (Ep cut), else VG in red cl. *Hadley.* $24/£15

GOTCH, PHYLLIS M. The Romance of the Boo-Bird Chick. Brimley Johnson, 1903. 1st ed. Sm 8vo. Color frontis, 14 color plts. Floral-patterned eps. Pict white bds. Internally Fine (bkpl; edges sl worn). *Bookmark.* $72/£45

Gotham and the Gothamites, a Medley. (By Samuel B.H. Judah.) NY: The Author, 1823. 1st ed. 56,93,(1)pp (foxed). Later 3/4 calf, marbled bds. BAL 11020. *M & S.* $275/£172

Gothic and Renaissance Art. Collection of the Late Thomas Fortune Ryan. NY: American Art Assoc/Anderson Galleries, 1933. Folio. 5 color plts. Vellum spine, bds. Fine. *Turtle Island.* $75/£47

GOTTSHALL, FRANKLIN H. Heirloom Furniture. Bonanza, 1957. VG in dj (sl worn, repaired). *Whittle.* $29/£18

GOUDY, FREDERIC. The Alphabet: Fifteen Interpretive Designs. NY: Mitchell Kennerley, 1918. 1st ed. Black cl, gilt. (Spine dull, ends, corners rubbed), else VG-. *Pacific**. $29/£18

GOUGH, BATTY M. (ed). To the Pacific and Arctic with Beechey. London: Hakluyt Soc, 1973. Fine in dj. *Explorer*. $48/£30

GOUGH, HUBERT. The Fifth Army. London, 1931. 1st Eng ed. 20 fldg maps. Good (name; mkd, sl rubbed; no dj). *Clearwater*. $64/£40

GOULARD, THOMAS. A Treatise on the Effects and Various Preparartions of Lead.... London: P. Elmsly, 1772. 3rd ed. Tp, (A2-[A4]),232pp; fldg table. Marbled eps. Rebound in full morocco w/raised bands, gilt spine. *Edwards*. $136/£85

GOULD, C. The Paintings of Correggio. London: Faber, 1976. 12 color plts. Good in dj. *Ars Artis*. $200/£125

GOULD, CHARLES N. Travels Through Oklahoma. Oklahoma City, 1928. 1st ed. Grn cl, gilt. (Cvrs soiled), else Good. *Larry Price*. $25/£16

GOULD, CHESTER. How Dick Tracy and Dick Tracy Jr Caught the Racketeers. NY: Cupples & Leon, (ca 1933). Cl-backed color pict bds. (Blank eps have tape mks.) Color dj (worn, marginal tears, fold). *Reisler*. $375/£234

GOULD, MICHAEL. Surrealism and the Cinema. South Brunswick/NY: A.S. Barnes, (1976). NF in dj. *Turtle Island*. $50/£31

GOULD, STEPHEN JAY. An Urchin in the Storm. NY: W.W. Norton, (1987). 1st ed. Maroon 1/2 cl, gilt, cream paper bds. VG in dj. *Cady*. $20/£13

GOULDEN, SHIRLEY. Tales from Japan. Super Splendour Books Series. W.H. Allen, 1961. Folio. Benvenuti (illus). 64pp. Pict bds (worn, soiled, neatly rebacked). *Hollett*. $104/£65

GOULDING, H. R. Old Lahore, Reminiscences of a Resident. Lahore, 1924. 2 lg fldg maps in rear pocket. *Hallam*. $104/£65

GOULEY, JOHN W. S. Diseases of the Urinary Organs: Including Stricture of the Urethra, Affections of the Prostate, and Stone.... NY, 1873. 1st ed. 368pp. Grn tooled cl. VG (corners worn). *Doctor's Library*. $85/£53

GOVE, JESSE A. The Utah Expedition, 1857-1858. Concord, NH: NH Hist Soc, 1928. 1st ed. 4 plts. (Lt shelfworn, sl stains to cvrs, fore-edges), else VG. Howes G279. *Pacific**. $104/£65

GOVER, ROBERT. The Maniac Responsible. NY: Grove, 1963. 1st ed. VG+ (name; sl shelfworn) in dj (sl edgeworn). *My Bookhouse*. $20/£13

Governess: Or, Little Female Academy. Being the History of Mrs. Teachum, and Her Nine Girls.... (By Sarah Fielding.) Phila: Dobson, 1791. 1st Amer ed. xii,228pp. Contemp calf (worn, cvr nearly detached; browned, soiled). *Oinonen**. $450/£281

Government of the Tongue. (By Richard Allestree.) Oxford: Theater, 1674. 1st ed, 2nd imp. Frontis, (2),(14),224pp. Gilt-tooled paneled calf. (Old name, old ink mks; glue to spine ends), else VG. *Pacific**. $219/£137

GOWANLOCK, THERESA and THERESA DELANEY. Two Months in the Camp of Big Bear. Park Dale: Times Office, 1885. 1st ed. Nice (lt worn, hinges neatly repaired). *Hermitage*. $75/£47

GOWANS, ALAN. Images of American Living. Phila: Lippincott, (1961). Orig ed. Fine in VG dj. *Turtle Island*. $55/£34

GOWER, RONALD. George Romney. London: Duckworth, 1904. 73 halftone, 16 photogravure plts, tissues. Teg. (Sm spine tear.) *Ars Artis*. $120/£75

GOWER, RONALD. The Great Historic Galleries of England. London: Sampson Low, 1881-82. 3 vols in 1. Sm folio. 24; 39; 18 plts. 1/2 morocco, gilt, raised cords. Fine. *Europa*. $80/£50

GOWER, RONALD. Sir Thomas Lawrence. London/Paris/NY, 1900. One of 600. Folio. Color frontisport. Marbled eps; teg, rest uncut. 1/2 morocco, marbled bds (orig limp paper wrappers bound in; lt spotted), gilt, raised bands. *Edwards*. $240/£150

GOWIN, EMMET. Emmet Gowin: Photographs. NY, 1976. 1st ed. Dj (sm tears). *Swann**. $103/£64

GOWIN, EMMET. Emmet Gowin: Photographs. NY: Knopf, 1976. 1st ed, 1st bk. 68 b/w plts. VG in dj (worn, repaired). *Cahan*. $125/£78

GOWING, LAWRENCE. Lucien Freud. (London, 1982.) Pict cl. Plastic dj. *Swann**. $46/£29

GOYTISOLO, JUAN. The Young Assassins. NY, 1959. 1st Amer ed. NF in VG+ dj (price-clipped). *Warren*. $50/£31

GRABAR, ANDRE and C. NORDENFALK. Early Medieval Painting from the Fourth to the Eleventh Century. Albert Skira, 1957. 101 tipped-in illus (98 color). Grn cl. Dj. *Maggs*. $64/£40

GRABAR, ANDRE. Byzantine Painting. Geneva: Skira, (1953). Fine in dj. *Petersfield*. $56/£35

GRABBE, EUGENE M. et al (eds). Handbook of Automation, Computation, and Control. NY: John Wiley, (1958-61). 3 vols. Fine set, vols 2 & 3 in djs. *Glaser*. $175/£109

GRABHORN, EDWIN. Some Remarks on the Printed Book. San Mateo, CA: Quercus, 1948. Inscribed presentation copy. VG (bkpl) in paper-cvrd bds. *Michael Taylor*. $32/£20

GRABHORN, JANE. The Compleat Jane Grabhorn: Hodge-Podge of Typographical Ephemera.... SF: Grabhorn-Hoyem, 1968. 1st ed. One of 400. 1/2 cl, dec bds. NF. *Pacific**. $98/£61

GRABHORN, ROBERT. Nineteenth Century Type Displayed in 18 Fonts Cast by United States Founders, Now in the Cases of the Grabhorn Press. SF: David Magee, 1959. One of 300 ptd. Signed by Edwin & Robert Grabhorn. Cl-backed patterned bds, morocco spine label. Fine in dj. *Pacific**. $98/£61

GRABO, CARL H. Peter and the Princess. Chicago: Reilly & Lee, 1920. 1st ed. 4to. 8 full-pg color plts by John R. Neill. Pict eps; teg. Grn linen, gilt, paste label. Good. *Reisler*. $250/£156

GRADIDGE, RODERICK. Dream-Houses. (NY): Brazillier, 1980. 20 photos. NF in dj (spine sl faded). *Hadley*. $51/£32

GRAF, ALFRED B. Exotica Pictorial Cyclopedia of Exotic Plants from Tropical and Near-Tropic Regions. NY, 1978. 9th ed. VG. *Larry Price*. $75/£47

GRAF, OSKAR MARIA. Prisoners All. Margaret Green (trans). NY: Knopf, 1928. 1st US ed. Gilt blue cl. VG in dj (chipped, split at flap fold). *Reese*. $40/£25

GRAFTON, SUE. F is for Fugitive. NY, 1989. 1st ed. Fine in Fine dj. *Warren*. $50/£31

GRAFTON, SUE. G Is for Gumshoe. NY, 1990. 1st Amer ed. Signed. Fine in Fine dj. *Polyanthos*. $35/£22

GRAFTON, SUE. G Is for Gumshoe. NY: Holt, 1990. 1st ed. Fine in Fine dj. *Beasley*. $35/£22

GRAFTON, SUE. H Is for Homicide. NY, 1991. 1st Amer ed. Signed. Fine in Fine dj. *Polyanthos*. $35/£22

GRAFTON, SUE. J is for Judgement. NY: Holt, (1993). 1st ed. Fine (bkseller's stamp) in dj (corner sl nicked). *Second Life*. $35/£22

GRAFTON, SUE. J is for Judgement. NY: Henry Holt, 1993. 1st ed. Inscribed. *Lame Duck*. $65/£41

GRAFTON, SUE. K is for Killer. NY: Holt, (1994). 1st ed. Fine (bkseller's stamp) in dj. *Second Life*. $35/£22

GRAFTON, SUE. K Is for Killer. NY, 1994. 1st Amer ed. Fine in Fine dj. *Polyanthos*. $25/£16

GRAFTON, SUE. L Is for Lawless. NY, 1995. 1st Amer ed. Signed. Fine in Fine dj. *Polyanthos*. $35/£22

GRAHAM, ANGUS. The Golden Grindstone. London: C&W, 1935. Frontis. Fine in VG dj. *High Latitude.* $50/£31

GRAHAM, CAROLINE. Death of a Hollow Man. Century, 1989. 1st UK ed. Fine in dj. *Williams.* $96/£60

GRAHAM, CAROLINE. The Envy of the Stranger. Century, 1984. 1st UK ed. Fine in dj (price-clipped). *Williams.* $120/£75

GRAHAM, CAROLINE. The Killings at Badger's Drift. Century, 1987. 1st UK ed. Fine in dj. *Williams.* $152/£95

GRAHAM, CAROLINE. Murder at Madingley Grange. Century, 1990. 1st UK ed. Fine in dj. *Williams.* $48/£30

GRAHAM, FRANK. The Brooklyn Dodgers. Putnam, 1945. Later ptg. VG + in VG dj. *Plapinger.* $75/£47

GRAHAM, FRANK. McGraw of the Giants. Putnam, 1944. 1st ed. VG + in Good + dj. *Plapinger.* $65/£41

GRAHAM, FRANK. The New York Yankees. Putnam, 1958. New, rev ed, 1st ptg. VG + in VG dj. *Plapinger.* $145/£91

GRAHAM, HARVEY. Eternal Eve. The History of Gynaecology and Obstetrics. GC: Doubleday, 1951. 1st Amer ed. VG. *Glaser.* $35/£22

GRAHAM, HENRY GREY. Scottish Men of Letters in the Eighteenth Century. A&C Black, 1908. 32 ports. (Fr bd mkd, spine head chipped, frayed.) *Hollett.* $40/£25

GRAHAM, J. A. The Sporting Dog. NY: Macmillan, 1904. 1st ed. One of 100. Frontis repro. Teg. 1/2 leather, marbled bds. VG + . *Mikesh.* $225/£141

GRAHAM, LLEWELLYN. The Romance of Texas Oil. Fort Worth: Tariff Pub, 1935. Good (dampstained) in pict stiff wraps. *Dumont.* $35/£22

GRAHAM, MARIA. Journal of a Residence in India. London, 1812. 1st ed. 4to. Hand-colored frontis, vii,211pp; 15 plts. Contemp calf (rebacked). *Maggs.* $520/£325

GRAHAM, MARIA. Journal of a Residence in India. Edinburgh: Constable, 1813. 2nd ed. 1/2-title, hand-colored engr frontis, 15 engr plts, 2 fldg (1 w/sm hole, sl tear at fold). Later 1/2 morocco. (Sl spotted; sl rubbed.) *Sotheby's*.* $349/£218

GRAHAM, PHILIP. Showboats. Austin: Univ of TX, 1951. VG in dj. *American Booksellers.* $45/£28

GRAHAM, R. B. CUNNINGHAME. Brought Forward. Duckworth, 1916. 1st ed. VG + . *Any Amount.* $32/£20

GRAHAM, R. B. CUNNINGHAME. Charity. London, 1912. 1st ed. NF (fep sl offset; sl rubbed). *Polyanthos.* $25/£16

GRAHAM, R. B. CUNNINGHAME. Doughty Deeds. London: Heinemann, 1925. 1st ed. 8 plts. Nice. *Cady.* $25/£16

GRAHAM, R. B. CUNNINGHAME. Father Archangel of Scotland. A&C Black, 1896. 1st ed. VG (edges sl bumped). *Any Amount.* $26/£16

GRAHAM, R. B. CUNNINGHAME. His People. Duckworth, 1906. 1st ed. Red cl, gilt. (Foxed; fr cvr sl scratched, spine ends sl bumped), else VG + . *Any Amount.* $32/£20

GRAHAM, R. B. CUNNINGHAME. Jose Antonio Paez. London: Heinemann, 1929. 1st ed. 9 plts, 1 map. (Edges, tp spotted; lower bd damped.) *Hollett.* $48/£30

GRAHAM, R. B. CUNNINGHAME. Mogreb-El-Acksa. NY: Viking, 1930. 1st ed. Frontis, map. (Sl rubbed, sm spine nick), o/w VG. *Worldwide.* $20/£13

GRAHAM, R. B. CUNNINGHAME. Pedro de Valdivia, Conqueror of Chile. London: Heinemann, 1926. 1st ed. Frontis, fldg map. (Spine faded, edge of lower bd sl spotted.) *Hollett.* $48/£30

GRAHAM, RON et al. A Study of the Colt Single Action Army Revolver. TX, 1976. Signed by Graham and John Kopec (co-author). (Lt worn.) *Oinonen*.* $110/£69

GRAHAM, STEPHEN. Balkan Monastery. London: Ivor Nicholson & Watson, 1936. 1st ed. Gray cl. (Blindstamp on ep; spine ends sunned), else Nice in pict dj (sl loss spine foot). *Reese.* $30/£19

GRAHAM, STEPHEN. Life and Last Words of Wilfrid Ewart. London, 1924. 1st Eng ed. Good (monograms on ll, lib labels). *Clearwater.* $40/£25

GRAHAM, STEPHEN. A Private in the Guards. London: Macmillan, 1919. 1st ed. Gilt-dec blue cl. (Ink inscrip dated 1919; sl rubbed), else Nice. *Reese.* $50/£31

GRAHAM, STEPHEN. Through Russian Central Asia. NY: Macmillan, 1916. 1st ed. 24 plts, dbl-pg map. (Sl rubbed, spine ends sl frayed), o/w VG. *Worldwide.* $85/£53

GRAHAM, STEPHEN. Tramping with a Poet in the Rockies. NY: D. Appleton, 1922. 1st ed, 2nd ptg. VG. *Perier.* $20/£13

GRAHAM, VICTOR. Growing Succulent Plants. Newton Abbot/Devon, 1987. Fine in dj. *Brooks.* $34/£21

GRAHAM, W. S. 2nd Poems. Poetry London, 1945. 1st Eng ed. Nice (lacks dj). *Clearwater.* $80/£50

GRAHAM, W. S. Implements in Their Places. London, 1977. 1st Eng ed. Inscribed. Fine in card wrappers. *Clearwater.* $88/£55

GRAHAM, W. S. The Nightfishing. London, 1955. 1st Eng ed. VG (eps tanned, fep sl wrinkled; fr cvr sl faded) in dj. *Clearwater.* $80/£50

GRAHAM, W. S. The Nightfishing. Faber & Faber, 1955. 1st ed. VG (feps lt browned, sl spotted; extrems sl rubbed, spine sl faded) in dj (nicked, sl rubbed, mkd). *Ulysses.* $136/£85

GRAHAM, W. S. The White Threshold. Faber & Faber, 1949. 1st ed. VG (feps sl spotted; top edge sl dusty) in dj (nicked, spotted, sl torn, rubbed, dusty, edges sl dknd, top edge of rear panel lacks sm piece). *Ulysses.* $104/£65

GRAHAM, WILLIAM A. The Custer Myth. Harrisburg, (1953). 1st ed. VG + in dj (worn, chipped). *Pratt.* $45/£28

GRAHAM, WILLIAM A. The Custer Myth. Harrisburg: Stackpole, (1953). 1st ed. VG in Good dj. *Perier.* $50/£31

GRAHAM, WILLIAM A. The Custer Myth...To Which Is Added, Important Items...and A Complete and Comprehensive Bibliography, by Fred Dustin. Harrisburg: Stackpole, (1957). 2nd ptg. NF in dj (sl worn). *Pacific*.* $29/£18

GRAHAM, WILLIAM A. The Reno Court of Inquiry. Harrisburg, (1954). 1st ed. Fldg map. (Sl cvr wear), o/w VG + . *Pratt.* $65/£41

GRAHAM, WILLIAM A. The Reno Court of Inquiry. Abstract of the Official Record of Proceedings of the Reno Court of Inquiry, Convened at Chicago, Illinois, 13 January 1879.... Harrisburg: Stackpole, (1954). Frontisport, facs, fldg map. NF in dj (sl dusty, few sm chips). *Pacific*.* $58/£36

GRAHAM, WILLIAM A. The Reno Court of Inquiry: Abstract of the Official Record of Proceedings. Harrisburg, PA: Stackpole, 1954. 1st ed. VG in dj. *Labordo.* $85/£53

GRAHAM, WILLIAM A. The Story of Little Big Horn. NY: Century, 1926. 1st ed. NF. *Labordo.* $175/£109

GRAHAM, WILLIAM A. The Story of the Little Big Horn, Custer's Last Fight. Harrisburg: Military Service Pub, (1945). 2nd ed. Black/red-stamped cl (rippled). Dj (spine ends chipped). *Dawson.* $50/£31

GRAHAM, WILLIAM A. The Story of the Little Big Horn: Custer's Last Fight. NY: Century, (1926). 1st ed. Engr frontis, 3 maps (2 fldg). Grn cl, gilt. (Inscrip; extrems sl rubbed), else VG. Howes G292. *Pacific*.* $127/£79

GRAHAM, WINSTON. Marnie. GC: Doubleday, 1961. 1st ed. (Bkpl), else Fine in Fine dj. *Between The Covers.* $175/£109

GRAHAME, JAMES. The Birds of Scotland and Other Poems. London/Edinburgh: Longman, Hurst et al/Wm. Blackwood, 1806. 1st ed. 248pp. Contemp 1/2 calf (newly rebacked, corners repaired). *Cox.* $64/£40

GRAHAME, KENNETH. Dream Days. John Lane, Bodley Head, 1930. 1st ed thus. 168pp; 28 illus by Ernest H. Shepard. Pict cl (spine, edges sl dknd). *Hollett.* $56/£35

GRAHAME, KENNETH. Dream Days. London: John Lane, Bodley Head, 1930. 1st ed illus by E. H. Shepard. De luxe ed. Ltd to 275 numbered, signed by Grahame and Shepard. 8vo. (xii),168pp. Teg, rest uncut. Orig 1/4 vellum-backed marbled paper bds. (Pastedown eps sl speckled), else Fine in card slip-case w/ptd paper label. *Sotheran.* $637/£398

GRAHAME, KENNETH. Fun o' the Fair. London/Toronto: J.M. Dent, (1929). 1st ed thus. 8vo. Roberta F.C. Waudby (illus). (vi),7-29pp. Fine in yellow paper wraps, stitched as issued. *Sotheran.* $125/£78

GRAHAME, KENNETH. The Golden Age. London: John Lane, Bodley Head, 1928. 1st ed de luxe illus by E. H. Shepard. Ltd to 275 numbered, signed by Grahame and Shepard. 8vo. (xii),166pp. Teg, rest uncut. Orig 1/4 vellum-backed marbled paper bds. (Pastedown eps sl browned), else Fine in card slip-case w/ptd paper label. *Sotheran.* $637/£398

GRAHAME, KENNETH. The Headswoman. London: John Lane, Bodley Head, 1921. One of 75. Signed. 8vo. 8 color plts. Vellum, dec-stamped bds. (Eps sl foxed), o/w Fine. *Heritage.* $750/£469

GRAHAME, KENNETH. Kenneth Grahame's Wind in the Willows. A Pop-Up Book. London: Methuen Children's Books, 1983. 5 pop-ups by Babette Cole. Glazed pict bds. VG. *Book-finders.* $45/£28

GRAHAME, KENNETH. The Reluctant Dragon. NY: HRW, 1983. 4to. Michael Hague (illus). Fine in Fine dj. *American Booksellers.* $30/£19

GRAHAME, KENNETH. The Wind in the Willows. London: Methuen, (1927). 1st ed thus. 8vo. 20 full-pg illus by Wyndham Payne. (Sl foxed.) Teg. Blue cl, gilt. Color pict dj (lt worn, dknd). *Reisler.* $350/£219

GRAHAME, KENNETH. The Wind in the Willows. NY: Heritage Press, (1940). 9 1/4 x 6. 12 color plts by Arthur Rackham. Blue cl, gilt. (Spine sunned), else VG in VG- slipcase (sl broken). *Pacific*.* $40/£25

GRAHAME, KENNETH. The Wind in the Willows. Methuen, 1908. 1st UK ed. NF (spine ends sl pushed) in re-issue dj. *Williams.* $3,200/£2,000

GRAHAME, KENNETH. The Wind in the Willows. London: Methuen, 1931. 1st ed illus by E. H. Shepard. 8vo. (vi),312pp. Pict eps; teg, rest deckled. Orig pub's full grn morocco, gilt. (Spine faded, sl browned, extreme tips of corners rubbed), o/w VG. *Sotheran.* $720/£450

GRAHAME, KENNETH. The Wind in the Willows. NY: Heritage, 1940. Lg 8vo. 12 color plts, 14 illus by Arthur Rackham. Red/blue pict cl, fr cvr w/design by Rackham stamped in yellow. Dj (few sm tears), pub's slipcase. *Christie's*.* $645/£403

GRAHAME, KENNETH. The Wind in the Willows. NY: LEC, 1940. Ltd to 2020 signed by Bruce Rogers (designer). 4to. 16 mtd color plts by Arthur Rackham on cream paper. Teg. Cl-backed dec bds. *Christie's*.* $773/£483

GRAHAME, KENNETH. The Wind in the Willows. LEC, 1940. One of 2020 signed by Bruce Rogers (designer). Arthur Rackham (illus). Fine in slipcase. *Swann*.* $862/£539

GRAHAME, KENNETH. The Wind in the Willows. Methuen Children's Books Ltd, 1971. 1st ed thus. One of 250 numbered, signed by E. H. Shepard (illus). Color eps. Aeg. Full dec morocco, gilt, raised bands. Fine (fr cvr sl mkd) in slipcase (sl mkd, rubbed, dusty). *Ulysses.* $1,000/£625

GRAHAME, KENNETH. The Wind in the Willows. NY: Holt, 1980. Lg 4to. Michael Hague (illus). Fine in Fine dj. *American Booksellers.* $35/£22

GRAINGE, WILLIAM. The Battles and Battle Fields of Yorkshire. York: James Hutton, 1854. 1st ed. Frontis map, xi,204pp. Blind-stamped cl, gilt. VG. *Hollett.* $104/£65

GRAMATKY, HARDIE. Creeper's Jeep. NY: Putnam, 1948. 1st ed. 7.5x9.75. 64pp. Good. *Cattermole.* $25/£16

GRAMATKY, HARDIE. Hercules. NY: Putnam, 1940. 1st ed. 8x10. 72pp. VG in dj. *Cattermole.* $25/£16

GRAMMATICUS, SAXO. The History of Amleth, Prince of Denmark. Copenhagen: LEC, 1954. One of 1500. Signed by Sigurd Vasegaard (illus). 1/2 pigskin, dec bds. Fine in slipcase (sm tear). *Pacific*.* $35/£22

GRAMMONT, COUNT. Memoirs of the Court of Charles the Second. Walter Scott (ed). London: Henry G. Bohn, 1853. Teg. Purple calf, gilt, brn/grn inlaid morocco spine labels; bound by Root & Son. (Cvrs irregularly sunned), else VG. *Pacific*.* $58/£36

GRAND, GORDON. Colonel Weatherford and His Friends. NY: Derrydale, 1933. One of 1450. Red cl. NF. *Biscotti.* $90/£56

GRAND, GORDON. Colonel Weatherford and His Friends. NY: Derrydale, 1933. One of 1450. Signed, inscribed. (Sl worn.) *Oinonen*.* $130/£81

GRAND, GORDON. Colonel Weatherford's Young Entry. NY: Derrydale, 1935. One of 1350. Signed, inscribed. (Sl worn.) *Oinonen*.* $70/£44

GRAND, GORDON. Old Man and Other Colonel Weatherford Stories. NY: Derrydale, 1934. One of 1150. Signed, inscribed. (Sl worn.) *Oinonen*.* $50/£31

GRAND, GORDON. Old Man. NY: Derrydale, 1934. One of 1150. Color frontis. Red cl. Fine. *Biscotti.* $100/£63

GRAND, GORDON. The Silver Horn. NY: Derrydale, 1932. Ltd to 950 numbered. Orig prospectus laid in. Red paper over bds. Fine. *Biscotti.* $300/£188

GRAND, GORDON. The Southborough Fox. NY: Derrydale, 1939. One of 1450. Signed. (Sl worn.) *Oinonen*.* $70/£44

GRAND, GORDON. The Southborough Fox. NY: Derrydale, 1939. One of 1450, signed. Red cl. Fine. *Biscotti.* $100/£63

GRAND, GORDON. Young Entry. NY: Derrydale, 1935. One of 1350. Red cl. Fine. *Biscotti.* $100/£63

Grandmamma Easy's New Little Stories About the Alphabet. Albany, NY: Sprague, (ca 1850). 8vo. 8pp. Illus paper wrappers (dusty, worn, spine chipped). *Reisler.* $200/£125

GRANGER, ALFRED HOYT. Charles Follen McKim: A Study of His Life and Work. Boston, 1913. (Extrems worn.) *Swann*.* $80/£50

GRANGER, BYRD H. Grand Canyon Place Names. Tucson, 1960. 1st ed. Map. VG in stiff magenta wraps. *Five Quail.* $15/£9

GRANT and CATES. A Handbook for Dissectors. Balt, 1940. 1st ed. (Ink dwg on ep), else VG. *Doctor's Library.* $35/£22

GRANT, BRUCE. How to Make Cowboy Horse Gear. Cambridge, 1956. Enlgd ed, 1st ed thus. VG in dj (worn). *Baade.* $32/£20

GRANT, BRUCE. Isaac Hull, Captain of Old Ironside. Chicago, (1947). 1st ed. Fine in dj (sl worn). *Pratt.* $25/£16

GRANT, CHARLES (ed). Night Visions 2. (Arlington Hts: Dark Harvest, 1985.) 1st ed. One of 300. NF in dj (sm chip bottom edge rear panel), slipcase. *Pacific*.* $81/£51

GRANT, CLAUDE. The Shikari, a Hunter's Guide. Westminster, 1914. (Cvrs damp mkd, affecting interior; lt dampstaining, esp last few pp.) Fair. *Hallam.* $88/£55

GRANT, DONALD. Personal Reminiscences of Royal Dornoch Golf Club, 1900-1925. (London: Donald Grant, 1979.) 1st ed. Inscribed, signed, dated 1979. Fine in dec wrappers. *Pacific*.* $98/£61

GRANT, ED. The Tame Trout: A Tale of the Maine Woods. SF: (F.P. & M.B. Farquhar), 1939. Ltd ed. Wrappers. (Cvrs sunned), else VG. *Pacific**. $52/£33

GRANT, FRANK (ed). Report of the Reunion of the Grant Family Association...in Washington D. C., April 27, 1922. Westfield, MA, 1922. (Pp browned) in wrapper (discolored, sl worn). *Woolman*. $20/£13

GRANT, GORDON. The Life and Adventures of John Nicol, Mariner. NY: Farrar & Rinehart, 1936. Pict cl. VG. *American Booksellers*. $65/£41

GRANT, J. C. B. A Method of Anatomy Descriptive and Deductive. London, 1948. 4th ed. VG. *Whitehart*. $40/£25

GRANT, JAMES AUGUSTUS. A Walk Across Africa. London, 1864. 1st ed. 8vo. xviii,453pp + 31pp pub's list; fldg map in rear pocket (sm splits to folds). Gilt-illus cl. (Tp inner margin replaced affecting lettering of pub; lt browned, ex-lib, bkpl, hinges cracked; soiled, spine chipped.) *Edwards*. $576/£360

GRANT, MAURICE HAROLD A Chronological History of the Old English Landscape Painters (in Oil). Leigh-on-Sea: F. Lewis, 1957-61. Ltd to 500. 8 vols. Fine set in djs. *Hollett*. $400/£250

GRANT, MAURICE HAROLD. A Dictionary of British Landscape Painters from the 16th Century to the Early 20th Century. Leigh-on-Sea, 1976. 2nd rpt w/supp. (Top edge sl damp-wrinkled.) *Washton*. $50/£31

GRANT, MAXWELL. The Shadow Laughs. NY: Street & Smith, (1931). 1st ed. Pict bds. (Spine ends sl rubbed), else NF. *Pacific**. $115/£72

GRANT, MRS. Memoirs of an American Lady. NY: Samuel Campbell, 1809. 2nd Amer ed. 344pp. Contemp 1/2 black calf, bds. (Hinges tender; spine, tips, corners rubbed, worn), else VG. Howes G302. *Chapel Hill*. $150/£94

GRANT, ROBERT. An Average Man. Boston: James R. Osgood, 1884. 1st ed. Brn cl. Fine. *Sumner & Stillman*. $65/£41

GRANT, ULYSSES S. Personal Memoirs. NY: Charles L. Webster, 1885-1886. 1st ed. 2 vols. Floral ptd eps. Dk grn cl, gilt. Good (lt aging; sl worn, dusty; sm stain vol 1 cvr). *Baltimore**. $85/£53

GRANT, ULYSSES S. Personal Memoirs. NY, 1885. 1st ed. 2 vols. 584; 647pp. (Bkpls, corners sl worn, vol 1 backstrip faded.) *Woolman*. $85/£53

GRANT, ULYSSES S. Personal Memoirs. NY, 1885. 1st ed. 2 vols. 584; 647pp. (Worn, sm piece torn from spine), o/w VG + . *Pratt*. $115/£72

GRANT, ULYSSES S. Personal Memoirs. NY, 1885. Sub's ed. 2 vols. Pub's 1/2 morocco, gilt. *Swann**. $230/£144

GRANT, VERNON. Tinker Tim, the Toy Maker. Racine: Whitman, (1934). 1st ed. 4to. 29pp. Pict bds. VG in VG dj. *Davidson*. $200/£125

GRANVILLE, A. B. A Catechism of Facts. Phila, 1832. 1st ed. VG (extrems sl worn) in ptd paper cvrd bds. *Doctor's Library*. $125/£78

GRANVILLE, A. B. An Historical and Practical Treatise on the Internal Use of Hydro-Cyanic (Prussic) Acid, in Pulmonary Consumption, and Other Diseases of the Chest.... Longman, Hurst, Rees, Orme, Brown, 1820. 2nd ed. xvii,(vii),417pp (lib stamps), ad leaf. Uncut. Orig bds, new paper spine, label. *Bickersteth*. $104/£65

GRASS, GUNTER. Dog Years. NY, 1965. 1st Amer ed. Fine in dj (2 sm nicks). *Polyanthos*. $25/£16

GRASS, GUNTER. Dog Years. NY, 1965. 1st Amer ed. Signed. NF in NF dj. *Warren*. $75/£47

GRASS, GUNTER. The Flounder. NY: Harcourt, (1978). 1st Amer ed. Signed. NF in dj (sm tear). *Captain's Bookshelf*. $100/£63

GRASS, GUNTER. The Flounder. LEC, 1985. One of 1000 signed. 3 vols. Fine in slipcase. *Swann**. $201/£126

GRAVES, ALFRED PERCIVAL. To Return to All That. Cape, 1930. 1st Eng ed. 4 b/w plts. VG (pencil notes rep, inscrip, frontis creased, top edge sl dusty; prelims, edges, eps spotted; feps partly browned, some pp sl mkd, thumbed; spine ends, cvrs sl bumped) in dj (nicked, sl torn, rubbed, mkd, dusty, price-clipped, edges sl dknd). *Ulysses*. $360/£225

GRAVES, ALGERNON. A Dictionary of Artists. Henry Graves, 1895. New, enlgd ed. xii,314pp (sm lib stamp, numbers). 1/4 calf (spine rubbed, corners worn), gilt. *Hollett*. $240/£150

GRAVES, CHARLES L. Hubert Parry. London: Macmillan, 1926. 1st ed. 2 vols. 12 plts. (Lib labels rear pastedowns; labels removed from upper bds.) *Hollett*. $48/£30

GRAVES, CHARLES S. Before the White Man Came. Yreka: Siskiyou News, 1934. Signed. Frontis. (Bottom of rear bd nicked, spine ends lt worn.) *Dawson*. $75/£47

GRAVES, CHARLES. Leather Armchairs. NY: Coward McCann, (1964). 1st Amer ed. Brn bds, white linen spine. Fine in dj. *Appelfeld*. $85/£53

GRAVES, CHARLES. The Story of St. Thomas's 1106-1947. Faber, 1947. 8 color plts. *Edwards*. $24/£15

GRAVES, J. A. My Seventy Years in California, 1857-1927. L.A.: Times-Mirror, 1927. 1st ed. 19 plts. Blue cl, gilt. (Few pp lt foxed), o/w Fine. *Pacific**. $29/£18

GRAVES, J. A. Out of Doors, California and Oregon. L.A.: Grafton Pub, 1912. VG. *Perier*. $75/£47

GRAVES, RICHARD PERCEVAL. The Brothers Powys. London: Routledge & Kegan Paul, 1983. 1st Eng ed. Fine (spine foot sl bumped) in dj. *Ulysses*. $56/£35

GRAVES, ROBERT and JOSHUA PODRO. Jesus in Rome. Cassell, 1957. 1st ed. VG in Good dj (sl soiled). *Virgo*. $40/£25

GRAVES, ROBERT and LAURA RIDING. A Pamphlet Against Anthologies. GC: Doubleday, Doran, 1928. 1st ed. Fine in dj (sl worn). *Lenz*. $400/£250

GRAVES, ROBERT. 5 Pens in Hand. Doubleday, 1958. 1st US ed. VG (bkpl) in dj (rubbed). *Williams*. $58/£36

GRAVES, ROBERT. Adam's Rib. Trianon, 1955. One of 2026. 36 orig wood-engrs by James Metcalf. Fine (bkpl) in VG dj (sl browned, closed tear to spine head). *Williams*. $51/£32

GRAVES, ROBERT. Advice from a Mother. Poem-of-the-Month-Club Ltd, 1970. Signed. Broadsheet. VG (sl creased). *Ulysses*. $152/£95

GRAVES, ROBERT. An Ancient Castle. Owen, 1980. 1st UK ed. Fine in Fine dj. *Martin*. $14/£9

GRAVES, ROBERT. Antigua Penny Puce. Majorca: Seizin, 1936. 1st UK ed, 1st issue w/'ytyle' for 'style' on pg 100, line 11. VG (bkpl, lacks dj). *Williams*. $51/£32

GRAVES, ROBERT. At the Gate. Poems 1974. Stellar, 1974. One of 536 signed of which 500 were for sale. Fine (bkpl) in dj. *Williams*. $104/£65

GRAVES, ROBERT. At the Gate: Poems. (London: Bertram Rota), 1974. 1st ed. One of 536 ptd. Signed. Fine in dj. *Pacific**. $98/£61

GRAVES, ROBERT. Beyond Giving: Poems. (London: Bertram Rota), 1969. 1st ed. One of 536 ptd. Signed. Fine in dj. *Pacific**. $86/£54

GRAVES, ROBERT. But It Still Goes On. London: Jonathan Cape, (1930). 1st ed, 1st state of leaf 157/8, w/reference to 'The Child She Bare' intact. Gilt grn cl. Fine in NF grn dj ptd in purple. *Reese*. $300/£188

GRAVES, ROBERT. Claudius the God. Arthur Barker, 1934. 1st UK ed. VG (bkpl) in dj (browned, edges worn). *Williams*. $136/£85

GRAVES, ROBERT. Collected Poems (1914-1947). London, 1948. 1st Eng ed. VG in dj (sl nicked). *Clearwater*. $80/£50

GRAVES, ROBERT. Collected Poems 1914-1947. Cassell, 1948. 1st UK ed. NF (bkpl) in VG dj (spine foot, fr panel sl chipped). *Williams.* $58/£36

GRAVES, ROBERT. Collected Poems 1965. Cassell, 1965. 1st UK ed. VG (bkpl; spine sl unevenly faded through wrapper) in dj (sm tape mks to rear). *Williams.* $29/£18

GRAVES, ROBERT. Collected Poems. Doubleday, 1961. 1st US ed, 1st ed thus. VG (bkpl; lacks dj). *Williams.* $19/£12

GRAVES, ROBERT. Colophon to Love Respelt. (London: Bertram Rota), 1967. 1st ed. One of 350 ptd. Signed. Fine in dj. *Pacific*. $86/£54

GRAVES, ROBERT. Contemporary Techniques of Poetry. London: Leonard & Virginia Woolf, 1925. 1st ed. Fair in semi-stiff illus wrappers. *Maggs.* $96/£60

GRAVES, ROBERT. Count Belisarius. Casssell, 1938. 1st UK ed. VG (bkpl; spine sl faded, lacks dj). *Williams.* $24/£15

GRAVES, ROBERT. Country Sentiment. Secker, 1920. 1st UK ed. VG (sm ink inscrip, bkpl; spine browned). *Williams.* $58/£36

GRAVES, ROBERT. The Crane Bag. Cassell, 1969. 1st UK ed. NF (ink name) in dj. *Williams.* $40/£25

GRAVES, ROBERT. The Crowning Privilege. Cassell, 1955. 1st ed. NF in dj. *Virgo.* $56/£35

GRAVES, ROBERT. The English Ballad. Benn, 1927. 1st UK ed. Fine (bkpl) in VG dj (sl unevenly browned). *Williams.* $200/£125

GRAVES, ROBERT. Fairies and Fusiliers. Heinemann, 1917. 1st UK ed. VG (bkpl; spine sl faded, nicked). *Williams.* $152/£95

GRAVES, ROBERT. The Feather Bed. Hogarth, 1923. 1st ed. One of 250 signed. Dec bds (spine sl rubbed). *Sotheby's*. $221/£138

GRAVES, ROBERT. The Feather Bed. Richmond: Hogarth, 1923. One of 250. Signed. Cl-backed patterned bds. (Bkpl; edges dknd.) *Kane*. $225/£141

GRAVES, ROBERT. Good-Bye to All That. London: Jonathan Cape, (1929). 1st ed, 2nd state, w/the ll bearing the offending text replaced w/cancels. VG in dj (dknd, chipped, split 1 joint mended on verso). *Reese.* $200/£125

GRAVES, ROBERT. Good-Bye to All That. London: Jonathan Cape, (1929). 1st ed, 1st issue, w/the text on pp290 and 341-3 intact. Port. Salmon cl, gilt. (Gilt leather bkpl), o/w NF in dj (sl dknd, sm chip, closed tear top of fr joint). *Reese.* $850/£531

GRAVES, ROBERT. Good-Bye to All That. Cape, 1929. 1st UK ed, 2nd issue w/Sassoon poem excised from pp 341-343. VG in dj (sl browned, few closed tears, edges sl worn). *Williams.* $208/£130

GRAVES, ROBERT. Good-Bye to All That. Cape, 1929. 1st UK ed, 1st issue w/Sassoon poem on pp 341-343 (replaced by asterisks in 2nd issue). VG in dj (price-clipped, spine sl browned, couple inconspicuous closed tears, spine extrems sl worn). *Williams.* $952/£595

GRAVES, ROBERT. The Green-Sailed Vessel Poems 1971. Stellar, 1971. One of 536 signed of which 500 were for sale. Fine (bkpl) in dj. *Williams.* $104/£65

GRAVES, ROBERT. The Green-Sailed Vessel: Poems. (London: Bertram Rota), 1971. 1st ed. One of 536. Signed. Fine in dj. *Pacific*. $86/£54

GRAVES, ROBERT. Hercules, My Shipmate. NY: Farrar, Straus & Cudahy, (1957). 3rd Amer imp. Dbl-pg map, single-pg map. Orange-gray cl. (Paper lt browned.) Dj (edges chipped). *Maggs.* $48/£30

GRAVES, ROBERT. Hercules, My Shipmate. NY: Creative Age, 1945. 1st ed. VG (shelfworn, pp yellowed) in dj (edgeworn). *My Bookhouse.* $47/£29

GRAVES, ROBERT. Homer's Daughter. London, (1955). 1st ed. VG in dj (badly chipped). *King.* $65/£41

GRAVES, ROBERT. I, Claudius. Arthur Barker, 1934. 1st UK ed. VG (sm stamp, bkpl; lacks dj). *Williams.* $104/£65

GRAVES, ROBERT. I, Claudius. Arthur Barker, 1934. 1st ed. Fldg family tree. VG (eps lt browned; top edge sl dusty, top/fore-edges sl mkd) in dj (nicked, sl rubbed, torn, creased, dusty, inside flaps, spine, edges browned, lacks sm piece). *Ulysses.* $880/£550

GRAVES, ROBERT. Impenetrability or The Proper Habit of English. Leonard & Virginia Woolf, 1926. 1st ed. Blue-grn bds (joints sl worn, spine faded). Good in glassine wrapper. *Maggs.* $200/£125

GRAVES, ROBERT. John Doyle. The Marmosite's Miscellany. Hogarth, 1925. 1st ed. Dec bds (top sl soiled). *Sotheby's*. $349/£218

GRAVES, ROBERT. John Kemp's Wager, a Ballad Opera. Oxford: Basil Blackwell, 1925. 1st ed. One of 750 ptd. Dec bds. (Worn.) *Maggs.* $128/£80

GRAVES, ROBERT. John Kemp's Wager. Oxford: Basil Blackwell, 1925. One of 100 numbered, signed. 1/4 vellum, patterned bds. *Sotheby's*. $312/£195

GRAVES, ROBERT. John Kemp's Wager. Oxford: Basil Blackwell, 1925. 1st Eng ed. VG (feps browned) in card wrappers (sl dusty, yapp edges rubbed, creased, spine sl dknd, spine ends sl bumped). *Ulysses.* $360/£225

GRAVES, ROBERT. Lars Porsena, or The Future of Swearing and Improper Language. London: Martin Brian & O'Keeffe, (1972). 1st ed. One of 100. Signed. Blue cl, gilt-lettered spine. Fine in slipcase. *Pacific*. $138/£86

GRAVES, ROBERT. Lawrence and the Arabs. London: Jonathan Cape, (1927). 1st ed. Port. Tan cl, gilt. (Bkpl, fr hinge cracking), else Good. *Reese.* $35/£22

GRAVES, ROBERT. Lawrence and the Arabs. Cape, 1927. 1st UK ed. Good + (bkpl, ink inscrip, pict of Lawrence pasted to fep). *Williams.* $26/£16

GRAVES, ROBERT. The Less Familiar Nursery Rhymes. London: Ernest Benn, (1927). 1st ed. VG in stapled white wrappers. *Maggs.* $64/£40

GRAVES, ROBERT. Mammon and the Black Goddess. GC, 1965. 1st Amer ed. Two-tone cl. VG in dj (edges worn). *King.* $35/£22

GRAVES, ROBERT. Man Does, Woman Is. Cassell, 1964. 1st UK ed. VG (ink name) in dj (sl rubbed, stained). *Williams.* $26/£16

GRAVES, ROBERT. The Meaning of Dreams. Cecil Palmer, 1924. 1st UK ed. Good + (bkpl; cvrs bumped, spine faded, browned). *Williams.* $77/£48

GRAVES, ROBERT. The More Deserving Cases: Eighteen Old Poems for Reconsideration. (N.p.): Marlborough College, 1962. 1st ed thus. One of 350 in cl, of 750 numbered, signed. Port. Polished buckram, gilt. Fine. *Reese.* $150/£94

GRAVES, ROBERT. Mrs. Fisher or The Future of Humour. London: Kegan Paul, Trench, Trubner, 1928. 1st ed. VG (sl worn) in dj (sl worn). *Lenz.* $275/£172

GRAVES, ROBERT. My Head! My Head! Secker, 1925. 1st UK ed. VG (bkpl) in dj (rear panel sl chipped). *Williams.* $216/£135

GRAVES, ROBERT. My Head! My Head! London: Martin Secker, 1925. One of 500. 1st issue: black-veined red cl backed w/black cl, no rule on tp, etc. VG (feps partly browned; prelims, edges, eps spotted; top edge dusty; spine ends sl bumped, cvrs sl rubbed) in dj (nicked, rubbed, dusty, sl spotted, mkd, frayed, sl soiled, browned). *Ulysses.* $560/£350

GRAVES, ROBERT. No More Ghosts. Faber, 1940. 1st UK ed. VG (bkpl; cvrs unevenly browned, lacks dj). *Williams.* $16/£10

GRAVES, ROBERT. Occupation: Writer. Cassell, 1951. 1st UK ed. VG + (ink name, bkpl) in VG dj (price-clipped, spine sl worn). *Williams.* $35/£22

GRAVES, ROBERT. On English Poetry. Heinemann, 1922. One of 1560. 2nd state binding w/cobbled design on spine, fr, rear cvrs VG (spine browned, bkpl). *Williams.* $58/£36

GRAVES, ROBERT. The Pier-Glass. Secker, (1921). One of 500. Good+ (bkpl; ink name; spine browned, ends sl chipped, spine label sl chipped). *Williams.* $104/£65

GRAVES, ROBERT. The Pier-Glass. London: Martin Secker, (1921). 1st ed. One of 500. Frontisport. Fine in black/yellow cobbled bds. Dj. *Maggs.* $400/£250

GRAVES, ROBERT. Poems 1914 to 1926. Heinemann, 1927. One of 1000. VG (sl foxed, spine label browned). *Williams.* $77/£48

GRAVES, ROBERT. Poems 1914-1927. Heinemann, 1927. One of 115 numbered, signed. Teg. 1/4 vellum. Dj (sl soiled). *Sotheby's**. $405/£253

GRAVES, ROBERT. Poems 1926-1930. Heinemann, 1931. 1st UK ed. VG+. *Williams.* $40/£25

GRAVES, ROBERT. Poems 1938-1945. Cassell, 1946. 1st UK ed. Fine (bkpl) in VG dj (spine sl faded). *Williams.* $40/£25

GRAVES, ROBERT. Poems 1953. Cassell, 1953. One of 250 signed. VG in orig tissue wrapper (sl browned, chipped, worn). *Williams.* $200/£125

GRAVES, ROBERT. Poems 1965-1968. Cassell, 1968. 1st UK ed. VG+ in dj. *Williams.* $32/£20

GRAVES, ROBERT. Poems 1970-1972. Cassell, 1972. 1st UK ed. Fine in dj. *Williams.* $40/£25

GRAVES, ROBERT. Poems About Love. Cassell, 1969. 1st UK ed. VG+ in dj. *Williams.* $45/£28

GRAVES, ROBERT. Poems and Satires 1951. Cassell, 1951. 1st UK ed. Fine (bkpl) in VG dj (spine sl browned). *Williams.* $45/£28

GRAVES, ROBERT. The Poems of Robert Graves. LEC, 1980. One of 2000 signed by Paul Hogarth (illus) and Freeman Keith (designer). Fine in slipcase. *Swann**. $34/£21

GRAVES, ROBERT. Poetic Unreason. Cecil Palmer, 1925. 1st UK ed. VG (bkpl; spine label browned, lt foxed). *Williams.* $77/£48

GRAVES, ROBERT. The Poor Boy Who Followed His Star. Cassell, 1968. 1st UK ed. VG+ in dj (price-clipped). *Williams.* $38/£24

GRAVES, ROBERT. Proceed, Sergeant Lamb. Random House, 1941. 1st US ed. Fine (bkpl) in VG dj (price-clipped, sl rubbed, few short closed tears). *Williams.* $58/£36

GRAVES, ROBERT. Robert Graves; Selected by Himself. Penguin Books, 1957. 1st ed. Fine in dec wrappers. *Maggs.* $32/£20

GRAVES, ROBERT. Sergeant Lamb of the Ninth. Methuen, 1940. 1st UK ed. VG- (bkpl, fldg map torn w/loss; cvrs sl mkd). *Williams.* $32/£20

GRAVES, ROBERT. Seven Days in New Crete. Cassell, 1949. 1st ed. VG (edges lt spotted, spine foot sl bumped) in dj (nicked, sl creased, edges sl rubbed). *Ulysses.* $104/£65

GRAVES, ROBERT. Seventeen Poems Missing from Love Respelt. (London: Bertram Rota), 1966. 1st ed. One of 330 ptd. Signed. Unopened. Fine in dj. *Pacific**. $98/£61

GRAVES, ROBERT. The Shout. Elkin Mathews, 1929. One of 530 signed. Fine (bkpl) in VG sl oversize dj (top edge sl creased). *Williams.* $240/£150

GRAVES, ROBERT. The Shout. London: Elkin Matthews & Marrot, 1929. 1st ed. One of 530 ptd. Signed. Dec bds. (Sl offset eps), else Fine in dj. *Pacific**. $259/£162

GRAVES, ROBERT. Steps. Cassell, 1958. 1st UK ed. VG+ (bkpl) in VG dj (price-clipped, sm mks, closed tears). *Williams.* $48/£30

GRAVES, ROBERT. The Tales of Unwisdom. Cassell, 1950. 1st UK ed. (Edges sl spotted), o/w VG in dj (soiled, worn). *Virgo.* $64/£40

GRAVES, ROBERT. Ten Poems More. Paris: Hours Press, 1930. 1st ed. One of 200 numbered, signed. Folio. VG (sm thumb-mk to 1/2-title) in photographic bds, grn roan spine, gilt. *Maggs.* $280/£175

GRAVES, ROBERT. They Hanged My Saintly Billy. Doubleday, 1957. 1st US ed. VG (bkpl) in dj (edges sl worn). *Williams.* $40/£25

GRAVES, ROBERT. They Hanged My Saintly Billy. Cassell, 1957. 1st ed. VG in dj (sl soiled, chipped, price-clipped, sm closed tear to bk fold). *Virgo.* $72/£45

GRAVES, ROBERT. Timeless Meeting: Poems. (London): Bertram Rota, 1966. 1st ed. One of 536 ptd. Signed. Fine in dj. *Pacific**. $98/£61

GRAVES, ROBERT. To Whom Else? Majorca: Seizin, 1931. One of 200 signed. VG (bkpl, cvrs sl rubbed). *Williams.* $280/£175

GRAVES, ROBERT. Welchman's Hose. Fleuron, 1925. One of 525 of which 500 were for sale. VG (bkpl; spine sl worn w/sl loss). *Williams.* $400/£250

GRAVES, ROBERT. Whipperginny. Heinemann, 1923. 1st UK ed. VG (bkpl; spine sl faded, extrems worn). *Williams.* $56/£35

GRAVES, ROBERT. Whipperginny. London, 1923. 1st Eng ed. Patterned bds (extrems sl rubbed). *Clearwater.* $104/£65

GRAY, A. The First American Library—A Short Account of the Library Company of Philadelphia 1731-1931. Phila, 1936. Good in ptd cvrs. *Moss.* $22/£14

GRAY, A. Gray's School and Field Book of Botany. NY, 1868. 236; 386pp (name, pp browned). (Soiled, corners, edges worn.) *Sutton.* $40/£25

GRAY, ALASDAIR et al. Lean Tales. Cape, 1985. 1st UK ed. Signed. Fine in dj. *Williams.* $40/£25

GRAY, ALASDAIR. 1982 Janine. (NY): Viking, (1984). 1st US ed. As New in dj. *Bernard.* $25/£16

GRAY, ASA. Gray's New Manual of Botany. B. L. Robinson and M. L. Fernald (rev). NY: Amer Book Co, 1908. 7th ed. Flexible leather. Good. *Archer.* $15/£9

GRAY, ASA. Manual of the Botany of the Northern U.S. S. Watson and J. Coulter (rev). NY: Amer Book Co, 1889. 6th ed. Good (fr bd dampstained). *Archer.* $20/£13

GRAY, CECIL. Gilles de Rais. London: Simpkin Marshall, (1941). One of 200 numbered, signed by Gray and Michael Ayrton (illus). Good (4pp sl soiled; spine cracked, browned, sl worn, foot defective; cvrs sl mkd, spotted, dusty; cvr edges browned, sl rubbed). *Ulysses.* $152/£95

GRAY, CHRISTOPHER. Sculpture and Ceramics of Paul Gauguin. Balt: Johns Hopkins, 1963. VG in dj (soiled, traces of flaps glued down). *Turtle Island.* $175/£109

GRAY, DAVID. Smith. London: Duffield, 1911. Inscribed presentation from W. Somerset Maugham. 4 b/w plts, 1 of which is also mtd on fr cvr. Good (bkpl, top edge dusty, rear hinge cracked; spine ends, corners bumped, rubbed; spine mkd, faded, worm hole to fr joint, rear cvr sl mkd). *Ulysses.* $400/£250

GRAY, DAVID. The Sporting Works of David Gray: Gallops I; Gallops II; Mr. Carteret. NY: Derrydale, 1929. Ltd to 750 numbered, signed sets. 3 vols. Orig prospectus laid in. Red cl. Fine in VG slipcase. *Biscotti.* $300/£188

GRAY, EDWARD F. Lief Eriksson Discoverer of America A.D. 1003. NY: Kraus Reprint, 1972. Rpt. Fldg map. VG. *Dumont.* $25/£16

GRAY, EDWARD. William Gray of Salem, Merchant. Boston: Houghton Mifflin, 1914. 1st ed. Ltd to 500 numbered. 8 engr plts. Grn cl, paper spine label. Good in slipcase. *Karmiole.* $60/£38

GRAY, ELIZABETH. The Cheerful Heart. Viking, 1959. 1st ptg. Kazue Mizamura (illus). 176pp. VG (name) in Good dj. *Price*. $22/£14

GRAY, HAROLD. The 'Pop-Up' Little Orphan Annie and Jumbo the Circus Elephant. Chicago: Pleasure Books, 1935. 8x9. Unpaginated. Pict bds. VG (ink, 1 pop-up sl loose; edgeworn). *My Bookhouse*. $225/£141

GRAY, HAROLD. Little Orphan Annie and Jumbo, the Circus Elephant. Chicago: Pleasure Books, (1935). 1st ed. 9 1/4 x 7 3/4. 3 pop-ups. Pict bds. (Last pop-up lacks center animal; soiled; fr cvr lacks piece from upper joint), else VG. *Pacific**. $81/£51

GRAY, HAROLD. Little Orphan Annie and Sandy. Racine: Whitman, 1933. 1st ed. 4 sq. Pict bds. (Old tape to upper 1/2 of tp gutter; spine, extrems sl rubbed, lower corners sl bumped), else VG. *Pacific**. $40/£25

GRAY, HAROLD. Little Orphan Annie and the Big Town Gunmen. Racine: Whitman, 1937. 1st ed. Cl-backed pict bds. (Soiled; rear hinge neatly cracked), else VG. *Pacific**. $40/£25

GRAY, HENRY. Anatomy, Descriptive and Surgical. Phila, 1887. 11th ed. 1100pp. Orig full calf. Good (1/2 of fep missing; scuffed, worn, shaken, spine torn). *Doctor's Library*. $50/£31

GRAY, HOWARD LEVI. English Field Systems. Harvard, 1915. 1st ed. (Sl shelfworn.) *Rybski*. $25/£16

GRAY, HUGH. Letters from Canada, Written During a Residence There in the Years 1806, 1807, and 1808. London: Longman, Hurst et al, 1809. 16,406pp; fldg map, 3 fldg tables. Contemp calf (rebacked). *Adelson*. $375/£234

GRAY, JAMES. The Illinois. NY, (1940). 1st ed. VG in dj (sl used). *King*. $20/£13

GRAY, JOHN HENRY. China: A History of the Laws, Manners, and Customs of the People.... William Gow Gregor (ed). London: Macmillan, 1878. 1st ed. 2 vols. 1/2-titles, xv,(i)blank,397,(1)imprint,(2)ads; xii,374,(2)ads; 137 line-engr plts. Blue cl, gilt. Sound (sl foxed, margins lt browned; worn, hinges cracking). *Morrell*. $136/£85

GRAY, JOHN S. Centennial Campaign: The Sioux War of 1876. (Ft. Collins, CO): Old Army, (1976). 1st ed. Fine in dj. *Pacific**. $109/£68

GRAY, NICOLETTE. XIXth Century Ornamented Types and Title Pages. Faber, 1938. 1st ed. 8 half-tone plts. Good. *Cox*. $45/£28

GRAY, ROBERT. The Birds of the West of Scotland. Glasgow: Thomas Murray & Sons, 1871. 1st ed. x,(i),520pp; complete w/15 tinted litho plts. Aeg. 3/4 sage grn morocco, gilt. VG (bkpl, few spots to plts). *Hollett*. $296/£185

GRAY, THOMAS. Elegy Written in a Country Church Yard. Cinncinnati, OH: Howe's Subscription Book Concern, 1867. Sq 12mo. Frontis, 24 leaves, 2pp ads; 32 VF 1/2-pg wood engrs. New black paper wrapper w/title label cut out from orig wrapper. *Hobbyhorse*. $75/£47

GRAY, THOMAS. Elegy Written in a Country Churchyard. LEC, 1938. Ltd to 1500 numbered, signed by Agnes Miller Parker (illus). Fine in slipcase. *Swann**. $115/£72

GRAY, THOMAS. Poems and Letters. London: Ptd at Chiswick Press, 1863. 1st ed thus. xvi,415pp; 4 mtd photo illus. Aeg. Contemp lt tan calf, raised bands, gilt. VG (extrems sl rubbed, few discolorations to cvrs). *Young*. $152/£95

GRAY, THOMAS. Poems and Letters. London: Ptd at the Chiswick Press, 1867. xi,415pp (lt foxed). Orig full calf (extrems rubbed), spine heavily gilt. Contents Clean. *Cullen*. $200/£125

GRAY, THOMAS. Poems and Letters. Chiswick, 1879. 1st ed thus. Frontisport, xvi,415pp. Marbled eps; gauffered edges, gilt inner dentelles, aeg. Prize binding by Riviere: full calf (worn), raised bands, gilt, black leather label. Text Fine (inscrip). *Hartfield*. $195/£122

GRAY, WILLIAM C. Camp-Fire Musings: Life and Good Times in the Woods. NY: A.D.F. Randolph, 1894. 1st ed. (Bkpl), else NF. *Pacific**. $40/£25

GRAY, WILLIAM H. A History of Oregon, 1792-1849. Portland, OR: Harris & Holman, 1870. 2nd issue, w/2 errata slips. Woodcut frontis, 624pp. Black pebbled cl (spine extrems lt frayed). Howes G342. *Karmiole*. $150/£94

GRAY, WILLIAM. Travels in Western Africa, in the Years 1818, 19, 20, and 21.... London: John Murray, 1825. 1st ed. xvi,413pp; fldg map, 14 plts (few lt foxed). Orig cl-backed bds, paper label. *Adelson*. $485/£303

GRAY, WILLIAM. Travels in Western Africa, in the Years 1818, 19, 20, and 21.... London: John Murray, 1825. 1st ed. 8vo. 1/2-title, frontis (lt foxed), xv,(i),413,(1)blank,(1)imprint; 10 aquatint plts, 4 lithos, engr fldg map (torn, creased w/o loss). Marbled edges. Contemp grn 1/2 calf, marbled bds, red label, gilt. VG (few plts marginally browned, offsetting to tp; sl rubbed). *Morrell*. $576/£360

GRAYSON, CHARLES (ed). The Sportsman's Hornbook. NY: Random House, 1933. One of 500. Prospectus laid in. Plain bds, leather spine (lt rubbed). *Dawson*. $100/£63

GRAYSON, WILLIAM J. The Hireling and the Slave, Chicora and Other Poems. Charleston, SC: McCarter, 1856. 3rd ed. (Extrems worn.) *Swann**. $138/£86

Great and Eccentric Characters, of the World, Their Lives and Their Deeds.... NY: Hurst, 1877. 1st ed. 799pp. (Sl foxed; sl rubbed, soiled, spine ends frayed), o/w VG. *Worldwide*. $25/£16

Great Britain, Atlantic Steam Ship of 3500 Tons. London, 1847. Thin folio. 14 fldg engr plts numbered 1-25. Cl-backed wrappers (worn, loose; dampstain in lower margins throughout). *Swann**. $230/£144

Greater America. Essays in Honor of Herbert Eugene Bolton. Berkeley/L.A.: Univ of CA, 1945. 1st ed. 12 maps (11 lg fldg). Fine in dj. *Argonaut*. $90/£56

Greatest Plague in Life. London: David Bogue, (1847). 1st ed. 12 etchings. Full tan polished calf, gilt line mitres on cvrs, gilt paneled spine, raised bands, leather spine labels, aeg, by Root. Good. *Appelfeld*. $250/£156

GREELEY, HORACE. The American Conflict: A History of the Great Rebellion in the United States of America, 1860-'64: Its Causes, Incidents and Results.... Hartford: O.D. Case, 1864-67. 1st ed. 2 vols. Marbled edges. Period 3/4 calf, marbled bds, red morocco spine labels, sl raised bands. (Vol 2 fr joint cracked through), else VG. *Pacific**. $161/£101

GREELEY, WILLIAM ROGER. The Essence of Architecture. NY, (1927). 1st Amer ed. NF (lt rubbed). *Polyanthos*. $30/£19

GREELY, ADOLPHUS W. Three Years of Arctic Service. NY, 1894. Lg fldg map. Dec cl (extrems sl worn). (4-inch tear in map repaired w/clear tape), o/w contents VG. *New Hampshire**. $70/£44

Green Envelopes. London: John Murray, (1929). 1st ed. Cl, bds, paper labels. (Foxing early and late, at edges), o/w NF in dj (sm nicks, smudges) w/litho facs of grn 'On Active Service' envelope. *Reese*. $175/£109

Green Envelopes. London, 1929. 1st Eng ed. VG (corner sl bruised; no dj). *Clearwater*. $64/£40

GREEN, ANNA KATHARINE. The Leavenworth Case. NY: Putnam, (1890s). Rpt. 475pp; fldg facs (tear repaired w/linen tape). Red cl. Good (fr hinge starting, tp pulled at bottom; bumped, rubbed, soiled). *Blue Mountain*. $25/£16

GREEN, BEN K. The Color of Horses. Flagstaff, (1974). 1st ed. 34 color plts. VG in dj (sm chips, tears). *Woolson*. $50/£31

GREEN, BEN K. Horse Tradin'. NY: Knopf, 1967. 1st ed. Fine in dj. *Labordo*. $60/£38

GREEN, BEN K. Some More Horse Tradin'. NY: Knopf, 1972. 1st trade ed. Grn cl, gilt. Fine in NF dj. *Harrington*. $45/£28

GREEN, BEN K. A Thousand Miles of Mustangin'. Flagstaff: Northland Press, (1972). 1st trade ed. Brn cl, gilt. Fine in NF dj (tape reinforcement on verso). *Harrington.* $50/£31

GREEN, BEN K. A Thousand Miles of Mustangin'. Flagstaff: Northland, 1972. 1st ed. NF in dj. *Dumont.* $75/£47

GREEN, BEN K. The Village Horse Doctor. NY: Knopf, 1971. 1st ed. VG in dj. *Labordo.* $45/£28

GREEN, BEN K. Wild Cow Tales. NY, 1969. 1st ed. Fine in dj. *Baade.* $60/£38

GREEN, CHARLES R. Early Days in Kansas. Olathe, KS: Charles R. Green, 1913. Map. (Pp browned, last few pp lt damp-stained), o/w Good in ptd wraps. *Brown.* $75/£47

GREEN, DONALD E. Panhandle Pioneer: Henry C. Hitch. Norman: Univ of OK, (1980). Fine in dj. *Lien.* $25/£16

GREEN, F. Some Personal Recollections of Lillie Hitchcock Coit. SF: Grabhorn, 1935. Ltd to 450. (Cvr sl faded), else VG. *Perier.* $60/£38

GREEN, F. Some Personal Recollections of Lillie Hitchcock Coit. SF: Grabhorn, 1935. 1st ed. One of 450. Signed by Edwin Grabhorn. Cl-backed orange bds, paper spine label. Fine. *Harrington.* $100/£63

GREEN, G. GILBERT. Cacti and Succulents. London, 1953. 1st ed. 17 color, 168 b/w photo plts. (Few bleach spots fr cvr), else VG. *Larry Price.* $25/£16

GREEN, GERALD. The Artists of Terezin. NY, (1978). Dj (wrinkled). *Argosy.* $50/£31

GREEN, HENRY. Nothing. NY, 1950. 1st Amer ed. (Bkpl, spine sl discolored), else VG in dj (edgeworn). *King.* $45/£28

GREEN, HENRY. Nothing. Hogarth, 1950. 1st ed. (Pp sl yellowed), o/w VG in dj (sl nicked, yellowed). *Virgo.* $160/£100

GREEN, HORACE. General Grant's Last Stand. NY, 1936. 1st ed. VG + . *Pratt.* $30/£19

GREEN, J. R. A Short History of the English People. NY: Harper, 1894. 4 vols. Teg. Red cl, gilt. NF. *Pacific*.* $46/£29

GREEN, JERRY. Year of the Tiger. Coward McCann, 1969. 1st ed. VG + in VG dj. *Plapinger.* $45/£28

GREEN, JOHN. Johnny Green of the Orphan Brigade. A. D. Kirwan (ed). (Lexington): Univ of KY, (1956). 1st ed. One of unspecified # of the 'Chickamauga Edition,' signed. Frontis. Red cl. (Eps browned, sticker removed fep, sig), else NF in dj (lt soiled). *Chapel Hill.* $120/£75

GREEN, JULIAN. Avarice House. NY, 1927. 1st Amer ed, 1st bk. NF (sl rubbed, spine sunned). *Polyanthos.* $30/£19

GREEN, JULIAN. Memories of Happy Days. Harper, (c1942). 1st ed. VG. *Book Broker.* $20/£13

GREEN, MOWBRAY A. The Eighteenth Century Architecture of Bath. Bath, 1904. One of 500. (Lib ink stamps, bkpl, fldg map loose, prelims bound out of order; fr hinge cracked, rear hinge detached; worn, rubbed, spine discolored.) *Edwards.* $64/£40

GREEN, PAUL. The Field God and In Abraham's Bosom. NY, 1927. 1st ed. VG in dj (rubbed, chipped). *King.* $75/£47

GREEN, PETER. Habeas Corpus and Other Stories. Cleveland: World, (1963). 1st Amer ed. VG in dj. *Cady.* $20/£13

GREEN, PHILIP JAMES. Sketches of the War in Greece.... London, 1828. 2nd ed. Contemp calf (extrems worn; bkpl). *Swann*.* $115/£72

GREEN, RALPH. A History of the Platen Jobber. Chicago: Phillip Reed, 1953. 1st ed. Ltd to 495 numbered. (Bkpl, ink name.) *Oak Knoll.* $65/£41

GREEN, RICHARD. The Works of John and Charles Wesley. London: The Author, 1896. 1st Eng ed. VG (rebound in cl). *Clearwater.* $104/£65

GREEN, SYDNEY. Furs to Furrows. Caldwell: Caxton, 1939. 1st ed. VG in dj (torn). *Perier.* $50/£31

GREEN, THOMAS HILL. Works. R. L. Nettleship (ed). London, 1885. 1st ed. 3 vols. New 1/2 calf. Fine set. *Young.* $320/£200

GREEN, THOMAS. The Universal Herbal. London: Caxton Press, n.d. 2nd ed, rev. Vol 2 (only). Frontis; 47 plts (of 50; plt at pg 267 supplied twice, hand-colored). 1/2 calf, marbled bds (sl worming to lower margin, fr hinge taped; worn, spine sl wormed w/loss). Internally Clean. *Edwards.* $160/£100

GREENAWAY, KATE. Almanack for 1883. London, (1882) 1883. 1st ed. 24mo. Cl-backed pict glossy bds (lt rubbed). *Swann*.* $172/£108

GREENAWAY, KATE. Almanack for 1884. Routledge, n.d. (1883). 1st Eng ed. Color frontis. Aeg. Wrappers. NF. *Ulysses.* $312/£195

GREENAWAY, KATE. Almanack for 1885. Routledge, n.d. (1884). 1st Eng ed. Frontis, 5 full-pg dwgs. Buckram-backed glazed pict bds. VG (ink/pencil mks to pp; cvrs sl mkd, dusty, edges rubbed; spine ends, corners sl bumped, bruised). *Ulysses.* $136/£85

GREENAWAY, KATE. Almanack for 1886. London: Routledge, (1885). 1st ed. 4x3. Cl-backed olive grn glazed pict bds. NF (inscrip). *Pacific*.* $98/£61

GREENAWAY, KATE. Almanack for 1886. Routledge, n.d. (1885). 1st Eng ed. Frontis, 5 full-pg dwgs. Buckram-backed glazed pict bds. VG (ink/pencil mks to pp; cvrs mkd, sl dusty, edges sl rubbed, bottom corners sl bumped, bruised). *Ulysses.* $136/£85

GREENAWAY, KATE. Almanack for 1887. Routledge, n.d. (1886). 1st Eng ed. Frontis, 4 full-pg dwgs. Buckram-backed glazed pict bds. VG (ink/pencil mks to pp, fep bottom edges sl worn; cvrs sl mkd, edges sl rubbed, bottom corners sl bumped, bruised). *Ulysses.* $136/£85

GREENAWAY, KATE. Almanack for 1888. Routledge, n.d. (1887). 1st Eng ed. Frontis, 4 full-pg dwgs. Buckram-backed glazed pict bds. VG (ink/pencil mks to pp; cvrs sl mkd, bottom edges sl rubbed, corners sl bumped, bruised). *Ulysses.* $136/£85

GREENAWAY, KATE. Almanack for 1890. London: Routledge, (1890). 1st ed. 24mo. (24)pp. Pale grn cl, gilt. Fine in ptd dj (2 sm nicks). *Sotheran.* $317/£198

GREENAWAY, KATE. Almanack for 1894. Routledge, n.d. (1893). 1st Eng ed. Frontis; 16 full-pg illus. Aeg. Dec gilt imitation morocco. Fine. *Ulysses.* $264/£165

GREENAWAY, KATE. Almanack for 1895. Routledge, n.d. (1894). 1st Eng ed. 16mo. Frontis, 16 full-pg illus. Aeg. Dec gilt imitation morocco. VG (cvrs mkd, dusty, sl bowed, spine rubbed). *Ulysses.* $720/£450

GREENAWAY, KATE. A Day in a Child's Life. London: Routledge, (1881). 1st ed, 1st issue. Slim sm 4to. Grn coated eps. Grn cl, lt grn glazed bds, beveled edges. (Sl foxed; sl worn, spotted, lt scattered discoloration.) *Baltimore*.* $80/£50

GREENAWAY, KATE. A Day in a Child's Life. London: Routledge, (1881). 1st ed. Sm 4to. Edmund Evans (engrs). 30pp. Grn cl-backed color paper over beveled bds. VG (lt soiled, edgeworn). *House.* $225/£141

GREENAWAY, KATE. A Day in a Child's Life. Routledge, 1881. 1st ed. Pict bds, spine. VG. *Green Meadow.* $152/£95

GREENAWAY, KATE. Kate Greenaway Pictures. London: Frederick Warne, 1921. 1st ed. Photogravure frontis, 20 mtd color plts. Grn cl. VG in dj (torn). *Davidson.* $300/£188

GREENAWAY, KATE. Kate Greenaway's Alphabet. London: Frederick Warne, (c. 1885). (Chipping along spine, joints), else VG- in pict yellow/grn wrappers. *Pacific*.* $40/£25

GREENAWAY, KATE. Kate Greenaway's Birthday Book for Children. Verses by Mrs. Sale Barker. London: Frederick Warne, (c. 1901). Sq 3.75. Pict cvr label. (Sl soiled, few birthdays filled in), else VG. *Pacific*.* $63/£39

GREENAWAY, KATE. Kate Greenaway's Book of Games. London: George Routledge & Sons, (1889). 1st ed. 4to. 64pp; 24 full color plts. All edges tinted yellow. Blue cl-backed grn glazed pict bds (corners lt worn, cvrs mkd). *Reisler*. $600/£375

GREENAWAY, KATE. Language of Flowers. London: Routledge, (1884). 1st ed. 5.75x4.5. Edmund Evans (engrs). Yellow eps; all edges stained yellow. Cl-backed glazed olive pict bds. (Foxed; cvrs scratched, extrems rubbed), else VG-. *Pacific**. $63/£39

GREENAWAY, KATE. Marigold Garden. London: Routledge, (1885). 1st ed, 1st issue. Edmund Evans (engrs). Grn eps. Glazed grn pict bds, brn cl spine. (Cvrs discolored, scraped), else VG. *Pacific**. $92/£58

GREENAWAY, KATE. Mother Goose or the Old Nursery Rhymes. London: Frederick Warne, n.d. (ca 1915). 12mo. Frontis, 1/2-title, 54pp; 44 full-pg chromolithos by Greenaway. Flowered dec eps. Full color pict label on bds, olive grn cl spine. Fine (2 corners sl rubbed). *Hobbyhorse*. $225/£141

GREENAWAY, KATE. Under the Window. London, (1878). 1st ed. Sm 4to. Pict bds (few chips bottom fore-edge). *Swann**. $172/£108

GREENBERG, DAN. Chewsday. NY: Stein & Day, (1968). 1st ed. VF in VF dj (spine sl rubbed). *Between The Covers*. $85/£53

GREENBERG, MARTIN. The Robot and the Man. NY: Gnome, (1953). 1st ed. Tan bds. (Tape residue to each fep; edges stained from old dj protector), else NF in dj (sm closed tears). *Other Worlds*. $40/£25

GREENBURG, DAN W. Sixty Years...Cattle Industry in Wyoming.... Cheyenne, WY: WY Stock Growers Assoc, 1932. 1st ed. VG+ in stiff pict wrappers. Howes S580. *Labordo*. $350/£219

GREENE, A. C. The Last Captive. Austin: Encino, 1972. 1st ed thus. NF in dj (insect damage). Howes J232. *Labordo*. $25/£16

GREENE, A. C. The Last Captive. Austin: Encino, 1972. 1st ed. Signed by Greene and the pub. Fine in dj. *Dumont*. $75/£47

GREENE, A. C. A Personal Country. NY: Knopf, 1969. 1st ed. Fine in dj. *Labordo*. $45/£28

GREENE, C. E. and D. YOUNG (eds). Encyclopaedia of Agriculture. London: William Green & Sons, 1907. 4 vols. Orig 1/2 morocco (vol 4 spine rubbed, lettering dull), gilt. VG set. *Hollett*. $96/£60

GREENE, DAVID L. and DICK MARTIN. The Oz Scrapbook. NY, (1977). 1st ed. Dj. *Kane**. $55/£34

GREENE, DONALD J. The Politics of Samuel Johnson. Yale Univ, 1960. 1st Eng ed. (1 corner tip sl bumped; no dj.) *Clearwater*. $40/£25

GREENE, EDWARD L. Landmarks of Botanical History. F. Egerton (ed). Stanford: Stanford Univ, 1983. Part 1 rpt of 1909 ed. 1st ed thus. 2 vols. Fine in NF djs. *Archer*. $100/£63

GREENE, EDWARD L. Landmarks of Botanical History. Frank N. Egerton (ed). Stanford, 1983. 2 vols. As New in dj. *Woolson*. $75/£47

GREENE, GRAHAM. Another Mexico. NY: Viking, 1939. 1st Amer ed of The Lawless Roads. Fine in dj (sm tear). *Lenz*. $500/£313

GREENE, GRAHAM. Babbling April. Oxford: Basil Blackwell, 1925. 1st ed, 1st bk. One of approx 300 issued. Inscribed to Eric Quayle. 8vo. (Foxed.) Pale paper bds, lettered in blue. Gray dj (soiled, lacks piece base of spine, corners chipped). *Sotheby's**. $2,208/£1,380

GREENE, GRAHAM. The Basement Room and Other Stories. Cresset, 1935. 1st ed, 1st issue. Grn cl, gilt. Good (feps spotted, pastedowns dampstained; lettering sl dull, few sl mks). *Hollett*. $240/£150

GREENE, GRAHAM. Brighton Rock. London: Heinemann, (1938). 1st ed. Red cl, gilt spine. VG (lt browned, edges lt foxed). *Heritage*. $250/£156

GREENE, GRAHAM. Brighton Rock. Heinemann, 1938. 1st UK ed. NF (pp sl browned). *Williams*. $560/£350

GREENE, GRAHAM. Brighton Rock. Heinemann, 1938. 1st ed. VG (pg edges sl browned; top edge sl spotted, sm snag to spine head; lacks dj). *Ulysses*. $720/£450

GREENE, GRAHAM. British Dramatists. London, 1942. 1st Eng ed. Nice in dj (sl rubbed). *Clearwater*. $80/£50

GREENE, GRAHAM. British Dramatists. London: Collins, 1942. 1st ed. Pict bds. (Eps browned), o/w NF in NF dj (sl edgeworn). *Agvent*. $100/£63

GREENE, GRAHAM. A Burnt-Out Case. Heinemann, 1961. 1st UK ed. Fine in NF dj (price-clipped). *Williams*. $48/£30

GREENE, GRAHAM. Collected Essays. London, 1969. 1st Eng ed. Very Nice in dj (sl torn, price-clipped). *Clearwater*. $88/£55

GREENE, GRAHAM. The Comedians. Bodley Head, 1966. 1st UK ed. Fine in Fine dj. *Martin*. $45/£28

GREENE, GRAHAM. The Confidential Agent. NY: Viking, 1939. 1st ed. Fine in dj (sl worn). *Lenz*. $500/£313

GREENE, GRAHAM. The End of the Affair. London: Heinemann, (1951). 1st ed. Fine in dj w/wraparound band. *Lenz*. $300/£188

GREENE, GRAHAM. England Made Me. GC: Doubleday Doran, 1935. 1st ed. Fine in Fine dj. *Lenz*. $750/£469

GREENE, GRAHAM. Getting to Know the General. Bodley Head, 1984. 1st UK ed. (Inscrip), o/w Fine in dj. *Virgo*. $24/£15

GREENE, GRAHAM. Getting to Know the General. Bodley Head, 1984. 1st UK ed. NF in dj (price-clipped). *Williams*. $26/£16

GREENE, GRAHAM. The Great Jowett. Bodley Head, 1981. One of 525 signed. Fine in glassine dj (sm spine tear). *Any Amount*. $136/£85

GREENE, GRAHAM. The Honorary Consul. Bodley Head, 1973. 1st UK ed. Mint in Mint dj. *Martin*. $26/£16

GREENE, GRAHAM. How Father Quixote Became a Monsignor. Hollywood: Sylvester & Orphanos, 1980. Ltd to 330 signed. Fine dec cl. *Truepenny*. $250/£156

GREENE, GRAHAM. In Search of a Character. Two African Journals. London: Bodley Head, (1961). 1st ed. This copy inscribed. Fine in dj. *Black Sun*. $500/£313

GREENE, GRAHAM. It's a Battlefield. GC: Doubleday Doran, 1934. 1st ed. Fine in dj (sl worn). *Lenz*. $750/£469

GREENE, GRAHAM. J'Accuse, the Dark Side of Nice. London, 1982. 1st ed. VG in wrappers. *Typographeum*. $15/£9

GREENE, GRAHAM. J'Accuse. Bodley Head, 1982. 1st UK ed. Fine in self-wrappers. *Williams*. $24/£15

GREENE, GRAHAM. Journey Without Maps. GC: Doubleday Doran, 1936. 1st ed. Fine in dj (sl worn). *Lenz*. $750/£469

GREENE, GRAHAM. The Labyrinthine Ways. NY: Viking, 1940. 1st Amer ed, 1st state, w/p165 transposed w/p256. Fine in Fine dj. *Lenz*. $850/£531

GREENE, GRAHAM. The Little Fire Engine. London: Bodley Head, (1973). 1st ed. Edward Ardizzone (illus). Pict bds. Fine. *Lenz*. $100/£63

GREENE, GRAHAM. The Little Horse Bus. London: Bodley Head, (1974). 1st ed. Edward Ardizzone (illus). Pict bds. Fine in Fine dj. *Lenz*. $100/£63

GREENE, GRAHAM. The Little Horse Bus. Max Parrish, 1952. 1st UK ed. Fine (bds sl warped) in VG dj (sl nicked, rubbed). *Williams*. $472/£295

GREENE, GRAHAM. The Little Steamroller. London: Bodley Head, (1974). 1st ed. Edward Ardizzone (illus). Pict bds. Fine in Fine dj. *Lenz*. $100/£63

GREENE, GRAHAM. The Little Steamroller. Doubleday, 1974. 1st ed. 9.5x8 oblong. Edward Ardizzone (illus). 46pp. VG- (name, date stamp, crayoned name) in Good dj (two 1/2-inch chips, creased). *Price*. $28/£18

GREENE, GRAHAM. The Little Train. London: Bodley Head, (1973). 1st ed. Edward Ardizzone (illus). Pict bds. Fine. *Lenz.* $100/£63

GREENE, GRAHAM. Loser Takes All. London: Heinemann, (1955). 1st ed. Fine in dj (sl worn). *Lenz.* $200/£125

GREENE, GRAHAM. The Man Within. London: Heinemann, (1929). 1st ed, 1st bk. Black cl, gilt spine. VG (spine faded, cocked, extrems sl rubbed, cvrs sl faded) in dj (lt soiled, spine sl browned). *Heritage.* $2,000/£1,250

GREENE, GRAHAM. The Ministry of Fear. Heinemann, 1943. 1st UK ed. VG (ink inscrip) in variant pastel yellow bds. *Williams.* $72/£45

GREENE, GRAHAM. The Ministry of Fear. NY: Viking, 1943. 1st US ed. VG + . *Beasley.* $75/£47

GREENE, GRAHAM. The Ministry of Fear. NY: Viking, 1943. 1st ed. Fine in dj (sl worn). *Lenz.* $500/£313

GREENE, GRAHAM. Monsignor Quixote. Bodley Head, 1982. 1st UK ed. Fine in Fine dj. *Martin.* $22/£14

GREENE, GRAHAM. Mr. Visconti...an Extract of Travels with My Aunt. London: Bodley Head, (1969). 1st ed. Edward Ardizzone (illus). Wrappers. Fine. *Black Sun.* $350/£219

GREENE, GRAHAM. The Name of Action. Heinemann, 1930. 1st UK ed. VG (sl bumped, creased). *Williams.* $280/£175

GREENE, GRAHAM. Nineteen Stories. London: Heinemann, (1947). 1st ed. Fine in Fine dj. *Lenz.* $350/£219

GREENE, GRAHAM. The Other Man. Bodley Head, 1983. 1st UK ed. Fine in Fine dj. *Martin.* $13/£8

GREENE, GRAHAM. Our Man in Havana. London, 1958. 1st Eng ed. Nice in dj (sl nicked, 1 closed tear). *Clearwater.* $80/£50

GREENE, GRAHAM. The Pleasure-Dome, the Collected Film Criticism 1935-40. John Russell Taylor (ed). London: Secker, (1972). Dj. *Petersfield.* $38/£24

GREENE, GRAHAM. The Potting Shed. London: Penguin Books, 1971. Uncorrected proof copy. (Pp sl browned; part of cvr dknd.) Ptd wrappers. *Black Sun.* $100/£63

GREENE, GRAHAM. The Power and the Glory. Heinemann, 1940. 1st UK ed. Almost Fine (contemp ink name, date) in NF dj (virtually invisible professional restoration to edges). *Williams.* $5,200/£3,250

GREENE, GRAHAM. A Quick Look Behind. L.A.: Sylvester & Orphanos, 1983. One of 330 signed. Bright blue cl, ptd paper spine label. Fine (spine sl faded) in cream cl open-end slipcase. *Heritage.* $200/£125

GREENE, GRAHAM. The Quiet American. NY, 1956. 1st Amer ed. VG in dj (edges frayed, sl torn; spine sunned). *King.* $30/£19

GREENE, GRAHAM. The Revenge: An Autobiographical Fragment. Privately ptd, 1963. One of 300. (Inscrip), else NF in wraps. *Any Amount.* $256/£160

GREENE, GRAHAM. A Sense of Reality. Bodley Head, 1963. 1st UK ed. Fine in dj. *Williams.* $88/£55

GREENE, GRAHAM. Stamboul Train. London, (1932). 1st ed. (Binding sl skewed.) *Swann*.* $115/£72

GREENE, GRAHAM. Stamboul Train. London: Heinemann, 1932. 1st ed. Cvrs in this copy measure vertically 189mm. Black buckram (spine damp-spotted, sides sl so; gilt dull, rubbed). Internally Fine. *Temple.* $54/£34

GREENE, GRAHAM. The Third Man and The Fallen Idol. London: Heinemann, (1950). 1st ed. Fine in dj (spine sl worn). *Lenz.* $300/£188

GREENE, GRAHAM. The Third Man and The Fallen Idol. London: Heinemann, 1950. 1st Eng ed. VG (erasure on tp; edges of 1/2-title, final blank browned) in dj (nicked, chipped, sl torn, rubbed, creased, spine dknd). *Ulysses.* $280/£175

GREENE, GRAHAM. The Third Man and The Fallen Idol. Heinemann, 1950. 1st UK ed. Fine in VG + dj (edges sl worn, few sm closed tears). *Williams.* $312/£195

GREENE, GRAHAM. Travels with My Aunt. NY, (1970). 1st Amer ed. NF in NF dj. *Polyanthos.* $25/£16

GREENE, GRAHAM. Travels with My Aunt. Bodley Head, 1969. 1st UK ed. Mint in Mint dj (price-clipped). *Martin.* $29/£18

GREENE, GRAHAM. Travels with My Aunt. Toronto/London, 1969. 1st ed. NF in NF dj (sm spine tear). *Polyanthos.* $40/£25

GREENE, GRAHAM. Ways of Escape. Bodley Head, 1980. 1st UK ed. Press rev laid in. Fine in Fine dj. *Martin.* $29/£18

GREENE, GRAHAM. Why Do I Write? London: Percival Marshall, 1948. 1st ed. Dec bds. VG (spine sl browned, sm ink stain fr cvr). *Maggs.* $144/£90

GREENE, GRAHAM. Why the Epigraph? Nonesuch, 1989. One of 950 signed. Fine in clear plastic wrapper. *Williams.* $112/£70

GREENE, HOMER. A Lincoln Conscript. Boston, (1909). 1st ed. VG (pg wrinkled, name). *Woolman.* $10/£6

GREENE, J. A. Evidence and the Custer Enigma. Kansas City, MO: Westerners, 1973. 1st ed. One of 100. Signed by Green and Tom Phillips (tp illus). Fldg map. Fine. *Pacific*.* $35/£22

GREENE, JACOB W. Greene Brothers' Clinical Course in Dental Prosthesis. Detroit, 1916. 4th ed. Frontis ports. VG. *Doctor's Library.* $35/£22

GREENE, W. T. Parrots in Captivity. Volumes 1-3 (of 4). London, 1884-87. 1st ed. Lg 8vo. 81 wood-engr plts, ptd in color and hand-finished. Orig cl (expertly rebacked retaining orig backstrips; lacks suppl w/9 plts). *Swann*.* $3,220/£2,013

GREENE, WELCOME ARNOLD. The Provident Plantation for Two Hundred and Fifty Years. Providence: J.A. & R.A. Reid, 1886. Dec cl. VG. *Zubal*.* $25/£16

GREENE, WILLIAM B. Mutual Banking. Columbus Junction, IA: E.H. Fulton, 1895?. 1st ed. VG + in wraps (fragile). *Beasley.* $85/£53

GREENHILL, BASIL and ANN GIFFARD. Westcountrymen in Prince Edward's Isle. David & Charles/Univ of Toronto, 1967. Fine (inscrip) in dj. *Explorer.* $32/£20

GREENHILL, F. A. Incised Effigial Slabs. Faber & Faber, 1976. 1st ed. 2 vols. 160 plts. Djs (sl soiled, chipped along top edge of vol 2). *Edwards.* $88/£55

GREENLY, A. H. A Bibliography of Father Richard's Press in Detroit. Ann Arbor, MI: William L. Clement's Library, 1955. Ltd to 750. Signed. Good. *Karmiole.* $50/£31

GREENLY, A. H. A Selective Bibliography of Important Books, Pamphlets and Broadsides Relating to Michigan History. Lunenburg, VT: Stinehour Press, 1958. One of 500. Frontis, 26 plts. Brn linen over olive linen. Fine. *Karmiole.* $75/£47

GREENOUGH, SARAH and JUAN HAMILTON. Alfred Stieglitz, Photographs and Writings. Washington, (1983). 1st ed. Folio. 73 repros. (Prelims, fore-edge sl soiled.) Dj (lt soiled, tape repair fr panel verso). *Swann*.* $126/£79

GREENWALT, EMMETT A. The Point Loma Community in California 1897-1942. Berkeley/L.A.: Univ of CA, 1955. 1st ed. VF in gray wrappers. *Argonaut.* $50/£31

GREENWAY, DALE and P. J. Kenya Trees and Shrubs. Nairobi/London: Buchanan's Kenya Estates/Hatchards, 1961. 1st ed. 31 color plts, fldg map. (Ex-lib; hinge repair), else Good in dj (chipped). *Fair Meadow.* $40/£25

GREENWELL, GRAHAM H. An Infant in Arms. War Letters of a Company Officer, 1914-1918. London, 1935. 1st Eng ed. VG (edges sl discolored, corner bumped) in dj (sl nicked, tanned). *Clearwater.* $120/£75

GREENWELL, WILLIAM and GEORGE ROLLESTON. British Barrows. Oxford: Clarendon, 1877. 1st ed. xi,763pp (new feps). Later textured cl, orig backstrip preserved, laid down. *Hollett.* $240/£150

GREENWOOD, GRACE. Haps and Mishaps of a Tour in Europe. Boston: Ticknor, Reed, & Fields, 1854. 1st ed. 437pp. Brn cl (sl worn), gilt, blind-stamped. VG. *Second Life*. $85/£53

GREENWOOD, JAMES. The Adventures of Reuben Davidger; Seventeen Years and Four Months Captive Among the Dyaks of Borneo. NY: Harper, 1866. 1st ed. (Name; joints rubbed, fr joint torn, spine ends frayed), else VG. *Pacific**. $58/£36

GREENWOOD, JAMES. The Purgatory of Peter the Cruel. London: Routledge, 1868. 1st ed. Lg sq 8vo. Ernest Griset (illus). (iv),6-164,(ii)pp. Aeg. Red grained cl, gilt. Nice (spine ends knocked, dknd, few sm closed splits, repairs, cvrs lt mkd). *Sotheran*. $237/£148

GREENWOOD, JEREMY. The Wood-Engravings of John Nash: A Catalogue. Liverpool: Wood Lea Press, 1987. One of 750. Folio. Cl-backed patterned bds. Cl slipcase. *Swann**. $172/£108

GREENWOOD, ROBERT (comp). The California Outlaw, Tiburcio Vasquez. Los Gatos: Talisman, 1960. 1st ed. Ltd to 975. VF in dj. Howes B313. *Argonaut*. $125/£78

GREENWOOD, ROBERT. California Imprints 1833-1862. Los Gatos, 1961. One of 750. (Lt worn.) Dj (frayed, soiled). *Oinonen**. $60/£38

GREENWOOD, ROBERT. California Imprints, 1833-1862. Los Gatos: Talisman, 1961. 1st ed. VG in dj (soiled, sm tear). *Pacific**. $63/£39

GREENWOOD, THOMAS. Public Libraries: A History.... Cassell, 1891. 4th ed. Frontis. Lib buckram (spine head torn). *Forest*. $29/£18

GREER, JOSEPH. A Physician in the House for Family and Individual Consultation. Chicago: J. H. Greer, (1921). Frontisport; 15 color plts. (Paper uniformly browned, brittle, inner hinges cracked; cvrs loose, soiled.) *Weber*. $40/£25

GREER, JOSEPH. Sex Science. Chicago, 1911. 1st ed. Grn cl. VG (extrems sl worn). *Doctor's Library*. $35/£22

GREEVER, WILLIAM S. The Bonanza West. Norman: Univ of OK, (1963). 1st ed. VG in dj. *Lien*. $35/£22

GREG, W. W. (ed). The Play of Antichrist from the Chester Cycle. OUP, 1935. 1st Eng ed. Corrigendum slip tipped-in. Fine (eps partly browned; spine foot sl bumped) in dj (sl mkd, sl creased, spine sl dknd). *Ulysses*. $120/£75

GREGER, DEBORA. Blank Country. SF, 1985. One of 130 signed by author & Madel Greger (illus). 3-color dbl-folded litho. Untrimmed. 1/4 blue cl, ptd label, ptd beige Roma bds. Fine. *Blackwell's*. $80/£50

GREGG, ANDREW. Drums of Yesterday: The Forts of New Mexico. Santa Fe: Press of the Territorian, 1968. Map. (Stamp, bds worn), else Good. *Dumont*. $25/£16

GREGG, ANDREW. New Mexico in the 19th Century—A Pictorial History. Albuquerque, 1968. 1st ed. VG in dj. *Dumont*. $35/£22

GREGG, JOSIAH. Commerce of the Prairies. Max L. Moorhead (ed). Norman: Univ of OK, 1954. 1st ed thus. NF in dj. Howes G401. *Labordo*. $75/£47

GREGORIETTI, G. Jewelry Through the Ages. NY: Crescent, c1969. VG in dj. *Blake*. $85/£53

GREGOROVITSH, DIMITRY. The Fisherman. NY: McBride, 1917. 1st Amer ed. VG. *Cady*. $20/£13

GREGORY, AUGUSTUS. New Comedies. NY/London: Putnam, 1913. Frontisport. Paper label. (Rear cvr foot sl stained.) Internally VG. *Dramatis*. $35/£22

GREGORY, DICK. Dick Gregory's Political Primer. James R. McGraw (ed). NY: Harper & Row, (1972). 1st ed. Fine in NF dj (sm nick). *Reese*. $35/£22

GREGORY, DICK. From the Back of the Bus. NY, 1962. 1st ed. Stiff pict wrappers. *Swann**. $46/£29

GREGORY, G. An History of the Christian Church, from the Earliest Period to the Present Time. London: C. & G. Kearsley, 1795. New ed. 2 vols. Frontispieces. Aeg. Ribbed morocco, gilt, sl raised bands, bound by J. Mackenzie. NF. *Pacific**. $75/£47

GREGORY, HERBERT E. The Geology and Geography of the Paunsaugunt Region, Utah. Washington, 1951. 5 plts (4 fldg maps in rear pocket). VG. *Five Quail*. $45/£28

GREGORY, HERBERT E. Geology of the Navajo Country. Washington, 1917. Fldg chart, 2 fldg maps in rear pocket. Wraps. (Spine strengthened, rear wrap replaced), else VG. *Dumont*. $135/£84

GREGORY, HERBERT E. and RAYMOND C. MOORE. The Kaiparowits Region. Washington: GPO, 1931. 31 plts, 3 VG lg full-color fldg maps in rear pocket. Gray heavy wraps (worn, soiled). Internally VG + . *Five Quail*. $135/£84

GREGORY, J. W. The Nature and Origin of Fiords. London: John Murray, 1913. 1st ed. Bkpl of Arthur Raistrick. (1st, last leaves sl spotted.) *Hollett*. $72/£45

GREGORY, LADY. A Book of Saints and Wonders Put Down Here by Lady Gregory According to the Old Writings and the Memory of the People of Ireland. London: John Murray, 1907. 1st Eng ed. Inscribed presentation. Linen-backed bds, paper spine labels. (Lt foxed; worn, labels chipped, partly worn away), o/w Good. *Holmes*. $275/£172

GREGORY, LADY. The Golden Apple. Murray, 1916. 1st ed. 8 color plts. Pict cl (Eps lt offset; lower bd sl damp-mkd), else NF in pict dj (browned, soiled, sl chipped). *Any Amount*. $144/£90

GREGORY, W. (ed). The Beckford Family. London/Bath, 1898. One of 250 ptd. Aeg. Full red levant morocco, gilt-paneled spine, raised bands, by Sangorski & Sutcliffe. Fine (bkpl). *Appelfeld*. $300/£188

GREINER, JAMES. Wager with the Wind; the Don Sheldon Story. Chicago: Rand McNally, (1974). 1st ed, 1st ptg. Fine in VG dj. *Perier*. $30/£19

GREINER, T. The New Onion Culture. NY: OJ, 1909. Grn cl. VG. *Larry Price*. $20/£13

GRENFELL, BERNHARD P. and ARTHUR S. HUNT. The Oxyrhynchus Papyri. Part 2 (only). London: Kegan Paul, Trench, Trubner, 1898. 1st ed. xvi,358pp; 8 tinted plts. Cl spine (frayed, lib #, bds rubbed). Internally VG (ex-lib). *Worldwide*. $125/£78

GRENFELL, WILFRED. A Labrador Doctor. London: Hodder & Stoughton, n.d. 1st ed. 14 plts. (Spine sl faded.) *Hollett*. $40/£25

GRESHAM, WILLIAM LINDSAY. Limbo Tower. NY: Rinehart, (1949). 1st ed. (Lt rubbed), else NF in VG dj (chipped). *Between The Covers*. $65/£41

GRESHAM, WILLIAM LINDSAY. Nightmare Alley. NY: Rinehart, (1946). 1st ed, 1st bk. Black cl. VG (eps lt browned, spine extrems sl rubbed) in dj (browned, lt chipped). *Heritage*. $50/£31

GREVILLE, CHARLES C. F. The Greville Memoirs, 1814-1860. Lytton Strachey and Roger Fulford (ed). London: Macmillan, 1938. ltd to 630. 8 vols incl index. Frontispieces. Teg. Red pub's cl. *Christie's**. $360/£225

GREY OF FALLODON, VISCOUNT. Fly Fishing. London, (1930). 1st ed. One of 150 w/extra plt, signed by Eric Fitch Daglish (illus). 4to. Vellum, gilt trout fly fr cvr. *Swann**. $690/£431

GREY, HOWARD and GRAHAM STUART. The Victorians by the Sea. London/NY: Academy Editions/St. Martin's, 1973. 1st ed. 132 photo-plts. VG in illus dj. *Cahan*. $60/£38

GREY, R. Memoria Technica, or Method of Artifical Memory.... Oxford: J. Vincent, 1841. New ed. xxiii,215pp. 1/2 calf (sl rubbed), gilt. *Hollett*. $72/£45

GREY, ROMER. The Fisherman Under the Southern Cross: A Story of Adventure in New Zealand. NY: Harper, 1930. 1st ed. VG in dj (spine sunned, sm tears to extrems, spine ends chipped). *Pacific**. $1,380/£863

GREY, ZANE. Adventures in Fishing. Ed Zern (ed). NY, (1952). 1st ed. (Bkpl, ink inscrip), else VG in dj (price-clipped, frayed). *King*. $65/£41

GREY, ZANE. Betty Zane. NY: Charles Francis, (1903). 2nd ed (so stated), 1st bk. Frontis port, 5 plts. Untrimmed. Gray cl (rubbed, dusting, spot stains). Text Good (early note). *Baltimore**. $210/£131

GREY, ZANE. The Call of the Canyon. NY: Harper, 1924. 1st ed. 4 plts. Pict-stamped orange cl. VG (eps sl browned; extrems lt rubbed, joints dknd) in dj (spine faded, lt chipped, tears, tape repairs). *Heritage*. $300/£188

GREY, ZANE. The Desert of Wheat. NY: Harper, (1919). 1st ed. Frontis. Gray-grn cl, gilt. (Ink name; cl sl rubbed), else VG. *Reese*. $60/£38

GREY, ZANE. Ken Ward in the Jungle. Harper, 1912. 1st ed. (Sm faded area spine base), else VG- in pict cl. *Fine Books*. $275/£172

GREY, ZANE. The Last of the Plainsmen. NY: Outing Publishing, 1908. 1st ed. Gilt-lettered pict cl. (Spine sunned), else VG. *Pacific**. $58/£36

GREY, ZANE. The Lost Wagon Train. NY: Harper, 1936. 1st ed. VG + (bumped) in VG + dj (nicked). *Unger*. $375/£234

GREY, ZANE. Majesty's Rancho. NY: Harper, 1938. 1st ed. VG (name) in VG dj. *Unger*. $250/£156

GREY, ZANE. The Mysterious Rider. NY: Harper, (1921). 1st ed. Frontis signed 'Frank Hoffman,' 4 plts. Pict-stamped grn cl. NF (name, 1921 date; spine ends sl rubbed) in dj (lt chipped, spine faded) signed 'Frank Tenney Johnson.' *Heritage*. $250/£156

GREY, ZANE. Nevada. NY: Harper, 1928. 1st ed. Fine in pict dj (spine ends lt chipped). *Else Fine*. $250/£156

GREY, ZANE. The Reef Girl. NY, 1977. 1st ed. Fine in NF dj. *Warren*. $40/£25

GREY, ZANE. Riders of the Purple Sage. NY, 1912. 1st ed. 'Published January, 1912' w/o code letters on tp verso. Frontis; 3 plts. (Lib stamps; fr hinge starting, spine end sl worn.) *Kane**. $110/£69

GREY, ZANE. Tales of Fishes. NY: Harper, 1919. 1st ed. Harper's code 'F-T' on c. pg. Color frontis. Teg. Gilt-lettered blue cl, pict cvr onlay. VG. *Pacific**. $207/£129

GREY, ZANE. Tales of Fresh-Water Fishing. NY/London: Harper, 1928. 1st ed. 48 plts. Orange photo eps. Grn cl, gilt, blindstamped pub's device on fr cvr. (Few sm scratches to cvr, spine ends lt rubbed), o/w NF in dj (price-clipped, 2 fingerprints on fr flap, sm edge tears). *Heritage*. $450/£281

GREY, ZANE. Tales of Lonely Trails. NY: Harper, (1922). 1st ed. Harper's code 'G-W' on copyright pg. Frontis. Gilt-lettered grn cl, pict cvr onlay. NF. *Pacific**. $58/£36

GREY, ZANE. Tales of Lonely Trails. NY, (1922). 1st ed. Signed, inscribed. Dj (lt soiled, spine chipped). *Swann**. $316/£198

GREY, ZANE. Tales of Southern Rivers. H&S, 1924. 1st Eng ed. VG in VG dj (lt worn, torn, dust-soiled). *Fine Books*. $175/£109

GREY, ZANE. Tales of Tahitian Waters. NY: Harper, 1931. 1st ed. Lt blue cl, gilt. (Spine head sl rubbed), else NF. *Pacific**. $316/£198

GREY, ZANE. Tappan's Burro and Other Stories. NY: Harper, (1923). 1st ed. Black cl, gilt, pict cvr label. (Spine dull), else VG. *Pacific**. $104/£65

GREY, ZANE. Tappan's Burro. NY: Harpers, (1923). 1st ed. Inscribed. (Sl soiled), else NF in VG + dj (sm nicks, tears). *Between The Covers*. $650/£406

GREY, ZANE. Thunder Mountain. NY: G&D, (1935). Signed. (Ink name; cvrs sl spotted, worn.) *King*. $85/£53

GREY, ZANE. The Thundering Herd. NY: Harper, 1925. 1st ed. 4 plts. Tan cl. VG (shelfworn) in dj (lt chipped, soiled). *Heritage*. $250/£156

GREY, ZANE. The Trail Driver. NY: Harper, 1936. Grey's blind-stamp. Fine in Fine full-color pict dj (spine ends sl rubbed), slip-case. *Unger*. $625/£391

GREY, ZANE. Twin Sombreros. NY: Harper, 1940. 1st ed. VG + in VG + dj (lt worn). *Unger*. $300/£188

GREY, ZANE. Under the Tonto Rim. NY: Harper, 1926. 1st ed. Bluish-grn cl. VG (contemp inscrip, eps lt browned; spine ends lt rubbed) in dj (lt chipped, soiled). *Heritage*. $350/£219

GREY, ZANE. The Vanishing American. NY: Harper, 1925. 1st ed. NF in pict dj (sl chipped). *Captain's Bookshelf*. $200/£125

GREY, ZANE. Wanderer of the Wasteland. NY: G&D, 1924. Photoplay ed. Fine in color photo dj (sl edgeworn). *Else Fine*. $135/£84

GREY, ZANE. Wild Horse Mesa. NY: Harper, 1928. 1st ed. Pict eps; top edge stained lt orange. Dec blue cl. (Spine ends sl rubbed), o/w NF in dj (lt chipped, soiled, tape-repaired). *Heritage*. $300/£188

GREY, ZANE. Wild Horse Mesa. NY: Harper, 1928. 1st ed. Inscribed. NF (edges sl soiled) in NF pict dj (sm tear rear panel). *Unger*. $950/£594

GREY, ZANE. Wildfire. NY: Grosset, 1917. Photoplay ed. Fine in Fine dj (sl rubbed). *Unger*. $125/£78

GRIAULE, MARCEL. Burners of Men, Modern Ethiopia. Edwin Gile Rich (trans). Phila/London: Lippincott, 1935. 1st ed. 16 plts, 1 map. (Ex-lib; sl rubbed, soiled, lib spine #), o/w VG. *Worldwide*. $25/£16

GRIBBLE, GEORGE (ed). Giacomo Casanova. Arthur Machen (trans). London: Routledge & Sons, 1930. 2 vols in 1. Orange cl. VG in dj (spine sl browned). *Maggs*. $48/£30

GRIERSON, JAMES. Saint Andrews as It Was and as It Is; Being the Third Edition of Dr. Grierson's Delineations.... Cupar: G.S. Tullis, 1838. 3rd ed. 12 copper plts. New eps. Later gilt-ruled calf, morocco spine label, raised bands. Fine. *Pacific**. $2,588/£1,618

GRIFFIN, G. W. New South Wales. Sydney, 1888. 293pp. (Lib bkpl, stamps, #s; sl soiled.) *Edwards*. $96/£60

GRIFFIN, JOHN S. A Doctor Comes to California: The Diary of John S. Griffin, Assistant Surgeon with Kearny's Dragoons, 1846-1847. SF: CA Historial Soc, 1943. 1st ed. Frontisport, 4 maps. Fine (bkpl). *Pacific**. $63/£39

GRIFFIN, JOHN. Memoirs of Captain James Wilson. Boston: Samuel T. Armstrong/Crocker & Brewster, 1822. 1st Amer ed. Engr frontis, 220pp (inscrips, sl soiled). Contemp calf (rubbed, spine top neatly repaired). *Karmiole*. $275/£172

GRIFFIN, LEPEL HENRY. The Great Republic. NY: Scribner & Welford, 1884. 1st Amer ed. vi,189pp. Red cl. *Mott*. $50/£31

GRIFFIS, WILLIAM ELLIOT. The Mikado's Empire. NY: Harper, 1876. 2nd enlgd ed. 2 parts in 1. 645,6pp. (Ex-lib; sl rubbed, spine ends sl frayed), o/w VG. *Worldwide*. $95/£59

GRIFFIS, WILLIAM ELLIOT. The Mikado's Empire. London, 1906. 11th ed. 2 vols. Map. (Bkpls; fr hinge cracked vol 1, extrems sl rubbed.) *Edwards*. $64/£40

GRIFFITH, BEATRICE. Pennsylvania Doctor. Harrisburg, 1957. 1st ed. VG in Good dj. *Doctor's Library*. $30/£19

GRIFFITH, G. W. E. My 96 Years in the Great West. (L.A., 1929.) (Lt rubbed.) *King*. $25/£16

GRIFFITH, LLEWELYN WYN. Up to Mametz. London: Faber & Faber, (1931). 1st ed. Blue cl, gilt. (Cl lt foxed), o/w NF in dj (lt nicked). *Reese*. $350/£219

GRIFFITH, R. H. Alexander Pope, a Bibliography. London: Holland, 1962. Rpt of 1922 ed. Ltd to 350. 2 vols. Black 1/4 buckram, marbled bds, gilt. Djs. *Maggs*. $208/£130

GRIFFITHS, MRS. True and Surprising Adventures, Voyages, Shipwrecks and Distresses of Mons. Pierre Viaud, a French Sea-Captain, and a Native of Bordeaux. (By Jean Gaspard Dubois-Fontanelle.) London: Ptd by S. Fisher, 1800. Engr frontis, engr tp, 88pp. New 1/2 calf. *Young.* $120/£75

GRIGGS, GEORGE. History of the Mesilla Valley or The Gadsden Purchase. Mesilla, NM, 1930. Internally Clean (names, pencil notes; lacks wraps) in later protective cvrs. *Dumont.* $275/£172

GRIGGS, NATHAN. Lyrics of the Lariat. NY: Fleming Revell, 1893. 1st ed. VG (edgeworn). *Labordo.* $200/£125

GRIGSON, GEOFFREY. The Contrary View: Glimpses of Fudge and Gold. London, 1974. 1st Eng ed. Nice in dj (rubbed). *Clearwater.* $32/£20

GRIGSON, GEOFFREY. The Englishman's Flora. London, 1955. 1st ed. Dj. *Edwards.* $120/£75

GRIGSON, GEOFFREY. Goddess of Love. London, 1976. 1st Eng ed. VG in dj. *Clearwater.* $40/£25

GRIGSON, GEOFFREY. A Herbal of All Sorts. London, 1959. 1st ed. Dj (spine lt faded). *Edwards.* $26/£16

GRIGSON, GEOFFREY. The Isles of Scilly and Other Poems. London, 1946. 1st Eng ed. (Cvrs sl bubbled.) Dj (sl torn). *Clearwater.* $56/£35

GRIGSON, GEOFFREY. John Craxton: Paintings and Drawings. Horizon, 1948. 1st Eng ed. VG in card wrappers. *Clearwater.* $88/£55

GRIGSON, GEOFFREY. A Master of Our Time: A Study of Wyndham Lewis. Methuen, 1951. 1st Eng ed. B/w frontis. VG in wrappers (sl creased, mkd, spine head bumped). *Ulysses.* $104/£65

GRIGSON, GEOFFREY. O Rare Mankind! London, 1963. 1st Eng ed. Dj (price-clipped). *Clearwater.* $24/£15

GRIGSON, GEOFFREY. Poets in Their Pride. Phoenix House, 1962. 1st ed. 10 b/w plts. VG (spine ends sl bumped, foot sl faded) in dj (worn). *Ulysses.* $56/£35

GRIGSON, GEOFFREY. Samuel Palmer, the Visionary Years. London: Kegan Paul, 1947. 1st Eng ed. 68 plts (2 color). Buckram. Fine in dj (sl rubbed, torn, nicked). *Ulysses.* $88/£55

GRIGSON, GEOFFREY. Thornton's Temple of Flora. Collins, 1951. Folio. Color frontis, 11 color, 24 b/w plts. (Lt spotting.) Dj (sl soiled, ragged). *Edwards.* $280/£175

GRIGSON, GEOFFREY. Wessex. London, 1951. 1st Eng ed. Pict bds. VG in dj (sl frayed). *Clearwater.* $32/£20

GRIGSON, GEOFFREY. Wild Flowers in Britain. London: Wm. Collins, 1944. 1st ed. VG in VG- dj. *Archer.* $10/£6

GRIGSON, JANE. The Art of Charcuterie. Knopf, 1968. 1st Amer ed. VG in VG- dj. *Book Broker.* $20/£13

GRIMALKIN. Cats. London: Sands, (1901). Lg 4to. Louis Wain (illus). 21 full-pg b/w dwgs. (Foxed, 1 pg w/marginal tears.) Dk blue cl. *Reisler.* $775/£484

GRIMBLE, AUGUSTUS. The Salmon Rivers of Scotland. London: Kegan Paul, Trench, Trubner, (1913). 3rd ed. 3 maps. Grn cl, gilt. (Tape offset to pastedowns), else NF. *Pacific*.* $40/£25

GRIMES, ABSALOM. Absalom Grimes, Confederate Mail Runner. M. M. Quaife (ed). New Haven: Yale Univ, 1926. 1st ed. Frontisport. Navy cl. Fine in dj. *Chapel Hill.* $250/£156

GRIMES, MARTHA. Rainbow's End. NY, 1995. Uncorrected proof. Fine. *Warren.* $25/£16

GRIMM, HERMAN. Life of Michaelangelo. Fanny Elizabeth Bunnett (trans). Boston: Little, Brown, 1886. 14th ed. 2 vols. Terracotta cl. VG. *Turtle Island.* $40/£25

GRIMM, JACOB and WILHELM. (GRIMM BROTHERS.) The Fairy Tales of the Brothers Grimm.... Mrs. Edgar Lucas (trans). London: Constable, 1909. Ltd to 750 signed by Arthur Rackham. 4to. 40 mtd color plts on white paper. Teg. Orig pict vellum (lt stained), gilt, mod pink silk ties. *Christie's*.* $1,472/£920

GRIMM, JACOB and WILHELM. (GRIMM BROTHERS.) German Popular Stories Tranlated from the Kinder und Haus Marchen Collected by M. M. Grimm from Oral Tradition. London/Dublin: James Robins/Joseph Robins, Jr, 1825/6. 3rd ed of vol 1, 1st issued in 1823; 1st ed of vol 2. 2 vols. 12mo. Etched tps, xii-217,220-240 notes; iv,244,246-256 notes pp; 20 etched plts by George Cruikshank. W/half-titles. Aeg, gilt inner dentelles. Full dk grn morocco by Riviere, spines w/5 raised bands, single rule to bands, elaborately gilt in dbl-ruled compartments w/thistle center tools set w/in a dec gilt surround, dated at base of spine, lettered in gilt compartments, triple-rule gilt panels to sides. VG set (offsetting from etched plts, gathering in vol 2 foxed). *Sotheran.* $2,400/£1,500

GRIMM, JACOB and WILHELM. (GRIMM BROTHERS.) Grimm's Fairy Tales. Phila: David McKay, (c. 1910). 10 chromolitho plts by E. H. Wehnert. Pict cl. VG. *Pacific*.* $69/£43

GRIMM, JACOB and WILHELM. (GRIMM BROTHERS.) Grimm's Fairy Tales. Paisley: Alexander Gardner, 1909. 1st ed. 8vo. Color frontis, 305pp; 11 full-pg b/w plts by John Hassall. (Eps foxed.) Teg. Red textured cl, gilt. *Reisler.* $250/£156

GRIMM, JACOB and WILHELM. (GRIMM BROTHERS.) Grimm's Fairy Tales. London: Constable, 1909. 1st ed. 4to. xv,325pp; 40 color plts by Arthur Rackham mtd-at-lg on heavier card, guards. Dk red cl, gilt. Very Nice (few plts sl creased; spine sl sunned). *Sotheran.* $880/£550

GRIMM, JACOB and WILHELM. (GRIMM BROTHERS.) Grimm's Fairy Tales. LEC, 1931. Ltd to 1500 numbered, signed by Fritz Kredel (illus) and Rudolf Koch (designer). Fine in slipcase. *Swann*.* $115/£72

GRIMM, JACOB and WILHELM. (GRIMM BROTHERS.) Grimm's Fairy Tales. Louis and Bryna Untermeyer (eds). NY: LEC, 1962. One of 1500 ptd. Signed by Lucille Corcos (illus). 4 vols. Grn/white patterned cl, gilt. NF in glassine, slipcases. *Pacific*.* $127/£79

GRIMM, JACOB and WILHELM. (GRIMM BROTHERS.) Grimm's Popular Tales and Household Stories. Boston: Crosby & Nichols, 1862. 3/4 red morocco, marbled bds, gilt. (Spine ends, extrems rubbed), else VG. *Pacific*.* $40/£25

GRIMM, JACOB and WILHELM. (GRIMM BROTHERS.) Hansel and Gretel. NY: G&D, (1946). Sq 8vo. 4 moveables by Julian Wehr. Spiral-bound pict bds (sl worn). VG (tp discolored). *Davidson.* $150/£94

GRIMM, JACOB and WILHELM. (GRIMM BROTHERS.) Household Stories from the Collection of the Bros. Grimm. Lucy Crane (trans). London: Macmillan, 1882. 1st ed. Walter Crane (illus). Grn cl, paper spine label. (Spine foot, label rubbed, head chipped), else VG. *Pacific*.* $40/£25

GRIMM, JACOB and WILHELM. (GRIMM BROTHERS.) Household Stories. London: Macmillan, 1899. 1st ed illus by Walter Crane. 8vo. (x),269,(ii)pp. Aeg. Mid-grn pict cl, gilt. NF. *Sotheran.* $93/£58

GRIMM, JACOB and WILHELM. (GRIMM BROTHERS.) Little Brother and Little Sister and Other Tales. London: Constable, (1917). 1st ed thus. 4to. 12 mtd color plts, 44 b/w dwgs by Arthur Rackham. Grn cl, gilt. Good in 2-color illus dj (worn, chip at spine foot). *Reisler.* $750/£469

GRIMM, JACOB and WILHELM. (GRIMM BROTHERS.) Little Brother and Little Sister. NY: Dodd Mead, (1917). 1st ed. Thick 4to. 251pp; 12 tipped-in color illus by Arthur Rackham. Illus eps. Red cl, gilt. VG. *Davidson.* $275/£172

GRIMM, JACOB and WILHELM. (GRIMM BROTHERS.) Little Brother, Little Sister. London: Constable, 1917. 1st ed. 4to. xi,250pp; 12 mtd color plts by Arthur Rackham, guards. Uncut edges. Mint grn cl, gilt. Fine (fep sl speckled). *Sotheran.* $589/£368

GRIMM, JACOB and WILHELM. (GRIMM BROTHERS.) Snow White. NY: Coward McCann, 1938. 1st ed. 6.25x8.25. Wanda Gag (illus). 43pp. Glossy bds. Good. *Cattermole.* $80/£50

GRIMM, JACOB and WILHELM. (GRIMM BROTHERS.) Snow-White and the Seven Dwarfs. Randall Jarrell (trans). NY: FSG, 1972. 1st ed. 9 1/4 x 12 1/4. Nancy Ekholm Burkert (illus). 32pp. Fine in dj. *Cattermole.* $75/£47

GRIMM, JACOB and WILHELM. (GRIMM BROTHERS.) The Story of Hansel and Gretel. London: Blackie & Son, (ca 1920). 4to. 12 full-pg color plts by Frank Adams. Cl-backed color pict bds (dusty, edges rubbed; sl separation frontis/tp). *Reisler.* $200/£125

GRIMM, JACOB and WILHELM. (GRIMM BROTHERS.) Tales from Grimm. NY: Coward McCann, 1936. 4th imp. Wanda Ga'g (illus). Blue cl, pict cvr. VG in VG dj. *Davidson.* $60/£38

GRIMSLEY, DANIEL A. Battles in Culpeper County, Virginia 1861-1865 and Other Articles. Orange, VA: Green, 1967. Facs rpt of 1st ed. Fine in stiff ptd gray wraps. *Chapel Hill.* $35/£22

GRIMWADE, A. G. The Queen's Silver. The Connoisseur, 1953. 1st ed. 64 plts. Cl-backed patterned bds, gilt. VG in dj (sl worn). *Hollett.* $104/£65

GRINDLAY, ROBERT MELVILLE. Scenery, Costumes and Architecture Chiefly on the Western Side of India. London: R. Ackermann, 1826-30. Folio. 2 vols in 1. Color vignette tp, litho tp for vol 2, 2 contents ll, 5 sub-titles; 36 Fine hand-color plts by J.B. Hogarth. Full morocco. (Cvrs detached, spine worn, edges gauffered.) *Kane*.* $4,300/£2,688

GRINNELL, GEORGE BIRD and CHARLES SHELDON. Hunting and Conservation. New Haven, 1925. (Sl worn.) *Oinonen*.* $120/£75

GRINNELL, GEORGE BIRD (ed). American Big Game in Its Haunts. NY, 1904. (Sm spine repair, cvrs mkd, spine sl faded.) Internally Good. *Hallam.* $136/£85

GRINNELL, GEORGE BIRD. The Fighting Cheyennes. NY: Scribner, 1915. 1st ed. Dec cl, gilt. (Ink name; sl worn, rubbed, soiled), o/w VG. Howes G433. *Pacific*.* $81/£51

GRINNELL, GEORGE BIRD. Hunting at High Altitudes. NY/London, 1913. (Sl worn.) Dj (tattered.) *Oinonen*.* $375/£234

GRINNELL, GEORGE BIRD. Jack in the Rockies or a Boy's Adventure with a Pack Train. London: W&R Chambers, 1909. (Spine sl faded.) *Perier.* $65/£41

GRINNELL, GEORGE BIRD. Pawnee Hero Stories and Folk-Tales. NY, 1889. 417pp. (Bkpl, fep, frontis detached; sl worn, fr, rear hinges cracked.) *Woolson.* $30/£19

GRINNELL, GEORGE BIRD. When Buffalo Ran. New Haven: Yale Univ, 1920. 1st ed. Frontis, 7 full-pg photo illus. Pict tan bds. Dj (sm chip, top edge worn, spine head sl chipped). *Dawson.* $100/£63

GRINNELL, J. Gold Hunting in Alaska. Elgin: David C. Cook, c1901. 1/2 cl, marbled paper over bds. Good. *Blake.* $75/£47

GRINNELL, JOSEPH and T. I. STORER. Animal Life in the Yosemite. Berkeley, 1924. 60 plts (12 color), 2 maps. (Sl loose, cvrs sl mkd, bottom of few pp sl damp-mkd.) *Hallam.* $77/£48

GRINNELL, JOSEPH and T. I. STORER. Animal Life in the Yosemite. Berkeley: Univ of CA, 1924. 1st ed. 12 color plts, 60 b/w plts, 2 color maps. Blue buckram, gilt. VG (extrems lt worn). *House.* $200/£125

GRINNELL, JOSEPH and T. I. STORER. Animal Life in Yosemite. Berkeley: Univ of CA, 1924. 12 color plts, 48 half-tone plts, 2 color fldg maps. Blue cl, gillt spine. (Ink names; cvrs sl rubbed), else NF. *Pacific*.* $161/£101

GRINNELL, JOSEPH and T. I. STORER. Animal Life in Yosemite. Berkeley: Univ of CA, 1924. 1st ed. Color frontis, 11 color plts, 48 half-tone plts, 2 color maps. (Extrems lt rubbed), else Fine. *Argonaut.* $250/£156

GRINNELL, JOSEPH and J. M. LINSDALE. Vertebrate Animals of Point Lobos Reserve, 1934-35. Washington, 1936. 39 plts, 1 map. Stiff wrappers (lib stamp, call #s). *Sutton.* $55/£34

GRINNELL, JOSEPH et al. Fur-Bearing Mammals of California. Berkeley: Univ of CA, 1937. 1st ed. 2 vols. 13 color plts. (Spine ends sl frayed vol 2.) Djs (chipped). *Dawson.* $200/£125

GRINNELL, JOSEPH et al. Vertebrate Natural History of a Section of Northern California Through the Lassen Park Region. Berkeley: Univ of CA, 1930. 1st ed. (Bkpl), else VG. *Pacific*.* $98/£61

GRISCOM, JOHN H. The Use of Tobacco, and the Evils, Physical, Mental, Moral, and Social, Resulting Therefrom. NY: Putnam, 1868. 1st ed. Grn cl, gilt. VG. *Pacific*.* $40/£25

GRISHAM, JOHN. The Firm. NY: Doubleday, (1991). 1st ed. Signed. Fine in dj. *Pacific*.* $150/£94

GRISHAM, JOHN. The Firm. NY, 1991. 1st ed. VG in VG dj. *Warren.* $60/£38

GRISHAM, JOHN. The Pelican Brief. NY: Doubleday, 1992. 1st ed. Fine in NF dj. *Pettler.* $35/£22

GRISHAM, JOHN. The Rainmaker. NY, 1995. 1st ed. Signed bkpl laid in. Fine in Fine dj. *Warren.* $30/£19

GRISTWOOD, A. D. The Somme (and) The Coward. London, 1928. 2nd imp. Good (no dj). *Clearwater.* $40/£25

GRISTWOOD, A. D. The Somme Including Also the Coward. London: Jonathan Cape, (1927). 1st ed. Gilt brn cl. (Sm ink name, spine sl sunned), else VG. *Reese.* $35/£22

GRISWOLD, FRANK GRAY. Some Fish and Some Fishing. NY: Lane, 1921. 1st ed. Grn bds (worn). Good. *Bowman.* $30/£19

GRISWOLD, FRANK GRAY. Some Fish and Some Fishing. NY: John Lane, 1921. 1st ed. Photogravure frontis. Cl-backed bds, gilt. Fine. *Pacific*.* $69/£43

GRISWOLD, HATTIE TYNG. Apple Blossoms. Chicago: Jansen, McClurg, 1878. 1st ed. Griswold's signature mtd on fep. 195pp. (Cvrs spotted), else Good. *Brown.* $12/£8

GRISWOLD, N. W. Beauties of California Including Big Trees, Yosemite Valley, Geysers, Lake Tahoe, Donner Lake, S. F. '49 and '83, etc. SF: H.S. Crocker, 1883. 1st ed. Wrappers dec w/chromolitho scene from the Calaveras grove. 'Eastern edition Price 50 [cents] Copyright 1883 by N.W. Griswold' ptd on fr wrapper. Does not have the ads called for on versos of cvrs; this copy has 26 color plts on 13 leaves. (Spine sl worn, sm stain rear wrapper, lt foxed), o/w NF. *Pacific*.* $460/£288

GRISWOLD, RUFUS W. and BENSON J. LOSSING. Washington: A Biography. NY: Virtue, 1856-1860. 1st ed, in orig 45 numbered parts. 91 steel-engr plts. Untrimmed, mostly unopened. Engr tan wraps. (Aging, dusting, some parts w/partial stains, incl plts; some wraps partly detached, most sl worn, chipped.) *Baltimore*.* $50/£31

GROEBER, KARL. Children's Toys of Bygone Days. NY, (1928). Folio. (Sig.) Dj, bd slipcase (cracked). *Swann*.* $126/£79

GROEBIL, RENE. The Eye of Love: a Love Poem in Photographs. London: Photography, 1954. 1st ed. 22 full-pg b/w photos. (Eps sl foxed), else VG in pict stiff wrappers (sl foxed). *Cahan.* $200/£125

GROGAN, EWART S. and ARTHUR H. SHARP. From the Cape to Cairo; the First Traverse of Africa from Cape to Cairo. Thomas Nelson & Sons, (c. 1915). New ed. Fldg map. Recent dk blue 1/2 morocco, cl sides, raised bands, gilt. Fine. *Sotheran.* $296/£185

GROHMANN, WILL. Paul Klee. NY: Abrams, (1954). 1st US ed. Black cl stamped in white (edges sl dusty). Text VG in color dj (sl worn, chipped, few sm tears). *Baltimore*.* $35/£22

323

GROHMANN, WILL. Wassily Kandinsky. London: Thames & Hudson, 1959. 40 tipped-in color plts, 20 b/w plts. (Sl worn.) *Ars Artis.* $400/£250

GROHMANN, WILL. Wassily Kandinsky: Life and Work. NY, ca 1958. Mtd color plts. (Lacks dj.) *Swann*.* $69/£43

Grolier 75. A Biographical Retrospective to Celebrate the Seventy-Fifth Anniversary of the Grolier Club in New York. NY, 1959. One of 1000 ptd. 75th anniversary dinner announcement inserted. VG + in slipcase. *Zubal*.* $50/£31

GROMOV, M. Across the North Pole to America. Moscow: Foreign Languages, 1939. VG in ptd wrapper. *High Latitude.* $25/£16

GRONOW, CAPTAIN. The Reminiscences and Recollections of Captain Gronow, Being the Anecdotes of the Camp, Court, Clubs, and Society, 1810-1860. London: John C. Nimmo, 1889. 2 vols. 20 hand-colored aquatint/etched plts, guards. Gilt-dec brn cl. (Spines dknd, heads chipped), else VG-. *Pacific*.* $196/£123

GROOM, WINSTON and DUNCAN SPENCER. Conversations with the Enemy. NY: Putnam, 1983. 1st ed. Fine in Fine dj. *Pettler.* $35/£22

GROOM, WINSTON. Only. NY, 1984. 1st ed. VG + in NF dj. *Warren.* $30/£19

GROPIUS, WALTER. The New Architecture and the Bauhaus. NY: MOMA, n.d. (1936). 1st Amer ed. (Ink name; cvrs sl soiled.) *King.* $95/£59

GROSE, FRANCIS. The Antiquities of Scotland. London: Hooper & Wigstead, 1797. 2 vols. Folio. 190 engr plts, incl tps. Contemp red straight-grain morocco (joints, corners rubbed), gilt. (Lt foxed, affecting plts.) *Swann*.* $230/£144

GROSE, FRANCIS. Military Antiquities Respecting a History of the English Army from the Conquest to the Present Time. London: T. Egerton & G. Kearsley, 1801. 2nd ed. 4to. 3 parts in 2 vols. 3 engr frontispieces, 3 engr tps, 139 engr plts. (Lt occasional spotting.) Contemp red morocco, gilt (spines lt faded, corners rubbed), gilt and gauffered edges. Attractive set. *Christie's*.* $685/£428

GROSSMAN, MARY LOUISE and JOHN HAMLET. Birds of Prey of the World. London, 1965. 1st UK ed. (Eps lt spotted). Dj (sl chipped, sl ragged fr edge). *Edwards.* $56/£35

GROSSMANN, EDWINA BOOTH. Edwin Booth. Recollections by His Daughter Edwina Booth Grossmann. NY, 1894. 1st Amer ed. Teg. Pict cvrs, gilt. Fine (spine sl rubbed). *Polyanthos.* $35/£22

GROSVENOR, EDWIN A. Constantinople. Boston, 1895. 2 vols. Slipcase (repaired). *Swann*.* $103/£64

GROSZ, GEORGE. Drawings. NY, 1944. Folio. Cl, dj. *Swann*.* $103/£64

GROSZ, GEORGE. Ecce Homo. NY, (1966). Folio. (Bkpl.) *Swann*.* $126/£79

GROSZ, GEORGE. A Little Yes and a Big No. NY, 1946. 1st Amer ed. NF (names; sl rubbed, sl soiled) in dj (edge chips, rubbed). *Polyanthos.* $30/£19

GROSZ, GEORGE. A Little Yes and A Big No. NY: Dial, 1946. 1st ed. Fine (sl soiled) in dj (lt chipped). *Beasley.* $85/£53

GROSZ, GEORGE. A Post-War Museum. London: Faber & Faber, 1931. 1st Eng ed. VG (spotting) in sewn wrappers (sl nicked, sl rubbed). *Ulysses.* $88/£55

GROTE, GEORGE. A History of Greece. London: John Murray, 1846-1856. 1st ed. 12 vols. Demy 8vo. Fine set in orig blind-emb brn cl, gilt. *Ulysses.* $3,840/£2,400

GROUT, A. J. Mosses with a Hand-Lens. NY: The Author/O.T. Louis, 1905. 2nd ed. (Shelf-worn), else VG. *Fair Meadow.* $30/£19

GROUT, A. J. Mosses with Hand-Lens and Microscope. NY: The Author, 1903. 1st ed. Blue cl. NF (few notes). *Archer.* $65/£41

GROUT, A. J. Mosses with Hand-Lens and Microscope. NY: The Author, 1924. 3rd ed. Good (ex-lib). *Archer.* $20/£13

GROVE, LADY. Seventy-One Days' Camping in Morocco. London: Longmans, Green, 1902. 1st ed. Port, 16 plts. Teg. (Cvrs sl faded, sl stained), else VG. *Morrell.* $72/£45

GROVER, EULALIE OSGOOD (ed). Mother Goose Rhymes. Joliet: P.F. Volland, (1925). 4to. (48)pp; 23 full-pg color illus by Frederick Richardson. Pict eps. Color pict grn bds (lt edgeworn). VG. *House.* $90/£56

GROVER, EULALIE OSGOOD. Kittens and Cats: A Book of Tales. Boston: Houghton Mifflin, (1911). 1st ed. 8vo. 39 full-pg photo illus. Tan-yellow cl. Good in beige dj (chipped, edges worn). *Reisler.* $200/£125

GROVER, EULALIE OSGOOD. Mother Goose. Joliet: P.F. Volland, (1915). 1st ed. 12x8.75. Frederick Richardson (illus). Pict cvr label. (Spine, extrems sunned), else VG. *Pacific*.* $127/£79

GROWELL, A. Three Centuries of English Booktrade Bibliography. NY: Dibdin Club, 1903. 1st ed. One of 550. Frontis, 11 plts. Teg, uncut. Orig 1/4 leather (lacks spine head, sl rubbed). *Forest.* $152/£95

GRUBB, DAVIS. The Night of the Hunter. Hamish Hamilton, 1954. 1st ed. VG (top edge sl mkd, dusty, spine ends sl bumped) in dj (nicked, sl dusty). *Ulysses.* $72/£45

GRUBB, FREDERICK. A Vision of Reality. C&W, 1965. 1st Eng ed. Fine (spine ends sl bumped) in dj (spine sl faded). *Ulysses.* $29/£18

GRUBB, NORMAN H. Cherries. London, 1949. 1st ed. 28 plts (12 color). (Lt spotted; sl soiled.) *Edwards.* $40/£25

GRUBB, SARAH. A Selection of Letters of the Late Sarah Grubb, (formerly Sarah Lynes). Sudbury: J. Wright, 1848. 1st ed. (viii),451pp. Orig blind-stamped cl (lacks sm piece at spine foot, 2 sm splits in joints), o/w Nice. *Young.* $72/£45

GRUBB, SARAH. Some Account of the Life and Religious Labors of Sarah Grubb.... London: Ptd by James Phillips, 1796. 3rd ed. viii,398pp. Old sheep (joints cracking). *Young.* $40/£25

GRUBER, FRANK. The Honest Dealer. NY: Farrar, 1947. 1st ed. (Lt worn, soiled), else NF in dj (ends lt nicked; lt rubbed). *Murder.* $37/£23

GRUELLE, JOHNNY. The Camel with the Wrinkled Knees. NY: McLoughlin Bros, 1943. 8.25x7.25. Pict bds. VG in dj (faint stain upper corner, spine ends chipped). *Pacific*.* $52/£33

GRUELLE, JOHNNY. The Cruise of the Rickety-Robin. Chicago: Manning, 1931. Sm folio. 16pp (incl cvrs); 13 full color illus. Good in color pict wrappers (marginal tears, folds, tape mks on spine). *Reisler.* $225/£141

GRUELLE, JOHNNY. Johnny Gruelle's Golden Book. Chicago: M.A. Donohue, (1925). Lg 4to. 96pp. Cl-backed color illus bds (edges lt chipped). *Reisler.* $100/£63

GRUELLE, JOHNNY. The Magical Land of Noom. Chicago: Donahue, (1922). 4to. 157pp; 12 full-pg color illus. Illus eps. Grn/blue cl, pict label. VG (spine ends bumped). *Davidson.* $300/£188

GRUELLE, JOHNNY. Marcella: A Raggedy Ann Story. Joliet: P.F. Volland, (1929). 1st ed. 8vo. Cl-backed color pict bds. VG in color pict pub's box (sides, corners worn). *Reisler.* $300/£188

GRUELLE, JOHNNY. My Very Own Fairy Stories. Chicago: P.F. Volland, (1917). 1st ed. 8vo. Full color pict bds (lt edgeworn). *Reisler.* $225/£141

GRUELLE, JOHNNY. Raggedy Andy Stories. Joliet: P.F. Volland, 1920. 1st ed. 6x9. Unpaginated. Pict bds. VG- (extrems, spine very scuffed; foxed, edge tears). *My Bookhouse.* $62/£39

GRUELLE, JOHNNY. Raggedy Ann and Andy and the Nice Fat Policeman. NY: Johnny Gruelle, 1942. 1st ed. 6.5x9. 95pp. Pict bds. VG (corner waterstained, shelfworn) in dj (edgeworn). *My Bookhouse.* $115/£72

GRUELLE, JOHNNY. Raggedy Ann and Andy. Akron, OH: Saalfield, 1944. 8vo. 6 full-pg tab-activated moveables by Julian Wehr. Color pict bds w/spiral binding. Full color pict dj (edges worn, spine ends chipped). *Reisler.* $375/£234

GRUELLE, JOHNNY. Raggedy Ann and the Golden Butterfly. NY: Johnny Gruelle, 1940. 1st ed. 6.5x9. 95pp. Pict bds. VG. *My Bookhouse.* $92/£58

GRUELLE, JOHNNY. Raggedy Ann and the Happy Toad. Springfield, MA: McLoughlin Bros, 1943. 8vo. 11 full-pg color plts by Justin C. Gruelle. Color pict bds. Good in full color dj (margins lt worn, chipped). *Reisler.* $110/£69

GRUELLE, JOHNNY. Raggedy Ann and the Laughing Brook. #63 of Westfield Classic Series. Springfield, MA: McLoughlin Bros, 1943. 8vo. 11 full-pg color plts by Justin C. Gruelle. Color pict bds (lt edgeworn). Full color dj (margins lt worn, chipped). *Reisler.* $110/£69

GRUELLE, JOHNNY. Raggedy Ann in Cookie Land. NY: Volland, 1931. 1st ed. 6x9. 95pp. VG (bkpl, pp sl browned; corners bumped). *My Bookhouse.* $105/£66

GRUELLE, JOHNNY. Raggedy Ann in the Deep Deep Woods. Chicago: M.A. Donoghue, (1930). 9x6. Pict bds. (Sl smoke damage lower pg extrems; extrems rubbed), else VG in dj (extrems rubbed). *Pacific*.* $46/£29

GRUELLE, JOHNNY. Raggedy Ann in the Garden. #62 of Westfield Classic Series. Springfield, MA: McLoughlin Bros, 1943. 8vo. 10 full-pg color plts by Justin C. Gruelle. Color pict bds (lt shelfworn). Full color dj (lt marginal wear, chipped). *Reisler.* $110/£69

GRUELLE, JOHNNY. Raggedy Ann in the Snow White Castle. NY: Johnny Gruelle, (1946). 1st ed. Justin C. Gruelle (illus). Cl-backed pict bds. (Extrems rubbed), else VG. *Pacific*.* $46/£29

GRUELLE, JOHNNY. Raggedy Ann's Alphabet Book. Joliet: P.F. Volland, (1925). 4th ed. 12mo. Full color pict bds. VG. *Reisler.* $125/£78

GRUELLE, JOHNNY. Raggedy Ann's Alphabet Book. NY: Volland, 1925. 6x7.5 inches. VG (sl rubbed). *American Booksellers.* $45/£28

GRUELLE, JOHNNY. Raggedy Ann's Magical Wishes. Chicago: Donohue, 1928. 8vo. Good (rep clipped; sl worn, mkd). *American Booksellers.* $45/£28

GRUELLE, JOHNNY. Raggedy Ann's Wishing Pebble. Joliet: P.F. Volland, (1925). 27th imp. 8vo. Unpaginated. Illus eps. VG (ink name, spotting, bkpl). *Davidson.* $125/£78

GRUENIG, PHILIP. The Doberman Pinscher. NY: OJ, 1939. 1st US ed. Good+. *October Farm.* $40/£25

GRUMBACH, DORIS. Chamber Music. NY: Dutton, (1979). 1st ed. As New in dj. *Between The Covers.* $125/£78

GRUMBACHER, M. Brushes and Artists' Material: Volume 2—Artists' Colors and Sets. NY/Toronto: Grumbacher, (1933). 1st ed. Spiral-bound bds. NF. *Pacific*.* $46/£29

GRUNDBERG, ANDY and KATHLEEN McCARTHY GAUSS. Photography and Art: Interactions Since 1946. Fort Lauderdale/LA/NY: Museum of Art/LA County Museum of Art/Abbeville, 1987. 1st ed. Frontis. Fine in dj. *Cahan.* $85/£53

GRUNDY, C. REGINALD. A Catalogue of the Pictures and Drawings in the Collection of Frederick John Nettlefold. London, 1933-8. 4 vols. 385 mtd color plts. Uncut. (Bkpls, marginal emb stamps, ll sl wrinkled; spines lt faded, remains of lib #s.) *Edwards.* $480/£300

GRUNER, LEWIS. Specimens of Ornamental Art. London, 1850. Folio. 80 litho plts. (Lt foxed, browned; sl dampstain top left edge few beginning ll.) *Swann*.* $2,760/£1,725

GRUNSKY, CARL E. Stockton Boyhood. Berkeley: Friends of the Bancroft Library, 1959. 1st ed. Fine. *Harrington.* $40/£25

GRZIMEK, B. et al (eds). Grzimek's Encyclopedia of Ethology. NY: Van Nostrand, 1977. 1st ed. Fine in VG+ dj. *Mikesh.* $60/£38

GUEDEL, ARTHUR E. Inhalation Anesthesia; a Fundamental Guide. NY: Macmillan, 1937. (1st 53 pp frequently underlined in pencil, 2 pp notes mtd to rear ll.) *Weber.* $75/£47

GUENTHER, E. The Essential Oils. NY: Van Nostrand, 1955/1949. 2 vols. VG. *Savona.* $56/£35

GUENTHER, KONRAD. A Naturalist in Brazil. Boston, 1931. 1st ed. 32 photo plts. Grn dec cl. Good+ (ex-private lib). *Larry Price.* $40/£25

GUERINOT, J. V. Pamphlet Attacks on Alexander Pope 1711-1744. Methuen, 1969. 1st ed. Dj (torn). *Forest.* $56/£35

GUERRA, FRANCISCO. American Medical Bibliography, 1639-1783. NY: Lathrop C. Harper, 1962. 1st ed. Navy cl, gilt. (Sl rubbed.) *Baltimore*.* $80/£50

GUEST, IVOR. The Dancer's Heritage. London: The Dancing Times, (1967). Signed by Margot Foneyn Price. Pb. VG. *Dramatis.* $30/£19

GUEST, THEODORA. A Round Trip in North America. London: Edward Stanford, 1895. 1st ed. Frontis, 4 prelim ll, 240pp; 15 plts. Red cl (spine faded), gilt. *Mott.* $75/£47

GUEVARA, ERNESTO CHE. Reminiscences of the Cuban Revolutionary War. NY, (1968). 1st ed. (Blindstamp), else VG in dj (sl worn). *King.* $25/£16

GUGGENHEIM, PEGGY. Out of This Century. NY, 1946. 1st ed. Red/yellow/black abstract design dj (sl rubbed, sl loss spine head). *Swann*.* $201/£126

GUICCIOLI, COUNTESS. My Recollections of Lord Byron; and Those of Eye-Witnesses of His Life. Hubert Jerningham (trans). London: Richard Bentley, 1869. 1st ed in English. 2 vols. x,459; vi,453pp. Teg. 3/4 dk brn morocco, marbled bds, gilt. VG set (few lt scuffs). *House.* $250/£156

Guide Book of Historic Charleston and Map. Charleston, SC: Lanneau's Art Store, 1912. Lg fldg map attached inside rear cvr. Fine in orig wrappers (sm tear to bottom of lower cvr). *Sadlon.* $25/£16

Guide to the Museum of the American Indian, Heye Foundation. NY: Museum of the American Indian, 1922-1924. 1st eds. 3 vols. Ptd buff wraps. Good (edges, spines dusty, sl chipped, sm tears, rear cvr vol 1 lacks chunk along fore-edge). *Baltimore*.* $50/£31

GUILLAUME, GEORGE. Architectural Views and Details of Netley Abbey. Southampton, 1848. Thin folio. Frontis (sl offset), (iv),35pp; 10 plts. Morocco. (Lt spotted, few margins sl thumped; fr joint split; worn, spine chipped.) *Edwards.* $120/£75

GUILLAUME, PAUL and THOMAS MUNRO. Primitive Negro Sculpture. NY: HB, (1926). 1st ed. Sound (blindstamps; edgeworn; lacks dj). *Agvent.* $85/£53

GUILLET, PETER. Timber Merchant's Guide. Also a Table, Whereby, at One View, May Be Seen the Solid and Superficial Measure of Any Square or Unequal Hewed Logs or Plank.... Balt: James Lovegrove, 1823. 1st ed. 8vo. 24pp,(86)pp of tables; 30 Fine color lithos (offset) by Henry Stone. Full contemp calf (skillfully rebacked, old label laid down). *M & S.* $2,000/£1,250

GUILLIM, JOHN. A Display of Heraldrie.... London: Jacob Blome, 1660. 4th ed. 3 hand-color plts. Full calf (rebacked, orig cvrs sl worn). *Kane*.* $275/£172

Guinness Book of Superlatives. NY, 1956. 1st ptg. As New in emb grn/gold cl. *Bond.* $40/£25

Guinness Pop-Up Book of Records. UK: Guinness Superlatives, 1986. 8pp pop-ups by John Farman. Glazed pict bds. VG. *Bookfinders.* $45/£28

GUINNESS, RUPERT (ed). The Guinness Book of Superlatives. (NY: Superlatives, Inc, 1956.) 1st ed. Lt grn cl, gilt. (Fr hinge cracked, portions of dj flaps mtd at fep; cvrs sl rubbed.) *Baltimore**. $30/£19

GUITERAS, RAMON. Urology, the Diseases of the Urinary Tract in Men and Women. NY, 1912. 1st ed. 2 vols. Good (inner hinges cracked). *Doctor's Library*. $110/£69

GULICK, SIDNEY L. Evolution of the Japanese. Social and Psychic. London, 1903. (Ex-lib, bkpl; feps lt browned; hinges cracked, corners, spine chipped.) *Edwards*. $64/£40

GULL, W. W. A Collection of the Published Writings of William Withey Gull. T.D. Acland (ed). New Sydenham Soc, 1894/6. 2 vols. ix,600pp, 19 color plts; frontisport, lxxii,184pp (crayon mks in margins, few ink notes). Blind-stamped cl. *Whitehart*. $40/£25

GULLICK, T. J. and J. TIMBS. Painting Popularly Explained Including Fresco Oil,.... London: Crosby Lockwood, 1885. 5th ed. Frontis, x,336pp. Blindstamp tp. *Ars Artis*. $40/£25

GULLIVER, LEMUEL. (Pseud of Jonathan Swift.) Travels into Several Remote Nations of the World. Chas. Bathurst, 1747. 5th ed. (x),296pp; 4 copperplts. Contemp sprinkled calf (lacks label, rubbed, sm cracks to hinges, backstrip head sl worn), gilt. Clean. *Cox*. $136/£85

GUN, NERIN E. Red Roses from Texas. Muller, 1964. 1st ed. VG + (eps, fore-edges sl foxed) in dj. *Any Amount*. $96/£60

GUNKI, MASAKATSU. Kabuki. Kodansha Internat'l, (1969). 1st ed. Good in dj, slipcase. *Rybski*. $50/£31

GUNN, DOUGLAS. Picturesque San Diego, with Historical and Descriptive Notes. Chicago: Knight & Leonard, 1887. 1st ed. 98pp; 72 photogravure plts. Floral eps, aeg. Orig full leather, gilt. (Cvr edges scuffed, worn, joints crudely repaired.) Internally VG + . *Pacific**. $92/£58

GUNN, M. J. Print Restoration and Picture Cleaning. London, 1922. 2nd ed. 18plts. (Cl stained.) *Ars Artis*. $40/£25

GUNN, THOM. Collected Poems. Faber, 1993. One of 150 signed. Fine in clear plastic wrapper. *Williams*. $240/£150

GUNN, THOM. Fighting Terms. NY: Hawk's Well, 1958. Ltd to 1500. NF in ptd wraps. *Polyanthos*. $50/£31

GUNN, THOM. The Garden of the Gods. Cambridge: Pym-Randall, 1968. 1st ed. Ltd to 226 signed. VG in heavy rose colored ptd paper wraps, sewn. *Cady*. $40/£25

GUNN, THOM. A Geography. Iowa City: Stone Wall Press, 1966. 1st ed. One of 220 ptd. Signed. Frontis. Mailing label from Stone Wall Press to poetry editor John Gill laid in. Fine in ptd red wrappers. *Pacific**. $104/£65

GUNN, THOM. The Menace. (SF): Manroot, (1982). One of 26 lettered, of 276 signed by Gunn & J.J. Hazard (illus). Fine in flexible plastic wrappers. *Reese*. $125/£78

GUNN, THOM. Moly. London: Faber & Faber, (1971). 1st ed. Fine in dj (price-clipped w/later price ptd). *Pacific**. $40/£25

GUNN, THOM. My Sad Captains and Other Poems. London: Faber & Faber, (1961). 1st ed. Fine in VG dj (price-clipped, sm spot, internal mend spine crown). *Reese*. $75/£47

GUNNISON, J. W. The Mormons, or Latter-Day Saints, in the Valley of the Great Salt Lake.... NY: George Munro's Son, (1887). xvii,13-168pp + (16)pp ads. (Contents browned, brittle, 2-inch tear to tp), else VG in pict wrappers. *Pacific**. $75/£47

GUNTHER, ERNA. Art in the Life of the Northwest Coast Indians. Portland: Portland Art Museum, (1966). (Ink notes), else VG in wraps. *Perier*. $35/£22

GUNTHER, JOHN. The Golden Fleece. NY: Random House/Legacy Bks, (1959). 1st ed. VF in VF dj (tiny sized rubbed spots). *Between The Covers*. $125/£78

GUNTHER, R. T. Oxford Gardens. OUP, 1912. (Feps lt browned; spine sl chipped.) *Edwards*. $29/£18

GUPPY, H. B. Observations of a Naturalist in the Pacific Between 1896 and 1899. London: Macmillan, 1903. 1st ed. 2 vols. Red cl, gilt spines. (Ex-lib w/mks, insect damage), else VG. *Pacific**. $52/£33

GUPTILL, A. B. Practical Guide to Yellowstone National Park. St. Paul, MN: F. Jay Haynes, (1890). 1st ed. Fldg map. (Dampstain lower cvr), o/w NF. *Sadlon*. $75/£47

GUPTILL, A. B. Yellowstone Park Guide: A Practical Hand-Book. St. Paul: F. Jay Haynes, 1894. 131,(5)pp; fldg map tipped to rear pastedown (as issued?). (Spien rubbed), else VG. *Pacific**. $98/£61

GUPTILL, ARTHUR L. Norman Rockwell, Illustrator. NY: Watson-Guptill Pub, (1970). 3rd ed. Fine in slipcase. *Turtle Island*. $75/£47

GUPTILL, ARTHUR L. Norman Rockwell, Illustrator. NY, 1946. 1st ed. (Bkpl), else VG in dj (sl worn). *King*. $50/£31

GUPTILL, ARTHUR L. Norman Rockwell, Illustrator. NY: Watson-Guptill, 1946. 1st ed. Signed by Rockwell. NF in dj (spine ends rubbed). *Pacific**. $127/£79

GURALNICK, PETER. Searching for Robert Johnson. NY, 1989. 1st ed. Fine (sm run) in NF dj. *Warren*. $50/£31

GURALNIK, DAVID B. The Making of a New Dictionary. A Paper Read Before the Rowfant Club November 30, 1951. Cleveland/NY: World, 1953. NF in paper wrappers. *Zubal**. $50/£31

GURDJIEFF, G. The Herald of the Coming Good: First Appeal to Contemporary Humanity. Paris, 1933. 1st ed. (Rear lacks subscription pp, tab partly removed from pg following preface), else VG in suede wrappers (extrems sl chipped, spine chipped, repaired). *Pacific**. $460/£288

GURNEY, IVOR. Poems...Principally Selected from Unpublished Manuscripts.... London: Hutchinson, (1954). 1st ed. One of 1000 ptd. Gilt red bds. Fine in white dj (lt soiled). *Reese*. $100/£63

GURNEY, IVOR. Severn and Somme. London: Sidgwick & Jackson, 1917. 1st ed. Pinkish red cl bds, ptd spine label. (Sl foxed, bds sl faded), o/w VG in dj (lacks lg piece lower edge of rear panel). *Reese*. $350/£219

GURNEY, JOSEPH JOHN. Memoirs of Joseph John Gurney. Joseph Bevan Braithwaite (ed). Norwich: Fletcher & Alexander, 1854. 1st ed. 2 vols. xii,542; vii,551pp; 4 fldg facs. Full polished calf, gilt, raised bands, dbl spine labels. Handsome set (eps spotted). *Hollett*. $224/£140

GURNEY, JOSEPH JOHN. A Winter in the West Indies. London: John Murray, 1840. Frontis, xvi,282,(ii)pp + 8pp pub's cat; 1 plt. (Sl marginal browning, sm stain frontis margin.) Calf-backed cl (rebound), raised bands, gilt. (Rear bd scratched.) *Edwards*. $200/£125

GUSSOW, H. T. and W. S. ODELL. Mushrooms and Toadstools. Ottawa: Minister of Agric., 1927. 1st ed. Grn cl. VG (bumped). *Archer*. $35/£22

Gustavus; or, the Macaw. A Story to Teach Children the Proper Value of Things. Translated from the German. Darton, Harvey & Darton, 1814. Only Eng ed. 12mo in 6's. Engr frontis, 174pp + (6)pp pub's cat. Orig grn roan-backed drab bds, gilt. Good (early name; sm area of damage, loss on tail edge of rear cvr). *Blackwell's*. $176/£110

GUTERSON, DAVID. The Country Ahead of Us, the Country Behind. NY, 1989. 1st ed, 1st ptg, 1st bk. Fine in NF dj. *Warren*. $200/£125

GUTERSON, DAVID. Family Matters: Why Homeschooling Makes Sense. NY: HBJ, (1992). 1st ed. Signed. Fine in dj. *Between The Covers*. $125/£78

GUTERSON, DAVID. Snow Falling on Cedars. NY: Harcourt Brace, 1994. 1st ed. VF in VF dj. *Unger*. $75/£47

GUTHRIE, A. B., JR. The Big Sky. NY: Sloane, 1947. 1st ed. One of 500 numbered, signed. Fine in NF trade dj & NF numbered dj (spine dknd). *Unger*. $450/£281

GUTHRIE, A. B., JR. Fair Land, Fair Land. Boston: Houghton Mifflin, 1982. 1st ed. Fine in dj. *House.* $20/£13

GUTHRIE-SMITH, H. Sorrows and Joys of a New Zealand Naturalist. Dunedin: Reed, 1936. 1st ed. One of 1000 signed. 5 maps. VG. *Mikesh.* $75/£47

GUTMAN, JUDITH MARA. Lewis W. Hine and the American Social Conscience. (NY, 1967.) 1st ed. (Binding defect on rear pastedown.) Contents Clean in dj (soiled, spine panel age-dknd). *Swann*.* $57/£36

GUTMAN, JUDITH MARA. Through Indian Eyes. NY: OUP/Internat'l Center of Photography, 1982. 1st ed. Fine in illus dj. *Cahan.* $85/£53

GUTTMAN, SAMUEL A. et al. Concordance to the Standard Edition of the Complete Psychological Works of Sigmund Freud. NY: Internat'l Universities Press, 1984. 2nd ptg. 6 vols. Folio. Brn buckram. Fine. *Gach.* $500/£313

GUY, WILLIAM A. Principles of Medical Jurisprudence. NY, 1845. 1st Amer ed. 711pp. Marbled bds (skillfully rebound) w/red buckram spine, gilt lettering. VG. *Doctor's Library.* $375/£234

GUYE, S. and H. MICHEL. Time and Space Measuring Instruments from the 15th to the 19th Century. NY: Praeger, 1971. Fine. *Blake.* $125/£78

GWALTNEY, JOHN LANGSTON. Drylongso: A Self-Portrait of Black America. NY: Random House, 1980. 1st ed. (Rmdr stamp), else Fine in NF dj. *Pettler.* $45/£28

GWYNN, AUBREY and R. NEVILLE HADCOCK. Medieval Religious Houses—Ireland. Longmans, 1970. 1st ed. VG in dj. *Hollett.* $72/£45

GWYNN, C. W. Imperial Policing. London, 1939. Enlgd ed. Fine (rebound). *Gretton.* $16/£10

GWYNN, JOHN. Liber Ardmachanus. The Book of Armagh. Dublin: Royal Irish Academy, 1913. One of 400, this copy ex-series. Uncut. Cl-backed wrappers (spine faded). *Sotheby's*.* $773/£483

GWYNN, STEPHEN. Claude Monet and His Garden. London: Country Life, 1934. (Spine dknd, cvr soiled.) Contents VG. *Quest.* $55/£34

GWYNN, STEPHEN. Fishing Holidays. London: Macmillan, 1904. 1st ed. Grn cl, gilt. VG. *Pacific*.* $40/£25

GWYNN, STEPHEN. Mungo Park and the Quest of the Niger. London, 1934. 1st ed. Frontisport, 6 plts. (Leaves roughly opened; sl spotted.) *Edwards.* $40/£25

GYSIN, BRION. To Master, a Long Goodnight. NY: Creative Age, 1946. 1st ed, 1st bk. (Initials partly erased), o/w NF in NF dj. *Warren.* $150/£94

H

H., R. The Angler's Sure Guide: Or, Angling Improved, and Methodically Digested. London: G. Conyers, 1706. 1st ed. 8vo. Frontis, engr plt. Old blindstamped calf (rubbed, upper joint splitting near spine head), red leather spine label. Sound. *Oinonen*.* $1,500/£938

HAANEL, EUGENE. On the Location and Examination of Magnetic Ore Deposits By Magnetometric Mesurement. Ottawa: Dept of the Interior, 1904. 6 plts, 8 fldg charts (5 colored). Bkpl of Arthur Raistrick. *Hollett.* $136/£85

HAART and AUDOUIN-DUBREUIL. The Black Journey, Across Africa with the Citroen Expedition. NY, 1928. *Hallam.* $56/£35

HAAS, ELISE S. Letters from Mexico. SF: Privately ptd, 1937. Ltd to 75. Signed presentation. Good. Brn cl over dec bds, paper spine label. *Karmiole.* $125/£78

HAAS, ERNST. The Creation. London: Michael Joseph, 1971. 1st ed. VG in dj (chipped). *Smith.* $85/£53

HABE, HANS. The Mission. M. Bullock (trans). NY, 1966. 1st ed. VG in dj (sl stained). *Typographeum.* $10/£6

HABENSTEIN, ROBERT W. and WILLIAM M. LAMERS. The History of American Funeral Directing. Milwaukee, WI, 1955. 1st ed. (Sl mildewed odor, label fr inside cvr), else Good. *King.* $35/£22

HABERLY, LOYD. John Apostate an Idyll of the Quays. Long Crendon Buckinghamshire: Seven Acres, 1927. 1st ed. Ltd to 125. Leather-backed dec bds (newly bound). *Cox.* $88/£55

HABERLY, LOYD. Pursuit of the Horizon. A Life of George Catlin, Painter and Recorder of the American Indian. NY: Macmillan, 1948. 1st ed. Brick cl. (Upper corners sl jammed), else Fine. *Argonaut.* $45/£28

HABICHT, FRANK. Young London: Permissive Paradise. Harrap, 1969. 1st ed. Sm folio. VG in dj (sl torn). *Sclanders.* $32/£20

HABINGTON, WILLIAM. The Poems of William Habington. Kenneth Allott (ed). University Press of Liverpool, 1948. 1st Eng ed. VG (top edge sl dusty; spine ends, corners sl bumped) in dj (nicked, sl creased, rubbed, dusty, browned). *Ulysses.* $72/£45

HACHIYA, MICHIHIKO. Hiroshima Diary, the Journal of a Japanese Physician August 6 - September 30, 1945. London, 1955. 1st ed. VG. *Doctor's Library.* $40/£25

HACK, MARIA. Winter Evenings; or, Tales of Travellers. London: Harvey & Darton, 1818-1824. 4 vols. 12mo. Full-pg copperengr frontis each vol, ix-219; 226; 211; 248pp. Orig marbled paper on bds, red roan spine, gilt. VG set (name labels, 3 sigs lt sprung; sl rubbed, spine heads bumped, chip vol 4 top). *Hobbyhorse.* $400/£250

HACKENBROCH, YVONNE. English Furniture. Thames & Hudson, 1958. Color frontis; 358 plts (20 color). (Lib ink stamp, bkpl; lt soiled, edges rubbed.) *Edwards.* $296/£185

HACKENBROCH, YVONNE. Meissen and Other Continental Porcelain, Faience and Enamel...in the Irwin Untermyer Collection. Cambridge, 1956-57. 2 vols. Folio. Djs (chipped). *Swann*.* $201/£126

HACKER, LILIAN PRICE. Susan. London: Hodder & Stoughton, (n.d. ca 1912). Lg 4to. 12 full-pg color plts. Ivory illus/dec bds, orig ribbon through spine. Good in orig box (worn). *Reisler.* $375/£234

HACKER, MARILYN. Separations. NY: Knopf, 1976. 1st ed. *Agvent.* $150/£94

HACKER, MARILYN. Taking Notice. NY: Knopf, 1980. 1st ed. Fine in Fine dj. *Beasley.* $30/£19

HACKLE, PALMER. Hints on Angling, with Suggestions for Angling Excursions in France and Belgium.... London: W.W. Robinson, 1846. 1st ed. Orig blindstamped grn cl, gilt. (Old cat entry mtd to fr pastedown, lib bkpl, stamp, hinges cracking; corners rubbed, spine ends chipped w/sm tears to cl), else VG-. *Pacific*.* $46/£29

HACKLE, SPARSE GREY. (Pseud of Alfred W. Miller.) Fishless Days. NY: Angler's Club of NY, 1954. 1st ed. One of 591. Paper labels. (Lt worn.) *Oinonen*.* $130/£81

HACKLE, SPARSE GREY. (Pseud of Alfred W. Miller.) His Life, His Stories, and His Angling Memories. Austin M. Francis (ed). NY: Anglers' Club of NY, 1993. One of 300. Frontis. (Lt worn.) Slipcase. *Oinonen*.* $160/£100

HACKWOOD, FREDERICK W. Good Cheer. T. Fisher Unwin, 1911. 1st ed. Color frontis, 24 plts. Teg, untrimmed. Pict cl, gilt. VG. *Hollett.* $72/£45

HADDOCK, JNO. A Souvenir: The Thousand Islands of the St. Lawrence River...Profusely Illustrated. Alexandria Bay, NY, 1895. 410pp; fldg map, fldg view. (Names, addresses, new eps; cvrs worn), o/w VG. *New Hampshire*.* $260/£163

HADER, BERTA and ELMER. Billy Butter. Macmillan, 1936. 1st ed. 12mo. 90pp; 6 full-pg color illus. Illus eps. Yellow bds. VG in dj (lt soiled). *Davidson*. $85/£53

HADER, BERTA and ELMER. Jamaica Johnny. NY: Macmillan, 1935. 1st ed. 12mo. 91pp (bkpl); 6 full-pg color lithos. Illus eps. Grn cl. VG in dj (lt torn). *Davidson*. $90/£56

HADER, BERTA and ELMER. Little Antelope, an Indian for a Day. Macmillan, 1962. 1st ed. 4to. Unpaginated. Gray lib cl. VG + (ex-lib; corners, edges sl worn, corners bumped). *Price*. $22/£14

HADER, BERTA and ELMER. Little Antelope: An Indian for a Day. NY: Macmillan, 1962. 1st ed. 4to. Color pict bds (lower edges sl rubbed). Full color dj (marginal tear). *Reisler*. $50/£31

HADFIELD, MILES and JOHN. Gardens of Delight. Boston: Little, Brown, 1964. 1st Amer ed. 46 color, b/w plts. (Name; sm water spot fr bd), else VG. *Fair Meadow*. $40/£25

HADFIELD, MILES et al. British Gardeners: A Biographical Dictionary. Zwemmer, 1980. VG in dj. *Hadley*. $77/£48

HADFIELD, WILLIAM. Brazil, the River Plate, and the Falkland Islands. London: Longman, Brown et al, 1854. vi,384pp; port, 3 fldg maps. 1/2 brn calf, marbled bds (rubbed). *Adelson*. $385/£241

HADLEY, C. J. Trappings of the Great Basin Buckaroo. Reno: Univ of NV, (1993). 1st ed. As New in dj. *Lien*. $40/£25

HAFEN, LEROY R. and W. J. GHENT. Broken Hand. Denver, 1931. 1st ed. Internally VG (ex-lib, loose; worn). Howes H10. *Woolson*. $125/£78

HAFEN, LEROY R. and W. J. GHENT. Broken Hand: The Life of Thomas Fitzpatrick, Chief of the Mountain Men. Denver: Old West, 1931. 1st trade ed. Dbl-pg map, 8 b/w plts. Dk grn ribbed cl, gilt. (Lt crease fep; spine gilt sl flecked, hinges w/recent neat repairs.) Text Clean, cvrs VG. Howes H10. *Baltimore**. $140/£88

HAFEN, LEROY R. and ANN W. (eds). The Far West and the Rockies 1820-1875. Glendale, CA: A.H. Clark, 1954-1961. 15 vols. 9.5x6.5 inches. Prospectus. Uniform grn cl. (Corners sl bumped), else Clean set. *King*. $1,500/£938

HAFEN, LEROY R. and ANN W. (eds). The Far West and the Rockies Historical Series, 1820-1875. Glendale: A.H. Clark, 1954-1961. 1st ptgs thus. 15 vols. Grn cl, gilt-lettered spines. Fine set. *Pacific**. $1,265/£791

HAFEN, LEROY R. and FRANCIS MARION YOUNG. Fort Laramie and the Pageant of the West, 1834-1890. Glendale, CA: A.H. Clark, 1938. 1st ed. Teg. (Bkpl; cvr sl stained.) *King*. $125/£78

HAFEN, LEROY R. and ANN W. Handcarts to Zion. Glendale: A.H. Clark, 1960. Pioneers' ed. Fine in dj (sl worn). *Pacific**. $40/£25

HAFEN, LEROY R. and ANN W. Old Spanish Trail: Santa Fe to Los Angeles. Glendale: A.H. Clark, (1968). 3rd ptg. Fldg map. Grn cl. Fine. *Harrington*. $80/£50

HAFEN, LEROY R. The Overland Mail, 1849-1869. Cleveland: A.H. Clark, 1926. 1st ed. Grn cl. VF. Howes H11. *Labordo*. $250/£156

HAFEN, LEROY R. Pikes Peak Gold Rush Guidebooks of 1859 by Luke Tierney, William B. Parsons and Summaries of the Other Fifteen. Glendale: A.H. Clark, 1941. 1st ed. Fine. *Labordo*. $150/£94

HAFEN, LEROY R. (ed). The Mountain Men and the Fur Trade of the Far West. Glendale: A.H. Clark, 1965-1972. 10 vols. Brn cl, gilt. Good (ex-lib, spine mks, ep pockets, shelfwear). *Pacific**. $431/£269

HAFENDORFER, KENNETH A. Perryville, Battle for Kentucky. Louisville, (1981). 1st ed. Fine in Fine dj. *Pratt*. $57/£36

HAFERKORN, HENRY E. The War with Mexico 1846-1848. N.p., 1970. Rpt of 1914 ed. VG. *Dumont*. $25/£16

HAFTMANN, WERNER (ed). Wols: Watercolors, Drawings, Writings. NY, ca 1965. Pict cvr label. Slipcase. *Swann**. $115/£72

HAGAN, JOHN W. Confederate Letters of John W. Hagan. Bell Irvin Wiley (ed). Athens, GA: Univ of GA, (1954). 1st ed. Frontisport. NF in ptd gray wraps (sl sunned). *Chapel Hill*. $45/£28

HAGAR, ANNA MARIE and EVERETT GORDON. The Historical Society of Southern California Bibliography of All Published Works. L.A.: Hist Soc, 1958. 1st ed. Fine in Fine dj. *Book Market*. $40/£25

HAGEN, LOIS D. A Parish in the Pines. Caldwell, 1938. 1st ed. Pict cl. (Rev copy label, bkpl affixed to fep; lower fr cvr corner bumped), else VG. *Baade*. $20/£13

HAGENBECK, L. Animals Are My Life. London: Bodley Head, 1956. 1st ed. VG. *Mikesh*. $27/£17

HAGERTY, DONALD J. Maynard Dixon. SF: CA Academy of Sciences, (1981). Color frontis, 8 pg exhibition cat laid in. White blind emb cl. Fine in slipcase (sl soiled). *Turtle Island*. $125/£78

HAGGARD, H. RIDER and ANDREW LANG. The World's Desire. Longmans, Green, 1890. Beveled bds. Good (sl spotted; spine bumped, lt sunned, cvrs sl mkd). *Tiger*. $80/£50

HAGGARD, H. RIDER. Allan and the Holy Flower. Longmans, Green, 1915. 1st Amer ed. VG-. *Fine Books*. $60/£38

HAGGARD, H. RIDER. Allan and the Ice-Gods. Hutchinson, (1927). 1st UK ed. Bound w/out the ads normally found. NF. *Williams*. $120/£75

HAGGARD, H. RIDER. Allan and the Ice-Gods. NY, 1927. 1st Amer ed. Dj (backed w/non-acidic rice paper, paper restoration at spine extrems, flap edges). *Swann**. $126/£79

HAGGARD, H. RIDER. Allan Quatermain. London: Longmans, Green, 1887. 1st ed. Dec grn cl. (Lacks plt; sl cocked, fr hinge neatly repaired; spine tips, corners sl worn.) *Agvent*. $200/£125

HAGGARD, H. RIDER. Ayesha: The Return of She. Ward, Lock, 1905. Good (lt spotted, joints cracked; spine bumped, hinges, corners rubbed). *Tiger*. $58/£36

HAGGARD, H. RIDER. Beatrice: A Novel. Longmans, Green, 1890. Pub's cat dated 3/90. Beveled bds. Good (sl spotted; spine bumped, sl sunned, cvrs sl mkd). *Tiger*. $88/£55

HAGGARD, H. RIDER. Belshazzar. NY, 1930. 1st Amer ed. Dj (backed w/non-acidic rice paper, few sm archival paper restorations). *Swann**. $80/£50

HAGGARD, H. RIDER. Benita. Cassell, 1916. 1st UK ed. VG (spine sl faded). *Williams*. $136/£85

HAGGARD, H. RIDER. Doctor Therne. Longmans, 1898. 1st UK ed. NF. *Williams*. $136/£85

HAGGARD, H. RIDER. Eric Brighteyes. Longmans, Green, 1891. Pub's cat dated 12/90. Beveled bds. VG (sl spotted, lacks initial blank; spine bumped, sl chipped). *Tiger*. $96/£60

HAGGARD, H. RIDER. Fair Margaret. Hutchinson, 1907. 1st UK ed. VG (spine sl browned). *Williams*. $112/£70

HAGGARD, H. RIDER. Finished. Ward Lock, 1917. 1st UK ed. VG + . *Williams*. $128/£80

HAGGARD, H. RIDER. A Gardener's Year. London, 1905. 2nd imp. 25 plts. Teg. (Spine faded.) *Henly*. $45/£28

HAGGARD, H. RIDER. Heart of the World. NY: Longmans, Green, 1895. 1st ed. Frontis, 347pp + 16pp pub's cat; 12 plts. Grn cl, gilt. Good (fr hinge cracked, rear hinge starting, slit to rep; feps offset, prelims lt dampstained; edges bumped, rubbed; cl split fr joint foot). *Blue Mountain*. $50/£31

HAGGARD, H. RIDER. Heart of the World. Longmans, 1896. 1st UK ed. VG (ink name). *Williams*. $104/£65

HAGGARD, H. RIDER. Jess. Smith, Elder, 1887. Good (sl spotted; rebacked w/orig backstrip relaid, recased, rubbed). *Tiger*. $64/£40

HAGGARD, H. RIDER. Jess. Smith Elder, 1887. 1st UK ed. VG (ink name; cvrs dull, fr cvr stained). *Williams*. $120/£75

HAGGARD, H. RIDER. Jess. London: Smith, Elder, 1887. 1st UK ed. One of 2000. (Spine faded, bottom edge badly worn, fr/rear cvrs lt spotted), o/w Good. *Bernard*. $125/£78

HAGGARD, H. RIDER. Joan Haste. Longmans, 1895. 1st UK ed. VG (spine sl worn, foxed). *Williams*. $112/£70

HAGGARD, H. RIDER. King Solomon's Mines. Cassell, 1885. 3rd issue w/spelling mistakes corrected. Pub's cat dated 5G.10.8, fldg map (torn). Pict cl. Good (new eps; spine bumped, chipped, sl sunned). *Tiger*. $264/£165

HAGGARD, H. RIDER. King Solomon's Mines. Cassell, 1885. Later issue of 1st ed w/2 minor textual misprints corrected, and ads to rear dated November rather than August 1885. Fine (sl foxed). *Williams*. $1,040/£650

HAGGARD, H. RIDER. King Solomon's Mines. London et al: Cassell, 1905. 1st illus ed. Fldg color map. Red pict binding, gilt. VG (spine sl faded, edges lt foxed). *Bernard*. $250/£156

HAGGARD, H. RIDER. Lysbeth. NY/London/Bombay, 1901. 1st Amer ed. (Spine top edge lacks sm piece), else VG. *Mcclintock*. $75/£47

HAGGARD, H. RIDER. Maiwa's Revenge. Longmans, 1888. 1st UK ed. Blue-grn bds. VG. *Williams*. $128/£80

HAGGARD, H. RIDER. Marie. Cassell, 1912. 1st UK ed. VG (bkpl, ink name; cvrs sl faded). *Williams*. $77/£48

HAGGARD, H. RIDER. Marion Isle. NY, 1929. 1st Amer ed. Dj (backed w/non-acidic rice paper, few sm archival paper restorations). *Swann**. $92/£58

HAGGARD, H. RIDER. Montezuma's Daughter. Longmans, Green, 1893. Pub's cat dated 11/93. Beveled bds. Good (lt spotted; spine bumped, chipped, sunned; corners rubbed). *Tiger*. $80/£50

HAGGARD, H. RIDER. Morning Star. Cassell, 1910. Pub's cat. Good (lt spotted; rebacked w/orig sunned backstrip relaid, cvrs sl mkd). *Tiger*. $32/£20

HAGGARD, H. RIDER. Nada the Lily. Longmans, 1892. 1st UK ed. VG- (cvrs sl browned, worn). *Williams*. $88/£55

HAGGARD, H. RIDER. Pearl-Maiden. London: Longmans, Green, 1903. 1st Eng ed. Blue cl. VG (lib bkpl, lt foxed; spine tips, corners sl worn). *Agvent*. $125/£78

HAGGARD, H. RIDER. The People of the Mist. NY, 1894. 1st Amer ed. 357pp. Pict cl (rubbed, discolored). *King*. $35/£22

HAGGARD, H. RIDER. Queen of the Dawn. NY, 1925. 1st Amer ed. Dj (extensively restored, backed w/non-acidic rice paper). *Swann**. $92/£58

HAGGARD, H. RIDER. Queen Sheba's Ring. Eveleigh Nash, 1910. 1st UK ed. VG. *Williams*. $120/£75

HAGGARD, H. RIDER. Queen Sheba's Ring. E. Nash, 1910. 1st ed. (Rear inner hinge starting; spine head lt rubbed), else VG. *Fine Books*. $165/£103

HAGGARD, H. RIDER. Regeneration. London: Longmans, Green, 1910. 1st Eng ed. VG (inscrip; edges, eps spotted; spine ends, 2 corners sl bumped). *Ulysses*. $104/£65

HAGGARD, H. RIDER. Regeneration: Being an Account of the Social Work of the Salvation Army in Great Britain. Longmans, Green, 1910. Good (ink inscrip; spine bumped). *Tiger*. $32/£20

HAGGARD, H. RIDER. She. London: Longmans, Green, 1887. 1st ed, 1st issue. Stamped presentation copy from pub. Dec cl. (2 bkpls, cat clipping, bkseller ticket fr pastedown; backstrip laid on w/loss of cl along edges.) Internally Fine. *Agvent*. $250/£156

HAGGARD, H. RIDER. She. London, 1887. 1st Eng ed, 1st issue. 8vo. Dbl-pg color litho frontis. Gilt-pict blue cl. Slipcase. *Swann**. $690/£431

HAGGARD, H. RIDER. Treasure of the Lake. NY, 1926. 1st Amer ed. Dj (backed w/non-acidic rice paper, few sm archival paper restorations). *Swann**. $115/£72

HAGGARD, H. RIDER. The Virgin of the Sun. London et al: Cassell, (1922). 1st UK ed. (Eps browned; spine sl dknd), o/w VG. *Bernard*. $45/£28

HAGGARD, H. RIDER. The Wanderer's Necklace. Cassell, 1914. 1st UK ed. VG (spine sl faded). *Williams*. $128/£80

HAGGARD, H. RIDER. When the World Shook. Cassell, 1919. 1st UK ed. VG (spine sl faded). *Williams*. $152/£95

HAGGARD, HOWARD W. The Lame, the Halt, and the Blind: The Vital Role of Medicine in the History of Civilization. NY, 1932. VG in Good dj. *Doctor's Library*. $50/£31

HAGUE, C. W. Printing for the Schools. Milwaukee: Bruce, (1943). (Ink inscrip; rubbed.) *Oak Knoll*. $35/£22

HAHN, EMILY. Aphra Behn. London: Cape, 1951. 1st Eng ed. VG (cvrs sl mkd, bumped) in dj (nicked, sl rubbed, mkd, dusty, browned). *Ulysses*. $48/£30

HAHNEMANN, SAMUEL. Organon of the Art of Healing. Phila, 1875. 5th Amer ed. 244pp. Good (extrems worn, outer hinges, top of spine chipped). *Doctor's Library*. $125/£78

HAIG, AXEL HERMAN. Axel Herman Haig and His Work. London: Fine Art Soc, 1905. 1st ed. One of ltd ed on lg paper. Signed on frontis; numbered, initialed by another on 1/2-title. Orig etching frontis, ptd tissue guards. Teg. 3/4 grn morocco, grn cl, gilt. Fine (#, initials). *Pacific**. $345/£216

HAIG-BROWN, RODERICK. Alison's Fishing Birds. Vancouver: Colophon Books, 1980. One of 500 numbered, signed by Valerie Haig-Brown, and w/mtd color vignette on tp signed by Jim Rimmer (illus). Uncut. (Lt worn.) *Oinonen**. $100/£63

HAIG-BROWN, RODERICK. Measure of the Year. NY: William Morrow, 1950. 1st ed. NF in VG dj (chipped). *Backman*. $45/£28

HAIG-BROWN, RODERICK. Return to the River. Toronto: McClelland & Stewart, (1946). 1st Canadian ed. Fine in VG + dj. *Authors Of The West*. $80/£50

HAIG-BROWN, RODERICK. Return to the River. NY: Morrow, 1941. 1st ed. VF in dj. *Bowman*. $75/£47

HAIG-BROWN, RODERICK. Return to the River. A Story of the Chinook Run. NY, 1941. Deluxe 1st ed. One of 520 numbered, signed by Haig-Brown and Charles De Feo (illus), and further signed & inscribed by Haig-Brown. Teg, uncut. 1/2 morocco (rubbed, soiled). *Oinonen**. $450/£281

HAIG-BROWN, RODERICK. The Western Angler: An Account of Pacific Salmon and Western Trout. NY: Derrydale, (1939). 1st ed. One of 950. Signed. 2 vols. 8 color plts. Red cl, gilt. (Fr cvr vol 1 sl sunned), else NF. *Pacific**. $748/£468

HAIG-THOMAS, DAVID. Tracks in the Snow. London: Hodder & Stoughton, 1939. Map. VG (sl worn). *High Latitude*. $40/£25

HAIGHT, ANNE LYON. Banned Books: Informal Notes on Some Books Banned for Various Reasons. NY, 1935. 1st Amer ed. Fine (sl sunned). *Polyanthos*. $35/£22

HAIGHT, SARAH. The Ralston-Fry Wedding and the Wedding Journey to Yosemite, May 20, 1858.... Francis P. Farquhar (ed). Berkeley: Friends of Bancroft Library, 1961. Ltd ed. Fine in ptd stiff wrappers. *Pacific**. $29/£18

HAIL, MARSHALL. Knight in the Sun. Boston, 1962. 1st ed. VF in Fine dj. *Bond*. $20/£13

HAILE, ELLEN. The Two Gray Girls. NY: Cassell, Petter, Galpin, (1880). 1st ed. 8vo. Kate Greenaway et al (illus). 258pp. Brn pict cl, gilt. VG (spine foot lt frayed, sl edgeworn). *House*. $50/£31

HAINES, ELIJAH M. Historical and Statistical Sketches, of Lake County, Illinois. Waukegan, IL, 1852 (i.e., 1853). Sm 8vo. W/the errata leaf. Fldg frontis. Orig yellow letterpress wrappers (sm edgetears). Cl fldg case. Howes H20. *Swann**. $747/£467

HAINES, FRANCIS. The Nez Perces. Norman: Univ of OK, (1955). 1st ed. 16 plts. Red cl. Fine in pict dj. *Argonaut*. $60/£38

HAINES, FRANCIS. The Plains Indians. NY: Thomas Y. Crowell, 1976. 1st ed. Signed. Good in dj (sl worn). *Dumont*. $30/£19

HAINES, FRANCIS. Red Eagles of the Northwest. Portland, OR: Scholastic, 1939. 1st ed. Frontis photo tipped-on. Rust cl, paper spine/fr cvr labels. Fine (spine sl faded). *Argonaut*. $125/£78

HAINES, FRANCIS. The Snake Country Expedition of 1830-1831. Norman: Univ of OK, 1971. Map. Good. *Dumont*. $25/£16

HAINES, HERBERT. A Manual of Monumental Brasses. Oxford/London: J.H. & Jas. Parker, 1861. 2 vols. Color frontis. (Spine ends worn.) *Bickersteth*. $56/£35

HAINES, HERBERT. A Manual of Monumental Brasses. Oxford/London, 1861. 2 parts. cclxiii; 286pp. Tooled cl (both backstrips sl chipped, few corners bumped). *Washton*. $150/£94

HAINES, REGINALD. General Gordon. Cambridge: Deighton Bell, 1902. Frontis port. VG. *Hollett*. $40/£25

HAINES, TOM. Flouring Mills of Montana Territory. N.p.: (Friends of Univ of MT Library, 1984). 1st ed. Fine in VG + dj. *Sagebrush*. $25/£16

HAINING, PETER. Movable Books. An Illustrated History. (London): New English Library, (1979). 1st ed. Black bds. Good in illus dj. *Karmiole*. $125/£78

HAISLET, JOHN (ed). Famous Trees of Texas. N.p.: TX Forest Service, 1970. 1st ed. Pict cl. NF. *Archer*. $27/£17

HAJEK, LUBOR. Japanese Graphic Art. Helena Krejcova (trans). Secaucus, NJ: Chartwell, 1976. 1st US ed. 113 plts. VG in dj. *Worldwide*. $25/£16

HAJIB, YUSUF KHASS. Wisdom of Royal Glory (Kutadgu Bilig). Robert Dankoff (trans). Chicago/London: Univ of Chicago, 1983. 1st ed. NF in dj. *Worldwide*. $20/£13

HAKLUYT, RICHARD. The Principal Voyages, Traffiques and Discoveries of the English Nation. NY, 1927. 8 vols. (Backstrips sl dknd.) *Swann**. $149/£93

HAKLUYT, RICHARD. The Principall Navigations Voiages and Discoveries of the English Nation. CUP, 1965. 2 vols. Fldg map. Djs (sl discolored). *Edwards*. $200/£125

HAKLUYT, RICHARD. The Principall Navigations, Voiages and Discoveries of the English Nation. Cambridge: Hakluyt Soc, 1965. 2 vols. Fldg facs map. Gilt-lettered blue cl. Fine in djs (sl shelfworn, spines sl faded). *Pacific**. $184/£115

HALAAS, DAVID FRIDTJOF. Boomtown Newspapers. Albuquerque, (1981). 1st ed. Frontis, map. NF in VG + dj. *Sagebrush*. $30/£19

HALBERT, HENRY S. and TIMOTHY H. BALL. The Creek War of 1813 and 1814. Chicago/Montgomery: Donohue & Henneberry/White, Woodruff, & Fowler, 1895. 1st ed. Frontisports, fldg map, 331,(iii)pp. Maroon cl, gilt. (Browned, lower hinge cracked, old stains fep edges; spine spotted, lt stains at cvrs.) Howes H28. *Baltimore**. $160/£100

HALDANE, J. S. Respiration. New Haven, 1922. 2 fldg charts. (Lt foxed; spine worn, fr hinge cracked.) *Whitehart*. $96/£60

HALDSTED, WILLIAM STEWART. Surgical Papers. Balt: Johns Hopkins, 1924. Signed by Harry W. Plath. 2 vols. Frontis, 103 plts (5 fldg, 2 color), fldg table. Teg. Fine in grn cl. *Weber*. $500/£313

HALE, CHRISTOPHER. Dead of Winter. CCD, 1941. 1st ed. VG (bds rubbed, edges sl worn) in Good dj (pieces out spine ends, edges rubbed; lt soiled). *Murder*. $40/£25

HALE, EDWARD EVERETT. Prospero's Island. NY: Dramatic Museum of Columbia Univ, 1919. One of 333. Paper label. VG. *Dramatis*. $35/£22

HALE, EDWARD EVERETT. Seven Spanish Cities and the Way to Them. Boston: Roberts Bros, 1883. 1st ed. v,328pp. (Cl rubbed, dust-soiled), o/w Good. *Brown*. $15/£9

HALE, EDWARD EVERETT. Tom Torrey's Tariff Talks. Boston: J. Stillman Smith, 1888. 1st ed. 40,58pp + 2pp ads. Pict cl bds. (Edgeworn), else VG. *Brown*. $25/£16

HALE, J. H. How to Tie Salmon Flies. London, 1892. 1st ed. Errata slip tipped in. Uncut. (Shelfworn, sl soiled.) *Oinonen**. $250/£156

HALE, JOHN P. Trans-Allegheny Pioneers. Cincinnati: Graphic Press, 1886. 1st ed. 330pp; fldg facs. Marbled eps. Grn cl, beveled bds, gilt. Text VG (lt aged, ink sig, stamps), cvrs Very Clean (extrems sl rubbed). Howes H32. *Baltimore**. $100/£63

HALE, KATHLEEN. Orlando the Marmalade Cat Buys a Farm. London: Country Life, 1942. 1st ed. 10.25x14. 32pp. VG in wraps. *Cattermole*. $350/£219

HALE, KATHLEEN. Orlando's Home Life. London: Penguin, (1942). 1st ed. Obl 8vo. 30pp. VG in pict paper wraps. *Sotheran*. $96/£60

HALE, KATHLEEN. Orlando's Invisible Pyjamas. London: Royle, (1947). 1st ed. Obl 8vo. 30pp. VG in color-ptd pict wraps. *Sotheran*. $96/£60

HALE, KATHLEEN. Orlando's Zoo. London: John Murray, (1954). 1st ed. Obl 8vo. 30pp. Fine in color-ptd paper wraps (sm splash mk). *Sotheran*. $96/£60

HALE, KATHLEEN. Orlando, the Frisky Housewife. London: Country Life, 1956. 1st ed. Royal 8vo. 32pp. Orange pict bds. Fine. *Sotheran*. $141/£88

HALE, LUCRETIA P. Alone in Rome. Rome: Ptd at Gould Memorial Home, 1883. Rpt. 1st separate bk ed after magazine pub. 27pp. VG in lt orange wraps (sl soiled) w/tipped-in slip. *Second Life*. $60/£38

HALE, MATTHEW. The History of the Common Law. London: G.G. & J. Robinson et al, 1794. 5th ed. 2 vols. Mod bds. Good set (browned). *Boswell*. $650/£406

HALE, NATHAN CABOT. Embrace of Life: The Sculpture of Gustav Vigeland. NY, (1969). Dj. *Swann**. $57/£36

HALE, NATHANIEL. Pelts and Palisades: The Story of Fur and the Rivalry for Pelts in Early America. Richmond: Dietz, (1959). (Ink inscrip), else VG in dj. *Perier*. $30/£19

HALES, PETER B. William Henry Jackson and the Transformation of the American Landscape. Phila: Temple Univ, 1988. VG in dj. *Dumont*. $45/£28

HALEY, ALEX. Roots. GC, (1976). 1st ed. VG + in dj (sl worn, 1.5-inch tear). *Pratt*. $100/£63

HALEY, ALEX. Roots. NY: Doubleday, (1976). Rpt. Inscribed. 1/4 gilt-stamped black cl, tan bds. (Spine ends sl rubbed), o/w Fine in dj. *Heritage*. $200/£125

HALEY, ALEX. Roots. GC: Doubleday, 1976. Inscribed, dated 3/4/89. VG (stamp, bkpl; upper corner bumped) in VG dj (price-clipped). *Agvent*. $275/£172

HALEY, ALEX. Roots. NY: Doubleday, 1976. 1st ed. One of 500 signed. Teg. Orig full leather, gilt-stamped spine. (Bkpl), o/w Fine in cardboard slipcase. *Heritage*. $450/£281

HALEY, ALEX. Roots. Johannesburg: Hutchinson, 1977. 1st South African ed. VG in VG + dj (price-clipped). *Pettler*. $35/£22

HALEY, J. EVETTS and WILLIAM C. HOLDEN. The Flamboyant Judge: James D. Hamlin. Canyon, TX: Palo Duro, 1972. 1st ed. Inscribed by Holden, signed by Haley. NF in dj (sl worn). *Dumont*. $125/£78

HALEY, J. EVETTS and ERWIN SMITH. Life on the Texas Range. Austin: Univ of TX, 1952. 1st ed. NF in slipcase (edgewear). *Labordo*. $165/£103

HALEY, J. EVETTS. Earl Vandale on the Trail of Texas Books. Canyon, TX: Palo Duro, 1965. One of 500. Signed by Haley and Carl Hertzog (ptr). Frontis. NF. *Dumont*. $165/£103

HALEY, J. EVETTS. Earl Vandale on the Trail of Texas Books. Canyon, TX: Palo Duro, 1965. 1st ed. Ltd to 500. Inscribed. Fine. *Sadlon*. $175/£109

HALEY, J. EVETTS. Focus on the Frontier. Amarillo, TX: Shamrock Oil & Gas Corp, 1957. 1st ed. Inscribed. Fine in wrapper. *Sadlon*. $85/£53

HALEY, J. EVETTS. Jeff Milton. Norman: Univ of OK, 1948. 1st ed, 1st issue w/name of John Campbell Greenway on p.421 in index is ptd upside down. Good. Howes H38. *Lien*. $75/£47

HALEY, J. EVETTS. Life on the Texas Range. Austin: Univ of TX, 1952. 1st ed. Inscribed. Fine in NF slipcase w/photo label. *Sadlon*. $200/£125

HALEY, J. EVETTS. Story of the Shamrock. Amarillo, TX: Shamrock Oil & Gas Corp, (1954). 1st ed. Inscribed. Grn wrappers (spine fold sl lightened) w/grn rawhide tie, slipcase (lt shelfworn). *Sadlon*. $75/£47

HALEY, J. EVETTS. The XIT Ranch of Texas. Norman: Univ of OK, 1949. 1st ed thus. NF in dj. *Labordo*. $65/£41

HALEY, WILLIAM. The Life of George Romney. Chichister: T. Payne, 1809. 1st ed. 12 engr plts (1 engr by William Blake). 3/4 red morocco, gilt-paneled spine, raised bands. Fine. *Appelfeld*. $325/£203

HALFORD, FREDERIC M. Dry Fly Entomology. A Brief Description of Leading Types of Natural Insects...with the 100 Best Patterns of Floating Flies. London, 1897. Deluxe ed. One of 100 numbered, signed. 2 vols. 4to. 28 plts (10 hand-colored), 100 artificial flies in 12 sunken mounts. Pub's gilt-lettered morocco. Superb (lt foxed; rubbed). *Oinonen**. $2,400/£1,500

HALFORD, FREDERIC M. Dry-Fly Fishing in Theory and Practice. London: Sampson Low et al, 1889. 1st ed. 289pp + ad; 26 plts. Brn cl, beveled edges. (Lt edgeworn, foxed), else VG. *Bowman*. $250/£156

HALFORD, FREDERIC M. Dry-Fly Fishing in Theory and Practice. London: Vinton, 1902. 4th ed. Dk blue cl, gilt. (Spine sl leaning, lt foxing), else VG. *Pacific**. $58/£36

HALFORD, FREDERIC M. The Dry-Fly Man's Handbook. London: Routledge, (1913). 1st ed. 43 plts. (Rear cvr sl stained), o/w VG. *Petersfield*. $240/£150

HALFORD, FREDERIC M. Floating Flies and How to Dress Them. London, 1886. 1st ed. 32-pg Sampson Low cat dated Oct 1885. Joseph D. Bates Jr.'s bkpl. 9 hand-colored plts. Uncut. (Shelfworn.) *Oinonen**. $280/£175

HALFORD, FREDERIC M. Making a Fishery. London: Horace Cox, 1895. 1st ed. Frontis port. Teg. Dk blue cl, gilt. *Pacific**. $109/£68

HALFORD, FREDERIC M. Making a Fishery. London: Cox, 1895. 1st ed. Photo frontis, 212pp; 4 plts. Teg. Blue cl, gilt. (Sm dull spot lower fr cvr), else VG. *Bowman*. $140/£88

HALFORD, FREDERIC M. Modern Development of the Dry Fly: The New Dry Fly Patterns, the Manipulation of Dressing Them and Practical Experiences of Their Use. London, (1910). Deluxe ed. Ltd to 75 numbered sets, signed. 2 vols. 4to. 9 color plts, 33 flies mtd in 9 sunken compartments. Teg, uncut. Red-stained 3/4 calf (rubbed, spine tips worn; foxed). *Oinonen**. $1,600/£1,000

HALFORD, W. C. The Mechanic's Own Book.... London: Bailey, n.d. (ca 1840). 32pp. New bds (spotted). *Marlborough*. $192/£120

HALFPENNY, WILLIAM and JOHN. Rural Architecture in the Chinese Taste. London: Robert Sayer, 1752. 2nd ed. 4 parts in 1 vol. 8vo. Engr general tp, 60 engr plts, 11 fldg. (Occasional lt spotting, fep loose, inscrip.) Contemp calf (fr cvr almost detached, rear cvr split but cords holding, worn.) *Christie's**. $864/£540

HALFPENNY, WILLIAM. Practical Architecture. London: Tho. Bowles, 1730. 5th ed. 3 prelims (engr tp, engr dedication, engr preface), 48 engr plts. Contemp calf (rubbed, 3/4-inch chip spine bottom, hinges starting). *Karmiole*. $450/£281

HALKETT, SAMUEL and JOHN LAING. Dictionary of Anonymous and Pseudonymous English Literature. Edinburgh/London, 1926-1962. New, enlgd ed. 9 vols. (Lt worn.) *Oinonen**. $425/£266

HALL, A. D. The Genus Tulipa. London, 1940. 40 color plts. (Pp tanned; flecked, bumped, spine faded, sm tear fore-edge fr cvr.) *Sutton*. $125/£78

HALL, BASIL. Account of a Voyage of Discovery to the West Coast of Corea.... London: John Murray, 1818. 1st ed. 4to. xvi,(i),222pp + cxxx + (lxxii)pp; 5 charts (2 fldg), 2 plain plts, 8 hand-colored aquatints. (Lt foxing mainly to margins, dust soiling.) Contemp bds (rebacked w/much of orig spine laid down, sympathetic repairs to rear bd; surface wear). *Edwards*. $1,600/£1,000

HALL, BASIL. Extracts from a Journal, Written on the Coasts of Chili, Peru, and Mexico, in the Years 1820, 1821, and 1822.... Edinburgh: Archibald Constable, 1824. 3rd ed. 2 vols. xx,379; xii,304,71pp; fldg chart. Contemp 1/2 calf (rubbed, joints cracked). Internally Clean. *Lefkowicz*. $150/£94

HALL, BASIL. The Great Polygot Bibles, Including a Leaf from the Complutensian of Acala, 1514-17. SF: Book Club of CA, 1966. One of 400 ptd. Prospectus laid in. Unsewn sheets in wrapper, purple cl box. Fine. *Pacific**. $288/£180

HALL, BASIL. Travels in North America, in the Years 1827 and 1828. Edinburgh: Robert Cadell, 1830. 3rd ed. 3 vols. xiv,421,(8) ads, fldg color map; vi,432; vii,436pp, 9 fldg tables. Uncut. Orig bds (spine worn), paper labels. (Card remnants pasted inside fr cvrs; spines chipped), o/w VF. Howes H47. *Mott*. $250/£156

HALL, BASIL. Travels in North America. Edinburgh, 1829. 3 vols. W/half-titles, 4pp ads. Fldg map (2-inch tear at edge), fldg table. 19th-cent 1/2 calf (backstrips defective; owner initials on tps, lt foxed, bkpls). Howes H47. *Swann**. $149/£93

HALL, BERT L. Roundup Years. (Kennebec & Pierre), 1956. 2nd ptg. (Sig, few ink notes; hinges professionally reinforced, bds cvrd w/lamination.) Cvrs VG-, text Fine. *Baade*. $100/£63

HALL, C. and G. GOODING. Flowers of the Islands in the Sun. NY: Barnes, 1966. 1st ed. Fine in VG + dj (price-clipped, torn). *Archer*. $25/£16

HALL, CARROLL D. (ed). Donner Miscellany: 41 Diaries and Documents. SF: Book Club of CA, 1947. One of 350 ptd. (Bkpl), else VG. *Pacific**. $63/£39

HALL, CHARLES A. Plant-Life. London: A. & C. Black, 1915. 50 color plts. (Rep lt browned; spine, fr hinge lt faded.) *Edwards*. $72/£45

HALL, CHARLES F. Arctic Research Expedition and Life Among the Esquimaux. NY: Harper, 1865. 1st ed. 595pp + ads; fldg map. VG (spine sl faded). *Walcot*. $224/£140

HALL, CHARLES F. Life with the Esquimaux: A Narrative of Arctic Experience in Search of Survivors of Sir John Franklin's Expedition. Sampson Low, Son & Marston, 1865. Popular ed. x,547pp,16 ads; 4 color plts; fldg map in rear pocket. Gilt-dec cl (carefully rebacked). VG. *Explorer*. $112/£70

HALL, CHARLES F. Narrative of the Second Arctic Expedition.... J. E. Nourse (ed). Washington: GPO, 1879. 1st ed. 1,644pp; 2 steel-engr ports, lg fldg map in rear pocket. Rose cl, gilt. Text, map Good. (Spine, edges sunned, ends frayed w/some tears, hinges cracked.) *Baltimore**. $80/£50

HALL, CYRIL. Modern Weapons of War. Blackie & Son, 1915. 1st ed. 36 b/w plts. Pict cl. VG (top edge dusty, spine ends, corners sl bumped, rubbed) in dj (worn, lacks spine piece). *Ulysses*. $104/£65

HALL, FREDERIC. The History of San Jose and Surroundings with Biographical Sketches.... SF: A.L. Bancroft, 1871. Inscribed. Fldg map. (Lt foxed, sm dk spots; extrems worn, sl soiled.) *Metropolitan**. $28/£18

HALL, FREDERICK. Letters from the East and from the West. Washington City: F. Taylor & Wm M. Morrison, (1840). 1st ed. 11,168pp (piece clipped fep, margins stained). Orig cl (very soiled), ptd paper label. Howes H64. *M & S*. $400/£250

HALL, GEORGE. The Gypsy's Parson. Sampson Low, Marston, n.d. xii,307pp; 44 plts. (Few spots.) *Hollett*. $56/£35

HALL, GRANVILLE DAVISSON. Lee's Invasion of Northwest Virginia in 1861. (Glencoe, IL: The Author), 1911. 1st ed. 'With compliments of the author' slip tipped to fr pastedown. Tan cl. NF. *Chapel Hill*. $175/£109

HALL, GRANVILLE STANLEY. Founders of Modern Psychology. NY: Appleton, (1912). Ptd red cl. *Gach*. $50/£31

HALL, H. R. The Ancient History of the Near East from the Earliest Times to the Battle of Salamis. London: Methuen, 1927. 7th ed. 33 plts, 14 maps. (Marginal ink notes; edges rubbed, spine ends frayed), o/w VG. *Worldwide*. $20/£13

HALL, H. R. Catalogue of Egyptian Scarabs, etc. in the British Museum, Volume I. London: British Museum, 1913. (Bkpl; lt bumped, rubbed.) *Archaeologia*. $650/£406

HALL, H. R. The Civilization of Greece in the Bronze Age. NY: R.V. Coleman, (1928). Frontis, 2 maps. (Corner bumped, sl shelfworn.) *Archaeologia*. $45/£28

HALL, H. R. The Civilization of Greece in the Bronze Age. London: Methuen, 1928. 1st ed. (Sl rubbed, lib spine #), o/w VG. *Worldwide*. $65/£41

HALL, HARRY H. A Johnny Reb Band from Salem: The Pride of Tarheelia. Raleigh: NC Confederate Centennial Commission, 1963. 1st ed. (Spine head repaired), else VG in ptd blue wraps. *Chapel Hill*. $35/£22

HALL, HENRY MARION. Woodcock Ways. NY, 1946. 1st ed. Dj (lt edgeworn). *Swann**. $69/£43

HALL, J. The Fauna of the Niagra Group in Central Indiana. NY, 1879. 99-210pp; 35 plts. Good. *Henly*. $51/£32

HALL, J. Palaeontology of New-York. Volume 1. Albany: C. Van Benthuysen, 1847. xxiii,338pp. (Rebacked, bds edgeworn), else Good. *Blake*. $100/£63

HALL, J. Palaeontology of New-York. Volume II. Albany: C. Van Benthuysen, 1852. viii,362pp; 85 + (19) plts. Good (recased, corners lt rubbed). *Blake*. $125/£78

HALL, J. Palaeontology of New-York. Volume III. Part II: Plates. Albany: C. Van Benthuysen, 1861. 141 litho plts, tissues. (Outside edges foxed, spine ends chipped), else Good. *Blake*. $100/£63

HALL, JAMES NORMAN. High Adventure. Boston: Houghton Mifflin, 1918. 1st ed. (Inscrip; top edge dusty), else VG + in VG dj. *Lame Duck*. $150/£94

HALL, JAMES NORMAN. High Adventure. Boston/NY: Houghton Mifflin, 1918. 1st ed. Frontis. Red cl stamped in black. NF in VG dj (chipped). *Reese*. $200/£125

HALL, JAMES W. Under Cover of Daylight. NY, 1987. 1st ed. NF in NF dj. *Warren*. $95/£59

HALL, JOSEPH (ed). King Horn. OUP, 1901. 1st Eng ed. Buckram. VG (spine ends sl bumped). *Ulysses*. $104/£65

HALL, MANLY P. Codex Rosae Crucis: A Rare and Curious Manuscript of Rosicrucian Interest. L.A.: Philosophers, 1938. 1st ed. Inscribed, signed. 1/2 red morocco, gilt. (Spine ends rubbed), else VG. *Pacific**. $86/£54

HALL, MANLY P. An Encyclopedic Outline of Masonic, Hermetic, Cabbalistic and Rosicrucian Symbological Philosophy.... H.S. Crocker, 1928. 1st ed. One of 550 signed. 48 full-pg color plts. Vellum spine. (2 plts w/long professionally mended tears, 2 other plts w/sm mended tears; fore-edge, bottom edge of bds worn, spine dust-soiled), else VG in wooden slipcase (worn). *Fine Books*. $475/£297

HALL, MARTIN HARDWICK. The Confederate Army of New Mexico. Austin, 1978. (Shelfworn), else Good. *Dumont*. $90/£56

HALL, MR. and MRS. S. C. The Book of the Thames.... London: Virtue, n.d. (ca 1898). New ed. xii,460pp. Pict cl, gilt. (Edges rubbed.) *Marlborough*. $120/£75

HALL, MRS. BASIL. The Aristocratic Journey...Written During a Fourteen Months Sojourn in America 1827-1828. Una Pope-Hennessy (ed). NY: Putnam, 1931. 1st ed. Paper labels. (Lt foxed.) *Mott*. $45/£28

HALL, MRS. S. C. Pilgrimages to English Shrines: Second Series. Arthur Hall, Virtue, 1853. Aeg. Dec cl. Good (sig, sl spotted; spine bumped, head chipped w/loss, corners rubbed, fr joint cracked). *Tiger*. $40/£25

HALL, MRS. S. C. Sketches of Irish Character. London: How & Parsons, 1842. Illus ed. 1st ed thus. 380pp. Marbled eps. 3/4 pebbled grn morocco, gilt, raised bands, marbled bds. VG. *Hartfield*. $195/£122

HALL, R. N. Pre-Historic Rhodesia. Phila, n.d. c.(1909). 1st ed. 8 maps, plans on 5 (4 fldg). Teg. (Lt marginal browning; spine sl chipped, faded.) *Edwards*. $136/£85

HALL, RADCLYFFE. (Pseud of Marguerite Radclyffe.) The Master of the House. London: Cape, 1932. 1st ed. One of 167 (of 172) numbered, signed. Teg, rest uncut. Orig vellum-backed cream cl (lt soiled, unevenly faded), gilt. Internally Good. *Maggs*. $72/£45

HALL, RADCLYFFE. (Pseud of Marguerite Radclyffe.) A Saturday Life. London: Arrowsmith, (1925). 1st ed. Pub's ads on dj rear, flaps. Dk grn cl. VG (edges, prelims, eps foxed) in pict dj (nicked). *Houle*. $450/£281

HALL, SAMUEL CARTER (ed). The Book of Gems. The Poets and Artists of Great Britain. London: Saunders & Otley, 1836-1838. 1st ed. 3 vols. xvi,304,(4); xvi,304,(4); xvi,304,(4)pp. Aeg. Gilt full blue morocco (hinges lt rubbed). *Karmiole*. $275/£172

HALL, THOMAS B. Medicine on the Santa Fe Trail. Dayton, OH: Morningside Bookshop, 1971. Ltd, signed ed. One of 1000. NF. *Glenn*. $40/£25

HALL, THOMAS B. Medicine on the Santa Fe Trail. (Dayton): Morningside Bookshop, 1971. 1st ed. One of 1000 signed. Fldg table. Blue cl (sl soiled). NF. *Harrington*. $55/£34

HALL, THOMAS C. John Hall: Pastor and Preacher. NY: Revell, (1902). 1st ed. Gilt-dec cl. *Ginsberg*. $75/£47

HALL, TOM S. Tramping Holidays in Scotland. Country Life, 1948. Rev, enlgd ed. 12 maps. VG in dj (chipped, defective). *Hollett*. $24/£15

HALL, TOM S. Tramping in Arran. Falkirk: Wayfaring Assoc, 1947. 3rd ed. 3 maps. VG. *Hollett*. $24/£15

HALL, TREVOR. Old Conjuring Books. London: Duckworth, 1972. 1st ed. One of 1000 signed. Dec cl. VG. *Dramatis*. $50/£31

HALL, TREVOR. Old Conjuring Books. Gerald Duckworth, 1972. 1st ed. Ltd signed, numbered ed. Frontis, 8 plts. Dj. *Forest*. $72/£45

HALL, WILLIAM H. and WILLIAM D. BERNARD. Narrative of the Voyages and Services of the Nemesis, from 1840 to 1843. London: Henry Colburn, 1844. 2 vols. 8vo. xvi,450; x,522pp; 3 fldg maps, 6 plts (lt foxed). 1/2 grn calf (rubbed), gilt. *Adelson*. $585/£366

HALL-DUNCAN, NANCY. The History of Fashion Photography. NY: Alpine Bk, 1979. 1st ed. Fine in dj (edges chipped). *Cahan.* $75/£47

HALLAHAN, WILLIAM H. The Ross Forgery. Indianapolis: Bobbs-Merrill, 1973. 1st ed. VG + (edges, cvrs lt spotted) in dj (lt edgeworn). *Janus.* $65/£41

HALLAM, HENRY. The Constitutional History of England from the Accession of Henry VII to the Death of George II. London: John Murray, 1846. 5th ed. 2 vols. xv,719; viii,624pp. 1/2 calf (dry, spines worn). *Zubal*.* $90/£56

HALLAM, HENRY. Introduction to the Literature of Europe, in the Fifteenth, Sixteenth, and Seventeenth Centuries. John Murray, 1843. 2nd ed. 3 vols. Contemp 1/2 calf, marbled bds (all vols rebacked). *Bickersteth.* $96/£60

HALLECK, FITZ-GREENE. The Poetical Works.... NY, 1858. 3rd ed. Folio, w/8vo contents trimmed and inlaid to size. 7 engr plts (incl frontisport, add'l tp). Extra-illus. Contemp grn morocco, gilt, by Pawson & Nicholson. (Joints rubbed.) *Swann*.* $517/£323

HALLENBECK, CLEVE and JUANITA H. WILLIAMS. Legends of the Spanish Southwest. Glendale: A.H. Clark, 1938. 1st ed. 8 photo plts, 1 fldg map. Lt blue cl. Good. *Karmiole.* $100/£63

HALLENBECK, CLEVE. The Journey of Fray Marcos de Niza. Dallas: University Press, 1949. 1st ed. Fine in dj. *Labordo.* $195/£122

HALLENBECK, CLEVE. Spanish Missions of the Old Southwest. GC, 1926. 72 leaves of photo plts. VG in VG dj, cardboard slipcase (broken). *New Hampshire*.* $75/£47

HALLENBECK, CLEVE. Spanish Missions of the Old Southwest. GC, 1926. (Sl edge worn, faded, else VG. *Dumont.* $100/£63

HALLER, ALBERTUS. First Lines of Physiology. William Cullen (trans). Edinburgh: Charles Elliot/G.G.J. & J. Robinson, 1786. 2 vols in 1. viii,288; (1)-278,(2)ads pp. Contemp calf (expertly rebacked). VG. *House.* $400/£250

HALLIBURTON, RICHARD. Book of Marvels. Indianapolis, (1937). Signed. (Ink inscrip, spine frayed, cvrs worn.) *King.* $35/£22

HALLIBURTON, RICHARD. His Story of His Life's Adventures as Told in Letters to His Mother and Father. Indianapolis, 1940. 1st ed. VF. *Bond.* $20/£13

HALLIWELL, JAMES ORCHARD. The Early History of Freemasonry in England. London: John Russell Smith, 1844. 2nd ed. 52pp. Contemp red 1/2 roan (extrems sl rubbed; bkpl). *Young.* $136/£85

HALLOCK, CHARLES. An Angler's Reminiscences. Cincinnati: Sportsmen's Review, 1913. 1st ed. Signed, inscribed by Fred E. Pond (intro). Red cl, gilt. (Spine ends rubbed), else NF. *Pacific*.* $173/£108

HALLOCK, CHARLES. The Sportsman's Gazetteer and General Guide. NY: Forest & Stream, 1880. 5th ed. 3 fldg hand-colored maps (lacks map in rear pocket). Red cl, gilt. Fine. *Pacific*.* $58/£36

HALLWARD, REGINALD FRANCIS. Flowers of Paradise. London: Macmillan, (1889). 1st ed. Slim 4to. (iii),4-39pp; 8 full-pg color plts. Dec peach eps. Purple cl-backed paper-cvrd bds. (Corners sl knocked), o/w Fine. *Sotheran.* $352/£220

HALPIN, WARREN T. Hoofbeats. Drawings and Comments. Phila, 1938. One of 1500 numbered. (Sl worn, cvrs spotted.) *Oinonen*.* $50/£31

HALSELL, H. H. The Old Cimarron. N.p., 1944. Signed. Good in dj (chipped, spotted). *Dumont.* $50/£31

HALSEY, ASHLEY, JR. Illustrating for the Saturday Evening Post. Arlington House, (1951). Good in dj (worn, chipped). *Rybski.* $50/£31

HALSMAN, PHILIPPE. Halsman Portraits. Yvonne Halsman et al (eds). NY: McGraw-Hill, 1982. 1st ed. 119 full-pg b/w plts. Fine in illus dj. *Cahan.* $85/£53

HALSMAN, PHILIPPE. Jump Book. NY, 1959. Signed, inscribed clipping affixed to fep. (Eps sl soiled, newspaper clipping mtd w/tape opposite tp; sl worn, corners bumped.) Dj (stained, worn). *Swann*.* $103/£64

HALSTEAD, B. W. Poisonous and Venomous Marine Animals of the World. Washington, 1965-67-70. 1st ed. 3 vols. (Names; lt scuffed, faded.) *Sutton.* $385/£241

HALSTED, WILLIAM STEWART. Surgical Papers by....(1852-1922). Johns Hopkins, 1924. 2 vols. (Bkpls.) *Rybski.* $125/£78

HAMBLEN, HERBERT ELLIOTT. The Story of a Yankee Boy: His Adventures Ashore and Afloat. NY: Scribner, 1898. 1st ed. 8vo. ix,(iii),339pp; 4 plts by Harry Edwards. Pict grayish blue cl, gilt. VG (spine sl faded, joint soiled). *Blue Mountain.* $25/£16

HAMBLY, W. D. Origins of Education Among Primitive Peoples. London, 1926. 1st ed. (Prelims lt browned; spine sl rubbed, sl cl loss top edge rear bd.) *Edwards.* $96/£60

HAMBURGER, MICHAEL. A Mug's Game. Cheadle Hulme, Cheshire: Carcanet, 1973. 1st Eng ed. NF (fore-edge sl spotted; spine foot sl bumped) in dj (sl faded, rubbed, few nicks). *Ulysses.* $32/£20

HAMERTON, PHILIP GILBERT. Drawing and Engraving. A&C Black, 1892. Color litho frontis, xxii,172pp (eps sl mkd); 22 plts. Teg, uncut. Buckram, gilt. *Hollett.* $72/£45

HAMERTON, PHILIP GILBERT. Etching and Etchers.... London, 1880. 3rd ed. Folio. 48 etchings (26 by various contemp artists, 22 by Amant-Durand). Orig 1/4 leather (spine ends chipped, joints worn, fr hinge cracked), gilt. (Lt offsetting from plts), o/w Clean internally. *Swann*.* $862/£539

HAMERTON, PHILIP GILBERT. The Graphic Arts: A Treatise.... London, 1882. Thick sm folio. Gilt vellum. *Swann*.* $258/£161

HAMERTON, PHILIP GILBERT. Landscape. London, 1885. One of 525. 1/4 morocco (extrems rubbed; hinges just starting). *Swann*.* $172/£108

HAMERTON, PHILIP GILBERT. Landscape. London, 1885. One of 525 numbered. Folio. 13 etched plts. (1st, last few ll foxed.) Orig imitation vellum (soiled, hinges cracked), gilt. *Swann*.* $230/£144

HAMERTON, PHILIP GILBERT. Man in Art. London, 1892. 1st ed. Sm folio. 46 plts. Uncut. Buckram. *Argosy.* $100/£63

HAMERTON, PHILIP GILBERT. Man in Art. London, 1892. Folio. 46 plts. Teg. Full crushed blue morocco, gilt. (Feps loose; spine sl rubbed.) *Kane*.* $110/£69

HAMERTON, PHILIP GILBERT. The Unknown River. Boston: Roberts Bros, 1872. 1st Amer ed. 36 etched plts (margins, versos foxed); pub's ad laid in. Aeg. Blue cl, gilt. Good (foxed, ink inscrip; bumped, spotted, rear cvr lt stained, sm spine tear). *Blue Mountain.* $45/£28

HAMILTON, ALEXANDER et al. The Federalist. LEC, 1945. Ltd to 1500 numbered, signed by Bruce Rogers (illus). 2 vols. Fine in slipcase. *Swann*.* $258/£161

HAMILTON, ALEXANDER et al. The Federalist or the New Constitution. NY: LEC,f 1945. One of 1500. Signed by Bruce Rogers (decs). 2 vols. Teg. 1/2 morocco, dec bds, gilt. Fine in glassine, slipcase. *Pacific*.* $127/£79

HAMILTON, ALEXANDER. Observations on Certain Documents Contained in...The History of the United States for the Year 1796.... Phila: John Fenno, 1797. 1st ed. 37,58pp (tp lt foxed). Contemp marbled paper-cvrd bds (sl rubbed), later calf spine. *Kane*.* $300/£188

HAMILTON, ALEXANDER. The Works of Alexander Hamilton. Henry Cabot Lodge (ed). NY: Putnam, (1903). 12 vols. Dk grn cl, maroon leather labels, gilt tops. Fine. *Appelfeld.* $200/£125

HAMILTON, ANTHONY. Memoirs of Count Grammont. London: William Miller & James Carpenter, 1811. New ed. 2 vols. ix,xxxvii,262; (iii),356pp; 64 copper engr ports. Marbled edges. Early calf, marbled bds later recased in lt brn calf w/orig black leather spine labels retained. (Sl foxing, offsetting from plts, some lt foxed; cvrs dknd, lt cracked, inner edges of cvrs crackled, dknd.) *Baltimore**. $80/£50

HAMILTON, CHARLES. Scribblers and Scoundrels. NY, 1968. Good in dj. *Dumont*. $35/£22

HAMILTON, CLAYTON. Studies in Stagecraft. NY: Henry Holt, (1914). VG. *Dramatis*. $30/£19

HAMILTON, COSMO. Paradise. Boston: Little, Brown, 1925. 1st US ed. Dec red cl. (Bkpl), o/w Nice in dj (sl chipped). *Reese*. $30/£19

HAMILTON, DAVID. Early Aberdeen Golf: Golfing Small-Talk in 1636. Glasgow/Oxford: Patrick, 1985. 1st ed. One of 450. Signed. Prospectus laid-in. Pict bds. Fine (emb stamp). *Pacific**. $150/£94

HAMILTON, DAVID. Early Golf at Edinburgh and Leith: The Account Books of Sir John Foulis of Ravelston. Glasgow: Patrick, 1988. 1st ed. One of 350. Signed. Dk grn cl, paper cvr, spine labels. Fine (emb stamp). *Pacific**. $127/£79

HAMILTON, DAVID. Early Golf at St. Andrews. Glasgow/Oban: Patrick, (1986). 1st ed. One of 350 ptd. 1 laid-in fldg facs. Pict blue bds, gilt. Fine (emb stamp). *Pacific**. $161/£101

HAMILTON, DAVID. Early Golf in Glasgow, 1589-1787. Oxford: Patrick, 1985. 1st ed. One of 250. Inscribed, signed. Prospectus laid-in. Ptd bds. NF (emb stamp). *Pacific**. $150/£94

HAMILTON, EDWARD. Recollections of Fly Fishing for Salmon, Trout, and Grayling, with Notes on Their Haunts, Habits and History. NY: OJ, 1885. 1st Amer ed. Frontis mezzotint engr. (Spine ends sl rubbed), else NF. *Pacific**. $58/£36

HAMILTON, ELIZABETH. The Cottagers of Glenburnie. Edinburgh: Ptd by James Ballantyne, 1808. 3rd ed. xv,408pp. Uncut. Calf-backed bds. *Young*. $56/£35

HAMILTON, GEORGE. The Elements of Drawing in Its Various Branches, for the Use of Students, etc. London: Phillips, 1827. viii + 93pp; 50 plts. Recent 1/2 morocco, marbled bds. VF. *Europa*. $192/£120

HAMILTON, HENRY W. and JEAN TYREE HAMILTON. The Sioux of the Rosebud. Norman: Univ of OK, (1971). 1st ed. Red-stamped turquoise cl. (Rear inner hinge weak.) Dj. *Dawson*. $50/£31

HAMILTON, IAN. Gallipoli Diary. London: Edward Arnold, 1920. 1st ed. 2 vols. Plum cl stamped in gilt/blind. VG set (spine gilt sl dull). *Reese*. $100/£63

HAMILTON, JOHN P. Travels Through the Interior Provinces of Colombia. London: John Murray, 1827. 2 vols. 4,332; 4,256pp (perf lib stamp on tps), errata; fldg map, 7 plts. Mod red buckram. *Adelson*. $385/£241

HAMILTON, MYRA. Kingdoms Curious. London: William Heinemann, 1905. 1st ed, 1st issue, w/fr cvrs stamped in black/gold. 4to. 6 illus by Arthur Rackham (5 full-pg). (Lt spotting.) Tan pict cl (spine lt browned, spotted), gilt. *Christie's**. $331/£207

HAMILTON, PATRICK. Hangover Square. NY: Random House, (1942). 1st Amer ed. VG in dj (sl worn, chipped). *Ash*. $120/£75

HAMILTON, PETER J. Colonial Mobile. Mobile, 1952. Rev ed. Fldg map. (Spine sl faded, top edge sl damp-puckering.) Howes H134. *Bohling*. $27/£17

HAMILTON, R. Ichtyology: British Fishes. Edinburgh: W.H. Lizars, 1852. 2 vols. 72 hand-colored plts, guards. Teg. Gilt-lettered red cl. (Spine feet chipped, part II w/repairs to spine cl, joints), else VG. *Pacific**. $345/£216

HAMILTON, RUTH. The Book of Ruth. NY: Ticknor & Fields, 1988. 1st ed, 1st bk. Fine in Fine dj. *Beasley*. $250/£156

HAMILTON, SINCLAIR. Early American Book Illustrators and Wood Engravers, 1670-1870. Princeton, 1958. 1st ed. *Argosy*. $175/£109

HAMILTON, THOMAS MARION. The Young Pioneer. Washington, 1932. Signed. (Ink sig, last few pp bumped; top rear cvr bumped), else VG. *Baade*. $50/£31

HAMILTON, W. H. The Desire of the Moth. London, 1925. 1st Eng ed. Good (spine sl chafed). *Clearwater*. $24/£15

HAMILTON, WALTER. French Book-Plates. George Bell, 1892. 1st ed. Ltd to 500. viii,176pp. Silk cl (hinges worn). Sound. *Cox*. $56/£35

HAMILTON, WILLIAM RICHARD. Remarks on Several Parts of Turkey. Part I. Aegyptica [All Published]. T. Payne/Cadell & Davies, 1809. 1st ed. 2 vols, incl Atlas vol. 4to, folio. Engr fldg dbl-pg map, 24 plts (few tears at folds). Bkpl of Sir Joseph Radcliffe, the Blackmer copy. Contemp grn calf, gilt. *Sotheby's**. $4,784/£2,990

HAMILTON, WILLIAM T. My Sixty Years on the Plains. E. T. Sieber (ed). NY: Forest & Stream, 1905. 1st ed. Port, 6 b/w plts. Crimson cl, gilt, mtd oval photo port fr cvr. VG (sl aged, handled; sl rubbed, dusty). Howes H139. *Baltimore**. $60/£38

HAMLEY, E. BRUCE. The Story of the Campaign of Sebastopol. London, 1855. Color frontis (margins stained), map, 8 litho plts. Binder's cl (fr cvr soiled). *Petersfield*. $58/£36

HAMLIN, C. S. Old Times in the Yukon. L.A.: Wetzel, (1928). 1st ed. Good + . *Perier*. $90/£56

HAMM, JEFFREY. Action Replay, an Autobiography. London, 1983. 1st ed. VG in dj. *Typographeum*. $28/£18

HAMMER, KENNETH (ed). Custer in '76: Walter Camp's Notes on the Custer Fight. (Provo): Brigham Young Univ, (1976). 1st ed. Tan cl, brn backstrip. Fine in Fine dj. *Harrington*. $65/£41

HAMMER, RICHARD. The Court-Martial of Lt. Calley. NY, (1971). 1st ed. Fine in dj (worn, repaired w/scotch tape). *Pratt*. $20/£13

HAMMERTON, J. A. In the Tracks of R. L. Stevenson and Elsewhere in Old France. Bristol: Arrowsmith, 1907. 1st ed. VG + . *Any Amount*. $22/£14

HAMMETT, DASHIELL. The Adventures of Sam Spade. NY: Lawrence E. Spivak, 1944. 1st ed. Pb orig. (Spine foot sl worn), o/w Fine in wrappers. *Mordida*. $250/£156

HAMMETT, DASHIELL. The Big Knockover. Lillian Hellman (ed). NY: Random House, (1966). 1st ed. Top edges stained grn. Black cl, gilt. (Spine ends sl rubbed), o/w Fine in dj (chipped, edges creased). *Heritage*. $85/£53

HAMMETT, DASHIELL. The Big Knockover. Lillian Hellman (ed). NY, 1966. 1st ed. Fine in NF dj. *Warren*. $75/£47

HAMMETT, DASHIELL. The Continental Op. NY, 1974. 1st ed. Fine in Fine dj. *Warren*. $50/£31

HAMMETT, DASHIELL. Dashiell Hammett Omnibus. Red Harvest; The Dain Curse; The Maltese Falcon. NY: Knopf, 1935. 1st collected ed. (Spine head sl torn), else VG in VG- dj (extrems, spine ends chipped, rubbed, head lacks sm piece). *Pacific**. $86/£54

HAMMETT, DASHIELL. The Glass Key. NY, 1931. 1st ed. 8vo. Dj (edges rubbed, loss of paper at spine extrems). *Swann**. $690/£431

HAMMETT, DASHIELL. The Thin Man. NY, 1924. 1st ed. (Ex-lib, sigs loose, bkpl; cvr sunned, bottom of cvrs frayed.) *King*. $150/£94

HAMMETT, DASHIELL. The Thin Man. NY, 1934. 1st ed. 8vo. Dj (sl edgeworn, sm chip spine head). *Swann**. $2,300/£1,438

HAMMETT, DASHIELL. The Thin-Man. NY: Knopf, 1934. 1st ed. 1st issue dj w/description of bk on fr flap (not reviews). (Cvrs faded; sm tears to dj at fr joint head, upper fr panel edge; 1.25-inch tear lower fr panel; spine ends chipped, sm tear to head), else VG in dj. *Pacific**. $1,725/£1,078

HAMMOND, C. CONRAD. Florida Gardens: Landscape Architecture. Miami, 1940. Good. *Brooks*. $95/£59

HAMMOND, DARYN. The Golf Swing: The Ernest Jones Method. NY: Brentano's, (c.1920). 1st Amer ed. Grn cl. (Adhesion residue from removed bkpl; spine ends rubbed), else VG. *Pacific**. $109/£68

HAMMOND, GEORGE P. The Adventures of Alexander Barclay, Mountain Man. Denver: Old West, 1976. 1st ed. Color frontis, 4 color plts, 3 fldg maps in rear pocket. Orig prospectus laid in. Brn cl. Fine in NF dj. *Harrington*. $65/£41

HAMMOND, GEORGE P. The Adventures of Alexander Barclay, Mountain Man. A Narrative of His Career, 1810 to 1855. His Memorandum Diary, 1845 to 1850. Denver: Old West, 1976. 1st ed. 5 full-color plts, 3 lg fldg maps in rear pocket. VF in pict dj. *Argonaut*. $75/£47

HAMMOND, GEORGE P. and DALE L. MORGAN (eds). Captain Charles M. Weber, Pioneer of the San Joaquin and Founder of Stockton, CA. Berkeley, CA, 1966. 1st ed. Ltd to 700. Folio. Color frontis. Good + . *Wantagh*. $75/£47

HAMMOND, GEORGE P. (ed). The Larkin Papers. Berkeley: Univ of CA, 1951-1968. Ltd to 1000 sets. 11 vols (10 vols + index). Grn cl. Fine set in djs. *Karmiole*. $600/£375

HAMMOND, GEORGE P. (ed). The Treaty of Guadalupe Hidalgo, February Second 1848. Berkeley: Friends of the Bancroft Library, (1949). One of 500 ptd. Fldg facs map in separate bds folder. 1/2 cl, patterned bds, paper spine label. NF. *Pacific**. $184/£115

HAMMOND, NATALIE HAYS. Anthology of Pattern. NY, 1949. 1st Amer ed. Fine (spine sunned) in NF box. *Polyanthos*. $75/£47

HAMMOND, NATALIE HAYS. Anthology of Pattern. NY: William Helburn, 1949. 1st ed. One of 750. Inscribed. 2-tone cl. Fine in box. *Appelfeld*. $100/£63

HAMMOND, S. H. Hunting Adventures in the Northern Wilds. Phila: J. Edwin Poter, 1865. 1st ed. Frontis. Red cl, gilt. (Spine ends chipped, extrems rubbed), else VG. *Pacific**. $58/£36

HAMMOND, WILLIAM A. Sleep and Its Derangements. Phila: Lippincott, 1878. Later ptg. (Lib stickers, notes on prelim), else Fine. *Beasley*. $85/£53

HAMNETT, NINA and OSBERT SITWELL. The People's Album of London Statues. Duckworth, 1928. One of 116 numbered, signed by both. (Cvrs dusty, sl mkd, handled; no dj.) *Clearwater*. $240/£150

Hamper of Mischief. London: Raphael Tuck & Sons, (ca 1890). 12mo. 8pp. Color pict wrappers. *Reisler*. $135/£84

HAMPSON, JOHN. Two Stories. London, 1931. One of 250 signed. (Lacks part of label; no dj.) *Typographeum*. $45/£28

HAMSUN, KNUT. Hunger. George Egerton (trans). London: Leonard Smithers, 1899. 1st Eng ed, 1st bk. Pict cl. VG (blindstamps on fep, 1/2-title; feps lt browned, prelims spotted, fr hinge cracked; spine ends, corners sl bumped, cvrs rubbed, spine dknd). *Ulysses*. $400/£250

HANBURY, MRS. DAVID. One Day in the Life of a Stag. London: Colburn, 1847. Pict cl (worn, spine gone, loose in binding, fraying; marginal chips, sl stains, soil). *Oinonen**. $70/£44

HANCHETT, LAFAYETTE. The Old Sheriff and Other True Tales. NY: Margent Press, 1937. 1st ed. Signed, inscribed. (Moisture stains on rear cvr), else Good. *Brown*. $40/£25

HANCOCK, RALPH and JULIAN WESTON. The Lost Treasure of Cocos Island. NY: Nelson, 1960. VG in dj. *American Booksellers*. $35/£22

Hand Shadow Stories. Boston: Taggard & Thompson, 1863. Toybook. 12mo. 30pp (2pp spotted); 8 engrs. Engr paper wrappers (lt dusty). *Reisler*. $125/£78

Hand-List of the Books Printed at the Ashendene Press MDCCCXC-MCMXXV. Ashendene Press, 1925. 1st Eng ed. NF in wrappers (sl creased, spine sl dknd). *Ulysses*. $240/£150

HANDASYDE. The Four Gardens. Phila: Lippincott, 1912. 1st Amer ed. 8vo. 8 full-pg color plts by Charles Robinson. Top edge tinted. Lavender cl, gilt. VG in glassine dj (edges sl frayed). *Reisler*. $225/£141

Handbook for Durham and Northumberland. London: Murray, 1873. New 2nd ed. VG. *Gretton*. $56/£35

Handbook for North Wales. London: Murray, 1874. 4th ed. Good (lacks map). *Gretton*. $24/£15

Handbook for Switzerland (1838). London: Murray, 1970. New ed. Fine in dj. *Gretton*. $11/£7

Handbook for Travellers in Central Italy and Florence. London: Murray, 1864. 6th ed. VG (rear pocket tightly closed, map probably never present). *Gretton*. $48/£30

Handbook for Travellers in Southern Germany. London, 1850. 5th ed. Clean (lacks map in rear, pp3-22 of ads removed). *Gretton*. $80/£50

Handbook for Travellers in Switzerland, and the Alps of Savoy and Piedmont. London, 1854. 6th ed. Pocket map. Clean (lacks map). *Gretton*. $64/£40

HANDERSON, H. E. Gilbertus Anglicus. Medicine of the Thirteenth Century. Cleveland, OH, 1918. One of 500. Frontisport. (Ink inscrip, 2 text pp detached; spine ends, corners sl worn.) *Whitehart*. $64/£40

HANDFIELD-JONES, R. M. Surgery of the Hand. Edinburgh: E. & S. Livingstone, 1946. 2nd ed. (Dj lt worn), else Fine. *Weber*. $75/£47

HANDLER, J. S. A Guide to Source Materials for the Study of Barbados History, 1627-1834. Carbondale/Edwardsville: SIU, 1971. Frontis map. Brn cl. Dj (sl torn). *Maggs*. $29/£18

Handley Cross; or, Mr. Jorrock's Hunt. (By Robert Surtrees.) Harrap, 1930. One of 1050 (of 2050). Teg. Scarlet bevel-edged cl, gilt backstrip (lt faded). Good (fr hinge sl weak) in dj (lacks sm piece), bd slipcase. *Blackwell's*. $64/£40

Handley Cross; or, Mr. Jorrocks's Hunt. (By Robert Smith Surtees.) London: Bradbury & Evans, 1854. 1st illus bk ed, 1st issue, w/'Illustrious Leech' in preface, etc. In this copy, there are no ads ptd on the 'yellow ends.' Pub's gilt-pict cl. (Sl worn.) Protective cl case provided. *Oinonen**. $160/£100

HANDLEY, JAMES. The Ocean, a Novel. London, 1941. 1st ed. Fine in dj (faded, torn). *Petersfield*. $19/£12

HANDLEY-TAYLOR, G. Bibliography of Monaco. St. James, 1968. Fine in dj. *Moss*. $29/£18

HANDLIN, W. W. American Politics, a Moral and Political Work, Treating of the Causes of the Civil War, the Nature of Government, and the Necessity for Reform. New Orleans: Ptd by Isaac T. Hinton, 1864. iv,107pp. Good (eps lt foxed; soiled, tips worn). *Cahan*. $125/£78

HANDY, W. C. The Father of the Blues. NY: Macmillan, 1941. 1st ed. VG (inscrip). *Beasley*. $40/£25

HANES, BAILEY C. Bill Doolin. Norman, 1968. 1st ed. Fine in dj (price-clipped). *Baade*. $40/£25

HANEY, JESSE. The Gilder's Manual; A Complete Practical Guide to Gilding in All Its Branches.... NY: Excelsior Pub, 1876. 1st ed. Pict cl. (Lt foxed), else VG. *Pacific**. $127/£79

HANFF, HELENE. The Duchess of Bloomsbury Street. Phila, 1973. 1st ed. As New in dj. *Bond*. $20/£13

HANKEY, CLEMENT. Bottles in the Smoke. London (etc): Longmans, Green, 1931. 1st ed. Red cl, stamped in black. (Sl dknd at edges), o/w VG in dj (lt smudged, spine crown chipped). *Reese*. $50/£31

HANKEY, DONALD. Letters of Donald Hankey: 'A Student in Arms'. Edward Miller (ed). London: Andrew Melrose, 1919. 1st ed. Brn cl, gilt. VG. *Reese*. $40/£25

HANKINS, MAUDE McGEHEE. Daddy Gander. Joliet: P.F. Volland, 1928. 1st ed. Ve Elizabeth Cadie (illus). Pict bds. (Sl adhesion residue to pastedowns, soiled), else VG. *Pacific**. $46/£29

HANLEY, JAMES. Nothing to Say. NY: Horizon, 1962. 1st Amer ed. NF in dj. *Pacific**. $29/£18

HANNA, A. J. Flight Into Oblivion. (Richmond): Johnson Pub, (1938). 1st ed. Signed. Pict gray cl. VG (few smudges to tp; lt soiled). *House.* $50/£31

HANNA, PHIL TOWNSEND. The Dictionary of California Land Names. L.A.: Automobile Club of Southern CA, 1946. 1st ed. Fine in dj. *Argonaut.* $75/£47

HANNA, PHIL TOWNSEND. Libros Californios, or Five Feet of California Books. L.A., 1958. One of 1000. Rpt. Signed by Lawrence Clark Powell (rev). VG. *Dumont.* $50/£31

HANNAH, BARRY. Boomerang. Boston, 1989. 1st Amer ed. Signed. Fine in Fine dj. *Polyanthos.* $30/£19

HANNAH, BARRY. Geronimo Rex. NY: Viking, (1972). 1st ed, 1st bk. Fine in Fine dj. *Lenz.* $125/£78

HANNAH, BARRY. Never Die. Boston, 1991. 1st Amer ed. Signed. Fine in Fine dj. *Polyanthos.* $30/£19

HANNAS, LINDA. The English Jigsaw Puzzle 1760 to 1890. Wayland, 1972. 1st ed. 67 plts (8 color). VG in dj (price-clipped). *Hollett.* $64/£40

HANNAY, JAMES. The Complete Works of William Hogarth. London Ptg & Pub Co, n.d. c.(1860). New, rev ed. 2 vols. xviii,201pp (lt spotted). 1/2 morocco, cl bds (edges sl wormed), dec gilt bands. *Edwards.* $256/£160

HANNEMAN, AUDRE. Ernest Hemingway. A Comprehensive Bibliography. Princeton Univ, 1967. Dj (margins lt chipped). *Zubal**. $40/£25

HANNEMAN, AUDRE. Ernest Hemingway: A Comprehensive Bibliography. Volume I. Princeton: Princeton Univ, (1969). 2nd ed. Black cl. Fine. *Pacific**. $81/£51

HANNIBAL, ALFRED. Last-Fitting and Pattern-Cutting. London: Burlington Pub Co, 1900. 4th ed. VG. *Hollett.* $29/£18

HANNOVER, EMIL. Pottery and Porcelain. London, 1925. 3 vols. (Sl worn), else VG in djs (worn). *King.* $175/£109

HANNUM, ALBERTA. Spin a Silver Dollar. NY: Viking, 1945. 1st ed. Fine in VG dj. *Book Market.* $35/£22

HANNUM, ANNA (ed). A Quaker Forty-Niner. (By Charles Edward Pancoast.) Phila: Univ of PA, 1930. 1st ed. Unopened. Brn cl. NF (spine sl faded). *Harrington.* $40/£25

HANO, ARNOLD. A Day in the Bleachers. Crowell, 1955. 1st ed. VG. *Plapinger.* $35/£22

HANS, FRED M. The Great Sioux Nation. Chicago: M.A. Donohue, (1907). 1st ed. Pict cvr label. (Ink mk; extrems worn), else VG. Howes H166. *Pacific**. $138/£86

HANSCOM, W. W. The Archaeology of the Cable Car. Walt Wheelock (ed). Pasadena: Socio-Technical Books, 1970. Deckled edges. VG + in dj (lt soiled). *Bohling.* $45/£28

Hansel and Gretel. London: Bancroft, 1961. V. Kubasta (illus). 8 dbl-pg pop-ups, incl fr cvr. VG in pict wraps. *Bookfinders.* $130/£81

HANSEN, HARVEY J. and JEANNE THURLOW MILLER. Wild Oats in Eden: Sonoma County in the 19th Century. Santa Rosa, 1962. 1st ed. (Sl adhesion damage rear pastedown), o/w Fine. *Pacific**. $23/£14

HANSEN, HARVEY J. et al. Wild Oats in Eden. Santa Rosa: Privately published, 1962. 1st ed. Uncut. Tan pict cl, gilt spine. Fine. *Pacific**. $63/£39

HANSEN, JOSEPH. Skinflick. Holt, 1979. 1st ed. Fine in dj. *Murder.* $45/£28

HANSEN, RON. The Assassination of Jesse James by the Coward Robert Ford. NY: Knopf, 1983. 1st ed. Signed. Fine in Fine dj (rear panel sl soiled). *Unger.* $125/£78

HANSEN, RON. Atticus. NY: Harper, 1996. 1st ed. Signed. Fine in Fine dj. *Unger.* $45/£28

HANSEN, RON. Desperadoes. NY: Knopf, 1979. 1st ed, 1st bk. Fine in Fine dj. *Unger.* $125/£78

HANSEN, RON. Mariette in Ecstasy. NY: Harper, 1991. 1st ed. Signed. Fine in Fine dj. *Unger.* $100/£63

HANSON, CHARLES, JR. The Plains Rifle. Harrisburg, PA: Stackpole, 1960. 1st ed. VG + in dj (chipped). *Labordo.* $65/£41

HANSON, JOHN W. Historical Sketch of the Old Sixth Regiment of Massachusetts Volunteers...1861, 1862, 1863, and 1864. Boston: Lee & Shepard, 1866. 1st ed. 352pp (sl browned; tp partly separated at gutter; bkpl); 3 ll w/vintage sm uncoated albumen photo ports, guards. Dk brn coated eps. Dk maroon cl (fr cvr lt spotted), gilt. *Baltimore**. $100/£63

HANSON, JOSEPH MILLS. The Conquest of the Missouri. Chicago: A.C. McClurg, 1909. 1st ed. Fldg map. Pict cl. (Orange pencil underlining, sl shaken; rubbed, soiled, spine dknd), else VG. Howes H177. *Pacific**. $29/£18

HAPPOLD, D. C. D. The Mammals of Nigeria. Oxford, 1987. 113 maps. *Sutton.* $125/£78

Happy Family. NY: McLoughlin Bros, (ca 1880). Little Showman Series. 4to. 3-tiered pop-up. Color pict bds hinged at top (edges chipped). Internally VG. *Reisler.* $385/£241

HARADA, JIRO. Japanese Gardens. MA, 1956. 1st ed. Cl, reamins of label (?). Dj (lt soiled, chipped w/loss). *Edwards.* $96/£60

HARADA, JIRO. The Lesson of Japanese Architecture. C. G. Holme (ed). London/NY: The Studio, 1936. 1st ed. Grn cl, gilt. (Sig; rubbed, spine, edges sunned, spine lettering dull.) Text Clean. *Baltimore**. $40/£25

HARBAUGH, H. Harbaugh's Harfe. Reading, PA, 1870. 1st ed. 6 full-pg steel-engr illus, guards. Emb crimson dec cl. As New. *Bond.* $120/£75

HARBER, GILES B. Report of...U. S. N. N.p. (Washington): GPO, n.d. (1884). 75pp; 4 plts, fldg map. VG in ptd wrapper. *High Latitude.* $95/£59

HARBOUR, HENRY. Where Flies the Flag. London: Collins, (1904). 1st ed. 8vo. 6 color plts by Arthur Rackham. (Tp head sl spotted, contemp inscrip.) Blue pict cl, gilt. *Christie's**. $166/£104

HARCOURT-SMITH, SIMON. The Last of Uptake. London: Batsford, 1942. 1st ed. One of 100 signed by Harcourt-Smith and Rex Whistler (illus). Teg, rest uncut. Orig grn morocco-backed cl. (Corner bumped), o/w Fine in slipcase. *Maggs.* $480/£300

HARCOURT-SMITH, SIMON. The Last of Uptake. London: Batsford, c. 1944. Dj. *Petersfield.* $109/£68

HARCUS, WILLIAM (ed). South Australia. London, 1876. xv,426pp; 2 fldg maps. Cl-backed bds (spine faded). *Edwards.* $152/£95

HARD, M. E. The Mushroom, Edible and Otherwise, Its Habitat and Its Time of Growth. Columbus, 1908. 1st ed. Gray cl. (Edgeworn, cvrs soiled), else Good. *Larry Price.* $40/£25

HARDCASTLE, EPHRAIM. Wine and Walnuts; or, After Dinner Chit-Chat. London: Longman, Hurst, Rees et al, 1824. 2nd ed. 2 vols. Marbled eps, teg. Period mottled calf, gilt, morocco spine labels. (Bkpls; spine heads, joints worn; label sl worn), else VG. *Pacific**. $69/£43

HARDENBROOK, WILLIAM TEN EYCK. Financial New York. NY, 1897. One of 1200 numbered. Folio. 3/4 leather (worn, cvr detached, foxed). *Oinonen**. $130/£81

HARDIE, MARTIN. English Coloured Books. Totowa, NJ: Rowman and Littlefield, (1973). Rpt. (Spine faded.) Dj. *Oak Knoll.* $45/£28

HARDIE, MARTIN. Frederick Goulding. Stirling, 1910. One of 350 numbered. Paper-vellum backed bds. *Swann**. $69/£43

HARDIE, MARTIN. Water-Colour Painting in Britain. Volume I (only of 3): The Eighteenth Century. Dudley Snelgrove (ed). London: Batsford, 1969. Rpt. Color frontis. Dj (sl torn, ragged). *Edwards.* $64/£40

HARDIE, MARTIN. Water-Colour Painting in Britan. Dudley Snelgrove (ed). London: Batsford, (1966-68). 3 vols. (Sl worn, sm wormhole in 1 spine foot). *Oinonen*.* $170/£106

HARDIN, A. N. The American Bayonet, 1776-1964. Phila, 1964. Dj (few edge chips). *Swann*.* $138/£86

HARDIN, JOHN WESLEY. The Life of John Wesley Hardin, from the Original Manuscript as Written by Himself. Seguin, TX: Smith & Moore, 1896. 1st ed, 1st state. NF in wrappers. Howes H188. *Labordo.* $275/£172

HARDIN, JOHN WESLEY. The Life of John Wesley Hardin. Seguin, 1896. 1st ed, 1st issue. 144pp. (Tp pulled from staples; lower corner fr cvr creased, cvrs lt foxed, spine chipped), else Good in dec wraps. Howes H188. *Baade.* $200/£125

HARDING, A. R. Ginseng and Other Medicinal Plants. Columbus, 1906. Revised ed. VG. *Doctor's Library.* $60/£38

HARDING, A. R. Ginseng and Other Medicinal Plants. Columbus, OH: A.R. Harding, c. 1936. Rev ed. (Browned), else VG. *Fair Meadow.* $35/£22

HARDING, ANNE and PATRICIA BOLLING. Bibliography of Articles and Papers on North American Indian Art. Washington, n.d. (1940). Good (rebound in cl). *Dumont.* $125/£78

HARDING, J. D. Lessons on Art. London: Bogue, 1849. 1st ed. Sm folio. Unpaginated. #89 plt, text never issued. Orig cl w/blind embossed framing, gilt cartouche (inner joints strengthened; spine split). *Europa.* $120/£75

HARDING, J. D. Lessons on Trees. London: David Bogue, 1850. 3ff; 30 litho plts. 1/2-leather (sl worn), marbled bds, gilt. Good. *Ars Artis.* $240/£150

HARDING, VALERIE. Faces and Figures in Embroidery. Batsford, 1979. 1st ed. Fine in dj. *Whittle.* $19/£12

HARDING, WALTER. The Days of Henry Thoreau. NY: Knopf, 1965. 1st ed. Red cl. VG + in dj (sl tears). *Lucas.* $40/£25

HARDING, WALTER. Thoreau's Library. Charlottesville, VA: Univ of VA, 1957. 1st ed. Stapled as issued; self-wrappers. VG (sl dust soiled). *Lucas.* $45/£28

HARDMAN, WILLIAM. A Trip to America. London: T. Vickers Wood, 1884. 1st ed. 110pp; map. (Shelfworn.) *Mott.* $60/£38

HARDWICH, T. FREDERICK. A Manual of Photographic Chemistry, Including the Practice of the Collodion Process. London: John Churchill, 1857. 4th ed. xvi,390pp. VG (crown, rear hinge sl worn). *Cahan.* $400/£250

HARDWICK, MICHAEL and MOLLIE. The Sherlock Holmes Companion. London: John Murray, 1962. 1st ed. Fine in NF dj (1 sm chip, lt edgeworn). *Janus.* $75/£47

HARDY, A. C. From Slip to Sea. Glasgow: James & Brown, 1926. Black cl, gilt. VG. *American Booksellers.* $40/£25

HARDY, CAMPBELL. Forest Life in Acadie. NY, 1869. 1st Amer ed. 371pp; 12 engr plts. Grn cl, gilt. (Lacks frontis), else VG. *Larry Price.* $125/£78

HARDY, FLORENCE EMILY. The Early Life of Thomas Hardy 1840-1891 [with] The Later Years of Thomas Hardy 1892-1928. London: Macmillan, 1928/1930. 1st eds. Grn cl, gilt. Fine in Fine djs. *Vandoros.* $400/£250

HARDY, G. and W. Wild Flowers in the Rockies. Saskatoon: H.R. Larson, 1949. 1st ed. VG. *Archer.* $30/£19

HARDY, G. H. A Mathematician's Apology. Cambridge, 1940. 1st Eng ed. Nice (fr cvr sl dented) in dj. *Clearwater.* $40/£25

HARDY, IZA DUFFUS. Between Two Oceans: or Sketches of American Travel. London: Hurst & Blackett, 1884. 1st ed. 4 prelim ll, pp 355,(16) ads. (Spine faded; soiled, rubbed.) *Mott.* $30/£19

HARDY, JOSEPH. A Picturesque and Descriptive Tour in the Mountains of the High Pyrenees. R. Ackermann, 1825. 1st ed. Engr frontis map, 24 mtd hand-colored aquatint plts. Contemp crimson straight-grained morocco (expertly rebacked), gilt. *Sotheby's*.* $957/£598

HARDY, THOMAS. A Changed Man, the Waiting Summer, and Other Tales Concluding with the Romantic Tales of a Milkmaid. London: Macmillan, 1913. 1st ed. Frontis photogravure. Teg. Fine in dk grn bold-ribbed cl, gilt. *Vandoros.* $195/£122

HARDY, THOMAS. The Famous Tragedy of the Queen of Cornwall. NY: Macmillaan, 1923. One of 1000. Cl-backed black bds, paper cvr label. NF in VG dj. *Pacific*.* $23/£14

HARDY, THOMAS. Far from the Madding Crowd. NY: Holt, 1874. 1st Amer ed w/ep ad dated November 1874. Part-pict cl (dust-mkd, grubby, extrems sl chafed; spine ends sl ragged; ink name, bkpl). *Clearwater.* $240/£150

HARDY, THOMAS. Far from the Madding Crowd. NY: Harper, 1895. 1st Amer ed. Etching, map. Gilt-dec grn cl. (Sm tear to spine head, lower fr cvr corner rubbed), else VG. *Pacific*.* $115/£72

HARDY, THOMAS. Far from the Madding Crowd. LEC, 1958. Ltd to 1500 numbered, signed by Agnes Miller Parker (illus). Fine in slipcase. *Swann*.* $103/£64

HARDY, THOMAS. Human Shows Far Phantasies, Songs, and Trifles. London: Macmillan, 1925. 1st ed. Gilt grn cl. (Narrow crack fr inner hinge), o/w VG in dj (lt edge-used). *Reese.* $85/£53

HARDY, THOMAS. Human Shows Far Phantasies. NY: Macmillan, 1925. 1st Amer ed. Grn cl, gilt. VF in Fine dj. *Macdonnell.* $100/£63

HARDY, THOMAS. Jude the Obscure. Osgood, McIlvaine, 1896. 1st ed, mixed state w/pp 38 and 47 numbered and pp 7, 16, 25, and 32 unnumbered. Fine. *Williams.* $312/£195

HARDY, THOMAS. Jude the Obscure. LEC, 1969. Ltd to 1500 numbered, signed by Agnes Miller Parker (illus). Fine in slipcase. *Swann*.* $92/£58

HARDY, THOMAS. Life's Little Ironies. London, (1894). 1st ed. Fine (contemp sig). *Swann*.* $103/£64

HARDY, THOMAS. The Mayor of Casterbridge. LEC, 1964. Ltd to 1500 numbered, signed by Agnes Miller Parker (illus). Fine in slipcase. *Swann*.* $92/£58

HARDY, THOMAS. Moments of Vision and Miscellaneous Verses. London, 1917. 1st ed. VG (bkpl; worn). *Bond.* $50/£31

HARDY, THOMAS. The Return of the Native. NY: Harper, 1929. 1st Leighton ed. One of 1500. Signed by Clare Leighton (illus). Tipped-in frontis. Cl-backed blue bds, paper spine label. (Sm corner fep lacking; extrems rubbed, spine label chipped, browned), else VG. *Pacific*.* $58/£36

HARDY, THOMAS. Satires of Circumstance. Macmillan, 1914. 1st UK ed. VG (bkpl; spine sl dull). *Williams.* $77/£48

HARDY, THOMAS. Selected Poems of Thomas Hardy. London: Medici Soc, 1921. 1st ed. Ltd to 1025. Woodcut frontisport. Linen-backed bds, paper labels. VG (bkpl). *Truepenny.* $175/£109

HARDY, THOMAS. Tess of the D'Urbervilles. London: James R. Osgood/McIlvaine, (1892). 1st ed, 2nd issue. 3 vols. Gilt-dec cvrs. (Lt chipped, soiled, spines sunned), else Fine set. *Polyanthos.* $450/£281

HARDY, THOMAS. Tess of the D'Urbervilles. NY, 1892. 1st Amer ed. 421pp. (Inner hinges cracked; cvrs rubbed, dknd; corners bumped, spine ends sl frayed.) *King.* $100/£63

HARDY, THOMAS. Tess of the d'Urbervilles. NY: Harper, 1892. 1st Amer ed. (Fr hinge starting; spine sl dknd, ends worn), else VG. *Pacific*.* $109/£68

HARDY, THOMAS. Tess of the D'Urbervilles. London: Macmillan, 1926. 1st illus ed, sm paper issue. Dk blue cl. Dj (torn). *Maggs*. $40/£25

HARDY, THOMAS. Tess of the D'Urbervilles. LEC, 1956. Ltd to 1500 numbered, signed by Agnes Miller Parker (illus). Fine in slipcase. *Swann**. $92/£58

HARDY, THOMAS. The Trumpet-Major. Marston, Searle, Low & Rivington, 1881. 1st 1-vol Eng ed. VG in red cl. *Fine Books*. $175/£109

HARDY, THOMAS. Under the Greenwood Tree. London: C&W, 1913. Fair in grn cl, gilt. (Inscrip; 3 stains rear cvr.) *Maggs*. $72/£45

HARDY, THOMAS. The Writings of Thomas Hardy in Prose and Verse. NY: Harper, 1920. Anniversary ed. One of 1250 sets. 21 vols. Ptd tissue guards. Teg; unopened. Red cl, gilt. Glassine. (Glassine chipped, torn), else Fine set. *Pacific**. $633/£396

HARDY, THOMAS. Yuletide in a Younger World. London: Ariel Poems, (1927). 1st Eng ed. Pict card wrappers (1 corner sl chipped). *Clearwater*. $40/£25

HARDY, W. J. Book-Plates. Kegan Paul, Trench, Trubner, 1897. 2nd ed. xiv,240pp; 44 plts. Uncut. Good in grn cl. *Cox*. $40/£25

HARDY, W. J. Book-Plates. Kegan Paul, Trench, Trubner, 1897. (Fr cvr sl spotted), else VG. *Fine Books*. $45/£28

HARE, A. J. C. The Rivieras. London, 1897. 1st ed. (Lt rubbed.) *Gretton*. $24/£15

HARE, A. J. C. The Story of Two Noble Lives. George Allen, 1893. 1st ed. 3 vols. x,381; 489; viii,495pp (eps, edges foxed); 64 plts. Contemp 1/2 calf (hinges, edges sl rubbed, scraped), gilt. *Hollett*. $192/£120

HARE, A. J. C. Walks in London. London, Vol 2 1901, vol 1 1923. 7th ed. 2 vols. Good + . *Gretton*. $19/£12

HARE, A. J. C. A Winter at Mentone. Wertheim, Mackintosh & Hunt, n.d. (1862). Fldg map (torn at fld). Good (pencil sig, sl spotted; spine bumped, sunned, chipped). *Tiger*. $104/£65

HARE, CYRIL. An English Murder. London: Faber & Faber, 1951. 1st ed. Red cl. (Sm mk rear cvr), o/w Nice. *Temple*. $16/£10

HARE, CYRIL. He Should Have Died Hereafter. London, 1958. 1st ed. Fine in dj (torn). *Petersfield*. $16/£10

HARE, CYRIL. That Yew Tree's Shade. London: Faber & Faber, 1954. 1st ed. Fine in dj (spine sl dknd, torn, price-clipped). *Mordida*. $85/£53

HARE, CYRIL. That Yew Tree's Shade. Faber, 1954. 1st UK ed. NF (ink name) in dj. *Williams*. $96/£60

HARE, DAVID. Slag. London, 1971. 1st ed. NF in orig wrappers. *Warren*. $40/£25

HARE, HOBART AMORY. Practical Diagnosis: The Use of Symptoms in the Diagnosis of Disease. Phila, 1896. 1st ed. 573pp; 13 color plts. Grn cl, gilt. (Sm stain on back cvr), o/w NF. *Doctor's Library*. $150/£94

HARGRAVE, JOHN. The Life and Soul of Paracelsus. London: Gollancz, 1951. 1st ed. VG in VG dj. *Middle Earth*. $75/£47

HARGREAVES, REGINALD. The Enemy at the Gate. Harrisburg, 1948. VG in Poor dj. *Clark*. $20/£13

HARGRETT, LESTER. A Bibliography of the Constitutions and Laws of the American Indians. Cambridge: Harvard Univ, 1947. VG in dj (clipped, faded). *Dumont*. $125/£78

HARGRETT, LESTER. The Gilcrease-Hargrett Catalogue of Imprints. Norman, 1972. 1st ed. VG in dj (chipped). *Dumont*. $50/£31

HARGRETT, LESTER. Oklahoma Imprints 1835-1890. NY: Bowker, 1951. 1st ed. (Sl worn.) *Oinonen**. $80/£50

HARGROVE, GEORGE. An Account of the Islands of Walcheren and South Beveland, Against Which the British Expedition Proceeded in 1809. Dublin, 1812. Frontis map. List of subs. Mod cl. *Swann**. $57/£36

HARGROVE, WILLIAM. History and Description of the Ancient City of York. York: Wm. Alexander, 1818. 2 vols. 407; 688pp + (ii); fldg hand-colored plan, 7 copper plts, 25 woodcuts. Marbled eps, edges. Early 1/2 calf, marbled bds, raised bands, gilt, leather spine labels. (Bkpl; rubbed, sl loss to corners.) *Edwards*. $320/£200

HARIOTT, JOHN. Struggles Through Life, Exemplified in the Various Travels and Adventures.... Phila, 1809. 1st Amer ed. 2 vols. Contemp tree calf (rubbed; foxed, tear vol 1 tp neatly repaired). Howes H220. *Oinonen**. $160/£100

HARKEY, IRA. Pioneer Bush Pilot. The Story of Noel Wien. Seattle: Univ of WA, (1974). (Corner torn off tp), else VG in dj (edgetorn). *Perier*. $50/£31

HARKNESS, WILLIAM HALE. Temples and Topees. NY: Derrydale, 1936. Ltd to 200 numbered. Brown pebble-grain cl. VF. *Biscotti*. $275/£172

HARLAN, JACOB WRIGHT. California '46 to '88. SF: Bancroft, 1888. Frontis, 242pp. (Extrems lt worn), else Clean. Howes H196. *Dumont*. $150/£94

HARLAN, R. Fauna Americana. Phila, 1825. 318,(1)pp (sl foxed, bkpl), errata. Contemp tree calf rebacked w/later calf (worn, fr cvr nearly detached, rear hinge tender). *Sutton*. $285/£178

HARLAND, MARGARET. The Yellow Witch Book. Reading/London: Petty & Sons, 1905. 1st ed. Obl 4to. 30pp lithos. Clbacked color illus bds (stained, dknd). *Reisler*. $350/£219

HARLEY, TIMOTHY. Lunar Science: Ancient and Modern. London: Swan Sonnenschein, Lowrey, 1886. (viii),89pp + 5pp ads. Dk grn cl, gilt. *Weber*. $75/£47

HARLOW, ALVIN F. Old Post Bags. NY: D. Appleton-Century, 1928. 1st ed. Fine in dj (sl chipped). Howes H199. *Labordo*. $150/£94

HARLOW, ALVIN F. Old Towpaths. NY: D. Appleton-Century, 1926. 1st ed. VG + in dj (chipped). Howes H200. *Labordo*. $150/£94

HARLOW, ALVIN F. Old Waybills. NY: D. Appleton-Century, 1934. 1st ed. Sturdy cl (rebound). VG. Howes H201. *Dumont*. $75/£47

HARLOW, NEAL. California Conquered: War and Peace on the Pacific 1846-1850. Berkeley: Univ of CA, (1982). 1st ed. Fine in dj (price torn off). *Pacific**. $23/£14

HARLOW, NEAL. California Conquered: War and Peace on the Pacific 1846-1850. Berkeley: Univ of CA, (1982). 1st ed. Signed, inscribed. Fine in dj. *Pacific**. $23/£14

HARLOW, NEAL. Maps and Surveys of the Pueblo Lands of Los Angeles. L.A.: Dawson's Book Shop, 1976. One of 375 ptd. Signed by Harlow and Grant Dahlstrom (ptr). 2 fldg facs maps loose in rep sleeve. 1/2 cl, patterned bds, gilt. Fine. *Pacific**. $173/£108

HARLOW, NEAL. The Maps of San Francisco Bay from the Spanish Discovery in 1769 to the American Occupation. SF: Book Club of CA, 1950. One of 375. 12.25x9. 19 plts. 1/2 red morocco, dec bds, gilt. Fine in dj. *Pacific**. $805/£503

HARLOW, NEAL. Maps of the Pueblo Lands of San Diego, 1602-1874. L.A.: Dawson's Book Shop, 1987. 1st ed. One of 375 ptd. 80 maps. Cl-backed dec bds. Fine. *Harrington*. $150/£94

HARLOW, NEAL. Maps of the Pueblo Lands of San Diego, 1602-1874. L.A.: Dawson's Book Shop, 1987. One of 375 ptd. Signed. 1/2 cl, bds w/facs map, gilt. Fine. *Pacific**. $150/£94

HARMAN, F. WARD. Ship Models Illustrated. NY: Marine Model, 1946. Tan paper over bds. Good. *American Booksellers*. $22/£14

HARMAN, S. W. Belle Starr the Female Desperado. Houston: Frontier, 1954. Rpt. (Browned), else Good in stiff wrappers. *Dumont*. $20/£13

HARMON, NOLAN. The Famous Case of Myra Clark Gaines. Baton Rouge: LA State Univ, 1946. Usable (worn, faded). *Boswell*. $25/£16

HARNDEN, HENRY. The Capture of Jefferson Davis. Madison, WI: (Ptd by Tracy, Gibbs), 1898 (i.e. 1899). 1st ed. Frontis, 105pp; port, facs of reward poster. Blue cl. NF (fep excised). *Chapel Hill*. $125/£78

HARNETT, CYNTHIA. The Writing on the Hearth. Minneapolis: Lerner, 1984. 1st of this ed. Garett Floyd (illus). 300pp. Fine in Fine dj. *Price*. $20/£13

Harp of a Thousand Strings. NY: Dick & Fitzgerald, (1858). 1st ed. Yellow eps. Blind brn cl (frayed, sl worn, sl discoloration lower cvr), gilt. Text Good (browned, old dampstain bottom 1/2 last 1/2 of text, several text cracks, 1 sig sprung). *Baltimore**. $85/£53

HARPENDING, ASBURY. The Great Diamond Hoax and Other Stirring Incidents in the Life of.... James H. Wilkins (ed). SF: James H. Barry, 1913. 1st ed. Frontis. Lt blue cl. Fine. *Argonaut*. $75/£47

HARPER, C. G. On the Road in Holland. London, 1922. 1st ed. (Lacks fep, 1/2-title margin sl affixed to pastedown, prelims lt browned.) *Edwards*. $56/£35

HARPER, C. G. A Practical Handbook of Drawing for Modern Methods of Reproduction. Chapman & Hall, 1894. White linen cl. Clean. *Moss*. $32/£20

HARPER, CHARLES. The Newmarket, Bury, Thetford and Cromer Road. London: Chapman & Hall, 1904. 1st ed. Good+. *October Farm*. $225/£141

HARPER, J. E. T. The Royal Navy at War. (London, 1941.) 2nd imp. Flexible cl. VG in dj (chipped, torn). *King*. $25/£16

HARRELL, JOHN M. The Brooks and Baxter War: A History of the Reconstruction Period in Arkansas. St. Louis: Slawson Ptg, 1893. 1st ed. 276pp. Maroon cl. VG- (lacks rep, contemp sig). Howes H216. *Chapel Hill*. $175/£109

HARRER, HEINRICH. Seven Years in Tibet. LEC, 1993. One of 300 signed. Wrapped in a red/yellow flag, held between 2 carved wooden bds. Fine. *Swann**. $258/£161

HARRER, HEINRICH. The White Spider. Hugh Merrick (trans). Rupert Hart-Davis, 1960. 2nd imp. 41 plts (1 color, 1 fldg). VG in dj. *Hollett*. $104/£65

HARRINGTON, ALAN. The Revelations of Dr. Modesto. NY: Knopf, 1955. 1st ed, 1st bk. Fine in dj (lt used). *Beasley*. $75/£47

HARRINGTON, ALAN. The Revelations of Dr. Modesto. NY: Knopf, 1955. 1st ed. Nice (ep lt dampstained, marginal repairs pp223-30, not affecting text) in dj (chip). *Bromer*. $100/£63

HARRINGTON, H. D. Manual of the Plants of Colorado. Denver, 1964. 2nd ed. Frontis map. VG. *Larry Price*. $40/£25

HARRIS, A. S. Andrea Sacchi. Oxford, 1977. 179 plt illu, 4 color plts. Good in dj. *Ars Artis*. $120/£75

HARRIS, ALBERT W. The Cruise of a Schooner. Chicago: Privately ptd, 1911. 1st ed. Pict cl. (Top 1 3/8-inches cut off blank prelim), else NF. *Baade*. $45/£28

HARRIS, BENJAMIN BUTLER. The Gila Trail. Norman: Univ of OK, 1960. 1st ed. Good in dj. *Dumont*. $25/£16

HARRIS, BURTON. John Colter: His Years in the Rockies. NY: Scribner, 1952. 1st ed. VF in pict dj (sl chipped). *Argonaut*. $175/£109

HARRIS, CHAPIN A. The Dental Art, a Practical Treatise on Dental Surgery. Balt: Armstrong & Berry, 1839. 1st ed. 384pp; 3 plts. Recent 1/4 calf, marbled bds. (Text lt spotted; rebound), o/w Good. *Brown*. $250/£156

HARRIS, CHARLES T. Memories of Manhattan: in the Sixties and Seventies. NY: Derrydale, 1928. Ltd to 1000. Blue cl backed over gray paper-cvrd bds. Fine. *Biscotti*. $100/£63

HARRIS, CLIVE (ed). The History of the Birmingham Gun-Barrel Proof House. Birmingham: Guardians of the Proof House, 1946. 1st ed. 26 plts. VG in dj (spine head sl frayed). *Hollett*. $104/£65

HARRIS, EDWARD. Up the Missouri with Audubon. John Francis McDermott (ed). Norman, 1951. Good in dj (faded). *Dumont*. $50/£31

HARRIS, ELIZABETH. The Common Press. London: Merrion, 1978. 1st UK ed. W/fldr of plans. Both in wrappers, in slipcase. Fine. *Michael Taylor*. $29/£18

HARRIS, FRANK. Elder Conklin and Other Stories. NY: Macmillan, 1894. 1st ed, 1st bk. Olive cl, gilt. NF. *Reese*. $150/£94

HARRIS, FRANK. Montes the Matador and Other Stories. NY, 1910. Inscribed presentation. (Hinges starting.) *Argosy*. $65/£41

HARRIS, FRANK. The Yellow Ticket. London: Grant Richards, 1914. 1st Eng ed, 1st issue w/12pp pub's ads dated Oct 1914. VG (edges, prelims sl spotted; spine sl dull, ends sl bumped, top fr cvr sl affected by damp). *Ulysses*. $88/£55

HARRIS, HELENA J. Southern Sketches. Cecil Gray; or, the Soldier's Revenge. Rosa Sherwood; or, the Avenger. New Orleans: Crescent Job Print, 1866. 1st ed. 20pp. NF in ptd wraps (lt soiled). *Chapel Hill*. $225/£141

HARRIS, JOEL CHANDLER. The Bishop and the Boogerman. NY: Doubleday, Page, 1909. 1st ed. 8vo. 184pp; 8 plts. Grn cl, gilt. VG (eps sl browned, extrems lt rubbed). BAL 7161. *Heritage*. $75/£47

HARRIS, JOEL CHANDLER. The Chronicles of Aunt Minervy Ann. London: J.M. Dent, 1899. 1st ed. VG in emb yellow cl, bds, gilt. *Smith*. $45/£28

HARRIS, JOEL CHANDLER. The Chronicles of Aunt Minervy Ann. NY: Scribner, 1899. 1st ed. 8vo. 210pp; 32 plts by A. B. Frost. Teg, rest untrimmed. Tan cl. VG (ink sig erasure; spine browned, extrems rubbed). BAL 7143. *Heritage*. $100/£63

HARRIS, JOEL CHANDLER. Daddy Jake, the Runaway, and Other Stories. NY: Century, 1889. 1st ed w/glazed bds. 4to. 145pp. Good (sl soil throughout; edges, corners worn, spine reinforced). *Davidson*. $185/£116

HARRIS, JOEL CHANDLER. Daddy Jake, the Runaway, and Short Stories Told After Dark. NY: Century, (1889). 1st ed. 4to. 145pp. Pict bds. Good (part of rep corner torn away; bds soiled, spine cocked, extrems rubbed). *Heritage*. $300/£188

HARRIS, JOEL CHANDLER. Little Mr. Thimblefinger and His Queer Country. Boston: Houghton Mifflin, (1894). 1st ed. Oliver Herford (illus). 8 1/4 x 5 3/4. Gilt-lettered pict cl. (1 plt detached), else NF. *Pacific**. $127/£79

HARRIS, JOEL CHANDLER. Mingo and Other Sketches in Black and White. Boston, 1893. 6th ed. Inscribed. Als glued to feps. (Inner hinges weak, sl rubbed.) *Kane**. $375/£234

HARRIS, JOEL CHANDLER. Mr. Rabbit at Home. Boston/NY: Houghton, Mifflin, 1896. Signed. 8vo. 304pp; 25 plts. All edges stained grn. Beige cl, gilt. VG (lt browned throughout; extrems lt rubbed). *Heritage*. $500/£313

HARRIS, JOEL CHANDLER. On the Plantation. NY: D. Appleton, 1892. 1st ed. 8vo. Frontis by E. W. Kemble, 233pp + (10)pp ads. Mustard cl, gilt spine. VG (1st few ll lt foxed; spine cocked, cvrs lt soiled). BAL 7124. *Heritage*. $200/£125

HARRIS, JOEL CHANDLER. Sister Jane: Her Friends and Acquaintances. Boston: Houghton, Mifflin, 1896. 1st ed. VG. *Pacific**. $46/£29

HARRIS, JOEL CHANDLER. Stories of Georgia. NY: American Book, 1896. 1st ed. 315pp, ads. (Sl shelfworn, cl lt dust soiled), else Good. BAL 7136 w/'W.P.I.' on tp verso. *Brown*. $50/£31

HARRIS, JOEL CHANDLER. The Tar-Baby and Other Rhymes of Uncle Remus. NY: D. Appleton, 1904. 1st ed. A.B. Frost & E.W. Kemble (illus). Frontis; 8 plts. (Glue stains gutter 1st blank l.) Tan-orange cl (sl soiled, shaken). BAL 7154. *Cummins.* $50/£31

HARRIS, JOEL CHANDLER. The Tar-Baby and Other Rhymes of Uncle Remus. NY: D. Appleton, 1904. 1st ed. A. B. Frost & E. W. Kemble (illus). Teg. Gilt-tooled salmon cl. (Old inscrip; soiled), else VG. BAL 7154. *Pacific**. $161/£101

HARRIS, JOEL CHANDLER. Uncle Remus Returns. Boston, 1918. 1st ed. A. B. Frost & J. M. Conde (illus). 8vo. Pict cl. *Swann**. $103/£64

HARRIS, JOEL CHANDLER. Uncle Remus, His Songs and His Sayings. NY: D. Appleton, 1881. 1st ed, 3rd state, w/'presumptuous' rather than 'presumptive' in the last line of p9 and w/reviews of this bk occupying the 1st pg of ads. 8pp undated ads. Frederic S. Church, James H. Moser (illus). Pict-dec olive brn cl. (Extrems sl rubbed, 1 sm scratch rear cvr), else Fine. *Sumner & Stillman.* $475/£297

HARRIS, JOEL CHANDLER. Uncle Remus, His Songs and His Sayings. NY, 1881. 1st ed, 1st issue, w/'presumptive' in the last line p9, and title not mentioned in ads at rear. Frederick S. Church & James H. Moser (illus). 8vo. Gilt-pict brn cl (spine top lt worn). Fine. BAL 7100. *Swann**. $805/£503

HARRIS, JOEL CHANDLER. Uncle Remus, His Songs and His Sayings. NY: D. Appleton, 1881. 1st ed. 8vo. Frederic Church & James Moser (illus). Pict ochre cl. Fine. *Appelfeld.* $1,500/£938

HARRIS, JOEL CHANDLER. Uncle Remus, His Songs and His Sayings. NY: D. Appleton, 1895. 8vo. Frederick Church and James Moser (illus). 231,(8)ads. Gilt-pict brn lettered tan cl. Good+ (lt dampstained, affecting lower rt corner of pp; spotted, soiled). *House.* $75/£47

HARRIS, JOEL CHANDLER. Uncle Remus, His Songs and His Sayings. NY: D. Appleton, 1910. New, rev ed. 8vo. xxiv,265,(4)ads; 112 illus (11 full-pg) by A. B. Frost. Teg. Pict red cl, gilt. VG (backstrip lt dknd). *House.* $75/£47

HARRIS, JOEL CHANDLER. Uncle Remus, His Songs and His Sayings. NY/London: D. Appleton, 1911. A. B. Frost (illus). 8vo. Teg. Pict brick red cl, gilt. Fine. *Glenn.* $85/£53

HARRIS, JOEL CHANDLER. Uncle Remus, His Songs and His Sayings. NY: LEC, 1957. One of 1500. Signed by Seong Moy (illus). Pict cl. Fine in slipcase. *Pacific**. $98/£61

HARRIS, JOEL CHANDLER. Uncle Remus: Being Legends of the Old Plantation. Mount Vernon: Peter Pauper Press, (1937). Ltd to 1100. 8vo. 8 full-pg illus by Fritz Eichenberg. Cl-backed dec bds (edges lt worn), paste label. VG. *Reisler.* $125/£78

HARRIS, JOEL CHANDLER. Wally Wanderoon and His Story-Telling Machine. NY: McClure, Phillips, 1903. 1st ed. Pict cl. (Name; spine ends frayed, extrems rubbed), else VG. *Pacific**. $57/£36

HARRIS, JOEL CHANDLER. Wally Wanderoon and His Story-Telling Machine. NY: McClure, Phillips, 1903. 1st ed. Karl Moseley (illus). 8 1/4 x 6. Pict cl. (Fr hinge starting, calling card to fep; spine ends rubbed), else VG. *Pacific**. $63/£39

HARRIS, JOHN. The Architect and the English Country House 1620-1920. (Washington): A.I.A., 1985. Fine in pict wraps. *Hadley.* $35/£22

HARRIS, JOHN. Buckingham Palace. London, 1968. 1st ed. 79 color plts. Dj (spine sl faded). *Edwards.* $72/£45

HARRIS, JOHN. The Description and Use of the Globes, and the Orrery. London: B. Cole/E. Cushee, 1757. 8th ed. Fldg frontis, viii,190pp + (2)pp ads; fldg plt, 5 fldg diags. Orig calf, leather spine label. (Bkpl, some plt folds splitting; worn, hinges cracked, corners showing.) *Weber.* $185/£116

HARRIS, JOHN. English Decorative Ironwork 1610-1836. Tiranti, 1960. 168 plts. VG in red cl. *Hadley.* $48/£30

HARRIS, JOHN. Gardens of Delight: The English Rococo Landscape of Thomas Robins the Elder. London: Basilisk, 1978. One of 515 numbered sets. 2 vols. Obl folio, atlas. 15 mtd color plts. Slipcases. *Swann**. $862/£539

HARRIS, LAURA. Pop-Up Cowboys and Indians. NY: Avon Kiddie Books, 1951. 22pp; 2 dbl-pg pop-ups by Julian Wehr. Illus bds. VG. *Bookfinders.* $75/£47

HARRIS, MARK. Bang the Drum Slowly. Knopf, 1956. 1st ed. VG in Good dj. *Plapinger.* $135/£84

HARRIS, MARK. It Looked Like For Ever. McGraw-Hill, 1979. 1st ed. Fine in VG dj. *Plapinger.* $27/£17

HARRIS, MARK. The Southpaw. Bobbs Merrill, 1953. 1st ed. Good+ in Good+ dj. *Plapinger.* $175/£109

HARRIS, MARK. A Ticket for a Seamstitch. Knopf, 1957. 1st ed. VG in Good+ dj. *Plapinger.* $45/£28

HARRIS, MARK. Trumpet to the World. NY, (1946). 1st ed, 1st bk. (Cvrs spotted), else Good in dj (soiled, edges chipped). *King.* $50/£31

HARRIS, MICHAEL. Poems. Dublin: Dolmen, (1965). 1st ed. Ltd to 500. VG in tan ptd wrappers. *Cady.* $10/£6

HARRIS, N. DWIGHT. Europe and the East. Boston/NY: Houghton Mifflin (Riverside), 1926. 1st ed. 7 color maps (1 dbl-pg). (Sl rubbed, spine faded), o/w VG. *Worldwide.* $30/£19

HARRIS, N. DWIGHT. The History of Negro Servitude in Illinois. Chicago, 1914. 1st ed. (Ink inscrip; cvr worn, soiled.) *King.* $65/£41

HARRIS, PHIL (ed). Hooked. NY: Pyramid, 1968. 1st ed. VG in wraps. *Beasley.* $25/£16

HARRIS, RICHARD (ed). The Reminiscences of Sir Henry Hawkins Baron Brampton. London: Edward Arnold, 1905. Maroon cl (worn), gilt. Sound. *Boswell.* $50/£31

HARRIS, RICHARD. Before and at Trial. What Should Be Done by Counsel, Solicitor and Client. Long Island: Edward Thompson, 1890. 1st Amer ed. Contemp sheep (very rubbed, fr joint cracked). Usable. *Boswell.* $75/£47

HARRIS, ROBERT. Enigma. London: Hutchinson, 1995. Signed, dated 4.ix.95. Fine (spine tail sl bumped) in dj. *Ulysses.* $72/£45

HARRIS, ROSEMARY. The Nice Girl's Story. London, 1968. 1st ed. Fine in dj. *Petersfield.* $19/£12

HARRIS, STANLEY. The Coaching Age. London: Richard Bentley, 1885. 468pp. Teg. 1/4 leather, raised bands. VG. *Perier.* $97/£61

HARRIS, STANLEY. The Coaching Age. London: Bentley, 1885. 3/4 morocco by Larkins, spine gilt. (Foxing; rubbed.) *Oinonen**. $130/£81

HARRIS, STANLEY. Old Coaching Days. London, 1882. (Shelfworn, foxed.) *Oinonen**. $110/£69

HARRIS, T. W. A Report on the Insects of Massachusetts Injurious to Vegetation. Cambridge, 1841. viii,459pp (eps browned, foxed, ink name). 1/2 calf (rubbed, scuffed). *Sutton.* $75/£47

HARRIS, THADDEUS M. Beauties of Nature Delineated. Charlestown, (MA): Samuel Etheridge, 1801. 2nd ed. 12mo. x,237pp. 3-pg preface, 1pg ad, 4pp contents misbound w/Part II placed before Part I. Full leather on bds. (Pencil notes on eps, owner stamp, lt foxed, edges browned; cvrs rubbed, frayed, partly detached, lg part of spine leather gone.) Internally Good. *Hobbyhorse.* $105/£66

HARRIS, THOMAS. Black Sunday. NY: Putnam, 1975. 1st ed, 1st bk. Fine in NF dj (price-clipped). *Lame Duck.* $200/£125

HARRIS, THOMAS. Red Dragon. NY, 1981. 1st ed. Fine in NF dj. *Warren.* $45/£28

HARRIS, THOMAS. The Silence of the Lambs. NY, 1988. 1st ed. Fine in Fine dj. *Warren.* $40/£25

HARRIS, W. S. Life in a Thousand Worlds. Boston: James H. Earle, (1905). 1st ed. Gilt-pict cl (sl dknd). *Swann**. $92/£58

HARRIS, WILLIAM C. (ed). The Angler's Guide Book and Tourists' Gazetteer of the Fishing Waters of the United States and Canada, 1885. NY: American Angler, (1884). 1st ed. Pinkish-tan cl, gilt. Fine. *Pacific**. $230/£144

HARRIS, WILLIAM. Rambles About Dudley Castle. Halesowen: William Harris, 1845. 110,(ii)pp (sm hole to 1 leaf, affecting 2 lines); 7 engr plts. Orig blind-stamped cl, gilt. *Hollett*. $136/£85

HARRIS, WILLIAM. The Wild Sports of Southern Africa. W. Pickering, 1841. 3rd ed. Lg 8vo. Add'l hand-colored litho frontis, 25 hand-colored litho plts, fldg map. Gilt edges. Mod grn 1/2 morocco. *Sotheby's**. $626/£391

HARRIS, WILLIAM. The Wild Sports of Southern Africa. London, 1852. 5th ed. 8vo. Color frontis, add'l color tp, xvi,359pp; 24 color plts, fldg map. (Lt browned, fore-edge some ll chipped.) Aeg. Cl bds (repairs, recased w/much of orig worn spine laid down; bds stained). *Edwards*. $720/£450

Harrison Weir's Pictures of Birds and Other Family Pets. London: Religious Tract Soc, (1879). 1st ed. 4to. (108)pp; 24 plts, guards. Mustard cl, onlaid pict vignette to upper cvr. Very Bright (lt internal speckling not affecting plts). *Sotheran*. $269/£168

HARRISON, BENJAMIN. Fortune Favors the Brave. L.A.: Ward Ritchie, 1953. 1st ed. Fine in VG dj. *Book Market*. $35/£22

HARRISON, CHARLES. English Art and Modernism, 1900-1939. London, 1981. 1st Eng ed. Fine in dj. *Clearwater*. $56/£35

HARRISON, CHARLES. Generals Die in Bed. NY: William Morrow, 1930. 1st ed. Pict eps. Tan cl stamped in red. Fine in dj (spine tanned, sm chip). *Reese*. $175/£109

HARRISON, D. Footsteps in the Sand. London: Benn, 1959. 1st ed. 8 photo plts. VG + in Good dj. *Mikesh*. $30/£19

HARRISON, DAVID L. (retold by). Cinderella. Kansas City: Hallmark, n.d. (1974). 5 dbl-pg pop-ups by Arlene Noel. Glazed pict bds. VG. *Bookfinders*. $50/£31

HARRISON, F. The Painted Glass of York. London, 1927. 46 plts hors texte. (Text sl spotted.) *Washton*. $75/£47

HARRISON, FRED. Hell Holes and Hangings. Clarendon, TX, 1968. 1st ed. Frontis. Buckram. NF in VG + dj. *Sagebrush*. $50/£31

HARRISON, FREDERIC. The Choice of Books and Other Literary Pieces. Macmillan, 1896. Ad leaf. Good (sig; spine bumped, sunned). *Tiger*. $19/£12

HARRISON, FREDERIC. Studies in Early Victorian Literature. London/NY: Edward Arnold, 1895. (viii),248pp, pub's inserted 32-pg cat at end dated Oct 1895. Uncut. Black coarse buckram, glazed white paper spine label. (Sm chip margin 1 leaf; spine label sl chipped, cracked), o/w Fine. *Temple*. $40/£25

HARRISON, FREDERIC. William the Silent. London: Macmillan, 1898. vi,260pp. Full prize grn calf (fr bd sl mkd). *Hollett*. $64/£40

HARRISON, G. B. John Bunyan: A Study in Personality. J.M. Dent, 1928. 1st Eng ed. NF (feps partly browned; spine tail sl bumped, sl faded) in dj (sl nicked, mkd, spine sl dknd). *Ulysses*. $32/£20

HARRISON, JIM. Farmer. NY, 1976. 1st ed. NF in NF dj (lt worn). *Warren*. $95/£59

HARRISON, JIM. Julip. NY, 1994. 1st ed. Fine in Fine dj. *Warren*. $30/£19

HARRISON, JIM. Legends of the Fall. (NY): Delacorte, (1979). 1st ed. Fine in Fine dj. *Lenz*. $75/£47

HARRISON, JIM. Plain Song. NY: Norton, (1965). 1st ed, 1st bk. Fine in dj (sl rubbed). *Lenz*. $275/£172

HARRISON, JIM. The Theory and Practice of Rivers. Seattle: Winn Books, 1986. 1st ed. Fine in cl slipcase. *Warren*. $75/£47

HARRISON, JIM. Warlock. (NY): Delacorte, (1981). 1st ed. Fine in Fine dj. *Lenz*. $40/£25

HARRISON, JIM. Warlock. NY, 1981. 1st ed. One of 250 numbered, signed. Slipcase. *Swann**. $57/£36

HARRISON, M. CLIFFORD. Home to the Cockade City! Dietz, 1942. 1st ed. VG in VG dj. *Book Broker*. $30/£19

HARRISON, MICHAEL. The Exploits of the Chevalier Dupin. Sauk City, WI: Mycroft & Moran, 1968. One of 1917. As New in dj. *Bernard*. $85/£53

HARRISON, MICHAEL. In the Footsteps of Sherlock Holmes. NY: Frederick Fell, (1960). 1st ed. VG in VG dj (edges lt worn). *Gravesend*. $60/£38

HARRISON, MICHAEL. The London of Sherlock Holmes. NY: Drake, (1972). 1st ed. NF in NF dj. *Gravesend*. $60/£38

HARRISON, MICHAEL. The World of Sherlock Holmes. NY: E.P. Dutton, 1975. 1st Amer ed. NF (lt bumped) in VG dj (spine spotted). *Blue Mountain*. $25/£16

HARRISON, TONY. Earthworks. Northern House Pamphlet Poets, 1964. 1st ed thus, 1st bk. VG in wraps (edges sl browned). *Virgo*. $112/£70

HARRISON, TONY. The Gaze of the Gorgon. Bloodaxe Books, 1992. 1st ed. Signed. Fine in dj. *Virgo*. $56/£35

HARRISON, TONY. Selected Poems. Viking, 1984. 1st ed thus. Fine in dj. *Virgo*. $32/£20

HARRISON, W. JEROME. Geology of the Counties of England. London, 1882. xxviii,346pp. (Tp, last few ll sl spotted, bkpl; joints rubbed; worn.) *Edwards*. $72/£45

HARRISON, WILLIAM HENRY. Aborigines of the Ohio Valley. Chicago, 1883. 8vo. Orig letterpress yellow wrappers. Fldg case. Howes H245. *Swann**. $517/£323

HARRISON, WILLIAM HENRY. A Discourse on the Aborigines of the Valley of the Ohio. Cincinnati: (Office of the Cincinnati Express), 1838. 1st ed. 51pp; VG fldg map. Marbled eps. Later dk brn morocco, pebbled cl, raised bands, gilt. James J. Hill bkpl. (Lt foxed; lib white ink # fr cvr, perf stamp tp, 1 text leaf; ink stamp, bkpl; edges, joints sl worn, faint vertical crease at center.) Howes H245. *Baltimore**. $200/£125

HARRISSON, J. A. B. and H. J. GALSWORTHY. Pad, or Minesweeper Nonsense Verse. London: Warren, n.d. (1944). 1st Eng ed. Signed by both authors. VG (tp sl foxed) in dj (nicked, creased, mkd, dknd). *Ulysses*. $56/£35

HARRISSON, TOM (ed). Borneo Jungle; An Account of the Oxford Expedition to Sarawak. Lindsay Drummond, 1938. 1st ed. 2 maps. All edges red. Brick-red cl. (Eps sl foxed), o/w VF. *Sotheran*. $152/£95

HARROP, D. A. A History of the Gregynog Press. Private Library Assoc, 1980. 1st ed. VG. *Whiteson*. $64/£40

HARROWER, JOHN. The Journal of.... Col. Williamsburg & Holt Rinehart, (c1963). Fritz Kredel (illus). VG (pencil notes) in Good dj. *Book Broker*. $20/£13

HARROWFIELD, DAVID L. Sledging into History. Auckland: Macmillan, 1981. Fine in dj. *Explorer*. $96/£60

HART, ANN CLARK. Clark's Point. SF: Pioneer, 1937. 17 plts, 3 facs. Leather-backed marbled bds, gilt spine. Fine in pict dj (few sm tears, chips to edges). *Pacific**. $29/£18

HART, B. H. LIDDELL. The Real War 1914-1918. London: Faber & Faber, (1930). 1st ed. Gilt red cl. VG in dj (sl nicked, dknd). *Reese*. $55/£34

HART, B. H. LIDDELL. Reputations Ten Years After. Boston: Little, Brown, 1928. 1st US ed. Gilt grn cl. Sound (dull, ex-lib, sl mks). *Reese*. $10/£6

HART, CHARLES HENRY. Catalogue of the Engraved Portraits of Washington. NY: Grolier Club, 1904. One of 425. *Swann**. $258/£161

HART, FRED H. The Sazerac Lying Club: A Nevada Book. SF: Henry Keller, 1878. 1st ed. Brick red cl, gilt. (Fr hinge starting; spine ends chipped, corners rubbed), else VG. *Pacific**. $86/£54

HART, GEORGE. The Violin. Dulau, 1885. 1st ed. xl,499pp; 22 wood-engr plts. Pict cl over beveled bds (nicely rebacked in matching levant morocco), gilt. *Hollett.* $192/£120

HART, GEORGE. The Violin. Dulau, 1885. 1st ed. xl,499pp; 22 wood-engr plts. Pict cl, gilt, beveled bds. (Nicely rebacked in matching levant morocco, gilt.) *Hollett.* $192/£120

HART, HERBERT M. Old Forts of the Southwest. Seattle: Superior, (1965). 1st ed. Fine in VG dj. *Perier.* $35/£22

HART, HORACE. Bibliotheca Typographica, A List of Books About Books. Rochester: The Printing House of Leo Hart, 1933. 1st ed. Prospectus, fldg broadside, 1953 bill of sale loosely inserted. Fine in dj (worn). *Oak Knoll.* $55/£34

HART, JAMES D. The Private Press Ventures of Samuel Lloyd Osbourne and R.L.S. SF: Book Club of CA, 1966. 1st ed. One of 500. Frontis, 11 full-pg facs, 13 add'l facs in rear pocket. Dec beige cl. Fine. *Harrington.* $65/£41

HART, ROY. Blood Kin. London: Scribner, 1991. 1st ed. Fine in dj. *Murder.* $40/£25

HART, SCOTT. The Moon Is Waning. NY: Derrydale, 1939. Ltd to 950 numbered. Unnumbered rev copy, slip laid in. Blue cl. VF. *Biscotti.* $150/£94

HART, THOMAS. Rope Driving; or, The Transmission of Power by Ropes. Blackburn: Thomas Hart, (c. 1920). VG. *Hollett.* $24/£15

HART, WILLIAM S. The Law on Horseback and Other Stories. L.A., (1935). Color frontis, full-pg photo. NF in Good+ dj. *Sagebrush.* $40/£25

HART, WILLIAM S. My Life East and West. Martin Ridge (ed). Chicago: R.R. Donnelley, 1994. Frontis. VG. *Lien.* $30/£19

HARTE, BRET. The Complete Poetical Works. London: C&W, 1886. 1st Eng ed. (Eps browned), o/w NF. BAL 7503. *Agvent.* $85/£53

HARTE, BRET. The Heathen Chinee: Plain Language from Truthful James. SF: John Henry Nash, 1934. One of 500. String-bound blue bds, paper spine label, chemise w/bone clasps. (Edges sl sunned), else NF. *Pacific*.* $150/£94

HARTE, BRET. The Luck of Roaring Camp. SF: Ransohoffs, 1947. One of 300 ptd. 1/2 cl, gilt-dec bds. (Portion of gilt illus on fr cvr rubbed, top corners lt bumped), else VG. *Pacific*.* $40/£25

HARTE, BRET. A Millionaire of the Rough-and-Ready. Kentfield: L-D Allen Press, 1955. One of 220. Fine. *Pacific*.* $127/£79

HARTE, BRET. Mliss. SF: Grabhorn, 1948. One of 300. 1/2 cl, paper spine label. (Bds sunned), else NF. *Pacific*.* $46/£29

HARTE, BRET. Poems. Boston: James R. Osgood, 1871. 1st ed. Grn cl-cvrd bds. (Sig, lib sticker; bumped), else Fine. *Metropolitan*.* $46/£29

HARTE, BRET. The Queen of the Pirate Isle. London, (1886). 1st Eng ed. Kate Greenaway (illus). Sm 4to. Cl-backed pict buckram. *Swann*.* $138/£86

HARTE, BRET. The Queen of the Pirate Isle. London: C&W, (1886). 1st ed. Kate Greenaway (illus). White eps; gold edges. Beige cl, color pict cvrs. VG (spine lt worn). *Davidson.* $300/£188

HARTE, BRET. The Queen of the Pirate Isle. Boston: Houghton Mifflin, (1887). 1st Amer ed. 8vo. 58pp; 28 color engrs. Aeg. Wheat-colored pict cl (lt foxed). VG. *Reisler.* $275/£172

HARTE, BRET. The Queen of the Pirate Isle. London: C&W, n.d. (1886). 1st ed. BAL's state B of binding w/sheet edges stained brnish-gold. Kate Greenaway (illus). Pict beige cl, gilt. Fine (spine ends, corners sl rubbed). BAL 7337. *Argonaut.* $175/£109

HARTE, BRET. Tales of the Gold Rush. LEC, 1944. One of 1200 signed by Fletcher Martin (illus). Fine in slipcase. *Swann*.* $40/£25

HARTE, BRET. The Writings of Bret Harte. Boston/NY: Houghton Mifflin, (1899). Riverside ed. 20 vols. Blue cl, gilt. (Lib stamps; sm shelf #, vol # on each spine foot), o/w VF set. *Hollett.* $240/£150

HARTFORD, W. P. The Motor Launch: How to Build and How to Run. Cleveland: Penton Pub, 1905. 1st ed. (Spine sl faded), else NF. *Pacific*.* $23/£14

HARTHAN, JOHN P. Bookbindings. London, 1961. 2nd ed. (Cl spotted.) *Typographeum.* $20/£13

HARTLEY, HARRIETT A. Needlework Practically Explained. A. Brown, n.d. (c. 1900). 2 fldg samplers. Pict cl. Good+ (corners worn, soil, upper hinge tender). *Whittle.* $29/£18

HARTLEY, JOHN. Grimes's Trip to America. Ten Letters from Sammywell to John Jones Smith. London: W. Nicholson, (1877). 1st ed. pp121,(7) ads. Pict bds (spine rubbed). *Mott.* $75/£47

HARTLEY, L. P. The Boat. NY, 1950. 1st Amer ed. Nice (spine ends sl bumped) in dj (sl torn, rubbed, dusty). *Clearwater.* $56/£35

HARTLEY, L. P. The Brickfield. Hamish Hamilton, 1964. 1st Eng ed. VG (spine ends sl bumped) in dj (sl rubbed, few tears rear panel). *Ulysses.* $32/£20

HARTLEY, L. P. The Go-Between. NY: Knopf, 1954. 1st Amer ed. Fine in NF dj (spine sl faded, 2 sm tears). *Between The Covers.* $65/£41

HARTLEY, L. P. The Harness Room. London, 1971. 1st Eng ed. Fine in dj (torn). *Clearwater.* $32/£20

HARTLEY, L. P. The Hireling. London, 1957. 1st Eng ed. Fine in dj (sl rubbed, nicked). *Clearwater.* $56/£35

HARTLEY, L. P. My Fellow Devils. London, 1951. 1st Eng ed. Good (cvrs handled) in dj (torn, grubby). *Clearwater.* $40/£25

HARTLEY, L. P. The Novelist's Responsibility. London: Hamish Hamilton, 1967. 1st Eng ed. Fine in dj (sl nicked, creased). *Ulysses.* $56/£35

HARTLEY, L. P. A Perfect Woman. London, 1955. VG in dj. *Typographeum.* $35/£22

HARTLEY, L. P. Poor Clare. London, 1968. 1st Eng ed. Nice (corner bumped) in dj. *Clearwater.* $40/£25

HARTLEY, L. P. Simonetta Perkins. London, 1925. 1st Eng ed. Buckram-backed batik bds (sl cocked). Very Nice in dj (sl chipped, neatly repaired). *Clearwater.* $240/£150

HARTLEY, L. P. The Travelling Grave and Other Stories. London, 1951. 1st Eng ed. Good (cocked, edges sl string-dented; spine head chafed) in dj (chipped, nicked). *Clearwater.* $40/£25

HARTLEY, L. P. Two for the River. London, 1960. 1st Eng ed. Fine in dj (sl dusty). *Clearwater.* $56/£35

HARTLEY, L. P. The West Window. NY, 1945. 1st Amer ed. Nice (rev clipping pasted to fep; corners bumped) in dj (sl nicked, rubbed, price-clipped). *Clearwater.* $88/£55

HARTLEY, L. P. The White Wand and Other Stories. London, 1954. 1st Eng ed. Very Nice in dj (sl rubbed, neatly repaired). *Clearwater.* $56/£35

HARTMAN, ROLAND C. and G. VICKERS. Hatchery Management. NY: OJ, 1932. 1st ed. Blue cl, gilt. Good+. *Larry Price.* $25/£16

HARTMAN, WILLIAM E. et al. Nudist Society: An Authoritative, Complete Study of Nudism in America. NY: Crown, (1970). 1st ed. Fine in dj. *Pacific*.* $52/£33

HARTMANN, FRANZ. The Principles of Astrological Geomancy. Boston: Occult, 1889. 1st ed. 136pp. VG+. *Middle Earth.* $145/£91

HARTMANN, HEINZ. Essays on Ego Psychology. Selected Problems in Psychoanalytic Theory. NY: International Universities Press, (1964). 1st ed. Blue cl. Fine in ptd dj. *House.* $50/£31

HARTMANN, SADAKICHI. The Valiant Knights of Daguerre. Berkeley: Univ of CA, 1978. 1st ed. Fine in dj (spine sunned). *Smith.* $100/£63

HARTNACK, HUGO. Unbidden House Guests. Tacoma: Hartnack Pub Co, 1943. Gilt red fabricoid. Fine. *Karmiole.* $50/£31

HARTNELL, NORMAN. Silver and Gold. Evans Bros, 1955. 1st ed. 46 plts, full-pg dwgs. VG. *Cox.* $29/£18

HARTOG, W. G. The Kiss in English Poetry. (London): A. M. Philpot, 1923. 1st ed. One of 500. (Fep, fr cvr written on, extrems rubbed), else VG-. *Pacific*.* $58/£36

HARTSHORNE, ALBERT. Hanging in Chains. Fisher & Unwin, 1891. 1st Eng ed. Parchment cvrs (mottled). Good. *Clearwater.* $80/£50

HARTSHORNE, ALBERT. Hanging in Chains. London: T. Fisher Unwin, 1891. 1st ed. Inscribed, signed. Frontis. Vellum. (Lettering nearly rubbed off cvr), else VG. *Pacific*.* $138/£86

HARTSHORNE, C. H. The Book Rarities in the University of Cambridge. Longman, Rees, Orme, Brown & Green, 1829. 1st ed. Frontis. (Lower inner hinge split.) Uncut. 19th-cent cl. *Forest.* $88/£55

HARTSHORNE, CHARLES and P. WEISS (eds). Collected Papers of Charles Sanders Peirce, Volume 4. Harvard Univ, 1933. 1st ed. Teg. Red cl, gilt. VG (ex-lib). *Larry Price.* $28/£18

HARTT, F. Drawings of Michelangelo. London: Thames & Hudson, 1971. 16 mtd color illus. Good in dj. *Ars Artis.* $136/£85

HARTZ, S. L. The Elseviers and Their Contemporaries. Amsterdam: Elsevier, 1955. 1st ed. *Forest.* $120/£75

Harvard Memorial Biographies. Cambridge: Sever & Francis, 1866. 1st ed. 2 vols. xix,477; iv,512pp (lt aging, few pp roughly opened); tipped-in errata slip rear of vol 2. Brn coated eps. Grn cl (sl worn, rippled), gilt. *Baltimore*.* $70/£44

HARVEY, ANDREW. A Full Circle. Deutsch, 1981. 1st ed. Fine in dj. *Any Amount.* $19/£12

HARVEY, ANDREW. A Journey in Ladakh. London, 1983. 1st Eng ed. Fine in dj. *Clearwater.* $56/£35

HARVEY, CLARA TOOMBS. Not So Wild, the Old West. Denver: Golden Bell, 1961. VG in dj. *Harvey,* $25/£16

HARVEY, E. NEWTON. A History of Luminescence, from the Earliest Times Until 1900. Phila: American Philosophical Soc, 1957. 1st ed. NF in dj. *Pacific*.* $127/£79

HARVEY, E. NEWTON. A History of Luminescence, from the Earliest Times until 1900. Phila: American Philosophical Soc, 1957. Fine (stamp) in dj. *Weber.* $150/£94

HARVEY, F. W. Gloucestershire Friends. London, 1917. 1st Eng ed. (Sl mkd.) *Clearwater.* $40/£25

HARVEY, FRANK. The Last Enemy. London, 1930. 1st Eng ed. Good (spine sl chafed). *Clearwater.* $32/£20

HARVEY, GEORGE ROWNTREE. A Book of Scotland. A&C Black, 1949. 1st ed. 31 color plts. (Feps spotted.) *Hollett.* $40/£25

HARVEY, HENRY. History of the Shawnee Indians, from the Year 1681 to 1854, Inclusive. Cincinnati: Ephraim Morgan, 1855. 1st ed, w/pencil presentation. 1st issue, w/spine lettering reading 'History of the Shawnee Indians,' w/o frontisport, w/preface dated Sept 21, 1855; 2nd issue had a frontis, preface was dated 'ninth month,' and spine incl Harvey's name. 316pp. Dk brn blind cl, gilt. (Pp lt rippled, sl foxed; spine ends chipped, extrems worn, sl flaking at lower spine.) Howes H275. *Baltimore*.* $130/£81

HARVEY, JOHN. Early Nurserymen. Phillimore, 1974. Fine in dj. *Hadley.* $26/£16

HARVEY, JOHN. Early Nurserymen. London: Phillimore, 1974. 16 plts. As New. *Quest.* $50/£31

HARVEY, JOHN. Gothic England: A Survey...1300-1550. Batsford, 1948. 2nd ed. VG in dj (chipped). *Hadley.* $35/£22

HARVEY, JOHN. Victorian Novelists and Their Illustrators. London, 1970. VG in dj (frayed). *Typographeum.* $45/£28

HARVEY, KATHERINE. The Best-Dressed Miners. (NY, 1969.) 1st ed. Fldg frontis, map. NF in VG + dj. *Sagebrush.* $55/£34

HARVEY, T. EDMUND. Saint Aelred of Rievaulx. London: H.R. Allenson, 1932. 1st ed. Presentation copy. Uncut. VG in dj (spine head chipped). *Hollett.* $32/£20

HARVEY, W. H. Memoir of W. H. Harvey. London, 1869. 1st ed. Frontis, 372pp. Grn cl, gilt. (Ex-lib; spine head chipped, edges cracked), else Good. *Larry Price.* $49/£31

HARVEY, W. H. Phycologia Britanica: or a History of British Sea-Weeds.... London, 1846-1851. 1st ed. 4 vols. 8vo. 360 Fine color plts. Grn 1/2 calf, gilt. (Eps sl foxed.) *Henly.* $832/£520

HARVEY, WILLIAM. The Anatomical Exercises. Geoffrey Keynes (ed). London: Nonesuch, (1928). Facs ed. One of 1450. Fldg plt. Full morocco. *Marlborough.* $320/£200

HARVEY, WILLIAM. The Anatomical Exercises...Concerning the Motion of the Heart and Blood [with] Discourse on the Heart by James de Back. London: Richard Lowndes & Math. Gilliflower, 1673. 2nd ed in English. 12mo. (24),107,(1); (20),172pp. Aeg. 19th-cent russia, gilt, morocco spine label. (Name dated 1697 to tp, tp verso, pp trimmed, sl stained, later eps; extrems rubbed, rebacked w/earlier spine strip laid on), else VG. *Pacific*.* $2,875/£1,797

HARVEY, WILLIAM. On Excision of the Enlarged Tonsil and Its Consequences in Cases of Deafness. London: Henry Renshaw, 1850. 1st ed. xii,121pp + ad leaf; 2 woodcut plts. Orig panelled blind-stamped cl, gilt. (Extrems sl bumped, worn.) *Hollett.* $136/£85

HARVEY, WILLIAM. Structural Survey of the Church of the Nativity Bethlehem. Oxford, 1935. 6 fldg plans, 23 plts. Good. *Washton.* $165/£103

HARWELL, RICHARD B. The Confederate Hundred. Urbana, IL, 1964 (1982). VG. *Dumont.* $40/£25

HARWELL, RICHARD B. The Confederate Hundred. N.p.: Beta Phi Mu, 1964. 1st ed. (Sl worn.) Glassine wrapper (sl frayed). *Oinonen*.* $100/£63

HARWELL, RICHARD B. Cornerstones of Confederate Collecting. Charlottesville: Univ of VA, 1953. 2nd ed. Tan cl. VG. *Chapel Hill.* $50/£31

HARWELL, RICHARD B. Cornerstones of Confederate Collecting. Univ of VA, 1953. 2nd ed. Ltd to 500. Facs tp. VG. *Book Broker.* $65/£41

HARWELL, RICHARD B. Cornerstones of Confederate Collecting. Charlottesville, VA, 1982. Numbered, ltd ed. VG. *Dumont.* $30/£19

HARWELL, RICHARD B. In Tall Cotton. Austin, 1978. (Bds sl soiled), else VG. *Dumont.* $125/£78

HARWELL, RICHARD B. More Confederate Imprints. VA State Lib, 1957. 2 vols. Paper cvr. VG (cvr stained vol 2). *Book Broker.* $45/£28

HARWELL, RICHARD B. (ed). The Confederate Reader. NY: Longmans, Green, 1957. 1st ed. Gray cl. Fine in Good dj (price-clipped, worn). *Chapel Hill.* $65/£41

HARWELL, RICHARD B. (ed). The Union Reader. NY: Longmans, Green, 1958. 1st ed. Blue cl. Fine in VG dj (price-clipped). *Chapel Hill.* $65/£41

HARWOOD, JOHN EDMUND. Select Poems. Whitehall: T. & J. Egerton, 1793. Period tree calf, gilt, morocco spine label. (Old name, fep clipped; joints cracked), else VG. *Pacific*.* $29/£18

HARWOOD, RONALD. The Genoa Ferry. Secker, 1976. 1st UK ed. VG + (sl bumped). *Williams.* $26/£16

HARWOOD, RONALD. The Girl in Melanie Klein. Secker, 1969. 1st UK ed. VG + (sm flaw fr cvr) in dj (sm tear strengthened to rear). *Williams.* $32/£20

HASFORD, GUSTAV. The Short Timers. NY: Harper & Row, 1979. 1st ed. Inscribed in 1979, in 3 different ink colors. Xeroxed rev sheet laid in. (Poorly bound), else Fine in dj. *Smith*. $500/£313

HASKELL, ARNOLD and MIN LEWIS. Infantilia. Dennis Dobson, 1971. 1st ed. 4to. Stanley Lewis (illus). 120pp. Dj. *Hollett*. $48/£30

HASKELL, ARNOLD and MIN LEWIS. Infantilia. The Archaeology of the Nursery. London, 1971. 1st ed. Fine in dj (price-clipped). *Polyanthos*. $30/£19

HASKELL, FRANCIS. Patrons and Painters. London: C&W, 1963. VG. *Turtle Island*. $45/£28

HASKINS, C. W. The Argonauts of California. NY: Fords, Howard & Hulbert, 1890. 1st ed. 501pp. (Ex-lib, removed spine label w/fading and rubbing, removed bkpls; cvrs soiled, extrems worn, hinge cracking after title), else VG. Howes H383. *Pacific**. $161/£101

HASKINS, CARYL P. The Amazon. NY, 1943. 1st ed. 13 photo plts. Tan linen cl. VG. *Larry Price*. $28/£18

HASKINS, DAVID GREENE. Ralph Waldo Emerson. Boston: Cupples, Upham, 1887. Lg paper ed. One of unknown # of ed deluxe. 12,151pp. Cl-backed bds, ptd paper label. *M & S*. $175/£109

HASLUCK, P. N. (ed). Cassell's Carpentry and Joinery. London, n.d. (c.1900). 12 color plts. Good+ (last 2 index pp damaged w/o loss, lacks plt). *Whittle*. $48/£30

HASSALL, JOHN. Double Dutch. Leeds: Alf Cooke, (ca 1920). 4to. 18pp; 6 full-pg plts. Good in illus stiff paper wrappers (restoration along spine). *Reisler*. $100/£63

HASSE, CHARLES EWALD. An Anatomical Description of the Diseases of the Organs of Circulation and Respiration. London, 1846. 400pp. Orig cl bds. VG (inner hinges loose; extrems sl worn). *Doctor's Library*. $125/£78

HASSELL, JOHN. Picturesque Rides and Walks.... For J. Hassell, 1817-1818. 2 vols. 120 hand-colored aquatint plts. Uncut. Later mottled calf by Riviere, gilt spines. (Lt dust-soiled, spotted in margins.) *Sotheby's**. $1,288/£805

HASSRICK, PETER H. Frederick Remington. Abrams/Amon Carter Museum, (1973). 1st ed. Fine in dj. *Truepenny*. $85/£53

HASSRICK, ROYAL B. History of Western American Art. NY: Exeter Books, (1987). 1st ed. Color frontis. Maroon cl, gilt. Fine in pict dj. *Argonaut*. $35/£22

HASSRICK, ROYAL B. The Sioux. Norman, (1964). 1st ed. Fine in Fine dj. *Pratt*. $70/£44

HASTED, EDWARD. The History and Topographical Survey of the County of Kent. Canterbury: The Author, 1778-1790. 1st ed. 3 vols only (of 4). 1 hand-colored fldg engr map, 31 maps, 44 plts. (Closed tears 3 leaves w/o loss, clear tear 1 plt, occasionally spotted.) Contemp tree calf (rebacked, recornered, fr cvr vol 1 detached, spine ends frayed, scuffed.) *Christie's**. $990/£619

Hastings Guide. (By J. Stell.) London: Barry, 1815. 4th ed. Frontis, iv,83,(1)pp; fldg map. Orig bds, ptd label. (Spine, joints worn, cracked.) *Marlborough*. $80/£50

HASTINGS, FRANK S. A Ranchman's Recollections. Chicago, 1921. 1st ed. Pict cl. (Upper backstrip sl split each corner), else VG. *Baade*. $65/£41

HASTINGS, JAMES (ed). A Dictionary of Christ and the Gospels. NY: Scribner, 1924. 2 vols. Frontis map vol 1. Black cl, gilt. (Ink name), else Fine set. *Argonaut*. $125/£78

HASTINGS, M. St. Stephen's Chapel and Its Place in the Development of Perpendicular Style in England. CUP, 1955. Frontis, 56 plts. Pub's cl. VG. *Peter Taylor*. $43/£27

HATCH, ALDEN and FOXHALL KEENE. Full Tilt. NY: Derrydale, 1938. Ltd to 950 numbered. Blue cl. NF. *Biscotti*. $100/£63

HATCH, FREDERICK H. and J. A. CHALMERS. The Gold Mines of the Rand. London: Macmillan, 1895. 1st ed. 1/2-title, xvii,(i)blank,306,(2)ads, errata slip; 5 fldg plans, 2 fldg tables, 2 lg fldg charts (repaired at folds) loose in rear pocket. Red cl. (Ink inscrip; hinges cracking, stained). Internally Sound. *Morrell*. $352/£220

HATCH, JAMES V. (ed). Black Theater, U.S.A.: 45 Plays by Black Americans, 1847-1974. NY: Free Press, (1974). (Upper tips bumped.) Ptd dj. *Petrilla*. $30/£19

HATCH, W. J. The Land Pirates of India. Phila: Lippincott, (1928). 1st ed. Fldg map. Red cl, gilt. Good. *Karmiole*. $75/£47

HATCH, W. J. The Land Pirates of India. Phila, n.d. c.(1928). 23 plts, fldg map. (Lt browned; sl cl loss to corners, joints splitting.) *Edwards*. $64/£40

HATCHER, EDMUND N. The Last Four Weeks of the War. Columbus, OH, 1892. 2nd ed. 416pp. (Spine lettering rubbed off; cvrs dknd, rubbed; corners bumped.) *King*. $50/£31

HATFIELD, EDWIN F. History of Elizabeth, New Jersey. NY: Carlton & Lanahan, 1868. 1st ed. 701pp. (Lib spine #, sl shelfworn), else Good. Howes H301. *Brown*. $75/£47

HATFIELD, EDWIN F. (comp). Freedom's Lyre. NY: S.W. Benedict, 1840. 2nd ed. 6,265pp (lacks fep). Orig cl. *M & S*. $175/£109

HATFIELD, JOHN T. Thirty-Three Years a Live Wire. Cincinnati, (ca 1895). 1st ed. 317pp. *Ginsberg*. $150/£94

HATTERAS, OWEN. (Pseud of H. L. Mencken and George Nathan.) Pistols for Two. NY: Knopf, 1917. 1st ed. VG in heavy rose colored paper wraps (spine sl faded). *Cady*. $125/£78

HATTERSLEY, RALPH. Andreas Feininger. Dobbs Ferry, NY: Morgan & Morgan, 1973. 1st ed. (Inscrip), o/w NF in dj. *Cahan*. $60/£38

HATTON, JOSEPH. Henry Irving's Impressions of America.... London: Sampson Low, 1884. 1st ed. 2 vols. (Bkpls removed; lt spotted.) *Mott*. $50/£31

HATTON, JOSEPH. The Lyceum 'Faust.' London: J.S. Virtue, n.d. (1886). Frontis. Cl-backed pict bds (edges worn, cvrs pulling; eps soiled). *Dramatis*. $30/£19

HATTON, JOSEPH. The New Ceylon. London, 1881. 1st ed. Frontis, xi,209,32ads pp; 3 maps (2 fldg). Pict cl, gilt. Fine (sm lib stamps). *Maggs*. $320/£200

HATTON, S. F. The Yarn of a Yeoman. London, (1930). 1st Eng ed. (No dj.) *Clearwater*. $32/£20

HAULTAIN, ARNOLD. The Mystery of Golf. Boston: Houghton Mifflin, 1908. 1st ed. One of 440. Cl-backed dec bds, gilt. (Emb stamp; spine ends, corners rubbed, sl soiled), else VG. *Pacific**. $1,610/£1,006

HAULTAIN, ARNOLD. The Mystery of Golf. NY: Macmillan, 1914. 2nd ed. Grn/white cl. (Spine lettering, white rubbed, white on fr cvr sl discolored), else VG. *Pacific**. $150/£94

HAULTAIN, ARNOLD. The Mystery of Golf. NY: Serendipity, 1965. 1st ed thus. 1/2 cl, dec bds, gilt. Fine in slipcase. *Pacific**. $127/£79

HAUPT-HEYDEMARCK, GEORG. War Flying in Macedonia. Claud W. Sykes (trans). London, (1935). 1st Eng ed. VG (name) in pict dj (sl nicked, torn, internal stains of old tape reinforcement). *Clearwater*. $152/£95

Haut Ton Directory of Portland, Oregon. Portland: C.H. McIsaac, 1888. 134pp. Floral ptd eps, edges stained red. Dk brn cl, gilt. VG (sl edgeworn). *Baltimore**. $75/£47

HAVEN, CHARLES T. A History of the Colt Revolver and the Other Arms Made...from 1836 to 1940. NY: William Morrow, 1940. 1st ed. Fine in dj (tears, chips, spine sl faded), slipcase (few scrapes, scratches). Howes H308. *Pacific**. $109/£68

HAVEN, CHARLES T. A History of the Colt Revolver. NY, 1940. 1st ed. (Lt worn.) *Oinonen**. $50/£31

HAVERKAMP-BEGEMANN, EGBERT. Drawings from the Clark Art Institute. Yale Univ, 1964. 2 vols. (Lt worn.) Slipcase. *Oinonen**. $50/£31

HAVIGHURST, WALTER. Upper Mississippi. NY, 1937. 1st ed. Grn cl. (Spine sl sunned), else VG. *Larry Price*. $17/£11

HAW, STEPHEN G. The Lilies of China. London/Portland, 1986. 1st ed. 8 color plts. Mint in dj. *Larry Price*. $30/£19

Hawbuck Grange; or, The Sporting Adventures of Thomas Scott, Esq. (By Robert Smith Surtees.) London, 1847. 1st ed, 1st issue, w/the date on tp, etc. W/the ad leaf of 'New Works' and Longman's 32-pg cat dated April 1847 at end. 8 plts by Phiz. Orig gilt-pict cl. (Sl soiled, foxed; shelfworn.) Slipcase provided. *Oinonen**. $80/£50

Hawbuck Grange; or, The Sporting Adventures of Thomas Scott, Esq. (By Robert Smith Surtees.) London, 1847. 1st ed, 1st issue, w/date on tp, and w/Longman's 32-pg cat at end. 8 engr plts by Phiz. Full red morocco by Bayntun. (Orig cvrs, part of spine bound in at end; sl worn.) Protective cl case provided. *Oinonen**. $110/£69

HAWEIS, H. R. Old Violins. George Redway, 1898. 1st ed. 293pp. Uncut. (Few spots eps; cl sl rubbed, spotted.) *Hollett*. $56/£35

HAWEIS, MRS. H. R. The Art of Beauty. London, 1878. 1st ed. Color frontis, xiv,298pp. 1/2 morocco, marbled bds, gilt. (Fr hinge tender; sl rubbed, spine soiled, bumped.) *Edwards*. $77/£48

HAWES, HARRY. Fish and Game: Now or Never. NY, 1935. 1st ed. VF in VG dj. *Bond*. $20/£13

HAWK, DAVE. Eighty Years on Bass. Corpus Christi, (1958). 1st ed. Pict wrappers (shelfworn). *Oinonen**. $50/£31

HAWKER, PETER. Instructions to Young Sportsmen in All That Relates to Guns and Shooting. London, 1824. 10 plts (4 hand-colored aquatints). 3/4 red leather (worn, fr hinge starting; eps replaced). *Oinonen**. $240/£150

HAWKER, PETER. Instructions to Young Sportsmen in All That Relates to Guns and Shooting. Longman, Rees, Orme, Brown, Green & Longman, 1833. 7th ed. Frontis, 16,(xxiv),(508)pp; 7 engr plts. Orig cl, morocco label (sl worn). Nice (sl loose, 1 leaf sl creased). *Ash*. $152/£95

HAWKER, PETER. Instructions to Young Sportsmen, in All That Relates to Guns and Shooting. Phila, 1846. 1st Amer ed. Mod cl. (Foxing throughout.) *Swann**. $172/£108

HAWKER, PETER. Instructions to Young Sportsmen, in All That Relates to Guns and Shooting. Phila, 1853. 2nd Amer ed. 10 engr plts (evenly browned). 19th-cent 1/2 leather, gilt. *Swann**. $172/£108

HAWKER, PETER. Instructions to Young Sportsmen, on the Choice, Care, and Management of Guns. London, 1816. 2nd ed. 6 plts + 1 extra loosely inserted. Uncut. Orig bds (rebacked w/paper label, corners bumped). *Petersfield*. $224/£140

HAWKER, R. S. The Prose Works. William Blackwood & Sons, 1893. 1st ed. Frontis, (iv),187,32pp. (Sm rust-mk on contents leaf; few sl mks.) *Hollett*. $136/£85

HAWKES, JOHN. The Beetle Leg. NY: New Directions, 1951. 1st ed, 1st issue (orange, not red cl). NF (pg ends lt foxed) in dj. *Smith*. $150/£94

HAWKES, JOHN. The Blood Oranges. New Directions, (1971). 1st ed. (Newspaper clipping offset rep), else VG in dj (sl worn, yellowed). *King*. $35/£22

HAWKES, JOHN. The Universal Fears. Northridge, CA: Lord John Press, 1978. 1st ed. Ltd to 275 numbered, signed. (Upper rt corners sl bumped), else VG. *King*. $65/£41

HAWKES, JOHN. Virginie, Her Two Lives. New Directions, (1982). 1st ed. Ltd to 300 numbered, signed. VG. *King*. $100/£63

HAWKESWORTH, JOHN (ed). The Adventurer. London: C. Hitch & L. Hawes et al, 1762. 4th ed. 4 vols. Calf, gilt, red morocco spine labels. (Old name to tps; glue to spine heads, upper joints), else VG. *Pacific**. $196/£123

HAWKESWORTH, JOHN. An Account of the Voyages Undertaken by the Order of His Present Majesty for Making Discoveries in the Southern Hemisphere. W. Strahan & T. Cadell, 1783. 2nd ed. 3 vols. 15 (of 52) engr plts. Contemp tree calf. (Spotted, 1 tp creased; worn, cvrs almost detached.) *Sotheby's**. $552/£345

HAWKESWORTH, JOHN. An Account of the Voyages Undertaken by the Order of His Present Majesty...Third Edition [of Cook's First Voyage]. London, 1785. 4 vols. 2 maps, 9 plts. Orig bds (rebacked w/calf). *Swann**. $460/£288

HAWKINS, JOHN. The Life of Samuel Johnson. Dublin: Chamberlain et al, 1787. 1st Dublin ed. ii,553,(19)pp. Uncut. 3/4 leather (rebound), raised bands, dbl leather labels. Internally Fine. *Hartfield*. $395/£247

HAWKINS, LAETITIA-MATILDA. Anecdotes, Biographical Sketches and Memoirs. London: Rivington, 1822. 1st ed. viii,(2),351pp. Recent Fine terra-cotta linen, red/gilt morocco label. VG. *Hartfield*. $295/£184

HAWKINS, WILLIAM G. Lunsford Lane; Or, Another Helper from North Carolina. Boston: Crosby & Nichols, 1863. 1st ed. Frontisport, 305pp. Brn cl. (Bkpl; cvrs lt spotted), else NF. *Chapel Hill*. $200/£125

HAWKINS, WILLIAM. A Treatise of the Pleas of the Crown. London, 1762. 4th ed. 2 vols. 266; 464pp + indexes. (Ink names, tp mtd; hinges cracked, cvrs worn, chipped.) *King*. $195/£122

HAWKS, FRANCIS et al. Revolutionary History of North Carolina. Raleigh, 1853. Pub's cl (soiled; lib bkpl). Howes H326. *Swann**. $161/£101

HAWKS, FRANCIS L. (ed). Narrative of the Expedition of an American Squadron to the China Seas and Japan, Performed in the Years 1852, 1853, and 1854.... NY/London: D. Appleton/Trubner, 1856. 1st trade ed. 8vo. vii,(i)errata,624pp; 10 fldg maps (1 lg). Red pict blindstamped pub's cl, gilt. Fine (sm stain to fore-edge of lg fldg map; 2 sm wormholes upper joint, spine ends sl worn). *Sotheran*. $720/£450

HAWLEY, HENRY. Faberge and His Contemporaries. Cleveland: Museum of Art, (1967). Color frontis, 64 plts (7 color). Fine in dj. *Turtle Island*. $55/£34

HAWLEY, ROYAL DE FOREST. The Hawley Collection of Violins. Chicago: Lyon & Healy, 1904. Ltd to 2000 numbered. (Article pasted to final blank.) Port, 36 plts. Red linen, gray bds (spine sl faded), paper spine label (sl rubbed). *Karmiole*. $350/£219

HAWLEY, W. M. Chinese Folk Design. Hollywood, CA, 1949. 1st Amer ed. NF (water-stained not affecting text) in dj (2 tears, water-stained). *Polyanthos*. $60/£38

HAWORTH, PAUL LELAND. On the Headwaters of the Peace River. NY: Scribner, 1917. 1st ed. 2 maps. Dk grn pict cl. VF. *Bowman*. $185/£116

HAWTHORNE, JULIAN. A Fool of Nature. NY: Scribner, 1896. 1st ed. Dec cl. (Lt marginal dust soiling few ll), o/w Nice. *Reese*. $45/£28

HAWTHORNE, NATHANIEL. The Blithedale Romance. Boston: Ticknor, Reed & Fields, 1852. 1st Amer ed, 1st ptg, w/the word 'Massachusetts' on the c. pg directly across from the phrase 'does not wish' on 1st pg of Preface. 4pp prelim ads dated April 1852. Blind-stamped brn cl. NF (sm worn spot fr joint, spine ends sl worn). *Sumner & Stillman*. $575/£359

HAWTHORNE, NATHANIEL. Complete Works. Boston/NY: Houghton Mifflin, 1886. Riverside ed. 'Thirteenth Edition.' 12 vols. Teg. Sturdy brn cl, red-brn leather spine labels. Good set (sl aged; sl spotted, worn). *Baltimore**. $50/£31

HAWTHORNE, NATHANIEL. Complete Works. Boston: Houghton Mifflin, 1891. Wayside ed. 25 vols. Frontis etching each vol. Marbled eps; teg. 3/4 lt brn polished calf, marbled bds, spines richly gilt, raised bands, dk red leather labels. (Spine heads of 4 or 5 vols lt worn), else Fine set. *Argonaut.* $1,250/£781

HAWTHORNE, NATHANIEL. Doctor Grimshaw's Secret. Julian Hawthorne (ed). Boston: James R. Osgood, 1883. 1st ed. xiii,368pp + 4pp facs ms inserted. Pict cl, gilt. (Spine ends rubbed), else NF. BAL 7642. *Pacific**. $52/£33

HAWTHORNE, NATHANIEL. Doctor Grimshawe's Secret. Julian Hawthorne (ed). Boston: Osgood, 1883. 1st ed, trade issue. Gray cl, gilt. (Sl dknd, spine ends sl frayed), o/w VG. BAL 7642. *Reese.* $100/£63

HAWTHORNE, NATHANIEL. Famous Old People: Being the Second Epoch of Grandfather's Chair. Boston: E.P. Peabody, 1841. 1st ed. (viii),(9)-158, blank. Orig purple P cl, black fr cvr label. VG (lt stained; spine foot sl frayed). BAL 7591. *House.* $180/£113

HAWTHORNE, NATHANIEL. The House of the Seven Gables. Boston, 1851. 1st ed, binding variant B, w/cat preceding tp dated May 1851. (Bkpl, remnants of another on fr pastedown; cl sl skewed.) *Swann**. $460/£288

HAWTHORNE, NATHANIEL. The House of the Seven Gables. LEC, 1935. Ltd to 1500 numbered, signed by Valenti Angelo (illus). Fine in slipcase. *Swann**. $46/£29

HAWTHORNE, NATHANIEL. The Marble Faun. Boston: Ticknor & Fields, 1860. 1st US ed, 1st ptg, w/text ptd in sigs of 8 leaves (although signed as 12pp); 2nd ptg had sigs of 12 leaves. 2 vols. Brn coated eps. Brn blind cl, gilt. Text Good (browned, foxing, lt spotted; cvrs worn, scuffed, ends frayed, chipped, spines sl turned). BAL 7621. *Baltimore**. $70/£44

HAWTHORNE, NATHANIEL. The Marble Faun. Boston: Ticknor & Fields, 1860. 1st ed, 1st ptg w/ads at rear dated March, 1860. 2 vols. 283,16pp ads; 284pp. Slate brn eps. Blind-dec brn cl, gilt. Good+ (spine ends chipped, edges, corners worn). BAL 7621. *House.* $100/£63

HAWTHORNE, NATHANIEL. The Marble Faun. Boston: Ticknor & Fields, 1860. 1st Amer ed, 1st ptg. 2 vols. (2),xi,(p.xii blank),(15)-283; 284pp. Blind-stamped cl, gilt spine. (Sl adhesion residue fr pastedowns from removed bkpls; spine ends chipped, corners sl rubbed)), else VG. BAL 7621. *Pacific**. $109/£68

HAWTHORNE, NATHANIEL. The Marble Faun. Boston: Ticknor & Fields, 1860. 1st ed, 2nd issue. 2 vols. 283 + 16pp pub's cat dated May 1860; 288pp. Blind-stamped brn cl, gilt. VG set. *Young.* $152/£95

HAWTHORNE, NATHANIEL. Mosses from an Old Manse. NY: Wiley & Putnam, 1846. 1st ed, later issue, bound as one. This copy has both imprints (T. B. Smith, Stereotyper, and R. Craighead's Power Press) on verso of 1st tp, and no imprints on verso of 2nd. Last leaf of vol 2 is used as tp for the cat. Both tps incl, 4-pg pub's cat plus add'l tp at rear. Orig blind grn cl, gilt spine lettering. (Sl foxed, browned, pencil squiggles fr blank; cvrs worn, edges frayed, old clear tape repairs to tears along joints, across spine w/loss of bottom inch). Text Good. BAL 7598. *Baltimore**. $80/£50

HAWTHORNE, NATHANIEL. Mosses from an Old Manse. Boston: Ticknor & Fields, 1854. 2nd ed; 1000 ptd. Pub's ads dated Sept 1854 at back of vol 2. 2 vols. Brn blind-stamped cl, gilt. (Sig, some ll spotted; lt rubbed, spines frayed), else VG. BAL 7615. *Cummins.* $100/£63

HAWTHORNE, NATHANIEL. Our Old Home: A Series of English Sketches. Boston: Ticknor & Fields, 1863. 1st ed, 1st state w/p399 imprinted w/an ad. 398pp,(399)ads. Blind-dec brn cl. VG+ (spine ends lt frayed). BAL 7626. *House.* $150/£94

HAWTHORNE, NATHANIEL. Passages from the French and Italian Note-Books. London: Strahan, 1871. 1st ed. 2 vols. Blue cl (spines sl dknd, lt rubbed). BAL 7636. *M & S.* $250/£156

HAWTHORNE, NATHANIEL. The Scarlet Letter. London: Methuen, (1920). 1st ed. Thick 4to. 31 mtd color plts by Hugh Thompson. Teg. Blue cl. Good. *Reisler.* $225/£141

HAWTHORNE, NATHANIEL. The Scarlet Letter. LEC, 1941. Ltd to 1500 numbered, signed by Henry V. Poor (illus). Fine in slipcase. *Swann**. $126/£79

HAWTHORNE, NATHANIEL. The Snow-Image and Other Twice-Told Tales. Boston: Ticknor, Reed & Fields, 1852. 1st ed, 1st issue w/cat dated Jan 1852 inserted at fr. 273pp. Brn cl. (Blindstamp; stain to reps, last 3 leaves; spine ends chipped), o/w VG. BAL 7607. *New Hampshire**. $100/£63

HAWTHORNE, NATHANIEL. Twice-Told Tales. LEC, 1966. Ltd to 1500 numbered, signed by Valenti Angelo (illus). Fine in slipcase. *Swann**. $115/£72

HAWTHORNE, NATHANIEL. A Wonder Book and Tangle-Wood Tales for Boys and Girls. NY, 1910. 1st Parrish ed. 9.5x7.5. 358pp (some pp roughly opened, few missing margin pieces); 10 full-pg color plts w/guards by Maxfield Parrish. Cl, pict label. (Worn, scratched.) *King.* $125/£78

HAWTHORNE, NATHANIEL. A Wonder Book and Tangle-wood Tales. NY: Duffield, 1910. 1st ed. 4to. 10 full-pg color plts by Maxfield Parrish, guards. Dk blue ribbed cl, color paste label. Fine. *Reisler.* $450/£281

HAWTHORNE, NATHANIEL. A Wonder Book for Boys and Girls. Boston: Houghton, Mifflin, 1893. 1st Amer ed. Walter Crane (illus). (Plt detached; spine ends, corners rubbed), else VG. *Pacific**. $46/£29

HAWTHORNE, NATHANIEL. A Wonder Book. NY: George H. Doran, (1922). Lg 8vo. xii,207pp; 24 color plts (16 tipped-in) by Arthur Rackham. Pict eps. Dk orange cl. Good+ (few smudges; faded). *House.* $135/£84

HAWTHORNE, NATHANIEL. A Wonder Book. London: Hodder & Stoughton, (1922). Ltd to 600 signed by Arthur Rackham (illus). 4to. 24 color plts (16 mtd on cream paper). (Inscrip.) Teg. Pict cl, gilt. *Christie's**. $1,013/£633

HAWTHORNE, NATHANIEL. A Wonder-Book for Girls and Boys. Chicago: Rand McNally, (1913). 1st ed illus by Milo Winter. 8vo. 254pp; 8 color plts. Pict eps. Blue cl w/color plt fr cvr. NF in VG color pict dj (lt edgeworn). *House.* $200/£125

HAWTREE, FRED. Colt and Co., Golf Course Architects: A Biographical Study of Henry Shapland Colt, 1869-1951, with His Partners C. H. Alison, J. S. F. Morrison and Dr. A. Mackenzie. Oxford: Cambuc Archive, (1991). 1st ed. One of 1000. Signed. Fine (emb stamps) in dj. *Pacific**. $86/£54

HAY, ANDREW M. A Century of Coconuts. NY, 1972. 1st ed. Ltd to 500 signed. VG. *Larry Price.* $35/£22

HAY, HELEN. Verses for Jock and Joan. NY: Fox, Duffield, 1905. Lg 4to. Charlotte Harding (illus). 6 full-pg color plts. Cl-backed color pict bds (edgeworn). *Reisler.* $300/£188

HAY, IAN. (Pseud of John Hay Beith.) Carrying on—After the First Hundred Thousand. Edinburgh, 1917. 1st ed. VG (no dj). *Typographeum.* $25/£16

HAY, IAN. (Pseud of John Hay Beith.) Carrying On—After the First Hundred Thousand. Edinburgh/London: William Blackwood, 1917. 1st ed. Gray cl, gilt. (Pencil inscrip, sl discolorations lower edges eps), else VG in pict dj (old inner reinforcement). *Reese.* $75/£47

HAY, IAN. (Pseud of John Hay Beith.) The Last Million. London: Hodder & Stoughton, (1919). 1st ed. Pale violet cl stamped in purple. (Ink name, sl foxing), o/w VG in pict dj (lt chipped, edge-creased). *Reese.* $75/£47

HAY, IAN. (Pseud of John Hay Beith.) One Hundred Years of Army Nursing. London: Cassell, (1953). *Petersfield.* $19/£12

HAY, JOHN. Jim Bludsoe of the Prairie Belle, and Little Breeches. Boston, 1871. 1st ed, 1st bk. Ptd orange wrappers (stitching loose, 2 sm stains). BAL 7739. Swann*. $69/£43

HAY, JOHN. The Pike County Ballads. Boston: Houghton Mifflin, (1912). 1st ed. 4to. Color frontis, 6 full-pg color plts. N. C. Wyeth (illus). Tan woven cl, color paste label. VG. Reisler. $225/£141

HAY, O. P. The Fossil Turtles of North America. Washington, 1908. 113 plts (last few tanned; lower corner 1st few pp lt dampstained, pp yellowed, tanned). Wrappers (soiled, chipped, esp rear wrapper, faded; call #s, lib stamp fr wrapper). Sutton. $575/£359

HAY, THOMAS ROBSON. Hood's Tennessee Campaign. NY: Neale, 1929. 1st ed. Complete w/4 maps (2 fldg). Blue cl. (Eps lt foxed; spine ends sl bumped), o/w VG. Chapel Hill. $175/£109

HAYDEN, ARTHUR. Chats on Cottage and Farmhouse Furniture. C. G. E. Bunt (ed). E. Benn, 1950. 2nd rev ed. (Ex-lib, stamps, lacks fep), o/w VG + . Whittle. $16/£10

HAYDEN, F. V. Preliminary Field Report of the United States Geological Survey of Colorado and New Mexico.... Washington, 1869. 155pp. VG (corner fep torn away, next pg taped, no loss to text). Sagebrush. $75/£47

HAYDEN, HORACE H. Geological Essays; or, an Enquiry into Some of the Geological Phenomena to Be Found in Various Parts of America, and Elsewhere. Balt: J. Robinson, 1820. 1st ed. viii,412pp; errata. Full contemp mottled calf (rebacked, edges worn). VG. House. $300/£188

HAYDEN, ROBERT E. Heart-Shape in the Dust. Detroit, (1940). 1st ed, 1st bk. Signed. 9x5.5 inches. 63pp. (Cvrs heavily soiled, sl frayed.) King. $2,500/£1,563

HAYDON, JAMES RYAN. Chicago's True Founder, Thomas J. V. Owen. A Pleading for Truth and Social Justice in Chicago History. Lombard, IL: Privately ptd, (1934). Sponsor's ltd ed. VG. Perier. $35/£22

HAYES, CHARLES W. A Long Journey. The Story of Daniel Hayes. Portland, ME, 1876. 1st ed. One of 100 ptd. 76pp. All edges red. Gilt-stamped cl. (Lib mks, sl worn.) Oinonen*. $60/£38

HAYES, ISAAC I. An Arctic Boat Journey in the Autumn of 1854. Boston: Brown, Taggard & Chase, 1860. xvii, 375pp; 2 fldg maps. Gilt stamped cl (dull, sl worn). Good. High Latitude. $75/£47

HAYES, ISAAC I. An Arctic Boat Journey, in the Autumn of 1854. Boston: Brown, Taggard & Chase, 1860. 1st ed. 2 lg b/w litho fldg maps, xvii,375pp. Brn coated eps. Blind brn cl, gilt. Good (fr hinge lt cracked, lt aged, spotted, maps w/few old misfolds; sl worn, rubbed, sl loss of spine gilt, ends lt frayed). Baltimore*. $80/£50

HAYES, ISAAC I. The Land of Desolation. NY: Harper & Bros, 1872. 21 plts. Dec cl (sl mottled). VG. High Latitude. $70/£44

HAYES, J. GORDON. Antarctica: A Treatise on the Southern Continent. London: Richards, 1928. 1st, only ed. 4 maps in pocket. VG (Spine sl sunned, sm mk at foot). Explorer. $144/£90

HAYES, J. GORDON. The Conquest of the North Pole. NY: Macmillan, 1934. 1st U.S. ed. 3 fldg maps. Fine in dj (chipped, torn). High Latitude. $55/£34

HAYES, J. GORDON. The Conquest of the South Pole. London: Thornton Butterworth, 1932. 1st ed. VG. High Latitude. $60/£38

HAYES, JESS G. Apache Vengeance. Albuquerque: Univ of NM, 1954. 1st ed. VG in dj. Labordo. $55/£34

HAYES, JESS G. Sheriff Thompson's Day. Tucson, 1968. 1st ed. Fine in dj (soiled, price-clipped). Baade. $45/£28

HAYES, JOHN. The Drawings of Thomas Gainsborough. (London, 1970.) 2 vols. Folio. Djs. Swann*. $69/£43

HAYES, JOHN. Gainsborough. Paintings and Drawings. London: Phaidon, 1975. 1st ed. 16 color plts. Dj. Edwards. $40/£25

HAYES, JOHN. The Landscape Paintings of Thomas Gainsborough. Ithaca, (1982). 2 vols. Folio. Djs. Swann*. $92/£58

HAYES, JOHN. Rowlandson. Watercolours and Drawings. London: Phaidon, 1972. 1st ed. Dj. Edwards. $40/£25

HAYES, JOSEPH. The Desperate Hours. NY, 1954. 1st Amer ed. Fine in dj (sm tear fr panel). Polyanthos. $25/£16

HAYES, M. HORACE. Points of the Horse: A Treatise on the Conformation, Movements, Breeds, and Evolution of the Horse. London: Hurst & Blackett, 1904. 3rd ed. Teg. Grn cl, gilt. (First/last few pp foxed), else NF. Pacific*. $98/£61

HAYES, RICHARD. Interest at One View, Calculated to a Farthing.... J. Johnson/G.G.J. & J. Robinson, 1789. 18th ed. 384pp. Orig sheep (hinges broken, but sides held on cords). Cox. $40/£25

HAYES, WILLIAM C. The Burial Chamber of the Treasurer Sobk-Mose from Er Rizeikat. NY: Arno, 1973. Archaeologia. $65/£41

HAYGOOD, TAMARA. Henry William Ravenel, 1814-1887. Tuscaloosa: Univ of AL Press, 1987. 1st ed. Fine in dj. Archer. $17/£11

HAYNE, COE. Race Grit: Adventures on the Border-Land of Liberty. Phila: Judson, (1922). 1st ed. 20 photo plts. Pict cl. (Inscrip.) Petrilla. $75/£47

HAYNES, ALFRED E. Man-Hunting in the Desert. London: Horace Cox, 1894. 1st ed. xxii,305pp; 2 maps (1 fldg), 11 plts (incl frontisport). Blue dec cl (recased, sl rubbed, stained). Sound. Morrell. $208/£130

HAYNES, J. E. Haynes New Guide and Motorist's Complete Road Log of Yellowstone National Park. St. Paul: J.E. Haynes, (1928). 39th ed. Fldg map. Color pict ptd flexible cl wrappers (sl rubbed, spine lightened). Sadlon. $25/£16

HAYNES, JAMES B. History of the Trans-Mississippi and International Exposition of 1898. N.p., 1910. 1st ed. Signed by Gurdon Wattles (pres of the expo). (Few dents, spots rear cvr), o/w Fine. Baade. $250/£156

HAYSTEAD, LADD. If the Prospect Pleases. Norman: Univ of OK, 1941. Good in dj (chipped). Dumont. $40/£25

HAYTER, C. An Introduction to Perspective. London: Kingsbury, (1825). 4th ed. Rev, enlgd. xxiii,300pp; 22 engr plts. Full leather (joints worn, spine labels damaged). Ars Artis. $96/£60

HAYTER, C. An Introduction to Perspective.... London: The Author, 1813. 1st ed. Engr frontis, 168pp; 14 engr plts. New plain wrappers. Ars Artis. $120/£75

HAYWARD, ARTHUR H. Colonial Lighting. Boston: B.J. Brimmer, (1923). 114 photo plts. Teg. Dec blue linen (spine faded). Good in dj (sl chipped). Karmiole. $100/£63

HAYWARD, J. F. Virtuoso Goldsmiths and the Triumph of Mannerism 1540-1620. London: Sotheby Parke Bernet, 1976. 24 color plts hors-texte. (Fr cvr edge nicked), o/w VF in dec color dj. Europa. $96/£60

HAYWOOD, CHARLES. A Bibliography of North American Folklore and Folksong. NY, (1951). One of (1500). NF (sl rubbed). Polyanthos. $60/£38

HAZ, NICHOLAS. Emphasis in Pictures. OH, (1937). 1st Amer ed. NF. Polyanthos. $35/£22

HAZARD, LUCY LOCKWOOD. The Frontier in American Literature. NY: Thomas Y. Crowell, 1927. 1st ed. VG in dj (rubbed, edgeworn). Howes H363. Cahan. $125/£78

HAZARD, SAMUEL. Annals of Pennsylvania, from the Discovery of the Delaware. Phila: Hazard & Mitchell, 1850. 1st ed. viii,664pp. Later cl. (Lib stamps; rebound), else Good. Howes H364. Brown. $35/£22

HAZARD, SAMUEL. Annals of Pennsylvania, from the Discovery of the Delaware. Phila: Hazard & Mitchell, 1850. 1st ed. viii,664pp. Yellow eps. Dk brn blind cl, gilt. (Lt aged; spine ends heavily chipped, sl worn.) Text Clean. Howes H364. *Baltimore**. $80/£50

HAZARD, WILLIS P. How to Select Cows; or the Guenon System Simplified.... Phila: J.M. Stoddart, 1879. 1st ed. 1 orig mtd photo. (Fep detaching), else VG. *Pacific**. $52/£33

HAZEN, ALLEN T. A Catalogue of Horace Walpole's Library. New Haven: Yale Univ, 1969. 1st ed. 3 vols. 12 plts. Dj. *Forest.* $136/£85

HAZLITT, W. C. Bibliographical Collections and Notes on Early English Literature. Reeves & Turner/Bernard Quaritch, 1876-1892. 1st ed. 5 vols. Uncut. *Forest.* $136/£85

HAZLITT, W. C. The Book Collector. London, 1904. 1st ed. Frontis. Grn cl. VG. *Gretton.* $27/£17

HAZLITT, W. C. Collection and Notes 1867-1876. Reeves & Turner, 1876. xi,498pp. VG. *Moss.* $112/£70

HAZLITT, W. C. Old Cookery Books and Ancient Cuisine. Elliot Stock, 1902. (Inner hinges shaken.) *Forest.* $19/£12

HAZLITT, WILLIAM. Characters of Shakespear's Plays. London: Taylor & Hessey, 1818. 2nd ed. W/half-title. Untrimmed. Blue-gray bds (fr bd detached, spine very worn). *Maggs.* $40/£25

HAZLITT, WILLIAM. Conversations of James Northcote, Esq., R.A. London: Henry Colburn & Richard Bentley, 1830. 1st ed. Engr frontis. Contemp 1/2 calf. (Ex-lib, lacks 1/2-title; frontis, tp stained; rebacked, stamps, labels.) *Maggs.* $176/£110

HAZLITT, WILLIAM. Criticisms on Art: And Sketches of the Picture Galleries of England...Edited by His Son. London: John Templeman, 1843. 1st ed. Full red polished calf (joints sl scuffed), gilt, grn leather label. *Maggs.* $120/£75

HAZLITT, WILLIAM. Lectures on the Dramatic Literature of the Age of Elizabeth. John Warren, 1821. 2nd ed. Contemp 1/2 leather over cl, raised bands, leather spine labels. Good (lt spotted; rubbed). *Tiger.* $48/£30

HAZLITT, WILLIAM. Lectures on the Dramatic Literature of the Age of Elizabeth; Delivered at the Surrey Institution. London: John Warren, 1821. 2nd ed. viii,356pp. Contemp 1/2 calf (lacks label, sm crack to top of fr joint), raised bands. *Young.* $64/£40

HAZLITT, WILLIAM. Lectures on the Dramatic Literature of the Age of Elizabeth; Delivered at the Surrey Institution. London: John Warren, 1821. 2nd ed (i.e. 2nd issue). W/half-title. Recent 1/2 calf (ex-lib, stamps, labels). *Maggs.* $80/£50

HAZLITT, WILLIAM. The Life of Napoleon Buonaparte. Second Edition, Revised by His Son. London: Office of the Illustrated London Library, 1852. 2nd ed. 4 vols. Engr frontispieces, engr/ptd tps each vol. VG set in grn emb cl, gilt. *Maggs.* $280/£175

HAZLITT, WILLIAM. Memoirs...with Portions of His Correspondence. William Carew Hazlitt (ed). London: Richard Bentley, 1867. 1st ed. 2 vols. Engr frontisport each vol, 1 other port vol 2; w/half-titles. Teg, by Zaehnsdorf. VG set in 1/2 dk blue morocco, gilt, marbled sides. *Maggs.* $240/£150

HAZLITT, WILLIAM. Notes of a Journey Through France and Italy. London: Hunt & Clarke, 1826. 1st ed, 2nd issue w/Hazlitt's name stamped on tp. 8vo. Engr frontis added. Uncut. Orig drab bds, grn cl spine, ptd paper label largely intact. *Maggs.* $520/£325

HAZLITT, WILLIAM. A Reply to Z. London: First Edition Club, 1923. One of 300. Teg. Buckram. VG (name plt, feps browned; spine sl faded, foot sl bumped). *Ulysses.* $58/£36

HAZLITT, WILLIAM. Table-Talk. London: Henry Colburn, 1824. 2 vols. 400; 401pp. Marbled eps; teg, silk ribbon markers. 3/4 black pebbled morocco, raised bands, gilt, marbled bds. Fine set. *Hartfield.* $295/£184

HAZLITT, WILLIAM. Table-Talk: Original Essays on Men and Manners. Edited by His Son. London: C. Templeman, 1845. 3rd ed. 2 vols. Teg, by Zaehnsdorf. VG in recent 1/2 dk blue crushed morocco, gilt, marbled sides. *Maggs.* $88/£55

HAZZARD, SHIRLEY. Cliffs of Fall and Other Stories. NY: Knopf, 1963. 1st Amer ed. NF in dj (price-clipped, sm chip, tear). *Hermitage.* $60/£38

HEAD, BARCLAY V. A Guide to the Principal Coins of the Greeks. British Museum, 1932. New ed. 50 plts. VF (ex-lib, label, 2 blind-stamps). *Hollett.* $64/£40

HEAD, F. B. Rough Notes Taken During Some Rapid Journeys Across the Pampas. John Murray, 1826. 2nd ed. xi,309pp (some ll badly creased). Old diced 1/2 morocco (worn, spine sl defective, repaired), gilt. *Hollett.* $192/£120

HEAL, AMBROSE. The London Furniture Makers...1660-1840. London, (1953). Dj. *Swann**. $92/£58

HEAL, AMBROSE. London Tradesmen's Cards of the XVIIIth Century. Batsford, 1925. Ltd to 950. 102 plts. Holland-backed marbled bds, gilt. (Stamp; lower edges sl rubbed.) *Hollett.* $192/£120

HEAL, AMBROSE. London Tradesmen's Cards. NY: Scribner, 1925. Frontis, 101 plts. Djs. *Marlborough.* $144/£90

HEALEY, B. J. The Plant Hunters. NY: Scribner, 1975. 1st ed. Good (bumped) in VG dj. *Archer.* $30/£19

HEALY and BIGELOW. Life Among the Indians. N.p.: Kickapoo Indian Agency, (c.1900). VG- in pict color wrappers (spine chipped, tear to fr wrapper w/old tape to verso). *Pacific**. $98/£61

HEALY, MICHAEL A. Report of the Cruise of the Revenue Marine Steamer Corwin in the Arctic Ocean in the Year 1885. Washington: GPO, 1887. 102pp; 4 color plts, 2 lg fldg maps. Clean (worn). *Explorer.* $128/£80

HEANEY, SEAMUS. After Summer. (Old Deerfield/Dublin): Deerfield Press/Gallery Press, (1978). 1st ed. One of 250 ptd. Signed. NF in dj (sm tears upper extrems). *Pacific**. $207/£129

HEANEY, SEAMUS. Among Schoolchildren. Belfast: Queen's Univ, 1983. 1st ed. Fine in stapled wrappers. *Between The Covers.* $85/£53

HEANEY, SEAMUS. Death of a Naturalist. London: Faber & Faber, (1966). 1st ed, 1st bk. Signed. (Upper extrems sl shelfworn), else VG. *Pacific**. $489/£306

HEANEY, SEAMUS. Door into the Dark. London: Faber & Faber, (1969). 1st ed. Fine (name) in Fine dj. *Dermont.* $200/£125

HEANEY, SEAMUS. Door into the Dark. London: Faber & Faber, 1969. 1st ed. Fine in NF dj (price-clipped). *Lame Duck.* $175/£109

HEANEY, SEAMUS. Dylan the Durable? On Dylan Thomas. (USA): Bennington College, 1992. One of 1000 numbered. Fine in wraps as issued. *Williams.* $40/£25

HEANEY, SEAMUS. Eleven Poems. Belfast: Festival Pub, n.d. (1965). 1st ed, 1st bk, 1st issue, ptd on laid paper, w/cvr device ptd in purple. VG (cvrs sl mkd, creased, dusty, spine sl browned). *Ulysses.* $1,200/£750

HEANEY, SEAMUS. Field Work. London: Faber & Faber, 1979. 1st ed. NF in stiff illus wraps. *Lame Duck.* $35/£22

HEANEY, SEAMUS. Field Work. London: Faber & Faber, 1979. 1st ed. Fine in dj. *Lame Duck.* $100/£63

HEANEY, SEAMUS. From the Republic of Conscience. Dublin: Amnesty Internat'l, 1985. 1st ed. New in pale grey stapled wrappers. *Dermont.* $35/£22

HEANEY, SEAMUS. Hailstones. Dublin: Gallery, 1984. One of 500 in wrappers signed. VG (top edge contents pg sl creased) in dj (top edge sl creased). *Ulysses.* $120/£75

HEANEY, SEAMUS. The Haw Lantern. London: Faber & Faber, (1987). 1st ed. Fine in Fine dj. *Dermont.* $35/£22

HEANEY, SEAMUS. A Lough Neagh Sequence. Manchester: Phoenix Pamphlet Poets Press, 1969. 1st ed. One of 950 (of 1000). Fine in ptd stiff glazed white stapled wrappers. *Blackwell's.* $160/£100

HEANEY, SEAMUS. North. Faber, 1975. 1st ed. Pale blue cl, gilt. Fine (eps browned) in dj (backstrip panel faded). *Blackwell's.* $160/£100

HEANEY, SEAMUS. North. NY: OUP, 1975. 1st US ed. (Extrems shelfworn), else NF in VG+ dj (spine faded, sm internal tear). *Lame Duck.* $200/£125

HEANEY, SEAMUS. Place and Displacement: Recent Poetry of Northern Ireland. (Cumbria): Dove Cottage, (1985). 1st ed. Fine (last pg sl creased) in stapled wrappers in dj. *Between The Covers.* $85/£53

HEANEY, SEAMUS. Poems and a Memoir. LEC, 1982. One of 2000 signed by Henry Pearson (illus) and Thomas Flanagan (intro). Fine in slipcase. *Swann*.* $258/£161

HEANEY, SEAMUS. Preoccupations. NY, 1980. 1st Amer ed. Signed proof copy. Ptd wrappers. *Swann*.* $201/£126

HEANEY, SEAMUS. The Redress of Poetry. Oxford: Clarendon, 1990. 1st ed. Fine in blue ptd wrappers. *Dermont.* $25/£16

HEANEY, SEAMUS. Robert Lowell, a Memorial Address and an Elegy. London/Boston: Faber & Faber, 1978. 1st ed. Sewn as issued in gray wrappers (spine sl faded). Fine. *Maggs.* $480/£300

HEANEY, SEAMUS. Seeing Things. Faber, 1991. One of 250 signed. Fine in slipcase. *Williams.* $176/£110

HEANEY, SEAMUS. Sweeney Astray. NY: FSC, (1984). 1st Amer ed. One of 350 numbered, signed. *Between The Covers.* $250/£156

HEANEY, SEAMUS. Sweeney Astray. Derry: A Field Day Publication, 1983. 1st ed. Fine in Fine dj. *Dermont.* $100/£63

HEAP, GWINN HARRIS. Central Route to the Pacific, from the Valley of the Mississippi to California. Phila: Lippincott, Grambo, 1854. 1st ed. Color frontis, 136pp + 46pp ads; 12 plts. Brn emb cl. (Lt stained, professionally rebacked w/orig spine laid down, cvr lt soiled, corners worn.) Howes H378. *Parmer.* $350/£219

HEARN, LAFCADIO. Barbarous Barbers and Other Stories. Ichiro Nishizaki (ed). (Tokyo): Hokuseido, (1939). Ltd to 250 (as indicated on tipped-on colophon, rep). Grn cl. (Lt tape stains fep; owner chop mk below colophon in tp.) Dj. BAL 8039. *Karmiole.* $100/£63

HEARN, LAFCADIO. Buying Christmas Toys and Other Essays. Ichiro Nishizaki (ed). (Tokyo): Hokuseido, (1939). Ltd to 180 (as indicated on tipped-in colophon, rep). Grn cl. Good in dj (sm inkstain top margin fr panel). BAL 8040. *Karmiole.* $100/£63

HEARN, LAFCADIO. Chita: A Memory of Last Island. NY, 1889. 1st ed. Dec stamped salmon cl (sl skewed). BAL 7918. *Swann*.* $345/£216

HEARN, LAFCADIO. Exotics and Retrospectives. Boston, 1898. 1st ed. Pict cl (spine rubbed; fr hinge cracked, but sound). *Swann*.* $201/£126

HEARN, LAFCADIO. Fantastics and Other Fancies. Boston, (1914). 1st Amer ed. NF (rubbed, spine sunned). *Polyanthos.* $45/£28

HEARN, LAFCADIO. Gleanings in Buddha-Fields. Boston, 1897. 1st ed. Gilt-dec blue cl. (Bkpl.) BAL 7929. *Swann*.* $230/£144

HEARN, LAFCADIO. Glimpses of Unfamiliar Japan. Boston, 1894. 1st ed. 2 vols. Pict silver-stamped black cl. (Lacks blank following ep vol 2.) BAL 7926. *Swann*.* $316/£198

HEARN, LAFCADIO. Glimpses of Unfamiliar Japan. Cambridge/Boston/NY: CUP/Houghton Mifflin, 1900. New ed. 2 vols. Dk blue dec cl, silvered. VF set (removed bkpl traces). *Sotheran.* $256/£160

HEARN, LAFCADIO. Gombo Zhebes. NY: Will H. Coleman, 1885. 1st ed. Grn cl, gilt/silver. VG (feps lt stained, rear pastedown bubbling; spine sl dknd, extrems lt rubbed). BAL 7914. *Heritage.* $500/£313

HEARN, LAFCADIO. In Ghostly Japan. Boston, 1899. 1st ed. Pict blue cl (lt rubbed, spine sl dknd). BAL 7934. *Swann*.* $201/£126

HEARN, LAFCADIO. Insects and Greek Poetry. NY: William Edwin Rudge, 1926. 1st ed. Ltd to 550. Blue bds, gilt. (Spine sl sunned), o/w Fine. BAL 7995. *Heritage.* $150/£94

HEARN, LAFCADIO. Japan. An Attempt at Interpretation. NY, 1904. 1st Amer ed. Color frontis. Dec cvrs, gilt. Fine (rear cvr sl bubbled; spine sl sunned). *Polyanthos.* $150/£94

HEARN, LAFCADIO. Japan. An Attempt at Interpretation. NY, 1904. 1st ed. Gilt-pict brn cl. (Contemp inscrip.) BAL 7941. *Swann*.* $201/£126

HEARN, LAFCADIO. A Japanese Miscellany. Boston, 1901. 1st issue. Teg, uncut. Pict cvrs, gilt. Fine (spine sl sunned). *Polyanthos.* $100/£63

HEARN, LAFCADIO. A Japanese Miscellany. Boston, 1901. 1st ed. Pict grn cl. BAL 7936. *Swann*.* $258/£161

HEARN, LAFCADIO. Kokoro, Hints and Echoes of Japanese Life. Boston, 1896. 1st ed. Grn cl (spine lt faded, tips rubbed). BAL 7928. *Swann*.* $201/£126

HEARN, LAFCADIO. Kotto. NY, 1902. 1st ed, 1st state. Gilt-pict olive grn cl. (Bkpl.) BAL 7938. *Swann*.* $258/£161

HEARN, LAFCADIO. Kwaidan. (NY/Tokyo: LEC, 1932.) One of 1500 numbered, signed by Fujita (illus). Sm 4to. Silk string-tied Japanese style silk-cvrd bds. Glassine dj, wrap-around rough silk folder. *Swann*.* $575/£359

HEARN, LAFCADIO. Kwaidan. Stories and Studies of Strange Things. Boston, 1904. 1st ed. Pict dk grn cl. BAL 7940. *Swann*.* $201/£126

HEARN, LAFCADIO. Lectures on Tennyson. Shigetsugu Kishi (ed). Tokyo: Hokuseido, (1941). Ltd to 500 (stated on colophon). Brn cl, paper labels. (Text foxed, sig, traces of tape removal feps.) BAL 8045. *Karmiole.* $75/£47

HEARN, LAFCADIO. Letters to a Pagan. Detroit, 1933. 1st ed. One of 550 numbered. Frontis port. 1/4 gilt cl. Dj, slipcase (crack at rear). *Swann*.* $258/£161

HEARN, LAFCADIO. Literary Essays. Ichiro Nishizaki (ed). (Tokyo): Hokuseido, (1939). 1st ed. Grn cl. Good in dj. BAL 8041. *Karmiole.* $100/£63

HEARN, LAFCADIO. The New Radiance and Other Scientific Sketches. Ichiro Nishizaki (ed). (Tokyo): Hokuseido, (1939). 1st ed. Grn cl, gilt. Good in dj (ink stain fr cvr). BAL 8042. *Karmiole.* $100/£63

HEARN, LAFCADIO. Out of the East. Boston, 1895. 1st Amer ed. Fine (sl soiled, spine sunned). *Polyanthos.* $125/£78

HEARN, LAFCADIO. The Romance of the Milky Way and Other Stories. Boston/NY: Houghton Mifflin, (1905). Apparent early ed, w/o extended spine ornamentation of 1st ed. Dk grn cl. VG (eps lt browned; spine extrems rubbed). *Heritage.* $75/£47

HEARN, LAFCADIO. The Romance of the Milky Way and Other Stories. Boston/NY, 1905. Partly unopened. *Edwards.* $64/£40

HEARN, LAFCADIO. The Romance of the Milky Way and Other Studies and Stories. Boston, 1905. 1st ed. (Spine extrems sl rubbed.) BAL 7943. *Swann*.* $161/£101

HEARN, LAFCADIO. Shadowings. Boston, 1900. 1st ed. Pict blue cl. (Bkpl, contemp inscrip.) BAL 7935. *Swann*.* $258/£161

HEARN, LAFCADIO. Some Chinese Ghosts. Boston: Roberts Bros, 1887. 1st ed. (4),185pp. Maple-leaf patterned eps. Dec mustard cl. (Names, sl offset to pp60-63), else VG in dj (spine ends sl chipped). *Pacific*.* $115/£72

HEARN, LAFCADIO. Some Chinese Ghosts. Boston, 1887. 1st ed. Pict red cl (lt rubbed; contemp sig). BAL 7916. *Swann**. $345/£216

HEARN, LAFCADIO. Some New Letters and Writings of Lafcadio Hearn. Sanki Ichikawa (ed). Tokyo, 1925. 1st ed. Ptd label. (2 copies of errata slip inserted at rear; sl discolored.) BAL 7992. *Swann**. $258/£161

HEARN, LAFCADIO. Stray Leaves from Strange Literature. Boston, 1884. 1st ed, 1st bk. Mustard yellow cl. (1/2-inch unobtrusive dampstain upper rt margin, not affecting text.) BAL 7912. *Swann**. $460/£288

HEARN, LAFCADIO. Two Years in the West Indies. NY, 1890. 1st ed. Gilt-pict grn cl (lt rubbed; bkpl). BAL 7920. *Swann**. $258/£161

HEARN, LAFCADIO. The Writings.... Boston: Houghton Mifflin, 1922. Lg paper ed. One of 750 numbered sets. 16 vols. 8vo. Orig parchment-backed silk bds, gilt. Fine set in djs. *Heritage*. $3,000/£1,875

HEARNE, LAFCADIO. The Romance of the Milky Way. Boston/NY: Houghton Mifflin, 1905. 1st ed. VG (spine lt soiled). BAL 7943. *Second Life*. $85/£53

HEARNE, LAFCADIO. The Romance of the Milky Way. Boston/NY: Houghton Mifflin, 1905. 1st ed. VF in dj (chipped, dust-stained, lacks 1-inch piece fr cvr, 1/2 inch piece from spine). BAL 7943. *Second Life*. $300/£188

HEARSAY, JOHN E. N. Bridge: Church and Palace in Old London. Murray, 1961. NF in dj. *Hadley*. $32/£20

HEARTMAN, CHARLES F. The New England Primer Issued Prior to 1830. NY, 1934. Ltd to 300. Uncut. Fine. *Polyanthos*. $50/£31

HEATH ROBINSON, W. Bill the Minder. NY: Holt, 1912. 1st US ed. 16 Fine mtd color plts, tissue guards. Grn cl, gilt, lg color illus mtd on fr cvr. (Fr hinge lt cracked, ink inscrip; spine sl rubbed.) *Baltimore**. $110/£69

HEATH ROBINSON, W. Bill the Minder. NY: Henry Holt, 1912. 1st Amer ed. 4to. 16 full-pg mtd color plts. Grn cl, gilt, color paste label. VG in pict dj (worn, chipped). *Reisler*. $1,250/£781

HEATH, CHRISTOPHER. A Manual of Minor Surgery and Bandaging for House-Surgeons, Dressers, and Junior Practitioners. J. & A. Churchill, 1883. 7th ed. xv,344pp + 16pg pub's cat dated April 1884. Maroon cl (spine faded, sl worn, cl on joints partly slit). *Bickersteth*. $88/£55

HEATH, E. G. The Grey Goose Wing. Greenwich, CT, (1972). 1st Amer ed. 22 color plts. (Corner bumped, edge sl frayed), else Good in dj (price-clipped, worn, sl tear). *King*. $95/£59

HEATH, THOMAS. Aristarchus of Samos, the Ancient Copernicus. Oxford: Clarendon, 1913. 1st Eng ed. Navy blue cl. Fine. *Weber*. $400/£250

HEATH, THOMAS. Mathematics in Aristotle. Oxford: Clarendon, 1949. Fine in dj. *Weber*. $125/£78

HEATHCOTE, J. M. et al. Tennis. Longmans, Green, 1890. 1st ed. xiv,484pp. Pict cl, gilt. Good (sl shaken, spotted, browned, lt worn, sm label fr cvr). *Ash*. $200/£125

HEATHERINGTON, A. A Practical Guide. Montreal: John Lovell, 1868. iv,179pp; 2 lg fldg charts. (Lacks geologic section, sl dampstained, insect damage to joints, rear hinge.) *Blake*. $85/£53

HEATON, MRS. CHARLES. The Life of Albrecht Durer of Nurnberg. London: Seeley, Jackson & Halliday, 1881. xv,373pp; port. (Ex-libris, stamp; extrems sl rubbed.) *Hollett*. $40/£25

HEBARD, GRACE RAYMOND and E. A. BRININSTOOL. The Bozeman Trail. Cleveland: A.H. Clark, 1922. 1st ed. 2 vols. Red cl. Fine set. Howes H382. *Labordo*. $550/£344

HEBARD, GRACE RAYMOND and E. A. BRININSTOOL. The Bozeman Trail. Glendale: A.H. Clark, 1960. 2nd ed. 1 vol. Blue cl. NF. *Labordo*. $185/£116

HEBARD, GRACE RAYMOND. The Pathbreakers from River to Ocean. Chicago: Lakeside, 1911. Inscribed. (Extrems sl worn.) Internally Good. *Dumont*. $45/£28

HEBARD, GRACE RAYMOND. Sacajawea. Glendale: A.H. Clark, 1957. One of 502 ptd. Fine. *Perier*. $125/£78

HEBER-PERCY, ALGERNON. Moab, Ammon, and Gilead. Market Drayton: Bennion, Horne, Smallman et al, 1896. 1st ed. vii,(i)list,101,(1)imprint; fldg map, 18 half-tone plts. Maroon cl, gilt (sl rubbed). Fine. *Morrell*. $184/£115

HEBERT, JOHN R. Panoramic Maps of Anglo-American Cities. Washington, 1974. VG in wraps. *Dumont*. $20/£13

HECHT, BEN. Erik Dorn. NY: Putnam/Knickerbocker, 1921. 1st ed. Yellow-grn cl. VG (few sl internal faults; cvrs sl worn). *Temple*. $32/£20

HECHT, BEN. The Sensualists. NY: Messner, (1959). 1st ed. VF in VF dj (sl rubbed). *Between The Covers*. $100/£63

HECK, EARL L. W. Augustine Herrman, Beginner of the Virginia Tobacco Trade.... Englewood, OH, 1941. VG. *Book Broker*. $25/£16

HECKLE, A. The Lady's Drawing Book and Complete Florist. London: Carington Bowles, 1764. Obl 4to. 24 plts (23 hand-colored). Old marbled paper-cvrd wraps. (Lt foxed, pp curled; loss at corners.) *Metropolitan**. $1,725/£1,078

HECKMAN, MARLIN L. Overland on the California Trail, 1846-1859. Glendale: Arthur Clark, 1984. 1st ed. Ltd to 500. Fine. *Book Market*. $125/£78

HECKMAN, WILLIAM L. Steamboating Sixty-Five Years on Missouri's Rivers. Kansas City: Burton, 1950. Gray pict cl. VG. *American Booksellers*. $55/£34

HEDDERWICK, PETER. A Treatise on Marine Architecture, Containing the Theory and Practice of Shipbuilding. Edinburgh: The Author, 1830. 2 vols. 4to. 28 engr plts, 1 engr recto verso. Contemp 1/2 calf. (Spotted, stained; rubbed.) *Sotheby's**. $626/£391

HEDGPETH, DON. Cowboy Artist: The Joe Beeler Story. Flagstaff, (1979). Morocco. Slipcase (rubbed). *Swann**. $80/£50

HEDGPETH, DON. Cowboy Artist; the Joe Beeler Story. Flagstaff, 1979. 1st ed. (Inscrip), else NF in dj. *Dumont*. $55/£34

HEDIGER, H. Studies of the Psychology and Behavior of Captive Animals in Zoos and Circuses. London: Butterworths, 1955. 1st ed. (Ex-lib, pocket, stamps, sm spine dot; sl pencilling), o/w Fine. *Beasley*. $40/£25

HEDIN, SVEN. A Conquest of Tibet. NY: Nat'l Travel Club, 1934. 1st ed. (Sl rubbed), o/w VG. *Worldwide*. $35/£22

HEDIN, SVEN. The Flight of Big Horse. NY: Dutton, 1936. 1st ed. 124 plts. (Sl rubbed, unevenly faded, sl soiled), o/w VG. *Worldwide*. $55/£34

HEDIN, SVEN. Through Asia. NY/London: Harper, 1899. 1st ed. 2 vols. xviii,649; xii,650-1255pp; 2 fldg maps. Teg. Lib buckram. VG (ex-lib). *Worldwide*. $145/£91

HEDREN, PAUL L. First Scalp for Custer. Glendale: A.H. Clark, 1980. One of 350. 2 maps. Buckram, gilt. *Dawson*. $100/£63

HEDRICK, U. P. A History of Horticulture in America to 1860. Portland: Timber Press, (1988). Fine in Fine dj. *Book Market*. $75/£47

Heedless Harry's Day of Disasters. London: Darton, n.d. (ca 1850). Sm 4to. 15pp. Full-pg wood-engr frontis, pict stiff paper self-wrappers. (Wrapper edges sl dknd), else VF. *Hobbyhorse*. $300/£188

HEGEMAN, ELIZABETH COMPTON. Navaho Trading Days. Univ of NM, (1963). 1st ed. VG + in dj. *Truepenny*. $95/£59

HEGGEN, THOMAS and JOSHUA LOGAN. Mister Roberts. NY: Random House, (1948). 1st ed. blue cl, gilt spine. (Spine cocked), o/w NF in dj (lt chipped, spine sl browned). *Heritage*. $125/£78

HEIB, DAVID L. Fort Laramie. Washington, 1961. Rpt. Fine in pict wraps. *Pratt.* $7/£4

HEIB, LOU. Collecting Tony Hillerman. Santa Fe, 1992. One of 200 numbered. Fine in wraps. *Dumont.* $35/£22

HEILBRON, W. C. Convict Life at the Minnesota State Prison. St. Paul, MN: W.C. Heilbron, 1909. 2nd ptg. Good+ in wrappers (worn, chipped). *Labordo.* $45/£28

HEILNER, VAN CAMPEN and FRANK STICK. The Call of the Surf. NY: Doubleday, Page, 1920. 1st ed, 1st bk. Color frontis. Blue cl. VG. *Biscotti.* $65/£41

HEILNER, VAN CAMPEN. A Book on Duck Shooting. NY: Knopf, 1943. 5th ptg. 16 color plts. Red cl. Fine in pict color dj (chipped). *Biscotti.* $125/£78

HEILPRIN, A. The Tower of Pelee. Phila: Lippincott, c1904. 3/4 cl over bds. Good. *Blake.* $125/£78

HEIN, O. L. Memories of Long Ago By an Old Army Officer. NY: Putnam, 1925. 1st ed. VG. *Lien.* $85/£53

HEINE, HEINRICH. The North Sea and Other Poems. William Stirling (trans). (London): Allan Wingate, (1947). 1st ed thus. One of 70 ptd. Black cl, gilt-lettered spine. (Spine head sl bumped), else VG. *Pacific*.* $75/£47

HEINE, HEINRICH. Poems of Heinrich Heine. LEC, 1957. Ltd to 1500 numbered, signed by Fritz Kredel (illus). Fine in slipcase. *Swann*.* $80/£50

HEINLEIN, ROBERT. Assignment in Eternity. PA: Fantasy, 1953. 1st ed. Fine in Fine 1st binding dj. *Warren.* $250/£156

HEINLEIN, ROBERT. Between Planets. NY: Scribner, 1951. 1st ed. NF in dj (rubbed). *Pacific*.* $207/£129

HEINLEIN, ROBERT. Farmer in the Sky. NY: Scribner, 1950. 1st ed. (Cl faded), else VG in VG dj (spine head rubbed). *Pacific*.* $161/£101

HEINLEIN, ROBERT. The Green Hills of Earth. Chicago: Shasta, (1951). 1st ed. Dj (sl chipped). *Kane*.* $190/£119

HEINLEIN, ROBERT. Have Space Suit—Will Travel. NY: Scribner, (1958). 1st ed. VG in dj (sl chipped, 2.5-inch tear to fr panel w/tape to verso sl showing through). *Pacific*.* $196/£123

HEINLEIN, ROBERT. Methuselah's Children. Hicksville: Gnome, (1958). 1st ed. (Pp browned; few spot-stains to fore-edge), else VG+ in dj (worn, torn, browned, spine ends lt chipped). *Other Worlds.* $100/£63

HEINLEIN, ROBERT. Rocket Ship Galileo. NY: Scribner, (1947). 1st ed, 1st bk. VG in dj (spine ends sl rubbed, 1.75-inch tear rear joint, crease rear panel). *Pacific*.* $489/£306

HEINLEIN, ROBERT. Rocket Ship Galileo. Scribner, 1947. 1st ed. Fine in VG+ dj (spine extrems sl worn). *Fine Books.* $500/£313

HEINLEIN, ROBERT. The Star Beast. NY: Scribner, (1954). 1st ed. NF in dj (smudge ink # to spine). *Pacific*.* $173/£108

HEINLEIN, ROBERT. Starman Jones. NY: Scribner, (1953). 1st ed. VG- in dj (chipped, lacks spine head piece, rear extrem sunned, rear panel discolored). *Pacific*.* $173/£108

HEINLEIN, ROBERT. To Sail Beyond the Sunset. NY: Ace/Putnam, (1987). 1st ed. NF in dj (few sm tears). *Antic Hay.* $25/£16

HEINS, HENRY HARDY. A Golden Anniversary Bibliography of Edgar Rice Burroughs. West Kingston: Grant, 1964. Complete ed. One of 1000. Fine in dj (lt soiled, sunned). *Pacific*.* $288/£180

HEISER, CHARLES B. The Sunflower. Univ of OK, 1976. 1st ed. 8 color plts. VG in dj. *Larry Price.* $28/£18

HEISTER, LAURENCE. A General System of Surgery, in Three Parts. J. Whiston, L. Davis, C. Reymers, 1768. 8th ed, rev. 2 vols in 1. 4to. xvi,456; (ii),414pp (sl spotted, lt browned, 2 early ink sigs, 1 dated 1778); 40 fldg engr plts (few w/sm slit in fold). Orig plain calf (rubbed, recased w/new old-style eps), orig sm morocco spine label. *Bickersteth.* $1,096/£685

HEITMAN, FRANCIS B. Historical Register and Dictionary of the United States Army, 1789-1903. Washington: Congress, 1903. 2 vols. (Silverfished; tips bumped, vol 1 lacks fep.) *Dawson.* $200/£125

HEITZMANN, C. Microscopical Morphology of the Animal Body in Health and Disease. NY, 1883. 1st ed. Signed presentation. 849pp. Grn pebbled cl. Good (inner hinges starting; extrems worn). *Doctor's Library.* $100/£63

HEIZER, ROBERT F. Francis Drake and the California Indians, 1579. Berkeley: Univ of CA, 1947. 1st ed. Frontis, 5 plts. Grn cl. Fine in dj (lt worn). *Argonaut.* $45/£28

HELD, JULIUS S. The Oil Sketches of Peter Paul Rubens. A Critical Catalogue. Princeton Univ, 1980. 2 vols. 71; 528 plts (24 color). Good in dj (sl torn). *Ars Artis.* $226/£141

HELD, R. BURNELL and M. CLAWSON. Soil Conservation in Perspective. Johns Hopkins, 1965. (Ex-private lib), else VG. *Larry Price.* $19/£12

HELFERICH, H. On Fractures and Dislocations. NY, 1899. 3rd ed. 130pp; 68 full-pg color plts. Good (ex-lib, inner hinges cracked; worn). *Doctor's Library.* $75/£47

Hell for Leather. NY: Derrydale, 1928. One of 350 numbered. 3 engrs. (Spine sl discolored.) *Woolson.* $225/£141

HELLER, JOSEPH. Catch-22. London, (1962). 1st Eng ed. Dj (price-clipped). *Swann*.* $103/£64

HELLER, JOSEPH. Catch-22. London: Jonathan Cape, (1962). 1st British ed. Cerise bds (sl shelfworn), gilt. Clean in dj (dusty, edgeworn, spine lt sunned). *Baltimore*.* $120/£75

HELLER, JOSEPH. Catch-22. NY: S&S, 1961. 1st ed. VG in VG dj (worn). *Unger.* $375/£234

HELLER, JOSEPH. Catch-22. NY, 1961. 1st ed, 1st bk. Dj (sl crimp spine top). *Swann*.* $431/£269

HELLER, JOSEPH. Closing Time. NY: S&S, 1994. 1st ed. Fine in Fine dj. *Unger.* $30/£19

HELLER, JOSEPH. God Knows. NY: Knopf, 1984. 1st ed. Fine in Fine dj. *Unger.* $30/£19

HELLER, JOSEPH. God Knows. NY, 1984. 1st ed. One of 350 numbered, signed. Dj, slipcase. *Swann*.* $57/£36

HELLER, JOSEPH. Good as Gold. NY, (1979). 1st ed. One of 500 numbered, signed. Slipcase. *Swann*.* $57/£36

HELLER, JOSEPH. Good as Gold. NY: S&S, 1976. 1st ed. Fine in Fine dj. *Unger.* $30/£19

HELLER, JOSEPH. We Bombed in New Haven. Cape, 1969. 1st UK ed. VG (cvrs sl mkd) in dj (sl browned, mkd). *Williams.* $58/£36

HELLER, NANCY G. Women Artists. London: Abbeville, 1991. Rev, expanded ed. Color pict limp bds. *Edwards.* $24/£15

HELLMAN, LILLIAN. Three. Boston, (1979). 1st ed. One of 500 numbered, signed. Slipcase. *Swann*.* $115/£72

HELLMAN, LILLIAN. Watch on the Rhine. NY: Privately pub, 1942. 1st deluxe ptg. Ltd to 349. NF in slipcase (battered). *Reese.* $225/£141

HELLYER, ARTHUR. Gardens of Genius. Hamlyn, 1980. VG in dj. *Hadley.* $32/£20

HELM, CLEMENTINE. Cecily (Elf Goldhair). Elisabeth P. Stork (trans). Phila: Lippincott, (1924). 1st ed. 9.25x7. Gertrude A. Kay (illus). Maroon cl, gilt, pict cvr label. Fine in NF dj (soiled, sm repairs to verso). *Pacific*.* $63/£39

HELM, ERNIE. Kill the Ump. (As told by Dusty Boggess.) Lone Star Brewing, 1966. Orig trade pb ed. VG. *Plapinger.* $50/£31

HELM, H. T. American Roadsters and Trotting Horses. Chicago, 1878. 13 photo-engr plts on coated paper, 2 wood-engr plts. Mod 1/2 red morocco. *Swann*.* $172/£108

HELM, H. T. American Roadsters and Trotting Horses. Chicago, 1878. 1st ed. 552pp. (Name label, extrems worn.) *King.* $200/£125

HELM, MYRA SAGER. Lorinda Bewley and the Whitman Massacre. Portland: Metropolitan, (1951). VG in dj (worn). *Perier.* $17/£11

HELME, ELEANOR. Suitable Owners. Eyre & Spottiswoode, 1948. 1st ed. Lg 8vo. 126pp; 4 mono plts by Lionel Edwards. (Spine foot sl faded), else VG + in pict dj (repaired). *Bookmark.* $32/£20

HELMS, ANTHONY Z. Travels from Buenos Ayres, by Potosi, to Lima. London: Richard Phillips, 1807. 2nd ed. xii,292pp (lt foxed); fldg map. Mod tan cl, black label. *Adelson.* $325/£203

HELPER, HINTON R. Dreadful California.... Lucius Beebe and Charles M. Clegg (eds). Indianapolis, (1948). VG in VG dj. *Sagebrush.* $15/£9

HELPER, HINTON R. The Land of Gold. Balt: Henry Taylor, 1855. 1st ed. 300pp. Blind-stamped cl. (Lacks fep, rear blank excised; tips, edges worn.) *Dawson.* $150/£94

HELPER, HINTON R. Nojoque: A Question for a Continent. NY: George W. Carleton, 1867. 1st ed. 479pp. Purple cl. VG (bkpl, sig; spine top frayed, corners worn). *Chapel Hill.* $200/£125

HELTZEL, VIRGIL B. A Check List of Courtesy Books in the Newberry Library. Chicago: Newberry Library, 1942. One of 600 ptd. VG + . *Zubal*.* $26/£16

HEMBROW, VICTOR. The Model Theatre. London/NY: The Studio, 1934. VG in dec stiff wraps. *Dramatis.* $18/£11

HEMENWAY, CHARLES W. Memoirs of My Day in and out of Mormondon. Salt Lake City: (Deseret News Co), 1889. 1st ed. Wood-engr frontisport, ix,265pp. (Rubberstamp fr pastedown, inked-out name, hinges cracked at eps; cvrs rubbed, else Good. *Pacific*.* $81/£51

HEMINGWAY, ERNEST. Across the River and into the Trees. London, (1950). 1st Eng ed. (Cl sl skewed.) Dj (spine extrems lt rubbed). *Swann*.* $103/£64

HEMINGWAY, ERNEST. Across the River and into the Trees. NY, 1950. 1st ed, 1st issue dj. (Bkpl, bkseller's stamp inside fr cvr), else Good in dj (price-clipped, heavily chipped, torn). *King.* $75/£47

HEMINGWAY, ERNEST. Across the River and into the Trees. NY, 1950. 1st ed. Dj (lt edgeworn, creased). *Swann*.* $115/£72

HEMINGWAY, ERNEST. By-Line: Ernest Hemingway. NY: Scribner, (1967). 1st ed. NF (pencil name erased) in NF dj (sm inner mend). *Reese.* $50/£31

HEMINGWAY, ERNEST. Death in the Afternoon. London: Jonathan Cape, (1932). 1st British ed, 1st issue dj in white, ptd in black/red. Color frontis, 81 photo plts. Orange cl. (Inscrip), else VG in dj (extrems chipped, closed long tears; spine head lacks piece removing word 'Death'). *Pacific*.* $81/£51

HEMINGWAY, ERNEST. Death in the Afternoon. NY: Scribner, 1932. 1st ed. Color frontis. Black cl, gilt spine. (Spine ends sl rubbed), else VG. *Pacific*.* $115/£72

HEMINGWAY, ERNEST. Death in the Afternoon. NY: Scribner, 1932. 1st ed, 2nd ptg. Color frontis. Fine in dj (extrems chipped; piece gone from spine head, lower corner fr panel; price-clipped). *Pacific*.* $138/£86

HEMINGWAY, ERNEST. A Farewell to Arms. NY: Scribner, 1929. 1st ed. VG. *New Hampshire*.* $80/£50

HEMINGWAY, ERNEST. A Farewell to Arms. NY, 1929. 1st ed, 1st state. Black cl. (Sig, feps browned; cvrs spotted, binding skewed, spine label rubbed.) Dj (sl browned, chipped, edge tears, ink 'discard' stamp rear panel). *Swann*.* $316/£198

HEMINGWAY, ERNEST. A Farewell to Arms. NY: Scribner, 1929. 1st ed, 1st issue w/o disclaimer notice on p(x). Black cl, gilt paper cvr/spine labels. (Name; chip spine label, foot sl rubbed), else VG in dj (spine ends chipped, spine, extrems dknd). *Pacific*.* $316/£198

HEMINGWAY, ERNEST. A Farewell to Arms. NY: Scribner, 1929. 1st trade ed, 1st issue, w/o disclaimer notice prior to text. Untrimmed. Black cl, gold paper labels. (Bkpl, eps lt browned from dj; corners sl worn.) VG color pict dj (spine, rear panel lt sunned, dusty, spine ends chipped, flap folds worn). *Baltimore*.* $375/£234

HEMINGWAY, ERNEST. A Farewell to Arms. NY: Scribner, 1929. 1st ed, 1st issue w/o the disclaimer notice on p(x). Black cl, gilt paper cvr/spine labels. NF in VG- dj (sm bumps to corners, spine ends chipped, torn, tape repairs to verso, upper joint lacks piece, tears, creases). *Pacific*.* $403/£252

HEMINGWAY, ERNEST. A Farewell to Arms. Cape, 1929. 1st UK ed. Fine in NF dj. *Williams.* $680/£425

HEMINGWAY, ERNEST. A Farewell to Arms. NY: Scribner, 1929. One of 510 signed. Royal 8vo. Blue eps. 1/2 vellum, pale blue bds, gilt-stamped black morocco spine label. VG (rebacked identically to pub's binding; bds unevenly browned, rear bd scraped) in cl open-end slipcase. *Heritage.* $3,000/£1,875

HEMINGWAY, ERNEST. A Farewell to Arms. NY, 1929. Deluxe ed. Ltd to 510 signed. Lg 8vo. 355pp. Partly unopened. 1/4 vellum, pale grn bds. VG + (bkpl) in slipcase (mended w/tape). *Truepenny.* $4,500/£2,813

HEMINGWAY, ERNEST. A Farewell to Arms. NY, 1929. 1st ed. One of 510 numbered, signed. Lg 8vo. 1/2 vellum, bds. Slipcase (top parted at seam). *Swann*.* $8,050/£5,031

HEMINGWAY, ERNEST. A Farewell to Arms. NY: Scribner, 1948. 1st illus ed. Gray cl, paper spine label. (Spine, label sl dknd), else Fine in slipcase (extrems sl dknd). *Pacific*.* $115/£72

HEMINGWAY, ERNEST. The Fifth Column and Four Stories of the Spanish Civil War. NY: Scribner, (1969). 1st ed. Orange cl, gilt. (1st few pp creased), o/w Fine in dj. *Heritage.* $100/£63

HEMINGWAY, ERNEST. The Fifth Column and Four Unpublished Stories of the Spanish Civil War. NY: Scribner, (1969). 1st ed. Fine in Fine dj (sm tear). *Between The Covers.* $100/£63

HEMINGWAY, ERNEST. The Fifth Column and the First Forty-Nine Stories. NY: Scribner, 1938. 1st ed. 8vo. Red cl, facs sig on fr cvr, gilt. Fine (spine ends lt rubbed) in dj (lt chipped, soiled). *Heritage.* $1,000/£625

HEMINGWAY, ERNEST. The Fifth Column and the First Forty-Nine Stories. Cape, 1939. 1st UK ed. NF in VG black dj (edges sl worn, lacks sm piece, black card affixed to verso). *Martin.* $77/£48

HEMINGWAY, ERNEST. The Fifth Column and the First Forty-Nine Stories. Cape, 1939. 1st UK ed. Fine in VG dj (sm chip, repaired). *Williams.* $312/£195

HEMINGWAY, ERNEST. The Fifth Column. A Play in Three Acts. NY: Scribner, 1940. 1st separate ed. 8vo. Gray cl. (Few brn stains on eps), o/w Fine in dj (reverse spine foot reinforced w/tape; spine lt browned); 1/4 morocco clamshell case. *Heritage.* $3,500/£2,188

HEMINGWAY, ERNEST. For Whom the Bell Tolls. NY: Scribner, 1940. 1st ed. NF. *Pacific*.* $46/£29

HEMINGWAY, ERNEST. For Whom the Bell Tolls. NY: Scribner, 1940. 1st ed. VG + (lacks dj). *Warren.* $50/£31

HEMINGWAY, ERNEST. For Whom the Bell Tolls. NY: Scribner, 1940. 1st ed. Beige cl. Fine in 1st issue dj (extrems sl torn). *Appelfeld.* $150/£94

HEMINGWAY, ERNEST. For Whom the Bell Tolls. NY, 1940. 1st ed, 1st issue dj. (Eps discolored, pp yellowed; worn) in dj (worn). *King.* $200/£125

HEMINGWAY, ERNEST. For Whom the Bell Tolls. NY, 1940. 1st ed. 1st issue dj (nick). *Swann*.* $431/£269

HEMINGWAY, ERNEST. For Whom the Bell Tolls. NY, 1940. 1st ed, 1st state. 8vo. Dj (2 tiny internal repairs). *Swann*.* $747/£467

HEMINGWAY, ERNEST. For Whom the Bell Tolls. Cape, 1941. 1st UK ed. (Edges sl worn), o/w NF. *Martin.* $19/£12

HEMINGWAY, ERNEST. For Whom the Bell Tolls. LEC, 1942. Ltd to 1500 numbered, signed by Lynd Ward (illus). Fine in slipcase. *Swann*.* $201/£126

HEMINGWAY, ERNEST. The Garden of Eden. Scribner, 1986. 1st US ed. NF in dj. *Williams.* $24/£15

HEMINGWAY, ERNEST. God Rest You Merry Gentlemen. NY: House of Books, 1933. 1st ed. One of 300. Orig red cl (sl faded), gilt. Orig plain glassine dj (torn, chipped) in cl, plexiglas clamshell box. *Kane*.* $850/£531

HEMINGWAY, ERNEST. Green Hills of Africa. NY: Scribner, 1935. 1st ed. (Spine, edges faded), else VG+ in VG+ dj (extrems lt nicked, torn). *Between The Covers.* $600/£375

HEMINGWAY, ERNEST. Green Hills of Africa. NY: Scribner, 1935. 1st ed. 8vo. Grn cl (spine sl faded). VG in dj (sl worn, rubbed). *Cummins.* $600/£375

HEMINGWAY, ERNEST. Green Hills of Africa. NY: Scribner, 1935. 1st ed. VG (sm brn fore-edge stains, 1 affects margin of few pp, inscrip; top edges lt foxed; spine faded) in VG- dj (two 2-inch spine tears, tape repair to verso). *Lame Duck.* $650/£406

HEMINGWAY, ERNEST. Green Hills of Africa. NY: Scribner, 1935. 1st ed. (Name; spine, extrems sunned), o/w VG in dj (spine head chipped, few sm creases, chips). *Pacific*.* $748/£468

HEMINGWAY, ERNEST. Green Hills of Africa. Cape, 1936. 1st UK ed. (Name, lt foxed; dw type on cl), o/w VG in VG dj (extrems sl shelfworn). *Any Amount.* $176/£110

HEMINGWAY, ERNEST. In Our Time. NY: Scribner, 1930. 2nd US ed. Black cl, gilt labels. Nice in VG dj (old reinforcements, few sm edge tears on verso). *Reese.* $300/£188

HEMINGWAY, ERNEST. Islands in the Stream. Collins, 1970. 1st UK ed. Fine in dj (price-clipped). *Williams.* $29/£18

HEMINGWAY, ERNEST. Men at War. NY, 1942. 1st ed. Dj (sm closed tear, spine extrems lt worn). *Swann*.* $230/£144

HEMINGWAY, ERNEST. Men Without Women. NY: Scribner, 1927. 1st ed. Black cl, ptd foil-finish labels. (Cl, labels sl rubbed, lt soiled), else VG (w/o dj). *Reese.* $60/£38

HEMINGWAY, ERNEST. Men Without Women. NY: Scribner, 1927. 1st ed, 2nd issue dj. 8vo. Black cl w/gold paper labels. VF. *Appelfeld.* $550/£344

HEMINGWAY, ERNEST. A Moveable Feast. London, (1964). 1st Eng ed. Dj (several inner tape repairs). *Swann*.* $115/£72

HEMINGWAY, ERNEST. A Moveable Feast. NY, (1964). 1st ed. Dj (price-clipped). *Swann*.* $126/£79

HEMINGWAY, ERNEST. A Moveable Feast. Cape, 1964. 1st UK ed. NF in dj. *Williams.* $29/£18

HEMINGWAY, ERNEST. The Old Man and the Sea. London: Jonathan Cape, (1952). 1st Eng ed. NF in dj (few sm tears upper extrems, spine sl sunned) w/price of 7s.6d. on rear flap. *Pacific*.* $196/£123

HEMINGWAY, ERNEST. The Old Man and the Sea. NY: Scribner, 1952. 1st ed. (Rubber stamp fep; offset from tape to cl, feps), else VG- in dj (spine ends sl rubbed). *Pacific*.* $219/£137

HEMINGWAY, ERNEST. The Old Man and the Sea. NY, 1952. 1st ed. NF in NF dj (price-clipped, 4 sm tape remnant spots). *Warren.* $300/£188

HEMINGWAY, ERNEST. The Old Man and the Sea. Reprint Soc, 1953. 1st illus ed. C.F. Tunnicliffe and Raymond Sheppard (illus). Fine in VG dj (sl nicked, dusty). *Williams.* $40/£25

HEMINGWAY, ERNEST. The Old Man and the Sea. LEC, 1989. One of 600 signed by Alfred Eisenstaedt (photos). Fine in slipcase. *Swann*.* $862/£539

HEMINGWAY, ERNEST. Selected Letters 1917-1961. Carlos Baker (ed). NY: Scribner, (1981). 1st ed. One of 500. Signed by Baker. Cl-backed bds, pub's cl slipcase. Good. *Holmes.* $125/£78

HEMINGWAY, ERNEST. Short Stories. (Copenhagen: Hansen & Nielsens Bogtrykerri, 1948.) 1st ed w/these illus. One of 175 numbered. 7 linoleum cuts by Dan Sterup-Hansen. Pict bds. *Swann*.* $69/£43

HEMINGWAY, ERNEST. The Spanish Earth. Cleveland: J.B. Savage, 1938. Illus ed, ltd to 1000. 2nd issue (plain eps). Tan cl. Fine. *Karmiole.* $350/£219

HEMINGWAY, ERNEST. The Sun Also Rises. NY, 1926. 1st ed, 1st issue w/'stopped' spelled 'stopppped' p181. 8vo. Fine (sl skewed) in dj (lt worn, sm closed tear fr joint). *Swann*.* $6,900/£4,313

HEMINGWAY, ERNEST. To Have and Have Not. Cape, 1937. 1st UK ed. Fine in VG dj (sl browned, closed tear, sl loss to spine head). *Williams.* $448/£280

HEMINGWAY, ERNEST. To Have and Have Not. NY: Scribner, 1937. 1st ed. 8vo. Black cl, facs sign on fr cvr. VG (bkpl, eps browned; spine extrems sl rubbed) in dj (lt chipped, soiled). *Heritage.* $600/£375

HEMINGWAY, ERNEST. Today Is Friday [caption title]. Stable Pamphlet, Number IV. (Englewood, NJ, 1926.) 1st ed. One of 300 numbered. Pict wrappers. Orig pub's envelope (lacks flap, sm tears, soil); cl slipcase. *Swann*.* $431/£269

HEMINGWAY, ERNEST. The Torrents of Spring. Paris: Crosby Continental Editions, 1932. 1st Continental Edition, sm paper issue. 12mo. Fine in ptd wrappers, glassine wrapper (sl torn), cl slipcase. *Holmes.* $750/£469

HEMINGWAY, ERNEST. The Torrents of Spring. London, 1933. 1st Eng ed. Dj (lt foxed, spine sl tanned). *Swann*.* $460/£288

HEMINGWAY, ERNEST. The Torrents of Spring: A Romantic Novel in Honor of the Passing of a Great Race. NY: Scribner, 1926. 1st ed. Dk grn cl lettered in red. (Sl offset feps; spine ends sl rubbed), else VG. *Pacific*.* $374/£234

HEMINGWAY, ERNEST. Winner Take Nothing. NY: Scribner, 1933. 1st ed. Black cl, gold labels. Fine. *Macdonnell.* $125/£78

HEMINGWAY, ERNEST. Winner Take Nothing. NY: Scribner, 1933. 1st ed. Top edge stained red. Black cl, gold paper labels. NF (extrems lt rubbed, few creases to spine label) in dj (chipped, sm edge tears). *Heritage.* $500/£313

HEMINGWAY, ERNEST. Winner Take Nothing. Cape, 1934. 1st UK ed. VG (bkpl, foxed; cvrs sl dusty). *Williams.* $56/£35

HEMMING, GEORGE WIRGMAN. Billiards Mathematically Treated. London: Macmillan, 1899. 1st ed. Presentation copy. 45pp. Grn cl, gilt. (Sm nick rear hinge), else VG. *Weber.* $50/£31

HEMON, LOUIS. Maria Chapdelaine. NY: Macmillan, 1924. 1st ptg of illus ed. Wilfred Jones (illus). Navy cl, stamped. VG. *Price.* $45/£28

HENDERSON, ALEXANDER. The History of Ancient and Modern Wines. London: Baldwin, Cradock & Joy, 1824. 1st ed. Period 1/2 cl, bds (orig?), spine label. (Added frontis, few mtd vignettes to tp, chapter tops; joints starting, spines torn), else VG-. *Pacific*.* $345/£216

HENDERSON, ARCHIBALD. George Bernard Shaw, His Life and Work. London: Hurst & Blackett, 1911. 1st ed. Sepia frontisport; 1 fldg facs. (Worn, fr cvr head bubbled.) *Dramatis.* $60/£38

HENDERSON, DAVID S. Fishing for the Whale. Dundee: Museum & Art Gallery, 1972. VG. *Hollett.* $32/£20

HENDERSON, G. F. R. The Civil War: A Soldier's View. Chicago: Univ of Chicago, (1958). 1st ed. Gray cl. NF in VG dj (sl rubbed). *Chapel Hill.* $45/£28

HENDERSON, G. F. R. Stonewall Jackson and the American Civil War. London/NY/Bombay: Longmans, Green, 1898. 1st ed. 2 vols. Lg 8vo. 550pp + 32pp ads; 641pp; complete w/2 ports, 33 fldg maps. Red cl. Very Nice set (lt scattered foxing; spine sl faded). Howes H408. *Chapel Hill*. $900/£563

HENDERSON, HAROLD GOULD and ROBERT TREAT PAINE (eds). Japanese Art. Newton, MA: University Prints, n.d. (ca 1945). 15 plts, loose as issued in cl portfolio. VG in slipcase. *Worldwide*. $65/£41

HENDERSON, JOHN B. The Cruise of the Tomas Barrera. NY/London: Putnam, 1916. 1 fldg map. Gilt-dec blue cl. Fine. *Parmer*. $50/£31

HENDERSON, LAWRENCE J. Blood. A Study in General Physiology. New Haven: Yale Univ, 1928. 1st ed. Fldg chart. VG. *Glaser*. $50/£31

HENDERSON, LOUIS. Strange Experiences. London, 1955. Fine in VG dj. *Middle Earth*. $25/£16

HENDERSON, M. R. Malayan Wild Flowers. London, 1954-1959. 2 vols. Djs. *Henly*. $77/£48

HENDERSON, PETER. Gardening for Pleasure. NY: OJ, 1884. (3)-v,(7),(9)-250,2pp ads. Dec grn cl, gilt. (Ex-lib, browned, rear ep separated; shelf-worn), else Good. *Fair Meadow*. $14/£9

HENDERSON, PETER. Gardening for Profit. NY: OJ, 1888. 376pp. Grn cl, gilt. (Cl wrinkled), else Good. *Larry Price*. $30/£19

HENDERSON, PETER. Practical Floriculture. NY: OJ, c. 1869. 1st ed. 3-249,3pp ads. Pict brn bds, gilt. (Browned; shelf-worn), else VG. *Fair Meadow*. $40/£25

HENDERSON, RANDALL. Sun, Sand and Solitude. L.A.: Westernlore, 1968. 1st ed. Signed. Fine in VG dj. *Book Market*. $45/£28

HENDERSON, ROBERT M. D.W. Griffith. The Years at Biograph. NY, 1970. 1st Amer ed. Fine in dj (sm edge nick). *Polyanthos*. $25/£16

HENDERSON, ROBERT W. Early American Sport. NY: Grolier Club, 1937. One of 400. Red morocco label. (Lt worn.) *Oinonen**. $30/£19

Henderson. A Guide to Audubon's Home Town in Kentucky. Northport, L.I., NY, (1941). 1st ed. Good + . *Wantagh*. $30/£19

HENDLEY, GEORGE. Narratives of Pious Children. NY: Amer Tract Soc, n.d. (ca 1850). 12mo. 62pp. Gilt edges. Blind-tooled cl on bds, gilt. Fine (dated dedication fep, lt foxed). *Hobbyhorse*. $75/£47

HENDLEY, THOMAS HOLBEIN. Damascening on Iron and Steel, as Practised in India. W. Griggs & Sons, 1892. 1st ed. 32 color plts, some w/gilt. Orig roan-backed bds (spine chipped, defective, bds loose). *Sotheby's**. $1,563/£977

HENDRICK, BURTON J. Statesmen of the Lost Cause. Boston: Little, Brown, 1939. 1st ed. Gray cl. NF. *House*. $25/£16

HENDRICKS, GORDON. Albert Bierstadt. NY: Abrams, 1973. Fine in dj. *Turtle Island*. $375/£234

HENDRICKS, GORDON. The Life and Works of Winslow Homer. NY, (1979). Obl folio. Dj. *Swann**. $69/£43

HENDRICKS, GORDON. The Photographs of Thomas Eakins. NY, 1972. 1st ed. *Swann**. $115/£72

HENDRICKS, STANLEY. Astronauts on the Moon. Kansas City: Hallmark, n.d. (1970). 4 dbl-pg pop-ups by Al Muenchen. Pict bds (extrems sl worn). Internally VG in dj. *Bookfinders*. $90/£56

HENLE, MARY (ed). Documents of Gestalt Psychology. Berkeley: Univ of CA, 1961. Red/gray cl. VG in dj (edgeworn). *Gach*. $57/£36

HENLEY, W. E. A Book of Verses. London: David Nutt, 1888. 1st ed. Yapped flexible gray bds. NF (yapped edges sl nicked, spine sl dknd). *Sumner & Stillman*. $175/£109

HENLEY, W. E. London Types. London: Heinemann, 1898. Library ed. Ltd to 275. Lg 4to. 12 full-pg plts by William Nicholson. Top edge tinted red. White cl (edges sl faded). Very Nice. *Reisler*. $1,275/£797

HENLEY, W. E. (ed). A London Garland. Macmillan, 1895. 1st ed. 203pp (spotted, 1 leaf w/chipped fore-edge). Orig full vellum (sl dknd), gilt. *Hollett*. $104/£65

HENNELL, THOMAS. Lady Filmy Fern, Or, The Voyage of the Window Box. Hamish Hamilton, 1980. 1st ed. Obl 4to. (41)pp; 18 full-pg color, 1 lg b/w illus by Edward Bawden. Pict bds. NF in pict dj. *Bookmark*. $40/£25

HENNEN, JOHN. Observations on Some Important Points in the Practice of Military Surgery, and in the Arrangement and Police of Hospitals. Edinburgh, 1818. 1st ed. x,(ii),508pp. Orig 1/2 calf (rebacked w/orig spine, labels eps preserved). VF (old ink name, lib stamp, pale waterstain last 1/4 of bk; sm ink # at spine foot). *Bickersteth*. $456/£285

HENNING, FRED. Fights for the Championship: The Men and Their Times. London: Liscensed Victuallers' Gazette, (1900). 1st ed. 2 vols. Red cl, gilt. (Spines faded, ends rubbed, chipped), else VG-. *Pacific**. $127/£79

HENNINGHAUSEN, LOUIS P. History of the German Society of Maryland. Balt: For sale by W.E.C. Harrison & Sons, 1909. 1st ed. Frontisport. Grn cl. VG. *Chapel Hill*. $85/£53

HENREY, BLANCHE. British Botanical and Horticultural Literature Before 1800. London: OUP, 1975. 1st ed. 3 vols. Gray cl, gilt. Fine in slipcase. *Pacific**. $374/£234

HENRI, ADRIAN. Autobiography. Jonathan Cape, 1971. 1st ed. Signed. NF (spine ends sl bumped) in dj (sl spotted). *Ulysses*. $19/£12

HENRY, ALEXANDER and DAVID THOMPSON. New Light on the Early History of the Great Northwest. Elliot Coues (ed). Minneapolis: Ross & Haines, (1965). One of 1500. Frontisport; fldg legend sheet, 3 fldg maps in rear pocket. (Corner lt bumped), else Fine in slipcase (2 corners bumped). *Pacific**. $98/£61

HENRY, ALICE. Women and the Labor Movement. NY: Doran, 1923. 1st ed. VG in wraps (chipped). *Beasley*. $65/£41

HENRY, ARNOLD K. The Hinge Graft. Balt: Williams and Wilkins, 1950. Fine. *Weber*. $75/£47

HENRY, E. R. Classificatoin and Uses of Finger Prints. London: HMSO, 1934. 7th ed. 2 fldg charts. (Cl sl spotted.) *Hollett*. $56/£35

HENRY, MARGUERITE. Always Reddy. NY: Whittlesey, 1947. 1st ed. 6.25x9.25. Wesley Dennis (illus). 79pp. Good in dj. *Cattermole*. $25/£16

HENRY, MARGUERITE. Argentina in Story and Picture. Whitman, 1941. 1st ed. 8x5 oblong. Kurt Wiese (illus). Unpaginated. Good (spine top bumped) in Good dj (1/2-inch chip). *Price*. $25/£16

HENRY, MARGUERITE. Auno and Tauno. Chicago: Whitman, 1940. 1st ed. 10.5x8.25. Gladys Rourke Blackwood (illus). 28pp. Pict cl. Fine in dj. *Cattermole*. $50/£31

HENRY, MARGUERITE. Gaudenzia Pride of the Palio. Rand McNally, 1960. 1st ed. 7.3x9.6. Lynd Ward (illus). 237pp. NF (neat bkpl) in VG + dj. *Price*. $43/£27

HENRY, MARGUERITE. Mexico in Story and Picture. Whitman, 1941. 1st ed. 8x5 oblong. Kurt Wiese (illus). Unpaginated. VG in Good dj. *Price*. $25/£16

HENRY, MARGUERITE. Stormy, Misty's Foal. Rand McNally, 1963. 1st ed. 7.3x9.6. Wesley Dennis (illus). 224pp. NF (neat bkpl) in VG + dj. *Price*. $40/£25

HENRY, O. (Pseud of William Sydney Porter.) Cabbages and Kings. NY: McClure, Phillips & Co, 1904. 1st issue, 1st bk. Black pict cl. VG (lt worn) in early custom black cl slipcase. *Dermont*. $225/£141

HENRY, O. (Pseud of William Sydney Porter.) The Gentle Grafter. NY: McClure, 1908. 1st ed, 1st ptg, w/pg 1 so paginated.
Red cl, reads 'McClure' at spine foot. VG (extrems sl rubbed, sl
glass ring rear cvr). *Sumner & Stillman*. $75/£47

HENRY, O. (Pseud of William Sydney Porter.) Let Me Feel Your
Pulse. NY: Doubleday, Page, 1910. 1st ed. Tan cl, pict label.
VF in glassine dj (chipped). BAL 16296. *Macdonnell*. $100/£63

HENRY, O. (Pseud of William Sydney Porter.) O. Henryana.
Seven Odds and Ends: Poetry and Short Stories. GC: Doubleday, Page, 1920. 1st ed. Ltd to 375. Nice in parchment
backed bds, gilt. *Cady*. $50/£31

HENRY, O. (Pseud of William Sydney Porter.) Postscripts.
NY/London: Harper, 1923. 1st ed. Red cl. Fine in NF dj (sl
shelfworn). *Sumner & Stillman*. $145/£91

HENRY, O. (Pseud of William Sydney Porter.) Strictly Business.
NY: Doubleday, Page, 1910. 1st ed. Nice. *Cady*. $25/£16

HENRY, O. (Pseud of William Sydney Porter.) The Voice of the
City and Other Stories. NY: LEC, 1935. Ltd to 1500 signed by
George Grosz (illus). Black buckram. Fine in purple buckram
slipcase (lt worn). *Truepenny*. $250/£156

HENRY, O. (Pseud of William Sydney Porter.) The Voice of the
City and Other Stories. Clifton Fadiman (ed). NY: LEC, 1935.
Ltd to 1500(?) signed by George Grosz (illus). 20 color plts.
Black buckram. Fine in purple buckram slipcase (sl worn). *Any
Amount*. $296/£185

HENRY, W. S. Campaign Sketches of the War with Mexico. NY:
Harper, 1847. 1st ed. Frontis, 331pp; 2 dbl-pg maps. Orig 1/2
calf, marbled bds, morocco spine label. Nice (19th-cent bkpl, lt
foxed). Howes H429. *Chapel Hill*. $175/£109

HENRY, WILL. Alias Butch Cassidy. NY: Random House, 1967.
1st ed. VG + in dj. *Labordo*. $75/£47

HENRY, WILL. Chiricahua. Phila: Lippincott, 1972. 1st ed. NF in
VG + dj (sl rubbed, trimmed). *Unger*. $125/£78

HENRY, WILL. Death of a Legend. NY: Random House, 1954.
1st ed. Fine in dj. *Labordo*. $85/£53

HENRY, WILL. The Fourth Horseman. NY: Random House,
1954. 1st ed. NF in VG + dj (worn). *Unger*. $175/£109

HENRY, WILL. From Where the Sun Now Stands. NY: Random
House, 1960. 1st ed. Fine in NF dj (few sm tears). *Unger*.
$100/£63

HENRY, WILL. The Gates of the Mountains. NY: Random
House, 1963. 1st ed. Fine in Fine dj (title background sl faded).
Unger. $75/£47

HENRY, WILL. I, Tom Horn. Phila: Lippincott, 1975. 1st ed. Fine
in dj. *Labordo*. $95/£59

HENRY, WILL. Journey to Shiloh. NY: Random House, 1960. 1st
ed. NF in VG + dj (price-clipped). *Unger*. $100/£63

HENRY, WILL. The Last Warpath. NY: Random House, 1966.
1st ed. Fine in NF dj (lt soiled). *Unger*. $75/£47

HENRY, WILL. No Survivors. NY: Random House, 1950. 1st ed,
1st bk. (Name), else VG in VG grn dj (chipped). *Unger*.
$275/£172

HENRY, WILL. Reckoning at Yankee Flat. NY: Random House,
1958. 1st ed. Fine in dj. *Labordo*. $55/£34

HENRY, WILL. Who Rides with Wyatt. NY: Random House,
1955. 1st ed. Fine in dj. *Labordo*. $75/£47

HENRY, WILLIAM CHARLES. Memoirs of the Life and Scientific
Researches of John Dalton. London: Cavendish Soc, 1854. 1st
ed. Engr frontis port, xv,249pp + (iv, bibliography),(vii, ads)pp; 3
fldg plts. Mod 1/2 polished calf, gilt, spine label, raised bands.
VG. *Hollett*. $240/£150

Hensel and Gretel. A Peepshow Book. London: C&W, 1975. 5
fldg-out scenes by Mary McClain. Glazed pict bds. VG. *Bookfinders*. $40/£25

HENSHALL, JAMES A. Book of the Black Bass. Cincinnati, 1889.
Pub's gilt-pict cl (extrems lt rubbed). Swann*. $80/£50

HENSHALL, JAMES A. Camping and Cruising in Florida. Cincinnati: Robert Clarke, 1884. 1st ed. 248pp, 4pp ads, 12pp title listing. Blue dec cl. VG. *Biscotti*. $175/£109

HENSHALL, JAMES A. Camping and Cruising in Florida. Cincinnati: Robert Clarke, 1888. 1st ed. Gray cl, gilt. (Hinges cracking,
bkpl, name), else VG. Pacific*. $137/£86

HENSHALL, JAMES A. Favorite Fish and Fishing. NY, 1908. 1st
ed. (Names, fr inner hinge cracked, extrems worn), else Good.
King. $40/£25

HENSHAW, JULIA W. Mountain Wild Flowers of Canada.
Toronto: William Briggs, 1906. 1st ed. 99 b/w plts. (Sl flaw xiii,
pencil note fep, pencil checks, some pp mkd by pressed flowers), else VG. *Fair Meadow*. $65/£41

HENSLOW, T. GEOFFREY. Ye Sundial Booke. London, 1914.
Frontisport. Fore, lower edges uncut. Japon bds, gilt. (Lt spotted,
fr hinge cracked; rear joints worn, rubbed, head bumped.) *Edwards*. $72/£45

HENSMAN, HOWARD. The Afghan War of 1879-80. W.H. Al-
len, 1881. 1st ed. xiii,list of maps,567pp; 10 fldg maps, plans.
Later black 1/2 morocco, marbled bds, gilt, raised bands. VG.
Sotheran. $560/£350

HENSON, JOSIAH. Truth Stranger Than Fiction. Boston: John P.
Jewett, 1858. 1st ed. Port, xii,212pp. (Lib bkpl, stamps, spine #),
o/w Good. *Brown*. $100/£63

HENTOFF, NAT. The Jazz Life. NY: Dial, 1961. 1st ed. VG in dj
(lt chipped). *Petrilla*. $30/£19

HENTY, G. A. At Aboukir and Acre, a Story of Napoleon's Invasion of Egypt. London: Blackie & Son, 1899. 1st ed.
(x),352,(32)ads pp. Olivine edges. Deep red cl. NF. *Sotheran*.
$141/£88

HENTY, G. A. At the Point of the Bayonet, a Tale of the Mahratta
War. London: Blackie & Son, 1902. 1st ed. Olivine edges. Dk
grn pict cl, gilt. Very Bright (1st 2 leaves sl speckled). *Sotheran*.
$157/£98

HENTY, G. A. At the Point of the Bayonet. NY: Scribner, 1901.
1st Amer ed. Wal Paget (illus). Pict grn cl. NF (few sm mks, 1
sm nick at spine top). *Sumner & Stillman*. $95/£59

HENTY, G. A. Both Sides the Border, a Tale of Hotspur and Glen-
dower. London: Blackie & Son, 1899. 1st ed. 8vo. (x),12-
384,32 ads pp; 12 monochrome illus by Ralph Peacock.
Olivine edges. Dk blue pict cl, gilt. VG (sm grn mks on few ll, 1
corner turned down; spine ends rubbed). *Sotheran*. $125/£78

HENTY, G. A. Both Sides the Border. Blackie & Son, 1899. 1st
ed. 384,32pp; 12 illus by Ralph Peacock. Blue dec cl (sl worn,
neatly recased; few spots), gilt. *Hollett*. $96/£60

HENTY, G. A. By Conduct and Courage. Blackie & Son, 1905.
1st ed. 384,32pp; 8 illus by William Rainey. Pict red cl (spine sl
faded), gilt. *Hollett*. $104/£65

HENTY, G. A. Captain Bayley's Heir. London/NY: Blackie &
Son/Scribner, n.d. Early Amer ed. 32pp undated ads; 12 full-pg
illus by H. M. Paget. Pict brn cl. Fine (1893 inscrip). *Sumner &
Stillman*. $110/£69

HENTY, G. A. Condemned as a Nihilist. NY: Scribner, 1892. 1st
Amer ed. 16pp ads dated 1892. Pict blue-gray cl. NF (sl cellotape stains to eps; sl soiled, extrems sl rubbed). *Sumner & Stillman*. $145/£91

HENTY, G. A. For the Temple. London/NY: Blackie & Son/Scrib-
ner, n.d. Early Amer ed. Solomon J. Solomon (illus). 32pp undated ads. Pict blue-gray cl, beveled. NF (January 1893 sig;
extrems sl rubbed). *Sumner & Stillman*. $95/£59

HENTY, G. A. In the Irish Brigade. NY: Scribner, 1900. 1st Amer
ed. Pict grn cl. VG (few ll sl proud; corners sl rubbed). *Sumner
& Stillman*. $85/£53

HENTY, G. A. In the Reign of Terror. The Adventures of a Westminster Boy. Blackie, 1888. 1st ed. Frontis, 351pp + 32pp pub's list; 7 plts. Maroon eps. Pale blue cl, gilt. VG (inscrip dated 8.1.88; backstrip sl dull). *Blackwell's*. $120/£75

HENTY, G. A. The Lion of St. Mark, a Tale of Venice. London: Blackie & Son, 1889. 1st ed. (x),12-384,32ads pp. Olivine edges. Bright red pict cl. Good (spine evenly faded, sl rubbed, sm damp spot to fr cvr). *Sotheran*. $317/£198

HENTY, G. A. A March on London, a Tale of Wat Tyler's Rising. London: Blackie & Son, 1897. 1st ed. 8vo. G. A. Henty & W. H. Margetson (illus). (x),352,32 ads pp. Olivine edges. Mid-blue pict cl. (Frontis verso, fep foxed, fore-edge of book block speckled.) Externally VF. *Sotheran*. $157/£98

HENTY, G. A. No Surrender! London: Blackie & Son, 1900. 1st Eng ed. Pict red cl. (Lacks fep), o/w NF. *Sumner & Stillman*. $80/£50

HENTY, G. A. No Surrender! A Tale of the Huguenot Wars. London: Blackie & Son, 1900. 1st ed. Gray eps; olivine edges. Dk red pict cl, gilt. Fine. *Sotheran*. $157/£98

HENTY, G. A. On the Irrawaddy, a Story of the First Burmese War. London: Blackie & Son, 1897. 1st ed. 8vo. W. H. Overend (illus). Frontis, (x),12-352,32 ads pp. Olivine edges. Slate blue pict cl, gilt. (Frontis verso lt browned), else Internally Clean. *Sotheran*. $157/£98

HENTY, G. A. Out with Garibaldi. A Story of the Liberation of Italy. London: Blackie & Son, 1901. 1st ed. Olivine edges. French-blue pict cl, gilt. Clean. *Sotheran*. $125/£78

HENTY, G. A. Queen Victoria. London: Blackie & Son, 1901. 1st ed thus. Plain edges. Purple cl, gilt. (Prize label to fep; spine sunned), o/w Very Clean. *Sotheran*. $157/£98

HENTY, G. A. Seaside Maidens. Jacksons of Ilkley, (1986). (Facs of orig ed publ by Tinsley Bros in 1880.) 8vo. Fine in color pict wraps, card slipcase. *Sotheran*. $45/£28

HENTY, G. A. St. Bartholomew's Eve. London: Blackie & Son, 1894. 1st ed. Gray eps; olivine edges. Dk grn pict cl, gilt. Very Nice (no pub's cat at rear; few sm closed spine nicks). *Sotheran*. $157/£98

HENTY, G. A. The Tiger of Mysore. Blackie & Son, 1896. 1st ed. 379,32pp; 12 illus by W. H. Margetson, 1 map. Pict grn cl, gilt. VG (sl rubbed, neatly recased). *Hollett*. $152/£95

HENTY, G. A. To Herat and Cabul. NY: Scribner, 1901. 1st Amer ed. Pict blue cl. NF (spine sl dknd, ends sl shelfworn). *Sumner & Stillman*. $85/£53

HENTY, G. A. To Herat and Cabul. London, 1902. 1st ed. Map. (Tp foxed.) *Petersfield*. $77/£48

HENTY, G. A. The Treasure of the Incas. NY: Scribner, 1902. 1st Amer ed. Map. Dk grn pict-dec cl. NF (sl rubbed). *Sumner & Stillman*. $115/£72

HENTY, G. A. True to the Old Flag. London: Blackie & Son, 1885. 1st ed. Brn eps; olivine edges. Brn pict cl. VG (inner hinge cracked, strengthened neatly w/transparent tape; spine sl rubbed). *Sotheran*. $317/£198

HENTY, G. A. When London Burned. NY: Scribner, 1894. 1st Amer ed. 16pp undated ads. Pict blue-gray cl. NF (sl soiled, rubbed). *Sumner & Stillman*. $125/£78

HENTY, G. A. With Buller in Natal. NY: Scribner, 1900. 1st Amer ed. Pict blue-gray cl. Fine. *Sumner & Stillman*. $115/£72

HENTY, G. A. With Cochrane the Dauntless. NY: Scribner, 1896. 1st Amer ed. 32pp undated ads. Pict blue-gray cl. VG (fr cvr sl rubbed, lg mk to rear). *Sumner & Stillman*. $75/£47

HENTY, G. A. With Kitchener in the Soudan. NY: Scribner, 1902. 1st Amer ed. 3 maps. Pict red cl. Fine. *Sumner & Stillman*. $95/£59

HENTY, G. A. With Lee in Virginia. London, (1890). Undated rpt. 380pp. Pict cl. VG. *Pratt*. $15/£9

HENTY, G. A. With the British Legion, a Story of the Carlist Wars. London: Blackie & Son, 1903. 1st ed, w/orig summary slip condensing the plot inserted at fr of bk. Olivine edges. Dk blue pict cl, gilt. NF. *Sotheran*. $157/£98

HENTY, G. A. Won by the Sword. London: Blackie & Son, 1900. 1st Eng ed. Pict blue-grn cl, beveled. Fine. *Sumner & Stillman*. $120/£75

HENTY, G. A. Yule Logs, Being Longman's Xmas Annual for 1898. London: Longmans, Green, 1898. 1st ed. xi,430pp. Aeg. Deep red pict cl, gilt. VG. *Sotheran*. $205/£128

HENTY, G. A. et al. Brains and Bravery. NY: E.P. Dutton, 1903. 1st Amer ed. 8 plts by Arthur Rackham. Pict cl, gilt. (Spine ends, extrems worn), else VG. *Pacific**. $150/£94

HEPBURN, A. BARTON. The Story of an Outing. NY: Harper, 1913. 1st ed. 1/4 brn cl over paper-cvrd bds, 4 corners cvrd in cl. NF. *Biscotti*. $75/£47

HEPPLEWHITE, A. The Cabinet-Maker and Upholsterer's Guide. London: Batsford, 1897. Facs of 1794 ed (3rd ed). Folio. (vi),24pp; 125 plts. Gilt-dec cl. (Lt spotting.) *Edwards*. $240/£150

HERBERT, A. P. The Ayes Have It. London: Methuen, 1937. 1st ed. Orange cl. NF. *Temple*. $32/£20

HERBERT, A. P. The Bomber Gipsy and Other Poems. London: Methuen, 1918. 1st ed. Red cl. VG in dj (sm tear). *Maggs*. $120/£75

HERBERT, A. P. Holy Deadlock. London: Methuen, (1934). 1st Eng ed. Nice. *Cady*. $15/£9

HERBERT, A. P. Independent Member. London, (1952). Inscribed, dated. 2 maps. Dj (torn). *Argosy*. $35/£22

HERBERT, A. P. The Secret Battle. NY: Knopf, 1920. 1st US ed. Blue cl. (Spotted, few mks to cl), o/w Good. *Reese*. $20/£13

HERBERT, AGNES. Casuals in the Caucasus; The Diary of a Sporting Holiday. John Lane, Bodley Head, 1912. 1st ed. Dk blue cl, gilt. (Edges sl spotted, spine ends sl worn), o/w Good. *Sotheran*. $157/£98

HERBERT, AGNES. Two Dianas in Alaska. London/NY, 1909. (Foxed throughout; spine discolored, edges rubbed.) *Oinonen**. $90/£56

HERBERT, AGNES. Two Dianas in Somaliland. London: J. Lane, (1908). 2nd ed. (2-inch tear at spine head), else VG. *Mikesh*. $30/£19

HERBERT, EDWARD. The Autobiography.... Gregynog, 1928. One of 300. Folio. 9 wood-engrs. Teg, others uncut. Brn buckram. VG (sl rubbed, mkd). *Cox*. $384/£240

HERBERT, FRANK. Chapterhouse: Dune. NY: Putnam, (1985). One of 750 numbered, signed. Fine in slipcase. *Antic Hay*. $100/£63

HERBERT, FRANK. Dune Messiah. NY: Putnam, (1969). 1st ed. (Name), else Fine in NF dj (spine ends, extrems sl rubbed). *Pacific**. $230/£144

HERBERT, FRANK. Dune. Phila, (1965). 1st ed. 8vo. Nice in dj (sl rubbed, white portion rear panel sl soiled). *Swann**. $1,265/£791

HERBERT, FRANK. Dune. London, 1966. 1st UK ed. NF (edges lt soiled) in VG dj (edgeworn, few short closed tears). *Warren*. $175/£109

HERBERT, FRANK. The Green Brain. NY: Ace, 1966. 1st ed. Pb orig. NF. *Warren*. $25/£16

HERBERT, FRANK. The White Plague. NY: Putnam, (1983). One of 500 numbered, signed. Blue cl. Fine in cl-cvrd slipcase. *Antic Hay*. $85/£53

HERBERT, GEORGE R. South-Sea Bubbles. NY: Appleton, 1872. 297,2 ads. (Cl rubbed, spine ends worn.) *Adelson*. $150/£94

HERBERT, GEORGE. The English Works of George Herbert. George Herbert Palmer (ed). Boston/NY: Houghton Mifflin, 1905. Lg paper ed. 1st ed thus. One of 150 sets. 6 vols. 5 ports, engrs, manuscripts, mtd, w/pg guards for each. Uncut. Bds, linen spines. Fine set. *Hartfield.* $450/£281

HERBERT, GEORGE. The Remains.... Pickering, 1841. 2nd Pickering ed, w/half-title, allowing it to stand as vol 1. Frontis. Orig cl, paper label. Good (lt mkd). *Cox.* $24/£15

HERBERT, GEORGE. The Works. London: Pickering, 1841. 2nd ed. 2 vols. Full roan, gilt. Fine. *Argosy.* $175/£109

HERBERT, H. J. G. Reminiscences of Athens and the Morea; Extracts from a Journal of Travels in Greece in 1839. John Murray, 1869. 1st, only ed. 8vo. xli,230,(ii) ads pp; fldg map. Grn cl, emb bds, gilt. (Map sl browned), o/w VG. *Sotheran.* $957/£598

HERBERT, HENRY WILLIAM. Frank Forester's Fugitive Sporting Sketches. Westfield, 1879. 3/4 morocco (orig wrappers bound in). *Swann*.* $138/£86

HERBERT, HENRY WILLIAM. Frank Forester's Horse and Horsemanship of the United States and British Provinces of North America. NY, 1857. 1st ed, earliest(?) state w/colon after 'NY' and full period after 'Broadway' in imprint in vol 1. 2 vols. 2 vignette tps, 10 pedigrees, 13 (of 14) mtd India proof plts. VG set (contemp newspaper clippings affixed to vol 1 eps; lt rubbed, spine ends evenly trimmed). BAL 8159. *Kane*.* $250/£156

HERBERT, HENRY WILLIAM. Frank Forester's Horse and Horsemanship of the United States and British Provinces of North America. NY: Stringer & Townsend, 1857. 1st ed. 2 vols. 552; 576pp + index; 16 engr plts. Blind-stamped, gilt, dec cl. VG (expert repairs to spine ends, joints). *House.* $300/£188

HERBERT, HENRY WILLIAM. Hints to Horse-Keepers, a Complete Manual for Horsemen.... NY: OJ, (1859). 1st ed. Brn cl, gilt. (Spine ends chipped), else VG. *Pacific*.* $98/£61

HERBERT, JAMES. Lair. New English Library, 1979. 1st UK ed. Fine in dj. *Williams.* $280/£175

HERBERT, JAMES. The Rats. New English Library, 1974. 1st UK ed, 1st bk. VG (sm ink # fep, foxed, sl mks to 1/2-title) in dj (worn, creased, spine sl damaged). *Williams.* $200/£125

HERBERT, JAMES. The Spear. New English Library, 1978. 1st UK ed. Inscribed. Fine in dj (price-clipped). *Williams.* $77/£48

HERBERT, LORD (ed). The Pembroke Papers 1734-1780.... London, 1942. 1st ed thus. VG (bkpl). *Gretton.* $27/£17

HERBERT, THOMAS. Memoirs of the Last Years of the Reign of King Charles I...To Which Is Added...a Letter from Sir Thomas Herbert to Sir William Dugdale. London: G. & W. Nicol, 1813. Engr frontisport, viii,222pp. Uncut. Pub's marbled bds (rebacked in linen). *Young.* $72/£45

HERBERT, WALLY. Across the Top of the World. London: Longmans, 1969. Map. Fine in dj. *Explorer.* $19/£12

HERCULES, FRANK. I Want a Black Doll. NY: S&S, 1967. 1st ed. Fine (bkpl) in NF dj (sm tears). *Beasley.* $30/£19

HERD, SANDY. My Golfing Life, Told to Clyde Foster. NY: E.P. Dutton, 1923. 1st Amer ed. (Bkpl, plts, lower fr joint stained; spine soiled), else VG. *Pacific*.* $109/£68

HERDER, J.G. The Spirit of Hebrew Poetry. James Marsh (trans). Burlington, (VT): Edward D. Smith, 1833. 1st ed. 2 vols. (Sig, browned.) Contemp calf-backed marbled bds (spine rubbed). *M & S.* $250/£156

HERDMAN, WILLIAM A. Founders of Oceanography and Their Work. London, 1923. 1st ed. 29 plts. (Sm lib label, ink mk to fep, rep; extrems sl rubbed.) *Edwards.* $77/£48

HERGE. The Adventures of Tintin: the Black Island. London: Methuen, 1961. 1st UK ed. 9x12. 62pp. VG (bds, spine worn). *Price.* $36/£23

HERGE. The Adventures of Tintin: the Shooting Star. London: Methuen, 1966. 1st UK ed. 9x12. 62pp. Good (name, phone; rear sl scuffed, hinge started, spine cracked, bd edges worn). *Price.* $28/£18

HERGESHEIMER, JOSEPH. Berlin. NY: Knopf, 1932. 1st ed. One of 125 on utopian heather laid paper, signed. Black cl, black bds. NF (extrems lt rubbed) in glassine wrapper (browned, chipped). *Heritage.* $150/£94

HERGESHEIMER, JOSEPH. The Limestone Tree. NY, 1931. 1st ed. One of 225. Signed. Dj (sl worn), box. *Kane*.* $23/£14

HERIOT, GEORGE. Travels Through the Canadas. London: Richard Phillips, 1807. 1st ed. 4to. Aquatint frontis, 25 (of 26) aquatint plts, incl 5 fldg, 1 fldg hand-colored map. (Offsetting from plts, lt spotted, lower margin of 3N torn away, upper margin 5 leaves creased, torn.) Marbled edges. Contemp 1/2 calf, marbled bds (fr joint split, inner fr hinges cracked, corners bumped). *Christie's*.* $685/£428

HERKOMER, HUBERT. Etching and Mezzotint Engraving. Macmillan, 1892. vii,107pp (eps spotted); 13 etchings. Uncut. Cream cl (soiled, spine dknd), gilt. *Hollett.* $152/£95

HERLIHY, JAMES LEO and WILLIAM NOBLE. Blue Denim. NY: Random House, (1958). 1st ed, 1st bk. (Faint erasure fep), else VF in VF dj (sl soiled). *Between The Covers.* $200/£125

HERLIHY, JAMES LEO. Midnight Cowboy. NY: S&S, (1965). 1st ed. Blue cl, gilt. (Spine sl faded), o/w NF in dj (rear panel, spine sl soiled; few spine creases). *Heritage.* $150/£94

Hermit; or, Unparalleld Sufferings and Surprising Adventures of Mr. Philip Quaill, an Englishman. London: Ptd for J. Wren, 1780. 12th ed. Old 1/2 leather, marbled paper bds. (Lt foxed; worn, hinges starting.) *Metropolitan*.* $172/£108

HERNANDEZ, FRANCES. The Catalan Chronicle of Francisco de Moncada. El Paso: Texas Western Press, 1975. 1st ed in English. NF in dj. *Dumont.* $40/£25

HERNDON, WILLIAM LEWIS and LARDNER GIBBON. Exploration of the Valley of the Amazon.... Washington, 1854. House of Representatives ptg. 3 vols. 52 plts, 2 fldg maps; separate folder w/3 fldg maps. (Maps weak, separated at folds, sl torn but complete; spines faded, map folder loose, lacks spine.) *Kane*.* $170/£106

HERNMARCK, CARL. The Art of the European Silversmith, 1430-1830. London, (1977). 2 vols. Sm folio. Djs, cl slipcase. *Swann*.* $57/£36

HERODOTUS. The Histories of Herodotus. Harry Carter (trans). Haarlem: LEC, 1958. One of 1500 ptd. Signed by Edward Bawden (illus). Brn buckram, beveled bds, emb port fr cvr. Fine in dec slipcase. *Pacific*.* $63/£39

HERODOTUS. The History of Herodotus of Halicarnassus. A. W. Lawrence (ed). Nonesuch Press, 1935. One of 675. Add'l pict tp, 9 maps. Teg, rest uncut. Orig vellum-backed cl, gilt. Dj. *Sotheby's*.* $478/£299

Heroes of the Plains, or Lives and Wonderful Adventures of Wild Bill, Buffalo Bill, Kit Carson, Capt. Payne, 'White Beaver,' Capt. Jack, Texas Jack, California Joe.... Phila: West Phila Pub, (1891). 1st ed. Frontis chromolitho, 612pp. (Fr hinge starting), else VG. *Pacific*.* $29/£18

HEROLD, STANLEY CARROLLTON. Analytical Principles of the Production of Oil, Gas, and Water from Wells; a Treatise.... Stanford: Stanford Univ, 1928. Fine in dj (lt worn). *Weber.* $45/£28

HERR, CHARLOTTE B. How Freckle Frog Made Herself Pretty. Chicago: P.F. Volland, (1913). 1st ed. 6.25x4.5. Frances Beem (illus). Pict bds. (Bds soiled), else VG. *Pacific*.* $29/£18

HERR, MICHAEL. Dispatches. NY: Knopf, 1977. 1st ed. Fine in NF dj. *Pettler.* $75/£47

HERR, MICHAEL. Dispatches. Picador, 1978. 1st UK ed. Pb orig. VG (sm label). *Williams.* $45/£28

HERR, PAMELA. Jessie Benton Fremont, American Woman of the 19th Century. NY: Franklin Watts, (1987). 1st ed. Fine in Fine dj. *Book Market.* $40/£25

HERRICK, ROBERT. One Hundred and Eleven Poems. (Waltham St. Lawrence): Golden Cockerel, 1955. One of 550. Teg. 1/4 vellum, gilt-stamped cl. Fine in slipcase. *Pacific*.* $259/£162

HERRICK, ROBERT. Wanderings. London: Cape, 1926. 1st Eng ed. NF (feps partly browned, edges sl spotted; spine foot sl bumped) in dj (sl spotted, sl nicked). *Ulysses.* $104/£65

HERRICK, SOPHIE B. The Wonders of Plant Life Under the Microscope. NY, 1883. 1st ed. 248pp. Grn cl, gilt. VG. *Larry Price.* $45/£28

HERRIMAN, GEORGE. Krazy Kat. NY: Henry Holt, (1946). 1st ed. Orange cl (Cvrs lt spotted), o/w Fine in dj (price-clipped, chipped, soiled, rear cvr torn). *Heritage.* $250/£156

HERRING, JAMES and JAMES B. LONGACRE. The National Portrait Gallery of Distinguished Americans. NY, 1834-1839. 1st bk ed. 4 vols. Tall 4to. Pub's deluxe binding: gilt-pict black morocco, spines gilt extra. *Swann*.* $690/£431

HERRING, RICHARD. Paper and Paper Making, Ancient and Modern. Longman, Brown, Green, and Longmans, 1856. 2nd ed. Frontis, xvi,125,(2)pp; 30 specimens of paper (1 fldg), 24pp pub's cat, 4 litho plts. Uncut. (sl rubbed, spine ends sl chipped). *Forest.* $408/£255

HERRIOT, JAMES. Let Sleeping Vets Lie. Joseph, 1973. 1st ed. VG in dj (sl dull). *Whiteson.* $16/£10

HERRIOT, JAMES. Vets Might Fly. Joseph, 1976. 1st ed. VG in dj (sl discolored). *Whiteson.* $16/£10

HERSCHEL, JOHN. Outlines of Astronomy. London: Longman, Brown, Green et al, 1849. 1st ed. 5 engr plts. Mod 1/2 blue levant morocco, gilt. (Tp, frontis sl fingered.) *Hollett.* $264/£165

HERSCHEL, JOHN. A Treatise on Astronomy. Phila: Carey, Lea & Blanchard, 1834. 396pp; 3 plts. (Foxed, water-stained, rough.) Internally Clean. *Bookcell.* $80/£50

HERSEY, JOHN. A Bell for Adano. NY, 1944. 1st ed. (Spine ends sl dknd), else VG in dj (chipped, worn). *King.* $35/£22

HERSEY, JOHN. Hiroshima. LEC, 1983. Ltd to 1500 numbered, signed by Hersey, Jacob Lawrence (illus), and Robert Penn Warren (intro). Fine in slipcase. *Swann*.* $632/£395

HERSEY, JOHN. Men on Baatan. NY, 1942. 1st ed, 1st bk. NF in VG dj (few tears, rear panel crinkled). *Warren.* $85/£53

HERSEY, JOHN. The Wall. LEC, 1957. Ltd to 1500 numbered, signed by William Sharp (illus). Fine in slipcase. *Swann*.* $69/£43

HERSHBERGER, H. R. The Horseman. A Work on Horsemanship...to Which Is Annexed a Sabre Exercise for Mounted and Dismounted Service. NY, 1844. 1st ed. 30 plts. Orig gilt-pict cl (shelfworn; sl foxed, soiled). *Oinonen*.* $140/£88

HERSHOLT, JEAN (ed). The Evergreen Tales. Group 1. LEC, 1948. One of 2500 sets signed. 3 vols. Fine in slipcase. *Swann*.* $126/£79

HERSHOLT, JEAN (ed). The Evergreen Tales. Group 2. LEC, 1949. One of 2500 sets signed by Hersholt and Robert Lawson (illus). 3 vols. Fine in slipcase. *Swann*.* $115/£72

HERSHOLT, JEAN (ed). The Evergreen Tales. Group 3. LEC, 1949. One of 2500 sets signed by Edward Ardizzone & Everett G. Jackson (illus) and Hersholt. 3 vols. Fine in slipcase. *Swann*.* $201/£126

HERSHOLT, JEAN (ed). The Evergreen Tales. Group 4. LEC, 1952. One of 2000 sets signed by Hersholt, Fritz Eichenberg, R. Bussoni and E. Metzel (illus). 3 vols. Fine in slipcase. *Swann*.* $115/£72

HERSHOLT, JEAN (ed). The Evergreen Tales. Group 5. LEC, 1952. One of 2000 sets signed. 3 vols. Fine in slipcase. *Swann*.* $138/£86

HERT, C. Tracking the Big Cats. Caldwell: Caxton, 1955. 1st ed. Fine in VG + dj. *Mikesh.* $75/£47

HERTER, GEORGE LEONARD and BERTHE. Bull Cook and Authentic Historical Recipes and Practices. Waseca, MN, (1964). 9th ed. VG. *Perier.* $17/£11

HERTRICH, WILLIAM. The Huntington Botanical Gardens 1905-1949. San Marino: Huntington Library, 1949. 1st ed. Ltd to 1000. Dec paper-cvrd bds, cl spine. Fine. *Quest.* $50/£31

HERTZ, EMANUEL. Abraham Lincoln: A New Portrait. NY: Liveright, (1931). 1st ed. 2 vols. Untrimmed. Navy buckram (sl rubbed, dusty), gilt. Internally VG. *Baltimore*.* $20/£13

HERTZ, EMANUEL. Report of the Select Committee Relative to the Soldiers' National Cemetery.... Harrisburg: Singerly & Myers; State Ptrs, 1864. Frontis litho map (browned), 111pp; toned fldg litho map. Blind black cl, gilt, sm old paper spine label. Cvrs VG. (Corners worn; ex-lib, bkpl, spine label mkd; sl foxed.) *Baltimore*.* $35/£22

HERVEY, A. B. Beautiful Wild Flowers of America. Boston: D. Lothrop, 1882. 156pp; 14 chromlithographs, guards (1 guard missing, 1 loose). Aeg. Dec cl. (Inscrip, notes; sl soiled), else VG. *Fair Meadow.* $150/£94

HERVEY, FREDERIC et al. The Naval History of Great Britain; from the Earliest Times to the Rising of the Parliament in 1779. London: William Adlard, 1779. 1st ed. 5 vols. Period calf, some morocco spine labels. (1 plt vol 5 mtd to fep; lacks most spine labels, glue to joints, spine ends), else VG set. Bkpls, sigs of George Henry Towry. *Pacific*.* $230/£144

HERVEY, JOHN and WALTER S. VOSBURGH. Racing in America 1665-1921. NY: Privately ptd for the Jockey Club, (1922-44). One of 800 numbered sets. 4 vols. Lg 4to. Uncut. Cl-backed bds, paper spine labels. (Sl worn.) *Oinonen*.* $900/£563

HERVEY, JOHN. Lady Suffolk; the Old Gray Mare of Long Island. NY: Derrydale, 1936. Ltd to 500 numbered. Vellum cl backed over mustard paper-cvrd bds. VF. *Biscotti.* $175/£109

HERVEY, JOHN. Memoirs of the Reign of King George II. Romney Sedgwick (ed). London: King's Ptrs, 1931. 1st ed. One of 900 sets. 3 vols. Frontisports each vol. Teg, uncut. Blue cl. Fine in box (sl worn). *Hartfield.* $325/£203

HERVEY, JOHN. Messenger. The Great Progenitor. NY: Derrydale, (1935). One of 500 numbered. Uncut. Paper cvr label. (Lt worn.) *Oinonen*.* $90/£56

HERVEY, JOHN. Racing in America, 1665-1865. NY: Privately ptd for The Jockey Club, (1944). 1st ed. One of 800 numbered sets. 2 vols. Thick sm folio. Top edges stained red-brn, untrimmed. Tan buckram, bds, ptd paper spine labels. (Edges sl rubbed.) Internally Fine. *Baltimore*.* $150/£94

HESS, HANS. Lyonel Feininger. NY: Abrams, (1961). (Several ll edges dampstained, not affecting text or plts.) Dj. *Swann*.* $201/£126

HESS, HANS. Lyonel Feininger. NY: Abrams, ca 1961. Color mtd repros. (Fep clipped.) Dj (lg chip fr panel). *Swann*.* $316/£198

HESSE, HERMAN. Steppenwolf. LEC, 1977. One of 1600 signed by Helmut Ackermann (illus). Fine in slipcase. *Swann*.* $46/£29

HESSE, MAX RENE. The White Flame. London: Faber & Faber, (1932). 1st ed. Gilt black cl. (Eps sl foxed, lt stain rep), else Good. *Reese.* $30/£19

HESSELS, J. H. Haarlem: The Birth-Place of Printing, Not Mentz. Elliot Stock, 1887. 1st ed. Uncut. *Forest.* $72/£45

HESTON, ALFRED M. Absegami: Annals of Eyren Haven and Atlantic City, 1609-1904. Volume I only. The Author, 1904. 1st ed. One of 500. Orig subscriber's copy w/his sig. Lg engr tinted map laid in. (Rebound w/orig fr cvr title transposed.) Contents Fine. *Heinoldt.* $45/£28

HESTWOOD, HAROLD K. Gawpy: Book One. Carmel-by-the-Sea, CA: Hestwood Studios, 1926. 1st ed. 4to. Cl-backed b/w pict bds (edges sl rubbed). *Reisler.* $75/£47

HETH, EDWARD HARRIS. Any Number Can Play. NY: Harper, 1945. 1st ed. Fine in Fine dj. *Between The Covers.* $50/£31

HETHERINGTON, A. L. The Early Ceramic Wares of China. London, 1922. Color frontis, 44 plts. Fore, lower edges uncut. (Cl sl sunned, spine sl chipped.) Internally VG. *Edwards.* $80/£50

HETHERINGTON, A. L. The Early Ceramic Wares of China. London, 1922. (Remnants of mtd cuttings on feps, pencil notes reps.) *Swann*.* $258/£161

HEWARD, BILL and DIMITRI GAT. Some Are Called Clowns. Crowell, 1974. 1st ed. VG + in VG + dj. *Plapinger.* $60/£38

HEWARD, CONSTANCE. Ameliaranne Keeps School. Harrap, 1946. 3rd ptg. Tall 8vo. 28 full-pg color illus by S.B. Pearse. Color pict eps. Pict bds. (Edges grazed), else VG. *Bookmark.* $27/£17

HEWARD, CONSTANCE. Ameliaranne Keeps Shop. Phila: David McKay, (1928). 1st Amer ed. Susan Beatrice Pearse (illus). 8vo. Cl-backed color illus bds. Good in color dj (dusting, lt edgewear). *Reisler.* $120/£75

HEWARD, CONSTANCE. The Twins and Tabiffa. Phila: Macrae Smith, 1923. Susan Beatrice Pearse (illus). 8vo. 121pp. Blue cl, color paste label. Good in full color dj (dusting). *Reisler.* $150/£94

HEWES, AGNES DANFORTH. A Boy of the Lost Crusade. Boston: Houghton Mifflin, 1923. 1st ed. 279pp. 4 plts, cvr plt by Gustaf Tenggren. VG (bottom rt corner of plt torn off 1/8-inch; corners, spine ends bumped). *Price.* $50/£31

HEWETT, D. F. et al. Mineral Resources of the Region Around Boulder Dam. Washington: USGS, 1936. 14 plts (8 fldg), 3 maps in rear pocket. VG (spine sunned, cvrs worn). *Five Quail.* $30/£19

HEWETT, DANIEL. The American Traveller; or, National Directory, Containing an Account of All the Great Post Roads, and Most Important Cross Roads, in the United States. Washington, 1825. 19th-cent 1/2 morocco. (Lt foxed; extrems rubbed.) Howes H453. *Swann*.* $460/£288

HEWETT, EDGAR L. The Chaco Canyon and Its Monuments. Albuquerque, 1936. VG in dj (chipped, taped). *Dumont.* $75/£47

HEWETT, EDGAR L. Kit Carson. He Led the Way. Santa Fe, NM, 1946. 1st ed. Photo port. Fine in gray ptd wrappers. *Argonaut.* $25/£16

HEWETT, EDGAR L. et al. The Physiography of the Rio Grande Valley, New Mexico, in Relation to Pueblo Culture. BAE Bulletin 54. Washington: GPO, 1913. 1st ed. Fldg panoramic frontis, map. Grn cl (spine dknd, extrems worn). VG + . *Harrington.* $35/£22

HEWETT, STEPHEN H. A Scholar's Letters from the Front. London, 1918. 1st Eng ed. Pub's rev slip. (Grubby, dust-mkd.) *Clearwater.* $88/£55

HEWITT, EDWARD R. Better Trout Streams. NY: Scribner, 1931. 1st ed. (Cvrs sunned), else VG; internally Fine. *Bowman.* $110/£69

HEWITT, EDWARD R. Hewitt's Trout Raising and Stocking. NY: Marchbanks, 1935. 1st ed. VF. *Bowman.* $150/£94

HEWITT, GRAILY. The Pen and Type-Design. London: First Edition Club, 1928. 1st ed. One of 250. Good in full deep red morocco (edges sl worn, sl discolored), gilt. *Maggs.* $216/£135

HEWITT, JOHN H. Shadows on the Wall or Glimpses of the Past. Balt: Turnbull Bros, 1877. 1st ed. Signed, inscribed. 249pp. Good (sl worn). Howes H456. *Brown.* $75/£47

HEWLETT, MAURICE (ed). The Fool Errant: Being the Memoirs of Francis-Anthony Strelley, Esq., Citizen of Lucca. Heinemann, 1905. Good (bkpl, sl cocked; spine bumped, chipped, sunned). *Tiger.* $16/£10

HEWLETT, MAURICE. Artemission: Idylls and Songs. Elkin Mathews/Scribner, 1909. Ltd to 250. VG (bkpl; spine lt sunned). *Tiger.* $32/£20

HEWLETT, MAURICE. A Ballad of 'The Gloster' and 'The Goeben.' Poetry Bookshop, n.d. (1914). 1st Eng ed. Folded sheet. Good (offsetting from illus; outer panel edges browned, 1/2-inch tear top edges). *Ulysses.* $58/£36

HEWLETT, MAURICE. Bendish: A Study in Prodigality. Macmillan, 1913. Pub's cat dated Autumn 1913. Teg. VG (sl spotted, bkpl; spine bumped). *Tiger.* $22/£14

HEWLETT, MAURICE. Flowers in the Grass. London: Constable, 1920. 1st ed. Pub's presentation blindstamp. Blue-gray bds, paper spine label. VG (w/o dj). *Reese.* $25/£16

HEWLETT, MAURICE. The Forest Lovers. Macmillan, 1909. New ed, 1st ed thus. Teg. Nice (sl spotted; spine bumped, sl sunned, cvrs unevenly sunned). *Tiger.* $22/£14

HEWLETT, MAURICE. The Life and Death of Richard Yea-and-Nay. Macmillan, 1900. Good (sl spotted, bkpl; spine bumped, cvr sl mkd). *Tiger.* $24/£15

HEWLETT, MAURICE. Quattrocentisteria: How Sandro Botticelli Saw Simonetta in the Spring. NY: Grolier Club, 1921. One of 300. Sm slim folio. Untrimmed paper w/unicorn water mk. Tan cl, marbled bds, ptd paper spine label. Text Nice (pg edges lt rippled; edges worn, dknd, spine ends lt frayed). *Baltimore*.* $45/£28

HEWLETT, MAURICE. Rest Harrow. Bernhard Tauchnitz, 1911. Copyright ed. Sprinkled edges. Contemp cl (spine bumped, sunned). Good (bkpl). *Tiger.* $16/£10

HEWLETT, MAURICE. Singsongs of the War. Poetry Bookshop, 1914. 1st Eng ed. Pict card wrappers (edges sl tanned). *Clearwater.* $56/£35

HEWLETT, MAURICE. The Stooping Lady. Macmillan, 1907. Teg. Good (sl spotted; spine bumped, cvr sl mkd). *Tiger.* $26/£16

HEWLETT, MAURICE. The Village Wife's Lament. London: Martin Secker, (1918). 1st ed. Gray bds, ptd spine label. Fine in NF dj. *Reese.* $40/£25

Hey Diddle Diddle Picture Book. Routledge, n.d. (1883). 1st combined ed. Obl 4to. 24 color plts by Randolph Caldecott. Pict cream-color cl. Sound (dust-stained). *Bookmark.* $64/£40

HEY, MAX H. An Index of Mineral Species and Varieties Arranged Chemically. London: British Museum, 1950. 1st ed. Blue cl, gilt. (Ex-lib), else VG. *Larry Price.* $30/£19

HEYEN, WILLIAM. Lord Dragonfly. NY: Vanguard, (1981). One of 150 numbered, signed. NF in dj, cardbd slipcase. *Antic Hay.* $50/£31

HEYER, GEORGETTE. The Black Moth. Boston: H-M, 1921. 1st ed, 1st bk. VG (lacks dj). *Else Fine.* $40/£25

HEYER, GEORGETTE. Death in the Stocks. NY: Dutton, 1970. 1st US ed. VG + (sl shelfworn) in dj (edgeworn). *My Bookhouse.* $27/£17

HEYER, GUSTAV RICHARD. The Organism of the Mind. An Introduction to Analytical Psychotherapy. NY: Harcourt, 1934. 1st ed. VG (lib mks, stamp; dot on spine). *Beasley.* $40/£25

HEYERDAHL, THOR. The Art of Easter Island. GC: Doubleday, 1975. 1st ed. 336 plts (16 color). Lt grn linen. Good in dj. *Karmiole.* $125/£78

HEYL, EDITH STOWE GODFREY (comp). Bermuda Through the Camera of James B. Heyl, 1868-1897. Hamilton, Bermuda: Distributed by the Bermuda Book Stores, 1951. 1st ed. Ltd to 1500 numbered. Frontis. Gilt-dec blue cl. VG. *Cahan.* $200/£125

HEYNEMAN, JULIE HELEN. Arthur Putnam, Sculptor. SF, 1932. One of 500. Leather spine. *Dawson.* $75/£47

HEYSINGER, ISAAC W. Antietam and the Maryland and Virginia Campaigns of 1862. NY: Neale, 1912. 1st ed. Maroon cl. (Sm ink stain lower fore-edge; spine sl faded), else NF. *Chapel Hill.* $165/£103

HEYWARD, DOROTHY and DU BOSE. Mamba's Daughters. NY: Farrar & Rinehart, (1939). 1st ed thus. Grn cl. NF (ink stamp; spine faded, 2 lt stains on foot) in dj (rear panel lt soiled). *Heritage.* $250/£156

HEYWARD, DU BOSE. Jasbo Brown and Selected Poems. NY: Farrar & Rinehart, (1931). 1st ed. (Name; dampstained), else VG in dj (extrems dampstained, sm tears). *Pacific*.* $35/£22

HEYWOOD, GERALD G. P. Charles Cotton and His River. Manchester: Sherratt & Hughes, 1928. 1st ed. Grn cl, gilt. (Spine head, corners sl worn), else VG. *Pacific*.* $288/£180

HEYWOOD, MARTHA SPENCE. Not By Bread Alone: The Journal of Martha Spence Heywood 1850-56. Juanita Brooks (ed). Salt Lake City: UT State Hist Soc, (1978). 1st ed. VG in dj. *Lien.* $25/£16

HEYWOOD, SAMUEL. A Vindication of Mr. Fox's History of the Early Part of the Reign of James the Second. London: J. Johnson, 1811. 1st ed. xl,424,lix pp. (Few ll rust spotted), o/w Very Clean in contemp calf (neatly rebacked). *Young.* $192/£120

HEYWOOD, THOMAS. The Life of Merlin, Sirnamed Ambrosius. His Prophesies, and Predictions Interpreted.... London, 1641. 1st ed. 4to. Frontis. 19th-cent calf. *Felcone.* $2,000/£1,250

HEYWOOD, V. H. (ed). Flowering Plants of the World. NY: Mayflower, 1978. 1st US ed. VG in dj. *Archer.* $50/£31

HEYWOOD, VALENTINE. British Titles. London: A&C Black, 1951. 1st ed. VG. *Hollett.* $40/£25

HIAASEN, CARL and WILLIAM D. MONTALBANO. A Death in China. NY: Atheneum, 1984. 1st ed. NF (top edge sl scuffed) in NF dj. *Warren.* $100/£63

HIAASEN, CARL. Double Whammy. NY: Putnam, 1987. 1st ed. Fine in NF dj. *Lame Duck.* $65/£41

HIAASEN, CARL. Tourist Season. NY: Putnam, 1986. 1st ed. Signed. VF in dj (edges lt worn). *Lame Duck.* $150/£94

HIBBARD, HOWARD. Poussin. The Holy Family on the Steps. NY, 1974. Good in dj. *Washton.* $25/£16

HIBBEN, F. Hunting American Lions. NY: Crowell, 1948. 1st ed. Dbl-pg sepia dwg. VG. *Mikesh.* $35/£22

HIBBEN, FRANK C. Kiva Art of the Anasazi at Pottery Mound. Las Vegas, NV, 1975. Signed. VG in dj. *Dumont.* $75/£47

HIBBEN, HENRY B. Navy-Yard, Washington. Washington: GPO, 1890. Senate Exec Doc 22. 1st ed. 240pp; 2 fldg plts. Mod 1/2 morocco. *Lefkowicz.* $100/£63

HIBBERD, SHIRLEY. The Amateur's Greenhouse and Conservatory. Groombridge, 1873. 1st ed. 272pp; 6 fldg litho color plts (incl frontis). VG in grn dec cl (nicked, spine head sl rubbed). *Hadley.* $128/£80

HIBBERD, SHIRLEY. The Fern Garden. London: Groombridge & Sons, 1878. 7th ed. 148pp + 20pp ads; 8 color plts, 40 wood engrs. Grn cl, gilt. (Fep removed), else VG. *Quest.* $110/£69

HIBBS, B. and P. DE KRUIF. Two Men on a Job. Curtis Publishing, 1938. 1st ed. (Rubbed, sm area effaced from fr panel), else VG in paper bds as issued. *Fine Books.* $30/£19

HICHBORN, PHILIP. Report on European Dockyards. Washington: GPO, 1886. 1st ed. Gilt-lettered blue cl. (Name), else VG. *Pacific*.* $58/£36

HICHENS, ROBERT. The Garden of Allah. NY: Grosset & Dunlap, (1936). 1st ed. (Fep corner lt clipped), else VF in VF dj. *Between The Covers.* $100/£63

HICKLIN, JOHN. The Handbook of Llandudno. Chester: Catherall & Pritchard, 1866. 11th thousand. (ii),162,(iv)pp; 12 engr vignettes on 8 card ll, fldg map. Blind-stamped cl (spine, edges faded), gilt. *Hollett.* $136/£85

HICKS, ELIAS. Journal of the Life and Religious Labors of.... NY, 1832. 451pp. New buckram (rebound; dampstains, foxing throughout). *Heinoldt.* $20/£13

HICKS, JAMES E. Nathan Starr, U.S. Sword and Arms Maker. Mt. Vernon, NY: The Author, (1940). Blue cl (lt soiled). *Glenn.* $20/£13

HICKS, JOHN W. The Theory of the Rifle and Rifle Shooting. London: Charles Griffin, 1919. 1st ed. Frontis, 7 tables (2 fldg; fore-edge of 1 sl worn). *Hollett.* $56/£35

Hide and Seek. National Geographic Action Book. Nat'l Geographic Soc, 1985. 6 dbl-pg pop-ups by Barbara Gibson. Glazed pict bds. VG. *Bookfinders.* $40/£25

HIEB, LOUIS A. Tony Hillerman: A Bibliography, from The Blessing Way to Talking God. Tucson: Press of the Gigantic Hound, 1990. One of 1000. Signed. Fine. *Pacific*.* $92/£58

HIELSCHER, KURT. Picturesque Spain. NY: Brentano, n.d. (ca 1920). 1st ed. (Rubbed, spine faded), o/w VG. *Worldwide.* $25/£16

HIEOVER, HARRY. (Pseud of Charles Bindley.) Bipeds and Quadrupeds. London: Newby, 1853. 3/4 red morocco by Zaehnsdorf (lt rubbed). *Oinonen*.* $80/£50

HIEOVER, HARRY. (Pseud of Charles Bindley.) Hints to Horsemen; Showing How to Make Money by Horses. London: Newby, 1856. Teg. 3/4 red morocco by Zaehnsdorf. (Orig cvr bound in at end; lt rubbed.) *Oinonen*.* $80/£50

HIEOVER, HARRY. (Pseud of Charles Bindley.) The Hunting-Field. London: Longman, 1850. Engr frontis. 3/4 red morocco by Zaehnsdorf. (Orig cvr bound in at end; lt rubbed.) *Oinonen*.* $80/£50

HIEOVER, HARRY. (Pseud of Charles Bindley.) The Pocket and the Stud; or, Practical Hints on the Management of the Stable. London, 1848. Engr frontis. 3/4 red morocco by Zaehnsdorf. (Orig cvr bound in at end; lt rubbed.) *Oinonen*.* $170/£106

HIEOVER, HARRY. (Pseud of Charles Bindley.) Practical Horsemanship. London: Longman, 1850. Engr frontis. Teg. 3/4 red morocco by Zaehnsdorf. (Orig cvr bound in at end; lt rubbed.) *Oinonen*.* $80/£50

HIEOVER, HARRY. (Pseud of Charles Bindley.) Precept and Practice. London: Newby, 1857. Teg. 3/4 red morocco by Zaehnsdorf. (Orig cvr bound in at end; rubbing; sm stain tp.) *Oinonen*.* $80/£50

HIEOVER, HARRY. (Pseud of Charles Bindley.) Sporting Facts and Sporting Fancies. London: Newby, 1853. 3/4 red morocco by Zaehnsdorf (lt rubbed). *Oinonen*.* $80/£50

HIEOVER, HARRY. (Pseud of Charles Bindley.) The Sporting World. London, 1858. 3/4 red morocco by Zaehnsdorf. (Orig cvr bound in at end; lt rubbed.) *Oinonen*.* $80/£50

HIEOVER, HARRY. (Pseud of Charles Bindley.) The Sportsman's Friend in a Frost. London: Newby, 1857. 3/4 red morocco by Zaehnsdorf (rubbed). *Oinonen*.* $80/£50

HIEOVER, HARRY. (Pseud of Charles Bindley.) Stable Talk and Table Talk, or Spectacles for Young Sportsmen. London, 1845-46. 2 vols. Teg. 3/4 red morocco by Zaehnsdorf. (Orig cvr/spine bound in at end each vol; lt rubbed.) *Oinonen*.* $140/£88

HIEOVER, HARRY. (Pseud of Charles Bindley.) The Stud, for Practical Purposes and Practical Men. London: Longman, 1849. 2 engr plts. Teg. 3/4 red morocco by Zaehnsdorf. (Orig cvr bound in at end; lt rubbed.) *Oinonen*.* $120/£75

HIEOVER, HARRY. (Pseud of Charles Bindley.) Things Worth Knowing About Horses. London, 1859. Teg. 3/4 red morocco by Zaehnsdorf. (Orig cvr/spine bound in at end; lt rubbed.) *Oinonen*.* $100/£63

HIEOVER, HARRY. (Pseud of Charles Bindley.) A Treatise on the Proper Condition for All Horses. London: Newby, 1852. 2 litho plts. Teg. 3/4 red morocco by Zaehnsdorf (lt rubbed). *Oinonen*.* $120/£75

HIEOVER, HARRY. The World: How to Square It. London: Newby, 1854. 3/4 red morocco by Zaehnsdorf. (Orig cvr bound in at end; lt rubbed.) *Oinonen**. $80/£50

HIGBE, KIRBY and MARTIN QUIGLEY. The High Hard One. Viking, 1967. 1st ed. Fine in VG+ dj. *Plapinger*. $85/£53

HIGGENBOTHAM, DON. The War of American Independence: Military Attitudes, Policies, and Practices, 1763-1789. NY: Macmillan, (1971). 1st ed. Blue cl. Fine in VG+ dj (sl chipped). *Harrington*. $35/£22

HIGGINS, C. A. To California Over the Santa Fe Trail. Chicago: Passenger Dept, Santa Fe, 1911. VG in wraps. *Book Market*. $20/£13

HIGGINS, DICK. City with All the Angles: A Radio Play. West Glover, NY: Unpublished Editions, 1974. 1st ed. Signed. 7 full-pg b/w photos. NF in illus stiff wrappers. *Cahan*. $65/£41

HIGGINS, ETHEL. Our Native Cacti. NY: De la Mare, 1931. 1st ed. Fine in Good dj (chipped). *Archer*. $15/£9

HIGGINS, GEORGE V. The Friends of Eddie Coyle. Secker, 1972. 1st UK ed, 1st bk. NF in dj. *Williams*. $96/£60

HIGGINS, GODFREY. Anacalypsis, an Attempt to Draw Aside the Veil of the Saitic Isis. London, 1836. 2 vols. 46 litho plts. Contemp 1/4 calf (needs rebacking). *Swann**. $431/£269

HIGGINS, HENRY H. Notes by a Field-Naturalist in the Western Tropics. Liverpool: E. Howell, 1877. 1st ed. (vii),205pp; fldg map, 18 plts. Dec red cl, gilt. (Lt foxed.) *Maggs*. $360/£225

HIGGINS, JACK. Storm Warning. NY: Holt, Rinehart & Winston, (1976). 1st ed. VG (sm abrasion rear cvr) in dj. *Antic Hay*. $25/£16

HIGGINSON, A. HENRY. As Hounds Ran. NY: Huntington Press, 1930. One of 990 numbered. Uncut. (Sl worn.) *Oinonen**. $110/£69

HIGGINSON, A. HENRY. British and American Sporting Authors. Berryville, VA, 1949. (Sl worn, sl stain spine foot.) *Oinonen**. $130/£81

HIGGINSON, A. HENRY. British and American Sporting Authors: Their Writings and Biographies. London: Hutchinson, 1951. 1st ed. 16 plts. VG in dj (soiling, sm tears extrms). *Pacific**. $173/£108

HIGGINSON, ELLA. Alaska: The Great Country. NY: Macmillan, 1908. 1st ed. VG. *Perier*. $50/£31

HIGGINSON, THOMAS WENTWORTH. Army Life in a Black Regiment. N.p., 1982. Time-Life rpt of 1870 orig. Aeg. Simulated leather. NF. *Sagebrush*. $22/£14

HIGHET, JOHN. The Scottish Churches. Skeffington, 1960. 1st ed. VG in dj. *Hollett*. $24/£15

HIGHSMITH, PATRICIA. The Black House. London: Heinemann, 1981. 1st ed. Steel-blue cl-textured bds. Fine in dj. *Temple*. $35/£22

HIGHSMITH, PATRICIA. The Blunderer. Cresset, 1956. 1st ed. VG (feps lt browned; top edge sl spotted, dusty, cvrs sl bowed, spine ends, corner sl bumped) in dj (nicked, creased, dusty, sl torn, chipped, internally repaired, flaps browned). *Ulysses*. $240/£150

HIGHSMITH, PATRICIA. Found in the Street. London: Heinemann, 1986. 1st ed. Lt blue cl-textured bds. Fine in dj. *Temple*. $22/£14

HIGHSMITH, PATRICIA. Mermaids on the Golf Course and Other Stories. London: Heinemann, 1985. 1st ed. Scarlet cl. NF in duj (inch tear at rear flap fold repaired w/ghost tape on verso). *Temple*. $38/£24

HIGHSMITH, PATRICIA. Slowly, Slowly, in the Wind. NY: Mysterious Press, (1979). 1st Amer ed. Grn cl, gilt spine. (Rmdr mk top edge), o/w Fine in dj. *Heritage*. $45/£28

HIGHSMITH, PATRICIA. The Snailwatcher and Other Stories. GC: Doubleday, 1970. 1st ed. Pub's file copy stamp fep. Fine in NF dj (spine folds sl rubbed). *Any Amount*. $38/£24

HIGHSMITH, PATRICIA. Strangers on a Train. NY: Harper, (1950). 1st Amer ed. (Tape offset to fr/rear cvrs), else VG-. *Pacific**. $29/£18

HIGHSMITH, PATRICIA. Those Who Walk Away. London: Heinemann, 1967. 1st ed. Dk charcoal bds. Fine in dj (sl mkd, frayed). *Temple*. $32/£20

HIGHSMITH, PATRICIA. The Tremor of Forgery. London: Heinemann, 1969. 1st ed. Orange bds. Fine in dj. *Temple*. $38/£24

HIGHSMITH, PATRICIA. The Two Faces of January. London: Heinemann, (1964). 1st ed. Blue bds, gilt. (Spine cocked), o/w Fine in dj (sl soiled, faded, lt edgeworn). *Heritage*. $150/£94

HIJUELOS, OSCAR. The Fourteen Sisters of Emilio Montez O'Brien. NY: FSG, 1993. 1st ed. Signed. VF in VF dj. *Unger*. $50/£31

HIJUELOS, OSCAR. The Mambo Kings Play Songs of Love. Hamilton, 1989. 1st UK ed. Fine in dj. *Williams*. $32/£20

HIJUELOS, OSCAR. The Mambo Kings Play Songs of Love. London: Hamish Hamilton, 1989. 1st British ed. Fine in dj. *Lame Duck*. $35/£22

HIJUELOS, OSCAR. The Mambo Kings Play Songs of Love. NY: FSG, 1989. NF in dj. *Lame Duck*. $50/£31

HILDBURGH, W. L. Medieval Spanish Enamels and Their Relation to the Origin and the Development of Copper Champleve Enamels of the Twelfth and Thirteenth Centuries. Oxford, 1936. 24 plts. (Sl worn.) *Washton*. $90/£56

HILDRETH, SAMUEL C. and JAMES R. CROWELL. The Spell of the Turf; the Story of American Racing. Phila, 1926. 1st ed. (Sl worn, faded.) *Woolson*. $25/£16

HILER, HILAIRE. From Nudity to Raiment. NY, 1930. Wrappers, pub's bd slipcase (cracked, repaired w/cellotape). *Swann**. $57/£36

HILL, A. V. First and Last Experiments in Muscle Mechanics. Cambridge, 1970. Mint. *Whitehart*. $29/£18

HILL, A. W. (ed). Poisonous Plants. Frederick Etchells & Hugh MacDonald, 1927. One of 350 numbered. 20 full-pg, 2 vignette wood-engrs by John Nash. VG (feps sl browned, pastedowns sl spotted; spine ends, corners sl bumped; lacks dj). *Ulysses*. $760/£475

HILL, AARON. The Dramatic Works of.... London: T. Lownds, 1760. 1st ed. 2 vols. (4),xx,(12),411; 404pp + (4)pp ads. Period calf, gilt. VG (bkpls). *Pacific**. $207/£129

HILL, ALEXANDER STAVELEY. From Home to Home. Ann Arbor: University Microfilms, 1966. Fldg map. VG. *Lien*. $15/£9

HILL, AMELIA LEAVITT. Garden Portraits. NY: Robert M. McBride, 1923. 1st ed. Pict cl, gilt. (Bkpl removed, inscrip), else VG. *Fair Meadow*. $30/£19

HILL, DOUGLAS. The Opening of the Canadian West. NY: John Day, (1967). 1st Amer ed. (Ink name), else Fine in Fine dj. *Perier*. $15/£9

HILL, ELIZABETH. The Widow's Offering. New London, (CT): Starr & Farnhm, 1856. 2nd ed. 281pp. VG (one sig pulled). *Second Life*. $75/£47

HILL, GEORGE BIRKBECK (ed). Colonel Gordon in Central Africa 1874-1879. London: Thos. de la Rue, 1881. Frontisport, xlii,456,(ix)pp; fldg map (sl torn), 2 plts. (Sl foxed, esp prelims; sl mkd, frayed.) *Hollett*. $136/£85

HILL, GRACE LIVINGSTON. An Unwilling Guest. Phila: Judson, 1902. 1st ed. Fine (inscrip; spine base sl rubbed). *Between The Covers*. $100/£63

HILL, H. W. Rowland Hill and the Fight for the Penny Post. London: Frederick Warne, 1940. 1st ed. Frontis port. VG in dj. *Hollett*. $40/£25

HILL, IDA THALLON. The Ancient City of Athens. London: Methuen, (1953). 2 plts. Dj (tattered). *Archaeologia*. $45/£28

HILL, JASPER S. The Letters of a Young Miner, Covering the Adventures of Jasper S. Hill...1849-1852. Doyce B. Nunis, Jr. (ed). SF: John Howell-Books, 1964. Fldg facs map. (Clear plastic dj chipped), else VG + . *Zubal**. $45/£28

HILL, JOE, JR. and OLA DAVIS HILL. In Little America with Byrd. Boston: Ginn & Co, c. 1937. Dbl pg map. Dec cl. VG. *High Latitude.* $30/£19

HILL, JOHN. The Family Herbal, or an Account of All Those English Plants, Which Are Remarkable for Their Virtues, and of the Drugs Which Are Produced by Vegetables of Other Countries. Bungay: Brightly & Kinnersley, n.d. (ca 1810). 54 color plts. Contemp calf-backed bds (shelfworn, soiled, stained, browned). *Oinonen**. $225/£141

HILL, JOSEPH J. The History of Warner's Ranch and Its Environs. L.A.: Privately ptd, 1927. One of 1000. 9 facs plts, ports. Brn cl. VG. *House.* $50/£31

HILL, JOSEPH J. The History of Warner's Ranch and Its Environs. L.A.: Privately ptd, 1927. One of 1000 numbered. (Shelfworn.) Internally Good. Howes 474. *Dumont.* $125/£78

HILL, OLIVER. The Garden of Adonis. London, (1923). 1st ed. (Hinges split, shaken; spine ends worn, corners bumped.) *Swann**. $149/£93

HILL, PATI. Slave Days: 29 Poems, 31 Photocopied Objects. N.p.: Pati Hill, 1975. 1st ed. 31 b/w images. NF (sl worn) in pict stiff wrappers. *Cahan.* $65/£41

HILL, PAUL. David Jones. London: Tate Gallery, (1981). Fine in dj. *Turtle Island.* $30/£19

HILL, SARAH JANE FULL. Mrs. Hill's Journal—Civil War Reminiscences. Chicago: R.R. Donnelley, 1980. Frontis. VG. *Lien.* $30/£19

HILL, SUSAN. Can It Be True? NY: Viking, 1988. 1st ed. 7.5x11. Angela Barrett (illus). 28pp. Fine in dj. *Cattermole.* $20/£13

HILL, T. ST. QUINTIN. The Voyage and Certain Songs. Oxford: Basil Blackwell, 1940. NF in maroon heavy paper wraps. *Cady.* $25/£16

HILL, VERNON. Ballads Weird and Wonderful. London: John Lane, Bodley Head, 1912. 1st ed. 25 full-pg collotype plts, guards (lt creased). Teg, rest uncut. Gray cl (spine sl browned), gilt. *Sotheran.* $109/£68

HILL, W. A. Historic Hays.... Hays, KS: News Pub, 1938. 1st ed. Pub notice laid in loose. Fine in wrappers. *Labordo.* $65/£41

HILL, WILLIAM L. Jackieboy in Rainbowland. Chicago: Rand McNally, (1911). 1st ed. Fanny Y. Cory (illus). 9 x 6 1/2. Reddish cl, pict cvr label. (Spine ends, corners sl rubbed), else VG. *Pacific**. $46/£29

HILL-TOUT, C. The Native Races of the British Empire. London: Arnold Constable, 1907. Fldg map. (Shelfworn.) Internally Good. *Dumont.* $75/£47

HILLARY, EDMUND and GEORGE LOWE. East of Everest. Hodder & Stoughton, 1956. 1st ed. 48 plts. VG in dj. *Hollett.* $48/£30

HILLARY, EDMUND and DESMOND DOIG. High in the Thin Cold Air. Hodder & Stoughton, 1963. 1st Eng ed. 31pp plts. VG in dj. *Hollett.* $40/£25

HILLCOURT, WILLIAM. Handbook for Patrol Leaders. NY: Boy Scouts of America, (1935). Silver Jubilee Edition. Pict silver stiff wrappers. Fine. *Pacific**. $46/£29

HILLER, LEJAREN A. Bypaths in Arcady: A Book of Love Songs. Poems by Kendall Banning. Chicago: Brothers of the Book, 1915. 1st ed. Folio. Uncut. Vellum-backed bds. (Lt foxed, bkpl; lt soiled.) *Swann**. $230/£144

HILLERMAN, TONY. The Blessing Way. (London): Macmillan, (1970). 1st Eng ed. Fine in dj. *Between The Covers.* $750/£469

HILLERMAN, TONY. The Dark Wind. NY: Harper & Row, (1982). 1st ed. Signed. Fine in dj. *Pacific**. $196/£123

HILLERMAN, TONY. The Ghostway. London: Victor Gollancz, 1985. 1st British ed. Signed. Fine in Fine dj. *Backman.* $45/£28

HILLERMAN, TONY. The Great Taos Bank Robbery. Albuquerque: Univ of NM, 1973. 1st ed. This copy w/single picture of Shiprock on rear panel of dj. Fine in dj (sm spots on rear panel, price-clipped). *Mordida.* $400/£250

HILLERMAN, TONY. The Great Taos Bank Robbery. Albuquerque: Univ of NM, 1973. 1st ed, 1st state dj w/one illus on rear panel. Signed. Fine in dj. *Smith.* $450/£281

HILLERMAN, TONY. Sacred Clowns. NY: Harper/Collins, 1993. 1st ed. Signed ltd ed. New in slipcase. *Perier.* $150/£94

HILLIARD, GRAY et al. An Atlas Accompanying Worcester's Epitome of Geography. Boston: Hilliard, et al, 1826. 10 maps. (Pencilled math to rear of few pp, maps foxed; spine chipped.) Stiff paper wraps. *Dumont.* $175/£109

HILLIER, BEVIS (ed). Punorama.... Whittington, 1974. One of 750. VG in ptd dj (2 sm tears, sl frayed). *Michael Taylor.* $40/£25

HILLIER, GEORGE. A Narrative of the Attempted Escapes of Charles the First from Carisbrook Castle. Richard Bentley, 1852. 1st ed. xiv,334,(i)pp; 2 plts (stained). Blind-stamped cl (sl mkd, faded), gilt. VG. *Hollett.* $136/£85

HILLIER, J. The Art of Hokusai in Book Illustration. Sotheby/Univ of CA, 1980. Fine in dj. *Moss.* $64/£40

HILLIER, J. Catalogue of the Japanese Paintings and Prints in the Collection of Mr. and Mrs. Richard P. Gale. (London, 1970.) 2 vols. Sm folio. (Bkpl removed, lib stamps.) Bd slipcase. *Swann**. $103/£64

HILLIER, J. Suzuki Harunobu: An Exhibition of His Colour-Prints and Illustrated Books.... Phila: Museum of Art, 1970. 1st ed. VG in dj. *Worldwide.* $65/£41

Hillingdon Hall; or, The Cockney Squire; A Tale of Country Life. (By Robert Smith Surtees.) London, 1845. 1st ed. 3 vols. Contemp olive-stained polished calf, morocco backs. (Sl foxed, soiled; rubbed.) *Oinonen**. $140/£88

HILLS, DELIA M. Whisperings of Time. SF: Keller, 1878. 1st ed. 172pp. Dec cl. *Ginsberg.* $75/£47

HILLS, J. W. River Keeper. The Life of William James Lunn. London: Bles, 1947. *Petersfield.* $48/£30

HILLS, J. W. A Summer on the Test. London: Philip Allan, (1924). 1st ed. One of 300. Signed. Grn cl, gilt. (Lacks etchings), o/w Fine. *Pacific**. $92/£58

HILLS, J. W. A Summer on the Test. London, (1924). One of 300 numbered, signed. 4to. 12 orig dry-point etchings. Uncut. 3/4 morocco (rubbed0. *Oinonen**. $850/£531

HILLS, J. W. A Summer on the Test. London: Philip Allan, 1930. 2nd ed. Grn cl, gilt. (Spine sunned), else VG. *Pacific**. $127/£79

HILLYER, ROBERT. The Death of Captain Nemo. NY: Knopf, 1949. 1st ed. As New in As New dj. *Between The Covers.* $125/£78

HILLYER, ROBERT. The Relic and Other Poems. NY: Knopf, 1957. 1st ed. As New in As New dj. *Between The Covers.* $125/£78

HILPRECHT, HERMAN V. (ed). Recent Research in Bible Lands. Phila: Holman, 1903. 1st ed. Fldg color map. Teg. (Edges sl rubbed, spine ends frayed), o/w VG. *Worldwide.* $40/£25

HILTON, HAROLD H. My Golfing Reminiscences. London: James Nisbet, 1907. 1st ed. Grn cl. (Emb stamp, tipped-in bkpl; spine head sl rubbed), else NF. *Pacific**. $345/£216

HILTON, HAROLD H. and GARDEN G. SMYTH. The Royal and Ancient Game of Golf. London: London & Counties, 1912. 1st ed. One of 900. 12.25x9.5. 3 color plts, 2 photogravures, guards. Aeg. Red morocco, gilt. (Name, fr hinge cracking, easily repairable; spine ends, extrems scuffed, leather faded, soiled), o/w VG. *Pacific**. $1,380/£863

HILTON, JAMES. The Dawn of Reckoning. T. Butterworth, 1925. 1st ed. VG + in VG pict dj (sl soiled, closed tears, spine head sl frayed, folds chipped). *Any Amount*. $352/£220

HILTON, JAMES. Good-Bye, Mr. Chips. (London): Hodder & Stoughton, 1934. 1st Eng ed. VG (rear cvr sl dampstained) in dj (bkpl fr flap, soiled, extrems chipped, sm tears, lower spine, rear panel discolored), wrap-around band. *Pacific**. $63/£39

HILTON, JAMES. Good-Bye, Mr. Chips. Boston, 1934. 1st ed. Dj (lt soiled). *Swann**. $92/£58

HILTON, JAMES. Good-Bye, Mr. Chips. Boston, 1934. 1st Amer ed. Fine (sm date stamp, sl rubbed) in dj (sm tear, spine sl sunned). *Polyanthos*. $95/£59

HILTON, JAMES. Good-Bye, Mr. Chips. (NY): Little, Brown, 1935. 1st illus ed. Ltd to 600 signed by Hilton and H. M. Brock (illus). VF in pinkish-tan paper bds backed in vellum, gilt. Ptd, numbered slipcase. *Bromer*. $350/£219

HILTON, JAMES. So Well Remembered. Little, Brown, 1945. 1st ed. Inscribed presentation. VG (ep edges, last 2 blanks browned; top edge dusty, spine ends, corner sl bumped, rear cvr sl mkd) in dj (sl nicked, rubbed, mkd, dusty, spine, edges browned, bookshop label pasted to rear flap). *Ulysses*. $120/£75

HILTON, JAMES. To You Mr. Chips. Hodder, 1938. 1st UK ed. Fine in VG dj. *Williams*. $96/£60

HILTON, JAMES. Without Armor. NY: William Morrow, 1934. 1st US ed. Red cl stamped in gilt/blind. (Sl dknd), o/w VG in pict dj (spine tanned, narrow loss spine crown, sm nicks). *Reese*. $100/£63

HILTON-SIMPSON, M. W. Among the Hill-Folk of Algeria. NY, 1921. Map. (Marginal browning; spine sl frayed.) *Edwards*. $96/£60

HIMES, CHESTER. A Case of Rape. NY: Targ, 1980. One of 350 signed. Fine in tissue dj, as issued. *Smith*. $125/£78

HIMES, CHESTER. Cast the First Stone. NY: Coward-McCann, (1952). 1st ed. Black cl, lt blue-gray bds. Text Clean (ink sig, bkseller ticket rear pastedown, orig receipt laid in; lt worn, edges dusty, corner lt bumped). Dj (chipped, sl worn, rear panel browned, lower flap fold worn, browned). *Baltimore**. $100/£63

HIMES, NORMAN E. Medical History of Contraception. Balt: Williams & Wilkins, 1936. 1st ed. Grn cl. Good in dj (sl soiled, chipped). *Karmiole*. $75/£47

HINCKLEY, F. LEWIS. A Directory of Antique Furniture. NY: Crown, 1953. VG in dj (sl worn). *Hollett*. $96/£60

HIND, ARTHUR M. Early Italian Engraving. NY/London, 1938. Vols 2 and 3 (of 3), being the plt vols of the set. Each one of 375 numbered. *Swann**. $373/£233

HIND, ARTHUR M. A History of Engraving and Etching. Boston/NY, 1923. (Sl worn, cvr faded, water-stained.) *Oinonen**. $30/£19

HIND, ARTHUR M. Nielli, Chiefly Italian of the XV Century, Plates, Sulphur Casts and Prints Preserved in the British Museum. London, 1936. *Swann**. $103/£64

HIND, ARTHUR M. Wenceslaus Hollar and His Views of London and Windsor in the Seventeenth Century. London, 1922. (Lt worn, sl stained.) *Oinonen**. $70/£44

HIND, ARTHUR M. Wenceslaus Hollar and His Views of London and Windsor in the Seventeenth Century. London: John Lane, 1922. Frontis. Brn buckram. (Inscrip), o/w Fine in dj. *Marlborough*. $200/£125

HIND, C. LEWIS. Turner's Golden Visions. London: T.C. & E.C. Jack, 1925. 50 tipped-in color plts. Later cl, gilt spine. VG. *Pacific**. $40/£25

HIND, HENRY YOULE. Narrative of the Canadian Red River Exploring Expedition of 1857. Longman et al, 1860. 1st ed. 2 vols. 20 chromoxylographs, 7 maps and plans (2 fldg), 1 fldg diag, half-titles. Contemp calf, gilt spines. *Sotheby's**. $626/£391

HINDE, G. J. Catalogue of the Fossil Sponges in the Geological Department of the British Museum (Natural History) wit Descriptions of New and Little-Known Species. London, 1883. viii,248pp; 38 plts. (Sl foxed, blind lib stamps; rebacked.) *Henly*. $96/£60

HINDE, THOMAS. Capability Brown. Hutchinson, 1986. NF in dj. *Hadley*. $40/£25

Hindenburg's March into London. (By Paul Georg Muench.) L.G. Redmond-Howard (trans). London: John Long, 1916. 1st British ed. Pict wrappers. Sound (paper sl tanned, sl foxed early/late; wrappers used, sm chips, creases, clean tear fr joint). *Reese*. $50/£31

HINDLIP, LORD. Sport and Travel. London: Fisher Unwin, 1906. 1st ed. Port, 2 fldg maps. Fine. *Maggs*. $760/£475

HINDS, JOHN. Conversations on Conditioning. The Grooms' Oracle, and Pocket Stable-Directory. London: For the Author, 1829. Fldg color frontis. Uncut. Cl-backed bds, paper spine label. (Sl foxed, soiled; shelfworn, label chipped.) Protective cl case provided. *Oinonen**. $170/£106

HINDS, JOHN. Conversations on Conditioning. The Grooms' Oracle, and Pocket Stable-Directory. London: For the Author, 1830. 2nd ed. Fldg color frontis. Uncut. Calf, tip-edge gilt. (Sl foxed, rubbed.) *Oinonen**. $110/£69

HINE, DARYL. The Prince of Darkness and Co. NY: Abelard-Schuman, (1961). 1st ed. VF in Fine dj (extrems sl rubbed). *Between The Covers*. $250/£156

HINE, ROBERT V. Bartlett's West. New Haven, 1968. Map. VG in dj. *Dumont*. $45/£28

HINE, ROBERT V. California's Utopian Colonies. San Marino: Huntington Library, 1953. 1st ed. 8 plts. VF in dj. *Argonaut*. $50/£31

HINE, ROBERT V. California's Utopian Colonies. San Marino, CA, 1953. 1st ed. Port, chart. Fine in VG + dj. *Sagebrush*. $60/£38

HINE, ROBERT V. Edward Kern and American Expansion. New Haven: Yale Univ, 1962. 1st ed. VF in dj. *Argonaut*. $35/£22

HINE, ROBERT V. In the Shadow of Fremont. Edward Kern and the Art of American Exploration, 1845-1860. Norman: Univ of OK, 1982. 2nd ed. 2 maps. Blue cl. VF in pict dj. *Argonaut*. $35/£22

HINE, ROBERT V. and SAVOIE LOTTINVILLE (eds). Soldier in the West. Letters of Theodore Talbot...1845-53. Norman, (1972). 1st ed. NF in NF dj. *Sagebrush*. $45/£28

HINGSTON, R. W. G. A Naturalist in Hindustan. London, 1923. 1st ed. 8 plts. (Rear hinge cracked, rear bd sl spotted.) *Edwards*. $64/£40

HINGSTON, R. W. G. Nature at the Desert's Edge. Boston: Small, Maynard, n.d. (ca 1930). (Marginal pencil mks; sl rubbed), o/w VG. *Worldwide*. $75/£47

HINSDALE, PETER. The Fabulous Porsche 917. Haessner, 1976. Rev 2nd ed, 1st ptg. Orig trade pb ed. VG. *Plapinger*. $100/£63

HINTON, A. HORSELY. Handbook of Illustration. NY/London: G. Gennert, (1894). Frontis, guard, 120pp,(18) ads. (Fr bd lt soiled, fep torn), else VG. *Cahan*. $250/£156

HINTON, J. W. Organ Construction. Weekes, 1902. 2nd ed. Frontisport, 17 plts. (Sigs; spine ends worn, top of rear hinge split, corners bumped.) *Hollett*. $88/£55

HINTON, S. E. Rumble Fish. NY, 1975. 1st ed. Advance rev copy w/slip laid in. Fine in NF dj. *Warren*. $50/£31

HIPKINS, A. J. Musical Instruments. Edinburgh: A&C Black, 1888. Signed ltd ed. One of 1040. Folio. xix,107pp; 50 color plts. Teg. Orig 1/2 morocco, gilt. VG (sl spotted; bds sl soiled, scraped, handsomely rebacked in matching morocco, gilt, raised bands). *Hollett.* $720/£450

HIPKINS, A. J. Musical Instruments. A&C Black, 1945. 48 color plts. (Sl spotted; corners sl rubbed.) *Edwards.* $136/£85

HIPKISS, EDWIN J. Eighteenth-Century American Arts: The M. and M. Karolik Collection. Cambridge: Harvard Univ, 1950. 2nd ed (so stated). Navy cl, gilt. (Lib white ink spine # partly removed, ink handstamps, card pocket; sl rubbed, worn.) Cvrs Good. *Baltimore*.* $100/£63

HIRSCHMAN, LOUIS J. Handbook of Diseases of the Rectum. St. Louis, 1909. 1st ed. 2 color plts. Fine (corners sl rubbed). *Doctor's Library.* $50/£31

HIRST, BARTON COOKE. A Text-Book of Diseases of Women. Phila: W.B. Saunders, 1903. 1st ed. Grn cl. VG + . *House.* $100/£63

HIRTH, KENNETH (ed). Trade and Exchange in Early Mesoamerica. Univ of NM, (1984). 1st ed. Good. *Rybski.* $55/£34

Historic Gallery of Portraits and Paintings.... London: Vernor, Hood & Sharpe, 1807. 1st ed. 7 vols. 19th-cent 3/4 brn calf, marbled bds, gilt spines, morocco spine labels. (Lt foxed; most spine labels chipped or lacking), else VG. *Pacific*.* $63/£39

Historic Homes of Alabama and Their Traditions. Birmingham, 1935. Ltd to 700 numbered. Two-tone gilt stamped cl. (Cvrs loose, lt worn, sl soiled.) *King.* $75/£47

Historic Houses of the United Kingdom. London: Cassell, 1892. 1/2 brn calf, backstrip gilt w/red leather label. *Petersfield.* $32/£20

Historical Atlas of the American West. Chicago: Rand McNally, 1969. 2nd ed. 15 map repros. VG. *Dumont.* $45/£28

Historical Collections and Report. Volume XXVII, 1954. Pierre, SD, 1954. VG. *Lien.* $50/£31

Historical Illustrations of the Origin and Progress of the Passions, and Their Influence on the Conduct of Mankind. London: Longman, Hurst et al, 1825. 1st ed. 2 vols in 1. (Lib stamps), else VG. *Pacific*.* $40/£25

Historical Journal of the American War. (By Thomas Pemberton.) Boston: Belknap, 1795. Apparently 1st separate ed. (1)leaf, 206pp. Contemp calf. (Bkpl removed, soiled, foxed, sl stained, browned; rubbed.) Howes P193. *Oinonen*.* $225/£141

Historical Remarks on the Castle of the Bastille. (By Brossais du Perray.) London: Gardner et al, 1789. Fldg plan. 1/4 calf. (Sig, sm lib stamp.) *Rostenberg & Stern.* $165/£103

Historical Sketch Book and Guide to New Orleans and Environs. NY: Will H. Coleman, 1885. 324pp; fldg map. (Lacks fr wrapper, rebound in later plain wraps), else Good. *Brown.* $20/£13

Historical Souvenir of Vermont with the Story of Old Vermont in Pictures from Drawings by R. F. Heinrich.... Chester, VT: Nat'l Survey Co, 1941. Map. Stiff ptd wrappers (extrems sl rubbed). *Sadlon.* $25/£16

History and Reminiscences of Dougherty County, Georgia. Albany, GA, 1924. 1st ed. (Fr inner hinge starting; shelfworn, rubbed), o/w VG. *Brown.* $35/£22

History and Roster of Maryland Volunteers, War of 1861-5. Volume II only. Balt: Guggenheimer, Weil, 1899. ix,287pp (few pp chipped). Maroon cl w/later black leather repairs to spine, corners (new eps). *Baltimore*.* $60/£38

History of Aladdin or the Wonderful Lamp. NY: Edwd. Dunigan, (ca 1848). 12mo. 8pp (incl cvrs). Good in stiff paper wrappers (spine lt worn). *Reisler.* $225/£141

History of an Apple Pie. NY: McLoughlin Bros, n.d. (ca 1870). Aunt Friendly's Colored Picture Books Series. 8vo. 6 leaves + 1pg ad rear wrapper; 6 VF full-pg chromolithos. VG (ink sig fr wrapper, top of fr cvr lt discolored). *Hobbyhorse.* $100/£63

History of Butte County, California. 1882.... Berkeley: Howell-North, 1973. Facs ed. Black cl, gilt. Fine in Fine dj. *Harrington.* $75/£47

History of Cattle Brands and How to Read Them. Carter Oil Co, (1955). Fine in wraps. *Perier.* $15/£9

History of Contra Costa County, California. Oakland: Brooks-Sterling, 1974. Facs of 1882 ed. Mustard cl. Fine. Howes C718. *Harrington.* $65/£41

History of Hindostan; Its Arts, and Its Sciences. (By Thomas Maurice.) London: W. Bulmer for the Author, 1795-1798. 1st ed. 2 vols. Engr frontis, (6),xxxiv,592,(2); engr frontis, xx,706,(2)pp; 17 plts (1 lg fldg, 1 dbl-pg). 19th-cent vellum, marbled bds (spines soiled, sm chips), red/grn morocco spine labels. *Karmiole.* $475/£297

History of Jenny Wren. London: For the Booksellers, n.d. (ca 1820). 12mo. 8pp + 1pg list on lower wrapper; 8 half-pg hand-colored wood engrs. (Top pg edges crudely opened), else Fine in pict grn paper wrappers. *Hobbyhorse.* $225/£141

History of King Pippin. London: Dean & Munday, n.d. (ca 1840). Sq 12mo. 15pp + 1pg list lower wrapper; 8 wood engrs. (Ink sig on fr wrapper, frontis), else Fine in pict yellow paper wrappers (lt soiled). *Hobbyhorse.* $150/£94

History of Little Tom Tucker. London: Ptd for the Booksellers, n.d. (ca 1820). 12mo. 8pp + 1pg list on lower wrapper. 8 wood engrs (some colored by child). Yellow pict paper wrappers. Good (top pg edges crudely opened, repaired). *Hobbyhorse.* $190/£119

History of Los Angeles County, California with Illustrations. (By John Albert Wilson.) Berkeley: Howell-North, 1959. 111 plts, color map. Prospectus laid in. Black buckram, gilt. Fine in ptd dj. *Pacific*.* $143/£89

History of Merced County, California with Illustrations, 1881. Fresno: CA History Books, 1974. Rpt of orig 1881 ed. Black cl, gilt. Fine. *Pacific*.* $58/£36

History of Napoleon Buonaparte. William Tegg, n.d. George Cruikshank (illus). xxii,655pp. Eps, edges marbled. Full blue polished calf, gilt. VG. *Hollett.* $104/£65

History of Placer County California with Illustrations and Biographical Sketches of Its Prominent Men and Pioneers. Oakland: Thompson & West, 1882. 1st ed. (2),vii-viii,(1),iv-vi,10-416pp; 84 lithos. Tan buckram (rebound); orig cl cvr, leather spine laid on. Good (sm tears, chips to pg edges, some tape-repaired; sm pieces of masking tape on plts; reversal of order of some early pp). *Pacific*.* $196/£123

History of Printing from its Beginnings to 1930. Millwood: Kraus Reprint, 1980. 1st ed. 4 vols. 4to. Fine. *Oak Knoll.* $750/£469

History of Printing. SPCK, (1862). 1st ed. Color frontis. Dec cl (spine head chipped; inner hinges shaken). *Forest.* $32/£20

History of Punch. London: Cassell, 1895. 1st Eng ed. 592pp. Marbled eps; aeg. Dec red leather, gilt, raised bands. VG (sl rubbed, dusty, mkd). *Ulysses.* $152/£95

History of Sam the Sportsman. London: Blackie & Son, (c. 1910). Frank Adams (illus). 11 x 8 1/2. Cl-backed bds, pict cvr label. (Extrems sl dknd, corners rubbed), else VG. *Pacific*.* $92/£58

History of San Luis Obispo County, California, with Illustrations and Biographical Sketches of Its Prominent Men and Pioneers. Berkeley, CA: Howell-North Books, 1966. Facs ptg of orig 1883 ed. Black cl, gilt. VF. *Argonaut.* $100/£63

History of Sandford and Merton, a Work Intended for the Use of Children. (By Thomas Day.) London: John Stockdale, 1786-1789. 3rd ed. 3 vols. 8vo. Vols 1 and 2 w/full-pg copper engr frontis by W. Skelton, w/imprint dated March 26, 1786; 281 + 3pp list; 306 + 6pp list; 308 + 4pp list. 3/4 leather, marbled paper on bds. Text Fine (pg 179 vol 2 restored at lower corner w/some text loss, few repaired tears, sl foxed, ragged edges). Good set (lib label inside fr cvr 1st vol; heavily rubbed, edges chipped). *Hobbyhorse.* $200/£125

History of Shipwrecks, and Disasters at Sea, from the Most Authentic Sources. London: Whittaker, Treacher, 1833. 2 vols. viii,343pp, 8 plts; iv,316pp, 8 plts. Grn cl, paper labels. VG (few ll sl foxed; sl loss vol 2). *Explorer.* $96/£60

History of Texas, or the Emigrant's Guide to the New Republic.... (A.B. Lawrence, intro.) NY: Nafis & Cornish, 1844. Orig sheets w/cancel tp and w/o dedication. 12mo. B/w litho frontis dated 1844, 275pp. Old calf (spine damaged). Sound. *M & S.* $500/£313

History of the 110th Infantry (10th Pa.) of the 28th Division, U. S. A. 1917-1919. (Greensburg, PA, 1920.) (Inner hinges sl cracked; cvrs lt worn, spotted w/sl fore-edge fray.) *King.* $45/£28

History of the 376th Regiment Between the Years of 1921-1945. (Wuppertal-Barmen, Germany): Regimental Hist Committee, Information & Education Office, (1945). 1st ed. Cream bds, gilt, blue cl spine (extrems lt frayed). *Karmiole.* $75/£47

History of the Abbey Church of St. Peter's Westminster, Its Antiquities and Monuments. London: R. Ackermann, 1812. 1st ed, 2nd issue. 2 vols. Engr plan, port, 81 hand-colored aquatint plts. (Occasional lt spotting, offsetting.) Contemp calf (worn). *Christie's*.* $270/£169

History of the American Field Service in France. Boston/NY: Houghton Mifflin, 1920. 1st ed. 3 vols. 3 maps on 2 fldg sheets in rear pocket vol 1. Teg, untrimmed, partly unopened. Navy buckram, gilt. Very Clean set in plain glassine djs, orig bd slipcase (heavy wear, lacks upper side). *Baltimore*.* $35/£22

History of the Calhoun Monument at Charleston, S.C. Charleston: Lucas, Richardson, 1888. vi,147pp. Orig wrappers. (Edgeworn, fr wrap fore-edge torn), o/w Good. *Brown.* $25/£16

History of the City of Denver, Arapahoe County, and Colorado. Chicago: O.L. Baskin, 1880. 1st ed. Dbl-pg frontis view, 652pp. Aeg. 3/4 morocco, brn cl, gilt. VG (extrems lt worn). Howes D262. *House.* $300/£188

History of the College of William and Mary...from Its Foundation, 1660 to 1874. J.W. Randolph & English, 1874. 183pp. Paper cvr. VG-. *Book Broker.* $50/£31

History of the Colonization of the Free States of Antiquity. (By William Barron.) London: T. Cadell, 1777. 1st ed. Recent marbled paper wraps. *Kane*.* $300/£188

History of the Military Transactions of the British Nation in Indostan, from the Year MDCCXLV. (By Robert Orme.) London: John Nourse, 1763. 1st ed. (6),416pp; 10 maps, plans (9 fldg). Contemp calf (scuffed, rebacked), portions of orig gilt spine laid down. *Karmiole.* $300/£188

History of the Pocasset Tragedy! New Bedford, 1879. Orig pict wrappers. *Swann*.* $258/£161

History of the Schuykill Fishing Company of the State in Schuykill, 1732-1888. Phila: By the Members, 1889. Uncut. 3/4 morocco (rubbed; lib mks, sl stained, soiled). Howes M636. *Oinonen*.* $225/£141

History of the Schuylkill Fishing Company of the State in Schuylkill, 1732-1888. Phila: Members of the State in Schuylkill, 1889. 1st ed. Frontis litho. 3/4 red calf, marbled bds, gilt, morocco spine label. (Bkpl; tp laid down on archival paper; sm crack fr joint), else VG. *Pacific*.* $316/£198

History of the Seventy-Seventh Division August 25th, 1917-November 11th, 1918. (NY, 1919.) 1st ed. Fldg map. Black cl (sl soiled, dknd, edgeworn). Internally VG. *Reese.* $55/£34

History of the United States Twelfth Armored Division: The Hellcats in World War II. 15 September, 1942-17 December, 1945. Baton Rouge, 1947. VG. *Clark.* $95/£59

History of the University of New Hampshire 1866-1941. Durham: Univ of NH, 1941. 1st ed. Fine in Good + dj. *Connolly.* $25/£16

History of the XVI Corps. Washington, (1947). 1st ed. (Ex-lib; worn.) *King.* $75/£47

History of Three Brothers. NY: Samuel Campbell, 1794. 1st Amer ed. Frontis, 106pp. Contemp calf-backed paper-cvrd bds (lib bkpl; worn, lower corner lacking, affecting few letters). *M & S.* $375/£234

History of White's. (By William Biggs Boulton.) London: Algernon Bourke, (1892). Ltd to 500 numbered sets. 2 vols. (2),xvi,258; (2),vi,260,(2),98,vipp (lt spotting). Dk blue cl (lt rubbed, soiled). *Karmiole.* $250/£156

History of Wonderful Inventions. London: Chapman, Hall, 1849. 2 hand-colored frontispieces, viii,120; 126pp; (inside hinges repaired w/cl tape; bkpls). Grn cl (recased, hinges cracked), stamped in blind, gilt-stamped spine (part missing replaced w/new cl). *Oak Knoll.* $85/£53

HITCH, CLOVE. A Handboook on Sailing. H. Roberts (ed). London: John Lane, 1904. Limp grn leather, backstrip (faded, sl torn). *Petersfield.* $24/£15

HITCHCOCK, EDWARD. Elementary Geology. NY: Mark H. Newman, 1845. 3rd ed. xii, 352pp; 3 fldg plts (2 hand-colored). Full calf. Good (rubbed; spine head chipped). *Blake.* $65/£41

HITCHCOCK, EDWARD. Ichnology of New England. A Report on the Sandstone of the Connecticut Valley, Especially Its Fossil Footmarks. Boston, 1858. 1st ed. 60 litho plts. (Shelfworn, shaken, foxed, sl stained, soiled.) *Oinonen*.* $150/£94

HITCHCOCK, EDWARD. Outline of the Geology of the Globe, and of the United States in Particular. Boston: Phillips, Sampson, 1854. 2nd ed. 136pp; 2 hand-colored fldg maps, 5 litho plts. VG (1 fldg map w/4-inch repaired tear w/sl paper loss, both w/creasing; ink name, inscrip dated 1858). *Pacific*.* $138/£86

HITCHCOCK, EDWARD. Outline of the Geology of the Globe, and of the United States in Particular. Boston, 1856. 3rd ed. 136pp; 2 lg fldg hand-colored maps, 6 plts. (Sl foxed at ends), o/w Fine. *Henly.* $120/£75

HITCHCOCK, EDWARD. Report on the Geology of Vermont. Claremont: Claremont Manufacturing, 1861. 1st ed, apparently a married set. 2 vols. (v),988pp; 7 full-pg maps (6 hand-colored), 3 fldg maps w/orig hand-coloring, 5 full-pg (1 fldg) b/w litho plts, 3 fldg hand-colored charts, 20 b/w oval litho plts. Dk grn-brn blind cl w/pattern, both later rebacked in grn cl, orig gilt-lettered portions of spines trimmed and mtd. Maps, charts, and plts NF (1 fldg map w/4-inch tear into details; text sl aged; cvrs sl worn). *Baltimore*.* $260/£163

HITCHCOCK, FRANK. A True Account of the Capture of Frank Rande. John W. Kimsey (ed). Peoria, IL: Ptd by J.W. Franks & Sons, 1897. 1st ed. Frontisport, 156,(2)pp (1/2-pg vertical tear in leaf pp111-112, no loss). Cl-backed ptd pict bds (sl soiled). *Wantagh.* $75/£47

HITCHCOCK, HENRY-RUSSELL. American Architectural Books. Minneapolis: Univ of MN, (1962). 2nd ed. Tan cl, red spine lettering. (Sl dusty, finger smudges.) Text Good. *Baltimore*.* $90/£56

HITCHCOCK, HENRY-RUSSELL. Early Victorian Architecture in Britain. New Haven: Yale Univ, 1954. 1st ed. Signed presentation. 2 vols. 200 photo plts. Pub's cl. Dj (torn, repaired). *Sotheran.* $128/£80

HITCHCOCK, HENRY-RUSSELL. Rococo Architecture in Southern Germany. Phaidon, 1968. 1st ed. VG in dj. *Hadley.* $54/£34

HITLER, ADOLF. Mein Kampf. NY: Reynal & Hitchcock, 1939. Special ed, w/14pp pamphlet tipped in at fr which begins 'The Following Individuals as a Committee Sponsor the Publication of this Annotated and Unexpurgated Edition of Mein Kampf.' Frontis, map. Red cl. (Sl worn, spine top lt chipped.) Dj. *Karmiole.* $100/£63

HITSCHMANN, EDUARD. Freud's Theories of the Neuroses. C. R. Payne (trans). NY: Journal of Nervous & Mental Disease Pub Co, 1913. 1st ed in English. VG in ptd brn wrappers (spine, edges chipped). *Gach.* $75/£47

HITSCHMANN, EDUARD. Freud's Theories of the Neuroses. NY: Moffat, Yard, 1916. 1st trade ed. Blue cl. *Gach.* $30/£19

HITT, ORRIE. Hotel Woman. NY: Valentine, 1971. 1st ed. NF (sl leaning) in NF dj. *Warren.* $35/£22

HITTEL, JOHN S. A History of the City of San Francisco and Incidentally of the State of California. SF: A.L. Bancroft, 1878. 1st ed. Signed, inscribed; 1-pg author letter tipped to rep. (5),6-498pp. Orange cl, gilt. VF (bkpl). *Pacific*.* $345/£216

HITTELL, JOHN S. Mining in the Pacific States of North America. SF: H.H. Bancroft, 1861. 1st ed. (5),vi-viii,(1),10-224pp. Red cl, gilt. (Lib #s; cvrs sl worn, soiled), o/w VG. *Pacific*.* $345/£216

HITTELL, THEODORE. The Adventures of James Capen Adams, Mountaineer and Grizzly Bear Hunter of California. SF: Towne & Bacon, 1860. 1st ed. 7.5x4.75. vi,(3),10-378pp; 12 plts, tissue guards. Brn pebbled cl, gilt spine. Bkpl of Robert Ernest Cowan. (Fep tear expertly repaired), o/w NF. *Pacific*.* $1,380/£863

HITTI, PHILIP K. The Makers of Arab History. NY: St. Martin's, 1968. 1st ptg. 8 maps. (Ex-lib, mks; scotch tape on cvrs), o/w VG in dj (lib sticker). *Worldwide.* $25/£16

HIVES, FRANK. Ju-Ju and Justice in Nigeria. London: John Lane, The Bodley Head, 1933. Orange cl (very worn, faded, joints splitting). Usable. *Boswell.* $50/£31

HJORTSBERG, WILLIAM. Alp. NY: S&S, (1969). 1st ed, 1st bk. Signed on ptd label pasted to fep. Fine in VG+ dj (sm price sticker mk fr panel, spine edge sl worn). *Bernard.* $85/£53

HJORTSBERG, WILLIAM. Alp. NY, 1969. 1st ed, 1st bk. Fine in Fine dj. *Warren.* $65/£41

HJORTSBERG, WILLIAM. Falling Angel. NY, 1978. 1st ed. VG+ in NF 1st state dj. *Warren.* $40/£25

HJORTSBERG, WILLIAM. Tales and Fables. Hollywood: Sylvester & Orphanos, 1985. Ltd to 330 signed. Fine dec cl. Slipcase. *Truepenny.* $100/£63

HOAGLAND, EDWARD. Cat Man. Boston: Houghton Mifflin, 1956. 1st ed, 1st bk. Top edge stained brn, untrimmed. Lt brn cl. VG (edges sl dusty) in dj (sl worn, chipped, tear along bottom of 1 fold, sm price sticker fr panel). *Baltimore*.* $40/£25

HOAR, GEORGE F. A Boy Sixty Years Ago. Boston: Perry Mason, (1898). 1st separate ed. Frontis, 40pp. Wrappers. VG (sl stain spot). *Lucas.* $20/£13

HOARE, DOROTHY. Some Studies in the Modern Novel. London: C&W, 1938. 1st ed. Fine in dj (sl tanned). *Reese.* $30/£19

HOARE, DOROTHY. The Works of Morris and of Yeats in Relation to Early Saga Literature. CUP, 1937. 1st ed. Paper spine label, extra paper label tipped-in. (Lt spotted.) Dj (sl spotted, browned, spine sl chipped). *Edwards.* $32/£20

HOATSON, FLORENCE. Lavender's Blue. Harrap, 1928. 1st ed. 8vo. Color frontis, 79pp. Blue-gray bds. (Sm crack spine foot), else VG+. *Bookmark.* $19/£12

HOBAN, RUSSELL. Bedtime for Frances. NY: Harper, 1960. 1st ed, 1st bk. 8.25x10.25. Garth Williams (illus). 32pp. Cl spine, pict bds. VG (sm tape stain fep) in dj (price-clipped, hand-stamped $2.75). *Cattermole.* $350/£219

HOBAN, RUSSELL. Bread and Jam for Frances. NY: Harper & Row, 1969. 1st ed. 8.25x10.25. Lillian Hoban (illus). 32pp. Cl spine, pict bds. VG in dj. *Cattermole.* $200/£125

HOBAN, RUSSELL. Kleinzeit. NY, (1974). 1st Amer ed. VG in dj (sl used). *King.* $35/£22

HOBAN, RUSSELL. La Corona and the Tin Frog. London: Cape, 1979. 1st Eng ed. Nicola Bayley (illus). 4to. Color pict laminated bds. Fine (spine ends sl bumped). *Ulysses.* $72/£45

HOBAN, RUSSELL. The Medusa Frequency. NY, 1987. 1st Amer ed. Fine in Fine dj. *Polyanthos.* $20/£13

HOBAN, RUSSELL. The Mouse and His Child. London: Faber & Faber, 1969. 1st Eng ed. Lillian Hoban (illus). NF (top edge spotted; spine head sl bumped) in dj (sm internally repaired nick). *Ulysses.* $152/£95

HOBAN, RUSSELL. Riddley Walker. NY: Summit, (1980). 1st US ed. Fine in dj (nicked). *Other Worlds.* $30/£19

HOBAN, RUSSELL. The Stone Doll of Sister Brute. NY: Macmillan, 1968. 1st ed. 5x7.25. Lillian Hoban (illus). 32pp. Pict bds. Fine in dj. *Cattermole.* $40/£25

HOBART, COTT (ed). Dialogues of Creatures Moralised. Kentfield: Allen, 1967. One of 130. 13x9.5. 122 woodcuts. Prospectus laid in. Fine. *Pacific*.* $546/£341

HOBBES, THOMAS. Leviathan, or the Matter, Forme, and Power of a Common-Wealth Ecclesiaticall and Civill. London, 1651. 2nd ed. Folio. Contemp calf. *Felcone.* $2,000/£1,250

HOBBS, GEORGE W. and BEN G. ELLIOTT. The Gasoline Automobile. NY: McGraw-Hill, 1915. 1st ed, 4th imp. Grn cl, gilt. VG. *Pacific*.* $35/£22

HOBBS, ROBERT. Robert Smithson: Sculpture. Ithaca: Cornell Univ, (1981). Fine in dj. *Turtle Island.* $65/£41

HOBBY, WILLIAM. An Inquiry into the Itinerancy, and the Conduct of the Rev. Mr. George Whitefield, an Itinerant Preacher.... Boston, 1745. 1st ed. 28pp. Sewn. (Notes, soiled.) *M & S.* $275/£172

HOBHOUSE, MRS. HENRY. I Appeal unto Caesar. London: George Allen & Unwin, (ca 1917). 3rd ed. Stiff ptd wrappers. (Text paper tanned; sm chips spine ends), else VG. *Reese.* $20/£13

HOBSON, GEOFFREY D. Bindings in Cambridge Libraries. CUP, 1929. 1st ed. Ltd to 230. Folio. 72 plts. Dj (torn, lacks top portion of fr cvr). *Sotheby's*.* $736/£460

HOBSON, HAROLD. Theatre. London, 1948. 1st ed. Inscribed. VG in dj. *Typographeum.* $25/£16

HOBSON, R. L. and A. L. HETHERINGTON. The Art of the Chinese Potter. London, 1923. One of 1500 numbered. 153 plts. (Spine sl faded.) *Swann*.* $172/£108

HOBSON, R. L. A Catalogue of Chinese Pottery and Porcelain in the Collection of Sir Percival David.... London: Stourton, 1934. One of 650 numbered. Folio. 180 plts. Blue silk (bottom edges worn) by Savgorski & Sutcliffe. Dj (edges worn). *Swann*.* $977/£611

HOBSON, R. L. A Catalogue of Chinese Pottery and Porcelain in the Collection of Sir Percival David.... Stourton Press, 1934. One of 650. Folio. 180 plts. Orig silk by Sangorski & Sutcliffe. Orig box (distressed, soiled). *Sotheby's*.* $1,104/£690

HOBSON, R. L. Catalogue of the Collection of English Pottery. British Museum, 1903. 42 plts (4 color). *Edwards.* $240/£150

HOBSON, R. L. Catalogue of the Leonard Gow Collection of Chinese Porcelain. 1931. One of 300 signed by Gow. Teg, rest uncut. Orig buckram, gilt. *Sotheby's*.* $386/£241

HOBSON, R. L. Chinese Ceramics in Private Collections. London, 1931. One of 650. 32 tipped-in color plts. Teg, rest uncut. (Lt soiled, sl stain.) *Edwards.* $240/£150

HOBSON, R. L. A Guide to Islamic Pottery of the Near East. British Museum, 1932. 40 plts. Ptd bds. VG. *Hollett.* $48/£30

HOBSON, R. L. The Later Ceramic Wares of China. London, 1925. One of 250 numbered, signed, w/5 add'l color plts. 76 plts. (Bkpl, prelims sl foxed.) Pigskin (rehinged). *Swann*.* $201/£126

HOBSON, R. L. The Wares of the Ming Dynasty. NY, 1923. One of 1500 numbered. Frontis (loose; rear hinge cracked). *Swann**. $161/£101

HOBSON, R. L. Worcester Porcelain. London, 1910. Folio. 109 plts (17 color). (Spine faded.) *Swann**. $402/£251

HOBSON, WILDER. American Jazz Music. NY: W.W. Norton, (1939). 1st ed. 6 plts. Pict cl. VG in pict dj (lt chipped). *Petrilla*. $100/£63

HOCHBERG, FRITZ. An Eastern Voyage. A Journal of the Travels.... London, 1910. 2 vols. 25 color plts. Teg. (Margins sl browned, sm ink stamp vol 1, vol 2 lacks fep; spines, edges faded, spine sl chipped.) *Edwards*. $136/£85

HOCKING, ANNE. The Best Laid Plans. GC: Doubleday, 1950. 1st ed. Fine in VG dj (edgeworn, spine sunned). *Janus*. $25/£16

HOCKNEY, DAVID. David Hockney, Photographs. London/NY, (1982). 1st ed. Dj (extrems faded, sl worn). *Swann**. $92/£58

HOCKNEY, DAVID. Paper Pools. Nikos Stangos (ed). London: Thames & Hudson, 1980. One of 1000 signed, and w/signed 6-color litho in separate folder. 4to. Blue cl. Blue paper wrapper. In orig cardbd box. *Christie's**. $1,141/£713

HODEIR, ANDRE. Toward Jazz. Noel Burch (trans). NY: Grove, (1962). 1st ed. VG in pict dj. *Petrilla*. $35/£22

HODGE, F. W. and THEODORE H. LEWIS (eds). Spanish Explorers in the Southern United States, 1528-1543. NY: Scribner, 1907. 1st ed. Frontis, 2 fldg maps. Dk grn cl, gilt. (Pencil sig, stamp.) *Dawson*. $100/£63

HODGE, F. W. Turquoise Work of Hawikuh New Mexico. NY: Museum of the American Indian, 1921. 2 color plts. NF in wraps. *Dumont*. $125/£78

HODGE, GENE MEANY. The Kachinas Are Coming. Flagstaff: Northland, 1967. Facs rpt of 1936 orig. 18 color plts. (Edges sl dusty), else NF. *Dumont*. $85/£53

HODGE, GENE MEANY. The Kachinas Are coming. Flagstaff: Northland Press, 1967. Facs ed of 1936 orig. 18 color plts. Brn leatherette-backed patterned bds. Fine. *Harrington*. $100/£63

HODGE, HIRAM C. Arizona as It Is. NY: Hurd & Houghton, 1877. 1st ed. Wood-engr frontis, 273pp; dbl-pg map. (Lt foxed; rubbed, worn), else VG. *Pacific**. $98/£61

HODGES, JAMES. War Betwixt the Two British Kingdoms Consider'd and the Dangerous Circumstances of Each.... London: John Taylor, 1705. 1st ed. (40),165 + (3) ad pp. Paneled calf, morocco spine label. (Cvrs worn, expertly rebacked), else VG. *Pacific**. $161/£101

HODGES, WILLIAM. Travels in India, During the Years 1780, 1781, 1782, and 1783. London: The Author, 1793. 1st ed. 14 plts, fldg map. Contemp calf (rubbed, worn, soiled, sl stained, foxed). *Oinonen**. $375/£234

HODGKIN, L. V. A Book of Quaker Saints. Edinburgh: T.N. Foulis, 1917. 1st ed. 7 tipped-in color plts. Uncut. (1 text leaf torn, taped.) *Hollett*. $48/£30

HODGKIN, R. H. A History of the Anglo-Saxons. London: Humphrey Milford, 1939. 2nd ed. 2 vols. Color frontis, 85 plts (3 color), 9 color fldg maps. Blue cl (sl rubbed, faded, bumped, shaken). *Maggs*. $45/£28

HODGKINSON, EATON (ed). Practical Essay on the Strength of Cast Iron and Other Metals. London: John Weale, 1860-61. 2nd ed. ix,384,32pp; 6 steel-engr plts. Blind-stamped cl, gilt. (Spine, fore-edges faded.) *Hollett*. $224/£140

Hodgson's Jackoo the Monkey. London: Hodgson & Co, 1822. 12mo. 12pp; VF wood engrs. Pict label on stiff paper wrappers. (Occasional spotting, strengthened at inner folds; rebacked, soiled, corners rounded.) Custom-made box w/spine label. *Hobbyhorse*. $400/£250

HODGSON, MARGARET and ROLAND PAINE. A Field Guide to Australian Wildflowers. Adelaide: Rigby, 1985. 7th ptg. 2 vols. 188 color plts, 1 map. (Sticker, notes), else VG in dj. *Fair Meadow*. $40/£25

HODGSON, MRS. WILLOUGHBY. Old English China. London, 1913. Folio. 80 plts (16 color). (Feps browned, text foxed; rubbed, shaken.) *Swann**. $46/£29

HODGSON, MRS. WILLOUGHBY. Old English China. London, 1913. 16 color plts. Fore, lower edges uncut. (Lt spotted; sl soiled, spine sl bumped.) *Edwards*. $72/£45

HODGSON, W. EARL. How to Fish. A&C Black, 1907. Fore/lower edge uncut. Color pict cl. (Tp, frontis edges lt browned, 2 add'l illus adhered to fr prelims.) *Edwards*. $40/£25

HODGSON, WILLIAM HOPE. Deep Waters. Sauk City: Arkham House, 1967. 1st ed. NF in dj (edges sl browned, spine head sl worn). *Other Worlds*. $100/£63

HODGSON, WILLIAM HOPE. The Dream of X. West Kingston, RI: Donald M. Grant, 1977. One of signed ltd ed. Signed by Stephen E. Fabian (illus). 14 color plts. Fine in dj, VG slipcase (lt sunned). *Bernard*. $75/£47

HODGSON, WILLIAM HOPE. The House on the Borderland and Other Novels. Sauk City: Arkham House, 1946. 1st ed thus. One of 3000. (Name), else NF in dj (spine ends rubbed). *Pacific**. $219/£137

HODGSON, WILLIAM HOPE. The House on the Borderland and Other Novels. Sauk City: Arkham House, 1946. 1st ed thus. (Bkpl; upper corners bumped, lower corners worn), else NF in dj (lt edgeworn, clear tape to 1 corner). *Other Worlds*. $250/£156

HODGSON, WILLIAM HOPE. The House on the Borderland. Sauk City, 1946. 1st Amer ed. Dj. *Swann**. $230/£144

HODNETT, EDWARD. English Woodcuts, 1480-1535. London: Bibliographical Society, 1935. 1st ed. Teg, untrimmed. Tan cl, lt brn bds. (Lib spine #, ink handstamps; cvrs lt worn.) Text VG. *Baltimore**. $20/£13

HODSON, A. W. Trekking the Great Thirst. London, 1913. 2nd ed. (Foxed, corners sl bumped, rubbed.) *Grayling*. $80/£50

HOEGH, LEO. Timberwolf Tracks: The History of the 104th Infantry Division 1942-1945. Washington, 1946. 1st ed. Good. *Clark*. $75/£47

HOEHLING, A. A. The Jeannette Expedition. Abelard Schuman, 1969. 1st Eng ed. VG in dj. *Walcot*. $19/£12

HOELLER, SUSANNE WINTERNITZ. Toscanini: a Photobiography. NY: Island Press, (1943). One of 300 numbered. Tan cl over brn cl; ptd label. VG (lt bumped, rubbed; cvr edges faded, spine lt spotted, rear cvr sl stained). *Blue Mountain*. $50/£31

HOETIS, THEMISTOCLES (ed). Zero Anthology No. 8. NY: Zero, (1956). 1st ed. VF in VF dj (sl soiled). *Between The Covers*. $85/£53

HOFFER, ERIC. The Ordeal of Change. NY, 1963. 1st Amer ed. NF (sl rubbed) in NF dj (sm tear). *Polyanthos*. $25/£16

HOFFER, FRANK W. et al. The Jails of Virginia. Appleton-Century, 1933. VG (several water-stain spots to fr cvr) in Good dj (water-damaged, spine chips). *Book Broker*. $45/£28

HOFFMAN, ABBIE. Steal This Book. NY: Pirate Editions, 1971. 1st ed. VG + (spine sl creased, sl rubbed) in wraps. *Sclanders*. $64/£40

HOFFMAN, ALICE. White Horses. NY: Putnam, 1982. 1st ed. Fine in Fine dj. *Pettler*. $45/£28

HOFFMAN, CARL. Saipan: The Beginning of the End. Washington, 1950. VG in custom binding. *Clark*. $85/£53

HOFFMAN, FELIX. The Wolf and the Seven Little Kids. Harcourt, 1959. 1st US ed. 12x6.5. Unpaginated. VG (sm corner bumps, thin bds edgeworn) in VG dj (1/2-inch chip, sm chips fr bottom, spine top). *Price*. $55/£34

HOFFMAN, FREDERICK J. Freudianism and the Literary Mind. Baton Rouge, LA: LA State Univ, 1945. Ptd tan cl. *Gach.* $27/£17

HOFFMAN, LOUIS. Puzzles Old and New. London: Frederick Warne, (1893). Early ed. Pict cl, gilt. VG. *Pacific*.* $138/£86

HOFFMAN, PROFESSOR. Later Magic. Routledge, n.d. Pict cl. (Feps adhered to pastedowns; fr hinge tender; damp spotted, extrems sl rubbed.) *Edwards.* $64/£40

HOFFMAN, PROFESSOR. Modern Magic. Phila: David McKay, n.d. Amer ed. Frontis. (Spine sunned, ends worn.) *Dramatis.* $30/£19

HOFFMAN, PROFESSOR. More Magic. Phila: David McKay, 1900. Early ed. Mauve cl. (Lt edgeworn), else VG. *Glenn.* $125/£78

HOFFMANN, E. T. A. Nutcracker. NY: Crown, 1984. One of 250 signed, w/orig litho by Maurice Sendak laid in. 4to. 102pp. Mint in slipcase. *Davidson.* $1,200/£750

HOFFMANN, E. T. A. The Tales of Hoffman. LEC, 1943. Ltd to 1500 numbered, signed by Hugo Steiner-Prag (illus). Fine in slipcase. *Swann*.* $103/£64

HOFFMANN, HEINRICH. Jimmy Sliderlegs and Other Stories with Funny Pictures. NY: George Sully, (ca 1870). 4to. Cl-backed color pict bds (rear cvr mkd). VG. *Reisler.* $375/£234

HOFFMANN, HEINRICH. Slovenly Peter. LEC, 1935. Ltd to 1500 numbered, signed by Fritz Kredel (illus). Fine in slipcase. *Swann*.* $201/£126

HOFHEIMER, CHARLES R. (ed) Tell It Like It Is. Norfolk, VA: Norfolk Ministerial Assoc, 1967. 1st ed. 36 b/w photos by David A. Harvey. NF in pict stiff wrappers. *Cahan.* $45/£28

HOFLAND, MRS. Africa Described, in Its Ancient and Present State.... Longman, Rees, Orme et al, 1828. 1st ed. viii,291,(i)pp; fldg map (sl browned, 1 fold neatly repaired). Contemp 1/2 calf, gilt, raised bands, black leather prize label, marbled bds. VG. *Sotheran.* $224/£140

HOFLAND, MRS. Africa Described. A.K. Newman, 1834. New ed. 12mo. Triple-fold frontis map, viii,292pp. Aeg. Bkpl of Marjorie Moon. Emb black refined leather, gilt. (Ink sig; tips sl worn), else Fine. *Bookmark.* $152/£95

HOFLAND, MRS. The Blind Farmer and His Children. London: J. Harris, 1816. 1st ed. Sm 8vo. VF full-pg copper-engr frontis w/imprint dated 1 Dec 1815; iv,183pp + 8pp list. Orig leather on bds (rebacked), gilt spine. VG (sl spotting in text, edges lt rubbed). *Hobbyhorse.* $195/£122

HOFLAND, T. C. The British Angler's Manual, or, The Art of Angling in England, Scotland, Wales and Ireland: With Some Account of the Principal Rivers, Lakes and Trout Streams. London, 1839. 1st ed. 14 Fine engr views, plts. Orig cl (shelfworn; sl foxed, soiled). *Oinonen*.* $90/£56

HOFMANN, WERNER. Caricature. From Leonardo to Picasso. London, 1957. 1st UK ed. 80 plts. Dj (sl chipped). *Edwards.* $32/£20

HOFMANN, WERNER. The Sculpture of Henri Laurens. NY, (1970). Dj. *Swann*.* $92/£58

HOFMEISTER, WILHELM. On the Germination, Development and Fructification of the Higher Cryptogamia, and the Fructification of the Coniferae. Frederick Curry (trans). London: Ray Soc, 1862. 1st ed in English. xvii,506pp; 65 plts (lacks plt 61, plt 63 duplicated). Teg. Emb blue cl. (Last few pp lt foxed; joints split, spine chipped w/loss; bumped w/sl loss.) *Edwards.* $48/£30

HOGAN, BEN with HERBERT WARREN WIND. Five Lessons: The Modern Fundamentals of Golf. NY: A.S. Barnes, (1957). 1st ed. Inscribed, signed. (Cvrs sl bowed), else VG in dj. *Pacific*.* $288/£180

HOGAN, INEZ. Nicodemus and His Little Sister. NY: E.P. Dutton, 1932. 1st ed. 12mo. 44 color illus. White bds, black/red lettering. Fine in matching dj (few spots). *Reisler.* $275/£172

HOGAN, INEZ. Nicodemus and His New Shoes. London: J.M. Dent & Sons, (1956). 1st Eng ed. 8vo. 54pp illus + text. 2-color pict bds. Clean in 2-color illus dj (chipped, dusty). *Reisler.* $100/£63

HOGARTH, BASIL. Writing Thrillers for Profit. London: A&C Black, March 1936. 1st ed. Errata slip tipped in before contents. Grn rough buckram. NF. *Temple.* $26/£16

HOGARTH, D. G. Life of Charles Doughty. OUP, 1928. 1st ed. Frontis, fldg map. All edges uncut. Grn cl, gilt. (Half-title, tp, frontis lt browned; spine sl faded), o/w VG. *Sotheran.* $312/£195

HOGARTH, WILLIAM The Works, Including the Analysis of Beauty and Five Days' Peregrination. John Nichols et al (eds). (By William Hogarth.) Phila: George Barrie & Son, 1900. 1st ed thus. One of 1000 sets. 10 vols. 4to. Mtd plts, dbl tissue guards. Uncut, teg. Red cl. Each vol in fitted cl slipcase. *Hartfield.* $895/£559

HOGARTH, WILLIAM. Anecdotes of Mr. Hogarth. Thomas Cook/G. & J. Robinson, 1803. viii,386pp. Contemp 1/2 calf (sl rubbed), gilt. *Hollett.* $120/£75

HOGARTH, WILLIAM. Hogarth's Graphic Works. Ronald Paulson (comp). New Haven/London: Yale Univ, 1965. 1st ed. 2 vols. Tan buckram (sl shelfworn, rubbed), black spine lettering. Texts Good (lt old dampstain top edge vol 1). Djs (chipped, sl worn, tears, old dampstain rear panel vol 1). *Baltimore*.* $70/£44

HOGARTH, WILLIAM. The Works. London/NY, ca 1875. 2 vols. Gilt-pict cl (tips rubbed w/some cl loss). *Swann*.* $115/£72

HOGBEN, LANCELOT. The Wonderful World of Archaeology. GC, 1955. 1st US ed. 9.5x12. Charles Keeping et al (illus). Unpaginated. Glossy pict bds. VG in Good dj (2-inch chips at corner, spine foot). *Price.* $25/£16

HOGG, J. The Microscope. London: Routledge, 1911. 15th ed. Frontis, 20 plts (10 color). VG (bkpl). *Savona.* $72/£45

HOGG, J. The Microscope: Its History, Construction and Application. London, 1871. 8th ed. xx,762pp. 9 plts (8 color). Pict cl, gilt. *Henly.* $72/£45

HOGG, JAMES. The Ettrick Shepherd. London: T.N. Foulis, (1912). 1st ed illus by Jessie M. King. 8vo. (iv),151,(iv)ads pp; mtd color tp, 6 Fine mtd color plts (1 dbl-pg), guards. Teg, rest uncut; unopened. Early cat description affixed to inner upper cvr. Pale gray cl-backed paper-cvrd bds, onlaid pict label to upper cvr, gilt. Fine. *Sotheran.* $269/£168

HOGG, JAMES. The Pilgrims of the Sun, a Poem. Edinburgh, 1815. 1st ed. Buckram. (Ex-lib.) *Argosy.* $50/£31

HOHL, REINHOLD. Alberto Giacometti. NY, (1971). Mtd color plts. Dj. *Swann*.* $201/£126

HOHMAN, ELMO PAUL. The American Whaleman. NY: Longmans, Green, 1928. Leather labels. VG. *High Latitude.* $45/£28

HOIG, STAN. Humor of the American Cowboy. Caldwell: Caxton Ptrs, 1958. 1st ed. Fine in dj. *Labordo.* $95/£59

HOIG, STAN. The Sand Creek Massacre. Norman: Univ of OK, (1961). 1st ed. Black cl. Fine in pict dj (lt worn). *Glenn.* $40/£25

HOIG, STAN. The Western Odyssey of John Simpson Smith. Glendale: A.H. Clark, 1974. 1st ed. Fine. *Harrington.* $40/£25

HOIG, STAN. The Western Odyssey of John Simpson Smith. Glendale, CA, 1974. 1st ed. One of 1613. Frontis. NF in dj. *Sagebrush.* $50/£31

HOLAND, HJALMAR R. Old Peninsula Days. Tales and Sketches of the Door County Peninsula. Ephraim, WI: Pioneer Pub, (1925). 1st ed. Map. (Inked-out name to fr pastedown; spine ends, corners sl rubbed.) *Sadlon.* $20/£13

HOLBEIN, HANS. The Dance of Death. London, 1816. 33 engr plts. Contemp 1/2 straight-grain morocco. (Foxed throughout; joints rubbed.) *Swann*.* $149/£93

HOLBEIN, HANS. The Dance of Death. London: J. Coxhead, 1816. 33 hand-colored copper plts. Mod 3/4 red calf, morocco spine labels. Fine. *Pacific**. $345/£216

HOLBEIN, HANS. Portraits of Illustrious Personages of the Court of Henry VIII, with Memoirs by Edmund Lodge. London: Bulmer, 1828. Sm folio. 82 engr plts. 1/2 morocco, gilt. (Marginal browning, lt spotting; worn, rubbed, fr cvr loose.) *Swann**. $690/£431

HOLBORN, MARK. Black Sun: the Eyes of Four. NY: Aperture, 1985. 1st ed. 2 fldg plts. Elkoh Hosoe, et al (photos). (Mk lower edge), else Fine in dj (lg closed tear repaired w/tape, old price-sticker on rear). *Cahan*. $40/£25

HOLBROOK, M. L. Eating for Strength. NY: Wood & Holbrook, 1875. 1st ed. VG. *Pacific**. $29/£18

HOLBROOK, STEWART H. The Columbia. NY: Rinehart, (1956). 1st ed. VG in VG dj. *Perier*. $50/£31

HOLBROOK, STEWART H. Machines of Plenty, Pioneering in American Agriculture. NY, 1955. 1st ptg. Frontis. VG in VG dj. *Sagebrush*. $40/£25

HOLCROFT, THOMAS. The Life of Thomas Holcroft, Written by Himself. Elbridge Colby (ed). London, 1925. One of 700. 2 vols. (Foxed; cvrs mottled, corner tips sl bumped, hinges cracked.) *Clearwater*. $80/£50

HOLDEN, GEORGE PARKER. The Idyl of the Split-Bamboo: A Carefully Detailed Description of the Rod's Building. Cincinnati: Stewart & Kidd, (1920). 1st ed. Grn cl, gilt. NF. *Pacific**. $196/£123

HOLDEN, QUEEN. Bunnies. Racine, WI: Whitman, (1929). 16mo. Color illus bds (corners lt worn). Color dj (folds lt worn). *Reisler*. $50/£31

HOLDEN, W. C. The Espuela Land and Cattle Company. Austin: TX State Hist Assoc, 1970. 1st ed. Fine in dj. *Labordo*. $35/£22

HOLDEN, W. C. The Spur Ranch. Boston: Christopher Pub House, 1934. 1st ed. VF in dj. Howes H583. *Labordo*. $350/£219

HOLDEN, WILLIAM CURRY. Teresita. Owings Mills, MD, 1978. Signed by Curry and Jose Cisneros (illus). VG in dj. *Dumont*. $50/£31

HOLDER, CHARLES FREDERICK. Along the Florida Reef. NY: D. Appleton, 1892. 1st ed. Gilt-dec pict red cl. (Lacks fep; sm spot fr joint), else VG. *Pacific**. $161/£101

HOLDER, CHARLES FREDERICK. The Channel Islands of California. Chicago: McClurg, 1910. 1st ed. Pict blue cl. (Tp foxed; spine sl sunned, cvrs sl soiled), else VG. *Pacific**. $150/£94

HOLDER, CHARLES FREDERICK. The Channel Islands of California: A Book for the Angler, Sportsman and Tourist. Chicago: A.C. McClurg, 1910. 1st ed. Blue cl. NF. *Pacific**. $196/£123

HOLDER, CHARLES FREDERICK. The Fishes of the Pacific Coast. NY: Dodge Pub, 1912. 1st ed. Grn paper over bds w/mtd pict. VG. *Biscotti*. $80/£50

HOLDER, CHARLES FREDERICK. Life in the Open: Sport with Rod, Gun, Horse and Hound in Southern California. NY: Putnam, 1906. 1st ed. Photogravure frontis. Teg. Grn cl, gilt. (Rubbed, sm bump fr cvr), else VG. *Pacific**. $81/£51

HOLDER, CHARLES FREDERICK. Recreations of a Sportsman on the Pacific Coast. NY, 1910. 1st ed. (Corners sl worn, sm damage mks on spine in title area.) Contents VG. *Woolson*. $75/£47

HOLDER, CHARLES FREDERICK. Recreations of a Sportsman on the Pacific Coast. NY: Putnam, 1910. 1st ed. Teg. Grn cl. VG. *Biscotti*. $85/£53

HOLDICH, T. HUNGERFORD. The Indian Borderland 1880-1900. London, 1901. 1st ed. Map. (Tp sl foxed; backstrip faded.) *Petersfield*. $80/£50

HOLDREDGE, HELEN. Firebelle Lillie. NY: Meredith Press, (1967). 1st ed. Purple cl. Fine in Fine dj. *Harrington*. $35/£22

HOLDREDGE, HELEN. Mammy Pleasant's Partner. NY: Putnam, (1954). 1st ed. VG in VG dj. *Book Market*. $18/£11

HOLDSWORTH, W. G. Cleft Lip and Palate. NY: Grune & Stratton, 1951. (Ink underlining), else Fine. *Weber*. $30/£19

HOLDSWORTH, WILLIAM S. Charles Dickens as a Legal Historian. New Haven: Yale Univ, 1928. *Boswell*. $85/£53

HOLE, CHRISTINA. The English Housewife in the Seventeenth Century. London: C&W, 1953. 7 half-tone plts. Lt red cl, gilt. Fine in dj (sl nicked, dusty). *Temple*. $19/£12

HOLE, CHRISTINA. Witchcraft in England. NY, 1947. 1st Amer ed. (Spine ends worn.) Internally VG. *Mcclintock*. $20/£13

HOLE, S. REYNOLDS. A Book About Roses. London: Edward Arnold, 1902. 19th imp, rev ed. Dec red cl. VG (bkpl, name, browned). *Fair Meadow*. $45/£28

Holiday Tales. Providence: Weeden & Peek, 1849. Sq 12mo. 3 vols in 1. 16,15,16pp + 1pg list on lower wrapper. 6 VF woodengr vignettes. Pict buff paper wrappers. Fine. *Hobbyhorse*. $120/£75

HOLINSHED, RAPHAEL. The First (-Second-Third) Volumes of Chronicles. London, (1587). 3 parts in 4 vols. Folio. Old calf, mod calfbacks (rubbed, cvrs signed, few lib stamps tps). Internally Sound, Clean. *Oinonen**. $3,300/£2,063

HOLLADAY, VIRGINIA. Bantu Tales. Louise Crane (ed). Viking, 1970. 1st ed. Rocco Negri (illus). 95pp. Pict cl. Fine. *Price*. $25/£16

HOLLAND, CECIL F. Morgan and His Raiders. NY, 1942. (Ink inscrip; cvr sl worn.) *King*. $65/£41

HOLLAND, CECIL F. Morgan and His Raiders. NY: Macmillan, 1942. 1st ed. Blue cl. VG in dj. *Chapel Hill*. $75/£47

HOLLAND, CLIVE. How to Take and Fake Photographs. London: C. Arthur Pearson, (1901). 1st ed. Fldg frontis panorama. Pict red cl. (Soiled, spine repaired, cl torn), else VG. *Pacific**. $35/£22

HOLLAND, CLIVE. Wessex. A&C Black, 1912. 75 color plts, guards. Teg. Dec cl (fr cvr sl faded). Good. *Cox*. $40/£25

HOLLAND, HENRY RICHARD LORD. Some Account of the Life and Writings of Lope Felix de Vega Carpio. London: Longman, Hurst et al, 1806. 1st ed. Frontis port. Gilt-ruled diced russia. (Fr joint cracked through, fr cvr neatly detached), else VG. *Pacific**. $46/£29

HOLLAND, LORD. Eve's Legend. London: Etchells & Macdonald, 1928. One of 300 ptd. Dec bds. NF in slipcase. *Pacific**. $46/£29

HOLLAND, MARION. A Big Ball of String. Random House, 1958. 1st ed. 64pp. Pict bds. VG (corners sl worn) in NF dj (dknd). *Price*. $25/£16

HOLLAND, RAY P. Nip and Tuck. NY: Knopf, 1946. New, rev ed. 1st ed thus. Pict eps. Burgundy cl. Fine in NF pict dj. *Biscotti*. $30/£19

HOLLAND, RAY P. Now Listen Warden. West Hartford, VT: Countryman, 1946. 1st ed. Deluxe ed ltd to 475 numbered, signed by author and Wesley Dennis (illus). 1/2 grn cl over grn paper-cvrd bds. Fine in slipcase (worn). *Biscotti*. $110/£69

HOLLAND, RAY P. Scattergunning. NY: Knopf/Borzoi, 1951. 1st ed. Color frontis. VG in dj. *Bowman*. $60/£38

HOLLAND, RAY P. Seven Grand Gun Dogs. NY: Thomas Nelson, 1961. 1st ed. Deluxe ed ltd to 250 numbered, signed by the author and Charles Liedl (illus). Color frontis. Brn buckram. Fine in Fine slipcase. *Biscotti*. $275/£172

HOLLAND, RAY P. Shotgunning in the Lowlands. West Hartford, (1945). One of 350 numbered, signed by Holland and Lynn Bogue Hunt (illus). 9 color plts. *Swann**. $230/£144

HOLLAND, RAY P. Shotgunning in the Uplands. NY: A.S. Barnes, (1945). 2nd ed. 8 color plts by Lynn Bogue Hunt. Tan cl, gilt. Fine. *Pacific**. $35/£22

HOLLAND, RUPERT SARGENT. Yankee Ships in Pirate Waters. Phila: Macrae Smith, (1931). 1st ed. Dbl-pg color illus tp, 4 color plts by Frank Schnoover. Pict eps. Orange lettered yellow cl. VG (cvrs soiled). *House.* $35/£22

HOLLAND, VYVYAN. Hand Colored Fashion Plates 1770 to 1899. B. T. Batsford, 1955. 1st ed. Color frontis. Nice (inscrip) in dj. *Forest.* $96/£60

HOLLANDER, JOHN. Spectral Emanations: New and Selected Poems. NY: Atheneum, 1978. 1st ed. One of 1000. (Edges sl dust mkd.) Dj (sm inner mend spine crown). *Reese.* $25/£16

HOLLAS, WILLIAM and ALICE. Early Recollections. Nelson: Coulton, 1952. Presentation from author's son. VG. *Hollett.* $32/£20

HOLLERAN, ANDREW. Dancer from the Dance. NY: Morrow, 1978. 1st ed. (Sm fore-edge abrasion), else VF in VF dj. *Between The Covers.* $75/£47

HOLLEY, JOSEPH WINTHROP. You Can't Build a Chimney from the Top. NY: William-Frederick, 1948. 1st ed. Port. VG in dj (chipped). *Petrilla.* $35/£22

HOLLEY, JOSEPH WINTHROP. You Can't Build a Chimney From the Top. William-Frederick, 1948. 1st ed. Inscribed presentation copy. VG-. *Book Broker.* $50/£31

HOLLEY, MARIETTA. Samantha at Saratoga. Phila: Hubbard, 1887. 1st ed. Frederick Opper (illus). 583pp. Grn cl, ptd pict. VG- (early name-card set on blank pg, rep chipped; spine ends rubbed). *Price.* $35/£22

HOLLEY, O. L. (ed). The Picturesque Tourist. NY: J. Disturnell, 1844. 1st ed. Engr extra tp, (iv),336pp + ad leaf; 6 b/w plts, 5 Good maps (1 fldg). Orig blind grn cl, gilt. (Lacks fep, sl browned, hinges cracked; sl worn, spine sl turned, ends chipped, frayed.) *Baltimore*.* $70/£44

HOLLIDAY, WALT. Mining Camp Melodies. Butte: Oates & Roberts, (1924). VG. *Perier.* $35/£22

HOLLING, H. C. Minn of the Mississippi. Boston: Houghton Mifflin, 1951. 1st ed. 86pp. NF in dj (chipped, bottom edge near corner sl worn). *Price.* $65/£41

HOLLING, H. C. Pagoo. Boston: Houghton Mifflin, 1957. 1st ed. 9x11. 87pp. VG+ (corners, spine ends bumped). *Price.* $28/£18

HOLLINGHURST, ALAN. Confidential Chats with Boys. Oxford: Sycamore, 1982. 1st Eng ed, 1st bk. NF in wrappers. *Ulysses.* $96/£60

HOLLINGHURST, ALAN. The Swimming Pool Library. NY, 1988. 1st Amer ed. Advance rev copy w/slips, author photo laid in. Fine in Fine dj. *Warren.* $50/£31

HOLLINGHURST, ALAN. The Swimming Pool Library. C&W, 1988. 1st ed. VG (pg edges sl browned; spine ends, corners sl bumped) in dj (spine sl faded, crease dusty). *Ulysses.* $104/£65

HOLLINGSHEAD, JOHN. The Story of Leicester Square. London: Simpkin, 1892. 76pp. Red cl. *Marlborough.* $104/£65

HOLLINGSHEAD, MICHAEL. The Man Who Turned on the World. Blond & Briggs, 1973. 1st ed. (Edges sl spotted), o/w NF- in dj (neat internally repaired sm tear). *Sclanders.* $80/£50

HOLLINGSWORTH, BUCKNER. Her Garden Was Her Delight. NY: Macmillan, 1962. 1st ed. Fine in VG- dj (torn). *Archer.* $25/£16

HOLLINGSWORTH, J. M. The Journal of Lieutenant John McHenry Hollingsworth of the First New York Volunteers.... SF: CA Hist Soc, 1923. One of 300. Color frontis. Blue cl, gilt spine. Fine (bkpl) in dj (lacks 1/2 of spine; dknd, worn). Howes H597. *Pacific*.* $63/£39

HOLLISTER, ISAAC. A Brief Narration of the Captivity of Isaac Hollister, Who Was Taken by the Indians...1763. Townsend, (MA): Otis Seaver, 1855. 8pp. Lib binder. *M & S.* $250/£156

HOLLISTER, OVANDO. Colorado Volunteers in New Mexico. Chicago: R.R. Donnelley, 1962. Frontis, map. VG. *Lien.* $30/£19

HOLLISTER, OVANDO. The Mines of Colorado. Springfield, 1867. Fldg map frontis, hand-colored in outline (sm tears). Pub's cl. (Lt foxed.) Howes H602. *Swann*.* $103/£64

HOLLISTER, OVANDO. The Mines of Colorado. NY, 1974. Rpt of 1867 orig. NF in VG+ dj. *Sagebrush.* $17/£11

HOLLISTER, PAUL M. Famous Colonial Houses. Phila: David McKay, 1921. 1st ed. 12 color plts. Teg. Gilt, dec blue cl. NF (extrems sl worn). *House.* $45/£28

HOLLON, W. EUGENE and RUTH BUTLER (eds). William Bollaert's Texas. Norman, 1956. 1st ed. VG in dj. *Dumont.* $40/£25

HOLLOPETER, W. C. Hay-Fever. Its Prevention and Cure. NY: Funk & Wagnalls, 1917. 1st ed. Frontis. Fine. *Glaser.* $60/£38

HOLLOWAY, OWEN E. French Rococo Book Illustration. Alec Tiranti, 1969. 1st ed. (Ex-lib.) Dj. *Forest.* $48/£30

HOLLOWELL, J. M. War-Time Reminiscences and Other Selections. (Goldsboro, NC): Goldsboro Herald, June 1939. 1st ed. Fine in brn ptd wraps. *Chapel Hill.* $300/£188

HOLLY, H. W. The Art of Saw-Filing. NY, 1890. 5th ed. 56pp; 24 engrs. (Margins lt browned.) *Edwards.* $32/£20

HOLMAN, A. M. and C. R. MARKS. Pioneering in the Northwest. Sioux City, IA, 1924. 1st ed. 2 vols. *Heinoldt.* $45/£28

HOLMAN, A. M. and C. R. MARKS. Pioneering in the Northwest. Sioux City, IA: Deitch & Lamar, 1924. 1st ed. VG. *Perier.* $85/£53

HOLMAN, LOUIS. The Graphic Processes: Intaglio, Relief, and Planographic. Boston: Charles Goodspeed, 1926. Folio. Text booklet (sm lib stamp), 28 leaflets w/37 mtd specimens. Contents loose in cl portfolio (spine lt worn) as issued. *Swann*.* $488/£305

HOLMAN, LOUIS. The Graphic Processes: Intaglio, Relief, Planographic. Boston, 1926. Folio. 32 mtd specimens. (Different copies of this ed were apparently issued w/varying numbers of specimens.) Loose in cl portfolio, as issued. (Worn, cvr soiled.) *Oinonen*.* $275/£172

HOLME, BRIAN. The Kate Greenaway Book. NY: Viking, 1976. 8vo. Kate Greenaway (illus). Fine in Fine dj. *American Booksellers.* $25/£16

HOLME, C. Children's Toys of Yesterday. London: The Studio, 1932. 4to. 128pp. Beige cl. VG (lt foxing, starting) in VG dj. *Davidson.* $135/£84

HOLME, C. and SHIRLEY B. WAINWRIGHT (eds). Decorative Art, 1927. London: The Studio, n.d. c.(1927). Color frontis, 7 color plts. Mod cl, leather spine label. *Edwards.* $48/£30

HOLME, C. He-Who-Came? London: Chapman & Hall, 1930. 1st ed. NF in dj w/color paper pict onlay. *Cady.* $30/£19

HOLME, C. Modern Etchings, Mezzotints and Drypoints. Studio, 1913. 1st ed. Teg. Beveled bds. (Lt spotted.) *Hollett.* $48/£30

HOLME, C. (ed). Art in Photography: With Selected Examples of European and American Work. London/Paris/NY: The Studio, 1905. 110 plts. VG in stiff wrappers (lt chipped). *Cahan.* $250/£156

HOLME, C. (ed). Colour Photography, and Other Recent Developments of the Art of the Camera. London/Paris/NY: The Studio, 1908. (Fr hinge cracked, margins yellowed; paper cvr label worn, faded.) *Swann*.* $258/£161

HOLME, C. (ed). Colour Photography, And Other Recent Developments of the Art of the Camera. London/Paris/NY: The Studio, 1908. 1st ed. 18 color plts, 95 b/w photos (most tipped-in). Teg. (Lt hand soil, erases; extrems rubbed), else NF. *Cahan.* $275/£172

HOLME, C. (ed). The Gardens of England in the Midland and Eastern Counties. Studio, 1908. 1st ed. Sm folio. 8 color, 128 half-tone plts. Sound (sides faded, mkd by damp). Cox. $24/£15

HOLME, RATHBONE and KATHLEEN M. FROST (eds). Decorative Art, 1943-1948. London: The Studio, n.d. c.(1948). 16 color plts. Dj (sl ragged, spine faded). Edwards. $58/£36

HOLMES, E. Report on an Exploration and Survey of the Territory of the Aroostook River, During the Spring and Autumn of 1836. Augusta: Smith & Robinson, 1839. 1st ed. 78,(1)pp. Ptd wrappers. VG (blank corners of some pp missing, wrapper spine torn). Lucas. $150/£94

HOLMES, EUGENIA KELLOGG. Adolph Sutro: A Brief Story of a Brilliant Life. SF: Press of SF Photo-Engr Co, 1895. 1st ed. 56pp. Gilt-dec cl. Fine (sm label). Pacific*. $138/£86

HOLMES, JACK D. L. Gayoso: The Life of a Spanish Governor in the Mississippi Valley, 1789-1799. LA State Univ, (1965). 1st ed. Nice in dj. Rybski. $55/£34

HOLMES, JAMES. Manuscript Notes on Weaving. Burnley: Lupton Bros, (c. 1905). VG (sl shaken, cl sl mkd). Hollett. $136/£85

HOLMES, JOHN CLELLON. Get Home Free. NY: Dutton, 1964. 1st ed. Fine in dj. Pharos. $75/£47

HOLMES, JOHN CLELLON. The Horn. NY: Random House, (1958). 1st ed. Fine in dj. Pharos. $150/£94

HOLMES, JOHN CLELLON. Nothing More to Declare. NY: Dutton, 1967. 1st ed. Errata slip laid in. Fine in dj. Pharos. $75/£47

HOLMES, JOHN CLELLON. Nothing More to Declare. Andre Deutsch, 1968. 1st UK ed. NF in dj. Sclanders. $24/£15

HOLMES, JULIA ARCHIBALD. A Bloomer Girl on Pike's Peak 1858. Agnes Wright Spring (ed). Denver: Western Hist Dept, Denver Public Library, (1949). Ltd ed. Paper-cvrd bds, paper label fr panel. (Spine sl rubbed), else NF in glassine dj (sunned, lt chipped). Hermitage. $40/£25

HOLMES, KENNETH L. Ewing Young, Master Trapper. Portland, OR: Peter Binford Foundation, (1967). 1st ed. Fine in pict dj. Argonaut. $50/£31

HOLMES, LOUIS A. Fort McPherson, Nebraska, Fort Cottonwood, N. T., Guardian of the Tracks and Trails. Lincoln, NE: Johnsen Pub, (1963). 1st ed. One of ltd, signed ed. Clipped Holmes sig affixed to limitation pg. Fine. Pacific*. $46/£29

HOLMES, M. Some Bibliographical Notes on the Novels of G. B. Shaw. London, (1928). Ltd to 500. Fine. Edrich. $40/£25

HOLMES, MAURICE. Captain James Cook, R.N., F.R.S.: A Bibliographical Excursion. London: Francis Edwards, 1952. 1st ed. One of 500. Buckram, gilt. (Spine faded), else NF. Pacific*. $196/£123

HOLMES, OLIVER WENDELL. The Autocrat of the Breakfast Table. LEC, 1955. Ltd to 1500 numbered, signed by Raymond J. Holden (illus). Fine in slipcase. Swann*. $46/£29

HOLMES, OLIVER WENDELL. The Autocrat of the Breakfast-Table. Boston: Houghton Mifflin, 1894. 1st ed thus. 2 vols. Howard Pyle (illus). Brick cl, gilt. Fine. Pacific*. $40/£25

HOLMES, OLIVER WENDELL. Collected Legal Papers. London: Constable, 1920. 1st Eng ed. Sound (rubbed, faded). Boswell. $150/£94

HOLMES, OLIVER WENDELL. The Common Law. Boston, 1881. 1st ed, the state w/'University Press: John Wilson & Son, Cambridge' on tp verso. 8vo. Reddish-brn cl (edges lt rubbed). Kane*. $950/£594

HOLMES, OLIVER WENDELL. The Common Law. Boston: Little, Brown, 1881. 1st ed. 8vo. 16,422pp. Brick red cl. VF (fep offset from newspaper port, near break in paper on pp xiii-xiv; sl corner wear). M & S. $1,500/£938

HOLMES, OLIVER WENDELL. The Complete Works of Oliver Wendell Holmes: Medical Essays. Boston, 1849. VG (ex-lib). Doctor's Library. $90/£56

HOLMES, OLIVER WENDELL. The One Hoss Shay. Boston: Houghton, Mifflin, 1892. 1st separate ed. Orig suede. VG (few sl mks). BAL 9034. Macdonnell. $125/£78

HOLMES, OLIVER WENDELL. The One Hoss Shay. Boston: Houghton, Mifflin, 1905. 1st illus ed. Howard Pyle (illus). Dec drab grn cl, gilt. (Spine ends, corners rubbed), else VG. Pacific*. $58/£36

HOLMES, OLIVER WENDELL. One Hundred Days in Europe. Boston: Houghton Mifflin, 1887. 1st ed. VG (inked date, bkpl) in grn emb cl, gilt. Smith. $40/£25

HOLMES, PRESCOTT. Animal Tales with Picture Puzzles. Phila: Henry Altemus, (1907). 1st ed. Color frontis. Pict cl. VG. Pacific*. $46/£29

HOLMES, PRESCOTT. Animal Tales with Puzzle Pictures. Phila: Henry Altemus, (1907). 1st ed. Pict cl. VG. Pacific*. $46/£29

HOLMES, RICHARD R. Victoria, Queen of England. London: Boussod, Valadon, 1897. 1st ed. Hand-colored frontis port. Teg. 3/4 brn morocco, gilt-paneled spine, raised bands. Fine. Appelfeld. $300/£188

HOLMES, T. R. E. A History of the Indian Mutiny. W.H. Allen, 1883. 1st ed. xvi,604pp (bkpl); 2 maps, 6 plans (mostly fldg). All eps, edges marbled. Contemp 1/2 calf, gilt. Hollett. $224/£140

HOLMES, THOMAS H. et al. The Nose: an Experimental Study.... Springfield, IL: Charles C. Thomas, (1950). VG in dj. Weber. $30/£19

HOLMS, A. CAMPBELL. Practical Shipbuilding. London: Longmans, Green, 1916. 3rd ed. 2 vols. Lg 8vo and obl folio. xiv,638; (4)pp; 115 plts. Blue linen. (Vol 2 soiled, extrems fraying). Karmiole. $175/£109

HOLP, P. E. The Golden Age and Other Sermons. Sioux Falls, SD: Dakota Bell, 1887. 1st ed. 220pp. Ginsberg. $150/£94

HOLT, ARDEN. Fancy Dresses Described. London: Debenham & Freebody, n.d. 4th ed. 16 color plts. (Lt spotted, gathering sl loose, plt detached, sl ragged; hinges cracked.) Edwards. $72/£45

HOLT, ARDEN. Fancy Dresses Described; or, What to Wear at Fancy Balls.... London, (1882). 3rd ed. 32 litho plts (16 color). (Bkpl; shaken.) Swann*. $69/£43

HOLT, L. EMMETT. The Diseases of Infancy and Childhood. NY: D. Appleton, 1899. xvii,1117pp; 7 color plts. Grn cl (lt rubbed). VG. House. $80/£50

HOLT, ROSA BELLE. Oriental and Occidental Rugs. NY, 1937. New, rev ed. 33 full-pg illus (12 color), map. (Lt spotted, color plts sl offset.) Edwards. $72/£45

HOLT, VINCENT M. Why Not Eat Insects. Hampton: E.W. Classey, 1967. (Ink name), else Fine in wraps. Perier. $25/£16

HOLTBY, WINIFRED. The Frozen Earth. Collins, 1935. 1st ed. (Sl dull), else Good in wrappers. Whiteson. $16/£10

HOLTBY, WINIFRED. South Riding. London: Collins, 1936. 1st ed. (Spine sl leaned), else Fine in pict dj (lt smudged, extrems rubbed). Bromer. $75/£47

HOLTON, ISAAC F. New Granada: Twenty Months in the Andes. NY: Harper, 1857. xvi,17-605pp; 2 fldg color maps. 1/2 grn calf, marbled bds (rubbed), gilt. Adelson. $335/£209

HOLUB, EMIL. Seven Years in South Africa. London, 1881. 1st Eng ed. 2 vols. Fldg map. Pict cl. (Lacks plt.) Maggs. $224/£140

HOLUB, EMIL. Seven Years in South Africa. Boston: Houghton Mifflin, 1881. 2 vols. xi,426; xi,479pp; fldg map, 60 plts. Pict cl (rubbed, rear cvr of vol 1 stained). Adelson. $325/£203

HOLUB, LEO. Leo Holub. Photographer. Stanford: Stanford Alumni Assoc, 1982. 1st ed. NF in dj. Smith. $150/£94

HOLWAY, JOHN. Voices from the Great Black Baseball Leagues. NY: Dodd, Mead, 1975. 1st ed. (Sl cocked), else VG + in dj (sl edgeworn). My Bookhouse. $87/£54

Holy Bible, Containing the Old and New Testaments and the Apocrypha. Boston: Hinkley, (1904). One of 1000 sets. 14 vols. Tall 8vo. 1/2 pigskin, raised bands w/King James device in 4 panels, title and Book in 2. (Lt rubbed, occasional dkng.) *Swann**. $546/£341

Holy Bible, Containing the Old and New Testaments. NY: Harper, 1846. 1st ed. Engr frontis, 1/2 title. Aeg. Contemp pub's deluxe blind-stamped full brn morocco. *Swann**. $373/£233

Holy Bible, Containing the Old and New Testaments. Phila: Mathew Carey, Oct 20, 1801. 9 engr plts. Orig full dk brn calf, red leather spine label. (Browned, sl foxed, lacks fr blanks, tears at tp top, sm chunk missing 1 leaf margin; worn, scuffed, tear at spine top partly into label.) *Baltimore**. $130/£81

Holy Bible, Conteyning the Old Testament and the New: Newly Translated Out of the Original Tongues: And with the Former Translations Diligently Compared and Reuifed...1611. [Cleveland, OH: World, n.d. (1965)]. Facs of King James Bible. One of 1500 numbered, ptd by offset lithography, bound by Amilcare Vizzi, Milan. Binding is a replica of an orig contemp binding. Fine in slipcase as issued. *Black Sun*. $900/£563

Holy Bible. Birmingham: John Baskerville, 1769. Aeg. Leather. (Rear hinge repaired, lt foxed, worn, fr bd detached.) *King*. $450/£281

Holy Bible. Trenton: Isaac Collins, 1791. 1st Bible ptd in NJ. Thick 4to. Contemp blind-stamped sheep (worn, cvrs loose; lacks final text leaf); binder's label of Craig & Lea of Wilmington. *Swann**. $632/£395

Holy Bible. London: Nonesuch, 1963. King James Version of 1611 Now Reprinted w/Apocrypha. 3 vols. Good. *Karmiole*. $85/£53

Holy Bible. Boston: R.H. Hinkley, n.d. (ca 1934). 14 vols. 3/4 pigskin, cl bds. (Few ll carelessly opened.) *Kane**. $275/£172

Holy Bible. Genesis. Nonesuch, 1924. One of 375. Imp 8vo. 28 ll; 12 woodcuts by Paul Nash. Untrimmed. Black bds, gilt. VG (feps sl browned; spine ends sl rubbed) in dj (sl defective, tape/tissue repairs). *Blackwell's*. $920/£575

Holy Bible: The King James Version. LEC, 1935-36. Ltd to 1500 numbered. 3 vols. Fine in slipcase. *Swann**. $161/£101

Holy Scriptures, Translated and Corrected by the Spirit of Revelation, by Joseph Smith, Jr., the Seer. Plano, IL: Church of Jesus Christ of the Latter-Day Saints, 1867. 6.75x4. 917,286pp. Aeg; gilt inner dentelles. Period full gilt-dec morocco. (Scuffed, lt stain rear cvr), else VG. *Pacific**. $518/£324

HOLYOAKE, GEORGE JACOB. Among the Americans. London: T.H. Roberts, 1881. 1st ed. Fldg frontis, 1 prelim l, pp79,(3),(4) ads. Orig ptd wrappers (spine sl chipped). *Mott*. $85/£53

HOLZWORTH, JOHN M. The Wild Grizzlies of Alaska. NY: Putnam, 1930. 1st ed. Color frontis. VG in Poor dj. *Perier*. $80/£50

Home-Making and House-Keeping. NY: Butterick, 1889. 1st ed. 398pp. VG. *Petrilla*. $35/£22

HOMER. Iliad of Homer. Mr. Pope (trans). London: Bernard Lintot, 1736. 6 vols. Old brn calf bds (expertly rebacked), gilt paneled spines, raised bands, red/grn spine labels. VG set. *Appelfeld*. $300/£188

HOMER. The Iliad. Maurice Hewlett (trans). Cresset, 1928. 1st ed. Ltd to 750. Uncut. VG in linen-backed cl. Dj (sl soiled). *Cox*. $45/£28

HOMER. The Odyssey. Alexander Pope (trans). Glasgow: Robert & Andrew Foulis, 1772. 3 vols. (4),172; (4),176; (4),156pp. Marbled eps; aeg. Period calf, morocco spine labels. (Margins sl trimmed), else VG set. *Pacific**. $184/£115

HOMER. The Odyssey. George Herbert Palmer (trans). Cambridge: Houghton, Mifflin, 1929. 1st ed illus by N. C. Wyeth. 10.25x7.5. 16 color plts. Gilt-dec red cl. (Hinges weak; spine ends rubbed, soiled), else VG. *Pacific**. $81/£51

HOMER. The Odyssey. Cambridge: Houghton, Mifflin, 1929. 1st Wyeth ed. One of 550 signed by N.C. Wyeth (illus) and Geo. Herbert Palmer (trans). 4to. 15 mtd color plts. Grn silk doubloure eps; teg. Beautifully bound in full red morocco, elaborate gilt-stamped panels on cvrs, spine gilt, raised bands, grn morocco inner panels, inner wide gilt borders. Fine. *Appelfeld*. $950/£594

HOMER. The Odyssey. T. E. Lawrence (trans). (London), 1932. 1st Lawrence ed. One of 530 signed by Bruce Rogers (designer). Sm folio. Orig black niger. *Swann**. $1,265/£791

HOMER. The Odyssey. T. E. Lawrence (trans). Emery Walker, Wilfred Merton & Bruce Rogers, 1932. Ltd to 530. Folio. Roundels in gold/black. Teg, rest uncut. Orig black morocco. Slipcase (worn). *Sotheby's**. $1,288/£805

HOMER. The Odyssey. LEC, 1981. One of 2000 signed by Barry Moser (illus). Fine in slipcase. *Swann**. $103/£64

Homes of American Authors; Comprising Anecdotal, Personal, and Descriptive Sketches by Various Writers. NY: D. Appleton, 1858. viii,374pp. Aeg. Full stamped leather (extrems rubbed). VG + (lt age-spotted). *Zubal**. $35/£22

HOMES, A. M. The Safety of Objects. NY: Norton, (1990). 1st ed. Fine in Fine dj. *Robbins*. $20/£13

HONE, PHILIP. The Diary of Philip Hone 1828-1851. Allan Nevins (ed). NY: Dodd, Mead, 1927. 1st trade of enlgd ed. 2 vols. Frontis. Red buckram w/ptd paper spine labels. Good (stained, foxed to eps, prelims; rear cvr lt soiled, fr cvr lt faded from removed labels). Howes H620. *House*. $45/£28

HONEY, W. B. English Pottery and Porcelain. A&C Black, 1962. 5th ed. 24 plts. (Sm dent to fr bd.) Dj. *Hollett*. $24/£15

HONEY, W. B. Victoria and Albert Museum. Glass. A Handbook for the Study of Glass Vessels of All Periods and Counties and a Guide to the Museum Collection. London, 1946. 72 plts. Good in wrappers. *Washton*. $45/£28

Honeyman Collection of Scientific Books and Manuscripts. London: Sotheby's, 1978-81. 7 vols. Price lists laid in, some prices in ink. (Lt worn.) *Oinonen**. $200/£125

HONIG, DONALD. Baseball in the '50's. Crown, 1987. 1st ed. VG + in VG + dj. *Plapinger*. $60/£38

Hood's Practical Cook's Book for the Average Household. Lowell, MA: C.I. Hood, 1897. 6th ed. 349pp. VG. *Perier*. $40/£25

HOOD, JOHN B. Advance and Retreat. New Orleans: By G.T. Beauregard for the Hood Orphan Memorial Fund, 1880. 1st ed. Frontisport, 358pp (ink stamps fr blank, tp; lt aging). Blue eps. Later dk gray buckram (sl dusty, lt spotted), leather spine label. Howes H622. *Baltimore**. $200/£125

HOOD, JOHN C. F. Icelandic Church Saga. SPCK, 1946. 1st ed. VG in dj (torn). *Walcot*. $16/£10

HOOD, THOMAS. The Epping Hunt. NY: Derrydale, 1930. One of 490 numbered. 6 hand-colored engrs. Vellum cl backed over red paper-cvrd bds. Fine. *Biscotti*. $150/£94

HOOD, THOMAS. Poems. Edward Moxon, 1846. 2nd ed. 2 vols. Frontis vol 1. Good (ink inscrip; spines bumped, sunned, foot nicked vol 1; corners rubbed). *Tiger*. $38/£24

HOOD, THOMAS. The Poetical Works of.... NY: Thomas Knox, (c. 1900). 3 vols. Marbled edges. 3/4 calf, marbled bds, gilt, morocco spine labels. Fine. *Pacific**. $98/£61

Hoofs, Claws and Antlers of the Rocky Mountains. (By Allen Grant Hallihan.) Denver, 1894. Sm folio. Pict cl (extrems worn, cvrs soiled; hinges cracked). *Swann**. $57/£36

HOOGERWERF, FRANK W. Confederate Sheet-Music Imprints. NY: Inst for Studies in American Music, (1984). 1st ed. Clean in white wraps (sl rubbed). *Baltimore**. $30/£19

HOOK, STELLA LOUISE. Little People and Their Homes in Meadows, Woods and Waters. NY: Scribner, 1888. 1st ed. Dan & Harry Beard (illus). Pict cl. (Sl soiled), else VG. *Pacific**. $69/£43

HOOKER, J. D. Himalayan Journals. London: Ward, Lock, (1905). 2nd ed. Fldg map, 13 full-pg plts. (Spine dknd, rubbed), else Good+. *Mikesh.* $150/£94

HOOKER, J. D. and JOHN BALL. A Journal of a Tour in Morocco and the Great Atlas. Macmillan, 1878. 1st ed. 8vo. xvi,499,(39 ads)pp; lg fldg wood-engr panorama, fldg plt, 6 full-pg wood-engr plts, fldg map. Olivine pict cl, gilt. VG (spine ends sl bumped, worn). *Sotheran.* $760/£475

HOOKER, WILLIAM FRANCIS. The Prairie Schooner. Chicago: Saul Bros, 1918. 1st ed. Color frontis. Fine. *Pacific*.* $52/£33

HOOKER, WILLIAM JACKSON. Journal of a Tour in Iceland in the Summer of 1809. London, 1811. Hand-colored frontis, 3 plts. Contemp 1/2 sheep (needs rebinding). *Swann*.* $402/£251

HOOLE, KEN. A Regional History of the Railways of Great Britain. Volume 4: The North East. London: David & Charles, 1974. 3rd rev ed. 44 plts, lg fldg map. VG in dj. *Hollett.* $32/£20

HOOPER, GEORGE. The Campaign of Sedan. London: Bell, 1897. Map. (Sl mkd.) *Stewart.* $64/£40

HOOPER, JANE WINNARD. Arbell: A Tale for Young People.... London: Routledge, 1858. 1st ed. 8vo. 306,14 ads pp; 4 full-pg illus by James Godwin. Coarse-stippled, blind-stamped blue cl, gilt. *Young.* $80/£50

HOOPER, ROBERT. The Anatomist's Vade-Mecum: Containing the Anatomy and Physiology of the Human Body. Windsor, 1809. 2nd Amer ed. 264pp. Full leather w/red spine label. VG (foxed, extrems sl worn). *Doctor's Library.* $200/£125

HOOPER, WILLIAM H. Ten Months Among the Tents of the Tuski, with Incidents of an Arctic Boat Expedition in Search of Sir John Franklin.... London: John Murray, 1853. xv,(i),417pp,(ii)ads; 4 color plts, fldg map. Good (ex-lib, sm stamps). *Explorer.* $512/£320

HOOPES, ALBAN W. The Road to the Little Big Horn and Beyond. NY: Vantage, (1975). 1st ed. Fine in dj. *Lien.* $25/£16

HOOVER, H. A. Early Days in the Mogollons. El Paso: TX Western Press, 1958. VG in pict wraps. *Truepenny.* $35/£22

HOOVER, HERBERT CLARK. A Remedy for Disappearing Game Fishes. NY: Huntington Press, 1930. 1st ed. One of 990 ptd. Cl-backed marbled bds. Fine (bkpl) in glassine (chipped), slipcase (cracked, stain to lower edge). *Pacific*.* $75/£47

HOOVER, HERBERT CLARK. A Remedy for Disappearing Game Fishes. NY: Huntington, 1930. One of 990 numbered. Uncut, unopened. Cl-backed bds (lt worn). Slipcase (scuffed). *Oinonen*.* $80/£50

HOPE, ANNE. Tommy, Tinker and Tip-Toes. A Tale of Three Little Kittens. England: J. Salmon, (1950). 8vo. 16pp. Good in full color ptd wrappers (lt worn). *Reisler.* $150/£94

HOPE, ANTHONY. The Dolly Dialogues. NY: Henry Holt, 1894. 1st Amer ed. 16mo. Frontis by Arthur Rackham, (4),195pp. Teg. Natural linen. VG (lettering rubbed). *House.* $45/£28

HOPE, ANTHONY. The Prisoner of Zenda. LEC, 1966. Ltd to 1500 numbered, signed by Donald H. Spencer (illus). Fine in slipcase. *Swann*.* $57/£36

HOPE, ARTHUR. Sorrento and Inlaid Work for Amateurs, with Original Designs. Chicago: John Wilkinson, 1876. 47pp,5pp ads; 16 plts. (Cardpocket mtd rep; shelfworn, edges worn, rear cvr rubbed), else Good. *Brown.* $75/£47

HOPE, LAURA LEE. The Bobbsey Twins and Baby May. NY: G&D, 1924. Thick ed. Bobbsey Twins #17; lists 32 titles on dj flap. 5x7.5. 242pp + ads. Lime grn cl. VG (shelfworn) in dj (sl edgeworn) w/illus of 2 children picking flowers. *My Bookhouse.* $27/£17

HOPE, LAURA LEE. The Bobbsey Twins on Blueberry Island. NY: G&D, 1917. #10; lists 10 titles. 5x7.5. 244pp + ads. VG+ (shelfworn) in dj (sl worn). *My Bookhouse.* $37/£23

HOPE, LAURA LEE. The Outdoor Girls at Cedar Ridge. NY: G&D, 1931. 1st ed. Outdoor Girls #21; lists to this title. 5x7.5. Walter S. Rogers (illus). 214pp. Good+ (cvr dampstained) in dj (sl edgeworn). *My Bookhouse.* $37/£23

HOPE, LAURA LEE. The Outdoor Girls at Spring Hill Farm. NY: G&D, 1927. Outdoor Girls #17; lists to #22. 5x7.5. 210pp + ads. VG (corners bumped) in dj (sl edgeworn). *My Bookhouse.* $37/£23

HOPE, LAURA LEE. The Outdoor Girls in the Air. NY: G&D, 1932. 1st ed. Outdoor Girls #22; lists only to this title. 5x7.5. 213pp + ads. VG+ (sl shelfworn) in full color illus dj (sl worn). *My Bookhouse.* $47/£29

HOPE, LAURA LEE. The Outdoor Girls on a Canoe Trip. NY: G&D, 1930. Outdoor Girls #20; lists 21 titles on dj flap. 5x7.5. 212pp + ads. Grn cl. VG+ (sl shelfworn) in full color illus dj (sl edgeworn). *My Bookhouse.* $47/£29

HOPE, LAURA LEE. The Outdoor Girls on a Hike. NY: G&D, 1929. Outdoor Girls #19; lists 21 titles on dj flap. 5x7.5. 236pp + ads. VG (inscrip; shelfworn) in full color illus dj (edgeworn). *My Bookhouse.* $42/£26

HOPE, THOMAS. Costume of the Ancients. London: William Miller, 1812. New ed. 2 vols. 300 copper plts. Contemp dbl-gilt-ruled diced russia, gilt/blind-tooled spines, raised bands, gilt-tooled turn-ins. (Bkpls; joints sl weakening), else VG. *Pacific*.* $403/£252

HOPE, THOMAS. An Historical Essay on Architecture. London, 1835. 2nd ed. 2 vols. 97 plts. Mod cl. (Lt foxed.) *Swann*.* $57/£36

HOPE, W. H. ST. JOHN. The Architectural History of the Cathedral Church and Monastery of St. Andrew at Rochester. Mitchell & Hughes, 1900. 1st ed. vi,220pp; 6 lg fldg plans (all but 1 colored, 1 w/color overlay), 1 color plt. VG. *Hollett.* $152/£95

HOPE, W. H. ST. JOHN. Heraldry for Craftsmen and Designers. London: John Hogg, 1913. 1st ed. (Sl faded, spine soiled), o/w VG. *Michael Taylor.* $29/£18

HOPE, W. H. ST. JOHN. Heraldry for Craftsmen and Designers. Pitman, n.d. (1913). 85 plts. Good+ (ex-lib, worn, soiled). *Whittle.* $22/£14

HOPEWELL-SMITH, A. An Introduction to Dental Anatomy and Physiology. Descriptive and Applied. Phila/NY, 1913. Presentation copy. Frontis; 5 plts. (Spine sl worn), o/w VG. *Whitehart.* $56/£35

HOPKINS, ALBERT A. (comp). Magic, Stage Illusions and Scientific Diversions. NY: Munn, 1898. (Rebound w/orig color pict cvr.) Internally NF. *Dramatis.* $150/£94

HOPKINS, D. R. Princes and Peasants: Smallpox in History. Univ of Chicago, (1983). Good in dj. *Rybski.* $45/£28

HOPKINS, EDWARD J. and EDWARD F. RIMBAULT. The Organ. Robert Cocks, 1878. 3rd ed. 3 vols. 3 lg fldg frontispieces, xxxvi,160; xxxi,625-628(index),159; xxxi,610-632,160-327pp. Blind-stamped cl (1 spine sl faded), gilt. *Hollett.* $136/£85

HOPKINS, F. POWELL. Fishing Experiences of Half a Century, with Instructions in the Use of the Fast Reel. London: Longmans, Green, 1893. 1st ed. Gilt-lettered pict cl. NF (bkpl, inscrip). *Pacific*.* $115/£72

HOPKINS, GARLAND EVANS. The First Battle of Modern Naval History. Richmond, VA: Dietz, 1943. 1st ed. One of 199 signed, inscribed. Blue cl. NF. *Chapel Hill.* $150/£94

HOPKINS, HENRY CLAYTON. The Moon-Boat and Other Verse. Phila: David McKay, (1918). 4to. 12 full-pg color plts by W. Philip Vinton Clayton. Tan cl (fr edge rubbed), gilt, color paste label. *Reisler.* $225/£141

HOPKINS, LUTHER W. From Bull Run to Appomattox: A Boy's View. Balt: Fleet-McGinley, (1911). 1st ed. Frontisport; fldg map. Maroon cl (worn, frayed; hinges very cracked), gilt. Good (shaken; ex-lib, bkpl fep, sm ink # c. pg). *Baltimore*.* $30/£19

HOPKINS, MANLEY. Hawaii: The Past, Present, and Future of Its Island-Kingdom.... London, 1866. 2nd ed. Gilt-pict cl. (Hinges starting.) *Swann*. $138/£86

HOPKINSON, CECIL. Collecting Golf Books 1743-1938. London: Constable, (1938). 1st ed. VG (emb stamp, corners dogeared) in ptd red wrappers (chipped, sl adhesion residue to lower joints, lacks sm piece of lower rear corner). *Pacific**. $1,093/£683

HOPKIRK, MARY. Queen Adelaide. London: John Murray, 1946. 8 plts. VG in dj. *Hollett*. $32/£20

HOPLEY, C. C. Snakes: Curiosities and Wonders of Serpent Life. London: Griffith/Farran, 1882. 1st ed. 614pp; 2 full-pg hand-colored engrs. 1/2 leather, marbled bds. VG+ (2 pp notes rep). *Mikesh*. $150/£94

HOPPIN, CHARLES A. (ed). The Washington Ancestry and Records of the McClain, Johnson, and Forty Other Colonial American Families. Greenfield, OH, 1932. One of 300 sets. 3 vols. Blue cl, gilt. Box. *Kane**. $140/£88

HOPPIN, JOSEPH CLARK. A Handbook of Attic Red-Figured Vases.... Cambridge: Harvard Univ, 1919. 2 vols. Teg. (Few pp foxed.) *Archaeologia*. $300/£188

HOPTON, WILLIAM. A Conversation on Mines, &c., Between a Father and Son. Manchester: Abel Heywood & Son, 1865. 2nd ed (4th thousand). Fldg frontis diag (sl torn), 174,(ii)pp. Blindstamped cl, gilt. (Sig, fr joint cracked, sl rubbed.) *Hollett*. $72/£45

HORACE. The Satires and Epistles of Horace. London: D. Browne & J. Walthoe, 1712. 2nd ed. Frontisport, (22),407,(1),61,(8)pp + 3pp ads. Contemp calf. (Spine worn), else VG. *Pacific**. $86/£54

HORAN, JAMES D. Across the Cimarron. NY: Crown, (1956). 1st ed. VG in dj. *Lien*. $20/£13

HORAN, JAMES D. Desperate Men, Revelations from the Sealed Pinkerton Files. NY, (1949). 1st ed. (Dj sl worn.) *King*. $25/£16

HORAN, JAMES D. Desperate Men. NY, 1949. Good in dj. *Dumont*. $35/£22

HORAN, JAMES D. The Life and Art of Charles Schreyvogel, Painter-Historian of the Indian-Fighting Army of the American West. NY: Crown Pub, (1969). VG+ in dj (edgeworn, sm tears). *Pacific**. $127/£79

HORAN, JAMES D. The Life and Art of Charles Schreyvogel. NY, 1969. Oblong folio. 36 full-color plts. Internally VG. Dj (worn, chipped). *Dumont*. $100/£63

HORAN, JAMES D. The McKenney-Hall Portrait Gallery of American Indians. NY, 1972. Sm folio. VG in dj. *Dumont*. $55/£34

HORE, J. P. History of the Royal Buckhounds. London, 1895. 1st ed. 'Subscription ed.' 400pp. (1st, last pp foxed, frontis sl loose; hinges sl split, cvrs soiled, worn.) *King*. $40/£25

HORGAN, PAUL. The Centuries of Santa Fe. NY, 1956. 1st Amer ed. NF in NF dj. *Polyanthos*. $25/£16

HORGAN, PAUL. Conquistadors in North American History. NY, 1963. 1st Amer ed. Fine in Fine dj. *Polyanthos*. $25/£16

HORGAN, PAUL. From the Royal City. Santa Fe: Rydal, 1936. Tls from Horgan laid in. NF (sl shelfworn). *Dumont*. $150/£94

HORGAN, PAUL. Great River: The Rio Grande in North American History. NY: Rinehart, 1954. 1st trade ed. Inscribed, signed. 2 vols. VG set in slipcase (worn). *Labordo*. $95/£59

HORGAN, PAUL. Great River: The Rio Grande in North American History. NY: Rinehart, 1954. 1st ed. 2 vols. 4 maps (3 dbl-pg). Black cl, gilt. Fine set in pict slipcase (lt worn). *Argonaut*. $125/£78

HORGAN, PAUL. Great River: The Rio Grande in North American History. NY: Rinehart, 1954. One of 1000. Signed. 2 vols. 2 dbl-pg maps. Pict eps; teg. NF in slipcase (sl shelfworn). *Pacific**. $259/£162

HORGAN, PAUL. The Habit of Empire. Santa Fe: Rydal, (1939). 1st ed. Signed. Gray cl. Fine in VG- dj (spine tanned, sm nicks). *Reese*. $225/£141

HORGAN, PAUL. One Red Rose for Christmas. Longmans, Green, 1952. 1st ed. VG+ (inscrip) in VG dj (sl chipped). *Authors Of The West*. $30/£19

HORLE, CRAIG W. (ed). Records of the Courts of Sussex County Delaware 1677-1710. Phila: Univ of PA, 1991. 1st ed. 2 vols. (Upper rt hand corners sl bumped), else VG set. *Brown*. $60/£38

HORLER, SYDNEY. The Curse of Doone. NY, 1930. 1st Amer ed. Good in dj (soiled, worn, edges frayed). *King*. $25/£16

HORLER, SYDNEY. Ring Up Nighthawk. London: Hodder & Stoughton, May 1947. 1st ed. Dull red cl. VF in dj (sl frayed). *Temple*. $29/£18

HORLER, SYDNEY. Virus X: A Paul Vivanti Story. Adelphi: Quality Press, 1945. 1st ed. Pale blue cl. (Paper sl browned), o/w Fine in dj (sl chipped, head sl torn). *Temple*. $29/£18

HORN, CALVIN. New Mexico's Troubled Years. Albuquerque: Horn & Wallace, 1963. 1st ed. VG in dj (sl worn). *Dumont*. $25/£16

HORN, DAVID. The Literature of American Music. Metuchen, NJ, 1977. VG. *Dumont*. $50/£31

HORN, MADELINE D. Farm on the Hill. NY: Scribner, 1936. 1st ed. Inscribed to Sterling Bunnell by both Horn and Grant Wood (illus). Sm 4to. 8 color plts. Blue cl (lt stain). VG in dj (1-inch piece missing spine top). *Davidson*. $200/£125

HORN, ROBERT. A Sketch by His Mother. Glasgow: Privately ptd, 1933. Leather spine label. Good (inscrip). *Clearwater*. $88/£55

HORN, STANLEY F. The Decisive Battle of Nashville. Baton Rouge: LA State Univ, (1956). 1st ed. Signed. Blue bds. Fine in pict dj (sl worn). *Argonaut*. $50/£31

HORN, STANLEY F. (ed). Tennessee's War 1861-1865, Described by Participants. Nashville: TN Civil War Centennial Commission, 1965. 1st ed. VG in dj. *Cahan*. $45/£28

HORN, TOM. Life of Tom Horn, Government Scout and Interpreter. Doyce B. Nunis, Jr. (ed). Chicago: R.R. Donnelley, 1987. Frontis. VG. *Lien*. $30/£19

HORNADAY, W. T. Camp-Fires on Desert and Lava. NY: Scribner, 1908. 1st ed. Color frontis, 2 maps. Teg. Red cl, gilt, pict cvr label. (Ink name; spine sl faded), else VG. *Pacific**. $98/£61

HORNADAY, W. T. Our Vanishing Wild Life. NY: Scribner, 1913. 1st ed. Good+. *Mikesh*. $27/£17

HORNADAY, W. T. Taxidermy and Zoological Collecting. NY, (1891). xix,362pp; 23 plts. (1 plt, tp tanned, 1 pg smudged; worn, stained.) *Sutton*. $68/£43

HORNE, BERNARD S. The Compleat Angler 1653-1967. Pittsburgh: Pittsburgh Bibliophiles, 1970. Ltd to 500. Color frontis. Grn buckram. Fine in Fine pict dj. *Biscotti*. $135/£84

HORNE, THOMAS HARTWELL. An Introduction to the Study of Bibliography. To Which Is Prefixed a Memoir on the Public Libraries of the Antients. Ptd by G. Woodfall, 1814. 1st ed. 2 vols. Fldg frontis, 9 plts. (1 gathering loose.) Uncut. 19-cent bds. *Forest*. $104/£65

HORNELL, JAMES. British Coracles and Irish Curraghs. Bernard Quaritch, 1938. 23 plts. VG (eps sl spotted) in dj. *Hollett*. $152/£95

HORNSBY, ROGERS and BILL SURFACE. My War with Baseball. Coward McCann, 1962. 1st ed. (Edgeworn), o/w VG in VG dj. *Plapinger*. $55/£34

HORNSBY, ROGERS. My Kind of Baseball. McKay, 1953. 1st ed. VG+ in VG dj. *Plapinger*. $60/£38

HORNUNG, E. W. The Camera Fiend. Scribner, 1911. 1st ed. VG+ in dj (chipped). *Fine Books*. $65/£41

HORNUNG, E. W. Mr. Justice Raffles. Smith, Elder, 1909. 1st ed. Pict cl. Nice (fep cracked, few mks, creases, sl shaken; rear cvr mkd). *Ash.* $160/£100

HORNUNG, E. W. Stingaree. NY: Scribner, 1905. 1st US ed. 8 b/w plts. (Spine, corners sl worn), o/w VG. *Bernard.* $35/£22

HOROVITZ, FRANCES. Water over Stone. Enitharmon Press, 1980. 1st Eng ed. Signed. VG (top corners sl bumped) in dj (sl nicked, dusty, spine sl dknd). *Ulysses.* $58/£36

HORSFIELD, THOMAS WALKER. The History, Antiquities and Topography of the County of Sussex. Lewes, 1835. 2 vols. 56 engr plts; list of subscribers, ad leaf end of vol 2. Contemp 1/2 morocco (worn, fr cvr vol 1 detached; spotted, discolored). *Sotheby's*.* $294/£184

HORSLEY, JOHN. Britannia Romana; or, The Roman Antiquities of Britain. London: John Osborn & Thomas Longman, 1732. 105 engr plts, maps (offsetting affecting 1st few maps). Early 19th-cent diced calf (cvrs detached, extrems bumped). *Christie's*.* $234/£146

HORST. Patterns from Nature. NY: J.J. Augustin, 1946. 1st ed. Frontis. VG (eps lt foxed) in illus dj (lacks few sm chips). *Cahan.* $150/£94

HORT, LIEUTENANT COLONEL. Penelope Wedgebone: The Supposed Heiress. London: J. & D.A. Darling, (1850). 1st ed. Brn cl-cvrd eps; teg. Later dk brn levant morocco, brn cl, raised bands, gilt. Text Clean (sl aged; sl worn, orig trimmed cl binding incl spine inserted at rear). *Baltimore*.* $110/£69

HORTON, THOMAS F. (ed). History of Jack County. Jacksboro, n.d. (1932). Wraps. (Ex-lib), else Good. *King.* $100/£63

HORVATH, FERDINAND HUSZTI. Captured! NY: Dodd, Mead, 1930. 1st ed. Gray cl stamped in red. Fine in pict dj (sl edge use, sm chip). *Reese.* $50/£31

HORWOOD, A. R. British Wild Flowers in Their Natural Haunts. Volume IV. London: Gresham, 1919. 1st ed. Good. *Archer.* $15/£9

HOSACK, DAVID. A Biographical Memoir of Hugh Williamson. NY: E. Bliss & E. White, 1821. 2nd ed. Frontisport, 78pp. Orig ptd wraps. (Foxed, offsetting from frontis to tp), else VG. *Chapel Hill.* $95/£59

HOSE, CHARLES and WILLIAM McDOUGALL. The Pagan Tribes of Borneo, a Description of Their Physical, Moral and Intellectual Condition.... Macmillan, 1912. 1st ed. 2 vols. 8vo. 143plts, 4 fldg maps vol 2. Blue pict cl, gilt. Good set (lt spotted; spine ends sl worn). *Sotheran.* $520/£325

HOSE, CHARLES and WILLIAM McDOUGALL. The Pagan Tribes of Borneo. Macmillan, 1912. 2 vols. 8vo. 2 color frontispieces, 4 fldg maps in vol 2, ad. (Spotting.) Pub's dk blue cl (sl mkd; bkpl), gilt. *Sotheby's*.* $827/£517

HOSE, CHARLES and WILLIAM McDOUGALL. The Pagan Tribes of Borneo. London: Macmillan, 1912. 1st ed. 2 vols. Demy 8vo. xiv,284; x,374pp; 4 fldg maps, 211 plts, 3 tables (2 on 9 fldg sheets). (Lt foxed, 1 map sl edge-frayed), o/w Fine in 1/2 blue crushed morocco (recently recased), blue cl, gilt. *Ulysses.* $960/£600

HOSEGOOD, NANCY. The Glass Island. Hodder & Stoughton, 1964. 1st ed. Map. VG + in dj. *Walcot.* $24/£15

HOSKYNS-ABRAHALL, JOHN. Western Woods and Waters. London, 1864. 1st ed. Frontis, fldg map. (Sl foxed, soiled; shelfworn.) Howes H657. *Oinonen*.* $30/£19

HOSMER, JAMES. History of the Expedition of Captains Lewis and Clark. Chicago: A.C. McClurg, 1902. 1st trade ed. 2 vols. Fldg map. VG- set (lt edgeworn). *Perier.* $160/£100

HOSMER, PAUL. Now We're Loggin. Portland: Metropolitan, 1930. 1st ed. Signed presentation. VG in dj. *Perier.* $30/£19

HOSTETLER, JOHN A. Annotated Bibliography on the Amish.... Scottdale: Mennonite Pub House, 1951. 1st ed. Good in ptd wraps. *Baltimore*.* $25/£16

HOTCHKIN, JAMES. A History of the Purchase and Settlement of Western New York.... NY: M.W. Dodd, 1848. xvi,600pp + ads. Later cl. (Lacks frontis; lib spine #), else Good. Howes H665. *Brown.* $45/£28

Hotels of Europe, America, Asia, Australasia and Africa.... London: J.P. Segg, 1890. viii,9-322pp; 11 dbl-pg color ptd maps. Aeg. Red cl (sl affected by damp, faded), gilt. Contents VG. *Marlborough.* $240/£150

HOTSON, LESLIE. Shakespeare's Motley. London, 1952. 1st Eng ed. VG in dj. *Clearwater.* $40/£25

HOTTEN, JOHN CAMDEN. Abyssinia and Its People. London: John Camden Hotten, 1868. 1st ed. Color engr frontis, vi,384,(8) pub's list; lg fldg map, 7 color engr plts. Blue marbled cl. VG (ad slip torn away, margins lt browned, 1 gathering roughly opened; upper hinge cracked, spine head well repaired, sl rubbed). *Morrell.* $176/£110

HOUART, VICTOR. Easter Eggs. Souvenir, 1978. 1st ed. VG in dj. *Hollett.* $48/£30

HOUDINI, HARRY. A Magician Among the Spirits. NY, 1924. 1st ed. Signed, inscribed. Lg 8vo. Errata slip laid in. (Spine soiled, dknd.) *Swann*.* $862/£539

HOUGEN, JOHN. The Story of the Famous 34th Infantry Division. San Angelo, 1949. 1st ed. VG. *Clark.* $125/£78

HOUGH, EMERSON. Mother of Gold. NY: Appleton, 1924. 1st ed, 1st ptg w/Appleton's '1' on last pg of text. Orange cl. VF in Good pict color dj. BAL 9363. *Macdonnell.* $75/£47

HOUGH, EMERSON. The Story of the Cowboy. NY: D. Appleton, 1897. 1st ed. Dec cl. NF. Howes H673. *Labordo.* $225/£141

HOUGH, EMERSON. The Story of the Outlaw. NY: Outing, 1907. 1st ed, 1st state w/ptr's rule at top of pg v. NF. Howes H674. *Labordo.* $225/£141

HOUGH, EMERSON. The Web. Chicago: Reilly & Lee, (1919). 1st ed. Lt brn cl stamped in black. NF in VG dj (dust-soiled, sm chips, rubs). *Reese.* $55/£34

HOUGH, EMERSON. The Web. Chicago: Reilly & Lee, (1919). 1st ed. Tan cl. VF in VG pict color dj. BAL 9354. *Macdonnell.* $100/£63

HOUGH, FRANKLIN B. Report Upon Forestry. US Dept of Agriculture, 1878. 650pp. Black cl, gilt. (Ex-lib; rebound.) *Larry Price.* $65/£41

HOUGH, HORATIO GATES. Diving, or an Attempt to Describe upon Hydraulic and Hydrostatic Principles. Hartford: John Russell, Jr, 1813. 1st ed. As issued, ptd and folded from folio leaf, w/o wraps. 8pp. Untrimmed, uncut. VG (sl browned, partial split along spine fold). *Baltimore*.* $130/£81

HOUGH, ROMEYN BECK. Handbook of the Trees. Lowville, NY: Romeyn B. Hough, 1936. 5th ptg. (Sl browned; spine sunned), else VG. *Fair Meadow.* $20/£13

Houghton Library, 1942-1967. A Selection of Books and Manuscripts in Harvard Collections. Cambridge, 1967. Sm folio. NF in clear plastic dj (chipped, torn). *Zubal*.* $45/£28

Houghton Library, 1942-1967. A Selection of Books and Manuscripts in Harvard Collections. Cambridge, 1967. (Lt worn.) Dj. *Oinonen*.* $60/£38

HOUGHTON, ELIZA P. DONNER. The Expedition of the Donner Party and Its Tragic Fate. L.A.: Grafton Pub Corp, 1920. Later ed. Grn cl, gilt. *Dawson.* $50/£31

HOUGHTON, W. British Fresh-Water Fishes. London: William MacKenzie, n.d. c.(1879). 1st ed. 2 vols in 1. xxvi,204pp; 41 color ptd wood block plts (tissue guard to frontis, 1 plt creased). Aeg, marbled eps. (Lt browned, ex-lib w/bkpl remains, ink stamps verso of plts, blanks). Gilt-edged 1/2 morroco w/blind-stamp (extrems, joints rubbed, sm splits to joint heads; spine chipped, rubbed.) *Edwards.* $1,200/£750

HOUGHTON, W. British Freshwater Fishes. William Mackenzie, n.d. Folio. 41 chromolitho plts. Contemp red 1/2 morocco. (Fep torn; sl rubbed.) Sotheby's*. $957/£598

HOUGLAND, WILLARD. Santos. NY, 1946. 8 full-pg photos, map. (Wraps soiled), else VG. Dumont. $35/£22

HOUSE, HOMER D. Wild Flowers of New York. Albany, 1918. 2 vols. 264 color plts. Grn cl, gilt. Kane*. $50/£31

HOUSE, HOMER D. Wild Flowers of New York. Albany, NY: Univ of the State of NY, 1918. 1st ed. 264 color plts. (Bds sl scuffed, corners bumped, spine sl worn), else VG. Fair Meadow. $120/£75

HOUSE, HOMER D. Wild Flowers. NY: Macmillan, 1935. 2nd ptg. 364 full-pg color illus. VG (bkpl; ex-lib). Quest. $50/£31

HOUSEHOLD, GEOFFREY. The Third Hour. London: C&W, 1937. 1st ed. (Pg edges, eps lt spotted), o/w NF in dj (spine sl dknd, few sm tears). Mordida. $175/£109

HOUSER, M. L. Young Abraham Lincoln and Log College. Peoria, IL: L.O. Schriver, 1942. 13 facs. Good + in pict card wraps. Wantagh. $30/£19

HOUSER, M. L. Young Abraham Lincoln Mathematician. Peoria, IL: Lester O. Schriver, 1943. 1st ed. Frontis. Good + in ptd wraps. Wantagh. $25/£16

Housewife's Reason Why: Affording to the Manager of Household Affairs Intelligible Reasons for the Various Duties She Has to Perform. (By Robert Kemp Philp.) London: Houlston & Wright, (1857). 1st ed. xli,(1)pp,(1)leaf,(45)-352pp, 2 ad ll tipped in at fr. Textured cl, gilt. VF (margins sl stained; spine, edges sl faded). Pirages. $150/£94

HOUSMAN, A. E. The Collected Poems of A. E. Housman. Cape, 1939. 1st ed. Buckram. VG (feps lt browned, faint inscrip fep, largely removed by ink solvent; sl mkd) in dj (sl torn, chipped, rubbed, creased, soiled, dusty, internally repaired, spine, edges sl dknd). Ulysses. $136/£85

HOUSMAN, A. E. The Collected Poems. London: Cape, 1959. 1st Eng ed. Buckram. NF (feps partly browned, sig; spine ends, bottom edges sl faded) in dj (sl nicked, creased, spotted, spine sl faded). Ulysses. $152/£95

HOUSMAN, A. E. Fifteen Letters to Walter Asburner. London: Tragara, 1976. One of 125. Petersfield. $80/£50

HOUSMAN, A. E. Last Poems. London: Grant Richards, 1922. 1st Eng ed. Signed. VG (spine ends, corners sl bumped, rubbed, spine sl mkd, faded) in dj (nicked, dusty, sl torn, rubbed, mkd, creased, sl dknd). Ulysses. $1,120/£700

HOUSMAN, A. E. The Name and Nature of Poetry. Cambridge, 1933. 1st ed. (Spine ends chipped, spine foot torn at outer hinges.) King. $25/£16

HOUSMAN, A. E. A Shropshire Lad. London, 1896. 1st ed, 1st bk. 12mo. 1/4 vellum, red ptd spine label. (Bkseller ticket rear pastedown.) 1/4 morocco fldg case. Swann*. $1,265/£791

HOUSMAN, LAURENCE (ed). War Letters of Fallen Englishmen. NY: Dutton, (ca 1930). 1st ed, US issue. Purple cl, gilt. Nice (2 leaves roughly opened at bottom, spine gilt tarnished) in VG white dj (smudged). Reese. $45/£28

HOUSMAN, LAURENCE (trans). Stories from the Arabian Nights. London: Hodder & Stoughton, (c. 1929). 9.25x6. 29 tipped-in color plts by Edmund Dulac. Grn cl, gilt. NF. Pacific*. $63/£39

HOUSMAN, LAURENCE (trans). Stories from the Arabian Nights. NY: George H. Doran, (c.1925). 8vo. 237pp; 16 tipped-in color plts by Edmund Dulac. Dec eps. Black pict red cl. VG (extrems rubbed). House. $80/£50

HOUSMAN, LAURENCE (trans). Stories from the Arabian Nights. London: Hodder & Stoughton, 1907. Ltd to 350 signed. Thick 4to. 133pp + preface; 50 full-pg mtd color plts by Edmund Dulac. Teg, orig ties present. White vellum, gilt. Good. Reisler. $3,500/£2,188

HOUSMAN, LAURENCE. Echo de Paris. London, 1923. One of 250 signed. Uncut. Dec cvrs. Fine (bkpl; label rubbed). Polyanthos. $35/£22

HOUSMAN, LAURENCE. Princes Badoura. London: Hodder & Stoughton, (1913). 1st ed. One of 750 signed by Edmund Dulac (illus). 4to. 10 mtd color plts. Teg. Cream dec linen. Good. Appelfeld. $650/£406

HOUSMAN, LAURENCE. Princess Badoura. London: Hodder & Stoughton, (1913). 1st ed. Sm 4to. White/pale grn cl, gilt. VG (edges lt foxed; lt scratches, sl soil fr cvr). Glenn. $375/£234

HOUSTON, C. STUART (ed). To the Arctic By Canoe 1819-1821. Montreal: Arctic Inst. of North America, McGill Queens Univ, 1974. Fine in dj. High Latitude. $45/£28

HOUSTON, C. STUART (ed). To the Arctic by Canoe 1819-1821. Montreal/London: Arctic Inst of North America/McGill-Queen's Univ, 1974. VG in dj. Explorer. $64/£40

HOUSTON, MARY G. Ancient Greek, Roman and Byzantine Costume and Decoration. London, 1965. 2nd ed. 8 color plts. (Lib ink stamp fep.) Dj. Edwards. $32/£20

Houston: A History and Guide. Houston: Anson Jones, 1942. 1st ed. VG in dj (sl soiled). Dumont. $60/£38

HOUTS, MARSHALL. From Gun to Gavel. NY: William Morrow, 1954. 1st ed. VG in dj. Lien. $25/£16

HOVEY, CHARLES MASON. The Fruits of America. Boston, 1848-56. 1st ed. 2 vols. 4to. 2 uncolored litho frontisports, 96 chromolithos by William Sharp. Contemp brn leather (spine ends worn, joints cracked or starting), gilt. Swann*. $4,140/£2,588

HOVEY, RICHARD. To the End of the Trail. NY, 1908. 1st Amer ed. Frontisport. NF. Polyanthos. $30/£19

HOVEY, SYLVESTER. Letters from the West Indies: Relating Especially to the Danish Island St. Croix.... NY, 1838. 1st ed. iv,(13)-212pp (foxed, lib label ep). Cl (shelfworn), paper spine label (scuffed). Oinonen*. $70/£44

HOW, LOUIS. Nursery Rhymes of New York City (with additions). NY: Harbor, 1931. 1st ed. 20 color wood-block illus by Ilse Bischoff. Cl-backed dec bds, gilt. Fine. Pacific*. $86/£54

HOWARD, BRIAN. Portrait of a Failure. Marie-Jacqueline Lancaster (ed). Blond, 1968. 1st ed. (Edges sl rubbed, rear cvr sl mkd, spine sl creased), else VG in dj (browned, soiled, chipped, closed tears, internally repaired, price-clipped). Virgo. $40/£25

HOWARD, CLIFFORD. Sex Worship: An Exposition of the Phallic Origin of Religion. Washington: Clifford Howard, 1897. 1st ed. Grn cl, gilt. (Pp lt pencil-mkd), else VG. Pacific*. $40/£25

HOWARD, DAVID SANCTUARY. Chinese Armorial Porcelain. London, (1974). 4to. Dj. Swann*. $1,035/£647

HOWARD, DOROTHY. Dorothy's World: Childhood in Sabine Bottom 1902-1910. Englewood Cliffs, NJ: Prentice-Hall, (1977). 1st ed. Fine in dj (lt edgeworn). Sadlon. $20/£13

HOWARD, F. E. and F. H. CROSSLEY. English Church Woodwork...1250-1550. London, (1917). (Tp becoming loose, few ll foxed; sl cocked, tips bumped.) Swann*. $57/£36

HOWARD, F. E. and F. H. CROSSLEY. English Church Woodwork...the Mediaeval Period 1250-1550. Batsford, 1927. 2nd ed. 16 full-pg collotype plts. Blue cl, gilt. Good + (ex-lib, stamps; worn, spine head chipped). Whittle. $64/£40

HOWARD, F. E. The Medieval Styles of the English Parish Church. NY, 1936. Good. Washton. $60/£38

HOWARD, FRANK. Colour as a Means of Art. London, n.d. c.(1879). Rpt. Color frontis, 17 color plts. (Pp19/20 almost detached, margins lt browned, marginal mks; rubbed, lt soiled.) Edwards. $56/£35

HOWARD, H. R. The History of Virgil A. Stewart.... NY: Harper, 1836. 1st ed. VG (lt foxed; lacks part of title label, cvrs worn). Howes H70. Labordo. $450/£281

HOWARD, JOHN GALEN. Brunelleschi. SF, 1913. Ltd to 480. Uncut. Fine (inscrip) in NF box (sl rubbed). *Polyanthos.* $45/£28

HOWARD, JOHN T., JR. A Bibliography of Theatre Technology. Westport: Greenwood, (1982). NF. *Dramatis.* $35/£22

HOWARD, JOHN. The State of the Prisons in England and Wales. Warrington, 1784. 3rd ed. 492pp + index; 22 copper plts. Period tree calf, gilt-roll borders, gilt-tooled, stamped spine, morocco spine label. (Bkpls; corners sl bumped, hinges chipped), else Nice. *King.* $395/£247

HOWARD, JOSEPH KINSEY. Montana High, Wide, and Handsome. New Haven: Yale Univ, 1968. Good in dj (sl worn). *Dumont.* $30/£19

HOWARD, L. O. The House Fly Disease Carrier.... London, 1912. Color frontis. (Sl fr cvr damp mk), o/w VG. *Petersfield.* $32/£20

HOWARD, MRS. B. C. Fifty Years in a Maryland Kitchen. Balt: Turnbull Bros, 1873. 1st ed. xvi,378pp. Old calf, bds. Text Good (few pp at fr/rear detached incl tp, which has old paper repair along fore-edge and sm abrasion across center; lacks spine, cvrs very worn, detached). *Baltimore*.* $50/£31

HOWARD, O. O. My Life and Experience Among Our Hostile Indians.... Hartford: E.D. Worthington, (1897). 1st ed. 10 color litho plts. (Tape repairs to fr gutters, incl tp; spine faded, ends frayed), else Good. *Pacific*.* $92/£58

HOWARD, O. O. My Life and Experiences Among Our Hostile Indians.... Hartford: A.D. Worthington, (1907). 1st ed. Frontisport, 10 chromolithos. Floral eps. Dk grn blind cl, gilt. (Fraying, spine sunned.) Contents Nice. Howes H710. *Baltimore*.* $60/£38

HOWARD, ROBERT E. The Coming of Conan. NY: Gnome, (1953). 1st ed. NF in dj (spine sl sunned, lower edges rubbed). *Pacific*.* $98/£61

HOWARD, ROBERT E. The Coming of Conan. NY: Gnome, 1953. 1st ed. Fine in Fine dj. *Warren.* $175/£109

HOWARD, ROBERT E. Conan the Barbarian. NY: Gnome, (1954). 1st ed. (Internally browned; sl soiled, lower edges rubbed), o/w NF in dj. *Pacific*.* $115/£72

HOWARD, ROBERT E. Conan the Barbarian. NY: Gnome, 1954. 1st ed. NF (bottom fore-edge lt stained) in Fine dj. *Warren.* $150/£94

HOWARD, ROBERT E. Conan the Conqueror. NY: Ace Books, (1950). Ace Double. Pict wraps (sl worn, one cvr sl creased). *King.* $35/£22

HOWARD, ROBERT E. Conan the Conqueror. NY: Gnome, 1950. 1st ed. Fine in NF dj. *Warren.* $225/£141

HOWARD, ROBERT E. Conan the Conqueror: The Hyborean Age. NY: Gnome, (1950). 1st ed. NF in dj (spine sl sunned). *Pacific*.* $150/£94

HOWARD, ROBERT E. Etchings in Ivory: Poems in Prose. Pasadena: Glenn Lord, 1968. 1st ed. One of 250. Fine in stiff wrappers. *Pacific*.* $98/£61

HOWARD, ROBERT E. King Conan: The Hyborean Age. NY: Gnome, (1953). 1st ed. NF in dj (rear panel soiled). *Pacific*.* $109/£68

HOWARD, ROBERT E. Skull-Face and Others. Sauk City: Arkham House, 1946. 1st ed. One of 3000. (Cvrs sl insect-damaged), else VG in dj (chipped, spine head, fr panel lack pieces). *Pacific*.* $138/£86

HOWARD, ROBERT E. Skull-Face and Others. Sauk City, 1946. 1st ed. Fine in dj. *Swann*.* $345/£216

HOWARD, ROBERT E. The Sword of Conan: The Hyborean Age. NY: Gnome, (1952). 1st ed. NF in dj. *Pacific*.* $109/£68

HOWARD, ROBERT E. and L. SPRAGUE DE CAMP. Tales of Conan. NY: Gnome, 1955. 1st ed. Fine in Fine dj. *Warren.* $95/£59

HOWARD, ROBERT E. and L. SPRAGUE DE CAMP. Tales of Conan. NY: Gnome, (1955). 1st ed. NF in dj. *Pacific*.* $69/£43

HOWARD, ROBERT M. Reminiscences. Columbus, GA: Gilbert Ptg, 1912. 1st ed. Frontisport. Tan cl. (Frontis lt foxed, sparse ink underlining; spine ends sl worn), o/w NF. *Chapel Hill.* $275/£172

HOWARD, ROBERT. The Duel of the Stags, a Poem.... London: Ptd by H. Hills, 1709. 1st ed ptd by Hills. 16pp (lt stained). Calf-backed bds. *Young.* $88/£55

HOWARD, WINEFRED. Journal of a Tour in the United States, Canada and Mexico. London: Sampson Low, Marston, 1897. 1st ed. xii,355pp; 37 half-tones. Grn cl (spot fr cvr). *Mott.* $50/£31

HOWARTH, DAVID. The Desert King. London: Collins, 1964. 1st ed. VG in dj. *Worldwide.* $35/£22

HOWARTH, PATRICK. Undercover: The Men and Women of the Special Operations Executive. Routledge & Kegan Paul, 1980. 1st Eng ed. VG (top edge sl dusty; spine tail sl bumped) in dj (sl mkd, rubbed, spine sl faded). *Ulysses.* $40/£25

HOWARTH-LOOMES, B. E. C. Victorian Photography. Ward Lock, 1974. VG in dj. *Hollett.* $48/£30

HOWAY, FREDERIC W. (ed). Voyage of the Columbia to the Northwest Coast, 1787-1790 and 1790-1793. (Boston): MA Hist Soc, 1941. 1st ed. 1/2 cl, gilt. (Corners showing), else VG. *Pacific*.* $184/£115

HOWE, BETTY. Patricia Mae: The Pig Whose Tail Would Not Curl. Springfield: McLoughlin Bros, 1942. Obl 4to. Multiple overlay pp. Color pict bds (edges worn), spiral binding (part of plastic missing). *Reisler.* $125/£78

HOWE, GEORGE. The Battle History of the 1st Armored Division, 'Old Ironsides'. Washington, 1954. VG. *Clark.* $65/£41

HOWE, HENRY M. The Metallurgy of Steel, Volume 1. NY, 1896. 4th ed. Folio. 392pp. Maroon cl, gilt. (Lib spine #, tp perf), else VG. *Larry Price.* $65/£41

HOWE, HENRY. Historical Collections of the Great West. Cincinnati, 1851. 1st ed. 2 vols in 1. Mod cl. Howes H721. *Swann*.* $126/£79

HOWE, JAMES VIRGIL. The Modern Gunsmith. Funk & Wagnalls, 1944. 2 vols. Fine set in djs. *Hollett.* $240/£150

HOWE, JAMES. The Celery Stalks at Midnight. Atheneum, 1983. 1st ed. Leslie Morrill (illus). 111pp. NF (spine head sl bumped) in NF dj. *Price.* $28/£18

HOWE, MAUDE. Sun and Shadow in Spain. Boston, 1908. Color frontis. Teg. Gilt-illus cl (spine chipped w/loss). *Edwards.* $32/£20

HOWE, OCTAVIUS T. and FREDERICK C. MATHEWS. American Clipper Ships, 1833-1858. Salem: Marine Research Soc, 1926-27. 1st ed. 2 vols. Color frontispieces. Blue cl, gilt. Fine set. *Argonaut.* $500/£313

HOWE, WILLIAM H. (ed). The Butterflies of North America. GC: Doubleday, 1975. Deluxe ed. Ltd to 200 numbered, signed. 97 color plts; extra loose color plt laid in. Aeg. Full red morocco. Fine in slipcase. *Karmiole.* $250/£156

HOWELL, ANTHONY. Sergei de Diaghileff. Turret, 1968. One of 50 (of 150) numbered, signed. Pamphlet. Fine in wrappers, dj (sl nicked). *Ulysses.* $88/£55

HOWELL, JOHN THOMAS. The Cactaceae of the Galapagos Islands. SF, 1933. 2 plts. Unopened. Self-wraps. *Brooks.* $21/£13

HOWELL, THOMAS. A Flora of Northwest America, Volume 1. Portland, OR, 1903. 1st ed. Grn cl, gilt. (Gilt title faint), else Good+. *Larry Price.* $95/£59

HOWELLS, JOHN MEAD. The Architectural Heritage of the Merrimack. NY, (1941). 1st ed. One of 1000. (Cvrs sl rubbed.) *King.* $85/£53

HOWELLS, JOHN* MEAD. The Architectural Heritage of the Piscataqua. NY, (1937). 1st ed. (Sl foxed, cvrs soiled, rubbed.) *King*. $75/£47

HOWELLS, JOHN MEAD. Lost Examples of Colonial Architecture. NY, 1931. One of 1100 numbered. Folio. Bd slipcase (cracked). *Swann**. $115/£72

HOWELLS, WILLIAM DEAN. The Coast of Bohemia, a Novel. NY: Harper, 1893. 1st ed. Red cl, gilt. NF. BAL 9679. *Macdonnell*. $30/£19

HOWELLS, WILLIAM DEAN. Familiar Spanish Travels. NY, 1913. 1st Amer ed. Teg. Illus pict cvrs, gilt. Fine (sm blind stamp). *Polyanthos*. $35/£22

HOWELLS, WILLIAM DEAN. The Flight of Pony Baker. NY/London: Harper, 1902. 1st ed, primary binding. Red pict cl. Fine. BAL 9748. *Macdonnell*. $75/£47

HOWELLS, WILLIAM DEAN. Impressions and Experiences. NY: Harper, 1896. 1st ed. Teg, uncut. Dec red cl, gilt. VG. BAL 9706. *Macdonnell*. $50/£31

HOWELLS, WILLIAM DEAN. The Lady of the Aroostook. Boston: Houghton, Osgood, 1879. 1st ed, 3rd ptg (with 'All rights reserved' added to the c. pg). Pict-dec brn cl. Fine. *Sumner & Stillman*. $45/£28

HOWELLS, WILLIAM DEAN. Literature and Life. Studies. NY/London: Harper, 1902. 1st ed. Presentation copy, inscribed Nov 15, 1902. Teg. (Extrems, spine edges sl rubbed, worn; few lt mks), o/w VG. BAL 9749. *Holmes*. $450/£281

HOWELLS, WILLIAM DEAN. Miss Bellard's Inspiration. NY: Harper, 1905. 1st ed. Grn dec cl, gilt. Fine. BAL 9760. *Macdonnell*. $40/£25

HOWELLS, WILLIAM DEAN. The Son of a Royal Langbirth. NY: Harper, 1904. 1st ed. Teg, uncut. Blue cl, gilt. Good (inscrip). BAL 9758. *Macdonnell*. $35/£22

HOWELLS, WILLIAM DEAN. Stops of Various Quills. NY, 1895. 1st ed, trade issue. Frontis. Gilt-pict tan cl. Dj (fr flap cracked, 1-inch chip spine base). BAL 9697. *Swann**. $103/£64

HOWELLS, WILLIAM DEAN. Suburban Sketches. NY/Cambridge: Hurd & Houghton/Riverside, 1871. 1st ed. Teg. Pub's cl. VG. BAL 9555, state B, w/imprint on tp 2 7/8 inches wide, sheet bulk of 2 7/8 inches. *Cummins*. $250/£156

HOWELLS, WILLIAM DEAN. Their Silver Wedding Journey. NY/London: Harper, 1899. 1st ed. 2 vols. Gray dec cl. Fine set. *Sumner & Stillman*. $85/£53

HOWELLS, WILLIAM DEAN. A Traveler from Altruria. NY, 1894. 1st ed. 318pp. (Ink name; corners bumped, spine sl sunned, cvr sl spotted.) *King*. $20/£13

HOWES, BARBARA. The Undersea Farmer. Pawlet: Banyan, 1948. 1st bk. One of 250 numbered. VF in glassine. *Pharos*. $95/£59

HOWES, PAUL G. The Giant Cactus and Its World. NY, 1954. 1 color plt. VG in dj (faded). *Brooks*. $22/£14

HOWES, WRIGHT. U.S.iana. NY, 1963. (Notes; extrems worn.) *Dumont*. $35/£22

HOWISON, JOHN. Sketches of Upper Canada, Domestic, Local, and Characteristic.... Edinburgh: Oliver & Boyd, 1821. 1st ed. 1/2 title, tp, (ix)-xvi,339pp. Uncut. Orig bds, ptd paper label. (Sig tp; sl worn), o/w Fine. *Mott*. $350/£219

HOWITT, SAMUEL. The British Sportsman. E. Orme, 1812. New ed. 4to. Add'l engr tp, 71 engr plts (some lt spotted). Gilt edges. Contemp purple morocco (rubbed), gilt. *Sotheby's**. $2,392/£1,495

HOWITT, WILLIAM. Homes and Haunts of the Most Eminnent British Poets. London: Routledge, 1877. Extra-illus w/74 mtd plts. Teg. 3/4 red calf, cl, gilt, morocco spine label. (Joints worn), else VG. *Pacific**. $127/£79

HOWITT, WILLIAM. The Rural and Domestic Life of Germany...in a General Tour, and During a Residence in the Country in 1840, 41 and 42. Phila: Carey & Hart, 1843. 2 vols. Orig letterpress wrappers (1 cvr loose). *Swann**. $57/£36

HOWLETT, E. Driving Lessons. NY: R.H. Russell & Son, 1894. 1st ed. Pict cl. NF. *Pacific**. $109/£68

HOWLEY, J. P. The Beothucks or Red Indians. Cambridge, 1915. 38 plts, photos. *Hallam*. $240/£150

HOWLEY, JAMES P. The Beothucks or Red Indians. CUP, 1915. 37 plts, 10 sketches. 2-tone cl. (Lib bkpls, ink stamps, lacks fep; fr joint sl bubbled, corners sl rubbed w/sl loss, rear bd lt stained.) *Edwards*. $264/£165

HOWORTH, HENRY H. History of the Mongols from the 9th to the 19th Century. NY: Burt Franklin, n.d. 5 vols. 2 maps. Grn cl, gilt. (Ex-lib, stamps, bkpls removed from rear pastedowns), else VG. *Pacific**. $127/£79

HOY, ANNE H. Fabrications: Staged, Altered, and Appropriated Photographs. NY: Abbeville, 1987. 1st ed. (Fep sl creased), else Fine in dj. *Cahan*. $75/£47

HOY, JIM. Cowboys and Kansas. Norman: Univ of OK, (1991). 1st ed. Fine in dj. *Lien*. $23/£14

HOY, P. C. A Brief History of Bradford's Battery, Confederate Guards Artillery. (Pontotoc, MS, 1932.) 2nd ed. Good in stiff wraps (lacks rear wrap, fr wrap chipped at lower corner, tape-repaired on verso). *Chapel Hill*. $375/£234

HOYLAND, JOHN. A Historical Survey of the Customs, Habits and Present State of the Gypsies. York: The Author, 1816. 1st ed. 265,(1)pp. Untrimmed. Orig paper-backed bds (sl worn), paper label. VG (sl foxed). *Second Life*. $250/£156

HOYLE, EDMOND. Hoyle's Games Improved. NY: George Long, 1823. Copper-engr frontis, (6),278pp; 2 plts. Brn pigskin (rebound), orig spine label laid down. *Karmiole*. $200/£125

HOYT, EDWARD JONATHAN. Buckskin Joe...Memoirs of Edwin Jonathan Hoyt. Glenn Shirley (ed). Lincoln, 1966. 1st ed. Fine in dj (sl worn, price-clipped). *Baade*. $27/£17

HOYT, ELISABETH (ed). Santa Claus' Dolls. Boston: W.A. Wilde, (1911). 1st ed. Josephine Bruce (illus). Pict bds. (Spine dknd), else VG. *Pacific**. $46/£29

HOYT, HENRY F. A Frontier Doctor. Boston: Houghton Mifflin, 1929. 1st ed. NF in dj. Howes H747. *Labordo*. $150/£94

HOYT, HENRY F. A Frontier Doctor. Doyce B. Nunis, Jr. (ed). Chicago: R.R. Donnelley, 1979. Frontis. VG. *Lien*. $30/£19

HOYT, JOHN C. and N. C. GROVER. River Discharge. NY, 1930. 4th ed. Blue cl, gilt. (Stamp), else VG. *Larry Price*. $25/£16

HOZIER, HENRY M. The British Expedition to Abyssinia. London: Macmillan, 1869. 1st ed. xi,271pp (lt marginal browning). Gilt-edged morocco-backed marbled bds (rebound). *Edwards*. $200/£125

HRDLICKA, ALES. The Aleutian and Commander Islands and Their Inhabitants. Phila: Wistar Inst of Anatomy and Biology, 1945. 1st ed. (Spine spotted), o/w VG. *Brown*. $60/£38

HUBBACK, J. H. and EDITH. Jane Austen's Sailor Brothers. John Lane/Bodley Head, 1906. Good (fore-edge lt spotted; spine bumped). *Tiger*. $56/£35

HUBBARD, CHARLES D. An Old New England Village. Portland, ME: Falmouth Pub, 1947. 1st ed. Review slip laid in. Black cl. Fine in pict dj (sm chip bottom of rear cvr). *House*. $45/£28

HUBBARD, ELBERT. Little Journeys to the Homes of Great Musicians: Frederick Chopin. East Aurora, 1901. 1st Amer ed. Suede cvrs, gilt. Fine (spine, edges sl sunned). *Polyanthos*. $25/£16

HUBBARD, ELBERT. Little Journeys to the Homes of Great Philosophers. Thoreau. East Aurora: Roycrofters, 1904. 1st ed. VG in wrappers. *Lucas*. $15/£9

HUBBARD, ELBERT. Ruskin and Turner. East Aurora: Roycroft Ptg Shop, 1896. One of 473 ptd. Signed. (Soiled, corners rubbed, spine dknd), else VG. *Pacific**. $69/£43

HUBBARD, HENRY VINCENT and THEODORA KIMBALL. Landscape Designs. NY: Macmillan, 1929. Rev ed. (Name, browned, one chapter underlined; spine worn), else Good+. *Fair Meadow*. $45/£28

HUBBARD, JOHN NILES. Sketches of the Life and Adventures of Moses Van Campen. Dansville, NY, 1841. 1st ed. 310pp (foxed). Contemp tree calf (rubbed, joints repaired). Howes H752. *Oinonen**. $110/£69

HUBBARD, L. RON. Dianetics: The Modern Science of Mental Health. NY: Hermitage House, (1950). 1st ed. VG in dj (spine head sl chipped, sm tear spine foot, 2 to extrems). *Pacific**. $75/£47

HUBBARD, L. RON. Dianetics: The Modern Science of Mental Health. NY, 1950. 1st ed. Dj (spine lt tanned). *Swann**. $103/£64

HUBBARD, L. RON. Final Blackout. Providence: Hadley, (1948). 1st ed. NF in dj (spine browned, ends lt worn, frayed, clear tape to spine foot). *Other Worlds*. $200/£125

HUBBARD, L. RON. Final Blackout. Providence: Hadley Pub, (1948). 1st ed. Ltd to 1000. (Name, offset from tape to tops of feps), else VG in dj (spine ends rubbed). *Pacific**. $345/£216

HUBBARD, L. RON. Triton and Battle of Wizards. L.A.: Fantasy, 1949. 1st ed. Blue binding variant. Fine in dj. *Levin*. $200/£125

HUBBARD, L. RON. Two Novels...Typewriter in the Sky [&] Fear. NY: Gnome, (1951). 1st ed. NF in dj (spine head chipped, flap creases sl dknd). *Pacific**. $115/£72

HUBBARD, PAUL B. (comp). Garlock Memories, a Tribute to East Kern County's Pioneer Citizens. Ridgecrest, CA: (Privately ptd, 1960). 1st ed. Fine in wraps. *Book Market*. $30/£19

HUBBARD, PREVOST. Dust Preventatives and Road Binders. NY, 1910. 1st ed, 1st thousand. (Ex-lib, ink stamps; sl rubbed, spine chipped.) *Edwards*. $24/£15

HUBBARD, W. L. Chats with Color-kin. Chicago: Bond Shop, 1909. 1st ed. Donn P. Crane (illus). 8 1/4 x 6 3/4. Pict cl. Fine. *Pacific**. $69/£43

HUBBARD, WILLIAM. A Narrative of the Indian Wars in New England. Worcester, 1801. Contemp sheep. Howes H756. *Swann**. $230/£144

HUBBLE, EDWIN POWELL. The Observational Approach to Cosmology. Oxford: Clarendon, 1937. 1st ed. Fine in dj. *Weber*. $120/£75

HUC, EVARISTE REGIS. The Chinese Empire. London: Longman, Brown et al, 1855. 2 vols. xxx,421,2 ads; vi,440pp,24 ads (lacks 1/2-titles); fldg map. Blue cl (spine ends worn). *Adelson*. $385/£241

HUC, M. The Chinese Empire. London, 1855. 2nd ed. 2 vols. xxxii,421pp + (ii)pub's ads; viii,440pp + 24pp pub's list; fldg frontis map. (Rear hinge vol 2 cracked through, foxing; cl loss to corners, dkng, vol 1 rebacked w/much of orig spine laid down, vol 2 spine chipped.) *Edwards*. $136/£85

HUC, M. Travels in Tartary, Thibet, and China, During the Years 1844-5-6. London: Nat'l Illustrated Library, (c.1860s). 2 vols. Fldg map. Dec cl, gilt. VG. *Pacific**. $403/£252

HUCKEL, J. F. (ed). American Indians: First Families of the Southwest. Kansas City, 1920. 2nd ed. Sm folio. 33 color plts. Heavy brn cvr stock, sketch laid on. Good+. *Five Quail*. $70/£44

HUCKEL, J. F. (ed). American Indians: First Families of the Southwest. Kansas City: Fred Harvey, 1928. 4th ed. (Extrems sl worn), else NF in color pict wrappers. *Pacific**. $52/£33

Huckleberry Hound and the Dog-Cat. World Distributors Manchester UK, 1974. 4 dbl-pg pop-ups. Glazed pict bds. VG. *Bookfinders*. $40/£25

HUDAK, JOSEPH. Gardening with Perennials Month by Month. NY: Quadrangle/NY Times, 1976. 1st ed. VG. *Fair Meadow*. $25/£16

HUDDLESTON, SISLEY. Paris Salons, Cafes, Studios. Phila/London: Lippincott, 1928. 1st ed. Top edges stained. Yellow pict cl. VG (sl dull). *Maggs*. $120/£75

HUDLESTON, WILFRID H. A Monograph of the British Jurassic Gasteropoda. Part 1, Number 3—Gasteropoda of the Inferior Oolite. London: Palaeontographical Soc, 1889. 137-192pp; 5 litho plts. Unopened. VG in mod grn wrappers. *Hollett*. $72/£45

Hudson's Bay Company, a Brief History. London: Hudson's Bay House, 1934. VG. *Perier*. $22/£14

Hudson's Bay Record Society: Publications. London: Chaplain Soc for Hudson's Bay Record Soc, 1938-1963. Ltd ed. Numbers I-XXII and XXIV only in 23 vols. Teg. Blue cl (spines worn). *Christie's**. $184/£115

HUDSON, ALMA. Peter Rabbit at the Circus. NY: Cupples & Leon, (1921). 12mo. 48pp; 8 full-pg color plts by Richard Hudson. Red ptd bds (sm spine area rubbed through), full color paste label fr cvr. *Reisler*. $85/£53

HUDSON, J. K. Letters to Governor Lewelling. Topeka: Topeka Capital Co, 1893. 1st ed. Signed, inscribed. 223pp. (Text browned; cl soiled), o/w Good. *Brown*. $75/£47

HUDSON, JOSHUA HILARY. Sketches and Reminiscences. Columbia, SC, 1903. 1st ed. (Shelfworn, cvrs spotted.) Howes H764. *Oinonen**. $80/£50

HUDSON, KENNETH. Working to Rule. London: Adams & Dart, 1970. 1st ed. VG in dj. *Hollett*. $40/£25

HUDSON, T. S. A Scamper Through America; or, Fifteen Thousand Miles of Ocean and Continent in Sixty Days. London: Griffith & Farran, 1882. 1st ed. pp xxii,289,30 ads. Dec cl (bubbled). *Mott*. $65/£41

HUDSON, TOM. Three Paths Along a River. Palm Desert: Desert-Southwest, (1964). 1st ed. Fine in VG dj. *Book Market*. $30/£19

HUDSON, W. H. Birds in Town and Village. London: J.M. Dent & Sons, 1919. 1st ed thus. 8vo. 8 full-pg color plts by Edward Detmold. Grn cl (lower edge fr cvr sl rippled), gilt. Ptd dj (tape repairs, spine chipped). *Reisler*. $225/£141

HUDSON, W. H. Birds of La Plata. London: J.M. Dent, 1920. 1st ed. One of 75 ptd for Great Britain (of 200). Signed. 2 vols. 11.5x8.25. 22 tipped-in color plts, extra suite of 22 mtd color plts, guards. Red/grn cl, gilt. (Paper portfolio containing extra suite torn along edges; vol 1 spine foot lt bumped), else VG. *Pacific**. $546/£341

HUDSON, W. H. British Birds. Longmans, Green, 1897. New ed. xxii,363pp; 8 Fine color plts. Good in russet cl (spine rubbed). *Cox*. $32/£20

HUDSON, W. H. A Crystal Age. NY: E.P. Dutton, 1916. 1st Amer ed. Signed on fep (possibly supplied). Teg. 3/4 dk grn morocco, gilt, raised bands. (Bkpl, foxed), else VG. *Pacific**. $52/£33

HUDSON, W. H. Far Away and Long Ago. LEC, 1943. Ltd to 1500 numbered, signed by Raul Rosarivo (illus) and Guillermo Kraft (pub). Fine in slipcase. *Swann**. $69/£43

HUDSON, W. H. Green Mansions. LEC, 1935. Ltd to 1500 numbered, signed by Edward A. Wilson (illus). Fine in slipcase. *Swann**. $46/£29

HUDSON, W. H. Green Mansions. Phila: Franklin Ptg, 1935. Signed by Edward A. Wilson (illus). 1/4 natural French linen, stamped in scarlet. Boxed. *Appelfeld*. $125/£78

HUDSON, W. H. A Little Lost Boy. Knopf, 1929. 3rd ptg. 4to. Frontis, 187pp; 10 full-pg color illus by Dorothy Lathrop. Illus eps. Grn cl bds, gilt. (Many pp poorly opened), o/w VG. *Davidson*. $95/£59

HUDSON, W. H. The Man Napoleon. London: George C. Harrap, 1915. 15 color plts. Pict cl (scratched, faded in patches; fore-edges spotted). *Hollett.* $32/£20

HUDSON, W. H. The Naturalist in La Plata. London, 1895. 3rd ed. x,394pp. (Bkpl, hinges cracked.) Illus cl (corners sl rubbed w/sl loss, spine sl chipped). *Edwards.* $40/£25

HUDSON, WILSON M. Andy Adams His Life and Writings. Dallas, 1964. Good in dj (sl worn). *Dumont.* $30/£19

HUEFFER, FORD MADOX. Between St. Dennis and St. George. London, 1915. 1st Eng ed. Orig gray card wrappers (very chipped, worn, rubber stamp on fr cvr). *Clearwater.* $32/£20

HUEFFER, FORD MADOX. The Critical Attitude. London: Duckworth, 1911. 1st Eng ed. Teg. Buckram. VG (feps sl browned, edges sl spotted; spine ends, corners sl bumped, edges sl rubbed). *Ulysses.* $104/£65

HUEFFER, FORD MADOX. The Feather. London: T. Fisher Unwin, 1892. 1st ed. 8vo. Frontis by Ford Madox Brown, (vi),212,(iv)pp, pub's list. White cl, design in blue to cvrs, eps, edges. VG (spine sl rubbed, sl yellowed). *Sotheran.* $429/£268

HUEFFER, FORD MADOX. Henry James. A Critical Study. Secker, 1913. 1st ed. Teg. (Sl foxed), else VG +. *Any Amount.* $56/£35

HUEFFER, FORD MADOX. On Heaven and Poems Written on Active Service. London/NY: John Lane, Bodley Head/John Lane, 1918. 1st ed, US issue, w/the dj copy at variance from British dj (imprint at spine foot is 'John Lane Company'). Fore/bottom edges untrimmed. Purple vertically ribbed cl. (Spine unevenly sunned), o/w VG in dj (partly defective, lacks most of spine, internal mends). *Reese.* $250/£156

HUEFFER, FORD MADOX. When Blood Is Their Argument. London/NY/Toronto: Hodder & Stoughton, 1915. 1st ed. This copy has tp w/variant imprint cited by Harvey in the Huntington copy, w/Toronto added to the imprint. Red cl stamped in black. (Edges lt foxed, rear inner hinge sl cracked), o/w VG. *Reese.* $175/£109

HUEFFER, FRANCIS. Half a Century of Music in England. Chapman & Hall, 1889. 1st ed. x,240pp. VG. *Hollett.* $40/£25

HUELSENBECK, RICHARD. Memoirs of a Dada Drummer. Hans J. Kleinschmidt (ed). NY: Viking, (1974). 1st ed in English. Fine in dj (spine faded). *Turtle Island.* $55/£34

HUES, ROBERT. A Learned Treatise of Globes, Both Celestial and Terrestriall.... London: P. Stephens & C. Meredith, 1639 (imprimatur dated 1638). 1st ed in English. 8vo. (38),186,(1)pp. Contemp calf (rebacked). VG (1 woodcut shaved close at fore-edge w/loss of a few text letters; 1st, last ll marginally dknd). *Glaser.* $2,400/£1,500

HUESTON, ETHEL. Calamity Jane of Deadwood Gulch. NY, 1937. (Worn.) *Dumont.* $35/£22

HUESTON, J. T. Dupuytren's Contracture. Edinburgh: E. & S. Livingstone, 1963. 1st ed. Fine. *Weber.* $75/£47

HUFFAKER, CLAIR. Nobody Loves a Drunken Indian. NY: McKay, 1967. 1st ed. Fine in VG + dj. *Pettler.* $40/£25

HUFFMAN, JAMES. Ups and Downs of a Confederate Soldier. NY: William E. Rudge's Sons, 1940. 1st ed. One of 400. Blue buckram, paper cvr label. Fine. *Chapel Hill.* $250/£156

HUFFORD, D. A. Death Valley; Swamper Ike's Traditional Lore: Why, When, How? L.A., 1902. Frontisport. (Red pencilling, underlining several pp), else VG in dec wrappers. *Sagebrush.* $55/£34

HUG, BERNAL D. History of Union County, Oregon. La Grande, OR: Union County Hist Soc, (1961). Fine. *Perier.* $65/£41

HUGES, CHARLES C. Eskimo Boyhood. Lexington: Univ Press of KY, (1974). 1st ed. Fine in dj. *Perier.* $30/£19

HUGESSEN, E. H. K. The Forest Fairy: Christmas in Switzerland. Boston: Dana Estes, (1896). 1st ed. L. J. Bridgman (illus). 7 1/2 x 5 1/2. Blue cl, gilt, oval pict cvr label. (Sm warped spot rear cvr), else NF. *Pacific*.* $92/£58

HUGHES, DOROTHY B. Ride the Pink Horse. NY: Duell, Sloan & Pearce, 1946. Inscribed. (Browned), else Good in dj (worn, chipped). *Dumont.* $35/£22

HUGHES, G. BERNARD. English, Scottish and Irish Table Glass from the Sixteenth Century to 1820. Batsford, 1956. 1st ed. Color frontis. VG. *Cox.* $56/£35

HUGHES, G. BERNARD. Small Antique Silverware. NY, 1957. 1st ed. (Prelims sl spotted.) Dj (sl chipped). *Edwards.* $64/£40

HUGHES, J. E. Eighteen Years on Lake Bangweulu. London: Field, n.d. (1932). 1st ed. 1/2-title, xvi,376pp; 70 plts. Orange cl (rubbed, soiled), gilt. Internally Clean. *Morrell.* $152/£95

HUGHES, JOHN T. Doniphan's Expedition; Containing an Account of the Conquest of New Mexico. Cincinnati: J.A. & U.P. James, 1848. 2nd ed, 2nd ptg. Fldg map. Orig ribbed pict cl (rebacked, hinges repaired). Howes H769. *Glenn.* $350/£219

HUGHES, LANGSTON. Ask Your Mama, 12 Moods for Jazz. NY, 1961. 1st ed. VG in dj. *King.* $150/£94

HUGHES, LANGSTON. Ask Your Mama: 12 Moods for Jazz. NY: Knopf, 1969. 2nd ptg. Cl-backed pict bds. Clean (ex-lib, bkpl, edges stamped) in illus dj (label). *Petrilla.* $50/£31

HUGHES, LANGSTON. Don't You Turn Back. NY, (1969). 1st ed. Pict dj. *Swann*.* $172/£108

HUGHES, LANGSTON. Fields of Wonder. NY, (1947). 1st ed. (Extrems soiled), else Good in dj (heavily chipped, spine worn). *King.* $125/£78

HUGHES, LANGSTON. Fine Clothes to the Jew. NY, 1927. 1st ed. (Spine faded, lower tips lt rubbed.) *Swann*.* $201/£126

HUGHES, LANGSTON. Freedom's Plow. NY: Musette Pubs, 1943. VG in wrappers (sl creased). *Ulysses.* $152/£95

HUGHES, LANGSTON. I Wonder as I Wander. NY, 1956. 1st ed. NF in NF dj. *Warren.* $175/£109

HUGHES, LANGSTON. Jim Crow's Last Stand. (Atlanta): Negro Pub Soc of America, (1943). 1st ed. Fine in sl marbled white wrappers, stamped in blue. *Bromer.* $235/£147

HUGHES, LANGSTON. Jim Crow's Last Stand. (NY): Negro Publication Soc of America, (1943). VG in ptd wrappers (lt soiled). *Heritage.* $350/£219

HUGHES, LANGSTON. The Langston Hughes Reader. NY: Braziller, 1958. 1st ed. NF in VG dj. *Agvent.* $75/£47

HUGHES, LANGSTON. Montage of a Dream Deferred. NY, (1951). 1st ed. (Pencil notes, short tape mk, browned from former paper insertion), else VG in dj (edges torn; chipped). *King.* $125/£78

HUGHES, LANGSTON. Simple Speaks His Mind. (NY): S&S, (1950). 1st ed. Ptd 'Comment' card laid in. (Name), else NF in dj (sm tear, rub to spine foot). *Pacific*.* $150/£94

HUGHES, LANGSTON. The Sweet Flypaper of Life. NY: S&S, 1955. 1st ed. Fine in VG dj (price-clipped). *Smith.* $500/£313

HUGHES, LANGSTON. Tambourines to Glory. NY, (1958). 1st ed. (Sl worn), else VG in dj (1/2-inch rear cvr chip). *King.* $125/£78

HUGHES, LANGSTON. The Weary Blues. NY: Knopf, 1926. 1st ed, 1st bk. Orange patterned bds backed in blue cl. (Fr cvr sl discolored, extrems lt rubbed), else Nice. *Bromer.* $500/£313

HUGHES, RICHARD B. Pioneer Years in the Black Hills. Agnes Wright Spring (ed). Glendale: A.H. Clark, 1957. 1st ed. Frontis. Unopened. 6 extraneous ll from another bk bound in at end (binder's error). *Dawson.* $100/£63

HUGHES, RICHARD. A High Wind in Jamaica. London, 1929. VG. *Typographeum.* $15/£9

HUGHES, RICHARD. The Innocent Voyage. LEC, 1944. Ltd to 1500 numbered, signed by Lynd Ward (illus). Fine in slipcase. *Swann**. $115/£72

HUGHES, ROBERT EDGAR. Two Summer Cruises with the Baltic Fleet, in 1854-5. London, 1855. Frontis, map. Gilt-pict cl. (bkpl; 1 sig loose.) *Swann**. $103/£64

HUGHES, RUPERT. The Patent Leather Kid and Several Others.... NY: G&D, (1927). 1st ed. Red cl. NF in pict dj (sm corner chips). *Reese*. $40/£25

HUGHES, STELLA. Hashknife Cowboy. Tucson, 1984. 1st ed. As New in dj. *Baade*. $37/£23

HUGHES, T. E. et al. History of the Welsh in Minnesota, Foreston and Lime Springs. N.p., 1895. 1st ed. Good. *Rybski*. $150/£94

HUGHES, TED. The Cat and the Cuckoo. London: Sunstone, n.d. One of 250 signed by Hughes and R. J. Lloyd (illus). Fine in dj, cl slipcase. *Ulysses*. $104/£65

HUGHES, TED. Cave Birds. Faber, 1978. 1st UK ed. VG + in dj (price-clipped). *Williams*. $40/£25

HUGHES, TED. The Earth Owl and Other Moon People. London, 1963. 1st ed. Fine in dj. *Petersfield*. $45/£28

HUGHES, TED. A Few Crows. Exeter: Rougemont, 1970. One of 150, this being one of the 75 unsigned copies. Simulated leather. Fine in dj. *Ulysses*. $120/£75

HUGHES, TED. Ffangs the Vampire Bat and the Kiss of Truth. London, 1986. 1st ed. Fine in dj. *Petersfield*. $26/£16

HUGHES, TED. Meet My Folks. London: Faber & Faber, 1961. 1st ed. 8vo. George Adamson (illus). Yellow pict bds. Fine in NF wrapper (spine head sl nicked, sm closed, repaired tear to top edge). *Sotheran*. $125/£78

HUGHES, TED. Meet My Folks. Bobbs Merrill, 1973. 1st US ed. NF in dj. *Williams*. $22/£14

HUGHES, TED. Moortown Diary. Faber, 1989. 1st ed thus. *Williams*. $24/£15

HUGHES, TED. Shakespeare's Poem. London: Lexham, 1971. One of 150 signed. Fine in wrappers, matching paper folder (sl creased). *Ulysses*. $104/£65

HUGHES, THERLE. English Domestic Needlework: 1660-1860. Lutterworth, 1961. 1st ed. 4 color plts. VG in dj. *Whittle*. $29/£18

HUGHES, THOMAS (ed). Gone to Texas. NY: Macmillan, 1884. 1st ed, Amer issue. xiii,(3),228pp. Grn cl. *Mott*. $150/£94

HUGHES, THOMAS. James Fraser, Second Bishop of Manchester. A Memoir 1818-1885. London: Macmillan, 1887. 1st ed. Frontisport, (10),368pp. *Mott*. $35/£22

HUGHES, THOMAS. Memoir of a Brother. Macmillan, 1873. 1st ed. Frontisport, xvi,178,58(pub's cat)pp. Brn chalked eps. Orig morocco-grain blue cl, gilt. Good (extrems, joints rubbed, gilt dull). *Blackwell's*. $104/£65

HUGHES, THOMAS. Memoir of Daniel Macmillan. Macmillan, 1882. Steel-engr frontis, conjugate letterpress tp, guard; (xvi),308pp. Top edge uncut, others rough trimmed. Sage grn smooth cl, gilt. (Tissue foxed, offsetting, eps foxed; rear cvr sl mottled), o/w Fine. *Temple*. $38/£24

HUGHES, THOMAS. Rugby, Tennessee, Being Some Account of the Settlement Founded on the Cumberland Plateau.... London: Macmillan, 1881. 1st ed. pp xi,168,32 ads. (Lt soiled.) *Mott*. $125/£78

HUGHES, THOMAS. Vacation Rambles. C.C. (ed). London: Macmillan, 1896. 2nd ed. x,420pp. NF. *Mott*. $50/£31

HUGHES, W. E. Chronicles of Blackheath Golfers. London: Chapman & Hall, 1897. 1st ed. 10x7.25. Frontisport, guards. Teg. Dk blue cl, gilt. (Hinges cracked, repairable; spine ends rubbed), else VG. *Pacific**. $2,875/£1,797

HUGHES, WENDELL L. Reconstructive Surgery of the Eyelids. St. Louis: Mosby, 1943. 1st ed. 36 plts. Fine. *Glaser*. $250/£156

HUGHES, WENDELL L. Reconstructive Surgery of the Eyelids. St. Louis: C.V. Mosby, 1943. 1st ed. 36 plts. Fine. *Weber*. $275/£172

HUGILL, BERYL. Bring on the Clowns. (Secaucus): Chartwell, (1980). VG in color pict dj. *Dramatis*. $25/£16

HUGO, RICHARD. A Run of Jacks. Minneapolis: Univ of MN, (1961). 1st ed, 1st bk. VG (edges rubbed; lacks dj). *Agvent*. $65/£41

HUGO, VICTOR The Hunchback of Notre Dame. LEC, 1930. 1st ed thus. One of 1500 signed by Frans Masereel (illus). 2 vols. Fine in wraps, tissue djs, cardboard folder (strengthened), slipcase (remade). *Fine Books*. $225/£141

HUGO, VICTOR. The Battle of Waterloo. LEC, 1977. One of 1600 signed by Drew Middleton (intro). Fine in slipcase. *Swann**. $34/£21

HUGO, VICTOR. Les Miserables. Carleton, 1862. 1st Amer ed. 5 vols bound in 1. VG + in 1/2 leather, raised spine. *Fine Books*. $475/£297

HUGO, VICTOR. Les Miserables. LEC, 1938. Ltd to 1500 numbered, signed by Lynd Ward (illus). 5 vols. Fine in slipcase. *Swann**. $172/£108

HUGO, VICTOR. Notre-Dame de Paris. LEC, 1930. Ltd to 1500 numbered, signed by Frans Masereel (illus). 2 vols. Fine in slipcase. *Swann**. $161/£101

HUGO, VICTOR. Notre-Dame de Paris. NY: LEC, 1955. One of 1500. Signed by Bernard Lamotte (illus). Pict cl, leather spine label. Fine in slipcase. *Pacific**. $23/£14

HUGO, VICTOR. The Outlaw of Iceland. Sir Gilbert Campbell (trans). C&W, 1899. New ed. Pub's cat dated September 1899. Pict cl. Good (spotted, soiled; spine bumped, corners rubbed, vents in hinges). *Tiger*. $26/£16

HUGO, VICTOR. The Toilers of the Sea. LEC, 1960. Ltd to 1500 numbered, signed by Tranquillo Marangoni (designer) and Giovanni Mardersteig (illus). Fine in slipcase. *Swann**. $46/£29

HUGO, VICTOR. The Works of.... Boston: Colonial Press, (c. 1900). Beacon ed. 23 vols. Teg. 3/4 dk blue morocco, marbled bds, gilt. (Spine ends sl rubbed), else VG set. *Pacific**. $287/£179

HUIDOBRO, VICENTE. Selected Poetry. NY: New Directions, 1981. (Blind-stamp), else Fine in dj. *Lame Duck*. $25/£16

HUISH, MARCUS B. British Water-Colour Art in the First Year of the Reign of King Edward the Seventh.... London: A&C Black, 1904. One of 500 signed. 62 color plts. Teg. (Bkpl, sl marginal spotting, feps lt spotted, hinges cracked.) Dec cl (spine chipped, frayed; joints, corners worn). *Edwards*. $96/£60

HUISH, MARCUS B. Happy England. A&C Black, 1909. New, expanded ed. 81 color plts, ptd tissue guards. Dec cl. Good (inscrip, eps browned, sl spotted, hinges cracked; spine ends, corners bumped, cvrs sl mkd, edges sl rubbed, spine faded). *Ulysses*. $296/£185

HUISH, ROBERT. The Public and Private Life of...George the Third.... London: Thomas Kelly, 1821. 1st ed. Frontis, 19 copper plts. Mod cl, gilt. (Plt stained; lt foxed), else VG. *Pacific**. $58/£36

HULANISKI, F. J. (ed). The History of Contra Costa County, California. Berkeley: Elms Pub Co, 1917. 1st ed. 7 steel-engr ports. Aeg. 3/4 brn morocco. VG + (sl spotted, worn, professionally recased, expert repairs to joints, extrems). *Harrington*. $225/£141

HULBERT, ARCHER BUTLER. Forty Niners: The Chronicle of the California Trail. Boston: Little, Brown, 1931. 1st ed. NF in dj. *Labordo*. $75/£47

HULBERT, ARCHER BUTLER. The Niagara River. NY/London: Putnam, 1908. Blue cl, illus onlaid to fr cvr, gilt. VG. *Cullen*. $150/£94

HULBERT, WILLIAM D. Forest Neighbors. NY, 1902. 1st ed. 16 plts; plt tipped on fr cvr. Brn cl, gilt. VG. *Larry Price.* $30/£19

HULBERT, WILLIAM D. White Pine Days on the Taquamenon. Lansing: Hist Soc of MI, 1949. 1st ed. 24 photo plts; photo tipped on fr cvr. VG. *Larry Price.* $30/£19

HULETT, T. G. Every Man His Own Guide to the Falls of Niagara. Buffalo, 1846. Frontis map. Letterpress wrappers (chipped, edges torn). *Swann*.* $115/£72

HULING, CHARLES C. American Candy Maker. Phila: Privately pub, 1902. 1st ed. (Top 1/4 cut off fep.) *Hollett.* $48/£30

HULL, BARLING. Thirty-Three Rope Ties and Chain Releases. Chicago: Arthur P. Felsman, (1915). Fine in pict wraps. *Dramatis.* $25/£16

HULL, F. M. Bee Flies of the World. Washington, 1973. Color frontis. Dj (lt worn). *Sutton.* $65/£41

HULLMANDEL, C. The Art of Drawing on Stone. London: Longman/The Author, 1835. New ed. Litho frontis, xii,79pp; 8 further plts. Contemp roan-backed floral cl. VG. *Europa.* $472/£295

HULME, F. EDWARD. Familiar Wild Flowers. London: Cassell, (c.1890's). Likely 1st ed. 5 vols. Dec cl, gilt. (Spine ends worn), else VG. *Pacific*.* $138/£86

HULME, F. EDWARD. Familiar Wild Flowers. London: Cassell, Petter & Galpin, (ca 1877). Series 1-5 in 5 vols. Contemp 1/2 calf, gilt. (Text lt spotted, bkpls; rubbed.) *Christie's*.* $162/£101

HULME, F. EDWARD. Flower Painting in Water Colors. London, c. 1890. 20 mtd color plts. *Henly.* $72/£45

HULME, JOHN (ed). Guillaume Chequespierre and the Oise Salon. NY, 1986. 1st US ed. VF in Fine dj. *Bond.* $15/£9

HULME, KERI. The Windeater/Te Kaihau. Hodder, 1987. 1st UK ed. VG + (sl browned) in dj. *Williams.* $24/£15

HULS, DON (comp). The Winter of 1890: (What Happened at Wounded Knee). N.p.: Don Huls, 1974. 1st bk ed. Pict wrappers. Fine. *Harrington.* $35/£22

HULTEN, K. G. PONTUS. and GERMANO CELANT. Italian Art 1900-1945. NY: Rizzoli, 1989. 1st ed. As New in dj. *Pacific*.* $58/£36

HULTEN, K. G. PONTUS. Jean Tinguely: 'Meta.' Boston, (1975). *Swann*.* $57/£36

HULTEN, K. G. PONTUS. Jean Tinguely: 'Meta.' Boston, (1975). One of 250 numbered of Amer ed. This copy signed. Wrap-around cl case w/lock. *Swann*.* $172/£108

HULTEN, K. G. PONTUS. The Machine as Seen at the End of the Mechanical Age. NY: MOMA, (1968). Orig metal. *Swann*.* $80/£50

HULTON, PAUL and DAVID BEERS QUINN. The American Drawings of John White 1577-1590. London, 1964. 2 vols. Folio. 160 plts, 76 color. Slipcase. *Swann*.* $345/£216

HULTON, PAUL. The Work of Jacques le Moyne de Morgues, a Huguenot Artist in France, Florida, and England. (London, 1977.) 2 vols. Sm folio. Slipcase. *Swann*.* $46/£29

Human Prudence, or the Art by Which a Man May Raise Himself and His Fortune to Grandeur. (By William de Britaine.) London: Richard Sare, 1702. 9th ed. (10),229 + (1)ad pg. Period dk calf. (Names, dates; glue along joints), else VG-. *Pacific*.* $161/£101

HUMBLE, B. H. On Scottish Hills. Chapman & Hall, 1946. 1st ed. VG in dj (worn, soiled, some loss). *Hollett.* $72/£45

HUMBLE, B. H. Tramping in Skye. Edinburgh: Grant & Murray, 1933. 1st ed. 15 plts, 5 maps. VG in dj (worn, defective). *Hollett.* $56/£35

HUME, DAVID. Essays and Treatises on Several Subjects. Edinburgh: Bell & Bradfute, 1800. New ed. 2 vols. iv,571; vii,(i),527pp. Marbled eps; blue sprinkled/polished edges. Contemp marbled brn calf, red morocco title labels, gilt, oval vol labels. Good (vol 1 lt loss at head of backstrip, fr joint split, tender). *Blackwell's.* $264/£165

HUME, DAVID. The History of England. A. Millar, 1767. New ed. 6 vols. 4to. Contemp grn morocco, gilt. (Lt soiled; rubbed, discolored.) *Sotheby's*.* $1,011/£632

HUME, DAVID. The Life of David Hume, Esq. For W. Strahan & T. Cadell, 1777. Half-title, engr frontis port, 1pg ads bound in at fr. Contemp calf. (Frontis offset onto tp, sm flaw on tp; sl rubbed, rebacked, new eps.) *Sotheby's*.* $442/£276

HUME, DAVID. Private Correspondence...with Several Distinguished Persons, Between the Years 1761 and 1776. London: Henry Colburn, 1820. 1st ed. Orig blind-stamped cl (recased). Sound (foxed). *Appelfeld.* $150/£94

HUME, JOHN R. The Industrial Archaeology of Scotland. II. The Highlands and Islands. London: Batsford, 1977. 1st ed. VG in dj (spine faded). *Hollett.* $40/£25

HUMFREVILLE, J. LEE. Twenty Years Among Our Hostile Indians. NY: Hunter, (1903). 2nd ed (so stated). Pict cl, gilt. (Hinges repaired, but still weak; stained, spine faded), else VG. Howes H790. *Pacific*.* $58/£36

HUMMEL, CHARLES F. With Hammer in Hand. Charlottesville, 1968. Signed, inscribed. *Swann*.* $69/£43

HUMMEL, RAY O. Southeastern Broadsides Before 1877. A Bibliography. Richmond: VA State Library, 1971. 1st ed. Blue cl. Fine. *Chapel Hill.* $60/£38

HUMPHREY, HERMAN. The Life and Labors of the Rev. T.H. Gallaudet, LL.D. NY: Robert Carter & Bros, 1857. 1st ed. Engr frontisport, 440pp. Black cl (extrems lt chipped). *Karmiole.* $75/£47

HUMPHREY, MAUD with ELIZABETH S. TUCKER. The Book of Pets. NY: Frederick A. Stokes, 1893. 1st ed. 4to. 12 full-pg color plts by Humphrey, each followed by a full-pg color plt by Tucker. Cl-backed color pict bds (edges rubbed). *Reisler.* $750/£469

HUMPHREY, MAUD. Children of the Revolution. NY: Frederick A. Stokes, 1900. 4to. 12 full-pg color plts. Cl-backed color pict bds (edges rubbed, worn, pencil mks erased). *Reisler.* $600/£375

HUMPHREY, MAUD. Little Continentals. NY: Frederick A. Stokes, 1900. 1st ed. 4to. Cl-backed color pict bds (dusty, edges worn, rear stained; rep corner clipped). *Reisler.* $275/£172

HUMPHREY, MAUD. Little Folk of '76. NY: Frederick A. Stokes, 1900. 1st ed. 4to. 6 full-pg color plts. Cl-backed color pict bds. (Lacks fep; edges worn, rubbed), o/w Clean. *Reisler.* $350/£219

HUMPHREY, MAUD. One, Two, Three, Four. Helen Gray Cone (verses). NY: Frederick A. Stokes & Brother, 1889. 1st ed. 8vo. 4 full-pg color plts. Cl-backed color illus bds (edges rubbed; foxing not affecting plts). *Reisler.* $200/£125

HUMPHREY, SETH K. Loafing Through Africa. Phila: Penn Pub, 1929. 1st ed. Grn pict cl, gilt. (Spine gilt sl worn), o/w VG. *Sotheran.* $237/£148

HUMPHREY, ZEPHINE. Cactus Forest. NY: E.P. Dutton, 1938. 1st ed. VG in dj (worn). *Lien.* $15/£9

HUMPHREYS, ARTHUR L. Old Decorative Maps and Charts. London/NY: Halton & Truscott Smith/Minton, Balch, 1926. 1st ed. One of 1500 numbered. Folio. 79 plts. (Spine faded), o/w Fine. *Lefkowicz.* $250/£156

HUMPHREYS, COLONEL. The Miscellaneous Works. NY, 1790. 1st ed. 348pp. Full contemp calf. VG. *M & S.* $95/£59

HUMPHREYS, H. N. and J. O. WESTWOOD. British Moths and Their Transformations. William Smith, 1843-1845. 1st ed. 2 vols. 4to. 124 hand-colored litho plts. Contemp 1/2 roan. (S! spotted; vol 1 spine head joints cracked.) *Sotheby's**. $589/£368

HUMPHREYS, H. N. Hans Holbein's Celebrated Dance of Death.... London: (Bernard Quaritch), 1868. Pub's brick cl, gilt. *Book Block*. $175/£109

HUMPHREYS, H. N. Illuminated Illustrations of Froissart. London: William Smith, 1844. 1st ed. 36 hand-colored, chromolitho plts. Aeg. Morocco, gilt. (Pg edges sl chipped), else VG. *Pacific**. $374/£234

HUMPHREYS, H. N. The Origin and Progress of the Art of Writing. London: Ingram Cooke, 1853. 1st ed. Aeg. Contemp blue gilt-stamped cl. Sound. *Appelfeld*. $250/£156

HUMPHREYS, W. J. Physics of the Air. Phila, 1920. 1st ed. *Argosy*. $75/£47

HUMPHRIES, SYDNEY. Oriental Carpets, Runners and Rugs and Some Jacquard Reproductions. London, 1910. 24 color plts. (Joints splitting.) *Swann**. $92/£58

HUNEKER, JAMES. Bedouins. NY, 1920. 1st Amer ed. NF (spine sl creased). *Polyanthos*. $30/£19

HUNEKER, JAMES. Melomaniacs. NY, 1902. 1st Amer ed. Teg, uncut. Pict cvrs, gilt. Fine (spine sl rubbed). *Polyanthos*. $35/£22

HUNGERFORD, EDWARD. The Story of the Baltimore and Ohio Railroad, 1827-1927. NY/London: Putnam, 1928. 1st ed. 2 vols. Pict eps, teg. Navy cl. (Sl loss of cl top edge each rear cvr.) VG djs (sl rubbed, chipped), orig plain bd slipcase. *Baltimore**. $100/£63

HUNGERFORD, EDWARD. Wells Fargo, Advancing the American Frontier. NY: Random House, (1949). 1st ed. VG in dj (torn). *Perier*. $30/£19

HUNGERFORD, EDWARD. Wells Fargo. NY: Random House, (1949). 1st ed. VG (cut-out pasted to fep in dj (sl worn). *Lien*. $30/£19

HUNGERFORD, JOHN B. Hawaiian Railroads. Hungerford, (1963). Good in dj. *Rybski*. $40/£25

HUNING, FRANZ. Trader on the Santa Fe Trail. Albuquerque, 1973. 1st ed. Signed by author's granddaughter (ed). VG in dj (sl worn). *Dumont*. $45/£28

HUNNEWELL, JAMES F. Illustrated Americana 1493-1889. N.p.: American Antiquarian Soc, 1890. 1st ed. One of 150. Inscribed, signed. Frontis. NF. *Pacific**. $52/£33

HUNT, AURORA. The Army of the Pacific. Glendale: A.H. Clark, 1951. 1st ed. One of 1023. Frontis, 16 plts, fldg map. Dk blue cl, gilt. Fine. *Argonaut*. $225/£141

HUNT, AURORA. Kirby Benedict, Frontier Federal Judge. Glendale: A.H. Clark, 1961. 1st ed. Fldg map. VG. *Lien*. $35/£22

HUNT, CECIL. How to Build a New World. London: Hutchinson, n.d. (1943). 1st Eng ed. Inscribed presentation from W. Heath Robinson (illus). Signed by Hunt and Robinson. Good (name, address; top edge sl dusty; prelims, edges, eps spotted; spine ends sl bumped). *Ulysses*. $360/£225

HUNT, CECIL. How to Run a Communal Home. London: Hutchinson, n.d. (1941). 1st Eng ed. Inscribed presentation from W. Heath Robinson (illus). Good (top edge dusty; spine ends, corners sl bumped, spine faded, cvrs cocked, rubbed). *Ulysses*. $360/£225

HUNT, ELVID. Fort Leavenworth 1827-1927. Fort Leavenworth: General Services School, 1926. 1st ed. (Lt edge stains 1st few pp), else VG in dj (worn edges). Howes H800. *Perier*. $97/£61

HUNT, FRAZIER and ROBERT. I Fought with Custer. NY, 1947. 1st ed. (Bkpl), else Good. *King*. $40/£25

HUNT, FRAZIER. Cap Mossman, Last of the Great Cowmen. NY: Hastings House, 1951. 1st ed. NF in dj (worn). *Labordo*. $65/£41

HUNT, FRAZIER. The Tragic Days of Billy the Kid. NY: Hastings House, (1956). 1st ed. Dj. *Dawson*. $40/£25

HUNT, G. H. Outram and Havelock's Persian Campaign. London, 1858. Later 1/2 morocco. (Lacks fep, bkpl.) *Swann**. $172/£108

HUNT, G. W. A History of the Hunt Family. Boston: McDonald, Gill, 1890. 1st ed. 79pp. (Lt rubbed.) *Kane**. $275/£172

HUNT, INEZ and WANETTA W. DRAPER. To Colorado's Restless Ghosts. (Denver, CO, 1960.) 1st ed. Good+ (sl sprung, bkpl, p189 soiled; sunned). *Sagebrush*. $27/£17

HUNT, J. (ed). Personality and the Behavior Disorders. NY: Ronald, 1944. 1st ed. 2 vols. NF (lib mks; dot on spine). *Beasley*. $50/£31

HUNT, LEIGH. Table-Talk. London: Edward Moxon, 1851. 1st ed. Aeg. Full tan polished calf (orig blue cl cvrs bound in), gilt. *Cummins*. $100/£63

HUNT, LEIGH. The Town. Smith, Elder, 1848. 1st ed. 2 vols. Orig tan cl. (Lacks 1/2-title vol 1; cl sl soiled.) *Sotheby's**. $91/£57

HUNT, LYNN BOGUE. An Artist's Game Bag. NY: Derrydale, 1936. One of 1225 numbered. Brn cl. NF in color pict dj. *Biscotti*. $300/£188

HUNT, RACHEL. William Penn, Horticulturist. Pittsburgh, 1953. 10 plts. *Maggs*. $19/£12

HUNT, ROBERT. A Manual of Photography. London/Glasgow: Richard Griffin, 1854. 4th ed. Color frontis, xii,329pp,32+8pp ads. (Spine expertly repaired, tips rubbed), else VG. *Cahan*. $500/£313

HUNT, ROCKWELL D. John Bidwell. Caldwell: Caxton Ptrs, (1942). 1st ed. NF in dj (few sm edge tears, price-clipped). *Pacific**. $63/£39

HUNT, T. Systematic Mineralogy Based on Natural Classification. NY: Scientific, 1892. 2nd ed. xvii,391pp+ads. VG. *Blake*. $250/£156

HUNT, W. BEN. Indian Silversmithing. Milwaukee: Bruce Publishing, (1952). 1st ed. Fine in VG dj. *Book Market*. $30/£19

HUNT, WILLIAM SOUTHWORTH. Frank Forester. A Tragedy in Exile. NY: Carteret Book Club, 1933. 1st ed. One of 200. Uncut. Leather spine label. (Lt worn.) Slipcase (scuffed). *Oinonen**. $150/£94

HUNTER, ALEXANDER. The Huntsman in the South. Volume 1. Virginia and North Carolina. (All Published). NY, 1908. 1st ed. Port. Pict cl (lt worn, spine tips frayed). *Oinonen**. $270/£169

HUNTER, ALEXANDER. Johnny Reb and Billy Yank. NY/WA: Neale, 1905. 1st ed. (Sl aging, lt dusty.) Grn cl (sl rubbed), gilt. *Baltimore**. $325/£203

HUNTER, ANOLE. Let's Ride to Hounds. NY: Derrydale, 1929. One of 850. 4 full-pg illus. Red cl (spine sl faded). NF. *Biscotti*. $125/£78

HUNTER, C. L. Sketches of Western North Carolina. Raleigh: Raleigh News Steam Job Print, 1877. 1st ed. 357,(1)pp. Grn cl. (Bkpl), else NF. Howes H810. *Chapel Hill*. $250/£156

HUNTER, D. The Diseases of Occupations. London, 1975. (Label removed), o/w VG. *Whitehart*. $64/£40

HUNTER, DARD. My Life with Paper. NY, 1958. 1st ed. Dj (chipped, dknd). *Kane**. $55/£34

HUNTER, DARD. Papermaking by Hand in America. Chillicothe: Mountain House Press, 1950. 1st ed. One of 210 numbered, signed. Folio. Color frontis view, 171 mtd facs. Orig 1/2 linen, patterned bds. Morocco-backed cl fldg case. *Swann**. $5,750/£3,594

HUNTER, DARD. Papermaking by Hand in America. Chillicothe, (OH): Mountain House, 1950. 1st ed. One of 210 (somewhat fewer were completed). Folio. Color frontis. Orig folded sheets laid into cl fldg box w/leather label by Gray Parrot. Fine. *M & S*. $9,500/£5,938

HUNTER, DARD. Papermaking Through Eighteen Centuries. NY: William Edwin Rudge, 1930. 1st ed. Frontis. Teg, untrimmed. Brn coated buckram (spine sl rubbed w/gouge to bottom portion of label affecting name), crimson leather spine label. Text Clean (bkpl) in felt-lined bd slipcase (sl dusting). *Baltimore*. $135/£84

HUNTER, DARD. Papermaking Through Eighteen Centuries. NY: William Edwin Rudge, 1930. 1st ed. Fldg frontis. Teg; unopened. Morocco spine label. NF. *Pacific*. $184/£115

HUNTER, DAVID SMITH. Golf Simplified: Cause and Effect. GC: Doubleday, Page, 1923. Paper cvr label. (Sl residue to fr pastedown from removed bkpl; spine foot w/sm chip), else NF. *Pacific*. $40/£25

HUNTER, EVAN. Mothers and Daughters. NY: S&S, 1961. 1st ed. NF in NF dj. *Between The Covers*. $175/£109

HUNTER, EVAN. Sons. GC: Doubleday, 1969. 1st ed. Black cl. VG in white dj (worn, dknd). *Reese*. $20/£13

HUNTER, GEORGE LELAND. Decorative Furniture. Grand Rapids, 1923. 23 color plts. (Sl shaken.) *Washton*. $100/£63

HUNTER, GEORGE LELAND. Italian Furniture and Interiors. NY, (1920). (2nd ed.) Folio. Contents loose in cl portfolio, as issued. 200 photo plts. (Sl marginal imperfections on tp.) *Swann**. $431/£269

HUNTER, JACK D. The Blue Max. NY: Dutton, 1964. 1st ed. Cl, dec bds. NF in dj. *Reese*. $55/£34

HUNTER, JOHN D. Manners and Customs of Several Indian Tribes Located West of the Mississippi. Phila, 1823. 1st ed. Contemp tree sheep. (Lib bkpl, ink stamp.) Howes H813. *Swann**. $126/£79

HUNTER, JOHN D. Manners and Customs of Several Indian Tribes Located West of the Mississippi.... Phila: The Author, 1823. 1st ed. 402pp. Old calf, leather spine label. Text Good (browned, sl foxed, some ll creased, lt stains, sig, lacks feps; worn, scuffed). Howes H813. *Baltimore**. $110/£69

HUNTER, JOHN D. Manners and Customs of Several Indian Tribes. Minneapolis, MN: Ross & Haines, 1957. Ltd to 1500. VG in dj. Howes H813. *Lien*. $20/£13

HUNTER, JOHN M. and NOAH H. ROSE. The Album of Gunfighters. N.p., 1951. Errata slip, author bios tipped-in. (Lt shelfworn), else VG. *Dumont*. $150/£94

HUNTER, JOHN M. and NOAH H. ROSE. The Album of Gunfighters. Bandera, TX, 1951. 1st ltd ed. One of 300. Signed by both and Warren Hunter (illus). Errata slip laid in. Pict cl. VG + in dj. Howes H814. *Labordo*. $450/£281

HUNTER, JOHN M. The Trail Drivers of Texas. Nashville: Cokesbury, 1925. 2nd ed. 2 vols in 1. Blue cl, gilt. VG (lt edgeworn). Howes H816. *House*. $180/£113

HUNTER, MILDRED C. Wuzzle and His Muzzle. Raphael Tuck, n.d. c1920. Sq 4to. Color frontis by Lawson Wood, 16pp. Buff wraps (mks, sl worn) w/shaped color pict onlay. *Bookmark*. $40/£25

HUNTER, MILTON R. Brigham Young the Colonizer. Independence, MO: Zion's, 1945. 3rd ed. Black bds. VG (stamp; lt bumped) in pict dj (rear cvr soiled, spine faded, chipped). *Blue Mountain*. $35/£22

HUNTER, NORMAN. The Home-Made Dragon. Bodley Head, 1971. 1st ed. 8vo. Fritz Wegner (illus). 96pp. VG + in pict dj. *Bookmark*. $27/£17

HUNTER, NORMAN. The Peculiar Triumph of Professor Branestawm. Bodley Head, 1970. 1st ed. 8vo. George Adamson (illus). Fine in pict dj (frayed). *Bookmark*. $32/£20

HUNTER, ROBERT. The Links. NY: Scribner, 1926. 1st ed. Inscribed by Hunter to his son, dated 1935. 8.75x6. Grn dec cl. (Emb stamp, sig, inscrip dated 1931; spine ends sl rubbed), else Fine. *Pacific**. $1,495/£934

HUNTER, SAM. Isamu Noguchi. NY: Abrams, n.d. Dj. *Swann**. $258/£161

HUNTER, SAM. Isamu Noguchi. NY: Abbeville, n.d. (1978). 1st ed. Folio. Fine in dj. *Cahan*. $300/£188

HUNTER, SAM. Joan Miro: His Graphic Work. (NY, 1958.) Pict cl. Dj (worn). *Swann**. $172/£108

HUNTER, W. S., JR. Hunter's Eastern Townships Scenery, Canada East. Montreal: John Lovell, 1860. 1st ed. Slim folio. 36pp; 1 full-pg engr map on thin paper, add'l pict tp, 13 Fine toned view plts, guards. Lt brn cl, gilt. (Spine heavily chipped, fr cvr nearly detached, cvrs sl worn, sunned, cl peeled from fr cvr corners.) *Baltimore**. $550/£344

HUNTER, W. W. Orissa. London, 1872. 2 vols. 2 frontispieces (1 color), 330; 219pp; fldg color map, plan, 13 plts. Marbled eps, edges. Gilt-edged 1/2 calf, marbled bds (extrems sl rubbed), morocco spine labels (2 worn w/loss). *Edwards*. $280/£175

HUNTFORD, ROLAND (ed). The Amundsen Photographs. NY: Atlantic Monthly, 1987. 1st US ed. Mint in dj. *Explorer*. $45/£28

HUNTFORD, ROLAND. Scott and Amundsen. Hodder & Stoughton, 1979. 1st ed. VG in dj. *Walcot*. $61/£38

HUNTINGTON, ANNIE OAKES. Studies of Trees in Winter. Boston: Knight & Millet, 1902. 1st ed. Teg. (Browned; shelf-worn, spine sunned), else Good. *Fair Meadow*. $30/£19

HUNTINGTON, ELLSWORTH. The Climatic Factor as Illustrated in Arid America. Washington: Carnegie Inst, 1914. 1st ed. 2 fldg maps. Orig ptd wrappers. (Rubbed, dknd), else VG. *Pacific**. $40/£25

HUNTINGTON, G. S. The Anatomy and Development of the Systemic Lymphatic Vessels in the Domestic Cat. Phila, 1911. (Pp tanned.) 138 plts. Wrappers (soiled, faded, call #s fr wrapper, worn, spine crudely repaired w/ cl tape). *Sutton*. $38/£24

HUNTLEY, ELIZABETH V. Peninsula Pilgrimage. Whittet & Shepperson, 1941. Signed. VG (edges browned; binding weak). *Book Broker*. $35/£22

HUNTON, JOHN. John Hunton's Diary. Wyoming Territory, 1885-89. L. G. Flannery (ed). Glendale: Clark, 1970. 1st ed. *Heinoldt*. $34/£21

HURD, PETER. The Lithographs. John Meigs (ed). Lubbock, TX: Baker Gallery, 1969. 2nd ed. Sm folio. 60 plts. NF in dj. *Dumont*. $60/£38

HURLEY, DANIEL. Cincinnati the Queen City. Cincinnati: Cincinnati Hist Soc, 1982. 1st ed. Gray cl. Fine in color, pict dj. *House*. $20/£13

HURLIMANN, BETTINA. Three Centuries of Children's Books in Europe. Brian Alderson (trans). Cleveland: World Pub Co, (1968). 1st ed in English. NF in dj. *Pacific**. $35/£22

HURLIMANN, BETTINA. Three Centuries of Children's Books in Europe. World, 1968. 1st US ed. 297pp. VG (lower rear corner sl stained) in VG dj. *Price*. $45/£28

HURLIMANN, MARTIN. Istanbul. London: Thames & Hudson, 1958. 1st ed. VG in dj (torn). *Worldwide*. $20/£13

HURST, ARTHUR et al. Medical Diseases of War. Balt: Williams & Wilkins, 1941. 2nd ed. (Lib mks; faint spine #s), else NF. *Beasley*. $45/£28

HURST, FANNY. Lummox. NY: Harper, 1923. 1st ed. One of 250. Signed. Cl-backed dec bds. NF. *Pacific**. $40/£25

HURST, GEORGE H. Colour: A Handbook of the Theory of Colour. Scott, Greenwood, 1900. 1st ed. 10 color plts. Patterned cl. Good (sl damage, spine replaced). *Whittle*. $56/£35

HURST, H. E. The Nile: A General Account of the River and the Utilization of Its Waters. London, 1952. 1st ed. 32 photo plts. Blue cl, gilt. VG in dj (chipped). *Larry Price*. $28/£18

HURST, JOHN THOMAS. A Hand-Book of Formulae, Tables, and Memoranda for Architectural Surveyors, and Others Engaged in Building. London: E. & F.N. Spon, 1895. 14th ed. iv,477pp + 17 ads. Aeg. Dk grn blind-stamped cl (sl worn). *Young.* $56/£35

HURST, SAMUEL H. Journal-History of the Seventy-Third Ohio Volunteer Infantry. Chillicothe, OH, 1866. 1st ed. 254pp. (Lacks fep (or frontis?), stained; pencil notes; loose, worn.) *King.* $175/£109

HURSTON, ZORA NEALE. Jonah's Gourd Vine. Phila, 1934. 1st ed, 1st bk. 7.5x5.5 inches. (Pp sl browned; cvr tops, top edge dknd; sm bump.) *King.* $750/£469

HURSTON, ZORA NEALE. Moses: Man of the Mountain. Phila: Lippincott, (1939). 1st ed. 8vo. Grn cl. VG (sm stain spine head, joints sl browned, extrems lt worn) in dj (chipped, sl soiled). *Heritage.* $750/£469

HURSTON, ZORA NEALE. Seraph on the Suwanee. NY: Scribner, 1948. 1st ed. Untrimmed. Tan cl (edges sl dusty). Text Fine, cvrs Nice in dj (sl chipped, sl edgeworn). *Baltimore*.* $240/£150

HURSTON, ZORA NEALE. Their Eyes Were Watching God. Phila: Lippincott, 1937. 1st ed. Fine in NF dj (few sm chips). *Lame Duck.* $2,850/£1,781

Hush-a-Bye Baby. NY: McLoughlin Bros, (ca 1880). Lg 4to. 6 full-pg chromolitho plts by J. H. Howard. Very Nice in gold highlighted full color paper wrappers (marginal chipping). *Reisler.* $335/£209

HUSMANN, GEORGE. The Cultivation of the Native Grape, and Manufacture of American Wines. NY: George E. Woodward, (1866). 1st ed. Grn cl, gilt spine. (Names; spine ends rubbed, spot fr cvr), else VG. *Pacific*.* $207/£129

HUSSEY, CHRISTOPHER. The Life of Sir Edwin Lutyens. London: Country Life, 1953. Special ed. 178 plts. VG. *Hollett.* $96/£60

HUSSEY, JOHN A. The History of Fort Vancouver and Its Physical Structure. WA State Hist Soc, (1957). One of 1000. Tipped-in color frontis. Dec cl. Fine. *Pacific*.* $81/£51

HUSSEY, JOHN A. (ed). The Voyage of the Racoon: A 'Secret' Journal...1813-1814. SF: Book Club of CA, 1958. 1st ed. Ltd to 400 ptd. Errata slip. Morocco-backed marbled bds. Fine. *Harrington.* $100/£63

HUTCHESON, MARTHA BROOKES. The Spirit of the Garden. Boston: Little, Brown, 1923. 1st ed. (Browned; bds sl scuffed, sm water stains), else VG. *Fair Meadow.* $60/£38

HUTCHINGS, J. M. Hutchings Guide and Souvenir of California. Yosemite Valley and the Big Trees. What to See and How to See It. SF: J.M. Hutchings, (1900). 5th ed. 2 maps. Ptd card from Foley's Studio laid in loose. Red bds, gilt, cl spine. (Rubberstamp; cvrs dull, rear stained), else VG. *Pacific*.* $92/£58

HUTCHINGS, J. M. In the Heart of the Sierras: The Yo Semite Valley, Both Historical and Descriptive.... Yo Semite Valley: Old Cabin, 1886. 1st ed, 1st issue. Inscribed presentation Oct 5, 1886. Frontis, (4),xii,13-496pp; port, 20 phototypes, 2 artotypes, 1 heliotype, 1 red plt, 3 wood-engr plts, 2 maps (1 fldg). Marbled eps; aeg. Full turkey morocco, gilt. (Port of Hutchings and following 3 leaves detached, hinge cracked after title, contents shaken, informally rebacked w/black cl, edges worn, corners showing), else Good. *Pacific*.* $1,495/£934

HUTCHINGS, J. M. Scenes of Wonder and Curiosity in California. SF: Hutchings & Rosenfield, (1860). 1st ed, 1st ptg. (3),4-236pp; 93 illus [one on p33 is not listed]. Black cl, gilt spine. (Pencil name dated 1860; lt water stains fr cvr), o/w Fine. *Pacific*.* $259/£162

HUTCHINGS, J. M. Scenes of Wonder and Curiosity in California. NY/SF: A. Roman, 1871. (4),5-292,(4)ads pp; 2 maps. Brn pebbled cl, gilt. (Spine ends sl chipped, sm tear rear cvr), o/w VG. *Pacific*.* $86/£54

HUTCHINGS, J. M. Seeking the Elephant, 1849. James Mason Hutchings' Journal of His Overland Trek to California. Glendale: A.H. Clark, 1980. 1st ed. Ltd to 750. Fine in unptd dj. *Book Market.* $65/£41

HUTCHINGS, MARGARET. The Book of the Teddy Bear. London, 1964. 1st ed. Blue bds, gilt. VG (ex-lib) in dj (adhesive plastic cvr). *Whittle.* $32/£20

HUTCHINGS, W. W. London Town, Past and Present. Cassell, 1909. 2 vols. (Sl staining fr bd vol 1, edges sl bumped, spines chipped w/loss.) *Edwards.* $72/£45

HUTCHINS, JAMES S. Boots and Saddles at the Little Bighorn. (Ft. Collins, CO): Old Army, (1976). 1st ed. One of 250. Signed. 2-tone cl. Fine. *Pacific*.* $52/£33

HUTCHINSON, ARTHUR H. Little Saints Annoy the Lord. Seattle: Greenwood, 1938. 1st ed. Signed presentation. VG. *Perier.* $35/£22

HUTCHINSON, C. ALAN. Frontier Settlement in Mexican California. New Haven: Yale Univ, 1969. 1st ed. Fine in VG dj. *Book Market.* $75/£47

HUTCHINSON, F. E. Medieval Glass at All Souls College. Faber, 1948. (Eps browned.) Dj. *Peter Taylor.* $32/£20

HUTCHINSON, HORACE G. The Book of Golf and Golfers. London: Longmans, Green, 1900. 3rd ed. Teg. Red cl, gilt. (Emb stamp, eps foxed; spine ends sl rubbed), else VG. *Pacific*.* $207/£129

HUTCHINSON, HORACE G. British Golf Links. London: J.S. Virtue, 1897. 4to. Pict cl, gilt. *Christie's*.* $630/£394

HUTCHINSON, HORACE G. British Golf Links: A Short Account of the Leading Golf Links of the United Kingdom. London: J.S. Virtue, 1897. 1st trade ed. 12.75x9.25. Pict cl, gilt. (Sl adhesion residue to fep; spine ends, corners sl rubbed), else VG. *Pacific*.* $978/£611

HUTCHINSON, HORACE G. Fifty Years of Golf. London: Country Life, (1919). 1st ed. Grn cl, gilt. (Emb stamp, eps offset from binder's glue; spine ends sl rubbed), else VG. *Pacific*.* $403/£252

HUTCHINSON, HORACE G. Golf. Longmans, Green, 1890. 1st ed. xiv,(464)pp. Dec cl (sl rubbed). Nice (leaf sl damaged from opening, browned, spotted). *Ash.* $312/£195

HUTCHINSON, HORACE G. Golf. London: Longmans, Green, 1892. 1st ed. One of 250 lg paper copies. 9.25x7.5. Teg. 3/4 blue morocco, orange cl, gilt. (Emb stamp, lacks tp, limitation pg; spine rubbed, scuffed), o/w VG. *Pacific*.* $920/£575

HUTCHINSON, HORACE G. (ed). Big Game Shooting. London: Country Life, 1905. 1st ed. 2 vols. Red cl, gilt. (Foxed; spine sunned), else VG. *Pacific*.* $259/£162

HUTCHINSON, HORACE G. (ed). The New Book of Golf. London: Longmans, Green, 1912. 1st ed. Red cl, gilt. (Emb stamp; fr hinge crudely reinforced, spine ends sl rubbed), else VG. *Pacific*.* $259/£162

HUTCHINSON, J. R. The Press-Gang Afloat and Ashore. NY: E. P. Dutton, 1914. 1st Amer ed. (Lt foxed; spine head sl torn.) *Lefkowicz.* $85/£53

HUTCHINSON, R. C. The Unforgotten Prisoner. London (etc): Cassell, (1933). 1st ed. Gilt red cl. (Fore-edge lt foxed), else NF in dj. *Reese.* $40/£25

HUTCHINSON, VERONICA (ed). Chimney Corner Fairy Tales. NY: Minton, Balch, 1928. 1st ed. 4to. 183pp; 6 color illus by Lois Lenski. VG (name stamp) in VG dj. *Davidson.* $140/£88

HUTCHINSON, VERONICA (ed). Chimney Corner Poems. NY: Minton, Balch, 1929. 1st ed. Lois Lenski (illus). VG in blue cl (sl soiled). *Second Life.* $45/£28

HUTCHISON, CLAUDE B. (ed). California Agriculture, by Members of the Faculty of the College of Agriculture, University of California. Berkeley: Univ of CA, 1946. 1st ed. Grn cl. Fine in dj (spine faded). *Argonaut.* $40/£25

HUTH, ALFRED HENRY (comp). A Catalogue of the Woodcuts and Engravings in the Huth Library. Chiswick, 1910. Ltd to 150. 12 plts. (Feps lt yellowed.) Teg, rest uncut. Morocco-backed bds (sl faded, rubbed). *Edwards*. $77/£48

HUTH, HANS. Lacquer of the West. Chicago/London, 1971. 16 color plts. Good +. *Washton*. $85/£53

HUTTON, CHARLES. A Course of Mathematics. London: G.G. & J. Robinson, 1799-98. Vol 1 2nd ed, vol 2 1st ed. 2 vols. iv,368; iv,364pp, w/errata leaf vol 2. Later marbled bds, cl spines. VG set. *Glaser*. $150/£94

HUTTON, HAROLD. Doc Middleton. Chicago, (1980). Frontis port, map. NF in VG + dj. *Sagebrush*. $22/£14

HUTTON, HAROLD. Vigilante Days. Chicago, 1978. VG in dj. *Dumont*. $40/£25

HUTTON, O. Life of the Right Reverend William Pinkney, D.D., LL.D., Fifth Bishop of Maryland. Washington: Gibson, 1890. 1st ed. (8),388pp; 1 photogravure, lengthy port. Dec cl. *Ginsberg*. $60/£38

HUTTON, S. K. By Eskimo Dog Sled and Kayak. Seeley Service, 1919. Map. VG. *Walcot*. $38/£24

HUTTON, W. The Scarborough Tour, in 1803. London: John Nichols, 1804. 1st ed. 318pp + 2pp ads. Mod 1/4 calf. *Marlborough*. $120/£75

HUTTON, WILLIAM RICH. Glances at California 1847-1853. San Marino: Huntington, 1942. 1st ed. Fine. *Book Market*. $20/£13

HUXLEY, ALDOUS. Along the Road: Notes and Essays of a Tourist. NY: George H. Doran, (1925). 1st Amer ed. One of 250. Signed. Teg. 3/4 parchment, paper spine label. VG. *Pacific**. $127/£79

HUXLEY, ALDOUS. Arabia Infelix and Other Poems. NY: Fountain Press, 1929. 1st Amer ed. One of 300 (of 692). Signed. Cl-backed yellow bds, gilt. (Sl soiled), else NF. *Pacific**. $63/£39

HUXLEY, ALDOUS. Beyond the Mexique Bay. C&W, 1934. 1st ed. One of 210 signed. Teg, rest untrimmed. Grn 1/4 buckram, patterned bd sides. (Spine faded), o/w VG. *Sotheran*. $285/£178

HUXLEY, ALDOUS. Brave New World. Chatto, 1932. 1st UK ed. NF (lacks dj). *Williams*. $144/£90

HUXLEY, ALDOUS. Brave New World. London: C&W, 1932. 1st trade ed. (Spine sl creased, ends lt rubbed), else VG. *Pacific**. $150/£94

HUXLEY, ALDOUS. Brave New World. London: C&W, 1932. 1st ed. Top edge stained blue. Blue cl, gilt spine. VG (spine browned, cocked, extrems lt rubbed) in dj (price-clipped, spine browned, extrems sl chipped). *Heritage*. $350/£219

HUXLEY, ALDOUS. Brave New World. London: C&W, 1932. 1st ed. Blue cl, gilt. Fine (sl crease from manufacturer) in dj (crown sl chipped). *Macdonnell*. $850/£531

HUXLEY, ALDOUS. Brave New World. London: C&W, 1932. 1st ed. VF (traces of paperclip fr blank) in orig dj (price-clipped, edge chipped). *Bromer*. $950/£594

HUXLEY, ALDOUS. Brave New World. GC: Doubleday, Doran, 1932. 1st Amer ed. Ltd to 250 signed. Teg. Cl-backed mauve bds. VF in matching slipcase (repaired, worn). *Bromer*. $1,250/£781

HUXLEY, ALDOUS. Brave New World. LEC, 1974. One of 2000 signed by Mary McAfee (illus). Fine in slipcase. *Swann**. $46/£29

HUXLEY, ALDOUS. Brief Candles. Chatto, 1930. 1st UK ed. NF in VG dj (sl dusty, browned). *Williams*. $56/£35

HUXLEY, ALDOUS. Brief Candles. NY: Fountain, 1930. One of 800 numbered, signed. Black cl. Fine in glassine dj (torn). *Dermont*. $200/£125

HUXLEY, ALDOUS. The Cicadas and Other Poems. London, 1931. 1st ed. NF (spine sl sunned). *Polyanthos*. $30/£19

HUXLEY, ALDOUS. Crome Yellow. London: C&W, 1921. 1st ed. Extra spine label tipped in back, as issued. VG- (shelfworn, spine dknd, dingy). *My Bookhouse*. $87/£54

HUXLEY, ALDOUS. The Defeat of Youth and Other Poems. (Oxford: B.H. Blackwell, 1918.) 1st ed. Pict grn/white bds, paper spine/cvr labels. (Spine, extrems rubbed, ends lt chipped), else VG. *Pacific**. $75/£47

HUXLEY, ALDOUS. The Devils of Loudun. London: C&W, 1952. 1st ed. Orange cl. Fine in dj. *Maggs*. $56/£35

HUXLEY, ALDOUS. Do What You Will. London: C&W, 1929. 1st ed. One of 260 signed. Teg. Cl-backed patterned bds, gilt. Fine. *Vandoros*. $450/£281

HUXLEY, ALDOUS. Do What You Will. Essays. London: C&W, 1929. 1st Eng ed. Fine. *Cady*. $30/£19

HUXLEY, ALDOUS. The Doors of Perception. London, 1945. 1st ed. (2pp discolored by newspaper cutting.) Dj. *Petersfield*. $40/£25

HUXLEY, ALDOUS. The Doors of Perception. C&W, 1954. 1st ed. NF- in dj (extrems worn, spine sl dknd). *Sclanders*. $56/£35

HUXLEY, ALDOUS. An Encyclopaedia of Pacifism. London, 1937. Cuttings laid in. Orig wraps (spine, edges sl dknd), o/w VG. *Edrich*. $19/£12

HUXLEY, ALDOUS. An Encyclopaedia of Pacifism. London: C&W, 1937. 1st ed. Yellow self-wrappers. (Eps sl foxed, sm ink correction p67; wrappers sl dusty), o/w Fine. *Temple*. $24/£15

HUXLEY, ALDOUS. Ends and Means. London: C&W, 1937. 1st ed. One of 160 signed. 1/4 yellow cl, dec bds, gilt. (Spine sl browned), o/w NF in 1/2 brn morocco clamshell case. *Heritage*. $400/£250

HUXLEY, ALDOUS. Ends and Means. An Enquiry into the Nature of Ideals and into the Methods Employed for Their Realization. London: C&W, 1937. 1st ed. One of 160 numbered, signed. Teg. Ptd paper bds, yellow cl spine, gilt. (Extrems sl rubbed), o/w NF. *Black Sun*. $300/£188

HUXLEY, ALDOUS. Essays Old and New. London: C&W, 1926. 1st ed. One of 650 ptd. Signed. Teg. 1/2 blue cl, marbled bds, gilt. NF. *Pacific**. $86/£54

HUXLEY, ALDOUS. Eyeless in Gaza. London: C&W, 1936. 1st ed. Top edge crimson, lower edges uncut. Old cream coarse rough buckram. Fine. *Temple*. $32/£20

HUXLEY, ALDOUS. Eyeless in Gaza. London: C&W, 1936. 1st Eng ed. NF (edges spotted; spine ends sl bumped) in dj (sl nicked, sl rubbed, spine faded). *Ulysses*. $152/£95

HUXLEY, ALDOUS. The Gioconda Smile. London: C&W, 1938. 1st Eng ed. Patterned paper bds. VG (top edge sl dusty; spine ends bumped) in dj (sl creased, sl browned). *Ulysses*. $58/£36

HUXLEY, ALDOUS. Heaven and Hell. C&W, 1956. 1st ed. VG in dj (sl rubbed, frayed, sl loss to spine head). *Sclanders*. $32/£20

HUXLEY, ALDOUS. Heaven and Hell. Chatto, 1956. 1st UK ed. NF (ink name) in VG dj (spine extrems worn). *Williams*. $35/£22

HUXLEY, ALDOUS. Jesting Pilate. London: C&W, 1926. 1st ed. Blue cl, gilt. VG in dj (spine ends chipped, head lacks piece, sm tears to extrems, sl yellowed, soiled). *Pacific**. $40/£25

HUXLEY, ALDOUS. Leda. London: C&W, 1920. 1st ed. One of 160. Signed. Frontis. 1/2 cl, paper spine label. (Bkpl, offset to eps; rear corners stained), else VG-. *Pacific**. $58/£36

HUXLEY, ALDOUS. Limbo. London: C&W, 1920. 1st ed. VG (shelfworn). *My Bookhouse*. $52/£33

HUXLEY, ALDOUS. Little Mexican. C&W, 1924. 1st ed. VG (eps lt browned; spine ends, top corners sl bumped, edges sl faded) in dj (nicked, rubbed, dusty, sl torn, spine, edges browned, spine sl creased). *Ulysses*. $200/£125

HUXLEY, ALDOUS. The Olive Trees and Other Essays. C&W, 1936. One of 160 numbered, signed. Teg. Buckram. VG (fore-edge sl spotted; spine sl faded; spine ends, corner sl bumped; rear cvr sl mkd). *Ulysses*. $520/£325

HUXLEY, ALDOUS. Point Counter Point. London, 1928. 1st ed. Dj (lt edgeworn, sl soiled). *Swann**. $57/£36

HUXLEY, ALDOUS. Point Counter Point. London: C&W, 1928. 1st ed. Good in orange-brn cl (sm mks to lower rear joint). Dj (edges sl chipped). *Maggs*. $96/£60

HUXLEY, ALDOUS. Point Counter Point. London, 1928. 1st ed. One of 256 numbered, signed. Grn buckram. *Swann**. $230/£144

HUXLEY, ALDOUS. Prisons. London: Trianon, (1949). 1st ed. One of 1000. (Sm bumps to corners), else NF. *Pacific**. $127/£79

HUXLEY, ALDOUS. Proper Studies. London: C&W, 1927. 1st ed. One of 260. Signed twice. Teg. Cl-backed marbled bds, gilt. (Bkpl; extrems, spine sl sunned; sl rubbed), else VG. *Pacific**. $58/£36

HUXLEY, ALDOUS. Texts and Pretexts. Chatto, 1932. 1st UK ed. NF (spine sl faded) in VG dj (sl browned, edges sl worn). *Williams*. $104/£65

HUXLEY, ALDOUS. Those Barren Leaves. London: C&W, 1925. 1st Eng ed. Extra paper title label tipped-in at end. Fine. *Cady*. $30/£19

HUXLEY, ALDOUS. Those Barren Leaves. C&W, 1925. 1st ed. VG (spine foot sl bumped) in dj (dusty, sl chipped, spine dknd). *Ulysses*. $152/£95

HUXLEY, ALDOUS. Time Must Have a Stop. NY: Harpers, 1944. 1st Amer ed. Fine in VG + dj (sm tears). *Between The Covers*. $100/£63

HUXLEY, JULIAN. Essays in Popular Science. London: C&W, 1926. 1st ed. 5 plts. VG. *Hollett*. $56/£35

HUXLEY, LEONARD. Life and Letters of Thomas Henry Huxley. London: Macmillan, 1903. 2nd ed. 3 vols. VG (lt foxed; spine ends worn). *Bookcell*. $50/£31

HUXLEY, T. H. An Introduction to the Classification of Animals. London, 1869. 1st separate ed. (5),147pp,(40pp cat dated Jan 1872). (Worn, backstrip splitting, fr joint very open, shaken.) *Sutton*. $75/£47

HUXLEY, T. H. T.H. Huxley's Diary of the Voyage of HMS Rattlesnake. Julian Huxley (ed). London: C&W, 1935. Fldg map. VG. *Explorer*. $80/£50

HUYGHE, RENE. Delacroix. London, 1963. 56 color plts. Dj (spine sl chipped). *Edwards*. $104/£65

HUYSHE, GEORGE L. The Red River Expedition. London: Macmillan, 1871. 1st ed. 1/2-title, xi,(i)list,275,(1)imprint; 3 fldg charts, fldg table, engr plt. Brn cl. VG (bkpl tipped to tp; sl rubbed). *Morrell*. $208/£130

HUYSHE, GEORGE L. The Red River Expedition. London: Macmillan, 1871. xii,275pp; 3 fldg maps, plt, fldg table. Orig cl (rebacked), leather label. *Adelson*. $325/£203

HUYSMANS, J. K. La-Bas: A Novel. Fortune, 1943. (Fore-edge spotted; spine bumped, chipped, fr hinge nicked.) *Tiger*. $32/£20

HYAMS, EDWARD. Capability Brown and Humphrey Repton. NY: Scribner, c. 1971. 1st US ed. (Lower left corner rear bd discolored), else VG in dj (lt soiled). *Fair Meadow*. $50/£31

HYAMS, EDWARD. English Cottage Gardens. Nelson, 1970. 1st ed. VG in dj. *Hadley*. $45/£28

HYAMS, EDWARD. Irish Gardens. NY: Macmillan, (1967). 15 color plts. (Foxed; worn), else VG. *Fair Meadow*. $35/£22

HYAMS, EDWARD. Ornamental Shrubs for the Temperate Zone Garden. NY: A.S. Barnes, (1972). 48 color, 48 b/w plts. VG in dj (chipped). *Fair Meadow*. $40/£25

HYDE, CHARLES L. Pioneer Days. NY, 1939. (Browned), else Good in dj (chipped). *Dumont*. $65/£41

HYDE, DAYTON O. The Last Free Man. NY: Dial, 1973. 1st ed. Fine in dj. *Perier*. $30/£19

HYDE, GEORGE E. A Life of George Bent. Norman, (1968). 1st ed. VG in VG dj. *Woolson*. $35/£22

HYDE, GEORGE E. Red Cloud's Folk, a History of the Oglala Sioux. Norman, 1937. 1st ed. VG + . *Pratt*. $55/£34

HYDE, H. MONTGOMERY (ed). Oscar Wilde. London, 1948. 1st ed. (Cvrs dampstained.) *Gretton*. $16/£10

HYDE, H. MONTGOMERY. Norman Birkett. London: Hamish Hamilton, 1965. VG in dj (sl worn). *Hollett*. $32/£20

HYDE, J. A. LLOYD. Oriental Lowestoft, Chinese Export Porcelain. Newport, Monmouthshire, 1964. (Spine sl faded.) *Swann**. $115/£72

HYDE, J. A. LLOYD. Oriental Lowestoft. NY, (1936). One of 1000 numbered. Frontis, 30 plts. (Lt soiled, spine ends worn.) *Swann**. $46/£29

HYDE, JOHN. Big Game Hunting for Boys. NY: McLoughlin, (1907). 1st ed. 10x8.25. Pict cl, gilt. (Soiled), else VG. *Pacific**. $46/£29

HYDE, JOHN. Thro' Wonderland with Lieut Schwatka; or, Alaska and the Isle Passage. St. Paul: Northern Pacific Railroad, 1886. Color pict paper wraps (chipped, lacks rear wrap, stamp on cvr). *Metropolitan**. $28/£18

HYDE, RALPH. Printed Maps of Victorian London. Dawson, 1975. *Marlborough*. $24/£15

HYLANDER, C. J. The World of Plant Life. NY: Macmillan, 1939. 1st ed. NF in dj (chipped, torn). *Archer*. $20/£13

HYLANDER, C. J. The World of Plant Life. NY: Macmillan, 1944. 4th ptg. (Name, address, date; shelf-worn), else VG. *Fair Meadow*. $30/£19

Hymns in Prose for Children. (By Mrs. Barbauld.) John Murray, 1866. Rpt. All edges red. Good (Ink inscrip, bkpl; spine bumped). *Tiger*. $40/£25

HYNE, CUTCLIFFE. Adventures of Captain Kettle. NY, 1898. 1st Amer ed. Frontis. (Sl worn.) Internally VG. *Mcclintock*. $12/£8

HYNE, CUTCLIFFE. More Adventures of Captain Kettle. Captain Kettle K. C. B. NY, (1903). 1st Amer ed. Color paste plt port. VG. *Mcclintock*. $35/£22

Hyperion. (By Henry Wadsworth Longfellow.) NY, 1839. 1st ed. 2 vols. Pub's cl-backed bds (needs rebinding). *Swann**. $103/£64

HYSLOP, T. B. Mental Handicaps in Golf. Balt: Williams & Elkins, 1927. 1st Amer ed. Dec grn cl, gilt. Fine (bkpl). *Pacific**. $81/£51

I

IBARGUENGOITIA, JORGE. Two Crimes. London: C&W, 1984. 1st British ed. Fine in dj. *Lame Duck*. $35/£22

IBN KHALLIKAN. Ibn Khallikan's Biographical Dictionary. Vols 2-4 only. Bn Mac Guckin de Slane (trans). Oriental Translation Fund of Great Britain & Ireland, 1843, 1868, 1871. 1/4 morocco (very worn). Internally VG (sl foxed). *Worldwide*. $200/£125

IBSEN, HENRIK. Brand: A Dramatic Poem. William Wilson (trans). Methuen, 1891. Pub's cat dated October 1892. Good (fore-edge lt spotted, sig; spine bumped, sl sunned). *Tiger*. $32/£20

IBSEN, HENRIK. Speeches and New Letters. Arne Kildal (trans). Frank Palmer, 1911. 1st ed. Frontis port. VG. *Cox*. $16/£10

IBSEN, HENRIK. Three Plays of Henrik Ibsen. LEC, 1964. Ltd to 1500 numbered, signed by Frederik Matheson (illus). Fine in slipcase. *Swann**. $80/£50

IBSEN, HENRIK. The Works of.... NY: Scribner, 1911-1912. 13 vols complete. Teg; uncut, partly unopened. Brn cl, gilt. VG (1 spine top snagged). *Houle*. $475/£297

ICAZA, JORGE. The Villagers. Carbondale, IL: Southern IL Univ, 1964. 1st authorized ed in English. NF in dj (spine faded). *Lame Duck*. $50/£31

Idaho. NY: OUP, 1950. Rev ed. VG in dj (edges chipped, worn). *Labordo*. $25/£16

IDDINGS, JOSEPH PAXSON. Rock Minerals, Their Chemical and Physical Characters and Their Determination in Thin Sections. NY: John Wiley, 1911. 2nd ed, 1st thousand. Fldg table, fldg color diag. Navy blue cl. NF. *Weber*. $50/£31

Ideal Fairy Tales. NY: McLoughlin Bros, 1897. Lg 4to. 16 full-pg chromolithos. Cl-backed color pict bds (edges rubbed, worn; text w/fingermks, dusty, worn). *Reisler*. $485/£303

Igloo Life: a Brief Account of a Primitive Arctic Tribe Living Near One of the Most Northern Trading Posts of Revillon Freres. (By Robert Flaherty.) NY: Privately ptd, 1923. 1st ed. Robert Flaherty (photos). (Short break to fr joint), else VG in illus bds. *Cahan*. $85/£53

IGO, JOHN. Los Pastores; An Annotated Bibliography with an Introduction. San Antonio, 1967. Fine in wraps. *Dumont*. $20/£13

IKBAL ALI SHAH, SIRDAR. The Golden East. London: Long, 1931. 1st ed. 32 plts. (Ex-lib, fep clipped; sl rubbed, soiled, lib spine #), o/w VG. *Worldwide*. $25/£16

ILLINGWORTH, CHARLES. The Story of William Hunter. London, 1967. Color frontis. *Edwards*. $32/£20

ILLINGWORTH, FRANK. Highway to the North. NY: Philosophical Library, (1955). VG in dj. *Perier*. $30/£19

Illinois at Shiloh. (Chicago: Ptd by M.A. Donohue, 1905?). 1st ed. 2 fldg maps in pocket, 12 plts. Ptd compliments slip laid in. (Cl sl soiled), o/w Fine. *Pirages*. $150/£94

Illuminated Bible, Containing the Old and New Testaments. NY: Harper, 1846. Frontis, extra pict tp. Contemp (pub's?) black morocco (rubbed, loose in casing, inner joints tape-strengthened, sl foxed, soiled), gilt. *Oinonen**. $110/£69

Illustrated Catalogue of the Complete Library of the Late Alfred Austin, Poet Laureate...Catalogue No. 44. Henry Sotheran, (c. 1915). *Forest*. $32/£20

Illustrated History of Plumas, Lassen and Sierra Counties, with California from 1513 to 1850. SF: Fariss & Smith, 1882. 10 7/8x7 5/8 inches. 507pp; map, 54 litho, 4 engr plts, 29 ports. (Repaired tears to margins of 1 plt, 1 leaf; foxed, spotted; rebacked, bds rubbed; edges, tips worn.) *Dawson*. $500/£313

Illustrations of British Hawk Moths, and Their Larvae. (By Theophilus Johnson.) (London), 1874. 8vo. 36 full-pg watercolor dwgs; ptd tp, 2pp index, 44pp text (numbered [3]-46). Teg, rest uncut. Olive morocco, gilt, by Tout. (Sl spotted.) *Sotheby's**. $6,440/£4,025

Illustrations of the History and Practices of the Thugs. And Notices of Some of the Proceedings of the Government of India, for the Suppression of the Crime of Thuggee. (By Edward Thornton.) London: Wm. H. Allen, 1837. 1st ed. (iv),475pp (tp margin blind-stamped). Contemp grn 1/2 calf (neatly rebacked), red morocco label, vellum corners. *Young*. $240/£150

Illustrations of the Landscape and Coast Scenery of Ireland. Dublin: William Frederick Wakeman, 1843. 4to. 24 Fine hand-colored acquatints after drawings by George Petrie et al. Plts dated 1835. Aeg. 3/4 19th-cent brn morocco, gilt paneled spine, raised bands. Fine. *Appelfeld*. $3,500/£2,188

Illustrious Men of the United States. Boston: J. Buffum, 1856. Sq 12mo. Full-pg wood engr frontis, 96pp; 30 full-pg engr ports. Aeg. Red cl on bds, gilt, blind dec. VG (2 pencil dedications fep; sm hole spine fold). *Hobbyhorse*. $100/£63

IMBER, SAMUEL J. Modern Yiddish Poetry: An Anthology. NY: East & West Pub, 1927. 1st ed. One of 850. Red cl, gilt. NF. *Pacific**. $40/£25

Impartial History of the War in America.... (By Edmund Burke?) London: R. Faulder & J. Milliken, 1780. 1st ed. Thick 8vo. xi,608,44pp; lg fldg copperplt map, 11 (of 12 or 13) copperplt ports. Contemp calf (rebacked in matching calf), orig crimson leather spine label laid down. (New blanks at fr/rear, lt browning, offsetting, map sl foxed, few sm edgetears, plts sl aged; sl scuffed, worn.) Text VG. Both Sabin and Howes call for 13 plts, although Sabin lists only 12; this vol lacks the port of Samuel Adams and one other (?) approx 16 1/2 x 21 1/4 inches. Howes B975. *Baltimore**. $975/£609

In Memoriam. (By Alfred Tennyson.) London: Edward Moxon, 1850. 1st ed, 1st issue w/misprints on pp2, 198, and w/o inserted ads dated February 1850. Half-title, (viii),210pp. Grn crushed morocco (recently rebound), raised bands, gilt. Fine in morocco-edged slipcase. Sig of first Lord Monteagle. *Young*. $480/£300

INCHBALD, MRS. A Simple Story. William Walker, 1846. Rpt. Frontis. Orig cl (spine bumped, chipped, badly rubbed). Good (grease mk fr cvr, 1st few ll). *Tiger*. $32/£20

INCHBALD, MRS. (ed). Collection of Farces and Afterpieces. Longman, Hurst, Rees, & Orme, 1809. 7 vols. Contemp 1/2 leather, marbled bds. Good (sl spotted; spines chipped, rubbed, lacks several spine labels, corners rubbed, hinges cracked but cords sound). *Tiger*. $112/£70

India House. A Descriptive Catalogue of the Marine Collection to Be Found at India House. Middletown, 1973. One of 1250. (Lt worn.) Slipcase. *Oinonen**. $70/£44

Indian Basket Weaving. L.A.: Whedon & Spreng, 1903. 6 related full-pg and fldg plts laid in (chipped); tipped-in price list at center. Woven flaxen wraps stamped in red (frayed, lettering partly worn). *Baltimore**. $160/£100

Indian Basket Weaving. L.A.: Whedon & Spring, 1903. Stiff burlap wraps (sl faded). Internally Good. *Dumont*. $225/£141

Indian Notes. Volumes 1-4. NY: Museum of the American Indian, Heye Foundation, Jan 1924-Oct 1927. 4 vols. Untrimmed. Orig plain tan buckram, leather spine labels. (Orig wraps bound in; cvrs dust-soiled, sl worn.) Texts Good. *Baltimore**. $110/£69

Indian Zoology. (By Thomas Pennant.) London: Hughs for Faulder, 1790. 2nd ed. Engr tp; 16 engr plts. (Foxing.) Old 3/4 calf (shelfworn, sl stained, soiled), mod calf back. *Oinonen**. $225/£141

Infant's Battledore. Castle Cary: S. Moore, n.d. (ca 1830). 12mo. 2pp + 1 flap. Pink dec cvr. (Lt fading along folds.) *Hobbyhorse*. $175/£109

INFANTE, G. CABRERA. See CABRERA INFANTE, G.

Infantry Exercise of the United States Army. Montpelier, VT, 1820. 3rd ed. 107pp; 9 engr plts. Contemp calf (rubbed; foxed, browned). *Oinonen**. $100/£63

INGALLS, RACHEL. Mrs. Caliban. London: F&F, (1982). 1st ed. Fine in dj. *Agvent*. $125/£78

INGALLS, RAYMOND G. Tumors of the Orbit and Allied Pseudo Tumors. Springfield, IL: Charles C. Thomas, (1953). Fine. *Weber*. $95/£59

INGE, WILLIAM. The Dark at the Top of the Stairs. NY: Random House, 1958. 1st ed. (Bkpl, sm sticker), else VG + in VG dj. *Pettler*. $25/£16

INGE, WILLIAM. A Loss of Roses. NY: Random House, (1960). 1st ed. VF in VF dj. *Between The Covers*. $250/£156

INGE, WILLIAM. Natural Affection. NY: Random House, (1963). 1st ed. VF in VF dj. *Between The Covers.* $200/£125

INGE, WILLIAM. Picnic. NY: Random House, (1953). 1st trade ed. Frontis. Fine in dj (sl tanned, few corner smudges). *Reese.* $85/£53

INGE, WILLIAM. Summer Brave and Eleven Short Plays. NY: Random House, (1962). 1st ed. VF in VF dj (sl soiled). *Between The Covers.* $200/£125

INGE, WILLIAM. Where's Daddy? NY: Random House, (1966). 1st ed. VF in Fine dj (sl rubbed). *Between The Covers.* $250/£156

INGELOW, JEAN. A Story of Doom and Other Poems. Longmans, Green, 1867. 1st ed. Half-title, (vi),296,(2)pp. Pale cream eps (browned). Grn cl, gilt. Good (lt foxed; joints, spine ends rubbed, sm split center of lower joint). *Blackwell's.* $48/£30

INGERSOLL, CHARLES JARED. Inchiquin, the Jesuits Letters, During a Late Residence in the United States of America. NY: I. Riley, 1810. 1st ed. v,165pp. Orig bds, paper spine label. (Spine worn, chipped, lacks portions), else Good. *Brown.* $35/£22

INGERSOLL, ERNEST. The Crest of the Continent. Chicago: R.R. Donnelley & Sons, 1888. 344pp. Dec grn cl, gilt. VG. *House.* $30/£19

INGHOLT, HARALD. Gandharan Art in Pakistan. (NY, 1957.) Dj. *Swann*.* $230/£144

INGLIS, ALEX. Northern Vagabond. Toronto: McClelland & Stewart, 1978. 1st ed. Map. VG in dj. *Walcot.* $22/£14

INGLIS, JAMES. Tent Life in Tigerland. London, 1892. Frontis (margins sl foxed); 22 color chromo-litho plts. Pict cl (joints sl loose). *Petersfield.* $224/£140

INGOLDSBY, THOMAS. (Pseud of Richard Harris Barham.) The Ingoldsby Legends. London, 1863. George Cruikshank, John Leech & John Tenniel (illus). Mod 1/2 polished crimson calf. Slipcase. *Swann*.* $230/£144

INGOLDSBY, THOMAS. (Pseud of Richard Harris Barham.) The Ingoldsby Legends. London: Richard Bentley, 1870. 2 vols. 8.5x5.25. Cruikshank et al (illus). Red cl, gilt. VG. *Pacific*.* $98/£61

INGOLDSBY, THOMAS. (Pseud of Richard Harris Barham.) The Ingoldsby Legends. London: J.M. Dent, 1898. 1st Rackham ed. 12 tinted plts by Arthur Rackham. Teg. 3/4 blue morocco over marbled bds, gilt paneled spine, raised bands. Fine. *Appelfeld.* $200/£125

INGOLDSBY, THOMAS. (Pseud of Richard Harris Barham.) The Ingoldsby Legends. London: J.M. Dent, 1907. 1st enlgd ed illus by Arthur Rackham. 4to. xix,549pp; 24 mtd full color plts, guards, 12 tinted plts. Teg, rest uncut. Grn cl, gilt. VG (sl rubbed, deckled edges sl speckled). *Sotheran.* $240/£150

INGOLDSBY, THOMAS. (Pseud of Richard Harris Barham.) The Ingoldsby Legends. London: J.M. Dent, 1907. Ltd to 560 signed. Thick, lg 4to. Arthur Rackham (illus). 24 mtd color plts, 12 full-pg tinted illus, 66 b/w dwgs. Teg. Full vellum, gilt. (Replaced ties.) Cl slipcase. *Reisler.* $1,250/£781

INGOLDSBY, THOMAS. (Pseud of Richard Harris Barham.) The Ingoldsby Legends. London: Macmillan, n.d. Complete Lib ed. 4 vols. Teg, rest uncut. (Ex-lib.) *Edwards.* $120/£75

INGRAHAM, CORINNE. The Wishing Fairy's Animal Friends. NY: Brantano's, (1921). 1st ed. 4to. 141pp; 8 full-pg color plts by Dugald Stewart Walker. Lt orange cl, color paste label. Color pict dj (lower edge sl chipped, fold in rear cvr). *Reisler.* $375/£234

INGRAHAM, JOSEPH. Journal of the Brigantine Hope on a Voyage to the Northwest Coast of North America, 1790-92. Mark D. Kaplanoff (ed). Barre, MA: Imprint Soc, 1971. One of 1950 ptd. 1/2 cl, paper spine label. Fine (lacks slipcase). *Pacific*.* $52/£33

INGRAM, JAMES. Memorials of Oxford. Oxford, 1837. 3 vols. Contemp straight-grained black morocco (rubbed, spines sl dried). Internally Sound. *Oinonen*.* $350/£219

INGRAM, JAMES. Memorials of Oxford. Oxford: John Henry Parker, 1837. 3 vols. 98 steel-engr plts, fldg engr plan. Gilt edges. Contemp pub's 1/2 morocco. (Sl spotting.) *Sotheby's*.* $552/£345

Ingres Centennial Exhibition 1867-1967. Cambridge: Fogg Art Museum, Harvard Univ, 1967. Good+ in dj. *Washton.* $90/£56

INGSTAD, HELGE. Land Under the Pole Star. London: Cape, 1966. VG in dj. *Explorer.* $29/£18

INGSTAD, HELGE. Nunamuit. London: Geo. Allen & Unwin, 1954. Color frontis, fldg map. VG in dj. *High Latitude.* $25/£16

Inheritance. (By Susan Ferrier.) Edinburgh, 1824. 1st ed. 3 vols w/half-titles. Early 1/2 calf. VF set. *Argosy.* $250/£156

INMAN, HENRY (comp.) Buffalo Jones' Forty Years of Adventures: A Volume of Facts Gathered from Experience, by Hon. C. J. Jones.... Topeka, KS: Crane, 1899. 1st ed. Inscribed, signed presentation by Jones. xii,469pp. Pict cl, gilt. (Fr hinge cracked; rubbed, soiled), else Good+. Howes I54. *Pacific*.* $63/£39

INMAN, HENRY. The Great Salt Lake Trail. NY, 1898. 1st ed. 13,529pp; port, 7 plts. (Cvr faded.) *Heinoldt.* $75/£47

INMAN, HENRY. The Old Santa Fe Trail. NY, 1897. 2nd ptg. Frederic Remington (illus). Frontisport (sm piece of paper stuck on lower portion), 493pp,index+3pp ads. Letter from author dated 1898 mtd in side fr cvr. (Foxed.) Howes I57. *Woolson.* $125/£78

INMAN, HENRY. The Old Santa Fe Trail. Topeka: Crane, 1916. Fldg map. Clean. Howes I57. *Dumont.* $85/£53

INMAN, HENRY. Tales of the Trail: Short Stories of Western Life. Topeka: Crane, 1898. 1st ed. viii,280pp. Edges stained yellow. Pict cl, gilt. (Bold sig, sl affecting imprint, offset to facing blank leaf; top pg edges overzealously stained yellow, few sl stains intruding to upper margins; spine sl sunned), else VG+. Howes I58. *Pacific*.* $173/£108

INN, HENRY. Chinese Houses and Gardens. NY: Bonanza, 1950. 2nd ed. Dec cl. NF in pict dj. *Quest.* $90/£56

INN, HENRY. Chinese Houses and Gardens. S.C. Lee (ed). NY, (1950). 1st Amer ed. Fine (lt rubbed) in dj (lg pieces missing). *Polyanthos.* $60/£38

INNES, GEORGE. The Works of George Innes...An Illustrated Catalogue Raisonne. LeRoy Ireland (comp). Austin, (1965). Color frontis. Dj. *Swann*.* $460/£288

INNES, HAMMOND. The Last Voyage, Captain Cook's Lost Diary. NY, (1978). 1st Amer ed. VG+ in VG+ dj. *Pratt.* $20/£13

International Competition for a New Administration Building for the Chicago Tribune MCMXXII.... (Chicago, 1923). Sm folio. 282 plts. Coarse cl (rebacked retaining orig backstrip). *Swann*.* $345/£216

International Sport: The Anglo-American Equestrian World. London, (1956-57). One of 250 numbered. Folio. Photogravure frontis, 72 ports. Red leather, gilt. (Joints cracked.) *Swann*.* $161/£101

Invert and His Social Adjustment. Balt: Williams & Wilkins, n.d. (ca 1929). (Extrems sl worn), else VG. *Brown.* $25/£16

IONESCO, EUGENE. Journeys Among the Dead. LEC, 1987. One of 1000 signed. Fine in slipcase. *Swann*.* $149/£93

IPCAR, DAHLOV. Sir Addlepate and the Unicorn. Doubleday, 1971. 1st ed. 9x11. Unpaginated. Fine in VG dj (spine sl worn, repaired). *Price.* $35/£22

IREDALE, TOM. Birds of New Guinea. Melbourne, 1956. 2 vols. 35 color plts; fldg map. Morocco-backed cl. (Bkpl, eps sl tapestained.) *Edwards.* $560/£350

IRELAND, ALLEYNE. The New Korea. NY: Dutton, 1926. 1st ed. Fldg map. Tipped in presentation label. (Bkpl; sl rubbed, soiled), o/w VG. *Worldwide.* $50/£31

IRELAND, LEROY. The Works of George Inness: An Illustrated Catalogue Raisonne. Austin, (1965). Sm folio. Dj (chipped, worn). *Swann*.* $747/£467

IRELAND, WILLIAM W. The Blot upon the Brain: Studies in History and Psychology. Edinburgh: Bell & Bradfute, 1885. 1st ed. VG + (bkpls, plt traces on eps). *Beasley.* $125/£78

IRIMIE, CORNEL and MARCELA FOSCA. Romanian Icons Painted on Glass. NY, 1970. 1st Amer ed. 149 color plts. Fine in dj. *Argosy.* $85/£53

Irish Fairy Tales, Folklore and Legends. London: Gibbings, 1904. 1st ed. Geoffrey Strahan (illus). 8vo. Grn cl, gilt. Nice (eps browned; sl rubbed). *Glenn.* $110/£69

Irish Portraits 1660-1860. Dublin: Nat'l Gallery of Ireland, 1969. Good in wrappers. *Washton.* $30/£19

IRISH, WILLIAM. (Pseud of Cornell Woolrich.) The Dancing Detective. Hutchinson, (1948). 1st UK ed. VG + in VG dj (sl dusty, sl worn w/sl loss along top edge). *Williams.* $58/£36

IRVINE, KEITH. The Rise of the Colored Races. NY: W.W. Norton, (1970). 1st ed. VG in illus dj. *Petrilla.* $35/£22

IRVING, HELEN (ed). The Ladies' Wreath: An Illustrated Annual. NY: J.C. Burdick, (c. 1840s). 1st ed. Aeg. Orig dec cl, gilt. VG. *Pacific*.* $63/£39

IRVING, JOHN. The Hotel New Hampshire. NY, (1981). 1st ed. Signed. Dj. *Swann*.* $69/£43

IRVING, JOHN. The Hotel New Hampshire. NY: Dutton, (1981). 1st ed. Signed. Fine in Fine dj. *Lenz.* $85/£53

IRVING, JOHN. The Pension Grillparzer. Logan, IA: Perfection Form, 1980. 1st ed. NF- in illus stapled wraps. *Lame Duck.* $150/£94

IRVING, JOHN. A Prayer for Owen Meany. NY: Morrow, (1989). 1st ed. Signed presentation. Fine in dj. *Antic Hay.* $85/£53

IRVING, JOHN. A Prayer for Owen Meany. NY: William Morrow, (1989). One of 250. Signed. Brn/gray cl, gilt. Fine in slipcase. *Pacific*.* $127/£79

IRVING, JOHN. Setting Free the Bears. NY: Random House, (1968). 1st ed, 1st bk. Signed. Fine in Fine dj. *Lenz.* $850/£531

IRVING, JOHN. The Water Method Man. NY, (1972). 1st ed. Signed. Nice in white dj (sl soiled). *Swann*.* $161/£101

IRVING, JOHN. The World According to Garp. NY: Dutton, (1978). 1st ed. (Rep cut irregularly, few sm nicks), else NF in NF dj (sm tear). *Between The Covers.* $150/£94

IRVING, JOHN. The World According to Garp. NY: Dutton, (1978). 1st ed. Signed. Fine in Fine dj. *Lenz.* $175/£109

IRVING, JOHN. The World According to Garp. Gollancz, 1978. 1st UK ed. Fine in dj. *Any Amount.* $32/£20

IRVING, LAWRENCE. A Selection of the Principal Voyages, Traffiques and Discoveries of the English Nation by Richard Hakluyt 1152-1616. Heinemann, 1926. 1st ed of this selected ed. 10 sepia illus tipped in. Dk blue cl, gilt. VG. *Sotheran.* $192/£120

IRVING, WASHINGTON. Abu Hassan and the Wild Huntsman. Boston: The Bibliophile Soc, 1924. 1st eds. Ltd to 455. 2 vols. Teg. Vellum-backed bds. VG in pub's slipcase (sl stained). *King.* $125/£78

IRVING, WASHINGTON. The Adventures of Captain Bonneville. Edgeley Todd (ed). Norman: Univ of OK, 1961. 1st ed thus. Fine in dj. Howes I85. *Labordo.* $65/£41

IRVING, WASHINGTON. The Alhambra. NY: Putnam, 1892. Author's rev ed. 2 vols. xii,266; vi,312pp; 31 photogravure plts. Teg. Dec cl. Good in blue linen djs. *Karmiole.* $85/£53

IRVING, WASHINGTON. The Alhambra. (Mount Vernon): LEC, 1969. One of 1500 ptd. Signed by Lima de Freitas (illus). Full brocade cl, morocco spine label. Fine in glassine. *Pacific*.* $29/£18

IRVING, WASHINGTON. The Angler. N.p.: A.S.W. Rosenbach, Dec 1931. One of 150, this copy not numbered. Uncut. Paper cvr label. (Cvrs scuffed, spine head chipped.) *Oinonen*.* $90/£56

IRVING, WASHINGTON. Astoria, or Anecdotes of an Enterprise Beyond the Rocky Mountains. Norman: Univ of OK, 1964. 1st ed thus. Fine in dj. Howes I81. *Labordo.* $65/£41

IRVING, WASHINGTON. A History of the Life and Voyages of Christopher Columbus. John Murray, 1828. 1st UK ed. 4 vols. xii,473; (6),490; viii,413; vii,489pp; 2 lg fldg maps. Marbled edges. VG set (ex-libris) in contemp 1/2 calf, marbled sides, dbl morocco labels, gilt. *Cox.* $288/£180

IRVING, WASHINGTON. A History of the Life and Voyages of Christopher Columbus. John Murray, 1828. 1st Eng ed. 4 vols. 8vo. 4 fldg maps (lt foxed). All edges marbled. Later 1/4 calf, raised bands, maroon labels, gilt, terracotta cl. VG set (sm newspaper cutting tipped on fep vol 1). *Sotheran.* $557/£348

IRVING, WASHINGTON. The Legend of Sleepy Hollow. Phila: David McKay, (1928). 4to. 8 full-pg color plts by Arthur Rackham. Teg. Brn cl w/full color paste label of The Headless Horseman and book title. Good in dj (wear, staining, some of which has transferred to spine cl). *Reisler.* $165/£103

IRVING, WASHINGTON. The Legend of Sleepy Hollow. London: George G. Harrap, 1928. 1st ed illus thus. 4to. Arthur Rackham (illus). (iv),5-102pp; 8 color plts. Pict eps; teg, untrimmed. Dk grn cl, gilt. NF. *Sotheran.* $317/£198

IRVING, WASHINGTON. Legends of the Alhambra. Phila: Lippincott, 1909. 1st ed thus. 7 color plts by George Hood. Blue cl w/picture paste-on. VG (rear hinge broken, shelfworn). *My Bookhouse.* $52/£33

IRVING, WASHINGTON. The Life and Voyages of Christopher Columbus. Boston, 1839. 1st Amer ed. Port, map. NF (lt foxed, sl soiled, rubbed; spine tear professionally mended). *Polyanthos.* $75/£47

IRVING, WASHINGTON. The Life and Voyages of Christopher Columbus.... NY: Putnam, 1892. Author's rev ed. Ltd to 402 sets. 3 vols. Color frontis pieces, xviii,400; xii,462; xiv,426pp (inner margins sl wormed); 5 etchings, 12 steel engrs, 13 photogravures, 43 mtd plts. Vellum-like bds (lt soiled), gilt. *Karmiole.* $250/£156

IRVING, WASHINGTON. Life of George Washington. NY, 1855-59. 1st issues. 5 vols. Frontisports. NF (few prelims sl foxed). *Polyanthos.* $200/£125

IRVING, WASHINGTON. The Life of Oliver Goldsmith, with Selections from His Writings. NY: Harper, 1840. 1st ed. 2 vols. Orig ptd tan muslin. (Foxed, mostly eps; vol 1 rebacked w/parts of orig backstrip laid down, dust soiled), o/w VG set in cl wrappers, 1/2 morocco fldg case (fr joint rubbed). BAL 10156. *Reese.* $150/£94

IRVING, WASHINGTON. Rip Van Winkle. London: George G. Harrap, (ca 1925). 1st UK ed(?). Royal 8vo. (x),84pp; 8 Fine color plts by N. C. Wyeth. Pict eps. Brn cl w/lg pict plt to fr cvr, gilt. NF in Very Clean matching pict wrapper (triangular tear to upper edge of fr wrap, sl loss, neatly repaired). *Sotheran.* $237/£148

IRVING, WASHINGTON. Rip Van Winkle. London: Heinemann, 1905. Ltd to 250 signed by Arthur Rackham (illus). 4to. 51 mtd color plts on brn paper. Teg. Orig pict vellum (sm stain fr cvr, lacks ties), gilt. *Christie's*.* $1,565/£978

IRVING, WASHINGTON. Rip Van Winkle. Heinemann, 1908. 1st Arthur Rackham illus ed. 51 tipped-in color plts. Pict cl, gilt. VG (1 plt sl creased). *Ash.* $120/£75

IRVING, WASHINGTON. Rip Van Winkle. LEC, 1930. Ltd to 1500 numbered, signed by Frederic W. Goudy (designer). Fine in slipcase. *Swann*.* $92/£58

IRVING, WASHINGTON. Three Choice Sketches by Geoffrey Crayon, Gent. San Mateo: Greenwood Press, 1941. One of 250. Buckram, paper spine label. Dj. *Dawson.* $75/£47

IRVING, WASHINGTON. A Tour on the Prairies. Phila: Carey, Lea, & Blanchard, 1835. 1st Amer ed. 274pp + 12pp ads. Orig bds (edgeworn, spotted; hinges reinforced), else Good. Howes I86. *Dumont.* $200/£125

IRVING, WASHINGTON. A Tour on the Prairies. John Francis McDermott (ed). Norman: Univ of OK, (1956). 1st ptg. *Mott.* $20/£13

IRVING, WASHINGTON. The Western Journals of.... John Francis McDermott (ed). Norman, 1944. 1st ed. Fldg map. (Bkpl, inscrip.) Internally Good in dj (sl worn). *Dumont.* $45/£28

IRVING, WASHINGTON. Works. NY: Putnam, (ca 1900). 10 vols. Teg. 1/2 red morocco, gilt. (Lt worn, few joints rubbed.) *Swann*.* $345/£216

IRVING, WASHINGTON. The Writings of.... NY: Putnam, 1895-96. Author's Autograph ed. 28 vols. Teg. 3/4 brn morocco, marbled bds, gilt, raised bands. (Bkpls, old names, lacks ms leaf; 1 joint cracked, taped, 1 hinge cracked), else VG set. *Pacific*.* $184/£115

IRWIN, DAVID. John Flaxman 1755-1826. London: Studio Vista/Christie's, 1979. NF in dj. *Turtle Island.* $60/£38

IRWIN, EYLES. A Series of Adventures in the Course of a Voyage Up the Red-Sea, on the Coasts of Arabia and Egypt. London, 1780. 1st ed, w/the half-title. 6 engr maps and plts. Mod lib buckram. (Ink lib stamps.) *Swann*.* $402/£251

IRWIN, R. British Bird Books—An Index to British Ornithology (1481-1948). Grafton, 1951. Good in dj. *Moss.* $72/£45

IRWIN, WALLACE. A Bird Cage. NY: B.W. Dodge, 1908. 1st ed. 11x8. Edna Morse (illus). Pict cl. VG. *Pacific*.* $69/£43

ISAACS, A. C. An Ascent of Mount Shasta: 1856. L.A.: Glen Dawson, 1952. 1st bk ed. One of 250 ptd. Cl-backed dec bds. (Spine sl dknd), else Fine. *Argonaut.* $75/£47

ISAACS, EDITH. The Negro in the American Theatre. NY: Theatre Arts, 1947. 1st ed. (Pencil marginalia; cvr edges stained, worn, sl dampened.) *Dramatis.* $35/£22

ISABELLE, JULANNE. Hemingway's Religious Experience. NY: Chip's Bookshop, 1964. 1st Amer ed. Fine (sl bumped). *Polyanthos.* $35/£22

ISEMONGER, R. M. Snakes of Africa. NY: Nelson, 1962. 1st ed. Pict bds. Fine in NF dj. *Mikesh.* $60/£38

ISHERWOOD, CHRISTOPHER. The Berlin Stories. (NY): New Directions, (1945). 1st Amer ed. VG in dj (spine ends rubbed). *Pacific*.* $63/£39

ISHERWOOD, CHRISTOPHER. Christopher and His Kind. Hollywood: Sylvester & Orphanos, 1976. Ltd to 130 signed by Isherwood & Don Bachardy (frontis, eps). Frontis. Raw Indian silk. *Truepenny.* $500/£313

ISHERWOOD, CHRISTOPHER. Lions and Shadows. Hogarth, 1938. 1st ed. 1st binding: blue cl lettered in black. Dj (sl worn, frayed). *Sotheby's*.* $202/£126

ISHERWOOD, CHRISTOPHER. A Meeting by the River. NY: S&S, (1967). 1st Amer ed. VF in VF dj (ink mk rear cvr). *Between The Covers.* $75/£47

ISHERWOOD, CHRISTOPHER. The Memorial. Hogarth, 1932. One of 1222. 1st binding of pink linen lettered in blue. VG (bkpl; top edge faded, bottom edge sl spotted, edges sl browned, spine ends, corner sl bumped) in dj (nicked, chipped, rubbed, mkd, sl torn, frayed, creased, spine, edges browned). *Ulysses.* $760/£475

ISHERWOOD, CHRISTOPHER. Sally Bowles. Hogarth, 1937. 1st ed. Signed. 8vo. Blue cl. Dj. *Sotheby's*.* $2,392/£1,495

ISHERWOOD, CHRISTOPHER. A Single Man. NY, 1964. 1st ed. VG in dj (sl spotted, discolored). *King.* $25/£16

ISHIZAWA, MASAO et al. The Heritage of Japanese Art. Tokyo/NY/SF: Kodansha Internat'l, 1982. 1st ed. Folio. 164 color plts, map. NF in dj. *Worldwide.* $65/£41

ISYS, COTSWOLD. An Angler's Strange Experiences, a Whimsical Medley, and an Of-Fish-All Record Without A-Bridge-Ment. London: Sampson Low et al, 1883. 1st ed. Gilt-lettered pict cl. (Soiling), else VG. *Pacific*.* $92/£58

ISYS, COTSWOLD. Lyra Piscatoria. London: Horace Cox, 1895. 1st ed. Gilt-lettered grn cl. (Fr hinge starting), else Fine. *Pacific*.* $40/£25

Itinerant Observations in America. Savannah: Estill, 1878. Rpt. 64pp. Unopened. Ptd wraps (dknd, spine ends splitting). Howes K142. *Bohling.* $45/£28

ITOH, TEIJI et al. The Japanese Garden, an Approach to Nature. New Haven, CT: Yale Univ, 1972. 1st ed. Fine in dj. *Fair Meadow.* $35/£22

ITOH, TEIJI. Kura: Design and Tradition of the Japanese Storehouse. Tokyo, (1973). Folio. Dj (price-clipped). *Swann*.* $103/£64

Ivanhoe, a Romance, with the Author's Last Notes and Additions. (By Walter Scott.) Paris: Baudry's European Library, 1842. 1st ed thus. xxiv,390 + (2) ads. Contemp French 1/4 calf (1-inch crack to top of fr joint). *Young.* $72/£45

IVES, EDWARD. A Voyage from England to India, in the Year MDCCLIV, and an Historical Narrative. London, 1773. Lib buckram. (Ink lib stamps throughout.) *Swann*.* $402/£251

IVES, JOSEPH C. Report upon the Colorado River of the West. Washington: GPO, 1861. 32 (of 38?) plts, maps (8 color). (Few maps w/tears repaired; lt stained, stamps on tp.) Mod brn 1/2 morocco, gilt spine. *Sotheby's*.* $405/£253

IVES, MARGUERITE. Seventeen Famous Outdoorsmen Known to Marguerite Ives. Chicago: Canterbury Press, 1929. 1st ed. One of 500. Signed. Gilt-lettered grn cl. (Sl insect damage fr cvr), else NF. *Pacific*.* $92/£58

IVIMEY, JOHN W. Complete Version of Ye Three Blind Mice. London: Frederick Warne, (1904). 1st ed. Obl 8vo. (16)pp; 16 full color plts, vignettes, by Walton Corbould. Pict eps. Gray paper-cvrd bds w/onlaid pict label. VG (sl creased, thumbed; sm split to spine head). *Sotheran.* $141/£88

IVINS, WILLIAM M. The Artist and the Fifteenth Century Printer. Valenti Angelo, 1940. One of 300. *Dawson.* $25/£16

IVY, ROBERT H. and LAWRENCE CURTIS. Fractures of the Jaws. Phila: Lea & Febiger, (1945). 3rd ed. VG in grn cl. *Weber.* $100/£63

IVY, ROBERT H. and LAWRENCE CURTIS. Fractures of the Jaws. Phila: Lea & Febiger, 1931. 1st ed. NF in maroon cl. *Weber.* $350/£219

IVY, ROBERT H. A Link with the Past. Balt: Williams & Wilkins, 1962. Frontis. Fine. *Weber.* $75/£47

J

JACBERNS, RAYMOND. Tabitha Smallways Schoolgirl. Chambers, 1912. 1st ed. 8vo. 304pp; 6 color plts by Mabel Lucy Attwell. Turquoise cl, gilt. (Inscrips, bkpls mtd on frontis verso, sl cockled; sl dampstain to lower margin edges, faded, lt rubbed, fingermks.) *Bookmark.* $80/£50

JACHNA, JOSEPH D. Light Touching Silver. Chicago: Center for Contemp Photography, 1980. 1st ed. One of 2500. 45 full-pg b/w photos. (Edge-sunned, stamp), else NF in ptd stiff wrappers. *Cahan.* $45/£28

Jack and the Beanstalk. An All-Action Treasure Hour Pop-Up Book. London: Murray's Children's Books, 1978. 6 dbl-pg pop-ups by V. Kubasta. Glazed pict bds. VG. *Bookfinders*. $45/£28

Jack and the Giants. London: Griffith & Farran, 1858. 2nd, New ed. Sm 4to. (viii),56pp; 31 engrs by Richard Doyle, incl frontis, tp spread. Dk blue cl, gilt. VG (lt thumbed, handled; sl mkd, dknd, gilt dull). *Sotheran*. $237/£148

Jack the Giant Killer. NY: Blue Ribbon Books, (1932). 4to. 96pp; 3 pop-ups, 1 dbl-pg pop-up by Harold Lentz. Pict bds. VG (lt stain 3pp). *Davidson*. $600/£375

JACKS, L. P. All Men Are Ghosts. Williams & Norgate, 1913. 1st ed. VG (feps lt browned; top edge sl dusty, spine ends, corners sl bumped, spine, edges sl faded, spine gilt oxidised) in dj (nicked, rubbed, sl chipped, inside, spine, edges browned). *Ulysses*. $248/£155

JACKSON, A. V. WILLIAMS. History of India. London: Grolier Soc, 1906-7. One of 200 sets. 9 vols. Color frontis each vol. 1/2 morocco (few sm spine chips), gilt. *Adelson*. $375/£234

JACKSON, A. Y. The Arctic 1927. Ontario: Penumbra, 1982. Mint in slipcase. *Explorer*. $42/£26

JACKSON, BASIL H. (ed). Recollections of Thomas Graham Jackson 1835-1924. OUP, 1950. NF in dj. *Hadley*. $35/£22

JACKSON, C. Second Annual Report on the Geology of the Public Lands.... Augusta: Luther Severance, 1838. xi,100pp,xxxvii. Good (new spine strip). *Blake*. $100/£63

JACKSON, CHARLES JAMES. An Illustrated History of English Plate, Ecclesiastical and Secular. Country Life/Batsford, 1911. 2 vols. Folio. Color frontis, 76 photogravure plts. Teg. Contemp 1/2 morocco. (Lt spotted.) *Sotheby's**. $405/£253

JACKSON, CHARLES T. Third Annual Report on the Geology of the State of Maine. Augusta: Smith & Robinson, 1839. 1st ed. 276pp + (64)pp cat, (1)pg errata. VG (blank fep lacks corner) in ptd wrappers (spine chipped). *Lucas*. $95/£59

JACKSON, CHARLES. English Goldsmiths and Their Marks. Macmillan, 1921. 2nd ed. Beveled bds (hinges split at heads). *Hollett*. $104/£65

JACKSON, CHARLES. The Lost Weekend. NY, (1944). 1st ed. VG in dj (spine ends frayed, extrems worn). *King*. $50/£31

JACKSON, CLARENCE S. Picture Maker of the Old West. NY, 1947. 1st ed. Good in dj (sl worn, taped). *Dumont*. $95/£59

JACKSON, DONALD (ed). Letters of the Lewis and Clark Expedition with Related Documents 1783-1854. Urbana: Univ of IL, 1962. 1st ed. Blue cl, gilt. VG in dj (few sm tears, top edge crinkled). *Pacific**. $69/£43

JACKSON, DONALD (ed). Letters of the Lewis and Clark Expedition with Related Documents 1783-1854. Urbana, IL: Univ of IL, 1978. 2nd ed. 2 vols. VF in slipcase, shrinkwrap. *Labordo*. $85/£53

JACKSON, DONALD. Voyages of the Steamboat Yellowstone. NY: Ticknor & Fields, 1985. 1st ed. (Bkpl), else Fine in dj. *Perier*. $35/£22

JACKSON, E. N. Ancestors in Silhouette Cut by August Edouart. London/NY: John Lane, 1921. 63 plts. (Spine frayed, spot fr cvr.) *Ars Artis*. $136/£85

JACKSON, E. N. A History of Hand-Made Lace. London/NY: L. Upcott Gill/Scribner, 1900. 1st ed. Half-title. Pub's dec cl, gilt. *Sotheby's**. $202/£126

JACKSON, F. H. The Shores of the Adriatic. NY: Dutton, 1908. 1st ed. Teg. (Eps sl foxed; rubbed, spine ends frayed), o/w VG. *Worldwide*. $45/£28

JACKSON, FREDERICK J. Notes on the Game Birds of Kenya and Uganda. London, 1926. 1st ed. 13 color plts. (Lt browned, prelims wormed; bds sympathetically repaired, rebacked w/much of orig spine laid down.) *Edwards*. $120/£75

JACKSON, HELEN HUNT. Ramona. Boston: Roberts Bros, 1884. 1st ed. Terra cotta cl, gilt. VG+ (top edge dknd). BAL 10456. *Labordo*. $450/£281

JACKSON, HELEN HUNT. Ramona. LEC, 1959. Ltd to 1500 numbered, signed by Everett Gee Jackson (illus). Fine in slipcase. *Swann**. $92/£58

JACKSON, HOLBROOK. Bernard Shaw. London: Grant Richard's, (1909). VG in dec wraps (worn). *Dramatis*. $30/£19

JACKSON, HOLBROOK. The Eighteen Nineties. London, 1913. 1st ed. (Fr hinge sl weak, cvrs sl spotted; no dj.) *Typographeum*. $45/£28

JACKSON, HOLBROOK. The Fear of Books. London/NY: Soncino/Scribner, 1932. 1st ed. One of 2000 numbered. Fine in dj (chipped). *Second Life*. $45/£28

JACKSON, HOLBROOK. The Printing of Books. Cassell, 1938. 1st ed. VG (feps lt browned, eps sl spotted; fore-edge sl soiled) in dj (nicked, rubbed, dusty, sl mkd, torn, creased, spine, edges browned). *Ulysses*. $88/£55

JACKSON, HOLBROOK. The Printing of Books. Cassell, 1947. 2nd ed. Dj. *Forest*. $35/£22

JACKSON, HOLBROOK. The Reading of Books. London: Faber, 1946. 1st ed. VG in dj. *Hollett*. $32/£20

JACKSON, JOHN. The Practical Fly Fisher; More Particularly for Grayling or Umber. London, 1854. 1st ed, w/the List of Subscribers. 10 Fine engr plts. (Shelfworn, sl soiled.) *Oinonen**. $275/£172

JACKSON, JOHN. The Practical Fly-Fisher; More Particularly for Grayling or Umber. London: John Slark, 1880. 3rd ed. 10 hand-colored copper plts. Gilt-lettered grn cl. NF (bkpl). *Pacific**. $173/£108

JACKSON, JOSEPH HENRY. Anybody's Gold, the Story of California's Mining Towns. NY: D. Appleton-Century, 1941. Fine in glassine dj. *Book Market*. $30/£19

JACKSON, JOSEPH HENRY. Anybody's Gold, the Story of California's Mining Towns. NY: D. Appleton-Century, 1941. 1st ed. Inscribed, signed. VG+ in dj. *Labordo*. $85/£53

JACKSON, JOSEPH HENRY. Bad Company. NY: Harcourt, Brace, (1949). 1st ed. VG in dj (spine head chipped, extrems rubbed). *Pacific**. $35/£22

JACKSON, JOSEPH HENRY. Gold Rush Album. NY: Scribner, 1949. 1st ed. VG+ in slipcase. *Labordo*. $50/£31

JACKSON, JOSEPH HENRY. Tintypes in Gold. NY: Macmillan, 1939. 1st ed. Illus eps. Good. *Lien*. $20/£13

JACKSON, KATHRYN. The Animal's Merry Christmas. NY: Golden, 1950. A Giant Golden Book. 76pp; lg pop-up inside fr cvr by Richard Scarry. VG. *Bookfinders*. $65/£41

JACKSON, LAWRENCE. A Letter to a Young Lady Concerning the Principles and Conduct of the Christian Life. F.C. & J. Rivington, 1818. 4th ed. Contemp full leather, raised bands, leather spine label. Good (ink inscrip, lt spotted; hinges, corners rubbed). *Tiger*. $56/£35

JACKSON, MARY ANNA. Memoirs of 'Stonewall' Jackson. Louisville: Prentice Press, (1895). Engr frontis port, xxiv,647pp. Floral-patterned eps. Olive cl (spine heavily worn, hinges severely cracked), gilt, fr cvr port. Text Good (sl foxed, rear blanks chipped), cvrs Fair. Howes J25. *Baltimore**. $70/£44

JACKSON, MELVIN H. Privateers in Charleston. 1793-1796. Washington: Smithsonian Inst, 1969. Dk blue/grn cl. (Cvrs sl worn, esp corners), else VG. *Parmer*. $55/£34

JACKSON, MRS. F. NEVILL. Silhouette. Methuen, 1938. 1st ed. 10 color plts laid onto black card, guards; 93 photo plts. VG in dj (sl torn, soiled). *Hollett*. $136/£85

JACKSON, MRS. F. NEVILL. Toys of Other Days. London: Country Life, 1908. 1st ed. Frontis. (Some pp roughly opened, lt foxed; tape repairs to cracked fr hinge.) *Dramatis*. $85/£53

JACKSON, MRS. F. NEVILL. Toys of Other Days. NY/London, 1968. Reissue. *Edwards.* $48/£30

JACKSON, SHELDON. Alaska and the Missions on the North Pacific Coast. NY: Dodd, Mead, (1880). 327pp. VG (ex-lib, sl mkd). *Perier.* $90/£56

JACKSON, SHELDON. Report on Education in Alaska.... Washington: GPO, 1886. 93pp; 2 fldg plts, 2 fldg maps. Black cl (dull, sl mkd), else Good. *High Latitude.* $75/£47

JACKSON, SHIRLEY. The Bird's Nest. NY: Farrar, Straus & Young, (1954). 1st ed. NF in dj (sl soiled, spine ends sl rubbed). *Pacific*.* $69/£43

JACKSON, SHIRLEY. The Bird's Nest. NY: Farrar Straus, (1954). 1st ed. Fine in dj (sl worn). *Lenz.* $85/£53

JACKSON, SHIRLEY. Come Along with Me. NY: Viking, (1968). 1st ed. Fine in Fine dj. *Lenz.* $60/£38

JACKSON, SHIRLEY. Hangsaman. NY: Farrar, 1951. 1st ed. (Stamp fep), else Fine in NF dj (sm chips, sm tear). *Beasley.* $100/£63

JACKSON, SHIRLEY. Hangsaman. (NY, 1951.) 1st ed. (Eps, edges sl foxed; spine ends sl frayed), else Good in dj (heavily worn; chipped). *King.* $75/£47

JACKSON, SHIRLEY. Raising Demons. Michael Joseph, 1957. 1st Eng ed. VG (feps partly browned; cvrs sl bowed, spine tail sl bumped) in dj (nicked, sl rubbed, creased, dusty, spine faded, edges sl dknd). *Ulysses.* $56/£35

JACKSON, SHIRLEY. The Sundial. NY: FSC, (1958). 1st ed. Fine in Fine dj (sl crease). *Between The Covers.* $150/£94

JACKSON, W. SPENCER (ed). Merry Minstrelsy: Everybody's Book of Humourous Poetry. Howe, (1892). Aeg. Beveled bds (spine bumped, sl chipped; ex-lib, stamp, bkpl, lt spotted). Good. *Tiger.* $19/£12

JACOB, GILES. The New Law-Dictionary. In the Savoy, 1750. 6th ed. 14x9.5 inches. (824)pp. Old leather (rebacked). (Sl foxed, inner fr hinge cracked), else Nice. *King.* $595/£372

JACOBI, CARL. Revelations in Black. Sauk City, 1947. 1st ed, 1st bk. NF in VG dj (top spine edge rumpled, folds sl worn). *Mcclintock.* $75/£47

JACOBI, CHARLES T. Some Notes on Books and Printing. Chiswick, 1892. 1st ed. Uncut. Buckram (soiled). *Forest.* $40/£25

JACOBI, LOTTE. Lotte Jacobi. Kelly Wise (ed). Danbury: Addison House, 1978. 1st ed. This copy signed twice by Jacobi. NF in dj. *Smith.* $150/£94

JACOBS, FRANCINE. The King's Ditch. CowardMG, 1971. 1st ed. 10x10. Jerry Pinkney (illus). Unpaginated. NF (flattened wrinkle) in VG dj (1/2-inch rear, 1/4-inch chip). *Price.* $28/£18

JACOBS, JOSEPH (ed). English Fairy Tales. London: David Nutt, 1890. 1st ed. 8vo. 250pp; 9 full-pg b/w illus by John Batten. Blue pict cl (spine sl faded). *Reisler.* $150/£94

JACOBS, ORANGE. Memoirs of Orange Jacobs. Seattle: Loman & Hanford, 1908. 1st ed. VG. Howes J37. *Perier.* $125/£78

JACOBS, W. W. Deep Waters. Hodder & Stoughton, (1919). 1st issue bound in beige pict cl w/pagination pb. Good (spine bumped, sunned, both hinge heads nicked, fr cvr sl rubbed). *Tiger.* $19/£12

JACOBS, W. W. The Lady of the Barge. NY: Dodd, Mead, 1902. 1st ed. 12 plts. Pict cl. (1 plt reinforced w/tape on verso; spine ends lt rubbed), o/w NF. *Heritage.* $225/£141

JACOBS, W. W. Night Watches. Hodder & Stoughton, 1914. 1st ed. 6 color plts. VG (spotted, bottom corners of few pp sl creased, 1/2-title, rep lt browned; top edge dusty, fr hinge cracked, spine ends sl bumped) in dj (nicked, rubbed, mkd, dusty, sl creased, torn, edges dknd, lacks 2 sm pieces). *Ulysses.* $200/£125

JACOBSEN, HERMANN. A Handbook of Succulent Plants. London, 1960. 1st Eng ptg. 3 vols. 3 maps. VG + in slipcases (seams sl damaged). *Brooks.* $175/£109

JACOBSON, YVONNE. Passing Farms: Enduring Values—California's Santa Clara Valley. Los Altos: William Kaufmann, (1984). 1st ed. Signed by Jacobson & Wallace Stegner (foreword). (Sm stain fore-edge of 1/2-title), else VG in dj (spine ends, corners sl rubbed). *Pacific*.* $150/£94

JACOBUSX. Untrodden Fields of Anthropology. NY: American Anthropology Soc, n.d. (ca 1900). 2 vols in 1. Grn linen cl. VG. *Larry Price.* $85/£53

JAFFE, BERNARD. Crucibles. The Lives and Achievements of the Gret Chemists. London: Jarrolds, 1931. 24 plts. (Feps, 1/2-title sl browned, spotted; spine lt faded.) *Hollett.* $40/£25

JAFFE, HANS L. C. Piet Mondrian. NY, n.d. 48 tipped-in color plts. Dj. *Edwards.* $80/£50

JAGENDORF, M. In the Days of Han. L.A.: Suttonhouse, 1936. 1st ed. 8vo. 168pp; 24 full-pg illus by Erwin Neumann. Metallic illus eps. Red cl bds, gilt. VG. *Davidson.* $45/£28

JAGENDORF, M. Penny Puppets, Penny Theatre, and Penny Plays. Indianapolis: Bobbs-Merrill, (1941). 1st ed. VG in color pict dj (worn). *Dramatis.* $20/£13

JAGOR, F. Travels in the Philippines. London: Chapman and Hall, 1875. 1st Eng ed. ix,(i),370pp; fldg map, 5 engr plts (incl frontis). Contemp brn cl, green morocco label, gilt. Sound (bkpl, lib stamp; 1st, last few ll, map foxed; sl rubbed, sl damp-spotted, hinges cracked). *Morrell.* $280/£175

James Cook, Surveyor of Newfoundland: Being a Collection of Charts of the Coasts of Newfoundland and Labradore.... SF: David Magee, 1965. Facs rpt. One of 365 ptd. 32pp; folder of 12 collotype facs plts (11 charts & a tp). Fine in wrappers, dropback linen box (sunned, shelfworn). *Pacific*.* $345/£216

JAMES, CROAKE. Curiosities of Law and Lawyers. NY: Funk & Wagnalls, 1899. Crimson cl (worn, faded). Sound. *Boswell.* $85/£53

JAMES, DAVID. Scott of the Antarctic. London: Convey, 1948. Ptd bds. VG in dj. *High Latitude.* $17/£11

JAMES, EDWARD. The Next Volume. London: James Press, 1932. 1st ed. One of 525 (ptd on rag paper). Imperial 8vo. Rex Whistler (illus). Full-pg plt. Teg, uncut, unopened. Brn cl, gilt. VG (eps sl speckled; sl rubbed). *Sotheran.* $797/£498

JAMES, EDWARD. Swans Reflecting Elephants: My Early Years. George Melly (ed). London, 1982. 1st Eng ed. Nice in dj. *Clearwater.* $40/£25

JAMES, G. P. R. The Gentleman of the Old School. Sims & McIntyre, 1852. Parlour Lib, 1st 1 vol ed. Good (spine bumped). *Tiger.* $32/£20

JAMES, G. P. R. The Gipsy: A Tale. Simms & McIntyre, 1849. Sprinkled edges. Contemp 1/2, marbled bds (sl rubbed; sig). Good. *Tiger.* $19/£12

JAMES, GEORGE WHARTON. Arizona the Wonderland. Boston: Page, (1920). 1st ed. 20 color plts, fldg color map. Teg. Color pict cvr label. Fine. *Pacific*.* $196/£123

JAMES, GEORGE WHARTON. Arizona. Boston, 1917. 1st imp. 12 color plts, fldg map. Dec cl, pict label. (Top/bottom backstrip starting to fray, extrems worn), else VG. *Baade.* $75/£47

JAMES, GEORGE WHARTON. In and Around the Grand Canyon. Boston, 1905. Grn cl. (Bkpl, news clipping), o/w VG +. *Five Quail.* $60/£38

JAMES, GEORGE WHARTON. Indian Basketry. Phoenix, AZ, 1902. 2nd ed. (Pub's ad glued to rep; rear hinge cracked, extrems rubbed.) *King.* $100/£63

JAMES, GEORGE WHARTON. Indian Blankets and Their Makers. NY: Tudor, 1937. 2nd ed. VG (ex-lib, mks). *Pacific*.* $52/£33

JAMES, GEORGE WHARTON. Indian Blankets and Their Makers. NY, 1937. New ed. (Lib ink stamps, labels, #s; upper hinge tender; worn.) *Edwards.* $77/£48

JAMES, GEORGE WHARTON. The Indians of the Painted Desert Region. Boston, 1903. 1st ed. Pict cl. (Ink inscrip; removal mks; lt worn, shaken.) *King.* $50/£31

JAMES, GEORGE WHARTON. The Lake of the Sky, Lake Tahoe. Pasadena: The Author, 1915. 1st ed. VG. *Perier.* $85/£53

JAMES, GEORGE WHARTON. Lake Tahoe, the Lake of the Sky. Chicago: Powner, 1956. 1st of this ed. Fine in VG dj. *Book Market.* $35/£22

JAMES, GEORGE WHARTON. New Mexico: The Land of the Delight Makers. Boston: Page, (1920). 1st ed. 8 color plts, fldg color map. Teg. Gilt-dec cl, color pict circular cvr label. Fine. *Pacific*.* $219/£137

JAMES, GEORGE WHARTON. New Mexico: The Land of the Delight Makers. Boston, 1920. 1st ed. Fldg map. Teg. (Sl worn), else NF. *Dumont.* $200/£125

JAMES, GEORGE WHARTON. The Old Franciscan Missions of California. Boston: Little, Brown, 1919. Later ed. (Sl shelf-worn), o/w Good. *Brown.* $25/£16

JAMES, GEORGE WHARTON. Practical Basket Making. Pasadena: George Wharton James, n.d. New ed. Fine. *Pacific*.* $46/£29

JAMES, GEORGE WHARTON. Through Ramona's Country. Boston: Little, Brown, 1909. (Bkpl; fr hinge starting), else Good. *Dumont.* $35/£22

JAMES, GEORGE WHARTON. What the White Race May Learn from the Indian. Chicago: Forbes, 1908. 1st ed. Red cl, gilt. (Lt stain lower corners fr cvr, 1st few pp), else NF. *Pacific*.* $150/£94

JAMES, GEORGE WHARTON. The Wonders of the Colorado Desert. Boston: Little, Brown, 1907. 2nd ptg. 2 vols. 33 plts. Blue/gray cl, gilt. (Hinge cracked between pp.xliv and 1; spines sl faded), o/w NF set. *Pacific*.* $259/£162

JAMES, GRACE. Green Willow and Other Japanese Fairy Tales. London: Macmillan, 1910. 1st ed. Royal 8vo. viii,280,(ii)pp; 40 Fine mtd color plts by Warwick Goble. Blue edges. Dk blue cl, gilt. VG (front 2 ll sl foxed). *Sotheran.* $520/£325

JAMES, HARRY C. Western Campfires. Flagstaff: Northland, 1973. 1st ed. Signed, inscribed. Fine in Fine dj. *Book Market.* $40/£25

JAMES, HENRY. The Ambassadors. LEC, 1963. Ltd to 1500 numbered, signed by Leslie Saalburg (illus). Fine in slipcase. *Swann*.* $69/£43

JAMES, HENRY. The Beast in the Jungle. Kentfield: Allen, 1963. One of 130. Prospectus laid in. Fine. *Pacific*.* $316/£198

JAMES, HENRY. Daisy Miller. LEC, 1969. Ltd to 1500 numbered, signed by Gustave Nebel (illus). Fine in slipcase. *Swann*.* $40/£25

JAMES, HENRY. The Finer Grain. NY: Scribner, 1910. 1st ed. Teg. Brn cl. VG (spine head lt frayed, back lt faded). BAL 10671. *House.* $35/£22

JAMES, HENRY. French Poets and Novelists. London: Macmillan, 1878. One of 1250. (Cl tips worn through, panels sl bubbled), else VG + . *Lame Duck.* $150/£94

JAMES, HENRY. Gabrielle de Bergerac. NY: Boni & Liveright, 1918. 1st ed. VG (spine dknd) in dj (chipped, rear panel lacks piece, spine dknd, verso discolored). *Pacific*.* $46/£29

JAMES, HENRY. Julia Bride. NY/London: Harper, 1909. 1st separate ed. Claret cl blindstamped w/hearts. NF (sl string dent on spine). *Sumner & Stillman.* $95/£59

JAMES, HENRY. Master Eustace. NY: Thomas Seltzer, 1920. 1st ed. NF in VG dj (extrems chipped, few 2-inch tears). *Lame Duck.* $275/£172

JAMES, HENRY. Mont Saint Michel and Chartres. (By Henry Adams.) Washington: Privately ptd, 1904. 1st ed. Inscribed on inserted leaf of stationery. 4to. Buckram (rebound at early date), orig cl backstrip, cvrs laid down. (Marginal paper cracks, chipping on 1st several ll not affecting text.) Cl fldg case. BAL 31. *Swann*.* $747/£467

JAMES, HENRY. Notes of a Son and Brother. London: Macmillan, 1914. 1st ed. Frontisport. Blue cl. (Bkpl; corners bumped), o/w Good. *Maggs.* $72/£45

JAMES, HENRY. The Outcry. London: Methuen, (1911). 1st Eng ed. Grn cl, gilt. NF. *Sumner & Stillman.* $165/£103

JAMES, HENRY. The Outcry. NY: Scribner, 1911. 1st ed. Teg. Brn cl. VG (spine lt faded). BAL 10674. *House.* $100/£63

JAMES, HENRY. A Passionate Pilgrim. Boston: James R. Osgood, 1875. 1st ed, 1st bk. 8vo. 496pp. Purple cl, gilt. VG (sm ink name; spine extrems lt frayed, hinges tender). BAL 10529. *Truepenny.* $950/£594

JAMES, HENRY. The Portrait of a Lady. OUP, 1947. 1st ed thus. Fine (spine foot sl bumped) in dj (sl nicked, creased, 1 internal repair). *Ulysses.* $88/£55

JAMES, HENRY. The Portrait of a Lady. LEC, 1967. Ltd to 1500 numbered, signed by Colleen Browning (illus). Fine in slipcase. *Swann*.* $40/£25

JAMES, HENRY. Portraits of Places. Boston: James R. Osgood, 1884. 1st Amer ed. viii,376pp. Gold cl, gilt spine. Good (sm dots on cvrs, sl shelfworn). *Cullen.* $40/£25

JAMES, HENRY. The Princess Casamassina. NY: Macmillan, 1886. 1st US, 1st 1-vol ed. VG. *Lame Duck.* $175/£109

JAMES, HENRY. The Private Life. NY: Harper, 1893. 1st Amer ed, primary binding state. 4pp undated ads. Dec blue-grn cl. NF (spine sl dull). *Sumner & Stillman.* $115/£72

JAMES, HENRY. The Question of Our Speech. Boston: Houghton Mifflin, 1905. 1st ed. One of 2000 designed by Bruce Rogers. VG + in ptd dj (extrems sl chipped). *Lame Duck.* $750/£469

JAMES, HENRY. Roderick Hudson. Boston: James R. Osgood, 1876. 1st ed, 1st ptg, 1st binding. One of 1572. Initial form of binding, w/'J.R. Osgood & Co.' spine imprint. Brn coated eps. Brn cl, sl beveled bds, gilt spine. (Lt aged; lib white ink spine #, ink handstamps to edges, ink # c. pg; spine ends chipped, frayed.) BAL 10531. *Baltimore*.* $45/£28

JAMES, HENRY. The Sacred Fount. Rupert Hart-Davis, 1959. 1st ed. Inscribed by Leon Edel (intro). VG (top edge faded, dusty; spine ends, corners bumped) in dj (worn). *Ulysses.* $40/£25

JAMES, HENRY. The Turn of the Screw. LEC, 1949. Ltd to 1500 numbered. Fine in slipcase. *Swann*.* $57/£36

JAMES, HENRY. Washington Square. NY: Harper, 1881. 1st ed. Frontis. Gilt-pict olive grn cl (tips, edges lt rubbed). Nice. *Swann*.* $431/£269

JAMES, HENRY. Washington Square. LEC, 1971. Ltd to 1500 numbered, signed by Lawrence Beall Smith (illus). Fine in slipcase. *Swann*.* $34/£21

JAMES, J. T. Journal of a Tour in Germany, Sweden, Russia, Poland in 1813-14. John Murray, 1819. 3rd ed. Eton presentation copy. 2 vols. xvi,470; iv,447pp; 12 aquatint plts. Marbled eps; all edges marbled. Contemp full calf, raised bands, gilt-tooled, black leather labels, bd edges gilt-tooled. (Sl offsetting from few plts; extrems rubbed), o/w VG set. *Sotheran.* $477/£298

JAMES, MONTAGUE RHODES. Abbeys. London, 1925. 1st ed. Color frontis, 106 plts (6 color), 13 fldg plans, color fldg map in rear pocket. Red paper-cvrd bds (sl bumped, rubbed; sm part fep cut out), spine cl. *Maggs.* $29/£18

JAMES, MONTAGUE RHODES. Address at the Unveiling of the Roll of Honour of the Cambridge Tipperary Club on July 12, 1916. CUP, 1916. 1st Eng ed. NF in wrappers (spine ends sl rubbed). *Ulysses.* $72/£45

JAMES, MONTAGUE RHODES. Bibliotheca Pepysiana...Part III. Mediaeval Manuscripts. London: Sidgwick & Jackson, 1923. Uncut. Cl-backed blue bds (sl bumped), paper spine label. *Maggs*. $96/£60

JAMES, MONTAGUE RHODES. The Collected Ghost Stories of M.R. James. Edward Arnold, 1931. 1st UK ed. NF (ink name) in VG dj (sl creased). *Williams*. $1,592/£995

JAMES, MONTAGUE RHODES. A Descriptive Catalogue of the Manuscripts in the Library of Corpus Christi College, Cambridge. Cambridge: CUP, 1909-1911. 2 vols. Brn cl. Orig wrappers, 1912 appendix bound in. *Maggs*. $144/£90

JAMES, MONTAGUE RHODES. A Descriptive Catalogue of the Manuscripts in the Library of Gonville and Caius College. Cambridge: CUP, 1907-1908. 2 vols. Black cl (spines faded, sl worn; ex-lib, stamps), gilt. *Maggs*. $120/£75

JAMES, MONTAGUE RHODES. A Descriptive Catalogue of the Manuscripts Other Than Oriental in the Library of King's College, Cambridge. Cambridge: CUP, 1895. 1st ed. Unopened. *Forest*. $136/£85

JAMES, MONTAGUE RHODES. The Five Jars. Edward Arnold, 1922. 1st UK ed. Fine (ink inscrip, foxed). *Williams*. $160/£100

JAMES, MONTAGUE RHODES. The Frescoes in the Chapel at Eton College. Eton College/Spottiswoode, 1907. One of 250. Tissue-guarded mtd facs. Teg. 1/2 buckram. Good (inscrip, eps lt spotted; cvrs rubbed, mkd, soiled, dusty; spine dknd, ends sl bumped). *Ulysses*. $264/£165

JAMES, MONTAGUE RHODES. Ghost Stories of an Antiquary. London: Edward Arnold, 1904. 1st ed. 8vo. James McBryde (illus). Beige linen, stamped in black/red. (Spine sl dknd, fr inner hinge repaired), o/w NF. *Cummins*. $800/£500

JAMES, MONTAGUE RHODES. A Guide to the Windows of King's College Chapel Cambridge. C.J. Clay & Sons, 1899. 1/2-title not called for, final blank; 38,(ii)pp. Issued w/o eps. Pale gray-grn wrappers, cut flush. (Lt pencil notes few ll), o/w Fine. *Temple*. $56/£35

JAMES, MONTAGUE RHODES. Some Remarks on Ghost Stories. Edinburgh: Tragara Press, 1985. One of 115 numbered. NF in patterned paper wrappers. *Ulysses*. $104/£65

JAMES, MONTAGUE RHODES. Suffolk and Norfolk. London, 1950. Rpt. VG in dj. *Gretton*. $24/£15

JAMES, MONTAGUE RHODES. A Thin Ghost and Others. Edward Arnold, 1919. 1st UK ed. VG. *Williams*. $77/£48

JAMES, MONTAGUE RHODES. Two Ancient English Scholars. Glasgow: Jackson, Wylie, 1931. Fine in wrappers. *Ulysses*. $56/£35

JAMES, MONTAGUE RHODES. The Western Manuscripts in the Library of Trinity College, Cambridge. Cambridge: CUP, 1900-1904. 4 vols. 17 plts. Blue cl (fr hinge vol 1 starting; headcaps sl bumped), gilt. *Maggs*. $360/£225

JAMES, P. D. Cover Her Face. NY: Scribner, (1966). 1st Amer ed, 1st bk. NF (blind stamp tp) in NF dj. *Dermont*. $250/£156

JAMES, P. D. Death of an Expert Witness. London, 1977. 1st ed. (Ep, tp sl spotted.) Dj. *Petersfield*. $48/£30

JAMES, P. D. Death of an Expert Witness. London: Faber & Faber, 1977. 1st ed. Signed. Scarlet bds. Fine in dj. *Temple*. $104/£65

JAMES, P. D. Devices and Desires. London: Faber & Faber, 1989. 1st ed. Fine in dj. *Murder*. $50/£31

JAMES, P. D. Devices and Desires. NY: Knopf, 1990. 1st US ed. Signed on tipped-in leaf. Fine in Fine dj. *Beasley*. $40/£25

JAMES, P. D. and T. A. CRITCHLEY. The Maul and the Pear Tree. Constable, 1971. 1st ed. Pict eps. Fine in dj. *Ulysses*. $200/£125

JAMES, P. D. Original Sin. London: Faber & Faber, 1994. 1st ed. One of 150 numbered, signed. Fine w/o dj as issued. *Murder*. $125/£78

JAMES, P. D. A Taste for Death. London: Faber & Faber, 1986. 1st ed. Fine in dj. *Murder*. $95/£59

JAMES, P. D. An Unsuitable Job for a Woman. London, 1972. 1st ed. Fine in dj. *Petersfield*. $96/£60

JAMES, PHILIP (ed). A Butler's Recipe Book 1719. Cambridge, 1935. 1st ed. Cl-backed ptd pink bds (sl browned). VG. *Cox*. $77/£48

JAMES, PHILIP. Early Keyboard Instruments. London, 1930. (Lt foxed; lt worn.) *Oinonen**. $110/£69

JAMES, ROBERT RHODES. Gallipoli. London, 1965. 1st ed. VG in dj (sl frayed). *Typographeum*. $45/£28

JAMES, THOMAS. Three Years Among the Mexicans and the Indians. (Chicago: Rio Grande, 1962.) Fac rpt of 1916 rpt ed. Frontisport. Maroon cl, gilt. Fine. *Argonaut*. $50/£31

JAMES, WILL. Cowboys North and South. NY: Scribner, 1925. 1st bk. Pict gray cl (lt soiled). VG. *House*. $50/£31

JAMES, WILL. Drifting Cowboy. NY: Scribner, 1925. 1st ed. Pict bds over brn linen spine. Fine. *Appelfeld*. $50/£31

JAMES, WILL. In the Saddle with Uncle Bill. NY: Scribner, 1935. 1st ed. (Ink name, bkpl; sunned, esp spine), else VG. *Pacific**. $98/£61

JAMES, WILL. Lone Cowboy. NY: Scribner, 1930. True 1st ed with the 'A' on c. pg. (Worn), else Good. *Dumont*. $95/£59

JAMES, WILL. Lone Cowboy. NY: Scribner, 1930. 1st ed. Photo frontisport. Grn cl, gilt. (Sl rubbed, faded), else VG in dj (sunned, edgeworn). *Pacific**. $173/£108

JAMES, WILL. Smoky, the Cowhorse. NY: Scribner, 1926. Inscribed presentation. (Lacks rep, shaken, hinges cracked at eps; worn), else Good. *Pacific**. $196/£123

JAMES, WILL. Smoky, the Cowhorse. NY: Scribner, 1926. 1st ed. (Ink inscrip; discolored fading to cvrs), else VG- in dj (sunned, chipped). *Pacific**. $288/£180

JAMESON, ANNA. Shakespeare's Heroines. London: Ernest Nister, (1904). 1st ed illus thus. 6 Fine chromolithos by W. Paget. Aeg. Mint grn pict cl. NF. *Sotheran*. $141/£88

JAMESON, ANNA. The Writings on Art of Anna Jameson. Boston, 1896. 5 vols. Contemp 1/2 polished maroon calf, gilt. (Joints rubbed, sm chip 1 head.) *Swann**. $103/£64

JAMESON, MALCOLM. Bullard of the Space Patrol. Andre Norton (ed). Cleveland: World, (1951). 1st ed. Signed. VG- in dj (fr panel, spine foot each lacks sm piece, ends chipped, long tear rear joint, sm tear top fr panel). *Pacific**. $127/£79

JAMESON, MRS. Memoirs of Celebrated Female Sovereigns. Routledge, n.d. (c1875). New ed. Frontis. Marbled edges. Contemp 1/2 leather, marbled bds, raised bands, leather spine label. VG (prize label). *Tiger*. $56/£35

JAMESON, MRS. Memoirs of the Early Italian Painters, and of the Progress of Painting in Italy. From Cimabue to Bassano. Charles Knight, 1845. 2 vols bound in one. Contemp cl (rebacked w/ orig backstrip relaid, corners rubbed), leather spine label. Good (bkpl). *Tiger*. $42/£26

JAMESON, STORM. Farewell to Youth. NY: Knopf, 1928. 1st US ed. Orange cl stamped in gilt/grn. NF in pict 'flapper' dj (lt worn, sm nicks, creased edge tear). *Reese*. $50/£31

JAMESON, STORM. The Pot Boils. London: Constable, 1919. 1st ed, 1st bk. Gray-grn cl. VG. *Temple*. $120/£75

JANIS, CHARLES G. Barbed Boredom. Irvington, NJ, 1950. Pict label. (Ink inscrip, tp tear at gutter; cvrs rubbed), else Good. *King*. $100/£63

JANIS, HARRIET and SIDNEY. Picasso: The Recent Years, 1939-1946. NY, 1947. One of 350 numbered, signed by Picasso. (Scattered soiling.) *Swann**. $287/£179

JANSON, CHARLES WILLIAM. The Stranger in America. London, 1807. 1st ed. 4to. 10 sepia-tinted aquatint plts, incl add'l tp; engr plan. Mod 1/2 morocco (extrems rubbed). Howes J59. *Swann**. $747/£467

JANSSON, TOVE. Comet in Moominland. London: Benn, 1946. 1st ed. 5x7.5. 192pp. VG. *Cattermole*. $40/£25

JANSSON, TOVE. Moominvalley in November. London: Benn, 1971. 1st ed. 5.75x8.5. 175pp. Fine in dj. *Cattermole*. $50/£31

Japanese Fairy Tale Series. No. 10: The Matsuyama Mirror. (Tokyo: Nishinomiya, n.d.) 1st ed. 12mo. (22)pp. Creped paper, french-folded; stabbed and tied. (Lower outer corner rear wrapper torn away.) *Karmiole*. $85/£53

Japanese Fairy Tale Series. No. 17: Schippeitaro. (Tokyo: Kobunsha, 1889.) 1st ed. 12mo. (26)pp. Creped paper, french-folded; stabbed and tied. Good. *Karmiole*. $85/£53

Japanese Fairy Tale Series. No. 6: The Mouse's Wedding. (Tokyo: Y. Nishinomiya, n.d.) 12mo. (22)pp. Creped paper, french-folded; stabbed and tied. Good. *Karmiole*. $85/£53

Japanese No Drama Costumes and Priest Robes. Providence: Art Museum/Rhode Island School of Design, April 6-May 10, 1937. NF in ptd Japanese paper wrappers. *Turtle Island*. $45/£28

JARDINE, WILLIAM. The Natural History of Humming-Birds. Edinburgh: W.H. Lizars, & Stirling & Kenney, 1833. 2 vols. 60 (of 64) hand-colored engr plts. Contemp 1/2 calf. (Vol 1 tp scratched; sm hole in p125-132 vol 1, affecting text, 2 plts; soiled; vol 2 hinges cracked; rubbed.) *Sotheby's**. $422/£264

JARDINE, WILLIAM. The Natural History of the Felinae. Edinburgh: The Naturalist's Library, 1834. 34 hand-colored plts. Uncut. New 1/2 black morocco, gilt. Orig grn paper ptd wrapper bound in. *Petersfield*. $83/£52

JARDINE, WILLIAM. The Natural History of the Ordinary Cetacea or Whales. Edinburgh: W.H. Lizars et al, 1837. Frontis, tissue (spotted), xv,264pp; 32 engr plts (29 hand-colored). Old binder's cl (sl rubbed), gilt. *Hollett*. $192/£120

JARDINE, WILLIAM. The Naturalist's Library. Edinburgh, 1843. 40 vols complete. 8vo. 40 half-titles, 40 add'l engr tps w/vignettes (25 color), 40 ports, 1278 plts (few spotted, loose). Orig cl (spines sl worn; some joints, hinges split). *Sotheby's**. $3,128/£1,955

JARDINE, WILLIAM. The Naturalist's Library: Mammalia. Edinburgh: W.H. Lizars, 1833-42. 1st ed. 13 vols. 3/4 dk grn morocco, marbled bds. NF. *Pacific**. $748/£468

JARMAN, W. U.S.A. Uncle Sam's Abscess, or Hell Upon Earth for U.S. Uncle Sam.... Exeter, 1884. 194pp. Good (tp chipped, folded; foxed, few pg edges turned) in wrappers (lacks fr wrap, rear wrap chipped, folded). *Benchmark*. $45/£28

JARRELL, RANDALL. The Animal Family. Pantheon, 1965. Apparent 1st ed. Maurice Sendak (illus). 180pp. Yellow cl, stamped w/pict. VG (inscrip). *Price*. $45/£28

JARRELL, RANDALL. The Bat-Poet. NY: Macmillan, 1964. 1st ed. 6x9. Maurice Sendak (illus). 43pp. Fine in dj. *Cattermole*. $100/£63

JARRELL, RANDALL. Blood for a Stranger. NY: Harcourt, Brace, 1942. 1st US ed. NF in dj (extrems lt worn), red cl-cvrd slipcase. *Lame Duck*. $250/£156

JARRELL, RANDALL. Fly by Night. NY: FSG, 1976. 1st ed. Sm 8vo. Maurice Sendak (illus). Fine in Fine dj. *American Booksellers*. $45/£28

JARRELL, RANDALL. Little Friend, Little Friend. NY: Dial, 1945. 1st ed. Presentation, inscribed on fep: 'To Philip Rahv from Randall Jarrell.' Stamped cl. VG (extrems sl faded) in dj (chipped, worn, inside rear panel separated but present). *Holmes*. $650/£406

JARVIS, C. S. Arab Command. The Biography of Col. F. W. Peake Pasha. London, 1942. 1st Eng ed. (Cvrs handled, sl spotted; corners bumped; lacks dj.) *Clearwater*. $56/£35

JARVIS, C. S. Three Deserts. London: John Murray, 1936. 1st ed. Frontis photo. Grn cl, gilt. VG in dj (sl chipped). *Maggs*. $136/£85

JASEN, DAVID A. A Bibliography and Reader's Guide to the First Editions of P. G. Wodehouse. Barrie & Jenkins, 1971. 1st ed. Frontis. (Ex-lib.) Dj. *Forest*. $24/£15

JASTROW, JOSEPH. The House That Freud Built. NY: Greenberg, (1932). Early ptg. Grey cl. Good (spine rubbed, shelfworn). *Gach*. $30/£19

JASTROW, MORRIS, JR. The War and the Bagdad Railway. Phila/London: Lippincott, 1918. 3rd imp. 8 plts, fldg map. (Bkpl; sl rubbed, soiled), o/w VG. *Worldwide*. $28/£18

JAVELLE, EMILE. Alpine Memories. W. H. Chesson (trans). T. Fisher Unwin, 1899. 1st ed. 4 plts. (Hinges sl rubbed.) *Hollett*. $96/£60

JAVITCH, GREGORY. A Selective Bibliography of Ceremonies, Dances, Music and Songs of the American Indian. Montreal, 1974. One of 300 numbered, signed. NF. *Dumont*. $100/£63

JAY, WILLIAM. An Inquiry into the Character and Tendency of the American Colonization, and American Anti-Slavery Societies. NY: Leavitt, Lord, 1835. 3rd ed. Peach cl, gilt spine. Good (bottom left corner 1st 25 pp dampstained; foxing, name; stained, faded, sl insect damage fr joint). *Blue Mountain*. $75/£47

JAY, WILLIAM. A Review of the Causes and Consequences of The Mexican War. Boston: Benjamin B. Mussey, 1849. 2nd ed. 333pp. (Sl shelfworn), else VG. *Brown*. $50/£31

JEAFFRESON, J. C. The Life of Robert Stephenson, F.R.S. London: Longman, Green et al, 1864. 1st ed. 2 vols. xv,363; xii,335,24pp; complete w/half-titles, 2 ports, 5 plts. Blue cl, gilt. (1 hinge cracked; extrems sl rubbed, spine tops sl rucked.) *Hollett*. $296/£185

JEAN, MARCEL (ed). The Autobiography of Surrealism. NY: Viking, 1980. 1st ed. Cl-backed paper over bds. (Fr soiled), o/w NF in dj. *Cahan*. $85/£53

JEAN-AUBRY, G. Joseph Conrad: Life and Letters. GC: Doubleday, Page, 1927. 1st ed. 2 vols. Teg. Blue cl, gilt spines. Fine. *Pacific**. $40/£25

JEFFCOAT, PERCIVAL R. Nooksack Tales and Trails. Ferndale, WA: Sedro-Woolley Courier Times, 1949. Memorial ed. Fine. *Perier*. $50/£31

JEFFERIES, RICHARD. The Amateur Poacher. London: Smith, Elder, 1896. New ed. Brn cl, gilt. Fine (bkpl, address label). *Pacific**. $46/£29

JEFFERIES, RICHARD. The Dewy Morn. Richard Bentley & Son, 1884. 1st ed. 2 vols. Silver-patterned eps vol 2. Grn pebble-grain cl. (Vol 2 tp soiled, spotting.) *Sotheby's**. $184/£115

JEFFERIES, RICHARD. Field and Hedgerow, Being the Last Essays of, Collected by His Widow. London: Longmans, 1889. 1st ed. Pict cl. (Foxed throughout.) *Petersfield*. $83/£52

JEFFERIES, RICHARD. The Gamekeeper at Home. London: Smith, Elder, 1892. New ed. Grn cl, gilt. (Lt foxed, rubbed), else VG. *Pacific**. $35/£22

JEFFERIES, RICHARD. Greene Ferne Farm. London: Smith, Elder, 1880. 1st Eng ed. Good (eps cracked at joints; foxed, bkpl; cl sl spotted, corners chafed, spine tanned, worn). *Clearwater*. $152/£95

JEFFERIES, RICHARD. Hodge and His Masters. Smith, Elder, 1880. 1st ed. 2 vols. Half-titles, ads at end of vol 2. Brn dec cl, gilt; blocking not uniform. *Sotheby's**. $294/£184

JEFFERIES, RICHARD. The Life of the Fields. Chatto, 1884. 1st Eng ed. Pict cl. (Name; mkd, handled, 2 corner tips bumped.) *Clearwater*. $104/£65

JEFFERIES, RICHARD. Nature Near London. Chatto, 1883. 1st Eng ed. 1/2 smooth grn calf, grn cl sides, by Sickers of London. (No ads; spine faded, 2 corner tips sl chafed.) *Clearwater.* $136/£85

JEFFERIES, RICHARD. The Toilers of the Field. London: Longmans, 1892. 1st ed. 24pp ads. (Foxed throughout; backstrip faded.) *Petersfield.* $83/£52

JEFFERIES, RICHARD. Wood Magic. Cassell, Petter, Galpin, 1881. 1st ed. 2 vols. Half-titles, ads at end. Dk grn dec cl (upper hinge vol 1 cracked). *Sotheby's*. $312/£195

JEFFERS, JO. Ranch Wife. NY: Doubleday, 1964. 1st ed. NF in dj. *Labordo.* $45/£28

JEFFERS, ROBINSON. Cawdor. NY, 1928. 1st ed. One of 375 numbered, signed. Cl-backed buckram. Slipcase (defective). *Swann*. $126/£79

JEFFERS, ROBINSON. Dear Judas and Other Poems. NY: Horace Liveright, 1929. 1st ed. NF in dj (spine head chipped, sm tear fr panel, soiled). *Pacific*. $40/£25

JEFFERS, ROBINSON. Dear Judas. NY, 1929. 1st ed. One of 375 signed. Vellum-backed bds. Slipcase. *Swann*. $126/£79

JEFFERS, ROBINSON. Descent to the Dead. NY: Random House, (1930). 1st ed. One of 500 signed. Vellum spine, cinnamon bds. (Spine lt soiled), o/w Fine in orig cardboard open-end slipcase (bottom splitting, wear). *Heritage.* $300/£188

JEFFERS, ROBINSON. Flagons and Apples. L.A.: Grafton, 1912. 1st ed, 1st bk. One of unstated ed of 500. Tan cl, brn bds, ptd paper labels. VG (eps sl browned; edges, spine sl rubbed; cvrs sl spotted, spine label browned, fr label sl foxed). *Baltimore*. $400/£250

JEFFERS, ROBINSON. Give Your Heart to the Hawks and Other Poems. NY: Random House, 1933. 1st ed. One of 200. Signed. Teg. 1/2 calf, marbled bds, gilt. (Spine dknd, esp head), else VG. *Pacific*. $138/£86

JEFFERS, ROBINSON. Hungerfield. SF: Grabhorn, 1952. 1st ed. One of 30 ptd. 12x8.5. 1/2 cl, paper spine label. (Sl foxed), else NF in later clamshell box, morocco spine label. *Pacific*. $4,025/£2,516

JEFFERS, ROBINSON. Medea. NY, 1946. 1st Amer ed. NF (corners sl rubbed). *Polyanthos.* $25/£16

JEFFERS, ROBINSON. Poems. SF: Book Club of CA, 1928. One of 310 ptd. Signed by Jeffers and Ansel Adams. Silver-print frontis photo by Adams. Grn cl, paper spine label. (Adhesion residue fep, hinge starting at tp; spine sunned), else VG in slipcase (tape-repaired). *Pacific*. $431/£269

JEFFERS, ROBINSON. The Selected Poetry of.... NY: Random House, (1938). 1st ed. (Spine sl dknd), else NF. *Pacific*. $104/£65

JEFFERS, ROBINSON. Solstice and Other Poems. NY, 1935. 1st ed. One of 320. Signed. *Swann*. $103/£64

JEFFERS, ROBINSON. Solstice and Other Poems. NY: Random House, 1935. 1st ed. One of 320 ptd. Signed. Cl-backed dec bds, paper spine label. (Offset from flaps to feps), else NF in dj (spine ends chipped). *Pacific*. $138/£86

JEFFERS, ROBINSON. Such Counsels You Gave to Me and Other Poems. NY: Random House, (1937). 1st ed. Signed. Dec maroon cl, gilt. VF in pict dj (spine dknd). *Argonaut.* $225/£141

JEFFERS, ROBINSON. Such Counsels You Gave to Me and Other Poems. NY: Random House, (1937). 1st ed. This copy inscribed. VF in dj. *Black Sun.* $425/£266

JEFFERS, ROBINSON. Thurso's Landing and Other Poems. NY: Liveright, (1932). 1st ed. One of 200 signed. Blue cl, beveled edges, gilt. Fine in orig cardboard open-end slipcase (faded, lt worn). *Heritage.* $375/£234

JEFFERS, ROBINSON. The Women at Point Sur. NY, (1927). 1st ed. One of 265 numbered, signed. Paper-backed bd. Slipcase (defective). *Swann*. $149/£93

JEFFERS, ROBINSON. The Women at Point Sur. NY: Random House, (1935). 5th ed. Signed, inscribed. 1/2 cl, purple bds, gilt. NF (bkpl). *Pacific*. $138/£86

JEFFERS, UNA. Visits to Ireland; Travel-Diaries of Una Jeffers. L.A., 1954. One of 300. Marbled bds, cl spine, paper spine label. Slipcase. *Dawson.* $250/£156

JEFFERSON, JOSEPH. The Autobiography. Fisher Unwin, (1890). 1st Eng ed. xv,501pp; 77 plts. Uncut. Blind-stamped cl (lt soiled). *Young.* $88/£55

JEFFERSON, ROBERT L. A New Ride to Khiva. NY: New Amsterdam Book, 1900. 1st US ed. Frontis, 31 half-tone plts. Pict olive cl. VG. *Morrell.* $144/£90

JEFFERSON, THOMAS. A Manual of Parliamentary Practice for the Use of the Senate of the United States. Washington: Samuel Harrison Smith, 1801. 1st ed. 12mo. Contemp sheep. *Swann*. $1,725/£1,078

JEFFERSON, THOMAS. Thomas Jefferson's Garden Book, 1766-1824. Phila, 1944. 1st ed. Port, 36 plts. (Pp tanned; lt soiled, spine foot worn.) *Sutton.* $90/£56

JEFFERSON, THOMAS. Thomas Jefferson's Letter of 20 May 1826 to James Heaton on the Abolition of Slavery. Walter Muir Whitehill (ed). Dumbarton Oaks Garden Library, 1967. One of 150. Inscribed by Whitehill. VG. *Book Broker.* $125/£78

JEFFERSON, THOMAS. The Writings of Thomas Jefferson. LEC, 1967. Ltd to 1500 numbered, signed by Lynd Ward (illus). Fine in slipcase. *Swann*. $103/£64

JEFFERYS, THOMAS. A Description of the Spanish Islands and Settlements on the Coast of the West Indies. Thomas Jefferys, 1762. 1st ed. 4to. 32 fldg engr maps, plans, 1st hand-colored in outline. (Sl worming touching image of plt 1, tp, prelims; browned.) Recent calf, gilt. *Sotheby's*. $2,208/£1,380

JEFFREYS, HAROLD. Cartesian Tensors. CUP, 1931. (Bkpl.) Dj. *Weber.* $50/£31

JEFFREYS, HAROLD. The Earth; Its Origin, History and Physical Constitution. CUP, 1952. 3rd ed. 10 plts. Navy blue cl. Fine. *Weber.* $40/£25

JEFFREYS, HAROLD. Earthquakes and Mountains. London: Methuen, (1950). 2nd ed. Dj (lt worn). *Weber.* $18/£11

JEFFREYS, JOHN GWYN. British Conchology. London: John Van Voorst, 1862-1869. 1st ed. 5 vols. Color frontispieces. 30 b/w, 102 color plts. (Hinges taped, spines faded, recased w/spine ends unattractively reinforced, sl loss to spine lettering vol 3.) *Edwards.* $800/£500

JEKYLL, FRANCIS. Gertrude Jekyll, a Memoir. London, 1934. 1st ed. VG-. *Gretton.* $56/£35

JEKYLL, GERTRUDE and CHRISTOPHER HUSSEY. Garden Ornament. London: Country Life, 1927. 2nd ed. Folio. 692 b/w plts. (Eps foxed; water stain 1/3 fr bd, corners bumped, bd edges shelf-worn), else Good. *Fair Meadow.* $300/£188

JEKYLL, GERTRUDE and LAWRENCE WEAVER. Gardens for Small Country Houses. London: Country Life, 1913. 2nd ed. Color frontis. Teg. (Inscrip, pp xxxv-xxxvi edge wrinkled; expertly rebacked in orig cl), else VG. *Fair Meadow.* $145/£91

JEKYLL, GERTRUDE and LAWRENCE WEAVER. Gardens for Small Country Houses. London, 1914. 3rd ed. (Extrems rubbed, cvrs lt scratched.) *Swann*. $115/£72

JEKYLL, GERTRUDE and EDWARD MAWLEY. Roses for English Gardens. Country Life, 1902. (Edges of ll spotted, occasionally intruding onto inner margins; faded, dampstained.) *Edwards.* $64/£40

JEKYLL, GERTRUDE. Color Schemes for the Flower Garden. London: Country Life, 1919. 4th ed. Color frontis, 109 half-tones, 6 fldg plans, diagrams. Blue cl, gilt. NF. *Quest.* $95/£59

JEKYLL, GERTRUDE. A Gardener's Testament. Francis Jekyll and G. C. Taylor (eds). London: Country Life, 1937. 1st ed. Lt grn cl, gilt. (Foxed, ink notes inside fr bd, fep removed, ink poem rep), else VG. *Fair Meadow*. $85/£53

JEKYLL, GERTRUDE. Home and Garden. London: Longmans, Green, 1900. 1st ed. 53 b/w plts. Red cl, gilt. (Bkpl, sl browned; shelf-worn, bds sunned.) *Fair Meadow*. $95/£59

JEKYLL, GERTRUDE. Lilies for English Gardens. London, 1901. 1st ed. 60 photo plts. Brn cl, gilt. VG. *Larry Price*. $75/£47

JEKYLL, GERTRUDE. Lilies for English Gardens. London, 1903. 2nd ed. (Lt foxed), else VG. *Larry Price*. $60/£38

JEKYLL, GERTRUDE. Wall and Water Gardens, with Chapters on the Rock Garden and the Heath Garden. London: Country Life, 1920. 6th ed. (Browned; shelf-worn, corners bumped), else VG. *Fair Meadow*. $110/£69

JEKYLL, GERTRUDE. Wall and Water Gardens. London: Country Life, n.d. 3rd ed. Buckram, gilt. (Margins lt foxed; cvr lt spotted), else VG. *Quest*. $90/£56

JEKYLL, GERTRUDE. Wood and Garden. Longmans, Green, 1904. Uncut. Good (bkpl) in buckram (spine sl faded), gilt. *Cox*. $56/£35

JELENSKI, CONSTANTIN. Leonor Fini. (NY, 1968.) 1st ed. Pict bds. (Sl worn.) *King*. $150/£94

JELINEK, GEORGE. Ellsworth, Kansas 1867-1947. Salina: Published by Consolidated, 1947. Orig stiff wraps. VG. *Brown*. $35/£22

JELINEK, GEORGE. Ellsworth, Kansas, 1867-1947. Salina, KS: Consolidated, 1947. 1st ed. Signed. NF in wrappers. *Labordo*. $40/£25

JELLICOE, G. A. Baroque Gardens of Austria. London: Ernest Benn, 1932. 1st ed. Tall folio. 40 photo plts. Blue linen over gray bds. Fine in dj (chipped). *Karmiole*. $250/£156

JELLICOE, G. A. The Gardens of Europe. London: Blackie, 1937. 1st ed. (Name; corners bumped, sm spine tear, shelf-worn), else Good. *Fair Meadow*. $40/£25

JELLICOE, G. A. The Gardens of Europe. London/Glasgow: Blackie & Sons, 1937. 1st ed. Fine in dj (worn). *Quest*. $125/£78

JENKIN, A. K. HAMILTON. The Cornish Miner. London: Allen & Unwin, 1948. 2nd ed. 14 plts. (Spine sl faded.) *Hollett*. $72/£45

JENKINS, A. O. Olive's Last Roundup. Loup City, NE: Sherman Country Times, n.d. 1st ed. Fine in wrappers. Howes J90. *Labordo*. $250/£156

JENKINS, G. NEIL. The Physiology of the Mouth. Oxford: Blackwell Scientific, (1954). 1st ed. (Dj lt worn), else Fine. *Weber*. $125/£78

JENKINS, GERAINT (ed). Studies in Folk Life: Essays in Honour of Iorwerth C. Peate. RKP, 1969. NF in dj. *Hadley*. $40/£25

JENKINS, GERAINT. The Craft Industries. London: Longman, 1972. 1st ed. 29 plts. VG in dj. *Hollett*. $40/£25

JENKINS, GERAINT. Traditional Country Craftsmen. London: Routledge & Kegan Paul, 1965. 1st ed. VG in dj. *Hollett*. $48/£30

JENKINS, HERBERT. The Life of George Borrow. London, 1912. Dec cl. VG. *Gretton*. $32/£20

JENKINS, J. T. A History of the Whale Fisheries from the Basque Fisheries of the Tenth Century to the Hunting of the Finner Whale at the Present Date. London: H.F.& G. Witherby, 1921. 12 plts. VG. *High Latitude*. $160/£100

JENKINS, J. T. The Sea Fisheries. London: Constable, 1920. 1st ed. Blue cl, gilt. (Foxed; spine ends bumped), else VG. *Pacific**. $29/£18

JENKINS, JOHN H. Audubon and Other Capers: Confessions of a Texas Bookmaker. Austin: Pemberton, 1976. 1st ed. (Stamp fr pastedown), else VG in dj (soiled). *Pacific**. $40/£25

JENKINS, JOHN H. Printer in Three Republics. Austin, 1981. Frontis. NF. *Dumont*. $35/£22

JENKINS, JOHN STILWELL. Voyage of the U.S. Exploring Squadron, Commanded by Captain Charles Wilkes...in 1838, 1839, 1840, 1841, and 1842. Auburn, 1850. 1st ed. Engr add'l tp, 8 plts (browned), full-pg map. (Lib stamp 1/2-title.) *Swann**. $172/£108

JENKINS, OLAF P. (ed). Geologic Guidebook of the San Francisco Bay Counties. SF: CA Division of Mines, 1951. 1st ed. 1 fldg diag. Tan cl. NF. *Harrington*. $40/£25

JENKINSON, HILARY. Mediaeval Tallies, Public and Private. Soc of Antiquaries, 1925. 8 plts. Mod 1/2 morocco (orig wrappers bound in), gilt. (Sl center fold throughout.) *Hollett*. $136/£85

JENKS, ROBERT W. The Brachial Telegraph. NY, 1852. 1st ed. (Lacks fep, foxed, worn.) *Oinonen**. $90/£56

JENKS, T. The Century World's Fair Book for Boys and Girls. Century, 1893. 1st ed. (Paper bds lt soiled), else VG in dj (lt worn). *Fine Books*. $225/£141

JENNER, GEORGE CHARLES. The Evidence at Large, as Laid Before the Committee of the House of Commons, Respecting Dr. Jenner's Discovery of Vaccine Inoculation. London: J. Murray, 1805. Final errata leaf. (Lacks 1/2-title, tp w/ragged tear in blank area, old repair at outer margin, stamps, few perf stamps, accession #, marginal soil, spotting.) Brn lib cl. *Christie's**. $154/£96

JENNESS, DIAMOND. The Indians of Canada. Ottawa, 1932. 1st ed. Fldg map in rear pocket. (Inner joint broken; sl shaken, sl worn.) *Oinonen**. $40/£25

JENNESS, DIAMOND. Report of the Canadian Arctic Expedition 1913-18. Vol XII: the Life of the Copper Eskimos. Ottawa: F.A. Acland, 1922. 2 maps. VG in ptd wrapper. *High Latitude*. $45/£28

JENNESS, DIAMOND. Report of the Canadian Arctic Expedition 1913-18. Vol XIII: Eskimo Folk-Lore. Part B: Eskimo String Figures. Ottawa: F.A. Acland, 1924. Map. VG in ptd wrapper. *High Latitude*. $25/£16

JENNEWEIN, J. LEONARD. Calamity Jane of the Western Trails. Huron, SD: Dakota Books, 1953. 2nd ed. Fine in wrappers. *Labordo*. $15/£9

JENNINGS, AL. Through the Shadows with O. Henry. NY: H.K. Fly, 1921. 1st ed. VG (fr hinge cracked). *Labordo*. $65/£41

JENNINGS, AL. Through the Shadows with O. Henry. NY: H.K. Fly, 1921. 1st ed. Blue pict cl. Fine. *Cummins*. $75/£47

JENNINGS, ARTHUR S. and G. C. ROTHERY. The Modern Painter and Decorator. Caxton, n.d. (c.1935). New ed. 3 vols. Dec cl, gilt. Good set (worn; joints of 2 vols worn, 1 splitting). *Whittle*. $56/£35

JENNINGS, ELIZABETH. A Dream of Spring. Celandine, 1980. One of 150. Signed by Jennings and Anthony Rossiter (illus). 1/4 cl, marbled bds. Fine. *Michael Taylor*. $96/£60

JENNINGS, ELIZABETH. Frost. Edinburgh/London: Oliver & Boyd, 1964. 1st Eng ed. VG in wrappers (sl creased, mkd, rubbed). *Ulysses*. $40/£25

JENNINGS, N. A. A Texas Ranger. NY: Scribner, 1899. 1st ed. VG (spine, edges lt foxed, cvrs sl worn). Howes J100. *Labordo*. $385/£241

JENNINGS, N. A. A Texas Ranger. Lakeside/R.R. Donnelley, 1992. Good. *Rybski*. $22/£14

JENNINGS, N. A. A Texas Ranger. Ben Procter (ed). Chicago: R.R. Donnelley, 1992. Frontis. VG. *Lien*. $30/£19

JENNINGS, O. On the Cure of the Morphia Habit Without Suffering. NY, 1901. 2nd ed. (Cl sl stained.) *Whitehart*. $64/£40

JENNINGS, SAMUEL. Orchids: And How to Grow Them in India and Other Tropical Climates. London: L. Reeve, 1875. 1st ed. Folio. 12x9. 49 hand-color litho plts. Later 3/4 morocco, cl, gilt. NF. *Pacific**. $1,955/£1,222

JENNISON, G. Noah's Cargo. London: Blackie, 1928. 1st ed. Pict cl, gilt. VG. *Mikesh.* $45/£28

JENSEN, LEE. The Pony Express. NY, 1955. 1st ed. Pict cl (sl edgeworn). VG. *Baade.* $30/£19

JENYNS, R. SOAME and WILLIAM WATSON. Chinese Art; the Minor Arts. NY, (1963-65). 2 vols. 425 plts (133 color). (Bkpl vol 1.) Djs, vol 2 w/slipcase, glassine outer wrapper. *Swann*.* $115/£72

JEPSON, WILLIS LINN. A Manual of the Flowering Plants of California. Berkeley: Univ of CA, 1925. 1st ed. VG in dec grn cl, gilt. *Fair Meadow.* $45/£28

Jericho Road; A Story of Western Life. (By John Habberton.) Chicago: Jansen, McClurg, 1877. 1st ed. Black cl. VG (lt rubbed, foxed). *Reese.* $35/£22

JERNIGAN, E. WESLEY. Jewelry of the Prehistoric Southwest. Albuquerque: Univ of NM, (1978). 1st ed. Fine in Fine dj. *Book Market.* $25/£16

JEROME, JEROME K. My Life and Times. Hodder & Stoughton, 1926. 1st ed. Color frontisport. VG (spotted; sl mkd, top edge sl dusty, spine ends, corners sl bumped, rubbed) in dj (nicked, rubbed, dusty, sl mkd, creased, spotted, spine, edges browned). *Ulysses.* $152/£95

JEROME, JEROME K. Three Men in a Boat. NY: Holt, 1890. 1st Amer ed. Lt blue bds. (Lt edgeworn, sl cocked), o/w VF. *Warren.* $95/£59

JEROME, JEROME K. Three Men in a Boat. LEC, 1975. One of 2000 signed by John Griffiths (illus). Fine in slipcase. *Swann*.* $34/£21

JERROLD, ALICE. A Cruise in the Acorn. Marcus Ward, tp dated 1875. 1st ed. This title advertised as '[just published].' Unrecorded variant (floral panel on cvr pictures foxgloves, blackberries and butterfly). Lg 8vo. 140pp,4pp ads; 6 illus on dec mts by Kate Greenaway. Dec dk grn cl w/floral-pict onlay, gilt. (Mks, mostly on eps, inscrip, partly erased sig; gilt rubbed, spine ends, corners worn), else Sound. *Bookmark.* $400/£250

JERROLD, DOUGLAS. The Truth About Quex. Ernest Benn, n.d. (1927). 1st Eng ed. VG (top edge dusty; spine ends, corners sl bumped) in dj (nicked, rubbed, dusty, sl chipped, dknd). *Ulysses.* $72/£45

JERROLD, WALTER (ed). The Big Book of Fables. London: Blackie & Son, (1912). 1st ed. 4to. Frontis (faint mount mks to recto), (xxiv),293pp; 11 color, 18 tinted plts by Charles Robinson. Pict eps; aeg. Red cl, gilt. Very Clean (spine sl faded). *Sotheran.* $360/£225

JESSE, CAPTAIN. The Life of George Brummell, Esq. London, 1886. One of 500. 2 vols. xxxii,363pp; xv,364+19pp ads; 40 color plts. Partly unopened. Leather spine labels (rubbed). (Margins lt stained, plts sl offset, eps browned; rear bd vol 1 damp-damaged.) *Edwards.* $72/£45

JESSE, EDWARD. An Angler's Rambles. London: John Van Voorst, 1836. 1st ed. (8),318pp. Teg. 3/4 maroon morocco, marbled bds, gilt. (Inscrip, bkpl; sl rubbed), else VG. *Pacific*.* $230/£144

JESSE, EDWARD. Gleanings in Natural History. John Murray, 1832-34. 1st eds. 2 vols. xi,313pp + (ii)pp ads; xi,321pp, fldg facs. 1/2 roan (sl rubbed), gilt. *Hollett.* $152/£95

JESSE, EDWARD. Gleanings in Natural History. London: John Murray, 1838. New ed. 2 vols. xi,352; v,383pp. Contemp 1/2 calf, marbled sides, gilt; twin red/black morocco labels. VG set (vol 1 almost invisibly re-hinged). *Young.* $72/£45

JESSE, GEORGE R. Researches into the History of the British Dog. London, 1866. 2 vols. 20 etched plts. Later 1/2 calf, gilt. *Swann*.* $230/£144

JESSE, JOHN HENEAGE. London: Its Celebrated Characters and Remarkable Places. Bentley, 1871. 1st ed. 3 vols. 8vo. Extra-illus w/130 engr plts. Teg. 1/2 blue morocco, spine gilt. *Sotheby's*.* $662/£414

JESSE, JOHN HENEAGE. Memoirs of the Pretenders and Their Adherents. George Bell & Sons, 1890. Frontis (sl spotted, stained), xii,564,32pp; 6 plts. (Fep removed; hinges sl rubbed.) *Hollett.* $40/£25

JEWELL, EDWARD ALDEN. Have We an American Art? NY: Longmans, Green, 1939. Stiff wrappers in dj. *Dawson.* $50/£31

JEWETT, JOHN HOWARD. The Baby Bears' Picnic. (Little Mother Series.) London: Ernest Nister, ca 1910. 16mo. R. C. Petherick (illus). Cl-backed color pict bds (edges, corners rubbed). *Reisler.* $250/£156

JEWETT, JOHN HOWARD. Christmas Stocking Series: Con the Wizard. NY: Frederick A. Stokes, (1905). 1st ed thus. 7.75x3.5. Edward R. Little & Oliver Herford (illus). Cl-backed pict bds. (Extrems rubbed), else VG. *Pacific*.* $46/£29

JEWETT, SARAH ORNE. Country By-Ways. Boston: Houghton Mifflin, 1881. 1st ed. One of 2000 ptd. 249pp. Grn cl (sl rubbed). VG. BAL 10878. *Second Life.* $125/£78

JEWETT, SARAH ORNE. The Country of the Pointed Firs. Boston: Houghton Mifflin, 1896. 1st ed, 2nd ptg (w/cancel tp). One of 984. 213pp. Grn sateen (sl rubbed, faded). VG. BAL 10910. *Second Life.* $150/£94

JEWETT, SARAH ORNE. The Life of Nancy. Boston: Houghton Mifflin, 1895. 1st ed. 322pp. (Spine faded, hinge sl tender), o/w VG in pub's cl. BAL 10906. *Second Life.* $85/£53

Jews of Czechoslovakia. Jewish Pub Soc of America, 1968-1984. 1st eds. 3 vols. Good in djs. *Rybski.* $110/£69

JHABVALA, RUTH PRAWER. Esmond in India. London, 1958. 1st Eng ed. VG in dj (sl dust-mkd, nicked, 1 sm closed tear). *Clearwater.* $64/£40

Jim Dine Designs for a Midsummer Night's Dream. NY: MOMA, (1968). VG in dec wraps. *Dramatis.* $16/£10

JIMENEZ, JUAN RAMON. Platero and I. Oxford: Dolphin, 1956. 1st ed in English. NF in VG+ dj (1 sm chip). *Lame Duck.* $45/£28

Jingles Illustrated. NY: Waterbury, (1885). Pamphlet. VG (bkpl) in color pict wrappers. *Rostenberg & Stern.* $45/£28

JOAD, C. E. M. The Horrors of the Countryside. London: Hogarth, 1931. Orig wraps. *Edrich.* $19/£12

JOAN, NATALIE. Lie-Down Stories. London: Blackie & Son, 1919. 1st ed. Royal 8vo. (iv),5-77pp; 8 color plts by Anne Anderson. Gray cl-backed bds w/lg onlaid illus by Anderson to upper cvr. (Eps sl speckled, browned), o/w VF in pict wrapper (lower wrap sl soiled, few sm repaired, closed tears) w/another plt. *Sotheran.* $237/£148

JOANNIDES, PAUL. Masaccio and Masolino: A Complete Catalogue. NY, (1993). Dj. *Swann*.* $57/£36

JOANS, TED. The Hipsters. NY: Corinth Books, 1961. 1st ed. Signed. Fine in wraps. *Warren.* $150/£94

JOANS, TED. Mehr Blitzliebe Poems. Hamburg, 1982. 1st ed. Signed. Fine in wraps. *Warren.* $30/£19

JOBSON, RICHARD. The Golden Trade; or, A Discovery of the River Gambra, and the Golden Trade of the Aethiopians by Richard Jobson, 1623.... Charles G. Kingsley (ed). Teignmouth, Devonsh: Speight & Walpole, 1904. 1st ed. One of 300. (Eps sl soiled; sl rubbed, corners sl dented), o/w VG. *Worldwide.* $125/£78

JOEL, DAVID. The Adventure of British Furniture 1851-1951. London, 1953. 1st ed. (Eps lt spotted.) Dj (sl ragged, repaired w/cellotape). *Edwards.* $56/£35

JOERG, WOLFGANG L. G. Brief History of Polar Exploration since the Introduction of Flying.... NY: American Geographical Soc, 1930. 2 lg fldg maps. NF in orig slipcase. *Explorer.* $51/£32

JOFFRE, MARSHALL. The Memoirs of Marshall Joffre. T. Bentley Mott (trans). London: Geoffrey Bles, (1932). 1st British ed. 2 vols. Brn cl, gilt. (Edges lt foxed), o/w VG set in djs (lt nicked, smudged). *Reese.* $75/£47

JOHANNSEN, ALBERT. The House of Beadle and Adams and Its Dime and Nickel Novels. Norman, 1950. 1st ed. 2 vols. NF. *Dumont.* $125/£78

JOHANNSEN, ERNST. Four Infantrymen. NY: Alfred H. King, 1930. 1st US ed. Gray cl. Fine in pict dj (sl edge-tanned, sm chip). *Reese.* $50/£31

John F. Kennedy Memorial Miniature: Inaugural Address, Wit, Wisdom, Eulogies. NY: Random House, (1966). 1st ed. 4 vols. Fine in VG slipcase. *Pacific*.* $98/£61

John Steinbeck. A Collection.... Santa Barbara: Bradford Morrow, 1980. 1st ed. Fine (corner sl bumped) in wraps. *Beasley.* $50/£31

John's Island Stud (South Carolina) 1750-1788. (By Fairfax Harrison.) Richmond: Privately ptd at Old Dominion Press, 1931. Uncut. Paper spine label. (Sl worn.) *Oinonen*.* $130/£81

JOHN, EVAN. (Pseud of Evan John Simpson.) Atlantic Impact 1861. NY: Putnam, (1952). 1st Amer ed. Dj. *Mott.* $25/£16

JOHN, GWEN. Luck of War. London/Glasgow/Boston: Gowans & Gray/LeRoy Phillips, 1922. 1st ed. Pict parchment over wrappers. (Few sm spots rear panel of parchment), o/w VG. *Reese.* $30/£19

JOHNS, GEORGE S. Philip Henson, the Southern Union Spy. St. Louis, 1887. 1st ed. 97pp; 3 plts. Ptd wrappers (chipped, frayed, soiled; sl worn). *Oinonen*.* $50/£31

JOHNS, ORRICK. Asphalt and Other Poems. NY, 1917. 1st Amer ed, 1st bk. Fine (name, address; spine sl sunned) in dj (spine sunned, rubbed, chipped). *Polyanthos.* $35/£22

JOHNS, W. E. Another Job for Biggles. Hodder, 1951. 1st UK ed. VG in dj. *Williams.* $64/£40

JOHNS, W. E. Biggles and the Dark Intruder. Knight Books, 1967. 1st ed. VG. *Green Meadow.* $40/£25

JOHNS, W. E. Biggles and the Leopards of Zinn. Brockhampton, 1960. 1st UK ed. Fine in dj. *Williams.* $96/£60

JOHNS, W. E. Biggles Breaks the Silence. Hodder, 1949. 1st UK ed. VG + in dj. *Williams.* $80/£50

JOHNS, W. E. Biggles Gets His Men. Hodder, 1950. 1st UK ed. NF in dj. *Williams.* $80/£50

JOHNS, W. E. Biggles Goes Home. H&S, 1960. 1st ed. VG in Nice dj. *Green Meadow.* $59/£37

JOHNS, W. E. Biggles in Mexico. Brockhampton, 1959. 1st ed. 8vo. 184pp; 6 color plts by Leslie Stead. NF in VG pict dj. *Bookmark.* $61/£38

JOHNS, W. E. Biggles of the Interpol. Brockhampton, 1957. 1st UK ed. NF in VG dj. *Martin.* $29/£18

JOHNS, W. E. Biggles Sees Too Much. Brockhampton, 1963. 1st ed. (Fep corner cut), o/w VG in Nice dj. *Green Meadow.* $136/£85

JOHNS, W. E. Biggles Takes It Rough. Brockhampton, 1963. 1st ed. VG in VG dj. *Green Meadow.* $88/£55

JOHNS, W. E. Biggles Works It Out. Hodder, 1951. 1st UK ed. VG + in dj. *Williams.* $80/£50

JOHNS, W. E. Kings of Space. H&S, 1954. 1st ed. VG in dj. *Green Meadow.* $24/£15

JOHNSGARD, P. A. Ducks, Geese, and Swans of the World. Lincoln, 1978. Dj (lt worn, tear). *Sutton.* $40/£25

Johnson's Map of the Vicinity of Richmond, and Peninsular Campaign in Virginia. NY: Johnson & Ward, c. 1862. Hand-colored dbl-pg folio map. (Sl edgeworn), o/w VG. *New Hampshire*.* $80/£50

JOHNSON, A. F. French Sixteenth Century Printing. Ernest Benn, 1928. 1st ed. 50 facs. Dec bds. Dj. *Forest.* $48/£30

JOHNSON, A. F. Italian XVI Century (Typography). NY: Scribner, 1926. 1st ed. 50 facs. Dec bds. Dj. *Forest.* $56/£35

JOHNSON, A. T. The Mill Garden. London, 1950. 1st ed. Dj (chipped). *Edwards.* $24/£15

JOHNSON, ALICE M. (ed). Saskatchewan Journals and Correspondence. Edmonton House, 1795-1800. Chesterfield House, 1800-1802. London: Hudson's Bay Record Soc, 1967. 1st ltd ed. Map. Fine in dj. *Perier.* $75/£47

JOHNSON, AMANDUS. Journal and Biography of Nicholas Collin, 1746-1831.... Phila, 1936. 1st ed. Fine in dj, pub's cardboard case. *Ginsberg.* $50/£31

JOHNSON, B. S. The Unfortunates. Panther Books, 1969. 1st UK ed. Fine w/intact wrap-around in VG orig box (spine faded, sl stained). *Williams.* $136/£85

JOHNSON, BARRY C. A British Museum Legend. Barry C. Johnson, 1984. 1st ed. 1 facs. *Forest.* $26/£16

JOHNSON, BARRY C. Lost in the Alps. Barry C. Johnson, 1985. 1st ed. Frontis. *Forest.* $32/£20

JOHNSON, CHARLES. British Poisonous Plants. London: Taylor & Francis, 1856. 28 hand-colored plts. Floral-emb cl bds (spine tender, glued). Very Nice. *Metropolitan*.* $172/£108

JOHNSON, CHARLES. The Lives and Actions of the Most Noted Highwaymen, Street-Robbers, Pirates, Etc. London: Thomas Tegg, 1839. 3rd ed. 1/4 calf over marbled bds (rubbed; foxed). VG. *Boswell.* $250/£156

JOHNSON, CLIFTON. Highways and Byways of the Rocky Mountains. NY, 1910. 1st ed. Teg. Pict cl. (Sl worn.) Poor dj. *King.* $35/£22

JOHNSON, CLIFTON. The Isle of the Shamrock. NY: Macmillan, 1901. 1st ed. Teg, untrimmed. Lt grn pict cl, gilt. VG in lt gray ptd dj (sl worn, chipped), grn bd slipcase (worn, scuffed, partial surface peeling). *Baltimore*.* $50/£31

JOHNSON, CROCKETT. Barnaby. NY: Henry Holt, (1943). Thick 8vo. 361pp. Blue textured cl (lt dusting). Color dj. *Reisler.* $150/£94

JOHNSON, DENIS. Angels. NY, 1983. 1st Amer ed. Fine (sl rubbed) in Fine dj. *Polyanthos.* $35/£22

JOHNSON, DENIS. The Veil. NY: Knopf, 1987. 1st ed. (Rmdr line on pg edge), else Fine in Fine dj. *Pettler.* $40/£25

JOHNSON, DIANA. Fantastic Illustration and Design in Britain, 1850-1930. Museum of Art, (1979). Fine in illus dj. *Metropolitan*.* $23/£14

JOHNSON, DIANE. Fair Game. NY: Harcourt Brace, (1965). 1st ed, 1st bk. Signed. Fine in Fine dj. *Lenz.* $125/£78

JOHNSON, DIANE. The Life of Dashiell Hammett. London: C&W/Hogarth, 1984. 1st ed. Frontis port. Yellow-orange cl-textured bds. Fine in dj (rear top edge sl chipped). *Temple.* $22/£14

JOHNSON, DOROTHY M. The Hanging Tree. NY: Ballantine, 1957. 1st ed. NF in VG + dj (rear panel soiled). *Unger.* $175/£109

JOHNSON, E. D. H. (ed). The Poetry of Earth. NY, 1966. 1st ed. VG in dj. *Larry Price.* $35/£22

JOHNSON, EDGAR. Sir Walter Scott, the Great Unknown. NY, (1970). 1st ptg. 2 vols. (Spines sl faded.) Slipcase (sl worn). *Woolson.* $35/£22

JOHNSON, F. M. Francis Cotes. London: Phaidon, 1976. 115 plts (4 color). VG in dj. *Ars Artis.* $72/£45

JOHNSON, FRANK H. and YATA HANEDA. Bioluminescence in Progress. Princeton: Princeton Univ, 1966. 1st ed. Black cl. VG + in dj. *House.* $75/£47

JOHNSON, FRANK M. Forest Lake and River: The Fishes of New England and Eastern Canada. Boston: (University Press), 1902. 1st ed. Chromolitho frontis, guard. Moire eps; teg, checkered gilt inner dentelles. Full sheep. (Fr joint cracked, extrms scuffed, straps detached, laid in loose), else VG. *Pacific*.* $86/£54

JOHNSON, G. Y. and F. H. BRAMWELL. A Catalogue of Masonic Pottery. York, 1951. 12 plts. (Cl sl spotted.) *Hollett.* $72/£45

JOHNSON, GENE. Ship Model Building. NY: Cornell Maritime, 1944. Blue cl. VG in dj (lt worn). *Parmer*. $45/£28

JOHNSON, GERALD W. America Grows Up. Morrow, 1960. 1st ed. Leonard E. Fisher (illus). 223pp. NF (name) in VG- dj. *Price*. $25/£16

JOHNSON, GRACE. Colter's Hell. L.A., (1938). 1st ed. Signed. Frontis. Promo blurb laid in. VG (name, date). *Sagebrush*. $32/£20

JOHNSON, GUION G. Ante-Bellum North Carolina: A Social History. Chapel Hill: Univ of NC, 1937. 1st ed. (Ink sig.) Lt grn buckram, gilt. Very Clean in ptd dj (lt rubbed, dusty, sl chipped). *Baltimore**. $25/£16

JOHNSON, HENRY LEWIS. Gutenberg and the Book of Books.... NY: William Edwin Rudge, 1932. One of 750. Folio. 4 facs. *Kane**. $60/£38

JOHNSON, HENRY. The Life and Voyages of Joseph Wiggins. London, 1907. 1st ed. Photogravure frontisport, fldg map. Teg. (1st/last few ll browned, bkpl; spine sl faded, rubbed.) *Edwards*. $56/£35

JOHNSON, J. Typographia, or the Printers Instructor. London, 1824. 2 vols. Engr add'l tps, frontispieces. Early 1/4 cl (needs rebinding). *Swann**. $172/£108

JOHNSON, JAMES WELDON (ed). The Book of American Negro Poetry. NY, (1922). 1st ed. Dj (price-clipped). *Swann**. $316/£198

JOHNSON, JAMES WELDON. Black Manhattan. NY: Knopf, 1930. 1st ed. Pict eps; top edge stained red. Gray cl. VG (eps sl soiled; spine dknd, lettering flaking). *Heritage*. $200/£125

JOHNSON, JAMES WELDON. Black Manhattan. NY, 1930. 1st ed. Signed, inscribed presentation. (Sl worn.) Dj (frayed, chips, splits). *Oinonen**. $400/£250

JOHNSON, JAMES. An Essay on Morbid Sensibility of the Stomach and Bowels.... London: Thomas and George Underwood, 1828. 5th ed. viii,174pp + [ii]pp ads (last leaf torn w/out loss; some ll lt soiled, creased). Calf-backed marbled bds, spine gilt. *Edwards*. $120/£75

JOHNSON, JOHN EVERETT (trans). Regulations for Governing the Province of the Californias...1781. SF: Grabhorn, 1929. 1st ed in English. Ltd to 300. 2 vols. Tan paper bds, ptd spine titles. Fine set (last 2 reps of 1 vol sl foxed; spines sl dknd). *Argonaut*. $175/£109

JOHNSON, JOHN. The Defense of Charleston Harbor...1863-65. Charleston: Walker, Evans & Cogswell, 1890. 1st ed. 276,(1),186pp; complete w/48 plts, maps, illus. Olive cl. Nice (few creases of maps delicate; lt soiled, edges rubbed). Howes J138. *Chapel Hill*. $350/£219

JOHNSON, JOSEPH FORSYTH. The Natural Principles of Landscape Gardening. The Author, (1874). 1st ed. ii,viii,152,12pp ads; 11 plts. (Inscrip, ink fep bottom; corners bumped, scuffed), else VG. *Fair Meadow*. $125/£78

JOHNSON, KAY. Human Songs. SF: City Lights, 1964. 1st ed. One of 400. Fine in wraps. *Beasley*. $30/£19

JOHNSON, KENNETH (ed). San Francisco as It Is. Georgetown: Talisman, 1964. Ltd to 1000. 16 plts. Paper spine label. Fine in pict dj. *Pacific**. $29/£18

JOHNSON, KENNETH. Aerial California: An Account of Early Flight in Northern and Southern California 1849 to World War I. L.A.: Dawson's Book Shop, 1961. 1st ed. One of 350 ptd. Paper spine label. (Spine sl sunned), else NF. *Pacific**. $86/£54

JOHNSON, KENNETH. The Life and Times of Edward Robeson Taylor. (SF): Book Club of CA, 1968. 1st ed. Ltd to 400 ptd. Fldg facs. Mostly unopened. Fine. *Harrington*. $40/£25

JOHNSON, KENNETH. The New Almaden Quicksilver Mine with an Account of the Land Claims Involving the Mine and Its Role in California History. Georgetown, CA: Talisman, 1963. One of 75 signed, w/2 pieces related contemp ephemera. Fldg map. Cl-backed pict bds. Fine. *House*. $65/£41

JOHNSON, LADY BIRD. A White House Diary. NY, (1970). 1st ed. Inscribed, signed on bkpl. Dj (sl chipped). *Argosy*. $150/£94

JOHNSON, LIONEL. The Art of Thomas Hardy. London/NY: Elkin Mathews, John Lane/Dodd, Mead, 1894. 1500 ptd. Frontis, guard; errata on last pg of prelims; (xii),276,(lxiv)pp, pub's inserted 16-pg cat dated 1894 at end. Uncut. Grn coarse buckram, gilt. (Press cutting laid on fep; spine faded), o/w Fine. *Temple*. $88/£55

JOHNSON, LIONEL. The Art of Thomas Hardy. London: John Lane, Bodley Head, 1923. 1st ed. 2 ports. (Extrems sl rubbed.) *Hollett*. $56/£35

JOHNSON, M. M. and C. T. HAVEN. Automatic Arms: Their History, Development and Use. NY, 1941. 1st ed. (Inner fr hinge cracked.) *Hallam*. $96/£60

JOHNSON, MARGARET S. Snowshoe Paws. Morrow, 1949. 1st ed. 64pp. Fine in VG dj. *Price*. $35/£22

JOHNSON, MARTIN. Lion. African Adventure with the King of Beasts. Knickerbocker, 1929. 2nd imp. Fldg map. (Remains of lib? bkpl; spine sl faded, rear joint sl frayed.) *Edwards*. $72/£45

JOHNSON, MERLE. A Bibliography of the Works of Mark Twain. Westport: Greenwood Press, (1974). 2nd ptg of photo rpt of 1935 orig ed. Red cl. Clean. *Baltimore**. $30/£19

JOHNSON, MERLE. Howard Pyle's Book of the American Spirit. NY: Harper, 1923. 1st ed. 12x9. 1/2 cl, pict cvr label. (Spine, upper extrems sunned), else VG. *Pacific**. $81/£51

JOHNSON, MYRTLE ELIZABETH and HARRY JAMES SNOOK. Seashore Animals of the Pacific Coast. NY: Macmillan, 1927. 1st ed. Gilt-dec cl. VG + . *Pacific**. $29/£18

JOHNSON, OLGA W. Flathead and Kootenai Series. Early Libby and Troy, Montana. The Author, (1958). VG in wraps w/plastic comb binding. *Perier*. $22/£14

JOHNSON, P. H. Six Proust Reconstructions. Macmillan, 1958. 1st ed. VG in dj (sl dull). *Whiteson*. $19/£12

JOHNSON, P. H. Thomas Wolfe. A Critical Study. Heinemann, 1947. 1st ed. VG + in VG- dj. *Any Amount*. $19/£12

JOHNSON, P. H. The Unspeakable Skipton. Macmillan, 1959. 1st ed. (Edges sl faded), else Good in dj (sl rubbed). *Whiteson*. $16/£10

JOHNSON, R. BRIMLEY. Jane Austen. London: Sheed & Ward, 1927. 1st Eng ed. Fine in tissue dj (torn, creased, repaired). *Ulysses*. $48/£30

JOHNSON, R. J. Specimens of Early French Architecture, Selected Chiefly from the Churches of the Ile de France. Newcastle-Upon-Tyne: The Author, 1864. Folio. 100 plts. Contemp 3/4 leather (worn, inner joint broken; sl soiled, foxed). Internally Sound. *Oinonen**. $120/£75

JOHNSON, RAY et al (eds). Mail Etc., Art. Univ of CO/Tyler School of Art/FL State Univ, 1980. 1st ed. 3 tipped-in plts. Fine in illus stiff wrappers. *Cahan*. $45/£28

JOHNSON, ROBERT and CLARENCE BUEL (eds). Battles and Leaders of the Civil War. NY, Century, (1887-1888). 4 vols. 750; 760; 752; 836pp. (Bkpls; leather backstrips sl faded, chipped; one outer hinge cracked 3-inches.) *Woolman*. $350/£219

JOHNSON, ROBERT and CLARENCE BUEL (eds). Battles and Leaders of the Civil War. NY: Century, (1887-88). 4 vols. 4to. 750; 760; 752; 836pp + index. Aeg. 3/4 brn morocco, cl, gilt dec. NF. Howes J145. *House*. $650/£406

JOHNSON, RONALD. The Book of the Green Man. NY: Norton, (1967). 1st ed. Fine in dj. *Reese*. $85/£53

JOHNSON, SAMUEL. A Diary of a Journey into North Wales, in the Year 1774. R. Duppa (ed). London: Robert Jennings, 1816. 1st ed, 1st ptg. 12mo. Errata slip mtd to end leaf; 2 facs plts. Marbled edges, eps. Later polished calf, gilt spine, leather labels. (Lacks 1/2 title; 2 bkpls; sl discolored), o/w Fine. *Cummins*. $500/£313

JOHNSON, SAMUEL. A Dictionary of the English Language. London, 1755. 1st ed. 2 vols. Folio. (Tp vol 1 supplied in facs, sm sig tear, margins sl dknd; rebacked, recornered in mod leather, orig worn calf cvrs retained.) Kane*. $2,100/£1,313

JOHNSON, SAMUEL. A Dictionary of the English Language. London: J. & P. Knapton et al, 1755. 1st ed. 2 vols. Folio. Contemp calf (rebacked retaining early 19th-cent morocco lettering pieces; vol 1 fr joint starting, vol 2 fr joint cracked; crease in vol 2 tp; lacks 3 leaves). 1/4 cowhide fldg cases. Swann*. $2,300/£1,438

JOHNSON, SAMUEL. A Dictionary of the English Language. London, 1765. 3rd ed. 2 vols. 17x10 inches. Unpaginated. Lib buckram, gilt-stamped morocco spine labels. (Ex-lib, sl stained; cvrs worn), else Good set. King. $1,495/£934

JOHNSON, SAMUEL. A Dictionary of the English Language. J.F. & C. Rivington et al, 1785. 6th ed. 2 vols. Folio. Engr frontis port (sl spotted, offset). Contemp calf (crudely rebacked preserving orig spine), later(?) bds from another set (spines rubbed; hinges repaired). Sotheby's*. $478/£299

JOHNSON, SAMUEL. A Dictionary of the English Language...To Which Are Added Walker's Principles of English Pronunciation.... Phila: James Maxwell, 1819. 1st Amer ed. 2 vols. Tall wide 4to. Frontisport. Period-style chestnut calf spines, marbled bds, raised bands, gilt. VG (sl foxed; nicely rebound). Hartfield. $1,950/£1,219

JOHNSON, SAMUEL. The History of Rasselas Prince of Abissinia. London/NY: J.M. Dent/E.P. Dutton, (1926). 1st ed w/Douglas Percy Bliss illus. Black cl, gilt. (Spine head chipped), else Fine. Glenn. $100/£63

JOHNSON, SAMUEL. Johnsoniana; Or, Supplement to Boswell: Being Anecdotes.... London, 1836. 1st ed, large paper issue. 45 steel-engrs. (Foxing, few sl margin stains.) Contemp calf (rubbed, foxed, fr cvr nearly detached, spine worn), gilt. Oinonen*. $120/£75

JOHNSON, SAMUEL. The Letters of Samuel Johnson...with Mrs. Thrale's Genuine Letters to Him. R. W. Chapman (ed). Oxford: Clarendon, 1952. 1st ed. 3 vols. Facs frontispieces. Maroon linen, gilt. NF set. Hartfield. $395/£247

JOHNSON, SAMUEL. Letters to and from the Late Samuel Johnson, LL.D. London: A. Strahan & T. Cadell, 1788. 1st ed, lacking the scarce errata slip, as usual. 2 vols. 8vo. Tp, xi,424pp. Contemp calf (rebacked, hinges splitting, corners bumped, labels chipped). Marlborough. $560/£350

JOHNSON, SAMUEL. The Lives of the Most Eminent English Poets; with Critical Observations on Their Works. London: C. Bathurst et al, 1781. 1st separate London ed. 4 vols. Frontisport. Period mottled calf, gilt. VG (bkpls, joints cracking or starting; extrems, spines dknd, 1 vol w/crack along spine). Pacific*. $127/£79

JOHNSON, SAMUEL. The Poetical Works. London: Osborne, Griffin et al, 1785. New ed, w/Irene ptd at the end. Sm 8vo. Half-titles present, viii,152pp. Early polished calf, leather label. Nice (fep replaced, early names; hinges worn). Hartfield. $325/£203

JOHNSON, SAMUEL. Prayers and Meditations. George Strahan (ed). London: Cadell & Davis, 1807. 4th ed. 230pp,1-pg ads. Fine full polished morocco, raised bands, gilt, red leather label. Fine (bkpl, notes). Hartfield. $295/£184

JOHNSON, SAMUEL. The Rambler. London: Dodsley, Owen et al, 1794. 4 vols. Fine recent brn polished calf, marbled bds, raised bands, gilt, red/grn leather labels. Fine set. Hartfield. $495/£309

JOHNSON, SAMUEL. The Rambler. Montrose: Ptd by D. Buchanan, 1800. 1st Montrose ed. 4 vols. 4 engr frontispieces. (Text sl spotted; sl rubbed), o/w VG set in full contemp calf, gilt spines, twin red morocco labels. Young. $176/£110

JOHNSON, SAMUEL. The Rambler. Phila: J.J. Woodward, 1827. New ed. 4 vols. 12mo. Full-pg copper-engr frontis each vol, v,257; vii,230; vii,259; vii,235pp + 2pp list. Mottled calf on bds, gilt. Good (handwritten lib pocket, card pasted inside rear cvr each vol, call # label on spine, handwritten lib labels; sl worn, lt foxed, lt splitting). Hobbyhorse. $250/£156

JOHNSON, SAMUEL. The Works of Samuel Johnson, LL.D. In Nine (Eleven) Volumes. Oxford: William Pickering, 1825. 1st ed. 11 vols. Port vol X, port vol IX. All vols w/half-titles. 19th-cent 1/2 red calf, marbled bds (extrems sl scuffed), gilt. Sound. Karmiole. $450/£281

JOHNSON, SAMUEL. The Works of Samuel Johnson. London: T. Longman et al, 1792. 12 vols. Frontisport. Period tree calf, gilt spines, red/grn morocco spine labels. (Bkpls; spines worn, 1 spine head torn), o/w VG set. Pacific*. $184/£115

JOHNSON, STANLEY C. The Medal Collector. Herbert Jenkins, 1921. 1st ed. 24 plts. VG in dj (sl chipped). Hollett. $48/£30

JOHNSON, T. B. The Hunting Directory; Containing a Compendious View of the Ancient and Modern Systems of the Chase. London: Sherwood, Gilbert & Piper, 1830. 312pp + 20 leaves pub's ads at end, dated variously 1831-1833. Uncut. Cl back, paper spine label. (Sl foxed; shelfworn, soiled.) Oinonen*. $100/£63

JOHNSON, THEOPHILUS. Illustrations of the Larvae and Pupae of British Lepidoptera, with Figures of the Food-Plant. (London), 1878. 8vo. 53 full-pg watercolor dwgs. Teg, rest uncut. Olive morocco, gilt, by Tout. (Sl spotting.) Sotheby's*. $5,888/£3,680

JOHNSON, THOMAS BURGELAN. The Hunting Directory. London, 1830. 7 engr plts. Mod grn calf, gilt. Swann*. $172/£108

JOHNSON, THOMAS CARY. The Life and Letters of Robert Lewis Dabney. Richmond, VA: Presbyterian Committee of Pub, (1903). 1st ed. Inscribed. Grn cl. (Inner hinges cracked), else VG. Chapel Hill. $150/£94

JOHNSON, VIRGINIA W. An English 'Daisy Miller.' Boston: Estes & Lauriat, 1882. 1st ed. 67pp. (Sl shelfworn, soiled), o/w Good. Brown. $20/£13

JOHNSON, W. FLETCHER. The Red Record of the Sioux. Life of Sitting Bull and History of the Indian War of 1890-91. Edgewood Pub, (1891). 544pp. VG in dec cl. Perier. $45/£28

JOHNSON, WILLIAM HENRY. A Bird's Eye View of Happenings in the Life of William Henry Johnson of Petersburg, Virginia. Petersburg: The Author, 1927. 1st ed. Port. (Spine bottom scuffed), o/w VG in ptd wraps. Petrilla. $175/£109

JOHNSTON, A. Narrative of the Operations of a Detachment in an Expedition to Candy, in the Island of Ceylon, in the Year 1804. London, 1810. Inscribed by 'The Author.' Fldg map (several clean tears at folds). Tree sheep (cvr loose; upper margin excised on dedication leaf, no loss; bkpl). Swann*. $149/£93

JOHNSTON, ALASTAIR J. The Clapcott Papers. Edinburgh: (Foulis), 1985. 1st ed. One of 400. Prospectus laid in. Gilt-dec cl. As New (emb stamp) in slipcase. Pacific*. $259/£162

JOHNSTON, ANNIE FELLOWS. Mary Ware the Little Colonel's Chum. Boston: Page, 1908. Stated 1st ptg. Pict cl. VG (corners sl bumped). Price. $25/£16

JOHNSTON, D. In Search of Swift. Dublin, 1959. 1st ed. Signed. VG in dj (torn). Gretton. $19/£12

JOHNSTON, DAVID E. The Story of a Confederate Boy in the Civil War. (Portland, OR: Glass & Prudhomme, 1914.) 1st ed. Frontisport. Red cl. Fine in VG ptd dj (few chips, tears). Chapel Hill. $500/£313

JOHNSTON, FRANCES BENJAMIN. The Early Architecture of North Carolina. Univ of NC, 1941. One of 900. Folio. (Lt worn.) Box (worn). Oinonen*. $190/£119

JOHNSTON, GEORGE. An Introduction to Conchology.... John Van Voorst, 1850. 1st ed. xvi,(616)pp. Aeg. Contemp 1/2 morocco, banded, gilt. Nice (sl rubbed, sl split, few ribbon mks). *Ash.* $136/£85

JOHNSTON, H. The Nile Quest. Alston Rivers, 1905. 1st ed. All edges uncut. Grn dec cl, gilt. VF. *Sotheran.* $240/£150

JOHNSTON, H. The River Congo from Its Mouth to Bolobo.... Sampson Low, Marston, 1895. 4th ed. xv,300,30,(ii)ads pp. Crimson cl, gilt. Good (eps, tp foxed; bds sl mkd). *Sotheran.* $200/£125

JOHNSTON, HANK. Death Valley Scotty, 'The Fastest Con in the West.' Corona Del Mar, CA: Trans-Anglo, (1974). 1st ed. Fine in Fine dj. *Book Market.* $25/£16

JOHNSTON, HARRY V. My Home on the Range. St. Paul, MN: Webb Pub, (1942). 1st ed. VG in dj (sl worn). *Lien.* $30/£19

JOHNSTON, I. N. Four Months in Libby, and the Campaign Against Atlanta. Cincinnati, 1864. 1st ed. 191pp. Ptd wrappers (rebacked, sl worn, lt dampstained). *Oinonen*.* $130/£81

JOHNSTON, J. E. Narrative of Military Operations, Directed, During the Late War Between the States. NY: D. Appleton, 1874. 1st ed. Port, 602pp + ads. (Cl worn, soiled), else Good reading copy. Howes J167. *Brown.* $75/£47

JOHNSTON, J. E. Narrative of Military Operations. NY: Appleton, 1874. 1st ed. Frontisport, 602pp + (6)pp ads; 11 maps, plans (1 fldg). Grn cl, gilt. (Lt shelfworn), else Very Bright. *Chapel Hill.* $375/£234

JOHNSTON, J. F. W. Lectures on Agricultural Chemistry and Geology. Edinburgh, 1844. 1st ed. 2 vols. 1047pp. 1/2 leather, marbled bds, ribbed spines, gilt. (Rear bd vol 1 damaged), else VG. *Larry Price.* $145/£91

JOHNSTON, JAMES H. A Ministry of Forty Years in Indiana. Indianapolis: Holloway, Douglass, 1865. Pamphlet. Removed. 30pp. VG (text lt spotted). *Brown.* $20/£13

JOHNSTON, JENNIFER. How Many Miles to Babylon. London: Hamish Hamilton, (1974). 1st ed. Gilt grn cl bds. Fine in dj (sl smudged). *Reese.* $30/£19

JOHNSTON, MARY. Cease Firing. Boston: Houghton Mifflin, 1912. 1st ed. 4 color plts by N.C. Wyeth. Gray cl, gilt. VG + (sl worn). *House.* $45/£28

JOHNSTON, MARY. Cease Firing. Boston/NY: Houghton Mifflin, 1912. 1st ed. One of 500 signed. Color frontis, 3 color plts by N. C. Wyeth. Unopened. Gray cl, paper spine label. VG (spine soiled). *Chapel Hill.* $275/£172

JOHNSTON, MARY. The Long Roll. Boston: Houghton Mifflin, 1911. 1st ed. 4 color plts by N. C. Wyeth. Gray cl, gilt. VG (bkpl; spine faded). *Chapel Hill.* $45/£28

JOHNSTON, MARY. To Have and To Hold. Boston and NY/Cambridge: Houghton Mifflin/Riverside, (1900). 1st trade ed. 8vo. Frontis, vi,(ii),403pp; 7 plts. Pict grn cl, gilt. VG (name; lt bumped, rubbed). *Blue Mountain.* $50/£31

JOHNSTON, PAUL. Biblio-Typographica. NY: Covici, 1930. One of 1050. Orig prospectus laid in. Uncut. Paper spine label. (Lt worn.) Dj (frayed, tape repairs on verso). *Oinonen*.* $60/£38

JOHNSTON, RICHARD. Follow Me! The Story of the Second Marine Division in World War II. NY, 1948. 1st ed. VG. *Clark.* $85/£53

JOHNSTON, TONY. Lorenzo the Naughty Parrot. NY: Harcourt, Brace, Jovanovich, 1992. 1st ed. 4to. Leo Politi (illus). Fine in Fine dj. *Davidson.* $30/£19

JOHNSTON, W. and A. K. The Scottish Tartans. Edinburgh: W. & A.K. Johnston, (c.1910). (Cutting on ep.) Dec grn cl. *Hollett.* $48/£30

JOHNSTONE, E. M. West by South Half South. Buffalo: Matthews Northrup, 1890. 1st ed. 99pp. Good in wrappers (lacks spine portions, worn). *Brown.* $60/£38

JOHNSTONE, HARRY. George Grenfell and the Congo. London: Hutchinson, 1908. 1st ed. 2 vols. Med 8vo. xxiii,xx,990pp; 6 maps (2 fldg). Teg. Fine set in djs (sl rubbed). *Ulysses.* $960/£600

JOHNSTONE, R. W. William Smellie. The Master of British Midwifery. Edinburgh/London, 1952. Color frontis port. *Edwards.* $29/£18

JOHNSTONE, W. G. and A. CROALL. The Nature Printed British Sea-Weeds. London, 1859-1860. 4 vols. 8vo. 4 addt'l engr tps; 1 plain, 221 color plts (few plts sl foxed). 1/2 calf (rubbed), gilt. Bkpl of R. Binney-Smith. *Henly.* $576/£360

JOHNSTONE, WILLIAM. Creative Art in Britain. London, 1950. Color frontis, 7 color plts, 206 b/w plts. (Margins sl browned, lib ink stamp fr pastedown; cl lt soiled, lt #.) *Edwards.* $40/£25

JOINVILLE, JEAN. The History of Saint Louis. (Newtown: Gregynog), 1937. One of 200 numbered. Folio. 17 hand-colored wood engrs by Reynolds Stone, 2 full-pg maps. Dk maroon oasis, gilt arms. *Swann*.* $1,840/£1,150

JOINVILLE, JEAN. Memoirs...Written by Himself. Thomas Johnes (trans). (London): Hafod Press, 1807. 2 vols. 3 engr plts, 3 maps. Contemp 1/2 russia, gilt. (Engr matter foxed, offset.) *Swann*.* $488/£305

Jolly Jump-Ups See the Circus. Springfield: McLoughlin Bros, (1944). Obl 8vo. 6 pop-ups. Color pict bds (lt edgeworn). VG. *Davidson.* $185/£116

JOLY, HENRI L. and KUMASAKU TOMITA. Japanese Art and Handicraft. London: Sawers-Valansot, 1976. Red cl. Fine in dj. *Appelfeld.* $100/£63

JOLY, HENRI L. (ed). Legend in Japanese Art. London, 1908. (Spine faded, lacks sm piece at top, rear joint cracked.) *Swann*.* $316/£198

JONCICH, GERALDINE. The Sane Positivist: A Biography of Edward L. Thorndike. Middletown, CT: Wesleyan Univ, (1968). Maroon cl, painted spine label. VG in dj (lt worn). *Gach.* $50/£31

JONES, A. BASSETT and LLEWELLYN LLEWELLYN. Malingering, or the Simulation of Disease. Phila: Blakiston, 1918. 1st ed. Brn buckram (rebound?, shaken, worn; ex-lib), gilt. *Beasley.* $100/£63

JONES, ADRIAN. Memoirs of a Soldier Artist. London, 1933. (Lt spotting.) *Edwards.* $56/£35

JONES, BARBARA and WILLIAM OUELLETTE. Erotic Postcards. London, 1977. 1st Eng ed. VG in dj. *Clearwater.* $56/£35

JONES, BARBARA. Follies and Grottoes. London, 1974. 2nd ed. Dj (spine faded). *Edwards.* $48/£30

JONES, BENCE. The Life and Letters...Faraday. London: Longmans, Green, 1870. 1st ed. 2 vols. Frontis each vol, vi,(4),427; (12),499pp. Complete w/half titles. Mod cl. VG set (frontis, tp vol 1 dampstained). *Glaser.* $225/£141

JONES, BERNARD E. (ed). Cassell's Cyclopaedia of Photography. London/NY/Toronto/Melbourne: Cassell, n.d. (1911). 24 full-pg plts. Blue cl, gilt. NF (inscrip). *Cahan.* $150/£94

JONES, BOBBY. Rights and Wrongs of Golf. N.p.: A.G. Spalding, (1936). 1st ed. Fine (emb stamp) in pict wrappers. *Pacific*.* $184/£115

JONES, BRIAN. Poems. Alan Ross, London Magazine Editions, 1966. 1st ed. Fine in brn flecked wrappers. *Maggs.* $56/£35

JONES, C. W. In Prison at Point Lookout. Martinsville, VA: Bulletin Ptg & Pub, (ca 1890). 1st ed. 9pp. VG in pict ptd wraps. *Chapel Hill.* $125/£78

JONES, CHARLES C. The Life and Services of Commodore Josiah Tattnall. Savannah: Morning News Steam Ptg House, 1878. 1st ed. Frontisport, 255,4pp. Rust cl. VG + (full-pg inscrip). Howes J201. *Chapel Hill.* $300/£188

JONES, CHARLES C. The Siege of Savannah.... Albany, NY: The Author, 1874. 1st ed. 184pp. Complete w/errata slip. NF in ptd wraps bound into mod grn cl. *Chapel Hill.* $250/£156

JONES, CHUCK. Chuck Amuck: The Life and Times of an Animated Cartoonist. NY: FSG, (1989). 1st ed. Signed, inscribed. Fine in dj. *Pacific*.* $58/£36

JONES, CLEMENT. John Bolton of Storrs 1756-1837. Kendal: Titus Wilson, 1959. 1st ed. 4 plts. VG. *Hollett.* $24/£15

JONES, DAN BURNE. The Prints of Rockwell Kent: A Catalogue Raisonne. Chicago, (1975). Dj. *Swann*.* $230/£144

JONES, DAVID. The Kensington Mass. (London): Agenda Editions, 1975. 1st ed. Fine in stiff ptd wrappers, acetate dj. *Dermont.* $30/£19

JONES, DAVID. The Sleeping Lord and Other Fragments. London: Faber & Faber, (1974). 1st ed. Fine in Fine dj. *Dermont.* $60/£38

JONES, DAVID. The Sleeping Lord and Other Fragments. London, 1974. 1st Eng ed. Fine in dj. *Clearwater.* $56/£35

JONES, DOUGLAS C. The Court-Martial of George Armstrong Custer. NY: Scribner, (1976). 1st ed. VG in dj. *Lien.* $30/£19

JONES, E. ALFRED. The Old Silver of American Churches. Letchworth: Arden, 1913. One of 506 numbered. Thick folio. 145 plts. (Rebacked retaining orig backstrip; eps renewed; bkpl, card pocket.) *Swann*.* $517/£323

JONES, E. H. The Road to En-Dor, Being an Account of How Two Prisoners of War at Yozgad in Turkey Won Their Way to Freedom. London: Bodley Head, 1920. (Binding faded.) *Petersfield.* $24/£15

JONES, EDGAR YOXALL. Father of Art Photography: O.G. Rejlander, 1813-1875. Greenwich, CT: NYGS, 1973. 1st ed. 80 b/w photos. VG in dj. *Cahan.* $65/£41

JONES, EDGAR. Autobiography of an Early Settler in New Zealand. Wellington: Coulls Somerville Wilkie, 1933. Grn cl. Poor (soiled, cracked; worn). *Parmer.* $50/£31

JONES, EDWARD ALFRED. The Old Silver of American Churches. Letchworth: Arden Press, 1913. One of 506. Folio. 145 plts. Teg, rest uncut. Grn buckram. (Fr hinge sl weak.) *Sotheby's*.* $515/£322

JONES, ELIAS. Revised History of Dorchester County, Maryland. Balt: Read-Taylor Press, 1925. 1st ed. Frontisport. Dk grn cl, gilt (dull). Text Very Clean, cvrs VG. *Baltimore*.* $80/£50

JONES, ELIZABETH ORTON. Twig. Macmillan, 1942. 3rd ed. 152pp. VG (fep creased) in Good dj (browned; corners, spine ends chipped, faded, spine rubbed). *Price.* $46/£29

JONES, ERNEST. The Life and Work of Sigmund Freud. NY: Basic Books, (1953/1955/1957). 1st Amer eds, trade issues. 3 vols. 8 plts; 10 plts; 14 plts. Blue cl w/painted labels. (Spine labels rubbed), else VG set. *Gach.* $100/£63

JONES, ERNEST. The Life and Work of Sigmund Freud. London: Hogarth, (1953/1955/1957). 1st British eds. 3 vols. 8 plts; 10 plts; 14 plts. Blue buckram. VG in djs (worn). *Gach.* $125/£78

JONES, F. W. The Principles of Anatomy as Seen in the Hand. London, 1949. 2nd ed. 2 plts. (Spine sl worn), o/w VG. *Whitehart.* $56/£35

JONES, FAYETTE ALEXANDER. New Mexico Mines and Minerals. Santa Fe, 1905. 1st ed. Dated 1904 on fr bd. (Bkpl removed), else Good. *Dumont.* $85/£53

JONES, GEORGE F. Myself and Others; or, Reminiscences, Recollections and Experiences...1811-1887...in Providence...and Philadelphia.... Phila: Globe Ptg House, (1887). 1st ed. 252pp. (Inner hinges cracked, but holding), else VG. *Petrilla.* $65/£41

JONES, GEORGE N. Flora of Illinois. Notre Dame, IN: Univ of Notre Dame, 1950. 2nd ed. Black cl. Fine. *Archer.* $35/£22

JONES, GWYN and THOMAS (trans). The Golden Cockerel Mabinogion, a New Translation from the White Book of Rhydderch and the Red Book of Hergest. Golden Cockerel, 1948. One of 550 numbered. Folio. 20 wood engrs by Dorothea Braby. Teg, rest untrimmed. Orig 1/2 orange morocco, maize buckram sides, gilt design fr cvr. VG. *Sotheran.* $797/£498

JONES, HENRY. The Heroine of the Cave. Dublin: Ptd by W. Spotswood, 1775. 1st Dublin ed. 60pp. Calf-backed bds. *Young.* $56/£35

JONES, HETTIE. Big Star Fallin' Mama: Five Women in Black Music. NY: Viking, (1974). 1st ed. VG in pict dj. *Petrilla.* $25/£16

JONES, HOLWAY R. John Muir and the Sierra Club. SF: Sierra Club, (1965). 64 plts. Grn/gray cl, gilt. Fine in pict dj. *Pacific*.* $23/£14

JONES, IDWAL. Ark of Empire. GC: Doubleday, 1951. 1st ed. Signed. 12 plts. Grn/gray cl. Fine. *Pacific*.* $35/£22

JONES, IDWAL. China Boy. L.A.: Primavera Press, (1936). Inscribed. Prospectus laid in. Patterned bds, cl spine. Dj (lt chipped). *Dawson.* $60/£38

JONES, IDWAL. Vines in the Sun. NY: William Morrow, 1949. VG in dj. *Perier.* $30/£19

JONES, IDWAL. Vines in the Sun. A Journey Through the California Vineyards. NY: William Morrow, 1949. 1st ed. Inscribed, signed presentation. Dec gray cl. Fine in pict dj. *Argonaut.* $60/£38

JONES, IFANO. A History of Printing and Printers in Wales to 1810 and of Successive and Related Printers to 1923. Cardiff: Ptd by Wm. Lewis, 1925. Subscribers list. Dk grn cl, gilt. VG. *Michael Taylor.* $136/£85

JONES, INIGO. The Designs of; Consisting of Plans and Elevations for Publick and Private Buildings. London: William Kent, 1727. 1st ed. 2 vols in 1. Folio. 97 full/dbl-pg, fldg plts, numbered 1-73 and 1-63 (some plts w/dbl #s). 19th-cent brn morocco (worn, cvrs detached, spine chipped; sl foxed, soiled, lacks port), gilt. Internally Clean. *Oinonen*.* $1,900/£1,188

JONES, INIGO. The Most Notable Antiquity of Great Britain, Vulgarly Called Stone-Heng...to Which Are Added, The Chorea Gigantum...and Mr. Webb's Vindication.... London: D. Browne et al, 1725. 2nd ed. 3 parts in 1 vol. Folio. 14 engr plts. Contemp panelled calf (rebacked retaining most of orig backstrip, corner of fr cvr restored, hinges reinforced; 18th-cent armorial bkpl). *Swann*.* $747/£467

JONES, J. WILLIAM (comp). Army of North Virginia Memorial Volume. Richmond: Randolph & English, 1880. 1st ed. 347pp. Brn cl, ptd paper spine label. (Lt worn, spine sl sunned), else VG. *Chapel Hill.* $350/£219

JONES, J. WILLIAM. Christ in the Camp. B.F. Johnston, 1887. 528pp. VG (edges, interior foxed; spine sl frayed, cvr cl bubbled). *Book Broker.* $75/£47

JONES, J. WILLIAM. Life and Letters of Robert Edward Lee. NY/Washington: Neale, 1906. 1st ed. Inscribed. 8vo. Frontisport, add'l ports. Grn cl. Fine in dj (lt worn). *Chapel Hill.* $950/£594

JONES, J. WILLIAM. Personal Reminiscences, Anecdotes, and Letters of Gen. Robert E. Lee. NY: Appleton, 1874. 1st ed. Frontisport, xvi,509,(2)pp. Dec grn cl. VG (sigs; extrems lt rubbed). *Chapel Hill.* $250/£156

JONES, JAMES. From Here to Eternity. NY: Scribner, 1951. 1st ed, 1st bk. Black cl, gilt. VG (eps sl browned; spine sl cocked, gilt flaking from 2 spine letters). *Heritage.* $100/£63

JONES, JAMES. From Here to Eternity. NY: Scribner, 1951. 1st ed, 1st bk, trade issue. Black cl bds, gilt. (Eps sl offset), o/w Fine in NF dj (3 sm mks). *Reese.* $200/£125

JONES, JAMES. From Here to Eternity. NY: Scribner, 1951. 1st ed, 1st bk, presentation issue. Ltd to about 1500 signed. Fine in Fine dj. *Bromer.* $500/£313

JONES, JAMES. The Pistol. NY: Scribner, (1958). 1st ed. VF in VF dj (sm scrape). *Between The Covers.* $200/£125

JONES, JOHN B. A Rebel War Clerk's Diary at the Confederate States Capital. Phila: Lippincott, 1866. 1st ed. 2 vols. 392; 480pp (lt browned, foxed; bkpls). Early dk brn sheep, marbled bds (worn; cvr panels detached vol 1; spines scuffed w/some loss of lettering), gilt. Howes J220. *Baltimore*.* $80/£50

JONES, JOHN B. A Rebel War Clerk's Diary at the Confederate States Capital. Howard Swiggett (ed). NY: Old Hickory Bookshop, 1935. New, enlgd ed. 2 vols. (Ex-lib; lt handled.) Navy buckram (sl worn), gilt. Cvrs Good. Howes J220. *Baltimore*.* $35/£22

JONES, JOHN B. A Rebel War Clerk's Diary. Phila, 1866. 1982 Time-Life Collector's Library of the Civil War edition. 2 vols. Leather. Fine. *Pratt.* $50/£31

JONES, KATHARINE M. Heroines of Dixie. Indianapolis: Bobbs-Merrill, (1955). 1st ed. 11 ports. Red cl, gilt. Fine in pict dj. *Argonaut.* $40/£25

JONES, LEROI. Blues People. NY, (1963). 2nd ptg. Signed. (Sl worn.) Wraps. *King.* $25/£16

JONES, LEROI. Dutchman and the Slave. NY, 1964. 1st ed. 1/2-cl. VG in dj (sl worn, one sl tear). *King.* $50/£31

JONES, LEROI. Dutchman and the Slave: Two Plays. NY: William Morrow, 1964. 1st ed. Top edge stained yellow. White cl, dk grn bds. OBIE award sticker fr cvr. VG dj (sl rubbed). *Baltimore*.* $50/£31

JONES, LEROI. Preface to a Twenty Volume Suicide Note. N.p., (1961). Inscribed, signed. Wraps (sl soiled). *King.* $25/£16

JONES, OWEN. The Grammar of Ornament. London: Bernard Quaritch, 1868. Thick folio. (i),157pp; 112 chromolitho plts, guards. Later eps; aeg. Beveled crimson cl, gilt. (Lt aged, dozen plts w/purple ink mks; ink mks, underlining to several text pp; skillfully rebacked, orig spine laid down; sl worn, frayed.) *Baltimore*.* $220/£138

JONES, OWEN. The Grammar of Ornament. London: Bernard Quaritch, 1868. Folio ed. 112 chromolitho plts, guards. Rose moire eps; aeg. Mod maroon morocco, gilt. (Tp, chromolitho tp reinforced w/archival tape to versos, 2nd tp extrems lack sm pieces), else NF in box. *Pacific*.* $431/£269

JONES, OWEN. Rock-Climbing in the English Lake District. Keswick: G.P. Abraham & Sons, 1900. 2nd ed. Frontisport, 31 plts. Black cl, gilt. Very Nice. *Hollett.* $280/£175

JONES, P. W. et al. Development of Fishes of the Mid-Atlantic Bight. Volumes I-VI (complete). Washington, 1978. 6 frontispieces; 2 lg fldg charts laid in. (Names; lt soiled, spotted, lt stained, corners bumped, rubbed.) *Sutton.* $400/£250

JONES, PETER (trans). Collection of Chippeway and English Hymns. NY: Methodist Book Concern, 1847. 2nd ed. Orig stamped bds. (Lt shelfworn), else VG. *Dumont.* $175/£109

JONES, RAYMOND F. Planet of Light. Phila: John C. Winston, (1953). 1st ed. VG in dj (spine ends, extrems rubbed, price/flaps clipped). *Pacific*.* $52/£33

JONES, ROBERT T. and O. B. KEELER. Down the Fairway: The Golf Life and Play of Robert T. Jones, Jr. NY: Minton, Balch, 1927. 1st ed. One of 300. Signed by both, and again by Jones on frontis. 9.5x6.5. Teg. 1/4 vellum, gilt cl. (Upper extrems of 1st 3pp; upper edge of fr cvr sl dampstained; upper fr cvr sl bowed), else VG. *Pacific*.* $4,313/£2,696

JONES, SAMUEL. The Siege of Charleston, and the Operations on the South Atlantic Coast in the War Among the States. NY: Neale, 1911. 1st ed. Frontisport. Tan buckram. (Eps foxed), else NF. *Chapel Hill.* $350/£219

JONES, TERRY and MICHAEL PALIN. Bert Fegg's Nasty Book for Boys and Girls. London: Eyre Methuen, 1974. 1st ed. 7.5x9.75. Martin & Holly Honeysett (illus). 60pp. Pict bds. VG. *Cattermole.* $35/£22

JONES, THEOPHILUS. A History of the County of Brecknock. Edwin Davies, 1898. One of 600. 2 vols in 1 (as issued). 2pp subs list; 2 fldg maps (1 torn w/o loss), 3 color plts. Dec eps. (Bkpl; sl shaken; spine faded intruding onto bds, spine chipped.) *Edwards.* $240/£150

JONES, THOM. The Pugilist at Rest. Boston: Little Brown, (1993). 1st ed, 1st bk. Fine in Fine dj. *Robbins.* $50/£31

JONES, THOM. The Pugilist at Rest. Boston: Little, Brown, 1993. 1st ed, 1st bk. Signed. Fine in Fine dj. *Lame Duck.* $100/£63

JONES, THOMAS G. Last Days of the Army of Northern Virginia. An Address Delivered...Richmond, Va., October 12th, 1893. (Richmond?, 1893?) 1st ed. 46pp. Fine in ptd wraps (spine lt worn). *Chapel Hill.* $250/£156

JONES, TOM and HARVEY SCHMIDT. The Fantasticks. NY: Drama Book Shop, 1964. 1st ed. Fine in dj (sm tear). *Between The Covers.* $150/£94

JONES, VIRGIL C. The Civil War at Sea. NY: Holt, Rinehart, Winston, (1960-62). 1st eds. 1st vol inscribed, dated May 18, 1962. Tls laid in, dated Jan 9, 1963. 3 vols. Three 5x7.5-inch glossy repros of illus in 2nd vol laid in. Blue/gray cl. Fine set in djs. *Chapel Hill.* $225/£141

JONES, VIRGIL C. Gray Ghosts and Rebel Raiders. NY: Henry Holt, (1956). 1st ed. Signed. Fine in dj (tattered). *Argonaut.* $60/£38

JONES, VIRGIL C. Ranger Mosby. Chapel Hill, (1944). 1st ed. VG + in dj (2 sm pieces torn away). *Pratt.* $60/£38

JONES, VIRGIL C. Ranger Mosby. Univ of NC, 1944. 1st ed. VG. *Book Broker.* $35/£22

JONES, W. Finger-Ring Lore. London: C&W, 1898. New ed. xvi,567pp + 32pp ads. Largely unopened. Pict cl. Good (cl sl worn). *Blake.* $150/£94

JONES, W. The Treasures of the Earth. NY: Putnam, 1872. xii,404pp. VG. *Blake.* $200/£125

JONES, WILLIAM and EDWARD A. FREEMAN. The History and Antiquities of Saint David's. London, 1856. 23 engr plts. Erratum slip. Later 19th-cent 1/2 morocco (extrems scuffed). *Swann*.* $149/£93

JONES, WILLIAM (ed). Jones's British Theatre. Dublin: William Jones, 1795. 9 vols. Period gilt-ruled mottled calf, gilt, morocco spine labels. VG set (bkpls). *Pacific*.* $345/£216

JONES, WILLIAM et al. Dissertations and Miscellaneous Pieces Relating to the History and Antiquities, the Arts, Sciences, and Literature, of Asia. Dublin, 1793. Contemp sheep (spine worn, joints cracked). *Swann*.* $201/£126

JONES, WILLIAM. The Works of Sir William Jones. London: G.G. & J. Robinson, 1799-1804. 1st Collected ed. 9 vols. Period tree calf, gilt, morocco labels. (Sl foxed, offset; vols 1, 2 w/eps, tp, fr cvrs detached; rubbed, extrems worn, joints cracked, tender), else VG. *Pacific*.* $374/£234

JONES, WILLIAM. The Works...with the Life of the Author, by Lord Teignmouth. London, 1807. 13 vols. 68 (of ?) engr plts on 62 (of ?) leaves. Uncut, largely unopened. Orig bds (portions missing from spine ends, some cvrs detached or starting; old stamps, some plts browned). *Swann*.* $402/£251

JONSON, BEN and DAVID GARRICK. Everyman in His Humour. London: J. & R. Tonson, 1755. 3rd ed. Frontis, 72pp. Calf-backed bds. Good. *Young.* $96/£60

JONSON, BEN. Volpone, or The Fox. LEC, 1952. Ltd to 1500 numbered, signed by Rene Ben Sussan (illus). Fine in slipcase. *Swann*.* $57/£36

JONSON, BEN. Volpone, or The Foxe, a New Edition. NY: John Lane, 1898. One of 1000. Frontis by Aubrey Beardsley. Gilt-pict blue cl, beveled edges. (Offset to eps, pastedowns; tips rubbed, sm closed nick spine head.) *Swann*.* $258/£161

JONSON, BEN. Volpone. Berlin: Bruno Cassirer, 1910. 1st ed in German. One of 650 (of 700). Brn bevelled cl, gilt. Fine. *Maggs.* $288/£180

JONSON, BEN. The Works of...to Which Is Added a Comedy, Called The New Inn, with Additions Never Before Published. London: Thomas Hodgkin, 1692. 3rd ed. Folio. (10),744pp + (2)pp ads. Mod 3/4 red morocco, cl, gilt. (Repairs to tp verso, margins of 1st few pp; worming), else VG. *Pacific*.* $316/£198

JORDAN, DAVID STARR (ed). The California Earthquake of 1906. SF: A.M. Robertson, 1907. 1st ed. Maroon pict cl. Fine. *Pacific*.* $219/£137

JORDAN, DAVID STARR. The Days of a Man, Being Memories of a Naturalist, Teacher, and Minor Prophet of Democracy. Yonkers-on-Hudson: World Book Co, 1922. One of 390. Signed. 2 vols. Teg. 1/2 morocco, cl, gilt. (Spines sunned), else VG. *Pacific*.* $81/£51

JORDAN, DAVID STARR. Factors in Organic Evolution. Stanford: Stanford Univ, n.d. (ca 1895). VG. *Mikesh.* $35/£22

JORDAN, DAVID STARR. The Story of the Innumerable Company. SF, 1896. 1st ed. 294pp; 19 photo plts. Grn cl, gilt. VG. *Larry Price.* $40/£25

JORDON, DAVID STARR. Matka and Kotik. SF: Whitaker & Ray, 1897. 1st ed. 68pp; map. Dec cl. VG. *High Latitude.* $35/£22

Jorrocks' Jaunts and Jollities. London, 1869. 3rd ed. 16 color plts. Mod 1/2 red levant, gilt. (Bkpl removed.) *Swann*.* $103/£64

Jorrocks' Jaunts and Jollities. London, 1901. 3/4 morocco, gilt. *Swann*.* $115/£72

JOSEPHSON, HANNAH. The Golden Threads: New England's Mill Girls and Magnates. NY: Duell, Sloan & Pearce, (1949). 1st ed. (Spine ends lt chipped.) Dj (reinforced). *Petrilla.* $20/£13

JOSEPHSON, KENNETH. The Bread Book. N.p.: Kenneth Josephson, 1973. 1st ed. 20 full-pg b/w photos. VG in stiff wrappers (fr wrapper damp-wrinkled). *Cahan.* $60/£38

JOSLIN, SESYLE. Baby Elephant's Trunk. (NY: Harcourt Brace, 1960.) 1st ed. Leonard Weisgard (illus). Fine in dj. *Pharos.* $45/£28

JOSSIC, YVONNE F. Stage and Stage Settings. Phila: H.C. Perleberg, n.d. (1933). Folio. Tp; 20 pict ll loose as issued. (Lib stamps; corners worn.) *Dramatis.* $40/£25

JOSTES, BARBARA DONOHUE (comp). John Parrott, Consul, 1811-1884. SF: (Compiler), 1972. 1st ed. Frontisport, 67 plts (1 dbl-pg fldg), 2 fldg charts, 3 maps (1 fldg). Grn cl, gilt. VF. *Argonaut.* $250/£156

JOUFFROY, ALAIN and JOAN TEIXIDOR. Miro Sculpture. NY, (1974). 2 dbl-pg color lithos by Miro. Dj. *Swann*.* $115/£72

JOURDAIN, MARGARET and F. ROSE. English Furniture: The Georgian Period (1750-1830). Batsford, 1953. 1st ed. Color frontis. (Bkpl; faded, lib #s spine.) *Edwards.* $72/£45

JOURDAIN, MARGARET. English Decoration and Furniture of the Early Renaissance (1500-1650). London: Batsford, (1924). (Lt worn, cvrs sl spotted.) *Oinonen*.* $80/£50

JOURDAIN, MARGARET. Regency Furniture 1795-1830. London: Country Life, 1965. Color frontis, 3 color plts. Dj (sl chipped). *Edwards.* $88/£55

Journal of a Horticultural Tour Through Some Parts of Flanders, Holland. (By P. Neill.) Edinburgh, 1823. xv,574,(2)pp; 7 engr plts (foxed). Orig bds (corners chipped away, backstrip partly perished, cvrs detached; offsetting from plts, pp tanned, bkpl, bk split apart in center). *Sutton.* $150/£94

Journal of a Naturalist. (By John Leonard Knapp.) London: John Murray, 1829. 1st ed. Fldg frontis, xii,403pp; 6 plts (4 dbl-pg). Contemp 1/2 calf, morocco label. Good. *Young.* $72/£45

Journal of Eight Days Journey from Portsmouth to Kingston upon Thames...to Which Is Added an Essay on Tea.... (By Jonas Hanway.) London, 1757. 2nd ed. 2 vols. Frontispieces. Early sheep (needs rebinding). *Swann*.* $230/£144

Journal of the Congress of the Confederate States of America, 1861-1865. Senate Doc No. 234. Washington, 1904-5. 7 vols. Tan lib buckram. *Kane*.* $300/£188

Journals and Other Documents on the Life and Voyages of Christopher Columbus. LEC, 1963. Ltd to 1500 numbered, signed by Lima de Freitas (illus). Fine in slipcase. *Swann*.* $46/£29

Journals of the Legislature of the State of California at Its Second Session. Ptd by Eugene Casserly, 1851. Contemp sheep-backed marbled bds (1 detached). Clean. *Boswell.* $350/£219

Journey from Aleppo to Damascus. (By John Green.) London, 1736. Engr fldg map (backed w/paper, sl loss at edges). Mod lib buckram. (Ink lib stamp, tp backed w/paper; some loss in margins, affecting several words of text; 1st/last gatherings w/outer corners retipped; final text leaf silked.) *Swann*.* $373/£233

Journey to the Western Islands of Scotland. (By Samuel Johnson.) London: T. Cadell, 1775. 1st ed. Tp, 384pp, 1f., errata. Speckled calf (rebacked, rubbed). *Marlborough.* $320/£200

JOYCE, ERNEST E. M. The South Polar Trail: The Log of the Imperial Trans-Antarctic Expedition. London: Duckworth, 1929. VG (erasure tp, sig; spine dknd, top worn). *Explorer.* $176/£110

JOYCE, ERNEST E. M. The South Polar Trail:...the Log of the Imperial Trans-Antarctic Expedition.... London: Duckworth, 1929. Signed inscription, 1934. Map. VG. *High Latitude.* $325/£203

JOYCE, JAMES. Anna Livia Plurabelle. London: Faber, (1930). 1st ed. Prospectus laid in. NF in wrappers (top edge sl rubbed, brittle). *Pharos.* $125/£78

JOYCE, JAMES. Anna Livia Plurabelle. NY: Crosby Gaige, 1928. 1st ed. One of 800 signed. 8vo. Orig pub's prospectus w/note on verso loosely inserted. (Sig, sl rust mks from paperclip to fep tops.) Brn cl, gilt. *Sotheby's*.* $1,379/£862

JOYCE, JAMES. Chamber Music. Boston: Cornhill, (1918). 1st (unauthorized) Amer ed. Grn cl, gilt. Fine. *Pacific*.* $259/£162

JOYCE, JAMES. Chamber Music. Boston: Cornhill, (n.d., 1918). 1st Amer ed, 1st bk. Fine (lacks orig unptd tissue dj). *Between The Covers.* $250/£156

JOYCE, JAMES. Chamber Music. Elkin Mathews, 1907. 1st ed. One of 509. 3rd binding variant w/thin wove transparent eps, poems in sig C poorly centered on pg. 8vo. (Eps sl foxed, bkpl.) Lt grn cl, lettered in gilt. *Sotheby's*.* $2,208/£1,380

JOYCE, JAMES. Collected Poems. NY: Viking, 1937. 1st Amer ed. One of 1000 ptd. Frontisport. VG (lacks dj). *Agvent.* $225/£141

JOYCE, JAMES. Dubliners. NY: Huebsch, 1916. 1st US ed. Lt blue-grn cl. (Lt aged, partial old dampstain at bulked top edge; spine, edges discolored.) Text Good. *Baltimore*.* $130/£81

JOYCE, JAMES. Dubliners. LEC, 1986. One of 1000 signed by Robert Ballagh (photos) and Thomas Flanagan (intro). Fine in slipcase. *Swann*.* $402/£251

JOYCE, JAMES. Exiles. NY: Huebsch, 1918. 1st Amer ed. Crown 8vo. 1/4 dk grn cl, gilt. VG (eps sl browned; tail corners rubbed) in dj (head/tail trimmed). *Blackwell's.* $920/£575

JOYCE, JAMES. Exiles: A Play in Three Acts. NY: B.W. Huebsch, 1918. 1st Amer ed. (Name, bkseller label; extrems worn, color rubbed off cl at ends, hinges; bds stained.) *Woolson.* $200/£125

JOYCE, JAMES. Finnegans Wake. London: Faber & Faber, (1939). 1st ed. 8vo. Red cl, gilt spine. (Eps lt foxed), o/w Fine in dj (top edge unevenly trimmed, loss of 1/8-inch). *Heritage.* $1,500/£938

JOYCE, JAMES. Finnegans Wake. NY: Viking, 1939. 1st Amer ed. VG (eps lt foxed; soiled, rubbed; lacks dj). *Agvent.* $100/£63

JOYCE, JAMES. Finnegans Wake. NY: Viking, 1939. 1st Amer ed. Fine in NF dj (2 long neatly-repaired tears, other tears). *Between The Covers*. $450/£281

JOYCE, JAMES. Finnegans Wake. Faber, 1939. 1st ed. Royal 8vo. (iv),628pp. Untrimmed. Rust-red linen, gilt. VG (eps foxed) in dj (ends chipped, 2 sm tears, sm snag rear panel). *Blackwell's*. $720/£450

JOYCE, JAMES. Finnegans Wake. NY: Viking, 1939. 1st ed. Buckram. VG (sig) in dj (sl chipped, nicked, edges sl rubbed, spine sl faded). *Ulysses*. $792/£495

JOYCE, JAMES. Finnegans Wake. London/NY: Faber & Faber/Viking, 1939. One of 425 signed. Royal 8vo. W/16pp (incl cvrs) pamphlet of corrections. Red buckram, gilt. Overall NF (spine lt browned) in 1/4 morocco slipcase w/fldg cl chemise. *Heritage*. $4,500/£2,813

JOYCE, JAMES. Finnegans Wake. (London/NY): Faber & Faber/Viking, 1939. 1st ed. Ltd to 425 signed. 8vo. Uncut. Smooth red brick buckram, spine gilt. Yellow slipcase (sl soiled). *Sotheby's**. $4,784/£2,990

JOYCE, JAMES. Giacomo Joyce. London: Faber & Faber, 1968. 1st Eng ed. Fine (fep gutters sl browned) in dj (spine sl faded). *Ulysses*. $72/£45

JOYCE, JAMES. The Mime of Mick, Nick and the Maggies. The Hague: Servire Press, 1934. 1st ed. One of 1000 ptd. Nice in ptd wrappers. *Appelfeld*. $350/£219

JOYCE, JAMES. Pomes Penyeach. Paris: Shakespeare & Co, 1927. 1st ed, trade issue. This copy has been inked the letter 'R,' but presumably not as issued. Label 'Price Two Shillings' affixed to rear bd; ptr's imprint 'Herbert Clarke, Paris' ptd on rear bd. Errata slip. Tan bds (lt soiled). VG. *Pacific**. $316/£198

JOYCE, JAMES. Pomes Penyeach. Paris: Shakespeare & Co, 1927. 1st ed. Pale grn bds. Good (spine sunned, fr cvr sl foxed). *Blackwell's*. $360/£225

JOYCE, JAMES. Pomes Penyeach. Paris: Shakespeare & Co, 1927. 1st ed w/errata slip. Fine (sl foxed). *Metropolitan**. $575/£359

JOYCE, JAMES. A Portrait of the Artist as a Young Man. The Egoist Ltd, 1917. 2nd ed. VG- (spine dull, dknd, sm nick). *Williams*. $280/£175

JOYCE, JAMES. A Portrait of the Artist as a Young Man. LEC, 1968. Ltd to 1500 numbered, signed by Brian Keogh (illus). Fine in slipcase. *Swann**. $103/£64

JOYCE, JAMES. Selected Letters of James Joyce. Richard Ellmann (ed). London: Faber & Faber, 1975. 1st Eng ed. NF (spine foot sl bumped) in dj (spine sl faded). *Ulysses*. $136/£85

JOYCE, JAMES. Tales Told of Shem and Shaun. Three Fragments from Work in Progress. Paris: Black Sun, 1929. 1st ed. One of 500. White paper cvrs w/fldg flaps, lettered in red/black. Tissue dj, red/gilt slipcase (partly split). *Sotheby's**. $827/£517

JOYCE, JAMES. Two Tales of Shem and Shaun. Faber & Faber, 1932. 1st London ed. Paper bds (edges, spine sl dknd; sig; address). Dj (very dknd along spine, water-stain, dust-soiling along edges). *Cox*. $48/£30

JOYCE, JAMES. Ulysses. (London): Egoist, 1922. 1st Eng ed. Ltd to 2000. 8vo. 8pg errata inserted after pg xi, final blank present. Marbled eps. Mod parchment bds (orig blue paper cvrs, spine bound in). Matching slipcase. *Sotheby's**. $920/£575

JOYCE, JAMES. Ulysses. Paris/London: Egoist Press/John Rodker, 1922. 1st Eng ed. 8vo. Teg. 1/2 blue morocco, blue cl, gilt, raised bands. VG (lt marginal browning throughout, lacks 7-pg errata; orig wrappers bound in, fr joint lt worn). *Heritage*. $1,500/£938

JOYCE, JAMES. Ulysses. Paris: John Rodker for the Egoist Press, 1922. 1st Eng ed. Thick 8vo. Fine in ptd blue wrappers (few sm stains fr cvr, edges lt rubbed); morocco slipcase. *Swann**. $2,530/£1,581

JOYCE, JAMES. Ulysses. London: Egoist Press, 1922. 1st Eng ed. One of 2000. 8-pg uncut errata booklet laid in. Orig blue ptd wrappers. (Extrems sl rubbed), else NF. *Pacific**. $3,450/£2,156

JOYCE, JAMES. Ulysses. Shakespeare, 1922. 1st ed. Ltd to 750. Initial, final blanks. Marbled eps; teg, rest untrimmed. (Orig blue paper fr/rear cvrs bound in.) Contemp vellum, spine lettered in gilt, turn-ins dec in gilt. Slipcase. *Sotheby's**. $4,048/£2,530

JOYCE, JAMES. Ulysses. Paris: Shakespeare, 1922. 1st ed. Ltd to 750 numbered. 8vo. Top edge sl trimmed. Blue wrappers (spine carefully restored). *Sotheby's**. $5,888/£3,680

JOYCE, JAMES. Ulysses. Shakespeare, 1922. 1st ed. Ltd to 750. 1 blank only (at end). (Sl browned.) All edges uncut. Mod crushed grn morocco by Michael Wilcox, spine w/raised bands, lettered in gilt. *Sotheby's**. $6,624/£4,140

JOYCE, JAMES. Ulysses. Paris: Shakespeare & Co, 1922. 1st ed. One of 150 on Verges d'Arches, from total of 1000. Thick 8vo. Orig blue wrappers. Superb. *Swann**. $18,400/£11,500

JOYCE, JAMES. Ulysses. Paris: Shakespeare & Co, 1926. 1st ed, 8th ptg. Teg. Contemp dk navy morocco, marbled bds, raised bands, gilt spine. (Ink sigs; edges, joints sl scuffed, rear joint cracked.) *Baltimore**. $90/£56

JOYCE, JAMES. Ulysses. Paris: Shakespeare, 1927. 9th ptg, 1st issue this ptg w/'Jonathan' spelled correctly on p[2]. 3/4 brn morocco (rubbed; detached at hinges; retains blue fr/rear wraps). *Agvent*. $350/£219

JOYCE, JAMES. Ulysses. Hamburg: Odyssey, 1932. 1st ed. 2 vols. Fine set (sigs) in wrappers, slipcase (repaired). *Pharos*. $350/£219

JOYCE, JAMES. Ulysses. LEC, 1935. Ltd to 1500 numbered, signed by Henri Matisse (illus). Fine in slipcase. *Swann**. $2,530/£1,581

JOYCE, JAMES. Ulysses. NY: LEC, 1935. Ltd to 1500 signed by Henri Matisse (illus). 4to. 6 soft-ground etchings, 20 lithos. VF in brn buckram w/cvr design in gold-emb relief. Orig slipcase (sl worn). *Bromer*. $3,500/£2,188

JOYCE, JAMES. Ulysses. NY: LEC, 1935. One of 250 (of 1500) signed by Joyce and Henri Matisse (illus). 4to. Bd slipcase (partly cracked). *Swann**. $8,050/£5,031

JOYCE, JAMES. Ulysses. NY: LEC, 1935. One of very few signed by both Henri Matisse (illus) and Joyce, out of a total limitation of 1500 signed by Matisse. 4to. Brn buckram, gilt. Fine in pub's slipcase (sl soiled). *Heritage*. $10,000/£6,250

JOYCE, JAMES. Ulysses. Bodley Head, 1969. Rev ed. NF (spine foot sl bumped) in dj (sl nicked, edges sl rubbed). *Ulysses*. $56/£35

JOYCE, P. W. English as We Speak It in Ireland. London: Longmans, 1910. Half-title, tp, v-x, contents leaf, 356pp + 4pp ads, pink errata slip (p290). Red cl, gilt. *Marlborough*. $120/£75

JOYCE, STANISLAUS. Recollections of James Joyce. Ellsworth Mason (trans). N.p.: James Joyce Soc, 1950. One of 750 numbered. VG (1 marginal ink mk, sm patch of browning 2pp; cvrs sl dusty; spine, cvr edges sl browned). *Ulysses*. $104/£65

Joyful Tales Jingles and Jokes for Little Kids. NY: McLoughlin, 1869. 8vo. 8pp. Color pict wrappers (sm spine split). *Reisler*. $200/£125

JOZSEF, ATTILA. Selected Poems and Texts. John Batki (trans). Cheadle, Cheshire: Carcanet, 1973. 1st Eng ed. Fine in dj (sl nicked). *Ulysses*. $40/£25

JUARROZ, ROBERTO. Vertical Poetry. W. S. Merwin (trans). (Santa Cruz: Kayak, 1977.) 1st ed. Fine in wrappers. *Pharos*. $30/£19

JUDD, GERRIT. Dr. Judd. Hawaii's Friend. Honolulu: Univ of HI, 1960. 1st ed. 1/2 cl. VG in dj (worn). *Parmer*. $35/£22

JUDD, J. W. Volcanoes. London, 1893. 5th ed. iv ads, xvi,381pp; 10 plts. Fine. *Henly*. $26/£16

JUDD, LAURA FISH. Sketches of Life in the Hawaiian Islands from 1828 to 1861. Chicago: R.R. Donnelley, 1966. Frontis, map. VG. *Lien.* $25/£16

JUDGE, A. W. (ed). Centre, Capstan and Automatic Lathes. London: Caxton, 1950. 2 vols. Fine. *Savona.* $40/£25

JUDSON, CLARA INGRAM. Flower Fairies. Chicago: Rand-McNally, (1915). 1st ed. (Pict cvr label sl stained), else VG. *Pacific*.* $69/£43

JUDSON, CLARA INGRAM. They Came From France. Boston: Houghton Mifflin, 1943. 1st ed. Lois Lenski (illus). 246pp. VG (name stamp, spine head rubbed). *Price.* $25/£16

JUDSON, PHOEBE GOODELL. A Pioneer's Search for an Ideal Home: A Book of Personal Memoirs. Tacoma: WA State Hist Soc, 1966. Rpt. Fine. Howes J274. *Perier.* $40/£25

Julia de Roubigne, a Tale. (By Henry Mackenzie.) London: W. Strahan, T. Cadell, W. Creech, 1782. 3rd ed. 2 vols. Marbled edges. Period calf, gilt, morocco spine labels. (Bkpls, spines lack some gilt), else NF. *Pacific*.* $161/£101

JULIEN, CARL. Beneath So Kind a Sky. Columbia: USC Press, 1947. One of 1500 signed by Julien & Chapman J. Milling (intro). Folio. Frontis, 89 full-pg b/w plts. Red cl. (1/2-title lt foxed), else NF in pub's pict slipcase (sl worn). *Chapel Hill.* $150/£94

JUNEK, OSCAR W. Isolated Communities. NY: American Book, 1937. 1st ed. VG. *Walcot.* $40/£25

JUNG, C. G. Memories, Dreams, Reflections. NY, 1963. 1st ed. VG. *Doctor's Library.* $30/£19

JUNG, C. G. Psychology and Alchemy. R. F. C. Hull (trans). NY: Pantheon Books, (1953). 1st complete collected ed in English. Black cl. NF in dj. *House.* $50/£31

JUNGER, ERNST. The Storm of Steel. Basil Creighton (trans). London: C&W, 1929. 1st British ed. Gilt red cl. VG in dj (lt edge-worn). *Reese.* $95/£59

JUNGK, ROBERT. Brighter Than a Thousand Suns. NY: Harcourt, Brace, 1958. 1st US ed. Fine in Good + dj (worn, chipped). *Bookcell.* $25/£16

JUNGMAN, BEATRIX. Holland. A&C Black, 1904. 75 color plts. Teg. Dec cl. (Lt browned; cl lt dampstained, spine chipped.) *Edwards.* $56/£35

JUNGMAN, BEATRIX. Norway. A&C Black, 1905. 1st ed. 75 color plts. Teg. Dec cl. (Lt browned; spine sl discolored, rubbed.) *Edwards.* $45/£28

JUNIUS. The Letters of Junius. London/Edinburgh/Glasgow: J. Mundell, 1798. viii,316pp. Later dk grn buckram, red morocco label. *Young.* $144/£90

JUNIUS. The Letters of Junius. C. W. Everett (ed). London: Faber & Gwyer, 1927. 1st Eng ed. 4 b/w plts, 1 chart. VG (spine ends sl bumped) in dj (sl rubbed, dusty, browned). *Ulysses.* $136/£85

JUNOT, LAURE. Memoirs of Napoleon, His Court and Family. London: Richard Bentley, 1836. 1st ed. 2 vols. (4),548; (4),520pp; 16 copper-engr ports, incl frontis both vols. 19th-cent 1/2 calf, marbled bds (extrems sl rubbed), gilt, brn morocco spine labels. *Karmiole.* $150/£94

JURIEU, PETER. The History of the Council of Trent. London: Henry Faithorne, etc., 1684. Engr frontis. Aeg. Full red straight-grain morocco, gilt-paneled spine. Fine. *Appelfeld.* $150/£94

JUSSERAND, J. J. English Wayfaring Life in the Middle Ages (XIVth Century). L. T. Smith (trans). London: T. Fisher Unwin, 1899. Special ed. Frontis, 451pp; 20 plts. Blue cl (spine faded, dampstained). *Maggs.* $13/£8

JUSTUS, MAY. Jerry Jake Carries On. Whitman, 1943. 1st ed. Christine Chisholm (illus). 64pp. Grn cl, full-pg plt pasted on. VG (reps show paper removal). *Price.* $25/£16

K

KABERRY, CHARLES. The Book of Baby Dogs. London: Henry Frowde/H&S, n.d., (1914). 4to. 120pp; 19 tipped-in illus by E.J. Detmold. Beige cl, pict paste-on. VG (corner bent, rear hinge crack). *Davidson.* $365/£228

KAFKA, FRANZ. America. Edwin & Willa Muir (trans). London: Routledge, 1938. 1st Eng ed. VG (sm bkseller label fr pastedown; cvrs sl mkd; spine ends, 2 corners sl bumped; spine sl dknd). *Ulysses.* $136/£85

KAFKA, FRANZ. Dearest Father. NY: Schocken, 1954. 1st ed. (Stamp), o/w Fine in dj (lt used, internally reinforced). *Beasley.* $50/£31

KAFKA, FRANZ. The Diaries of Franz Kafka 1910-1923. Max Brod (ed). London: Secker & Warburg, 1948. 1st Eng ed. 2 vols. Facs. VG in djs. *Hollett.* $48/£30

KAFKA, FRANZ. The Great Wall of China. The Muirs (trans). London: Martin Secker, 1933. 1st ed in English. VG + in dj (fold splits at spine head). *Lame Duck.* $250/£156

KAFKA, FRANZ. In the Penal Colony. LEC, 1987. One of 800 signed by Michael Hafftka (illus). Fine in slipcase. *Swann*.* $172/£108

KAFKA, FRANZ. Letters to Friends, Family and Editors. Calder, 1978. 1st UK ed. NF in dj. *Williams.* $40/£25

KAFKA, FRANZ. The Metamorphosis. A.L. Lloyd (trans). London: Parton, 1937. 1st ed in English. (Extrems shelfworn; lacks dj), else NF in 1/4 cl, paper-cvrd bds. *Lame Duck.* $950/£594

KAFKA, FRANZ. Metamorphosis. LEC, 1984. Ltd to 1500 numbered, signed by Jose Luis Cuevas (illus). Fine in slipcase. *Swann*.* $258/£161

KAFKA, FRANZ. The Trial. NY: Knopf, 1937. 1st Amer ed. Flexible bds. (Eps sl dknd), else NF in VG dj (spine sl tanned, lt irregular tanning base of fr panel). *Between The Covers.* $450/£281

KAFKA, FRANZ. The Trial. Willa and Edwin Muir (trans). CT: LEC, 1975. One of 2000. Signed by Alan E. Cober (illus). Full leather, gilt. Fine in Fine box. *Polyanthos.* $95/£59

KAGAN, DIANE. Who Won Second Place at Omaha? NY: Random House, 1975. 1st ed. Meryl Joseph (photos). NF in dj. *Smith.* $125/£78

KAGAN, SOLOMON R. American Jewish Physicians of Note. Boston: Boston Medical Soc, 1942. 1st ed. (Spine lt sunned), else Fine. *Beasley.* $45/£28

KAHIN, GEORGE McTURNAN and JOHN W. LEWIS. The United States in Vietnam. NY: Dial, 1967. 1st ed. NF in dj (soiled, torn). *Dermont.* $35/£22

KAHL, VIRGINIA. Plum Pudding for Christmas. NY: Scribner, 1956. 1st ed. 8.25x10.25. 32pp. VG in dj. *Cattermole.* $35/£22

KAHLENBERG, MARY HUNT and ANTHONY BERLANT. The Navajo Blanket. L.A., 1972. (Bkpl; spine faded), else VG in dj. *Dumont.* $70/£44

KAHN, EDGAR M. Andrew Smith Hallidie: A Tribute to a Pioneer California Industrialist. SF: (Edgar M. Kahn), 1953. 1st ed. One of 275. Brn cl. Fine. *Harrington.* $35/£22

KAHNWEILER, D. H. Juan Gris, His Life and Work. London: Thames & Hudson, 1969. Enlgd ed. 24 mtd color illus. Good in dj. *Ars Artis.* $400/£250

KAHNWEILER, D. H. Juan Gris. NY: Valentin, 1947. *Swann*.* $57/£36

KAHNWEILER, D. H. The Sculptures of Picasso. London: Rodney Phillips, 1949. Pict bds. *Petersfield.* $48/£30

KAHRL, WILLIAM. L. The California Water Atlas. State of CA, (1979). 1st ed. Sq folio. 1/2 black leatherette, blue cl. (Few sl spots fr cvr), else Fine. *Argonaut.* $275/£172

KAIN, ROBERT C. June 25-26, 1876 in the Valley of the Little Big Horn. Newfane, VT, (1969). VG. *Woolson.* $30/£19

KAIN, SAUL. (Pseud of Siegfried Sassoon.) The Daffodil Murderer. Richmond, 1913. 1st ed. Good (bkpl remains inside fr cvr) in daffodil yellow wrappers (sl soiled, foxed). *Blackwell's.* $200/£125

KAINEN, JACOB. George Clymer and the Columbian Press. Taylor & Taylor, 1950. One of 350. *Dawson.* $30/£19

KAKONIS, TOM. Criss Cross. NY, 1990. 1st ed. Fine in NF dj. *Warren.* $35/£22

KAKONIS, TOM. Michigan Roll. NY, 1988. 1st ed. Fine in Fine dj. *Warren.* $50/£31

KALASHNIKOFF, NICHOLAS. My Friend Yakub. Scribner, 1953. 1st ed. Feodor Rojankovsky (illus). 249pp. NF (spine head sl rubbed, rear lt soiled) in VG dj. *Price.* $30/£19

KALISCHER, A. C. Beethoven's Letters. A. Eaglesfield-Hull (ed). J. S. Shedlock (trans). Dent, 1926. 1st Eng ed. 15 plts. (Spine lettering sl dull.) *Hollett.* $72/£45

KALLIR, JANE. Egon Schiele: The Complete Works. NY, (1990). Dj. *Swann*.* $230/£144

KALLIR, OTTO. Grandma Moses. NY, (1973). 1/2 cl. (Lt worn.) Dj. *Oinonen*.* $30/£19

KALLMAN, CHESTER. Elegy. NY: Tibor De Nagy Gallery, (1951). One of 500. 1st bk. Fine in stapled illus wrappers. *Dermont.* $50/£31

KALM, PETER. Travels into North America; Containing Its Natural History, and a Circumstantial Account of Its Plantations and Agriculture in General. Warrington/London, 1770-71. 1st ed in English, 1st issue. 3 vols. Lg fldg map. Mod calf. *Felcone.* $3,800/£2,375

KAMINSKY, MAX. My Life in Jazz. London: Andre Deutsch, 1964. 1st Eng ed. Fine in dj (sl rubbed). *Ulysses.* $40/£25

KAMINSKY, STUART. He Done Her Wrong. NY: St. Martin's, 1983. 1st ed. Fine in Fine dj (spine head sl worn). *Beasley.* $35/£22

KAMPEN, NICOLAAS GODFRIE. The History and Topography of Holland and Belgium. London: George Virtue, (1837). Engr add'l tp, fldg map. Pub's gilt-pict morocco. (Bkpls.) *Swann*.* $316/£198

KANAVEL, ALLEN B. Infections of the Hand. Phila/NY: Lea & Febiger, 1916. 4th ed, rev. Color frontis. Maroon cl. (Sl wrinkle to bottom text block), else Fine. *Weber.* $65/£41

KANAVEL, ALLEN B. Infections of the Hand: A Guide to the Surgical Treatment of Acute and Chronic Suppurative Processes.... Phila, 1925. 5th ed. Brn cl. (Extrems sl worn), o/w Good. *Doctor's Library.* $75/£47

KANDEL, LENORE. The Love Book. SF: Stolen Paper, 1966. 1st ed, 2nd state of the cvr design. NF in wraps. *Beasley.* $35/£22

KANDINSKY, WASSILY. Point and Line to Plane. Hilla Rebay (ed). Rebay & Howard Dearstyne (trans). NY: Solomon R. Guggenheim Foundation, 1947. 1st ed. Black cl, gilt. VG. *Reese.* $100/£63

KANE, ELISHA KENT. Arctic Explorations. Phila: Childs & Peterson, 1857. 2 vols. Extra engr tps, engr frontisports, lg fldg map, 1 full-pg map, fldg chart. Blind brn cl, gilt. Sound set (sl foxed, spotted; worn, frayed, spine ends chipped). *Baltimore*.* $60/£38

KANE, ELISHA KENT. Arctic Explorations: The Second Grinnell Expedition in Search of Sir John Franklin, 1853, '54, '55. Phila, 1857. 2 vols. Contemp 1/2 calf, gilt (sm surface imperfection fr cvrs). *Swann*.* $57/£36

KANE, FRANK. Grave Danger. NY: Ives Washburn, 1954. 1st ed. (Pg edges sl dknd, bkpl), o/w VG in dj (spine sl dknd). *Mordida.* $35/£22

KANE, JOSEPH N. Famous First Facts. NY, 1934. *Argosy.* $85/£53

KANE, THOMAS L. Alaska and the Polar Regions. Lecture...May 7, 1868. NY: Journeyman Printer's Co-operative, 1868. 32pp. Fine in ptd wrapper (sl stain on back). *High Latitude.* $140/£88

KANE, THOMAS LEIPER. The Private Papers and Diary of Thomas Leiper Kane, a Friend of the Mormons. SF: Gelber-Lilienthal, 1937. 1st ed. Ltd to 500 ptd. Frontis, plt, facs letter. Paper spine label. Fine (2 corners sl bumped). *Harrington.* $120/£75

KANER, H. The Sun Queen. Llandudno: Kaner Pub, 1946. 1st ed. (Sm clip fep corner), else NF in dj (edgeworn, sl chipped). *Other Worlds.* $25/£16

KANIN, FAY and MICHAEL. Rashomon. NY: Random House, (1959). 1st ed. VF in VF dj. *Between The Covers.* $150/£94

KANIN, GARSON. The Live Wire. NY, (1951). 1st Amer ed. Fine (bkpl, sm stamp) in dj (spine sunned). *Polyanthos.* $20/£13

KANIN, GARSON. One Hell of an Actor. NY: Harper, (1977). 1st ed. VF in VF dj. *Between The Covers.* $65/£41

Kansas City Social Register from 1948. Kansas City: Kansas City Social Directory, (1948). Orig pebbled leatherette (lt worn). *Glenn.* $25/£16

Kansas. NY: Viking, 1939. 1st ed. VG in dj (spine ends lack pieces). *Labordo.* $65/£41

KANTOR, MacKINLEY. Andersonville. NY: World, (1955). 1st trade ed. NF (lt sunned) in VG dj (torn, lt rubbed). *Between The Covers.* $75/£47

KANTOR, MacKINLEY. The Work of Saint Francis. Cleveland: World, (1958). 1st ed. (Fep sl creased), else VF in VF dj. *Between The Covers.* $125/£78

KAPLAN, EMANUEL B. Functional and Surgical Anatomy of the Hand. Phila: Lippincott, (1953). Dj remnant. *Weber.* $120/£75

KAPLAN, LOUIS. A Bibliography of American Autobiographies. Madison, 1962. Good. *Dumont.* $25/£16

KAPPLER, CHARLES J. (ed). Indian Affairs. Laws and Treaties. Washington: GPO, 1904. 2 vols. Later plain black buckram, gilt. (Ex-lib, cl tape shelf stickers on spines, bkpl, card pockets, ink stamps; sl worn.) Texts Good. *Baltimore*.* $110/£69

KAPROW, ALLEN. Assemblage, Environments and Happenings. NY, (1965?). Wrappers (lt worn). *Swann*.* $201/£126

KARABUDA, BARBRO. Goodbye to the Fez. Maurice Michael (trans). London: Dobson, 1959. 1st ed. VG in dj (tattered). *Worldwide.* $30/£19

KARALUS, KARL E. and ALLAN W. ECKERT. The Owls of North America. (North of Mexico). GC, 1974. Special ed. Ltd to 250 numbered, signed by both. 60 color plts (1 mtd). Aeg. Full grn morocco, gilt. Fine in slipcase. *Karmiole.* $250/£156

KARINTHY, FRIGYES. A Journey Round My Skull. NY, 1939. 1st ed. VG (text foxed) in dj (tattered). *Doctor's Library.* $25/£16

Karl Bodmer's America. (Lincoln): Univ of NE, (1984). 1st ed. Fine in dj. *Pacific*.* $69/£43

KARLSTROM, PAUL J. Louis Michel Eilshemius. NY, (1978). Dj. *Swann*.* $103/£64

KAROLEVITZ, ROBERT F. et al. Flight of Eagles...1919-1920. Brevet, 1974. 1st ptg. Nice in dj. *Rybski.* $55/£34

KAROLIDES, NICHOLAS J. The Pioneer in the American Novel, 1900-1950. Norman: Univ of OK, (1967). 1st ed. Fine in NF dj (spine faded). *Harrington.* $35/£22

KAROLIK, M. and M. Collection of American Paintings 1815-1865. Boston: Museum of Fine Arts, 1949. 233 plts. (Bds worn.) *Metropolitan*.* $28/£18

KAROLIK, M. and M. The M. and M. Karolik Collection of American Water Colors and Drawings, 1800-1875. Boston: Museum of Fine Arts, 1962. 2 vols. (Lt worn.) Slipcase (worn). *Oinonen*.* $80/£50

KARPEL, BERNARD (ed). Arts in America: A Bibliography. Washington, (1979). 4 vols. Folio. (Lt worn.) *Swann*.* $138/£86

KARSH, YOUSUF. Faces of Destiny. Chicago: Ziff-Davis, 1946. 1st ed. Signed, dated 1947. Fine in VG dj (few closed tears). *Smith*. $125/£78

KARSH, YOUSUF. Karsh Portraits. Boston: NYGS, 1976. 1st ed. Fine in dj. *Smith*. $125/£78

KARSH, YOUSUF. Karsh. Boston: NYGS, 1983. 1st ed. Signed. Fine in dj. *Smith*. $150/£94

KARSH, YOUSUF. Portraits of Greatness. NY, (1959). 1st ed. Folio. (Marginally age-dknd.) Dj (lacks rear panel). *Swann**. $115/£72

KARSH, YOUSUF. Portraits of Greatness. NY: Thomas Nelson, 1959. 1st ed. 96 full-pg b/w gravures. Promo material laid in. VG in dj. *Cahan*. $125/£78

KARSH, YOUSUF. Yousuf Karsh and John Fisher See Canada. Chicago: Rand McNally, 1960. 1st ed. NF in dj. *Smith*. $30/£19

KARSHAN, DONALD H. Picasso Linocuts 1958-1963. NY: Tudor Pub, (1968). 100 plts (21 color), errata slips. NF in dj. *Turtle Island*. $85/£53

KART, LAWRENCE. That Old Ball Game. David R. Phillips (ed). Regenry, 1975. 1st ed. VG + in VG dj. *Plapinger*. $85/£53

KARTESZ, JOHN and ROSEMARIE. A Synonymized Checklist of the Vascular Flora of the U.S., Canada, and Greenland. Chapel Hill: Univ of NC, 1980. 1st ed. Fine. *Archer*. $22/£14

KASTLE, HERBERT. The Movie Makers. NY: Bernard Geis, (1968). 1st ed. VF in VF dj. *Between The Covers*. $85/£53

KATZ, D. MARK. Custer in Photographs. NY: Bonanza Books, (1990). Bonanza rpt. Brn cl. Fine in Fine dj. *Harrington*. $50/£31

KATZ, FRIEDRICH. The Secret War in Mexico. Chicago: Univ of Chicago, 1981. 1st ed. VG in dj. *Lien*. $30/£19

KATZ, HARRY N. (ed). Kinks: A Book of 250 Helpful Hints for Hunters, Anglers and Outers. Chicago: Outer's Book Co, 1917. 1st ed. Pict cl. Fine. *Pacific**. $29/£18

KATZ, LESLIE GEORGE. Choreography by George Balanchine: a Catalogue.... Nancy Lassalle and Harvey Simmons (comps). NY: The Eakins Press Foundation, (1983). 1st ed. Ltd to 2000. Folio. Frontisport. Tan cl, blue spine label. NF (sm stain foreedge). *Blue Mountain*. $45/£28

KAUFFELD, CARL. Snakes and Snake Hunting. NY, 1957. 1st ed. 8 photo plts. VG in dj. *Larry Price*. $30/£19

KAUFFELD, CARL. Snakes and Snake Hunting. NY: Hanover, 1957. 1st ed. NF in VG dj. *Mikesh*. $37/£23

KAUFFER, E. McKNIGHT. Posters by E. McKnight Kauffer. NY: MOMA, 1937. 1st ptg. Fine in illus wrappers. *Turtle Island*. $50/£31

KAUFFMAN, HENRY J. The Pennsylvania-Kentucky Rifle. Harrisburg, PA: Stackpole Books, 1960. 1st ed. NF in dj. *Labordo*. $85/£53

KAUFMAN, BOB. Solitudes Crowded with Loneliness. NY: New Directions, 1965. 1st ed. Wraps (lt worn, short inscrip inside fr wrap). *Beasley*. $40/£25

KAUFMAN, LEWIS et al. Moe Berg: Athlete, Scholar, Spy. Little, Brown, 1974. 1st ed. Fine in VG dj. *Plapinger*. $55/£34

KAVANAGH, DAN. (Pseud of Julian Barnes.) Duffy. London: Cape, (1980). 1st ed. Fine in dj (pub's price sticker fr flap). *Reese*. $85/£53

KAVANAGH, DAN. (Pseud of Julian Barnes.) Duffy. Cape, 1980. 1st UK ed, 1st issue. Fine in dj. *Williams*. $88/£55

KAVANAGH, DAN. (Pseud of Julian Barnes.) Going to the Dogs. Viking, 1987. 1st UK ed. Fine in dj. *Williams*. $24/£15

KAVANAGH, DAN. (Pseud of Julian Barnes.) Going to the Dogs. Viking, 1987. 1st UK ed. Signed as 'Dan Kavanagh'. Fine in dj. *Williams*. $40/£25

KAVANAGH, JULIA. Woman in France During the Eighteenth Century. NY: Putnam, 1893. One of 100 lg paper. 2 vols. 10x6.75. Marbled eps; teg. Fine gilt-dec full dk blue morocco, leather spine labels. Vol 1 w/inset circular color port in fr cvr. (Internally foxed), else NF set in custom-made marbled slipcase. *Pacific**. $546/£341

KAVANAGH, MORGAN. Origin of Language and Myths. Sampson Low, 1871. 1st ed. 2 vols. xl,436; 594pp. (Book-label.) *Young*. $104/£65

KAVANAGH, PATRICK. A Soul for Sale. London: Macmillan, 1947. 1st Eng ed. VG (edges sl spotted; cvrs sl mkd) in dj (sl nicked, rubbed, mkd, dusty, price-clipped, sl browned). *Ulysses*. $152/£95

KAY, GERTRUDE ALICE. Us Kids and the Circus. Akron: Saalfield, 1928. 6.5x8.5. Unpaginated. Pict bds. VG (ink mk; corners bumped). *My Bookhouse*. $72/£45

KAY, HELEN. City Springtime. NY: Hastings House, (1957). 1st ed. Barbara Cooney (illus). 8vo. Yellow cl, dk blue lettering/decs. Good in color dj (2 sm chips). *Reisler*. $65/£41

KAY, ROSS. The Go Ahead Boys and the Mysterious Old House. NY: Barse & Hopkins, 1916. Go Ahead Boys #3; lists 6 titles on dj flap. 5x7.5. 232pp + ads. (Inscrip dated 1921; sl shelfworn), else VG + in dj (sl edgeworn). *My Bookhouse*. $42/£26

KAY, STEPHEN. Travels and Researches in Caffraria: Describing...Southern Africa. NY, 1834. 1st Amer ed. Map. Tree sheep. (Joints starting.) *Swann**. $172/£108

KAY, TERRY. To Dance with the White Dog. Atlanta: Peachtree, (1990). 1st ed. Signed. Fine in 1st issue ($15.95 price) dj. *Captain's Bookshelf*. $75/£47

KAYE, M. M. The Far Pavilions. Allan Lane, 1978. Proof copy. Fine in oversize dj (lower edges sl creased). *Any Amount*. $45/£28

KAYE, MOLLIE. Potter Pinner Meadow. London: Collins, (1948). 1st ed in this format. 8vo. Margaret Tempest (illus). Meadow grn cl-backed bds (edge rubbed). *Reisler*. $60/£38

KAYE-SMITH, SHEILA and G. B. STERN. Talking of Jane Austen. London: Cassell, 1944. 2nd ed. (Eps sl spotted.) Dj (sl chipped, faded). *Hollett*. $32/£20

KAYE-SMITH, SHEILA. Iron and Smoke. London: Cassell, (1928). 1st ed. Gilt blue cl. VF in pict dj (sm closed edge tear), cl slipcase, leather label. *Reese*. $75/£47

KAYE-SMITH, SHEILA. Iron and Smoke. London: Cassell, 1928. 1st ed. Lt blue buckram. (Sm fox spot to prelims), o/w Fine in dj. *Temple*. $48/£30

KAYE-SMITH, SHEILA. Joanna Godden Married and Other Stories. London: Cassell, (1926). 1st Eng ed. VG in dj. *Cady*. $25/£16

KAYE-SMITH, SHEILA. Kitchen Fugue. NY: Harper, 1945. 1st Amer ed. (Sm paper remnant rear bd), else Fine in NF dj (sm tear). *Between The Covers*. $85/£53

KAYE-SMITH, SHEILA. The Secret Son. NY: Harper, 1942. 1st Amer ed. Fine in NF dj (sl soiled, few sm tears). *Between The Covers*. $85/£53

KAYE-SMITH, SHEILA. Selina Is Older. London: Cassell, 1935. 1st ed. Salmon cl. NF in dj (frayed, sl chipped). *Temple*. $42/£26

KAYE-SMITH, SHEILA. The Village Doctor. London: Cassell, 1929. 1st ed. Dk blue buckram. Fine in dj (frayed, sl chipped). *Temple*. $48/£30

KAYE-SMITH, SHEILA. Willow's Forge and Other Poems. London: Erskine Macdonald, 1914. 1st ed. Gilt brn cl. Good. *Reese*. $22/£14

KAZANJIAN, VARAZTAD HOVHANNES and JOHN MARQUIS CONVERSE. The Surgical Treatment of Facial Injuries. Balt: Williams & Wilkins, 1949. (Pp 87-98 underlined in ink.) *Weber*. $125/£78

KAZANTZAKIS, NIKOS. Freedom or Death. Jonathan Griffin (trans). NY: S&S, 1956. 1st ed. Dated rev slip laid in. Fine in dj (sl rubbed). *Pharos.* $150/£94

KAZANTZAKIS, NIKOS. Zorba the Greek. London: John Lehmann, (1952). 1st ed in English. Pink bds. VG (eps lt browned; spine extrems lt rubbed, dk spots rear cvr) in dj (dk stains rear cvr). *Heritage.* $300/£188

KAZANZAKIS, NIKOS. Zorba the Greek. Carl Wildman (trans). Lehmann, 1952. 1st ed. VG (feps lt browned; spine ends sl bumped, bottom edge sl mkd) in dj (sl rubbed, dusty, internally browned). *Ulysses.* $200/£125

KAZIN, ALFRED. The Open Street. NY: Privately ptd, 1948. 1st ed. Ltd to 1000. Fine in shiny speckled black bds. *Warren.* $50/£31

KAZIN, ALFRED. Starting Out in the Thirties. Boston: Atlantic, (1965). 1st ed. Inscribed. Fine in VG+ dj (lt soiled). *Between The Covers.* $75/£47

KEABLE, ROBERT. Standing By: War-Time Reflections in France and Flanders. London: Nisbet, (1919). 1st ed. Red cl stamped in black. VG (eps tanned; lt foxed) in Good dj (sl chipped, dknd). *Reese.* $55/£34

KEAN, ABRAM. Young and Old Ahead, A Millionaire in Seals, Being the Life History of.... London: Heath, Cranton, 1935. 8 plts. VG in dj. *High Latitude.* $45/£28

KEAN, ROBERT GARLICK HILL. Inside the Confederate Government, the Diary of.... Edward Younger (ed). NY: OUP, 1957. 1st ed. Signed by Younger. Frontisport. (Lower corners sl bumped), else Fine in pict dj (spine faded). *Argonaut.* $50/£31

KEARNY, THOMAS. General Philip Kearny. NY: Putnam, 1937. Errata. VG in dj (worn). *Dumont.* $100/£63

KEATE, GEORGE. An Account of the Pelew Islands.... London, 1789. 3rd ed. Frontis port, fldg map, 15 plts. Contemp tree sheep (worn, rebacked; sm bkpl). *Swann*.* $201/£126

KEATING, BERN. An Illustrated History of the Texas Rangers. Chicago, 1975. 1st ptg. Silver-stamped cl. NF in dj. *Baade.* $42/£26

KEATING, H. R. F. The Sheriff of Bombay. CCC, 1984. 1st ed. (Pg edges sl browned), o/w VG in dj. *Virgo.* $19/£12

KEATING, WILLIAM (comp). Narrative of an Expedition to the Source of St. Peter's River. Phila, 1824. 1st ed. 2 vols. Fldg map, 15 plts. 19th-cent 1/2 sheep. (Bkpls, lib stamps; foxed, browned; extrems worn.) Howes K20. *Swann*.* $373/£233

KEATS, EZRA JACK. Louie. Atheneum, 1975. 1st ed. 9.3x8.2. Unpaginated. VG (thumbed wrinkles) in VG dj. *Price.* $25/£16

KEATS, JOHN. Isabella or the Pot of Basil. Edinburgh: T.N. Foulis, (1907). Tall 12mo. 6 tipped-in color plts (incl tp) by Jessie M. King. Gray cl, color paste label, gilt. Good. *Reisler.* $90/£56

KEATS, JOHN. Lamia, Isabella, The Eve of Saint Agnes, and Other Poems. Golden Cockerel, 1928. One of 500 numbered. Sm folio. Teg, rest uncut. Orig 1/4 sharkskin, spine lettered in gilt, grn buckram sides. Fine. *Sotheran.* $1,117/£698

KEATS, JOHN. The Letters of John Keats. M.B. Forman (ed). London, 1935. 2nd ed, rev. VG. *Gretton.* $40/£25

KEATS, JOHN. The Poems of John Keats. LEC, 1966. Ltd to 1500 numbered, signed by David Gentleman (illus). Fine in slipcase. *Swann*.* $46/£29

KEATS, JOHN. Poems. London, 1817. 1st ed, 1st bk. Sm 8vo. 1/2-title in facs. Uncut. Contemp bds (rebacked; lacks initial blank). *Swann*.* $7,475/£4,672

KEATS, JOHN. The Poetical Works and Other Writings of John Keats. H. Buxton Forman (ed). NY: Scribner, 1938-39. Hampstead ed. Signed by Forman & John Masefield (intro). 8 vols. Frontisport. Teg. Leather spine labels. Glassine. (1 vol lacks glassine), else NF. *Pacific*.* $489/£306

KEATS, JOHN. The Poetical Works. London, 1866. Engr port. Aeg. Later full polished crimson calf, gilt. (Crown lt rubbed.) *Swann*.* $103/£64

KEATS, JOHN. Unpublished Poem to His Sister Fanny. Boston: Bibliophile Society, 1909. 1st ed. One of 489. Fine (bkpl). *Pacific*.* $46/£29

KEDROV, M. S. Book Publishing Under Tzarism. NY: Workers Library, 1932. 1st ed. Fine in wraps. *Beasley.* $30/£19

KEEBLE, K. COREY. European Bronzes in the Royal Ontario Museum. Toronto, 1982. Good in dj (worn). *Washton.* $75/£47

KEELER, HARRY STEPHEN. The Marceau Case. Dutton, 1936. 1st ed. (Edges, spine worn, cvrs soiled), else VG in home-made acetate dj. *Murder.* $30/£19

KEELER, O. B. The Autobiography of an Average Golfer. NY: Greenberg, 1925. 1st ed. Gray cl. VG (emb stamp, hole to fep). *Pacific*.* $127/£79

KEELER, O. B. The Boy's Life of Bobby Jones. NY: Harper, 1931. 1st ed. Grn cl, gilt. Fine (emb stamp, sig). *Pacific*.* $259/£162

KEELEY, GERTRUDE. Story of Wild Flowers for Young People with Flower Alphabet. NY: Hurst, (1914). 1st ed. 10x6. Pict cvr label. VG. *Pacific*.* $150/£94

KEEN, RALPH HOLBROOK. Little Ape and Other Stories. London: Hendersons, 1921. 1st Eng ed. 4 plts by John Austen. Pict buckram. VG (tear to inner margin 1 plt, not affecting image; eps browned, edges sl spotted; cvrs dusty, sl mkd, fr cvr sl creased, spine sl dknd, bumped). *Ulysses.* $152/£95

KEENE, CAROLYN. The Bungalow Mystery. NY: G&D, 1937. Thick ed w/internal illus, white spine dj. Nancy Drew #3; lists 13 titles on dj flap. 5x7.5. 204pp. VG (spine faded, shelfworn) in dj (ragged). *My Bookhouse.* $155/£97

KEENE, CAROLYN. Nancy's Mysterious Letter. NY: G&D, 1932. 1st ed. Thick ed w/internal illus, white spine dj. Nancy Drew #8. 5x7.5. 209pp + ads. VG- (soiled, browned, worn) in dj (worn). *My Bookhouse.* $380/£238

KEENE, CAROLYN. A Three-Cornered Mystery. NY: G&D, 1935. Thick purple (early) ed. Dana Girls #4; lists to #6. 5x7.5. Glossy frontis, 217pp + ads. (Spine damstained), else VG+ in dj (sl worn). *My Bookhouse.* $180/£113

KEENE, DONALD. Bunraku: The Art of the Japanese Puppet Theatre. Kodansha Internat'l, (1965). 1st ed. 11 tipped-in color illus. VG (lacks sm phono-sheet recording). *Rybski.* $100/£63

KEENE, JOHN HARRINGTON. Fishing Tackle, Its Materials and Manufacture: A Practical Guide. London, (1886). 1st ed. Bkpl, sig of Vernon S. Hidy. Gilt-pict red cl (lt worn). *Oinonen*.* $250/£156

KEEPING, CHARLES. The Garden Shed. London: OUP, 1971. 1st ed. 11.25x9. 32pp. Pict bds. Fine in dj. *Cattermole.* $75/£47

KEEPING, CHARLES. Joseph's Yard. NY: Watts, 1969. 8.6x11.1. Unpaginated. Fine in VG dj (1.5-inch tear to spine foot). *Price.* $35/£22

KEEPING, CHARLES. Through the Window. OUP, 1970. 1st ed. Obl 4to. Pict bds. NF in pict dj. *Bookmark.* $56/£35

KEES, HERMANN. Ancient Egypt: A Cultural Topography. T. G. H. James (ed). London: Faber & Faber, 1961. 25 plts, 11 maps. Dj. *Archaeologia.* $65/£41

KEES, WELDON. Poems 1947-1954. SF: Adrian Wilson, 1954. 1st ed. Cl-backed dec bds, paper spine label. (Soiling), else VG. *Pacific*.* $98/£61

KEESE, JOHN. The Floral Keepsake. NY: Leavitt & Allen, 1854. 1st ed. 30 hand-color engr plts. Aeg. Gilt-dec red cl. (Spine ends, joints sl chipped), else VG. *Pacific*.* $207/£129

KEIL, CHARLES. Urban Blues. Chicago: Univ of Chicago, 1966. 1st ed. Fine in dj (rumpled). *Beasley.* $25/£16

KEILLOR, GARRISON. Lake Wobegon Days. NY: Viking, 1985. 1st ed. Fine in dj. *Virgo.* $56/£35

KEIR, DAVID. The House of Collins. Collins, 1952. 1st ed. 13 plts. VG in dj. *Hollett.* $40/£25

KEIR, JAMES. An Account of the Life and Writings of Thomas Day, Esq. London: Stockdale, 1791. 144pp. VG in recent wrappers. *Hartfield.* $95/£59

KEITH, ARTHUR. The Engines of the Human Body. London: Williams and Norgate, 1919. 1st ed. Fldg plt. VG (rubbed). *Weber.* $175/£109

KEITH, ELMER. Elmer Keith's Big Game Hunting. Boston: Little, Brown, 1948. Stated 1st ed. Color frontis. VG + in VG dj (several sm pieces torn from edges incl 1/2-inch piece from spine head). *Backman.* $150/£94

KEITH, ELMER. Hell I Was There. L.A.: Peterson Pub, (1979). Fine in dj. *Perier.* $50/£31

KEITH, ELMER. Keith's Rifles for Large Game. Huntington, 1946. (Lt worn.) *Oinonen*.* $190/£119

KEITH, ELMER. Shotguns—by Keith. Harrisburg, PA: Stackpole, 1950. 1st ed. VG in dj. *Labordo.* $85/£53

KEITH, ELMER. Sixgun Cartridges and Loads. Onslow County, (1936). Flexible cl. *Swann*.* $69/£43

KEITH, ELMER. Sixguns. Harrisburg: Stackpole, (1955). 1st trade ed. Color frontis. Grn cl. Fine in VG color pict dj (few sm seamed tears). *House.* $80/£50

KEITH, THOMAS. An Introduction to the Theory and Practice of Plane and Spherical Geometry.... 1826. 5th ed. xxviii,442pp, ad leaf; 5 fldg plts. Uncut. Orig bds (new paper spine, ptd label, old eps preserved). *Bickersteth.* $40/£25

KEITH, THOMAS. A New Treatise on the Use of the Globes, or A Philosophical View of the Earth and Heavens. NY: S. Wood, 1819. 3rd Amer ed. 352pp (lt foxed); 5 fldg plts. Orig full calf. *Cullen.* $125/£78

KEITH, THOMAS. A New Treatise on the Use of the Globes. London: Longmans, Brown, 1845. xxiv,364pp; 7 fldg copper-engr plts. Orig black cl, gilt. (Spine head frayed.) *Hollett.* $48/£30

KEITHAHN, EDWARD L. Native Alaskan Art in the State Historical Museum. Juneau: AK Hist Assoc, 1959. VG in wraps. *Perier.* $15/£9

KEITHLEY, RALPH. Buckey O'Neill. Caldwell, ID, 1949. 2nd ptg. (Cvrs lt worn, sl sunned w/bumped corners.) *King.* $25/£16

KELDER, DIANE (ed). Stuart Davis. NY: Praeger, (1971). 10 color plts. NF in dj. *Turtle Island.* $45/£28

KELEHER, JULIA and ELSIE RUTH CHANT. The Padre of Isleta. Santa Fe: Rydal, 1940. (Spine faded), else VG. *Dumont.* $125/£78

KELEHER, WILLIAM A. The Fabulous Frontier. Santa Fe: Rydal, (1946). 2nd ptg. Blue cl. NF in dj (soiled). *Argonaut.* $60/£38

KELEHER, WILLIAM A. The Maxwell Land Grant. Albuquerque: Univ of NM, (1984). 3rd ed. Dj. *Dawson.* $20/£13

KELEHER, WILLIAM A. New Mexicans I Knew: Memoirs, 1892-1969. Albuquerque: Univ of NM, (1983). 2nd ed. Dj. *Dawson.* $20/£13

KELEHER, WILLIAM A. Violence in Lincoln County 1869-1881. Albuquerque, 1957. 1st ed. Fine in dj (sl edgeworn). *Baade.* $67/£42

KELEHER, WILLIAM A. Violence in Lincoln County, 1869-1881: A New Mexico Item. Albuquerque: Univ of NM, (1957). 1st ed. Signed. Frontis. Fine in dj (sm tear to spine head). *Argonaut.* $150/£94

KELEMEN, P. Medieval American Art, Survey. NY: Macmillan, 1946. 2 vols. Map. *Petersfield.* $61/£38

KELL, JEAN B. A Greeting Story of Santa. N.p.: Cove Gully Farm Studio, (ca 1952). 8vo. Brook White (illus). Stiff bds w/slot in fr cvr to fit Santa doll (present). Good. *Reisler.* $200/£125

KELL, JOSEPH. (Pseud of Anthony Burgess.) Inside Mr. Enderby. London, 1963. 1st Eng ed. (Ex-lib?, stamp, ink-name, label removed; spine sl tanned.) Dj (sl mkd, pub-clipped). *Clearwater.* $200/£125

KELLER, DAVID H. Life Everlasting and Other Tales of Science Fiction, Fantasy, and Horror. Sam Moskowitz and Will Sykora (eds). Newark: Avalon, 1947. 1st ed. One of 1000. Bibliography of Keller laid in. (Spine lettering worn off), else VG in dj (chipped, spine browned). *Pacific*.* $63/£39

KELLER, DAVID H. The Solitary Hunters and The Abyss. Phila: New Era Pub, 1948. 1st ed. Signed. (Stamp, note), else VG in dj (spine ends chipped, corners rubbed). *Pacific*.* $63/£39

KELLERMAN, BERNARD. The Tunnel. NY: Macaulay, 1915. 1st US ed. (Name; rear hinge cracked, spine slanted), else VG in pict binding. *Other Worlds.* $20/£13

KELLEY, WILLIAM FITCH. Pine Ridge, 1890. Alexander Kelley and Pierre Bovis (eds). SF: Pierre Bovis, 1971. 1st bk ed. One of 2000. Lg fldg map. Brn cl. Fine in Fine dj. *Harrington.* $50/£31

KELLEY, WILLIAM MELVIN. Dancers on the Shore. GC: Doubleday, 1964. 1st ed. Fine in NF dj. *Beasley.* $50/£31

KELLEY, WILLIAM MELVIN. Dem. GC: Doubleday, 1967. 1st ed. Fine in NF dj (sm tear rear panel). *Beasley.* $50/£31

KELLOG, VERNON. Fighting Starvation in Belgium. GC: Doubleday, Page, 1918. 1st ed. Port. Gilt gray cl. (Sm adhesion spot of dj to fr cvr), else VG in dj (ragged). *Reese.* $18/£11

Kellogg's Funny Jungleland. W.K. Kellogg, 1909. 24 interchangeable outfits for animals. (Lt cvr wear), o/w VG. *Davidson.* $40/£25

KELLOGG, CHARLES. Charles Kellogg. The Nature Singer. His Book. Morgan Hill, CA, 1929. 1st ed. One of 1000. Frontisport. VG. *Sagebrush.* $30/£19

KELLOGG, JOHN HARVEY. Tobaccoism. Battle Creek, 1946. Rev ed. VG in ptd wrappers. *Doctor's Library.* $50/£31

KELLOGG, ROBERT H. Life and Death in Rebel Prisons. Hartford: L. Stebbins, 1865. 1st ed. Wood-engr frontis, 398pp + ad leaf. (Ink stamp.) Dk brn cl (spine sl frayed), gilt. Cvr VG. *Baltimore*.* $90/£56

KELLOGG, SANFORD C. The Shenandoah Valley and Virginia 1861 to 1865. NY/Washington: Neale, (1903). 1st ed. Blue cl. NF. *Chapel Hill.* $325/£203

KELLY, CHARLES and HOFFMAN BIRNEY. Holy Murder. NY: Minton, Balch, 1934. 1st ed. VG. *Labordo.* $60/£38

KELLY, CHARLES and DALE MORGAN. Old Greenwood. The Story of Caleb Greenwood. Georgetown: Talisman, 1965. 1st rev ed. Ltd to 750. Map. Fine in dj (sl chipped). *Argonaut.* $100/£63

KELLY, CHARLES. Outlaw Trail: A History of Butch Cassidy and His Wild Bunch. Salt Lake City: The Author, 1938. 1st ed. One of 1000 unnumbered. Dk maroon pebbled cl, gilt. (Pencil underlining 1 pg, sticker mtd fr pastedown, tp margin; lt shelfworn, sl rubbed.) Text Clean, cvrs VG in color pict dj (sl worn, chipped, sm tears top edge, clear tape repairs verso). Howes K58. *Baltimore*.* $140/£88

KELLY, F. M. Shakespearian Costume for Stage and Screen. A&C Black, 1938. 1st ed. 10 plts (1 fldg). VG +. *Whittle.* $24/£15

KELLY, FANNY. Narrative of My Captivity Among the Sioux Indians. Clark and Mary Lee Spence (eds). Chicago: R.R. Donnelley, 1990. Frontis. VG. *Lien.* $30/£19

KELLY, GEORGE. Reflected Glory. NY: Samuel French, (1937). 1st ed. (Fep corner clipped), else VF in VF dj. *Between The Covers.* $225/£141

KELLY, JAMES. Field Artillery Material. Columbia, 1920. 1st ed. (1 illus torn; worn), o/w VG. *Pratt.* $75/£47

KELLY, LAWRENCE C. The Navajo Indians and Federal Indian Policy, 1900-1935. Univ of AZ, (1968). VG in dj. *Perier.* $25/£16

KELLY, LEROY VICTOR. The Range Men. Toronto: William Briggs, 1913. 1st ed. Pict cl (sl worn). VG +. Howes K66. *Labordo.* $850/£531

KELLY, LUTHER S. Yellowstone Kelly. M. M. Quaife (ed). New Haven: Yale Univ, 1926. 1st ed. Fine in dj (neat tape reinforcements on recto at top/bottom edges, rubbed, price-clipped). *Pacific**. $81/£51

KELLY, PLYMPTON J. We Were Not Summer Soldiers. Tacoma, 1976. 1st ed. Fine in Fine dj. *Pratt*. $17/£11

KELLY, R. TALBOT. Egypt. London: A&C Black, 1906. Rpt. Dec cl, gilt. (Spine sl dull), else Fine. *Pharos*. $60/£38

KELLY, THOMAS. Practical Masonry, Bricklaying and Plastering, Both Plain and Ornamental. The Author, 1837. 232pp; 60 full-pg engr plts. (Plts foxed; lacks spine, orig bds present but defective.) *Whittle*. $136/£85

KELLY, WALT. Beau Pogo. NY, 1960. 1st ed. Pict wraps. (Cvrs sl discolored.) *King*. $25/£16

KELLY, WALT. The Pogo Sunday Brunch. NY, 1959. 1st ed. Pict wraps. (Paper sl browned; cvrs rubbed w/sl tears, creases), else Good. *King*. $22/£14

KELLY, WALT. Uncle Pogo So-So Stories. NY: S&S, 1953. 1st ed. Slim 4to. Pict gray eps. Scarce trial binding of yellow cl w/black spine lettering, sm black vignettes fr cvr. (Lt rubbed, edgeworn.) Text Nice. *Baltimore**. $60/£38

KELMAN, JAMES. The Busconductor Hines. Polygon Books, 1984. 1st ed. Fine in dj. *Ulysses*. $152/£95

KELMAN, JAMES. A Chancer. Polygon, 1985. 1st ed. Fine in dj. *Ulysses*. $104/£65

KELMAN, JOHN. The Holy Land. A&C Black, 1902. 1st ed. One of 500. 92 color plts by John Fulleylove. Teg. (Prelims lt browned, guard sl affixed to frontis at inner margin; sl soiled, spine sl stained.) *Edwards*. $200/£125

KELSEY, D. M. History of Our Wild West and Stories of Pioneer Life. Chicago: Thompson & Thomas, (1901). 1st ed. Good in pict cl. *Lien*. $50/£31

KELSEY, HENRY. The Kelsey Papers. Ottawa, 1929. 1st ed. Facs, fldg map. Fine in stiff wrappers (soiled, stained). *Argonaut*. $125/£78

KELTIE, J. SCOTT. The Partition of Africa. London: Edward Stanford, 1893. 1st ed. xv,(i),498pp (lacks 1/2-title); 16 maps, charts (14 fldg, 1 color). Grn cl, gilt. VG (carelessly opened ll; recased, extrems sl rubbed). *Morrell*. $192/£120

KEMBLE, EDWARD C. A History of California Newspapers, 1846-1858. Los Gatos: Talisman, 1962. 1st bk ed. One of 750. Rev copy. Pict eps. Brn cl, paper spine label. Fine in NF dj (spine sl dknd, spotted). *Harrington*. $65/£41

KEMBLE, EDWARD C. A History of California Newspapers, 1846-1858. Los Gatos: Talisman, 1962. 1st ed. Ltd to 750. Frontis, 1 plt. Pict eps. Orange cl, paper spine label. Fine in pict dj. *Pacific**. $86/£54

KEMBLE, EDWARD C. A Kemble Reader: Stories of California, 1846-1848. Fred Blackburn Rogers (ed). SF: CA Hist Soc, 1963. 1st bk ed. One of 1000 ptd. Unopened. Orange cl. Fine (spine sl faded) in Fine acetate shipping wrapper. *Harrington*. $50/£31

KEMBLE, FANNY. Fanny: The American Kemble. Fanny Kemble Wister (ed). Tallahassee, 1972. 1st ed. Dj. *Mott*. $25/£16

KEMBLE, FRANCES ANNE. Journal of a Residence on a Georgian Plantation in 1838-1839. NY: Harper & Bros, 1863. 337,7,(2)pp. Internally Good (spine, hinges repaired). Howes K70. *Dumont*. $100/£63

KEMBLE, FRANCES ANNE. Journal of a Residence on a Georgian Plantation in 1838-1839. NY: Harper, 1863. 1st Amer ed, 1st issue, w/'about' repeated in line 6, p314. pp337,10 ads. VF (spine sl faded). *Mott*. $125/£78

KEMBLE, FRANCES ANNE. Journal of a Residence on a Georgian Plantation in 1838-1839. NY: Harper, 1863. 1st Amer ed. Blind-stamped black cl, gilt. Fine. Howes K70. *Hermitage*. $200/£125

KEMBLE, FRANCES ANNE. Record of a Girlhood. Richard Bentley, 1878. 1st ed. 3 vols. Half-titles present, (vi),299; (iv),336; (iv),321pp. Marbled eps, edges. Contemp 1/2 tan calf, gilt raised bands, marbled bds, red title labels, grn vol labels. Good (rubbed, backstrips heads worn, labels chipped). *Blackwell's*. $240/£150

KEMBLE, JOHN HASKELL. The Panama Route, 1849-1869. Berkeley/L.A.: Univ of CA, 1943. 1st ed. 9 plts, 2 maps. (Fr cvr sl spotted), else VF in dj. *Argonaut*. $175/£109

KEMBLE, JOHN HASKELL. San Francisco Bay, a Pictorial Maritime History. Cambridge: Cornell Maritime Press, 1957. 1st ed. Red cl. Fine in Fine dj. *Harrington*. $45/£28

KEMEYS, JOHN GARDNER. Free and Candid Reflections. Dublin, 1785. 1st Dublin ed. iv,(7)-127pp. Orig marbled bds, speckled calf corners, mod speckled calf spine, morocco spine label. (Bkpl.) *Edwards*. $320/£200

KEMP, IAN. British G.I. in Vietnam. Robert Hale, 1969. 1st ed. VG (spine ends, 2 corners sl bumped) in dj (edges sl rubbed). *Ulysses*. $72/£45

KEMP, J. Ore Deposits of the United States and Canada. NY: Scientific, 1906. 3rd ed. Good (spine foot cl chipped). *Blake*. $40/£25

KEMP, OLIVER. Wilderness Homes: A Book of the Log Cabin. NY: Outing Pub, 1908. (Ink name, bad ding in rear spine edge), else VG. *Perier*. $27/£17

KEMPSON, E. G. H. and G. W. MURRAY (eds). Marlborough, Town and Countryside. Whittington, 1978. One of 400. Signed by eds and Richard Kennedy (illus). Fine in ptd dj (top edge sl nicked). *Michael Taylor*. $96/£60

Kempton-Wace Letters. (By Jack London and Anna Strunsky.) Isbister, 1903. 1st British ed. Teg; mostly unopened. Dec cl. Good (pencil notes, few ll roughly opened, sl creases, spots). *Ash*. $120/£75

Kemsley Manual of Journalism. London: Cassell, (1950). 1st ed. (Eps sl foxed), else Fine in Fine dj (sm tear, sl rubbed). *Between The Covers*. $300/£188

KENDALL, EDWARD AUGUSTUS. Travels Through the Northern Parts of the United States, in the Years 1807 and 1808. NY: I. Riley, 1809. Only ed. 3 vols. xi,(1),330; vi,309; vi,312pp. Contemp tree calf, leather labels. VF. Howes K74. *Mott*. $500/£313

KENDALL, GEORGE W. Across the Great Southwestern Prairies. Ann Arbor, 1966. Facs rpt. 2 vols. 2 frontispieces, map. VG. *Dumont*. $45/£28

KENDALL, GEORGE W. Narrative of the Texas Santa Fe Expedition. NY, 1844. Vol 2 only. 406pp; 3 plts. (Name; worn, spotted.) *Woolson*. $100/£63

KENDALL, GEORGE W. Narrative of the Texas Santa Fe Expedition. Chicago, 1929. Fldg map. (Lt worn.) *Woolson*. $30/£19

KENDALL, GEORGE. Henry Alken. Studio, 1929. Complete w/8 tipped-in color plts. (Few spots.) Orig wrappers. *Hollett*. $48/£30

KENDALL, JOHN. The Life of Thomas Story. London: Ptd by James Phillips, 1786. 1st ed thus. 383pp. Contemp calf. VG. *Young*. $80/£50

KENDALL, RICHARD (ed). Degas by Himself. London, 1989. Rpt. (Spine tail bumped.) Dj (spine tail sl torn). *Edwards*. $40/£25

KENDRICK, A. F. and C. E. C. TATTERSALL. Hand-Woven Carpets, Oriental and European. London: Benn, 1922. 1st ed. One of 1000 sets. 2 vols. Crown 4to. xi,198pp; xi + 205 plts (19 color), 2 maps. Full buckram (sl mkd). NF set. *Ulysses*. $800/£500

KENDRICK, JOHN (trans). The Voyage of Sutil and Mexicana, 1792. Spokane: A.H. Clark, 1991. 1st ed thus. Frontisports, 6 maps. Blue cl. Fine in dj. *Argonaut*. $75/£47

KENEALLY, THOMAS. Confederates. NY: Harper & Row, (1980). 1st Amer ed. Inscribed. Gray cl. Fine in dj. *Chapel Hill.* $60/£38

KENEALLY, THOMAS. Ned Kelly and the City of Bees. Boston: Godine, 1981. 1st US ed. NF in VG + dj. *Pettler.* $45/£28

KENEALLY, THOMAS. The Place at Whitton. London, 1964. 1st ed. NF (lacks dj). *Warren.* $50/£31

KENEALLY, THOMAS. The Playmaker. NY: S&S, (1987). 1st Amer ed. (Sm erasure fep), else Fine in Fine dj. *Between The Covers.* $45/£28

KENEALLY, THOMAS. The Playmaker. Hodder & Stoughton, 1987. 1st ed. VG in VG dj. *Whiteson.* $40/£25

KENEALLY, THOMAS. Schindler's Ark. London, (1982). 1st ed. Signed, inscribed. Dj. *Swann*.* $201/£126

KENEALLY, THOMAS. Schindler's Ark. London, 1982. 1st Eng ed. Fine in dj (price-clipped). *Clearwater.* $112/£70

KENEALLY, THOMAS. Schindler's Ark. Hodder, 1982. 1st UK ed. Fine in dj. *Williams.* $192/£120

KENEALLY, THOMAS. Schindler's List. NY, 1982. 1st Amer ed. NF in NF dj. *Warren.* $90/£56

KENNAN, GEORGE. The Salton Sea. NY, 1917. 1st ed. 7 photo plts. Blue cl, gilt. VG (ex-lib). *Larry Price.* $49/£31

KENNAN, GEORGE. Tent Life in Siberia and Adventures Among the Koraks and Other Tribes in Kamchatka and N. Asia. London: S. Low, Son & Marston, 1873. ix,425pp; fldg map. Gilt-dec cl. Good (sl mkd). *Walcot.* $88/£55

KENNARD, JOSEPH SPENCER. Masks and Marionettes. NY: Macmillan, 1935. 1st ed. Frontis port. VG. *Dramatis.* $45/£28

KENNEALLY, J. J. The Complete Inner History of the Kelly Gang and Their Pursuers. Melbourne: Reviews Pty, n.d. (ca 1920s). 1st ed. Good in pict wrapper (lacks rear wrap, spine chipped, worn). *Brown.* $35/£22

KENNEDY, EDWARD G. The Etched Work of Whistler. NY: Grolier Club, 1910. Ltd to 402. 5 vols plts, 1 vol text. Few add'l plts loosely inserted (lacks 3 repros). Brn 1/2 morocco (plts), cl-backed bds (text). (Sl rubbed.) *Sotheby's*.* $552/£345

KENNEDY, G. W. The Pioneer Campfire in Four Parts. Portland, OR: Clarke-Kundret Ptg, 1914. Good. *Lien.* $15/£9

KENNEDY, JOHN F. The Strategy of Peace. Harper, 1960. 1st ed. VG in dj (sl torn). *Whiteson.* $48/£30

KENNEDY, JOSEPH. Preliminary Report on the Eighth Census, 1860. Washington: GPO, 1862. 37th Congress, 2d Session, Senate issue. Copy of Anthony Kimmel. xvi,294pp (sl browned, foxed). Blind brn cl (rear cvr spotted; spine ends frayed), gilt. Cvrs Good. *Baltimore*.* $20/£13

KENNEDY, L. Sub-Lieutenant. London, 1944. VG in VG dj. *Clark.* $18/£11

KENNEDY, LOUISE VENABLE. The Negro Peasant Turns City-ward. NY: Columbia, 1930. 1st ed. VG (lib bkpl, spine #s, pocket). *Beasley.* $40/£25

KENNEDY, MARGARET. A Century of Revolution. Methuen, 1922. 1st ed, 1st bk. (Stamp; spine faded, ends sl bruised, cl sl mkd), o/w VG. *Any Amount.* $38/£24

KENNEDY, MICHAEL S. The Assiniboines, from the Account of the Old Ones Told to First Boy. Norman: Univ of OK, 1961. 1st ed thus. NF in dj (creased, chipped). *Labordo.* $50/£31

KENNEDY, MICHAEL S. (ed). The Red Man's West. NY: Hastings House, (1965). 1st ed. Signed. VG in dj. *Lien.* $50/£31

KENNEDY, OLIVE (ed). Letters from a Portuguese Nun. Whittington, 1986. One of 200. Signed by Olive and Richard Kennedy (illus). Paper-cvrd bds. Fine in slipcase. *Michael Taylor.* $88/£55

KENNEDY, RICHARD. A Boy at the Hogarth Press. Whittington, 1972. One of 495. Signed. (Sm gold smudge rep; lacks dj), o/w VG in pink paper-cvrd slipcase (rubbed, mkd) not called for. *Michael Taylor.* $216/£135

KENNEDY, ROBERT F. Just Friends and Brave Enemies. NY, 1962. 1st Amer ed. NF in dj (sl rubbed). *Polyanthos.* $35/£22

KENNEDY, ROBERT F. The Pursuit of Justice. NY/Evanston/London: Harper & Row, (1964). 1st ed. Signed. Fine in dj. *Bernard.* $300/£188

KENNEDY, W. M. Sportsmen's Association, of Cheat Mountain, 1889. Cheat Mountain, WV, 1889. 1st ed. Frontis, 2 fldg maps. (Pencil list rep, sl insect damage to cvrs), else VG. *Pacific*.* $207/£129

KENNEDY, WILLIAM. The Ink Truck. NY: Dial, 1969. 1st ed, 1st bk. Fine in NF dj (sl rubbed, lt paperclip mk fr panel). *Agvent.* $600/£375

KENNEDY, WILLIAM. Ironweed. NY: Viking, (1983). 1st ed. Signed, inscribed March 1983. NF in dj (sm tear rear panel). *Pacific*.* $173/£108

KENNEDY, WILLIAM. Legs. NY: C-Mc, (1975). 1st ed. NF in VG dj (tears; spine, corners worn). *Agvent.* $125/£78

KENNEDY, WILLIAM. O Albany! NY: Viking, 1983. 1st ed. (Inscrip), else NF in VG + dj. *Pettler.* $45/£28

KENNEDY, WILLIAM. Texas: The Rise, Progress, and Prospects of Texas.... London, 1841. 2nd ed. 2 vols. 8vo. 4 maps. Early calf (rebacked). Howes K92. *Swann*.* $3,220/£2,013

KENNEDY, WILLIAM. Wonders and Curiosities of the Railway or Stories of the Locomotive in Every Land. Chicago: Griggs, 1884. xvi,254pp. Pict cl. (Ex-lib, stamp, hinges cracked.) *Bohling.* $20/£13

KENNETT, BASIL. Romae Antiquae Notitia: Or, The Antiquities of Rome. London: J. Tonson et al, 1763. 13th ed. 2 parts. 14 copper plts. Calf, morocco spine label. (Fr joint, spine label w/sl glue, fr cvr sunned), else VG. *Pacific*.* $58/£36

KENNEY, JAMES F. (ed). The Founding of Churchill. London: J.M. Dent & Sons, 1932. 5 plts. (Lt ring on fr), else VG. *High Latitude.* $45/£28

KENNEY, LOUIS A. Catalogue of the Rare Astronomical Books in the San Diego State University Library. San Diego State Univ, 1988. Ltd to 1000 numbered. 16 color plts. Fine in slipcase. *Glaser.* $125/£78

KENNION, R. L. By Mountain, Lake, and Plain, being Sketches of Sport in Eastern Persia. London, 1911. Color frontis. Dec cl (sl faded). *Petersfield.* $256/£160

KENNION, R. L. Sport and Life in the Further Himalaya. Edinburgh: Blackwood, 1910. 1st ed. 1/2-title, xii,330,32 pub's list; 53 plts (incl frontis). Blue cl (hinges cracked, spine faded, sl rubbed), gilt. Internally Good (lt foxed, esp upper margins, inscrip). *Morrell.* $192/£120

KENOYER, NATLEE. The Firehorses of San Francisco. L.A.: Westernlore, 1970. 1st ed. Brn patterned cl, gilt. Fine in VG + dj. *Harrington.* $40/£25

KENRICK, WILLIAM. The New American Orchardist. Boston, 1835. 2nd ed. 418pp. Orig blind-stamped cl, gilt. (Foxed, tp torn w/loss of word 'Orchardist'). *Brooks.* $89/£56

KENT, ALEXANDER. Command a King's Ship. London: Hutchinson, (1973). 1st ed. Fine in NF dj (sl worn). *Between The Covers.* $150/£94

KENT, ALEXANDER. The Inshore Squadron. Hutchinson, 1978. 1st Eng ed. NF (spine head sl bumped) in dj. *Ulysses.* $48/£30

KENT, ALEXANDER. Signal-Close Action! London: Hutchinson, (1974). 1st ed. Richard Bolitho bkmk laid in. (Sl cocked), else NF in NF dj (crown sl worn). *Between The Covers.* $125/£78

KENT, ALEXANDER. Success to the Brave. Hutchinson, 1983. 1st Eng ed. Fine in dj (sl creased). *Ulysses.* $40/£25

KENT, ALEXANDER. A Tradition of Victory. Hutchinson, 1981. 1st Eng ed. NF in dj (sl creased). *Ulysses.* $40/£25

KENT, ALEXANDER. A Tradition of Victory. London, 1981. 1st Eng ed. Signed. Nice (edges sl faded, spine creased) in dj. *Clearwater.* $56/£35

KENT, H. W. The Work of Bruce Rogers, Jack of All Trades: Master of One.... NY: OUP, 1939. 1st ed. Frontis, 22 plts, facs. VG in dj (rubbed). *Cox.* $72/£45

KENT, H. W. (comp). Bibliographical Notes on One Hundred Books Famous in English Literature. NY: Grolier Club, 1903. 1st ed. One of 305 (of 308). Untrimmed. Vellum-backed lt gray bds, gilt spine. (Sl foxed, bkpls; sl worn, partly dust-soiled, corners lt bumped.) *Baltimore*.* $90/£56

KENT, ROCKWELL. Beowulf. NY: Random House, 1932. 1st ed. One of 950 ptd. Signed w/thumbprint. Sm folio. 6 full-pg illus. Gray cl. Fine. *Turtle Island.* $350/£219

KENT, ROCKWELL. A Birthday Book. NY: Random House, 1931. One of 1850 numbered, signed. Silk eps. Pict silk cl. Fine, w/o dj as issued. *Dermont.* $250/£156

KENT, ROCKWELL. A Birthday Book. NY: Random House, 1931. 1st ed. One of 1850 numbered, signed. Silk eps. Pict silk cl. Fine. *Argonaut.* $300/£188

KENT, ROCKWELL. The Bookplates and Marks of Rockwell Kent. NY: Random House, 1929. 1st ed. One of 1250 ptd. Signed. Prospectus laid in. NF in dj. *Pacific*.* $259/£162

KENT, ROCKWELL. How I Make a Wood Cut. Pasadena: Esto Publishing, 1934. One of 1000. 4 full-pg engrs. Paper cvr label. *Dawson.* $125/£78

KENT, ROCKWELL. Later Bookplates and Marks. NY: Pynson Ptrs, 1937. 1st ed. One of 1250. Signed. Coral cl. NF (spine foot sl frayed) in Good dj (worn, splitting at folds, spine foot lacks sm piece, reinforced w/clear tape). *House.* $200/£125

KENT, ROCKWELL. N by E. NY: Random House, 1930. 1st ed. One of 900 ptd on special watermkd paper, signed by Kent. Blue silver-stamped cl. Fine in box. *Appelfeld.* $250/£156

KENT, ROCKWELL. A Northern Christmas. NY: American Artists Group, c. 1941. Ptd bds. (Feps extracted), else VG in ptd dj. *High Latitude.* $30/£19

KENT, ROCKWELL. This Is My Own. NY: Duell, Sloan & Pearce, (1940). Signed. Dec cl. Fine. *Pacific*.* $46/£29

KENT, ROCKWELL. Voyaging, Southward from the Strait of Magellan. NY: Putnam, 1924. 1st ed. Teg. Beige pict cl. Fine (rear corners sl worn). *Appelfeld.* $150/£94

KENT-SAVILLE, W. The Naturalist in Australia. London, 1897. Tall 4to. xv,302pp (names, sl marginal dampstaining to 2 plts, 1 text leaf; pp tanned); port (sl foxed, sm dampstain lower corner), 50 collotype, 9 chromolitho plts. Dec cl (edges rubbed, corners bumped, lt stained). *Sutton.* $685/£428

Kentish Traveller's Companion. (By Thomas Fisher.) Rochester/Canterbury, T. Fisher/Simmons & Kirkby, 1779. 1st ed. iv,248,(8)pp; 3 fldg maps. Contemp tree calf, red morocco spine label. (Fr hinge cracked.) *Karmiole.* $200/£125

KENTON, EDNA (ed). Black Gown and Redskins. London, 1956. Map. Good in dj. *Dumont.* $35/£22

KENYON, KATHLEEN M. Archaeology in the Holy Land. NY/Washington: Praeger, 1971. 3rd ed, 2nd ptg. VG in dj. *Worldwide.* $25/£16

KEOLEIN, ARDASHES H. The Oriental Cook Book: Wholesome, Dainty and Economical Dishes.... Sully & Kleinteich, 1913. VG-. *Book Broker.* $65/£41

KEPES, GYORGY (ed). The Man-Made Object. London: Studio Vista, 1966. Dj (sl rubbed). *Edwards.* $40/£25

KEPES, GYORGY. The New Landscape in Art and Science. Chicago: Paul Theobald, (1956). 1st ed. NF in dj (sm chips). *Turtle Island.* $75/£47

KEPHART, HORACE. Camp Cookery. NY: Outing Pub, 1910. 1st ed. Dec cl. VG. *Pacific*.* $35/£22

KEPHART, HORACE. Our Southern Highlanders. NY, 1913. 1st ed. Teg. (Sm sticker), else VG. *King.* $35/£22

KEPPEL, GEORGE. Narrative of a Journey Across the Balcan.... Henry Colburn & Richard Bentley, 1831. 1st ed. Eton presentation copy. 2 vols. 8vo. Color aquatint frontis, xvi,463; xiii,465pp; 3 maps (2 fldg). All edges marbled. Full contemp calf (neatly rebacked), emb fore-edges on all bds, raised bands, black labels, gilt. VG set (fldg maps lt foxed, ink inscrip; corners sl rubbed). *Sotheran.* $957/£598

KEPPEL, GEORGE. Personal Narrative of a Journey from India to England...in the Year 1824. Henry Colburn, 1827. 2nd ed, 1st bk. 2 vols. 8vo. 2 color frontispieces, xii,336; vii,326pp; 1 fldg map, 1 color litho plt. Orig 1/2 calf (neatly rebacked, preserving orig labels), gilt, marbled bds. VG set (bkpls; corners sl rubbed). *Sotheran.* $797/£498

KEPPEL, HENRY. The Expedition to Borneo of H.M.S. Dido for the Suppression of Piracy. NY, 1846. Fldg frontis map. (Lt foxed, prelim gathering carelessly opened.) *Swann*.* $230/£144

KER, ANNIE. Papuan Fairy Tales. London: Macmillan, 1910. 1st ed. 13 photo plts. Dk grn cl (spine lt frayed). *Karmiole.* $75/£47

KER, N. R. Medieval Libraries of Great Britain, a List of Surviving Books. Royal Hist Soc, 1964. 2nd ed. Fine in dj. *Gretton.* $19/£12

KERBY, ROBERT LEE. The Confederate Invasion of New Mexico and Arizona 1861-1862. Tucson: Westernlore, 1981. Fine in Fine dj. *Book Market.* $20/£13

KERCHEVAL, SAMUEL. A History of the Valley of Virginia. Woodstock, VA: John Gatewood, 1850. 2nd ed. 347pp. Contemp brn calf. (Bkpl, sigs, lt foxed, rubbed), else VG. Howes K102. *Chapel Hill.* $350/£219

KEROUAC, JACK. The Americans. NY: Grossman, 1969. Rev, enlgd ed. Fine in Fine dj. *Lenz.* $225/£141

KEROUAC, JACK. Big Sur. London: Andre Deutsch, 1963. 1st ed. NF in orange dj (sl faded, extrems rubbed, 1/2-inch chip [present] to top of rear edge). *Smith.* $225/£141

KEROUAC, JACK. The Dharma Bums. NY, 1958. 1st ed. NF in NF dj (short closed tear, rubbed). *Warren.* $300/£188

KEROUAC, JACK. Doctor Sax. Faust Part Three. Andre Deutsch, 1977. 1st UK ed. (Edges sl foxed, spine partly leaned), o/w NF in dj. *Sclanders.* $40/£25

KEROUAC, JACK. Lonesome Traveler. NY: McGraw-Hill, 1960. 1st ed. VG + in VG dj (interior clear-tape reinforcement, spine chipped). *Pettler.* $150/£94

KEROUAC, JACK. Lonesome Traveler. Andre Deutsch, 1962. 1st UK ed. NF in dj. *Sclanders.* $64/£40

KEROUAC, JACK. Maggie Cassidy. Panther, (states 1960, actually 1962). 1st UK pb ed, 2nd issue, w/red-haired Maggie in blue jeans depicted on fr cvr. NF (pp sl tanned, sl creased). *Sclanders.* $16/£10

KEROUAC, JACK. Maggie Cassidy. NY: Avon, 1959. 1st ed. NF (lt creased) in wraps. *Beasley.* $40/£25

KEROUAC, JACK. On the Road. NY, 1957. 1st ed. NF (spine edges lt worn, sl spotted) in 2nd ptg dj w/Fine fr panel (sl nicked, edges rubbed, ptd price partly erased). *Warren.* $500/£313

KEROUAC, JACK. On the Road. NY: Viking, 1957. 1st ed. 8vo. Top edge stained red. Black cl. (Spine cocked, extrems sl rubbed), o/w NF in dj (torn, chipped). *Heritage.* $750/£469

KEROUAC, JACK. On the Road. NY, 1957. 1st ed. 8vo. Dj (several internal archival tape repairs). *Swann*.* $977/£611

KEROUAC, JACK. On the Road. London: Andre Deutsch, 1958. 2nd imp. NF (sl leaning) in NF dj. *Warren.* $250/£156

KEROUAC, JACK. On the Road. London: Andre Deutsch, 1958. 1st ed. 8vo. VG (fep offset) in dj (rubbed; closed tear, fold to top of rear panel). Smith. $650/£406

KEROUAC, JACK. Satori in Paris. NY, (1966). 1st ed. (Felt-tip pen scribbles inside fr cvr; corners bumped), else VG in dj. King. $60/£38

KEROUAC, JACK. Satori in Paris. NY: Grove, 1966. 1st ed. Fine in dj. Smith. $150/£94

KEROUAC, JACK. The Subterraneans. Andre Deutsch, 1960. 1st UK ed. VG in dj (sl torn, rubbed). Sclanders. $48/£30

KEROUAC, JACK. The Subterraneans. London: Andre Deutsch, 1960. 1st UK ed. NF in NF dj (spine sunned). Beasley. $200/£125

KEROUAC, JACK. Tristessa. NY: Avon, 1960. 1st ed. VG-. Warren. $30/£19

KEROUAC, JACK. Tristessa. NY: Avon, 1960. Pb orig. NF (2-inch crease top fr panel). Warren. $45/£28

KEROUAC, JACK. Tristessa. NY: Avon, 1960. 1st ed. VG (sl chewed down corner) in wraps. Beasley. $45/£28

KEROUAC, JACK. Tristessa. NY: Avon, 1960. Pb orig. NF in wraps. Beasley. $50/£31

KEROUAC, JACK. Vanity of Duluoz. NY: Coward-McCann, (1968). 1st ed. VG (gilt spine lettering dulled) in dj (sl worn). Lenz. $150/£94

KEROUAC, JOHN. The Town and the City. NY, (1950). 1st ed, 1st bk. VG in dj (price-clipped, edges torn, chipped). King. $295/£184

KEROUAC, JOHN. The Town and the City. NY: Harcourt, (1950). 1st ed, 1st bk. 8vo. Fine in dj (worn). Second Life. $600/£375

KEROUAC, JOHN. The Town and the City. Eyre & Spottiswoode, 1951. 1st UK ed, 1st bk. VG (sl foxed) in Nice dj. Williams. $960/£600

KERR, JOHN. The Golf-Book of East Lothian. Edinburgh: T. & A. Constable, 1896. 1st ed. One of 500 sm paper copies. 9.75x7. Pict brn cl, gilt. NF (bkpl, emb stamp). Pacific*. $1,725/£1,078

KERR, PHILIP. The Pale Criminal. Viking, 1990. 1st ed. NF in dj. Ulysses. $200/£125

KERR, R. Nature Through Microscope and Camera. London: R.T.S., 1905. VG (rear bd sl stained, prize label). Savona. $45/£28

KERRIDGE, PHILIP MARKHAM. An Address on Angling Literature, including Some Mysteries and Personal Observations.... Fullerton: Sultana Press, (1970). One of ltd ed. Signed, inscribed. 1/2 calf, cl, fly on hook in plastic on fr cvr, gilt. Fine in slipcase. Pacific*. $207/£129

KERRY, ALMON AARON. Sixty Years of Logging. Taft, OR: The Author, 1962. 1st ed. Fine. Perier. $20/£13

KERSH, GERALD. Brain and Ten Fingers. London: Heinemann, 1943. 1st Eng ed. VG (spine ends, 2 corners sl bumped) in dj (nicked, rubbed, dusty, sl creased, browned). Ulysses. $58/£36

KERSTING, RUDOLPH (comp). The White World. NY: Lewis, Scribner, 1902. Inscribed by Wm. Brewer. VG (sl worn). High Latitude. $65/£41

KERTESZ, ANDRE. Day of Paris. NY: J.J. Augustin, (1945). 1st ed. Tan cl (hinges lt cracked; spine lt frayed; lt dusty). Cvrs Good. Baltimore*. $80/£50

KERTESZ, ANDRE. Day of Paris. NY, (1945). 1st ed. (Eps, bottom edge sl soiled.) Dj (soiled, badly worn). Swann*. $230/£144

KERTESZ, ANDRE. Distortions. Nicolas Ducrot (ed). NY: Knopf, 1976. 1st ed. Fine in dj. Cahan. $185/£116

KERTESZ, ANDRE. From My Window. Boston, 1981. 1st ed. NF in NF dj. Warren. $75/£47

KERTESZ, ANDRE. From My Window. Boston: NYGS, 1981. 1st ed. 53 color photos. VG (corner bumped) in illus dj. Cahan. $75/£47

KERTESZ, ANDRE. J'Aime Paris. NY: Grossman, 1974. 1st ed. NF in dj (short closed tear to rear panel). Smith. $175/£109

KERTESZ, ANDRE. J'Aime Paris. Photographs Since the Twenties. NY, 1974. 1st ed. NF in NF dj (lt rubbed). Warren. $175/£109

KERTESZ, ANDRE. A Lifetime of Perception. Toronto, 1982. 1st ed. (Rear hinge split, fr cvr sl spotted.) Dj (rubbed, damp-stained). Swann*. $80/£50

KERTESZ, ANDRE. On Reading. NY, 1971. 1st ed. (Sm tear last leaf; extrems sl worn.) Dj (rubbed, yellowed). Swann*. $69/£43

KERTESZ, ANDRE. Sixty Years of Photography, 1912-1972. NY, 1972. 1st ed. 224 repros. (Interior sl age-dknd.) Dj (age-dknd, torn). Swann*. $103/£64

KESEY, KEN. Demon Box. (NY): Viking, (1986). 1st ed. Red eps. 1/4 black cl, red bds. Fine in dj (lt soiled). Heritage. $50/£31

KESEY, KEN. Kesey's Garage Sale. NY: Viking, (1973). 1st ed. Gray eps; top edge stained grn. 2-tone blue cl. (Ink inscrip, spine ends faded), o/w NF. Heritage. $50/£31

KESEY, KEN. One Flew Over the Cuckoo's Nest. London: Methuen, 1962. 1st British ed. (Top pg edges sl foxed; spine rolled), else NF in VG + dj (laminate peeling). Lame Duck. $275/£172

KESEY, KEN. Sometimes a Great Notion. NY, 1964. 1st ed, 1st issue w/pub's logo, the Viking ship. NF (inscrip) in VG + dj (few short tears, edgeworn). Warren. $150/£94

KESEY, KEN. Sometimes a Great Notion. NY: Viking, 1964. 1st ed, 1st issue of this novel, w/Viking ship logo to 1/2-title. VG (spine top faded) in dj (4 glue/paper residues). Lame Duck. $175/£109

KESSEL, JOSEPH. The Lion. Knopf, 1962. 1st illus ed. 7.3x10.3. Harper Johnson (illus). 186pp. Fine in VG dj. Price. $30/£19

KESSELL, JOHN L. Kiva, Cross, and Crown. The Pecos Indians and New Mexico, 1540-1840. Washington: Nat'l Park Service, 1979. 1st ed. Simulated leather, gilt. Fine. Argonaut. $150/£94

KESSELL, JOHN L. Mission of Sorrows: Jesuit Guevavi and the Pimas, 1691-1767. Tucson: Univ of AZ, (1970). 1st ed. Brn cl, gilt. Fine in NF dj (sl rubbed). Harrington. $55/£34

KESSLER, HENRY H. Accidental Injuries: The Medico-Legal Aspects of Workmen's Compensation and Public Liability. Phila, 1931. 1st ed. (Inner hinges cracked; extrems worn), o/w Good. Doctor's Library. $75/£47

KESSLER, HENRY H. Cineplasty. Springfield, IL: Charles C. Thomas, (1947). 1st ed. Fine in dj. Weber. $125/£78

KESTEN, HERMANN. Happy Man. Edward Crankshaw (trans). NY: A.A. Wynn, 1947. 1st ed. 18 full-pg illus. Good + (fr cvr creased, sl stained, corners sl bumped). Any Amount. $26/£16

KESTER, JESSE Y. The American Shooter's Manual. NY: Derrydale, 1928. One of 375 numbered. Grn cl backed over lt grn paper-cvrd bds. VF. Biscotti. $175/£109

KETCHUM, HIRAM. General McClellan's Peninsula Campaign. (NY), 1864. 72pp. (Dampstained) in self-wrapper. Woolman. $40/£25

KETCHUM, WILLIAM C., JR. Western Memorabilia. Maplewood, 1980. Stated 1st ed. Padded 'Classics Edition.' Fine in dj. Baade. $65/£41

KETTEL, KARSTEN. Peripheral Facial Palsy: Pathology and Surgery. Springfield, IL: Charles C. Thomas, 1959. Fine in dj. Weber. $150/£94

KETTELL, SAMUEL (ed). Specimens of American Poetry.... Boston, 1829. 1st ed. 3 vols. Fore-edges untrimmed. Orig cl-backed bds. (Rubbed, spine labels chipped, cl loss along spines, vol 3 cvrs nearly detached.) Kane*. $80/£50

KETTLE, RUPERT. Strikes and Arbitrations: With the Procedure and Forms Successfully Adopted in the Building Trade at Wolverhampton.... London/Wolverhampton: Simpkin, Marshall/W. Parke, 1866. 1st ed. 48pp. New 1/2 calf. Fine. *Young.* $224/£140

KETTLEWELL, JOHN. Beaver. T. Werner Laurie, n.d. (1922). 1st ed. Inscribed. Good+ in pict wraps (rebacked, soiled, edges worn). *Any Amount.* $32/£20

KEULEMANS, TONY and JAN COLDEWEY. Feathers to Brush: The Victorian Bird Artist John Gerard Keulemans, 1842-1912. (The Netherlands: Privately ptd, 1982.) One of 500. Signed by both. 3/4 morocco, gilt. Fine. *Pacific*.* $184/£115

KEWLEY, CHARLES and HOWARD FARRAR. Fishing Tackle for Collectors. Sothebys, 1987. 1st ed. 16 color plts. VG in dj. *Hollett.* $56/£35

KEY, TED. The Biggest Dog in the World. Dutton, 1960. 1st ed. 7x9. 44pp. Good in dj (chipped). *Price.* $20/£13

KEYES, E. D. From West Point to California. Oakland: Biobooks, 1950. Blue cl. VF. *Parmer.* $30/£19

KEYES, EDWARD L. Lewis Atterbury Stimson, M.D. NY: Knickerbocker, 1918. 1st ed. Frontis. Blue cl. NF. *Chapel Hill.* $150/£94

KEYES, FRANCES PARKINSON. Once on Esplanade. NY: Dodd Mead, 1947. 1st ed. 5.75x8. Addison Burbank (illus). 202pp. Fine in dj. *Cattermole.* $75/£47

KEYNES, GEOFFREY. A Bibliography of Dr. John Donne. Cambridge, 1932. 4th ed. Frontisport, 12 collotype plts. Black/red cl. Dj (sl grubby). *Maggs.* $40/£25

KEYNES, GEOFFREY. Bibliography of William Hazlitt. London: Nonesuch, 1931. 1st Eng ed. One of 750. 4 collotype plts. NF (feps partly browned; spine foot, 2 corners sl bumped) in dj (sl creased, sl faded). *Ulysses.* $200/£125

KEYNES, GEOFFREY. Blake Studies, Notes on His Life and Works in Seventeen Chapters. London, 1949. 1st ed. 48 plts. Grn buckram. VG. *Gretton.* $64/£40

KEYNES, GEOFFREY. Dr. Timothie Bright 1550-1615. London: Wellcome Historical Medical Library, 1962. 12 plts. Red cl. *Maggs.* $19/£12

KEYNES, GEOFFREY. The Library of Edward Gibbon. Bibliographical Soc, 1950. Fine in dj. *Gretton.* $88/£55

KEYNES, GEOFFREY. The Life of William Harvey. Oxford: Clarendon, 1966. 1st ed. Color frontis, 32 plts. VG. *Glaser.* $75/£47

KEYNES, GEOFFREY. William Blake's Engravings. London: Faber & Faber, 1950. 118 plts. Gray cl. Dj (few sm tears). *Maggs.* $104/£65

KEYNES, GEOFFREY. William Blake's Engravings. London: Faber, 1950. Good. *Ars Artis.* $136/£85

KEYNES, GEOFFREY. William Blake's Water-Colours Illustrating the Poems of Thomas Gray. Chicago: J. Philip O'Hara/Trianon Press, 1972. 1st ed. 16 color repros. Blue cl. Good in dj. *Karmiole.* $75/£47

KEYNES, JOHN MAYNARD. The Economic Consequences of Mr. Churchill. Tavistock Square: Leonard & Virginia Woolf, 1925. 1st ed. One of 7000 ptd. VG in grn ptd paper wrappers (spine sl worn, few sm tears). *Maggs.* $240/£150

KEYNES, JOHN MAYNARD. The Economic Consequences of the Peace. NY: Harcourt Brace, 1920. 1st ed. VG (sl foxed; sl worn). *Lenz.* $125/£78

KEYNES, JOHN MAYNARD. The General Theory of Employment Interest and Money. London: Macmillan, 1936. 1st ed. Fine. *Lenz.* $400/£250

KEYNES, JOHN MAYNARD. The General Theory of Employment, Interest and Money. London: Macmillan, 1936. 1st ed. 8vo. Forest grn cl. Fine in dj (spine, extrems browned, lt chipped). *Glenn.* $1,000/£625

KEYNES, JOHN MAYNARD. The Means to Prosperity. London, 1933. VG in orig wraps. *Edrich.* $29/£18

KEYNES, JOHN MAYNARD. A Short View of Russia. London: Hogarth, 1925. 1st Eng ed. VG (edges sl spotted, spine rubbed) in wrappers (sl dusty). *Ulysses.* $136/£85

KEYNES, JOHN MAYNARD. A Treatise on Money. NY: Harcourt, Brace, (1930). 1st Amer ed. 2 vols. Brn cl. Good in djs (sl chipped, spine sl dknd). *Karmiole.* $250/£156

KEYWORTH, SAMUEL. Form-Growth. A Practical Handbook on the Human Figure. London, 1895. 98pp + (iii)pp ads. Emb cl. (Lib ink stamps, margins sl thumbed; sl rubbed, soiled; #.) *Edwards.* $32/£20

KHAYYAM, OMAR. Rubaiyat. London: Hodder & Stoughton, (1913). 1st ed. Lg 4to. Rene Bull (illus). Rust-brn cl, gilt. (Few prelims, edges lt foxed), o/w Fine. *Reisler.* $500/£313

KHAYYAM, OMAR. Rubaiyat. London: Collins Clear-Type Press, (1928). 1st ed. 4to. 4 full-pg mtd color plts by Charles Robinson. Aeg. Blue limp leather, gilt. Good in textured dj (worn), color pict box (worn). *Reisler.* $350/£219

KHAYYAM, OMAR. Rubaiyat. Edward Fitzgerald (trans). London: Hodder & Stoughton, (c. 1909). 20 tipped-in color plts by Edmund Dulac. Red cl, gilt. (Spine, extrems insect-damaged), else VG- in Good box. *Pacific*.* $98/£61

KHAYYAM, OMAR. Rubaiyat. Edward Fitzgerald (trans). London, 1903. Sm 8vo. Beige silk doublures and eps (lt spotted). Olive morocco by Ramage, gilt. *Swann*.* $575/£359

KHAYYAM, OMAR. Rubaiyat. LEC, 1936. Ltd to 1500 numbered, signed by Valenti Angelo (designer). Fine in slipcase. *Swann*.* $149/£93

KHAYYAM, OMAR. Rubaiyat. London: George G. Harrap, n.d. 16 tipped-in color plts by Willy Pogany. Grn cl (lt bumped), gilt. NF in Fair dj (soiled, dknd, sm pieces out of spine; rear panel torn w/pieces out). *Blue Mountain.* $75/£47

KHEIRALLAH, GEORGE. Arabia Reborn. Albuquerque, NM: Univ of NM, 1952. 1st ed. 17 plts. (Sl rubbed, soiled), o/w VG. *Worldwide.* $45/£28

KIDD, J. H. Personal Recollections of a Cavalryman. Ionia, MI, 1908. Time-Life 1983 Collector's Library of the Civil War rpt. Leather, gilt. Fine. *Pratt.* $30/£19

KIDD, J. H. Personal Recollections of a Cavalryman. Ionia, MI, 1908. 1st ed. (Inner hinges cracked, ink name; rear cvr stained, spine sunned, frayed; rear corners gnawed, fr corners bumped.) *King.* $250/£156

KIDDER, ALFRED VINCENT. An Introduction to the Study of Southwestern Archaeology with a Preliminary Account of the Excavations at Pecos. New Haven: Dept of Archaeology, Phillips Academy, 1924. 2nd ptg. Fldg frontis, 49 photo plts. Grn cl, gilt. (Cvrs lt scratched), else Fine. *Argonaut.* $125/£78

KIDDER, D. (ed). Mines and Mining. NY: Lane & Scott, 1851. 212pp + (12)pp ads. 1/2 calf, marbled bds. (Dk waterstain.) *Blake.* $50/£31

KIDDER, DANIEL P. Mormonism and the Mormons. NY: G. Lane & P.P. Sandford, 1842. 1st ed. 342pp. Contemp calf (lt scuffed), leather label. Howes K122. *M & S.* $250/£156

KIDDER, GLEN M. Railway to the Moon. Kidder, 1969. Ltd to 1500 numbered. VG in dj. *Rybski.* $45/£28

KIDDER, J. EDWARD, JR. Japanese Temples, Sculpture, Paintings, Gardens, and Architecture. Tokyo/Amsterdam, n.d. (1964). VG. *King.* $100/£63

KIDDER, TRACY. House. Boston: HM, 1985. 1st ed. Fine in Fine dj. *Between The Covers.* $50/£31

KIDSON, JOSEPH R. and FRANK. Historical Notices of the Leeds Old Pottery. Leeds, 1892. One of 250. Frontisport, 161pp; 20 plts. Uncut. (Margins sl thumbed, bkpl, fr hinge sl tender; soiled, sl rubbed, spine sl bumped.) *Edwards.* $152/£95

KIDWELL, CLARA SUE. Choctaws and Missionaries in Mississippi, 1818-1918. Norman: Univ of OK, (1995). 1st ed. Fine in dj. *Lien.* $20/£13

KIEFER, ANSELM. Anselm Kiefer: Watercolours 1970-1982. London: Anthony d'Offay Gallery, (1983). One of 850 numbered, signed by Kiefer. 32 color plts. *Swann**. $172/£108

KIEFER, F. J. The Legends of the Rhine from Basle to Rotterdam. L. W. Garnham (trans). Mayence: David Kapp, 1870. 2nd ed. Frontis. Aeg. VG in gilt-pict binding. *Other Worlds.* $35/£22

KIERNAN, R. H. Lawrence of Arabia. London: George G. Harrap, 1935. 1st ed. Orange cl. Good (sl dusty). *Maggs.* $48/£30

KIERNAN, R. H. Lawrence of Arabia. London: George G. Harrap, 1935. 1st ed, Amer issue. Orange cl. Clean in dj (edges sl worn). *Maggs.* $72/£45

KIERNAN, R. H. The Unveiling of Arabia. London: George G. Harrap, 1937. 1st ed. Grn cl. (Sm spine stain), o/w Fine in dj. *Maggs.* $64/£40

KIHN, W. LANGDON. Portraits of American Indians. NY: Art Museum of Santa Fe, 1922. 9 plts (1 color). VG in wraps (sl soiled). *Dumont.* $275/£172

KIJEWSKI, KAREN. Wild Kat. Huntington Beach: James Cahill, 1994. One of 150. Signed. Cl-backed marbled bds, gilt. As New. *Pacific**. $63/£39

KILBOURNE, S. A. and G. BROWN GOODE. Game Fishes of the United States. NY: Winchester, 1972. Ltd to 1000 numbered. Portfolio bound in. Elephant folio. 20 loose color plts within bound-in portfolio. Dec 1/2 blue leather, gilt, over blue paper-cvrd bds. Fine in orig shipping carton. *Biscotti.* $135/£84

Kilgour Collection of Russian Literature, 1750-1920. Cambridge: Harvard College Library, 1959. 1st ed. Crimson cl, gilt. Nice (sl dusty, handled, spine lt sunned). *Baltimore**. $80/£50

KILMER, JOYCE. The Circus and Other Essays. NY: Laurence J. Gomme, 1916. 1st ed. Inscribed, signed, dated 1916. Red cl. (Few spots, spine dull), else VG. *Pacific**. $69/£43

KILMER, JOYCE. Trees and Other Poems. NY, (1914). 1st ed, 1st issue. Tan bds, label fr cvr. *Swann**. $57/£36

KILMON, JACK and HOOPER SHELTON. Rattlesnakes in America. Sweetwater, TX: (Shelton, 1981). Fine in dj. *Perier.* $25/£16

KILPATRICK, JAMES. My Seventy Years with Clydesdales. Glasgow: Henry Munro, 1949. 1st ptg. VG + in Good+ dj. *October Farm.* $95/£59

KIMBALL, CHARLES P. The San Francisco City Directory...September 1, 1850. SF: Journal of Commerce, 1850 (but ca 1890). 2nd rpt ed. 139pp, ads on both pastedowns. Maroon pebble-grain cl, gilt. Fine. Howes K134. *Harrington.* $100/£63

KIMBALL, FISKE. The Creation of the Rococo. Phila, 1943. 1/4 cl (sl splayed; last few plts sl foxed). *Washton.* $65/£41

KIMBALL, FISKE. Domestic Architecture of the American Colonies and of the Early Republic. NY, 1922. 1st ed. (Cvr sl stained, spine worn, rear cvr damaged near spine.) *King.* $75/£47

KIMBALL, FISKE. Mr. Samuel McIntire, Carver. Portland: Southworth-Anthoensen for the Essex Inst, 1940. One of 675. Orig prospectus, order form laid in. (Lt worn.) Slipcase (scuffed). *Oinonen**. $160/£100

KIMBALL, FISKE. Mr. Samuel McIntire, Carver: The Architect of Salem. Portland, 1940. One of 675. (Sl foxed.) *Swann**. $161/£101

KIMBALL, MARIA BRACE. A Soldier-Doctor of Our Army: James B. Kimball, Late Colonel and Assistant Surgeon-General, U.S. Army. Boston: Houghton, Mifflin, 1917. 1st ed. Inscribed, signed presentation. Gilt-dec cl. Fine (sm rubberstamp). Howes K137. *Pacific**. $207/£129

KIMBALL, NELL. Nell Kimball: Her Life as an American Madam. Stephen Longstreet (ed). NY: Macmillan, 1970. 1st ed. Fine in VG dj. *Connolly.* $32/£20

KIMES, WILLIAM and MAYMIE B. John Muir, a Reading Bibliography. Fresno: Panorama West Books, 1986. 1st ed. Fine. *Perier.* $97/£61

KIMES, WILLIAM. and MAYMIE B. John Muir: A Reading Bibliography. Fresno: Panorama West, 1986. Revised. Fine. *Book Market.* $100/£63

KIMMEL, STANLEY. The Mad Booths of Maryland. Indianapolis, (1940). 1st ed. (Sl lib mks), else Good. *King.* $35/£22

KINDIG, JOE. Thoughts on the Kentucky Rifle in Its Golden Age. York, 1960. Dj. *Swann**. $103/£64

KINDIG, JOE. Thoughts on the Kentucky Rifle in its Golden Age. (Wilmington, DE, 1960.) 1st ed. (Ink inscrip), else VG in dj (torn, frayed). *King.* $150/£94

KINDIG, JOE. Thoughts on the Kentucky Rifle in Its Golden Age. NY: Bonanza Books, n.d. Good in dj. *Zubal**. $35/£22

King Gobble's Feast, or The Fatal Effects of Pride. NY: McLoughlin Bros, 1883. Dame Dingles Series. Tall 8vo. 4 leaves + 1pg list on lower wrapper. Eight 2/3pg chromolithos, all engr and signed by Cogger. Pict paper wrappers. Near Mint. *Hobbyhorse.* $215/£134

KING, BEN. Southland Melodies. Chicago: Forbes, 1911. 1st illus ed. Essie Collins Matthews & Leigh Richmond Miner (illus). Photo frontis. Lt grn pict cl. VG (edges sl rubbed). *Baltimore**. $60/£38

KING, BLANCHE BUSEY. Under Your Feet. The Story of the American Mound Builders. NY: Dodd, Mead, 1939. 1st ed. Inscribed, signed. Color frontis. Grn cl. VG in color, pict dj (edge chipped). *House.* $35/£22

KING, C. The Natural History of Precious Stones and of the Precious Metals. London: Bell & Daldy, 1870. xi,364pp; 7 plts. Good. *Blake.* $100/£63

KING, CHARLES. An Apache Princess, a Tale of the Indian Frontier. NY, 1903. 1st ed. Teg. Color photo label. (Hinges weak, cvr sl stained, dknd.) *King.* $35/£22

KING, CHARLES. Campaigning with Crook and Stories of Army Life. NY: Harper, 1890. 1st ed. xi,295pp + (8)pp. Gilt-dec cl. (Few spots, extrems lt rubbed), else NF. *Pacific**. $58/£36

KING, CHARLES. Indian Campaigns: Sketches of Cavalry Service in Arizona and on the Northern Plains. Harry H. Anderson (ed). (Ft. Collins, CO): Old Army, (1984). One of 250. Signed by Anderson. 2-tone cl. Fine. *Pacific**. $98/£61

KING, CHARLES. Trials of a Staff Officer. Phila: L.R. Hamersly, 1891. 1st ed. 214,(8)pp. Grn cl, gilt. VG (tape repair fep; extrems sl worn, rubbed). *Harrington.* $75/£47

KING, CLARENCE. The Helmet of Mambrino. NY/London: Putnam, 1904. 1st ed. Frontisport, 8 plts. Uncut, teg. Vellum-backed bds, gilt. (Pencil name, notes; vellum worn, discolored, corners worn), o/w VG. *Pacific**. $127/£79

KING, CLARENCE. The Helmet of Mambrino. SF: Book Club of CA, 1938. Ltd to 350 ptd. Vellum-backed marbled bds, gilt spine. Fine in slipcase. *Pacific**. $52/£33

KING, CLARENCE. Mountaineering in the Sierra Nevada. Boston: James R. Osgood, 1872. 1st ed, 1st issue. (6),292pp. Maroon cl, gilt spine. (Offset to tp; spine faded, ends lt rubbed; cvrs lt soiled), o/w NF. Howes K148. *Pacific**. $345/£216

KING, CLARENCE. Mountaineering in the Sierra Nevada. Boston: Houghton, Osgood, 1879. 6th ed. (2),v,(2),308pp; 2 fldg color litho maps. Grn cl, gilt spine. (Inscrip, lt foxed; sl nick rear joint, extrems lt rubbed), else NF. *Pacific**. $138/£86

KING, CLARENCE. Mountaineering in the Sierra Nevada. Francis Farquhar (ed). NY: W.W. Norton, (1935). Frontis, 7 plts. Blue cl, gilt. (Few spots tp), else Fine. *Pacific**. $40/£25

KING, CLIVE. Me and My Million. Crowell, 1979. 1st Amer ed. 160pp. VG in Fair dj. *Price.* $20/£13

KING, EDWARD. The Great South: A Record of Journeys. Hartford, CT: American Pub, 1875. 1st ed. Frontis, 802,ivpp. Pict grn cl. (Extrems lt rubbed), else VG. Howes K149. *Chapel Hill.* $125/£78

KING, FRANCIS. Flights. Hutchinson, 1973. 1st UK ed. NF in dj. *Williams.* $32/£20

KING, FRANK M. Longhorn Trail Drivers. L.A.: The Author, 1940. 1st ed. One of 400. Signed. Fabricoid. VG + (faded). Howes K150. *Labordo.* $225/£141

KING, FRANK M. Mavericks: The Salty Comments of an Old-Time Cowpuncher. Pasadena, CA: Trail's End Pub, (1947). 1st ed. Color frontis. VG in dj (worn). *Lien.* $50/£31

KING, FRANK M. Pioneer Western Empire Builders. Pasadena: Trail's End, 1946. 1st ed. (Sl worn.) *Dumont.* $60/£38

KING, FRANK M. Wranglin' the Past. Pasadena, CA: Trails End, 1946. 1st rev ed. VG in dj. *Labordo.* $75/£47

KING, GEORGE S. The Last Slaver. NY: Putnam, 1933. 1st ed. Blue cl, gilt. VG. *American Booksellers.* $60/£38

KING, J. ANTHONY. Twenty-Four Years in the Argentine Republic. London: Longman, Brown, 1846. 1st ed. xii, 442,2,32 pub's lists. Orig purple ribbed/blindstamped cl. (Sl foxed; joint repaired), o/w VG. *Morrell.* $152/£95

KING, J. C. H. Artificial Curiosities from the Northwest Coast of America. London: British Museum Publications, (1981). 1st ed. 103 plts (16 color). Grn cl, gilt. Fine in dj. *Pacific*.* $138/£86

KING, J. T. and N. W. LESLIE. Aeroplane Construction and Assembly. Minneapolis, (1918). (Name, notes fep; fr pastedown sl discolored, worn; corners worn.) *Woolson.* $60/£38

KING, JEFF. Where the Two Came to Their Father: A Navajo War Ceremonial. (Princeton): Princeton Univ, 1969. 18 loose plts. Cl-backed wrappers. NF in box. *Pacific*.* $207/£129

KING, JESSIE M. How Cinderella Was Able to Go to the Ball. A Brochure on Batik. London: G.T. Foulis, (1924). 1st ed. 8vo. (xvi),17-55; 17 mtd color plts. White pict paper-cvrd bds. Very Nice (corner tips worn, edges rubbed, sl spine abrasions). *Sotheran.* $957/£598

KING, JESSIE M. The Little White Town of Never Weary. George C. Harrap, (1917). 1st ed. 4to. (vi),7-154pp; 4 full-color plts mtd-at-large. Pale grn pict cl. Excellent (fore-edge of book block sl speckled). *Sotheran.* $797/£498

KING, MARTIN LUTHER, JR. Stride Toward Freedom. NY, (1958). 1st ed. Dj (rubbed, chipped). *Swann*.* $103/£64

KING, MARTIN LUTHER, JR. Stride Toward Freedom. NY, (1958). 1st ed, 1st bk. Dj (sl edgeworn, spine faded, sm closed tear at head). *Swann*.* $126/£79

KING, MOSES. King's Views of the New York Stock Exchange. NY: King, 1897. Slim tall folio. 96pp + orig pict wraps. Olive cl, gilt. (Sl aged, dusty, hinges cracked; sl worn, spine bottom frayed, lacks lower 2 inches.) *Baltimore*.* $50/£31

KING, MRS. E. L. Hunting Big Game in Africa. Privately ptd, ca 1926. (Cvrs sl soiled), else VG. *Hallam.* $160/£100

KING, MRS. FRANCIS. The Well Considered Garden. NY: Scribner, 1915. 2nd ptg. (Browned; corners bumped), else VG. *Fair Meadow.* $35/£22

KING, MRS. FRANCIS. The Well Considered Garden. NY: Scribner, 1915. Fldg plan. Dec cl, gilt. VG (spine sl faded). *Quest.* $40/£25

KING, RUFUS. The Case of the Dowager's Etchings. NY: Doubleday, Doran, 1944. 1st ed. Gray cl. (Spine ends sl rubbed), o/w Fine in dj (spine lt browned, extrems chipped). *Heritage.* $100/£63

KING, STEPHEN and PETER STRAUB. The Talisman. West Kingston, 1984. 1st ed. 2 vols. (Lt worn.) Slipcase. *Oinonen*.* $40/£25

KING, STEPHEN. The Bachman Books: Four Early Novels by Stephen King. NY: NAL, (1985). Advance proof. Fine in ptd orange wrappers. *Pacific*.* $230/£144

KING, STEPHEN. Carrie. GC: Doubleday, 1974. 1st ed. Signed, inscribed presentation, 8/22/80. (Lt worn.) Dj. *Oinonen*.* $475/£297

KING, STEPHEN. Carrie. NY: Doubleday, 1974. 1st ed. Fine in dj. *Pacific*.* $575/£359

KING, STEPHEN. Carrie. NY, 1974. 1st ed, 1st bk. 8vo. Dj. *Swann*.* $690/£431

KING, STEPHEN. Christine. West Kingston, (1983). 1st ed. One of 1000 signed by King & Stephen Gervais (illus). Dj, slipcase. *Swann*.* $172/£108

KING, STEPHEN. Christine. West Kingston: Grant, (1983). One of 1000 numbered, signed by King and Stephen Gervais (illus). (Lt worn.) Dj, slipcase. *Oinonen*.* $225/£141

KING, STEPHEN. Cujo. NY: Viking, (1981). 1st ed. Black cl, tan bds. (Spine ends sl rubbed), o/w Fine in dj (lt edgeworn). *Heritage.* $50/£31

KING, STEPHEN. Cujo. NY: Mysterious Press, (1981). One of 750 numbered, signed. Gilt-dec cl. (Sl worn.) Slipcase. *Oinonen*.* $130/£81

KING, STEPHEN. Cujo. NY, (1981). 1st ed. Signed, inscribed. Dj (lt worn). *Swann*.* $230/£144

KING, STEPHEN. Cujo. NY: Mysterious, (1981). 1st ed. One of 750. Signed. Gilt-dec maroon cl. Fine in slipcase. *Pacific*.* $374/£234

KING, STEPHEN. The Dark Tower II: The Drawing of the Three. (West Kingston, RI): Donald Grant, (1987). 1st ed. Ltd to 850 signed by King and Phil Hale (illus). 10 color plts. Mint in Mint dj, cl slipcase. *Bromer.* $475/£297

KING, STEPHEN. The Dark Tower III: The Waste Lands. Hampton Falls, NH: Donald M. Grant, (1991). 1st ed. Ltd to 1250 signed by King and Ned Dameron (illus). 12 color plts (10 dbl-pg). Mint in dj, cl slipcase. *Bromer.* $350/£219

KING, STEPHEN. The Dark Tower: The Gunslinger. (West Kingston): Donald M. Grant, (1982). 1st Trade ed. One of 10,000 issued. (Spine ends sl rubbed), else NF in dj. *Pacific*.* $345/£216

KING, STEPHEN. Different Seasons. NY: Viking, (1982). 1st ed. Inscribed, dated 1983. Fine in dj. *Bromer.* $285/£178

KING, STEPHEN. Dolan's Cadillac. Lord John, 1989. One of 1000 signed, numbered. 1/4 cl, dec bds. *Martin.* $264/£165

KING, STEPHEN. Dolan's Cadillac. Northridge, CA: Lord John, 1989. 1st ed. Ltd to 1000 signed. VF. *Bromer.* $275/£172

KING, STEPHEN. Firestarter. NY, (1980). 1st ed. Signed, inscribed. Dj. *Swann*.* $287/£179

KING, STEPHEN. Firestarter. Huntington Woods, 1980. One of 725 numbered, signed by King and Michael Whelan (illus). (Lt worn.) Dj (sl edgeworn), slipcase. *Oinonen*.* $250/£156

KING, STEPHEN. Firestarter. Huntington Woods: Phantasia, 1980. 1st ed. One of 725. Signed, dated July 6, 1980. Blue cl. Fine in dj, slipcase. *Pacific*.* $374/£234

KING, STEPHEN. My Pretty Pony. NY: Whitney Museum, 1988. 1st ed. One of 280 deluxe copies signed by King and Barbara Kruger (illus). Folio. Leather-backed brushed steel, digital timepiece mtd on fr cvr. Orig mailing box. *Swann*.* $1,495/£934

KING, STEPHEN. My Pretty Pony. (NY: Borzoi, 1989.) 1st Trade ed. Dec bds. Fine in slipcase. *Pacific*.* $52/£33

KING, STEPHEN. My Pretty Pony. (NY, 1989.) 1st trade ed. VG in slipcase. *King.* $65/£41

KING, STEPHEN. Night Shift. GC: Doubleday, 1978. 1st ed. VG in dj (spine head, corners rubbed, spine foot chipped, ends, corners sl bumped). *Pacific*.* $403/£252

KING, STEPHEN. Night Shift. NY, 1978. 1st ed. Dj (lt rubbed). *Swann*.* $460/£288

KING, STEPHEN. Nightmares and Dreamscapes. London: Hodder & Stoughton, (1993). Ltd ed, w/bkpl signed by King affixed to 1/2-title. (Lt worn.) Slipcase. Oinonen*. $75/£47

KING, STEPHEN. Pet Sematary. GC: Doubleday, 1983. 1st ed. Advance uncorrected proof. Color pict wraps (handled, creases, spine w/cracks). Text Good. Baltimore*. $70/£44

KING, STEPHEN. Salem's Lot. GC: Doubleday, 1975. 1st ed. Untrimmed. Black cl, red bds, gilt spine. VG (spine head sl worn) in 2nd state color pict dj (spine head chipped, several creases, 3-inch tear top of rear panel, few sm edge tears, crease along fr flap edge; price-clipped, $7.95 price ptd along top edge). Baltimore*. $240/£150

KING, STEPHEN. Salem's Lot. GC: Doubleday, 1975. 1st ed, 2nd state dj w/misprint 'Father Cody' and $8.95 price clipped off, restamped w/$7.95. VG in dj (spine ends rubbed, sm tear fr panel). Pacific*. $403/£252

KING, STEPHEN. The Shining. NY: Doubleday, 1977. 1st ed. VG in dj (spine head, extrems rubbed, foot chipped, 1-inch tear rear joint, w/crease). Pacific*. $138/£86

KING, STEPHEN. The Shining. GC: Doubleday, 1977. 1st ed. Signed. Stamped 'With compliments of Doubleday & Company, Inc.' on fr pastedown. (Lt worn, top edge sl soiled.) Dj (sl frayed, soiled). Oinonen*. $200/£125

KING, STEPHEN. The Shining. GC: Doubleday, 1977. 1st ed. Fine in NF dj (few sm scuffs rear panel). Between The Covers. $300/£188

KING, STEPHEN. Skeleton Crew. (Santa Cruz): Scream/Press, 1985. One of 1000. Signed by King & J. K. Potter (illus). Color fold-out laid in loose, as issued. Black cl. Fine in dj, slipcase. Pacific*. $259/£162

KING, STEPHEN. Skeleton Crew. Santa Cruz: Scream, 1985. One of 1000 numbered, signed by King and J. K. Potter (illus), and w/color fold-out laid in loose, as issued. (Sl worn.) Dj, slipcase. Oinonen*. $275/£172

KING, STEPHEN. The Stand. GC, 1978. 1st ed. (Ink name; spine ends chipped; worn, sl stained) in dj (edges frayed). King. $75/£47

KING, STEPHEN. The Stand. GC: Doubleday, 1978. 1st ed. (Vertical fold 1st few ll), else VG in dj (edgeworn, several 1-inch closed tears). Other Worlds. $95/£59

KING, STEPHEN. The Stand. GC: Doubleday, 1978. 1st ed, 1st issue w/$12.95 price on flap. VG in dj (sm tears spine ends, sl creasing spine, extrems). Pacific*. $109/£68

KING, STEPHEN. The Stand. GC: Doubleday, 1978. 1st ed, 1st issue w/$12.95 price on flap. (Spine ends sl shelfworn), else NF in dj. Pacific*. $150/£94

KING, STEPHEN. The Stand. The Complete and Uncut Edition. NY, (1990). Deluxe ed. One of 1250 numbered, signed by King and Bernie Wrightson (illus). Aeg. Full gilt-stamped leatherette. (Sl worn.) Orig silk-lined wooden box. Oinonen*. $300/£188

KING, W. J. HARDING. A Search for the Masked Tawareks. London, 1903. 1st ed. Fldg map. (Feps lt browned, spine lt faded.) Edwards. $120/£75

KING, W. KENT. Tombstones for Bluecoats. Marion Station, MD, 1981. Typescript facs. 5 vols. VG + in wrappers. Pacific*. $115/£72

KING-HALL, EDITH. Adventures in Toyland. London: Blackie & Son, (c.1920's). 1st ed. 7.75x5.5. Alice B. Woodward (illus). Pict cl. (Foxed; extrems sl rubbed), else VG. Pacific*. $58/£36

KING-SMITH, DICK. Pigs Might Fly. Viking, 1980. 1st ed. Mary Rayner (illus). 158pp. VG (spine ends sl dampstained) in VG dj (sl dampstained). Price. $25/£16

KINGDON-WARD, FRANK. Pilgrimage for Plants. London: George C. Harrup, 1960. 1st ed. 36 plts. (Taplinger name pasted over Harrup; bd edges sunned), else VG in dj (chipped). Fair Meadow. $80/£50

KINGDON-WARD, FRANK. Plant Hunter in Manipur. London: J. Cape, 1952. 1st ed. Blue cl. VG in VG- dj (price-clipped). Archer. $100/£63

KINGDON-WARD, FRANK. Rhododendrons. NY, 1950. Color frontis, 4 b/w photo plts. VG. Larry Price. $49/£31

KINGLAKE, ALEXANDER WILLIAM. The Invasion of the Crimea: Its Origin and an Account of Its Progress Down to the Death of Lord Raglan. William Blackwood, 1863-87. Vol 1 2nd ed, rest 1st eds. 8 vols. 8vo. Half-titles present, 5 fldg frontispieces (incl a tinted view, 2 plans, 2 maps), 65 maps, plans (45 fldg). Marbled eps; marbled, gilt-hatched edges, Contemp brn tree calf, gilt, by Riviere, backstrips a paler calf, not faded, red morocco title labels, grn vol labels. VG (prelim ll foxed some vols, bkpl, shelf label fr pastedowns). Blackwell's. $1,040/£650

Kings County Resources, Illustrated. (Hanford): W.W. Barnes, 1897-98. 1st ed. 8.5x11.5. (7),14-148,(6)pp. Blue cl, gilt. (Water stain lower rt corners, gilt dull), o/w Fine. Pacific*. $690/£431

KINGSLEY, CHARLES, JR. The Saint's Tragedy; Or, The True Story of Elizabeth of Hungary. London, 1848. 1st ed, 1st bk. NF (sl rubbed, title label sl chipped). Polyanthos. $60/£38

KINGSLEY, CHARLES. The Life and Works of.... London, 1901-1903. Ltd to 525 sets. 19 vols. 9x6 inches. Teg. Bound by Blackwell in 3/4 brown morocco w/gilt-stamped spine w/raised bands. (One vol sl scraped, some sl scuffed), else VG set. King. $1,500/£938

KINGSLEY, CHARLES. The Water Babies. Phila: David McKay, (1915). 1st Amer ed. 8vo. 12 full-pg color plts by Mabel Lucie Attwell. Blue cl (spine sl faded, rear hinge cracked; tp spotted), gilt. Reisler. $175/£109

KINGSLEY, CHARLES. The Water Babies. London: Hodder & Stoughton, (1919). 1st UK ed illus by Jessie Willcox Smith. 4to. (xiii),3-240pp; 12 mtd color plts, guards. Blue pict cl, gilt. Very Nice (sm hole rep; lt rubbed). Sotheran. $360/£225

KINGSLEY, CHARLES. The Water Babies. London: T.C. & E.C. Jack, (1924). 1st ed illus thus. Royal 8vo. (vi),7-80pp; 12 color plts by Anne Anderson. Cream cl w/onlaid pict label to upper cvr. (Prize label to inner upper bd, cvrs sl soiled.) Sotheran. $240/£150

KINGSLEY, CHARLES. The Water Babies. London: Macmillan, 1885. Linley Sambourne (illus). 8vo. Aeg. Navy blue cl, gilt. VG (lt foxed, edgeworn). Glenn. $85/£53

KINGSLEY, CHARLES. The Water Babies. London: Macmillan, 1890. 8vo. Linley Sambourne (illus). (viii),330pp + 60pg pub's cat. Teg. 1/2 red calf, spine w/raised bands, gilt. Fine. Sotheran. $157/£98

KINGSLEY, CHARLES. The Water Babies. London: Macmillan, 1909. 1st ed. 4to. 32 full-pg mtd color plts by Warwick Goble. Aeg. Grn cl (spine cl sl pulled), gilt. Reisler. $600/£375

KINGSLEY, CHARLES. The Water Babies. London: Macmillan, 1909. 1st ed illus by Warwick Goble. Royal 8vo. x,273,(iii)pp; 32 mtd color plts (few w/sm corner creases). Aeg. Grn cl, gilt. Very Nice (eps browned; spine sl sunned). Sotheran. $605/£378

KINGSLEY, CHARLES. The Water Babies. NY: Dodd, Mead, 1916. 1st ed thus. 8vo. 362pp; 12 full-pg color illus by Jessie W. Smith. Teg. Grn cl, round pict onlay. VG + (ink name). Davidson. $450/£281

KINGSLEY, CHARLES. The Water Babies. London: Macmillan, 1922. 16 full-pg color plts by Warwick Goble. Red cl, gilt. Fine in Fine dj. Cullen. $125/£78

KINGSLEY, CHARLES. Westward Ho! LEC, 1947. Ltd to 1500 numbered, signed by Edward A. Wilson (illus). Fine in slipcase. Swann*. $34/£21

KINGSLEY, G. H. Notes on Sport and Travel. London, 1900. Frontis. VG (ex-lib, stamp; binding discolored, rubbed); contents VF. Grayling. $56/£35

KINGSLEY, HENRY. Leighton Court. Boston: Ticknor & Fields, 1866. 1st Amer ed. (6),190pp (lt soiled, foxed). Teg. 19th-cent brn morocco, marbled bds. *Karmiole*. $75/£47

KINGSLEY, JOHN STERLING. (ed). The Standard Natural History. Boston: S.E. Cassino, 1885. 6 vols. 4to. 3/4 tan polished calf, gilt paneled spines, raised bands, red leather labels, marbled edges. VG set. *Appelfeld*. $600/£375

KINGSLEY, MARY. Travels in West Africa. Macmillan, 1897. 3rd ed. xvi,736pp; 2 litho plts; 16 full-pg illus. Teg. Later full red morocco, gilt, raised bands. Good (lt browned throughout). *Sotheran*. $240/£150

KINGSLEY, NELSON. Diary of Nelson Kingsley a California Argonaut of 1849. Berkeley: Univ of CA, 1914. Wraps. (Spine sl frayed), o/w Good. *Dumont*. $45/£28

KINGSOLVER, BARBARA. The Bean Trees. NY: Harper & Row, (1988). 1st ed, 1st bk. Signed presentation. Tan cl, lt brn bds. VF in Fine color pict dj. *Baltimore**. $160/£100

KINGSOLVER, BARBARA. The Bean Trees. London: Virago, 1988. 1st ed, 1st bk. Fine in dj. *Smith*. $65/£41

KINGSOLVER, BARBARA. The Bean Trees. NY, 1988. 1st ed. Fine in NF dj (top edge fr panel sl crinkled). *Warren*. $150/£94

KINGSTON, W. H. G. In New Granada. London: Thomas Nelson & Sons, 1879. 1st ed. Grn pict cl, gilt. NF (vol sl askew). *Sumner & Stillman*. $145/£91

KINGSTON, W. H. G. Ned Garth. London/NY: SPCK/Pott, Young, n.d. (1878). 1st ed. 4pp undated ads. Dec dk grn cl. NF (sl askew, extrems sl rubbed). *Sumner & Stillman*. $115/£72

KINGSTON, W. H. G. The Two Supercargoes or, Adventures in Savage Africa. Sampson Low, Marston, Searle, et al, 1878. Aeg. Orig pict beveled bds (spine bumped, sunned, sl chipped, corners rubbed, cl bubbling rear cvr). Good (prize plt, new fep). *Tiger*. $32/£20

KINKLE, ROGER D. The Complete Encyclopedia of Popular Music and Jazz, 1900-1950. New Rochelle: Arlington House, (1974). 1st ed. 4 vols. VG in ptd djs. *Petrilla*. $150/£94

KINLOCH, ALEXANDER. Large Game Shooting in Thibet, the Himalayas.... Calcutta: Thacker, Spink, 1892. 3rd ed. viii,291pp + 16pp pub's ads; 35 plts, fldg map (sl torn). (Prelims lt browned, fep affixed to pastedown inner margin; spine, corners chipped; spine lt faded, sl mkd.) *Edwards*. $320/£200

KINLOCH, ALEXANDER. Large Game Shooting in Thibet, the Himalayas.... Calcutta, 1892. 3rd rev, enlgd ed. Fldg map. VG (inner hinge cracked, prelims sl foxed; fr cvr sl mkd). *Hallam*. $336/£210

KINNEAR, J. R. History of the Eighty-Sixth Regiment Illinois Volunteer Infantry, During Its Term of Service. Chicago: Tribune Company's Book & Job Ptg Office, 1866. 1st ed. 139pp. Black cl, gilt. VG (inscrip, foxed; extrems worn). *Wantagh*. $250/£156

KINNELL, GALWAY. Flower Herding on Mount Monadnock. Boston: Houghton Mifflin, 1964. 1st ed. Fine in dj (lt tanned). *Reese*. $60/£38

KINNELL, GALWAY. The Past. Boston, 1985. 1st ed. One of 200 numbered, signed. 1/4 morocco. Slipcase. *Swann**. $115/£72

KINNELL, GALWAY. What a Kingdom It Was. Boston: Houghton Mifflin, 1960. 1st ed, 1st separate bk. Fine in NF dj (2 closed edge tears). *Reese*. $150/£94

KINNEY, PETER. The Early Sculpture of Bartolomeo Ammanati. NY: Garland, 1976. (Cl sl worn.) *Washton*. $125/£78

KINNEY, ROBERT. The Bachelor in New Orleans. New Orleans: Bob Riley Studios, (c1942). (Inscrip; lt worn), else NF in color illus stiff wrappers. *Cahan*. $50/£31

KINO, EUSEBIO F. Kino's Historical Memoir of Pimeria Alta. Herbert Eugene Bolton (ed). Cleveland: A.H. Clark, 1919. 1st ed. 2 vols. 7 plts, maps (1 lg fldg). Unopened, uncut, teg. Red cl, gilt. (Few extrems sl bumped), else Fine. Howes K169. *Pacific**. $518/£324

KINROSS, LORD. The Innocents at Home. London: John Murray, (1959). 1st ed. Dj. *Mott*. $20/£13

KINROSS, LORD. Within the Taurus. NY: Morrow, n.d. (ca 1955). 15 plts, dbl-pg color map. (Sl foxed; sl rubbed, soiled), o/w VG. *Worldwide*. $18/£11

KINSELLA, THOMAS. The Messenger. Dublin: Peppercanister, 1978. Signed. Fine in dj. *Ulysses*. $152/£95

KINSELLA, THOMAS. Notes from the Land of the Dead. Dublin: Cuala, 1972. One of 500 numbered. Inscribed presentation. Linen. VG (sig; fr cvr sl mkd, spine sl spotted, spine label sl rubbed, creased). *Ulysses*. $200/£125

KINSELLA, THOMAS. A Selected Life. (Dublin): Peppercanister, 1972. 1st ed. One of 150 ptd. Signed. 1/2 morocco, blue cl, gilt. Fine. *Pacific**. $138/£86

KINSELLA, THOMAS. Song of the Night and Other Poems. Dublin: Peppercanister, 1978. Signed. Fine in tissue dj (sl frayed). *Ulysses*. $152/£95

KINSELLA, THOMAS. A Technical Supplement. Dublin: Peppercanister, 1976. One of 550 signed. Buckram. Fine (spine foot sl bumped) in plain dj. *Ulysses*. $152/£95

KINSELLA, W. P. Box Socials. NY: Ballantine, 1992. 1st US ed. Signed. Fine in Fine dj. *Unger*. $50/£31

KINSELLA, W. P. Dance Me Outside. Boston: Godine, 1986. 1st US ed. Signed. Fine in Fine dj. *Unger*. $75/£47

KINSELLA, W.P. Shoeless Joe. Boston: Houghton Mifflin, 1982. 1st ed. Fine in dj. *Lame Duck*. $275/£172

KINSEY, D. J. The Water Trail. L.A.: Dept of Water & Power, 1928. 1st ed. VG + in wraps. *Book Market*. $30/£19

KINSLEY, D. A. Favor the Bold. NY: Holt, Rinehart & Winston, 1967/1968. 1st ed. 2 vols. VG in dj. *Dumont*. $60/£38

KIP, LEONARD. California Sketches with Recollections of the Gold Mines. L.A.: N.A. Kovach, 1946. One of 750. Map. Grn cl. Fine in tan ptd dj. Howes K174. *House*. $35/£22

KIPLING, RUDYARD. An Almanac of Twelve Sports. London: Heinemann, 1898. 1st ed. 4to. William Nicholson (illus). Cl-backed pict bds (rebacked, new eps). *Reisler*. $400/£250

KIPLING, RUDYARD. The Art of Fiction. London, 1926. 1st ed. Frontis, 8pp. Orange wrappers. *Swann**. $57/£36

KIPLING, RUDYARD. Captains Courageous. NY: Century, 1897. 1st Amer ed. NF (lt worn; lacks dj). *Between The Covers*. $125/£78

KIPLING, RUDYARD. Captains Courageous. A Story of the Grand Banks. London: Macmillan, 1898. 1st ed. Blue cl, gilt. Fine. *Cummins*. $300/£188

KIPLING, RUDYARD. The Complete Stalky and Co. London: Macmillan, 1929. 1st Eng ed. 17 full-pg dwgs. Aeg. Red leather, gilt. VG (1/2-title browned; spine sl faded) in card slipcase (rubbed, partly split). *Ulysses*. $152/£95

KIPLING, RUDYARD. The Day's Work. London: Macmillan, 1898. 1st ed. VG in blue cl, gilt. *Maggs*. $72/£45

KIPLING, RUDYARD. Debits and Credits. London, 1926. 1st ed. Teg. Gilt-dec cvrs. NF (name; sl rubbed) in dj (lt chipped, sm tear rear cvr; spine sunned). *Polyanthos*. $65/£41

KIPLING, RUDYARD. Debits and Credits. London: Macmillan, 1926. 1st ed. VF in red cl. Dj. *Maggs*. $72/£45

KIPLING, RUDYARD. Debits and Credits. London, 1926. Teg. Fine (bkpl) in dj (sl rubbed, sm chip) in chemise, slipcase (sl rubbed). *Polyanthos*. $150/£94

KIPLING, RUDYARD. Debits and Credits. London: Macmillan, 1926. 1st ed. Pict eps, teg. Red cl, gilt. VG in dj. *Houle*. $275/£172

KIPLING, RUDYARD. Departmental Ditties, Barrack-Room Ballads and Other Verses. NY: United States Book Co, (1890). 1st ed thus, 1st issue w/'Lovell' on spine & c. notice on tp verso. Teg. Red cl, gilt. (Sl eraser mk on tp), else Fine in later chemise, 1/2 moroco slipcase. *Pacific**. $431/£269

KIPLING, RUDYARD. A Diversity of Creatures. Macmillan, 1917. 1st ed. Teg. VG in red cl, gilt. *Cox.* $24/£15

KIPLING, RUDYARD. Doctors. An Address Delivered to the Students of the Medical School of the Middlesex Hospital, 1st October, 1908. London: Macmillan, 1908. 1st ed. 2 plts. VG in stiff wrappers. *Hollett.* $48/£30

KIPLING, RUDYARD. France at War. GC: Doubleday, Page, 1915. 1st US ed. Tan bds, pict label. VG (sl use at edges, sm spot on fr fore-corner). *Reese.* $30/£19

KIPLING, RUDYARD. From Sea to Sea: Letters of Travel. NY: Doubleday & McClure, 1899. 1st ed. 2 vols. Grn cl. *Mott.* $45/£28

KIPLING, RUDYARD. The Glory of the Garden. Whittington, 1989. One of 100 hand-colored by Judith Verity (illus). Signed by Verity. Fine in stiff paper wrappers, color label. Slipcase. *Michael Taylor.* $368/£230

KIPLING, RUDYARD. Independence. Rectorial Address Delivered at St. Andrews, October 10, 1923. London: Macmillan, 1923. 1st ed. Red cl (extrems faded), gilt. *Maggs.* $24/£15

KIPLING, RUDYARD. The Irish Guards in the Great War. London: Macmillan, 1923. 1st ed. 2 vols. Teg. Red cl, gilt. Fine set in djs. *Reese.* $150/£94

KIPLING, RUDYARD. The Jungle Book and The Second Jungle Book. London: Macmillan, 1894/1895. 1st eds. 2 vols. 8vo. J.I. Kipling, W.H. Drake & P. Frezeny (illus). Aeg. Blue gilt-stamped cl (sl worn). Nice in linen fldg box. *Appelfeld.* $850/£531

KIPLING, RUDYARD. The Jungle Book. London: Macmillan, 1908. 1st ed. 8vo. 314pp + ads (sl shelfworn, sl foxed); 16 full-pg color plts by Maurice & Edward Detmold. Teg. Red cl, gilt. *Reisler.* $200/£125

KIPLING, RUDYARD. The Jungle Book. NY: Century, 1913. 1st Amer ed. 8vo. 331pp; 16 full color plts by Maurice & Edward Detmold. Teg. Grn pict cl (lt shelfworn), gilt. *Reisler.* $200/£125

KIPLING, RUDYARD. The Jungle Books. LEC, 1968. Ltd to 1500 numbered, signed by David Gentleman (illus). Fine in slipcase. *Swann**. $57/£36

KIPLING, RUDYARD. Just So Stories. London: Macmillan, 1902. 1st ed. 4to. Dk red pict cl (sl wrinkle rear cvr). Nice (few spots to blank eps). *Reisler.* $550/£344

KIPLING, RUDYARD. Just So Stories. Macmillan, 1902. 1st UK ed. VG + (sl foxed). *Williams.* $560/£350

KIPLING, RUDYARD. Just So Stories. (NY): Doubleday Page, 1927. Lg 8vo. 249pp; 12 color plts by Gleeson. Color pict eps. Pict red ribbed cl. (Spine gilt sl dull), o/w VG. *House.* $45/£28

KIPLING, RUDYARD. Kim. London, 1901. 1st Eng ed. Gilt-pict red cl. (Sl skewed.) *Swann**. $103/£64

KIPLING, RUDYARD. Kim. NY: LEC, 1962. One of 1500. Signed by Robin Jacques (illus). 1/2 leather, gilt-dec cl. Fine in glassine, slipcase. *Pacific**. $35/£22

KIPLING, RUDYARD. Land and Sea. London: Macmillan, 1923. 1st ed. (Offsetting to eps from dj, which is chipped at extrems.) *Agvent.* $100/£63

KIPLING, RUDYARD. Letters of Marque. Allahabad: A.H. Wheeler, 1891. 1st ed. One of 1000 ptd. Blue/red cl, gilt. (Bkpl; corner stained, fr joint, hinge cracked, spine ends rubbed), else VG in later chemise, 1/2 moroco slipcase. *Pacific**. $173/£108

KIPLING, RUDYARD. Letters of Travel (1892-1913). London: Macmillan, 1920. 1st ed. Red cl. Fine in dj (sl chipped). *Mott.* $50/£31

KIPLING, RUDYARD. Letters of Travel (1892-1913). London: Macmillan, 1920. 1st Eng ed. Teg. Buckram. NF (spine ends, 2 corners sl bumped) in dj (sl nicked, creased, spine sl dknd). *Ulysses.* $96/£60

KIPLING, RUDYARD. Many Inventions. London: Macmillan, 1893. 1st ed. Edges rough-trimmed. Blue cl, gilt. VG (sm nick to spine head). *Maggs.* $80/£50

KIPLING, RUDYARD. Many Inventions. London: Macmillan, 1893. 1st ed. Gilt-dec blue cl, gilt. Fine in later chemise, slipcase w/morocco spine label. *Pacific**. $138/£86

KIPLING, RUDYARD. Many Inventions. London, 1893. 1st ed. Gilt-dec cl. Bkpl of Harry Buxton Forman. *Swann**. $230/£144

KIPLING, RUDYARD. The Naulahka, a Story of West and East. London: Heinemann, 1892. 1st ed. Peach cl, gilt. Good (sl rubbed). *Macdonnell.* $65/£41

KIPLING, RUDYARD. Plain Tales from the Hills. Calcutta: Thacker & Spink, 1888. 1st ed, 1st issue w/cat at rear dated Dec 1887. Pict olive-grn cl (discoloration, tips bumped, spine extrems lt rubbed). 1/4 morocco slipcase. *Swann**. $230/£144

KIPLING, RUDYARD. Plain Tales from the Hills. London: Macmillan, 1890. 3rd ed. W/ad leaf, 59-pg pub's cat dated February 1890. VG in blue cl, gilt. *Maggs.* $144/£90

KIPLING, RUDYARD. Poems, 1886-1929. NY, 1930. 1st Amer ed. One of 525 numbered, signed. 3 vols. (Ex-lib.) *Swann**. $402/£251

KIPLING, RUDYARD. Poems, 1886-1929. GC, 1930. 1st Amer ed. Ltd to 537 signed. 3 vols. 4to. Paper-parchment bds. VG set (bkpls, old tape, tape residue). *Truepenny.* $500/£313

KIPLING, RUDYARD. Puck of Pook's Hill. NY: Doubleday, Page, 1906. 1st Amer ed. 8vo. 4 color illus by Arthur Rackham. Teg. Grn dec cl. *Appelfeld.* $85/£53

KIPLING, RUDYARD. Sea and Sussex. GC, 1926. One of 150 numbered, signed. 1/4 imitation vellum, gilt. Bd slipcase (bottom panel damaged). *Swann**. $230/£144

KIPLING, RUDYARD. Sea and Sussex. London, 1926. One of 500 lg paper copies signed. 24 mtd color plts by Donald Maxwell. 1/4 vellum. (Partial browning feps.) Dj (top/bottom edges chipped), bd slipcase. *Swann**. $316/£198

KIPLING, RUDYARD. Sea Warfare. London: Macmillan, 1916. 1st collective ed. Largely unopened, edges rough-trimmed. Gilt blue cl. NF in largely complete dj (split, mended). *Reese.* $85/£53

KIPLING, RUDYARD. The Second Jungle Book. Macmillan, 1895. 1st UK ed. Fine (bkpl, sl foxed). *Williams.* $232/£145

KIPLING, RUDYARD. The Song of the English. London: Hodder & Stoughton, (1909). 1st ed thus. 4to. 30 full-pg mtd color plts by W. Heath Robinson. Dk blue cl, gilt. (Cl worn, spotted.) *Reisler.* $350/£219

KIPLING, RUDYARD. The Song of the English. London: Hodder & Stoughton, (1915). W. Heath Robinson (illus). 4to. Cream cl blocked in navy. VG (cl soiled at edges) in dj (soiled). *Glenn.* $325/£203

KIPLING, RUDYARD. Songs of the Sea. London, 1927. One of 500 lg paper copies signed. 12 mtd color plts by Donald Maxwell. 1/4 vellum. (Partial browning feps.) *Swann**. $316/£198

KIPLING, RUDYARD. Songs of the Sea. NY: Doubleday, 1927. One of 150 numbered, signed. Paper bds, vellum spine. Fine in glassine dj, box. *Cullen.* $450/£281

KIPLING, RUDYARD. Tales of East and West. LEC, 1974. One of 2000 signed by Charles Raymond (illus). Fine in slipcase. *Swann**. $34/£21

KIPLING, RUDYARD. They. Macmillan, 1905. 1st ed. Gilt-dec white cl (dull). Internally Good. *Whiteson.* $26/£16

KIPLING, RUDYARD. Thy Servant a Dog. Told by Boots. London: Macmillan, 1930. 1st ed. Red cl. Fine in dj. *Maggs.* $48/£30

KIPLING, RUDYARD. Twenty Poems from Rudyard Kipling. London: Methuen, 1918. Good (name) in ptd wraps (spine chipped, worn). Cullen. $95/£59

KIPLING, RUDYARD. Under the Deodars. A.H. Wheeler, (1888). 1st ed. 8vo. Ad leaf at beginning, 4 ll of ads at end, add'l ad leaf tipped-in to 1st pg of text. (Bkpl.) Grayish-grn wrappers, lettering, design on fr cvr and on rear cvr in black. VF in chemise, 1/4 black morocco slipcase. Sotheby's*. $1,472/£920

KIPLING, RUDYARD. The Works of.... GC: Doubleday, Page, 1914. Seven Seas ed. One of 1050. Signed. 24 vols. 1/2 cl, paper spine labels. (Spines, extrems browned), else VG. Pacific*. $460/£288

KIPLING, RUDYARD. The Writings in Prose and Verse of Rudyard Kipling. NY: Scribner, 1925-37. 32 vols. Teg. Fr cvr medallions, gilt. (Sl discoloration rear cvr of vol 1, spines sunned), else VG. Pacific*. $288/£180

KIPLING, RUDYARD. The Writings in Prose and Verse.... NY: Scribner, 1916. 'Outward Bound' ed. 32 vols. 8vo. Teg. Contemp 1/2 black morocco, spines gilt. Fine set. Swann*. $977/£611

KIPLING, RUDYARD. The Years Between. London: Methuen, 1919. 1st Eng ed. Unopened. Buckram. Fine in dj (sl rubbed, creased) w/orig ptd price (7/6) on spine blocked out, 8/6 stamped below. Ulysses. $72/£45

KIPPING, ROBERT. Sails and Sail-Making, with Draughting, and the Centre of Effort of the Sails. London: Lockwood & Co, 1871. Grn cl, gilt, paper spine label. (Names; spine sunned), else VG. Pacific*. $40/£25

KIRBY, FREDERICK VAUGHAN. In Haunts of Wild Game. Edinburgh/London: William Blackwood, 1896. Photogravure frontis port, fldg color map. Mod 1/2 red morocco. Christie's*. $216/£135

KIRBY, MARY and ELIZABETH. The World at Home. T. Nelson & Sons, 1876. xii,296pp. Aeg. Dec red cl, gilt, beveled bds (sl mkd, extrems sl rubbed, spine lt faded). Hollett. $56/£35

KIRBY, W. F. European Butterflies and Moths. London: Cassell, Petter & Galpin, 1882. 1st ed. 1 plain, 61 hand-colored wood-engr plts. Contemp grn roan. (Blue wax mk to tp, clean tear to plt 37, margins lt browned; worn.) Christie's*. $349/£218

KIRBY, W. F. European Butterflies and Moths. Cassell, Petter, Galpin, 1882. 1st ed. 61 hand-colored plts, 1 uncolored. Gilt edges. Pict cl, gilt. (Few ll sl loose, hinges cracked.) Sotheby's*. $422/£264

KIRBY, W. F. European Butterflies and Moths. Cassell, 1889. 4to. 62 plts (61 hand-colored). Aeg. Sotheby's*. $662/£414

KIRCHEISEN, F. M. Jovial King. H. J. Stenning (trans). London: Elkin Mathews & Mariot, n.d. (ca 1950). 16 plts. (Spine dull.) Stewart. $48/£30

KIRCHENHOFFER, H. The Book of Fate. C.S. Arnold, 1824. 5th ed. Lg fldg linen-backed frontis table (sl repaired), xxxiv,31pp (1st few ll edges sl fragile, repaired, lower margins sl damped). Uncut. Mod 1/2 levant morocco, gilt. Hollett. $152/£95

KIRCHOFF, THEODORE. Handbook of Insanity for Practitioners and Students. NY: William Wood, 1893. 1st ed. 11 plts. Fine (stamps). Beasley. $75/£47

KIRK, WILLIAM. Right Off the Bat. Dillingham, 1911. Later ptg?. Good +. Plapinger. $130/£81

KIRKALDY, ANDRA. Fifty Years of Golf: My Memories. NY: E.P. Dutton, (1921). 1st Amer ed. Frontis. Grn cl, gilt. (Emb stamp; spine sl dknd, ends rubbed), else VG. Pacific*. $161/£101

KIRKBRIDGE, JOHN. The Northern Angler; or Fly-Fisher's Companion. London: R. Groombridge et al, 1840. 2nd ed. Frontis copper-engr plt. Grn cl, gilt. NF (bkpls). Pacific*. $196/£123

KIRKE, EDMUND. (Pseud of James Roberts Gilmore.) Down in Tennessee and Back by Way of Richmond. NY: Carleton, 1864. 1st ed. 282pp + ads. VG + (lt shelfworn). Chapel Hill. $60/£38

KIRKLAND, C. M. Western Clearings. Lonodn: Wiley & Putnam, 1846. 1st Eng ed. 238pp + (4)pp ads. Orig grn cl. (Fr inner hinge cracked), else VG. BAL 11149. Chapel Hill. $250/£156

KIRKLAND, FRAZAR. Cyclopaedia of Commercial and Business Anecdotes.... NY: Appleton, 1864. 1st ed. 2 vols. Marbled edges. 3/4 dk grn morocco, marbled bds, gilt, sl raised bands. VG. Pacific*. $63/£39

KIRKLAND, JOHN (ed). The Modern Baker, Confectioner and Caterer. London: Gresham Pub, 1927. New rev ed. 4 vols. 25 color plts. Good set (2 bds damped at edges). Hollett. $104/£65

KIRKMAN, J. S. The Arab City of Gedi. OUP, 1954. 35 plts. (Cl sl dampstained.) Dj (stained, creased). Edwards. $77/£48

KIRKPATRICK, D. L. (ed). Twentieth-Century Children's Writers. NY: St. Martin's, 1983. 2nd ed. VG + in dj. Zubal*. $25/£16

KIRKPATRICK, DORIS. The City and the River: Fitchburg, Massachusetts. (N.p.): Fitchburg Hist Soc, 1971. 1st ed. Black cl. Fine in pict dj. House. $25/£16

KIRKUP, JAMES. A Correct Compassion and Other Poems. London: OUP, 1952. 1st Eng ed. NF (feps sl browned; fr cvr sl bumped) in dj (sl rubbed, price-clipped, sl dknd). Ulysses. $56/£35

KIRKUP, JAMES. The Drowned Sailor. London: Grey Walls Press, 1947. 1st ed, 1st bk. Blue cl. (Edges of bds sl dusty), o/w Good in dj (sl dusty). Maggs. $80/£50

KIRKWOOD, EDITH BROWN. Animal Children. P.F. Volland, 1913. 26th ed. M. T. Ross (illus). 8vo. 95pp. Illus eps. Yellow bds, paper pict cvr. VG (lt edgeworn, corners bumped). Davidson. $100/£63

KIRMSE, MARGARET. Dogs in the Field. NY: Derrydale, (1935). One of 685 numbered. W/paper folder continaing 6 add'l plts. Obl folio. Frontis drypoint by Kirmse signed in pencil, 24 plts. 1/2 cl. Glassine dj (corners sl chipped), pub's 2-piece box (silk ribbon torn, lid dknd along edges, few minor cracks). Swann*. $805/£503

KIRMSE, MARGARET. Dogs. NY: Derrydale, 1930. One of 750. 4to. 77 plts, incl signed frontis drypoint by Kirmse. 1/2 cl (spine dknd, top of rear cvr faded). Swann*. $575/£359

KIRSCHENBAUM, B. The Religious and Historical Paintings of Jan Steen. Oxford: Phaidon, 1977. Color frontis, 132 b/w plts. Good in dj. Ars Artis. $80/£50

KIRST, HANS HELLMUT. Last Stop Camp 7. NY, 1969. VG in dj. Typographeum. $15/£9

KIRST, HANS HELLMUT. Night of the Long Knives. J. M. Brownjohn (trans). London, 1976. 1st ed. VG in dj. Typographeum. $18/£11

KIRST, HANS HELLMUT. A Time for Payment. J. M. Brownjohn (trans). London, 1976. 1st ed. VG in dj. Typographeum. $16/£10

KIRSTEIN, LINCOLN. Elie Nadelman. NY, 1973. One of 3075. Folio. (Lt worn.) Dj. Oinonen*. $70/£44

KIRSTEIN, LINCOLN. For My Brother. London: Hogarth, 1943. 1st ed. (Last 6 pp top corners creased, top edge dusty), o/w VG in dj (sl soiled; spine chipped). Virgo. $96/£60

KIRSTEIN, LINCOLN. Nijinsky Dancing. NY, (1975). 1st ed. Obl short folio. Dj (chipped). Argosy. $75/£47

KIRSTEIN, LINCOLN. Pavel Tchelitchew Drawings. NY, 1947. Dj. Swann*. $149/£93

KIRSTEIN, LINCOLN. Portrait of Mr. B: Photographs of George Balanchine. NY: Ballet Soc, 1984. 1st ed. VG + (sl shelfworn) in dj (sl edgeworn, sl faded). My Bookhouse. $32/£20

KIRSTEIN, LINCOLN. Rhymes and More Rhymes of a P. F. C. NY: New Directions, 1966. 1st Amer ed. NF in NF dj. Warren. $45/£28

KIRWAN, RICHARD. An Estimate of the Temperature of Different Latitudes. London: P. Elmsly, 1787. 1st ed. viii,114pp. Errata. Mod 1/4 calf, marbled bds, dk brn morocco spine label, corner tips. VG (lt foxed). *Weber*. $500/£313

KISKADDON, BRUCE. Western Poems. L.A.: Western Livestock Journal, (1935). (Bkpl), else Fine in wraps. *Perier*. $50/£31

KISMARIC, SUSAN. Jan Groover. NY: MOMA, 1987. 1st ed. 37 plts. VG in pict stiff wrappers. *Cahan*. $40/£25

KISSAM, RICHARD S. The Nurse's Manual, and Young Mother's Guide. Hartford, (CT): Cooke, 1834. 1st ed. 7,143pp. Orig cl (rubbed), leather label. *M & S*. $275/£172

KITCHIN, C. H. B. Mr. Balcony. London: Leonard & Virginia Woolf, 1927. 1st ed. Blue buckram. NF. *Temple*. $120/£75

KITCHIN, GEORGE. A Survey of Burlesque and Parody in English. Edinburgh/London, 1931. 1st Eng ed. Good in dj (torn). *Clearwater*. $64/£40

KITCHINER, WILLIAM. The Economy of the Eyes. Hurst, Robinson, 1824. 1st ed. Frontis (waterstain, sl offset onto tp), viii,246pp,ad leaf; fldg plt. Orig bds (sl stained, bumped), ptd paper label. *Bickersteth*. $232/£145

Kitten Eleven. London: Bancroft, 1965. 5 dbl-pg pop-ups by V. Kubasta. VG in wraps. *Bookfinders*. $70/£44

KITTO, JOHN. The History of Palestine from the Patriarchial Age to the Present Time. Boston: Gould & Lincoln, 1860. 1st ed. vi,426pp. (Sl foxed, sl affected by dampness mainly marginally; sl rubbed, soiled, spine top frayed, chipped), o/w Good. *Worldwide*. $35/£22

KITTON, FREDERICK G. The Dickens Country. A&C Black, 1925. Rpt. Good (lacks dj). *Tiger*. $10/£6

KLABER, DORETTA. Primroses and Spring. NY: Barrows, c. 1966. 1 color plt. (Eps browned), else VG. *Fair Meadow*. $18/£11

KLABER, DORETTA. Rock Garden Plants. NY: Bramwell House, c. 1959. VG in dj. *Fair Meadow*. $15/£9

KLABER, DORETTA. Violets of the U.S. Cranbury, NJ: Barnes, 1976. Sm folio. (Trace of water stain to fr cvr, spine.) Contents Fine. Dj (chipped). *Quest*. $55/£34

KLAPPHOLZ, LOWELL (ed). Gold! Gold! NY: Robert M. McBride, (1959). 1st ed. Rev copy. NF in dj. *Glenn*. $30/£19

KLAUBER, L. M. Rattlesnakes: Their Habits, Life Histories and Influence on Mankind. Berkeley: Univ of CA, (1972). 2nd ed. 2 vols. Dec cl. NF in VG djs, slipcase. *Mikesh*. $350/£219

KLEIN, HERMANN. Thirty Years of Musical Life in London 1870-1900. Heinemann, 1903. 1st ed. (Cl sl mkd, spine faded.) *Hollett*. $56/£35

KLEIN, WILLIAM. Mister Freedom. Paris, (1970). Folio. (Extrems sl worn.) *Swann**. $115/£72

KLEIN, WILLIAM. Moscow. NY, (1964). 1st ed. Folio. (Final plt creased, gatherings split; worn, lt soiled, backstrip shaken.) *Swann**. $287/£179

KLEIN, WILLIAM. Tokyo. NY, (1964). 1st ed. Folio. (Ink notes; extrems sl worn.) Dj (chipped, worn). *Swann**. $402/£251

KLEIN, WILLIAM. Tokyo. NY, 1964. 1st ed. NF (lacks dj). *Warren*. $175/£109

KLENCKE, HERMANN. Lives of the Brothers Humboldt, Alexander and William. Juliette Bauer (trans). NY: Harper, 1853. 1st ed in English. 2 parts in 1 vol. Frontisport, 2 tps, 398pp + 10pp ads; port. Dk brn blind-stamped cl. Fine (bkpl). *Weber*. $80/£50

KLETT, MARK. Traces of Eden: Travels in the Desert Southwest. Boston: Godine, 1986. 1st ed. 16 full-pg photos. Fine in dj (lt rubbed). *Cahan*. $60/£38

KLIMA, SLAVA (ed). Joseph Spence: Letters from the Grand Tour. Montreal/London, 1975. Good. *Washton*. $45/£28

KLIMAS, JOHN. Wild Flowers of Connecticut. NY: Walker, 1968. 1st ed. Fine in dj. *Archer*. $15/£9

KLINCK, RICHARD E. Land of Room Enough and Time Enough. Univ of NM, 1953. 1st ed. Yellow/black pict bds. VG + . *Five Quail*. $35/£22

KLINE, OTIS ADELBERT. The Outlaws of Mars. NY: Avalon Books, (1961). (Corners sl bumped), else VG in dj (clean tear). *King*. $25/£16

KLINE, OTIS ADELBERT. The Planet of Peril. (Chicago): A.C. McClurg, 1929. 1st ed. Signed. Grn cl. (Spine extrems sl faded, spine sl warped), else VG in later chemise, slipcase. *Pacific**. $184/£115

KLINE, OTIS ADELBERT. The Port of Peril. Providence: Grandon, 1949. 1st ed thus. NF in dj (sm edge tears, spine sl browned). *Other Worlds*. $35/£22

KLINE, OTIS ADELBERT. The Prince of Peril. Chicago: A.C. McClurg, 1930. 1st ed. Fine in dj, later chemise, slipcase. *Pacific**. $345/£216

KLINEFELTER, WALTER. A Bibliographical Check-List of Christmas Books. Portland, 1937. One of 1500. Uncut, unopened. Paper cvr label. (Sl worn.) *Oinonen**. $60/£38

Klondike: The Chicago Record's Book for Gold Seekers. Chicago Record, c1897. 555pp + ads. Pict cl. Good (sl foxed; cl rubbed). *Blake*. $50/£31

KLUCKHOHN, CLYDE and DOROTHEA LEIGHTON. Children of the People. Cambridge, 1948. VG in dj. *Dumont*. $40/£25

KLUCKHOHN, CLYDE and DOROTHEA LEIGHTON. The Navajo. Cambridge, 1958. VG in dj. *Dumont*. $35/£22

KLUNZINGER, C. B. Upper Egypt. London, 1878. 1st Eng ed. xvi,408pp + errata slip; 4 plts. Mod eps. Orig cl (rebacked w/orig spine laid down, sl soiled, corners worn). *Edwards*. $120/£75

KNAPP, ANDREW and WILLIAM BALDWIN. The Newgate Calendar. Liverpool: Nuttall, Fisher & Dixon, 1809-10. 4 vols. xiii,559,(vii); 544,(viii); 560,(viii); 511,(viii)pp; 30 steel-engr plts (foxed). Old 1/2 calf (neatly rebacked to match w/raised bands, spine labels), gilt. *Hollett*. $440/£275

KNAPP, ELDER JACOB. Autobiography of Elder Jacob Knapp. NY, 1868. 1st ed. 9,(26),341,(6)pp. *Ginsberg*. $50/£31

KNAUSS, JAMES OWENS. Territorial Florida Journalism. Deland, FL: FL State Hist Soc, 1926. One of 360 numbered. Frontis, 2 plts, 6 facs in rear pocket. Unopened. Black cl, purple bds, paper labels. Fine in pub's slipcase. *Karmiole*. $200/£125

KNEELAND, FRANK H. et al. Mining Equipment and Mine Organization and Safety, Ventilating Equipment, Erecting Work. NY, 1915. 1st ed, 3rd imp. Maroon cl, gilt. (Edgeworn), else Good + . *Larry Price*. $30/£19

KNEELAND, SAMUEL. An American in Iceland. Boston: Lockwood, Brooks, 1876. 1st ed. viii,326pp. Good (sl rubbed). *Walcot*. $88/£55

KNERR. The Katzenjammer Kids. Kenosha, WI: John Martin's House, (1945). Obl 4to. 2 moveables (1 turning wheel, 1 dbl-pg pop-up). Stiff paper color pict cvrs, spiral binding. Good. *Reisler*. $375/£234

KNICKERBOCKER, DIEDRICH. (Pseud of Washington Irving.) A History of New York, from the Beginning of the World to the End of the Dutch Dynasty. NY, 1809. 1st ed. 2 vols. Fldg plt. Crushed levant. Fine. *Felcone*. $1,100/£688

KNICKERBOCKER, H. R. et al. Danger Forward. Washington, (1947). (Edges spotted, cvr sl worn), else Good. *King*. $60/£38

KNIGHT, AUSTIN M. Modern Seamanship. NY: Van Nostrand, 1901. 1st ed. 136 plts. (Rubbed, sl shaken.) *Lefkowicz*. $75/£47

KNIGHT, CAPTAIN. Diary of a Pedestrian in Cashmere and Thibet. London: Richard Bentley, 1863. 1st ed. 8vo. xiv,385,(1)blank,8 pub's list; 8 tinted lithos (incl frontis), 8 engr plts. Grn pebble dec cl, gilt. (Foxed, lacks 1/2-title; damp-spotted, rubbed, spine ends repaired, some gatherings loose but complete.) *Morrell*. $496/£310

KNIGHT, CHARLES. London. London, 1841. 6 vols. Blind-emb cl. (Lt marginal browning, some hinges tender; corners, spines rubbed, sl cl loss, spines lt faded.) *Edwards.* $120/£75

KNIGHT, CHARLES. London...Revised and Corrected to the Present Time by E. Walford. London: Charles Knight, 1841. 6 vols. Each vol w/5 steel-engr plts (incl engr vignette tp as called for). Recent 1/4 calf, marbled bds. *Marlborough.* $240/£150

KNIGHT, CHARLES. Old England: A Pictorial Museum of Regal, Ecclesiastical..., and Popular Antiquities. London: James Sangster, (c. 1880s). 2 vols. Aeg. Blindstamped red cl, gilt. (Joints cracked), else VG. *Pacific*.* $127/£79

KNIGHT, CHARLES. Old England: A Pictorial Museum.... London: Forbes, Sangster, (later 19th-cent). (New ed.) 2 vols. Folio. 20 color relief plts. (Spines faded.) *Swann*.* $69/£43

KNIGHT, CHARLES. The Old Printer and the Modern Press. London: John Murray, 1854. 1st ed. xii,314,(2)pp. Blind stamped cl (head of spine chipped). *Oak Knoll.* $50/£31

KNIGHT, CHARLES. Shadows of the Old Booksellers. Bell & Daldy, 1865. 1st ed. 320pp. Tipped-in letter dated 1829. 1/4 calf, marbled bds. *Moss.* $96/£60

KNIGHT, HENRY GALLY. The Ecclesiastical Architecture of Italy. From the Time of Constantine to the Fifteenth Century. London: Henry Bohn, 1843. 2 vols. 2 chromolitho titles, 81 plts, most tinted lithos, incl 3 chromolithos by Owen Jones. (Occasional mainly marginal spotting, staining.) Contemp 1/2 morocco (heavily rubbed, inner hinges weak). *Christie's*.* $2,341/£1,463

KNIGHT, JOHN ALDEN. Black Bass. NY: Putnam, 1949. 1st ed. 3 color plts. VG + in dj. *Bowman.* $45/£28

KNIGHT, LAURA. A Book of Drawings. London: John Lane, 1923. Ltd to 500 signed. Frontis, 20 plts (4 color). Cl-backed paper-cvrd bds (extrems rubbed, label scuffed; text lt spotted). *Christie's*.* $258/£161

KNIGHT, OLIVER. Fort Worth, Outpost on the Trinity. Norman, 1953. 1st ed. (Dusty), else Good in dj. *Dumont.* $40/£25

KNIGHT, WILLIAM. Aspects of Theism. London, 1893. 1st ed. 220pp. Brn cl, gilt. VG (ex-lib). *Larry Price.* $49/£31

KNIGHTS, L. C. Drama and Society in the Age of Jonson. C&W, 1937. 1st ed. Inscribed presentation. Als loosely inserted. VG (bkpl; edges spotted, spine sl faded, ends sl bumped) in dj (rubbed, frayed, internally repaired, price-clipped, spine dknd). *Ulysses.* $104/£65

KNIPE, WILLIAM (ed). Criminal Chronology of York Castle. York, 1867. 1st Eng ed. (Hinges cracked.) *Clearwater.* $80/£50

KNOPF, ADOLPH. A Geologic Reconnaissance of the Inyo Range and the Eastern Slope of the Southern Sierra Nevada, California. Washington: GPO, 1918. 1st ed. Pocket map. VG in wraps (loose). *Book Market.* $75/£47

KNOTT, CARGILL G. (ed). Napier Tercentenary Memorial Volume. London: Royal Soc of Edinburgh, 1915. 1st ed. Color frontis, 15 plts. Teg. White buckram. (Corner bumped, spine dust-soiled), else VG. *Weber.* $225/£141

KNOWER, DANIEL. The Adventures of a Forty-Niner. Albany: Weed-Parsons, 1894. 1st ed. 200pp. Maroon cl, gilt. VG. *Cullen.* $100/£63

KNOWLES, ALISON. Journal of the Identical Lunch. SF: Nova Broadcast, 1971. (Lt rubbed), else Fine in pict stiff wrappers. *Cahan.* $100/£63

KNOWLES, JAMES D. Memoir of Roger Williams. Boston: Lincoln, 1834. Frontis, 437,(ii)pp. Emb cl, paper spine label. (Bkpl, spotted, lower hinge tender, joints splitting; lt soiled, bumped, spine faded, chipped w/loss.) *Edwards.* $72/£45

KNOWLES, JOHN A. Essays in the History of the York School of Glass-Painting. London, 1936. 63 plts hors texte. (Cl sl soiled, bds sl bubbled, corners sl bumped.) Internally VG. *Washton.* $150/£94

KNOWLES, JOSIAH N. Crusoes of Pitcairn Island. Richard S. Dillon (ed). L.A.: Glen Dawson, 1957. 1st ed. One of 250 ptd. Frontis, 2 maps. Pict eps. Cl-backed ptd bds. (Bd edges sl dknd), else Fine. *Argonaut.* $50/£31

KNOWLSON, JOHN C. The Yorkshire Cattle-Doctor and Farrier. Otley: William Walker, 1864. 24th thousand. Engr frontis, xiv,272pp; fldg chart. Blind-stamped cl (sl faded), gilt. *Hollett.* $120/£75

KNOX, ALEXANDER. The Climate of the Continent of Africa. CUP, 1911. 1st ed. Fldg color map, fldg diag, 11 fldg color maps in rear pocket. Partly nopened. VG (sl stain part of fr bd). *Hollett.* $104/£65

KNOX, DR. Fish and Fishing in the Lone Glens of Scotland, with a History of the Propagation, Growth, and Metamorphoses of the Salmon. London: G. Routledge, 1854. 1st ed. 3/4 tan cl, marbled bds, gilt, morocco spine label. (Sm # stamp bottom of contents pg), else NF. *Pacific*.* $184/£115

KNOX, DUDLEY W. Naval Sketches of the War in California Reproducing Twenty-Eight Drawings Made in 1846-47 by William H. Meyers, Gunner on the U.S. Sloop-of-War Dale. NY: Random House, 1939. One of 1000 ptd. 28 plts colored w/linoleum blocks. 1/2 white morocco, marbled bds, raised bands, spine label, gilt. (Spine sl soiled, rubbed), o/w Fine. *Pacific*.* $259/£162

KNOX, GEORGE. Giambattista and Domenico Tiepolo: A Study and Catalogue Raisonne of the Chalk Drawings. Oxford, 1980. 2 vols. Djs. *Swann*.* $149/£93

KNOX, J. P. A Historical Account of St. Thomas.... NY: Scribner, 1852. 1st ed. 8vo. i-xii,13-272pp; fldg litho plt. Black emb cl, gilt. Good (map lt browned; fore-edges sl bumped, spine ends sl chipped). *Sotheran.* $637/£398

KNOX, RONALD. Off the Record. London/NY: Sheed & Ward, (1953). 1st ed. Fine in NF dj. *Reese.* $30/£19

KNOX, RONALD. Stimuli. London/NY: Sheed & Ward, (1951). 1st ed. Nice (ink inscrip) in dj (spine sunned). *Reese.* $30/£19

KNOX, ROSE B. Miss Jimmy Deane: And What Happened at Pleasant Meadows. GC: Doubleday, 1946. 9 full-pg illus. VG in pict dj (taped on verso). *Petrilla.* $25/£16

KNOX, THOMAS W. The Boy Travellers on the Congo. London: Sampson Low, Marston, 1888. 1st London ed. Frontis, xii,355,(1)imprint. Blue pict cl (upper hinge cracking, rear cvr damp-stained, fr cvr sl stained, spine, edges rubbed). Internally Sound (sl foxed). *Morrell.* $72/£45

KOBLER, JOHN. Afternoon in the Attic. NY, 1950. 1st Amer ed. Fine. *Polyanthos.* $40/£25

KOCH, J. P. Survey of Northeast Greenland. Kobenhavn, 1917. 7 maps (4 fldg). VG in ptd wrapper. *High Latitude.* $145/£91

KOCH, ROBERT. Louis C. Tiffany's Glass, Bronzes, Lamps. NY: Crown, 1971. 1st ed. Color frontis. Cl-backed bds, gilt. VG. *Hollett.* $72/£45

KOCK, ROBERT. Louis C. Tiffany, Rebel in Glass. NY, 1964. 1st ed. Relevant news clippings loosely inserted. Dj (lt soiled, sl chipped). *Edwards.* $56/£35

KOEBEL, W. H. Argentina Past and Present. A&C Black, 1914. 1st ed thus. 32 color plts, map. (Spine split, repaired, sl loose.) *Hallam.* $72/£45

KOEHN, ALFRED. The Art of Japanese Flower Arrangement (Ikebana). (Kobe), Japan/London: J.L. Thompson/Kegan Paul, Trench, (1933). 1st ed. 64 full-pg photo illus. Pict cl, gilt. (Ink inscrip; spine ends sl worn), o/w Fine. *Sotheran.* $120/£75

KOESTLER, ARTHUR. The Age of Longing. London, 1951. VG in dj (frayed, sl foxed). *Typographeum.* $15/£9

KOESTLER, ARTHUR. The Ghost in the Machine. Hutchinson, 1967. 1st ed. NF in dj (sl creased). *Ulysses.* $58/£36

KOHL, J .G. Kitchi-Gami (Great Lake). MN: Ross/Haines, (1956). One of 1500. Facs rpt. Fine in NF dj. *Mikesh.* $60/£38

Koko's Circus. NY: Animated Book Co, 1942. 1st ed. Moveable. 12x9. Spiral-bound pict bds. (Spine head rubbed), else VG. *Pacific**. $58/£36

KOKOSCHKA, OSKAR. Forty-Eight Plates in Photogravure. James S. Plaut (ed). Boston/NY: Inst of Contemporary Art/Chanticleer Press, (1948). 1st ed. 8 color, 48 b/w plts, guards, 2 Fine orig full-pg lithos by Kokoschka bound in. Tan cl (edges sl sunned, worn). Text Nice. *Baltimore**. $45/£28

KOLBENHEYER, F. G. A Winter Chronicle. London: John Lane, Bodley Head, (1938). 1st Eng ed. NF in dj. *Cady*. $25/£16

KOLDEWAY, KARL. The German Arctic Expedition of 1869-70 and a Narrative of the Wreck of the 'Hansa' in the Ice.... London: Sampson, Low, 1874. 1st Eng ed. viii,590; 4 color lithos, 2 maps. Dec cl (sl rubbed). Good. *Walcot*. $456/£285

KOLLMANN, PAUL. The Victoria Nyanza. London, 1899. 1st ed. ix,254pp; fldg map (tape repairs). (Prelims lt browned, sm ink spots fep; top edge fr bd, fore-edge faded; spine chipped.) *Edwards*. $320/£200

KOLLWITZ, KAETHE. Diaries and Letters of Kaethe Kollwitz. Hans Kollwitz (ed). Richard & Clara Winston (trans). Chicago: Henry Regnery, 1955. 1st ed. NF (edges sl rubbed) in dj (spine sunned). *Hermitage*. $125/£78

KOLPACOFF, VICTOR. The Prisoners of Quai Dong. NY: NAL, (1967). 1st ed. VG in VG dj. *Dermont*. $25/£16

KOMISARJEVSKY, THEODORE. The Costume of the Theatre. NY: Henry Holt, (1932). (Edges, backstrip faded; paint stained.) *Dramatis*. $25/£16

KOMROFF, M. (ed). Contemporaries of Marco Polo. London: Cape, 1928. 1st ed. Black cl (sl rubbed). *Maggs*. $48/£30

KONVITZ, JEFFREY. The Sentinel. NY: S&S, (1974). 1st ed. (Rmdr mk bottom edge, pg edges sl browned), else Fine in Fine dj. *Between The Covers*. $85/£53

KOOIMAN, HELEN. Walter Knott, Keeper of the Flame. Fullerton: Plycon, (1973). 1st ed. Fine in VG dj. *Book Market*. $35/£22

KOONTZ, DEAN R. Anti-Man. NY: Paperback Library, 1970. 1st ptg. Pb orig. Fine. *Warren*. $30/£19

KOONTZ, DEAN R. The Bad Place. NY: Putnam, (1900). One of 250 numbered, signed. (Lt worn.) Slipcase. *Oinonen**. $60/£38

KOONTZ, DEAN R. Beastchild. Lynbrook: Charnel House, 1992. One of 750 numbered, signed by Koontz and Pamela Lee (illus). Japanese fabric (sl worn). Cl slipcase. *Oinonen**. $60/£38

KOONTZ, DEAN R. Dark of the Woods and Soft Come the Dragons. NY: Ace Double, 1970. 1st ptg. Pb orig. Fine in wraps. *Warren*. $30/£19

KOONTZ, DEAN R. The Eyes of Darkness. Arlington Heights: Dark Harvest, 1989. One of 400, this copy lettered 'P/C,' signed by Koontz and Phil Parks (illus). (Sl worn.) Dj, slipcase. *Oinonen**. $30/£19

KOONTZ, DEAN R. The House of Thunder. Arlington Heights: Dark Harvest, 1988. One of 550 numbered, signed by Koontz and Phil Parks. (Sl worn.) Dj, slipcase. *Oinonen**. $40/£25

KOONTZ, DEAN R. The Key to Midnight. Arlington Heights: Dark Harvest, 1989. One of 550 numbered, signed by Koontz and Phil Parks (illus). (Sl worn.) Dj, slipcase. *Oinonen**. $30/£19

KOONTZ, DEAN R. Lightning. NY, 1988. One of 200 numbered, signed. Uncut. Morocco-backed bds by Denis Gouey as issued. (Sl worn.) *Oinonen**. $60/£38

KOONTZ, DEAN R. Mr. Murder. NY, 1993. Uncorrected proof. Glossy wraps. *Warren*. $35/£22

KOONTZ, DEAN R. Night Chills. NY: Athenaeum, 1976. 1st ed. (Sm sticker shadow fep), else Fine in Fine dj. *Between The Covers*. $125/£78

KOONTZ, DEAN R. The Servants of Twilight. Arlington Heights: Dark Harvest, 1988. One of 450 numbered, signed by Koontz and Phil Parks (illus). (Sl worn.) Dj, slipcase. *Oinonen**. $30/£19

KOONTZ, DEAN R. Star Quest. NY: Ace, (1968). 1st ed. VG + (spine, corner crease) in pict wrappers. *Other Worlds*. $20/£13

KOONTZ, DEAN R. Starblood. NY: Lancer, 1972. 1st ptg. Pb orig. NF in wraps. *Warren*. $30/£19

KOONTZ, DEAN R. Twilight Eyes: A Novel of Fear. London: Allen, 1987. 1st ed. (Lt mk fep from sticker removal), else Fine in Fine dj. *Between The Covers*. $125/£78

KOONTZ, DEAN R. A Werewolf Among Us. NY: Ballantine, 1973. 1st Amer ed. Pb orig. NF in wraps. *Warren*. $30/£19

KOPIT, ARTHUR L. Oh Dad, Poor Dad, Mamma's Hung You in the Closet and I'm Feelin' So Sad. NY: Hill & Wang, (1960). 1st ed. Signed. VG (stain to margin of 1st pp, bd bottoms) in VG + dj (sl rubbed). *Between The Covers*. $150/£94

KOPPETT, LEONARD. The New York Mets: The Whole Story. Macmillan, 1970. 1st ed. VG in Good + dj. *Plapinger*. $45/£28

Koran, Commonly Called the Alcoran of Mahomet. Springfield: Isaiah Thomas, Oct 1806. 1st Amer ed. Old calf (corners sl curled; foxing, brn spots). *Metropolitan**. $172/£108

Koran...Translated into English Immediately from the Original Arabic; with Explanatory Notes...by George Sale, Gent. Phila, 1833. New ed. 2 vols. Uncut. (Lt foxed, ex-lib; worn, spines faded, vol 1 rear joint cracked.) *Swann**. $161/£101

Koran: Selected Suras. NY: LEC, 1958. One of 1500. Signed by Valenti Angelo (decs). Dec buckram bound in Islamic style. Fine in glassine, blue cl box. *Pacific**. $127/£79

KORESHOFF, DEBORAH R. Bonsai. Portland: Timber, 1984. 1st ed. 31 color plts. VG in dj. *Fair Meadow*. $40/£25

KORNBLUTH, CYRIL M. Takeoff. GC: Doubleday, 1952. 1st ed. (Lt stain along outside edge of eps), o/w VG + in dj. *Bernard*. $85/£53

KORNBLUTH, JESSE (ed). Notes from the New Underground. NY: Ace, 1968. 1st pb ed. VG. *Sclanders*. $13/£8

KORNILOVICH, A. L. Arts of Russia. 17th and 18th Centuries. James Hogarth (trans). London, 1967. 2 vols. 149 color plts. Djs (chipped). *Edwards*. $72/£45

KORNS, J. RODERIC. West from Fort Bridger.... Salt Lake City: UT State Hist Soc, 1951. 1st ed. 5 maps (2 fldg in rear pocket). Fine (sl bump upper edge fr cvr). *Argonaut*. $175/£109

KOSINSKI, JERZY. The Painted Bird. Boston: Houghton Mifflin, 1965. 1st ed. Fine in dj (sl worn). *Lenz*. $250/£156

KOSLOFF, LOU. California Bit and Spur: A History and Development. (Newport Beach, 1982.) One of 1000 numbered, signed. Cowhide. Cl slipcase. *Swann**. $103/£64

KOSMOS, GEORGE. Alaska Sourdough Stories. Seattle: Robert Seal/G. West Pub, (1956). VG in wraps. *Perier*. $20/£13

KOSTOFF, SPIRO. The Orthodox Baptistry of Ravenna. New Haven, 1965. Good. *Washton*. $65/£41

KOVIC, RON. Born on the Fourth of July. NY: McGraw-Hill, 1976. 1st ed. NF in dj (closed tear). *Smith*. $60/£38

KOVIC, RON. Born on the Fourth of July. NY, 1976. 1st ed. NF in NF dj. *Warren*. $95/£59

KOZIKOWSKI, RENATE. Sophie's Hideaway. NY: Harper, 1983. 6 dbl-pg pop-ups by Ray Marshall. Glazed pict bds (extrems lt worn). *Bookfinders*. $30/£19

KRACAUER, SIEGFRIED. From Caligari to Hitler. London, 1947. 1st Eng ed. Good (cvrs sl handled, mkd) in dj (worn, very repaired). *Clearwater*. $56/£35

KRAITSIR, CHARLES. Glossology. NY: Putnam, 1852. 1st ed. 240pp. (Spine chipped.) *M & S*. $225/£141

KRAKEL, DEAN. The Saga of Tom Horn. Laramie, 1954. (Lt ink notes, tipped-in photos show glue shadow on inner border; binding cocked), else VG in dj (badly torn, chipped). *Baade.* $135/£84

KRAL, VICTOR E. Mineral Resources of Nye County, Nevada. (Reno, NV), 1951. 1st ed. Maps in rear pocket. VG+ in wrappers. *Sagebrush.* $75/£47

KRAMER, FREDERICK L. The White House Gardens. NY: Great American Eds, 1973. 1st ed. 22 color plts by Harold Sterner. (Pp 49-55 lt stained bottom rt corner), else VG in dj (lt chipped, browned). *Fair Meadow.* $40/£25

KRAMER, HILTON. Milton Avery Paintings 1930-1960. NY, (1962). Sm folio. (Sm lib label tp, bkpl.) *Swann*.* $115/£72

KRAMER, JACK. Bromeliads. NY, 1981. 1st ed. Fine in dj. *Brooks.* $44/£28

KRAMER, W. The Aural Surgery of the Present Day. New Sydenham Soc, 1863. ix,154pp. Blind-stamped cl. (Sm lib stamps; sl worn), o/w VG. *Whitehart.* $40/£25

KRAMM, JOSEPH. The Shrike. NY: Random House, (1952). 1st ed. VF in VF dj. *Between The Covers.* $275/£172

KRANTZ, JUDITH. Mistral's Daughter. NY, 1983. 1st ed. Inscribed presentation, dated November 16, 1982. Dj. *Argosy.* $30/£19

KRARUP-NIELSEN, A. The Dragon Awakes. London, 1928. Frontisport, dbl-pg map. Dj (ragged, loss to edges). *Edwards.* $96/£60

KRASHENINNIKOV, STEPAN P. Explorations in Kamchatka, North Pacific Scimitar. E. A. P. Crownhart-Vaughan (trans). Portland: OR Hist Soc, 1972. Blue cl, gilt. Fine. *Pacific*.* $46/£29

KRASNA, NORMAN. Kind Sir. NY: Dramatists Play Service, (1954). 1st ed. VF in VF dj. *Between The Covers.* $125/£78

KRASSNER, PAUL. How a Satirical Editor Became a Yippie Conspirator in Ten Easy Years. NY: Putnam, 1971. 1st ed. NF in VG+ dj. *Sclanders.* $32/£20

KRATVILLE, WILLIAM W. The Mighty 800. Omaha: Kratville Pub, 1967. Pict bds. (Sl shelfworn), else NF. *My Bookhouse.* $27/£17

KRAUS, GEORGE. High Road to Promontory. Palo Alto: American West Pub, (1969). 1st ed. Red cl. Fine in VG+ dj (sl rubbed). *Harrington.* $45/£28

KRAUS, HENRY. Gold Was the Mortar. Routledge, 1979. VG in dj. *Hadley.* $48/£30

KRAUSE, HERBERT and GARY D. OLSON. Prelude to Glory. Sioux Falls, SD: Brevet, (1974). 1st ed. VG in dj. *Lien.* $45/£28

KRAUSS, RUTH. The Birthday Party. Harper & Row, 1957. 6.5x4.75 inches. Maurice Sendak (illus). Pict bds. Good (ex-lib). *American Booksellers.* $25/£16

KRAUSS, RUTH. The Bundle Book. NY: Harper, 1951. 1st ed. Helen Stone (illus). Obl 12mo. Unpaginated. Illus eps. Orange cl. VG (corners bumped, lt spot fr bd) in dj (torn). *Davidson.* $60/£38

KRAUSS, RUTH. A Hole Is to Dig. NY: Harper, 1952. 1st ed. Maurice Sendak (illus). 16mo. 48pp. Grn pict eps. VG in dj (lt worn) priced $1.50. *Davidson.* $200/£125

KREHBIEL, HENRY EDWARD. Afro-American Folksongs. NY, (1914). 5th issue. (Cvrs rubbed, dknd.) *King.* $65/£41

KREISLER, FRITZ. Four Weeks in the Trenches. Boston/NY: Houghton Mifflin, 1915. 1st US ed, 7th imp. Port. Sm promo flyer laid in. Grn cl stamped in silver. VG. *Reese.* $15/£9

KREYMBORG, ALFRED. Funnybone Alley. NY: Macaulay, (1927). Ltd to 500 signed. 4to. 7 mtd full color plts by Boris Artzybasheff. Purple cl (spine sl faded). *Reisler.* $175/£109

KRICK, ROBERT K. Neale Books; An Annotated Bibliography. N.p., 1977. Fine. *Dumont.* $35/£22

KRIDER, JOHN. Krider's Sporting Anecdotes, Illustrative of the Habits of Certain Varieties of American Game. H. Milnor Klapp (ed). Phila, 1853. Engr frontis, 1 plt. (Sl foxed; shelfworn.) *Oinonen*.* $100/£63

KRIEBEL, LAWRENCE C. The Doings of the Alphabet. NY: McLoughlin Bros, (ca 1880). Lg 4to. 6 full-pg color plts. Good in color pict wrappers (spine chipped, splitting). *Reisler.* $80/£50

KRIM, SEYMOUR (ed). The Beats. Greenwich: Gold Medal, 1960. 1st ed. NF (spine slant) in wraps. *Beasley.* $25/£16

KRIM, SEYMOUR. Shake It for the World, Smartass. NY: Dial, 1970. 1st ed. NF in dj (edges sl worn). *Sclanders.* $24/£15

Kriss Kringles's Christmas Tree. NY/Phila: E. Ferrett, 1846. Sm sq 8vo. Wood-engr add'l tp, 14 plts. Gilt/blind-stamped cl. (Label remnant, inscrip fr pastedown.) *Swann*.* $460/£288

KROEBER, A. L. Handbook of the Indians of California. Washington: BAE, 1925. 1st ed. 2 maps in rear pocket. Olive cl. *Dawson.* $100/£63

KROEBER, A. L. Handbook of the Indians of California. Washington: GPO, 1925. 1st ed. 2 maps in rep pocket. Grn cl, gilt. (Sl shaken, spine ends sl bumped), else VG. Howes K268. *Pacific*.* $104/£65

KRONENBERG, M. Notes on English Printing in the Low Countries (Early 16th Century). Bibliographical Soc, 1928. Unopened. VG in ptd cvrs. *Moss.* $24/£15

KRONINGER, ROBERT H. Sarah and the Senator. Berkeley: Howell-North, 1964. 1st ed. Gray cl. Fine in pict dj. *Argonaut.* $40/£25

KRUMGOLD, JOSEPH. Sweeney's Adventure. Random House, c.1942. 9x11.3. Tibor Gergely (illus). Unpaginated. Pict bds (corners worn, edges rubbed). Internally VG. *Price.* $20/£13

KRUMREY, KATE WARNER. Saga of Sawlog. Denver: Big Mountain, 1965. 1st ed. Signed. NF in dj (worn). *Labordo.* $60/£38

KRUSE, ANNE APPLEGATE. The Halo Trail. Drain, OR: Drain Enterprise, 1954. Fine in wraps. *Perier.* $20/£13

KRUSI, HERMANN. Handbook of Perspective Drawing. NY: Appleton, 1874. 1st ed. 65pp. *Marlborough.* $200/£125

KRUTCH, JOSEPH WOOD. The Gardener's World. NY: Putnam, 1959. (Rear hinge starting, shaken.) *Quest.* $30/£19

KRUTCH, JOSEPH WOOD. Henry David Thoreau. (NY): William Sloane Associates, (1948). 1st ed. Frontis. Grn cl. VG (lacks dj). *Lucas.* $15/£9

KRUTCH, JOSEPH WOOD. Herbal. Boston: Putnam, 1965. 1st ed. Folio. Dec paper-cvrd bds, cl spine. Fine in dj. *Quest.* $70/£44

KRUTCH, JOSEPH WOOD. The Last Boswell Paper. Woodstock, VT: Friends of Philip & Fanny Duschnes, Dec 1951. 1st separate ptg. One of 600. VG in ptd wrappers (sl dust soil). *Lucas.* $40/£25

KRUTCH, JOSEPH WOOD. The Twelve Seasons: A Perpetual Calendar for the Country. NY: Sloane, (1949). 1st ed. Fine in VG+ dj (sl loss at crown, sm tears). *Between The Covers.* $55/£34

KRYTHE, MAYMIE. Port Admiral: Phineas Banning, 1830-1885. SF: CA Hist Soc, 1957. 1st ed. Ltd to 1000 ptd. VF in pict dj. *Argonaut.* $75/£47

KUBASTA, V. How Columbus Discovered America. London: Bancroft, 1960. 8pp; dbl-pg pop-up. (Wheel on fr replaced w/wheel from later ptg.) Wraps. *Bookfinders.* $130/£81

KUBASTA, V. Jack and the Beanstalk. Brown Watson, 1981. 1st ed thus. Pop-up bk. 6 action pics. Glazed bds. VG+. *Green Meadow.* $40/£25

KUBASTA, V. The Tournament. London: Bancroft, 1961. Dbl-pg pop-up. (Knight replaced w/facs.) Wraps. *Bookfinders.* $100/£63

KUBLER, GEORGE. The Religious Architecture of New Mexico. Colorado Springs: Taylor Museum, 1940. 1st ed. One of 750. Fldg map. VG in wraps (spotted, creased). *Dumont.* $195/£122

KUBRICK, STANLEY. Stanley Kubrick's Clockwork Orange. NY: Abelard-Schuman, (1972). 1st ed. As New in As New dj. *Between The Covers.* $150/£94

KUCHLER, A. W. Vegetation Mapping. NY: Ronald, 1967. 1st ed. Good (ex-lib). *Archer.* $25/£16

KUCK, LORAINE E. The Art of Japanese Gardens. NY: John Day, 1941. Special ed. Color illus tipped on frontis. 64 b/w plts. (Eps browned, foxed; bkpl; sunned), else VG. *Fair Meadow.* $75/£47

KUDLACEK, JAN. Petrushka. Watts, 1971. 1st US ed. 8.5x11.5. 64pp. Fine in NF dj. *Price.* $40/£25

KUENEN, A. National Religions and Universal Religions. London/Edinburgh: Williams & Norgate, 1882. 1st ed. xii,339,8pp. (Pencil mks few pp; edges rubbed, spine ends sl frayed), o/w VG. *Worldwide.* $45/£28

KUES, BARRY S. Fossils of New Mexico. Albuquerque: Univ of NM, 1982. 1st ed. Signed. VG in dj. *Dumont.* $35/£22

KUGY, JULIUS. Son of the Mountains. H. E. G. Tyndale (trans). London: Thomas Nelson, 1938. 1st ed. 8 plts, map, port. (Spine sl rubbed.) *Hollett.* $64/£40

KUHLMAN, CHARLES. Did Custer Disobey Orders at the Battle of the Little Big Horn. Harrisburg, PA: Stackpole, (1957). 1st ed. Fine in wraps. *Perier.* $35/£22

KUHLMAN, CHARLES. Gen. George A. Custer: A Lost Trail and the Gall Saga.... Billings, MT: Privately pub by the Author, 1940. 1st ed. *Labordo.* $150/£94

KUHLMAN, CHARLES. Legend into History. Harrisburg, PA: Stackpole, 1952. 2nd ed w/additions. VG in dj (worn, tape repaired). *Labordo.* $125/£78

KUMIN, MAXINE. The Abduction. NY: Harper & Row, (1971). 1st ed. NF in NF dj. *Robbins.* $25/£16

KUMLIEN, L. L. Hill's Book of Evergreens. Dundee, IL, 1936. 1st ed. VG in grn cl, gilt. *Larry Price.* $28/£18

KUMM, H. K. W. From Hausaland to Egypt, Through the Sudan. London, 1910. 1st ed. Frontisport, 2 maps (1 fldg), 6 color plts. *Edwards.* $144/£90

KUNARD, R. The Book of Card Tricks. Chicago: Frederick J. Drake, n.d. (c. 1930). Color pict bds. VG. *Dramatis.* $30/£19

KUNDERA, MILAN. The Farewell Party. Peter Kussi (trans). John Murray, 1977. 1st ed. NF (spine foot, corner sl bumped, fr cvr sl mkd) in dj (sl mkd, sl browned). *Ulysses.* $72/£45

KUNDERA, MILAN. The Joke. NY, 1969. 1st Amer ed. VG + in VG + dj (2 short closed tears). *Warren.* $75/£47

KUNDERA, MILAN. Laughable Loves. Suzanne Rappaport (trans). John Murray, 1978. 1st ed. NF (fep sl mkd; spine foot sl bumped) in dj. *Ulysses.* $72/£45

KUNDERA, MILAN. The Unbearable Lightness of Being. NY: Harper & Row, (1984). 1st Amer ed. Fine in dj. *Pacific*.* $52/£33

KUNDERA, MILAN. The Unbearable Lightness of Being. Michael Henry Heim (trans). London: Faber & Faber, 1984. 1st Eng ed. VG (inscrip, top edge dusty; spine head bumped, cvrs sl cocked) in dj (sl creased). *Ulysses.* $72/£45

KUNDERA, MILAN. The Unbearable Lightness of Being. Faber, 1984. 1st UK ed. Proof copy. VG in ptd wrappers. *Williams.* $72/£45

KUNHARDT, DOROTHY. Junket Is Nice. NY: Harcourt, Brace, 1933. 1st ed, 1st bk. Obl 4to. Cl-backed illus bds (sm spot fr cvr). Clean. *Reisler.* $200/£125

KUNHARDT, DOROTHY. Lucky Mrs. Ticklefeather. NY: HBJ, 1935. 1st ed. 10x7. 64pp. Cl spine, pict bds. Good. *Cattermole.* $50/£31

KUNHARDT, DOROTHY. Now Open the Box. NY: Harcourt, Brace, 1934. 1st ed. Obl 4to. Cl-backed pict bds (lt dusty). *Reisler.* $175/£109

KUNISAKE, JIHEI. Kamisuki Chohoki. Charles E. Hamilton (trans). Berkeley: The Book Arts Club/Univ of CA, 1948. 1st ed in English. Cl spine, marbled bds. Fine. *Turtle Island.* $125/£78

KUNITZ, STANLEY. Intellectual Things. NY: Doubleday, Doran, 1930. 1st ed, 1st bk. Fine in dj (sl worn). *Second Life.* $150/£94

KUNOS, IGNACZ (ed). Forty-Four Turkish Fairy Tales. London: George G. Harrap, (1913). 1st ed. Thick 4to. Willy Pogany (illus). Teg. Tan cl. Good in pict dj (spine ends lt chipped). *Reisler.* $675/£422

KUNSTLER, WILLIAM M. The Minister and the Choir Singer. London: Victor Gollancz, 1964. 1st Eng ed, 1st bk. Lt blue cl (spine faded). NF in Good ptd yellow dj (short tears, sm tape stains; rear cvr sl creased, spine chipped, 1/4 inch piece out). *Blue Mountain.* $45/£28

KUNZ, G. Birth Stones, Natal Stones, Sentiments and Superstitions. NY: Tiffany, c1927. 31st ed. Pb. VG. *Blake.* $50/£31

KUNZ, G. Rings for the Finger. Phila: Lippincott, c1917. 1st ptg. Signed presentation. Pict cl. (Plts, adjacent pp lt foxed), else VG. *Blake.* $350/£219

KUNZ, VIRGINIA BRAINARD. Muskets to Missiles: A Military History of Minnesota. St. Paul: Minnesota Statehood Centennial Commission, 1958. 1st ed. VG in softcvrs. *Lien.* $15/£9

KUPPER, WALTER and PIA ROSHARDT. Cacti. NY, 1960. 60 full-pg color plts. VG in dj (sm tears). *Brooks.* $29/£18

KUPPER, WINIFRED. The Golden Hoof. NY, 1945. 1st ed. VG (lt worn). *Baade.* $25/£16

KUPPER, WINIFRED. The Golden Hoof. NY: Knopf, 1945. 1st ed. VG + in dj. *Labordo.* $65/£41

KURTZ, DONNA CAROL. The Berlin Painter. Oxford: Clarendon, 1983. Dj. *Archaeologia.* $125/£78

KURZ, OTTO. Bolognese Drawings of the XVII and XVIII Centuries in the Collection...at Windsor Castle. London/Oxford: Phaidon, 1955. 77 plts hors-texte. (Spine sl faded), o/w Fine. *Europa.* $96/£60

KURZ, OTTO. Fakes. A Handbook for Collectors and Students. Faber & Faber, 1948. 1st ed. Dj (lt soiled, sl chipped). *Edwards.* $48/£30

KUTTNER, HENRY. Fury. (London): Dobson, (1954). 1st UK ed. (Eps browned), else NF in dj (sl defects from old dj protector). *Other Worlds.* $65/£41

KUYKENDALL, WILLIAM L. Frontier Days. N.p.: J.M. & H.L. Kuykendall, 1917. 1st ed. VG. Howes K284. *Labordo.* $250/£156

KYGER, JOANNE. The Tapestry and the Web. SF: Four Seasons Foundation, 1965. Ltd to 1000. 1st bk. Signed presentation. NF in ptd wraps. *Polyanthos.* $25/£16

KYLE, FRANK. Chrysanthemums. London, 1952. 1st ed. Color frontis, 24 photo plts. VG in dj (torn). *Larry Price.* $18/£11

KYNE, PETER B. They Also Serve. NY: Cosmopolitan Book Corp, 1927. 1st ed. Frontis. Olive grn cl, gilt. NF in pict dj (sl sunned, nicks). *Reese.* $45/£28

KYNE, PETER B. The Three Godfathers. NY: Cosmopolitan, 1924. 1st ed. (Lt foxing frontis verso; few sm spots fr bd), else Fine in dj (chips, tears). *Between The Covers.* $85/£53

KYNE, PETER B. Tide of Empire. NY: Cosmopolitan, 1928. 1st ed. Fine in NF pict dj. *Unger.* $150/£94

L

L'AMOUR, LOUIS. Hopalong Cassidy and the Rustlers of West Fork. Doubleday, 1951. 1st ed. NF in VG + dj (lt worn, torn). *Fine Books.* $675/£422

L'AMY, JOHN H. Jersey Folk Lore. Jersey: J.T. Bigwood, 1927. 1st ed. Frontis, 8 plts, dbl-pg map. (Sl water-stain to frontis), o/w Good. *Cox.* $29/£18

L'ENGLE, MADELEINE. A Wind in the Door. NY: FSG, 1973. 1st ed. 8vo. 211pp. Grn cl bds, gilt. VG in Good dj. *Davidson.* $35/£22

LA BRANCHE, GEORGE M. L. The Dry Fly and Fast Water: Fishing with the Floating Fly on American Trout Streams.... NY: Scribner, 1914. 1st ed. Grn cl, gilt. (Spine ends sl rubbed), else NF. *Pacific*.* $173/£108

LA BREE, BEN. Camp Fires of the Confederacy.... Louisville, 1898. 1st ed. Color pict cl (spine faded, rubbed, soiled; sl shaken). *Kane*.* $75/£47

LA FARGE, OLIVER. The Enemy Gods. Boston: Houghton Mifflin, 1937. 1st ed. VG in dj (sl edgeworn, rubbed). *Smith.* $30/£19

LA FARGE, OLIVER. Santa Eulalia: The Religion of a Chuchumation Indian Town. Chicago: Univ of Chicago, (1947). 1st ed. (Shelf wear), else Good in VG dj. *Perier.* $35/£22

LA FAYETE, EUGENE. French Family Cookbook. London: Paris Pub, 1885. 1st ed. 160pp. VG. *Perier.* $60/£38

LA FONTAINE. Fables de la Fontaine. Boston: Alphabet Press, 1981. 1st ed. Marie Angel (illus). Folio. As New in slipcase. *Davidson.* $85/£53

LA FONTAINE. The Fables of La Fontaine. Margaret Wise Brown (trans). NY: Harper, (1940). 1st ed. Andre Helle (illus). 4to. 39pp. Pict cl-backed bds. VG (edges rubbed, corners worn). *Davidson.* $100/£63

LA FONTAINE. A Hundred Fables of La Fontaine. London: John Lane, 1900. 1st ed. Percy J. Billinghurst (illus). 4to. Grn cl (lt edgeworn). *Reisler.* $250/£156

LA GORCE, JOHN O. (ed). The Book of Fishes. Nat'l Geographic Soc, 1952. Fine in dj. *Larry Price.* $35/£22

LA MONT, VIOLET. Ballet in Pop-Up Action Pictures. London: Publicity Products, 1953. 4 dbl-pg pop-ups. Internally VG in illus wraps (extrems worn). *Bookfinders.* $70/£44

LA PRADE, ERNEST. Alice in Orchestralia. Doubleday, 1926. 1st ed. NF in VG dj (2 closed tears, sl soiled, worn). *Any Amount.* $35/£22

LA ROCHE, R. Pneumonia: Its Supposed Connection, Pathological and Etiological, with Autumnal Fevers. Phila, 1854. 1st ed. 502 pp. *Fye.* $200/£125

LA RUE, E. C. Water Power and Flood Control of Colorado River Below Green River, Utah. Washington: USGS, 1925. 79 plts. Orange wraps. Good + . *Five Quail.* $75/£47

LA SPINA, GREYE. Invaders from the Dark. Sauk City: Arkham House, 1960. 1st ed. Fine in NF dj (price-clipped). *Other Worlds.* $90/£56

LA WALL, CHARLES H. Four Thousand Years of Pharmacy. Phila: Lippincott, 1927. 1st ed. VG. *Glaser.* $75/£47

LABARTE, M. JULES. Handbook of the Arts of the Middle Ages and Renaissance. John Murray, 1855. xxxvi,443pp (feps spotted). Marbled edges. Old 1/2 calf, marbled bds (spine sl scuffed), gilt, spine label. *Hollett.* $120/£75

LABAT, GASTON. Regional Anesthesia. Phila: W.B. Saunders, 1924. Maroon cl (sl rubbed; bkpl). *Weber.* $75/£47

LABAT, GASTON. Regional Anesthesia. Phila, 1928. 2nd ed. VG (sl underlining, penciling; extrems sl worn). *Doctor's Library.* $200/£125

LABBAN, KUSHYAR IBN. Principles of Hindu Reckoning. Martin Levey & Marvin Petruck (trans). Madison/Milwaukee: Univ of WI, 1965. 1st ed. 31 plts. NF in dj. *Worldwide.* $45/£28

LABOULAYE, EDOUARD. Laboulaye's Fairy Book. NY/London: Harper, (1920). 1st ed thus. Edward C. McCandlish (illus). 8vo. Color pict pastedown. Tan cl. NF (few marginal tears). *Glenn.* $100/£63

LACHAMBRE, H. and A. MACHURON. Andree and His Balloon. Westminster: Constable, 1898. 1st ed. 306pp. Gilt-dec cl. VG. *Walcot.* $80/£50

LACHAMBRE, H. and A. MACHURON. Andree's Balloon Expedition in Search of the North Pole. NY: Frederick Stokes, (1898). 1st ed. (Spine dull, ends sl rubbed), else VG. *Pacific*.* $52/£33

LACHICOTTE, ALBERTA MOREL. Georgetown Rice Plantations. Columbia, SC: The State Co, 1955 (1956). 2nd ptg. Signed. Gray cl. VG (lt foxed) in dj (worn, tattered). *Chapel Hill.* $40/£25

LACKINGTON, JAMES. Memoirs of the First Forty-Five Years of the Life of J. Lackington, Bookseller.... London, 1803. New ed. Engr frontis port, extraneous hand-colored aquatint plt bound in. Later straight-grain morocco (joints rubbed). *Swann*.* $201/£126

LACKINGTON, JAMES. Memoirs of the First Forty-Five Years of the Life.... The Author, 1792. 2nd ed. Stipple engr frontisport (browned, as is tp), 486pp. Later 19th-cent half calf (rubbed, lt worn; lacks label). *Cox.* $88/£55

LADA-MOCARSKI, VALERIAN. Bibliography of Books on Alaska Published Before 1868. New Haven: Yale Univ, 1969. 1st ed. Fine in NF dj (sl edgeworn). *Pacific*.* $288/£180

LADD, WILLIAM and ROBERT GROSS. Abdominal Surgery of Infancy and Childhood. Phila, 1948. 1st ed. *Fye.* $75/£47

Ladies Calling, in Two Parts. (By Richard Allestree.) Oxford: Theater, 1673. 2nd ed. (24),95,(1)pp. Calf. (New eps, lacks prelims [if any] to tp; lower rear joint starting), else VG. *Pacific*.* $98/£61

LADIES OF CHICAGO. The Home Cook Book. Chicago: J. Fred Waggoner, 1877. 4th ptg. 400pp. (Cvr spots), else VG. *Perier.* $65/£41

LADOUX, GEORGES. Marthe Richard, the Skylark. Warrington Dawson (ed). London (etc): Cassell, (1932). 1st ed in English. Port. Blue cl. (Sl foxed), o/w NF in dj (lt edgeworn). *Reese.* $30/£19

LADURIE, EMMANUEL LE ROY. Carnival in Romans. M. Feeney (trans). NY, 1979. 1st ed. VG in dj. *Typographeum.* $20/£13

Lady's Narrative, 1834. Webster & Larkin, 1874. VG (fore-edge sl spotted, ink inscrip; spine bumped). *Tiger.* $128/£80

LAENNEC, R. T. H. A Treatise on Mediate Auscultation, and on Diseases of the Heart and Lungs. London, 1846. 862pp; 6 engr plts (1 partly hand-colored; engr port present). Recent 1/4 leather, marbled bds. *Fye.* $400/£250

LAENNEC, R. T. H. A Treatise on the Diseases of the Chest and on Mediate Auscultation.... NY, 1838. 784pp. Recent leatherette. (Lib stamp tp), o/w VG. *Fye.* $275/£172

LAFAYETTE, MARQUIS DE. A Complete History of the Marquis de Lafayette, Major General in the Army of the United States of America...By an officer in the late army. NY: Robert Lowry, 1826. 504pp; port, 3 plts. Full contemp Spanish calf (rubbed, hinges worn, lt browned). *Adelson.* $175/£109

LAFFIN, JOHN (ed). Letters from the Front 1914-1918. London: J.M. Dent, (1973). 1st ed. Gilt plum bds. Fine in NF dj w/pub's price sticker on flap. *Reese.* $25/£16

LAFOND, GEORGE. Covered with Mud and Glory. Edwin G. Rich (trans). Boston, 1918. (Name.) *Clearwater.* $40/£25

LAFONTAINE, GARY. Trout Flies. Proven Patterns. Helena, MT, (1993). Deluxe ed. One of 250 numbered, signed. 1/2 leather (lt worn). Slipcase w/built-in sunken mount containing 3 actual hand-tied trout flies. *Oinonen**. $250/£156

LAGERKVIST, PAR. Barabbas. NY: Random House, (1951). 1st ed. VF in Fine dj (sm tear, sl rubbed). *Between The Covers.* $150/£94

LAGERKVIST, PAR. The Death of Ahasuerus. NY: Random House, (1962). 1st Amer ed. VF in VF dj (sl rubbed). *Between The Covers.* $125/£78

LAGERKVIST, PAR. The Eternal Smile and Other Stories. NY: Random House, (1954). 1st Amer ed. As New in Fine dj. *Between The Covers.* $150/£94

LAGERKVIST, PAR. Herod and Mariamne. NY: Knopf, 1968. 1st ed. Fine in Fine dj. *Between The Covers.* $125/£78

LAGERKVIST, PAR. The Holy Land. NY: Random House, (1966). 1st Amer ed. VF in VF dj (sl rubbed). *Between The Covers.* $100/£63

LAGERKVIST, PAR. Pilgrim at Sea. NY: Random House, (1964). 1st Amer ed. VF in VF dj (sl rubbed). *Between The Covers.* $100/£63

LAGERKVIST, PAR. The Sibyl. NY: Random House, (1958). 1st Amer ed. (Sm fore-edge spot), else VF in VF dj. *Between The Covers.* $150/£94

LAGERKVIST, PAR. The Sibyl. London: C&W, 1958. 1st ed in English. Pale brn cl-textured bds. Fine in dj. *Temple.* $24/£15

LAGERLOF, SELMA. The Diary of Selma Lagerlof. Velma Swanston Howard (trans). GC: Doubleday, Doran, 1936. 1st ed. (Lt sunned), else Fine in NF dj. *Hermitage.* $35/£22

LAINE, TANNER. Cow Country. Herford, TX, 1969. 1st ed. Good. *Dumont.* $35/£22

LAING, ALEXANDER. The Cadaver of Gideon Wyck. NY, 1934. 1st ed, 1st bk. Dj (sm tear fr joint, sl edgeworn, lt dampstaining along fore-edge). *Swann**. $172/£108

LAING, ALEXANDER. Travels in the Timannee, Kooranko, and Soolima Countries in Western Africa. London: John Murray, 1825. Fldg engr map, 7 engr plts. (Lt spotting, browning, mainly to plts.) Contemp 1/2 calf (extrems chipped, rubbed), spine gilt. *Christie's**. $270/£169

LAING, SAMUEL. The Heimskringla of The Sagas of the Norse Kings. Rasmus B. Anderson (ed). London: John C. Nimmo, 1889. 2nd ed. One of 310. 4 vols. 2 maps. Blue cl, gilt. (Bkpls; spine ends rubbed, chipped, spines sl dull), else VG. *Pacific**. $138/£86

LAING, SAMUEL. Journal of a Residence in Norway During the Years 1834, 1835 and 1836. London: Longman, 1851. New ed. Mod brn calf (rebound). *Petersfield.* $56/£35

LAIRD, HELEN. Carl Oscar Borg and the Magic Region. Layton, UT, 1986. 1st ed. NF in dj. *Dumont.* $60/£38

LAKE, FRED and HAL WRIGHT. A Bibliography of Archery. Manchester, England: Simon Archery Foundation, 1974. Mottled grn cl. VF in VF color ptd dj. *Biscotti.* $90/£56

LAKE, STUART N. Wyatt Earp Frontier Marshal. Boston: Houghton Mifflin, 1931. (Bkpl; lt worn), else VG. *Dumont.* $30/£19

LAKE, STUART N. Wyatt Earp, Frontier Marshal. Boston: Houghton Mifflin, 1931. 1st ed. NF in dj (worn, chipped). *Labordo.* $185/£116

LAKES, ARTHUR. Prospecting for Gold and Silver. Scranton: Colliery Engineer Co, 1895. 1st ed. 207pp. (Sl edgeworn), else VG. *Brown.* $75/£47

LAKING, GUY FRANCIS. The Furniture of Windsor Castle. London: Bradbury, Agnew, 1905. 47 leaves of mtd photogravure plts. Pigskin over beige cl. Fine. *Karmiole.* $350/£219

LAMB, ARTHUR H. Tragedies of the Osage Hills. Pawhuska, OK: Osage Printery, n.d. (ca1935). 1st ed. VG (sm tear spine head) in pict wrappers. *Lien.* $150/£94

LAMB, CHARLES and MARY. Mrs. Leicester's School. NY: Henry M. Onderdonk, 1844. 2nd Amer ed. 12mo. Engr frontis, 166pp. Gilt/blind-stamped blue cl (spine lt frayed). *Karmiole.* $75/£47

LAMB, CHARLES and MARY. Mrs. Leicester's School. J.M. Dent, n.d. (c.1899). Obl lg 8vo. x,128pp; 40 color plts by Winifred Green. Pict bds (sl soiled, extrems sl frayed; bkpl, sig). *Hollett.* $104/£65

LAMB, CHARLES and MARY. Tales from Shakespeare. London: Ernest Nister, (1901). 1st ed illus thus. 6 Fine chromolithos by W. Paget. Aeg. Gray pict cl, gilt. Very Nice (sm tear rep; spine sl rubbed). *Sotheran.* $141/£88

LAMB, CHARLES and MARY. Tales from Shakespeare. London: J.M. Dent, 1909. 1st Rackham ed. One of 750 signed by Arthur Rackham (illus). Thick 4to. 13 mtd color plts. Teg; silk ties. Full gilt-stamped vellum. Nice. *Appelfeld.* $1,250/£781

LAMB, CHARLES (ed). Specimens of English Dramatic Poets, Who Lived About the Time of Shakespeare: With Notes. Longman et al, 1808. 1st ed. Sm 8vo. Half-title present, xii,484pp. Dk blue silk eps; teg, rest untrimmed. Late 19th-cent crushed polished dk blue morocco, by W. Root, gilt, dec raised bands, red morocco onlay center of fr cvr, blue silk marker. VG. *Blackwell's.* $520/£325

LAMB, CHARLES. The Complete Correspondence and Works of Charles Lamb. London, 1870. 4 vols. Contemp tree calf (few spine heads repaired), gilt extra, red/grn labels. *Swann**. $149/£93

LAMB, CHARLES. A Dissertation upon a Roast Pig. Rochester: Leo Hart, 1932. 1st ed. One of 950. Vellum-backed rice paper-cvrd bds. Fine. *Pacific**. $63/£39

LAMB, CHARLES. A Dissertation upon Roast Pig. Sampson Low, Marston, n.d. C. O. Murray (illus). Color frontis, 62,(ii)pp. Aeg. Gilt cl, beveled bds. Fine (bkpl). *Hollett.* $224/£140

LAMB, CHARLES. Eliana: Being the Hitherto Uncollected Writings of Charles Lamb. Edward Moxon, 1864. Final blank; 437,(iii)pp. Top edge uncut; eps coated yellow; binder's ticket on rep. Beveled dk grn fine morocco cl, gilt. Good. *Temple.* $104/£65

LAMB, CHARLES. The Letters of Charles Lamb, with a Sketch of His Life. Thomas Noon Talfourd (ed). Edward Moxon, 1837. 2 vols. 1/2-title, engr frontisport each vol; 1 plt vol 2; all plts w/guards; 2pp integral ads at end of vol 2. Full brn buckram. (Plts foxed, offsetting onto tissues, adjacent pp; recently rebound), o/w internally NF. *Temple.* $64/£40

LAMB, CHARLES. The Life, Letters and Writings of...Edited by Percy Fitzgerald. London: Gibbings, 1897. 6 vols. Teg. 3/4 grn morocco, marbled bds by Blackwell, gilt. VG set (backs sl faded). *House.* $250/£156

LAMB, CHARLES. A Masque of Days. London: Cassell, 1901. 1st ed illus by Walter Crane. Gray/yellow pict eps. Color pict paper over bds. VG (lt edgeworn, cvrs soiled). *House.* $225/£141

LAMB, CHARLES. A Masque of Days. Cassell, 1901. 1st ed. 4to. Walter Crane (illus). 40pp. Cl-backed pict bds. (Feps, edges spotted), o/w VG in dj (edges chipped, torn, lacks backstrip). *Hollett.* $288/£180

LAMB, CHARLES. The Works. London: C. & J. Ollier, 1818. 1st ed. 2 vols. Teg. 3/4 grn calf, marbled bds, morocco spine labels, raised bands. (Bkpls, eps sl foxed), else VG. *Pacific**. $207/£129

LAMB, CHARLES. The Works. C. & J. Ollier, 1818. 1st collected ed. 2 vols. Bound w/o 1/2-titles. Yellow burnished edges. Recent 1/4 calf, raised bands, labels, marbled bds. Fine. *Temple.* $320/£200

LAMB, DANA S. Bright Salmon and Brown Trout. (Barre: Barre Publishers, 1964.) 1st ed. One of 1500 ptd. Mustard cl, gilt. Fine in acetate, slipcase. *Pacific**. $161/£101

LAMB, DANA S. Green Highlanders and Pink Ladies. Barre: Barre Publishers, 1971. 1st ed. One of 1500 ptd. Signed. Grn cl, gilt. Fine in glassine, slipcase. *Pacific**. $161/£101

LAMB, DANA S. On Trout Streams and Salmon Rivers. Barre: Barre Publishers, 1963. 1st ed. One of 1500 ptd. Grn cl, gilt. Fine in VG slipcase (sl rubbed). *Pacific**. $219/£137

LAMB, DANA S. Some Silent Places Still. Barre: Barre Publishers, 1969. 1st ed. One of 1500. Frontis. 1/2 cl, bds. Fine in slipcase. *Pacific**. $161/£101

LAMB, DANA S. Where the Pools Are Bright and Deep. (NY): Winchester, (1973). 1st trade ed. VG in dj (sm tear fr panel top). *Pacific**. $58/£36

LAMB, DANA S. Woodsmoke and Water Cress. Barre: Barre Publishers, 1965. 1st ed. One of 1500 ptd. Brn cl, gilt. Fine in acetate. *Pacific**. $161/£101

LAMB, EDGAR. Stapeliads in Cultivation. London, 1957. 127 photo plts (27 color). Fine in dj (sm tears). *Brooks*. $42/£26

LAMB, FRANK W. Indian Baskets of North America. Riverside, CA: Riverside Museum, (1972). Signed. Fine in VG dj. *Perier*. $75/£47

LAMB, J. The Child's Primer; or First Book for Primary Schools. Burlington, (VT): Chauncey Goodrich, 1830. 12mo. 72pp + 1pg ad on lower cvr. VF woodcuts. Orig dec ptd buff paper on bds (lt browned, sm adhesive spot, lower bd cracked along spine). Overall Fine. *Hobbyhorse*. $325/£203

LAMB, ROBERT BYRON. The Mule in Southern Agriculture. Univ of CA, 1963. 1st ed. Signed. Good in wraps. *Rybski*. $30/£19

LAMBARD, WILLIAM. The Duties of Constables, Borsholders, Tythingmen, and Such Other Lovve Ministers of the Peace.... London: For Ralfe Newberie, 1594. Sm 8vo. 80pp. Mod calf, gilt spine. Good (last pg dusty; some headlines, pg #s shaved). *Sokol*. $1,360/£850

LAMBERT and RATCLIFFE. The Bodley Head 1887-1987. Bodley Head, 1987. 1st ed. 31plts, 15 facs. Pub's ptd presentation slip. Fine in dj. *Cox*. $24/£15

LAMBERT, C. and S. The Voyage of the 'Wanderer'.... G. Young (ed). London: Macmillan, 1883. 23 color plts, map. Cvr inlays. (Sl foxed; backstrip rubbed, sl torn, corners bumped.) *Petersfield*. $51/£32

LAMBERT, CLARA. The Story of Alaska. Harper, 1940. 1st ed. 10x11. Cornelius DeWitt (illus). Unpaginated. VG (1941 name; facing pp of color illus browned) in Good dj (2-inch spine chip). *Price*. $30/£19

LAMBERT, D. H. (ed). Shakespeare Documents. London, 1904. 1st ed. Fine (sl soiled). *Polyanthos*. $25/£16

LAMBERT, JOSEPH I. One Hundred Years with the Second Cavalry. Fort Riley, KS: Capper Ptg, 1939. 1st ed. Blue cl, gilt. (Bold pencil sig, blindstamp), else Fine. *Pacific**. $259/£162

LAMBERT, OSMUND. Angling Literature in England. Sampson Low, Marston, Searle, and Rivington, 1881. 1st ed. Teg, uncut. Full parchment. *Forest*. $56/£35

LAMBERT, SAMUEL W. When Mr. Pickering Went Fishing. NY: Brick Row Bookshop, 1924. 1st ed. Signed, inscribed. Fine in VG dj. *Pacific**. $63/£39

LAMBERT, WARD L. Practical Basketball. Chicago, 1932. 1st ed. Pict cl. (Spine almost detached; cvrs worn, loose.) *King*. $35/£22

LAMBETH, JOSEPH A. Lambeth Method of Cake Decoration and Practical Pastries. London: Virtue, 1937. 2nd ed. Port. (Extrems sl rubbed.) *Hollett*. $152/£95

LAMBROU, ANDREAS. Fountain Pens, Vintage and Modern. Sothebys, 1990. 39 color plts. VG in dj. *Hollett*. $48/£30

LAMBURN, JOAN. Mr Soloski's Cats. Cape, 1948. 1st ed. 4to. Tony Stoney (illus). Lattice-patterned bds. NF in illus dj (worn). *Bookmark*. $24/£15

Lamentations of Jeremiah. (Newtown: Gregynog), 1933. One of 110 (of 250) bound in oasis. Folio. 21 illus by Blair Hughes-Stanton. Wood-engr calligraphic tp. Deep blue oasis blocked in blind. *Swann**. $2,530/£1,581

LAMERS, WILLIAM M. The Edge of Glory: A Biography of General William S. Rosecrans, U.S.A. Harcourt, (1961). 1st ed. VG in dj (sl worn). *Rybski*. $75/£47

LAMONT, CORLISS. Remembering John Masefield. London: Kaye & Ward, 1972. 1st ed. (Damped.) Dj. *Hollett*. $40/£25

LAMONT, JAMES. Seasons with the Sea-Horses; or, Sporting Adventures in the Northern Seas. NY, 1861. (Bkpl.) *Swann**. $138/£86

LAMPMAN, EVELYN SIBLEY. The City Under the Back Steps. Doubleday, 1960. 1st ed. Honore Valintcourt (illus). 210pp. VG+ (bd edge bumped, spine ends chipped) in VG+ dj. *Price*. $75/£47

LAMPMAN, EVELYN SIBLEY. Crazy Creek. Doubleday, 1948. 1st ed. Grace Paull (illus). 213pp. Red cl w/dwg. VG (name) in dj (remnant, lacks 1/2 of rear panel). *Price*. $35/£22

LAMPMAN, EVELYN SIBLEY. Treasure Mountain. Doubleday, 1949. 1st ed. Richard Bennett (illus). 206pp. Good+ (2 names; corners bumped). *Price*. $25/£16

LAMPSON, ROBIN. Laughter Out of the Ground. NY: Scribner, 1935. 1st ed. One of 260 numbered, signed. 2-tone cl, black spine label, gilt. VF. *Argonaut*. $75/£47

LAMSON J. Round Cape Horn. Voyage of the Passenger-Ship James W. Paige...1852. Bangor, 1878. 1st, only ed. Inscribed by Hazel Lamson. 156pp. Cl, marbled paper over bds. (Sm piece of paper stuck on fep, cracked inner hinges; edges worn, hinges cracked.) *Woolson*. $150/£94

LAMSON, J. Round Cape Horn. Bangor, 1878. Pub's 1/2 cl (extrems rubbed), paper cvr label. (Lt dampstained.) Howes L48. *Swann**. $103/£64

LANCASTER, CLAY. The Japanese Influence in America. NY: Walton H. Rawls, 1963. 9 color plts. NF in dj. *Turtle Island*. $125/£78

LANCASTER, I. The Soaring Birds. A Mechanical Problem. (Wrapper title.) (Chicago?), ca 1900. 1st ed. 22pp. Orig ptd wraps (lib sticker). *M & S*. $275/£172

LANCASTER, ROY. Plant Hunting in Nepal. Croom Helm, 1981. NF in dj. *Hadley*. $32/£20

LANCE, LONG. Long Lance. NY: Cosmopolitan Book, 1928. 1st ed. VG. *Labordo*. $55/£34

Land of Enchantment. London: Cassell, 1907. 1st ed. 4to. Arthur Rackham (illus). Aeg. Full maroon morocco w/gilt floral panels on cvrs, gilt paneled spine, raised bands. Fine (orig cl cvrs bound in at the end). *Appelfeld*. $600/£375

LANDER, RICHARD and JOHN. Journal of an Expedition to Explore the Course and Termination of the Niger: With a Narrative of a Voyage Down That River to Its Termination. NY: J. & J. Harper, 1832. 1st Amer ed. 2 vols. 2 maps (1 fldg), 3 plts. Orig cl. (Foxed; vol 1 joints repaired), else VG. *Pacific**. $92/£58

LANDES, RUTH. The Ojibwa Woman. NY: Comunbia Univ, 1938. 1st ed. Red cl, gilt. (Sig fep), else Fine. *Hermitage*. $85/£53

LANDIS, C. S. .22 Caliber Rifle Shooting. Onslow County: Small-Arms, 1932. 1st ed. VG in dj (soiled, tattered). *Bowman*. $65/£41

LANDIS, HENRY G. How to Use the Forceps. 1880. 1st ed. 203pp. VG. *Doctor's Library*. $150/£94

LANDON, MARGARET. Never Dies the Dream. GC: Doubleday, 1949. 1st ed. (Sl cocked), else Fine in VG dj (sm tears). *Between The Covers*. $65/£41

LANDON, MELVILLE D. Kings of the Platform and Pulpit. Chicago: Werner Co, 1895. 570pp; 7 facs. Flowered eps. Dec cl, gilt. VG. *Connolly.* $45/£28

LANDOR, WALTER SAVAGE. Dry Sticks, Fagoted. Edinburgh: James Nichol, 1858. 1st ed. Pub's ads at end. Grn cl dec in blind. (Prelims sl foxed.) *Sotheby's*.* $147/£92

LANDOR, WALTER SAVAGE. Dry Sticks, Fagoted. Edinburgh/London: James Nichol/James Nisbet, 1858. 1st ed. 8pp undated ads. Blindstamped grn cl. VG (lacks feps; sl edgewear). *Sumner & Stillman.* $325/£203

LANDOR, WALTER SAVAGE. The Hellenics.... Edinburgh: James Nichol, 1859. New ed. xi,(i),279,(1)pp. Aeg. Grn morocco-grain cl, gilt. *Cox.* $48/£30

LANDOR, WALTER SAVAGE. Imaginary Conversations. NY: LEC, 1936. 1st ed. One of 1500 signed. Patterned bds, spine label. (Spine sl faded), else VG + . *Any Amount.* $104/£65

LANDOR, WALTER SAVAGE. Letters of Walter Savage Landor: Private and Public. Stephen Wheeler (ed). Duckworth, 1899. Teg. Buckram. Good (fore-edge spotted, lt spotted, 'snowpake' mk tp verso, possibly obliterating a shelf #; spine bumped, sunned, cvrs sl grubby). *Tiger.* $29/£18

LANDOR, WALTER SAVAGE. The Poetical Works of.... Stephen Wheeler (ed). Oxford: Clarendon, 1937. 1st ed. 3 vols. NF. *Agvent.* $75/£47

LANDOR, A. HENRY SAVAGE. See SAVAGE-LANDOR, A. HENRY

LANDSEER and HERRING. Aunt Louisa's Choice Present, Comprising Famous Horses, Noted Horses, Famous Dogs, Noted Dogs. London: Frederick Warne, (c. 1860s-80s). 24 chromolithos. Blue cl, gilt. (Hinges, joints cracked; extrems rubbed, dknd), else Good. *Pacific*.* $173/£108

LANDSTEINER, KARL. The Specificity of Serological Reactions. Springfield, 1936. 1st ed in English. *Fye.* $200/£125

LANDWEHR, JOHN. Studies in Dutch Books with Coloured Plates Published 1662-1875. The Hague, 1976. (Bkpl.) Dj. *Swann*.* $115/£72

LANDY, EUGENE E. The Underground Dictionary. NY: S&S, 1971. 1st ed. Fine in NF dj. *Beasley.* $40/£25

LANE, ALLEN STANLEY. Emperor Norton, the Mad Monarch of America. Caldwell, ID: Caxton, 1939. 1st ed. VF in pict dj. *Argonaut.* $150/£94

LANE, C. K. Rabbits, Cats and Cavies: Descriptive Sketches.... London: J.M. Dent, 1903. 1st ed. Teg. Grn cl, gilt. (Shelfworn, sm tear rear joint), else VG. *Pacific*.* $46/£29

LANE, E. W. (ed). The Thousand and One Nights, Commonly Called in England, the Arabian Nights' Entertainments. London, 1841. 3 vols. Uncut. Emb cl. (Margins lt browned; spines faded, ends bumped, chipped w/sl loss.) *Edwards.* $77/£48

LANE, E. W. (ed). The Thousand and One Nights; or, the Arabian Nights' Entertainments. NY: Harper, 1848. 1st Amer ed. 2 vols. Orig cl, gilt, dec spines. (Foxed; faded, corners rubbed, spine ends chipped), else VG-. *Pacific*.* $173/£108

LANE, FREDERICK CHAPIN. Venetian Ships and Shipbuilders of the Renaissance. Balt: Johns Hopkins, 1934. 1st ed. Blue linen, gilt. Good. *Karmiole.* $60/£38

LANE, SHELDON (ed). For Bond Lovers Only. NY: Dell, 1965. 1st Amer ed. Pb orig. Fine in wrappers. *Mordida.* $65/£41

LANE-POOLE, STANLEY. The Mohammadan Dynasties. Westminster: Constable, 1894. 1st ed. xxviii,361,2pp. Lib buckram. (Ex-lib; sl rubbed, lib spine sticker), o/w VG. *Worldwide.* $45/£28

LANES, S. G. The Art of Maurice Sendak. Bodley Head, 1981. 1st End ed. 97 color, 167 monochrome plts (incl moveable plt). Fine in pict cl. *Moss.* $112/£70

LANG, ANDREW. The All Sorts of Stories Book. Longmans, Green, 1911. 1st ed. xvi,377pp (few spots to eps); 5 color plts by H. J. Ford. Purple cl (spine faded), gilt. *Hollett.* $104/£65

LANG, ANDREW. Angling Sketches. London: Longmans, Green, 1891. 1st ed. 3 etchings. Grn cl, gilt. (Spine sl dknd), else NF. *Pacific*.* $58/£36

LANG, ANDREW. The Animal Story Book. Longmans, Green, 1896. 1st ed. H. J. Ford (illus). xiv,400pp. Pict cl (sl worn; few spots), gilt extra. *Hollett.* $120/£75

LANG, ANDREW. Ballads and Lyrics of Old France: with Other Poems. London: Longmans, Green, 1872. 1st ed, 1st bk. x,164pp. Good (foxed; bumped, soiled, cvrs foxed, spine dknd). *Blue Mountain.* $40/£25

LANG, ANDREW. Ballads of Books. Longmans, Green, 1888. 1st ed. xx,157pp. Teg, rest untrimmed. Blue cl, gilt. *Bickersteth.* $48/£30

LANG, ANDREW. The Blue Fairy Book. London: Longmans, Green, 1889. 1st ed. 8vo. 8 full-pg plts by H. J. Ford and G. P. Jacomb Hood. (Prelims sl foxed, eps replaced.) Aeg. Blue cl, gilt (dull). *Reisler.* $750/£469

LANG, ANDREW. The Book of Dreams and Ghosts. Longmans, 1897. 1st ed. Crown 8vo. xviii,301pp + 32pp pub's list. Teg, rest roughtrimmed. Pale blue cl. Good (bkpls, margins, eps lt browned). *Blackwell's.* $80/£50

LANG, ANDREW. The Book of Romance. London: Longmans, Green, 1902. 1st ed. H. J. Ford (illus). 3/4 blue morocco, floral emblematic tooling on spine, raised bands, gilt top, by Zaehnsdorf. Fine. *Appelfeld.* $150/£94

LANG, ANDREW. Books and Bookmen. Longmans, Green, 1887. 2nd ed. Beveled bds. Good (spine bumped). *Tiger.* $19/£12

LANG, ANDREW. The Brown Fairy Book. Longmans, 1904. 1st ed. Crown 8vo. Frontis, guard, xiii,350pp; 8 colorptd plts by H. J. Ford. Gilt edges. Mid brn cl, gilt. Good (name). *Blackwell's.* $200/£125

LANG, ANDREW. Cock Lane and Common-Sense. London: Longmans, Green, (1894). 8vo. 357pp + 24pp ads. Red cl (spine soiled), gilt. VG. *Davidson.* $125/£78

LANG, ANDREW. The Crimson Fairy Book. London: Longmans, Green, 1903. 1st ed. 8vo. 8 full-pg color plts, 35 full-pg b/w dwgs by H. J. Ford. Aeg. Crimson cl, gilt (spine sl dull). *Reisler.* $250/£156

LANG, ANDREW. The Green Fairy Book. London: Longmans, Green, 1892. 1st ed. H. J. Ford (illus). 8vo. Aeg. Grn cl, gilt. (Cl worn along rear spine edge, lt shelfworn.) *Reisler.* $250/£156

LANG, ANDREW. How to Fail in Literature: A Lecture. Field & Tuer, Leadenhall Press, 1890. 1st ed. 95,(iv)pp (lib stamp, few marginal blind-stamps). Uncut (edges sl dusty). Orig leather-grained wrappers (neatly rebacked). *Hollett.* $72/£45

LANG, ANDREW. Johnny Nut and the Golden Goose. London: Longmans, Green, 1887. 1st ed. Imperial 8vo. Am. Lynen (illus). (x),45pp. Teg. Lt blue dec cl. Very Bright (spine sl rubbed, lower corner tip worn). *Sotheran.* $141/£88

LANG, ANDREW. Letters to Dead Authors. Longmans, Green, 1886. Tp conjugate w/half-title; final blank; x,234,(ii)pp. Teg, rest uncut. 1/4 vellum, gilt, cerise buckram sides. (Spine foxed), o/w Fine. *Temple.* $35/£22

LANG, ANDREW. Lost Leaders. NY: Longmans, 1889. 1st ed. (Bds sl rubbed), else VG + . *Any Amount.* $26/£16

LANG, ANDREW. Notes and Names in Books. Chicago, 1900. One of 110. Uncut. Blue bds (sl soiled), paper cvr label. *Dawson.* $50/£31

LANG, ANDREW. The Olive Fairy Book. London: Longmans, Green, 1907. 1st ed. 8vo. 8 full-pg color plts by H. J. Ford. Aeg. Olive cl, gilt. VG in dj (lacks spine). *Reisler.* $550/£344

LANG, ANDREW. The Red Book of Animal Stories. Longmans Green, 1899. 1st ed. xvii,379pp; 32 plts by H. J. Ford. Aeg. Red pict cl (spine sl faded, head sl worn), gilt extra. *Hollett.* $120/£75

LANG, ANDREW. The Red Fairy Book. Phila: McKay, (1924). 1st ed thus. 285pp; 8 full-pg color illus by Gustaf Tenggren. Pict eps; teg. Red cl, pict paste-on. VG + . *Davidson.* $285/£178

LANG, ANDREW. The Red True Story Book. London: Longmans, Green, 1895. 1st ed. Henry J. Ford (illus). Gilt pict-dec red cl. NF (few sm dampstains). *Sumner & Stillman.* $150/£94

LANG, ANDREW. Rhymes a la Mode. Kegan Paul, Trench, 1885. 1st ed. Frontis, viii,(2),139pp. Beveled edges, teg, rest uncut. Smooth grn cl, gilt. VG. *Cox.* $29/£18

LANG, ANDREW. St. Andrews. London, 1893. 1st ed. xvi,347pp + 24pp pub's cat; 8 plts. (Browned; spine sl rubbed.) *Edwards.* $96/£60

LANG, ANDREW. The True Story Book. London: Longmans, Green, 1893. 1st ed. H. J. Ford et al (illus). 8vo. Aeg. Dk blue cl, gilt. Good. *Reisler.* $175/£109

LANG, ANDREW. The Violet Fairy Book. Longmans, 1901. 1st ed. Crown 8vo. Frontis, guard, xii,398pp; 8 colorptd plts by H. J. Ford. Gilt edges. Violet cl, gilt. VG (inscrip, rubberstamp). *Blackwell's.* $320/£200

LANG, ANDREW. The Violet Fairy Book. London: Longmans, Green, 1901. 1st ed. 8vo. 8 full-pg color plts, 25 full-pg b/w plts. Aeg. Violet cl (lt shelfworn), gilt. *Reisler.* $385/£241

LANG, D. M. Catalogue of Georgian and Other Caucasian Printed Books in the British Museum. London, 1962. 1st ed. Fine in NF dj. *Polyanthos.* $35/£22

LANG, H. O. History of the Williamette Valley. Portland: Geo. H. Himes, Ptr, 1885. 902pp. Orig full leather (spine starting to split). *Perier.* $275/£172

LANG, JOHN D. and SAMUEL TAYLOR, JR. Report of a Visit to Some of the Tribes of Indians, Located West of the Mississippi River. NY: M. Day, 1843. 1st ed. 34pp. Orig ptd wrappers bound into mod gilt-lettered lib cl. VG (lib mks; wrappers, tp chipped, stained, but expertly silked; sl foxed, stained). Howes L72. *Harrington.* $110/£69

LANG, LINCOLN ALEXANDER. Ranching with Roosevelt. Phila: Lippincott, 1926. 1st ed. Grn cl. VG + . *Labordo.* $70/£44

LANG, W. H. Australia. T.C. & E.C. Jack, 1900. 12 color full-pg illus, 2 maps. All edge marbled. Full contemp tree calf prize binding, gilt, raised bands. (Sl foxed), o/w Fine. *Sotheran.* $205/£128

LANGDON, DAVID. Orange Roofs, Golden Arches. (NY): Knopf, 1986. NF in dj (dusty). *Hadley.* $32/£20

LANGE, DOROTHEA and PAUL TAYLOR. An American Exodus: A Record of Human Erosion. NY: Reynal & Hitchcock, 1939. 1st ed. Fine in illus dj (rear sl dusty). *Cahan.* $500/£313

LANGE, DOROTHEA and MARGARETTA K. MITCHELL. To a Cabin. NY: Grossman, 1973. 1st ed. (Linen bds sl soiled), else Fine in dj. *Hermitage.* $45/£28

LANGE, JOHN. (Pseud of Michael Crichton.) Zero Cool. NY: Signet, 1969. Pb. VG- (inside cvrs foxed) in wraps. *Warren.* $25/£16

LANGE, MONIQUE. The Kissing Fish. Richard Howard (trans). NY: Criterion, (1960). 1st Amer ed. VF in VF dj. *Between The Covers.* $65/£41

LANGFORD, NATHANIEL PITT. Vigilante Days and Ways. Boston: J.G. Cupples, 1890. 1st ed. Inscribed, signed. 2 vols. Brn cl. Fine set. Howes L78. *Labordo.* $600/£375

LANGFORD, NATHANIEL PITT. Vigilante Days and Ways. Chicago, 1912. (Bkpl, pencil note, sm newsprint piece stuck inside fr cvr; sl worn, spotted.) Howes L78. *Woolson.* $60/£38

LANGHANS, EDWARD A. Restoration Promptbooks. Carbondale: Southern IL Univ, (1981). VG in slipcase. *Dramatis.* $40/£25

LANGLEY, HENRY G. A Street and Avenue Guide of San Francisco. SF: Henry G. Langley, 1875. (15 ads),106,(25 ads)pp. Grn cl, gilt. (Lacks map, fr hinge cracked), o/w VG. *Pacific*.* $127/£79

LANGLEY, NOEL. The Tale of the Land of Green Ginger. NY: William Morrow, 1937. 1st ed. 4to. 143pp. Grn cl. VG (sl foxing) in VG dj. *Davidson.* $135/£84

LANGLEY, NOEL. The Tale of the Land of Green Ginger. NY: William Morrow, 1938. 4to. 143pp; 5 full-pg vignettes in full color. Grn linen on bds. (Dated ink inscrip inside fr cvr; spine edges sl worn), else Fine. *Hobbyhorse.* $95/£59

LANGRIDGE, IRENE. William Blake. Study of His Life and Work. London: Geo. Bell, (1904). 1st ed. Gilt-stamped grn cl, gilt top. *Appelfeld.* $50/£31

LANGSTON, W., JR. Permian Amphibians from New Mexico. Berkeley: Univ of CA, 1953. 1st ed. Fine in wraps. *Mikesh.* $20/£13

LANGTON, JANE. Dark Nantucket Moon. NY: Harper, 1975. 1st ed. NF in NF dj. *Janus.* $75/£47

LANGTON, ROBERT. The Childhood and Youth of Charles Dickens. Hutchinson, 1891. Rev ed, 1st ptg. Frontis, guard. (Feps strengthened; neat restoration to spine head), o/w VG. *Temple.* $19/£12

LANGUM, DAVID J. Law and Community on the Mexican California Frontier. Norman: Univ of OK, (1987). 1st ed. VG in dj. *Lien.* $30/£19

LANIER, HENRY. A. B. Frost. The American Sportsman's Artist. NY: Derrydale, (1933). One of 950. (Pencil inscrip; sl worn.) *Oinonen*.* $180/£113

LANIER, HENRY. A. B. Frost: The American Sportsman's Artist. NY: Derrydale, (1933). One of 950. Folio. (Spine lettering heavily rubbed, ends worn.) *Swann*.* $161/£101

LANKESTER, E. RAY. Monograph of the Okapi. London, 1910. 48 plts (2 color). Buckram-backed cl (corners sl bumped). *Sutton.* $475/£297

LANKESTER, MRS. British Ferns.... W.H. Allen, 1884. New, enlgd ed. (4),127pp; 16 color litho plts. VG in pict cl (sl rubbed). *Cox.* $29/£18

LANMAN, CHARLES (ed). The Japanese in America. NY: University Pub, 1872. 1st ed. Dec red cl, gilt. (Few pp creased; soiled, spine ends chipped, repaired), else VG. *Pacific*.* $150/£94

LANMAN, CHARLES (ed). The Japanese in America. NY: University Pub Co, 1872. 1st ed. Frontis, (2),352pp; plt, port. Orange cl, gilt. Good. *Karmiole.* $175/£109

LANMAN, CHARLES (ed). Journal of Alfred Ely. NY, 1862. 1st ed. 359pp; port. (Inner fr hinge cracked; spine ends chipped, extrems frayed.) *King.* $75/£47

LANMAN, CHARLES. Adventures in the Wilds of the United States and British American Provinces. Phila: John W. Moore, 1856. 1st Amer ed. 2 vols. Red cl, gilt. (Soiled, cvr spots, vol I joints torn, spines rubbed), else VG-. *Pacific*.* $86/£54

LANMAN, CHARLES. Letters from the Alleghany Mountains. NY: Putnam, 1849. 2nd ed. 198pp + (18)pp ads. Orig dk grn cl. (Name, spine sl worn), else VG. Howes L89. *Chapel Hill.* $225/£141

LANSDALE, JOE R. The Nightrunners. Arlington Heights: Dark Harvest, 1987. One of 300 numbered, signed by Lansdale, Dean R. Koontz (intro), and Gregory Manches (illus). (Sl worn.) Dj, slipcase. *Oinonen*.* $40/£25

LANSFORD, WILLIAM DOUGLAS. Pancho Villa. L.A.: Sherbourne Press, (1965). 1st ed. Fine in Fine dj. *Book Market.* $30/£19

LANYON, ANDREW. Snap! London: Gordon Fraser, 1974. 1st ed. 47 b/w photos. Fine in illus stiff wrappers. *Cahan.* $35/£22

LAPHAM, MACY H. Criss Cross Trails. Berkeley, 1949. 1st ed. Inscribed. VG (few sm dimples in cvrs) in dj (chipped). *Baade*. $75/£47

LAPP, RUDOLPH M. Archy Lee: A California Fugitive Slave Case. Mallette Dean, 1969. One of 500. *Dawson*. $45/£28

LARDEN, WALTER. Inscriptions from Swiss Chalets. Oxford: Horace Hart, 1913. 52 plts. (Few pencilled notes, feps browned.) *Hollett*. $136/£85

LARDNER, RING. Bib Ballads. Chicago: Vollard, (1915). 1st ed, 1st bk. One of 500. Brn cl. VG (name). *Second Life*. $350/£219

LARDNER, RING. The Ecstasy of Owen Muir. NY, 1954. 1st Amer ed. NF (name) in dj (spine sunned, few chips). *Polyanthos*. $25/£16

LARDNER, RING. Gullible's Travels, Etc. Indianapolis: Bobbs-Merrill, (1917). 1st ed. Color frontis. (Bkpl; spine/fr cvr lettering flaked), o/w VG. *Bernard*. $100/£63

LARDNER, RING. Lose with a Smile. NY: Scribner, 1933. 1st ed. VG in dj (sunned, spine ends, extrems rubbed, price-clipped). *Pacific**. $104/£65

LARDNER, RING. Lose with a Smile. NY: Scribner, 1933. 1st ed. Grn cl. Fine in dj (sl used, spine ends lt rubbed). *Dermont*. $200/£125

LARDNER, RING. The Real Dope. Indianapolis: Bobbs-Merrill, (1919). 1st ed. Frontis. Blue bds stamped in red. (Ink inscrip; spine crown chipped), else Good. *Reese*. $85/£53

LARDNER, RING. Treat 'Em Rough: Letters from Jack the Kaiser Killer. Indianapolis: Bobbs-Merrill, (1918). 1st ed. Grn cl, pict cvr label. NF. *Pacific**. $69/£43

LARGE, R. GEDDES. The Skeena, River of Destiny. Vancouver: Mitchell, (1962). 2nd ed. Signed. VG in dj. *Perier*. $25/£16

LARKEY, JOANN LEECH. Davisville '68. Davis Historical & Landmarks Commission, 1969. 1st ed. Pict eps. Gilt-dec leather-textured fabricoid. Fine. *Connolly*. $55/£34

LARKIN, MARGARET. Singing Cowboy. NY, 1931. 1st ed. (Extrems worn, hinges strengthened.) Internally Good. *Dumont*. $55/£34

LARKIN, PHILIP. All What Jazz, a Record Diary 1961-68. NY, (1970). 1st Amer ed. (Fr cvr faded), else Good in dj (spotted, bumped). *King*. $25/£16

LARKIN, PHILIP. Aubade. (Salem, OR: Ptd at the Penstemon Press for Charles Seluzicki), 1980. 1st ed. One of 250 initialled by Larkin and ptr. Full-pg illus. Untrimmed. Fine in plain pale gray wrappers, matching envelope. *Blackwell's*. $344/£215

LARKIN, PHILIP. The Explosion. London: Poem-of-the-Month Club, 1970. One of 1000 signed. Broadsheet (sl tanned). *Clearwater*. $160/£100

LARKIN, PHILIP. A Girl in Winter. Woodstock, NY: Overlook, (1976). 1st Amer ed. Fine in Fine dj. *Dermont*. $45/£28

LARKIN, PHILIP. High Windows. London, 1974. 1st Eng ed. Fine (eps sl foxed) in dj (sl faded). *Clearwater*. $64/£40

LARKIN, PHILIP. High Windows. Faber, 1974. 1st ed. (Spine ends sl rubbed), o/w Good in dj (spine sl yellowed). *Virgo*. $72/£45

LARKIN, PHILIP. High Windows. Faber, 1974. 1st ed. Pale gray cl, gilt. Fine in dj. *Blackwell's*. $96/£60

LARKIN, PHILIP. Required Writing. NY: FSG, (1984). 1st Amer ed. Fine in Fine dj. *Dermont*. $35/£22

LARKIN, PHILIP. Required Writing. Miscellaneous Pieces 1955-1982. London, 1984. 1st hb ed. Fine in dj. *Clearwater*. $96/£60

LARKIN, PHILIP. Selected Letters of: 1940-1985. Anthony Thwaite (ed). Faber, 1992. 1st ed. Mint in dj. *Virgo*. $32/£20

LARKIN, PHILIP. The Whitsun Weddings. Faber, 1964. 1st ed. (Eps, fore-edge sl spotted), o/w VG in dj (sl soiled). *Virgo*. $144/£90

LARKIN, PHILIP. The Whitsun Weddings. Faber, 1964. 1st ed. Purple cl, gilt. VG in dj. *Blackwell's*. $160/£100

LARKIN, THOMAS O. The Larkin Papers. George Peter Hammond (ed). Berkeley: Univ of CA, 1951-1968. 1st ed. 10 vols. Frontispieces. (Worn, insect damage cvrs), else VG in djs. *Pacific**. $575/£359

LARKIN, THOMAS O. The Larkin Papers.... Volume I, 1822-1842. Berkeley: Univ of CA, 1951. Fine in dj. *Argonaut*. $100/£63

LARKIN, THOMAS O. The Larkin Papers.... Volume VI, 1847. Berkeley: Univ of CA, 1959. (Sl dampstain rear cvr), else Fine in dj (soiled, stained). *Argonaut*. $50/£31

LARNED, J. N. History for Ready Reference. Springfield: C.A. Nichols, 1895. 5 vols. Lt crimson coated buckram, ptd paper spine labels. Text VG (lt aged; cvrs lt sun-streaked, spines faded, labels rubbed, chipped). *Baltimore**. $30/£19

LARNED, J. N. The Literature of American History; A Bibliographical Guide. Columbus: Long's College Book Co, 1953. Rpt of 1902 ed. VG. *Dumont*. $65/£41

LARREY, DOMINIQUE JEAN. Observations on Wounds, and Their Complications. E. F. Rivinus (trans). Phila: Key, Mielke & Biddle, 1832. 1st US ed. viii,332pp; 2 b/w plts at rear. Old calf, leather spine label. Good (lt browned, sl foxed, scattered spot stains; fr cvr detached, cvrs lt warped, worn, scuffed, spot stains). *Baltimore**. $240/£150

LARRIMORE, LIDA. The Blossoming of Patricia-the-Less. Phila: Penn, 1924. 1st ed. 6.5x8.5. Hattie Longstreet Price (illus). Color frontis, 253pp. Blue cl w/picture paste-on. VG (inscrip; shelfworn, sl scratched). *My Bookhouse*. $32/£20

LARRISON, EARL J. Owyhee: The Life of a Northern Desert. Caldwell, ID, 1957. 1st ed. Color frontis. NF in VG + dj. *Sagebrush*. $60/£38

LARTIGUE, J. H. Boyhood Photos of J. H. Lartigue. (Lausanne): Ami Guichard, (1966). 1st ed. Gilt-stamped maroon cl. (Mtd illus on fr cvr rubbed, scratched), else Fine. *Karmiole*. $275/£172

LARTIGUE, J. H. Diary of a Century. Hammondsworth/NY: Penguin, 1978. 1st wrapper ed. Fine. *Cahan*. $40/£25

LASERON, CHARLES F. South with Mawson. London/Sydney: George G. Harrap, 1947. NF in dj (worn, split on fold). *Explorer*. $64/£40

LASKEY, J. C. A Description of the Series of Medals Struck at the National Medal Mint by Order of Napoleon Bonaparte. London: H.R. Young, 1818. 1st ed. Engr frontis. Green buckram spine, plain bds. (Prelims lt foxed, stamps), else Sound. *Turtle Island*. $250/£156

LASKI, HAROLD J. The Crisis and the Constitution: 1931 and After. London: Hogarth/Fabian Soc, 1932. 1st Eng ed. VG (edges spotted) in wrappers. *Ulysses*. $56/£35

LASKI, HAROLD J. Law and Justice in Soviet Russia. Hogarth, 1935. 1st Eng ed. Wrappers. VG (sig fr cvr; cvrs sl rubbed, creased, partly dknd). *Ulysses*. $56/£35

LASKI, M. Little Boy Lost. Cresset, 1949. 1st ed. (Sl dull), else Good in dj (dull, sl rubbed). *Whiteson*. $21/£13

LASKI, MARGHANITA. Love on the Super-Tax. Cresset, 1944. 1st UK ed. Fine in VG dj (edges sl worn; dusty, price-clipped). *Williams*. $56/£35

LASKY, MELVIN. Utopia and Revolution. Macmillan, 1976. 1st UK ed. Signed, inscribed presentation. NF (spine sl creased; lacks dj). *Any Amount*. $45/£28

LASKY, VICTOR. Robert F. Kennedy: The Myth and the Man. NY, (1968). Inscribed, signed. Dj. *Argosy*. $40/£25

LASSAIGNE, JACQUES. The Ceiling of the Paris Opera. NY, (1966). Dj. *Swann**. $316/£198

LASSAIGNE, JACQUES. Drawings and Watercolors for The Ballet. NY, (1969). Signed by Chagall. Dj, mylar outer wrapper, bd slipcase. *Swann**. $345/£216

LASSAIGNE, JACQUES. Spanish Painting from the Catalan Frescoes to El Greco. Stuart Gilbert (trans). Skira, (1952). 2 vols. Coarse natural linen. Fine set (bkpl). *Truepenny*. $75/£47

LASSO DE LA VEGA, GARCIA. The Odes and Sonnets of Garcia Lasso de la Vega. (London): Aquila, 1930. One of 250. Inscribed in 3-lines, signed by George W. Jones (designer). Gilt-stamped vellum, marbled bds. Good. *Karmiole*. $150/£94

Last Egyptian: A Romance of the Nile. (By L. Frank Baum.) Phila: Edward Stern, 1908. 1st ed, 1st state w/o ptr's imprint on c. pg. 7.25x5. 287pp; 8 color plts by Francis P. Wightman. Baughman's copy w/his Oz bkpl. Blue cl, pict cvr label. (Spine relettered in white), else VG. *Pacific**. $92/£58

Last of the Mohicans. NY: McLoughlin Bros, (ca 1890). Narrow 8vo (shapebook). 14pp. Good in full color pict wrappers (worn). *Reisler*. $85/£53

Last of the Mohicans: A Narrative of 1757. Phila: Carey & Lea, 1826. 1st ed. 2 vols. xi,(1),282; (2),289pp. Mod 3/4 grn morocco, marbled bds, gilt. (Bkpls, browned, lt foxed, last pg vol 2 creased, sm tear tp top, name, sl trimmed), else VG. BAL 3833. *Pacific**. $1,380/£863

Last of the Mohicans; A Narrative of 1757. (By James F. Cooper.) London: John Miller, 1826. 1st British ed. 3 vols. Untrimmed. Orig drab bds. (Bkpl each vol, edges foxed, spotted; neatly rebacked in gray paper w/ms labels, new eps; sl worn orig labels laid in), o/w VG. BAL 3833. *Reese*. $1,000/£625

LATHAM, CHARLES. The Gardens of Italy. London, 1905. 2 vols. Folio. (1st flys lacking, lib pockets to rear cvrs; sl loose, worn.) *Woolson*. $250/£156

LATHAM, CHARLES. In English Homes. London, 1908-09. 3 vols, mixed set: Vol 1 from 3rd ed, 1909; vol 2 from 2nd ed, 1908; vol 3 from 1st ed, 1909. Folio. (Bkpls; extrems worn, vols 1, 3 rear cvrs becoming loose.) *Swann**. $69/£43

LATHAM, JEAN LEE. Carry On, Mr. Bowditch. Boston: Houghton Mifflin, 1955. 1st ed. 8vo. John O'Hara Cosgrave II (illus). Dk grn cl. Good in full color dj (spine sl worn). *Reisler*. $250/£156

LATHAM, PETER M. Lectures on Subjects Connected with Clinical Medicine, Comprising Diseases of the Heart. London, 1846. 2nd ed. 2 vols. 374; 419pp. *Fye*. $300/£188

LATHAM, SIMON. Falconry or the Faulcons Lure and Cure in Two Books. (and) New and Second Booke of Faulconry. London: Thomas Harper for John Harison, 1633. 1st collected ed. 4to. (xxiv),148,(iv); (xxiv),147,(i)pp, 2nd part bound 1st. Contemp English speckled sheep, triple line borders, red morocco label. VG (Evelyn lib label; spine head chipped). *Sokol*. $4,720/£2,950

LATHROP, DOROTHY P. The Little White Goat. NY: Macmillan, 1933. 1st ed. Obl 4to. Full color frontis, 15 b/w plts. Yellow-orange cl (margins dknd). Full color dj (worn, fr edges spotted). *Reisler*. $250/£156

LATHROP, ELISE. Historic Houses of Early America. NY: Tudor, 1936. Frontis, 67 photo plts. Pict eps. NF. *Connolly*. $30/£19

LATIMER, DEAN and JEFF GOLDBERG. Flowers in the Blood. NY, 1981. 1st Amer ed. Fine in NF dj. *Warren*. $35/£22

LATIMORE, SARAH BRIGGS and GRACE CLARK HASKELL. Arthur Rackham: A Bibliography. L.A.: Suttonhouse, 1936. One of 550 signed by both. Prospectus laid in. Patterned bds, cl spine. Slipcase. *Dawson*. $300/£188

LATROBE, C. I. Journal of a Visit to South Africa, in 1815 and 1816. NY: James Eastburn, 1818. 1st Amer ed. 7,392pp. Old 3/4 calf, marbled bds (fr hinge weak). *M & S*. $275/£172

LATROBE, CHARLES JOSEPH. The Rambler in North America.... NY, 1835. 1st US ed. 2 vols. 2pp Harpers cat vol 2. Orig cl (ex-lib, spine ends worn). *Kane**. $80/£50

LATTA, FRANK F. Black Gold in the Joaquin. Caldwell: Caxton, 1949. 1st ed. Fine in VG dj. *Book Market*. $35/£22

LATTA, FRANK F. Dalton Gang Days. Santa Cruz, 1976. 1st ptg. Pict cl. Fine w/o dj as issued. *Baade*. $60/£38

LATTA, FRANK F. Death Valley '49ers. Santa Cruz: Bear State, (1979). 1st ed. Fine. *Book Market*. $40/£25

LATTA, FRANK F. Joaquin Murrieta and His Horse Gangs. Santa Cruz, CA: Bear State Books, (1980). 1st ed. Frontis. Tan cl, gilt. As New. *Argonaut*. $50/£31

LATTA, FRANK F. Joaquin Murrieta and His Horse Gangs. Santa Cruz: Bear State Books, (1980). 1st ed. Color frontisport. Pict eps. Tan cl, gilt. Fine. *Harrington*. $60/£38

LATTA, FRANK F. Saga of Rancho El Tejon. Santa Cruz: Bear State Books, (1976). 1st ed. Fine. *Book Market*. $28/£18

LATTA, FRANK F. Tailholt Tales. Santa Cruz, 1976. 1st ptg. Pict cl. Fine w/o dj probably as issued. *Baade*. $60/£38

LATTA, ROBERT R. Reminiscences of Pioneer Life. Kansas City, MO: Franklin Hudson, 1912. 1st ed. Partly unopened. (Pg edges sl scorched; stained, water-damaged), else Good + . *Pacific**. $86/£54

LATTIMORE, ELEANOR. The Search for Christina. Morrow, 1964. 1st ed. 112pp. VG in dj (1-inch, edgeworn). *Price*. $25/£16

LATTIMORE, ELEANOR. Turkestan Reunion. NY: Day, 1934. 1st ed. (Lib spine #, edges rubbed, spine faded, soiled, ends sl frayed), o/w Good. *Worldwide*. $30/£19

LATZKO, ANDREAS. Lafayette. London: Methuen, (1936). Frontis. Good. *Stewart*. $48/£30

LAU, T. Greek Vases: Their System of Form and Decoration. E. H. Greenleaf (trans). Boston: Tilton, 1879. 12 color litho plts. Pict bds (shelfworn, spine worn, chipped; margins sl stained). *Oinonen**. $90/£56

LAUBIN, REGINALD and GLADYS. The Indian Tipi: Its History, Construction, and Use. Norman: Univ of OK, (1957). 1st ed. Fine in dj. *Pacific**. $58/£36

LAUFE, ABE (ed). An Army Doctor's Wife on the Frontier. Pittsburgh: Univ of Pittsburgh, 1962. 1st ed. VG in dj (edgetorn). *Perier*. $40/£25

LAUFFER, CHARLES. Resuscitation From Electric Shock, Traumatic Shock, Drowning, Asphyxiation From Any Cause. NY, 1913. 1st ed. *Fye*. $75/£47

LAUGHLIN, CLARENCE JOHN. New Orleans and its Living Past. Text by David L. Cohn. Boston: Houghton Mifflin, 1941. 1st ed. One of 1000 numbered. Signed by Laughlin and Cohn. Folio. 62 gravure plts. Leather spine label. Fine in pub's slipcase (rubbed). *Cahan*. $750/£469

LAUGHLIN, JAMES (ed). Spearhead-10 Years' Experimental Writing in America. NY: New Directions, 1947. British issue w/Falcon Press stamp on tp and dj price 21/-. NF (spine tail sl bumped) in dj (sl rubbed, spotted, spine sl dknd). *Ulysses*. $61/£38

LAUGHLIN, JAMES. This Is My Blood. (Covelo): Yolla Bolly, (1989). Ltd to 255. Ptd wrappers of Phillipine Cogon grass paper, ptd mylar dj. *Truepenny*. $155/£97

LAUGHLIN, LEDLIE IRWIN. Pewter in America. Boston: Houghton Mifflin, 1940. 1st ed. 2 vols. 78 b/w photo plts. Untrimmed. Tan buckram, gray cl, gilt-lettered black leather spine labels. (Sl rubbed, shelfworn, labels partly scuffed, nicked.) Texts VG (bkpls). *Baltimore**. $40/£25

LAUGHLIN, LEDLIE IRWIN. Pewter in America. Boston, 1940. 2 vols. Uncut. 2-tone cl (sl worn), leather spine labels (sl scuffed). *Oinonen**. $90/£56

Laughter Book for Little Folks. NY: James Miller, (ca 1869). 4to. Grn blind-stamped cl, gilt. (Few pg edges sl rough; edges, spine foot worn.) *Reisler*. $750/£469

LAUGHTON, B. Philip Wilson Steer, 1860-1942. OUP, 1971. Frontis, 215 plts. Good in dj. *Ars Artis*. $120/£75

LAUMER, KEITH. The Great Time Machine Hoax. NY, 1964. 1st ed. VG in dj (sl rubbed). *King.* $50/£31

LAUMER, MARCH et al. The Green Dolphin of Oz. (Bellaire): Vanitas, (1978). 1st ed. Lau Shiu-Fan (illus). Red cl, pict cvr label. NF. *Pacific*.* $86/£54

LAUNAY, ANDRE. Caviar and After: The Truth About Luxury Foods. Macdonald, (c1964). 1st ed. VG in Good dj. *Book Broker.* $35/£22

LAURENS, HENRY. The Physiological Effects of Radiant Energy. NY, 1933. 1st ed. *Fye.* $100/£63

LAURIE, A. P. The Brush-Work of Rembrandt and His School. OUP, 1932. Frontisport; 127 b/w plts. Fore-edge uncut, partly unopened. VG (contents ll sl spotted) in dj (sl discolored, sm nick). *Edwards.* $64/£40

LAURIE, ALEX and D. C. KIPLINGER. Commercial Flower Forcing. Phila: Blakiston, 1950. 5th ed. VG. *Fair Meadow.* $20/£13

LAURIE, JOSEPH. The Homoeopathic Domestic Medicine. NY, 1877. 1044pp. Brn 1/2 calf, gilt. Good + (edgeworn). *Larry Price.* $80/£50

LAUT, AGNES C. The Blazed Trail of the Old Frontier. NY, 1926. 1st ed. Lg fldg map. (Sm piece of tape to tp; rebound.) *Heinoldt.* $60/£38

LAUT, AGNES C. The Blazed Trail of the Old Frontier: Being the Log of the Upper Missouri Historical Expedition.... NY: Robert M. McBride, 1926. 1st ed. Gilt-pict grn buckram. (Few hinges tender; rubbed, spine sl faded), else VG. Howes L143. *Pacific*.* $86/£54

LAVALLETTE, COUNT. Memoirs of Count Lavallette. London: Henry Colburn & Richard Bentley, 1831. 2nd ed. 2 vols. Extra-illus w/85 ports, incl hand-colored frontis. Teg. Blue morocco, gilt, raised bands. (Bkpls), o/w NF set. *Pacific*.* $115/£72

LAVATER, JOHN CASPAR. Essays on Physiognomy, Designed to Promote the Knowledge and the Love of Mankind. Henry Hunter (trans). London: John Murray et al, 1789-1792. 1st ed in English. 3 vols in 5. Lg 4to. Morocco eps; teg. Period or sl later 3/4 gilt-ruled morocco, marbled bds, raised bands. Internally NF (bkpls, sl foxed, soiled; rubbed, extrems worn, joints cracked). *Pacific*.* $633/£396

LAVENDER, DAVID. Bent's Fort. NY: Doubleday, 1954. 1st ed. Fine in Fine dj. *Book Market.* $15/£9

LAVENDER, DAVID. The Fist in the Wilderness. GC, 1964. 1st ed. (Sl worn.) *Woolson.* $20/£13

LAVENDER, DAVID. The Great Persuader. GC, 1970. 1st ed. (Sl worn) in dj (lacks sm pieces, sm tears). *Woolson.* $25/£16

LAVENDER, DAVID. Land of Giants. GC, 1958. 1st ed. VG in dj (small tears). *Woolson.* $20/£13

LAVENDER, DAVID. One Man's West. GC, 1943. 1st ed. Inscribed. NF in dj. *Baade.* $65/£41

LAVENDER, DAVID. The Southwest. NY, 1980. 1st ed. Signed by Lavender and dj designer. NF in dj. *Dumont.* $40/£25

LAVER, JAMES. Nymph Errant. London: Heinemann, 1932. 1st ed. Signed presentation dated June 1932. Rose buckram. (Spine sl faded, corner bruised), o/w Fine. *Temple.* $16/£10

LAVERAN, C. L. A. Paludism. London, 1893. 1st ed in English. 197pp. *Fye.* $100/£63

LAVIN, MARY. The House in Clewe Street. London: Michael Joseph, 1945. 1st ed. Grn cl. (Eps lt foxed), o/w VG. *Temple.* $35/£22

LAVOISIER. Elements of Chemistry, in a New Systematic Order, Containing All the Modern Discoveries. Edinburgh: William Creech, 1799. Stated 4th ed. 592pp; 13 fldg copper-engr plts, 2 fldg tables. Period calf. (Lacks feps, cl tape repairs to hinges covering gutter margin of 1/2-title, old rubberstamps, central hinge cracked w/tape repair, plts foxed; worn, spine cracked, crudely repaired w/cl tape), else Good. *Pacific*.* $109/£68

LAW, P. and J. BECHERVAISE. Anare. Melbourne: Oxford Univ, 1957. 1st ed. VG. *High Latitude.* $40/£25

LAW, P. and J. BECHERVAISE. Anare: Australia's Antarctic Outposts. Melbourne: OUP, 1957. VG in dj. *Explorer.* $48/£30

LAW, REUBEN D. The Founding and Early Development of the Church College of Hawaii. St. George, 1972. Errata laid in. VG. *Benchmark.* $15/£9

LAW, WILLIAM. A Collection of Letters on the Most Interesting and Important Subjects and on Several Occasions. J. Richardson, 1760. 1st ed. 8vo. (iv),220,(4)pp. Early 19th-cent 1/2 red roan (rebacked w/orig backstrip laid down, bkpl), marbled bds (rubbed). Good (sig, uniformly lt browned throughout). *Blackwell's.* $120/£75

LAWLER, JOHN. Book Auctions in England in the Seventeenth Century (1676-1700) with a Chronological List of the Book Auctions of the Period. London: Stock, 1898. 1st ed, lg-paper copy. Uncut. (Lt worn.) *Oinonen*.* $120/£75

LAWLER, RAY. Summer of the Seventeenth Doll. NY: Random House, (1957). 1st Amer ed. VF (fr bd sl flawed) in VF dj (sl soiled). *Between The Covers.* $125/£78

LAWRENCE, A. W. (ed). T. E. Lawrence—by His Friends. Cape, 1937. 1st Eng ed. 8 b/w plts. VG (spine ends, corners sl bumped) in dj (nicked, rubbed, sl torn, creased, dusty, browned). *Ulysses.* $248/£155

LAWRENCE, ALEXANDER A. James Johnston, Georgia's First Printer. Savannah, 1956. 1st ed. (Spine sl discolored), else Good in dj (dknd). *King.* $35/£22

LAWRENCE, D. H. Assorted Articles. Secker, 1930. 1st UK ed. Fine in VG dj (few sm closed tears). *Williams.* $96/£60

LAWRENCE, D. H. Assorted Articles. London: Martin Secker, 1930. 1st ed. Red cl, gilt. NF (spine sl faded, extrems lt rubbed) in dj (lt chipped, soiled). *Heritage.* $125/£78

LAWRENCE, D. H. Birds, Beasts and Flowers. Martin Secker, 1923. 1st UK ed. VG (fr hinge sl wormed) in dj (sl chipped, dusty, faded). *Williams.* $112/£70

LAWRENCE, D. H. Birds, Beasts and Flowers. London: Cresset, 1930. 1st illus ed. One of 500 numbered. Folio. Teg, rest uncut. Orig 1/4 vellum, marbled bds. VG (sm mk fr joint). *Maggs.* $400/£250

LAWRENCE, D. H. The Captain's Doll. NY: Seltzer, 1923. 1st Amer ed. Gray cl. Fine. *Appelfeld.* $85/£53

LAWRENCE, D. H. The Collected Letters of D. H. Lawrence. Harry T. Moore (ed). NY: Viking, 1962. 1st ed. 2 vols. Fine in djs (2 lt blue lines), NF pub's slipcase. *Smith.* $75/£47

LAWRENCE, D. H. The Collected Poems of D. H. Lawrence. London: Martin Secker, 1928. 1st Eng ed. 2 vols. Buckram. VG set (edges, prelims spotted; feps browned; cvrs sl rubbed). *Ulysses.* $88/£55

LAWRENCE, D. H. England, My England. NY, 1922. 1st ed. Dj. *Swann*.* $201/£126

LAWRENCE, D. H. Etruscan Places. London: Martin Secker, 1932. 1st ed. Frontis, 19 plts. Blue cl. VG in dj (extrems sl worn). *Maggs.* $400/£250

LAWRENCE, D. H. Fantasia of the Unconscious. NY: Thomas Seltzer, 1922. 1st ed. Blue cl, gilt. Good (emb stamp; cvrs soiled, spine lettering faded). *Heritage.* $75/£47

LAWRENCE, D. H. Fantasia of the Unconscious. London: Martin Secker, 1923. 1st Eng ed. One of 1000 ptd. Fore-edge uncut. Maroon cl, ptd paper spine label. Sound (eps foxed) in dj (unevenly browned, esp spine, extrems sl chipped). *Maggs.* $400/£250

LAWRENCE, D. H. Fire and Other Poems. SF: Book Club of CA, 1940. One of 300. Paper spine label. (Offset from lg bkpl to fr pastedown), else NF. *Pacific*.* $196/£123

LAWRENCE, D. H. Glad Ghosts. Benn, 1926. 1st ed. Ltd to 500. Good in wrappers. *Whiteson.* $38/£24

LAWRENCE, D. H. Glad Ghosts. London: Benn, 1926. One of 500. NF (traces of tape on eps) in wrappers. *Lenz.* $200/£125

LAWRENCE, D. H. Kangaroo. London, (1923). 1st ed. Dj (spine lt faded). *Swann*. $149/£93

LAWRENCE, D. H. Kangaroo. NY: Thomas Seltzer, 1923. 1st Amer ed. Blue cl. VG (emb stamp; cvrs lt soiled, extrems lt rubbed). *Heritage.* $75/£47

LAWRENCE, D. H. Lady Chatterley's Lover. The Hague: Heinemann, (1956). White cl. Fine (fr pastedown yellowed from tape) in dj (sl chipped, worn). *Glenn.* $30/£19

LAWRENCE, D. H. Lady Chatterley's Lover. N.p.: Privately ptd, 1928. Ltd to 1500. Early pirate ed. (Spine crudely taped.) *King.* $35/£22

LAWRENCE, D. H. Lady Chatterley's Lover. Florence: Privately ptd, 1928. 1st ed. Ltd to 1000 signed. 8vo. Orig prospectus attached to pastedown. Mulberry-colored bds (fr hinge partly cracked, spine ends sl chipped), ptd in black, fr cvr w/phoenix design, white paper spine label. *Sotheby's*. $2,115/£1,322

LAWRENCE, D. H. Lady Chatterley's Lover. Florence: Privately ptd, 1928. 1st ed. Ltd to 1000 signed. 8vo. Mulberry-colored bds, white paper spine label, Lawrence Phoenix design on fr cvr. Cream dj. *Sotheby's*. $4,416/£2,760

LAWRENCE, D. H. Last Poems. Richard Aldington (ed). London: Heinemann, (1935). Teg, rest untrimmed. 1/4 black cl over dec bds. *Maggs.* $80/£50

LAWRENCE, D. H. Last Poems. Richard Aldington and Giuseppe Orioli (eds). Florence: G. Orioli, 1932. One of 700 (of 750). Fore/bottom edges untrimmed. Brn bds. (Spine label sl worn, spine worn, fore-edge foxed), o/w VG. *Maggs.* $320/£200

LAWRENCE, D. H. The Letters of D. H. Lawrence. Aldous Huxley (ed). London: Heinemann, (1932). One of 525. Parchment-cvrd bds, yapp edges. (Tears to parchment rear cvr), else VG. *Pacific*. $63/£39

LAWRENCE, D. H. Love Among the Haystacks. Girard, KS: Haldeman-Julius, (1941). (Sm chip to tip of last blank leaf), else NF in black stiff paper wrappers, paper title label fr cvr. *Black Sun.* $75/£47

LAWRENCE, D. H. Love Among the Haystacks. London: Nonesuch, 1930. 1st ed. One of 1600 numbered. Fore/lower edges untrimmed. Canvas-backed yellow buckram bds (sl dust-soiled), black leather label. *Maggs.* $104/£65

LAWRENCE, D. H. Love Among the Haystacks. London: Nonesuch, 1930. 1st ed. One of 1600 numbered. Linen-backed bds (lt soiled), spine label. *Swann*. $161/£101

LAWRENCE, D. H. Love Poems and Others. London, 1913. 1st ed. Teg. (Cvrs worn, dknd.) *King.* $200/£125

LAWRENCE, D. H. The Man Who Died. Martin Secker, 1931. 1st ed. Ltd to 2000. Teg, rest uncut. Orig grn buckram. (Faded), o/w Good. *Cox.* $32/£20

LAWRENCE, D. H. The Man Who Died. London: Martin Secker, 1931. 1st Eng ed. One of 2000. Teg, rest uncut. Orig grn buckram, gilt. VG (feps browned; spine faded). *Maggs.* $64/£40

LAWRENCE, D. H. The Man Who Died. London, 1931. One of 2000. (Ep browned; part of dj laid in.) *Typographeum.* $85/£53

LAWRENCE, D. H. Mornings in Mexico. London: Martin Secker, 1927. 1st Eng ed. Buckram. VG (bkpl, edges sl spotted; spine ends, corners sl bumped). *Ulysses.* $88/£55

LAWRENCE, D. H. Nettles. London: Faber & Faber, 1930. Clbound issue. NF (spine head sl bumped) in tissue dj (torn, chipped, defective). *Ulysses.* $104/£65

LAWRENCE, D. H. New Poems. London: Martin Secker, 1918. 1st ed. One of 500. 3/4 leather by Root & Son. VG. *Metropolitan*. $57/£36

LAWRENCE, D. H. One Lover Among Many. E. Haldeman-Julius. Girard, KS: Haldeman-Julius, n.d. NF in ptd wrappers. *Cahan.* $25/£16

LAWRENCE, D. H. Pansies. London, (1929). 1st ed. One of 250 numbered, signed. Vellum-backed dec bds. Dj (sl soiled, tears). *Swann*. $345/£216

LAWRENCE, D. H. Pansies. Brooklyn, NY: Privately ptd, 1929. One of 1000 signed, numbered by Frieda Lawrence. Fine in grn bds w/o dj as issued. *Warren.* $75/£47

LAWRENCE, D. H. Phoenix. The Posthumous Papers. Edward D. McDonald (ed). London: Heinemann, 1936. 1st Eng ed. Fine in brn cl, gilt. *Maggs.* $72/£45

LAWRENCE, D. H. The Plumed Serpent (Quetzalcoatl). London: Secker, (1926). 1st ed. Fine in brn cl. Beige dj (sl chipped, rear cvr soiled). *Bromer.* $475/£297

LAWRENCE, D. H. The Plumed Serpent. London: Martin Secker, 1926. 1st ed. Chocolate-brn cl, gilt. Poor dj. *Maggs.* $72/£45

LAWRENCE, D. H. Pornography and Obscenity. London, 1929. VG in orig wraps. *Edrich.* $19/£12

LAWRENCE, D. H. The Prussian Officer. London: Duckworth, (1914). 1st ed, 1st issue. Blue cl, gilt. (Spine lt faded), else NF. *Bromer.* $250/£156

LAWRENCE, D. H. Psychoanalysis and the Unconscious. NY: Thomas Seltzer, 1921. 1st Amer ed. (Spine foot chipped, head sl rubbed, extrems sl browned), else VG. *Pacific*. $92/£58

LAWRENCE, D. H. Rawdon's Roof. London, 1928. 1st ed. One of 500 numbered, signed. Dec bds. Dj repeating bd design. *Swann*. $345/£216

LAWRENCE, D. H. Sea and Sardinia. NY: Thomas Seltzer, 1921. 1st ed. 8 color plts, b/w map. Cream cl, grn bds, ptd paper spine label. VG (spine sl soiled, label lt chipped, lt stains to bds). *Heritage.* $125/£78

LAWRENCE, D. H. Sun. Privately ptd, 1929. One of 500 cl-backed, patterned-painted bds. VG- (tips, lower spine worn, loss of cl). *Warren.* $75/£47

LAWRENCE, D. H. Tortoises. NY: Thomas Seltzer, 1921. 1st ed. Fore/lower edges uncut. Pict bds. VG (text sl thumbed; edges sl worn). *Maggs.* $200/£125

LAWRENCE, D. H. Tortoises. Williamsburg: Chelonidae, 1983. One of 90 w/an extra suite of plts signed by Alan James Robinson (illus) and encl in a separate folder. 1/4 vellum. 1/4 vellum fldg box. *Swann*. $431/£269

LAWRENCE, D. H. Touch and Go. London: C.W. Daniel, 1920. 1st ed. Orange paper bds, blue lettering labels. VG (spine label sl faded). *Maggs.* $104/£65

LAWRENCE, D. H. The Virgin and the Gypsy. London: Martin Secker, (1930). 1st ed. Fine in VG dj (spine ends rubbed, spine faded, sl soiled). *Pacific*. $115/£72

LAWRENCE, D. H. (trans). The Story of Dr. Manente. Florence: G. Orioli, 1929. 1st ed. One of 1000 numbered. *Heritage.* $100/£63

LAWRENCE, GUY. Forty Years on the Yukon Telegraph. Vancouver, BC: Mitchell, (1965). VG (lacks dj). *Perier.* $25/£16

LAWRENCE, HENRY MONTGOMERY. Essays, Military and Political, Written in India. London, 1859. (Bkpl; shaken.) *Swann*. $201/£126

LAWRENCE, JOHN. The History and Delineation of the Horse...the Character of the Race-Horse, and the Business of the Turf.... London: Albion, 1809. 1st ed. Engr tp, dedication, frontis, 12 plts. Uncut. Contemp bds (shelfworn, soiled; tips, edges worn; foxing). *Oinonen*. $160/£100

LAWRENCE, JOSEPHINE. Man in the Moon Stories Told Over the Radio-Phone. NY: Cupples & Leon, (1922). 1st ed. 8vo. 121pp; 8 full-pg color plts by Johnny Gruelle. Blue cl, full color paste label, gilt. Very Nice (sl spotted; spine gilt sl faded). *Reisler.* $375/£234

LAWRENCE, RICHARD. Elgin Marbles, from the Parthenon at Athens. London: Thomas Davidson, 1818. 1st ed. Folio. 50 copper-engr plts. Period 3/4 morocco, marbled bds, gilt. (Heavily scuffed, few scratches, scrapes), else VG. *Pacific**. $633/£396

LAWRENCE, RUTH. Genealogical Histories of Ledyard, Cass, Livingston, Prince and Allied Families. NY, 1925. Sm folio. Extra-illus. Watered silk eps. Morocco, gilt. *Swann**. $69/£43

LAWRENCE, T. E. The Letters of T. E. Lawrence. David Garnett (ed). NY: Doubleday, Doran, 1939. 1st Amer ed. Fore/lower edges uncut. Brn cl. VG in dj (sl dust-stained, worn). *Maggs*. $48/£30

LAWRENCE, T. E. The Letters of T. E. Lawrence. David Garnett (ed). NY: Doubleday, Doran, 1939. 1st US ed. Frontis. Gilt blue cl. (Ep gutters dknd), o/w NF in VG dj (lt dust-spotted, price-clipped). *Reese*. $85/£53

LAWRENCE, T. E. Letters to E. T. Leeds. J. M. Wilson (ed). Whittington, 1988. One of 650 stated. 1/4 cl, ptd paper sides. Fine in slipcase. *Michael Taylor*. $232/£145

LAWRENCE, T. E. Men in Print. London: Golden Cockerel, 1940. One of 500. Sm folio. Teg, rest uncut. Orig morocco-backed bds. VG (bkpl; sm stain fr bd). *Maggs*. $480/£300

LAWRENCE, T. E. Minorities. J. M. Wilson (ed). London, 1971. 1st ed. VG in dj (sl frayed). *Typographeum*. $30/£19

LAWRENCE, T. E. The Mint. London: Cape, 1955. 1st trade ed. Blue cl. Fine in dj (sl soiled). *Maggs*. $32/£20

LAWRENCE, T. E. The Mint: A Day-Book of the R.A.F. Depot Between August and December 1922 with Later Notes by 352087 A/C. Ross. London: Jonathan Cape, (1955). 1st ed. One of 2000. 1/4 morocco, gilt. Fine in VG slipcase (soiled). *Pacific**. $150/£94

LAWRENCE, T. E. Oriental Assembly. A. W. Lawrence (ed). London: Williams & Norgate, 1939. 1st ed. Brn buckram. Fine in dj (spine sl dknd). *Maggs*. $136/£85

LAWRENCE, T. E. Revolt in the Desert. London: Cape, 1927. 1st British trade ed. Port. Polished tan buckram, gilt. (Bkpl; spine sl sunned), o/w NF. *Reese*. $85/£53

LAWRENCE, T. E. Revolt in the Desert. Jonathan Cape, 1927. 1st ed. One of 315 lg paper copies. 19 plts, fldg map tipped-in at end. Teg. Brn buckram bds, dk brn pigskin spine. Bkpl of Tom Hickinbotham. Dj. *Sotheby's**. $1,563/£977

LAWRENCE, T. E. Revolt in the Desert. NY: George H. Doran, 1927. 1st US (ltd) ed. One of 250. Super royal 8vo. xx,336pp; 18 plts (11 color), fldg map. Fine (bkpl of Maxwell Steinhardt; lacks box) in blue buckram, brn leather title label. Dj (tanned, defective, spine head tear). *Ulysses*. $1,840/£1,150

LAWRENCE, T. E. Revolt in the Desert. Jonathan Cape, 1927. 1st ed, lg paper issue. Ltd to 315 numbered, of which 300 were for sale. Royal 8vo. Fldg map, 19 plts (11 color), guards. Teg, rest uncut, largely unopened. Orig 1/4 dk brn pigskin, brn buckram sides, gilt. VG (neat internal repairs, bkpl) in dj. *Sotheran*. $2,320/£1,450

LAWRENCE, T. E. Secret Despatches from Arabia. Golden Cockerel, 1939. 1st ed. Ltd to 1000. 8vo. Frontis, orig pub's prospectus loosely inserted. Teg. White linen bds, black morocco spine by Sangorski & Sutcliffe. Orig box. *Sotheby's**. $1,104/£690

LAWRENCE, T. E. Secret Dispatches from Arabia. Golden Cockerel, (1939). 1st ed. One of 1000. Super royal 8vo. Frontisport, 173pp. Teg, rest uncut. Cream cl (sl spotted), 1/4 niger morocco. NF in card slipcase (sl damaged). *Ulysses*. $1,120/£700

LAWRENCE, T. E. Seven Pillars of Wisdom. London: Jonathan Cape, (1935). 1st trade ed, actual 3rd Eng ed. 47 plts, 4 fldg maps. Partly unopened. Brn cl, gilt. NF (sm brn stain fep corner, offsetting to dj flap extending through 1st 3 leaves; spine extrems sl rubbed, rear cvr discolored) in dj (lt soiled, few chips). *Heritage*. $350/£219

LAWRENCE, T. E. Seven Pillars of Wisdom. London: Jonathan Cape, (1935). 1st British public ed, ltd issue. One of 750 numbered. Teg. 1/4 pigskin, polished buckram, gilt. (Lt rubbed), else VG. *Reese*. $750/£469

LAWRENCE, T. E. Seven Pillars of Wisdom. GC: Doubleday, Doran, 1935. One of 750. Frontisport. 1/4 calf, gilt. (Spine dknd, crackling), else VG in slipcase (stained). *Pacific**. $161/£101

LAWRENCE, T. E. Seven Pillars of Wisdom. GC: Doubleday, Doran, 1935. 1st Amer trade ed. 48 plts, 4 maps. Gray buckram, gilt. (Tape residue on eps, bkpl), o/w NF in dj (lt soiled, edges repaired). *Heritage*. $250/£156

LAWRENCE, T. E. Seven Pillars of Wisdom. London: Jonathan Cape, 1935. 1st Eng ed. One of 750. 4to. Teg. Pigskin-backed cl. *Christie's**. $699/£437

LAWRENCE, T. E. Seven Pillars of Wisdom. Cape, 1935. 1st trade ed. One of 750. VG (ink inscrip; spine sl scuffed, sm tear). *Williams*. $1,040/£650

LAWRENCE, T. E. Seven Pillars of Wisdom. Cape, 1940. 4th Eng ed. 8 b/w plts, 4 maps. VG (feps browned; bottom edges sl rubbed, spine ends sl bumped) in dj (nicked, sl rubbed, mkd, dusty, spine, edges sl dknd). *Ulysses*. $136/£85

LAWRENCE, T. E. Seven Pillars of Wisdom. Jonathan Cape, September 1935. Trade ed, 5th imp. (Sl foxed.) Marbled eps; teg. Variant issue specially bound in blue crushed morocco, blue/white head, tail bands. *Sotheby's**. $442/£276

LAWRENCE, T. E. Shaw-Ede...Letters to H. S. Ede 1927-1935. London: Golden Cockerell, (1942). One of 500. W/'Notice to Purchasers' laid in. 1/4 black niger morocco, cream cl, by Sangorski & Sutcliffe. VG + (sl foxed). *House*. $500/£313

LAWRENCE, T. E. T. E. Lawrence to His Biographer Robert Graves [with] T. E. Lawrence to His Biographer Liddell Hart. London: Faber & Faber, 1938. 1st eds. One of 1000 numbered sets, signed by Robert Graves & Liddell Hart in respective vols. 2 vols. Demy 8vo. ix,187; ix,233pp; 3 plts. Red/gray buckram. Fine set in cellophane djs (1 defective w/ptd paper inner flaps), slipcase (sl mkd). *Ulysses*. $960/£600

LAWRENCE, T. E. T. E. Lawrence to His Biographer, Robert Graves [with] T. E. Lawrence to His Biographer, Liddell Hart. Faber & Faber, 1938. 1st ed. Ltd to 1000 numbered, signed by Graves and Hart. 2 vols. 8vo. Frontispieces. Teg, rest untrimmed. Buckram, 1 vol red, the other gray. VG set (1 spine sl faded) in slipcase. *Sotheran*. $797/£498

LAWRENCE, THOMAS. Engravings from the Choicest Works of.... London: Henry Graves, 1836. 1st ed. Lg folio. 53 steel-engr plts. Aeg. 3/4 red morocco, marbled bds, gilt. (Rubbed, soiled, dknd, joints cracked), else VG. *Pacific**. $173/£108

LAWRENCE, WILLIAM. Lectures on Physiology, Zoology, and the Natural History of Man, Delivered at the Royal College of Surgeons. For J. Callow, 1819. 1st ed. 8vo. 12 plts (7 fldg), 8pp ads at fr. (Plts spotted.) Uncut, unopened. Orig bds (spine sl worn). 1/4 calf book-box. *Sotheby's**. $589/£368

LAWRENCE, WILLIAM. Lectures on Physiology, Zoology, and the Natural History of Man. Salem, MA, 1828. 1st Amer ed. 494pp. Recent cl. *Fye*. $100/£63

LAWRIE, W. H. Border River Angling. Oliver & Boyd, 1939. 1st ed. 5 plts. (Few spots; spine sl faded.) *Hollett*. $40/£25

LAWRIE, W. H. English Trout Flies. S. Brunswick/NY: A.S. Barnes, (1969). 1st US ed. 5 color, 9 b/w plts. VG + in dj. *Bernard*. $25/£16

Laws of the State of Illinois, Passed by the Eighteenth General Assembly, at Its Second Session.... Springfield: Ptd by Lanphier & Walker, 1854. Sheep-backed bds (joints cracked; foxed). Sound. *Boswell*. $50/£31

Laws of the United States, in Relation to the Naval Establishment, and the Marine Corps. N.p., n.d. (1814). 1st ed. 15.7 cm. 144,ix,pp. Contemp calf-backed marbled bds. VG (contemp sig). *Lefkowicz.* $750/£469

Laws of Wiskonsan Territory, Passed by the Fourth Legislative Assembly, at Madison, the Seat of Government.... Madison, WI: W.W. Wyman, 1844. Contemp 3/4 sheep, bds (early sig to fr cvr, extrems rubbed, spine scuffed, ends chipped; 1st, last ll sl foxed). *Sadlon.* $200/£125

Laws, Memorials and Resolutions of the Territory of Montana, Passed...December 6, 1869.... Helena: Robert E. Fisk, Public Printer, 1870. 163pp + errata slip. Ptd grn wrappers. Cl clamshell case (faint stain). *Dawson.* $400/£250

LAWSON, A. The Modern Farrier. London: G. Virtue, 1841. 24th ed. Frontis, engr tp, iv,616pp; 7 engr plts. Mod full levant blind-ruled morocco over heavy bds, French grooves, onlaid spine label. (Soiling, browning, few edge repairs, old ms recipes on fep.) *Hollett.* $104/£65

LAWSON, ANDREW C. The California Earthquake of April 18, 1906. Washington: Carnegie Inst of Washington, 1908-1910. 2 vols in 3 + atlas. 11.75x9. 145 plts, 3 maps. Ptd gray wrappers. Atlas: 25 maps, 15 seismographs; cl. (Several ll w/piece cut from top margin; spines, corners sl worn; atlas cl soiled, spine deteriorating, chipped, fr hinge split), o/w VG. *Pacific*.* $1,380/£863

LAWSON, H. Children of the Bush. Methuen, 1902. 1st ed. (Eps foxed; cvrs sl dust-soiled), else VG. *Fine Books.* $65/£41

LAWSON, JOHN CUTHBERT. Modern Greek Folklore and Ancient Greek Religion. New Hyde Park, NY: University Books, 1964. 1st ed. 27 plts. VG in dj. *Worldwide.* $30/£19

LAWSON, LIZZIE and ROBERT ELLICE MACK. Christmas Roses. NY: Dutton, (1886). 1st US ed. Sm 4to. 10 NF chromolitho plts. Brn cl, glazed chromolitho bds. (Eps browned, brittle, 1 fep detached; plts lt foxed, some guards browned, chipped; spine, edges lt worn, cvrs rubbed, worn.) Text VG. *Baltimore*.* $80/£50

LAWSON, PETER AND SON. The Agriculturist's Manual. London, 1836. xv,430,(ii)pp (sl browned). Contemp cl-backed bds (worn, rubbed). *Edwards.* $136/£85

LAWSON, ROBERT. The Fabulous Flight. Boston: Little Brown, 1949. 1st ed. 152pp. VG (tape pull fep, lower corner wrinkled 1st 3pp) in Good- dj (edgeworn, sm corner chips, rear crayoned). *Price.* $65/£41

LAWSON, ROBERT. Mr. Revere and I. Boston: Little Brown, 1953. 1st ed. 8vo. 152pp. VG (name; spine ends, corners bumped, sm tear in cl). *Price.* $40/£25

LAWSON, ROBERT. Robbut, a Tale of Tails. NY: Viking, 1948. 1st ed. 8vo. 94pp. Illus eps. VG in VG dj. *Davidson.* $120/£75

LAWSON, ROBERT. They Were Strong and Good. NY: Viking, 1940. 1st ed. 4to. Tan cl. Good in dj (dusty, margins chipped). *Reisler.* $225/£141

LAWSON, ROBERT. The Tough Winter. NY: Viking, 1954. 1st ed. 6.25x9.5. 128pp. VG in dj. *Cattermole.* $60/£38

LAWTON, EBA ANDERSON (ed). History of the 'Soldier's Home.' NY: Putnam, 1914. 1st ed. 17 facs plts. Dec cl, gilt. VG. *Connolly.* $45/£28

LAWTON, EDWARD. Lectures on Science, Politics, Morals, and Society. St. Louis, (MO): James M. Crawford, 1862. 1st ed. 132,81pp. *M & S.* $125/£78

LAWTON, MARY. A Lifetime with Mark Twain. NY: Harcourt, Brace, (1925). 1st ed. Red cl, gilt. VG. BAL II:252. *Macdonnell.* $45/£28

LAY, WILLIAM and CYRUS M. HUSSEY. A Narrative of the Mutiny, on Board the Ship Globe, of Nantucket, in the Pacific Ocean, Jan. 1824. And the Journal of a Residence of Two Years on the Mulgrave Islands. New-London, 1828. 1st ed. Contemp sheep. *Felcone.* $1,500/£938

LAYARD, AUSTEN H. Discoveries Among the Ruins of Nineveh and Babylon. NY, 1853. 1st Amer ed. 586pp. (Sl foxed; rebound using orig cvrs), else Nice. *King.* $135/£84

LAYARD, AUSTEN H. Nineveh and Its Remains. NY: Putnam, 1850. 2 vols. viii,326,36; 373pp. (Ex-lib, lt foxed, spotted; sl rubbed, spine ends frayed, lib spine #), o/w VG. *Worldwide.* $175/£109

LAYARD, AUSTEN H. A Popular Account of Discoveries at Nineveh. John Murray, 1854. New ed. Eton presentation copy. Engr frontis, xxiii,360pp; 5 fldg plans. Full contemp calf prize binding, gilt, raised bands. VG (ink inscrip). *Sotheran.* $157/£98

LAYARD, GEORGE S. Suppressed Plates, Wood Engravings, &c. London: A&C Black, 1907. 1st ed. 'Presentation Copy,' so stamped in blind on tp. Teg. Dk grn cl, gilt. Text Good (sl aged; sl worn, frayed). *Baltimore*.* $30/£19

LAYER, A. P. The Simplicity of the Golf Swing. London: L. Upcott Gill, 1911. 1st ed. Red cl. (Stamp, sm sticker; spine head soiled, frayed), else VG-. *Pacific*.* $52/£33

LAYNE, J. GREGG. Books of the Los Angeles District. L.A.: Dawson's Book Shop, 1950. One of 200. Prospectus laid in. *Dawson.* $100/£63

LAZAREV, VIKTOR. Old Russian Murals and Mosaics from the XI to the XVI Century. London, 1966. 9 color plts. Good in dj. *Washton.* $85/£53

LAZAREV, VIKTOR. Old Russian Murals and Mosaics. London: Phaidon, (1966). Map. Fine in dj. *Turtle Island.* $80/£50

LE BRUN, CORNELIUS. Travels into Muscovy, Persia, and Part of the East-Indies. London: A. Bettesworth et al, 1737. 1st ed in English. 2 vols. Folio. Copper-engr frontisport, (6),246; (2),223,(11)pp; 3 dbl-pg copper-engr maps, 118 copper-engr plts. Period full calf (rebacked w/mod calf), raised spine bands, morocco labels. VG (staining to lower corners, margins, esp in vol 2, where it sometimes intrudes onto plts or text; orig cvrs worn). *Pacific*.* $1,955/£1,222

LE CAIN, ERROL. King Arthur's Sword. London: Faber & Faber, (1968). 1st ed, 1st bk. 4to. Color pict bds. (Spot on 1/2 title; sl shelfworn), o/w Very Nice in full color illus dj (lt marginal wear). *Reisler.* $200/£125

LE CARRE, JOHN. Call for the Dead. Gollancz, 1961. 1st UK ed. VG (pencil name erased) in 2nd imp dj (lacks sm spine piece, sm tear). *Williams.* $720/£450

LE CARRE, JOHN. The Little Drummer Girl. NY: Knopf, 1983. Special ed for Book of the Month Club. Ltd to 1048 signed. All edges stained maroon. Cream cl over blue cl. Fine in open-end reddish-brn cl slipcase. *Heritage.* $150/£94

LE CARRE, JOHN. A Perfect Spy. London, (1986). 1st ed. One of 250 numbered, signed. 1/4 cl. *Swann*.* $149/£93

LE CARRE, JOHN. The Russia House. London, 1989. 1st ed. Signed. VG in dj. *Typographeum.* $75/£47

LE CARRE, JOHN. The Spy Who Came in from the Cold. Gollancz, 1963. 1st UK ed. Variant brn pub's binding, which probably precedes usual blue binding, as the blue version was retained in all rpts of the 1st ed. NF in dj (spine head sl worn). *Williams.* $384/£240

LE CLERC, M. The Compleat Surgeon. London, 1727. 6th ed. xviii,96pp. Contemp Cambridge calf. (Eps, tp lt foxed, blank pg torn, bkpl; sl worn, new leather label), o/w VG. *Whitehart.* $560/£350

LE CONTE, JOSEPH. A Compend of Geology. NY/Cincinnati/Chicago: American Book Co, (1884). 1st ed. (8),399pp. Black pebbled cl, gilt. Fine (bkpl). *Pacific*.* $35/£22

LE CONTE, JOSEPH. A Journal of Ramblings Through the High Sierra of California by the University Excursion Party. SF: Sierra Club, (1960). Rpt of 1875 ed. Ltd to 2500. VF in pict dj. *Argonaut.* $125/£78

LE CONTE, JOSEPH. A Journal of Ramblings Through the High Sierras of California by the University Excursion Party. SF: Sierra Club, 1930. One of 1500 ptd. Gravure frontisport, 3 plts, facs of orig tp. 1/2 cl, paper spine label. Fine. *Pacific**. $98/£61

LE CORBEAU, ADRIEN. The Forest Giant. J. H. Ross (trans). GC: Doubleday, Doran, 1936. 8 full-pg b/w wood engrs by Agnes Parker. Dk grn cl, gilt (faded), deckle-edged. Good (bkpl, stamp; lt bumped, rubbed, edge stained) in Fair dj (torn, bottom edge stained red; spine torn, piece out). *Blue Mountain*. $35/£22

LE CORBUSIER. Concerning Town Planning. Clive Entwistle (trans). New Haven: Yale Univ, 1948. 1st US ed. Tan cl. Clean (top edge dusty, edges sl aged) in dj (edges sl chipped, worn; spine, edges dusty, worn). *Baltimore**. $20/£13

LE CORBUSIER. My Work. James Palmes (trans). Architectural Press, 1960. 1st Eng ed. 2 color plts. VG in dj (lower edge folded). *Hollett*. $96/£60

LE CORBUSIER. My Work. Architectural Press, 1960. 1st ed. (Inscrip), else NF in dj (sl creased). *Hadley*. $109/£68

LE COUTEUR, J. D. Ancient Glass in Winchester. Winchester, 1920. 40 plts hors texte. (Eps stained), o/w VG. *Washton*. $75/£47

LE COUTEUR, J. D. English Medieval Painted Glass. London, 1932. 2nd ed. 52 plts hors texte. (Sl foxed.) *Washton*. $45/£28

LE FLEMING, CHRISTOPHER. The Peter Rabbit Music Books. Book II: 6 Easy Duets. London: J&W Chester, 1935. 9.5x12. Beatrix Potter (illus). 31pp. VG (spine split; extrems worn). *My Bookhouse*. $125/£78

LE GALLIENNE, EVA. At 33. NY: Longmans, 1940. Rpt ed. Inscribed. VG in dj (sl chipped, worn). *Second Life*. $45/£28

LE GALLIENNE, RICHARD. George Meredith: Some Characteristics. Elkin Mathews, 1890. One of 750. Blank precedes 1/2-title; frontisport, 1 plt, guards; (xvi unpaginated),168,(lxxv),viipp, ptr's imprint leaf following last pg of text; last pg of added text w/ptr's imprint; 8pp integral ads at end. Uncut; white laid eps. Blackish grn buckram, gilt. (Margins lt browned; spine gilt sl dull), o/w Fine. *Temple*. $56/£35

LE GALLIENNE, RICHARD. Omar Repentant. London: Grant Richards, 1908. 1st Eng ed. Parchment cvrs (bowed, sl mkd, soiled, edges browned, sl spotted). VG in dj (chipped, torn, rubbed, dusty, sl soiled, browned, missing sm pieces, fr flap detached but present). *Ulysses*. $152/£95

LE GALLIENNE, RICHARD. The Silk-Hat Soldier and Other Poems. London/NY/Toronto: John Lane/Bell & Cockburn, 1915. 1st ed. Pict mauve wrappers. (Edges sl sunned), o/w Nice. *Reese*. $50/£31

LE GALLIENNE, RICHARD. Volumes in Folio. Bodley Head, 1889. 1st ed. One of 250 (of 300). Inscribed. (xii),90,(1)ads pp. Untrimmed. 1/4 white bds, ptd label, gray bd sides. (Lt foxed, feps browned, bkpls; cvrs dust-soiled, joints cracked, spine foot sl defective.) Later protective blue cl portfolio w/in 1/4 dk blue morocco/blue cl bk-form slipcase. *Blackwell's*. $264/£165

LE GUIN, URSULA. The Farthest Shore. Gollancz, 1973. 1st UK ed. (Spine sl faded), o/w Fine in Fine dj. *Martin*. $45/£28

LE GUIN, URSULA. Very Far Away from Anywhere Else. NY: Atheneum, 1976. 1st ed. 5.75x8.5. 89pp. Fine in dj. *Cattermole*. $45/£28

LE LOYER, PIERRE. A Treatise of Specters or Straunge Sights, Visions and Apparitions...Witches, Sorcerers, Enchanters, and Such Like. London, 1605. 1st ed in English. 4to. Errata leaf in skillful pen facs. 19th-cent calf. *Felcone*. $1,200/£750

LE MARQUAND, H. S. and F. H. W. TOZER. Endocrine Disorders in Childhood and Adolescence. London, 1954. 2nd ed. *Fye*. $35/£22

LE MAY, ALAN. The Unforgiven. NY: Harper, 1957. 1st ed. Fine in NF dj (lt rubbed, few sm spine bruises). *Unger*. $225/£141

LE MOYNE, JACQUES. The Work of Jacques Le Moyne de Morgues. A Huguenot Artist in France, Florida and England. London: British Museum Pub, (1977). 1st ptg. 2 vols. 144 plts (16 color). Gilt, grn cl w/matching slipcase. Fine set. *House*. $125/£78

LE NETREL, EDMOND. Voyage of the Heroes Around the World with Duhaut-Cilly in the Years 1826, 1827, 1828 and 1829. Blanche Collet Wagner (trans). L.A.: Glen Dawson, 1951. 1st ed in English. One of 200 ptd. Maroon cl. Fine (bkpl). *Argonaut*. $50/£31

LE QUEUX, WILLIAM. Devil's Dice. Chicago/NY, 1897. 1st ed. Pict red, black, white cl, gilt. VG (spine lt faded). *Mcclintock*. $85/£53

LE QUEUX, WILLIAM. The Invasion of 1910. London, 1906. 1st ed. Pict stamped red cl. (Contemp sig.) *Swann**. $126/£79

LE ROUX, HUGUES and JULES GARNIER. Acrobats and Mountebanks. A. P. Morton (trans). London: Chapman & Hall, 1890. 1st ed in English. Pict cl, gilt. (Spine ends chipped, upper fr joint cl torn, corners rubbed), else VG. *Pacific**. $92/£58

LE SAGE, ALAIN-RENE. The Adventures of Gil Blas de Santillane. Tobias Smollett (trans). London: Thomas McLean et al, 1819. 1st ed thus. 3 vols. Teg. 3/4 red morocco, marbled bds, raised bands, gilt; bound by Riviere. (Joints sl rubbed), else NF. *Pacific**. $150/£94

LE SAGE, ALAIN-RENE. The Adventures of Gil Blas of Santillane. LEC, 1938. Ltd to 1500 numbered, signed by John Austen (illus). 2 vols. Fine in slipcase. *Swann**. $34/£21

LE SAGE, ALAIN-RENE. Asmodeus; or The Devil on Two Sticks. London: Joseph Thomas, 1841. 3/4 grn morocco, gilt, raised bands, bound by Root & Son. (Lt foxed; spine sl dknd), else VG. *Pacific**. $75/£47

LE SIEG, THEO. The Many Mice of Mr. Brice. London: William Collins, 1974. Roy McKie (illus). 2 pop-ups, 11pp pull tabs. String, rubber band intact. Glazed pict bds. VG. *Bookfinders*. $30/£19

LEA, REBA FITZPATRICK. The Lea Family in Nelson County Virginia. (Brown-Morrison, 1945). Inscribed. VG-. *Book Broker*. $45/£28

LEA, TOM. Bullfight Manual for Spectators. Nourse: San Carlos, 1949. 1st Amer ed. Fine in pict overhanging wraps. *Connolly*. $40/£25

LEA, TOM. The Hands of Cantu. Boston: Little, Brown, (1964). 1st ed. Color frontis. Gold cl. Fine in VG+ dj (sl chipped). *Harrington*. $45/£28

LEA, TOM. The Hands of Cantu. Boston, 1964. 1st ed. Fine in dj (sl worn, sl chipped). *Baade*. $37/£23

LEA, TOM. The King Ranch. Boston/Toronto: Little, Brown, (1957). 1st trade ed, 2nd state, w/'for Alice' on p507. 2 vols. Fine in pub's slipcase (lt shelfworn). *Sadlon*. $75/£47

LEA, TOM. The King Ranch. Boston, (1957). 1st trade ed. 2 vols. VG in slipcase (sl worn, ends cracked). *Woolson*. $125/£78

LEA, TOM. The King Ranch. Boston: Little, Brown, (1957). 1st ed, 1st ptg w/p507 beginning 'Alice.' 2 vols. 2-tone buckram. Fine in slipcase (extrems worn). *Pacific**. $173/£108

LEA, TOM. The King Ranch. Kingsville, TX: The King Ranch, 1957. Ltd to 3000. 2 vols. Crash linen in facs of saddle blankets woven and used on the King Ranch, having a 'W' in the center, slipcase cvrd w/like material. VG. *Lien*. $1,200/£750

LEA, TOM. A Picture Gallery: Paintings and Drawings. Boston: Little, Brown, (1968). 1st ed. 2 vols. 35 plts (12 color) loose in portfolio. 2-tone brn cl (sl rubbed, handled). VG+. *Harrington*. $130/£81

LEA, TOM. Western Beef Cattle. Dallas, 1950. 1st ed. (Sl worn, creased) in wrappers. *Woolson*. $40/£25

LEA, TOM. Western Beef Cattle: A Series of Eleven Paintings by Tome Lea Depicting the Origin and Development of the Western Range Animal. (Austin): Encino, (1967). 1st ed. One of 850. Fine in slipcase (sl shelfworn). *Pacific**. $75/£47

LEACH, A. F. The Schools of Medieval England. London: Methuen, 1916. 2nd ed. Red cl (spine sl faded, sl bumped). *Maggs*. $32/£20

LEACH, A. J. Early Day Stories, the Overland Trail Animals and Birds That Lived Here.... Norfolk, NE: Privately ptd, 1916. 1st ed. Signed. Port. Recent cl, paper label. (Lt soiled; rebound), else Good. Howes L162. *Brown*. $100/£63

LEACH, BERNARD. A Potter's Portfolio. NY, 1951. 60 plts. Bd slipcase. *Swann**. $287/£179

LEACH, CHRISTOPHER. The Send-Off. London: C&W, 1973. 1st ed. Scarlet bds. Fine in laminated dj (sl scored, peeling over rear gutter). *Temple*. $26/£16

LEACH, FRANK A. Recollections of a Newspaperman. SF: Samuel Levinson, 1917. 1st ed. Inscribed. Reddish-brn cl, gilt. Fine. *Harrington*. $50/£31

LEACH, HENRY (ed). Great Golfers in the Making, by Thirty-Four Famous Players. Phila: George W. Jacobs, (c. 1907). 1st Amer ed. Frontisport. Pink cl, gilt. (Name, bkpl; soiled, insect damage, # written on spine, sm chip to spine haed), else VG-. *Pacific**. $138/£86

LEACH, JONATHAN. Rough Sketches of the Life of an Old Soldier: During a Service in the West Indies. London, 1831. 19th-cent 1/2 calf. *Swann**. $69/£43

LEACH, JOSEPH. The Typical Texan. Dallas: Southern Methodist Univ, 1952. VG in dj. *Lien*. $25/£16

LEACH, JULIAN G. Insect Transmission of Plant Diseases. NY, 1940. 1st ed. Brn cl, gilt. VG (ex-lib). *Larry Price*. $30/£19

LEACH, MacEDWARD (ed). The Book of Ballads. NY: LEC, 1967. One of 1500 ptd. Signed by Fritz Kredel (illus). 1/4 grn cl, red bds. Fine in glassine, slipcase. *Pacific**. $58/£36

LEACOCK, STEPHEN. Canada, the Foundations of Its Future. Montreal: (Seagram), 1941. Private, ltd ed. 6 color plts. Ribbon markers. Boxed. *Heinoldt*. $25/£16

LEACOCK, STEPHEN. The Hohenzollerns in America. NY/London/Toronto: John Lane/John Lane, Bodley Head/S.B. Gundy, 1919. 1st US ed. Grn cl stamped in dk grn. NF in pict dj (lt frayed, tanned). *Reese*. $185/£116

LEACOCK, STEPHEN. Merry Christmas. William Henry Rudge, 1917. Ltd to 200. Lt blue bds (corners rubbed, spine dknd, joints worn), gilt. VG internally. *Blue Mountain*. $50/£31

LEAF, MUNRO. Ferdinand the Bull. Racine: Whitman, 1938. VG in pict wraps (rear spine reinforced, corner replaced). *Davidson*. $85/£53

LEAF, MUNRO. Gordon the Goat. Phila: Lippincott, 1944. 1st ed. 6.25x8.25. 48pp. Good in dj. *Cattermole*. $40/£25

LEAF, MUNRO. Health Can Be Fun. Stokes, 1943. 1st ed. 8vo. 55pp. Red cl, stamped. VG (corners 1/8-inch bumped, lt water-trace top edge). *Price*. $26/£16

LEAF, MUNRO. Noodle. NY: Frederick A. Stokes, 1937. 1st ed. Ludwig Bemelmans (illus). Obl 4to. Illus Noodle bkmk laid into bk along w/order form for this and other Munro Leaf titles. Tan cl, black lettering, port. Good in color pict dj. *Reisler*. $250/£156

LEAF, MUNRO. Sam and the Superdroop. NY: Viking, 1948. 1st ed. 8vo. Grn cl (lower edge sl bumped). Color dj (worn, sl chipped). *Reisler*. $85/£53

LEAF, MUNRO. The Watchbirds. NY: Stokes, 1939. 4to. VG red cl. *American Booksellers*. $25/£16

LEAF, MUNRO. Wee Gillis. London: Hamish Hamilton, 1938. 1st ed. Royal 8vo. Robert Lawson (illus). (vii),8-70pp. Tartan-ptd pict bds. (Eps sl foxed), o/w Fine. *Sotheran*. $77/£48

LEAKE, R. E. Letters of a V.A.D. London: Andrew Melrose, (ca 1918). 1st ed. Blue cl (Ink inscrip Christmas 1920), o/w VG in dj (lt sunned, smudged). *Reese*. $50/£31

LEAKE, WILLIAM MARTIN. Journal of a Tour in Asia Minor. John Murray, 1824. 1st ed. 8vo. 1/2-title, fldg engr map, 3 plts (2 offset), 2pp ads at end, w/add'l sig 2A from another work mistakenly bound in at end. Contemp calf. (Bkpl, lib stamps, sl spotted; sl worn, rebacked, repaired.) *Sotheby's**. $643/£402

LEAKEY, JOHN. The West That Was, From Texas to Montana. Dallas: Southern Methodist Univ, (1958). 1st ed. VG in dj (sl worn). *Lien*. $35/£22

LEALE, JOHN. Recollections of a Tule Sailor by John Leale (1850-1932), Master Mariner.... SF: George Fields, 1939. 1st ed. 2 maps, 16 plts. White canvas. *Pacific**. $58/£36

LEAMING, JAMES. Contributions to the Study of Diseases of the Heart and Lungs. NY, 1884. 1st ed. 276pp. *Fye*. $50/£31

LEAR, EDWARD. Book of Nonsense and More Nonsense. London/NY: Frederick Warne, n.d. (ca 1920). Obl 8vo. Brick-colored pict cl. NF (lt edgeworn). *Glenn*. $150/£94

LEAR, EDWARD. A Book of Nonsense. London: Frederick Warne, (1870). 1st colored ed. 4to. Tp, 112 color ptd illus. (Tp lt soiled, repaired at margin, 1 leaf repaired; lt spotted.) Contemp 1/2 morocco (rather worn, fr cvr detached). *Christie's**. $120/£75

LEAR, EDWARD. Edward Lear's Journals. Herbert van Thal (ed). NY: Coward, 1952. 1st ed. 260pp. VG (2-inch bruise/tear inside rear hinge, top) in VG dj. *Price*. $30/£19

LEAR, EDWARD. The Journal of a Landscape Painter in Corsica. London: R.J. Bush, 1870. 1st ed. Map. Brn cl (extrems sl worn). Fine. *Appelfeld*. $400/£250

LEAR, EDWARD. Journals of a Landscape Painter in Albania. Richard Bentley, 1851. 1st ed. 8vo. 20 tinted litho plts, litho map. (Sl spotting, offsetting.) *Sotheby's**. $736/£460

LEAR, EDWARD. The Jumblies. NY: Young Scott Books, (1968). 1st ed. Signed by Edward Gorey (illus). Fine in dj. *Pacific**. $58/£36

LEAR, EDWARD. The Jumblies. London: Warne & Co, 1923. Rpt. 7.25x8.75. Leslie Brooke (illus). 78pp. Cl spine, bds w/pict onlay. VG. *Cattermole*. $25/£16

LEARY, TIMOTHY. Eagle Brief. SF: City Lights, 1970. 1st ed. Fine in wraps. *Beasley*. $30/£19

LEARY, TIMOTHY. High Priest. NY: World, (1968). 1st ed. Fine in dj (sl worn). *Lenz*. $65/£41

LEARY, TIMOTHY. High Priest. NY, 1968. 1st pb ed. NF (lt worn) in wraps. *Warren*. $25/£16

LEARY, TIMOTHY. The Politics of Ecstasy. MacGibbon & Kee, 1970. 1st UK ed. NF (pg edges sl tanned) in dj. *Sclanders*. $48/£30

LEARY, TIMOTHY. What Does WoMan Want? Dexter, OR: 88 Books, 1976. 1st ed. Ltd to 5000 numbered (this copy unnumbered, out-of-series). No errata slip. Fine in wraps. *Sclanders*. $26/£16

LEASK, HAROLD G. Irish Castles and Castelled Houses. Dundalk, 1944. 2nd ed. 1/2 cl, bds. Good. *Washton*. $35/£22

LEATHAM, A. E. Sport in Five Continents. London, 1912. 1st ed. Teg. (Ex-lib, bkpl, feps lt browned; spine sl rubbed, sl discolored.) *Edwards*. $77/£48

LEATHAM, DIANA. They Built on Rock. Glasgow: Celtic Art Soc, 1948. 4 maps. (Extrems sl rubbed.) *Hollett*. $40/£25

Leaves from the Medicine Tree. N.p.: Lethbridge Herald, 1960. 1st ed. VG (cvrs lt worn, soiled). *Labordo*. $100/£63

Leaves of Grass. (By Walt Whitman.) Phila: McKay, 1888. 1st ed thus, 'printed from the plates of Leaves of Grass, 1884, with the annex 'Sands at Seventy,' p384-404, bound in at end.' Ochre cl. (Discoloration, fr hinge started.) BAL 21433. *Swann**. $460/£288

LEAVITT, DAVID. The Lost Language of Cranes. Viking, 1987. 1st UK ed. Fine in dj. *Any Amount.* $38/£24

LEBEL, ROBERT. Marcel Duchamp. (NY, 1959.) (Cvrs scratched, extrems rubbed.) *Swann*.* $115/£72

LEBEL, ROBERT. Marcel Duchamp. (NY, 1959.) 1st Amer ed. Madrid 1984 exhibition poster laid in. Pict wrappers (edges sl rubbed). *Swann*.* $287/£179

LECHFORD, THOMAS. Note-Book Kept by Thomas Lechford...from June 27, 1638 to July 29, 1641. Cambridge: John Wilson & Son, 1885. xviii,460pp. (Pp dkng, extrems rubbed.) *Zubal*.* $26/£16

LECHFORD, THOMAS. Notebook Kept by Thomas Lechford...June 27, 1638, to July 29, 1641. Cambridge: John Wilson & Son, 1885. 1st pub ed. xxviii,460pp. (Sl shelfworn, spine ends rubbed), o/w VG. *Brown.* $20/£13

LECONTE, JOHN L. The Coleoptera of Kansas and Eastern New Mexico. Washington City: Smithsonian Inst, 1859. Sm folio. vi,58pp; map, 2 plts. Wraps in later hb binding. (Fr wrap chipped), else Good. *Dumont.* $150/£94

LECOUNT, J. M. Holy Hill: Its History. Hartford, WI: Le Count, 1891. 1st ed. 256pp. *Ginsberg.* $75/£47

LECTOR, OLIVER. Letters from the Dead to the Dead. London: Bernard Quaritch, 1905. 1st ed. Teg, uncut. (Feps lt spotted; partly faded.) *Hollett.* $40/£25

LEDUC, VIOLETTE. The Taxi. NY: FSG, (1972). 1st Amer ed. VF in VF dj. *Between The Covers.* $75/£47

LEE, ALBERT. Portraits in Pottery. Boston, (1931). 1st ed. Teg. Two-tone cl. (Pencil drawing on rep; cvrs sl worn.) *King.* $60/£38

LEE, ANDREW. (Pseud of Louis Auchincloss.) The Indifferent Children. NY: Prentice-Hall, (1947). 1st ed, 1st bk. NF in VG dj (sm edge nicks, sm chip spine crown). *Reese.* $225/£141

LEE, AUSTIN. Sheep's Clothing. London: Cape, 1955. 1st ed. Signed. Fine in dj (lt soiled). *Mordida.* $65/£41

LEE, BOB and DICK WILLIAMS. Last Grass Frontier, the South Dakota Stock Grower Heritage. Sturgis, SD: Black Hills, 1964. 1st ed. Fine. *Labordo.* $55/£34

LEE, BRIAN NORTH. Bookplate Designs of Claud Lovat Fraser. Nevada City: Ptd by Harold Berliner, (1985). Full burgundy cl, paper spine label. *Truepenny.* $75/£47

LEE, BRIAN NORTH. Early Printed Book Labels. (Ravelston): Private Libraries Assoc, 1976. 1st ed. One of 2200. Maroon cl, gilt. Fine in acetate. *Pacific*.* $46/£29

LEE, CLARENCE. The Instrumental Detection of Deception, the Lie Test. Springfield, 1953. 1st ed. 249pp. *Fye.* $100/£63

LEE, EDWIN. A Treatise on Nervous Disorders. London: John Churchill, 1838. 2nd ed. Handwritten note, 'Presented by the Author'. VG (bkpl; spine chip). *Beasley.* $125/£78

LEE, FREDERIC P. The Azalea Book. Princeton: Van Nostrand, c. 1965. 2nd ed. VG in dj. *Fair Meadow.* $45/£28

LEE, GUS. China Boy. (NY): Dutton, (1991). 1st ed, 1st bk. Fine in dj (price-clipped). *Bernard.* $35/£22

LEE, GUS. China Boy. NY: Dutton, 1991. 1st ed, 1st bk. NF in dj. *Smith.* $45/£28

LEE, GYPSY ROSE. The G-String Murders. NY, 1941. 1st ed. Dj (spine head lt rubbed, chip). *Swann*.* $138/£86

LEE, HARPER. To Kill a Mockingbird. Phila/NY: Lippincott, (1960). 1st ed, advance rev copy. 8vo. Orig ptd rev slip w/hand-stamped release date laid in. Text Clean in ptd off-white stiff wraps (sl rubbed, dusty, spine folds sl worn, spine lt rippled), later faint hand-lettering in ink at spine. *Baltimore*.* $1,100/£688

LEE, HARPER. To Kill a Mockingbird. London: Heinemann, 1960. UK proof. VG + in brn ptd wrappers (spot fr panel). *Smith.* $450/£281

LEE, HENRY. Memoirs of the War in the Southern Department of the United States. Phila, 1812. 1st ed. 2 vols. 8vo. Frontispieces. Early 1/2 calf (extrems rubbed). Howes L202. *Swann*.* $575/£359

LEE, HERBERT PATRICK. Policing the Top of the World. Toronto: McClelland & Stewart, 1928. 2 maps. (Lt soiled, blank fep out), else VG. *High Latitude.* $40/£25

LEE, HOLME. (Pseud of Harriet Parr.) Hawksview. Chapman & Hall, 1874. New ed. Pict bds (spine bumped, chipped, hinges, corners rubbed; rep torn w/loss of text, ads). Good. *Tiger.* $29/£18

LEE, HOLME. (Pseud of Harriet Parr.) Kathie Brande; A Fireside History of a Quiet Life. Smith, Elder, 1860. New ed. Good (ink inscrip, sl spotted; spine bumped, chipped, sunned). *Tiger.* $42/£26

LEE, IDA. Commodore Sir Jon Hayes. London, 1912. Frontisport, fldg map. (Rebacked, much of orig faded spine laid down; bds sl faded.) *Edwards.* $88/£55

LEE, JAMES. Golf in America: A Practical Manual. NY: Dodd, Mead, 1895. 1st ed. Silver/grn-lettered cl. (Emb stamp; spine sl soiled, sl dknd), else VG. *Pacific*.* $1,495/£934

LEE, JOHN DOYLE. A Mormon Chronicle. The Diaries of John D. Lee 1848-1876. Robert Glass Cleland and Juanita Brooks (eds). San Marino, CA: Henry Huntington Library, 1955. 1st ed. 2 vols. NF set in djs (vol 2 w/closed tear). *Labordo.* $200/£125

LEE, JOHN S. Sacred Cities. Cincinnati: Williamson & Cantwell, 1878. 266pp; 5 plts. (Sl rubbed, soiled, faded), o/w VG. *Worldwide.* $30/£19

LEE, LAURIE. The Bloom of Candles. John Lehmann, 1947. 1st ed. VG in ptd dj (sl soiled). *Cox.* $40/£25

LEE, LAURIE. The Firstborn. Hogarth, 1963. 1st UK ed. VG in dj (price-clipped). *Williams.* $40/£25

LEE, LAURIE. The Sun My Monument. Hogarth, 1944. 1st ed. VG. *Cox.* $32/£20

LEE, LAURIE. The Voyage of Magellan. John Lehmann, 1948. 1st Eng ed. VG (feps partly browned; spine ends, corners sl bumped) in dj (nicked, rubbed, dusty, sl mkd, spotted, browned). *Ulysses.* $152/£95

LEE, MABEL BARBEE. Cripple Creek Days. NY, 1958. Good in dj. *Dumont.* $35/£22

LEE, MRS. R. Taxidermy. Longman, Brown et al, 1843. 6th ed. iv,244,32pp. Orig blind-stamped cl (edges sl faded, spine head sl frayed), gilt. *Hollett.* $104/£65

LEE, NORMAN. Klondike Cattle Drive: The Journal of Norman Lee. Vancouver: Mitchell, 1964. 2nd ptg. Fine in dj. *Labordo.* $25/£16

LEE, REBECCA S. Mary Austin Holley. Austin: Univ of TX, 1962. Good in dj (chipped). *Dumont.* $35/£22

LEE, ROBERT E. Recollections and Letters of General Robert E. Lee. GC, 1924. 2nd ed. (Bkpl, backstrip discolored, sl worn.) *Woolman.* $15/£9

LEE, ROBERT. Fort Meade and the Black Hills. Lincoln: Univ of NE, 1991. VG in dj (worn). *Dumont.* $25/£16

LEE, TANITH. The Castle of Dark. London: Macmillan, 1978. 1st ed. 5.25x8. 180pp. Fine in dj. *Cattermole.* $30/£19

LEE, WAYNE C. Scotty Philip: the Man Who Saved the Buffalo. Caldwell: Caxton, 1975. 1st ed. Dj. *Dawson.* $30/£19

LEE, WILLIAM. Daniel Defoe: His Life, and Recently Discovered Writings.... London: John Camden Hotten, 1869. 1st ed. 3 vols. Lib buckram, cl labels. Fine. *Argosy.* $175/£109

LEE, WILLIAM. (ed). Personal and Historical Sketches...of and by Members of the Seventh Regiment; Michigan Volunteer Cavalry 1862-1865. Detroit, 1990. Rpt of (1901) ed. *King.* $25/£16

LEE, WILLIS T. et al. Part B: The Overland Route, with a Side Trip to Yellowstone Park. Washington: USGS, 1961. 29 fldg color maps. Good+ (spine chipped, cvrs worn). *Five Quail.* $30/£19

LEECH, JOHN. Pictures of Life and Character. London, n.d. c.(1843-1850). Vols 1-3. Aeg. Orig gilt/black illus cl. (Spotting, hinges cracked; spines faded, ends sl worn.) *Edwards.* $120/£75

LEECH, SAMUEL. Thirty Years from Home.... Boston: John M. Whittemore, 1847. 15th ed. Frontis, 305,(1 ad)pp; 3 plts incl in pagination. Orig cl (spine ends sl worn, 1 joint sl damaged; stamps). VG. *Lefkowicz.* $90/£56

LEEDS, CHARLES S. Old Home Week Letters. Carlisle, 1908-1909. (Sl shelfworn), else Good. *Brown.* $20/£13

LEEPER, D. R. The Argonauts of 'Forty-Nine. Columbus: Long's College Book Co, 1950. 1st ptg of Long's College Book Co rpt. Dec grn cl, gilt: facs of orig pub's binding. Fine in ptd dj. Howes L226. *House.* $45/£28

LEEPER, D. R. The Argonauts of Forty-Nine. Columbus, OH: Long's College Book Co, 1950. VG (tp lt foxed) in dj (sl worn). Howes L226. *Lien.* $25/£16

LEEPER, WESLEY THURMAN. Rebels Valiant. (Little Rock, AR: Pioneer, 1964.) 1st ed. Gray bds. Fine in dj. *Chapel Hill.* $80/£50

LEES, CARLTON B. Gardens, Plants, and Man. NJ: Prentice-Hall, 1970. 1st ed. (Sm rectangle cut from top rt corner 1/2 title), else VG in dj. *Fair Meadow.* $25/£16

LEES, G. ROBINSON. Life and Adventure Beyond Jordan. London: Charles H. Kelly, n.d. (1906). 1st ed. 304pp; 8 color plts. Teg. Grn pict cl, gilt. VG (sl rubbed). *Morrell.* $120/£75

LEES, J. CAMERON. The Abbey of Paisley, from Its Foundation till Its Dissolution. Paisley: Alex Gardner, 1878. Frontis, xx,340pp + clxxxv,errata,(i)pub's ads; fldg facs, 1 plt, 1 plan. Marbled eps; teg, rest uncut. Gilt-edged 1/2 morocco, cl bds, gilt. *Edwards.* $200/£125

LEES-MILNE, JAMES. The Age of Adam. Batsford, 1947. 1st Eng ed. Color frontis. VG (edges, eps sl spotted; spine ends sl bumped, tail sl faded) in dj (sl rubbed, nicked, creased, spine sl dknd). *Ulysses.* $88/£55

LEES-MILNE, JAMES. Baroque in Italy. London: Batsford, 1959. 1st Eng ed. VG (sm mk fep; spine ends, corners bumped, sl rubbed) in dj (nicked, rubbed, dusty, sl creased, mkd, sl dknd). *Ulysses.* $120/£75

LEES-MILNE, JAMES. Caves of Ice: Diaries 1946 and 1947. London: C&W/Hogarth, 1983. 1st ed. (Top edge sl dusty; sm bump lower edge rear cvr), else VG in dj. *Virgo.* $45/£28

LEES-MILNE, JAMES. Heretics in Love. London: C&W, 1973. 1st ed. VG in dj. *Virgo.* $40/£25

LEES-MILNE, JAMES. Midway on the Waves. London, 1985. 1st Eng ed. Fine in dj. *Clearwater.* $48/£30

LEES-MILNE, JAMES. Roman Mornings. London: Allan Wingate, 1956. 1st Eng ed. NF (bottom corners sl bumped) in dj (chipped, nicked, sl rubbed, spine faded, bottom rear panel sl defective). *Ulysses.* $72/£45

LEES-MILNE, JAMES. Saint Peter's. London, 1967. 1st Eng ed. Fine in dj (sl nicked). *Clearwater.* $48/£30

LEES-MILNE, JAMES. Tudor Renaissance. London: Batsford, 1951. 1st Eng ed. Very Nice in dj (sl nicked). *Clearwater.* $56/£35

LEET, AMBROSE. A Directory to the Market Towns, Villages, Gentlemen's Seats and Other Noted Places in Ireland.... Dublin, 1814. 2nd ed. Contemp sheep (worn, fr cvr loose). *Swann*.* $126/£79

LEFFINGWELL, WILLIAM B. Shooting on Upland, Marsh and Stream. Chicago: Rand McNally, 1890. 473pp. Beveled edges. VG (lt edgeworn); internally Fine. *Bowman.* $50/£31

LEFFINGWELL, WILLIAM B. Wild Fowl Shooting. Chicago: Rand McNally, 1889. 373pp + 17pp ads. Grn cl, gilt. (Lt edge-worn), else VG+. *Bowman.* $75/£47

LEFORS, JOE. Wyoming Peace Officer. Laramie, 1953. 1st ed. NF (dk area to fr cvr) in plain dj. *Baade.* $150/£94

LEFORS, JOE. Wyoming Peace Officer. Laramie, WY: Laramie Ptg, 1953. 1st ed. Fine in dj. *Labordo.* $225/£141

LEGAT, NICOLAS. Ballet Russe. Paul Dukes (trans). London: Methuen, (1939). 1st ed. 7 color, 24 monotone plts. Illus red cl. Good in dj (soiled, chipped). *Karmiole.* $125/£78

LEGEAR, CLARA EGLI. A List of Geographical Atlases in the Library of Congress, with Bibliographical Notes. Volumes 5-8. Washington: Library of Congress, 1958-1974. 1st eds. Blue buckram (sl rubbed, worn), gilt. Texts Good (erasures feps, 1 vol w/old ink sig cvrd by black felt-tip). *Baltimore*.* $300/£188

LEGER, EVELYN ST. The Tollhouse. London: Smith, Elder, 1915. 1st ed. Gilt plum cl. (Spine stamping sl dull), else NF in Good dj (lt worn, lg chip spine toe). *Reese.* $35/£22

LEGGE, THOMAS. Industrial Maladies. Oxford, 1934. *Fye.* $100/£63

LEHMANN, JOHN. Autobiography, The Whispering Gallery, I Am My Brother, The Ample Proposition. London, 1955, 1960, 1966. 1st ed. 3 vols. VG in dj. *Typographeum.* $65/£41

LEHMANN, JOHN. Thrown to the Woolf's. Weidenfeld & Nicolson, n.d. (c. 1978). 1st ed. NF in VG dj. *Virgo.* $32/£20

LEHMANN, KARL. Samothrace: Excavations Conducted by the Institute of Fine Arts, New York University.... NY: Pantheon, 1962-4. 1st ed. 2 vols. VG in dj (sl soiled). *Worldwide.* $125/£78

LEHMANN, NICHOLAS. Out of the Forties. (Austin): TX Monthly, (1983). 1st ed. Fine in illus dj (price-clipped). *Cahan.* $45/£28

LEHMANN, R. C. (ed). Charles Dickens as Editor. London: Smith, Elder, 1912. 1st ed. Sepiatone photogravure frontis port, 3 sepiatone photogravure ports, guards. Lower edges uncut. Red beaded linen grain cl. Nice. *Temple.* $144/£90

LEHMANN, ROSAMOND. A Note in Music. Chatto, 1930. 1st UK ed. (Cut edge sl foxed), o/w NF in VG dj. *Martin.* $38/£24

LEHMANN, ROSAMOND. A Note in Music. London: C&W, 1930. 1st Eng ed. VG (edges, eps browned; spine ends sl bumped) in dj (nicked, rubbed, dusty, sl mkd, chipped, browned). *Ulysses.* $88/£55

LEHMANN, V. W. Forgotten Legions: Sheep in the Rio Grande Plain of Texas. El Paso: Texas Western, Univ of TX, 1969. 1st ed after ltd ed of 300. Ltd to 2000. Frontis photo, map. Fine in Fine dj. *Connolly.* $50/£31

LEHMANN-HAUPT, HELLMUT. Art Under a Dictatorship. NY: OUP, 1954. 45 plts. VG in dj. *Turtle Island.* $55/£34

LEHMANN-HAUPT, HELLMUT. Fifty Books About Bookmaking. NY: Columbia Univ, (1933). Fine. *Oak Knoll.* $10/£6

LEHMANN-HAUPT, HELLMUT. The Life of the Book. London/NY: Abelard-Schuman, (1957). 1st ed. Presentation. Fine in dj. *Oak Knoll.* $65/£41

LEIBER, FRITZ. The Demons of the Upper Air. N.p.: (Roy A. Squires, 1969). 1st ed. One of 275 ptd. Signed. Fine in stiff brn wrappers, paper cvr label, VG ptd envelope. *Pacific*.* $63/£39

LEIBER, FRITZ. Gather, Darkness! NY: Pellegrini & Cudahy, 1950. 1st ed. VF in pict dj (corners sl rubbed). *Else Fine.* $100/£63

LEIBER, FRITZ. The Leiber Chronicles. Fifty Years of Fritz Leiber. Martin H. Greenberg (ed). Arlington Heights: Dark Harvest, 1990. One of 500 numbered, signed. (Sl worn.) Dj, slipcase. *Oinonen*.* $30/£19

LEIBER, FRITZ. Night's Black Agents. Sauk City, WI, 1947. 1st ed, 1st bk. Inscribed, signed. NF in VG dj (price-clipped, sl worn). *Mcclintock.* $125/£78

LEIBER, FRITZ. Night's Black Agents. Sauk City, 1947. 1st ed. (Lt offset to pastedowns.) Dj. *Swann**. $138/£86

LEIBER, FRITZ. Two Sought Adventure. NY: Gnome, (1957). 1st ed, 1st binding (bds). (Pp browned), else NF in Fine dj (sl worn, sm closed tear). *Other Worlds*. $150/£94

LEIBOVITZ, ANNIE. Photographs 1970-1990. NY: Harper Collins, 1991. 1st ed. Inscribed. Folio. Fine in dj. *Smith*. $150/£94

LEIBOVITZ, ANNIE. Photographs, Annie Leibovitz 1970-90. NY, (1991). Ltd to 326 numbered, signed. Folio. (Spine sl worn.) Slipcase (sl rubbed). *Swann**. $258/£161

Leicestershire Sketch Book. London: Eyre & Spottiswoode, 1935. 1st ed. Lg 4to. Lionel Edwards (illus). xv,100pp; 8 Fine color plts, 26 monochrome plts. Blue cl. Fine in pict dj (triangular loss at lower corner, sm chips at spine ends). *Sotheran*. $317/£198

LEICHHARDT, F. W. LUDWIG. The Letters of F. W. Ludwig Leichhardt. M. Aurousseau (ed). Cambridge: University Press, 1968. 1st ed. 3 vols. Frontis, 2 maps (1 fldg). VG in dj (sl torn). *Worldwide*. $150/£94

LEIDY, J. Contribution to the Extinct Vertebrate Fauna of the Western Territories. Washington: USDI, 1873. 1st ed. 359pp; 37 engr plts. 1/2 leather, gilt-dec cl (heavily rubbed). Internally NF. *Mikesh*. $150/£94

LEIFCHILD, J. R. Cornwall: Its Mines and Miners. Longman, Brown et al, 1855. 1st ed. xii,303pp. Mod cl, gilt. VG. *Hollett*. $280/£175

LEIGH, FRANCES BUTLER. Ten Years on a Georgia Plantation Since the War. London: R. Bentley, 1883. 1st ed. xi,347pp. (Spine faded.) Howes L242. *Maggs*. $240/£150

LEIGH, WILLIAM R. The Western Pony. NY: Harper, (1933, but 1935). Rpt of 1933 ed. 6 tipped-in color plts, guards. NF. *Pacific**. $104/£65

LEIGHLY, JOHN. California as an Island. SF: Book Club of CA, 1972. One of 450. 25 plts, all but 2 dbl-pg, 1 fldg. 1/2 gilt-lettered brn morocco, dec bds. (Lg oily stain rear cvr), else VG. Internally Fine. *Pacific**. $460/£288

LEIGHLY, JOHN. California as an Island. SF: Book Club of CA, 1972. One of 450 ptd. 13.75x8.75. 25 plts (24 dbl-pg, 1 fldg). 1/2 gilt-lettered brn morocco, dec bds. Fine. *Pacific**. $805/£503

LEIGHTON, ALEXANDER H. and DOROTHEA C. The Navaho Door: An Introduction to Navaho Life. Cambridge: Harvard Univ, 1945. 2nd ptg. (Ink name), else VG + in dj (spine faded). *Pacific**. $35/£22

LEIGHTON, CLARE. Country Matters. NY, 1937. 1st Amer ed. NF (rubbed) in dj (sm chip, tear, sl soiled). *Polyanthos*. $35/£22

LEIGHTON, CLARE. Four Hedges. A Gardener's Chronicle. NY, 1935. 1st Amer ed. Fine (spine, edge sunned). *Polyanthos*. $35/£22

LEIGHTON, CLARE. Four Hedges: A Gardener's Chronicle. London: Gollancz, 1935. 3rd ptg. Aeg. Contemp full dk brn morocco, raised bands, gilt. (Extrems sl worn.) Text Very Clean, cvrs VG. *Baltimore**. $80/£50

LEIGHTON, CLARE. Growing New Roots. SF: Book Club of CA, 1976. 1st ed. One of 500. Signed. Fine. *Turtle Island*. $150/£94

LEIGHTON, CLARE. Southern Harvest. London: Gollancz, 1943. 1st ed. (Spine faded), else Fine. *Quest*. $50/£31

LEIGHTON, CLARE. Wood-Engraving and Woodcuts. London: The Studio, 1932. 10 photos tipped in. Block-ptd paper over bds, cl spine. (Prelims sl foxed; spine ends frayed, bd margins dampstained.) *Turtle Island*. $100/£63

LEIGHTON, DOROTHEA and CLYDE KLUCKHOHN. Children of the People. Cambridge: Harvard Univ, 1947. 1st ed. VG in dj (worn). *Lien*. $25/£16

LEIGHTON, JOHN. The Life of Man, Symbolised by the Months of the Year, in a Series of Illustrations. Richard Pigot (ed). London: Longmans, Green, Reader & Dyer, 1866. 1st ed. Aeg, gilt inner dentelles. Blind-tooled emb dk grn morocco, raised bands. (Joints sl rubbed, spine sl dknd), else VG. *Pacific**. $69/£43

LEINBAUGH, HAROLD P. and JOHN D. CAMPBELL. The Men of Company K. NY, (1985). 1st ed. VG + in VG + dj. *Pratt*. $22/£14

LEIRIS, MICHEL and FERNAND MOURLOT. Joan Miro Lithographs. NY, (1972). Vol 1 (of 6). 11 lithos. Dj. *Swann**. $402/£251

LEISER, ERIC. The Dettes. A Catskill Legend. Fishkill: Willowkill, (1992). One of 200 numbered, signed by Leiser and the Dettes. W/3 actual flies tied by the Dettes inside a special display mount designed by Don Leyden built into the slipcase. 1/2 calf (lt worn). Slipcase. *Oinonen**. $400/£250

LEITCH, A. A Scottish Fly-Fisher. Paisley: Alexander Gardner, 1911. 1st ed. Grn cl, gilt. (Bkpl; hinges starting), else NF. *Pacific**. $46/£29

LEITCH, R. P. A Course of Painting in Neutral Tint. Cassell, (ca 1876). 3rd ed. 32pp, 2 ad ll; 24 color plts. (Sm stamp; cvrs faded.) *Bickersteth*. $48/£30

LEITCH, R. P. A Course of Water-Colour Painting. London: Cassell, n.d. (ca 1880). 37pp; 24 mtd chromolithos. *Ars Artis*. $56/£35

LEJARD, ANDRE (ed). French Tapestry. Paul Elek, 1946. 1st UK ed. Good + (bds rubbed). *Whittle*. $29/£18

LELAND, CHARLES G. Leatherwork: A Practical Manual.... Pitman, 1922. 3rd imp. Blind-dec cl, gilt. VG (sl worn). *Whittle*. $24/£15

LELAND, THOMAS. The History of Ireland from the Invasion of Henry II, with a Preliminary Discourse on the Antient State of That Kingdom. Dublin: R. Moncrieffe, 1773. 1st ed. 3 vols. 10x8. Full calf, raised bands, morocco spine labels. (Joints vol 3 starting; cvrs sl scraped), else VG. *Pacific**. $690/£431

LELONG, B. M. Culture of the Citrus in California. Sacramento, St. Board Hort, 1902. 27 plts. Black cl, gilt. (Cl repaired), else Good. *Larry Price*. $49/£31

LEM, STANISLAW. A Perfect Vacuum. NY, 1979. 1st ed. Advance rev copy w/slip laid in. Fine in Fine dj (short closed tear to spine head). *Warren*. $35/£22

LeMAITRE, JULES. On the Margins of Old Books. Clarence Stratton (trans). NY, 1929. 1st Amer ed. (Rear hinge sl cracked), o/w VF. *Bond*. $20/£13

LeMESURIER, A. B. Hare-Lips and Their Treatment. Balt: Williams & Wilkins, 1962. 1st ed. (Bkpl.) *Weber*. $30/£19

LEMON, KENNETH. The Covered Garden. Museum, 1962. VG in dj. *Hadley*. $24/£15

LEMPRIERE, JOHN. A Classical Dictionary. London: T. Cadell, 1839. Unpaginated. Teg. 19th-cent red morocco, pebbled cl. Good. *Karmiole*. $250/£156

LEMPRIERE, WILLIAM. A Tour from Gibraltar to Tangier, Sallee, Mogodore, Santa Cruz, Tarudant.... The Author, 1791. 1st ed. xl,464pp; lg fldg map (lt browned). Contemp tan 1/2 calf (neatly rebacked), flat spine, black leather label, gilt, marbled bds. VG (extrems lt rubbed, paper to marbled bds apparently marbled over ptd text). *Sotheran*. $400/£250

LEMPRIERE, WILLIAM. A Tour From Gibraltar to Tangier. London: The Author, 1791. 1st ed. xl,464pp. Contemp 1/2 calf, marbled bds, black label, gilt. VG (sl foxed, 2 leaves at end browned, soiled). *Morrell*. $296/£185

LENNON, JOHN. A Spaniard in the Works. NY, 1965. 1st ed. Pict bds. (Ink scribbles; extrems rubbed, dented), else VG. *King*. $35/£22

LENSKI, LOIS. Blue Ridge Billy. Phila: Lippincott, (1946). 1st ed. 8vo. 80 litho illus. Aqua cl (edges sl faded). Full color pict dj (margins sl torn). *Reisler.* $80/£50

LENSKI, LOIS. Blue Ridge Billy. Phila: Lippincott, 1946. 2nd ed. Good (ex-lib). *Price.* $20/£13

LENSKI, LOIS. Judy's Journey. Phila: Lippincott, 1947. 1st ed. 8vo. Orange cl. Good in illus dj (worn, sm hole in rear cvr). *Reisler.* $100/£63

LENSKI, LOIS. Mr. and Mrs. Noah. NY: Crowell, 1948. 1st ed. 5.75x5. 48pp. Good. *Cattermole.* $40/£25

LENSKI, LOIS. Ocean-Born Mary. NY: Frederick A. Stokes, 1939. 1st ed. 8vo. 4 full-pg b/w dwgs. Aqua cl, gilt. Good in color dj (corners sl worn). *Reisler.* $100/£63

LENSKI, LOIS. Peanuts for Billy Ben. Phila: Lippincott, 1952. 1st ed. 8vo. Grn cl. Good in color dj (sl worn). *Reisler.* $85/£53

LENSKI, LOIS. Shoo-Fly Girl. Phila: J.B. Lippincott, (1963). 1st ed. 8vo. Violet cl (edges lt faded). Pict dj (edges lt worn). *Reisler.* $85/£53

LENSKI, LOIS. Songs of Mr. Small. OUP, 1954. 1st ed. 40pp. VG (corners, spine ends sl worn). *Price.* $60/£38

LENSKI, LOIS. We Live in the South. Phila: Lippincott, 1952. 1st ed. 8vo. Maroon cl. Good in color dj (spine lt worn). *Reisler.* $85/£53

LENTZ, HAROLD B. The Pop-Up Mother Goose. NY: Blue Ribbon, 1934. 1st ed. 4 color pop-ups. Pict bds. VF. *Appelfeld.* $350/£219

LENYGON, FRANCIS. Furniture in England from 1660 to 1760. Batsford, 1914. 1st ed. Folio. Color frontis. Mod 1/2 scarlet levant morocco, gilt. VG. *Hollett.* $224/£140

LEODHAS, SORCHE NIC. Always Room for One More. NY: Holt, Rinehart & Winston, (1965). 1st ed. Obl 8vo. Nonny Hogrogian (illus). Maroon bds. Good in full color dj. *Reisler.* $135/£84

LEONARD, ARTHUR G. How We Made Rhodesia. London: Kegan Paul et al, 1896. 356pp. Pict cl (spine ends worn). *Adelson.* $110/£69

LEONARD, ELMORE. Bandits. NY, 1987. 1st ed. Signed. NF in NF dj. *Warren.* $30/£19

LEONARD, ELMORE. The Bounty Hunters. NY, 1954. 1st ed, 1st bk. Wrappers (joints worn, sl skewed). *Swann*.* $172/£108

LEONARD, ELMORE. Dutch Treat. NY: Arbor House, (1977). One of 350. Signed. Aqua cl, gilt. Fine in slipcase. *Pacific*.* $46/£29

LEONARD, ELMORE. Escape from Five Shadows. NY: Dell, 1957. 1st pb ed. Signed. (Date stamp), o/w VG + . *Warren.* $50/£31

LEONARD, ELMORE. Forty Lashes Less One. NY: Bantam, 1972. 1st ed. Fine (slant to sl worn spine) in wraps. *Beasley.* $40/£25

LEONARD, ELMORE. Get Shorty. NY, 1990. 1st Amer ed. Signed. Fine in Fine dj. *Polyanthos.* $40/£25

LEONARD, ELMORE. Glitz. NY: Mysterious Press, (1985). One of 500. Signed. Dk blue cl, silver. Fine. *Pacific*.* $40/£25

LEONARD, ELMORE. Hombre. NY: Ballantine 526k, 1961. 1st ed. Fine in wraps. *Beasley.* $100/£63

LEONARD, ELMORE. Killshot. NY, 1989. 1st ed. Signed. NF in NF dj. *Warren.* $30/£19

LEONARD, ELMORE. Notebooks. Northridge: Lord John Press, 1991. One of 300. Signed. Fine. *Pacific*.* $40/£25

LEONARD, ELMORE. Stick. NY: Arbor House, 1983. 1st ed. Signed. Fine in Fine dj (nick). *Unger.* $75/£47

LEONARD, ELMORE. Swag. NY: Delacorte, 1976. 1st ed. Fine in Fine dj (spine nick). *Unger.* $150/£94

LEONARD, JOHN. The Naked Martini. NY: Delacorte, (1964). 1st ed, 1st bk. Fine in Fine dj. *Lenz.* $65/£41

LEONARD, THOMAS H. From Indian Trail to Electric Rail. Atlantic Highlands Journal, 1923. 1st ed. Signed. (Lacks frontisport, 1st 4pp lt stained, tp w/few holes; rebound.) *Heinoldt.* $35/£22

LEONARD, ZENAS. Narrative of the Adventures of Zenas Leonard, Written by Himself. Chicago, 1934. Lakeside Classic. Fldg map. VG (ep, edges lt foxed). Howes L264. *Baade.* $30/£19

LEONOWENS, ANNA HARRIETTE. The English Governess at the Siamese Court. Boston: Fields, Osgood, 1870. 1st ed. (Fr hinge starting; spine sl soiled, ends rubbed), else VG. *Pacific*.* $258/£161

LEOPOLD, ALDO. Report on a Game Survey of the North Central States. Madison: American Game Assoc, 1931. 1st ed. (Fr hinge starting), else VG. *Pacific*.* $35/£22

LEOPOLD, ALDO. Round River: From the Journals of Aldo Leopold. NY: Oxford, 1953. 1st ed. Fine in NF dj (2 sm nicks). *Between The Covers.* $250/£156

LEOPOLD, ALDO. A Sand County Almanac. NY: Oxford, (1949). 1st ed. Fine in NF dj (sm chips). *Between The Covers.* $200/£125

LEOPOLD, RUDOLF. Egon Schiele: Paintings, Watercolours, Drawings. (NY, 1973.) 4to. 228 plts (84 color). Dj. *Swann*.* $977/£611

LEOVY, HENRY J. The Laws and General Ordinances of the City of New Orleans.... New Orleans, 1857. 1st ed. xxvi,439pp (foxed, browned). Mod cl. *Oinonen*.* $50/£31

LEPPER, GARY M. A Bibliographical Introduction to Seventy-Five Modern American Authors. Berkeley, 1976. VG in dj. *Dumont.* $30/£19

LEPSIUS, CARL RICHARD. Discoveries in Egypt, Ethiopia, and the Peninsula of Sinai, in the Years 1842-1845. London, 1852. Chromolitho frontis, fldg engr map, uncolored litho plt. Mod 1/2 brn oasis, gilt. *Swann*.* $258/£161

LEPSIUS, R. A Tour from Thebes to the Peninsula of Sinai. C. H. Cottrell (trans). London, 1846. 1st Eng ed. (iv),92pp. Orig blind-stamped cl (edgeworn, sm ink spot fr bd joint). *Maggs.* $360/£225

LERICHE, R. and A. POLICARD. The Normal and Pathological Physiology of Bone: Its Problems. St. Louis, 1928. 1st ed in English. *Fye.* $60/£38

LEROUX, GASTON. The Phantom of the Opera. Indianapolis: Bobbs-Merrill, (1911). 1st Amer ed. (Soiled, spine ends rubbed), else VG. *Pacific*.* $173/£108

LEROW, CAROLINE B. English as She Is Taught. London: T. Fisher Unwin, 1887. 'Second Edition.' Untrimmed. Tan bds w/lizard-skin pattern. (Lt aged, sl foxed; edges, joints sl worn, lt scuffed.) BAL 3420. *Baltimore*.* $40/£25

LESLIE, CHARLES ROBERT. Autobiographical Recollections. Tom Taylor (ed). London, 1860. 2 vols. Frontisport (sl offset), lxxxviii,255; 325pp (prelims sl spotted). Marbled eps, edges. Full calf, gilt, leather title labels. *Edwards.* $200/£125

LESLIE, CHARLES ROBERT. Life and Letters of John Constable. London: Chapman and Hall, 1896. New ed. 3 ports. Teg. (Loose, sl mkd, backstrip sl torn). *Petersfield.* $72/£45

LESLIE, LIONEL A. D. Wilderness Trails in Three Continents. London, 1931. 1st ed. (Sl damp-mkd.) *Petersfield.* $64/£40

LESLIE, NOEL. Three Plays...Waste, The War-Fly, For King and Country. Boston: Four Seas, 1920. 1st US ed. Bds, paper spine label. (Ink name eradicated from pastedown), o/w Nice. *Reese.* $25/£16

LESLIE, PETER. The Liberation of the Riviera. NY, (1980). 1st ed. Map. VG + in VG + dj. *Pratt.* $17/£11

LESLIE, SHANE. Jutland. A Fragment of Epic. London: Ernest Benn, 1930. 1st ed. Gilt lt blue cl. (Edges lt foxed), o/w Fine in dj. *Reese.* $75/£47

LESSING, DORIS. African Stories. Michael Joseph, 1964. 1st UK ed. Signed. Fine in VG dj (price-clipped). *Williams*. $120/£75

LESSING, DORIS. Briefing for a Descent into Hell. NY, 1971. 1st Amer ed. Fine in Fine dj. *Polyanthos*. $25/£16

LESSING, DORIS. Canopus in Argos: Archives. NY: Knopf, 1979-83. 1st ed. 5 vols. Fine in djs. *Hermitage*. $100/£63

LESSING, DORIS. The Habit of Loving. NY: Thomas Y. Crowell, (1957). 1st Amer ed. Blue cl. (Top edge sl foxed), o/w Fine in dj (spine top lt rubbed). *Heritage*. $75/£47

LESSING, DORIS. A Man and Two Women. MacGibbon & Kee, 1963. 1st UK ed. Fine in NF dj. *Williams*. $40/£25

LESSING, DORIS. The Real Thing. (NY): Harper Collins, (1992). 1st US ed. Fine in dj. *Second Life*. $25/£16

LESSING, DORIS. A Small Personal Voice. NY, 1974. 1st Amer ed. NF in NF dj. *Polyanthos*. $25/£16

LESSING, JULIUS. Ancient Oriental Carpet Patterns After Pictures and Originals of the Fifteenth and Sixteenth Centuries. London, 1879. Folio. 30 chromolitho plts. Contents loose in mod cl portfolio. (Some plt margins lt soiled, chipped around edges, w/hand-written institutional #s.) *Swann**. $1,150/£719

LESTER, C. EDWARDS and ANDREW FOSTER. The Life and Voyages of Americus Vespucius; with Illustrations Concerning the Navigator, and the Discovery of the New World. NY: Baker & Scribner, 1846. 1st ed. Frontis, later tipped-in hand-colored litho, fldg family tree. Orig brn cl, gilt. VG. *Pacific**. $86/£54

LESTER, C. EDWARDS. The Artists of America. NY, 1846. *Swann**. $57/£36

LESTER, GEORGE. In Sunny Isles. London: Charles H. Kelly, 1897. 1st ed. Frontisport, xvi,144pp; 15 plts. Edges gilt, beveled. Grn cl, gilt. VG (lt foxed). *Morrell*. $104/£65

LESTER, GEORGE. In Sunny Isles: Chapters Treating Chiefly of the Bahama Islands and Cuba. Charles H. Kelly, 1897. 1st ed. xv,144pp (sl foxed). Aeg. Pict grn cl, gilt. *Sotheran*. $192/£120

LESTER, JOHN ERASTUS. The Yo-Semite: Its History, Its Scenery, Its Development. Providence: Privately ptd for the author, 1873. 1st ed. (2),40pp. Partly unopened. Fine in orig gray ptd wrappers (lt soiled). *Pacific**. $173/£108

LESTER, W. W. and WILLIAM J. BRONWELL. A Digest of the Military and Naval Laws of the Confederate States...to the End of the First Congress.... Columbia, 1864. 329,(1)pp. Contemp cl-backed bds. (Broken, pp brittle.) *Oinonen**. $200/£125

LESTGER, KATHERINE M. and B. V. OERKE. An Illustrated History of Those Frills and Furbelows of Fashion.... Peoria: Manual Arts, (1940). 1st ed. Brn cl. Fine. *Appelfeld*. $85/£53

LESURE, THOMAS B. Adventures in Arizona. San Antonio: Naylor, 1956. 1st ed. (Lt damp mk lower edge of pp), o/w VG in Good+ dj. *Connolly*. $25/£16

LESURE, THOMAS B. Adventures in Arizona. San Antonio: Naylor, 1956. 1st ed. VG+ in dj. *Labordo*. $60/£38

LETCHWORTH, WILLIAM P. The Insane in Foreign Countries. NY/London: Putnam, 1889. 1st ed. xii,374pp; 21 b/w plts, tissue guards. Brn patterned eps; teg, untrimmed. Dk navy cl, beveled bds, gilt. VG (edges sl aged, sl rubbed; sm spots on spine). *Baltimore**. $90/£56

Letter from the Secretary of the Treasury, Transmitting Report Upon the Mineral Resources of the States and Territories West of the Rocky Mountains. Washington: GPO, 1867. 321pp. Fair (ex-lib). *Lien*. $50/£31

Letter on American History. (By William B. Reed.) Phila, 1847. 1st ed. Pamphlet. Inscribed. 39pp. Orig ptd wraps (backed w/old scotch tape). *M & S*. $125/£78

Letters from Albion to a Friend on the Continent, Written in the Years 1810, 1811, 1812 to 1813. London: Gale, Curtis, & Fenner, 1814. 1st ed. 2 vols. iv,260,(2); (4),281,(3)pp. Uncut. Drab bds (spines very chipped; labels soiled). *Karmiole*. $100/£63

Letters from an American Farmer...Conveying Some Idea of the Late and Present Interior Circumstances of the British Colonies in North America. (By Michel-Guillaume de Crevecoeur.) London, 1782. 1st ed. 8vo. 2 fldg engr maps. Mod 1/4 vellum. (Lt foxed, offsetting from maps, lib stamp on tp, lacks half-title.) Howes C883. *Swann**. $920/£575

Letters from Barbary, France, Spain, Portugal, &c. By an English Officer. (By Alexander Jardine.) T. Cadell, 1790. 2nd ed. 2 vols. Errata leaf at end of vol 2. Contemp calf (joints weak; inscrips, sl browned). *Sotheby's**. $275/£172

Letters on Chivalry and Romance. (By Richard Hurd.) London: A. Millar, W. Thurlbourn, J. Woodyer, 1762. 2nd ed. (4),120pp. Period tree calf. (Fr joint cracked through at top), else VG. *Pacific**. $46/£29

LETTS, JOHN M. A Pictorial View of California; Including a Description of the Panama and Nicaragua Routes.... NY: Henry Bill, 1853. 8vo. 224pp + (1) ad; 48 litho plts. Blind-stamped pict cl, gilt. VG (extrems lt worn). Howes L300. *House*. $700/£438

LETTS, NOAH HARRIS and THOMAS ALLEN BANNING. Pioneers. Paul M. Angle (ed). Chicago: R.R. Donnelley, 1972. Map. VG. *Lien*. $25/£16

LEVAILLANT, FRANCOIS. Travels into the Interior Parts of Africa. London: G.G. & J. Robinson, 1796. 2nd Eng ed. 2 vols. 8vo. xxiv,376; (ii),403,(l)pp; 12 engr plts (2 fldg). Recent 1/2 calf, gilt, red/grn labels, marbled bds. (Lt foxed.) *Morrell*. $640/£400

LEVENSON, SAM. In One Era and Out the Other. NY, (1973). Inscribed. Dj. *Argosy*. $25/£16

LEVER, CHARLES. Charles O'Malley. The Irish Dragoon. London: Service & Paton, 1897. 1st ed. 8vo. 2pp ads; 16 wood-engr illus by Arthur Rackham. (Sig.) Uncut. Maroon cl, gilt. *Christie's**. $203/£127

LEVER, TRESHAM. Lessudden House, Sir Walter Scott and the Scotts of Raeburn. Boydell, 1971. 1st ed. VG in dj (sl worn). *Hollett*. $32/£20

LEVERTOV, DENISE. The Blue Rim of Memory. NY: Huntington, 1979. 1st ptg. Ltd to 500 signed. Fine. *Polyanthos*. $15/£9

LEVERTOV, DENISE. A Door in the Hive. (NY, 1989.) 1st ed. VG in dj. *King*. $20/£13

LEVERTOV, DENISE. Life in the Forest. NY, (1978). 1st ed. One of 150 numbered, signed. Slipcase. *Swann**. $92/£58

LEVERTOV, DENISE. Life in the Forest. (NY, 1978.) 1st ed. Ltd to 150 numbered, signed. VG in slipcase. *King*. $100/£63

LEVERTOV, DENISE. Wanderer's Daysong. Copper Canyon, (1981). 1st ed. Ltd to 240 signed. (Spine sl faded, top corners sl bumped), else VG. *King*. $85/£53

LEVERTOV, DENISE. With Eyes at the Back of Our Heads. New Directions, (1959). 1st ed. Fine in dj (sl used). *Dermont*. $60/£38

LEVEY, MICHAEL. The Later Italian Pictures. Phaidon, 1964. 211 plts (6 tipped-in color). Dj (edges sl browned). *Edwards*. $58/£36

LEVI, PETER. The Light Garden of the Angel King. William Collins Sons, 1972. 1st ed. 18 full-pg b/w photos. VG (spine ends, corners bumped) in dj (nicked, rubbed, sl torn, creased, chipped, spine sl faded). *Ulysses*. $88/£55

LEVI, PETER. Shakespeare's Birthday. London, 1985. VG in wrappers. *Typographeum*. $10/£6

LEVI, PRIMO. The Wrench. William Weaver (trans). London, 1987. 1st Eng ed. Very Nice in dj (price-clipped). *Clearwater*. $40/£25

LEVI, WENDELL M. Making Pigeons Pay. NY: OJ, 1947. Blue cl (cvrs soiled), gilt. Good. *Larry Price*. $19/£12

LEVIN, GAIL. Synchromism and American Color Abstraction, 1910-1925. NY: George Braziller/Whitney Museum, (1978). Illus stiff wrappers. *Turtle Island*. $45/£28

LEVIN, IRA. The Boys from Brazil. NY: Random House, (1976). 1st ed. VG (edges lt faded) in dj (extrems lt worn). *Bromer.* $125/£78

LEVIN, IRA. Rosemary's Baby. NY: Random House, (1967). 1st ed. NF in dj (spine ends sl rubbed). *Pacific**. $52/£33

LEVIN, IRA. This Perfect Day. NY: Random House, 1970. 1st ed. (Ink prices), else Fine in NF dj. *Pettler.* $20/£13

LEVIN, MARTIN (ed). Five Boyhoods. GC: Doubleday, 1962. 1st ed. NF in dj (sl edgeworn, edge tear). *Dermont.* $100/£63

LEVIN, MEYER. Compulsion. NY: S&S, (1959). 1st ed. VF (pp sl dknd) in VF dj. *Between The Covers.* $200/£125

LEVIN, MEYER. Compulsion. NY: S&S, 1959. 1st ed. Fine in Fine dj. *Dermont.* $75/£47

LEVINE, BERNARD R. Knifemakers of Old San Francisco. (SF): Badger Books, (1978). 1st ed. Signed. Fine in NF dj (few sm tears). *Pacific**. $58/£36

LEVINE, BERNARD R. Knifemakers of Old San Francisco. (SF): Badger Books, (1978). 1st ed. Signed. Gray cl. VF in dj (sl chipped). *Argonaut.* $150/£94

LEVINE, PHILIP. Red Dust. (Santa Cruz: Kayak Press, 1971.) One of 1200 ptd. Fine in wrappers. *Pacific**. $75/£47

LEVINE, SAMUEL and W. PROCTOR HARVEY. Clinical Auscultation of the Heart. Phila, 1950. 1st ed. *Fye.* $40/£25

LEVINE, SAMUEL. Coronary Thrombosis: Its Various Clinical Features. Balt, 1931. 1st ed. *Fye.* $125/£78

LEVINGER, LEE J. A Jewish Chaplain in France. NY: Macmillan, 1922. 1st ed, later imp. Frontis. Gilt blue cl. (Sm blindstamp ep; fr cvr sl soiled), else VG. *Reese.* $18/£11

LEVINSON, ANDRE. The Designs of Leon Bakst for The Sleeping Princess, a Ballet in Five Acts after Perrault, Music by Tchaikovsky. London, 1923. 1st ed in English. Ltd to 1000 numbered, this copy out-of-series. Folio. Port, 56 mtd color repros. Orig 1/4 vellum. *Swann**. $690/£431

LEVIS, HOWARD C. A Descriptive Bibliography of the Most Important Books in the English Language Relating to the Art and History of Engraving and the Collecting of Prints. London, 1912-1913. One of 350 numbered. Supp and index bound in at end, w/separate title dated 1913. Uncut, unopened. Paper spine label. (Eps foxed, rear inner hinge broken; worn, soiled.) *Oinonen**. $225/£141

LEVISON, J. B. Memoirs for My Family. SF: John Henry Nash, 1933. 1st ed. One of 200. Inscribed. Linen-backed brn bds, paper spine label. (Label sl crinkled), o/w Fine. *Harrington.* $225/£141

LEVISON, J. J. and M. F. The Home Book of Trees and Shrubs. NY: Knopf, 1949. 2nd ed. VG. *Fair Meadow.* $25/£16

LEVITT, HELEN and JAMES AGEE. A Way of Seeing. NY, (1965). 1st ed. (Lt soiled.) Dj (rubbed). *Swann**. $287/£179

LEVY, EDWARD. The Beast Within. NY: Arbor House, (1981). 1st ed. Fine in dj. *Bernard.* $25/£16

LEVY, ESTHER. Jewish Cookery Book, on Principles of Economy, Adapted for Jewish Housekeepers. Phila, 1871. 1st ed, w/errata slip preceding tp. 8vo. Pub's blue cl. (Lt stained, soiled; rubbed, spotted.) *Swann**. $1,265/£791

LEVY, IRWIN ROBERT. Acrylic Inlays, Crowns and Bridges. Phila, 1950. 1st ed. Red cl. VG. *Doctor's Library.* $40/£25

LEVY, JULIEN. Arshile Gorky. NY, (1966). Mylar dj. *Swann**. $201/£126

LEVY, JULIEN. Surrealism. NY: Black Sun, 1936. 1st ed. One of 1500. Pict bds. VG (bds sl browned, extrems lt rubbed). *Heritage.* $300/£188

LEVY, JULIEN. Surrealism. NY: Black Sun, 1936. One of 1500. This copy inscribed, signed. (Fep partly excised.) Pict bds. Joseph Cornell dj (chips, edge tears, lt soiled, price clipped). *Swann**. $373/£233

LEVY, JULIEN. Surrealism. NY: Black Sun Press, 1936. One of 1500. Pict bds. Dj (sl browned). *Swann**. $460/£288

LEVY, ROBERT (ed). Diseases of the Coronary Arteries and Cardiac Pain. NY, 1936. 1st ed. (Ex-lib.) *Fye.* $75/£47

LEVY, YANK. Guerilla Warfare. London: Penguin Books, 1941. 1st ed. Fine in ptd wrappers. *Maggs.* $56/£35

LEVY-BRUHL, LUCIEN. Primitives and the Supernatural. NY: Dutton, 1935. 1st ed in English. VG (lib stamps; spine sl worn, faint #s). *Beasley.* $30/£19

LEVY-BRUHL, LUCIEN. The Soul of the Primitive. London: Allen & Unwin, 1928. 1st ed in English. VG (lib stamps, sticker traces; faint spine #). *Beasley.* $35/£22

LEWES, GEORGE HENRY. The History of Philosophy from Thales to Comte. London: Longmans, Green, 1880. 5th rev ed. 2 vols. (ii),(cxiv),410,(2); (ii),x,773,(3)pp. Emb brn cl. NF. *Gach.* $100/£63

LEWIN, LOUIS. The Incidental Effects of Drugs. A Pharmacological and Clinical Handbook. NY, 1882. 1st ed in English. 239pp. *Fye.* $400/£250

LEWIN, RONALD. Rommel as Military Commander. Princeton, 1968. VG. *Clark.* $30/£19

LEWIS, ALFRED HENRY. Wolfville Nights. NY: Frederick A. Stokes, 1902. 1st ed. VG. *Labordo.* $50/£31

LEWIS, ALUN. Ha! Ha! Among the Trumpets. London: George Allen & Unwin, 1945. 1st ed. Black cl. VG in dj (sl soiled). *Maggs.* $56/£35

LEWIS, ANGELO J. Conjurer Dick. London/NY: Frederick Warne, n.d. (1885). 1st ed. Frontis. Gilt-pict cl, beveled edges. (Skillfully rebacked w/orig spine cl laid down, edges soiled.) *Dramatis.* $200/£125

LEWIS, BERNARD (ed). Islam and the Arab World. NY: Knopf/American Heritage, 1976. 1st US ed. Folio. VG in dj (torn). *Worldwide.* $75/£47

LEWIS, BERNARD. Behind the Type: The Life Story of Frederic W. Goudy. Pittsburgh: Carnegie Inst of Technology, 1941. VG in 1/4 cl, paper over bds. *Michael Taylor.* $32/£20

LEWIS, C. DAY. See DAY-LEWIS, C.

LEWIS, C. S. Beyond Personality. London: Geoffrey Bles, 1944. 1st Eng ed. VG (inscrip, edges sl spotted) in dj (rubbed, nicked, spotted, dknd). *Ulysses.* $72/£45

LEWIS, C. S. Beyond Personality. The Christian Idea of God. London: Geoffrey Bles, Centenary Press, 1944. 1st ed. Cream cl. Fine in dj. *Maggs.* $80/£50

LEWIS, C. S. Beyond the Bright Blur. NY, 1963. Ltd ed. Fine in tissue dj. *Warren.* $30/£19

LEWIS, C. S. Christian Behaviour. London: Geoffrey Bles, 1943. 1st ed. Orange cl, gilt. VG in dj (sm spine nicks). *Macdonnell.* $200/£125

LEWIS, C. S. Christian Behaviour. A Further Series of Broadcast Talks. London: Geoffrey Bles, Centenary Press, 1943. 1st ed. Orange cl. *Maggs.* $48/£30

LEWIS, C. S. English Literature in the 16th Century Excluding Drama. Oxford, (1954). 1st UK ed. Fine (name) in VG dj (chipped). *Authors Of The West.* $75/£47

LEWIS, C. S. The Great Divorce. London: Geoffrey Bles, Centenary Press, 1945. 1st ed. Pale lemon cl. Dj (extrems sl chipped). *Maggs.* $48/£30

LEWIS, C. S. The Horse and His Boy. London: Geoffrey Bles, (1954). 1st ed. (Spine sunned), else VG in dj (spine sunned, head sl chipped, price-clipped). *Pacific**. $403/£252

LEWIS, C. S. The Horse and His Boy. Bles, 1954. 1st UK ed. VG in dj (rear panel sl browned, sl worn, spine faded). *Williams.* $400/£250

LEWIS, C. S. The Last Battle. A Story for Children. Bodley Head, 1956. 1st ed. Crown 8vo. Pauline Baynes (illus). 184pp. Pale blue bds. VG in dj (sm tear, 2 sm spots rear panel, backstrip panel sl sunned). *Blackwell's*. $720/£450

LEWIS, C. S. Letters to Malcolm, Chiefly on Prayer. Bles, 1964. 1st UK ed. NF in VG dj (sl browned, short closed tear to spine head). *Williams*. $38/£24

LEWIS, C. S. The Lion, the Witch, and the Wardrobe. London: Geoffrey Bles, 1950. 1st ed. 8vo. Pauline Baynes (illus). (iv),5-172pp. Teg. 1/2 dk grn calf over grn cl sides, gilt, brn leather lettering spine label. Fine. *Sotheran*. $520/£325

LEWIS, C. S. The Lion, the Witch, and the Wardrobe. Bles, 1950. 1st ed. Crown 8vo. Colorptd frontis by Pauline Baynes, 173pp. Lime-grn cl. Good (spine, rear cvr head faded) in dj (spine ends, fr panel head chipped). *Blackwell's*. $1,040/£650

LEWIS, C. S. The Magician's Nephew. NY: Macmillan, 1955. 1st Amer ed. Pauline Baynes (illus). 8vo. Grn cl. Good in color dj (tears, wear). *Reisler*. $200/£125

LEWIS, C. S. The Magician's Nephew. London: Bodley Head, 1955. 1st ed. 8vo. Grn cl. Good in color dj (spine sl worn). *Reisler*. $1,000/£625

LEWIS, C. S. Miserable Offenders. Cincinnati: Forward Movement Publications, n.d. 12pp. VG in wrappers (sl mkd, spotted, dusty). *Ulysses*. $120/£75

LEWIS, C. S. Prince Caspian. Bles, 1951. 1st UK ed. VG + (spine faded) in VG dj. *Williams*. $760/£475

LEWIS, C. S. Prince Caspian: The Return to Narnia. Geoffrey Bles, (1951). 1st UK ed. VG (name; cvr blotched, rubbed). *Authors Of The West*. $150/£94

LEWIS, C. S. Prince Caspian: The Return to Narnia. London: Geoffrey Bles, (1951). 1st ed. 'First published in 1951' on p(196). VG- in dj (spine ends, corners heavily chipped, tear along rear flap crease, spine sl leaned; price-clipped). *Pacific**. $230/£144

LEWIS, C. S. The Problem of Pain. London: Centenary Press, 1940. 1st Eng ed. VG (edges lt spotted) in dj (sl rubbed, frayed, nicked, spotted, spine sl dknd). *Ulysses*. $104/£65

LEWIS, C. S. Reflections on the Psalms. NY: HB&Co, (1958). 1st Amer ed. Fine in NF dj (sm tears, sl rubbed). *Between The Covers*. $65/£41

LEWIS, C. S. Reflections on the Psalms. Bles, 1958. 1st UK ed. NF in dj. *Williams*. $45/£28

LEWIS, C. S. Rehabilitations and Other Essays. OUP, 1939. 1st Eng ed. NF (spine foot sl bumped) in dj (nicked, sl rubbed, creased, internally repaired, sl dknd, sm stain fr panel). *Ulysses*. $200/£125

LEWIS, C. S. Transposition and Other Addresses. London: Geoffrey Bles, 1949. 1st ed. Fine in red wrappers w/corresponding wrapper. *Maggs*. $64/£40

LEWIS, C. S. Vivisection. London: National Anti-Vivisection Soc, n.d. (1947). 1st Eng ed. B/w frontis photo. VG (spine head, bottom corners sl creased) in blue wrappers ptd in white (mkd, sl rubbed, edges dknd). *Ulysses*. $200/£125

LEWIS, C. S. The Voyage of the Dawn Treader. NY: Macmillan, (1952). 1st Amer ed. Pauline Baynes (illus). 8vo. Gray-blue cl, dk-blue spine lettering. (Sl fading to gutter.) Dj (lt faded). *Reisler*. $350/£219

LEWIS, C. S. The Voyage of the Dawn Treader. London: Geoffrey Bles, (1952). 1st ed. 8vo. Pauline Baynes (illus). Pale blue cl (faded, dknd). Color pict dj (worn). *Reisler*. $450/£281

LEWIS, C. T. COURTNEY. George Baxter (Colour Printer): His Life and Work. London: Sampson Low, Marston, 1908. 1st ed. Frontis, 30 plts. Teg, uncut. (Spine head sl torn.) *Forest*. $77/£48

LEWIS, C. T. COURTNEY. The Picture Printer of the Nineteenth Century, George Baxter, 1804-1867. London: Sampson Low, Marston, 1911. 1st ed. Grn cl (hinges rubbed), gilt w/cameo plt fr cvr. *Oak Knoll*. $250/£156

LEWIS, CHARLES LEE. Books of the Sea: An Introduction to Nautical Literature. Annapolis: US Naval Inst, (1943). 1st ed. Dj (soiled, sl chipped). *Lefkowicz*. $35/£22

LEWIS, CHARLES LEE. Matthew Fontaine Maury. Annapolis: US Naval Inst, 1927. 1st ed. Blue cl. (Lt offsetting to reps, bkpl; top edge rear cvr sl faded), else NF in dj (soiled, lt chipped). *Chapel Hill*. $50/£31

LEWIS, D. B. WYNDHAM. The Shadow of Cervantes. London: Hollis & Carter, 1962. 1st ed. 9 plts. VG in dj (sl worn, price-clipped). *Hollett*. $40/£25

LEWIS, DIO. Our Digestion; or, My Jolly Friend's Secret. Phila, 1872. 1st ed. Fine engr frontis, 407pp. *Fye*. $95/£59

LEWIS, DIO. Talks About People's Stomachs. Boston, 1870. 1st ed. 320pp. *Fye*. $40/£25

LEWIS, ELEANOR. (ed). Darkroom. (NY): Lustrum, 1977. 1st ed. Ptd wrappers (lt worn), else VG. *Cahan*. $40/£25

LEWIS, ELISHA J. The American Sportsman: Containing Hints to Sportsmen.... Phila: J.B. Lippincott, 1879. Color litho frontis. (Old names; spine rubbed), else VG. *Pacific**. $46/£29

LEWIS, FLORENCE. China Painting. London: Cassell, 1883. 1st ed. 16 chromolithos. (Foxed throughout, not affecting plts; hinges loose), o/w VG. *Hermitage*. $150/£94

LEWIS, J. MOORMAN. Pioneer Doctor. 1951. 1st ed. NF in VG dj. *Doctor's Library*. $30/£19

LEWIS, JANET. The Earth-Bound, 1924-1944. Aurora, NY: Wells College, 1946. 1st ed. Ltd to 300 ptd. Prospectus laid in. (Spine lt faded), else Fine. *Bromer*. $200/£125

LEWIS, JOHN FREDERICK. Lewis's Sketches of Spain and Spanish Character, Made During His Tour in That Country in the Years 1833-4. F.G. Moon & John F. Lewis, (1836). Folio. Litho tp (sm strip lacking from fore-margin), 21 (of 25) tinted litho plts. Later 1/2 calf retaining orig cl sides. (Foxing, sl soil; rubbed.) *Sotheby's**. $1,656/£1,035

LEWIS, JOHN. The 20th Century Book. Its Illustration and Design. Herbert, 1984. 2nd ed. Folio. New in dj. *Cox*. $32/£20

LEWIS, JOHN. Collecting Printed Ephemera. (London): Studio Vista, (1976). 1st ed. Fine in dj. *Oak Knoll*. $55/£34

LEWIS, JOHN. A Handbook of Type and Illustration. Faber, 1956. 1st ed. VG in dj (sl frayed). *Cox*. $29/£18

LEWIS, JOHN. Printed Ephemera. Ipswich: W.S. Cowell, (1962). 1st ed. Fine in dj. *Oak Knoll*. $85/£53

LEWIS, JOHN. The Twentieth Century Book. London: Studio Vista, 1967. 1st ed. VG in dj. *Michael Taylor*. $45/£28

LEWIS, LLOYD. Captain Sam Grant. Little, 1950. 1st ed. Good in dj (chipped, worn). *Rybski*. $25/£16

LEWIS, M. D. S. Antique Paste Jewelry. Kate Foster (ed). Boston: Boston Book and Art, (1970). 8 color, 48 b/w plts. VG in dj. *Turtle Island*. $60/£38

LEWIS, M. G. The Castle Spectre. Dublin: Ptd by G. Folingsby, 1799. 1st Dublin ed. v,(i),78pp. Calf-backed bds. *Young*. $120/£75

LEWIS, M. G. The Life and Correspondence of M. G. Lewis, with Many Pieces in Prose and Verse. London: Henry Colburn, 1839. 1st ed. 2 vols. Frontisport. Orig bds (expertly rebacked in morocco), gilt. (Extrems sunned), else VG. *Pacific**. $207/£129

LEWIS, M. G. (trans). Abaellino, the Bravo of Venice. (By Heinrich Zschokke.) Woodstock, VT: Ptd by David Watson, 1830. 159pp. Orig ptd paper-cvrd bds, muslin spine. (Spine worn, bds, fr cvr fore-edge rubbed), o/w VG. *Brown*. $75/£47

LEWIS, MERIWETHER and WILLIAM CLARK. The Journal of Lewis and Clark. Bernard De Voto (ed). Boston: Houghton, Mifflin, (1953). Fine in dj (sl shelfworn). *Pacific**. $46/£29

LEWIS, MERIWETHER and WILLIAM CLARK. The Journals of the Expedition Under the Command of Capts. Lewis and Clark to the Sources of the Missouri.... Nicholas Biddle (ed). NY: Heritage, (1962). 2 vols. 16 color plts, lg fldg map. Cl-backed dec bds. Fine in NF slipcases. *Harrington*. $85/£53

LEWIS, MERIWETHER and WILLIAM CLARK. The Journals of the Expedition Under the Command of Capts. Lewis and Clark.... NY: LEC, 1962. One of 1500. Dec cl, morocco spine labels. Fine in glassine, slipcase. *Pacific**. $184/£115

LEWIS, MERIWETHER and WILLIAM CLARK. Journals of the Expedition under the Command of Capts. Meriwether Lewis and William Clark. LEC, 1962. Ltd to 1500 numbered. 2 vols. Fine in slipcase. *Swann**. $126/£79

LEWIS, MERIWETHER and WILLIAM CLARK. Original Journals of the Lewis and Clark Expedition, 1804-1806. Reuben Gold Thwaites (ed). NY: Dodd, Mead, 1904-1905. 1st ltd ed. One of 200 numbered sets on Van Gelder. 15 vols. Sm folio. Separate atlas vol w/56 maps and plts on 62 sheets. Untrimmed. Orig gilt-stamped grn buckram. (Lib spine labels removed, perf stamps, ink stamps last pg each vol, bkpls; sl edgeworn, some spine ends sl pulled.) Texts Very Clean. Bkpls of James Hill. Howes L320. *Baltimore**. $2,000/£1,250

LEWIS, MERIWETHER and WILLIAM CLARK. Original Journals of the Lewis and Clark Expedition, 1804-1806. Reuben Gold Thwaites (ed). NY: Antiquarian Press, 1959. 2nd ed. One of 750 sets. 7 text vols + atlas of 54 maps. 9 1/8x6 1/4 inches. Buckram (spines lt sunned). *Dawson*. $500/£313

LEWIS, MERIWETHER and WILLIAM CLARK. Travels to the Source of the Missouri River and Across the American Continent to the Pacific Ocean. London: Longman, Hurst, Rees et al, 1814. 1st Eng ed. xxiv,663pp + 1pg ads; lg fldg map, 3 single-pg maps, 2 sm-format pub's cats. Uncut. Orig gray bds (expertly rebacked), orig spine label. *Dawson*. $6,000/£3,750

LEWIS, MICHAEL. Armada Guns. George Allen & Unwin, (1961). 1st ed. Good in dj. *Rybski*. $85/£53

LEWIS, NORMAN. Naples '44. Collins, 1978. 1st UK ed. NF in VG dj (rear flap sl creased). *Williams*. $32/£20

LEWIS, OSCAR and CARROL D. HALL. Bonanza Inn. NY: Knopf, 1939. 1st ed. Signed by both. Frontis, 15 plts. Mauve cl, gilt. VG in Good dj (chipped). *Connolly*. $50/£31

LEWIS, OSCAR. The First 75 Years. SF: Book Club of CA, 1987. 1st ed. One of 1200 ptd. Terra cotta bds, teal cl backstrip. Fine. *Harrington*. $65/£41

LEWIS, OSCAR. George Davidson, Pioneer, West Coast Scientist. Berkeley: Univ of CA, 1954. 1st ed. Fine in Fine dj. *Book Market*. $20/£13

LEWIS, OSCAR. Lafcadio Hearn and His Biographers. SF, 1930. 1st ed. One of 350. Inscribed by Edwin Grabhorn. Port. 1/4 cl. Japanese-style fldg slipcase w/silk and bone fasteners. *Swann**. $345/£216

LEWIS, OSCAR. Lola Montez: The Mid-Victorian Bad Girl in California. SF: Colt, (1938). Ltd ed. One of 750. Signed. Inscribed by Jane Grabhorn. Cl-backed red bds, paper spine label. Fine. *Harrington*. $80/£50

LEWIS, OSCAR. Second Reading: Selections from the Quarterly News-Letter, 1933-1963. Plantin Press, 1965. One of 425. *Dawson*. $45/£28

LEWIS, OSCAR. Silver Kings. NY: Knopf, 1947. 1st ed, 2nd ptg. 17 plts. VG in Good dj. *Connolly*. $25/£16

LEWIS, OSCAR. Silver Kings. NY: Knopf, 1947. 1st ed. Signed. VG in dj (sl worn). *Lien*. $35/£22

LEWIS, ROY HARLEY. A Cracking of Spines. London: Hale, 1980. 1st ed. Fine in dj (head lt rubbed). *Murder*. $75/£47

LEWIS, ROY HARLEY. Fine Bookbinding in the Twentieth Century. David & Charles, 1984. 1st ed. 33 color, 82 monochrome plts. VG in dj. *Cox*. $32/£20

LEWIS, ROY HARLEY. Where Agents Fear to Tread. London: Hale, 1984. 1st ed. Fine in dj. *Murder*. $65/£41

LEWIS, SAMUEL. A Topographical Dictionary of Ireland.... London, 1849. 2nd ed. 2 vols + Atlas (together 3 vols). (Needs rebinding.) *Swann**. $258/£161

LEWIS, SINCLAIR. Babbitt. NY: Harcourt, Brace, (1922). 1st ed, 1st state w/'Purdy' at 49.4. Blue cl. NF. *Macdonnell*. $125/£78

LEWIS, SINCLAIR. Babbitt. NY: Harcourt, Brace, (1922). 1st ed, 1st issue. Signed. (Lacks 1st blank.) Dj (several tape mends, 1-inch closed tear rear joint). *Swann**. $460/£288

LEWIS, SINCLAIR. Cass Timberlaine. Cape, 1946. 1st UK ed. Fine in VG dj. *Williams*. $72/£45

LEWIS, SINCLAIR. Dodsworth. NY, 1929. 1st Amer ed. NF (sl rubbed, spine sl sunned). *Polyanthos*. $30/£19

LEWIS, SINCLAIR. Dodsworth. London, 1929. 1st Eng ed. Secondary binding: orange cl lettered in black (1 corner sl bumped). Dj (sl mkd, rubbed, price-clipped). *Clearwater*. $72/£45

LEWIS, SINCLAIR. Elmer Gantry. NY, (1927). 1st ed, 1st issue. (Name.) Dj (price-clipped, chipped, sl soil). *Swann**. $230/£144

LEWIS, SINCLAIR. The God-Seeker. NY, 1949. 1st Amer ed. Fine (sl rubbed) in dj (rubbed, few sm tears). *Polyanthos*. $25/£16

LEWIS, SINCLAIR. Keep Out of the Kitchen. (NY), 1929. 1st ed. Fine. *Pharos*. $400/£250

LEWIS, SINCLAIR. Main Street. NY, 1920. 1st Amer ed. NF (sl rubbed). *Polyanthos*. $60/£38

LEWIS, SINCLAIR. Main Street. NY, 1920. 1st ed. (Inner fr hinge cracked; edges, eps sl spotted; cvrs rubbed), else Good. *King*. $95/£59

LEWIS, SINCLAIR. Main Street. NY: LEC, 1937. One of 1500 signed by Grant Wood (illus). Fine in slipcase (sl defective). *Pharos*. $400/£250

LEWIS, SINCLAIR. Main Street. LEC, 1937. Ltd to 1500 numbered, signed by Grant Wood (illus). Fine in slipcase. *Swann**. $690/£431

LEWIS, SINCLAIR. The Man Who Knew Coolidge. NY: Harcourt, Brace, (1928). 1st ed. Blue cl. (Few mks to rear cvr), else Good. *Macdonnell*. $45/£28

LEWIS, SINCLAIR. The Man Who Knew Coolidge. London: Cape, 1928. 1st Eng ed. Fine (spine ends sl bumped) in dj (sl creased, nicks). *Ulysses*. $104/£65

LEWIS, SINCLAIR. Selected Short Stories of Sinclair Lewis. NY: Doubleday Doran, 1935. 1st ed. Fine in NF dj (tears at upper spine folds). *Beasley*. $75/£47

LEWIS, T. PERCY. The Trade's Cake Book. Maclaren & Sons, n.d. (c.1914). 1st ed. 40 plts. (Plt 8 repeated, 10 omitted), o/w VG in dec cl, gilt. *Cox*. $56/£35

LEWIS, THOMAS A. The Guns of Cedar Creek. NY, (1988). 1st ed. Fine in Fine dj. *Pratt*. $27/£17

LEWIS, THOMAS. Clinical Disorders of the Heartbeat. NY, 1916. 3rd ed. *Fye*. $75/£47

LEWIS, THOMAS. Clinical Electrocardiography. NY, 1919. 2nd ed. *Fye*. $100/£63

LEWIS, THOMAS. Diseases of the Heart. NY, 1933. 1st ed. *Fye*. $50/£31

LEWIS, THOMAS. The Soldier's Heart and the Effort Syndrome. London, 1940. 2nd ed. (Backstrip spotted.) *Fye*. $100/£63

LEWIS, THOMAS. Vascular Disorders of the Limbs. London, 1936. 1st ed. *Fye*. $75/£47

LEWIS, WILLIAM. Chess for Beginners; in a Series of Progressive Lessons.... Chapman & Hall, 1846. 3rd ed. Colorptd frontis, vi,(ii),155pp; 23 plts. Yellow chalked eps. Orig morocco-grain red cl, gilt. Good (bkseller's ticket; joint ends w/sm unobtrusive splits). *Blackwell's.* $120/£75

LEWIS, WYNDHAM. America, I Presume. (NY): Howell, Soskin, (1940). 1st ed. (Spine faded.) *Mott.* $50/£31

LEWIS, WYNDHAM. Blasting and Bombardiering. London: Eyre & Spottiswoode, 1937. 1st ed, 2nd binding. One of 500 thus. Frontisport. Flexible orange cl. (Crease in rep, edges lt foxed), o/w NF in pict white dj (lt soiled, dknd, smudges, sign of price sticker on spine). *Reese.* $150/£94

LEWIS, WYNDHAM. The Childermass, Section I. London: C&W, 1928. 1st ed. (Soiled; spine dknd), else VG in dj (spine dknd, ends, extrems rubbed). *Pacific*.* $40/£25

LEWIS, WYNDHAM. Count Your Dead: They Are Alive! London: Lovat Dickson Ltd, (1937). 1st ed. Top edges blue. Yellow cl. Dj (spine sl browned, closed tear along fr joint and across spine, corners sl worn). *Maggs.* $160/£100

LEWIS, WYNDHAM. Filibusters in Barbary. London: Grayson & Grayson, 1932. 1st ed. Dec yellowish tan cl (sl dusty, corner bumped). *Maggs.* $72/£45

LEWIS, WYNDHAM. Left Wings over Europe: or, How to Make a War About Nothing. London: Jonathan Cape, (1936). 1st ed, 1st ptg w/misprint 'QUEAN' on p2. Red cl (rubbed). Julian Symons' copy, w/sig dated Aug 1940. *Maggs.* $64/£40

LEWIS, WYNDHAM. Paleface. Chatto, 1929. 1st UK ed. VG (spine sl browned). *Williams.* $96/£60

LEWIS, WYNDHAM. Tarr. London: Methuen, 1951. 2nd rev ed. VG in gray cl. Dj (head sl chipped). *Maggs.* $48/£30

LEWIS, C. DAY. See DAY-LEWIS, C. $10/£10

LEWKOWITSCH, J. Chemical Technology and Analysis of Oils, Fats and Waxes. George H. Warburton (ed). London, 1921. 6th ed. 3 vols. Grn cl, gilt. VG. *Larry Price.* $75/£47

LEWTON, VAL. Rasputin and the Empress. NY: Grosset & Dunlap, (1933). 1st ed. Dec eps. (Fep corner clipped), else VF in dj (sl short; faint rubberstamp bottom fr cvr). *Between The Covers.* $100/£63

LEXER, ERICH and ARTHUR DEAN BEVAN. General Surgery. Dean Lewis (trans). NY/London: D. Appleton, 1910. 2 color plts. Red cl. (Ex-lib, stamps, underlined in ink, sm waterstain across top corner throughout; hinges split, loose, shaken.) *Weber.* $80/£50

LEYBOURN, THOMAS. The Mathematical Questions, Proposed in the Ladies' Diary, and Their Original Answers, Together with Some New Solutions, from its Commencement in the Year 1704 to 1816. London: J. Mawman, 1817. 1st ed. 8vo. 4 vols. xi,415; (4),416; (4),400; (4),440,(2)pp. Complete w/all 1/2-titles, appendix, index of contributors, errata leaf vol 4. Orig 1/2 calf, marbled bds, spines gilt w/raised bands. Fine set (very nicely rebacked). *Glaser.* $1,200/£750

LEYDSTON, G. FRANK. Impotence and Sterility with Aberrations of the Sexual Function and Sex-Gland Implantation. Chicago, 1917. 1st ed. *Fye.* $75/£47

LEYMARIE, JEAN. Balthus. Geneva/London: Skira/Macmillan, 1979. Frontis, 48 mtd color plts, 16 monochrome. VF. *Europa.* $112/£70

LEYMARIE, JEAN. Dutch Painting. (Geneva): Skira, (1956). Folio. 114 full color repros tipped-in. NF in VG dj. *Turtle Island.* $65/£41

LEZAMA LIMA, JOSE. Paradiso. NY: FSG, 1974. 1st ed in English. NF in NF dj. *Lame Duck.* $125/£78

LEZARD, ADELE. The Great Gold Reef. Indianapolis, 1937. 1st ed. Fldg map, 14 photo plts. Orange cl. VG. *Larry Price.* $25/£16

LHEVINNE, ISADORE. Napoleons All. NY: Mohawk Press, 1931. 1st ed. Black cl. VG in pict dj (sm spine sticker). *Reese.* $35/£22

LHOYD, H. and DAVID POWEL (eds). The Historie of Cambria, Now Called Wales: A Part of the Most Famous Yland of Brytanie. London: John Harding, 1811. Mod cl, leather spine label. (Old lib stamp, name; new binding), else VG. *Pacific*.* $127/£79

LIARDET, FRANCIS. Professional Recollections on Points of Seamanship, Discipline, &c. Portsea/London: William Woodward/Longman, 1849. 1st and only ed. Litho frontis, (6),x,317,(4)pp; color litho plt. (Prelims, frontis foxed; rubbed.) *Lefkowicz.* $200/£125

Libby Chronicle. Albany: Louis N. Beaudry, (1889). 1st ed. Frontisport, (iv),51pp (lt aging). Brn pebbled cl (edges sl worn, fr hinge cracked), gilt. *Baltimore*.* $70/£44

LIBERMAN, ALEXANDER (ed). The Art and Technique of Color Photography. NY: S&S, 1951. 1st ed. Irving Penn, et al (photos). Folio. NF in dj (sl rubbed). *Cahan.* $85/£53

LIBERMAN, ALEXANDER (ed). The Art and Technique of Color Photography. NY, 1951. 1st ed. (Eps foxed; rubbed, spine agedknd.) Dj (chipped, worn, tape repairs to reverse). *Swann*.* $138/£86

LICHTENSTEIN, GASTON. Thomas Jefferson as War Governor. Wm. Byrd, 1925. Paper over bd (top spine torn off). *Book Broker.* $85/£53

Lichtenstein. London: Ernest Nister, No. 695, (1900). 1st ed. Olive-grn cl. Fine. *Sotheran.* $93/£58

LIDDELL, MARY. Little Machinery. GC: Doubleday, Page, (1926). 1st ed. 4to. 62pp (2 pp w/stuck spot); every other pg w/full-pg color illus. Cl-backed color pict bds (lt mkd, dusty). *Reisler.* $250/£156

LIDDELL, T. HODGSON. China, Its Marvel and Mystery. NY: Lane, 1910. 1st US ed. 40 color plts. Teg. (Edges rubbed, soiled, spine ends sl frayed, sl silverfished), o/w VG. *Worldwide.* $75/£47

LIDDLE HART, B. H. Sherman, the Genius of the Civil War. (London): Ernest Benn Ltd, 1930. Port. VG (fr hinge cracked). *Cullen.* $45/£28

LIDDLE HART, B. H. The Tanks, the History of the Royal Tank Regiment. London: Cassell, (1959). 2 vols. Djs. *Cullen.* $350/£219

LIEB, FRED and STAN BAUMGARTNER. The Philadelphia Phillies. Putnam, 1953. 1st ed. Fine in VG+ dj. *Plapinger.* $350/£219

LIEB, FRED. The Baseball Story. Putnam, 1950. 1st ed. VG in Good dj. *Plapinger.* $60/£38

LIEB, FRED. Baseball, As I Have Known It. Coward McCann, 1977. 1st ed. Fine in VG dj. *Plapinger.* $40/£25

LIEB, FRED. The Boston Red Sox. Putnam, 1947. 1st ed. VG+ in Fine dj (spine faded). *Plapinger.* $85/£53

LIEB, FRED. Connie Mack. Putnam, 1945. 1st ed. VG in Good+ dj. *Plapinger.* $65/£41

LIEB, FRED. The Detroit Tigers. Putnam, 1946. 1st ed. VG in Good dj. *Plapinger.* $65/£41

LIEBER, O. The Assayer's Guide. Phila: Baird, 1893. 2nd ed. xvi,283pp + 32pp ads. Good. *Blake.* $50/£31

LIEBIG, G. A., JR. and GEORGE ROHE. Practical Electricity in Medicine and Surgery. Phila, 1890. 1st ed. 383pp. *Fye.* $200/£125

LIEBIG, JUSTUS. Animal Chemistry, or Organic Chemistry in its Application to Physiology and Pathology. London, 1843. 2nd ed. 384pp. 1/2 leather (rear bd nearly detached; ex-lib). *Fye.* $200/£125

LIEBIG, JUSTUS. Researches on the Chemistry of Food, and the Motion of the Juices in the Animal Body. William Gregory (ed). Lowell, MA, 1848. 1st Amer ed. 219pp. *Fye.* $200/£125

LIEBKNECHT, KARL. Militarism. NY: B.W. Huebsch, 1917. 1st US ed. Olive grn cl stamped in gilt/white. (Few clippings offset, few pencil underscores, cl sl discolored toward spine foot), else Nice in dj (soiled, stain spine foot). *Reese.* $75/£47

LIEBLING, A. J. Back Where I Came From. NY, 1938. 1st ed, 1st bk. NF in VG dj (spine split, head chipped). *Warren.* $300/£188

LIEBLING, A. J. Mink and Red Herring. NY, 1949. 1st ed. NF in VG dj (spine edges chipped). *Warren.* $125/£78

LIEBLING, A. J. Normandy Revisited. NY: S&S, 1958. 1st ed. VG+ in VG dj (sm sticker fr flap). *Pettler.* $45/£28

LIEBLING, A. J. The Press. NY: Ballantine, 1961. 1st ed, pb orig. (Spine slanted), else VG in wrappers. *Pettler.* $12/£8

LIEBLING, A. J. The Telephone Booth Indian. NY, 1942. 1st ed. NF (name, date, place) in VG dj (2 thumb-size chips at spine, top fr panel; spine folds split). *Warren.* $175/£109

LIEBLING, A. J. (ed). The Republic of Silence. NY: Harcourt, (1947). 1st ed. Fine in dj (sl rubbed, dknd). *Reese.* $50/£31

LIEDERMAN, EARLE. The Science of Wrestling and the Art of Jiu-Jitsu. NY, 1924. 2nd ed. Frontis port. Gilt-dec cl (sl worn). *Edwards.* $48/£30

Life and Adventures of Arthur Clenning. (By Timothy Flint.) Phila: Tower & Hogan, 1828. 1st ed. 2 vols. Contemp calf-backed bds (shelfworn, spines dried; foxed, browned, sl stained, soiled). Contemp bkseller's ticket tipped to fr pastedown vol 1. BAL 6115. *Oinonen*.* $50/£31

Life and Adventures of Bampflyde-Moore Carew, Commonly Called King of the Beggars...to Which Is Added, A Dictionary of the Cant Language Used by the Medicants. Bath: J. Browne, 1802. Frontisport. Period calf. (Upper margins of 1st few pp wormed; spine worn), else VG. *Pacific*.* $52/£33

Life and Adventures of Don Quixote de la Mancha. (By Miguel de Cervantes Saavedra.) London: Hurst, Robinson, 1820. New ed. 4 vols. 8vo. Full-pg frontis each vol, xx,371; iv,388; vi,367; viii,436pp; 5 Fine full-pg copper engrs by Charles Heath each vol. Marbled eps, red speckled fore-edges. 3/4 leather (lt dried, sl chipped) w/corners, marbled paper on bds, 4 raised bands, vol 4 w/orig black spine label. VG set (shelfworn, reattached upper bd on vol 4). *Hobbyhorse.* $190/£119

Life and Correspondence of John Paul Jones, Including His Narrative of the Campaign of the Liman. NY, 1830. 1st ed. Frontisport, 556pp. Orig full leather. (Lacks errata slip; sl rubbed), o/w VG. Howes S91. *New Hampshire*.* $70/£44

Life and Exploits of S. Glenn Young: World-Famous Law Enforcement Officer. Herrin, IL, n.d. Good. *Rybski.* $75/£47

Life and Remains of the Rev. Edward Daniel Clarke, LL.D. (By William Otter.) London: George Cowie, 1824. 1st ed. Engr frontisport (foxed), x,670pp. Old calf, purple patterned silk (extrems sl scuffed), gilt. *Karmiole.* $275/£172

Life in California: During a Residence of Several Years in That Territory, Comprising a Description...By an American. (By Alfred Robinson.) London: H.G. Collins, 1851. 1st Eng ed. xiv,182pp (tp sl soiled)+ 10 ads. New 1/2 calf. *Young.* $136/£85

Life in South Africa. (By Mary Anne Broome.) Phila: Lippincott, 1877. 1st ed. 136+4pp ads (lt waterstain margin 1st 14pp). Brn cl (extrems lt frayed, spine faded). *Karmiole.* $75/£47

Life of a Fox, Written by Himself. (By Thomas Smith.) London, 1843. 1st ed. 5 litho plts. Teg. 3/4 red morocco by Root. (Orig cvr bound in at end; lt worn.) *Oinonen*.* $100/£63

Life of Isaac W. Sprague, the Living Skeleton. NY: NY Popular Pub, (1882). VG in pink pict wraps (sl soiled). *Dramatis.* $120/£75

Life of Jack London. (By H. M. Tichenor.) Girard, KS: Haldeman-Julius, (1923). Ptd wrappers. (Browned.) *Heritage.* $20/£13

Life of John Buncle, Esq. (By Thomas Amory.) London: J. Noon/Johnson & Davenport, 1756/1766. 1st eds. 2 vols. Tall thick 8vo. 511; 532pp. Contemp calf, gilt. Nice set (bkpl; nicely rebacked, w/orig labels laid down). *Hartfield.* $695/£434

Life of Mahomet; or, The History of That Imposture Which Was Begun...by Him in Arabia.... NY: Evert Duyckinck, 1813. 2nd Amer ed. 12mo. 118pp. Plain paper on bds (sm spot), cl spine. Internally Fine. *Hobbyhorse.* $125/£78

Life of Rev. Amand Parent. Toronto: William Briggs, 1887. Port, 235pp. (Worn, soiled), else Good. *Brown.* $15/£9

Life of the Boston Bard. Mt. Pleasant: Marshall, 1825. 1st ed. Calf, leather label. Good (pencil mks on blanks; fr joint partly split). *Agvent.* $75/£47

Life, Voyages and Adventures of Bampfylde-Moore Carew. (By Robert Goadby.) London: J. Barker et al, n.d. (1790). Engr frontisport, (iv),212pp. Contemp 1/2 calf, marbled bds. (Sl foxed; rubbed, joints repaired.) *Morrell.* $128/£80

LIFSON, DAVID S. The Yiddish Theatre in America. NY, (1965). 1st Amer ed. Fine in dj (sl rubbed, few sm nicks). *Polyanthos.* $30/£19

Light and Shadows of European History. (By Samuel Griswold Goodrich.) Boston: Bradbury, Soden, 1844. 8vo. Full-pg engr frontis, vi,320pp. 3/4 leather w/corners, marbled paper on bds, black spine label. Good (foxed, ink date, fep ripped across; lt soiled, corners rubbed). *Hobbyhorse.* $90/£56

LIGHTBOWN, RONALD. Mantegna. With a Complete Catalogue of the Paintings, Drawings and Prints. Oxford: Phaidon/Christie, 1986. 16 color plts. VF in dj. *Europa.* $200/£125

Lightning Express. NY: McLoughlin Bros, 1881. Toybook. 4to. 20pp; 10 full-color illus incl cvrs. Good in full color pict wrappers (worn, spine resewn, rear cvr repaired). *Reisler.* $150/£94

LIGHTWOOD, JAMES T. Charles Dickens and Music. Charles H. Kelly, 1912. Frontis. Teg. Good (lt spotted, new eps; spine bumped). *Tiger.* $38/£24

LIGON, RICHARD. A True and Exact History of the Island of Barbadoes...Together with the Ingenio That Makes the Sugar. London, 1673. Folio. Fldg map, 6 plts, fldg table, index leaf. Contemp calf (rebacked). *Felcone.* $3,000/£1,875

LIKINS, MRS. J. W. Six Years Experience as a Book Agent in California. SF: Book Club of CA, 1992. Terra cotta cl. *Rostenberg & Stern.* $50/£31

LILIEN, OTTO M. History of Industrial Gravure Painting up to 1920. Lund Humphries, 1972. Good in dj (worn). *Rybski.* $50/£31

LILIENTHAL, OTTO. Birdflight as the Basis of Aviation. London: Longmans, Green, 1911. 1st ed in English. 8vo. Frontisport, 8 fldg litho plts (1 plt strengthened at outer edge). Grn cl. NF (sl shelfworn). *Glaser.* $850/£531

LILLARD, RICHARD G. The Great Forest. NY, 1948. 24 plts. Grn cl. VG. *Larry Price.* $25/£16

Lille Before and During the War. Michelin Tyre, 1919. 1st ed. Fep stamped 'complimentary copy.' VG in card wrappers (dusty, sl soiled, nicked, creased, w/orig price overstamped). *Ulysses.* $72/£45

LIMB, SUE and PATRICK CORDINGLEY. Captain Oates, Soldier and Explorer. London: Batsford, 1982. VG in dj. *Explorer.* $29/£18

LIMBECK, R. R. The Clinical Pathology of the Blood. London, 1901. 1st ed. *Fye.* $75/£47

LIMEBEER, ENA. To a Proud Phantom. Richmond, 1923. One of 250. Marbled paper bds. VG (sl bowed, top edge sl dusty, spine ends, corners sl bumped, bruised, title lable on fr cvr dknd, spotted). *Ulysses.* $360/£225

LINCOLN, ABRAHAM. Address of Hon. Edward Everett, at the Consecration of the National Cemetery at Gettysburg...with the Dedicatory Speech of President Lincoln. Boston, 1864. 1st authorized ptg of Gettysburg Address. Frontis map. Orig cl (extrems worn, backstrip reinforced w/cl tape). *Swann*.* $460/£288

LINCOLN, ABRAHAM. Anecdotal Lincoln. Chicago: Thompson & Thomas, 1900. 1st ed. Pict cl, silver. Fine. *Connolly.* $45/£28

LINCOLN, ABRAHAM. Discoveries and Inventions: A Lecture...Delivered in 1860. SF: John Howell, 1915. 1st ltd ed. One of 250 numbered. Signed presentation, 1916, by pub. Teg, untrimmed. Orig full dk grn-brn levant morocco, gilt. VG (sm text crack; spine lt sunned). *Baltimore*.* $25/£16

LINCOLN, ABRAHAM. The Literary Works of Abraham Lincoln. LEC, 1942. Ltd to 1500 numbered, signed by John Steuart Curry (illus). Fine in slipcase. *Swann*.* $126/£79

LINCOLN, ABRAHAM. The Writings of Abraham Lincoln. Arthur Lapsley (ed). NY: Putnam, (1905). Constitutional ed. 8 vols. Frontisport each vol; endowment fund slip laid in. Teg. Brn buckram, gilt, leather labels. Clean set (lt worn). *House.* $350/£219

LINCOLN, ALMIRA H. Lectures on Botany. Hartford, 1836. 186pp. Brn full calf, gilt. Good + . *Larry Price.* $145/£91

LINCOLN, MARY JOHNSON. Mrs. Lincoln's Boston Cook Book. Boston: Roberts Bros, 1884. 1st ed, later issue, w/p.xvi not a blank, and w/o 4pp ads at end. 3/4 cl. (Sl foxed, stained, soiled, tp cresed; shelfworn.) *Oinonen*.* $180/£113

LINCOLN, WILLIAM ALEXANDER. The Art and Practice of Marquetry. London, 1971. 1st ed. Dj. *Edwards.* $26/£16

LINCOLN, WILLIAM S. Alton Trials. NY: John F. Trow, 1838. 1st ed. B/w litho frontis. 158pp + ad notice (sl foxed, lacks portion of fep, sig). Plain brn cl (spotted, partial deterioration). Text Good. Howes L348. *Baltimore*.* $90/£56

LIND, L. R. Studies in Pre-Vesalian Anatomy. Phila, 1975. 1st ed. *Fye.* $100/£63

LINDBERGH, ANNE MORROW. North to the Orient, [by plane], Washington to Hankow. London: Chatto, 1937. Dj. *Petersfield.* $34/£21

LINDBERGH, CHARLES A. The Spirit of St. Louis. NY: Scribner, 1953. Presentation ed. Signed. NF (lacks dj). *Warren.* $450/£281

LINDBERGH, CHARLES A. We. NY: Putnam, 1927. 1st ed. Ltd to 1000 signed. Untrimmed. Vellum-backed bds. NF. *Second Life.* $900/£563

LINDERMAN, FRANK B. Indian Why Stories: Sparks from War Eagle's Lodge-Fire. NY: Scribner, 1915. 1st ed. Pict cvr label. NF. *Pacific*.* $259/£162

LINDERMAN, FRANK B. Recollections of Charley Russell. Norman: Univ of OK, 1963. 1st ed. Fine in dj (chipped). *Labordo.* $85/£53

LINDERMAN, FRANK B. Recollections of Charley Russell. H. G. Merrian (ed). Norman: Univ of OK, (1963). 1st ed. Good (spine ends sl worn). *Lien.* $50/£31

LINDERMAN, FRANK B. Red Mother. NY: John Day, (1932). 1st ed. Good (dampstained; scorched, stained). *Pacific*.* $23/£14

LINDGREN, ASTRID. Springtime in Noisy Village. Viking, 1966. 1st Amer ed. 11x9. Ilon Wikland (illus). Unpaginated. NF in VG dj (1/2-inch tear, sm chips to spine). *Price.* $45/£28

LINDGREN, WALDEMER. The Tertiary Gravels of the Sierra Nevada of California. Washington: GPO, 1911. 1st ed. Fldg profile, maps, loose in rep envelope. VG in wrappers (soiled, worn, rear wrapper detached but present, eradicated rubber-stamp to fr wrapper). *Pacific*.* $98/£61

LINDMAN, MAJ. Flicka, Ricka, Dicka and the Girl Next Door. Chicago: Albert Whitman, 1945. 6th ptg. 4to. Unpaginated. 12 full-pg color illus. Red cl, pict label (lib binding). VG. *Davidson.* $85/£53

LINDMAN, MAJ. Snipp Snapp Snurr and the Gingerbread. Chicago: Albert Whitman, 1932. 1st ed. Sm 4to. Unpaginated. 10 color plts. Brn cl, pict onlay (lib binding). VG in art deco dj (lt torn). *Davidson.* $130/£81

LINDNER, LESLIE. The Journal of Beatrix Potter. London/NY: Frederick Warne, (1966). 8vo. 448pp. Grn cl, gilt. VG in VG dj. *Davidson.* $60/£38

LINDQUIST, EMORY K. Smoky Valley People. Lindsborg, KS: Bethany College, 1953. 1st ed. VG in dj (sl worn). *Brown.* $25/£16

LINDSAY, CRESSIDA. No, John, No. NY: Clarkson Potter, (1967). 1st Amer ed. Fine in Fine dj. *Between The Covers.* $50/£31

LINDSAY, DAVID M. A Voyage to the Arctic in the Whaler Aurora. Boston: Dana Estes, 1911. 1st ed. Gilt-pict cl. VG (sl rubbed). *Walcot.* $88/£55

LINDSAY, DIANA ELAINE. Our Historic Desert: the Story of the Anza-Borrego Desert. (San Diego: Copley Books, 1973.) Dj. *Dawson.* $40/£25

LINDSAY, FRANK W. Dramatic Parody by Marionettes in Eighteenth Century Paris. NY: King's Crown, 1946. VG in ptd wraps. *Dramatis.* $35/£22

LINDSAY, HOWARD and RUSSELL CROUSE. The Great Sebastians. NY: Random House, (1956). 1st ed. VF in VF dj. *Between The Covers.* $150/£94

LINDSAY, HOWARD and RUSSELL CROUSE. Happy Hunting. NY: Random House, (1957). 1st ed. VF in VF dj. *Between The Covers.* $150/£94

LINDSAY, J. SEYMOUR. Iron and Brass Implements of the English House. London, 1964. Rev, enlgd ed. Dj (sl chipped, spine soiled). *Edwards.* $64/£40

LINDSAY, J. SEYMOUR. Iron and Brass Implements of the English House. Tiranti, 1970. Rev, enlgd ed. NF in dj. *Hadley.* $45/£28

LINDSAY, JACK. William Blake. Fanfrolico, 1929. 2nd ed. Buckram-backed bds (soiled, worn). *Cox.* $29/£18

LINDSAY, MARTIN. The Epic of Captain Scott. London: Falcon, 1948. New ed. Fldg map. Fine in dj. *Explorer.* $16/£10

LINDSAY, VACHEL. Collected Poems. NY: Macmillan, 1925. 1st rev, illus ed, ltd issue. One of 350 numbered, signed. Pict eps. Dec bds. (2 sm tape shadows fep; spine ends sl tanned), o/w NF in Good slipcase (joints bruised, cracked). *Reese.* $125/£78

LINDSAY, VACHEL. Going-to-the-Sun. NY: Appleton, 1923. 1st ed. NF. *Agvent.* $50/£31

LINDSAY, VACHEL. Rhymes to Be Traded for Bread.... (Springfield, IL, 1912.) 1st ed. 8vo. Orig self-wraps (sm tears). Stapled as issued. *M & S.* $750/£469

LINDSAY, VACHEL. Springfield Town Is Butterfly Town. Kent, OH: Kent State, 1969. 1st ed. 8x9.25. 72pp. Pict bds. Good in dj. *Cattermole.* $40/£25

LINDSEY, ROBERT. The Falcon and the Snowman. NY, 1979. 1st ed. NF in NF dj. *Warren.* $35/£22

LINGENFELTER, RICHARD E. The Newspapers of Nevada 1858-1958. SF: John Howell, 1964. 1st ed. Fine in dj. *Book Market.* $150/£94

LININGTON, ELIZABETH. Policeman's Lot. NY: Harper, 1968. 1st ed. Fine in NF dj (price-clipped). *Janus.* $20/£13

LINK, MAE MILLS et al. Medical Support of the Army Air Forces in World War II. USAF: Office of Surgeon General, 1955. Good. *Rybski.* $65/£41

LINK, RICHARD. Fossils. N.p.: Richard Link, 1972. 1st ed. 23 full-pg b/w photos. (Stamp), else Fine in pict stiff wrappers. *Cahan.* $35/£22

LINKLATER, MAGNUS. Scotland. Collins, 1984. 1st ed. VG in dj. *Hollett.* $32/£20

LINNEY, E. J. A History of the Game of Bowls. London, 1933. 1st ed. Marbled eps. Gilt-ruled morocco (rebound), dec gilt-edged raised bands. *Edwards.* $200/£125

LINS DO REGO, JOSE. Plantation Boy. NY: Knopf, 1966. 1st ed. NF in dj. *Lame Duck.* $65/£41

LINS, OSMAN. Avalovara. Gregory Rabassa (trans). NY: Knopf, 1980. 1st US ed. Fine in dj. *Bernard.* $35/£22

LINSLEY, D. C. Morgan Horses.... NY: Saxton, 1857. 1st ed. (Professionally rebound using orig bds.) *October Farm.* $295/£184

LINSLEY, LESLIE. Scrimshaw. A Traditional Folk Art, a Contemporary Craft. NY: Hawthorn Books, 1976. 2nd ptg. VG (worn) in dj (worn). *Parmer.* $45/£28

LINTIER, PAUL. My Seventy-Five: Journal of a French Gunner. London: Peter Davies, 1929. 2nd ed in English. Frontis. Gilt red cl. VG in pict dj (lt foxed). *Reese.* $85/£53

LINTON, W. J. Wood-Engraving: A Manual of Instruction. London: George Bell, 1884. 1st ed. One of 500. x,127pp. Brn cl, beveled bds, gilt. (Possibly ex-lib, w/removal evidence of cl tape at 2 portions of spine; sl worn, edges frayed, ring stain fr cvr.) Text Good (sl aged, tp/frontis leaf detached, chipped). *Baltimore*.* $40/£25

LION-GOLDSCHMIDT, DAISY. Ming Porcelain. London, (1978). 41 color plts. Dj. *Swann*.* $115/£72

LIPCHITZ, JACQUES. My Life in Sculpture. NY: Viking, (1972). 1st ed. NF in dj (price-clipped). *Turtle Island.* $45/£28

LIPPE, ADOLPHUS. Text Book of Materia Medica. Phila, 1866. 1st ed. 717pp. Recent cl. *Fye.* $200/£125

LISH, GORDON. Dear Mr. Capote. NY, 1983. 1st ed. Fine in Fine dj. *Warren.* $40/£25

LISH, GORDON. Peru. NY, 1986. 1st ed. NF in NF dj. *Warren.* $25/£16

LISIANSKY, UREY. A Voyage Round the World, in the Years 1803, 4, 5, and 6. London: John Booth et al, 1814. 1st ed in English. 11x8.5. Stipple-engr frontisport, xxi,(2),388pp; 10 hand-colored copper-engr maps on 8 sheets (3 fldg), 3 copper-engr plts, 2 hand-colored aquatint plts. Old mottled bds (rebacked, recornered in calf), gilt, raised bands. (Lt offsetting, foxing to contents), else NF. Howes L372. *Pacific*.* $5,175/£3,234

LISPECTOR, CLARICE. The Apple in the Dark. NY: Knopf, 1967. 1st ed. NF in dj (price-clipped, sm closed tear to fr cvr). *Lame Duck.* $85/£53

LISSNER, IVAR. Man, God and Magic. NY: Putnam, 1961. 1st ed in English. 64 plts. VG in Fair dj. *Connolly.* $32/£20

List of Natural Flies That Are Taken by Trout, Grayling and Smelt, in the Streams of Ripon. (By Michael Theakston.) Ripon, 1853. 1st ed. x,154pp; 8 litho plts. 3/4 black morocco (rebacked, preserving most of older spine; rubbed), gilt. Internally Clean (Dean Sage's bkpl). *Oinonen*.* $350/£219

LISTER, CHARLES. Letters and Recollections. London, 1917. 2nd ed. (Cvrs very mkd.) *Clearwater.* $40/£25

LISTER, RAYMOND. Old Maps and Globes. London: Bell & Hyman, (1979). Rev ed, 1st w/this title. Red cl. Fine in dj. *Argonaut.* $100/£63

LISTER, RAYMOND. The Paintings of William Blake. CUP, 1986. 1st ed. 75 color plts. Dj. *Edwards.* $40/£25

LISTON, ROBERT. Elements of Surgery. Phila, 1842. 1st Amer ed. 640pp. Gray marbled bds (skillfully rebound) w/dk leather spine, red spine label. VG. *Doctor's Library.* $265/£166

Literary Hours; by Various Friends. (By Walter Savage Landor.) (Liverpool): Privately ptd, 1837. 1st ed. Frontis. Orig cl (lacks spine; eps foxed). *Sotheby's*.* $147/£92

Little American Farmer. NY: McLoughlin Bros, (1908). Folio. 7 leaves. Floral eps. Chromolitho pict paper on bds, red cl spine. NF (cvrs lt dusted, shelfworn). *Hobbyhorse.* $450/£281

Little Blue Eyes. London: Dean & Son, ca 1908. Sm folio. Black coated eps. Dk navy ribbed cl, gilt, applied die-cut chromolitho illus on fr cvr. (Shaken, loose w/in loose sigs, sm adhesions few ll, sm edge tears, wear few ll; sl edgeworn, corner bumped.) *Baltimore*.* $90/£56

Little Boys' and Girls' Own Primer, by Mrs. Teachem. NY: Kiggins & Kellogg, n.d. (ca 1885). 12mo. Full-pg wood-engr tp, 16pp + 1pg list on lower wrapper. Pict gray paper wrappers (sm chip 1 corner). *Hobbyhorse.* $120/£75

Little Brighthope's Stories: Pea-Hen at Home; or the Swan's Bridal Day. Phila: Davis, Porter & Coates, (ca 1860). 12mo. 8pp. VG in orange-yellow illus paper wrappers. *Reisler.* $200/£125

Little Charley's Stories of Great Men. Phila: C.G. Henderson, 1858. 12mo. Full-pg wood-engr frontis, 32pp + 16pp ads. Pict paper on bd; ad on rear cvr. (Ink sig, eps discolored; cvrs lt rubbed, missing part of spine, sm tear affecting last word of title), else VG. *Hobbyhorse.* $85/£53

Little Folks' Fair and What We Saw There. London: Ernest Nister, (ca 1896). Lg 4to. 34pp (incl 17pp color plts). Cl-backed color illus bds (sm marginal tear, fr hinge sl lifted, edges lt worn). Bright. *Reisler.* $350/£219

Little Keepsake; or, Easy Lessons, in Words of One Syllable. New Haven: Sidney Babcock, (c. 1830). 3 3/4 x 2 1/4. Orig ptd yellow wrappers. (Name inside fr wrapper and top of fr wrapper), else NF. *Pacific*.* $46/£29

Little Miss Moffet and Other Rhymes. N.p.: McLoughlin Bros, 1886. 1st ed. 13 3/4 x 11 1/4. Chromolitho wrappers. (Spine rubbed, sl soiled, creasing bottom rt corner), else NF. *Pacific*.* $87/£54

Little Nancy, or, The Punishment of Greediness. Phila: Morgan & Yeager, n.d. (ca 1824). 1st ed. Sq 12mo. 8pp + 4 leaves + 1pg list on rear wrapper; 4 full-pg copper engrs. Buff stiff paper wrappers. Fine (last leaf lt foxed; lower spine corner sl chipped). *Hobbyhorse.* $325/£203

Little Pets Story Book. London: Ernest Nister, (ca 1906). Royal 8vo. Mtd chromolitho frontis, (66)pp. Cl-backed pict bds. Very Bright (few sl internal mks). *Sotheran.* $125/£78

Little Red Riding Hood. Lombard, IL: Gargoyle, (1988). Ltd to 1000 signed. 12mo. Charles Vess (illus). Red cl, gilt. As New in full color dj. *Reisler.* $75/£47

Little Red Riding Hood. London: Raphael Tuck & Sons, (ca 1892). 12mo. Expanding toybook. Cl-backed color pict bds (rubbed; paper chipped; loose in binding). *Reisler.* $175/£109

Little Red Riding Hood. NY: Blue Ribbon, 1934. Illustrated Pop-Up Edition. 20x24 cm. C. Carey Cloud & Harold B. Lentz (illus). 3 dbl-pg pop-ups. Pict bds (extrems sl worn, sm spine chip). *Bookfinders.* $250/£156

Little Red Riding Hood. NY: Blue Ribbon, 1934. C. C. Cloud and Harold Lentz (illus). 3 VG pop-ups. VG (sl soil, corners bumped). *Davidson.* $285/£178

Little Red Riding Hood. NY: Blue Ribbon, 1934. Sq 4to. 3 dbl-pg full color pop-ups by C. Carey Cloud and Harold B. Lentz. Full color pict bds. VG. *Reisler.* $285/£178

Little Red Riding Hood. NY: Duenewald, 1944. 17x21 cm. Julian Wehr (engineer). 6 tab-operated movable plts. Pict bds, spiral binding. VG-. *Bookfinders.* $130/£81

Little Rosebuds. NY: Frederick A. Stokes, 1898. 1st ed. 4to. 6 full-pg color plts by Maud Humphrey & Elizabeth S. Tucker. Cl-backed color pict bds (worn; lacks blank feps, tear to lower edge of frontis). *Reisler.* $300/£188

Little Small Red Hen. Phila: Henry Altemus, (ca 1920s). 16mo. 58pp + ads; 26 illus. Cl-backed dec bds, color paste label. Good in color dj (edges, folds worn). *Reisler.* $40/£25

Little Stories About Mark Twain. NY: Harper, (1911). 1st ed. Fine in ptd wrappers. *Macdonnell.* $100/£63

Little Suck-a-Thumb (Aunt Grumble's Series). NY: McLoughlin Bros, (ca 1870). 12mo. 7pp. (Spine loose, sm hole at back.) 2-color pict wrappers. *Reisler.* $85/£53

LITTLE, ARTHUR W. From Harlem to the Rhine. NY, (1936). 1st ed. (Spine faded.) *Swann*.* $80/£50

LITTLE, BRIAN. Birmingham Buildings. David & Charles, 1971. VG in dj. *Hadley.* $26/£16

LITTLE, FRANCES. Little Sister Snow. NY: Century, 1909. 1st ed. Sm 8vo. 140pp; 12 color plts by Genjiro Kataoka. Gray cl, gilt. VG (rear corners sl bumped, 1/4-inch rough area fr edge each bd). *Price.* $65/£41

LITTLE, JAMES A. Jacob Hamblin. SLC, UT: Juvenile Instructor Office, 1881. 144pp. Blue cl. (Name), o/w Good. *Five Quail.* $150/£94

LITTLE, JAMES M. Erosional Topography and Erosion. SF: Privately ptd, 1940. 1st ed. Brn cl, gilt. VG (ex-lib). *Larry Price.* $40/£25

LITTLE, MRS. ARCHIBALD. In the Land of the Blue Gown. London: T. Fisher Unwin, 1908. 2nd ed. 32 plts (incl frontis). Top edges trimmed, rest uncut. Maroon pict cl, gilt. Good. *Morrell.* $40/£25

LITTLEJOHN, B. F. Texas History Stories. Richmond, 1901. (Tp stamp; worn), else Good. *Dumont.* $25/£16

LITTLEJOHN, DAVID et al. Orders, Decorations, Medals and Badges of the Third Reich. Volume 2. R. James Bender, (1973). 1st ed. Good. *Rybski.* $35/£22

LITTLEJOHN, F. J. Legends of Michigan and the Old North West. Allegan, MI: Northwestern Bible & Pub Co, 1875. 1st ed. Steel-engr frontis port, 566pp (marginal tear 1 leaf, not affecting text). Pebbled brn cl, gilt. Howes L392. *Karmiole.* $125/£78

Littlest One's Third Book. Harrap, 1928. 1st ed. 8vo. 58pp; 4 color plts by Margaret Tarrant. Grey bds. NF in pict dj (sl worn, sl dusty). *Bookmark.* $48/£30

LITZMANN, BERTHOLD. Letters of Clara Schumann and Johannes Brahms 1853-1896. Edward Arnold, 1927. 1st ed. 2 vols. VG in djs (1 sl defective at spine foot). *Hollett.* $120/£75

LIVEING, EDWARD. Attack: An Infantry Subaltern's Impressions of July 1st, 1916. London: Heinemann, (1918). 1st ed. Dec buff bds. (Text browned, cracking at gutters), o/w VG in pict dj. *Reese.* $50/£31

LIVELY, PENELOPE. According to Mark. Heinemann, 1984. 1st UK ed. Signed. Mint in Mint dj. *Martin.* $22/£14

LIVELY, PENELOPE. According to Mark. Heinemann, 1984. 1st UK ed. Signed. Fine in dj. *Williams.* $38/£24

LIVELY, PENELOPE. Cleopatra's Sister. NY, 1993. 1st Amer ed. Fine in Fine dj. *Polyanthos.* $20/£13

LIVELY, PENELOPE. Moon Tiger. Deutsch, 1987. 1st UK ed. Signed. Mint in Mint dj. *Martin.* $54/£34

LIVELY, PENELOPE. Next to Nature, Art. Heinemann, 1982. 1st UK ed. Signed. Fine in Fine dj. *Martin.* $22/£14

Living Talmud: The Wisdom of the Fathers and Its Classical Commentaries. Judah Goldin (ed). NY: LEC, 1960. One of 1500 ptd. Signed by Ben-Zion (illus). Teg. 1/2 vellum, buckram, gilt. (Spine sl discolored), else NF in slipcase. *Pacific*.* $63/£39

Living Talmud: The Wisdom of the Fathers. LEC, 1960. Ltd to 1500 numbered, signed by Ben-Zion (illus). Fine in slipcase. *Swann*.* $161/£101

LIVINGSTON, EDWARD M. A Clinical Study of the Abdominal Cavity and Peritoneum. NY: Hoeber, 1932. 1st ed. 2-toned cl. NF. *Glaser.* $85/£53

LIVINGSTON, JANE. M. Alvarez Bravo. Boston/Washington, (1978). 1st ed. Dj (sl worn, spine sl discolored). *Swann*.* $126/£79

LIVINGSTON, LIDA (ed). Dali, a Study of His Art-in-Jewels, the Collection of the Owen Cheatham Foundation. Greenwich, CT, (1965). 35 tipped-in color plts (incl 4 loose in folders). VG (1 plt torn, creased) in slipcase (worn, split). *King.* $75/£47

LIVINGSTONE, DAVID and CHARLES. Narrative of an Expedition to the Zambesi and Its Tributaries and of the Discovery of the Lakes Shirwa and Nyassa, 1858-1864. John Murray, 1865. 1st ed. 8vo. Fldg engr frontis; xiv,(i),608pp; lg fldg color map. Pict purple cl, gilt. (Spine sl faded, rubbed), o/w VG. *Sotheran.* $560/£350

LIVINGSTONE, DAVID and CHARLES. A Narrative of an Expedition to the Zambesi and Its Tributaries; and of the Discovery of the Lakes Shirwa and Nyasa, 1858-1864. NY: Harper, 1866. 1st Amer ed. xxii,638pp + 6 ad pp; fldg map. Later grn buckram, gilt. (Sm map tear; soiled), else VG. *Pacific*.* $86/£54

LIVINGSTONE, DAVID. Family Letters, 1841-1856. Volume Two, 1849-1856. I. Schapera (ed). London: C&W, 1959. Mottled blue-grn cl. Fine in dj. *Temple.* $19/£12

LIVINGSTONE, DAVID. Livingstone's Private Journals, 1851-1853. I. Schapera (ed). London: C&W, 1960. 3 maps. Brick red cl, gilt. Fine in dj. *Temple.* $22/£14

LIVINGSTONE, DAVID. Missionary Travels and Researches in South Africa. John Murray, 1857. 1st ed. Fldg frontis, ix,(i),1-8,8*,8,9-711pp; 24 plts, fldg map. Brn blind-stamped cl, gilt. (Repair to frontis; joints somewhat repaired), o/w VG. *Sotheran.* $360/£225

LIVINGSTONE, DAVID. Missionary Travels and Researches in South Africa. NY, 1858. 1st Amer ed. 732pp + 3 fldg maps. Black cl, gilt. Good+. *Larry Price.* $145/£91

LIVINGSTONE, DAVID. Missionary Travels and Researches in South Africa; Including a Sketch of Sixteen Years' Residence in the Interior of Africa. London, 1857. 1st ed. 687pp + fldg map. Later 1/4 leather, marbled bds. *Fye.* $400/£250

LIVINGSTONE, PETER. Poems and Songs. Edinburgh: Mould & Tod, 1881. xii,(13)-143pp. Red cl (mkd, spine dknd). Good (contents sl loose). *Explorer.* $40/£25

LIVINGSTONE, W. P. Shetland and the Shetlanders. Thomas Nelson, 1947. 1st ed. 31 plts. VG. *Hollett.* $32/£20

LIVINGSTONE-LEARMONTH, DAVID. The Horse in Art. Studio Pub, 1958. 101 plts (4 color). VG in dj (upper corners sl chipped). *Hollett.* $136/£85

LIVIUS, TITUS. The First Five Books of the Roman History. John Bellenden (trans). Edinburgh: W. & C. Tait, 1822. 1st ed thus. 19th-cent 3/4 dk blue morocco, marbled bds, gilt. (Bkpl), else NF. *Pacific*.* $86/£54

LIVY. The History of Early Rome. Aubrey de Selincourt (trans). Verona: LEC, 1970. One of 1500 ptd. Signed by Giovanni Mardersteig (designer) & Raffae Scorzelli (illus). 1/2 brn linen, patterned bds, leather spine label. Fine in glassine, slipcase (sl sunned). *Pacific*.* $63/£39

LIVY. The History of Early Rome. LEC, 1970. Ltd to 1500 numbered, signed by Raffaele Scorzelli (illus) and Giovanni Mardersteig (designer). Fine in slipcase. *Swann*.* $80/£50

LLOSA, MARIO VARGAS. See VARGAS LLOSA, MARIO

LLOYD GEORGE, DAVID. War Memoirs. London: Ivor Nicholson & Watson, 1933-1936. 1st Eng ed. 6 vols. VG set (names, edges spotted) in djs (sl frayed, rubbed, spotted; dj of vol 6 faded, torn, internally repaired). *Ulysses.* $280/£175

Lloyd's Register of American Yachts. NY: Lloyds, 1931. Tan cl (sl spotted). VG. *American Booksellers.* $55/£34

Lloyd's Register of Shipping. London: Register Books, 1977. Folio. Blue/gold cl (sm rust stain fr cvr). VG. *American Booksellers.* $60/£38

LLOYD, ALBERT B. Uganda to Khartoum. London: T. Fisher Unwin, n.d. (1911). 1st ed, 3rd imp. 48 plts. Grn p¡ct cl. Good (lt foxed, upper hinge cracked). *Morrell.* $88/£55

LLOYD, B. E. Lights and Shades in San Francisco. SF: A.L. Bancroft, 1876. 1st ed. 8.5x5.5. Frontis, (7),8-523pp; 18 wood-engr plts. Marbled eps. Contemp full grn morocco, gilt, raised bands. (Bkpl; sm dents in leather fr cvr), o/w NF. Howes L404. *Pacific*.* $518/£324

LLOYD, CHRISTOPHER. Mr. Barrow of the Admiralty. Collins, 1970. 1st ed. Map. VG in dj. *Walcot.* $19/£12

LLOYD, CHRISTOPHER. The Well-Tempered Garden. London, 1970. 1st ed. Dj. *Edwards.* $32/£20

LLOYD, CHRISTOPHER. The Well-Tempered Garden. NY: Dutton, 1971. 1st US ed. Fine in dj. *Archer.* $35/£22

LLOYD, H. EVANS (trans). Travels in the Interior of North America. London: Ackermann, 1843. Text vol only (lacks map and atlas vols). 4to. xii,520pp. Aeg. (Binding oddly repaired, new leather spine w/orig gilt laid down, tips recovered in leather over old leather, inner hinges repaired w/lib tape.) VG. Howes M443. *Cahan.* $650/£406

LLOYD, HUGH. The Mysterious Arab. NY: G&D, 1931. Hal Keen #5; dj lists 7 titles. 5x7.5. Bert Salg (illus). 237pp + ads. VG + (sl shelfworn) in dj (sl chipped). *My Bookhouse.* $62/£39

LLOYD, HUMPHREY. Elementary Treatise on the Wave-Theory of Light. London: Longmans, Green, 1873. 3rd ed. xi,247pp. Marbled edges. Contemp calf, gilt. VG (joints started, few rubs, scratches). *Glaser.* $135/£84

LLOYD, J. IVESTER. The People of the Valley. Country Life, 1943. 1st ed. Lg 8vo. T. Ivester Lloyd & Stanley Lloyd (illus). 73pp. Dj (sl worn). *Hollett.* $24/£15

LLOYD, J. U. Elixirs: Their History, Formulae, and Methods of Preparation.... Cincinnati, 1883. 2nd ed. 187pp. (Cvrs spotted.) Contents Fine. *Fye.* $150/£94

LLOYD, JAMES T. Lloyd's Steamboat Directory and Disasters on the Western Waters. Cincinnati: The Author, 1856. 46 maps. Fair (foxed; waterstained, hinges cracked). Howes L406. *Cullen.* $350/£219

LLOYD, JOHN H. The History, Topography, and Antiquities of Highgate. Highgate: Ptd by the Subscribers, 1888. Ltd ed. Engr frontis, dbl-pg map. Mod morocco-backed bds. *Christie's*.* $80/£50

LLOYD, JOHN URI. Warwick of the Knobs. NY: Dodd, Mead, 1901. 1st ed. Frontis, 15 plts. Port laid on fr cvr. NF. *Connolly.* $42/£26

LLOYD, L. The Game Birds and Wild Fowl of Sweden and Norway. London: Day and Son Ltd, 1867. 2nd ed. xviii,599pp; 47 chromo plts (of 48 but w/plt of Great Grey Shrike not called for), map (possibly photocopy) in rear pocket, 4 full-pg woodcuts. Aeg. (Lacks pp xix-xx list of illus, pp 593-4 of general index; pp 387-8, 1 plt washed w/stain towards inner margin; outer margin pp387-399 chipped affecting 3 plts , frontis chipped to outer margin; sympathetically recased.) *Edwards.* $192/£120

LLOYD, L. The Game Birds and Wildfowl of Sweden and Norway. Frederick Warne, 1867. 2nd ed. 48 chromolitho plts (loose; 1 leaf torn; worn). *Sotheby's*.* $202/£126

LLOYD, L. Scandinavian Adventures. London: Richard Bentley, 1854. 1st ed. 2 vols. Med 8vo. xxi,512; xi,527pp; 12 tinted litho plts by Edm. Walker, litho map. Aeg. VG set in 1/4 grn calf, gilt, tan leather labels, cl bds. *Ulysses.* $1,040/£650

LLOYD, L. J. John Skelton: An Account of His Life and Writings. Oxford: Basil Blackwell & Mott, 1938. 1st Eng ed. VG (top edge sl dusty; bumped, spine ends bumped, cvrs sl mkd) in dj (nicked, sl creased, rubbed, dusty, browned, spine sl dampstained). *Ulysses.* $51/£32

LLOYD, NATHANIEL. A History of the English House from the Primitive Times to the Victorian Period. London: Architectural Press, 1949. Rpt. (Spine faded.) *Edwards.* $77/£48

LLOYD, SETON. Twin Rivers. London: Oxford, 1947. Frontis, 12 plts, 4 maps. Dj. *Archaeologia.* $45/£28

LOBEL, ANITA. On Market Street. NY: Greenwillow Books, (1981). Ltd to 250 signed. 4to. Full color poster laid in. Wine cl, gilt. As New in color dj. *Reisler.* $200/£125

LOBEL, ARNOLD. Frog and Toad All Year. NY: Harper & Row, 1976. 1st ed. Signed w/orig Lobel Frog character. 8vo. VG in VG dj. *American Booksellers.* $60/£38

LOBEL, ARNOLD. A Zoo for Mister Muster. NY: Harper & Row, 1962. 1st ed, 1st bk. 10x7.5. 32pp. Cl spine, pict bds. VG (lt soil, fr hinge opened) in dj. *Cattermole.* $40/£25

LOBO ANTUNES, ANTONIO. An Explanation of the Birds. NY: Grove Weidenfeld, 1991. 1st ed. Fine in dj. *Lame Duck.* $25/£16

LOBO, JEROME. A Voyage to Abyssinia.... Samuel Johnson (trans). London: Elliot & Kay, 1789. 2nd ed. (4),500pp. 19th-cent 1/2 black calf, gilt. *Swann*.* $460/£288

LOBSTEIN, JOHN. A Treatise on the Structure, Functions, and Diseases of the Human Sympathetic Nerve. Phila, 1831. 1st ed in English. 157pp + plts. Orig bds (rebacked w/new eps). *Fye.* $175/£109

LOCA, LA. (Pseud of Pamala Karol.) Adventures on the Isle of Adolescence. SF: City Lights, 1989. 1st ed. Signed. Fine in pict stiff wraps. *Any Amount.* $22/£14

LOCKE, A. The Tigers of Trengannu. NY: Scribner, 1954. 1st Amer ed. VG in dj. *Bowman.* $25/£16

LOCKE, A. The Tigers of Trengannu. London, 1954. (Sl foxed.) *Grayling.* $26/£16

LOCKE, JOHN. An Essay Concerning Human Understanding.... Boston: David Carlisle, 1803. 1st Amer ed. 3 vols. li,328; xvi,368; x,329pp. Period tree calf, red leather spine labels. (Browned; lib paper spine stickers w/white inked lib #s on labels; worn, scuffed, joints cracked, peeling, spines scraped, gouged.) *Baltimore*.* $130/£81

LOCKE, JOHN. Letters Concerning Toleration. Ptd for A. Millar et al, 1765. Frontisport, (viii),399,(1)pp. Contemp brn mottled calf (rebacked), raised bands, orig red label (relaid). Good (inscrip dated 1849; corners, edges repaired). *Blackwell's.* $136/£85

LOCKE, W. J. The Mountebank. London/NY/Toronto: John Lane, Bodley Head/Ryerson Press, 1921. 1st ed. Dec red cl. Fine in pict dj (sl frayed, nicked). *Reese.* $50/£31

LOCKHART, JOHN GIBSON. Ancient Spanish Ballads. London, 1842. Aeg. 1/2 red morocco, gilt extra, by Root. *Swann*.* $258/£161

LOCKHART, R. H. BRUCE. Memoirs of a British Agent. London: Putnam, 1932. 1st ed. 3 plts. (Piece cut from fep.) *Hollett.* $32/£20

LOCKHART, ROBERT BRUCE. My Rod, My Comfort. London: Dropmore Press, 1949. 1st ed. One of 550. Unopened, teg. 1/4 vellum, grn cl, gilt. (Emb stamp rep), else Fine. *Pacific*.* $196/£123

LOCKHART, ROBERT BRUCE. Scotch. Putnam, 1970. VG in dj (price-clipped). *Hollett.* $24/£15

LOCKLEY, FRED. Captain Sol. Tetherow, Wagon Train Master. Portland: Fred Lockley, n.d. 1st ed. VG in orig wraps. *Brown.* $25/£16

LOCKLEY, FRED. History of the Columbia River Valley from the Dalles to the Sea. Chicago: S.J. Clarke, 1928. 3 vols. Fine set. *Perier.* $250/£156

LOCKLEY, FRED. To Oregon by Ox-Team in '47.... Portland: The Author, n.d. 16pp. (Lt dampstain along blank margin, not affecting text), o/w Good in orig wraps (lt soiled, sunned). *Brown.* $25/£16

LOCKLEY, RONALD. The Lodge Above the Waterfall. Drumnadrochit: Divach, 1987. Orig card wrappers. VG in dj. *Hollett*. $32/£20

LOCKRIDGE, ROSS. Raintree County. Boston: Houghton Mifflin, 1948. 1st ed, 1st bk. Fine in dj (sl worn). *Lenz*. $125/£78

LOCKWOOD MARSH, W. Aeronautical Prints and Drawings. Halton & Truscott Smith, 1924. 1st ed. Working copy. Color frontis, 87 plts. (Cl dampstained affecting some text, plts.) *Forest*. $56/£35

LOCKWOOD, A. G. B. Gardens of Colony and State. NY, 1931-1934. 2 vols. Folio. (Name, vol 2 half-title lt foxed; vol 1 bds dknd, faded, spotted, soiled; edges rubbed.) *Sutton*. $600/£375

LOCKWOOD, CHARLES A. and HANS CHRISTIAN ADAMSON. Tragedy at Honda. Phila: Chilton, (1960). 1st ed. Gray cl. Dj (sl edgeworn). *Dawson*. $100/£63

LOCKWOOD, E. Natural History, Sport, and Travel. London, 1878. Nice (cl lt mkd). *Grayling*. $104/£65

LOCKWOOD, FRANK C. The Apache Indians. NY: Macmillan, 1938. 1st ed. Fine in dj. Howes L415. *Labordo*. $125/£78

LOCKWOOD, FRANK C. Arizona Characters. L.A.: Times-Mirror, 1928. 1st ed. VG+ in dj (worn). *Labordo*. $135/£84

LOCKWOOD, FRANK C. Arizona Characters. L.A.: Times-Mirror, 1928. Frontis. Dj (edges tape repaired), slipcase. *Dawson*. $150/£94

LOCKWOOD, FRANK C. Life in Old Tucson, 1854-1864. Tucson Civic Comm, (1943). Good. *Rybski*. $55/£34

LOCKWOOD, FRANK C. The Life of Edward E. Ayer. Chicago: A.C. McClurg, 1929. Frontis, 25 full-pg photo illus. Teg. Tan buckram, brn buckram spine, gilt. (Rear bd sl bumped.) Slipcase (lt worn). *Dawson*. $50/£31

LOCKWOOD, FRANK C. The Life of Edward E. Ayer. Chicago: A.C. McClurg, 1929. 1st ed. Pict eps; teg, unopened. Blue cl, dk blue cl backstrip. Fine. *Harrington*. $55/£34

LOCKWOOD, FRANK. Pioneer Days in Arizona. NY: Macmillan, 1932. 1st ed. Good (spine head lt worn). *Lien*. $125/£78

LOCKWOOD, HAZEL. The Golden Book of Birds. NY: S&S, (1945). 3rd ed. 7x8. Feodor Rojankovsky (illus). Unpaginated. Pict bds. VG- (extrems worn) in dj (ragged). *My Bookhouse*. $52/£33

LOCKWOOD, ISABEL INGERSOLL. Oriental Brasses and Other Objects for Temple and Household Use. Glendale: A.H. Clark, 1935. One of 500. 75 plts. Grn cl. Fine. *Metropolitan**. $40/£25

LOCKWOOD, JAMES D. Life and Adventures of a Drummer-Boy; or, Seven Years a Soldier. Albany: John Skinner, 1893. 1st ed. Frontisport, 191pp. Pict cl. (Recased w/new eps, cvrs rubbed, faded, else VG. Howes L418. *Pacific**. $173/£108

LOCKWOOD, LEE. Castro's Cuba, Cuba's Fidel. NY: Macmillan, 1967. 1st ed. Pict eps. VG in dj (lg closed tear). *Cahan*. $45/£28

LOCKWOOD, LUKE VINCENT. Colonial Furniture in America. NY: Scribner, 1951. 3rd ed (so stated). 2 vols. Brick-red buckram, gilt spine. (Bkpls.) Orig labeled bd slipcase (sl worn). *Baltimore**. $50/£31

LODGE, DAVID. The British Museum Is Falling Down. NY, 1965. 1st Amer ed. NF in VG dj (soiled, torn). *Warren*. $75/£47

LODGE, DAVID. The British Museum Is Falling Down. Macgibbon & Kee, 1965. 1st UK ed. Fine in VG dj (spine faded). *Williams*. $440/£275

LODGE, DAVID. Graham Greene. NY/London: Columbia Univ, 1966. VG in wrappers (corners sl creased). *Ulysses*. $120/£75

LODGE, DAVID. Nice Work. Secker, 1988. (Margins yellowed), else Fine in dj. *Any Amount*. $26/£16

LODGE, DAVID. The Picturegoers. London: Macgibbon & Kee, 1960. 1st ed, 1st bk. NF in NF dj. *Dermont*. $400/£250

LODGE, R. B. Bird-Hunting Through Wild Europe. London: Culley, (1908). Pict cl (backstrip tears; fore-edge, tp sl foxed). *Petersfield*. $72/£45

LOEB, CHARLES H. The Future Is Yours: The History of the Future Outlook League, 1935-1946. Cleveland: Future Outlook League, (1947). 1st ed. Frontis. VG+ in pict dj (chipped). *Petrilla*. $65/£41

LOEB, HAROLD. The Way It Was. NY: Criterion Books, 1959. 1st ed. Fine in VG dj. *Pettler*. $45/£28

LOEDERER, RICHARD A. Voodoo Fire in Haiti. NY: Literary Guild, (1935). 1st ed. VG in dj (chipped, sm tears). *Pacific**. $69/£43

LOEHR, MAX and LOUISA HUBER. Ancient Chinese Jades from the Grenville L. Winthrop Collection in the Fogg Art Museum, Harvard University. Cambridge, 1975. 1st ed. *Swann**. $172/£108

LOEHR, MAX. Ancient Chinese Jades. Cambridge, MA: Fogg Art Museum, 1975. Orig ed. Color frontis. (Inscrips.) *Turtle Island*. $125/£78

LOEHR, MAX. Chinese Landscape Woodcuts. Harvard, 1969. Good in dj. *Rybski*. $50/£31

LOEL, W. and W. H. COREY. The Vaqueros Formation, Lower Miocene of California. Berkeley: Univ of CA, 1932. 1st ed. 62 plts, 2 maps. NF in wraps. *Mikesh*. $37/£23

LOEWENBERG, ALFRED. Annals of Opera 1597-1940. Geneve: Societas Bibliographica, (1955). Rev, corrected 2nd ed. (Spine, edges sunned; shelfworn, fr hinge starting.) *Dramatis*. $50/£31

LOFTIE, W. J. Kensington, Picturesque and Historical. Leadenhall Press, 1888. xix,285,lxivpp + 7pp ads. (Feps lt browned; cl sl discolored, mkd.) Dj (chipped w/loss.) *Edwards*. $120/£75

LOFTING, HUGH. Doctor Dolittle and the Green Canary. Phila: Lippincott, (1950). 1st ed. 8vo. Color frontis, 51 full-pg b/w dwgs. Yellow pict cl. Color illus dj (edgeworn). *Reisler*. $150/£94

LOFTING, HUGH. Doctor Dolittle and the Secret Lake. Phila: J.B. Lippincott, (1948). 1st ed. 8vo. Color frontis, 45 dwgs. Orange cl, color paste label. Good in full color dj (lacks pieces, worn). *Reisler*. $125/£78

LOFTING, HUGH. Doctor Dolittle in the Moon. NY: Frederick A. Stokes, (1928). 1st ed. (Bkpl), else Fine in VG dj (spine head chipped, flaps clipped). *Pacific**. $173/£108

LOFTING, HUGH. Doctor Dolittle in the Moon. NY: Frederick A. Stokes, (1928). 1st ed. 8vo. 2 full-pg color illus, 70 b/w dwgs. Violet cl (few sl rubbed spots), color pict paste label. Dj (edges stained). *Reisler*. $200/£125

LOFTING, HUGH. Doctor Dolittle's Caravan. NY: Frederick A. Stokes, (1926). 1st ed. 8vo. Blue cl, color paste label. (Marginal water stains to prelims.) Full color dj (stained, chipped). *Reisler*. $200/£125

LOFTING, HUGH. Doctor Dolittle's Garden. NY: F.A. Stokes, (1927). 1st ed. 8vo. Color frontis, viii,327pp. Color pict eps. Grn cl, w/color plt on cvr. Fine in VG dj (lt soiled, edges chipped). *House*. $125/£78

LOFTING, HUGH. Doctor Dolittle's Garden. NY: Frederick A. Stokes, (1927). 1st ed. (Bkpl), else NF in VG dj (spine ends chipped, few sm tears to extrems). *Pacific**. $173/£108

LOFTING, HUGH. Doctor Dolittle's Garden. London: Cape, 1945. Color frontis. Color pict eps. (Spine faded), else VG. *Quest*. $35/£22

LOFTING, HUGH. Doctor Dolittle's Post Office. Stokes, 1923. 1st ed. 359pp. NF (top edge sl dusty, spine ends sl bumped). *Price*. $150/£94

LOFTING, HUGH. Doctor Dolittle's Puddleby Adventures. NY: Lippincott, (1952). 1st ed. 8vo. Color frontis. Pink cl. Good in color pict dj (worn). *Reisler*. $125/£78

LOFTING, HUGH. Doctor Dolittle's Return. NY: Frederick A. Stokes, 1933. 1st ed. Pict cvr label. (Label sl rubbed), else VG. *Pacific**. $46/£29

LOFTING, HUGH. Doctor Dolittle's Return. NY: Frederick A. Stokes, 1933. 1st ed. 8vo. Full color frontis, 14 full-pg b/w plts. Orange dec cl (spine sl dknd), color paste label. *Reisler.* $110/£69

LOFTING, HUGH. Doctor Dolittle's Zoo. NY: Frederick A. Stokes, (1925). 1st ed. 8vo. Full-color frontis, 88 b/w dwgs. Gray cl (sl mkd), color paste label. Pict dj (stained, pieces missing along fr flap, chipped along fold). *Reisler.* $200/£125

LOFTING, HUGH. Doctor Dolittle's Zoo. Cape, 1926. 1st ed. VG. *Green Meadow.* $56/£35

LOFTING, HUGH. Noisy Nora. NY: F. A. Stokes, (1929). 1st ed. 12mo. 4 full-pg color plts. Full color eps. Pink ribbed cl, color paste label. (Corner sl worn), o/w VG in Nice full color dj (marginal folds). *Reisler.* $250/£156

LOFTING, HUGH. The Story of Doctor Dolittle. NY: Frederick A. Stokes, 1920. 1st ed. 8vo. Full-color frontis, 33 b/w illus. Orange cl, full color paste label. Good in full color dj (wear, lacks spine pieces). *Reisler.* $950/£594

LOFTING, HUGH. The Twilight of Magic. Cape, 1931. 1st ed. Lois Lenski (illus). Pict cl. VG. *Green Meadow.* $56/£35

LOFTING, HUGH. The Voyages of Doctor Dolittle. NY: Frederick Stokes, (1923). 4th ed. Signed. Color frontis. Pict cvr label. Good (hinges cracking, bkpl, date stamps; shelfworn). *Pacific**. $92/£58

LOFTING, HUGH. The Voyages of Doctor Dolittle. Stokes, 1923. 6th ptg. Gray cl w/plt. VG (top edge dusty) in dj (remnant, lacks 2-inches of spine, tape pull affecting text). *Price.* $50/£31

Log of Cleopatra's Barge II, 1928-1942. Boston: Privately ptd, 1948. Frontisport. Teg. 1/4 morocco, marbled bds, gilt, paper cvr label. Fine. *Pacific**. $46/£29

LOGAN, C. A. Physics of the Infectious Diseases. Chicago, 1878. 1st ed. 212pp. *Fye.* $100/£63

LOGAN, HERSCHEL C. Buckskin and Satin. Harrisburg, PA: Stackpole, (1954). 1st ed. Signed. Fine in Fine dj. *Book Market.* $45/£28

LOGAN, HERSCHEL C. Hand Cannon to Automatic. Huntington, WV: Standard Publications, 1944. 1st ed. Fine. *Book Market.* $45/£28

LOGAN, JOSHUA. The Wisteria Trees. NY: Random House, (1950). 1st ed. VF in VF dj. *Between The Covers.* $250/£156

LOGAN, MRS. JOHN A. Thirty Years in Washington or Life and Scenes in Our National Capital. Worthington, 1901. Good. *Rybski.* $35/£22

LOGAN, WILLIAM. The Great Social Evil. London: Hodder & Stoughton, 1871. 1st ed. 240pp. Brn cl. VF. *Sumner & Stillman.* $165/£103

LOGUE, CHRISTOPHER. Puss in Boots. London: Cape, 1976. 4 dbl-pg pop-ups by Nicola Bayley. Glazed pict bds. VG. *Bookfinders.* $70/£44

LOGUE, CHRISTOPHER. Songs. NY, 1960. 1st Amer ed. Fine in Fine dj. *Polyanthos.* $25/£16

LOGUE, LARRY M. A Sermon in the Desert. Urbana: Univ of IL, (1988). 1st ed. As New in dj. *Perier.* $27/£17

LOHMAN, S. W. The Geologic Story of Canyonlands National Park. Washington: USGS, 1974. Map. VG + . *Five Quail.* $10/£6

LOKVIG, TOR and CHUCK MURPHY. Star Trek, the Motion Picture. The Pop-Up Book. NY: Wanderer Books/S&S, 1980. 5 dbl-pg pop-ups. Glazed pict bds. VG. *Bookfinders.* $40/£25

LOLIEE, FREDERIC. Women of the Second Empire. A. M. Ivimy (trans). London: Lane, 1907. 51 plts. Teg. Good. *Stewart.* $80/£50

LOMAX, ALAN. Mister Jelly Roll. NY: Duell, Sloan & Pearce, 1950. 1st ed. Fine in NF dj (spine sl dknd, sm chip to head). *Beasley.* $60/£38

LOMAX, ALFRED L. Pioneer Woolen Mills in Oregon. History of Wool and the Woolen Textile Industry in Oregon 1811-1875. Portland: Binfords & Mort, (1941). 1st ed. Special author's copy. Signed presentation. Fine in 1/4 blue leather w/wool cl. *Perier.* $75/£47

LOMAX, JOHN A. Adventures of a Ballad Hunter. NY: Macmillan, 1947. 1st ed. VG in dj. *Labordo.* $60/£38

LOMAX, JOHN A. Cow Camps and Cattle Herds. Austin: Encino, 1967. 1st ed. One of 750. Signed. VF. *Labordo.* $95/£59

LOMAX, JOHN A. Cowboy Songs and Other Frontier Ballads. NY: Sturgis & Walton, 1910. 1st ed. Pict cl. NF. *Labordo.* $275/£172

LOMAX, JOHN A. Cowboy Songs and Other Frontier Ballads. NY: Macmillan, 1924. (Spine faded), else Good. *Dumont.* $30/£19

LOMMIS, ANDREW. Creative Illustration. NY: Viking, 1947. Fine in pict dj (bumped, stained). *Metropolitan**. $149/£93

LOMMIUS, JODOCUS. A Treatise of Continual Fevers.... Thomas Dale (trans). London, 1732. 1st ed in English. 8 ll, 1-452pp, 2 ll ads. Contemp full calf (worn, rubbed). *Kane**. $160/£100

London Almanack. London: For the Company of Stationers, 1823. 24pp, (n.n.), 4pp view. (Red duty stamp.) Cream morocco, gilt. Matching slipcase. *Marlborough.* $480/£300

London Cyclist Battalion. London, 1932. 1st Eng ed. VG (cvr edges faded, back cvr cracked). *Clearwater.* $152/£95

LONDON, CHARMIAN. The Book of Jack London. NY: Century, 1921. 1st ed. 2 vols. 14 inserted photo plts vol 1, 16 inserted photo plts vol 2. Grn cl, gilt. NF set (extrems sl rubbed). *Heritage.* $350/£219

LONDON, CHARMIAN. Our Hawaii. NY: Macmillan, 1917. 1st ed. Blue cl, gilt. NF (bkpl, extrems lt rubbed). *Heritage.* $250/£156

LONDON, JACK and HERBERT HERON. Gold: A Play in Three Acts. Oakland: Holmes Book Co, 1972. 1st ed. One of 1000. Fine in dj. *Pacific**. $92/£58

LONDON, JACK. The Abysmal Brute. NY: Century, 1913. 1st ed, 1st issue, w/yellow stamping. Olive cl. VG (bkpl; spine cocked, dknd; cvrs soiled; extrems sl rubbed). BAL 11945. *Heritage.* $150/£94

LONDON, JACK. The Abysmal Brute. NY: Century, 1913. 1st ed. Frontis. Variant (probably later) grn cl. NF in dj (spine head lacks 1.5 inches, affecting title; tape repairs to verso). BAL 11945. *Pacific**. $345/£216

LONDON, JACK. Adventure. London: Thomas Nelson, (1911). 1st ed. Color frontis. Dec eps. Grn cl, gilt. (Fr hinge cracking; white on spine mostly rubbed off), else VG. BAL 11928. *Pacific**. $150/£94

LONDON, JACK. Adventure. NY: Macmillan, 1911. 1st Amer ed. Dk blue cl. (Hinges starting; spine ends rubbed, lettering worn off), else VG-. BAL 11928. *Pacific**. $63/£39

LONDON, JACK. Adventure. NY: Macmillan, 1911. 1st Amer ed. Variant binding: red cl lettered in white. (Name; spine faded, lt spot fr cvr, partial lettering wearing off), else VG. BAL 11928. *Pacific**. $104/£65

LONDON, JACK. Adventure. NY, 1911. 1st Amer ed. Pict cl (rubbed; fr inner hinge weak). *Swann**. $115/£72

LONDON, JACK. The Apostate. Girard, KS: The Appeal to Reason, 1906. 1st separate ed. 16pp. Ptd wrappers (chipped, detached but present). BAL 11897. *Heritage.* $175/£109

LONDON, JACK. Before Adam. NY: Macmillan, 1907. 1st ed. Color frontis, 7 color plts, 2-pg inserted map. Lt brn buckram. (Name; spine sl dknd), else NF. BAL 11903. *Pacific**. $98/£61

LONDON, JACK. Before Adam. NY: Macmillan, 1907. 1st ed. 7 full-pg color plts. Tan buckram. Good (some ll w/upper outer corners torn away, reps browned; spine dknd, sm stain rear cvr, extrems sl rubbed). BAL 11903. *Heritage.* $100/£63

LONDON, JACK. Burning Daylight. NY: Macmillan, 1910. 1st ed. State w/Macmillan spine imprint, 3 blank ll at rear, p(366) blank. 8 plts. Blue cl. VG. BAL 11918. *Pacific*.* $92/£58

LONDON, JACK. Burning Daylight. NY, 1910. 1st ed. Frontis. Pict blue cl. *Swann*.* $172/£108

LONDON, JACK. Burning Daylight. NY: Macmillan, 1910. 1st ed. State w/Macmillan spine imprint and 1 blank leaf at rear. 8 plts. Blue cl. Fine. BAL 11918. *Pacific*.* $316/£198

LONDON, JACK. Burning Daylight. Bernhard Tauchnitz, 1911. Copyright ed. Contemp cl. Good (spine bumped, cvrs unevenly sunned w/sl mks). *Tiger.* $29/£18

LONDON, JACK. The Call of the Wild. NY: Macmillan, 1903. 1st ed. Pict eps; teg, untrimmed. Ribbed gray-grn cl, gilt. (1/2-title wrinkled, few finger smudges tp margin; sl rubbed, flaking to fr cvr illus). Cvrs Good. BAL 11876. *Baltimore*.* $280/£175

LONDON, JACK. The Call of the Wild. NY: Macmillan, 1903. 1st ed. Color frontis. Teg. Vertically-ribbed grn cl, gilt. (Spine ends, joints sl rubbed, sl shelfworn), else VG in dj (spine head, corners sl chipped, sm tears to extrems). BAL 11876. *Pacific*.* $1,725/£1,078

LONDON, JACK. The Call of the Wild. LEC, 1960. Ltd to 1500 numbered, signed by Henry Varnum Poor (illus). Fine in slipcase. *Swann*.* $80/£50

LONDON, JACK. The Cruise of the Dazzler. NY: Century, 1902. 1st ed. (Text sl soiled.) Illus cl (rubbed, soiled, shaken, spine faint). BAL 11872. *Cummins.* $150/£94

LONDON, JACK. The Cruise of the Snark. NY: Macmillan, 1911. 1st ed. Color frontis, 1 b/w plt inserted. Teg. Blue cl, gilt, pict label fr cvr. (Bkpl, spine ends lt rubbed), o/w Fine. BAL 11929. *Heritage.* $600/£375

LONDON, JACK. The Cruise of the Snark. NY: Macmillan, 1911. 1st ed. Color frontis. Teg. Blue-grn cl, gilt, pict cvr label. Fine. BAL 11929. *Pacific*.* $633/£396

LONDON, JACK. A Daughter of the Snows. Phila: Lippincott, 1902. 1st ed. 4 color plts, incl frontis. Red cl. (Sl internal soil; spine sunned), else VG. BAL 11874. *Pacific*.* $161/£101

LONDON, JACK. Daughters of the Rich. Oakland: Holmes Book Co, 1971. 1st ed. Fine in wrappers. *Pacific*.* $46/£29

LONDON, JACK. Daughters of the Rich. Oakland: Holmes Book Co, 1971. 1st ed. Fine in wrappers. *Pacific*.* $58/£36

LONDON, JACK. Dutch Courage and Other Stories. NY: Macmillan, 1922. 1st ed. Frontis port, 7 plts. Red cl, gilt. (Eps sl browned, foxed), o/w NF in dj (spine sl browned, rear panel sl soiled, spine top chipped, fr flap unevenly trimmed, torn), 1/4 blue morocco clamshell case. BAL 11985. *Heritage.* $2,750/£1,719

LONDON, JACK. Dutch Courage. NY, 1922. 1st ed. 8vo. Pict red cl, gilt spine. Dj (lacks part of spine, extrems chipped). *Swann*.* $517/£323

LONDON, JACK. The Faith of Men and Other Stories. NY: Macmillan, 1904. 1st ed. Teg. Lt blue cl. (Sl lacquering to spine, ends sl rubbed), else NF. BAL 11878. *Pacific*.* $288/£180

LONDON, JACK. The Game. NY: Macmillan, 1905. 1st ed, 2nd issue, w/rubberstamp on c. pg. Pict eps; teg. Blue-grn cl. (Lt aged, fr hinge sl weak; sl rubbed, lt worn, spotted.) Cvrs Good. BAL 11886. *Baltimore*.* $25/£16

LONDON, JACK. The Game. NY, 1905. 1st ed. Frontis, 5 plts. Pict grn blue-grn cl. (Name.) *Swann*.* $69/£43

LONDON, JACK. The Game. NY: Macmillan, 1905. 1st ed, 2nd issue, w/the rubber stamp on copyright pg. Color frontis. Pict eps, teg. Grn cl. VG (extrems, joints lt rubbed, cvrs lt soiled). BAL 11886. *Heritage.* $200/£125

LONDON, JACK. The God of His Fathers and Other Stories. NY: McClure, Phillips, 1901. 1st ed. Blue cl, gilt. (Adhesion residue, offset from tape to eps; spine ends sl rubbed), else VG. BAL 11870. *Pacific*.* $150/£94

LONDON, JACK. Hearts of Three. London, (1918). 1st ed. Blue cl (worn, rubbed). *Swann*.* $287/£179

LONDON, JACK. Hearts of Three. NY: Macmillan, 1920. 1st ed. Red cl, gilt spine. Good (bkpl, hinges cracked, eps lt browned; cvrs soiled, spotted, extrems rubbed) in maroon cl open-end slipcase. BALL 11982. *Heritage.* $200/£125

LONDON, JACK. Hearts of Three. NY: Macmillan, 1920. 1st ed. Fine in dj (few chips, expertly repaired tears). *Lame Duck.* $2,500/£1,563

LONDON, JACK. The House of Pride and Other Tales of Hawaii. NY: Macmillan, 1912. 1st ed. Frontis. Lt grn cl. (Bkpl, name; spine ends sl rubbed), else NF. BAL 11936. *Pacific*.* $460/£288

LONDON, JACK. The Human Drift. NY, 1917. 1st ed. Frontisport. Red cl, gilt. *Swann*.* $345/£216

LONDON, JACK. The Iron Heel. NY: Macmillan, 1908. 1st ed. Dk blue cl. (Spine ends lt rubbed), else NF. BAL 11908. *Pacific*.* $196/£123

LONDON, JACK. The Iron Heel. NY, 1908. 1st ed. Gilt-pict deep blue cl. (Sl shaken, corner bumped.) *Swann*.* $230/£144

LONDON, JACK. Jack London by Himself. London: Mills & Boon, (n.d., 1913). 1st Eng ed. 8pp (incl cvrs). Wrappers (sl browned). *Heritage.* $75/£47

LONDON, JACK. The Jacket (The Star Rover). London: Mills & Boon, n.d. (but 1918). 1st ed. Blue-grn cl, gilt. (Spine sl sunned, ends frayed), else VG-. BAL 11962. *Pacific*.* $288/£180

LONDON, JACK. Jerry of the Islands. NY: Macmillan, 1917. 1st ed. Red-brn pict cl, gilt. VG. BAL 11973. *Macdonnell.* $85/£53

LONDON, JACK. Jerry of the Islands. NY, 1917. 1st ed. Frontis. Red cl. *Swann*.* $115/£72

LONDON, JACK. Jerry of the Islands. NY: Macmillan, 1917. Advance rev copy w/perf stamp on tp. Color frontis. Red cl. (Spine dknd, ends sl rubbed), else VG. BAL 11973. *Pacific*.* $633/£396

LONDON, JACK. John Barleycorn. NY: Century, 1913. 1st ed, 2nd ptg, w/3 blank leaves following p343. Frontis, 7 plts. Dk grn cl, gilt. (Spine ends bumped, few scratches rear cvr), o/w NF. BAL 11946. *Heritage.* $250/£156

LONDON, JACK. A Klondike Trilogy: Three Uncollected Stories. Earle Labor (ed). Santa Barbara: Neville, 1983. 1st ed thus. One of 300. Fine. *Pacific*.* $63/£39

LONDON, JACK. The Little Lady of the Big House. Macmillan, 1916. 1st ed, 1st state binding w/spine lettering in gold. VG +. *Fine Books.* $185/£116

LONDON, JACK. Lost Face. NY: Macmillan, 1910. 1st ed. Frontis, 5 plts. Dk blue cl. (Shelfworn), else NF. BAL 11915. *Pacific*.* $161/£101

LONDON, JACK. Lost Face. NY, 1910. 1st ed. Frontis, 5 plts. Pict grn cl. *Swann*.* $287/£179

LONDON, JACK. Love of Life and Other Stories. NY: Macmillan, 1907. 1st ed. Blue cl, rule border on fr cvr yellow instead of silver. (Fr hinge sl weak; spine ends, rear cvr edge rubbed), else VG +. BAL 11904. *Pacific*.* $259/£162

LONDON, JACK. Love of Life and Other Stories. NY, 1907. 1st ed. Gilt-pict dk blue cl. Fine. *Swann*.* $316/£198

LONDON, JACK. Martin Eden. NY, 1909. 1st ed. Frontis. Dec stamped dk blue cl. *Swann*.* $258/£161

LONDON, JACK. Michael, Brother of Jerry. NY, 1917. 1st ed. Frontis. Red cl. *Swann*.* $126/£79

LONDON, JACK. Michael, Brother of Jerry. NY: Macmillan, 1917. 1st ed. Color frontis. VG (spine dknd, gilt faded, cvr lt soiled). BAL 11974. *Heritage.* $150/£94

LONDON, JACK. Michael, Brother of Jerry. NY: Macmillan, 1917. 1st ed. Color frontis. Red cl. (Name), else VG. BAL 11974. *Pacific*.* $184/£115

LONDON, JACK. Moon-Face and Other Stories. NY: Macmillan, 1906. 1st ed. Teg. Blue cl, initials R.R in center of dec on fr cvr in lt grn, not cream. (Eps sl foxed; spine ends sl rubbed), else VG. BAL 11895. *Pacific*.* $98/£61

LONDON, JACK. The Night Born. NY: Century, 1913. 1st ed, 1st ptg w/1 blank leaf at rear. Color frontis. Gray-blue cl. (Spine ends sl rubbed, sm wrap spot to mid-spine), else VG. BAL 11942. *Pacific*.* $86/£54

LONDON, JACK. An Odyssey of the North. Girard, KS: Haldeman-Julius, (1920). 1st separate publication. Good (bkpl; browned) in wrappers (browned). *Heritage.* $25/£16

LONDON, JACK. The People of the Abyss. Toronto: George Morang, 1903. 1st Canadian ed. Frontis. Blue cl, gilt. (Spine ends sl rubbed), else VG. BAL 11877. *Pacific*.* $109/£68

LONDON, JACK. The People of the Abyss. NY: Macmillan, 1903. 1st ed. Frontis. Teg. Gray-blue cl. (Sl shaken; spine ends, corners rubbed, fr corner bumped), else VG. BAL 11877. *Pacific*.* $259/£162

LONDON, JACK. The Red One. NY: Macmillan, 1918. 1st ed. Frontisport. Dec brn bds. Fair (spine dknd, joints cracked, brn paint to fr joint) in dj (tape-repaired tears, extrems chipped, upper spine lacking). *Pacific*.* $288/£180

LONDON, JACK. The Red One. NY, 1918. 1st ed. 8vo. Pict bds (spine extrems worn). *Swann*.* $546/£341

LONDON, JACK. The Red One. NY: Macmillan, 1918. 1st ed. Frontisport. Dec brn bds. Fine. *Pacific*.* $805/£503

LONDON, JACK. The Red One. NY: Macmillan, 1918. 1st ed. 8vo. Frontis. Tan bds. VG (eps, edges browned, foxed; expert repair to joints, backstrip) in dj (sl soiled, shelfworn, expert restoration), 1/4 morocco clamshell case. BAL 11977. *Heritage.* $3,500/£2,188

LONDON, JACK. Revolution and Other Essays. London: Mills & Boon, (1910). 1st British ed. Possibly pub later than 1910. Lt blue cl. (Name), else VG- in dj (spine ends, flap creases chipped, reinforcements verso). *Pacific*.* $104/£65

LONDON, JACK. Revolution and Other Essays. NY: Macmillan, 1910. 1st ed, variant (remainder?) binding, w/spine imprint: Macmillan. Brn cl. Fine. BAL 11916. *Pacific*.* $316/£198

LONDON, JACK. The Road. NY: Macmillan, 1907. 1st ed. Frontis, 47 photo plts. Teg. Lt gray cl, gilt. (Lacks last 2 ad pp, staining to pp(225-226); rubbed, lettering, black design faded, rear hinge cracked), else Good. *Pacific*.* $69/£43

LONDON, JACK. The Scarlet Plague. NY, 1915. 1st ed. Pict deep red cl (spine head worn, sl cl loss). *Swann*.* $345/£216

LONDON, JACK. The Sea Sprite and the Shooting Star. (N.p.: Privately ptd, Nov 1932.) 1st ed. Single sheet folded lengthwise. Fine. *Heritage.* $150/£94

LONDON, JACK. The Sea-Wolf. NY, 1904. 1st ed, 2nd ptg. 6 plts. Blue cl (few sm spine spots). BAL 11882. *Kane*.* $160/£100

LONDON, JACK. The Sea-Wolf. London: Macmillan, 1904. 1st ed. 6 plts. Teg. Blue cl. NF (eps lt browned, few fox mks; extrems sl rubbed). BAL 11882, binding B. *Heritage.* $350/£219

LONDON, JACK. The Sea-Wolf. NY: Macmillan, 1904. 1st ed, preferred issue w/gilt spine lettering. Frontis, 5 plts. Blue cl. (Fr hinge cracking; spine ends, corners lt worn), else VG. BAL 11882. *Pacific*.* $403/£252

LONDON, JACK. The Sea-Wolf. NY, 1904. 1st ed. Frontis, 5 plts. Pict blue cl. *Swann*.* $431/£269

LONDON, JACK. The Sea-Wolf. Bernhard Tauchnitz, 1912. Copyright ed. 2 vols. Contemp cl, leather spine labels. Good (bkpls; spines bumped, sunned). *Tiger.* $32/£20

LONDON, JACK. The Sea-Wolf. NY: Heritage, 1961. Full-color frontis, full-color endpiece. 'Sandglass' laid in. Pict cl. NF (name) in NF slipcase. *Connolly.* $25/£16

LONDON, JACK. The Sea-Wolf. LEC, 1961. Ltd to 1500 numbered, signed by Fletcher Martin (illus). Fine in slipcase. *Swann*.* $138/£86

LONDON, JACK. Smoke and Shorty. London: Mills & Boon, (1920). 1st British ed. Red cl. (Possibly lacks prelim pg; sl soiled), else VG. BAL 12006. *Pacific*.* $52/£33

LONDON, JACK. Smoke Bellew. NY, 1912. 1st ed. Frontis, 7 plts. Pict dk blue cl (lt rubbed). *Swann*.* $115/£72

LONDON, JACK. Smoke Bellew. NY: Century, 1912. 1st ed. Frontis, 7 plts. Blue cl. VG (fr hinge starting; cvrs soiled, scratched, extrems sl rubbed). BAL 11939. *Heritage.* $200/£125

LONDON, JACK. A Son of the Sun. GC: Doubleday, Page, 1912. 1st ed. Frontis, 3 plts. Navy blue cl. (Names), else NF. BAL 11937. *Pacific*.* $196/£123

LONDON, JACK. A Son of the Sun. GC: Doubleday, Page, 1912. 1st ed. Frontis, 3 plts. Navy blue cl. NF in dj (spine head/fr panel lacks piece, soil, extrems rubbed, stain to lower fr panel). BAL 11937. *Pacific*.* $1,380/£863

LONDON, JACK. The Son of the Wolf. Boston, 1900. 1st ed, 1st state. Blanck's 1st binding. Frontis. Silver-pict gray cl (lt rubbed, sl askew). *Swann*.* $345/£216

LONDON, JACK. The Son of the Wolf: Tales of the Far North. Boston: Houghton Mifflin, 1900. 1st ed, 1st ptg, 1st bk. 1st issue binding w/no dots flanking the ampersand in pub's name on spine. Frontis, (8),251,(1)pp. Gray cl. (Bkpl; silver stamping sl tarnished), o/w NF. BAL 11869. *Pacific*.* $546/£341

LONDON, JACK. The Son of the Wolf: Tales of the Far North. Boston: Houghton, Mifflin, 1900. 1st ed, 1st ptg, 1st issue binding w/no dots flanking ampersand in pub's name on spine. Frontis. Gray cl stamped in silver. (Name; fr, middle hinges starting; silver stamping sl tarnished), o/w VG. BAL 11869. *Pacific*.* $633/£396

LONDON, JACK. South Sea Tales. NY: Macmillan, 1911. 1st ed. Color frontis. Blue cl. (Adhesion residue rep, eps soiled; lettering worn off, extrems rubbed), else VG-. *Pacific*.* $109/£68

LONDON, JACK. South Sea Tales. Bernhard Tauchnitz, n.d. (1913). Copyright ed. Good in paper wrappers (chipped, dusty). *Tiger.* $19/£12

LONDON, JACK. The Strength of the Strong. NY, 1914. 1st ed. Frontis. Gilt-dec blue cl (spine lt rubbed). *Swann*.* $258/£161

LONDON, JACK. The Strength of the Strong. NY: Macmillan, 1914. 1st ed. Frontis. Blue cl. (Sl adhesion residue, tape offset eps), else NF. BAL 11955. *Pacific*.* $288/£180

LONDON, JACK. Tales of the Fish Patrol. NY/London: Macmillan, 1905. 1st ed, w/'Published Sept. 1905' on c. pg. Frontis; 6 plts. Dec blue cl. (Lt discoloration), else VG. BAL 11887. *Cummins.* $150/£94

LONDON, JACK. Tales of the Fish Patrol. NY, 1905. 1st ed. Frontis, map, 6 plts. Pict blue cl. (Bkpl, lib bkpl tipped on slip on rear pastedown; spine extrems lt rubbed.) *Swann*.* $373/£233

LONDON, JACK. Tales of the Fish Patrol. NY: Macmillan, 1905. 1st ed. Map, 7 plts. Teg. Blue cl. NF. BAL 11887. *Pacific*.* $431/£269

LONDON, JACK. Theft: A Play in Four Acts. NY: Macmillan, 1910. 1st ed, 1st issue w/1 blank leaf in rear, later issue binding. Brn cl, spine lettered in black. (Soil, sl spine warping), else VG. BAL 11919. *Pacific*.* $805/£503

LONDON, JACK. When God Laughs and Other Stories. NY: Macmillan, 1911. 1st ed. Frontis, 5 plts. Olive grn cl. (Spine ends lt rubbed), else NF. BAL 11926. *Pacific*.* $196/£123

LONDON, JACK. When God Laughs. NY, 1911. 1st ed. Frontis, 5 plts. Dec-stamped grn cl. Swann*. $460/£288

LONDON, JACK. White Fang. NY: Macmillan, 1906. 1st ed, 2nd issue w/the tipped-in tp. Frontis, 7 color plts. Blue-grn cl, gilt. (Hinges cracked, spine ends sl rubbed, lower corners sl bumped), else VG. BAL 11896. Pacific*. $98/£61

LONDON, JACK. White Fang. LEC, 1973. One of 2000 signed by Lydia Dabcovich (illus). Fine in slipcase. Swann*. $80/£50

LONE, E. MIRIAM. Some Noteworthy Firsts in Europe During the Fifteenth Century. NY: Lathrop C. Harper, 1930. One of 425, this not numbered, ptd by Fred Anthoensen. Uncut. Simulated vellum w/wallet flaps. (Lt worn.) Slipcase. Oinonen*. $50/£31

Long Island and Where to Go!! A Descriptive Work Compiled for the Long Island R.R. Co. NY: Lovibond & Jackson, 1877. 1st ed. Frontis fldg map. Pict wrappers. (Tears to map creases, sm tears to joints, cvrs sl dampstained), else VG. Pacific*. $150/£94

Long Journey. (By Charles W. Hayes.) Portland, ME, 1876. 1st ed. One of 100 ptd. 76pp. Good (ex-lib). Howes H344. M & S. $175/£109

Long Live the Queen. London: Juvenile Productions, n.d. (1953). 4 dbl-pg pop-ups. VG- in illus wraps. Bookfinders. $110/£69

LONG, A. L. Memoirs of Robert E. Lee. NY: J.M. Stoddart, 1887. 2nd ed. Frontisport, 707pp. Grn cl. (Lib bkpl, blindstamp, inscrip), else VG. Chapel Hill. $95/£59

LONG, A. L. Memoirs of Robert E. Lee. Marcus J. Wright (ed). London: Sampson, Low, Marston et al, 1886. 1st Eng ed. Frontisport, 707pp. Teg. Orig 1/2 red morocco, grn cl. VG (lt foxed; spine worn). Chapel Hill. $150/£94

LONG, A. W. Irish Sport of Yesterday. Boston: Houghton Mifflin, 1923. 1st ed. Grn cl, paper spine label. Fine. Pacific*. $40/£25

LONG, BASIL. British Miniaturists 1520-1860. Holland, 1966. 32 plts. VG in dj. Hollett. $96/£60

LONG, C. A. The Mammals of Wyoming. Lawrence, 1965. 82 maps. Wrappers (name). Sutton. $30/£19

LONG, C. CHAILLE. Central Africa: Naked Truths of Naked People. NY: Harper, 1877. 1st Amer ed. xv,(i),330,6 ads pp; 21 wood-engr plts; 1 fldg color map. Brn dec cl, gilt. (Few ink notes; spine ends sl rubbed), o/w Fine. Sotheran. $360/£225

LONG, FRANK BELKNAP. The Goblin Tower. Denver: New Collector's Group, 1949. 1st ed thus. One of 500. (Extrems sl browned), else Fine in pict wrappers. Pacific*. $92/£58

LONG, H. P. My First Days in the White House. Telegraph Press, 1935. 1st ed. VG+ in VG dj (lt worn, torn, sl chipped). Fine Books. $175/£109

LONG, HANIEL. Pinon Country. NY: Duell, Sloan & Pearce, 1941. Good in dj (worn, chipped). Dumont. $35/£22

LONG, HANIEL. Pittsburgh Memoranda. Santa Fe: Writers' Editions, (1935). One of 1000 numbered, signed. Black buckram. Fine in Fine dj. Dermont. $125/£78

LONG, HANIEL. The Power Within Us. Nevada City: Harold Berliner, (1975). Ltd to 750. Full buckram. Truepenny. $75/£47

LONG, KATHERINE W. and SAMUEL A. SICILIANO. Yuma from Hell-Hole to Haven. Yuma: Yuma County Chamber of Commerce, 1950. 1st ed. 3 dbl-pg illus. Fine in pict heavy wrappers. Connolly. $20/£13

LONG, MARGARET. The Shadow of the Arrow. Caldwell: Caxton, 1941. 1st ed. VG in dec cl. Perier. $17/£11

LONG, MARGARET. The Shadow of the Arrow. Caldwell, ID: Caxton Ptrs, 1941. 1st ed. 5 maps. Gray pict cl. Fine in VG dj (tears on fr panel, stabilized, repaired). Harrington. $45/£28

LONG, MARGARET. The Shadow of the Arrow. Caldwell: Caxton, 1950. Rev ed. 25 plts, 5 maps. Brn pict cl. Fine in pict dj (price-clipped). Pacific*. $58/£36

LONG, PERRIN and ELEANOR BLISS. The Clinical and Experimental Use of Sulfanilamide, Sulfapyridine and Allied Compounds. NY, 1939. 1st ed. Fye. $100/£63

LONG, STEPHEN H. Account of An Expedition From Pittsburgh to the Rocky Mountains. Barre, 1972. Ltd to 1950 numbered. VG in VG slipcase. Woolson. $50/£31

LONG, STEPHEN H. Voyage in a Six-Oared Skiff to the Falls of Anthony I, 1817. Phila: Henery B. Ashmead, 1860. Nice (spine replaced). Metropolitan*. $172/£108

LONG, T. B. 70 Years a Cowboy. (Regina): The Author, 1959. 1st ed. Signed. Fine in wraps. Perier. $45/£28

LONG, WILLIAM J. How Animals Talk. Harper, 1919. Stated 1st ed. 4to. 302pp; 8 glossy plts by Charles Copeland. Teg. Prize-plt tipped in on fep, emblem stamped on rear cvr. NF. Bookmark. $40/£25

LONGACRE, JAMES B. and JAMES HERRING. The National Portrait Gallery of Distinguished Americans. Volumes III-IV (of 4). Phila/NY: Henry Perkins or Longacre/Herring, 1836-1839. Half-titles, extra engr tps, 74 Good steel-engr port plts, guards. Yellow coated eps; aeg. Orig full scarlet morocco, gilt. (Foxed, sm stains, some plts browned, foxed; sl worn, lt scuffed.) Cvrs VG. Howes H443. Baltimore*. $200/£125

LONGACRE, WILLIAM A. (ed). Reconstructing Prehistoric Pueblo Societies. Albuquerque, 1970. 1st ed. (Pencil notes), else Good in dj (chipped). Dumont. $40/£25

LONGFELLOW, H. W. The Courtship of Miles Standish, and Other Poems. Boston: Ticknor & Fields, 1858. 1st US ed, 1st state. 12-pg pub's cat dated Oct 1858 inserted at rear. Dk brn coated eps. Blind dk brn cl, gilt spine. (Lt aged; sm nick spine foot.) Cvrs VG. BAL 12122. Baltimore*. $80/£50

LONGFELLOW, H. W. The Golden Legend. London, 1851. 1st Eng ed, 1st state. (Ink inscrip; spine sunned, ends chipped; outer hinge sl torn, hinges weak.) King. $75/£47

LONGFELLOW, H. W. The Golden Legend. Boston: Ticknor, Reed & Fields, 1851. 1st ed. Oct 1851 cat. VG (sigs; corners, spine tips worn). BAL 12102. Agvent. $100/£63

LONGFELLOW, H. W. The Poems of Henry Wadsworth Longfellow. LEC, 1944. One of 1100 signed by Boyd Hanna (illus). Fine in slipcase. Swann*. $172/£108

LONGFELLOW, H. W. The Poets and Poetry of Europe. Phila: Carey & Hart, 1845. 1st ed, 1st ptg. 779pp. Aeg. Orig full maroon morocco, gilt. Fine (spine sunned). BAL 12078. Macdonnell. $300/£188

LONGFELLOW, H. W. The Skeleton in Armor. Boston: James R. Osgood, 1877. 1st separate ed. Pict terra cotta cl, gilt. Fine. BAL 12550. Macdonnell. $65/£41

LONGFELLOW, H. W. The Song of Hiawatha. Boston: Houghton Mifflin, 1891. 1st Remington ed. 22 photogravure plts by Frederic Remington; ptd tissue guards. Pict sheep, gilt. (19th c. inscribed card mtd to fep; fr joint leather sl torn, spine ends lt rubbed), else VG. Pacific*. $207/£129

LONGFELLOW, H. W. Tales of a Wayside Inn. Boston: Ticknor & Fields, 1863. 1st ed. VG (bkpl removed, paper aging; spine faded, corners, spine sl worn). BAL 12136. Agvent. $150/£94

LONGFIELD, CYNTHIA. The Dragonflies of the British Isles. London, 1937. 1st ed. Color frontis. (Spine head sl rubbed, sl warped.) Edwards. $32/£20

LONGHURST, HENRY. Adventure in Oil. London: Sidgwick & Jackson, 1959. 1st ed. Fine in dj. Hollett. $56/£35

LONGHURST, MARGARET H. Catalogue of Carvings in Ivory. London, 1927-29. 2 vols. (Vol 2 fr cvr stained, sl bowed.) Swann*. $287/£179

LONGLEY, MICHAEL. Patchwork. Dublin: Gallery, 1981. One of 500 signed by Longley and Jim Allen (illus). Cl-backed paper bds, fr cvr label. Fine. Ulysses. $72/£45

LONGLEY, MICHAEL. Ten Poems. Belfast: Festival Pub, n.d. (1965). 1st ed, 1st bk, 1st issue, ptd on laid paper, w/cvr device ptd in purple. VG (cvrs sl mkd, dusty, sl creased, edges sl browned) in wrappers. *Ulysses.* $280/£175

LONGMAN, C. J. and H. WALROND. Archery. Longmans, Green, 1894. 1st ed. xvi,534,(ii)pp. Pict cl, gilt. VG (few prelim ll roughly opened; spotted, mostly edge). *Ash.* $136/£85

LONGMAN, W. Tokens of the Eighteenth Century Connected with Booksellers and Bookmakers. Longmans, Green, 1916. 1st ed. Letter from Ernest Hartland, plus a letter reply from Longman laid in. Frontis, 11 plts. Dj (torn). *Forest.* $104/£65

LONGSTREET, HELEN D. Lee and Longstreet at High Tide. Gainesville: The Author, 1904. 1st ed. Frontis, 14 plts, ports. (Lt foxed.) Teg, untrimmed. Tan buckram (sl rubbed, edges sl worn). *Baltimore*.* $100/£63

LONGSTRETH, MORRIS. Rheumatism, Gout, and Some Allied Disorders. NY, 1882. 280pp. (Chipped, scuffed, corners worn), o/w Good. *Doctor's Library.* $50/£31

LONGSWORTH, BASIL NELSON. Memorandum of Thoughts, Reflections, and Transactions. Fairfield, WA: Ye Galleon, 1972. Ltd to 500. VG. Howes L458. *Lien.* $15/£9

LONGUS. Daphnis and Chloe. George Thornley (trans). London: Geoffrey Bles, 1925. 1st Eng ed. 16 plts (14 color) by John Austen. Buckram, gilt. NF (spine foot sl bumped) in dj (rubbed, nicked, creased, spine sl dknd, repaired tear top of fr panel). *Ulysses.* $200/£125

LONGUS. Daphnis and Chloe. George Thornley (trans). London (but ptd in France): A. Zwemmer, 1937. Ltd to 250 signed by Aristide Maillol (illus), and w/an extra suite of 55 woodcuts unbound as issued in 1/4 vellum portfolio (surface abrasion to 1 woodcut, sl discoloration). Orig vellum (lt stained). Slipcase. *Christie's*.* $883/£552

LONGWELL, DENNIS. Steichen: The Master Prints, 1895-1914—The Symbolist Period. NY: MOMA, (1978). 1st ed. Color frontis; 72 full-pg gravure repros. NF in matching dj. *Baltimore*.* $50/£31

Longworth's American Almanac, New-York Register, and City Directory, for the Fifty-Third Year of American Independence. NY: Thomas Longworth, 1828. 664pp, incl pair of tps and duplicate preface ll. Later tan cl, marbled bds. (Feps detached, chipped; browned, sl foxed, sl stained; old paper repair, ink notes 1st tp; cvrs sl worn, handwritten ink date on spine.) *Baltimore*.* $80/£50

LONN, ELLA. Foreigners in the Confederacy. Chapel Hill: Univ of NC, 1940. 1st ed. Frontisport, add'l ports. Gray cl. Fine in dj. *Chapel Hill.* $400/£250

LONNROTH, ERIK. Lawrence of Arabia. Ruth Lewis (trans). London: Valentine, Mitchell, 1956. 1st ed. Pale blue cl. (Fr hinge sl weak; spine sl spotted.) *Maggs.* $56/£35

LONSDALE and KAPLAN. A Guide to Sunken Ships in American Waters. Arlington: Compass, 1964. Grn cl. VG in dj. *American Booksellers.* $80/£50

Look at Animals. Jolly Jump-Ups. London/Somerset: Purnell & Sons, 1967. 4 dbl-pg pop-ups. Glazed pict bds (spine torn). *Bookfinders.* $55/£34

LOOKER, S. J. To the Immortal Memory of Richard Jefferies. London, 1939. Inscribed presentation. VG in orig wraps. *Edrich.* $16/£10

LOOMIS, ALFRED. Lectures on Diseases of the Respiratory Organs, Heart and Kidneys. NY, 1878. 1st ed. 549pp. Leather. *Fye.* $125/£78

LOOMIS, B. F. Pictorial History of the Lassen Volcano. SF: CA Press, (1926). 1st ed. Port, 2 maps (1 fldg). Orig postcard of eruption of Lassen Peak of May 22, 1915 by another photographer laid in. Brn cl, gilt, mtd cvr illus. Fine. *Pacific*.* $40/£25

LOOMIS, FREDERIC. Hunting Extinct Animals in Patagonian Pampas. NY: Dodd, Mead, 1913. Signed presentation. Red cl, gilt. Fine. *Cullen.* $85/£53

LOOMIS, LEANDER V. A Journal of the Birmingham Emigrating Company.... Edgar M. Ledyard (ed). Salt Lake City: Privately ptd, 1928. 1st ed. Ltd to 300 signed by Loomis' daughter & the daughter of the captain of the Birmingham Co. Inscribed, signed presentation by Ledyard's wife. Lg fldg map tipped to rep. Brn cl, gilt. Fine in pict dj (dknd). Howes L464. *Argonaut.* $300/£188

LOOMIS, NOEL M. The Texas-Santa Fe Pioneers. Norman, 1958. 1st ed. Fldg map. VG in dj. *Dumont.* $50/£31

LOONEY, J. THOMAS. Shakespeare Identified in Edward de Vere the Seventeenth Earl of Oxford. London: Cecil Palmer, (1920). 1st ed. NF. *Captain's Bookshelf.* $35/£22

LOPEZ, BARRY. Arctic Dreams. London: Macmillan, 1986. Fine in dj. *Explorer.* $22/£14

LOPEZ, BARRY. River Notes. Kansas City, MO: Andrews, McMeel, 1979. 1st ed. Fine in Fine dj. *Warren.* $150/£94

LORAC, E. C. R. Dangerous Domicile. London: CCC, 1957. 1st ed. (Pg edges sl dknd, top edge lt spotted), o/w VG in dj (tear, spine ends sl worn). *Mordida.* $85/£53

LORAC, E. C. R. Murder on a Monument. Collins, 1958. 1st UK ed. NF in dj. *Williams.* $72/£45

LORANT, STEFAN. Pittsburgh. The Story of an American City. GC: Doubleday, (1964). 1st ed. Gray cl. VG + in color, pict dj. *House.* $45/£28

LORCA, FEDERICO GARCIA. See GARCIA LORCA, FEDERICO

Lord Bateman (Uncle Frank's Series). NY: McLoughlin Bros, (ca 1860). 12mo. 8pp (lt foxed). Color pict wrappers. *Reisler.* $125/£78

LORD, JAMES. Alberto Giacometti Drawings. NY, (1971). Folio. Dj. *Swann*.* $230/£144

LORD, JOHN. Frontier Dust. Natalie Shipman (ed). Hartford, 1926. 1st ed. Ltd to 1000. *Heinoldt.* $15/£9

LORD, WALTER. A Night to Remember. NY: Henry Holt, (1955). 1st ed. NF in dj (lt chipped). *Glenn.* $35/£22

LORE, JOHN M., JR. An Atlas of Head and Neck Surgery. Phila: W.B. Saunders, (1962). 1st ed. 202 plts. (Bkpl.) *Weber.* $60/£38

LORETTE, LOUIS. The Lorette System of Pruning. Emmaus: Rodale, 1946. 1st ed thus. Fine in NF dj. *Archer.* $20/£13

LORREQUER, HARRY (ed). Arthur O'Leary: His Wanderings and Ponderings in Many Lands. London: Henry Colburn, 1844. 1st ed. 3 vols. 10 full-pg plts by George Cruikshank. Thick marbled eps; gilt inner dentelles. Full lt tan calf by Bradstreets, gilt, raised bands, red/grn morocco title/author labels. Good. *Young.* $336/£210

LORREQUER, HARRY (ed). Charles O'Malley, the Irish Dragoon. Dublin, 1841. 1st ed, early issue. 2 vols. 348; 336pp. Binder's cl. (Plts foxed, one frontis sl repaired; fr outer hinges torn 1 inch; rubbed), else Good set. *King.* $95/£59

Lorsch Gospels. NY: Braziller, (1967). Fine facs of ms. One of 1000 numbered. Folio. Separate text pamphlet laid in. Cl w/vellum back, gilt. (Lt worn.) Slipcase. *Oinonen*.* $80/£50

Los Angeles Corral. Brand Book Six. 1956. 1st ed. Ltd to 400. Fine in VG dj. *Book Market.* $60/£38

Los Angeles Corral. Brand Book Seven. (1957.) 1st ed. Ltd to 475. Fine in Fine dj. *Book Market.* $60/£38

Los Angeles Corral. Brand Book Eight. (1959.) 1st ed. Ltd to 525. Fine in Fine dj. *Book Market.* $75/£47

Los Angeles Corral. Brand Book Nine. (1961.) 1st ed. Ltd to 500. Fine in VG dj. *Book Market.* $40/£25

Los Angeles Corral. Brand Book Ten. 1963. 1st ed. Ltd to 525. Signed by 19 Westerners. Fine in Fine dj. *Book Market.* $50/£31

Los Angeles Corral. Brand Book Eleven. 1964. 1st ed. Ltd to 525. Signed by about 25 Westerners. Fine. *Book Market.* $150/£94

Los Angeles Corral. Brand Book Thirteen. (1969.) 1st ed. Fine in Fine dj. *Book Market.* $40/£25

Los Angeles Corral. Brand Book Fourteen. (1974.) 1st ed. Ltd to 500. Fine in Fine dj. *Book Market.* $50/£31

Los Angeles Corral. Brand Book Sixteen. 1982. 1st ed. Fine in Fine dj. *Book Market.* $30/£19

Los Angeles Corral. The San Francisco Vigilance Committee of 1856. L.A.: Westerners Silver Anniversary Publication, (1971). 1st ed. Ltd to 500. Fine. *Book Market.* $85/£53

LOSKIEL, GEORGE HENRY. History of the Mission of the United Brethren Among the Indians of North America. Christian Ignatius La Trobe (trans). London: Brethren's Soc, 1794. 1st Eng ed. 3 vols in 1. xii,159,234,233,(22)pp (lacks fldg map). 1/2 calf, raised bands, grn morocco label. *Young.* $152/£95

LOSKIEL, GEORGE HENRY. History of the Mission of the United Brethren. London, 1794. xii,159,234,231,(xxi)pp (w/o map, not bound in?). Calf-backed marbled bds (rebound), gilt, morocco spine label. (Sl soiled, ink stamps.) *Edwards.* $448/£280

LOSSING, BENSON J. Pictorial History of the Civil War in the United States of America. Phila/Hartford: George W. Childs/T. Belknap, 1866-1868. 1st ed, mixed issue. 3 vols. Marbled edges. Orig plain sheep (cvr panels detached, scuffed; spines dknd, crackled). Internally VG (few ll detached). *Baltimore*.* $25/£16

LOTH, DAVID. The Erotic in Literature. NY, 1961. VG in dj. *Typographeum.* $18/£11

LOTHROP, EATON S., JR. A Century of Cameras from the Collections of the International Museum of Photography at George Eastman House. Dobbs Ferry, NY: Morgan & Morgan, 1973. 1st ed. NF (edges rubbed) in dj (rubbed). *Cahan.* $50/£31

LOTHROP, S. K. Treasures of Ancient America. Skira, (1964). Folio. Pict dj (edges bumped). *Metropolitan*.* $86/£54

LOTHROP, S. K. et al. Robert Woods Bliss Collection. Pre-Columbian Art. London: Phaidon, 1957. Gilt-dec cl. *Petersfield.* $56/£35

LOUBAT, ALPHONSE. The American Vine Dresser's Guide. NY: D. Appleton, 1872. Facs rpt. Frontis, 123pp. Nice. *M & S.* $100/£63

LOUBAT, ALPHONSE. Vine Dresser's Guide. NY: Appleton, 1872. 123pp. VG. *Fair Meadow.* $25/£16

LOUDON, ARCHIBALD. A Selection of Some of the Most Interesting Narratives, or Outrages.... (Harrisburg: Harrisburg Pub, 1888.) 2nd ed. One of 100 numbered sets. 2 vols. x,301; (i),357pp + limitation leaf at fr vol I. Untrimmed. Black cl, ptd paper spine labels. Good (lt aged, sl shaken, old clippings mtd at fr blank, verso of limitation leaf vol 1, verso last text pg vol II, ink sig, dated 1889, bkpls removed; sl edgeworn.) Howes L487. *Baltimore*.* $280/£175

LOUDON, J. C. (ed). Hortus Britannicus. A Catalogue of All the Plants, Indigenous, Cultivated in, or Introduced to Britain. London: Longman, Rees, Orme, et al, n. d. c.(1832). 2nd ed w/Feb 1832 supplement. (iv) pub's list,xxiv,602pp + 16pp pub's cat. (Feps foxed; sl soiled, extrems sl worn.) *Edwards.* $80/£50

LOUDON, JANE W. British Wild Flowers. William Smith, 1846. 1st ed. 4to. 57 (of 60) hand-colored litho plts. (Spotted, lt browned; lacks plts 55-57, pp265-289 of text.) *Sotheby's*.* $736/£460

LOUDON, JANE W. The Ladies' Flower-Garden of Ornamental Perennials. London: William Smith, 1843-44. 1st ed. 2 vols. 4to. 84 (of 96) hand-colored litho plts (5 torn, few tears affecting illus, margins crudely repaired, 3 plts detached; some ll spotted). Orig pub's cl (rebacked, orig spine relaid 1 vol; worn). *Christie's*.* $2,701/£1,688

LOUGHLIN, G. F. Mineral Resources of the United States, 1919. Parts 1 and 2. GPO, 1922. 2 vols. Good. *Rybski.* $50/£31

LOUIS, E. C. A. Pathological Researches on Phthisis. C. Cowan (trans). London, 1835. li,388pp. Orig cl. (Corners sl worn, re-backed w/o title), o/w VG. *Whitehart.* $64/£40

LOUIS, PIERRE. Anatomical, Pathological and Therapeutic Researches on the Yellow Fever of Gibraltar of 1828. Boston, 1839. 1st ed in English. 374pp. *Fye.* $150/£94

LOUIS, PIERRE. Researches on Phthisis, Anatomical, Pathological and Therapeutical. London, 1854. 2nd ed. 571pp. *Fye.* $75/£47

LOUP, SAINT. Renault. Bodley Head, 1957. 1st Eng ed. VG in dj (sl defective). *Hollett.* $56/£35

LOUYS, PIERRE. Cyprian Masques. Fortune, (1929). One of 1350. 6 plts. 1/4 buckram, marbled bds (sl damp-spotted, corners bumped). VG. *Any Amount.* $35/£22

LOUYS, PIERRE. Satyrs and Women. Pierre Loving (trans). NY: Covici Friede, 1930. 1st ed thus. One of 1250 ptd. Signed by Majeska (illus). Blue cl. (Spine, upper extrems sl dull), else VG. *Pacific*.* $104/£65

LOUYS, PIERRE. The Songs of Bilitis. Alvah C. Bessie (trans). NY: Macy-Masius, 1926. One of 2000. Signed by Willy Pogany (illus). 10x7. (Spine lettering worn off), else VG in slipcase (broken). *Pacific*.* $63/£39

LOUYS, PIERRE. The Twilight of the Nymphs. Fortune, (1928). 1st ed. 4 plts. (Cl sl dknd, bds sl bowed, sl bubbled), else VG. *Any Amount.* $38/£24

LOUYS, PIERRE. The Twilight of the Nymphs. London: Fortune, (1928). One of 1200. Cecil Beaton (illus). Tan cl, gilt. (Sl soiled), else NF. *Pacific*.* $81/£51

Love of an Unknown Soldier Found in a Dug-Out. London/NY: John Lane, Bodley Head, 1918. 'Sixth Edition.' Frontis. Grn cl. Good. *Reese.* $20/£13

LOVE, EDWIN M. Rocking Island. NY: Thomas Nelson & Sons, (1927). 1st ed. 6 color plts, 12 b/w full-pg illus. Plum cl, gilt, w/ color plt on cvr. Fine. *House.* $65/£41

LOVE, EDWIN M. Rocking Island. NY: Thomas Nelson, 1927. 1st ed. 7x9. 182pp. Blue cl, gilt, w/picture paste-on. VG (corners bumped, spine faded, shelfworn). *My Bookhouse.* $47/£29

LOVE, J. F. The Fall and Rise of Cushan and Other Poems. Stoneman Press, 1911. 1st ed. (Spine tear), else NF. *Fine Books.* $225/£141

LOVE, ROBERTUS. The Rise and Fall of Jesse James. NY, 1926. 2nd ptg. Dec cl. (Sig; cvr corners lt worn), else VG. Howes L521. *Baade.* $40/£25

LOVE, ROBERTUS. The Rise and Fall of Jesse James. NY: Putnam, 1926. 1st ed. VF. Howes L521. *Labordo.* $225/£141

LOVECRAFT, H. P. At the Mountains of Madness and Other Novels. August Derleth (ed). Sauk City: Arkham House, 1964. 1st ed thus. VG- in dj (extrems rubbed, closed tears, spine ends chipped, lower spine creased). *Pacific*.* $40/£25

LOVECRAFT, H. P. At the Mountains of Madness. West Kingston: Donald M. Grant, (1990). One of 1000 signed by Fernando Duval (illus). Silver-gilt pict leatherette (sl worn). *Oinonen*.* $30/£19

LOVECRAFT, H. P. Beyond the Wall of Sleep. Sauk City: Arkham House, 1943. 1st ed. One of 1200. Tall 8vo. Black cl, gilt spine. VG (contemp news clipping mtd to fr pastedown, eps browned; edges sl dusty) in complete dj (sl sunned, spine sl dknd, sl chipped, few sm tears). *Baltimore*.* $700/£438

LOVECRAFT, H. P. Beyond the Wall of Sleep. Sauk City, 1943. 1st ed. Lg 8vo. Dj (2 nicks fr joint top). *Swann*.* $920/£575

LOVECRAFT, H. P. Beyond the Wall of Sleep. August Derleth and Donald Wandrei (eds). Sauk City: Arkham House, 1943. 1st ed. One of 1217 ptd. (Bkpl, name), else VG in dj (spine ends chipped, sm tears to foot, corners). *Pacific*.* $920/£575

LOVECRAFT, H. P. Dagon and Other Macabre Tales. Sauk City: Arkham House, 1965. 1st ed. Fine in dj. *Levin.* $150/£94

LOVECRAFT, H. P. Dreams and Fancies. Sauk City, 1962. 1st ed. Dj. *Swann**. $103/£64

LOVECRAFT, H. P. Dreams and Fancies. Sauk City: Arkham House, 1962. 1st ed. NF in NF dj. *Other Worlds*. $135/£84

LOVECRAFT, H. P. Dreams and Fancies. Sauk City, WI: Arkham House, 1962. 1st ed. Gray eps. Black cl, gilt. (Spine ends sl rubbed, gilt sl faded), o/w Fine in dj. *Heritage*. $200/£125

LOVECRAFT, H. P. and AUGUST DERLETH. The Lurker at the Threshold. Sauk City, 1945. 1st ed. Dj. *Swann**. $115/£72

LOVECRAFT, H. P. Marginalia. Sauk City, 1944. 1st ed. Dj. *Swann**. $230/£144

LOVECRAFT, H. P. Marginalia. Sauk City: Arkham House, 1944. 1st ed. VG + (lower corners bumped) in VG + dj (corners nicked). *Other Worlds*. $300/£188

LOVECRAFT, H. P. The Outsider and Others. Sauk City: Arkham House, 1939. 1st ed. One of 1200. Tall 8vo. Black cl, gilt spine. VF (top edge sl dusty) in complete NF dj (spine sl sunned, few sm chips). *Baltimore**. $950/£594

LOVECRAFT, H. P. The Outsider and Others. August Derleth and Donald Wandrei (eds). Sauk City: Arkham House, 1939. 1st ed. One of 1200. (Name), else NF in dj (spine head, fr corner sl rubbed). *Pacific**. $1,955/£1,222

LOVECRAFT, H. P. Something About Cats and Other Pieces. August Derleth (ed). Sauk City: Arkham House, 1949. 1st ed. VF in dj (sl rubbed, faded). *Bromer*. $225/£141

LOVECRAFT, H. P. Something About Cats. Sauk City, 1949. 1st ed. Dj. *Swann**. $115/£72

LOVECRAFT, H. P. Supernatural Horror in Literature. NY: Ben Abramson, 1945. 1st ed. Red cl, gilt. (Lower extrems sl stained), else VG. *Pacific**. $98/£61

LOVECRAFT, H. P. and AUGUST DERLETH. The Survivor and Others. Sauk City: Arkham House, 1957. 1st ed. (Upper corners sl worn), else NF in dj. *Pacific**. $86/£54

LOVECRAFT, H. P. and AUGUST DERLETH. The Watchers Out of Time and Others. Sauk City: Arkham House, 1974. 1st ed. One of 5000. VG in dj (sl used). *King*. $40/£25

LOVEJOY, ESTHER POHL. Certain Samaritans. NY, 1933. New ed. Signed. VG in dj (tattered). *Doctor's Library*. $50/£31

LOVEJOY, JOSEPH C. and OWEN. Memoir of the Rev. Elijah P. Lovejoy; Who Was Murdered in Defence of the Liberty of the Press. NY: Taylor, 1838. Bds, paper spine. Howes L522. *Rostenberg & Stern*. $250/£156

LOVELACE, RALPH MILBANKS. Astarte. London: Christophers, 1921. New ed. 8 plts, 2 facs. (few marginal blind stamps, lib accession stamp verso tp; faded, spine soiled, #s.) *Hollett*. $48/£30

LOVELL, JOHN H. The Flower and the Bee. NY: Scribner, 1918. 1st ed. 119 b/w plts. VG. *Fair Meadow*. $30/£19

LOVER, SAMUEL. The Lyrics of Ireland. Houlston & Wright, 1858. 1st ed. xxv,360pp (few marginal blind-stamps, stamp on tp verso). Blind-stamped cl (edges sl worn, spine sl dull), gilt. *Hollett*. $104/£65

LOVERIDGE, A. Reptiles of the Pacific World. NY, 1945. 4 plts. (Stamp to pg edges; fr cvr spotted, spine sunned.) *Sutton*. $35/£22

LOVERIDGE, A. Tomorrow's a Holiday. NY: Harper, 1947. 1st ed. NF in VG dj. *Mikesh*. $25/£16

LOVESEY, PETER. Butchers and Other Stories of Crime. NY: Mysterious, 1985. 1st ed. NF in dj (sl shelfworn). *My Bookhouse*. $32/£20

LOVESEY, PETER. Wobble to Death. London: Macmillan, 1970. 1st Eng ed. NF (edges browning; corners sl bumped) in dj (sl nicked, rubbed, creased, pub's sticker fr panel). *Ulysses*. $200/£125

LOVETT, ROBERT. Infantile Paralysis in Massachusetts During 1910. Boston, 1911. *Fye*. $35/£22

LOVETT, ROBERT. Lateral Curvature of the Spine and Round Shoulders. Phila, 1916. 3rd ed. Grn cl. NF. *Doctor's Library*. $100/£63

LOVETT, ROBERT. The Treatment of Infantile Paralysis. Phila, 1916. *Fye*. $125/£78

Loving Ballad of Lord Bateman. (By William Makepeace Thackeray.) London, 1839. 1st ed, 1st issue, w/'Vine' for 'Wine' p21. George Cruikshank (illus). Sq 18mo. Orig gilt-pict flexible grn cl. Fine (few ll loose from binding) in full morocco solander case by Zaehnsdorf. *Swann**. $747/£467

LOW, A. P. Report on the Dominion Government Expedition to Hudson Bay and the Arctic Islands on Board the D.G.S. Neptune 1903-1904. Ottawa, 1906. 1st ed. Pict cl, gilt. *Maggs*. $280/£175

LOW, CHARLES RATHBONE. History of the Indian Navy (1613-1863). London: Richard Bentley, 1877. 1st ed. 2 vols. (xxviii),541; vi,591pp. Mod lib buckram. Sound set (lib stamps). *Lefkowicz*. $100/£63

LOW, D. On the Domesticated Animals of the British Islands. London: Longman, n.d. (1845). 767pp. VG (ex-lib). *Mikesh*. $45/£28

LOW, DAVID. With All Faults. Amate, 1973. 1st UK ed. Signed presentation. Fine in Fine dj (sl spotted). *Martin*. $29/£18

LOW, FREDERICK F. Some Reflections of an Early California Governor Contained in a Short Dictated Memoir.... Robert H. Becker (ed). (Sacramento): Sacramento Book Collectors Club, 1959. One of 310 ptd. Color frontis. 1/2 linen, patterned cl, leather spine label. Fine. *Pacific**. $46/£29

LOW, JOHN L. Concerning Golf. London: Hodder & Stoughton, 1903. 1st ed. Grn cl, gilt. (Emb stamp, pp browned; spine ends, joints sl rubbed), else VG. *Pacific**. $86/£54

LOW, JOHN L. F. G. Tait: A Record, Being His Life, Letters, and Golfing Diary. London: J. Nisbet, (1900). 1st ed. Photogravure frontisport. Red cl, gilt. (Emb stamp; fr cvr spotted, spine ends rubbed, foot smudged), else VG. *Pacific**. $98/£61

LOW, SUSANNE M. An Index and Guide to Audubon's Birds of America. NY, 1988. 435 plts. NF in dj. *Dumont*. $50/£31

LOWE, C. M. Changing Pictures. London: Ernest Nister, (ca 1920). 4to. 6 dbl half-wheel transformations, each w/full color illus and 2 half-circle turning transformation panels. Color pict bds (edges rubbed, spine worn; pulls restored). *Reisler*. $1,475/£922

LOWE, E. J. Our Native Ferns; or, a History of the British Species and Their Varieties. London, 1867. 2 vols. vii,348; vii,492pp; 79 color plts. (New eps; sl soiled, worn.) *Henly*. $80/£50

LOWE, ROBERT W. A Biographical Account of English Theatrical Literature. London: John C. Nimmo, 1888. One of 100 numbered. x,394pp + 24pp ads. Deckled edges. Gilt blue linen, marbled bds. (Recently rebound; fr bd lt scuffed.) *Karmiole*. $150/£94

LOWE, ROBSON. The British Postage Stamp. Nat'l Postal Museum, 1968. 1st ed. (Lt tape-mks to feps.) Dj. *Hollett*. $104/£65

LOWELL, GUY. American Gardens. Boston: Bates & Guild, 1902. 1st ed. 112 photo plts. Pict grn cl, gilt. (Hinges neatly cracked; spine dknd, torn along joints, ends frayed), else VG-. *Pacific**. $69/£43

LOWELL, JAMES RUSSELL. Among My Books. Boston, 1876. True 1st ed. VF. *Bond*. $40/£25

LOWELL, JAMES RUSSELL. Among My Books. Boston: James R. Osgood, 1876. 1st ed, 1st issue, w/the error 'Belles-Letters' under author's name on tp. Terra cotta cl, beveled. Fine (few sm cvr mks). *Sumner & Stillman*. $175/£109

LOWELL, JAMES RUSSELL. The Bigelow Papers. Cambridge: George Nichols, 1848. 1st ed. 12,xxxii,163pp. Orig brn cl (Blanck's binding 'A'). VG (spine ends lt chipped, lt faded). BAL 13068. *House*. $90/£56

LOWELL, JAMES RUSSELL. Conversations on Some of the Old Poets. Cambridge, 1845. 1st Amer ed. Teg. 1/2 leather, marbled cvrs, gilt. Fine (bkpl, sl rubbed). *Polyanthos.* $60/£38

LOWELL, JAMES RUSSELL. Democracy and Other Addresses. Boston, 1887. 2nd issue. One of 1010 ptd. Fine (spine sl rubbed). *Polyanthos.* $30/£19

LOWELL, JAMES RUSSELL. Political Essays. Boston: Houghton, Mifflin, 1888. 1st ed. 326pp. Teg. Grn cl, gilt w/beveled sides. Fine. BAL 13198. *House.* $100/£63

LOWELL, ROBERT. For the Union Dead. NY, (1964). 1st ed. VG in dj (sl frayed, dknd). *King.* $35/£22

LOWELL, ROBERT. Life Studies. London, 1959. 1st ed. Fine in dj (spine sunned, few sm chips, price-clipped). *Polyanthos.* $60/£38

LOWELL, ROBERT. Life Studies. London, 1959. 1st ed. (Sl dust mk to ep from dj flap.) Dj (sl faded). *Petersfield.* $64/£40

LOWELL, ROBERT. The Voyage and Other Versions of Poems by Baudelaire. London: Faber & Faber, 1968. 1st ed. One of 200 signed by Lowell and Sidney Nolan (illus). Blue cl. Fine in slipcase. *Maggs.* $320/£200

Lower St. Lawrence, Or Quebec to Halifax, via Gaspe and Pictou. To Which Is Appended Mr. Wood's Description of the River Saguenay also, Legends of the St. Lawrence.... Quebec, 1862. Fldg frontis map, 122pp. (Sl foxed, soiled; lt worn.) *Oinonen*.* $250/£156

LOWER, MARK ANTONY. English Surnames. An Essay on Family Nomenclature.... London: John Russell Smith, 1849. 3rd ed. 2 vols. xxiv,264; vi,243pp + 16 ads. Fine set in orig blind-stamped cl, gilt. *Young.* $120/£75

LOWINSKY, RUTH. Lovely Food. A Cookery Notebook [and] More Lovely Food. London: Nonesuch, 1931/1935. 2 vols. Djs (vol 2 stuck to binding). *Maggs.* $96/£60

LOWMAN, AL. Printer at the Pass. San Antonio, 1972. VG. *Dumont.* $100/£63

LOWMAN, AL. Printing Arts in Texas. Austin, 1975. One of 395. Sm folio. NF. *Dumont.* $175/£109

LOWNDES, WILLIAM THOMAS. The Bibliographer's Manual of English Literature. London: Bell, n.d. (ca 1870s). New ed. 4 vols. Orig 1/2 brn leather (rubbed). *Oinonen*.* $110/£69

LOWNDES, WILLIAM THOMAS. The Bibliographer's Manual of English Literature.... Bell & Daldy, 1865. New ed. 6 vols. Contemp 1/2 morocco, gilt. (Sl rubbed), o/w Nice set. *Forest.* $200/£125

LOWNE, BENJAMIN THOMPSON. The Anatomy and Physiology of the Blow-Fly. London, 1870. vi,(ii),121pp; 10 plts (partly hand-colored). (Margins lt browned; corners rubbed w/some loss; rebacked, much of orig spine laid down.) *Edwards.* $136/£85

LOWRY, LOIS. Number the Stars. Boston: Houghton Mifflin, 1989. 1st ed. 8vo. Black cl, gilt. As New in full color dj. *Reisler.* $65/£41

LOWRY, MALCOLM. Dark as the Grave Wherein My Friend Is Laid. Cape, 1969. 1st UK ed. NF in dj. *Williams.* $40/£25

LOWRY, MALCOLM. Under the Volcano. NY: Reynal & Hitchcock, (1947). 1st ed. 1st binding: gray cl. VG in dj (spine head, corners chipped; sm tear fr panel top; sm scrape spine affecting title). *Pacific*.* $288/£180

LOWRY, MALCOLM. Under the Volcano. NY: Reynal & Hitchcock, 1947. 1st ed. VG (stamp, lacks dj). *Warren.* $125/£78

LOWRY, MALCOLM. Under the Volcano. NY: Reynal & Hitchcock, 1947. 1st ed. VG in dj (chips missing). *Smith.* $200/£125

LOWRY, MALCOLM. Under the Volcano. NY: Reynal & Hitchcock, 1947. 1st ed. VG + in VG dj (chipped, short tears to extrems, sm stain to rear panel). *Warren.* $275/£172

LOWTHER, GEORGE. The Adventures of Superman. NY: Random House, (1942). 1st ed. Joe Schuster (illus). Fine in VG dj (spine foot, extrems rubbed, head chipped). *Pacific*.* $575/£359

LUBBOCK, BASIL. The Arctic Whalers. Glasgow: Brown, Son & Ferguson, 1937. 1st ed. Fldg plan. (Sl mk on spine), else VG. *High Latitude.* $80/£50

LUBBOCK, BASIL. The Arctic Whalers. Glasgow: Brown, Son & Ferguson, 1937. 1st ed. 51 plts. NF. *Explorer.* $88/£55

LUBBOCK, BASIL. The Arctic Whalers. Glasgow: Brown, Son & Ferguson, 1955. Facs of 1st ed of 1937. Fine (lacks tp) in dj. *Explorer.* $32/£20

LUBBOCK, BASIL. The Log of the 'Cutty Sark.' Boston: Charles E. Lauriat, 1924. VG + (sl shelfworn) in most of dj. *My Bookhouse.* $82/£51

LUBBOCK, BASIL. The Log of the Cutty Sark. Glasgow: Brown, Son & Ferguson, 1954. 2 fldg plans. Fine. *Explorer.* $64/£40

LUBBOCK, BASIL. The Nitrate Clippers. Glasgow: Brown, Son & Ferguson, (1966). Rpt of 1932 1st ed. Frontis, 1 fldg illus. Blue cl, gilt. Fine in pict dj (sl chipped). *Argonaut.* $60/£38

LUBBOCK, BASIL. The Opium Clippers. Boston, 1933. (Name, lt worn, foxed.) *Woolson.* $75/£47

LUBBOCK, BASIL. The Opium Clippers. Glasgow: Brown, Ferguson, 1933. 1st ed. Frontisport, 2 fldg plans, color plt. Blue cl, gilt/silvered. (Blindstamp, lt pencil mks; corners bumped), else NF. *Parmer.* $295/£184

LUBBOCK, JOHN. A Contribution to Our Knowledge of Seedlings. London, 1892. 1st ed. 2 vols. 608; 646pp. (Feps lt browned.) *Edwards.* $136/£85

LUCAN. Pharsalia. Robert Graves (trans). Penguin, 1956. 1st UK ed. Orig pb. VG (ink name, sm label fr cvr). *Williams.* $19/£12

LUCAS, A. Ancient Egyptian Materials and Industries. London: Edward Arnold, (1962). 4th ed. Dj (tattered). *Archaeologia.* $150/£94

LUCAS, E. V. A Group of Londoners. Minneapolis: Edmund D. Brooks & Friends, 1913. 1st ed. Titled bds, cl spine. Fine. *Black Sun.* $100/£63

LUCAS, E. V. The Vermillion Box. London: Methuen, (1916). 1st ed. Red cl stamped in gilt/blind. (Lt foxed), o/w NF in pict dj (few sm closed tears rear panel). *Reese.* $85/£53

LUCAS, E. V. (ed). Runaways and Castaways. Wells Gardner Darton, 1908. 1st ed. 8vo. Color frontis, color pict tp plt, xxx,310pp,14pp ads; 18 b/w plts. Dbl-spread illus eps. Pict wine-red cl, gilt. NF. *Bookmark.* $80/£50

LUCAS, E. V. (ed). Runaways and Castaways. Wells Gardner Darton, 1908. 1st ed. Color frontis. Teg. Gilt pict cl. VG + . *Green Meadow.* $96/£60

LUCAS, GEORGE. The Diary of George A. Lucas. Princeton: Princeton Univ, (1979). 2 vols. Fine in djs. *Turtle Island.* $100/£63

LUCAS, VICTORIA. (Pseud of Sylvia Plath.) The Bell Jar. London: Heinemann, (1963). 1st ed. Black cl, gilt. (Ink inscrip, note), o/w Nice in dj (frayed, shelfworn). *Reese.* $800/£500

LUCIA, ELLIS. The Saga of Ben Holladay. NY: Hastings House, (1959). 1st ed. VG in dj. *Lien.* $30/£19

LUCIAN OF SAMOSATA. Lucian's True Story. London, 1894. One of 250 numbered. Aubrey Beardsley (illus). Buckram (spine dknd, extrems worn). *Swann*.* $138/£86

LUCIE-SMITH, EDWARD. Art Today. From the Abstract Expressionism to Superrealism. London: Phaidon, 1977. 1st UK ed. Dj. *Edwards.* $40/£25

LUCIE-SMITH, LUCIE. A Game of French and English. Turret Books, 1965. One of 100 signed. Fine in wrappers. *Ulysses.* $56/£35

LUCRETIUS. De Rerum Natura: Of the Nature of Things. L.A.: LEC, 1957. One of 1500. Signed by Paul Landacre (illus). Full dk blue morocco, gilt. Fine in slipcase. *Pacific**. $109/£68

LUCRETIUS. De Rerum Natura: Of the Nature of Things. L.A.: Ward Ritchie, 1957. Signed by Paul Landacre (illus). Full maroon morocco, spine in six compartments, gilt. Fine in box. *Appelfeld*. $125/£78

LUCRETIUS. De Rerum Natura: Of the Nature of Things. L.A.: LEC, 1957. One of 1500 ptd. Signed by Paul Landacre (illus). Full dk blue morocco, gilt. Fine in slipcase. *Pacific**. $150/£94

LUCRETIUS. Of the Nature of Things. LEC, 1957. Ltd to 1500 numbered, signed by Paul Landacre (illus). Fine in slipcase. *Swann**. $92/£58

Lucy Locket (The Doll with the Pocket!). Minneapolis: Gordon Volland, (1928). 5th ed. 8vo. 120pp. Dec cl-backed pict bds. VG. *Reisler*. $75/£47

LUCY, HENRY W. Gideon Fleyce. NY: Henry Holt, 1883. 1st Amer ed. Mustard-yellow cl. NF (spine head sl worn). *Sumner & Stillman*. $30/£19

LUD. Relief to Royalty: The Story of James J. Braddock, World's Heavyweight Champion. N.p., (1936). 1st ed. Inscribed, signed by Braddock, dated 1936. Grn cl, gilt. Fine (inscrip). *Pacific**. $259/£162

LUDEWIG, HERMANN E. The Literature of American Local History. A Bibliographical Essay. NY: The Author, 1846. 1st ed. xx,180pp. (Foxed, lt worn.) *Oinonen**. $120/£75

LUDLAM, HARRY. Captain Scott: The Full Story. London: Foulsham, 1965. Fine in dj. *Explorer*. $26/£16

LUDLOW, EDMUND. Memoirs of Edmund Ludlow. London: T. Becket et al, 1771. 1st ed. Engr frontis, xii,558,20,(30)pp. Contemp calf (handsomely rebacked; bd edges worn). *Karmiole*. $300/£188

LUDLOW, FITZHUGH. The Heart of the Continent. NY: Hurd & Houghton, 1870. 1st ed. Brn cl. NF. *Labordo*. $225/£141

LUDLUM, ROBERT. The Icarus Agenda. NY: Random House, (1988). 1st ed. NF in dj. *Antic Hay*. $17/£11

LUDLUM, ROBERT. The Osterman Weekend. NY, 1972. 1st Amer ed. Fine in NF ptd acetate dj. *Polyanthos*. $75/£47

LUDLUM, ROBERT. The Scarlatti Inheritance. NY: World, 1971. 1st ed. Fine in Fine acetate dj (sm corner chips). *Mordida*. $200/£125

LUDOVICI, ANTHONY M. Nietzsche and Art. London: Constable, 1911. Orig ed. Frontis, 8 plts. VG (prelims foxed). *Turtle Island*. $55/£34

LUDWIG, EMIL. July '14. C. A. Macartney (trans). London/NY: Putnam, (1929). 1st British ed. Black cl, gilt. (Lt foxed), o/w Nice in dj. *Reese*. $45/£28

LUEBKE, FREDERICK et al (eds). Mapping the North American Plains. Norman: Univ of OK, 1987. 1st ed. VG in dj. *Labordo*. $55/£34

LUGARD, F. D. The Rise of Our East African Empire, Early Efforts in Nyasaland and Uganda. William Blackwood & Sons, 1893. 1st ed. 2 vols. xix,(i),563,32ads; ix,(i),682pp; 2 fldg color maps. Red dec cl, gilt. Good set (bkpls; lt soiled, spines lt faded). *Sotheran*. $317/£198

LUGARD, F. D. The Rise of Our East African Empire. London: William Blackwood, 1893. 1st ed. 2 vols. 1/2-titles, frontisport, xx,563,(1)blank,32 pub's list; x,682pp; 130 plts (14 color), 9 color maps (2 loose pockets vol 1). Red dec cl, gilt. Good (rubbed, damp stain affecting rear cvr vol 2, hinges weak). *Morrell*. $216/£135

LUHAN, MABEL DODGE. Winter in Taos. NY: Harcourt, Brace, (1935). 1st ed. Pale cl. (Sl mottled; sm ink spot back panel), o/w VG (lacks dj). *Hermitage*. $85/£53

LUHAN, MABLE DODGE. Winter in Taos. NY: Harcourt, Brace, 1935. 1st ed. Good in dj (chipped, lt soiled). *Dumont*. $125/£78

LUKE, PETER. Hadrian VII. NY: Knopf, 1969. 1st ed. (Name; sl shelfworn), else VG + in dj (sl edgeworn). *My Bookhouse*. $47/£29

LUKIS, PARDEY. Tropical Hygiene for Anglo-Indians and Indians. Calcutta, 1914. 2nd ed. *Fye*. $125/£78

LULL, EDWARD P. History of the United States Navy-Yard at Gosport, Virginia.... Washington: GPO, 1874. 1st ed. 64pp; 3 fldg plans. (Cvrs sl spotted.) *Lefkowicz*. $100/£63

LUM, DYER. The Spiritual Delusion. Phila: Lippincott, 1873. 1st ed. NF (name stamp). *Beasley*. $200/£125

LUMHOLTZ, CARL. Among Cannibals: An Account of Four Years' Travels in Australia.... Rasmus B. Anderson (trans). NY: Scribner, 1896. xx,395,4pp; 3 (of 4) color plts, 25 full-pg illus, 2 fldg color maps. (Edges rubbed, sl soiled, spine ends frayed, lower corner of rear cvr chipped, sl shaken), o/w VG. *Worldwide*. $65/£41

LUMHOLTZ, CARL. Through Central Borneo: An Account of Two Years' Travel...1913 and 1917. NY: Scribner, 1920. 1st ed. 2 vols. 81 (of 95) plts, 1 fldg map. (Lib spine stickers, fr inner hinges strengthened; edges worn, spine ends frayed), o/w Good. *Worldwide*. $65/£41

LUMMER, OTTO. Contributions to Photographic Optics. Silvanus P. Thompson (trans). London: Macmillan, 1900. 1st ed. Teg. Grn cl. Good. *Young*. $96/£60

LUMMIS, CHARLES F. The Enchanted Burro. Chicago: Way & Williams, 1897. 1st ed. (10),277pp. (Lib stamp), else Good. *Dumont*. $65/£41

LUMMIS, CHARLES F. The Gold Fish of Gran Chimu. Boston: Lamson, Wolffe, 1896. 1st ed. Fine. *Pacific**. $52/£33

LUMMIS, CHARLES F. The Land of Poco Tiempo. NY: Scribner, 1893. 1st ed. xii,310pp. (Sl worn, dusty), else NF in mod slipcase. *Dumont*. $200/£125

LUMMIS, CHARLES F. The Land of Poco Tiempo. NY: Scribner, 1902. 1st ed. Dec cl, gilt. (Spine ends sl rubbed), else VG. *Pacific**. $86/£54

LUMMIS, CHARLES F. Some Strange Corners of Our Country. NY: Century, 1892. 1st ed. Frontis, xii,270pp. Pict cl, gilt (extrems lt worn). *Dawson*. $50/£31

LUMMIS, CHARLES F. The Spanish Pioneers. Chicago: A.C. McClurg, 1893. 1st ed. Frontis, 292pp; 8 full-pg photo illus. Pict cl (tips bumped; sm nick bottom edge fr bd). *Dawson*. $40/£25

LUMMUS, AARON. The Life and Adventures of Dr. Caleb. Boston: The Author, 1822. 1st ed. Contains leaf w/recommendations & subscriber list. 230,(2)pp (ex-lib, lacks fep). Contemp calf (worn). *M & S*. $225/£141

LUMSDEN, HARRY (ed). The Records of the Trades House of Glasgow A. D. 1713-1777. Glasgow: Trades House of Glasgow, 1934. One of 500. Frontis, 4 plts. Teg. (Margins browned.) *Edwards*. $136/£85

LUND, EDWARD. Hunterian Lectures on Some of the Injuries and Diseases of the Neck and Head, the Genito-Urinary Organs, and the Rectum. London: J. & A. Churchill, 1886. 116pp; 4 plts. Dk grn cl. (Sl rubbed; fr inner hinge starting), else VG. *Weber*. $125/£78

LUNDEBERG, AXEL and FREDERICK SEYMOUR. The Great Roosevelt African Hunt; and the Wild Animals of Africa.... N.p.: D.B. McCurdy, 1910. Blue pict cl. NF. *Biscotti*. $50/£31

LUNN, ARNOLD. Mountain Jubilee. Eyre & Spottiswoode, 1943. 1st ed. 17 plts. VG in dj (worn, chipped). *Hollett*. $40/£25

LUQUER, LEA M. Minerals in Rock Sections. NY, 1913. 4th ed. Fldg chart. Brn cl, gilt. VG. *Larry Price*. $35/£22

LURIE, ALISON. Foreign Affairs. NY: Random House, 1984. 1st ed. Fine in Fine dj. *Unger.* $65/£41

LUSHINGTON, HENRY. A Great Country's Little Wars; or, England, Afghanistan, and Sinde. London, 1844. Orig cl, paper spine label. (Bkpl; sm chip spine top.) *Swann*.* $126/£79

LUST, HERBERT C. Giacometti: The Complete Graphics and 15 Drawings. NY, (1970). Folio. Dj. *Swann*.* $345/£216

LUTHER, TAL. High Spots of Custer and Battle of the Little Big Horn Literature (and a Few Low Spots). Kansas City Westerners, (Dec 1967). Signed. Fine. *Dumont.* $45/£28

LUTIE, AUNT. Merry Christmas. NY: Shugg, (ca 1872). Lg 4to. 4 full-pg color illus (1 dbl-pg) by Alfred Kappes. Good in full color paper wrappers (spine taped). *Reisler.* $375/£234

LUTZ, E. G. Practical Engraving and Etching. Scribner, 1933. 1st ed. VG + in dj (soiled, torn). *Whittle.* $29/£18

LUTZ, FRANCIS EARLE. Richmond in World War II. Dietz, 1951. VG. *Book Broker.* $35/£22

LUTZ, WILLIS J. William D. Wittliff, a Bibliography. Dallas, 1975. (Sl soiled), else Fine in wraps. *Dumont.* $25/£16

LYALL, ALFRED C. Asiatic Studies, Religious and Social. London: Murray, 1882. 1st ed. xx,332pp. Mainly unopened. (Few pencil mks; sl rubbed, spine ends sl frayed), o/w VG. *Worldwide.* $45/£28

LYALL, EDNA. (Pseud of Ada Ellen Bayly.) Donovan: A Modern Englisham. Hurst & Blackett, 1886. 4th ed. Pub's cat. Good (ink inscrip, lt spotted; spine bumped). *Tiger.* $16/£10

LYALL, EDNA. (Pseud of Ada Ellen Bayly.) We Two: A Novel. Hurst & Blackett, 1886. 3rd ed. Good (lt spotted; spine bumped). *Tiger.* $16/£10

LYALL, GAVIN. The Secret Servant. NY, 1980. 1st Amer ed. Fine (sl rubbed) in dj (2 sm tears). *Polyanthos.* $20/£13

LYDEKKDER, R. A Geographical History of Mammals. London: CUP, 1896. 1st ed. Color fldg map frontis, 400pp. Maroon cl, gilt. Good + (ex-lib). *Larry Price.* $28/£18

LYDEKKER, R. Catalogue of the Ungulate Mammals in the British Museum. London, 1913-1916. 6 vols. Frontisport. (Ex-lib w/labels, cardholders; cl sl discolored; fore-edges 2 vols lt dampstained.) *Edwards.* $120/£75

LYDEKKER, R. The Royal Natural History. London, 1893-1896. 6 vols. 72 color plts. (lib ink stamps, labels, sl spotted, joint sl worn in vol 1; corners sl rubbed, spines sl bumped, sm split to head of 1st 3 vols, spine #s.) *Edwards.* $144/£90

LYDEKKER, R. The Sportsman's British Bird Book. London, 1908. (Sm nick.) *Edwards.* $56/£35

LYELL, CHARLES. Elements of Geology. Boston: Hilliard, Gray, 1841. 2nd Amer ed. 2 vols. Orig cl (sl worn). NF set. *M & S.* $350/£219

LYELL, CHARLES. The Geological Evidences of the Antiquity of Man. London, 1873. 4th, last ed. xix,572pp; 2 plts. 1/2 calf. (Eps foxed, spine faded.) *Henly.* $67/£42

LYELL, CHARLES. Principles of Geology. John Murray, 1830-1833. 1st ed. 3 vols. 8vo. 3 frontispieces (those to vols 2, 3 hand-colored aquatints); 5 plts, 3 maps (2 color), 2 fldg (plus a duplicate); half-titles vols 1, 3. (Lacks ad leaf at end of vol 3, spotted.) Mod 1/2 calf, gilt. *Sotheby's*.* $3,864/£2,415

LYELL, CHARLES. Principles of Geology. London, 1835. 4th ed. 4 vols. w/frontis, 7 maps (3 hand-colored, 5 fldg); 1 fldg hand-colored, 3 plain, 4 fldg plts. Uncut. New 1/2 calf, gilt. (Vol 1 lacks 1/2-title, end of vol 2 waterstained), o/w Fine. *Henly.* $400/£250

LYELL, CHARLES. Principles of Geology. London, 1850. 8th ed. Frontis, xvi,811pp; 7 maps, 4 plts. Pict gilt cl. (Frontis, tp sl foxed), o/w Fine. *Henly.* $90/£56

LYELL, CHARLES. A Second Visit to the United States of North America. NY: Harper, 1849. 1st Amer ed. 2 vols. pp273; 287,(12) ads. Orig brn cl (Eps foxed), else VF. Howes L574. *Mott.* $300/£188

LYELL, CHARLES. The Student's Elements of Geology. NY: Harper, 1871. 1st ed. xxiv,640pp + 4pp. VG (sm chip spine top). *Blake.* $50/£31

LYELL, CHARLES. Travels in North America, Canada, and Nova Scotia, with Geological Observations. London: John Murray, 1855. 2nd ed. 2 vols. xiii,2,316; viii,errata,272pp; 2 maps (1 color fldg), 5 plts. Grn cl (spines faded, ends chipped). Howes L575. *Adelson.* $325/£203

LYELL, CHARLES. Travels in North America. London, 1845. 1st Eng ed. 2 vols. Map, 6 plts. Pub's cl. (Sl foxed; backstrips lt faded), o/w Nice. Howes L575. *Swann*.* $316/£198

LYELL, CHARLES. Travels in North America. London: John Murray, 1845. 1st ed. 2 vols. (i-v),vi-vii,(viii-ix),x-xiii,(xiv),(1),2-316; (i-iii),iv-viii,(1),2-254,255-261,(262),(263),264-272pp, (1),2-12pp pub's ad; color fldg view, color fldg map. All edges trimmed. Grn cl, gilt. Very Nice. *Vandoros.* $500/£313

LYELL, JAMES P. R. (ed). Mrs. Piozzi and Isaac Watts. Grafton, 1934. 1st Eng ed. (Mkd, rubbed.) *Clearwater.* $48/£30

LYFORD, CARRIE A. Quill and Beadwork of the Western Sioux. (Washington): Education Division, U.S. Office of Indian Affairs, (1940). 1st ed. Frontis. Buckram. (Spine, fore-edges sl dknd), else Fine. *Argonaut.* $75/£47

LYKKEJAEGER, HANS. (Pseud of Andrew M. Smith.) Luck of the Wandering Dane. Phila, 1885. 1st ed. 130pp. Ptd wrappers. Howes S572. *Ginsberg.* $600/£375

LYLE, R. C. The Aga Khan's Horses. London, 1938. 1st ed. Color frontis, 7 color plts. (Feps browned, ex-lib; spine lt soiled, fr bd dampstained.) *Edwards.* $32/£20

LYLE, ROYSTER, JR. and PAMELA HEMENWAY SIMPSON. The Architecture of Historic Lexington. Charlottesville: Univ of VA, 1977. 1st ed. Signed by authors and Sally Munger Mann (photos). (Inscrip), else NF in dj (sl damp-wrinkled). *Cahan.* $125/£78

LYMAN, GEORGE. The Book and the Doctor. SF: Privately published, 1933. Ltd to 50 ptd. 2 dwgs by Valenti Angelo. Paper-cvrd bds, paper cvr label. Fine. *Pacific*.* $127/£79

LYMAN, GEORGE. John Marsh, Pioneer. NY: Scribner, 1930. Ltd to 150. Signed. Frontisport, 18 plts, 4 inserted facs. Pict eps. 2-tone red cl, black morocco spine label. Fine. *Pacific*.* $161/£101

LYMAN, HENRY. Insomnia; and Other Disorders of Sleep. Chicago, 1885. 1st ed. 239pp. *Fye.* $100/£63

LYMINGTON, LORD. Spring Song of Iscariot. Paris: Black Sun, 1929. One of 125 numbered. Ptd white wrappers, glassine dj (soiled). *Swann*.* $80/£50

LYNCH, ARTHUR. Human Documents. London: Bertram Dobell, 1896. (xii),304,(iii),(i blank)pp. 2 leaves integral ads at end. Uncut. Ribbed grn cl, gilt. NF (sl mk fr cvr). *Temple.* $32/£20

LYNCH, B. The Prize Ring. London: Country Life, 1925. One of 750. Marbled bds over vellum spine (spotted). *Appelfeld.* $150/£94

LYNCH, B. The Prize Ring. London: Country Life, 1925. 1st ed. One of 750. 1/4 vellum, dec bds, gilt, cvr label. (Extrems, corners rubbed), else VG. *Pacific*.* $196/£123

LYNCH, JEREMIAH. Three Years in the Klondike. London, 1904. 1st ed. Fldg map. (Eps foxed, inscrip; lt worn, spine foot bumped.) *Woolson.* $150/£94

LYNCH, JEREMIAH. Three Years in the Klondike. Dale Morgan (ed). Chicago: R.R. Donnelley, 1967. Lakeside Press ed. Fine. *Perier.* $27/£17

LYNCH, JEROME and JOSEPH FELSEN. Tumors of the Colon and Rectum: Their Pathology, Diagnosis and Treatment. NY, 1925. 1st ed. *Fye.* $100/£63

LYNCH, V. E. Thrilling Adventures. Portland: The Author, 1928. 1st ed. Frontis. Good+ (pencil name; spine edges worn, few nicks to cvr). *Backman.* $50/£31

LYNCH, W. F. Narrative of the United States' Expedition to the River Jordan and the Dead Sea. Phila: Blanchard & Lee, 1853. 9th ed. xx,509,16pp; 28 plts, 2 fdlg maps. Orig morocco. (Ex-lib, foxed, maps torn w/no loss; edges rubbed, scuffed, spine top taped w/lib cl, lib spine label), o/w VG. *Worldwide.* $65/£41

LYNES, GEORGE PLATT. Photographs 1931-1955. Pasadena: Twelvetrees, (1983). Folio. Wrappers (extrems sl worn). *Swann*.* $57/£36

LYON, DANNY. The Bikeriders. NY: Macmillan, (1968). VG in VG dj. *Dermont.* $50/£31

LYON, DANNY. The Bikeriders. NY: Macmillan, 1968. 1st ed, pb issue. 1st bk. (Rear cvr w/closed tear, spine foot sl worn), o/w NF-. *Sclanders.* $56/£35

LYON, DANNY. The Destruction of Lower Manhattan. Toronto, (1969). 1st ed. (Corners bumped.) Dj (worn, yellowed). *Swann*.* $126/£79

LYON, P. Observations on the Barrenness of Fruit Trees. Edinburgh: C. Stewart, 1813. Frontis, 80pp + 16pp ads. Early re-backed bds. (Ex-lib w/ink stamp to verso of repaired tp, foxing, pastedowns sl damaged from label removal.) *Edwards.* $128/£80

LYON, PETER. The Wild, Wild West. NY, 1969. 1st ed. Fine in dj (sl worn, price-clipped). *Baade.* $20/£13

LYON, WILLIAM S. Gardening in California. L.A.: George Rice, 1904. 3rd rev ed. Paper pict inset on fr cvr. *Quest.* $50/£31

LYONS, ALBERT and JOSEPH PETRUCELLI. Medicine: An Illustrated History. NY, 1987. Dj. *Fye.* $80/£50

LYONS, T. A. The Magnetism of Iron and Steel Ships. Washington: GPO, 1884. 123pp; 20 plts. (Bkpls, emb lib stamp.) *Lefkowicz.* $35/£22

LYONS, WILLIAM and BARNES WOODHALL. Atlas of Peripheral Nerve Injuries. Phila, 1949. 1st ed. *Fye.* $200/£125

LYRE, PINCHBECK. (Pseud of Siegfried Sassoon.) Poems by.... Duckworth, 1931. 1st ed. Black bds. VG (sl foxed) in tissue dj. *Blackwell's.* $80/£50

LYSNAR, FRANCES BREWER. New Zealand. Auckland: Brett Ptg & Pub, 1915. 1st ed. (Sl shelf-worn), else Good. *Brown.* $30/£19

LYTLE, HORACE. No Hunting? Dayton, OH: Field Sports Pub, 1928. 1st ed. Photo frontis. Pict eps. Brn dec cl. Fine in NF pict dj. *Biscotti.* $60/£38

LYTLE, HORACE. Point! NY: Derrydale, 1941. One of 950. Brn cl. Fine. *Biscotti.* $175/£109

LYTTELTON, GEORGE. Dialogues of the Dead. London: W. Sandby, 1760. 2nd ed. xii,320,i(erratum)pp. Contemp 1/4-calf, raised bands, red label. (Joints cracking.) *Young.* $77/£48

LYTTON, BULWER. The Last Days of Pompeii. NY: Scribner, 1926. 1st ed. 7x9.5. 425pp. Picture paste-on cvr. VG (spotted, sl shelfworn) in dj (edgeworn). *My Bookhouse.* $105/£66

LYTTON, LORD. The Haunted and the Haunters. Simpkin, Marshall, Hamilton, et al, 1925. Rpt. Good (sig; spine bumped, bubbled cl along hinges, corners bumped; lacks dj). *Tiger.* $48/£30

M

M'CLINTOCK, FRANCIS L. The Voyage of the Fox in Arctic Seas. Boston: Ticknor & Fields, 1860. Authors ed. xxiv,375pp; 4 maps (3 fldg). Orig blind-stamped brn cl (recased). Fine. *Explorer.* $176/£110

M'COLLESTER, SULLIVAN HOLMAN. After-Thoughts of Foreign Travel in Historic Lands and Capital Cities. Boston: New England Pub, 1882. 1st ed. Frontis, viii,375pp. (Sl rubbed), o/w VG. *Worldwide.* $25/£16

M'COLLESTER, SULLIVAN HOLMAN. Babylon and Nineveh Through American Eyes. Boston: Universalist Pub House, 1892. 1st ed. Frontis, 184pp; 12 plts. (Sl spotted, sl rubbed, spine ends frayed), o/w VG. *Worldwide.* $45/£28

M'COLLUM, WILLIAM. California as I Saw It: Pencillings by the Way of Its Gold and Gold Diggers and Incidents of Travel by Land and Water. Dale L. Morgan (ed). Los Gatos, CA: Talisman, 1960. 2nd ed. One of 750. Fine in dj. Howes M55. *Pacific*.* $46/£29

M'CORMICK, S. J. Portland Directory for 1880. Portland: F.L. M'Cormick, 1880. viii,318pp, several ad ll on different colored paper. Ptd bds, black leather spine. (Rebacked, new eps, orig spine laid down, bds worn, lt stained.) *Dawson.* $200/£125

M'CRIE, THOMAS. Life of Andrew Melville. Edinburgh: William Blackwood, 1824. 2nd ed. 2 vols in one. xv,480; vii,550pp; 1 facs (spotted). Contemp mid-tan 1/2 calf, raised bands, black morocco label. VG. *Young.* $72/£45

M'INTOSH, CHARLES. The Book of the Garden. Edinburgh/London: William Blackwood, 1853-1855. 1st ed. 2 vols. x,776,viii; iv,867pp; 34 plts. Grn cl, gilt. Good (hinges cracked, split, spines sunned; lt spotted). *Baltimore*.* $210/£131

M'LAREN, E. T. Dr. John Brown and His Sister Isabella. Edinburgh: David Douglas, 1890. 4th ed. 60,(ii)pp; 3 plts. VG. *Hollett.* $40/£25

M'LEAN, JOHN. Notes of a Twenty-Five Years' Service in the Hudson's Bay Territory. London: Richard Bentley, 1849. 2 vols. Sm 8vo. xii,(13)-308; vii,(i),(9)-328pp. Orig blind-stamped blue cl. VG (2 sigs loose vol 1; spine head vol 1 chipped, lib sticker remains on spine). *Explorer.* $1,120/£700

M'LEOD, JOHN. Narrative of a Voyage in His Majesty's Late Ship Alceste, to the Yellow Sea, Along the Coast of Corea.... London, 1817. 1st ed. Uncolored engr frontis port (offsetting onto tp), 4 hand-colored aquatint plts. Contemp cl-backed bds. (Fr cvr, opening ll loose.) *Swann*.* $316/£198

M'LEOD, JOHN. Narrative of a Voyage in His Majesty's Late Ship Alceste. London: John Murray, 1818. 2nd ed. Frontisport (stained), (viii),288pp; 5 hand-colored plts. (Soiled, browned, several ll creased, incl 1 plt.) Contemp 1/2 calf, marbled bds (surface loss, corners rubbed, spine rubbed w/loss to head), spine label (chipped). *Edwards.* $152/£95

M'MAHON, BERNARD. The American Gardener's Calendar, Adapted to the Climates and Seasons of the United States. Phila: A. M'Mahon, 1839. 9th ed. 3/4 morocco. (Foxed), else VG. *Pacific*.* $69/£43

Ma-Ka-Tai-Me-She-Kia-Kiak; Or, Black Hawk, and Scenes in the West. (By E. H. Smith.) NY: Edward Kearney, 1848. 1st ed. Frontis. Orig cl (rebacked, corners rubbed; 1st, last ll sl foxed), gilt. *Sadlon.* $40/£25

MABIE, PETER. The A to Z Book. Whitman, (1929). 4to. NF in pict wraps. *Davidson.* $60/£38

MABLE, HAMILTON WRIGHT. Nature and Culture. NY: Dodd, Mead, 1904. 1st ed thus. Frontis, 23 full-pg collotypes. Teg. (Lt foxed), else NF. *Cahan.* $85/£53

MAC GAHAN, J. A. Campaigning on the Oxus and the Fall of Khiva. Sampson, Low, Marston et al, 1874. 1st ed. x,438pp; 1 color fldg map. Full contemp calf (spine rubbed), raised bands, gilt (worn). Internally VG. *Sotheran*. $360/£225

MAC ORLAN, PIERRE. Vlaminck. NY, (1958). One of 2000 numbered. 5 litho plts, 1 color, 42 add'l plts. (1/2-title, frontis loose.) Color pict wrappers, plastic dj, slipcase. *Swann**. $373/£233

MacALLESTER, OLIVER. A Series of Letters, Discovering the Scheme Projected by France, in MDCCLIX.... London, 1767. 2 vols in 1. Mod cl. (Tp, dedication leaf damaged in outer margin; 1/2 the vol w/dampstaining and mold damage in outer margin.) *Swann**. $80/£50

MacARTHUR, ARTHUR. After the Afternoon. NY: Appleton-Century, 1941. 1st ed. VG + in dj (price-clipped, sm chip, tape). *Other Worlds*. $25/£16

MacARTHUR, CHARLES. War Bugs. London, (1929). 1st Eng ed. Fine in pict dj (sl dust-mkd). *Clearwater*. $152/£95

MacARTHUR, CHARLES. War Bugs. London: Hutchinson, (ca 1929). 1st British ed. Brn cl. (Foxed early/late), else Nice. *Reese*. $35/£22

MacARTHUR, DOUGLAS. Reminiscences, General of the Army. NY, (1964). Special ed. Ltd to 1750 numbered, signed. (Spine yellowed), else Good in slipcase (soiled, rubbed). *King*. $395/£247

MacARTHUR, MILDRED YORBA. California-Spanish Proverbs. (SF): Colt Press, 1954. One of 450 ptd. Unopened. 1/4 vellum, dec bds, gilt. Fine. *Pacific**. $58/£36

MACARTNEY, MERVYN E. The Practical Exemplar of Architecture.... London: Architectural Review, 1907-28. 6 vols. Sm folio. 677 plts. Contents loose in cl-backed bd folders (some corners worn) as issued. *Swann**. $575/£359

MACASKILL, W. R. Out of Halifax, a Collection of Sea Pictures. NY: Derrydale, 1937. 1st state for U.S.A. *Cullen*. $125/£78

MACAULAY, JAMES. Across the Ferry: First Impressions of America and Its People. London: Hodder & Stoughton, 1871. 1st ed. 424pp. Grn cl (corners rubbed). *Mott*. $75/£47

MACAULAY, JAMES. The Gothic Revival 1745-1845. London, 1975. 1st ed. VG in dj. *Gretton*. $72/£45

MACAULAY, LORD. The Miscellaneous Writings. T.F.E. (ed). Longman, Green, Longman, & Roberts, 1860. 2 vols. Fine engr frontisport vol 1; blank before 1/2-title; xvi,395,(i); (viii),440pp; erratum slip tipped in at end of contents; pub's 24-pg cat dated Sept 1859 at end. Eps coated lt caramel, ads on pastedowns, binder's ticket vol 1; uncut. Dk caramel ripple grain cl, gilt. (Frontis lt dampstained; 1 sig sl proud; patchy fading to cvrs), o/w VG. *Temple*. $104/£65

MACAULAY, ROSE. Catchwords and Claptrap. London: Hogarth, 1926. 1st ed. Paper-cvrd bds (faded, spine browned, edges rubbed). Good- (pencil notes rep). *Virgo*. $40/£25

MACAULAY, ROSE. The Writings of E. M. Forster. Hogarth, 1938. 1st ed. VG (top edge sl dusty, spine ends sl bumped) in dj (nicked, sl rubbed, mkd, dusty, spine, edges browned, spine foot sl soiled). *Ulysses*. $120/£75

MACAULAY, THOMAS BABINGTON. Lays of Ancient Rome. Longman, Brown, Green, Longmans, 1842. 1st ed. 191pp. Orig cl (rebacked preserving orig spine, eps; sm label; inscrip rubbed out). *Bickersteth*. $192/£120

MACAULAY, THOMAS BABINGTON. Lays of Ancient Rome. London: Longman, Brown, Green & Longmans, 1842. 1st ed. Orig brn cl (fr joint starting, inner hinge cracked). VG in 1/4 red morocco slipcase w/chemise. *Cummins*. $300/£188

MACAULAY, THOMAS BABINGTON. The Works. Longman, Brown et al, 1844-61. 12 vols. 8vo. All edges marbled. 1/2 calf, gilt, raised bands, spine labels, marbled bds. VG set. *Hollett*. $560/£350

MACAULEY, JAMES. The Classical Country House in Scotland 1660-1800. Faber, 1987. VG in dj. *Hadley*. $45/£28

MACBEAN, LACHLAN. Pet Marjorie. Stirling: Simpkin, Marshall et al/Eneas Mackay, 1914. 4th ed. 128,(1)pp; 14 tinted plts, guards, family tree. Watered cl (spine, edges faded, fr hinge lt water-stained). *Hollett*. $40/£25

MACBETH, GEORGE. The Broken Places. London: Scorpion, 1963. 1st ed, 1st bk. Rev copy, w/pub's 'Review copy' stamp w/pub date. Off-white cl. VG in dj. *Maggs*. $72/£45

MacBETH, R. G. Romance of the Canadian Pacific Railway. Ryerson, (1924). Good. *Rybski*. $35/£22

MACBRIDE, THOMAS H. In Cabins and Sod-Houses. Iowa City: State Hist Soc, 1928. 1st ed. Port, 2 plts. Teg. (Spine ends worn, shelfworn), else Good. *Brown*. $15/£9

MacCAIG, N. The Sinai Sort. Hogarth, 1957. 1st ed. Fine in dj (spine faded, price sticker removed). *Fine Books*. $30/£19

MacCANN, WILLIAM. Two Thousand Miles' Ride Through the Argentine Provinces. London: Smith, Elder, 1853. 1st ed. 2 vols. 8vo. 2 color frontispieces, xiv,295,12 ads; x,323pp; fldg map, 4 litho plts. Dec cl (sl worn). *Maggs*. $840/£525

MacCARTHY, DESMOND. Portraits. London, 1931. 1st ed. One of 150 signed. VG (no dj). *Typographeum*. $45/£28

MacCORMACK, WILLIAM. Antiseptic Surgery: An Address Delivered at St. Thomas's Hospital with the Subsequent Debate to Which are Added a Short Statement.... London, 1880. 1st ed. 286pp. (Sl lib mk on spine.) *Fye*. $400/£250

MacCREAGH, G. White Waters and Black. NY: Century, 1926. 1st ed. Pict cl, gilt. VG. *Mikesh*. $25/£16

MACCURDY, JOHN T. War Neuroses. Cambridge: CUP, 1918. 1st ed. Fine (name, few stamps). *Beasley*. $65/£41

MacDERMOT, H. E. Sir Thomas Roddick: His Work in Medicine and Public Life. Canada, 1938. VG (rebound in lib binding). *Doctor's Library*. $30/£19

MacDIARMID, HUGH. The Islands of Scotland. Batsford, 1939. 1st ed. VG (eps browned; edges spotted, spine sl faded, ends sl bumped) in dj (rubbed, sl mkd, price-clipped, spine sl dknd). *Ulysses*. $72/£45

MacDIARMID, JOHN. Lives of British Statesmen. London: Longman, Hurst, Rees, & Orme, 1807. 1st ed. Engr frontisport, xii,577,(2),29pp. Contemp calf (neatly rebacked). *Young*. $128/£80

MacDONALD, BETTY. Mrs. Piggle-Wiggle's Farm. Phila: Lippincott, 1954. Stated 1st ed. 5.5x8. Maurice Sendak (illus). 128pp. VG in dj ($2.00). *Cattermole*. $250/£156

MacDONALD, CHARLES BLAIR. Scotland's Gift: Golf. NY: Scribner, 1928. 1st trade ed. 10x7.5. Color frontis, fldg map. Red cl, gilt. Fine (emb stamp) in Fair slipcase (tape-repaired). *Pacific**. $575/£359

MacDONALD, DONALD. Tales and Traditions of the Lews. Stornoway: Mrs. MacDonald, 1967. Map. VG in dj. *Hollett*. $56/£35

MacDONALD, GEORGE E. Thumbscrew and Rack. NY: Truth Seeker, (c.1900). 1st ed. NF in pict wrappers. *Pacific**. $40/£25

MacDONALD, GEORGE. Alec Forbes of Howglen. Hurst & Blackett, n.d. (c1880). Rpt. Frontis. Good (lt spotted; spine bumped). *Tiger*. $38/£24

MacDONALD, GEORGE. At the Back of the North Wind. NY: Macmillan, (1924). 1st ed thus. 8vo. Color frontis, 376pp; 12 full-pg b/w illus by D. Bedford. Blue cl. VG. *Davidson*. $100/£63

MacDONALD, GEORGE. At the Back of the North Wind. London: Strahan, 1871. 1st ed. Arthur Hughes (illus). Brothers Dalziel (engrs). Red cl, gilt. VG (sm stain fep, sl shaken; extrems sl rubbed, spine ends chipped). *Pacific**. $431/£269

MacDONALD, GEORGE. At the Back of the North Wind. Phila, 1919. 1st ed thus. 9.5x7. 342pp; 8 full-pg color plts + tp by Jesse Willcox Smith. Teg. Pict label. (Loose, cvrs soiled, 1 illus loose.) King. $95/£59

MacDONALD, GEORGE. At the Back of the North Wind. Phila: David McKay, 1919. 1st ed. 8vo. 342pp; 8 full-pg color illus by Jessie Willcox Smith. Illus eps; teg. Gray cl, pict onlay. VG. Davidson. $125/£78

MacDONALD, GEORGE. At the Back of the North Wind. Phila: David McKay, 1919. 1st trade ed. 8 color plts by Jessie Wilcox Smith. Gilt-dec cl, pict cvr label. Fine in NF dj (spine head chipped, tape repair to verso). Pacific*. $316/£198

MacDONALD, GEORGE. A Book of Strife in the Form of the Diary of an Old Soul. Arthur C. Fifield, 1906. New ed. Frontisport. Good (fore-edge lt spotted; spine bumped). Tiger. $48/£30

MacDONALD, GEORGE. Fairy Tales. Greville MacDonald (ed). London: Arthur C. Fifield, 1904. 1st ed thus. 8vo. Arthur Hughes (illus). Teg. Blue cl, gilt. Nice (few fox spots). Reisler. $200/£125

MacDONALD, GEORGE. The Golden Key. NY: FSG, (1967). 1st ed, 1st issue. 8vo. 10 full-pg b/w dwgs by Maurice Sendak. Blue cl, gilt. Good in illus dj (worn). Reisler. $75/£47

MacDONALD, GEORGE. The Light Princess and Other Fairy Tales. NY: Putnam, (1893). 1st ed thus. Maud Humphrey (illus). Dec cl. (Spine dull), else NF. Pacific*. $115/£72

MacDONALD, GEORGE. The Light Princess. NY: FSG, (1969). 1st ed. 8vo. 10 full-pg b/w dwgs by Maurice Sendak. Blue cl, gilt. VG in illus dj (price-clipped). Reisler. $75/£47

MacDONALD, GEORGE. The Princess and Curdie. London: J.M. Dent, (1949). 1st ed thus. 8vo. 8 full-pg color plts by Charles Folkard. Maroon/wheat dec cl. Good in full color dj. Reisler. $100/£63

MacDONALD, GEORGE. The Princess and Curdie. Macmillan, 1927. 1st ed thus. Dorothy Lathrop (illus). Blue cl, stamped, gilt. Good (fep heavily erased w/1/16-inch hole; corners bumped). Price. $50/£31

MacDONALD, GEORGE. The Princess and the Goblin. Phila: Lippincott, (1907). 8vo. 305pp; 12 full-pg color illus by Maria Kirk. Illus eps. Pict stamped red cl. VG. Davidson. $165/£103

MacDONALD, JOHN D. Bright Orange for the Shroud. Phila: Lippincott, 1972. 1st bk ed. VG + (top edge of pp lt foxed; extrems sl shelfworn) in dj (spine sl faded). Lame Duck. $275/£172

MacDONALD, JOHN D. A Deadly Shade of Gold. Phila: Lippincott, 1974. 1st hb ed. Fine in NF dj (sl rubbed, nicked). Unger. $200/£125

MacDONALD, JOHN D. Dress Her in Indigo. Greenwich: Fawcett/Gold Medal, (1969). Pb orig. VG + (pg edges sl browned; sl scrape spine, lt worn). Between The Covers. $65/£41

MacDONALD, JOHN D. The Empty Trap. NY: Popular Library, (1957). 1st pb ed. Nice in pict wraps. King. $25/£16

MacDONALD, JOHN D. The Girl in the Plain Brown Wrapper. Greenwich: Fawcett/Gold Medal, (1968). Pb orig. VG (spine creases). Between The Covers. $50/£31

MacDONALD, JOHN D. Good Old Stuff. NY, 1982. 1st ed. NF in NF dj (short closed tear top of rear panel). Warren. $50/£31

MacDONALD, JOHN D. The House Guests. GC: Doubleday, 1965. 1st ed. NF in dj (sl dampstain spine head, sm tear fr panel). Pacific*. $52/£33

MacDONALD, JOHN D. Murder in the Wind. NY, 1960. 1st Amer ed. Pb orig. NF. Warren. $25/£16

MacDONALD, JOHN D. Nightmare in Pink. Greenwich: Fawcett/Gold Medal, (1964). Pb orig. Fine (pp sl browned). Between The Covers. $100/£63

MacDONALD, JOHN D. Wine of the Dreamers. NY: Greenberg, (1951). 1st ed. Bkpl signed by MacDonald mtd to fep. (Sl adhesion residue from former dj to extrems), else VG in dj (spine sl sunned, ends sl rubbed). Pacific*. $127/£79

MacDONALD, JOHN ROSS. (Pseud of Ross Macdonald.) Experience with Evil. Cassell, 1954. 1st Eng ed. VG (rep mkd, top edge dusty, edges sl spotted; spine tail sl bumped) in dj (nicked, dusty, sl rubbed, creased). Ulysses. $152/£95

MacDONALD, JOHN ROSS. (Pseud of Ross Macdonald.) Find a Victim. Cassell, 1955. 1st Eng ed. VG (edges lt spotted, top edge dusty) in dj (nicked, rubbed, creased, dusty, sl dknd). Ulysses. $152/£95

MacDONALD, PHILIP. Patrol. London (etc): W. Collins, (1927). 1st ed. Dk blue cl stamped in red. VG in VG pict dj (spine dknd, sm mend fr panel corner). Reese. $250/£156

MacDONALD, R. Opals and Gold. Phila: Lippincott, n.d (ca 1928). VG in dj (worn). Blake. $65/£41

MacDONALD, ROSS. (Pseud of Kenneth Millar.) Archer at Large. NY: Knopf, 1970. Omnibus ed. Fine in dj (spine sl faded). Mordida. $35/£22

MacDONALD, ROSS. (Pseud of Kenneth Millar.) Black Money. NY, 1966. 1st ed. 1/4 cl. Dj (lt rubbed, sl discoloration rear panel). Swann*. $69/£43

MacDONALD, ROSS. (Pseud of Kenneth Millar.) The Blue Hammer. NY, 1976. 1st ed. Advance rev copy w/slip laid in. NF in dj. Warren. $50/£31

MacDONALD, ROSS. (Pseud of Kenneth Millar.) The Ferguson Affair. NY, 1960. 1st ed. Signed. Dj (extrems lt soiled, rubbed). Swann*. $161/£101

MacDONALD, ROSS. (Pseud of Kenneth Millar.) The Goodbye Look. NY: Knopf, 1969. 1st ed. Fine in VG + dj (lt edgeworn). Janus. $45/£28

MacDONALD, ROSS. (Pseud of Kenneth Millar.) The Goodbye Look. NY, 1969. 1st ed. Fine in NF dj. Warren. $75/£47

MacDONALD, ROSS. (Pseud of Kenneth Millar.) The Instant Enemy. NY: Knopf, 1968. 1st ed. (Spine ends sl faded), else VG in dj (spine ends, top of rear panel sl chipped, price-clipped). Pacific*. $46/£29

MacDONALD, ROSS. (Pseud of Kenneth Millar.) The Instant Enemy. NY: Knopf, 1968. 1st ed. NF in NF dj. Janus. $85/£53

MacDONALD, ROSS. (Pseud of Kenneth Millar.) The Name Is Archer. NY: Bantam, 1955. 1st ed. Pb orig. NF. Janus. $85/£53

MacDONALD, ROSS. (Pseud of Kenneth Millar.) Sleeping Beauty. NY, 1973. 1st ed. Fine in NF dj. Warren. $35/£22

MacDONALD, ROSS. (Pseud of Kenneth Millar.) The Underground Man. Collins, 1971. 1st UK ed. NF in VG dj. Williams. $38/£24

MacDONALD, ROSS. (Pseud of Kenneth Millar.) The Underground Man. NY, 1971. 1st ed. NF in Fine dj. Warren. $40/£25

MacDONALD, W. A. A Farewell to Commander Byrd. NY: Coward-McCann, 1929. Only issue in bk form. Orig ptd paper wrapper. Fine in dj (sl chipped). Explorer. $56/£35

MacDONALD, WILLIAM. Poems. Edinburgh: The Author, 1809. 1st ed. viii,157,(1) blank pp + 14pp sub's list. Unpressed, untrimmed, unopened. Orig paper-backed gray bds, ptd paper label (worn). VG. Blackwell's. $240/£150

MacDONOUGH, GLEN and ANNA ALICE CHAPIN. Babes in Toyland. NY: Fox Duffield, 1904. 1st ed. Sm 4to. Color frontis, (x),180pp; 6 color plts by Ethel Franklin Betts. Fair (lt soiled, ink name, plts loose; pict cl bumped, rubbed, rear cvr stained, spine faded; inner hinges cracked, shaken). Blue Mountain. $35/£22

MacDOUGALL, ARTHUR R., JR. Dud Dean and His Country. NY: Coward-McCann, (1946). 1st ed. One of 450. Signed. Color frontis. Fine. Pacific*. $92/£58

MacDOUGALL, ARTHUR R., JR. Where Flows the Kennebec. NY: Coward-McCann, 1947. 1st ed. Grn buckram. NF in NF pict dj. *Biscotti.* $50/£31

MacDOUGALL, ELISABETH B. and RICHARD ETTING-HAUSEN. The Islamic Garden. N.p. Dumbarton Oaks, 1976. 36 plts. Mint. *Hadley.* $48/£30

MacDOUGALL, ELISABETH B. (ed). Medieval Gardens. (Washington): Dumbarton Oaks, 1986. Fine in grn cl. *Hadley.* $56/£35

MacDOUGALL, ELISABETH B. (ed). Medieval Gardens. Washington: Dumbarton Oaks, 1986. VF. *Europa.* $62/£39

MacDOUGALL, MARGARET O. (ed). Robert Bain's the Clans and Tartans of Scotland. Collins, 1954. Aeg. Orig padded tartan silk, gilt. VG in orig box (edges sl rubbed). *Hollett.* $48/£30

MACE, JEAN. The History of a Mouthful of Bread. Mrs. Alfred Gatty (trans). NY: American News, (1866). 1st Amer ed. Grn cl, gilt. VG. *Pacific*.* $40/£25

MACE, JEAN. The History of a Mouthful of Bread. NY, 1868. 1st Amer ed. 399pp. *Fye.* $75/£47

MACFADDEN, B. The Truth About Tobacco. NY, 1922. 1st ed. VG (extrems sl worn). *Doctor's Library.* $30/£19

MACFARLAN, ALLAN A. (ed). American Indian Legends. L.A.: LEC, 1968. One of 1500 ptd. Signed by Everett Gee Jackson (illus). 1/2 undyed fawnskin, natural wood veneer bds, spine label. Fine in glassine, slipcase. *Pacific*.* $81/£51

MacFARLANE, C. The Lives and Exploits of Banditti and Robbers in All Parts of the World. London: Thomas Tegg & Son, 1837. Blank or ad leaf preceding 1/2-title; Fine steel-engr frontis, 3 plts, guards; viii,408pp. All edges sprinkled blue. Early grn 1/2-calf, raised bands, gilt, bds stippled grn. (Bound w/o 1/2-title and initial blank or ad leaf; calf sl faded), o/w Fine. *Temple.* $35/£22

MacFARLANE, C. A Memoir of the Duke of Wellington. London, 1852. 272pp. 3/4 red leather, marbled bds. (Spine sl dull), else VG. *King.* $75/£47

MacFIE, HARRY. Wasa-Wasa, a Tale of the Trails and Treasure in the Far North. Hans Westerlund (trans). NY: W.W. Norton, (1951). 1st ed. VG in dj. *Perier.* $30/£19

MACFIE, RONALD CAMPBELL. Heredity, Evolution, and Vitalism. NY: William Wood, 1912. 1st ed. Blue cl, gilt. VG. *House.* $35/£22

MACGIBBON, DAVID and THOMAS ROSS. The Ecclesiastical Architecture of Scotland from the Earliest Christian Times to the Seventeenth Century. Edinburgh: David Douglas, 1896-1897. Royal 8vo. xiii,(1),483,(1),(16, pub's ads); xx,564; xiv,649,(1)pp. Aeg. Pub's cl, gilt thistle device to fr bds, spine gilt-lettered. Fine set. *Sotheran.* $557/£348

MacGILL, PATRICK. The Diggers: The Australians in France. London: Herbert Jenkins, 1919. 1st ed. Red cl. Fine in pict dj (lt worn, nicked, sm chip lower rear edge, closed tear). *Reese.* $35/£22

MacGILL, PATRICK. The Red Horizon. London: Herbert Jenkins, 1916. 1st ed. Red cl stamped in black. VG in pict dj (sl rubbed, spine tanned). *Reese.* $85/£53

MacGILL, PATRICK. Soldier Songs. London: Herbert Jenkins, 1917. 1st ed. Grn cl. Fine in VG pict dj (lt nicked). *Reese.* $35/£22

MacGILLIVRAY, WILLIAM. The Natural History of Dee Side and Braemar. Edwin Lankester (ed). Privately ptd, 1855. 1st ed. Inscribed. Woodcut frontis, xx,507pp; 2 extending color maps (1 fully color). Red cl (spine head sl chipped, frayed), gilt. *Hollett.* $352/£220

MacGOWAN, J. How England Saved China. London, 1913. 1st ed. Teg. (Lt foxed, blindstamp tp.) *Edwards.* $120/£75

MacGREGOR, ALASDAIR ALPIN. Behold the Hebrides! or Wayfaring in the Western Isles. W. & R. Chambers, 1925. 1st ed. VG. *Hollett.* $40/£25

MacGREGOR, ALASDAIR ALPIN. The Haunted Isles. Alexander MacLehose, 1933. 1st ed. 20 plts (incl color tp). (Hinges sl rubbed.) *Hollett.* $32/£20

MacGREGOR, ALASDAIR ALPIN. Islands by the Score. Michael Joseph, 1971. 1st ed. VG in dj (price-clipped). *Hollett.* $32/£20

MacGREGOR, ALASDAIR ALPIN. Over the Sea to Skye. W. & R. Chambers, 1930. 40 plts. (Hinges sl rubbed.) *Hollett.* $40/£25

MacGREGOR, ALASDAIR ALPIN. The Peat-Fire Flame. Moray, 1937. 1st ed. (Fr joint sl strained.) *Hollett.* $56/£35

MacGREGOR, ALASDAIR ALPIN. Searching the Hebrides with a Camera. George G. Harrap, 1933. 1st ed. (Sl rubbed.) *Hollett.* $40/£25

MacGREGOR, ALASDAIR ALPIN. Somewhere in Scotland. Robert Hale, 1950. Color frontis. VG in dj (sl worn, repaired, price-clipped). *Hollett.* $40/£25

MacGREGOR, ALASDAIR ALPIN. Summer Days Among the Western Isles. T. Nelson/T.C. & E.C. Jack, 1929. 1st ed. Color frontis. VG. *Hollett.* $64/£40

MacGREGOR, ALASDAIR ALPIN. The Turbulent Years. Methuen, 1945. 1st ed. 16 plts. (Eps sl spotted; top edges sl dknd.) *Hollett.* $48/£30

MacGREGOR, ALASDAIR ALPIN. Vanished Waters. Methuen, 1946. 3rd ed. 17 plts. (Spine faded.) *Hollett.* $32/£20

MacGREGOR, ALEXANDER. Highland Superstitions. Stirling: Eneas Mackay, 1951. VG in dj (price-clipped). *Hollett.* $40/£25

MacGREGOR, FRANCES M. COOKE et al. Facial Deformities and Plastic Surgery,a Psychosocial Study. Springfield, IL: Charles C. Thomas, (1953). Fine in dj. *Weber.* $60/£38

MacGREGOR, GREGORY A. Deus ex Machina. SF: Studebaker, 1975. 1st ed, 1st bk. Ltd to 1000. 41 full-pg b/w photos. NF in pict stiff wrappers (sl spotted). *Cahan.* $50/£31

MACH, ERNST. The Analysis of Sensations and the Relation of the Physical to the Psychical. C.M. Williams (trans). Chicago/London: Opern Court, 1914. Olive grn cl. Fine. *Weber.* $45/£28

MACHADO, ANTONIO. I Never Wanted Fame. Robert Bly (trans). St. Paul: Ally, 1979. 1st ed. Pamphlet. Fine in illus wraps. *Lame Duck.* $25/£16

MACHEN, ARTHUR. The Angels of Mons. NY/London: Putnam, 1915. 1st US ed. Tan bds, pict stamped in dk brn. Fine in NF dj (sm nicks). *Reese.* $55/£34

MACHEN, ARTHUR. The Angels of Mons. London: Simpkin, Marshall (et al), 1915. 1st ed. Gray bds pict stamped in blue. (Sm erasure fr bd), o/w VG +. *Reese.* $75/£47

MACHEN, ARTHUR. Fantastic Tales; or, The Way to Attain. Carbonnek: Privately ptd, 1923. One of 1050. Signed. Blue/cream bds, gilt spine. (Corners sl rubbed), else VG. *Pacific*.* $52/£33

MACHEN, ARTHUR. The London Adventure, or, The Art of Wandering. London: Martin Secker, (1924). 1st ed. One of 200. Signed. Blue bds, paper spine label. (Lt foxing; dampstaining to lower spine, upper corners), else VG in glassine. *Pacific*.* $35/£22

MACHEN, ARTHUR. The Terror. London: Duckworth, (1917). 1st ed. Pale blue bds, ptd in dk blue. (Browned, sm chip extreme upper margin of tp), o/w Fine in pict dj. *Reese.* $100/£63

MACHEN, ARTHUR. The Terror. London, 1917. 1st Eng ed. Good (tp hinge weak; sl dust-mkd, tanned). *Clearwater.* $72/£45

MACHEN, ARTHUR. The Terror. London: Duckworth, 1917. 1st ed. Fine (pp browned). *Else Fine.* $75/£47

MACHEN, ARTHUR. Things Near and Far. London, 1923. 1st Eng ed. Good in dj (sl rubbed, dust-mkd). *Clearwater.* $120/£75

MACHIAVELLI, NICCOLO. The Prince. N. H. T. (trans). Kegan Paul, Trench, 1882. One of 750. xi,181,(i)pp. Teg. Cl, beveled bds (sl worn), gilt. *Hollett.* $72/£45

MACHIAVELLI, NICCOLO. The Prince. Hill Thomson (trans). NY: LEC, 1954. One of 1500. Teg. Beveled full Florentine morocco, gilt. Fine in slipcase. *Pacific*.* $98/£61

MACHIAVELLI, NICCOLO. The Prince. LEC, 1954. Ltd to 1500 numbered. Fine in slipcase. *Swann*.* $149/£93

MACINNES, COLIN. Absolute Beginners. London: MacGibbon & Kee, 1959. 1st ed. Red cl. Fine in dj. *Maggs.* $120/£75

MacINNES, HAMISH. West Highland Walks: Two. Hodder & Stoughton, 1979. 1st ed. VG. *Hollett.* $19/£12

MacINNES, HELEN. Assignment in Brittany. Boston: LB, 1942. 1st ed. Fine in NF dj. *Between The Covers.* $75/£47

MacINNES, HELEN. While Still We Live. Boston: LB, 1944. 1st ed. Fine in Fine dj (sl worn). *Between The Covers.* $65/£41

MACINTYRE, D. Narvik. London, 1959. 1st ed. VG in VG dj. *Clark.* $25/£16

MACINTYRE, DONALD. Hindu-Koh: Wanderings and Wild Sport in the Himalayas. Edinburgh, 1891. (Foxed throughout; sl shaken, tips worn.) *Oinonen*.* $100/£63

MACINTYRE, DONALD. Hindu-Koh: Wanderings and Wild Sport on and Beyond the Himalayas. London, 1889. Color frontis (sl stained). 1/2 leather (rebacked w/old spine replaced). (Margins sl browned.) *Petersfield.* $157/£98

MACINTYRE, DONALD. Hindu-Koh: Wanderings and Wild Sport on and Beyond the Himalayas. London: William Blackwood, 1889. 1st ed. 1/2-title, color litho frontis, xx,464,24 pub's list; 8 plts. Grn dec cl (recased w/new eps, rubbed, stained), gilt. Internally Good (sl browned). *Morrell.* $208/£130

MACINTYRE, DONALD. Hindu-Koh: Wanderings and Wild Sport on and Beyond the Himalayas. London, 1891. New ed. *Petersfield.* $112/£70

MACINTYRE, DUGALD. Highland Gamekeeper. Seeley Service, n.d. (1930). 1st ed. Fine in dj. *Hollett.* $48/£30

MACINTYRE, W. IRWIN. Colored Soldiers. Macon: J.W. Burke, 1923. 1st ed. Port. Olive cl stamped in black. (Ink inscrip), else VG. *Reese.* $45/£28

MACK, CONNIE. My 66 Years in the Big Leagues. Phila, (1950). 1st ed. Pict wraps. (Cvrs sl soiled.) *King.* $35/£22

MACK, EFFIE MONA. The Indian Massacre of 1911 at Little High Rock Canyon, Nevada. (Sparks, NV, 1968.) 1st ed. One of 1000. Signed. NF. *Sagebrush.* $125/£78

MACK, JAMES D. Matthew Flinders, 1774-1814. Nelson, 1966. 1st ed. Good in dj. *Rybski.* $35/£22

MACK, LIZZIE and ROBERT ELLICE MACK. Christmas Tree Fairy. NY: E.P. Dutton, (ca 1880). 8vo. 6 full-pg chromolitho plts. Cl-backed color pict bds (lt dusty; fr hinge cracked). *Reisler.* $200/£125

MACK, ROBERT E. When All Is Young. NY: E.P. Dutton, (ca 1880). 8vo. Harriet M. Bennett (illus). Cl-backed color pict bds (stained). *Reisler.* $200/£125

MacKAY, DONALD. The Lumberjacks. Toronto, (1978). 1st ed. NF in VG + dj. *Sagebrush.* $45/£28

MacKAY, DOUGLAS. The Honourable Company. Indianapolis: Bobbs-Merrill, (1936). 1st ed. Frontis, 47 photo plts. VF in pict dj (sl chipped). *Argonaut.* $125/£78

MacKAY, GEORGE HENRY. Shooting Journal of George Henry Mackay 1865-1922. Cambridge, MA: Privately ptd, 1929. One of 300. Port. 1/2 cl w/paper-cvrd bds (lt worn). *Oinonen*.* $150/£94

MacKAY, HELEN. Stories for Pictures. NY: Duffield, 1912. 1st ed. 8vo. 8 full-pg color plts by Dugald Stewart Walker. Cl-backed stamped bds, gilt. Good in orig illus dj (worn, lacks piece). *Reisler.* $150/£94

MacKAY, JAMES. An Encyclopedia of Small Antiques. NY, 1975. 1st US ed. 32 color plts. Dj (spine lt faded). *Edwards.* $32/£20

MacKAY, JAMES. St. Kilda—Its Posts and Communications. Edinburgh: Scottish Postmark Group, 1963. 1st ed. Laid-in color frontis (sl adhesions damage to verso). VG. *Hollett.* $72/£45

MacKAY, MALCOLM S. Cow Range and Hunting Trail. NY/London: Putnam, 1925. 1st ed. 1925 signed presentation. Untrimmed. Dk grn cl, gilt. Nice (sl foxed; lt dusty). Howes M120. *Baltimore*.* $90/£56

MacKAY, WILLIAM. Ex-Soldier We Are Dead. London: Albert E. Marriott, (ca 1930). 1st ed. Red cl stamped in black. (Ink name, edges lt foxed), o/w VG in pict dj (sm price sticker shadow fr panel, lt discoloration spine crown). *Reese.* $55/£34

MacKENZIE, ALEXANDER SLIDELL. Case of the Somers' Mutiny. NY: Tribune Office, 1843. 1st ed. 30,ii pp. Mod cl. VG (tp spotted, inner margins lt dampstained). *Lefkowicz.* $195/£122

MacKENZIE, ALEXANDER SLIDELL. Life of Stephen Decatur. Boston: Charles C. Little & James Browne, 1846. 1st ed. Engr tp, (xii),443pp; port, facs. Later lib cl. Sound (lib label, other lib mks). Howes M136. *Lefkowicz.* $60/£38

MACKENZIE, ALEXANDER. The Prophecies of the Brahan Seer. Stirling: Eneas Mackay, 1924. 1st ed. Uncut. VG (fore-edge spotted) in pict dj. *Maggs.* $80/£50

MACKENZIE, ALEXANDER. Voyages from Montreal, on the River St. Laurence, Through the Continent of North America...In the Years 1789 and 1793. With a Preliminary Account.... London: Cadell, Davies et al, 1801. 1st ed. 4to. Stipple-engr frontisport, (2),viii,cxxxii,412,(2)pp; 3 fldg copper-engr maps, 1 hand-colored. Marbled eps. Mod full tree calf, gilt, morocco lettering piece. NF (lt offset from port, maps, sm gutter tear to tp expertly repaired, several neatly repaired crease tears to maps, sl foxing). Howes M113. *Pacific*.* $5,750/£3,594

MACKENZIE, ALISTER. Dr. Mackenzie's Golf Architecture. H. R. Grant (comp). Worcestershire: Grant Books, 1993. One of 700 ptd. Signed by Shirley Grant. Frontisport. Grn cl, gilt. As New. *Pacific*.* $98/£61

MACKENZIE, ALISTER. Golf Architecture: Economy in Course Construction and Green-Keeping. London: Simpkin et al, (1920). 1st ed. Grn cl. NF (emb stamp, name). *Pacific*.* $1,495/£934

MACKENZIE, COMPTON. Ben Nevis Goes East. London, 1954. 1st ed. Fine in dj. *Petersfield.* $16/£10

MACKENZIE, COMPTON. Calvary. London: John Lane/Bodley Head, 1942. 1st Eng ed. 29 full-pg b/w dwgs. NF (spine foot sl bumped) in dj (sl rubbed, sl dknd). *Ulysses.* $56/£35

MACKENZIE, COMPTON. Extremes Meet. London (etc): Cassell, (1928). 1st ed. Gilt black cl. (Lt foxed early/late), else Fine in pict dj (closed tear top of rear joint). *Reese.* $100/£63

MACKENZIE, COMPTON. Extremes Meet. GC: Doubleday, Doran, 1928. 1st US ed. Yellow cl. (Few smudges), else Good in pict dj (lg chunk missing lower edge fr panel). *Reese.* $25/£16

MACKENZIE, COMPTON. Gallipoli Memories. London, 1929. 1st ed. VG in dj. *Typographeum.* $45/£28

MACKENZIE, COMPTON. Gallipoli Memories. GC: Doubleday, Doran, 1930. 1st US ed. Gilt red cl. NF in VG pict dj (lt edgeworn, rubbed). *Reese.* $45/£28

MACKENZIE, COMPTON. My Life and Times Octave Five 1915-1923. London: C&W, 1966. 1st ed. Gilt blue cl. Fine in dj. *Reese.* $20/£13

MACKENZIE, COMPTON. The South Wind of Love. London: Rich & Cowan, (1937). 1st ed. Gilt blue cl. (Fore-edge lt foxed), o/w Nice in pict dj (short tears at spine ends). *Reese.* $35/£22

MACKENZIE, COMPTON. Sylvia and Michael: The Later Adventures of Sylvia Scarlett. London: Martin Secker, 1919. 1st ed. Black cl stamped in grn. (Eps foxed), else Good in dj (chipped, creased, dknd). *Reese.* $65/£41

MACKENZIE, COMPTON. The Three Couriers. London (etc): Cassell, (1929). 1st ed. Gilt black cl. Fine in VG pict dj (sm nick, corner rubs, narrow adhesion scar fr flap fold). *Reese.* $85/£53

MACKENZIE, COMPTON. Water on the Brain. London, 1933. 1st ed. Fine in dj (sl torn). *Petersfield.* $24/£15

MACKENZIE, FAITH COMPTON. Mandolinata. Fourteen Stories. London: Cope & Fenwick, 1931. 1st ed. Ltd to 330 signed. Nice in terra cotta buckram, gilt. *Cady.* $40/£25

MACKENZIE, GEORGE STEUART. Travels in the Island of Iceland, During the Summer of the Year MDCCCX. Edinburgh: Constable, 1812. 2nd ed. 4to. (xvii),491pp; 3 maps (1 lg fldg), 4 fldg charts, 8 color aquatints, 6 engrs. Later 1/2 calf. (Lt foxing affecting 3 plts.) *Maggs.* $800/£500

MACKENZIE, GEORGE. Memoirs of the Affairs of Scotland. Edinburgh, 1821. Lg paper copy. xii,332pp (bkpl, sig). Aeg. Old diced calf (edges scraped, restored, rebacked in matching calf), gilt. *Hollett.* $152/£95

MACKENZIE, J. B. The Six-Nations Indians in Canada. Toronto: Hunter, Rose, (1896). 151pp. Fine in blue cl, gilt. *Cullen.* $125/£78

MACKENZIE, JAMES. Diseases of the Heart. London, 1908. 1st ed. 386pp. (Backstrip faded.) *Fye.* $275/£172

MACKENZIE, JAMES. Diseases of the Heart. Oxford, 1913. 3rd ed. (Fep missing; lt foxed, sl worn.) *Whitehart.* $51/£32

MACKENZIE, JAMES. Reports of the St. Andrew's (James MacKenzie) Institute for Clinical Research. Vols I and III. London, 1922-1926. 2 vols. 208; 227pp. *Fye.* $125/£78

MACKENZIE, MORELL. Hayfever and Paroxysmal Sneezing, Their Etiology and Treatment with an Appendix on Rose Cold. London, 1889. 5th ed. 96pp. *Fye.* $75/£47

MACKENZIE, MORELL. The Use of the Laryngoscope in Diseases of the Throat. Phila, 1865. 1st Amer ed. 160pp. *Fye.* $350/£219

MACKENZIE, MURDO. Contrast Psychology. London: George Allen & Unwin, (1952). Red cl. VG in dj (lt worn). *Gach.* $25/£16

MACKENZIE, W. C. A Short History of the Scottish Highlands and Isles. Paisley: Alexander Gardner, 1906. 18 plts, color map. (Cl used.) *Hollett.* $24/£15

MacKENZIE, WILLIAM L. The Lives and Opinions of Benj'n Franklin Butler, United States District Attorney for the Southern District of New-York.... Boston: Cook & Co, 1845. 152pp (lt age-spotted). Mostly unopened. Paper wrappers (extrems chipped). *Zubal*.* $24/£15

MACKIE, MRS. Willy's Book of Birds. London: Darton & Hodge, 1862. Dbl-pg hand-colored litho frontis, tp, (vi),44pp; 6 hand-colored lithos. Aeg. Dk grn blind-stamped cl, gilt. VG (few sm internal mks, handling). *Sotheran.* $237/£148

MACKIE, P. JEFFREY. The Keeper's Book. London, 1910. 7th ed. Tipped-in illus. Teg. (Cvrs soiled, 2nd cvr label missing?.) *King.* $40/£25

MACKIE, THOMAS T. et al. A Manual of Tropical Medicine. Phila, 1949. VG in cl-cvrd wrappers (extrems sl worn). *Doctor's Library.* $45/£28

MACKINNON, FRANK DOUGLAS. Inner Temple Papers. London: Stevens & Sons, 1948. Sound (foxed, browned). *Boswell.* $50/£31

MACKINTOSH, ALEXANDER. The Driffield Angler. Gainsborough, (1806). 1st ed. Engr frontis. Mod 1/2 grn morocco (sl scuffed), gilt. *Swann*.* $373/£233

MACKINTOSH, ALEXANDER. The Modern Fisher. Derby: Henry Mozeley, (c1820). 1st ed (?). 249,(3)pp. Orig bds (rehinged, stained; inner margin of 1st gatherings partly stained not affecting text). *Young.* $192/£120

MACKLEY, GEORGE. Wood Engraving. London: Nat'l Magazine Co, (1948). 1st ed. Fine in dj. *Bromer.* $285/£178

MACKLIN, HERBERT W. The Brasses of England. NY, 1907. 3 plts. (Cl sl worn, soiled.) *Washton.* $75/£47

MACLAGAN, ERIC. Italian Sculpture of the Renaissance. The Charles Eliot Norton Lectures for the Years 1927-1928. Cambridge, 1935. (Cl dknd, extrems sl rubbed.) *Washton.* $65/£41

MACLAGAN, T. J. The Germ Theory Applied to the Explanation of the Phenomena of Disease. London, 1876. 1st ed. 258pp (tp, prelims stained). *Fye.* $125/£78

MACLAGAN, T. J. Rheumatism: Its Nature, Its Pathology and Its Successful Treatment. NY, 1886. 1st Amer ed. 277pp. *Fye.* $125/£78

MACLAREN-ROSS, J. The Funny Bone. London: Elek Books, 1956. 1st ed. Grn cl, gilt. VG in dj (sl dusty). *Maggs.* $80/£50

MACLAREN-ROSS, J. Memoirs of the Forties. London: Alan Ross, 1965. 1st Eng ed. VG (top edge sl spotted, dusty, spine ends sl bumped) in dj (sl creased, spine, edges sl dknd). *Ulysses.* $104/£65

MACLAREN-ROSS, J. The Weeping and the Laughter. London, 1953. 1st Eng ed. Very Nice in dj (sl rubbed, spine head chipped). *Clearwater.* $80/£50

MACLAY, EDGAR STANTON. A History of American Privateers. NY, 1899. 1st ed. xl,519pp; 14 plts. (Spine ends worn, rear hinge tender.) Emb stamps of W.M.P. Dunne. *Lefkowicz.* $100/£63

MacLEAN, ALISTAIR. Athabasca. London, 1980. VG in dj. *Typographeum.* $16/£10

MacLEAN, ALISTAIR. The Guns of Navarone. Collins, 1957. 1st UK ed. Fine in dj (price-clipped). *Williams.* $48/£30

MacLEAN, ALISTAIR. H.M.S. Ulysses. London: Collins, 1955. 1st ed, 1st bk. VG in dj (lt chipped, repaired). *Glenn.* $100/£63

MacLEAN, ALISTAIR. South by Java Head. Collins, 1958. 1st UK ed. VG in dj (price-clipped). *Williams.* $29/£18

MacLEAN, ALISTAIR. Where Eagles Dare. London: Collins, 1967. 1st ed. Fine in dj. *Mordida.* $60/£38

MacLEAN, ANGUS. Cuentos. Fresno: Pioneer, (1979). 1st ed. Signed by MacLean & illus. Pict yellow cl. NF. *House.* $20/£13

MacLEAN, ANGUS. The Curse of the Feathered Snake and Other Stories. Fresno: Pioneer, (1981). 1st ed. Signed by MacLean & illus. Map. Tan cl. NF. *House.* $20/£13

MACLEAN, CATHERINE MACDONALD. Dorothy Wordsworth: The Early Years. C&W, 1932. Good (fore-edge sl spotted; spine bumped; lacks dj). *Tiger.* $29/£18

MACLEAN, LACHAN. An Enquiry into the Nature, Causes, and Cure of Hydrothorax. Hartford, CT, 1814. 1st Amer ed. 187: 176pp. Paperbacked bds (backstrip cracked, chipped). Internally Fine. *Fye.* $400/£250

MACLEAN, NORMAN. A River Runs Through It. Chicago: Univ of Chicago, 1976. 1st ptg. VF in VF dj (minute wear). *Bowman.* $900/£563

MacLEISH, ARCHIBALD. America Was Promises. NY: Duell, (1939). 1st ed. VG in dj. *Reese.* $25/£16

MacLEISH, ARCHIBALD. The Happy Marriage and Other Poems. Boston: Houghton Mifflin, 1924. 1st ed. Partly unopened. Fine. *Lame Duck.* $150/£94

MacLEISH, ARCHIBALD. Land of the Free. NY: Harcourt Brace, 1938. 1st ed. 88 photo plts by Dorthea Lange, et al. (Bkpl), else VG in illus dj (edges worn). *Cahan.* $150/£94

MacLEISH, ARCHIBALD. New Found Land. Boston, 1930. 1st Amer ed. One of 500. Blue bds. Slipcase (sl worn). *Swann*.* $46/£29

MacLEISH, ARCHIBALD. The Trojan Horse. Boston: Houghton Mifflin, 1952. Ltd ed. Tipped-in frontis. VG in wrappers. *Pharos.* $25/£16

MACLENNON, R. J. Golf at Gleneagles. Glasgow: McCorquo-dale, (1921). 1st ed. Color litho fldg map. Pict bds. (Residue from removed bkpl; spine sl chipped), else VG. Pacific*. $489/£306

MACLEOD, DAWN. A Book of Herbs. Duckworth, 1968. VG in dj. Hadley. $19/£12

MACLEOD, FIONA. The Laughter of Peterian. Constable, 1897. 1st ed. 4 b/w plts. Pale blue pict cl, gilt. (Ep sl soiled, foxed; spine sl faded), else VG + . Any Amount. $48/£30

MACLEOD, JOHN. The Fuel of Life: Experimental Studies in Nor-mal and Diabetic Animals. Princeton, 1928. 1st ed. (Ex-lib.) Fye. $75/£47

MACLEOD, RODERICK. On Rheumatism in its Various Forms, and on the Affections of Internal Organs, More Especially the Heart and Brain, to Which it Gives Rise. London, 1842. 1st ed. 164pp. (Ex-lib.) Fye. $250/£156

MACLURE, WILLIAM. Opinions on Various Subjects, Dedicated to the Industrious Producers. New-Harmony, IN, 1831. 1st ed, 1st issue. 2 vols in 1. Sheep. Felcone. $1,000/£625

MACMAHON, A. R. Far Cathay and Farther India. London: Hurst and Blackett, 1893. 1st ed. 1/2-title, frontis, xii,340pp; 7 plts. Red cl, gilt. Good (prelims, last few ll foxed; cvrs sl soiled, spine dknd). Morrell. $128/£80

MACMAHON, A. R. The Karens of the Golden Chersonese. Lon-don: Harrison, 1876. 1st ed. v,(iii),423,(1)imprint; fldg map, 6 color lithos. Maroon cl. (Tp sl frayed, lib mks, partly deleted, sl browned; recased w/new eps, spine ends neatly repaired.) Mor-rell. $352/£220

MacMARTIN, D. F. Thirty Years in Hell or The Confessions of a Drug Fiend. Topeka: Capper Ptg Co, (1921). 1st ed. Grn cl. VG (eps browned; sl worn). Reese. $125/£78

MacMICHAEL, H. A. A History of the Arabs in the Sudan. CUP, 1922. 1st ed. 2 vols. Med 8vo. xxii,348; viii,488pp; fldg map in vol 2 rear pocket. VG in grn cl (lt spotted). Ulysses. $1,760/£1,100

MacMICHAEL, WILLIAM. The Gold-Headed Cane. NY, 1915. 1st ed thus. 1/2 vellum. (Ex-lib; marginal water stain few ll; back-strip soiled.) Fye. $50/£31

MacMICHAEL, WILLIAM. The Gold-Headed Cane. NY, 1925. Fair (inner hinges cracked). Doctor's Library. $25/£16

MacMICHAEL, WILLIAM. The Gold-Headed Cane. NY, 1932. Grn cl. VG. Doctor's Library. $45/£28

MacMICHAEL, WILLIAM. Journey from Moscow to Constanti-nople. John Murray, 1819. 1st ed w/plts in 2nd state. 4to. viii,272pp; 6 aquatints. Full contemp calf (rebacked preserving orig spine), gilt, maroon leather label. Good (extrems sl bumped). Sotheran. $1,277/£798

MACMILLAN, C. et al. Postelsia: the Year Book of the Minnesota Seaside Station, 1906. St. Paul: Privately ptd, 1906. One of 500. Prospectus laid in. Partly uncut. Pict cl, gilt. NF. Mikesh. $50/£31

MACMILLAN, DONALD. Etah and Beyond. Boston: Houghton Mifflin, 1927. VG. High Latitude. $35/£22

MACMILLAN, DONALD. Four Years in the White North. NY: Harper & Bros, (1918). 1st ed. Teg. VG. High Latitude. $45/£28

MACMILLAN, H. F. Tropical Planting and Gardening. London: Macmillan, 1935. 4th ed. VG- (bds sl worn). Archer. $30/£19

MacMULLEN, JERRY. Paddle-Wheel Days in California. Stan-ford: Stanford Univ, (1960). Fine in Fine dj. Book Market. $15/£9

MacMULLEN, JERRY. Paddle-Wheel Days in California. Stan-ford, 1944. VG in dj (chipped). American Booksellers. $40/£25

MacMUNN, G. F. The Armies of India. A&C Black, 1911. 72 color plts by A. C. Lovett. Blind-emb cl (sl worn; lt browned, 1 plt detached). Edwards. $152/£95

MacNEICE, LOUIS. Autumn Journal. Faber & Faber, 1939. 1st ed. Largely unopened. VG (top edge sl dusty, sm split in fr hinge, bottom edges sl rubbed, bumped, dknd) in dj (nicked, chipped, rubbed, dusty, sl creased, mkd, spine, edges dknd). Ulysses. $360/£225

MacNEICE, LOUIS. The Last Ditch. Dublin: Cuala, 1940. One of 450. Linen-backed paper bds, spine label. VG (stamps; spine foot sl bumped, corners rubbed, label rubbed, dknd). Ulysses. $280/£175

MACNUTT, J. SCOTT. A Manual for Health Officers. NY, 1915. Fye. $100/£63

MACON, T. J. Life Gleanings. Richmond, VA: W.H. Adams, 1913. 1st ed. VG + . Chapel Hill. $75/£47

MACPHEE, G. GRAHAM. Climbers' Guide to Ben Nevis. Scot-tish Mountaineering Club, 1954. 1st ed. (Spine faded.) Hollett. $24/£15

MACPHERSON, DUNCAN. Gateway to Skye. Stirling: Eneas Mackay, 1946. 1st ed. (Spine faded.) Hollett. $24/£15

MacPHERSON, H. A. History of Fowling. Edinburgh: Douglas, 1897. (Sl shelfworn, soiled.) Oinonen*. $100/£63

MacPHERSON, H. A. and A. J. STUART-WORTLEY. The Par-tridge. London, 1894. 2nd ed. 276pp; 12 plts. Tan dec cl. VG. Larry Price. $30/£19

MacPHERSON, H. A. A Vertebrate Fauna of Lakeland. Edin-burgh, 1892. civ,552pp + (xx) ads pp; 2 chromolitho, 6 etched plts, 1 fldg map, 9 woodcuts. Teg. (Spine faded intruding onto bds.) Edwards. $120/£75

MACPHERSON, JAMES. The History of Great Britain, from the Restoration to the Accession of the House of Hanover. London: W. Strahan & T. Cadell, 1775. 1st ed. 2 vols. Period calf, gilt, raised bands, new morocco spine labels. (Bkpls; glue to joints, spine ends), else VG. Pacific*. $75/£47

MACPHERSON, JAMES. Original Papers; Containing the Secret History of Great Britain.... London: W. Strahan & T. Cadell, 1775. 1st ed. 2 vols. Tree calf, morocco spine labels. (Bkpls; glue to spine ends, along joints), else VG-. Pacific*. $115/£72

MACPHERSON, W. G. et al (eds). History of the Great War: Based on Official Documents. Medical Services: Hygiene of the War. London, 1923. 2 vols. (Last few pp vol 2 lt water-stained; cl mkd), o/w VG set. Whitehart. $80/£50

MacQUARRIE, GORDON. Stories of the Old Duck Hunters and Other Drivel. Zack Taylor (ed). Harrisburg: Stackpole, 1967. Fine in NF ptd dj. Biscotti. $40/£25

MACQUEEN-POPE, W. Ghosts and Greasepaint. London, 1951. 1st ed. VG in dj (torn). Gretton. $10/£6

MACQUER, PIERRE JOSEPH. Elements of the Theory and Prac-tice of Chymistry. Edinburgh: Alexander Donaldson, 1768. 3rd ed in English. 3 vols. xv,(1),298,(2); vii,(1),273; vi,284pp; 6 cop-per-engr plts. Period calf, gilt spines, morocco labels, raised bands. (Crossed-out ink names, 1 plt lacks top 2 inches; scuffed, extrems worn), else VG. Pacific*. $104/£65

MACQUOID, PERCY and RALPH EDWARDS. The Dictionary of English Furniture. London: Offices of Country Life, 1924-1927. 1st ed. 3 vols. Tall folio. Teg. Dk grn cl, gilt. (1 pg lacks bottom 1/2; lib ink handstamps, white ink spine #s mostly re-moved; sl worn, spine ends frayed.) Texts Good. Baltimore*. $100/£63

MACQUOID, PERCY and RALPH EDWARDS. The Dictionary of English Furniture. 1954. 2nd ed. 3 vols. Folio. Teg. (Eps sl spotted; hinges reinforced w/cl.) Sotheby's*. $810/£506

MACQUOID, PERCY. A History of English Furniture. Lawrence & Bullen, 1904-1908. 4 vols. Folio. Edges gilt. Contemp red 1/2 morocco, gilt, by Townsend. (Plts, prelims, final ll spotted; sl off-setting onto tissue guards.) Sotheby's*. $883/£552

MACQUOID, PERCY. A History of English Furniture. London: Medici Soc, 1923. 4 vols. Lg folio. Teg. Rose buckram, gilt. (Sl handled; lib ink handstamps; spine ends frayed, spines lt sunned.) Baltimore*. $200/£125

MACQUOID, PERCY. A History of English Furniture. Lawrence & Bullen, 1938. 1st ed. 4 vols. Lg folio. 60 color plts. VG in maroon buckram over beveled bds. Cox. $400/£250

MACQUOID, PERCY. A History of English Furniture. The Age of Mahogany (only). London/NY, 1906. Teg. Morocco-backed cl bds, gilt. (Lib ink stamps, label remains fep; joints sl rubbed.) Edwards. $120/£75

MACRAY, W. D. Annals of the Bodleian Library, Oxford A.D. 1598-A.D. 1867. Oxford: Clarendon, 1890. 2nd ed. Frontis, xi,545pp; 3 plts. Uncut. Maroon cl (spine sl faded, headcaps bumped; inscrip). Maggs. $56/£35

MACROBIN, J. An Introduction to the Study of Practical Medicine. London, 1835. viii,226pp. 3/4 calf, marbled bds. (Lib stamp, ink mks; rebacked w/new leather label), o/w VG. Whitehart. $136/£85

MADDEN, BETTY I. Art, Crafts, and Architecture in Early Illinois. Urbana: Univ of IL, (1974). Orig ed. NF in dj. Turtle Island. $55/£34

MADDEN, DAVID. The Beautiful Greed. NY: Random House, (1961). 1st ed. (Fr inner hinge sl cracked), o/w Fine in NF dj (sm tear). Reese. $55/£34

MADDEN, ONYX. The Mysterious Chronicles of Oz or, The Travels of Ozma and the Sawhorse. Santa Monica: Dennis-Landman, (1985). 1st ed. 9x6.75. J. Noel (illus). Fine in dj. Pacific*. $40/£25

MADDEN, R. R. The Shrines and Sepulchres of the Old and New World. London, 1851. 2 vols. xii,562; (vi),692pp; add'l litho tps, 7 litho plts. Orig blind-emb cl (recased; marginal browning; spines faded, sl chipped). Edwards. $72/£45

MADDOW, BEN and COLE WESTON. Edward Weston, His Life and Photographs. NY: Aperture, (1979). Obl folio. (Extrems sl worn.) Swann*. $80/£50

MADDOW, BEN. Faces. A Narrative History of the Portrait in Photography. Constance Sullivan (ed). Boston, (1977). 1st ed. (Top corner bumped.) Dj (rubbed). Swann*. $80/£50

Madison, Dane County and Surrounding Towns; Being a History and Guide.... Madison, WI: Wm. J. Park, 1877. 1st ed. (Sl foxed; recased w/orig backstrip, cvr panels laid on.) Sadlon. $100/£63

MAEL, PIERRE. Under the Sea to the North Pole. Samson Low, Marston, (1894). New, cheaper ed. 8vo. 244pp,32pp ads dated 1894; 16 full-pg illus. Scarlet cl, gilt. VG + (few joints shaken). Bookmark. $35/£22

MAETERLINCK, MAURICE. The Blue Bird. NY: Dodd Mead, 1911. 1st trade ed. 24 tipped-in color plts by F. Cayley Robinson. Dec blue cl. Fine. Cullen. $125/£78

MAETERLINCK, MAURICE. Hours of Gladness. London: George Allen, (1912). 1st ed. Lg 4to. 20 mtd color plts by E. Detmold. White cl, gilt. Good in dec gray dj. Reisler. $685/£428

MAETERLINCK, MAURICE. My Dog. London: George Allen, 1913. 1st ed. 8vo. (iv),5-63pp; 6 color plts by Cecil Aldin, guards. Brn cl w/onlaid color plt to upper bd. Fine. Sotheran. $141/£88

MAFFITT, JOHN NEWLAND. Pulpit Sketches. Louisville, KY: W. Harrison Johnston, 1839. 1st ed. 178pp. Contemp full sheep. (Inner hinges repaired, inscrips), else VG. Chapel Hill. $150/£94

MAGARET, HELENE. Father DeSmet Pioneer Priest of the Rockies. NY, 1940. Frontis. Internally Good in dj (chipped). Dumont. $30/£19

MAGEE, DAVID. A Course in Correct Cataloguing; or, Notes to the Neophyte. SF, 1977. 1st collected ed. Ltd to 1000. 2 plts. Mint in ptd wrappers. Argonaut. $50/£31

MAGEE, DAVID. The Hundredth Book: A Bibliography of the Publications of the Book Club of California.... SF: Grabhorn, 1958. One of 400. Patterned bds, cl spine. Dawson. $175/£109

MAGEE, DAVID. The Hundredth Book: A Bibliography of the Publications of the Book Club of California.... SF: Book Club of CA, 1958. One of 400 ptd. 1/2 cl, dec bds, paper spine label. (Offset to eps; fr cvr corner sl nicked), else NF. Pacific*. $259/£162

MAGEE, DAVID. Infinite Riches: The Adventures of a Rare Book Dealer. NY: Paul S. Eriksson, (1973). 1st ed. Fine in dj. Pacific*. $23/£14

MAGEE, JUDY. Cavern of Crime. Smithland, KY: Livingston Ledger, 1973. 1st ed. VG in pict heavy wrappers. Connolly. $17/£11

MAGGIO, JOE. Company Man. NY: Putnam, (1972). 1st ed. Fine in dj (sl worn, few sm tears). Antic Hay. $25/£16

MAGGS BROS. Catalogue 418: French Literature. Maggs Bros, 1922. Good in dec cvrs. Moss. $40/£25

MAGGS BROS. Catalogue 509: Bibliotheca Typographica. Maggs Bros, 1928. Ptd cvrs (spine worn). Moss. $29/£18

MAGNUSSEN, DANIEL O. Peter Thompson's Narrative of the Little Bighorn Campaign 1876. Glendale: A.H. Clark, 1974. One of 1000. Fldg map. NF. Dumont. $100/£63

MAGOUN, F. ALEXANDER. The Frigate Constitution and Other Historic Ships. Salem, MA: Marine Research Soc, 1928. VG (scuffed, shelfworn). My Bookhouse. $210/£131

MAGRITTE, RENE. Exhibition of Paintings by Rene Magritte. NY: Sidney Janis Gallery, December 1-December 31, 1977. Ptd wrappers. Turtle Island. $25/£16

MAGRUDER, GENEVIEVE KRATKA. The Upper San Joaquin Valley 1772-1870. Bakersfield: Kern County Hist Soc, 1950. 1st ed. Fine in VG dj. Book Market. $45/£28

MAHAN, ALFRED THAYER. Great Commanders. Admiral Farragut. NY: D. Appleton, c.1892. One of 1000 lg paper cc. 333pp; 2 ports, 5 plans, maps (1 fldg). 2 kinds of gold-colored cl (lt soiled, corners bumped), paper spine label (rubbed). Parmer. $350/£219

MAHAN, ALFRED THAYER. The Life of Nelson. Boston: Little, Brown, 1897. 1st ed. 2 vols. (xxviii),454; xvi,427pp. Fine set. Lefkowicz. $165/£103

MAHAN, ALFRED THAYER. The Life of Nelson: The Embodiment of the Sea Power of Great Britain. Boston, 1897. 1st ed. 2 vols. 454; 427pp. (Bkpl, names; extrems lt worn.) Woolson. $100/£63

MAHAN, ALFRED THAYER. Sea Power in Its Relations to the War of 1812. Sampson Low, Marston, 1905. 1st ed (London issue of the American sheets, w/cancel tps). 2 vols. Teg. VG set (few sm mks, nicks). Ash. $200/£125

MAHAN, ALFRED THAYER. Types of Naval Officers Drawn from the History of the British Navy.... Boston: Little, Brown, 1901. 1st ed. VG (ep over rear inner hinge split). Lefkowicz. $100/£63

MAHAN, ALFRED THAYER. Types of Naval Officers Drawn from the History of the British Navy.... Sampson Low, Marston, 1902. 1st ed (London issue of American sheets, w/cancel tp). Teg. Nice (few sm mks, nicks). Ash. $152/£95

MAHAN, JAMES CURTIS. Memoirs. Lincoln: Franklin, (1919). 1st ed. Blue watered cl (edges sl worn), gilt. Internally VG; cvrs Good. Baltimore*. $40/£25

MAHFOUZ, NAGUIB. The Journey of Ibn Fattouma. NY: Doubleday, 1992. 1st ed. Fine in dj. Any Amount. $19/£12

MAHFOUZ, NAGUIB. The Time and the Place and Other Stories. Denys Johnson-Davies (trans). NY: Doubleday, 1991. 1st ed. Fine in dj. Any Amount. $19/£12

MAHON, DEREK. The Snow Party. OUP, 1975. 1st ed. VG (date inside rear cvr, edges sl rubbed) in wrappers. Ulysses. $58/£36

MAHON, DEREK. Twelve Poems. Belfast: Festival Pub, n.d. (1965). 1st ed, 1st bk, 1st issue, ptd on laid paper, w/cvr device ptd in purple. VG (cvrs sl mkd, dusty, spine sl browned) in wrappers. *Ulysses*. $400/£250

MAHON, TERENCE (ed). Cold Feet. London: Chapman & Hall, (1929). 1st ed. Black cl stamped in gilt/blind. VG (2 stamps) in pict dj (sl chipped). *Reese*. $65/£41

MAHOOD, RUTH I. (ed). Photographer of the Southwest: Adam Clark Vroman, 1856-1916. L.A.: Ward Ritchie, 1961. 1st ed. Orange/white dec cl. Fine in orig clear vinyl dj w/ptd title. *Pacific**. $46/£29

MAHR, AUGUST. The Visit of the 'Rurik' to San Francisco in 1816. Stanford: Stanford Univ, 1932. 7 plts. (Paper dknd), else VG. *Pacific**. $98/£61

MAHR, AUGUST. The Visit of the 'Rurik' to San Francisco in 1816. Stanford: Stanford Univ, 1932. 1st ed. Frontis, 6 plts. Facs of orig cl, gilt (newly bound). Fine. *Argonaut*. $125/£78

MAHURIN, MATT. Photographs. Pasadena, (1989). 1st ed. Folio. 47 repros. Dj (extrems sl worn). *Swann**. $115/£72

MAIDEN, CECIL. Speaking of Mrs. McKluskie. NY: Vanguard, 1962. 1st ed. 7.25x9.5. Hilary Knight (illus). 43pp. Fine in dj. *Cattermole*. $40/£25

MAILER, NORMAN. An American Dream. NY: Dial, 1965. 1st ed. 1/4 blue cl, gray bds, silver facs sig fr bd. (Eps irregularly faded, spine ends rubbed), o/w NF in dj (spine sl dknd, lt chipped). *Heritage*. $125/£78

MAILER, NORMAN. Ancient Evenings. Boston, (1983). 1st ed. Signed. Dj. *Argosy*. $60/£38

MAILER, NORMAN. The Armies of the Night. (NY, 1968.) 1st ed. VG in dj. *King*. $35/£22

MAILER, NORMAN. Cannibals and Christians. NY: Dial, 1966. 1st ed. VF in Fine dj (extrems rubbed). *Between The Covers*. $100/£63

MAILER, NORMAN. Deaths for the Ladies and Other Disasters. NY, (1962). 1st ed. (Corners sl bumped), else Good in dj (edges frayed; torn). *King*. $40/£25

MAILER, NORMAN. The Faith of Graffiti. NY: Praeger, 1974. 1st ptg. One of 350 signed by Mailer, Mervyn Kurlansky & John Naar (documenters). Folio. Black cl. Fine (corner sl bumped) in open-end slipcase. *Heritage*. $150/£94

MAILER, NORMAN. Marilyn. (NY: G&D, 1973.) Ltd, signed ed. Signed by Mailer and Lawrence Schiller. White cl. Fine in clamshell case w/photo label on fr. *Heritage*. $250/£156

MAILER, NORMAN. The Naked and the Dead. London, (1949). 1st Eng ed. One of 240 numbered, specially bound. Pub's full red morocco, gilt. (Sl dampstain bottom edge, affecting only sm part of tp, verso of fep.) *Swann**. $126/£79

MAILER, NORMAN. The Naked and the Dead. London: Allan Wingate, 1949. 1st Eng ed. Black cl, gilt. Fine in dj. *Maggs*. $80/£50

MAILER, NORMAN. Of a Small and Modest Malignancy, Wicked and Bristling with Dots. Northridge, CA: Lord John Press, 1980. 1st ed. Ltd to 300 numbered, signed. Cl-backed marbled bds. VG in slipcase. *King*. $100/£63

MAILER, NORMAN. Of Women and Their Elegance. NY: S&S, (1980). 1st ed. (Black line bottom pg edges), else Fine in dj (1 sm chip). *Bernard*. $60/£38

MAILER, NORMAN. Tough Guys Don't Dance. NY, (1984). 1st ed. One of 350 numbered, signed. Slipcase. *Swann**. $115/£72

MAILER, NORMAN. The White Negro. (SF): City Lights, (1957). Later ptg w/$.50 price on cvr. NF in pict wraps. *Agvent*. $45/£28

MAILER, NORMAN. The White Negro. SF: City Lights, 1960. 3rd issue, w/$.75 cvr price. VG+ in wraps. *Sclanders*. $11/£7

MAILS, THOMAS E. Dog Soldiers, Bear Men and Buffalo Women. Englewood Cliffs: Prentice-Hall, (1973). 1st ed. VG in dj (price-clipped). *Pacific**. $81/£51

MAILS, THOMAS E. The Mystic Warriors of the Plains. GC: Doubleday, 1972. Orig ed. 32 color plts. Fine in dj. *Turtle Island*. $100/£63

MAIR, CHARLES. Tecumseh, A Drama and Canadian Poems. Toronto, 1926. 1st ed thus. Gilt-dec spine. Fine (sl rubbed). *Polyanthos*. $45/£28

MAIRET, ETHEL M. A Book on Vegetable Dyes. Douglas Pepler, 1916. Partly unopened. Mod 1/2 black levant morocco, gilt. Orig black wrappers (very stained) bound in at end. VG (fep repaired, sl dampstained in places). *Hollett*. $224/£140

MAIRET, PHILIP. Pioneer of Sociology. Lund Humphries, 1957. 1st ed. Articles loosely inserted. VG in dj. *Hollett*. $40/£25

MAIS, S. P. B. England of the Windmills. London, 1931. 1st ed. (Leading corners browned.) Dj (chipped w/loss). *Edwards*. $40/£25

MAIS, S. P. B. I Return to Scotland. Christopher Johnson, 1947. 1st ed. 15 plts, 11 maps. (Lib label on fep.) *Hollett*. $24/£15

MAISON, K. E. Honore Daumier. (Greenwich, CT): NYGS, (1968). Orig ed. One of 800 (of 1500). 2 vols. Vol 1: The Paintings, Vol 2: The Watercolours and Drawings. 325 plts. Fine in slipcase. *Turtle Island*. $650/£406

MAISON, K. E. Honore Daumier. Catalogue Raisonne of the Paintings, Watercolours and Drawings. London: Thames & Hudson, 1968. Ltd to 1500. 2 vols. 4to. Teg. Slipcase. *Christie's**. $515/£322

MAISON, K. E. Themes and Variations. London, 1960. 1st ed. 31 tipped-in color plts. (Margins sl browned, bkpl.) Dj (sl ragged). *Edwards*. $48/£30

MAITLAND, WILLIAM. The History of London from Its Foundation to the Present Time. London: Samuel Richardson, 1739. 1st ed. 25 engr plts, 4 fldg. Contemp 1/2 calf. (Tp repaired at margin, 1 plt cropped, few marginal tears, stained; rubbed, lacks rear cvr.) *Christie's**. $368/£230

MAITLAND, WILLIAM. The History of London from Its Foundation to the Present Time. London: For T. Osborne et al, 1756. 2 vols. 121 engr plts, 9 fldg (few sl creased or shaved; few holes or short tears to text). Contemp calf (joints split, heavily rubbed). *Christie's**. $1,531/£957

MAJNO, GUIDO. The Healing Hand: Man and Wound in the Ancient World. Cambridge: Harvard Univ, 1975. 1st ed. 6 plts. Fine in dj. *Weber*. $50/£31

MAJOR, CLARENCE. The Dark and Feeling. Reflections on Black American Writers and Their Works. NY: Third Press, (1974). 1st ed. Fine in NF dj (sm spine tear). *Agvent*. $50/£31

MAJOR, HOWARD. The Domestic Architecture of the Early American Republic: The Greek Revival. Phila/London: Lippincott, 1926. 1st ed. Teg, untrimmed. Navy buckram, gilt. VG (sl rubbed, shelfworn, spine sl sunned; text sl handled). *Baltimore**. $50/£31

MAJOR, J. KENNETH and MARTIN WATTS. Victorian and Edwardian Windmills and Watermills from Old Photographs. London: Batsford, 1977. 1st ed. VG in dj. *Hollett*. $48/£30

MAJOR, MABEL et al. Southwest Heritage. Albuquerque, 1938. Frontis. (Few pp sl foxed; spine faded), else Good. *Dumont*. $35/£22

MAJORS, ALEXANDER. Seventy Years on the Frontier. Prentiss Ingraham (ed). Chicago: Rand McNally, 1893. 1st ed. 325pp + (3)pp ads. Blue cl, gilt. (Damage to pastedown from removed bkpl; extrems lt rubbed), else NF. Howes M232. *Pacific**. $104/£65

MAKINS, F. K. Herbaceous Garden Flora. London: Dent, 1957. 1st ed. Fine in VG dj. *Mikesh*. $20/£13

MALAMUD, BERNARD. God's Grace. NY: FSG, (1982). One of 300 numbered, signed. Cardbd slipcase. *Antic Hay*. $150/£94

MALAMUD, BERNARD. God's Grace. NY: FSG, 1982. 1st ed. One of 300 signed. Fine in pub's slipcase. *Cady*. $50/£31

MALAMUD, BERNARD. The Stories of Bernard Malamud. NY: FSG, (1983). One of 300. Signed. Grn/blue cl, gilt spine. Fine in slipcase. *Pacific**. $75/£47

MALCOLM, ALEXANDER. A New Treatise of Arithmetick and Book-Keeping.... Edinburgh: John Mosman & William Brown, 1718. 1st ed. 4to. (12),194,(20),(25),(36),(2),(1),(15),(24),(1 blank),(2),(4),(51),(1 ads)pp. Contemp calf. VG (leaf L14 torn, no loss, browned; fr joint started, rear joint tender; extrems rubbed, worn). *Glaser*. $750/£469

MALCOLM, HOWARD. Travels in South-Eastern Asia, Embracing Hindustan, Malaya, Siam and China. Boston: Gould, Kendall, & Lincoln, 1839. 2nd ed. 2 vols in 1. 272; 322 + 8pp ads; 5 engr plts, engr fldg map. Orig blind, gilt-stamped brn cl. Good. *Karmiole*. $350/£219

MALCOLM, HOWARD. Travels in the Burman Empire. Edinburgh, 1840. Frontis map. Wrappers (lacks rear cvr; several sm tears in text margins). *Swann**. $161/£101

MALCOLM, JAMES PELLER. Anecdotes of the Manners and Customs of London During the Eighteenth Century. London, 1808. 50 plts. Contemp 1/2 sheep (worn, fr cvr loose; tp wrinkled, 1 plt torn into image; ex-lib, w/ink stamp on tp, verso of all plts). *Swann**. $138/£86

MALCOLM, JOHN. Sketch of the Political History of India. London: William Miller, 1811. viii,549pp. (Lib blindstamps, lt browned.) Contemp marbled bds, vellum corners, rebacked in 18th-cent style mod mottled calf, gilt, raised bands, spine label. *Edwards*. $200/£125

MALDEN, H. E. (ed). The Victoria History of the County of Surrey. Westminster, 1902-12. 4 vols. Frontispieces (1 color). Teg. Red cl, gilt. (Lib ink stamps; vol 2 tp detached, hinges cracked, feps lt browned; spines sl faded, chipped.) *Edwards*. $320/£200

MALET, HAROLD E. Annals of the Road; or, Notes on Mail and Stage Coaching in Great Britain. London, 1896. 10 color plts. Later 1/2 red morocco, gilt. *Swann**. $149/£93

MALET, RAWDON. When the Red Gods Call. London, (1934). (3 pp badly opened w/margins sl worn), o/w VG in dj. *Petersfield*. $80/£50

MALINOWSKI, BRONISLAW. Argonauts of the Western Pacific. London, 1932. 2nd imp. 5 maps, 65 plts. *Argosy*. $75/£47

MALINOWSKI, BRONISLAW. The Sexual Life of Savages in North-Western Melanesia. NY: Harcourt, Brace, 1929. 1st US ed. 91 plts, 1 map. (Sl rubbed, sl damped), o/w VG. *Worldwide*. $35/£22

MALKUS, ALIDA S. The Dragon Fly of Zuni. NY: Harcourt, Brace, (1928). 1st ed. Dec eps. Brn cl. (Corner sl jammed), else Fine. *Argonaut*. $35/£22

MALLARME, STEPHANE. Un Coup de Des. LEC, 1992. One of 300 signed by Ellsworth Kelly (illus). Fine in slipcase. *Swann**. $2,300/£1,438

MALLARY, CHARLES D. Memoirs of Elder Edmund Botsford. Charleston: W. Riley, 1832. 240pp. Later buckram. (Lib spine #, rebound), else Good. *Brown*. $30/£19

MALLEA, EDUARDO. The Bay of Silence. NY: Knopf, 1944. 1st ed. NF in dj (price-clipped). *Lame Duck*. $100/£63

MALLESON, G. B. Herat: The Granary and Garden of Central Asia. London, 1880. Map. *Petersfield*. $72/£45

MALLESON, G. B. The Indian Mutiny. Seeley, 1891. 2nd ed. xiv,(ii),421,(i)pp. All edges marbled. Contemp full calf prize binding, gilt, raised bands. (Top fore-edge sl browned), o/w Fine. *Sotheran*. $208/£130

MALLET, DAVID. The Life of Francis Bacon, Lord Chancellor of England. A. Millar, 1740. 1st ed. viii,197,(3)ads pp. Contemp calf, red morocco label. (Inscrip, lower inner corner water-stained throughout but obtrusive only to prelims and at end; also affecting cvr, dknd.) *Cox*. $120/£75

MALLET, THIERRY. Glimpses of the Barren Lands. NY: Revillon Freres, 1930. Ptd paper bds (sl worn). Internally clean. *Explorer*. $32/£20

MALLIS, ARNOLD. American Entomologists. New Brunswick: Rutgers Univ, 1971. 1st ed. NF in Good dj. *Connolly*. $35/£22

MALLORY, WALTER H. China: Land of Famine. NY: American Geographical Soc, 1926. 1st ed. (Sl rubbed, soiled), o/w VG. *Worldwide*. $35/£22

MALLOWAN, M. E. L. Nimrud and Its Remains. NY: Dodd, Mead, (1966). 1st ed. 2 vols + separate map folder. 8 lg fldg maps/plans. Blue linen. Good in djs, pub's cardboard slipcase. *Karmiole*. $350/£219

MALMQUIST, O. N. The First 100 Years: A History of the Salt Lake Tribune.... Salt Lake City, 1971. Signed. VG in dj. *Benchmark*. $20/£13

MALONE, BARTLETT YANCEY. Whipt 'Em Everytime. William Whatley Pierson, Jr. (ed). Jackson, TN: McCowat-Mercer, 1960. 1st ed. Gray cl. (Bkpl), else Fine in dj. *Chapel Hill*. $50/£31

MALONE, DUMAS. Edwin A. Alderman. Doubleday, Doran, 1930. 1st ed. Good-. *Book Broker*. $20/£13

MALONEY, ALICE BAY (ed). Fur Brigade to the Bonaventura. John Work's California Expedition 1832-1833 for the Hudson's Bay Co. SF, 1945. One of 500. Frontisport, port, fldg map. Partly unopened. Ptd label fr panel, spine. (Cvrs lt rubbed, spine label sl worn), o/w VG +. *Sagebrush*. $125/£78

MALONEY, MARY T. The Legend of Nonnenwerth, and Other Poems. San Jose, CA: Owen, 1876. 1st ed. 126pp. Dec cl. *Ginsberg*. $75/£47

MALONEY, TOM (ed). U. S. Camera, 1941. NY: Duell, Sloan & Pearce, (1940). 1st ed. 2 vols. Paper cvr labels. (Spines sl lightened.) Pub's slipcase (taped, shelfworn). *Sadlon*. $65/£41

MALONEY, TOM (ed). U. S. Camera, 1943. NY: Duell, Sloan & Pearce, (1942). 1st ed. (Eps sl spotted; few sm spots, spine sl dull, ends rubbed.) *Sadlon*. $20/£13

MALONEY, TOM (ed). U. S. Camera, 1945. The U.S.A. at War. NY: Duell, Sloan & Pearce, (1944). 1st ed. (Spine sl lightened, few sm spots.) *Sadlon*. $20/£13

MALONEY, TOM (ed). U. S. Camera, 1952. (NY: U.S. Camera Pub, 1951.) 1st ed. Fine in dj (sl edgeworn). *Sadlon*. $20/£13

MALORY, THOMAS. The Death of King Arthur. London: Macmillan, 1928. One of 525. 12 wood-engrs by Catherine Donaldson. Unopened. Vellum-backed bds. NF (bkseller label rep; cvrs sl mkd, dusty). *Ulysses*. $152/£95

MALORY, THOMAS. Le Morte d'Arthur. H. Oskar Sommer (ed). London: David Nutt, 1889-1891. Ltd to 108 signed by pub. 3 vols. xviii,861;230;338pp. Full red buckram, orig ptd wrappers bound in. Fine set. *Truepenny*. $300/£188

MALORY, THOMAS. Le Morte d'Arthur. 1893-1894. One of 300. 3 vols. 5 dbl-pg, 15 full-pg illus. Teg. Fine contemp full vellum by Birdsall & Son. (Lt spotting, mainly to frontispieces.) *Sotheby's**. $7,451/£4,657

MALORY, THOMAS. Le Morte d'Arthur. London, 1898. 1st Beardsley ed. One of 1500. 2 vols. 4to. Frontis by Aubrey Beardsley. Gilt-dec cl. (Sl archival reinforcement tp gutter vol 1; rear cvrs lt dampstained, sl worn.) *Swann**. $690/£431

MALORY, THOMAS. Le Morte d'Arthur. London: Dent, 1926. 3rd ed. Ltd to 1600. 4to. 2 tissue-guarded etched plts by Aubrey Beardsley. Teg, rest uncut, largely unopened. Black cl, gilt. (Prelims sl speckled), o/w Fine. *Sotheran*. $797/£498

MALORY, THOMAS. Le Morte d'Arthur. London: Golden Cockerell, 1936. Signed by Robert Gibbings (illus). 3 vols. 1/4 blue linen, pattern paper sides. Fine in box (extrems worn). Appelfeld. $250/£156

MALORY, THOMAS. Le Morte d'Arthur. LEC, 1936. Ltd to 1500 numbered, signed by Robert Gibbings (illus). 3 vols. Fine in slipcase. Swann*. $258/£161

MALOT, HECTOR. Nobody's Boy. NY: Cupples & Leon, 1916. 1st ed. 5.5x8. Johnny Gruelle (illus). 372pp + ads. Blue cl w/sm round picture paste-on. VG- (spotted, shelfworn). My Bookhouse. $52/£33

MALOUF, DAVID. Antipodes. Chatto, 1985. 1st UK ed. NF in dj (spine ends sl bumped). Williams. $29/£18

MALOUF, DAVID. First Things Last. Poems. Univ of Queensland, 1980. 1st Eng ed. Laminated card wrappers (faded). Clearwater. $48/£30

MALOUF, DAVID. Fly Away Peter. Chatto, 1982. 1st UK ed. NF in dj. Williams. $48/£30

MALOUF, DAVID. Johnno. NY: George Braziller, 1978. 1st US ed. Signed. Fine in Fine dj. Beasley. $65/£41

MALRAUX, ANDRE and ANDRE PARROT. The Arts of Mankind. Michael Ross (trans). NY: Golden Press, (1968). Fine in pict dj (lg tears at seams). Metropolitan*. $28/£18

MALRAUX, ANDRE. The Metamorphosis of the Gods. Stuart Gilbert (trans). London: Secker & Warburg, 1960. 1st ed in English. Fine in dj. Reese. $50/£31

MALRAUX, ANDRE. The Psychology of Art. Museum Without Walls. S. Gilbert (trans). NY, 1949-50. 3 vols. Uniform cl, gilt. VF set. Europa. $112/£70

MALRAUX, ANDRE. The Voices of Silence. Stuart Gilbert (trans). GC: Doubleday, 1953. 1st Amer issue. (Bkpl), else Fine in dj, slipcase. Reese. $75/£47

MALSCH, BROWNSON. Lone Wolf. Austin, TX: Shoal Creek Pub, (1980). 1st ed. Fine in dj. Lien. $20/£13

MALTHUS, THOMAS ROBERT. An Essay on the Principle of Population.... London, 1803. New ed. 4to. Uncut. Orig bds (artlessly rebacked w/cl; lt dampstain corner of fr cvr, opening ll; lt foxed, bkpl removed). Swann*. $2,300/£1,438

MALTHUS, THOMAS ROBERT. Principles of Political Economy Considered with a View to Their Practical Application. London, 1820. 1st ed. 8vo. Murray's June 1820 8pp cat at end. (Marginal brownstaining throughout; lacks 1/2-title.) Uncut. Later cl. Oinonen*. $500/£313

MALTHUS, THOMAS ROBERT. Principles of Political Economy. John Murray, 1820. 1st ed. 8vo. W/initial and final blanks. Contemp polished calf, gilt. (Heavy spotting to ll in sig C, other ll lt foxed; joints partly cracked.) Sotheby's*. $1,104/£690

MALTZ, ALBERT. Black Pit. NY, (1935). 1st Amer ed, 1st bk. NF in dj (chips, nicks, rubbed). Polyanthos. $45/£28

MALTZ, MAXWELL. New Faces, New Futures. NY: Richard R. Smith, 1936. Blue cl (sl rubbed; few sl mks in text). Weber. $75/£47

MAMET, DAVID. The Hero Pony. Poems. NY: Grove, 1990. 1st ed. NF in dj. Any Amount. $19/£12

MAMET, DAVID. Sexual Perversity in Chicago and the Duck Variations. NY: Grove, (1974). 1st ed. Fine in Fine dj (sm tear, extrems sl dknd). Between The Covers. $150/£94

MAMET, DAVID. The Shawl and Prairie du Chien. NY: Grove, (1985). 1st ed. (Sm spot bottom edge), else Fine in Fine dj (sl rubbed). Between The Covers. $65/£41

Man of Feeling. (By Henry MacKenzie.) London: W. Strahan, 1783. New ed. Engr frontis, viii,278pp. Old calf (worn). Reading copy. Young. $64/£40

MANBY, CHARLES W. Tom Racquet, and His Three Maiden Aunts. London: Willoughby, n.d. 1st ed. Robert Cruikshank (illus). (Spine, extrems sl browned), else VG. Pacific*. $46/£29

MANCERON, CLAUDE. Austerlitz. G. Unwin (trans). London: Allen & Unwin, (1963). 8 sketch maps, 14 plts. Good. Stewart. $48/£30

MANCHESTER, HERBERT. Four Centuries of Sport in America, 1490-1890. NY: Derrydale, 1931. One of 850. Folio. Swann*. $230/£144

MANCHESTER, WILLIAM. A World Lit Only by Fire. Boston: Little, Brown, 1992. 1st ed. Signed on tipped-in leaf. Fine in Fine dj. Beasley. $40/£25

MANDEL, MIKE. Myself: Timed Exposures. L.A.: Mike Mandel, 1971. 1st ed, 1st bk. 34 full-pg b/w photos. (Sl sunned), else Fine in pict stiff wrappers. Cahan. $125/£78

MANDERSON, CHARLES F. The Twin Seven-Shooters. NY: F. Tennyson Neely, (1902). 1st ed. Frontisport. Blue cl, gilt. (Lacks fep, pieces of 1/2-title, frontis; rep tape-repaired), else VG. Pacific*. $29/£18

MANGAN, FRANK J. Bordertown, the Life and Times of El Paso del Norte. El Paso, 1964. VG- in pict wraps (lt shelfworn, sl waviness fr cvr). Baade. $15/£9

MANGIN, A. The Mysteries of the Ocean. London, 1874. New, rev ed. 470pp; 15 hand-colored plts. Aeg. Pict gilt cl. (Sl foxed; refixed in case.) Henly. $120/£75

MANGUM, CHARLES. The Legal Status of the Negro. Chapel Hill: Univ of NC, 1940. Blue cl. Sound (ex-lib?, owner stamps). Boswell. $125/£78

Manhattan Silver Mining Company of Nevada. Report of Adelberg and Raymond. NY: Wm. C. Bryant, 1865. 1st ed. 9.25x5.5. 21pp. (Paper sl aged), else NF in ptd wrappers, stapled into mod marbled stiff wrappers. Pacific*. $920/£575

MANHOFF, BILL. The Owl and the Pussycat. GC: Doubleday, 1965. 1st ed. VF in VF black dj (sl rubbed). Between The Covers. $250/£156

MANHOOD, H. A. Little Peter the Great. London, 1931. 1st ed. One of 550 signed. Frontis. Teg, rest uncut. Yellow cl. Fine in clear plastic dj. Maggs. $32/£20

MANKIEWICZ, JOSEPH L. All About Eve. NY: Random House, (1951). 1st ed. Fine in dj (price-clipped, lt dampstain along bottom of rear panel, few sm tears, sl rubbed). Between The Covers. $150/£94

MANKOWITZ, WOLF. Wedgwood. Spring Books, (1966). (Cvr sl faded.) Dj (worn, repaired). Rybski. $50/£31

MANKOWITZ, WOLF. Wedgwood. London, 1953. 8 color plts. (Shaken, backstrip sunned.) Washton. $40/£25

MANLEY, J. J. Notes on Game and Game Shooting. London: The Bazaar, 1880. 389pp + ads. Brn cl, gilt. VF. Bowman. $75/£47

MANLY, WILLIAM L. Death Valley in '49. NY/Santa Barbara: Wallace Hebbard, (1929). 3rd ed, w/typographical error on p488, 2nd paragraph, line 6: the name Henry Dale is in error (appears correctly as Henry Wade in 1st ed). Frontis, 16 plts. Uncut. Black cl, gilt. (Name stamps; sm tear 1 plt), o/w NF in pict dj. Howes M255. Pacific*. $46/£29

MANLY, WILLIAM L. Death Valley in '49. L.A.: Borden Pub, (1949). Fldg map. Pict cl. Dj (chipped). Dawson. $40/£25

MANLY, WILLIAM L. Death Valley in '49. San Jose: Pacific Tree & Vine Co, 1894. 1st ed. Port, 498pp. (Ex-lib, bkpl removed, sm blindstamp, shelfwear), else VG. Howes M255. Brown. $150/£94

MANLY, WILLIAM L. Death Valley in '49. San Jose: Pacific Tree & Vine Co, 1894. 1st ed. Frontisport, (11),12-498pp; 3 plts. Yellow cl, gilt spine. NF (extrems sl rubbed, spine sl dull). Howes M255. Pacific*. $196/£123

MANLY, WILLIAM L. Death Valley in '49. San Jose, CA, 1894. 1st ed. Frontisport, (xiii),13-498pp. 1933 sales slip for bk laid in. VG + (inscrip; extrems sl worn). Sagebrush. $300/£188

MANLY, WILLIAM L. Death Valley in '49. San Jose, CA: Pacific Tree & Vine, 1894. 1st ed. Mustard cl (lt worn, faded). VG. Howes M255. *Labordo.* $300/£188

MANLY, WILLIAM L. The Jayhawker's Oath and Other Sketches. Arthur Woodward (ed). L.A.: Warren F. Lewis, 1949. 1st ed. 36 plts, fldg facs map. Pict eps. Beige linen. Fine. *Pacific*.* $23/£14

MANN, ETHEL (ed). An Englishman at Home and Abroad 1792-1828. London: Heath Cranton, 1930. 1st ed. 12 plts. VG in dj (defective). *Hollett.* $48/£30

MANN, F. O. Grope Carries On. London: Faber & Faber, (1932). 1st ed. Reddish cl stamped in grn. Fine in dj. *Reese.* $85/£53

MANN, FRANKLIN W. The Bullet's Flight from Powder to Target. NY, 1909. (Internally lt worn; tips worn, bottom edge discolored, spine tips sl frayed.) *Oinonen*.* $70/£44

MANN, IDA. Developmental Abnormalities of the Eye. Cambridge, 1937. 1st ed. *Fye.* $100/£63

MANN, JAMES. Wallace Collection: European Arms and Armour. London: The Trustees, 1962. 5th ed. 2 vols. Color frontis, 104 plts hors-texte; plts 105-208. Uniform rexine. VF set. *Europa.* $32/£20

MANN, MATTHEW (ed). A System of Gynecology by American Authors. Phila, 1887. 1st ed. 2 vols. 1189; 1180pp. *Fye.* $250/£156

MANN, RALPH. After the Gold Rush. Stanford, 1982. 1st ed. Sm map. VG in VG dj. *Woolson.* $15/£9

MANN, THOMAS. The Beloved Returns. NY: Knopf, 1940. 1st US ed. VG+ in dj (sl edgeworn). *My Bookhouse.* $57/£36

MANN, THOMAS. The Beloved Returns. NY, 1940. 1st Amer ed. One of 395 numbered, signed. 8vo. 1/2 cl. (Bds lt faded.) *Swann*.* $690/£431

MANN, THOMAS. The Black Swan. LEC, 1990. One of 375 signed by John Hejduk (illus). Fine in slipcase. *Swann*.* $575/£359

MANN, THOMAS. Death in Venice. LEC, 1972. Ltd to 1500 numbered, signed by Felix Hoffmann (illus). Fine in slipcase. *Swann*.* $92/£58

MANN, THOMAS. Early Sorrow. London: Martin Secker, 1929. 1st Eng ed. Floral patterned eps. Nice. *Cady.* $25/£16

MANN, THOMAS. Joseph in Egypt. H. T. Lowe-Porter (trans). NY: Knopf, 1938. 1st Amer ed. 2 vols. Color chart rear vol 1. Dk grn cl (vol 2 cvrs lt rubbed), gilt. Orig glassine (rear vol 1 torn; vol 2 sl chipped). Cream, pink paper-cvrd ptd slipcase. NF in VG slipcase (soiled, bumped). *Blue Mountain.* $50/£31

MANN, THOMAS. Joseph the Provider. NY, 1944. 1st Amer ed. Fine in Fine dj. *Polyanthos.* $35/£22

MANN, THOMAS. The Letters of Thomas Mann to Caroline Newton. Princeton Univ, 1971. 1st Amer ed. Fine in glassine dj (few snags). *Polyanthos.* $25/£16

MANN, THOMAS. The Magic Mountain. NY: LEC, 1962. One of 1500. Signed by Felix Hoffmann (illus). Cl-backed gilt-lettered bds, paper spine labels. Fine in glassine, slipcase. *Pacific*.* $81/£51

MANN, THOMAS. The Magic Mountain. LEC, 1962. Ltd to 1500 numbered, signed by Felix Hoffmann (illus). 2 vols. Fine in slipcase. *Swann*.* $172/£108

MANN, THOMAS. Nocturnes. NY: Equinox Cooperative Press, 1934. 1st Amer ed. One of 1000 signed. Lynd Ward (illus). Blue cl, silver spine label. NF (ink inscrip; label chipped, spine faded, top edge fr cvr rubbed) in remnants of orig box. *Heritage.* $250/£156

MANN, THOMAS. A Sketch of My Life. (NY): Harrison of Paris, (1930). 1st ed. One of 75. Signed. 7.75x5.25. Vellum-backed bds, gilt. (Sm piece of removed bkpl, sm red ink mk fep), else NF. *Pacific*.* $575/£359

MANN, THOMAS. This Peace. NY: Knopf, 1938. 1st Amer ed. VG (spine rubbed) in VG dj (spine chipped). *Agvent.* $25/£16

MANN, THOMAS. Thomas Mann's Addresses...1942-1949. Washington, 1963. 1st Amer ed. NF in ptd wraps. *Polyanthos.* $25/£16

MANN, THOMAS. The Transposed Heads. NY: Knopf, 1941. 1st Amer ed. Fine in dj (spine sl toned). *Smith.* $50/£31

MANN, THOMAS. The Transposed Heads: A Legend of India. H. Lowe-Porter (trans). (Kentfield): Allen, 1977. One of 140. Prospectus laid in. Patterned cl, paper spine label. Fine. *Pacific*.* $431/£269

MANN, W. Six Years' Residence in the Australian Provinces. London: Smith, Elder, 1839. 1st ed. (ii) half-title, vi,360pp; fldg map (torn w/o loss). Grn ribbed blindstamped cl, gilt. Sound (foxed, joints cracked). *Morrell.* $208/£130

MANNERS, VICTORIA and G. C. WILLIAMSON. Angelica Kauffmann, R.A.: Her Life and Her Works. NY: Brentano's, (1924). 1st US ed. 79 full-pg repros. Untrimmed, partly unopened; top edge stained red-orange. White cl, slate bds, dk brn leather spine label. (Eps partly browned; edges worn, finger smudges.) *Baltimore*.* $80/£50

MANNING, E. F. The Coming of Father Christmas. London: Frederick Warne, (1892). Obl 4to. Aeg. Color pict 1/2 cl (corners sl worn). Nice. *Reisler.* $575/£359

MANNING, FREDERIC. Scenes and Portraits. London: Peter Davies, 1930. Rev, enlgd ed, trade issue. Tan cl. NF. *Reese.* $30/£19

MANNING, FREDERIC. Scenes and Portraits. Peter Davies, 1930. One of 250 signed on lg paper. VG (fr cvr sl dented). *Clearwater.* $104/£65

MANNING, GEORGE C. Basic Design of Ships. NY: D. Van Nostrand, 1945. 1st ed. Errata slip bound in. (Errata area browned), else VG+. *My Bookhouse.* $27/£17

MANNING, OLIVIA. Growing Up. London: Heinemann, 1948. 1st Eng ed. VG (inscrip; spine ends, corners sl bumped) in dj (nicked, rubbed, mkd, dusty, sl chipped, torn, creased, price-clipped, sl dknd, spine head frayed). *Ulysses.* $120/£75

MANNING, OLIVIA. The Rain Forest. London: Heinemann, 1974. 1st Eng ed. VG (top edge sl spotted; spine head sl buped) in dj (nicked, edges sl browned). *Ulysses.* $40/£25

MANNING, ROBERT. Book of Fruits: Being a Descriptive Catalogue.... Salem: Ives & Jewett, 1838. 1st ed. (Sl foxed), else VG in VG later marbled wrappers. *Pacific*.* $69/£43

MANNING-SANDERS, JOAN. Drawings and Paintings. NY: William Edwin Rudge, 1929. 1st Amer ed. (Spine faded), else VG. *Hermitage.* $45/£28

MANNIX, B. Mines and Their Story. Phila: Lippincott, 1913. Pict cl. VG (lt foxed). *Blake.* $145/£91

MANNOCK, JOHN. The Poor Man's Controversy. (London), 1769. Only ed. 135,(1)pp. Mod blue morocco. *Young.* $224/£140

MANOS, CONSTANTINE. A Greek Portfolio. NY: Viking, 1972. 1st ed. 112 plts. VG+ in dj. *Smith.* $100/£63

Mansfield Park: A Novel. (By Jane Austen.) London: T. Egerton, 1814. 1st ed. 3 vols. 12mo. Contemp calf. (Lt foxed; lacks 1/2 titles, final blank vol 2, final ad leaf vol 3; spine tops worn, joints cracked or starting.) *Swann*.* $2,185/£1,366

MANSFIELD, KATHERINE. The Dove's Nest and Other Stories. London, 1923. 1st Eng ed. (Foxed; spine foot sl bumped.) Dj (sl rubbed, internally reinforced w/tape). *Clearwater.* $128/£80

MANSFIELD, KATHERINE. Prelude. Richmond: Hogarth, (1918). 1st ed. One of 300. Later issue w/o line block on fr wrapper. (Lt foxed.) Dk blue paper wrappers (edges sl creased, sm tears on edges, spine). Collector's box. *Sotheby's*.* $699/£437

MANSFIELD, KATHERINE. To Stanislaw Wyspianski. (Privately ptd for Bertram Rota), 1938. 1st ed in English. One of 100. Fore-edges untrimmed. Fine in stiff gray sewn wrappers. *Blackwell's.* $320/£200

MANSFIELD, T. C. Carnations in Colour and Cultivation. London: Collins, 1952. 2nd ptg. 64 color plts. Pict grn cl, gilt. VG in dj (lacks triangular piece). *Fair Meadow.* $25/£16

MANSION, HORACE. Old French Nursery Songs. London: George C. Harrap, (ca 1925). 4to. (iv),5-87pp; 8 color plts by Anne Anderson. Blue cl-backed pict bds. Externally NF (1st, last 2 leaves speckled). *Sotheran.* $157/£98

MANSO, LEO. Firehouse. Rainbow Playbook, World, 1949. 1st ed. 9.3x10.5. 8 fld-down pp spiral bound w/groove for pole; 4 fldg scenes. As New unflded diorama pieces laid in. VG (facs Dalmatian, plain dowel pole replaced, 2 lt creases to pp, creased engine bumper) in VG dj (lt soiled, one 1/2-inch soil spot, 1-inch tear spine head, extrems sl worn). *Price.* $85/£53

MANSON, GRANT CARPENTER. Frank Lloyd Wright to 1910. NY, (1958). 1st ed. (Spine ends worn), else Good in dj (frayed). *King.* $95/£59

MANSON, J. B. The Life and Work of Edgar Degas. London: Studio, 1927. 1st ed. Teg, uncut. Vellum spine (lt sunned, lt rubbed). Fine. *Polyanthos.* $125/£78

MANSON, J. B. The Life and Work of Edgar Degas. Geoffrey Holme (ed). London: Studio, 1927. 1st ed. Photogravure frontis, 73 monotone plts, 8 mtd color plts. Vellum-like spine (soiled). (Edges lt rubbed.) *Karmiole.* $100/£63

MANSON, PATRICK. Tropical Diseases. Cassell, 1898. 1st ed. xvi,607pp, 4 ad ll; 2 color plts. Mod buckram, gilt. (Pale oval lib stamp dated 1898.) *Bickersteth.* $240/£150

MANSON, PATRICK. Tropical Diseases. NY: William Wood, 1903. 3rd ed. 2 color plts. Grn cl. (Ink, emb stamps), o/w VG + . *House.* $50/£31

MANT, ALICIA CATHERINE. The Young Naturalist, a Tale. H. Holloway, 1824. 1st ed. 12mo. Wood-engr frontis by W. Hughes, (ii),218,(1)pp. Orig 1/4 black roan, marbled bds. Good (name, 2 sealing wax mks on fr pastedown; rubbed). *Blackwell's.* $136/£85

MANTELL, G. A. Geological Excursions Round the Isle of Wight, and Along the Adjacent Coast of Dorsetshire. London, 1847. 1st ed. 430pp; 19 plts, hand-colored fldg map. (Cl neatly re-backed preserving spine.) *Henly.* $224/£140

MANTELL, G. A. The Geology of the South-East of England. London, 1833. Frontis, tp, xix,415pp; 5 plts, fldg hand-colored map (torn, repaired). Orig bds, recent 1/2-calf, gilt. (Frontis, plts sl foxed.) *Henly.* $264/£165

MANTELL, GIDEON. The Journal of Gideon Mantell. E. Cecil Curwen (ed). OUP, 1940. 1st ed. 4 plts, map. Dj (chipped, sl loss, sl soiled). *Edwards.* $61/£38

MANTER, ETHEL. Rocket of the Comstock, the Story of John William MacKay. Caldwell, 1950. 1st ed. Pict cl. NF in dj (chipped, sl worn, price-clipped). *Baade.* $40/£25

MANTLE, MICKEY and PHIL PEPE. My Favorite Summer 1956. NY, (1991). Signed by Mantle. Dj. *Argosy.* $250/£156

MANTLE, MICKEY. Education of a Baseball Player. S&S, 1967. 1st ed. VG in VG dj. *Plapinger.* $50/£31

Manual of the Coniferae.... Chelsea: James Veirch & Sons, Royal Exotic Nursery, 1881. 1st ed. (i),350pp. Dk blue-grn coated eps. Dk brn cl, gilt. (Lt aged, fr hinge lt cracked.) Cvrs VG. *Baltimore*.* $60/£38

Manual of the Police Department of the City of Buffalo. Buffalo: Ptg House of Matthews & Warren, 1873. 162pp. Presentation slip from the Clerk of the Board of Police tipped in. Aeg. Full morocco, gilt. VG (lacks tip of last few ll, no loss; extrems rubbed). *Cahan.* $125/£78

MANVELL, ROGER (ed). Experiment in the Film. Grey Walls, 1949. 1st ed. NF in dj (price-clipped). *Sclanders.* $32/£20

MANVILL, MRS. Lucinda; Or The Mountain Mourner. Johnstown, (NY): W. & A. Child, 1807. 1st ed. 12mo. 150pp. Contemp plain sheep. Excellent. *M & S.* $1,250/£781

MANWARING, ELIZABETH WHEELER. Italian Landscape in Eighteenth Century England. NY: OUP, 1925. Sound working copy (ink notes, disfiguring marginalia; hinges cracked). *Clearwater.* $56/£35

MANZONI, ALESSANDRO. The Betrothed (I Promessi Sposi). LEC, 1951. Ltd to 1500 numbered, signed by Bruno Bramanti (illus) and Giovanni Mardersteig (designer). Fine in slipcase. *Swann*.* $40/£25

MAPES, DAVID P. History of the City of Ripon. Milwaukee: Cramer, Aikens & Cramer, 1873. 1st ed. Engr frontis port, 281pp; 2 plts. VG (spine top sl chipped). *Connolly.* $85/£53

MAPPLETHORPE, ROBERT. Black Book. NY, (1986). 1st ed. Signed. (Fep lt soiled.) Dj (sl rubbed). *Swann*.* $258/£161

MAPPLETHORPE, ROBERT. Certain People: A Book of Photographs. Pasadena, (1985). 1st ed. Signed. Folio. (Sl marginally age-dknd; extrems sl worn.) Dj (rubbed). *Swann*.* $316/£198

MAPPLETHORPE, ROBERT. The Perfect Moment. Phila, (1988). 1st ed. Signed. Photo-pict wrappers (rubbed). *Swann*.* $258/£161

MAPPLETHORPE, ROBERT. Robert Mapplethorpe. Text by Patti Smith. N.p.: Bellport, 1987. 1st ed. Dj (rubbed, soiled). *Swann*.* $126/£79

MARAN, RENE. Batouala. Cape, 1922. 1st ed in English. One of 1050. Linen-backed patterned bds, paper labels. (Eps offset), o/w NF. *Any Amount.* $26/£16

MARAN, RENE. Batouala. NY: Thomas Seltzer, 1922. 1st ed. VG (2-inch tear rear joint). *Beasley.* $45/£28

MARAN, RENE. Batouala. LEC, 1932. Ltd to 1500 numbered, signed by Miguel Covarrubias (illus). Fine in slipcase. *Swann*.* $115/£72

MARBLE, HENRY CHASE. The Hand; a Manual and Atlas for the General Surgeon. Phila/London: W.B. Saunders, (1961). Fine. *Weber.* $50/£31

MARBURY, MARY ORVIS. Favorite Flies and Their Histories. Boston: Charles T. Branford, 1955. 32 color plts, 6 engrs. Dk grn cl. Fine in VG pict dj. *Biscotti.* $100/£63

MARBURY, MARY ORVIS. Favorite Flies and Their History. Boston: Houghton Mifflin, 1892. 1st ed. 32 chromolithos. Teg. Grn cl, gilt. VG (lacks tp, frontis; spine ends, extrems rubbed). *Pacific*.* $288/£180

MARCELIN, PIERRE and PHILIPPE THOBY-MARCELIN. The Beast of the Haitian Hills. NY: Rinehart, 1946. 1st US ed. VG + in VG- dj (price-clipped, chip to fr cvr). *Lame Duck.* $50/£31

MARCELIN, PIERRE and PHILIPPE THOBY-MARCELIN. The Pencil of God. Boston: Houghton Mifflin, 1951. 1st US ed. Inscribed by Thoby-Marcelin in 1951. (Feps offset), else VG + in VG dj (price-clipped, spine head lt chipped). *Lame Duck.* $175/£109

MARCH, BENJAMIN. Chinese Shadow-Figure Plays and Their Making. Paul McPharlin (ed). Detroit: Puppetry Imprints, 1938. 1st ed. White fabricoid, black ptd bds. Good. *Karmiole.* $60/£38

MARCH, JOSEPH MONCURE. The Wild Party. NY, 1929. 1st ed. One of 200. VG in VG dj. *Warren.* $175/£109

MARCH, JOSEPH MONCURE. The Wild Party. NY, 1994. New ed. Fine in Fine dj. *Warren.* $30/£19

MARCH, JOSEPH MONCURE. The Wild Party. NY, 1994. New ed. Signed by Art Spiegelman (illus). Fine in Fine dj. *Warren.* $55/£34

MARCH, RICHARD. The Mountain of the Upas Tree. London: Editions Poetry, (1948). Signed presentation. (Backstrip sl faded.) *Petersfield.* $24/£15

MARCH, WILLIAM. (Pseud of William E. M. Campbell.) Come in at the Door. NY: Smith & Haas, 1934. 1st ed. NF in dj (lt chipped). *Beasley.* $65/£41

MARCH, WILLIAM. (Pseud of William E. M. Campbell.) Company K. London: Gollancz, 1933. 1st British ed. Black cl stamped in red. (Ink named dated 1933), o/w VG in house-style dj (sl tanned, sm chips, internal mends to spine ends). *Reese.* $125/£78

MARCH, WILLIAM. (Pseud of William E. M. Campbell.) Company K. NY: Harrison Smith & Robert Haas, 1933. 1st ed, 1st bk. Pale grn cl, dec in black. (Spine sl sunned), o/w VG in glassine (torn but largely present) dj. *Reese.* $300/£188

MARCH, WILLIAM. (Pseud of William E. M. Campbell.) Trial Balance, the Collected Short Stories of.... NY: Harcourt, Brace, (1945). 1st collected ed. Brn cl stamped in white. Fine in NF dj (sm tear spine crown mended on verso). *Reese.* $85/£53

MARCHAND, HENRY L. The French Pornographers. NY, 1965. 1st Amer ed. NF in dj (sm nick, lt rubbed). *Polyanthos.* $25/£16

MARCHANT, BESSIE. A V.A.D. in Salonika. London, (1917). 1st Eng ed. Pict cl. (Fep creased, inscrip; sl handled.) Pict dj (very torn). *Clearwater.* $88/£55

MARCHINI, G. Italian Stained Glass Windows. NY, n.d. 93 tipped-in color, 36 b/w plts, 4 color transparencies, 18 diags. (Sl spotted.) *Washton.* $90/£56

MARCY, RANDOLPH B. Exploration of the Red River of Louisiana, in the Year 1852. Washington: Robert Armstrong, 1853. Tipped-in note 'with the respects of R. B. Marcy.' 65 plts (plt 18 botanical, not issued). Blind-stamped cl. (Dampstaining throughout.) *Metropolitan*.* $172/£108

MARCY, RANDOLPH B. The Prairie Traveler. NY, 1859. 1st ed. Fldg map. (Worn, fr joint sl worming.) Howes M279. *Oinonen*.* $350/£219

MARCY, RANDOLPH B. The Prairie Traveler. London: Trubner, 1863. xvi,251,24pp; fldg map. (Ex-lib; needs rebinding.) Internally Good. Howes M278. *Dumont.* $175/£109

MARCY, RANDOLPH B. The Prairie Traveller. NY: Harper, 1859. 1st ed. 340pp; VG fldg map (tiny edge tear just into details). Later plain grn buckram, gilt. (Sl aged, sl foxed, ex-lib, perf blind-stamp tp, 1pg; ink stamps last text leaf, map verso.) Howes M279. *Baltimore*.* $460/£288

MARCY, RANDOLPH B. Thirty Years of Army Life on the Border. NY, 1866. 1st ed. (Rear joint stained, blistered.) Howes M280. *Swann*.* $103/£64

MARCY, RANDOLPH B. Thirty Years of Army Life on the Border. NY: Harper & Bros, 1866. 442pp. Good (browned; hinges, extrems repaired). Howes M279. *Dumont.* $125/£78

MARDEN, PHILIP SANFORD. Travels in Spain. Boston/NY: Houghton Mifflin, 1910. 2nd ed. Map. All edges uncut. Pict blue cl, gilt. VG (some ll uncut, ink inscrip). *Sotheran.* $109/£68

MAREY, E. J. Animal Mechanism: A Treatise on Terrestrial and Aerial Locomotion. NY: D. Appleton, 1874. 1st US ed. xvi,283pp + (12)pp ads; 117 wood-engr illus. Dec red cl. Fine. *Cahan.* $300/£188

MARGARET, THE RANEE OF SARAWAK. (Margaret Brooke.) My Life in Sarawak. Methuen, 1913. 1st ed. Uncut. Dk grn cl, gilt. (Eps sl browned), o/w Bright. *Sotheran.* $237/£148

MARIACHER, GIOVANNI. Italian Blown Glass. NY: McGraw-Hill, (1961). 1st ed. 84 color plts tipped in. White bds. Good in dj. *Karmiole.* $125/£78

MARIE, PIERRE. Lectures on Diseases of the Spinal Cord. Montagu Lubbock (trans). New Sydenham Soc, 1895. 1st Eng ed. xix,512pp. Blind-stamped cl (spine top chipped), gilt. *Hollett.* $152/£95

MARIE, QUEEN OF ROUMANIA. The Dreamer of Dreams. London, (1915). Edmund Dulac (illus). 6 tipped-in color plts. (Spine sl dknd.) *Kane*.* $150/£94

MARIE, QUEEN OF ROUMANIA. Ordeal. The Story of My Life. NY, 1935. 1st Amer ed. Pict cvrs, gilt. Fine. *Polyanthos.* $30/£19

Marihuana and Health: A Report to the Congress from the Secretary, Department of Health, Education, and Welfare. Washington, 1971. 1st ed. VG in ptd wrappers (extrems sl worn). *Doctor's Library.* $20/£13

MARINARO, VINCENT. A Modern Dry-Fly Code. NY: Crown, (1970). Deluxe ed. One of 350. Signed. Gilt-lettered calf. As New in slipcase. *Pacific*.* $230/£144

MARINE, WILLIAM M. The British Invasion of Maryland, 1812-1815. Louis Henry Dielman (ed). Balt: Society of the War of 1812 in MD, 1913. 2nd ed, 'Patron's Edition.' One of 128 numbered. Fldg frontis map. Dk grn cl, gilt. (Sl handled, fr hinge splitting; lt edgeworn.) Text Good, cvrs Clean. *Baltimore*.* $70/£44

MARION. Mummy's Bedtime Story Book. London: Cecil Palmer, (1929). 1st ed. Lg 4to. 12 full-pg color plts by Jessie M. King. Color pict bds. (Mk from paper clip on few prelim pp; spine top sl worn), o/w VG. *Reisler.* $2,000/£1,250

MARK, MARY ELLEN. Falkland Road. Prostitutes of Bombay. NY, 1981. 1st ed. NF in VG + dj (1-inch tear at lower spine). *Warren.* $50/£31

MARKEVITCH, MARIE ALEXANDRE. The Epicure in Imperial Russia. SF: Colt, 1941. 1st ed. One of 500. Red bds, tan linen backstrip, red paper spine label. (Sm tape stain fep, rep; corners sl worn), o/w Fine. *Harrington.* $45/£28

MARKHAM, ALBERT H. The Cruise of the 'Rosario' Amongst the New Hebrides and Santa Cruz Islands, Exposing the Recent Atrocities Connected with the Kidnapping of Natives in the South Seas. London: Sampson, Low, Marston et al, 1873. 1st ed. Fldg map. Pict royal blue cl, gilt. Good (map chipped, fr hinge cracked; spine ends cl replaced). *Pacific*.* $46/£29

MARKHAM, ALBERT H. The Great Frozen Sea: A Personal Narrative of the Voyage of the 'Alert' During the Arctic Expedition of 1875-6. London: C. Kegan Paul, 1880. 4th ed. xix,384pp; map. Good (top edge faded, spine ends worn; sl browned). *Explorer.* $45/£28

MARKHAM, ALBERT H. Life of Sir John Franklin and the Northwest Passage. London: George Philip & Son, (1891). xii,324pp; 9 plts and ports, 7 maps (2 fldg). Grn cl. VG. *Explorer.* $80/£50

MARKHAM, ALBERT H. A Whaling Cruise to Baffin's Bay and The Gulf of Boothia, and an Account of the Rescue of the Crew of the Polaris. London: Sampson, Low, et al, 1875. 2nd ed. xxxi,307pp; 8 plts, fldg map. Dec cl (extrems rubbed). VG. *High Latitude.* $185/£116

MARKHAM, ALBERT H. A Whaling Cruise to Baffin's Bay and the Gulf of Boothia. London: Sampson Low, Marston, 1875. 2nd ed. xxxi,(i)blank,307,(1)blank,40 pub's list dated February 1875; fldg map, 7 engr plts. Blue cl, gilt. Sound (some ll dustsoiled, lt spotted, pencil mks to 1 leaf; rebacked, hinges cracked, corners rubbed). *Morrell.* $176/£110

MARKHAM, C. A. The 'New' Pewter Marks and Old Pewter Ware. London, 1928. 2nd ed. Frontis; 11 plts. (Eps lt spotted; hinges cracked, spine sl faded.) *Edwards.* $48/£30

MARKHAM, C. A. Pewter Marks and Old Pewter Ware. Reeves & Turner, 1909. 1st ed. Teg. (Cl sl rubbed, mkd.) *Hollett.* $77/£48

MARKHAM, CLEMENTS (ed). Early Spanish Voyages to the Strait of Magellan. London: Hakluyt Soc, 1911. 1st ed. 3 fldg maps. (1 leaf carelessly opened, marginal tears, eps browned; cvrs dull.) *Lefkowicz.* $150/£94

MARKHAM, CLEMENTS. Cuzco: A Journey to the Ancient Capital of Peru. London: Chapman & Hall, 1856. 1st ed. iv,420pp; 8 color lithos, fldg map. Grn cl (spine extrems lt frayed, hinges rubbed). *Karmiole.* $300/£188

MARKHAM, CLEMENTS. A Life of John Davis, the Navigator, 1550-1605, Discoverer of the Davis Straits. London: George Philip & Son, 1889. vi,(ii)301pp + 4pp ads; 4 maps (3 fldg). Unopened. Brn cl, gilt. VG. *Explorer.* $64/£40

MARKHAM, CLEMENTS. Peruvian Bark. London: John Murray, 1880. 1st ed. xxiii,(i)blank,550pp; 3 fldg maps. Brn cl, gilt. (Lt foxed), else VG. *Morrell.* $144/£90

MARKHAM, FRED. Shooting in the Himalayas. London, 1854. Frontis, fldg map. 1/2 calf (neatly rebacked). *Petersfield.* $480/£300

MARKHAM, GERVASE and ROBERT VENABLES. The Pleasures of Princes or Good Mens Recreations by Gervase Markham.... London: Cresset, 1927. One of 650. Teg. 3/4 dk grn morocco, cl, gilt, raised bands; bound by Bayntun. Fine. *Pacific*.* $161/£101

MARKHAM, GERVASE. Markham's Master-Piece, Containing All Knowledge Belonging to the Smith, Farrier, or Horse-Leech. E. Okes & T. Passenger, 1668. 10th ed. 4to. Add'l engr tp by R. Elstrak (neatline just shaved), 2 fldg woodcuts (1 w/tear repaired). Contemp calf (rebacked retaining spine, rubbed, corners repaired; internally sl spotted). *Sotheby's*.* $846/£529

MARKHAM, VIRGIL. The Devil Drives. NY, 1932. 1st Amer ed. NF (2 cup ring mks fr cvr) in dj (chipped). *Polyanthos.* $30/£19

MARKMAN, EARNEST. 10,000 Miles in a Balloon! St Louis: Mercantile Pub, 1873. 1st ed. 16mo. Frontis, 1/2 title, 96pp. Ptd wrappers (dated 1876). *M & S.* $525/£328

MARKOVITS, RODION. Siberian Garrison. George Halasz (trans). NY: Horace Liveright, 1929. 1st US ed. Red cl stamped in black/gilt. (Sl nick spine foot), o/w Nice in pict dj (sl dknd, lt chipped, tears at joints). *Reese.* $50/£31

MARKOVITS, RODION. Siberian Garrison. George Halasz (trans). Peter Davies, 1929. 1st Eng ed. Fine in dj (sl nicked, torn). *Clearwater.* $56/£35

MARKS, CLAUDE. From the Sketchbooks of the Great Artists. NY, 1972. Good. *Washton.* $40/£25

MARKS, EDWARD B. They All Had Glamour. NY: Julian Messner, (c. 1944). VG in color pict dj (worn). *Dramatis.* $25/£16

MARKS, ROBERT. Merle Armitage Bibliography. NY: E. Weyhe, (1956). One of 500. Wrappers. *Dawson.* $40/£25

Marlene Dietrich: Ten Stills. (By Marlene Dietrich.) (NY: MOMA, 1965). 1st ed. Stiff card folder with 10 b/w stills laid in. VF (stamp on rear; fldr corners sl bumped). *Between The Covers.* $100/£63

MARLOWE, CHRISTOPHER. Edward the Second. Kensington: Aquila Press, 1929. One of 500. Teg, rest untrimmed. Orig parchment, red blazon fr cvr, gilt. VG in slipcase. *Maggs.* $56/£35

MARLOWE, CHRISTOPHER. Four Plays. Havelock Ellis (ed). NY: LEC, 1966. One of 1500 ptd. Signed by Albert Decaris (illus). 1/2 grn morocco, natural linen, gilt, blind-stamped. Fine in glassine, slipcase (sunned). *Pacific*.* $46/£29

MARLOWE, CHRISTOPHER. The Tragical History of Doctor Faustus. (London): Hacon & Ricketts, 1903. Blind-tooled grn cl, gilt. (Spine ends sl rubbed), else NF. *Pacific*.* $196/£123

MARLOWE, CHRISTOPHER. The Works and Life of Christopher Marlowe. R. H. Case (ed). London: Methuen, 1930-1951. 1st Eng ed. 6 vols. NF set (spine ends sl bumped) in djs (3rd dj torn, repaired, rest w/sl dknd spines, nicked, rubbed, all w/price stickers on spines). *Ulysses.* $400/£250

MARLOWE, HUGH. (Pseud of Jack Higgins.) Seven Pillars to Hell. NY: Abelard Schuman, 1963. 1st ed. NF in dj (lt soiled). *Murder.* $35/£22

MARMELSZADT, WILLARD. Musical Sons of Aesculapius. NY: Froben, 1946. Only ed. Inscribed, dated May 1958. Dj (edge sl frayed, chipped). *Bickersteth.* $240/£150

MARPLES, MORRIS. University Slang. London: Williams & Norgate, 1950. 1st Eng ed. Fine (feps partly browned) in dj (sl nicked, spine dknd). *Ulysses.* $56/£35

MARQUAND, JOHN P. So Little Time. Boston: Little, Brown, 1943. 1st ed. Tan cl stamped in gilt/blue. (Ep gutters foxed), else Fine in dj (spine sunned). *Reese.* $25/£16

MARQUAND, JOHN P. The Unspeakable Gentleman. NY: Scribner, 1922. 1st ed. VG (shelfworn, spotted) in dj (tattered, torn). *My Bookhouse.* $52/£33

MARQUEZ, GABRIEL GARCIA. See GARCIA MARQUEZ, GABRIEL

MARQUIS, DON. Archy's Life of Mehitabel. GC: Doubleday, 1933. 1st ed. VF in dj. *Captain's Bookshelf.* $150/£94

MARQUIS, DON. The Cruise of the Jasper B. NY: Appleton, 1916. 1st ed, 1st ptg. Blue cl, gilt. VG. *Macdonnell.* $20/£13

MARQUIS, DON. Danny's Own Story. NY, 1912. 1st Amer ed, 1st bk. Pict cvrs. NF. *Polyanthos.* $50/£31

MARQUIS, DON. Danny's Own Story. GC: Doubleday, Page, 1912. 1st ed, 1st bk. E. W. Kemble (illus). Pict label. (Fr hinge tender), else VG. *Captain's Bookshelf.* $75/£47

MARQUIS, DON. A Variety of People. NY, 1929. 1st Amer ed. NF (sl rubbed, sunned). *Polyanthos.* $25/£16

MARQUIS, DON. When the Turtles Sing. NY: Doubleday, 1928. 1st ed. Red cl, labels. VG. *Macdonnell.* $15/£9

MARQUIS, THOMAS. Wooden Leg. Minneapolis, MN: Midwest, 1931. 1st ed. NF in dj. *Labordo.* $175/£109

MARRIC, J. J. (Pseud of John Creasey.) Gideon's Vote. London: Hodder & Stoughton, 1964. 1st ed. Fine in NF dj (rubbed). *Janus.* $30/£19

MARRIOTT, ALICE. Greener Fields. Experiences Among the American Indians. NY: Thomas Y. Crowell, (1953). 1st ed. Signed. VG in dj. *Perier.* $50/£31

MARRIOTT, ALICE. The Valley Below. Norman: Univ of OK, 1949. 1st ed. VG in dj. *Lien.* $35/£22

MARRIOTT, ALICE. Winter Telling Stories. NY: Thomas Y. Crowell, 1947. 1st ed. Signed. VG in dj (lt worn). *Dumont.* $95/£59

MARRIOTT, WILLIAMS. Infant Nutrition. St. Louis, 1930. 1st ed. *Fye.* $75/£47

MARROT, H. V. A Bibliography of the Works of John Galsworthy. London: Elkin Mathews & Marrot, 1928. Port, color plt. (Bkpl, fep, 1/2-title loose; inner joint broken.) *Maggs.* $56/£35

MARRYAT, CAPTAIN. A Diary in America, with Remarks on Its Institutions. (Part first). London: Longman, Orme, Brown et al, 1839. 1st ed. 3 vols. 2 prelim ll, 321; (4),319; (4),311pp,(1) errata. (Feps cracked vol 2; bkpls.) Orig cl-backed bds (spines faded), paper labels (piece missing from vol 2 affecting title). Howes M300. *Mott.* $150/£94

MARRYAT, FLORENCE. Life and Letters of Captain Marryat. NY: D. Appleton, 1872. 1st Amer ed. 2 vols. xi,260; vii,300pp. 3pp als laid in. Blue cl (lt worn, soiled). *Mott.* $50/£31

MARRYAT, FLORENCE. A Moment of Madness and Other Stories. Bernhard Tauchnitz, 1883. Copyright ed. Contemp 1/2 leather, marbled bds. Good (bkpl, sl rubbed). *Tiger.* $26/£16

MARRYAT, FLORENCE. Tom Tiddler's Ground. London: Swan Sonnenshein, Lowrey, 1886. 1st ed. Inscribed; inscribed presentation card tipped-in. 2 prelim ll, 212pp. Orange cl (fr inner hinge starting), gilt. NF (bkpl). *Mott.* $100/£63

MARRYAT, FRANK S. Borneo and the Indian Archipelago, with Drawings of Costume and Scenery. London: Longman, Brown et al, 1848. 1st ed. 10.5x6.75. viii,232pp; 22 litho plts (incl frontis, added tp). Marbled eps; aeg. Period 3/4 gilt-ruled morocco, raised bands. (Bkpl; extrems, joints scuffed), else NF. *Pacific*.* $920/£575

MARRYAT, FRANK S. Borneo and the Indian Archipelago. Longman, 1848. Tinted litho pict add'l tp, 21 tinted litho plts. 19th-cent purple 1/2 morocco (sl rubbed), gilt. *Sotheby's*.* $1,104/£690

MARRYAT, FRANK S. Mountains and Molehills or Recollections of a Burnt Journal. London: Longman, Brown, Green, Longmans, 1855. 1st Eng ed. xii,444pp; 8 color litho plts. 19th-cent calf, marbled bds (spine worn; hinges, corners scuffed). Howes M299. *Karmiole*. $275/£172

MARRYAT, FREDERICK. Narrative of the Travels and Adventures of Monsieur Violet, in California, Sonora, and Western Texas.... Leipzig: Bernh. Tauchnitz, June 1843. 1st ed. vi,384pp; fldg map. Contemp gilt-stamped calf, patterned paper-cvrd bds (lt rubbed). *Karmiole*. $200/£125

MARRYAT, JOSEPH. A History of Pottery and Porcelain, Mediaeval and Modern. London: John Murray, 1857. 2nd ed. xxiv,472pp; 6 VG chromolitho plts. Untrimmed. Lt brn cl, gilt. Good (text lt aged; spine recently repaired, ends chipped, sm cracks into lettering). *Baltimore**. $35/£22

MARSDEN, C. and H. S. JACKSON. Rebutia. London, 1968. 14 color plts. Fine in dj (lt worn). *Brooks*. $29/£18

MARSDEN, WILLIAM. The History of Sumatra. Kuala Lumpur/NY/London: OUP, 1966. Photo rpt of 1811 3rd ed. 26 b/w plts, lg fldg map. Crimson cl, gilt. Fine in dj (lt worn), orig bd slipcase (sl dusty, worn). *Baltimore**. $35/£22

MARSH, CHARLES F. (ed). The Hampton Roads Communities in World War II. Univ of NC, (c1951). VG in Good dj. *Book Broker*. $20/£13

MARSH, EDWARD (ed). Georgian Poetry, 1916-1917. Poetry Bookshop, 1917. 1st Eng ed. (Spine sl chafed.) *Clearwater*. $56/£35

MARSH, EDWARD (ed). Georgian Poetry, 1920-1922. Poetry Bookshop, 1922. 1st Eng ed. (Edge sl nicked, corner bumped.) *Clearwater*. $56/£35

MARSH, EDWARD. A Number of People. NY: Harper, 1939. 1st US ed. Brn cl. VG in dj (sm chips top edge). *Reese*. $45/£28

MARSH, GEORGE P. The Camel. Boston: (Gould & Lincoln), 1856. 1st ed. Pub's silky ribbed brn cl, gilt spine. VF. *Book Block*. $385/£241

MARSH, GEORGE P. The Earth as Modified by Human Action. NY, 1898. 629pp. Brn cl, gilt. VG. *Larry Price*. $49/£31

MARSH, JAMES B. Four Years in the Rockies; or, The Adventures of Isaac P. Rose Giving His Experience as a Hunter and Trapper.... New Castle, PA: W.B. Thomas, 1884. 1st ed. 262pp. Dk grn cl (rebound), gilt spine label. Fine (lacks frontisport, 3 leaves w/sm stain lower blank border). *Argonaut*. $475/£297

MARSH, JAMES B. Four Years in the Rockies; or, The Adventures of Isaac P. Rose.... New Castle: W.B. Thomas, 1884. 1st ed. Wood-engr frontisport, 262pp. Pict-dec mustard yellow cl, black lettering. (Lt aged; spine ends lt frayed, cvrs lt rubbed.) Text Clean. Recent protective clamshell box of morocco/brn cl over bds. Howes M306. *Baltimore**. $500/£313

MARSH, NGAIO. Black As He's Painted. Boston: Little, Brown, 1974. 1st US ed. Fine in Fine dj. *Janus*. $35/£22

MARSH, NGAIO. Clutch of Constables. London: CCC, 1968. 1st ed. Scarlet cl. (Sm mk rep), o/w Fine in dj. *Temple*. $19/£12

MARSH, NGAIO. Died in the Wool. Boston: Little, Brown, 1945. 1st US ed. Fine in NF dj (lt edgeworn, sl rubbed). *Janus*. $75/£47

MARSH, NGAIO. Tied Up in Tinsel. Boston: Little, Brown, 1972. 1st US ed. Fine in Fine dj. *Janus*. $30/£19

MARSH, NGAIO. When in Rome. London: Collins, 1970. 1st ed. Scarlet bds. Fine in dj (sl nicked, sl browned). *Temple*. $16/£10

MARSHAL, L. BIRKETT (ed). Rare Poems of the Seventeenth Century. CUP, 1936. 1st Eng ed. Buckram-backed paper bds. NF (spine ends sl bumped) in dj (price-clipped, spine sl dknd). *Ulysses*. $40/£25

MARSHALL, AGNES B. Mrs. Marshall's Larger Cookery Book of Extra Recipes. London: Marshall's School of Cookery, 1902. 1st ed. Frontis port. (Prelims sl spotted, joints cracked.) *Hollett*. $136/£85

MARSHALL, CHARLES. An Aide-de-Camp of Lee. Frederick Maurice (ed). Boston, 1927. 1st ed. (Sl worn, faded), o/w Fine. *Pratt*. $55/£34

MARSHALL, CHRISTOPHER. Extracts from the Diary of Christopher Marshall...1774-1781. William Duane (ed). Albany: Joel Munsell, 1877. 330pp. Later cl. (Inner margin tp reinforced on verso; shelfworn, edges, spine worn), else Good. Howes M310. *Brown*. $50/£31

MARSHALL, H. The History of Kentucky. Frankfort, 1824. 2nd ed. 2 vols. 8x5 inches. 465; 524pp. Old sheep. (Ink inscrip, lib bkpl; hinges broken, cvr heavily worn, spines badly chipped, foxed.) *King*. $450/£281

MARSHALL, H. RISSIK. Coloured Worcester Porcelain of the First Period (1751-1783). Newport, Monmouthshire: Ceramic Book Co, 1954. 1st ed. 31 color plts. Teg. Blue cl. Good. *Karmiole*. $150/£94

MARSHALL, H. RISSIK. Coloured Worcester Porcelain of the First Period (1751-1783). Newport, 1954. One of 1200 signed. Blue leather, gilt. (Fr joint staring.) *Swann**. $230/£144

MARSHALL, JAMES WILSON and EDWARD GOULD BUFFUM. From Mexican Days to the Gold Rush. D. B. Nunis, Jr. (ed). Chicago: R.R. Donnelley, 1993. Frontis. VG. *Lien*. $30/£19

MARSHALL, JOHN. The Life of George Washington, Commander in Chief of the American Forces.... Phila: C.P. Wayne, 1804-7. 5 vols. 8vo + atlas 4to. xxii,488,45, port; v,565,67; vii,576,28; viii,626,16; vii,779,36pp; atlas. 10 maps. Contemp Amer tree calf (rubbed), red/black labels; atlas in 1/2 tan calf. Howes M317. *Adelson*. $785/£491

MARSHALL, JOHN. A Manual of the Injuries and Surgical Diseases of the Face, Mouth, and Jaws. Phila: S.S. White Dental Mfg, 1909. 3rd ed, rev, enlgd. 6 color plts. VG (sig, pencil notes; corners starting to show). *Weber*. $90/£56

MARSHALL, LOGAN (ed). Fairy Tales of All Nations. Phila: John C. Winston, (1910). 1st ed. 8vo. 30 full-pg color plts. Grn cl, gilt, color paste label. VG in pub's cardbd box (edgeworn, corners cracked), color paste label. *Reisler*. $150/£94

MARSHALL, M. H. The Scottish Curlers in Canada and U.S.A. Edinburgh: T. & A. Constable, 1924. (Sm spine stain.) *Hollett*. $72/£45

MARSHALL, PAULE. Brown Girl, Brownstones. NY: Random House, 1959. 1st ed, 1st bk. NF in dj. *Lame Duck*. $750/£469

MARSHALL, PAULE. The Chosen Place, the Timeless People. NY: Harcourt, Brace & World, 1969. 1st ed. Fine in NF dj (few sm patches of surface loss to fr panel, edges). *Lame Duck*. $250/£156

MARSHALL, PAULE. Praisesong for the Widow. NY: Putnam, 1983. 1st ed. (Stamp to top pg edge), else Fine in Fine dj. *Pettler*. $65/£41

MARSHALL, ROBERT. Arctic Wilderness. Berkeley: Univ of CA, 1956. 2nd ptg. Fldg map. VG in dj. *Perier*. $30/£19

MARSHALL, S. L. A. Crimsoned Prairie. NY: Scribner, (1972). Fine in VG dj. *Perier*. $30/£19

MARSHALL, W. TAYLOR and THOR METHVEN BOCK. Cactaceae. Sakonnet, 1977. 163 b/w plts, 31 plts of dwgs. Grn cl. Fine. *Brooks*. $55/£34

MARSHALL, WILLIAM. A Phrenologist Amongst the Todas. Longmans, Green, 1873. 1st ed. xx,271pp; 26 plts. Brn cl, gilt. (Extrems sl bumped), o/w VG. *Sotheran*. $392/£245

MARSHALL, WILLIAM. The Rural Economy of Gloucestershire.... G. Nicol, 1796. 2nd ed. 2 vols. xxxii,332; xxiii,(i),367,(17)index pp. Contemp 1/2 calf (hinges broken but secure, edges worn, lacks vol 2 backstrip piece), marbled paper sides, morocco labels. Internally Good. *Cox*. $152/£95

MARSHALL-CORNWALL, JAMES. Marshall Massena. Oxford: OUP, 1965. 10 maps, 12 plts. Good. *Stewart.* $48/£30

MARSON, T. B. The Scotch Shorthorn. Edinburgh: Scottish Shorthorn Breeders Assoc, 1946. Inscribed presentation. 2 duplicated extracts from other works loosely inserted. Orig blue cl (rebacked in matching levant morocco), gilt. *Hollett.* $104/£65

MARSTON, E. Sketches of Some Booksellers of the Time of Dr. Samuel Johnson. London: Sampson Low, Marston, 1902. Frontisport, 8 plts. Vellum-backed maroon cl (spine sl rubbed, headcaps sl bumped; bkpl), gilt. *Maggs.* $32/£20

MARSTON, E. Thomas Ken and Izaak Walton: A Sketch of Their Lives and Family Connection. London: Longmans, Green, 1908. 1st ed. Blue cl, gilt. (Joints sl rubbed), else VG. *Pacific*.* $40/£25

MARSTON, LAURA A. The Wonderful, Astounding, Mysterious and Strange History. Balt, 1850. Orig letterpress wrappers (chipped, later careless stitching; some corners turned, other minor faults). *Swann*.* $172/£108

MARSTON, MARY GILMAN. George White Marston: A Family Chronicle. (L.A.): Ward Ritchie, 1956. One of 500 sets. 2 vols. Blue cl, gilt. VG in pub's blue bd slipcase. *Houle.* $95/£59

MARSTON, R. B. Walton and Some Earlier Writers on Fish and Fishing. NY: A.C. Armstrong & Son, (1894). 1st Amer ed. Grn cl, gilt. (Spine foot rubbed, head nicked), else VG. *Pacific*.* $104/£65

MARTI-IBANEZ, FELIX. Centaur: Essays on the History of Medical Ideas. NY: MD Publications, (1958). 1st ed. Black cl. VG + in dj (edges lt chipped). *House.* $35/£22

MARTIN, AUGUST. Pathology and Therapeutics of the Diseases of Women. Ernest W. Cushing (trans). Boston: E.W. Cushing, 1890. 2nd Amer ed. xxxiv,681pp; 68 b/w photo plts. Marbled eps. Contemp dk brn morocco, purple cl, raised bands, gilt. (Lt aged; sl worn, scuffed; hinges reinforced.) Text Clean. *Baltimore*.* $40/£25

MARTIN, CY. Whiskey and Wild Women. NY: Hart Pub, 1974. 1st ed. Fine in dj. *Labordo.* $40/£25

MARTIN, DEBORAH B. History of Brown County, Wisconsin Past and Present. Chicago: S.J. Clarke, 1913. 1st ed. 2 vols. Marbled edges. Orig 3/4 morocco (sl rubbed), gilt. Internally Clean. *Sadlon.* $200/£125

MARTIN, DEBORAH B. and SOPHIE BEAUMONT. Old Green Bay (1634-1899). NY: Cheltenham, 1899. 1st ed. Map. Ptd bds (few sm spots, spine ends, corners sl chipped). *Sadlon.* $50/£31

MARTIN, DON JOSE. Memorial and Proposals of Senor Don Jose Martin on the Californias. Henry R. Wagner (trans). (SF: Grabhorn), 1945. 1st ed in English. One of 250 ptd. Grn/yellow patterned bds, grn cl spine strip, paper label. Fine. *Harrington.* $85/£53

MARTIN, DOUGLAS D. The Earps of Tombstone. Tombstone, AZ, (1959). 1st ed. Map. (Pg corners sl bumped), else Very Clean in wrappers. *Sagebrush.* $22/£14

MARTIN, DOUGLAS D. The Earps of Tombstone. Tombstone Epitaph, 1959. Map. Good in heavy wrappers (soiled, bent). *Connolly.* $10/£6

MARTIN, DOUGLAS D. Tombstone's Epitaph. Albuquerque: Univ of NM, 1951. VG in dj. *Dumont.* $30/£19

MARTIN, DOUGLAS D. Tombstone's Epitaph. (Univ of NM, 1951.) 1st ed. Good (lacks dj). *King.* $35/£22

MARTIN, FRANKLIN H. Fifty Years of Medicine and Surgery. Chicago, 1934. 1st ed. Grn cl. VG (extrems sl worn). *Doctor's Library.* $30/£19

MARTIN, FREDERICK. The History of Lloyd's and of Marine Insurance in Great Britain.... London, 1876. *Petersfield.* $34/£21

MARTIN, FREDERICKA. Sea Bears—The Story of the Fur Seal. Phila: Chilton, (1960). 1st ed. VG in dj. *Perier.* $30/£19

MARTIN, GEORGE R. R. Songs the Dead Men Sing. Niles: Dark Harvest, 1983. One of 500 signed, this copy lettered 'P/C.' 1st Dark Harvest bk. (Sl worn.) Dj, slipcase. *Oinonen*.* $90/£56

MARTIN, GEORGE R. R. Songs the Dead Men Sing. Niles: Dark Harvest, 1983. 1st ed. One of 500. Signed. Fine in dj, slipcase (sl sunned). *Pacific*.* $150/£94

MARTIN, GEORGE W. The First Two Years of Kansas. Topeka, KS: State Ptg Office, 1907. 1st ed. NF in ptd wraps (few sm chips on rear wrap). Howes M335. *Chapel Hill.* $95/£59

MARTIN, H. B. Great Golfers in the Making. NY: Dodd, Mead, 1932. 1st ed. Pict cl. (Emb stamp, partly removed bkpl, tape repairs to pp89/90), else VG. *Pacific*.* $40/£25

MARTIN, H. B. How to Play Golf. NY: Modern Sports Pub, (1936). 1st ed thus. NF in pict wrappers. *Pacific*.* $109/£68

MARTIN, H. T. Castorologia or the History and Traditions of the Canadian Beaver. London, 1892. xvi,238pp; 14 plts, 2 maps. Gilt-dec cl (sm tears to spine head, signs of damp, mostly to spine, eps; ex-lib). *Sutton.* $115/£72

MARTIN, J. W. Float Fishing and Spinning in the Nottingham Style.... London: Sampson Low, Marston, Searle & Rivington, 1885. 2nd ed. 9 wood-engr plts. Cl-backed color litho pict bds. (Corners, cvrs sl rubbed), else VG. *Pacific*.* $86/£54

MARTIN, JACK. Border Boss. San Antonio, 1942. 1st ed. Pict cl. VG (sig) in dj (badly chipped, worn). Howes M336. *Baade.* $100/£63

MARTIN, JAMES. The Influence of Tropical Climates on European Constitutions.... London, 1856. 2nd ed. 599pp. Recent cl (new eps). *Fye.* $250/£156

MARTIN, JOHN RUPERT. The Ceiling Paintings of the Jesuit Church in Antwerp. London: Phaidon, (1968). Fine in dj (torn). *Turtle Island.* $65/£41

MARTIN, JOHN RUPERT. The Farnese Gallery. Princeton, 1965. (Top edge sl soiled.) Dj. *Washton.* $225/£141

MARTIN, JOHN. An Account of the Natives of the Tonga Islands, in the South Pacific Ocean. Boston: Charles Ewer, 1820. 1st Amer ed. Frontisport, fldg map (laid-on later backing cl). Mod 3/4 morocco, marbled bds, gilt, raised bands. (Spine sunned), else NF. *Pacific*.* $137/£86

MARTIN, K. The British Public and the General Strike. Hogarth, 1926. 1st ed. (Faded, spine label sl mkd), else Good. *Whiteson.* $29/£18

MARTIN, PETER. Pursuing Innocent Pleasures: The Gardening World of Alexander Pope. (CT): Archon, 1984. Fine in pub's cl. *Hadley.* $40/£25

MARTIN, R. E. (ed). Breeding Endangered Species in Captivity. London: Academic, 1975. 1st ed. Pict bds, gilt. Fine in VG dj. *Mikesh.* $50/£31

MARTIN, R. M. The Hudson's Bay Territories and Vancouver's Island. London: T. & W. Boone, 1849. Linen-backed fldg map. 3/4 leather, marbled paper-cvrd bds. VG (few text notes; sl worn). *Metropolitan*.* $201/£126

MARTIN, R. M. The Indian Empire. London Ptg & Pub Co, (1858-1861). 3 vols. 3 engr add'l tps, 2 dbl-pg maps hand-colored in outline, 121 plts (2 plts, 1 text leaf partly torn; spotted, sl soiled). Contemp 1/2 calf (rubbed, soiled). *Sotheby's*.* $478/£299

MARTIN-SANTOS, LUIS. Time of Silence. NY: HBW, 1964. 1st US ed. Rev slip laid in. NF in dj. *Lame Duck.* $65/£41

MARTINDALE, THOMAS. Sport Indeed. Phila: Jacobs, 1901. Teg. Pict cl. VG (sm repair spine head). *Bowman.* $40/£25

MARTINDALE, THOMAS. With Gun and Guide. Phila: George W. Jacobs, 1910. 1st ed. Frontis. Teg. Multi-colored cvr, gilt. NF in variant binding. *Backman.* $60/£38

MARTINEAU, HARRIET. Autobiography. Maria Weston Chapman (ed). Boston: Houghton Mifflin, 1881. 4th ed. 2 vols. Engr frontisports, 594; 596pp; 4 engrs bound in. Pub's cl (rear cvr vol 2 waterstained; spine extrems worn). Good. *Second Life.* $65/£41

MARTINEAU, HARRIET. British Rule in India: A Historical Sketch. Smith, Elder, 1857. VG (sig, sl spotted; spine bumped, cvrs sl dusty). *Tiger.* $96/£60

MARTINEAU, HARRIET. Feats on the Fiord. Routledge, n.d. (1875). Color frontis. Pub's cat dated August 1875. Aeg. Beveled bds (spine bumped, sunned, corners sl rubbed). Good. *Tiger.* $26/£16

MARTINEAU, HARRIET. Harriet Martineau's Autobiography. Maria Weston Chapman (ed). Boston: James R. Osgood, 1877. 1st Amer ed. 2 vols. Frontis, x,(l),594; frontis, vi,(l),596pp; 4 plts. Brn cl (sl flecked; long scratch mk fr cvr vol 1). VF. *Mott.* $100/£63

MARTINEAU, HARRIET. Illustrations of Political Economy. No. III: Brooke and Brooke Farm. Boston: Leonard C. Bowles, 1832. 1st Amer ed. (202)pp. Purple cl. VG (foxed). *Lucas.* $150/£94

MARTINEAU, HARRIET. Illustrations of Political Economy. No. VII. Cousin Marshall. Boston: Bowles, 1833. 1st US ed. 187pp. Orig linen cvrd bds (sl dknd, worn), paper label. VG. *Second Life.* $75/£47

MARTINEAU, HARRIET. Retrospect of Western Travel. NY: Harper, 1838. 1st Amer ed. 2 vols. Orig cl (faded), paper labels (very rubbed). Howes M348. *Mott.* $100/£63

MARTINEAU, HARRIET. Society in America. NY: Saunders & Otley, 1837. 1st Amer ed. 2 vols. 1 prelim l, xvi,iv,395; (8) ads,1 leaf,ii,420pp (pencil sig, notes; foxed). Orig cl (rebacked, old backs laid down), paper labels (sl chipped). Howes M350. *Mott.* $150/£94

MARTINEAU, HARRIET. Society in America. NY: Sanders & Otley, 1837. 1st US ed. 2 vols. 395; 420pp. Pub's cl; paper label, ads vol 2. NF. Howes M350. *Second Life.* $450/£281

MARTINEZ, JOSE LONGINOS. Journal of Jose Longinos Martinez. Lesley Byrd Simpson (ed). (SF): John Howell-Books, 1961. 2nd ed. Ltd to 1000 ptd. 3 fldg maps, charts. Uncut. Gray/grn cl, gilt. VF. *Argonaut.* $125/£78

MARTINEZ, PABLO L. A History of Lower California. Ethel Duffy Turner (trans). Mexico, D.F.: Editorial Baja California, 1960. 1st ed in English. One of 3000. Red cl, gilt. (Sm bruise fore-edge of rear bd), o/w Fine. *Harrington.* $65/£41

MARTINEZ, RAYMOND J. The Miser's Cup. New Orleans: Paul F. Veith, 1946. 1st ed. Signed, inscribed. (Sl shelfworn), else Good. *Brown.* $10/£6

MARTON, A. M. The New Treatise on the Modern Methods of Carbon Printing. Bloomington, IL: A.M. Marton, 1905. 2nd ed. (Table of contents stained, affecting several words; extrems lt rubbed), else VG. *Cahan.* $85/£53

MARTYN, FANNY. Gunilda; or, Sketches of Life in a Country Town. Tinsley Bros, 1875. Good (ex-lib, stamp, fore-edge lt spotted; spine bumped). *Tiger.* $58/£36

MARTYN, MRS. S. The Ladies' Wreath: An Illustrated Annual. NY: J.M. Fletcher, 1851. 1st ed. (Foxed; lt ring fr cvr), else VG. *Pacific*.* $46/£29

MARVELL, ANDREW. The Poems and Letters.... H. M. Margoliouth (ed). Oxford: Clarendon, (1952). 2nd ed. 2 vols. 2 frontispieces, 3 plts, 1 facs full-pg illus. Dk blue cl, gilt. VG (sig, note). *Blackwell's.* $216/£135

MARVELL, ANDREW. The Works...Poetical, Controversial and Political, Containing Original Letters, Poems, and Tracts, Never Before Printed.... The Editor, 1776. 3 vols. Frontisport, inserted add'l sub's leaf in vol 1, (x),lvii,(i),648; (vi),583; (vi),(i)-iv,(5)-559pp. Mottled eps; yellow edges. Dour mod 1/2 brn morocco, raised bands, gilt, brn cl sides. Good (tp lt soiled, dust-soiled, spotted, prelims, final ll browned, waterstain upper corners of prelim gatherings vol 1). *Blackwell's.* $320/£200

MARVIN, ARTHUR T. The Olive. SF, 1888. 146pp; 16 plts. Flora eps. Dec grn cl, gilt. VG. *Brooks.* $175/£109

MARX, HARPO and ROWLAND BARBER. Harpo Speaks! NY, 1961. 1st ed. VG + in VG dj (spine split 1/2 way down, 2-inch tear across spine). *Warren.* $50/£31

MARX, KARL. Capital: A Critical Analysis of Capitalist Production. Frederick Engels (ed). Samuel Moore and Edward Aveling (trans). London, 1887. 1st Eng ed. 2 vols. 8vo. Partially unopened. Maroon cl. VG (sl foxed; spines sl faded). *Heritage.* $2,750/£1,719

MARX, ROBERT F. Shipwrecks of the Western Hemisphere: 1492-1825. NY, (1971). 1st ptg. NF in NF dj. *Sagebrush.* $35/£22

Mary Had a Little Lamb. (Akron): Saalfield, (c. 1910). 5 x 3 1/2. Pict cvrs, all ptd on muslin. NF. *Pacific*.* $75/£47

Mary Putnam Jacobi, M.D., a Pathfinder in Medicine, with Selections from Her Writings and a Complete Bibliography. Women's Medical Association of New York City (eds). NY: Putnam, 1925. 1st ed. Frontisport. VG (few spots on cvrs, lt worn). *Glaser.* $75/£47

MARY, PRINCESS. Princess Mary's Gift Book. London: Hodder & Stoughton, (1915). 1st ed. 8vo. Cream cl. (Eps browned), o/w Fine in dj (soiled). *Glenn.* $100/£63

Mary, Mary Pop-Up. UK: Burnley, n.d. (194?). 18x24 cm. Dbl-pg pop-up by J. Walmsley Heap. VG in pict wraps. *Bookfinders.* $65/£41

Maryland Directory. Balt: J. Frank Lewis, 1882. xxii,584pp + 3 (of 4) ll of ads on salmon paper at fr/rear. Navy cl-backed salmon bds w/ads, gilt spine. Good (1 ad leaf defective, pp145-146 torn out and lacking; cvrs sl worn, scuffed). *Baltimore*.* $120/£75

MASEFIELD, JOHN. The Battle of the Somme. London: Heinemann, 1919. 1st ed. One of 250 numbered (of 268). 1/2 parchment, bds. VG. *Reese.* $60/£38

MASEFIELD, JOHN. Captain Margaret. London: Grant Richards, 1908. 1st ed. Dk gray cl, gilt. Fine. *Maggs.* $48/£30

MASEFIELD, JOHN. The Dream. London: Heinemann, (1922). 1st ed. One of 800 numbered, signed by Masefield & Judith Masefield (illus). Paper label. (Spine, label sl tanned), else Nice. *Reese.* $40/£25

MASEFIELD, JOHN. Gallipoli. London: Heinemann, 1916. 1st ed. Red cl. VG. *Maggs.* $48/£30

MASEFIELD, JOHN. Good Friday, a Play in Verse. London: Heinemann, (1917). 1st separate trade ed. VG in dj (spine toe torn). *Reese.* $25/£16

MASEFIELD, JOHN. King Cole. NY, 1922. 1st US ed. (Sig), else As New w/o dj as issued. *Bond.* $25/£16

MASEFIELD, JOHN. Live and Kicking Ned. Heinemann, 1939. 1st ed. VG (top edge sl faded, cvrs sl mkd, cocked, spine ends sl bumped) in dj (sl nicked, creased, mkd, dusty, spine faded). *Ulysses.* $88/£55

MASEFIELD, JOHN. A Mainsail Haul. NY: Macmillan, 1913. 2nd ed, 1st US ptg. Inscribed, signed Christmas 1913. Brn cl, gilt. (Worn, scuffed), else Good. *Reese.* $25/£16

MASEFIELD, JOHN. The Midnight Folk. London, 1927. 1st Eng ed. VG in VG pict dj (sl chipped, top edge rubbed). *Clearwater.* $64/£40

MASEFIELD, JOHN. Midsummer Night and Other Tales in Verse. NY: Macmillan, 1928. 1st US ed, ltd issue. One of 150 numbered, signed. Paper label. Fine in VG slipcase. *Reese.* $75/£47

MASEFIELD, JOHN. Multitude and Solitude. London: Grant Richards, 1909. 1st ed. Grn cl, gilt. Good (sl dull, rubbed). *Reese.* $35/£22

MASEFIELD, JOHN. The Old Front Line; or The Beginning of the Battle of the Somme. London: Heinemann, 1917. 1st British ed. Red cl stamped in blind. VG in pict dj (lt nicked). *Reese.* $50/£31

MASEFIELD, JOHN. A Poem and Two Plays. London: Heinemann, (1919). 1st ed. (Paper tanned), else Nice in dj (price sticker fr panel). *Reese.* $25/£16

MASEFIELD, JOHN. Right Royal. London: Heinemann, 1920. 1st British trade ed. NF in dj (tanned, spine nick). *Reese.* $25/£16

MASEFIELD, JOHN. Sard Harker. London: Heinemann, 1924. One of 380 signed, numbered. Vellum-backed bds. (Bkpl, lt foxed, hinges weak), o/w Nice. *Pharos.* $125/£78

MASEFIELD, JOHN. The Street of To-Day. London: J.M. Dent, 1911. 1st ed. (Spine tanned, sm nick), else Good. *Reese.* $30/£19

MASEFIELD, JOHN. The Wanderer of Liverpool. Heinemann, 1930. One of 525, signed. Full blue buckram in orig box. Fine. *Williams.* $160/£100

MASEFIELD, JOHN. With the Living Voice. London, 1924. VG in orig wraps. *Edrich.* $16/£10

MASKELL, ALFRED. Ivories. Methuen, 1905. 1st ed. 88 plts. (Cl sl worn, mkd.) *Hollett.* $136/£85

MASON, A. E. W. At the Villa Rose. London: Hodder & Stoughton, 1910. 1st ed. Good in red cl, gilt. *Maggs.* $160/£100

MASON, A. E. W. The Broken Road. Bernhard Tauchnitz, 1907. Copyright ed. Sprinkled edges. Contemp 1/2 leather over cl. VG (sig; spine sl sunned). *Tiger.* $21/£13

MASON, A. E. W. The Prisoner in the Opal. London: Hodder & Stoughton, (1928). 1st ed. Blue cl, gilt. Pict dj (extrems chipped). *Maggs.* $400/£250

MASON, ARTHUR. Salt Horse. NY: Sears, 1927. 1st ed. VG in dj. *American Booksellers.* $25/£16

MASON, BERNARD S. Dances and Stories of the American Indian. NY: Ronald, (1944). Good in pict cl (spine head lt worn). *Lien.* $25/£16

MASON, BOBBIE ANN. In Country. NY: Harper Row, (1985). 1st ed. Signed. Fine in dj. *Second Life.* $65/£41

MASON, BOBBIE ANN. In Country. Chatto, 1986. 1st UK ed. Fine (pp sl browned) in dj. *Williams.* $32/£20

MASON, CHARLOTTE. The Ladies' Assistant for Regulating and Supplying the Table; Being a Complete System of Cookery.... J. Walter, 1787. 6th ed. Half-title present, (xx),484,(20)pp. Mod 1/4 brn calf, raised bands, grn morocco label, gilt, marbled bds. Good (foxed, blank head margins stained). *Blackwell's.* $400/£250

MASON, GEORGE HENRY. The Costume of China. London: William Miller, (1821). Folio. 14x10. 60 hand-color stipple-engr plts by Pu-Qua. Aeg. Full maroon ribbed morocco, gilt. Fine (bkpls). *Pacific*.* $978/£611

MASON, GEORGE. A Supplement to Johnson's English Dictionary. NY: H. Caritat, 1803. 1st Amer ed. (269)pp. Contemp calf (outer hinges cracking). *M & S.* $275/£172

MASON, HERBERT L. A Flora of the Marshes of California. Berkeley: Univ of CA, 1969. 2nd ptg. (Name), else VG. *Fair Meadow.* $45/£28

MASON, JOHN. Paper Making as an Artistic Craft. Leicester: Twelve by Eight, 1963. Ltd ed. Signed. 9 samples of handmade paper. Stiff wrappers. *Forest.* $51/£32

MASON, JOHN. A Treatise on Self-Knowledge. Edinburgh: James Ballantyne, 1806. xx,264pp. Marbled eps. Dec-gilt full calf (joints, edges rubbed), leather spine label. (Lt spotted, tp head lt browned.) *Edwards.* $40/£25

MASON, KENNETH. Abode of Snow. London: Rupert Hart-Davis, 1955. 1st ed. Frontis, 16 maps, diags. Grn cl. NF (spine ends, corners rubbed) in dj (worn). *Argonaut.* $90/£56

MASON, LOUIS B. The Life and Times of Major John Mason, 1600-1672. NY: Putnam, 1935. 1st ed. VG in dj (sl worn). *Lien.* $25/£16

MASON, MICHAEL. The Arctic Forests. London: Hodder & Stoughton, 1924. 2 fldg maps. Dec cl (lt foxed). VG. *High Latitude.* $135/£84

MASON, OTIS TUFTON. Basket-Work of the North American Aborigines. Washington: GPO, 1890. 1st separate ptg. 291-306pp + 111 illus on 64 plts. Fine in orig ptd wrappers (lacks rear wrapper, fr wrapper soiled). *Argonaut.* $100/£63

MASON, SAMUEL, JR. Historical Sketches of Harford County, Maryland. Darlington, MD: Little Pines Farm, 1940. 1st ed. Ltd to 250. Frontis. VG. *Connolly.* $50/£31

MASPERO, GASTON. The Dawn of Civilisation. A. H. Sayce (ed). M. L. McClure (trans). London, 1901. 4th ed. 3 tinted plts. (Sl browned; sl bubbled, spine sl rubbed.) *Edwards.* $72/£45

MASPERO, GASTON. The History of Egypt, Chaldea, Syria, Babylonia, and Assyria. London, 1903-6. One of 1000 sets. 13 vols. 3/4 leather, marbled bds (scuffed, worn, some hinges weak). *Swann*.* $149/£93

Massachusetts Register. Boston: James Loring, 1842. 1st ed. 252pp. Leather (corners, bds worn). VG. *Connolly.* $47/£29

MASSER, PHYLLIS D. Presenting Stefano Della Bella: 17th-Century Printmaker. MMA, 1971. 1st ed. Sm pict onlay. Fine in dj. *Whittle.* $19/£12

MASSETT, STEPHEN C. The First California Troubadour. Oakland, 1954. 1st CA ed. Ltd to 500. (Sl worn.) *Woolson.* $25/£16

MASSEY, G. BETTON and F. H. MORSE. Galvanic Currents and Low Voltage Wave Currents in Physical Therapy. Boston, 1927. 1st ed. Red cl. (Ex-lib, foxed), o/w VG. *Doctor's Library.* $75/£47

MASSEY, MARY ELIZABETH. Bonnet Brigades, American Women and the Civil War. NY, 1966. 1st ed. Fine in dj (lt worn). *Pratt.* $60/£38

MASSIE, ALAN. Change and Decay in All Around I See. Bodley Head, 1978. 1st ed, 1st bk. Fine in dj. *Any Amount.* $29/£18

Master Henry's Visit at Mrs. Green's and His Return. Troy, NY: Merriam & Moore, n.d. (ca 1835). 12mo. Full-pg engr frontis, 24pp + 1pg list on lower wrapper. The engr at p14 is signed by Anderson w/monogram AA. Pict brn paper wrappers. VG (lt foxing, rubbing along spine). *Hobbyhorse.* $100/£63

MASTERS, EDGAR LEE. Lincoln the Man. NY, 1931. One of 150 numbered, signed. 3/4 cl. Slipcase (worn). *Swann*.* $201/£126

MASTERS, EDGAR LEE. Maximilian: A Play in Five Acts. Boston: Richard D. Badger/The Gorham Press, 1902. 1st ed. Signed. Bds, paper labels. Good (chipped, spine head sl cracked, few sl cracks to hinges). *Antic Hay.* $350/£219

MASTERS, EDGAR LEE. Spoon River Anthology. LEC, 1941. Ltd to 1500 numbered, signed by Masters and Boardman Robinson (illus). Fine in slipcase. *Swann*.* $201/£126

MASTERS, EDGAR LEE. Spoon River Anthology. NY: LEC, 1942. One of 1500 signed by Masters and Boardman Robinson (illus). Buckram. (Spine sl soiled; lacks slipcase), else Fine. *Pharos.* $250/£156

MASTERS, EDGAR LEE. Toward the Gulf. NY, 1918. 1st ed. Signed. NF (bkpl). *Agvent.* $125/£78

MASTERS, JOHN. The Compleat Indian Angler. London: Country Life, 1938. 1st Eng ed, 1st bk. Color frontis, 32 b/w plts. VG (edges lt spotted; cvrs sl mkd, spine ends sl bumped, head split) in dj (torn, rubbed, nicked, spine head defective). *Ulysses.* $200/£125

MASTERS, JOHN. Nightrunners of Bengal. Michael Joseph, 1951. 1st UK ed, 1st bk. VG (sl flaw fr cvr) in dj (sm nicks). *Williams.* $120/£75

MASTERSON, VINCENT VICTOR. The Katy Railroad and the Last Frontier. Norman: Univ of OK, 1952. 1st ed. Fine in dj. *Labordo.* $75/£47

MASTERSON, WHIT. (Pseud of Bill Miller and Robert Wade.) All Through the Night. Dodd, 1955. 1st ed. VG (pp edges lt foxed; lt worn) in dj (spine sunned, lt soiled). *Murder.* $65/£41

MASTERSON, WHIT. (Pseud of Bill Miller and Robert Wade.) The Gravy Train. Dodd, 1971. 1st ed. (Edges lt worn), else NF in dj (lt rubbed). *Murder.* $37/£23

MATHER, FRED. Modern Fishculture in Fresh and Salt Water. NY: Forest & Stream, 1900. 1st ed. Gray cl, gilt. VG. *Pacific*.* $40/£25

MATHER, R. E. and F. E. BOSWELL. Hanging the Sheriff. Salt Lake City, 1987. 1st ed. As New in dj. *Baade.* $25/£16

MATHERS, E. POWYS. The Books of the Thousand Nights and One Night. Casanova, 1923. One of 750. 16 vols. Color frontispieces. Teg, rest uncut. Japon-backed bds, gilt. (Feps lt browned; lt soiled, lower portion of spine vol 14 sl stained.) *Edwards.* $400/£250

MATHERS, E. POWYS. Procreant Hymn. Golden Cockerel, 1926. One of 200. 8vo. 5 copperplt engrs by Eric Gill. Teg, rest untrimmed. White buckram, gilt. Good (feps lt foxed, sm neat unobtrusive shelf # corner of rear pastedown; backstrip lt dknd). *Blackwell's.* $680/£425

MATHERS, E. POWYS. Sung to Shahryar. London: Casanova Soc, 1925. One of 50 lg paper, numbered, signed. VG. *Williams.* $240/£150

MATHES, J. HARVEY. The Old Guard in Gray. Researches in the Annals of the Confederate Historical Association. Sketches of Memphis Veterans.... Memphis, TN: S.C. Toof, 1897. 1st ed. 8vo. Frontis, 298pp. Orig cl (spotted, soiled). Copy of 1908 resolution on death of Frederick Wolf laid in. VG; internally Fine. *M & S.* $600/£375

MATHES, MICHAEL. Mexico on Stone. Artichoke Press, 1984. One of 550. *Dawson.* $125/£78

MATHES, MICHAEL. Spanish Approaches to the Island of California, 1628-1632. Greenwood, 1975. One of 400. *Dawson.* $50/£31

MATHES, MICHAEL. Spanish Approaches to the Island of California, 1628-1632. SF: Book Club of CA, 1975. One of 400 ptd. Facs map. Dec bds, paper spine label. Fine. *Pacific*.* $63/£39

MATHESON, JOHN. England to Delhi. London: Longmans, Green, 1870. 1st ed. xvi,539,(1)pp; 12 engr plts, map. Maroon cl. (Sl foxed, soiled, one leaf creased, ink inscrip; faded, hinges well repaired.) *Morrell.* $120/£75

MATHESON, RICHARD. The Beardless Warriors. Boston, 1960. 1st ed. VG (name, date, sl leaning) in VG dj (worn). *Warren.* $35/£22

MATHESON, RICHARD. Collected Stories. L.A.: Dream Press, (1989). One of 500 signed. Full simulated leather (lt worn). *Oinonen*.* $50/£31

MATHESON, RICHARD. Ride the Nightmare. NY: Ballantine Bks, (1959). 1st ed. (Spine sl dknd), else Nice in pict wraps. *King.* $40/£25

MATHESON, ROBERT. A Handbook of the Mosquitoes of North America. Springfield, IL: C. Thomas, 1929. 1st ed. VG + . *Archer.* $40/£25

MATHEWS, CATHARINE VAN CORTLANDT. Andrew Ellicott: His Life and Letters. NY: Grafton, (1908). 1st ed. One of 1000. (Spine top lt worn.) *Ginsberg.* $125/£78

MATHEWS, HARRY. Selected Declarations of Dependence. Calais: Z Press, 1977. 1st ed. NF in wraps. *Beasley.* $30/£19

MATHEWS, HARRY. The Sinking of Odradek Stadium and Other Novels. NY: Harper, 1975. 1st ed. Fine in Fine dj. *Beasley.* $60/£38

MATHEWS, JOHN JOSEPH. Wah-Kon-Tah, the Osage and the White Man's Road. Norman: Univ of OK, 1932. 1st ed. Frontis, 1 fldg illus. Pict eps. Fine in dec dj. *Argonaut.* $45/£28

MATHEWS, JOSEPH. A Treatise on Diseases of the Rectum, Anus and Sigmoid Flexure. NY, 1897. 2nd ed. 545pp. 1/2 leather. *Fye.* $100/£63

MATHEWSON, CHRISTY. First Base Faulkner. Dodd Mead, 1916. (1st ed.) VG + . *Plapinger.* $65/£41

MATHEWSON, CHRISTY. Pitching in a Pinch. NY: Putnam, 1912. 1st ed. Signed boldly, dated June 3, 1912. Fair (margins dampstained, sig not affected, tp edge chipped; hinges repaired, spine lettering faded). *Between The Covers.* $2,850/£1,781

MATHIAS, ANDREW. The Mercurial Disease. Phila: Edward Parker/Kimber & Richardson, 1811. 1st Amer ed. (5),250pp. Full contemp calf, leather label. *M & S.* $225/£141

MATHIAS, HENRY VINCENT. Five Week's Sport in the Interior of the Himalayas. London, 1865. 1st ed. 132pp. Orig blind-stamped cl (recased, edgeworn). *Maggs.* $440/£275

MATHIEU, PIERRE-LOUIS. Gustave Moreau. Boston: NYGS, 1976. Good in dj. *Ars Artis.* $168/£105

MATHIEU, PIERRE-LOUIS. Gustave Moreau. NY, 1985. 52 tipped-in plts (40 color). Good + in dj, slipcase. *Washton.* $65/£41

MATHISON, THOMAS. The Goff: Facsimiles of Three Editions of the Heroi-Comical Poem. (Far Hills, NJ): U.S.G.A., 1981. 1st ed. One of 1400 ptd. 1/4 cl, gilt. Fine (emb stamp) in slipcase. *Pacific*.* $345/£216

MATISSE, HENRI. Jazz. NY, (1983). Folio. 1/4 cl fldg portfolio case, contents loose as issued. Slipcase. *Swann*.* $138/£86

Matrix 3. Whittington, (1983). Copy no. XLVI of 50 specials. Fine in slipcase. *Michael Taylor.* $1,040/£650

Matrix 5. Whittington, (1985). Copy no. I of 80 specials. Fine in slipcase. *Michael Taylor.* $800/£500

Matrix 6. Whittington, (1986). Copy no. III of 100 specials. Fine in slipcase. *Michael Taylor.* $720/£450

Matrix 6. (Manor Farm: Whittington Press, 1986.) 1st ed, ltd to 900 numbered copies. Stiff paper wrappers (bkpl). *Oak Knoll.* $250/£156

Matrix 8. Whittington, (1988). Copy no. III of C specials. Fine in slipcase. *Michael Taylor.* $640/£400

Matrix 9. (Manor Farm: Whittington Press, 1989.) Ltd to 925, this one of 820 bound for trade ed. Fine in stiff paper wrappers. *Oak Knoll.* $200/£125

Matrix 11. Herefordshire: Whittington Press, 1991. Ltd to 955, this one of 850 bound thus. Stiff paper wrappers (bkpl). *Oak Knoll.* $225/£141

Matrix 14. Whittington, (1994). Copy no. 15 of 95 specials. Fine in slipcase. *Michael Taylor.* $320/£200

Matrix 15. A Review for Printers and Bibliophiles. Whittington, Winter 1995. 1st ed. Ltd to 950. Sm folio. New in pict bds. Dj. *Cox.* $200/£125

MATTERS, LEONARD. Through the Kara Sea. London: Skeffington & Son, 1932. Map. Very Nice. *High Latitude.* $75/£47

MATTES, MERRILL. The Great Platte River Road. Volume XXV. NE State Hist Soc, 1969. 1st ed. VG in dj. *Labordo.* $50/£31

MATTHES, FRANCOIS E. Geological History of the Yosemite Valley. Washington: GPO, 1930. 1st ed. 46 plts, 6 fldg maps, profiles (3 in rear pocket). Tan buckram, gilt; gilt owner name fr cvr. (Lt adhesive mks on tp, rep), o/w Fine. *Pacific**. $69/£43

MATTHES, FRANCOIS E. Geological History of the Yosemite Valley. Washington: GPO, 1930. 1st ed. 46 plts, 6 fldg maps, plts (3 in rear pocket). Tan buckram. NF (few sl stains feps; rebound). *Harrington*. $100/£63

MATTHES, FRANCOIS E. Sequoia National Park: A Geological Album. Fritiof Fryxell (ed). Berkeley: Univ of CA, 1950. 1st ed. Fine (bkpl) in pict dj. *Argonaut*. $60/£38

MATTHEWS, ERNEST. Topsy in Toyland. (#2 in The Piccaninnies Picture Pocket Books.) London: Sands, (ca 1910). 24mo. 96pp (lacks fep); 22 full-pg color illus by M. York Shuter. Red cl (worn, lettering rubbed). *Reisler*. $100/£63

MATTHEWS, ETTA LANE. Over the Blue Wall. Univ of NC, 1937. 1st ed. James Daugherty (illus). 328pp. VG in Good dj (chipped). *Price*. $40/£25

MATTHEWS, HARRY. Tlooth. GC: Doubleday, 1966. 1st ed. Pub's file copy stamp on fep. (Top edge dusty), o/w Fine in NF dj (spine sl faded). *Any Amount*. $48/£30

MATTHEWS, L. H. South Georgia. London: Simpkin Marshall, 1931. 1st ed. Map. VG (sl mkd). *Walcot*. $256/£160

MATTHEWS, LEONARD. The Long Life in Review. (St. Louis, 1928.) 1st ed. (Spine sl faded.) *Ginsberg*. $450/£281

MATTHEWS, SALLIE REYNOLDS. Interwoven: A Pioneer Chronicle. El Paso: Carl Hertzog, 1958. One of 1500 unnumbered. Untrimmed. Brick-red/tan cl, gilt, sm ptd fr cvr label. Ink presentation by author's son. VG (lt shelfworn) in thick clear plastic wrapper (few sm tears). Howes M426. *Baltimore**. $45/£28

MATTHEWS, WILLIAM F. Bookbinding. Gollancz, 1929. 1st ed. Frontis, 7 plts. (Spine faded, fr hinge torn.) *Forest*. $61/£38

MATTHEWS, WILLIAM. Hydraulia; an Historical and Descriptive Account of the Water Works of London. London: Simpkin, Marshall, 1835. 1st ed. Frontisport, xx,454pp + 1 ad leaf at rear; 5 Fine fldg engr maps, 12 engr plts. Orig dk grn cl, orig ptd paper spine label. (Lt aged, sm chunk lacking tp bottom margin; sl edgeworn, label browned, spine head sl chipped, fr hinge nearly split.) *Baltimore**. $200/£125

MATTHIESSEN, PETER. Far Tortuga. NY: Random House, 1975. 1st ed. (Spine head faded), else NF in VG + dj (price-clipped). *Lame Duck*. $75/£47

MATTHIESSEN, PETER. In the Spirit of Crazy Horse. NY: Viking, (1983). 1st ed. VG in dj. *Perier*. $100/£63

MATTHIESSEN, PETER. In the Spirit of Crazy Horse. NY: Viking, (1983). 1st ed, 1st issue. Dk brn cl, lt brn bds, gilt. NF (sl shelfworn, edges sl dusty) in NF pict dj. *Baltimore**. $120/£75

MATTHIESSEN, PETER. In the Spirit of Crazy Horse. NY: Viking, (1983). 1st ed. VG in dj. *Lien*. $175/£109

MATTHIESSEN, PETER. In the Spirit of Crazy Horse. NY: Viking, 1983. 1st ed. (Lt shelf-soiled), else VG in dj (clipped, flap edge creased). *Dumont*. $125/£78

MATTHIESSEN, PETER. In the Spirit of Crazy Horse. NY: Viking, 1983. 1st ed, suppressed state. NF in dj. *Labordo*. $150/£94

MATTHIESSEN, PETER. Oomingmak. NY, (1967). 1st Amer ed. Signed. Fine in Fine dj. *Polyanthos*. $65/£41

MATTHIESSEN, PETER. Oomingmak. NY: Hastings House, 1967. 1st ed. Signed. Fine in Fine dj. *Smith*. $85/£53

MATTHIESSEN, PETER. The Partisans. London, (1956). 1st Eng ed. (Offset, foxing to eps.) Dj (white rear panel sl soiled). *Swann**. $46/£29

MATTHIESSEN, PETER. The Shorebirds of North America. NY: Viking, (1967). 1st ed. Folio. (Inscrip), else NF in VG dj (price-clipped, few internal repairs, sm tears). *Between The Covers*. $220/£138

MATTHIESSEN, PETER. Wildlife in America. NY, 1959. 1st ed. Pict cl. NF in dj (spine rubbed, price-clipped, edge reinforced w/tape). *Baade*. $50/£31

MATTHIESSEN, PETER. Wildlife in America. NY, 1959. 1st ed. 8 color plts, 1 map. Illus eps. (Prelims lt foxed.) Dj (lt scuffed). *Sutton*. $75/£47

MATTSON, MORRIS. The American Vegetable Practice, or A New and Improved Guide to Health. Boston: Daniel Hale, 1841. 2 vols in 1. 8vo. 24 color plts. Full leather. (Some repairs to pp, foxed throughout, affecting plts; fr bd detached.) *Metropolitan**. $603/£377

MATZ, B. W. Dickensian Inns and Taverns. London: Cecil Palmer, 1923. 2nd ed. (Fore-edge sl spotted; spine head bumped.) *Hollett*. $32/£20

MAUDSLAY, ALFRED P. Life in the Pacific Fifty Years Ago. London: Routledge, 1930. 1st ed. VG. *Pacific**. $29/£18

MAUDSLAY, ROBERT. Texas Sheepman. Winifred Kupper (ed). Austin: Univ of TX, 1951. 1st ed. VG in dj. *Lien*. $50/£31

MAUDSLEY, HENRY. Body and Mind. NY: Appleton, 1872. 1st ed. VG (bkpl; spine repaired, lacquered over). *Beasley*. $60/£38

MAUGE, GILBERT. (Pseud of Edmee de la Rochefoucauld.) The Unknown Quantity. Shane Leslie (trans). London: Fortune, 1928. One of 800 (of 845). Uncut. Brn cl (spine sl dknd). *Maggs*. $48/£30

MAUGHAM, ROBIN. The Green Shade. (NY): NAL, (1966). 1st Amer ed. VF in Fine dj (sl rubbed). *Between The Covers*. $85/£53

MAUGHAM, ROBIN. Line on Ginger. London: Chapman & Hall, 1949. Inscribed presentation. VG (sl ink mks margins of 4pp, sm mk tp, top edge dusty) in dj (nicked, rubbed, dknd). *Ulysses*. $58/£36

MAUGHAM, ROBIN. North African Notebook. London: Chapman & Hall, 1948. 1st Eng ed. VG (sig, edges sl spotted; spine head sl bumped, rear cvr sl mkd) in dj (dusty, sl rubbed, nicked, repaired; defective rear panel). *Ulysses*. $40/£25

MAUGHAM, W. SOMERSET. Ah, King. London: Heinemann, (1933). 1st ed. Fine (fore-edge lt foxed) in NF dj (lt rubbed, 1/16 inch short). *Between The Covers*. $275/£172

MAUGHAM, W. SOMERSET. The Art of Fiction: an Introduction to Ten Novels and Their Authors. GC: Doubleday, 1955. 1st Amer ed. VG. *Between The Covers*. $125/£78

MAUGHAM, W. SOMERSET. Ashenden, or The British Agent. Leipzig: Bernhard Tauchnitz, 1928. Hb ed. NF (rear cvr sl mkd). *Ulysses*. $58/£36

MAUGHAM, W. SOMERSET. Ashenden: Or the British Agent. GC: Doubleday, Doran, 1928. 1st US ed. Blue cl stamped in orange. (Cl sl sunned through dj), o/w VG in dj (sl nicked, frayed, lg chips spine ends). *Reese*. $350/£219

MAUGHAM, W. SOMERSET. The Book-Bag. Florence: G. Orioli, 1932. 1st ed. One of 750 signed. Frontisport inserted. Uncut. 1/2 white canvas, blue bds, gilt. (Bd extrems sl faded), else Fine in dj (lt soiled, chipped). *Argonaut*. $350/£219

MAUGHAM, W. SOMERSET. Books and You. GC: Doubleday, 1940. 1st Amer ed. VF in Fine dj (lt rubbed, price-clipped, corner sl nicked.) *Between The Covers*. $150/£94

MAUGHAM, W. SOMERSET. Cakes and Ale. Heinemann, (1954). 1st ed thus. One of 1000 signed by Maugham and Graham Sutherland (illus). Orig litho. Fine in orig acetate (browned, chipped) in slipcase. *Williams*. $360/£225

MAUGHAM, W. SOMERSET. Cakes and Ale. London, 1930. 1st Eng ed. Fine (foxed; cvrs sl bowed) in dj. *Clearwater*. $200/£125

MAUGHAM, W. SOMERSET. Catalina. London: Heinemann, (1948). 1st ed. Lettered in silver. Fine in VF dj (price-clipped). *Between The Covers*. $150/£94

MAUGHAM, W. SOMERSET. Creatures of Circumstance. GC: Doubleday, 1947. 1st Amer ed. VF in dj (less than 1/8 inch shorter than bk), else VF. *Between The Covers*. $125/£78

MAUGHAM, W. SOMERSET. Don Fernando. Heinemann, 1935. 1st UK ed. Inscribed presentation copy. Good (spine re-backed w/loss replaced) in dj (edges worn, creased w/loss to spine). *Williams*. $400/£250

MAUGHAM, W. SOMERSET. East of Suez. Heinemann, 1922. 1st UK ed. Signed. VG (cvrs sl faded). *Williams*. $144/£90

MAUGHAM, W. SOMERSET. First Person Singular. Heinemann, 1931. 1st UK ed. VG in dj (spine head sl nicked). *Williams*. $312/£195

MAUGHAM, W. SOMERSET. France at War. GC: Doubleday, 1940. 1st Amer ed, 1st hb ed. (Fep corner clipped), else VF in VF dj. *Between The Covers*. $150/£94

MAUGHAM, W. SOMERSET. Great Novelists and Their Novels. Phila: Winston, 1948. 1st ed. (Top corner rear bd sl bumped), else VF in VF dj. *Between The Covers*. $125/£78

MAUGHAM, W. SOMERSET. The Letters of...to Lady Juliet Duff. Rasselas/Pacific Palisades, 1982. One of 274. Frontisport. Prospectus laid in. Paper labels. Fine. *Any Amount*. $72/£45

MAUGHAM, W. SOMERSET. Liza of Lambeth. London: T. Fisher Unwin, 1897. 1st ed, 1st bk. (8),242,(6) ads. Grn cl, gilt. Good (bkpl, eps browned, fr hinge repaired; spine sl browned, cocked, extrems sl rubbed, cvrs lt soiled). *Heritage*. $850/£531

MAUGHAM, W. SOMERSET. Liza of Lambeth. London, 1947. Jubilee ed. One of 1000 signed. Vellum-backed pict bds (corners sl bumped, chafed). Nice (eps foxed, bkpl) in dj (chipped, worn). *Clearwater*. $136/£85

MAUGHAM, W. SOMERSET. Liza of Lambeth. London: Heinemann, 1947. Jubilee ed. One of 1000 signed. Add'lly dated by author 'October 12, 1947.' Teg, rest uncut. Orig 1/4 vellum, Chinese rose paper patterned bds, black leather, gilt label. (Eps lt foxed), else Fine in Fine dj. *Vandoros*. $375/£234

MAUGHAM, W. SOMERSET. Loaves and Fishes. London: Heinemann, 1924. 1st ed. Red cl. NF. *Pacific**. $63/£39

MAUGHAM, W. SOMERSET. The Making of a Saint. London: T. Fisher Unwin, 1898. 2nd ed. Dk grn cl (sl scuffed), gilt. *Maggs*. $72/£45

MAUGHAM, W. SOMERSET. The Making of a Saint. Boston: L.C. Page, 1898. 1st US ed, 1st issue w/'In Press' under this title in ads and gold lettering on spine. VG (ink name; spine sl browned). *Williams*. $552/£345

MAUGHAM, W. SOMERSET. Maugham's Encore. GC: Doubleday, 1952. 1st Amer ed. VF in VF dj (sl rubbed). *Between The Covers*. $150/£94

MAUGHAM, W. SOMERSET. Maughamiana: The Writings of William Somerset Maugham. London: Heinemann, (1950). 1st ed. VG in dj (spine foot area sl discolored). *Pacific**. $63/£39

MAUGHAM, W. SOMERSET. The Moon and Sixpence. London: Heinemann, 1919. 1st ed. Signed. (Interior browned; corners bumped), else VG. *Pacific**. $138/£86

MAUGHAM, W. SOMERSET. Of Human Bondage with a Digression on the Art of Fiction. (Washington: Library of Congress), 1946. 2nd ptg. (Bottom corner sl bumped), else Fine in stapled wrappers. *Between The Covers*. $35/£22

MAUGHAM, W. SOMERSET. Of Human Bondage with a Digression on the Art of Fiction. Washington: Library of Congress, 1946. One of 800 ptd of which this is one of 500 signed. VG. *Williams*. $200/£125

MAUGHAM, W. SOMERSET. Of Human Bondage. GC: Doubleday, Doran, 1936. 1st illus ed. One of 751. Signed. Teg. Tan cl, gilt. (Offset from removed bkpl), else NF. *Pacific**. $219/£137

MAUGHAM, W. SOMERSET. Of Human Bondage. LEC, 1938. Ltd to 1500 numbered, signed by John Sloan (illus). 2 vols. Fine in slipcase. *Swann**. $632/£395

MAUGHAM, W. SOMERSET. Orientations. London: T. Fisher Unwin, 1899. Apparently an unrecorded variant w/sheets of the 1st ed, w/new 1/2- title and tp in black but w/tp dated 1899, and bound in what is probably the 1st issue binding as described by Stott. (Paper over fr hinge sl cracked; sl foxed), else VF. *Between The Covers*. $750/£469

MAUGHAM, W. SOMERSET. The Painted Veil. NY: Grosset & Dunlap, (1934). 1st ed. (Fep corner lt clipped), else VF in VF dj. *Between The Covers*. $100/£63

MAUGHAM, W. SOMERSET. The Painted Veil. Heinemann, 1925. 1st Eng ed, 2nd issue, 1st state, 'Author's Note' leaf inserted, name of 'Hong Kong' changed to 'Tching-Yen' throughout by the insertion of cancel ll. Crown 8vo. (ii),289pp. Tail edges untrimmed. Mid blue cl, gilt, Maugham symbol fr cvr. VG (eps sl browned; rear hinge sl weak) in illus dj (sl chipped, sm tear). *Blackwell's*. $536/£335

MAUGHAM, W. SOMERSET. Points of View. London, (1958). 1st ed. VG in dj (rubbed, sl tears). *King*. $45/£28

MAUGHAM, W. SOMERSET. Princess September and the Nightingale. NY: Oxford, 1939. 1st ed. Variant gray cl. VF in VF- dj (sl rubbed). *Between The Covers*. $450/£281

MAUGHAM, W. SOMERSET. Purely for My Pleasure. GC: Doubleday, 1963. 1st Amer ed. Folio. VF in cl, papercvrd bds in slipcase (sm scrape). *Between The Covers*. $125/£78

MAUGHAM, W. SOMERSET. Quartet: Four Stories. GC: Doubleday, 1949. 1st Amer ed. VF in VF dj. *Between The Covers*. $150/£94

MAUGHAM, W. SOMERSET. Rain and Other Stories. NY: G&D, (1921). Good in dj (chipped, rubbed). *King*. $22/£14

MAUGHAM, W. SOMERSET. Seventeen Lost Stories. Craig V. Showalter (comp). GC: Doubleday, 1969. 1st ed. VF in VF dj. *Between The Covers*. $100/£63

MAUGHAM, W. SOMERSET. The Summing Up. GC, 1954. 1st, Deluxe ed. Ltd to 391 signed. Full gray buckram. VF in slipcase (lt sunned, scuffed). *Truepenny*. $250/£156

MAUGHAM, W. SOMERSET. Then and Now. London, (1946). 1st ed. (Spine sl worn), else Good. *King*. $35/£22

MAUGHAM, W. SOMERSET. Then and Now. GC: Doubleday, 1946. 1st Amer ed. (Fep top corner clipped), else VF in VF dj (sl rubbed). *Between The Covers*. $100/£63

MAUGHAM, W. SOMERSET. Then and Now. London, 1946. 1st ed. Proof copy. Ptd buff wrappers. *Swann**. $201/£126

MAUGHAM, W. SOMERSET. Trio. GC: Doubleday, 1950. 1st Amer ed. VF in VF dj (sl rubbed). *Between The Covers*. $125/£78

MAUGHAM, W. SOMERSET. The Unconquered. NY: House of Books, 1944. 1st ed. One of 300 numbered, signed. Black cl, gilt. *Reese*. $250/£156

MAUGHAM, W. SOMERSET. The Vagrant Mood, Six Essays. London, (1952). 1st ed. (Corners sl bumped), else Good in dj (worn, badly chipped). *King*. $35/£22

MAUGHAM, W. SOMERSET. The Vagrant Mood: Six Essays. GC: Doubleday, 1953. 1st ed. VF in VF dj (sl rubbed). *Between The Covers*. $100/£63

MAUGHAM, W. SOMERSET. A Writer's Notebook. London: Heinemann, (1949). 1st ed. VF in VF 1st issue dj (price-clipped). *Between The Covers*. $200/£125

MAUGHAM, W. SOMERSET. A Writer's Notebook. London, (1949). Presentation copy. Inscribed, signed. Good (bkpl, stamps; cvr sl worn). *King*. $295/£184

MAUGHAM, W. SOMERSET. A Writer's Notebook. GC: Doubleday, 1949. 1st Amer ed. VF in VF black dj (1/8 inch short, sl rubbed). *Between The Covers*. $100/£63

MAUGHAM, W. SOMERSET. A Writer's Notebook. GC: Doubleday, 1949. One of 1000. Signed. Red cl, gilt spine. Fine in slipcase. *Pacific**. $196/£123

MAUGHAM, W. SOMERSET. A Writer's Notebook. Heinemann, 1949. 1st ed. One of 1000 signed. Teg, rest rough-trimmed. Orig 1/4 cream vellum, black leather label, dk blue buckram. Fine in bd slipcase. *Blackwell's*. $336/£210

MAUGHAM, W. SOMERSET. The Writer's Point of View. London: Nat'l Bk League, 1951. 1st ed. Pamphlet. VF in stiff wrappers in VF dj (price-clipped, sl smudged). *Between The Covers*. $125/£78

MAUND, BENJAMIN. The Botanic Garden. Vol I only. London: B. Groombridge, n.d. 4to. Engr tp, 24 hand-colored engr plts. (Few plts lt dampstained, some margins browned, some spotting.) Marbled edges. Contemp 1/2 calf, bds (extrems rubbed). *Christie's**. $648/£405

MAUND, BENJAMIN. The Botanic Garden: Volume IV. London: Simpkin & Marshall, 1831-2. 24 hand-colored plts. 1/2 old leather, marbled paper-cvrd bds. (Lt foxed, incl tp; sl rubbed, edges through, sl soiled.) *Metropolitan**. $402/£251

MAURETTE, MARCELLE. Anastasia. NY: Random House, (1955). 1st ed. VF in VF dj (1/16 inch short). *Between The Covers*. $125/£78

MAURICE, FREDERICK. Robert E. Lee, the Soldier. Boston, 1925. 1st ed. Table. VG+ (lt underlining, notes). *Pratt*. $45/£28

MAURICE, FREDERICK. Robert E. Lee, the Soldier. Boston/NY: Houghton Mifflin, 1925. 1st ed. Frontisport, fldg map tipped in at rear. Blue cl. NF. *Chapel Hill*. $65/£41

MAURICE, KLAUS and OTTO MAYR. The Clockwork Universe. NY: Neale Watson, 1980. Fine in Fine dj. *Bookcell*. $35/£22

MAURICE, THOMAS. Indian Antiquities, or Dissertations, Relative to the Antient Geographical Divisions, the Pure System of Primeval Theology.... London: John White, 1806. 7 vols. 8.25x5. 29 fldg copper-engr plts. Period 3/4 straight-grain morocco, marbled bds, gilt. (Bkpls, sl foxed, offset, vol 1 frontis sl torn; rubbed, scuffed), else VG. *Pacific**. $288/£180

MAURICEAU, A. M. The Married Woman's Private Medical Companion. NY, 1849. xiii,238pp. Orig cl (Lt browned, 1/3 of tp clipped, affecting text; worn, scuffed, extrems rubbed), else Good. *Brown*. $100/£63

MAUROIS, ANDRE. Chateaubriand. NY, 1938. 1st Amer ed. NF (name, bkpl; sl rubbed). *Polyanthos*. $25/£16

MAUROIS, ANDRE. Chelsea Way. Hamish Miles (trans). Elkin Mathews & Marrot, 1930. One of 530 numbered, signed. Cl-backed patterned paper bds. VG (bkpl, feps lt browned; top edge dusty, bottom edges sl rubbed) in matching dj (nicked, rubbed, dusty, sl torn, creased, spine, edges browned). *Ulysses*. $72/£45

MAURY, DABNEY H. Recollections of a Virginian in the Mexican, Indian and Civil Wars. Scribner, 1894. 1st ed. Frontisport. Good+ (ex-lib, edges browned, soiled; cvr spotted, rear hinge torn at bottom). *Book Broker*. $100/£63

MAURY, DABNEY H. Recollections of a Virginian in the Mexican, Indian, and Civil Wars. NY: Scribner, 1894. 1st ed. Frontisport, xi,279pp. Gray cl. VG (feps foxed, sm closed tear top of fep, 1/2-title; spine sl browned). Howes M440. *Chapel Hill*. $150/£94

MAURY, MATTHEW FONTAINE. Explanations and Sailing Directions to Accompany the Wind and Current Charts.... Washington: C. Alexander, 1851. 315,(1 blank, 2 contents)pp; 12 plts, charts. Orig ptd wrappers (soiled, spine chipped, defective; lt foxed, marginal dampstains). *Lefkowicz*. $250/£156

MAWE, JOHN. Instructions for the Use of the Blow-Pipe, and Chemical Tests, with Additions and Observations Derived from the Recent Publication of Professor Berzelius. London: The Author, 1825. 4th ed. vii,66pp+(2) ads (1st few ll lt dampstained, ad leaf corner cut just affecting a letter). New paper-cvrd bds. *Young*. $104/£65

MAWE, JOHN. The Linnaen System of Conchology.... London, 1823. Frontis, xv,207pp; 36 hand-colored plts. Contemp calf by Quinton of Norwich (neatly rebacked preserving spine), gilt. Good. *Henly*. $456/£285

MAWE, JOHN. The Voyager's Companion; or, Shell Collector's Pilot. Longmans, Hurst et al/The Author, 1821. 1st ed. xiv,56pp; 2 hand-colored plts. Contemp full black blind-stamped roan (neatly recased), gilt. *Hollett*. $256/£160

MAWSON, DOUGLAS. The Home of the Blizzard. Heinemann, 1915. 1st ed. 2 vols. 3 fldg maps in rear pocket. 1/2 blue calf (rebound), marbled bds. VG. *Walcot*. $448/£280

MAWSON, DOUGLAS. The Home of the Blizzard: Being the Story of the Australasian Antarctic Expedition, 1911-1914. London: Heinemann, 1915. 2 vols. 3 fldg maps. VG. *Explorer*. $480/£300

MAWSON, DOUGLAS. The Home of the Blizzard: Being the Story of the Australasian Antarctic Expedition, 1911-1914. London: Hodder & Stoughton, 1930. 1st reissue of 1-vol popular ed. 3 fldg maps. VG. *Explorer*. $67/£42

MAWSON, P. Mawson of the Antarctic. Longmans, 1964. 1st ed. VG in dj. *Walcot*. $32/£20

MAWSON, THOMAS. The Art and Craft of Garden Making. London/NY: Batsford/Scribner, 1907. 3rd ed. Sm folio. Teg. Dec grn cl, gilt. (Lower bd edge waterstained), else VG. *Fair Meadow*. $275/£172

MAXFIELD, ALBERT and ROBERT BRADY, JR. Roster and Statistical Record of Company D, of the Eleventh Regt. Maine Infantry Vols.... NY, 1890. VG in ptd wraps. *Wantagh*. $50/£31

Maxims and Hints for an Angler: Embellished with Humorous Engravings, Illustrative of the Miseries of Fishing. To Which Are Added Maxims and Hints for a Chess Player. (By Richard Penn.) Phila, 1855. 1st Amer ed. Pub's grn cl (shelfworn; foxed, sl soiled, 1st sig loose), gilt. *Oinonen**. $60/£38

MAXWELL, HERBERT. Flowers, a Garden Notebook. Glasgow: Maclehouse, Jackson, 1923. 1st ed. 12 color plts. Uncut. (Inscrip, inner hinge starting), else VG. *Quest*. $80/£50

MAXWELL, HERBERT. Salmon and Sea Trout. How to Propagate, Preserve, and Catch Them in British Waters. London, 1898. One of 130 numbered, lg paper copies. Pub's cl (lt worn, sl shaken; foxed). *Oinonen**. $100/£63

MAXWELL, HERBERT. Scottish Gardens. London: Edward Arnold, 1908. 1st ed. Teg. Dec cl. *Christie's**. $37/£23

MAXWELL, HU. The History of Randolph County, West Virginia from Its Earliest Settlement to the Present.... Morgantown, WV: Acme Pub, 1898. 1st ed. Speckled edges. Recent burgundy full polished calf, gilt panels, gilt paneled spine compartments, raised bands. Fine. *Sadlon*. $125/£78

MAXWELL, JOHN STIRLING. Shrines and Homes of Scotland. Maclehose, 1937. 1st ed. Uncut. VG in dj (sl rubbed, chipped). *Hollett*. $48/£30

MAXWELL, W. AUDLEY. Crossing the Plains. (SF: Sunset Publishing House, 1915.) 1st ed. Frontis. VG in orig brn wrappers (rear wrapper replaced, fr wrapper edge repaired), gilt. *House*. $60/£38

MAXWELL, W. AUDLEY. Crossing the Plains. (SF: Sunset Pub House, 1915.) 1st ed. Frontis. Gilt-ptd brn wraps. (Sm hole blank fep; edges lt chipped), o/w VG. *Chapel Hill*. $110/£69

MAXWELL, W. H. The Fortunes of Hector O'Halloran, and His Man, Mark Anthony O'Toole. NY: D. Appleton, 1843. 1st ed. 23 plts by John Leech. (Spine sunned, sl leaning, ends chipped), else VG. *Pacific**. $52/£33

MAXWELL, WILLIAM. Ancestors. NY: Knopf, 1971. 1st ed. NF in VG dj (few closed tears). *Pettler.* $25/£16

MAXWELL, WILLIAM. Over by the River. NY: Knopf, 1977. 1st ed. Fine in Fine dj. *Pettler.* $25/£16

MAXWELL, WILLIAM. Time Will Darken It. NY: Harper, 1948. 1st ed. VG + in VG dj (price-clipped, edges chipped). *Pettler.* $45/£28

MAY, EARL CHAPIN. The Circus from Rome to Ringling. NY: Duffield & Green, (c. 1932). Inscribed. Pict cl, gilt (spine faded). *Dramatis.* $25/£16

MAY, FRANCES. Beyond the Argentine. London: W.H. Allen, 1890. 1st ed. viii,148pp; fldg map, engr plt. Red cl, gilt. (Spine sl faded), else Fine. *Morrell.* $104/£65

MAY, HANS. Reconstructive and Reparative Surgery. Phila: F.A. Davis, 1947. 1st ed. Black cl (freckled w/some water spots), gilt. *Weber.* $100/£63

MAY, PERCY. The Chemistry of Synthetic Drugs. London, 1911. 1st ed. *Fye.* $100/£63

MAY, R. The Advantages of Early Religion. Phila: Sunday & Adult School Union, 1820. 2nd ed. VF pict wood engr tp + 1 on fr wrapper. VG (text lt foxed; ink sig verso fr wrapper). *Hobby-horse.* $55/£34

MAY, ROBERT L. (adapted by). Rudolph the Red-Nosed Reindeer. A Golden Pop-Up Book. Racine, WI: Western Pub, 1983. 3 dbl-pg pop-ups by Darrell Baker. Glazed pict bds. VG. *Bookfinders.* $30/£19

MAYDON, H. C. Big Game Shooting in Africa. London: Seeley, Service, 1951. 55 plts. (Cl lt rubbed.) *Adelson.* $110/£69

MAYER, ALFRED GOLDSBOROUGH. Medusae of the World. Washington, 1910. 3 vols. 4to. (Pp tanned.) 73 color, 3 plain plts. Wrappers (lib stamps, call #s, faded, lt soiled, spine ends chipped; 1-inch tear to fr panel vol 3). *Sutton.* $800/£500

MAYER, ALFRED M. (ed). Sport with Gun and Rod in American Woods and Waters. NY, (1883). Pict cl. *Swann*.* $149/£93

MAYER, ALFRED M. (ed). Sport with Gun and Rod in American Woods and Waters. NY, (1883). 1st ed. 2 vols. Uncut. Pub's pict cl. (Sl worn.) *Oinonen*.* $170/£106

MAYER, ALFRED M. (ed). Sport with Gun and Rod in American Woods and Waters. NY: Century, 1883. 1st ed. 2 vols. 888pp; 11 japan proof etchings, 27 full-pg plts. Dec cl, beveled bds (sl bumped; 1 joint sl cracked), gilt. Very Nice set. *Hollett.* $288/£180

MAYER, ALFRED M. (ed). Sport with Gun and Rod in American Woods and Waters. Edinburgh, 1884. 2 vols. Mod cl. *Swann*.* $92/£58

MAYER, BRANTZ. Captain Canot. London: Appleton, 1854. 460pp. Brn emb cl. VG (spine worn). *American Booksellers.* $100/£63

MAYER, GRACE M. Once Upon a City. NY: Macmillan, 1958. 1st ed. Folio. Fine in Good dj. *Connolly.* $75/£47

MAYER, GRACE M. Once Upon a City: New York from 1890 to 1910. NY: Macmillan, 1958. 1st ed. Percy Claude Byron (photos). (Inscrip), else VG in dj (worn, soiled). *Cahan.* $85/£53

MAYER, MARIANNA. The Unicorn and the Lake. NY: Dali, 1982. 4to. Michael Hague (illus). Fine in Fine dj. *American Booksellers.* $30/£19

MAYER, MERCER. East of the Sun and West of the Moon. NY: Four Winds, 1980. 1st ed. Obl 4to. 47pp; 18 full-pg color illus. Burgundy cl, gilt. VG (inscrip) in dj (lt torn). *Davidson.* $40/£25

MAYERS, F. J. Carpet Designs and Designing. Leigh-on-Sea: F. Lewis, 1934. 1st ed. Color frontis, 32 VG plts. Grn cl, gilt. VG (ex-lib). *Whittle.* $45/£28

MAYHEW, EDWARD. The Illustrated Horse Doctor. NY: D. Appleton, 1862. 1st ed. Pict grn cl, gilt. (Owner label, name), else VG. *Pacific*.* $81/£51

MAYHEW, G. P. Rage or Raillery, the Swift Manuscripts at the Huntington Library, California. London, 1967. 1st ed. Signed presentation. VG in dj. *Gretton.* $29/£18

MAYHEW, HENRY and BIRKETT FOSTER. The Upper Rhine. Routledge, 1858. Sm 4to. xv,448pp; 20 Very Clean steel-engr plts. Aeg. Dec cl, gilt extra. Very Nice (fr joint sl cracked; hinges, edges sl rubbed). *Hollett.* $560/£350

MAYHEW, HENRY. 1851; or, The Adventures of Mr. and Mrs. Sandboys. London, (1851). 1st ed, in orig 8 parts. Wood-engr tp, 9 (of 10) etched plts by Cruikshank. Wrappers (part 2 backstrip imperfect). 1/4 morocco slipcase. *Swann*.* $138/£86

MAYHEW, HENRY. German Life and Manners as Seen in Saxony at the Present Day. London: Wm. H. Allen, 1864. 2 vols. Color frontis each vol, xiv,612; iv,661pp. (Sl pencil marginalia.) 1/2 morocco (rubbed, dknd). *Zubal*.* $55/£34

MAYHEW, HENRY. The Wonders of Science. London: W. Kent, 1858. 3rd ed. xvi,424pp; 8 full-pg engrs. Contemp 1/2 calf, gilt extra. (Tp sl spotted; sl rubbed, scraped.) *Hollett.* $48/£30

MAYNARD, CHARLES J. A Manual of North American Butterflies. Boston: De Wolfe, Fiske. 1891. 1st ed. 10 hand-color plts. Brn cl, gilt. (Spine ends sl rubbed), else NF. *Pacific*.* $403/£252

MAYNE, ARTHUR. British Profile Miniaturists. London: Faber & Faber, 1970. 1st ed. 73 plts (8 color). Dj. *Edwards.* $32/£20

MAYNE, JONATHAN. Thomas Girtin. Leigh-on-Sea: F. Lewis, 1949. One of 500. 4 tipped-in color plts, 45 monochrome plts. VG in dj. *Hollett.* $104/£65

MAYNE, JONATHAN. Thomas Girtin. Leigh-On-Sea: Lewis, 1949. One of 500. Frontisport tipped-in; 4 tipped-in color plts, 45 monochrome. Deckle edges. Fine. *Europa.* $120/£75

MAYNE, WILLIAM. The Long Night. Oxford: Basil Blackwell, 1959. 1st ed. 8vo. 31pp; 4 b/w illus by D. Watkins-Pitchford. Illus bds. VG (lg lib stamp). *Bookmark.* $32/£20

MAYNE, WILLIAM. The Mouldy. NY: Knopf, 1982. 1st Amer ed. Nicola Bayley (illus). 8vo. Unpaginated. Mint in Mint dj. *Davidson.* $45/£28

MAYNE, WILLIAM. Royal Harry. Hamilton, 1971. 1st ed. 8vo. 158pp. VG + in pict dj (sl frayed). *Bookmark.* $24/£15

MAYNE, WILLIAM. Underground Alley. OUP, 1958. 1st ed. 8vo. Marcia Lane Foster (illus). (Tips faded), else NF in pict dj (frayed). *Bookmark.* $51/£32

MAYO, CHARLES H. and WILLIAM J. Collected Papers by the Staff of St. Mary's Hospital, Mayo Clinic. 1905-1909. Phila, 1911. 1st ed. *Fye.* $125/£78

MAYO, HERBERT. Observations on Injuries and Diseases of the Rectum. London, 1833. 1st ed. 220pp. 1/4 leather. (1-inch missing top of spine), o/w VG. *Fye.* $100/£63

MAYO, JIM. (Pseud of Louis L'Amour.) Utah Blaine [with] Desert Showdown by Brad Ward. NY: Ace, (1954). Pb orig. NF (lt spine crease, sl rubbed). *Between The Covers.* $125/£78

MAYO, KATHERINE. Soldiers What Next! London (etc): Cassell, (1934). 1st ed. Gilt reddish-orange cl. (Ink sig dated 1939), else VG in dj (lt edgeworn). *Reese.* $35/£22

MAYO, LAWRENCE SHAW. John Wentworth Governor of New Hampshire, 1767-1775. Cambridge: Harvard Univ, 1921. (Blindstamped names; corners worn, paper label rubbed, sl chipped.) *Woolson.* $35/£22

MAYO, MARGARET ELLEN (ed). The Art of South Italy. Richmond: VA Museum of Fine Arts, (1982). 6 color plts. Stiff wraps (sl shelfworn). *Archaeologia.* $125/£78

MAYOL, LURINE. Talking Totem Pole. NY: Saalfield, 1930. 4to. Edward Morgan (illus). VG in Good dj. *American Booksellers.* $30/£19

MAYOR, A. HYATT. Artists and Anatomists. NY, 1984. 1st ed. Dj. *Fye.* $40/£25

MAYOR, SUSAY. Collecting Fans. Studio Vista, 1980. 1st ed. VG in dj. *Hollett.* $48/£30

MAZER, CHARLES and LEOPOLD GOLDSTEIN. Clinical Endocrinology of the Female. Phila, 1932. 1st ed. *Fye.* $75/£47

MAZZULLA FRED and JO. Al Packer, a Colorado Cannibal. Denver, CO, 1968. 1st ed. Signed by both. Pict cl. Fine. *Labordo.* $55/£34

MAZZULLA, FRED and JO. Brass Checks and Red Lights. Denver, CO, 1966. 1st ed. Letter from Henry Clifford to Fred Rosenstock laid in loose. NF. *Labordo.* $45/£28

McADAM, ROGER WILLIAMS. Priscilla of Fall River. NY: Stephen Daye, 1956. VG in dj. *American Booksellers.* $35/£22

McAFEE, ANNALENA. The Visitors Who Came to Stay. NY: Viking, 1984. 1st ed. 9.75x11.5. Anthony Browne (illus). 32pp. Glossy bds. VG. *Cattermole.* $30/£19

McAFEE, ROBERT B. History of the Late War in the Western Country. Lexington: Ptd by Worsley & Smith, Reporter Office, 1816. 1st ed. (6),534,(2)pp (lacks tp, browned, spotted). Contemp calf (worn, fr hinge splitting). Howes M9. *Brown.* $200/£125

McAFEE, ROBERT B. History of the Late War in the Western Country. Bowling Green, OH: Historical Pub, 1919. 2nd ed. VG + . Howes M9. *Labordo.* $85/£53

McAFEE, ROBERT B. History of the Late War in the Western Country. Bowling Green: Historical Pub, 1919. Rpt, or 2nd ed. (Blank margins few ll lt smudged; extrems rubbed), else VG. Howes M9. *Brown.* $100/£63

McALPINE, WALLACE. Heart and Coronary Arteries: An Anatomical Atlas.... NY, 1975. 1st ed. Fine (ex-lib). *Fye.* $100/£63

McARTHUR, LEWIS A. Oregon Geographic Names. (Portland), 1928. 1st ed. Presentation. VG. *Perier.* $50/£31

McBAIN, ED. The 87th Precinct. NY, 1959. 1st ed. Dj (lt rubbed). *Swann*.* $69/£43

McBAIN, ED. Doll. NY: Delacorte, 1965. Fine in NF dj (price-clipped). *Unger.* $100/£63

McBAIN, ED. Hail to the Chief. NY: Random House, 1973. 1st ed. Signed. Fine in Fine dj (few wrinkles). *Unger.* $100/£63

McBAIN, ED. Long Time No See. NY: Random House, 1977. 1st ed. Fine in Fine dj. *Unger.* $75/£47

McBAIN, ED. Sadie When She Died. GC: Doubleday, 1972. 1st ed. Fine in NF dj (sl chipped). *Unger.* $75/£47

McBAIN, ED. So Long as You Both Shall Live. NY: Random House, 1976. 1st ed. Fine (pp dknd) in Fine dj. *Unger.* $75/£47

McBAIN, ED. Vespers. NY, (1990). 1st ed. VG in dj. *King.* $15/£9

McBRIDE, JOHN R. History of the Thirty-Third Indiana Veteran Volunteer Infantry During the Four Years of Civil War. Indianapolis, 1900. 1st ed. (Sl warped), else Good. *King.* $150/£94

McBRIDE, WILL. Show Me! Helga Fleischhauer-Hardt (text). NY: St. Martin's, 1975. 1st ed in English. Folio. (Corner sl bumped), else VG in pict stiff wrappers. *Cahan.* $60/£38

McBRYDE, JAMES. The Story of a Troll-Hunt. CUP, 1904. Parchment-backed paper bds. VG (feps browned, pastedowns bubbled; cvrs sl rubbed, mkd, soiled; spine ends, corners sl bumped). *Ulysses.* $312/£195

McCABE, GILLIE CARY. The Story of an Old Town: Hampton, Virginia. Old Dominion, 1929. Inscribed. Good (foxed throughout; cl worn). *Book Broker.* $25/£16

McCABE, JAMES D. Life and Campaigns of General Robert E. Lee. Atlanta/Phila et al: Nat'l Pub, (1866). 1st ed. Frontisport, 717pp + (1)pg ad; 7 fldg maps (2 w/tears, no loss). Orig 1/2 calf, morocco spine labels. Nice (partial label fr cvr). *Chapel Hill.* $350/£219

McCABE, JOSEPH. George Bernard Shaw: A Critical Study. London: Kegan Paul, 1914. 1st ed. Sepia frontisport. (Sl sunned, soiled.) *Dramatis.* $30/£19

McCABE, JOSEPH. Talleyrand. A Biographical Study. London: Hutchinson, 1906. Frontisport; 25 ports. Orig buckram. Good. *Stewart.* $48/£30

McCAFFREY, ANNE. Dragonsong. NY: Atheneum, 1976. 1st ed. Fine in dj. *Pacific*.* $173/£108

McCAFFREY, ANNE. Habit Is an Old Horse. Seattle: Dryad, (1986). 1st ed. One of 342. Signed. As New in pict wrappers. *Other Worlds.* $35/£22

McCALL, GEORGE ARCHIBALD. New Mexico in 1850: A Military View. Robert W. Frazer (ed). Norman, (1968). 1st ed. Map. Fine in NF dj. *Sagebrush.* $37/£23

McCALLUM, NEIL. It's an Old Scottish Custom. Dennis Dobson, 1951. 1st ed. VG in dj. *Hollett.* $32/£20

McCAMMON, ROBERT R. Swan Song. Arlington Heights: Dark Harvest, 1989. One of 650 numbered, signed by McCammon and Charles Lang (illus). Simulated leather (sl worn). Dj, slipcase. *Oinonen*.* $50/£31

McCANDLESS, BYRON and GILBERT GROSVENOR. Flags of the World. Washington: Nat'l Geographic Soc, 1917. 1st ed. (Lacks fep; edgewear, spotting), else VG. *Connolly.* $45/£28

McCARRISON, ROBERT. The Thyroid Gland in Health and Disease. London, 1917. 1st ed. *Fye.* $150/£94

McCARTHY, ALBERT et al. Jazz on Record: A Critical Guide to the First 50 Years, 1917-1967. London: Hanover Books, (1968). 1st ed. VG in illus dj. *Petrilla.* $45/£28

McCARTHY, ALBERT et al. Jazz on Record: A Critical Guide to the First 50 Years, 1917-1967. London: Hanover Books, 1968. 1st ed. VG (tear upper fr joint). *Beasley.* $25/£16

McCARTHY, CORMAC. All the Pretty Horses. N: Knopf, 1992. 1st ed. Fine in dj. *Pacific*.* $161/£101

McCARTHY, CORMAC. All the Pretty Horses. NY: Knopf, 1992. 1st ed. Fine in NF dj. *Lame Duck.* $250/£156

McCARTHY, CORMAC. All the Pretty Horses. NY: Knopf, 1992. 1st ed. VF in VF dj. *Unger.* $275/£172

McCARTHY, CORMAC. All the Pretty Horses. London: Picador, 1993. 1st British ed. One of 3000 ptd. Fine in Fine dj. *Pettler.* $100/£63

McCARTHY, CORMAC. Blood Meridian or the Evening Redness in the West. Picador, 1989. 1st UK ed. (Corners lt bumped), else NF in NF dj (spine panel sl creased). *Any Amount.* $240/£150

McCARTHY, CORMAC. Blood Meridian. NY: Random House, 1985. 1st ed. NF in dj. *Lame Duck.* $650/£406

McCARTHY, CORMAC. Child of God. NY: Random House, 1973. 1st ed. (Rmdr stamp on bottom pg edge), else NF in NF dj (price-clipped, spine sl peeling). *Pettler.* $550/£344

McCARTHY, CORMAC. The Crossing. NY: Knopf, 1994. 1st ed. Fine in Fine dj (price-clipped). *Pettler.* $25/£16

McCARTHY, CORMAC. The Crossing. NY: Knopf, 1994. 1st ed. Fine in dj. *Lame Duck.* $35/£22

McCARTHY, CORMAC. The Orchard Keeper. NY: Random House, 1965. 2nd ptg, 1st bk. VG in VG dj (price-clipped, spine foot chipped, fr fold worn). *Pettler.* $200/£125

McCARTHY, CORMAC. Outer Dark. NY, 1968. 1st ed. NF in NF dj (few sm chips, short tears at extrems). *Warren.* $600/£375

McCARTHY, CORMAC. The Stonemason. (Hopewell): Ecco Press, (1994). 1st ed. One of 350. Signed. Black cl, gilt. As New in slipcase. *Pacific*.* $184/£115

McCARTHY, CORMAC. The Stonemason. Hopewell: Ecco, 1994. 1st ed. One of 7500 ptd. Fine in Fine dj. *Pettler.* $40/£25

McCARTHY, CORMAC. Suttree. NY: Random House, 1979. 1st ed. (Rmdr stamp, fep offset), else VG in dj. *Lame Duck.* $1,000/£625

McCARTHY, DESMOND. William Somerset Maugham: 'The English Maupassant' an Appreciation by Desmond McCarthy with a Bibliography. London: Heinemann, 1934. 1st ed. VF in stapled wrappers. *Between The Covers*. $65/£41

McCARTHY, E. T. Incidents in the Life of a Mining Engineer. Routledge, 1919. 2nd imp. VG. *Hollett*. $104/£65

McCARTHY, JUSTIN. Reminiscences. London: C&W, 1899. 2nd ed. 2 vols. xii,444,32; vi,489,4pp; port. (Spines sl faded.) *Hollett*. $48/£30

McCARTHY, MARY. Ideas and the Novel. NY: Harcourt, (1980). 1st ed. Signed, dated 1982. Nice in dj (price-clipped). *Reese*. $55/£34

McCARTHY, MARY. Venice Observed. NY, 1957. 2nd ed. Pict cvrs. NF (spine professionally mended). *Polyanthos*. $35/£22

McCARTY, CLARA S. The Story of Boxwood. Dietz, n.d. VG. *Book Broker*. $50/£31

McCARTY, JOHN L. Maverick Town, the Story of Old Tascosa. Norman, 1946. 2nd ptg. Pict cl. VG in dj (sl worn, repaired tear, price-clipped). *Baade*. $20/£13

McCAULEY, LOIS B. Maryland Historical Prints, 1752 to 1889. Balt: MD Hist Soc, (1972). 1st ed. Grn buckram, gilt. NF in color pict dj (lt rubbed). *Baltimore**. $100/£63

McCAUSLAND, HUGH. The English Carriage. London: Batchworth, 1948. 1st ed. VG in Good dj. *October Farm*. $65/£41

McCLELLAN, ELISABETH. Historic Dress in America, 1607-1800. Phila: George W. Jacobs, n.d. (ca 1917). 2nd ed. 2 vols. Gilt/blind-stamped blue cl. Fine set in djs. *Karmiole*. $300/£188

McCLELLAN, GEORGE B. The Mexican War Diary of George B. McClellan. William Starr Myers (ed). Princeton: Princeton Univ, 1917. 1st ed. Inscribed by Myers, dated May 22, 1917. Frontis, 3 plts. Dk red cl. VG (emb lib stamps). *Chapel Hill*. $50/£31

McCLELLAN, GEORGE B. Report on the Organization and Campaigns of the Army of the Potomac. NY: Sheldon, 1864. 1st public ed. 480pp; 4 maps (incl fldg frontis). Dk brn blind cl (worn, scuffed; lacks bottom 1/2 of spine, rest of spine chipped, cracked), gilt. Internally VG (lt aging, foxed). *Baltimore**. $35/£22

McCLELLAN, GEORGE B. Senate Report of the Secretary of War, Communicating the Report of Capt. George B. McClellan...in 1855 and 1856. Washington: Nicholson Ptr, 1857. 360pp; 41 plts, lg map loosely inserted. Orig cl. (Rebacked, sl rubbed), o/w VG. *Worldwide*. $180/£113

McCLELLAN, R. GUY. The Golden State: A History of the Region West of the Rocky Mountains.... Phila: William Flint, 1874. Steel-engr frontis, (13)-711pp. Orig law calf, morocco spine label. (Foxing, extrems rubbed), else VG. *Pacific**. $138/£86

McCLELLAND, NANCY. Duncan Phyfe and the English Regency, 1795-1830. NY, (1939). One of 350 numbered, signed. Sm folio. (Fr cvr soiled, spine faded.) *Swann**. $172/£108

McCLENAHAN, RICHARD L. Some Scottish Quaichs, a Monograph. Skokie, IL: Privately ptd, (1955-1968). 2 vols. Vol I ltd to 100; vol II ltd to 150. Both vols signed, inscribed. Color frontis. Uniformly bound in unbleached coarse linen. Good. *Karmiole*. $100/£63

McCLINTOCK, JOHN S. Pioneer Days in the Black Hills. Deadwood, SD: John S. McClintock, 1939. 1st ed. Fabrikoid. VG (spine top tender, closed tears). Howes M42. *Labordo*. $195/£122

McCLOSKEY, ROBERT. Centerburg Tales. Viking, 1951. 1st ed. 191pp. VG + . *Price*. $30/£19

McCLOSKEY, ROBERT. Time of Wonder. NY: Viking, (1957). 1st ed. 4to. Dk blue cl (edge lt faded; 2 scotch tape mks on fep). Full color pict dj (edges worn, tear). *Reisler*. $350/£219

McCLURE, F. A. The Bamboos. Cambridge: Harvard, 1966. 1st ed. VG. *Archer*. $40/£25

McCLURE, MICHAEL. The Beard. Coyote Books, 1967. Ltd to 5000. Signed presentation. Fine in pict wraps. *Polyanthos*. $25/£16

McCLURE, MICHAEL. Little Odes and the Raptors. LA: Black Sparrow, 1969. 1st ed. One of 200 numbered, signed. Fine in NF glassine dj. *Sclanders*. $35/£22

McCLURE, MICHAEL. The New Book/A Book of Torture. NY: Grove, 1961. 1st Amer ed. VG in wraps. *Warren*. $30/£19

McCLURE, MICHAEL. Passage. Big Sur: Jonathan Williams, 1956. 1st ed, 1st bk. One of 200 ptd. 4to. (Edges lt tanned), else NF in sewn ptd wrappers. *Reese*. $550/£344

McCLURE, ROBERT E. Some Found Adventure. GC: Doubleday, Page, 1926. 1st ed. Gilt grn cl. Good (pencil inscrip, few ll spotted; cl sl dust-mkd) in pict dj (lg chips rear panel). *Reese*. $35/£22

McCLURE, ROY et al (eds). Burns, Shock, Wound Healing and Vascular Injuries. Phila, 1943. 1st ed. *Fye*. $75/£47

McCOMAS, E. S. A Journal of Travels. (Portland, OR): Champoeg, 1954. One of 500 ptd. 3 plts. Dec cl. (Corner sl bumped), else Fine. *Pacific**. $29/£18

McCONATHY, DALE and DIANA VREELAND. Hollywood Costume—Glamour! Glitter! Romance! NY, 1976. Patterned cl. Lettered mylar dj. *Swann**. $92/£58

McCONKEY, KENNETH. Edwardian Portraits. Images in an Age of Opulence. Woodbridge, 1987. 101 b/w, 36 color plts. Good in dj. *Washton*. $50/£31

McCONNELL, JOSEPH CARROLL. The West Texas Frontier. (Jacksboro, TX/Palo Pinto, TX: Gazette Print/TX Legal Bank & Book Co, 1933/1939.) 1st ed. 2 vols. (4),334; (4),348pp. Vol 1 in red buckram, vol 2 in blue buckram. (Text pp partly creased at top outer corners, lt waterstains to prelims; vol 1 spine rubbed.) Vol 2 VG. *Karmiole*. $650/£406

McCONNOCHIE, A. I. The Deer and Deer Forests of Scotland. London, 1923. Pict gilt cl (lt rubbed). Contents Fine. *Grayling*. $160/£100

McCORD, DAVID. The Crows. NY, 1934. 1st Amer ed. NF (sm nick fr cvr, spine sunned). *Polyanthos*. $25/£16

McCORKLE, JILL. July 7th. Chapel Hill: Algonquin, 1984. 1st ed, 1st bk. Signed. NF in dj (2 sm closed tears). *Robbins*. $175/£109

McCORMACK, JOHN. Channel Island Churches. Phillimore, 1986. 1st ed. 92 plts (9 color). VG in dj. *Hollett*. $72/£45

McCORMICK, E. H. The Expatriate. Wellington: New Zealand Univ, 1954. Orig ed. Frontisport. NF in VG dj. *Turtle Island*. $60/£38

McCORMICK, ROBERT R. The War Without Grant. NY, 1950. 1st ed. Fine in dj (lt worn). *Pratt*. $40/£25

McCORMICK, WILFRED. The Double Steal. NY: David McKay, 1961. 1st ed. Rocky McCune #9. 5.5x8. 180pp. VG (corners bumped) in dj (sl edgeworn, rear dingy). *My Bookhouse*. $47/£29

McCOY, JOSEPH G. Historic Sketches of the Cattle Trade of the West and Southwest. Kansas City, MO: Ramsey, Millett & Hudson, 1874. 1st ed. Grn cl, binding state A w/head of Texas longhorn emb on cvr. This copy w/ads. VG (cvrs lt rubbed, edges worn, closed tear near spine top, spine foot tender). Howes M72. *Labordo*. $1,950/£1,219

McCOY, JOSEPH G. Historic Sketches of the Cattle Trade of the West and Southwest. Columbus: Long's College Book Co, 1951. Facs of Kansas City, 1874 ed. Terracotta cl, gilt. NF (spine foot sl worn) in VG dj. *Pacific**. $52/£33

McCOY, JOSEPH G. Historic Sketches of the Cattle Trade of the West and Southwest. Columbus: Long's College Book Co, 1951. Facs rpt. Ptd eps. Brn cl, gilt. Fine in VG dj (spine dknd, chipped, soiled). Howes M72. *Harrington*. $65/£41

McCOY, JOSEPH G. Historic Sketches of the Cattle Trade of the West and Southwest. Ralph P. Bieber (ed). Glendale: A.H. Clark, 1940. Rpt ed. Fine. *Labordo*. $185/£116

McCRACKEN, DAVID R. Four Months on a Jap Whaler. NY: Nat'l Travel Club, c. 1948. VG in dj (tattered). *High Latitude*. $30/£19

McCRACKEN, HAROLD. The Charles M. Russell Book. GC: Doubleday, (1957). Color frontis. Padded morocco, pict cvr label. (Bkpl; spine sunned), else VG. *Pacific**. $40/£25

McCRACKEN, HAROLD. The Charles M. Russell Book. GC: Doubleday, (1957). Full padded leather. NF in slipcase (lt shelfworn). *Pacific**. $92/£58

McCRACKEN, HAROLD. The Charles M. Russell Book. NY, 1957. 1st trade ed. Lg folio. Fine in dj (frayed). *Heinoldt*. $60/£38

McCRACKEN, HAROLD. The Charles M. Russell Book. GC, 1957. 1st ed. Sm folio. (Bkpl), else VG in dj (few sm tears). *Woolson*. $85/£53

McCRACKEN, HAROLD. Frederic Remington: Artist of the Old West. With a Bibliographical Check List of Remington Pictures and Books. Phila: J.B. Lippincott, (1947). 1st ed. 48 plts. Fine in dj (edges lt worn). *Pacific**. $46/£29

McCRACKEN, HAROLD. George Catlin and the Old Frontier. NY: Dial, 1959. 1st ed. VG in dj (sl worn). *Dumont*. $45/£28

McCRACKEN, HAROLD. George Catlin and the Old Frontier. NY, 1959. 1st ed. Good in dj (worn). *Dumont*. $65/£41

McCRACKEN, HAROLD. George Catlin and the Old Frontier. NY: Dial, 1959. 1st ed. One of 250 numbered, bound in leather, w/extra color plt tipped-in at fr. Signed. 2 color frontispieces (1 tipped-in). Orig full leather, gilt. VF in slipcase. *Argonaut*. $375/£234

McCRACKEN, HAROLD. Portrait of the Old West. With a Biographical Check List of Western Artists. NY: McGraw-Hill, (1952). 1st ed. (Extrems lt worn), else NF in dj. *Pacific**. $52/£33

McCRACKEN, RUSSELL. The Elegant Elephant. Chicago: Rand McNally, 1944. Slottie Book complete w/punch-out toy. 7.5x10. Susanne Suba (illus). 28pp. VG + (sl shelfworn) in dj (edgeworn). *My Bookhouse*. $78/£49

McCRACKEN, W. D. The New Palestine: An Authoritative Account.... Boston: Page, 1922. 1st ed. 56 plts (8 color), fldg map. Teg. (Sl rubbed), o/w VG. *Worldwide*. $65/£41

McCRAE, JOHN. In Flanders Fields and Other Poems.... NY: Putnam, 1919. 1st US ed. Port. Fine in Good dj (few chips, tears, 1 old external tape mend). *Reese*. $85/£53

McCREADY, T. L., JR. Increase Rabbit. NY: Ariel Books, (1958). 1st ed. 8vo. Yellow cl. VG in full color dj. *Reisler*. $475/£297

McCREIGHT, M. I. Firewater and Forked Tongues. Pasadena, CA: Trail's End Pub, (1947). 1st ed. Color frontis. VG in dj. *Lien*. $45/£28

McCULLERS, CARSON. The Ballad of the Sad Cafe. Boston, 1951. 1st ed. VG in dj (frayed, rubbed). *King*. $50/£31

McCULLERS, CARSON. Clock Without Hands. Boston: Houghton Mifflin, 1961. 1st ed. (Spine ends sl chafed), o/w VF (parts of dj mtd/pasted to fep). *Pirages*. $35/£22

McCULLERS, CARSON. The Member of the Wedding. Boston: Houghton Mifflin, 1946. 1st ed. VF in VF dj. *Bromer*. $350/£219

McCULLERS, CARSON. Sweet as a Pickle and Clean as a Pig. Boston, 1964. 1st ed. Fine in Fine dj. *Warren*. $75/£47

McCUNE, BILLY. The Autobiography of Billy McCune. SF: Straight Arrow Bks, 1973. 1st ed. (Rmdr mk), else Fine in NF illus dj. *Cahan*. $85/£53

McCUTCHAN, PHILIP. Cameron's Raid. London: Weidenfeld & Nicolson, 1984. 1st Eng ed. Fine (spine ends sl bumped) in dj (sl creased). *Ulysses*. $48/£30

McCUTCHEON, GEORGE BARR. Books Once Were Men. NY, 1931. Ltd to 1000. Fine in slipcase (broken). *Truepenny*. $45/£28

McCUTCHEON, JOHN. John McCutcheon's Book. Chicago: Caxton Club, 1948. Ltd to 1000 ptd. Folio. Lt grn dec cl. Good. *Karmiole*. $85/£53

McDANIEL, JOHN M. The Turkey Hunter's Book. Clinton: Amwell, 1980. One of 1000 numbered, signed by McDaniel and Donald Shoffstall (illus). Slipcase. *Swann**. $103/£64

McDERMOTT, JOHN F. George Caleb Bingham River Portraitist. Norman, 1959. 1st ed. Good in dj (chipped). *Dumont*. $65/£41

McDERMOTT, JOHN F. Private Libraries in Creole Saint Louis. Balt: Johns Hopkins, 1938. (Bkpl), else VG + in 1/4 cl. *Zubal**. $30/£19

McDERMOTT, JOHN F. Seth Eastman: Pictoral Historian of the Indian. Norman, 1961. (Shelfworn; lacks dj), else Good. *Dumont*. $45/£28

McDERMOTT, JOHN F. Travelers on the Western Frontier. Urbana, IL, (1970). 1st ed. Dj. *Ginsberg*. $50/£31

McDERMOTT, JOHN F. Travelers on the Western Frontier. Urbana: Univ of IL, 1970. VG in dj (sl worn). *Dumont*. $35/£22

McDONALD, ANGUS. Old McDonald Had a Farm. Boston: Houghton Mifflin, 1942. 1st ed. Fine in Good dj. *Connolly*. $22/£14

McDONALD, GREGORY. Flynn's In. NY: Mysterious Press, (1984). 1st ed. One of 250 signed. Blue cl, gilt. Fine in dj (corner sl creased), cl slipcase. *Heritage*. $75/£47

McDONALD, LUCRETIA F. Apple Seeds. Phila/Chicago: H.J. Smith, 1892. Signed. 116pp. (Cl lt spotted), else Good. *Brown*. $50/£31

McDONALD, WILLIAM N. A History of the Laurel Brigade. Bushrod C. Washington (ed). (Balt): Mrs. Kate S. McDonald, 1907. 1st ed. Grn cl, gilt. VG (bkpl, sl shaken; sl rubbed, dusty). Howes M87. *Baltimore**. $350/£219

McDONALD, WILLIAM N. A History of the Laurel Brigade...Edited by Bushrod C. Washington. Published by Mrs. Kate S. McDonald. (Balt: Sun Job Ptg Office), 1907. 1st ed. Lg 8vo. Frontisport. Grn cl, gilt. (Sig on recto of frontis), else Fine. *Chapel Hill*. $800/£500

McDOUGALL, GEORGE F. The Eventful Voyage of H. M. Discovery Ship 'Resolute' to the Arctic Regions in Search of Sir John Franklin and the Missing Crews of H. M. Discovery Ships.... London: Longman, Green, 1857. 1st ed. xl,530pp; fldg map. 1/4 brn calf (rebound). Good + (foxed throughout). *Walcot*. $448/£280

McDOUGALL, W. Modern Materialism and Emergent Evolution. NY: Van Nostrand, 1929. 1st ed. VG + . *Mikesh*. $30/£19

MCDOWALL, ARTHUR. Peaks and Frescoes: A Study of the Dolomites. London, 1928. 14 color plts. *Argosy*. $50/£31

McDOWELL, FRANK et al. Surgery of Face, Mouth, and Jaws. St. Louis: C.V. Mosby, 1954. 1st ed. Fine. *Weber*. $175/£109

McELROY, JOSEPH. A Smuggler's Bible. NY: Harcourt, Brace & World, (1966). 1st ed, 1st bk. Red dj. *Dermont*. $250/£156

McELROY, ROBERT. Jefferson Davis. NY: Harper, 1937. 1st ed. 2 vols. Red cl. (Spines sl faded), else Fine set. *Chapel Hill*. $80/£50

McELWAINE, EUGENE. The Truth About Alaska. The Author, 1901. 1st ed. (Names; spine ends, corners frayed; cvrs sl dknd), else Good. *King*. $125/£78

McEWAN, IAN. The Child in Time. London, 1987. VG in dj. *Typographeum*. $25/£16

McEWAN, IAN. The Child in Time. Boston, 1987. 1st Amer ed. Signed presentation. Fine in Fine dj. *Polyanthos*. $30/£19

McEWAN, IAN. First Love Last Rites. Cape, 1975. 1st ed, 1st bk. Fine in dj. *Any Amount*. $176/£110

McEWAN, IAN. The Imitation Game. Cape, 1981. 1st UK ed. Fine (sm label) in dj. *Williams*. $77/£48

McEWAN, IAN. In Between the Sheets and Other Stories. London: Cape, 1978. 1st Eng ed. VG (top edge sl dusty; spine foot, corners sl bumped, cvrs sl mkd) in dj (sl creased, mkd, spine sl faded, fr panel internally soiled). *Ulysses*. $200/£125

McEWAN, IAN. In Between the Sheets. Cape, 1978. 1st UK ed. Signed. NF in Fine dj. *Martin*. $61/£38

McEWAN, IAN. In Between the Sheets. Cape, 1978. 1st ed. Fine in NF dj. *Any Amount*. $88/£55

McEWEN, JOHN B. An Introduction to an Unpublished Edition of the Pianoforte Sonatas of Beethoven. OUP, 1932. 1st ed. VG. *Hollett*. $48/£30

McFADDEN, CYRA. The Serial. NY, 1977. 1st ed. VG + in spiral binder. *Warren*. $30/£19

McFADDEN, DOROTHY. Touring the Gardens of Europe. NY: D. McKay, 1965. 1st ed. Fine in dj. *Archer*. $25/£16

McFALL, HALDANE. The Book of Lovat Claud Fraser. London: J.M. Dent, 1923. 1st trade ed. 21 plts (8 color). Dec color eps. Color ptd paper over bds (rubbed), cl spine (faded). Internally Clean. *Turtle Island*. $125/£78

McFARLAND, DENNIS. The Music Room. Boston: Houghton Mifflin, 1990. 1st ed. Fine in Fine dj. *Beasley*. $45/£28

McFARLAND, J. HORACE. Memoirs of a Rose Man. Emmaus: Rodale, 1949. 1st ed. VG (bumped) in dj (chipped, rubbed). *Archer*. $15/£9

McFARLING, LLOYD (ed). Exploring the Northern Plains, 1804-1876. Caldwell: Caxton, 1955. 1st ed. (Sm stain to top pg edges), else NF in dj (extrems sl rubbed). *Pacific**. $58/£36

McFARLING, LLOYD (ed). Exploring the Northern Plains, 1804-1876. Caldwell: Caxton Ptrs, 1955. 1st ed. Tan cl. Fine in Fine dj. *Harrington*. $65/£41

McFARLING, LLOYD. Exploring the Northern Plains. Caldwell, ID, 1955. Good (dusty) in dj (sl soiled). *Dumont*. $55/£34

McFEE, WILLIAM. The Harbour-Master. GC: Doubleday, Doran, 1931. 1st ed. One of 377. Signed. Teg. Fine. *Pacific**. $40/£25

McFEE, WILLIAM. The Harbour-Master. GC: Doubleday, Doran, 1932. 1st ed. Gilt blue cl. VF in dj. *Reese*. $50/£31

McFEE, WILLIAM. Letters from an Ocean Tramp. London: Cassell, 1908. 1st ed, 1st issue. Signed, inscribed presentation. Eps, frontis signed by Warwick Goble (illus). VG in VG specifically made box w/morocco back, gilt. *Cullen*. $325/£203

McFEE, WILLIAM. North of Suez. GC: Doubleday, Doran, 1930. 1st ed. One of 350 numbered, specially ptd and bound, signed. Teg. Linen-backed blue bds, pict onlay, pict label. Fine in plastic wrapper (sl chipped), slipcase (tanned, rubbed). *Reese*. $75/£47

McFEELY, WILLIAM S. Grant. A Biography. NY: W.W. Norton, (1981). 1st ed. Black cl, bds. Fine in dj. *House*. $20/£13

McGAFFEY, ERNEST. Poems of Gun and Rod. NY: Scribner, 1892. 1st ed. Pict cl, gilt. Fine (bkpl). *Pacific**. $58/£36

McGAHERN, JOHN. The Dark. NY: Knopf, 1966. 1st Amer ed. As New in dj. *Between The Covers*. $125/£78

McGAW, MARTHA. Stevenson in Hawaii. Honolulu: Univ of HI, 1950. 1st ed. Signed. One of 2000. VG + . *Any Amount*. $29/£18

McGEE, EMMA R. Life of W. J. McGee. Farley, IA: Privately ptd, 1915. Brn cl, gilt. (Lt worn), o/w VG + . *Five Quail*. $65/£41

McGILL, WILLIAM M. Caverns of Virginia. Univ of VA, 1933. VG. *Book Broker*. $75/£47

McGILLYCUDDY, JULIA B. McGillycuddy Agent. Stanford, 1941. 1st ed. Pict cl. VG (owner ink info) in dj (quite chipped). *Baade*. $75/£47

McGILLYCUDDY, JULIA B. McGillycuddy, Agent. Stanford: Stanford Univ, (1941). 1st ed. VG + in dj (sl worn, spine faded, price-clipped). *Pacific**. $58/£36

McGINLEY, PHYLLIS. The B Book. NY: Crowell-Collier, 1962. 1st ed. 7.75x11.5. Robert Jones (illus). 64pp. Pict bds. Good. *Cattermole*. $25/£16

McGINNIES, WILLIAM G. Discovering the Desert. Tucson, 1981. Fine in dj. *Brooks*. $24/£15

McGIVERN, ED. Ed McGivern's Book on Fast and Fancy Revolver Shooting and Police Training. Springfield, MA: King-Richardson, 1938. 1st ed. Inscribed, signed. NF. *Labordo*. $275/£172

McGIVERN, ED. Ed McGivern's Book on Fast and Fancy Revolver Shooting and Police Training. Boston, 1946. (Cvrs sl worn.) *King*. $45/£28

McGLASHAN, C. F. History of the Donner Party. SF: Ptd by A. Carlisle, 1922. Signed, dated Aug 6, 1925. Grn cl. Good (text browned; cvrs stained, rubbed). Howes M102. *House*. $90/£56

McGLASHAN, C. F. History of the Donner Party. SF: Ptd by A. Carlisle, 1929. Grn cl. Good (inscrip, partly bled through tp; extrems rubbed). *House*. $30/£19

McGLOIN, JOHN BERNARD. Eloquent Indian. Stanford, CA: Stanford Univ, (1949). 1st ed. VG. *Lien*. $20/£13

McGOWAN, EDWARD. Narrative of Edward McGowan, Including a Full Account of the Author's Adventures and Perils While Persecuted.... SF: Thomas C. Russell, 1917. Ltd to 200. Brn pebbled cl, paper spine label. Fine. Howes M103. *Pacific**. $127/£79

McGOWAN, EDWARD. The Strange and Eventful History of Parker H. French. L.A.: Glen Dawson, 1958. 1st bk ed. Ltd to 225 ptd. 2 facs (1 fldg). Fine. *Argonaut*. $60/£38

McGRAW, ELOISE JARVIS and LAUREN McGRAW WAGNER. Merry Go Round in Oz. Chicago, (1963). 1st ed, primary binding w/9.25 inch color paste-downs on cvrs. (Ink name, address.) *Kane**. $90/£56

McGRAW, ELOISE JARVIS and LAUREN McGRAW WAGNER. Merry Go Round in Oz. Chicago: Reilly & Lee, (1963). 1st ed. Inscribed, signed by Eloise Jarvis McGraw. 9x6.5. Dick Martin (illus). Pict cl, secondary binding w/fr cvr design reduced, etc. Fine in VG dj (spine head chipped). *Pacific**. $316/£198

McGRAW, ELOISE JARVIS and LAUREN MCGRAW WAGNER. Merry Go Round in Oz. Chicago: Reilly & Lee, (1963). 1st ed. 8vo. Dick Martin (illus). 303pp; full-pg pict map. Illus eps. NF in NF dj. *Davidson*. $675/£422

McGREGOR, JOHN. British America. Edinburgh: William Blackwood, 1832. 1st ed. 2 vols. 9 engr maps, 3 fldg (sl offset onto text, bkpl). Contemp calf gilt (lt rubbed, scuffed), morocco labels. *Christie's**. $270/£169

McGREW, R. BROWNELL. Brownell McGrew. Kansas City: Lowell Press, 1978. 1st ed. Fine in Fine dj. *Book Market*. $40/£25

McGROARTY, JOHN STEVEN. Mission Memories. L.A.: Neuner Corp, 1929. 1st ed. Tipped-in color frontis. Brn paper-cvrd bds, pict inset fr cvr. Fine in VG + dj (sl chipped). *Harrington*. $40/£25

McGUANE, THOMAS. The Bushwacked Piano. NY, 1971. 1st ed. NF in VG + dj (2 closed tears, sl rubbed). *Warren*. $95/£59

McGUANE, THOMAS. The Bushwhacked Piano. NY: S&S, (1971). 1st ed. Fine in dj (sl dknd). *Lenz*. $150/£94

McGUANE, THOMAS. Keep the Change. Boston, 1989. 1st Amer ed. Fine in Fine dj. *Polyanthos*. $20/£13

McGUANE, THOMAS. Ninety-Two in the Shade. NY, 1973. 1st ed. NF in NF dj. *Warren*. $75/£47

McGUANE, THOMAS. Nothing But Blue Skies. Boston: Houghton Mifflin, 1992. 1st ed. Blue cl backed over blue paper-cvrd bds. Fine in Fine ptd dj. *Biscotti*. $25/£16

McGUANE, THOMAS. The Sporting Club. NY: S&S, (1968). 1st ed, 1st bk. NF in dj (sl offset to fr panel from former price label). *Pacific**. $58/£36

McGUIRE, J. A. In the Alaska-Yukon Gamelands. Cincinnati: Stewart Kidd, 1921. 1st ed. Untrimmed. NF. *Connolly.* $35/£22

McHALE, TOM. Farragan's Retreat. NY: Viking, (1971). 1st ed. (Sm spot at topstain), o/w NF in dj. *Bernard.* $30/£19

McHENRY, LAWRENCE C. Garrison's History of Neurology. Springfield, 1969. 1st ed. VG in good dj. *Doctor's Library.* $200/£125

McILHANEY, EDWARD. Recollections of a '49er. Kansas City, 1908. 1st ed. Orig bds (extrems worn, watermkd). Howes M111. *Dumont.* $125/£78

McILHANY, WILLIAM H. Klandestine. New Rochelle, NY: Arlington House, 1975. 1st ed. NF in dj. *Labordo.* $65/£41

McINERNY, RALPH. Jolly Rogerson. NY, 1967. Advance rev copy w/slip laid in. Fine in NF dj. *Warren.* $50/£31

McINTIRE, JAMES. Early Days in Texas. Kansas City, MO: McIntire Pub, 1902. 1st ed. Grn pict cl. VG (pp browned; silverfishing to cvrs). Howes M113. *Labordo.* $1,000/£625

McINTOSH, JAMES and PAUL FILDES. Syphilis From the Modern Standpoint. London, 1911. 1st ed. *Fye.* $150/£94

McINTOSH, MARIA J. Woman in America. NY: Appleton, 1850. 1st ed. 155pp + (12)pp ads. Orig emb brn cl. VG (foxed; spine extrems chipped, corners worn). *Chapel Hill.* $165/£103

MCINTYRE, ANTHONY. The Shell Book of British Buildings. David & Charles, 1984. Fine in dj. *Hadley.* $24/£15

McIVOR, WILLIAM GRAHAM. Notes of the Propagation and Cultivation of the Medicinal Cinchonas. Madras: Gantz Bros, 1867. ii,33pp; 9 litho fldg plts. Paper label. (Lib stamps on tp, head of each plt; faded, corners sl bumped.) *Hollett.* $104/£65

McKAY, CLAUDE. Banjo. NY: Harper, 1929. 1st ed. Patterned eps, bds. (Spine ends lt worn), else NF in NF orange/black illus dj. *Pettler.* $500/£313

McKAY, CLAUDE. Harlem Glory. Chicago: Charles H. Kerr, 1990. 1st ed. Fine in wrappers. *Heritage.* $30/£19

McKAY, CLAUDE. Home to Harlem. NY: Harper, 1928. 1st ed. 3/4 cl, dec bds. VG. *Pacific**. $109/£68

McKAY, G. L. and C. LARSEN. Principles and Practice of Butter-Making. NY/London, 1908. 2nd ed, 1st thousand. (Eps lt dampspotted, corner fep sl torn, pp103/4 torn w/text loss; lt soiled, spotted, label remains spine tail.) *Edwards.* $24/£15

McKAY, GEORGE L. A Bibliography of the Writings of Sir Rider Haggard. London: Bookman's Journal, 1930. One of 475. Addenda tipped to limitation pg. Brn cl, gilt spine. Fine. *Pacific**. $288/£180

McKAY, WILLIAM D. The Scottish School of Painting. Duckworth, 1906. 1st ed. (Eps spotted, sl shaken; cl worn.) *Hollett.* $48/£30

MCKECHNIE, SAMUEL. Popular Entertainments Through the Ages. London: Sampson Low, Marston, n.d. (1932). 1st ed. Color frontis. VG. *Dramatis.* $60/£38

McKEE, ALEXANDER. Dresden, 1945: The Devil's Tinderbox. Dutton, (1984). 1st ed. Good in dj. *Rybski.* $27/£17

McKEE, ALEXANDER. Ice Crash. Disaster in the Arctic 1928. Souvenir, 1979. 1st ed. Fine in dj. *Walcot.* $24/£15

McKEEN, SILAS. A History of Bradford, Vermont...First Settlement in 1765...Events Which Have Occurred Down to 1874.... Montpelier, VT: J.D. Clarke, 1875. 1st ed. (Sig sl sprung; rubbed, spine ends, corners frayed.) *Sadlon.* $35/£22

McKELVEY, SUSAN DELANO. Botanical Exploration of the Trans-Mississippi West 1790-1850. Jamaica Plain: Arnold Arboretum, 1955. 2 fldg maps inside rear cvr pocket. (Sl worn.) Orig glassine wrapper (sl chips). *Oinonen**. $180/£113

McKELVEY, SUSAN DELANO. The Botanical Exploration of the Trans-Mississippi West. Jamaica Plain, MA, 1955. 7 fldg maps, 2 in rear pocket. (Lt worn), else NF. *Dumont.* $225/£141

McKELVEY, SUSAN DELANO. The Lilac. NY, 1928. 1st ed. 172 plts. (Foxed; spine discolored, cvrs sl stained.) *King.* $150/£94

McKELVEY, SUSAN DELANO. Yuccas of the Southwestern United States. Part 2. Jamaica Plain, 1947. 65 full-pg b/w photos. VG in wrappers. *Brooks.* $175/£109

McKELVEY, SUSAN DELANO. Yuccas of the Southwestern United States. Part I. Jamaica Plain, 1938. Inscribed, dated June 23, 1938. 80 full-pg b/w photos. Blindstamp of Wm. Trelease. Internally VG in wrappers (fr wrap cut away). *Brooks.* $345/£216

McKENNA, DOLORES. Tom Mitten's Cousins. NY: Sam'l Gabriel Sons, (1923). 8vo. Cl-backed color pict bds (corners lt rubbed). *Reisler.* $85/£53

McKENNA, RICHARD. The Sons of Martha and Other Stories. NY: Harper & Row, (1967). 1st ed. Fine in dj. *Pharos.* $20/£13

McKENNEY, J. WILSON. Desert Editor. Georgetown: Wilmac Press, 1972. 1st ed. Map. Fine in Good dj. *Connolly.* $32/£20

McKENNEY, J. WILSON. On the Trail of Peg Leg Smith's Lost Gold. Palm Desert: Desert Press, 1957. 1st ed. Fine in heavy pict wrappers. *Connolly.* $20/£13

McKENNEY, THOMAS L. History of the Indian Tribes of North America.... Phila: Rice, Rutter, 1865. 3 vols. 8vo. 121 hand-colored lithos (plt 17 w/chipped edges; frontis vol 3 detached, edges chipped). Aeg. Full pub's tooled brn morocco (sl rubbed), gilt. Internally Fine. *Kane**. $9,100/£5,688

McKENNEY, THOMAS L. and JAMES HALL. The Indian Tribes of North America. Edinburgh, 1933-34. 3 vols. 2 photogravure ports, 123 color plts, 2 color fldg maps. *Swann**. $373/£233

McKENZIE, THOMAS. My Life as a Soldier. St. John: McMillan, 1898. 1st ed. Inscribed. Frontis, (11),202pp; port. Dec cl. *Ginsberg.* $125/£78

McKEOWN, MARTHA FERGUSON. The Trail Led North. NY: Macmillan, 1948. 1st ed. Signed. Good in dj (worn). *Lien.* $20/£13

McKIM, RANDOLPH H. A Soldier's Recollections. NY, 1910. 1st ed. (Spine chipped, hinges loose, stained, worn, soiled.) *King.* $195/£122

McKIM, RANDOLPH H. The Soul of Lee. London: Longmans, Green, 1918. 1st ed. Frontisport. Blue cl. (Pencil name, lt notes eps, margins, occasional pale foxing), else VG + . *Chapel Hill.* $125/£78

McKINLEY, ASHLEY. The South Pole Picture Book. NY: Samuel W. Miller, 1934. Map. Orig ptd illus wrapper. VG. *Explorer.* $40/£25

McKINNEY, ROLAND. Eakins. NY: Crown, (1942). 8 color plts. VG in dj. *Turtle Island.* $65/£41

McKINNON, IAN. Garroot: Adventures of a Clydeside Apprentice. Jonathan Cape, 1933. 8vo. Tan cl. Dj (spine sl soiled). *Sotheby's**. $1,619/£1,012

McKINSTRY, BYRON N. The California Gold Rush Overland Diary of Byron N. McKinstry 1850-1852. Glendale, CA: A.H. Clark, 1975. Fine in dj. *Pacific**. $81/£51

McKITTERICK, DAVID (ed). Stanley Morison and D. B. Updike. Selected Correspondence. Scolar Press, 1980. 1st ed. 20 fac plts. Good in dj. *Cox.* $19/£12

McKNIGHT, EDWIN T. Geology of the Area Between Green and Colorado Rivers, Grand and San Juan Counties, Utah. Washington: USGS, 1940. 3 color fldg maps in rear pockets. (Map pocket repaired), o/w VG. *Five Quail.* $50/£31

McLARTY, MARGARET C. Illustrating Medicine and Surgery. Balt: Williams & Wilkins, 1960. Fine. *Weber.* $65/£41

McLEAN, JAMES L., JR. Cutler's Brigade at Gettysburg. Balt, 1987. 1st ed. Ltd to 300. VG + . *Pratt.* $50/£31

McLEAN, RUARI. George Cruikshank. NY: Pellegrini & Cudahy, (1948). NF in Good dj. *Turtle Island.* $35/£22

McLEAN, RUARI. Victorian Book Design and Colour Printing. Faber, 1972. 2nd ed. Dj. *Edwards.* $120/£75

McLELLAN, ISAAC. Haunts of Wild Game, or, Poems of Woods, Wilds and Waters. Charles Barker Bradford (ed). NY: Charles Barker Bradford, (1896). 1st ed. Teg. Dec grn cl, gilt. Fine (tipped-in bkpl). *Pacific*.* $46/£29

McLELLAN, ROY DAVIDSON. The Geology of the San Juan Islands. Seattle: Univ of WA, 1927. Text VG (lack fldg map), cvrs Good- (lacks rear cvr). Gray wraps. *American Booksellers.* $50/£31

McMACKEN, JOSEPH G. Geology of the Grand Coulee. Spokane: Author, 1938. 1st ed. Map inner fr cvr. Fine in pict wrappers. *Connolly.* $25/£16

McMEEKIN, McLENNAN. The First Book of Horses. Franklin Watts, 1949. Probably 1st ed. Pers Crowell (illus). 45pp. NF (bkpl) in Good dj (edgeworn). *Price.* $20/£13

McMILLAN, GEORGE. The Old Breed: A History of the First Marine Division in World War II. Washington, 1949. 1st ed. VG. *Clark.* $150/£94

McMILLAN, TERRY. Waiting to Exhale. NY: Viking, 1992. 1st ed. Fine in Fine dj. *Pettler.* $40/£25

McMILLAN, TERRY. Waiting to Exhale. (NY, 1992.) 1st ed. (Fr cvr sl spotted.) Dj. *Swann*.* $80/£50

McMULLAN, JOSEPH V. Turkoman Rugs. Cambridge, MA, 1966. Map. Pict bds. *Petersfield.* $34/£21

McMULLEN, ROY. The World of Marc Chagall. NY: Doubleday, 1968. 1st ed. Folio. Izis Bidermanas (photos). VG (bkpl) in dj (sl worn). *Cahan.* $75/£47

McMURRAY, W. J. History of the Twentieth Tennessee Regiment Volunteer Infantry, C.S.A. Nashville: Publication Committee, 1904. 1st ed. Lg 8vo. Frontisport, add'l ports. 1pg typed prospectus laid in. Black cl. (Neat bkpl; corner bumped, sm hole near bottom of rear gutter), else VG + . *Chapel Hill.* $650/£406

McMURTRIE, DOUGLAS C. The Book, The Story of Printing and Bookmaking. NY: Covici-Friede, 1937. 1st ptg. (Bkpl; sl bumped at head of spine.) *Oak Knoll.* $50/£31

McMURTRIE, DOUGLAS C. The Disabled Soldier. NY: Macmillan, 1919. 1st ed, 1st bk. Blue cl. VG. *Dermont.* $200/£125

McMURTRIE, DOUGLAS C. Early Printing in Wisconsin. Seattle: Frank McCaffrey, 1931. One of 300. Presentation copy from ptr w/signed, ptd slip tipped to fep. Folio. Uncut, unopened. Leather spine label. (Sl worn.) *Oinonen*.* $100/£63

McMURTRIE, DOUGLAS C. The Golden Book. Chicago: Pascal Covici, 1927. 1st ed, ltd to 2000. Teg (sl flaked off). Blue cl, gilt. *Oak Knoll.* $65/£41

McMURTRY, LARRY. Cadillac Jack. NY, 1982. 1st ed. NF in NF dj (few creases to fr panel). *Warren.* $30/£19

McMURTRY, LARRY. In a Narrow Grave: Essays on Texas. Austin: Encino Press, (1968). 1st ed. NF in dj. *Pacific*.* $259/£162

McMURTRY, LARRY. The Last Picture Show. NY: Dial, 1966. 1st ed. Fine in Fine dj. *Lenz.* $375/£234

McMURTRY, LARRY. Leaving Cheyenne. NY: Harper & Row, (1963). 1st ed. VG in dj (sm scrape lower spine, price-clipped, new price stamped on fr flap). *Pacific*.* $345/£216

McMURTRY, LARRY. Lonesome Dove. NY: S&S, (1985). 1st ed. (Emb name, ink name), else NF in dj. *Pacific*.* $109/£68

McMURTRY, LARRY. Lonesome Dove. NY: S&S, (1985). 1st ed. Black cl over black bds, gilt. NF (spine sl stressed, foot sl rubbed) in dj (price-clipped, few creases, chip). *Heritage.* $225/£141

McMURTRY, LARRY. Lonesome Dove. NY: S&S, 1985. 1st ed. Signed. Fine in Fine dj. *Unger.* $300/£188

McMURTRY, LARRY. Moving On. NY: S&S, (1970). 1st ed. (Rmdr mk bottom edges), else NF in dj (price-clipped). *Pacific*.* $86/£54

McMURTRY, LARRY. Moving On. NY: S&S, 1970. 1st ed. Signed. Dj (lt worn, soiled). *Dumont.* $150/£94

McMURTRY, LARRY. Somebody's Darling. NY: S&S, (1978). 1st ed. Blue cl, gilt. (Spine extrems sl rubbed), o/w Fine in dj (edges lt browned). *Heritage.* $100/£63

McMURTRY, LARRY. Splendors and Miseries of Being an Author Bookseller. NY, 1995. Only ed. One of 750 ptd. Pb. As New. *Bond.* $15/£9

McMURTRY, LARRY. Streets of Laredo. NY: S&S, 1993. 1st ed. Signed. VF in VF dj. *Unger.* $75/£47

McMURTRY, LARRY. Terms of Endearment. NY: S&S, (1975). 1st ed. Inscribed. VF in dj (extrems lt worn). *Bromer.* $400/£250

McMURTRY, LARRY. Terms of Endearment. NY: S&S, 1975. 1st ed. Fine in dj (lt used, sm tear spine foot). *Beasley.* $50/£31

McNAB, ROBERT. The Old Whaling Days. New Zealand: Whitcombe & Tombs, 1913. 1st ed. Good + (rubbed). *Walcot.* $96/£60

McNAB, ROBERT. The Old Whaling Days. Golden Press, 1975. Rpt. VG in dj. *Walcot.* $18/£11

McNAIL, STANLEY. Something Breathing. Sauk City: Arkham House, 1965. 1st ed. Lighter of the 2 grn bindings. Fine in Fine dj (2 sm closed tears). *Other Worlds.* $275/£172

McNAIR, JAMES B. Rhus Dermatitis...Its Pathology and Chemotherapy. Univ of Chicago, (1923). 1st ed. VG (lib stamp tp). *Glaser.* $45/£28

McNAIR, JAMES B. Simon Cameron's Adventures in Iron, 1837-1846. L.A.: The Author, (1949). 1st ed. one of 500. VG in dj. *Perier.* $35/£22

McNALLY, WILLIAM. Evils and Abuses in the Naval and Merchant Service Exposed. Boston: Cassady & March, 1839. 1st ed. viii,201,(errata)pp. Orig bds (fr cvr loose). *Lefkowicz.* $225/£141

MCNAMARA, BROOKS. The American Playhouse in the Eighteenth Century. Cambridge: Harvard Univ, 1969. 1st ed. 53 plts. Pub's cl. VG in dj. *Dramatis.* $40/£25

McNANNEY, MARY ALICE. The Wabash Story. N.p., March 15, 1955. 1st ed. Fine in pict wrappers (lt browned on edges). *Connolly.* $25/£16

McNEAL, THOMAS ALLEN. When Kansas Was Young. NY: Macmillan, 1922. 1st ed. Good + (cvrs soiled). *Labordo.* $55/£34

McNEELY, S. BLAKE. Bits of Charm in Old Mobile. Mobile: (Privately ptd, 1946). 2nd ptg. 60 full-pg photos. Grn cl. VG. *House.* $30/£19

McNEER, MAY. Stranger in the Pines. Boston: Houghton Mifflin, 1971. 1st ed. Lynd Ward (illus). 8vo. Grn cl. Good in color pict dj (fr lacks piece). *Reisler.* $35/£22

McNEIL, KATHERINE. Gary Snyder. A Bibliography. NY: Phoenix Book Shop, 1983. 1st ed. Fine in wraps. *Beasley.* $25/£16

McNEILL, F. MARIAN. Iona: A History of the Island. Blackie, 1951. 3rd ed. VG. *Hollett.* $24/£15

McNEILL, GEORGE E. Factory Children. Report Upon the Schooling and Hours of Labor.... Senate Doc No 50. Boston: Wright & Potter, 1875. 1st ed. 76pp. Orig ptd wrappers. *M & S.* $175/£109

McNIFF, WILLIAM J. Heaven on Earth. Oxford, OH: Mississippi Valley, 1940. 1st ed. Signed. VG in dj. *Lien.* $45/£28

McNITT, FRANK. The Indian Traders. Norman: Univ of OK, (1962). 1st ed. Color frontis. VF in pict dj. *Argonaut.* $90/£56

McPHARLIN, PAUL. The Puppet Theatre in America. NY: Harper, (1949). 1st ed. VG in pict dj (spine ends chipped). *Dramatis*. $40/£25

McPHEE, COLIN. Music in Bali: A Study in Form.... New Haven/London: Yale Univ, 1966. (Sl damped), o/w VG in dj (sl torn, soiled). *Worldwide*. $125/£78

McPHEE, JOHN. Alaska: Images of the Country. SF: Sierra Club, (1981). 1st ed. One of 500 numbered, signed by McPhee and Galen Rowell (photos). Slipcase. *Swann**. $126/£79

McPHEE, JOHN. Annals of the Former World. NY, 1981. 1st ed. One of 450 numbered, signed. 2 vols. Slipcase. *Swann**. $80/£50

McPHEE, JOHN. La Place de la Concorde Suisse. NY: FSG, 1984. 1st ed. One of 200 numbered, signed. Fine in slipcase. *Smith*. $125/£78

McPHEE, JOHN. Wimbledon: A Celebration. NY: Viking, (1972). 1st ed. Grn cl. Fine in dj (spine head worn, few internally mended tears). *Antic Hay*. $45/£28

McPHERSON, JAMES ALAN et al. Railroad: Trains and Train People in American Culture. Random House, (1976). 1st ed. Nice in dj (lacks piece). *Rybski*. $40/£25

McPHERSON, JAMES ALAN. Elbow Room. Boston, 1977. 1st ed. NF in NF dj (extrems lt rubbed). *Warren*. $30/£19

McPHERSON, JAMES ALAN. Elbow Room. Boston: Atlantic-Little Brown, 1977. 1st ed. (Name, date), else Fine in NF dj (price-clipped). *Pettler*. $100/£63

McPHERSON, JAMES M. The Negro's Civil War. NY, (1965). 1st ed. VG+ in dj (sl worn, chipped). *Pratt*. $32/£20

McQUADE, JAMES. The Cruise of the Montauk to Bermuda, The West Indies and Florida. NY: Thomas R. Knox, 1885. 1st ed. xv,441pp. Gilt, black pict grn cl (cvrs spotted, edges lt worn). VG. *House*. $55/£34

McQUOWN, F. R. Fine-Flowered Cacti. London, 1965. 1st ed. Color frontis. VG in dj (chipped). *Brooks*. $24/£15

McQUOWN, F. R. Fine-Flowered Cacti. Newton Abbot/Devon, 1971. Rev ed. Color frontis. (Leaf carelessly opened resulting in margin tear), else Fine in dj. *Brooks*. $25/£16

McRAE, HUGH. Satyrs and Sunlight. London: Fanfrolico, 1928. One of 550. Fore/lower edges uncut. Orig grn morocco. VG (some plts offset; spine sl faded). *Maggs*. $200/£125

McRAE, MILTON. Forty Years in Newspaperdom. NY: Brentano's, 1924. 1st ed. Frontis. (Fr inner hinge cracked, neatly repaired; spine ends worn), else Good. *Connolly*. $20/£13

McREYNOLDS, EDWIN C. Oklahoma: A History of the Sooner State. Norman: Univ of OK, (1954). 1st ed. VG in dj. *Lien*. $35/£22

McREYNOLDS, EDWIN C. The Seminoles. Norman: Univ of OK, (1957). 1st ed. Red cl. NF in VG dj (sl dampstain, sl affecting lower inner corners of bds; sl chipped, rubbed). *Harrington*. $35/£22

McTYEIRE, H. N. Duties of Masters to Servants: Three Premium Essays. Charleston, SC: Southern Baptist Publication Soc, 1851. 1st ed. 151,(1)pp. (Stain from old sticker tp; spotted, spine faded.) *M & S*. $200/£125

McVICKAR, ARCHIBALD. History of the Expedition...of Captains Lewis and Clark. NY: A.L. Fowle, 1900. Fldg map. VG. *Perier*. $97/£61

McVICKER, MARY LOUISE. The Writings of J. Frank Dobie: A Bibliography. Lawton: Museum of the Great Plains, (1968). 1st ed. Frontisport. Fine in dj. *Argonaut*. $60/£38

McVICKER, MARY LOUISE. The Writings of J. Frank Dobie: A Bibliography. Lawton, 1968. Ltd to 500 numbered, signed. NF in slipcase. *Dumont*. $65/£41

McVOY, LIZZIE CARTER and RUTH BATES CAMPBELL. A Bibliography of Fiction by Louisianians and on Louisiana Subjects. Baton Rouge, 1935. Good in wraps. *Dumont*. $30/£19

McWATTERS, GEORGE S. Knots Untied, or Ways and Byways in the Hidden Life of American Detectives. Hartford: Burr & Hyde, 1872. 665pp. Good+ (extrems very worn). *My Bookhouse*. $42/£26

McWATTERS, GEORGE S. Knots Untied: Or, Ways and By-ways in the Hidden Life of American Detectives. Hartford: J.B. Burr, 1872. 1st ed. Calf, leather spine label. VG. *Pacific**. $29/£18

McWHINEY, GRADY. Attack and Die. University, AL, (1982). 1st ed. Fine in Fine dj. *Pratt*. $32/£20

McWILLIAM, CANDIDA. A Case of Knives. London, 1988. 1st Eng ed. Fine in dj. *Clearwater*. $40/£25

McWILLIAM, CANDIDA. A Little Stranger. London, 1989. 1st Eng ed. Fine in dj. *Clearwater*. $32/£20

McWILLIAMS, CAREY. Factories in the Field. Boston, 1939. 1st ed. (Spine lt spotted), else Good in dj (edge frayed, sl stained). *King*. $35/£22

McWILLIAMS, CAREY. Louis Adamic and Shadow-America. L.A.: Arthur Whipple, (1935). Paper spine/cvr labels. Dj. *Dawson*. $100/£63

McWILLIAMS, MARGARET. Manitoba Milestones. Toronto: J.M. Dent, 1928. 1st ed. Signed. Full-color frontis, 35 plts (2 color). Dec cl. Fine. *Connolly*. $30/£19

MEACHAM, A. B. Wigwam and War-Path. Boston: John P. Dale, 1875. 1st ed. Frontis, xxiv,700pp + ad leaf; 19 full-pg engr illus. Blind-stamped cl, gilt (spine ends, tips lt worn; sm chip to spine head; inner hinges weak). *Dawson*. $200/£125

MEACHAM, A. B. Wigwam and War-Path. Boston, 1875. 2nd and rev ed. 700pp. Debossed cl, silver-stamped. Good (worn esp. at corners, fabric worn through 1 spot on lower fr spine; new eps, book resewn). *Baade*. $250/£156

MEACHAM, WALTER. Bonneville the Bold. Portland: The Author, 1934. 1st ed. Map. VG. *Perier*. $25/£16

MEAD, ELWOOD. Plans of Structures in Use on Irrigation Canals in the United States. Washington: GPO, 1903. 22 plts. Dk grn cl, gilt. (Extrems worn, sm discoloration fr cvr edge), else NF. *Weber*. $50/£31

MEAD, JAMES R. Hunting and Trading on the Great Plains, 1859-1875. Norman: Univ of OK, (1986). 1st ed. Blue cl. Fine in pict dj. *House*. $25/£16

MEAD, JAMES R. Hunting and Trading on the Great Plains, 1859-1875. Schuyler Jones (ed). Norman: Univ of OK, (1986). 1st ed. VG in dj. *Lien*. $30/£19

MEAD, RICHARD. The Medical Works of.... Dublin, 1767. 511pp; 4 fldg plts, 1 fldg plan (1/2 of plan missing). Buckram (rebound). Good. *Doctor's Library*. $265/£166

MEAD, ROBERT D. Ultimate North. NY: Doubleday, 1976. 1st ed. VG in dj (sl torn). *Walcot*. $19/£12

MEADE, L. T. A Bunch of Cousins and the Barn 'Boys'. London: W. & R. Chambers, (c. 1910). 1st ed. 4 plts by Hilda Cowham. Pict orange cl, gilt. (Foxed), else VG. *Pacific**. $35/£22

MEADOWS, DON. The American Occupation of La Paz. L.A.: Glen Dawson, 1955. 1st ed. One of 300 ptd. Black cl-backed ptd red bds. *Argonaut*. $45/£28

MEADOWS, DON. The American Occupation of La Paz. L.A.: Glen Dawson, 1955. 1st ed. Ltd to 300 signed. Fine. *Book Market*. $60/£38

MEADOWS, DON. Baja California 1533-1950. L.A.: Glen Dawson, 1951. 1st ed. Fine. *Book Market*. $30/£19

MEADOWS, DON. Baja California 1533-1950. L.A.: Glen Dawson, 1951. 1st ed. Dec tan cl. Fine. *Argonaut*. $90/£56

MEADOWS, KENNY. Heads of the People or Portraits of the English. London: Robert Tyas, 1840. 1st ed. 2 vols. Teg. 3/4 crushed morocco, marbled bds (orig cl spine strips mtd to prelims), gilt spines, raised bands; bound by Zaehnsdorf. Fine. *Pacific**. $115/£72

MEAKIN, BUDGETT. Life in Morocco and Glimpses Beyond. London: C&W, 1905. 1st ed. 24 plts. (Sl rubbed, soiled, spine ends frayed, spine sticker), o/w VG. *Worldwide*. $40/£25

MEAKINS, JONATHAN C. and H. WHITRIDGE DAVIES. Respiratory Function in Disease. Edinburgh: Oliver & Boyd, 1925. 1st ed. VG. *Glaser*. $35/£22

MEANY, TOM et al. Boston Red Sox. Barnes, 1956. 1st ed. VG in VG dj. *Plapinger*. $75/£47

MEANY, TOM et al. The Magnificent Yankees. Barnes, 1952. 1st ed. VG in Good dj. *Plapinger*. $55/£34

MEANY, TOM. Joe DiMaggio: Yankee Clipper. Barnes, 1951. 1st ed. (Sm spine chip), o/w VG. *Plapinger*. $40/£25

MEANY, TOM. Ralph Kiner: The Heir Apparent. Barnes, 1951. 1st ed. VG + . *Plapinger*. $45/£28

MEANY, TOM. Stan Musial: The Man. Barnes, 1951. 1st ed. VG. *Plapinger*. $60/£38

MEANY, TOM. Ted Williams: Hitting Unlimited. Barnes, 1951. 1st ed. VG. *Plapinger*. $55/£34

MEARES, JOHN. Voyages Made in the Years 1788 and 1789, from China to the North West Coast of America.... London: Logographic, 1790. Early ed. 2 vols. 8.5x5.25. xii,lxxii,363; (4),332,(62),(1)pp; 8 fldg maps, 4 copper plts (2 fldg). Period tree calf, gilt, morocco spine labels. (Tape repair to 1 pg), else NF set. Howes M469. *Pacific**. $1,035/£647

MEARNS, DAVID C. (ed). The Lincoln Papers. GC: Doubleday, 1948. 2 vols. Frontisport each vol. Tan buckram. Fine in VG djs. *House*. $40/£25

MEARNS, DAVID C. (ed). The Lincoln Papers. NY: Doubleday, 1948. 1st ed. 2 vols. 2 frontispieces. Beige linen. Boxed. *Appelfeld*. $45/£28

Medical Extracts. On the Nature of Health, and the Laws of the Nervous and Fibrous Systems.... (By Robert John Thornton.) London: J. Johnson et al, 1798. 3rd ed. 3 vols. (4),iii,(66),(4),cxxxi,134; (2),ii,(71),(4),xlvi,(135)-334; (3),(93),335-657pp; 7 hand-colored plts (4 fldg). Contemp full mottled calf (worn, broken). Good set. *Glaser*. $250/£156

MEDICAL SOCIETY OF THE CITY AND COUNTY OF NEW-YORK. Report on the Epidemic Small Pox and Chicken Pox.... NY: G. Forman, 1816. 1st ed. 28pp. Mod 3/4 cl over marbled bds. VG (lt foxed). *Glaser*. $200/£125

MEDLEY, JULIUS GEORGE. An Autumn Tour in the United States and Canada. London: Henry S. King, 1873. 1st ed. Ptd presentation-slip tipped in. pp vii,180,(2) + 32 ads. Dec grn cl. *Mott*. $125/£78

MEEK, MARCELLUS W. Fur Rabbits. L.A.: Southland, 1927. 2nd ed. (Sl underlining.) Wrappers. *Hollett*. $32/£20

MEEKER, ARTHUR. Prairie Avenue. NY: Knopf, 1949. 1st ed. Presentation inscribed, signed. VG in pict dj (sl worn). *Cady*. $30/£19

MEEKER, DAVID. Jazz in the Movies: A Guide to Jazz Musicians, 1917-1977. New Rochelle: Arlington House, (1977). 1st US ed. Pict glazed bds. VG. *Petrilla*. $35/£22

MEEKER, E. Hop Culture in the United States. Puyallup, Washington Territory: E. Meeker & Co, (1883). 1st ed. 170pp; 4 plts; trade card for George W. Elkins laid in. NF (rubberstamps on tp). *Pacific**. $138/£86

MEEKER, EZRA. The Busy Life of Eighty Five Years of Ezra Meekers Ventures and Adventures. Seattle: The Author, (1916). Signed presentation. VG in dec cl. *Perier*. $65/£41

MEEKER, EZRA. Pioneer Reminiscences of Puget Sound. Seattle: Lowman & Hanford, 1905. 1st ed. Signed. VG. *Perier*. $95/£59

MEEKER, EZRA. Pioneer Reminiscences of Puget Sound: The Tragedy of Leschi.... Seattle: Lowman & Hanford, 1905. 1st ed. Frontis. Blue cl, gilt. NF (rubbed, corners, spine ends sl bumped). Howes M377. *Argonaut*. $150/£94

MEESE, WILLIAM A. Abraham Lincoln. Moline, IL, (1908). 1st ed. Frontisport. Ptd card wraps bound in cl. *Wantagh*. $50/£31

MEGGENDORFER, LOTHAR. The Dolls House. London/NY: Kestrel/Viking, 1978. Glazed pict bds. VG. *Bookfinders*. $50/£31

MEGGENDORFER, LOTHAR. Lothar Meggendorfer's International Circus. London/NY: Kestrel/Viking, 1983. 6 fold-out panels w/pull-down scenes. Glazed pict bds. VG. *Bookfinders*. $50/£31

MEGGENDORFER, LOTHAR. Surprise! Surprise! NY: Viking, 1982. 5pp pull-tab moving pictures. Glazed pict bds. (Bkpl removed inside fr cvr), o/w VG. *Bookfinders*. $40/£25

MEHL, DIETER. The Elizabethan Dumb Show. Methuen, 1965. 1st Eng ed. Fine in dj (sl creased). *Ulysses*. $32/£20

MEHNERT, KLAUS. The Russians in Hawaii 1804-1819. Honolulu: Univ of HI, (1939). 1st ed. Frontis. Fine in ptd gray wrappers (extrems dknd). *Argonaut*. $75/£47

MEIER-GRAEFE, JULIUS. Degas. London, 1923. 1st ed. One of 1000. NF (sl soiled, sm spine nick, sl rubbed). *Polyanthos*. $125/£78

MEIGS, ARTHUR. A Study of the Human Blood-Vessels in Health and Disease. Phila, 1907. 1st ed. *Fye*. $150/£94

MEIGS, CHARLES D. Woman: Her Diseases and Remedies, Series of Letters to His Class. Phila, 1854. 3rd ed. 672pp. Full calf (repaired). Poor (ex-lib, foxed, eps damaged). *Doctor's Library*. $40/£25

MEIGS, CORNELIA. The Covered Bridge. NY: Macmillan, 1936. 1st ed. 5.75x6.5. Marguerite de Angeli (illus). 145pp. VG in dj. *Cattermole*. $35/£22

MEIGS, CORNELIA. Mother Makes Christmas. NY: G&D, 1940. 1st ed. Lois Lenski (illus). Sq 4to. Cl-backed color pict bds. Good in color dj (lt marginal wear). *Reisler*. $50/£31

MEIGS, JOHN (ed). Peter Hurd: The Lithographs. (Lubbock): Baker Gallery, 1968. One of 300. Inscribed, signed, titled (orig litho frontis) by Hurd. Olive grn morocco. Fine in slipcase. *Pacific**. $288/£180

MEIKLE, HENRY W. Scotland. Thomas Nelson & Sons, 1947. 105 plts (9 color). VG. *Hollett*. $48/£30

MEINE, FRANKLIN (ed). Tall Tales of the Southwest. NY: Knopf, 1930. 1st ed. Fine in dj. *Labordo*. $85/£53

MEINERTZHAGEN, FREDERICK. The Art of the Netsuke Carver. London: Routledge/Kegan Paul, 1956. 1st ed. 16 plts. (Sl rubbed), o/w VG. *Worldwide*. $35/£22

MEINERTZHAGEN, RICHARD. Army Diary 1899-1926. London: Oliver & Boyd, 1960. 1st ed. 39 plts. Fine in dj (sl rubbed). *Ulysses*. $256/£160

MEINERTZHAGEN, RICHARD. Birds of Arabia. Edinburgh/London: Oliver & Boyd, 1954. 1st ed. 4to. 28 plts. Tan cl. *Christie's**. $736/£460

MEINERTZHAGEN, RICHARD. Kenya Diary 1902-1906. Oliver & Boyd, 1957. 1st ed. (Bkpl), else NF in Good+ dj (spine chipped). *Any Amount*. $136/£85

MEINERTZHAGEN, RICHARD. Middle East Diary 1917-1956. London: Cresset, 1959. 1st ed. Map. Fine in dj (sl tanned). *Ulysses*. $272/£170

MEINERTZHAGEN, RICHARD. Nicoll's Birds of Egypt. London: Hugh Rees, 1930. 1st ed. 2 vols. Frontisport, 3 maps, 37 plts. Grn cl. (Inner hinges strengthened; bumped.) *Christie's**. $386/£241

MEISEL, LOUIS K. Photorealism. NY, (1982). 3rd ptg. Folio. Dj. *Swann**. $57/£36

MEISS, MILLARD and ELIZABETH H. BEATSON. The Belles Heures of Jean, Duke of Berry. NY, 1974. Good in dj. *Washton*. $50/£31

MEISS, MILLARD. French Painting in the Time of Jean de Berry: The Boucicant Master. London: Phaidon, 1968. Color frontis, 497 plts (bottom edge crinkled, separated w/abrasion, not affecting illus). Maroon cl. Dj. *Maggs.* $48/£30

MEISTER, MICHAEL W. and M. A. DHAKY (eds). Encyclopedia of Indian Temple Architecture. South India. Upper Dravidadesa. Early Phase, A. D. 550-1075. Phila, 1986. 2 vols. Good in dj. *Washton.* $175/£109

MELDOLA, RAPHAEL. The Chemistry of Photography. London: Macmillan, 1891. xiv,382pp, 6 ads. VG (lt worn). *Cahan.* $85/£53

MELENDY, H. B. and B. GILBERT. The Governors of California: Peter H. Burnett to Edmund G. Brown. Georgetown: Talisman, 1965. 1st ed. Ltd to 1000. Fine in dj (spine dknd). *Argonaut.* $100/£63

MELLEN, PETER. The Group of Seven. Toronto, 1970. Dj, slipcase. *Swann*.* $57/£36

MELLICK, ANDREW D., JR. Lesser Crossroads. Hubert G. Schmidt (ed). Rutgers Univ, 1948. 1st ed. Dec cl. VG in Good dj. *Connolly.* $25/£16

MELLON, J. African Hunter. Long Beach: Safari, (1986). 2nd ed. Fine in Fine dj. *Mikesh.* $150/£94

MELTZER, DAVID. Poems. SF: Donald & Alice Schenker, n.d. One of 25. Signed by Meltzer & Donald Schenker. Cl-backed pict flexible bds. (Soiled), else VG. *Pacific*.* $63/£39

MELVILLE, A. PATTERSON (ed). Duval's Artistic Anatomy. London, 1911. Rev ed. 104 woodcuts. *Fye.* $75/£47

MELVILLE, GEORGE W. In the Lena Delta. Boston: Houghton Mifflin, 1885. xiii,497pp; 4 maps. Good+ (spine ends sl rubbed). *Walcot.* $93/£58

MELVILLE, GEORGE W. In the Lena Delta. Melville Philips (ed). Boston: Houghton Mifflin, 1885. 1st ed. xvi,498pp + 8pp ads (inner fr hinge starting); 16 plts, 4 dbl-pg maps. Dec olive cl (spine extrems lt worn). *Karmiole.* $125/£78

MELVILLE, HERMAN. Battle-Pieces and Aspects of the War. NY: Harper, 1866. 1st ed. 8vo. 272pp. Terra-cotta cl, beveled edges. NF in custom red cl chemise, full morocco slipcase. BAL 13673. *Chapel Hill.* $2,000/£1,250

MELVILLE, HERMAN. Billy Budd and Beneto Cereno. LEC, 1965. Ltd to 1500 numbered, signed by Robert Shore (illus). Fine in slipcase. *Swann*.* $69/£43

MELVILLE, HERMAN. Israel Potter: His Fifty Years of Exile. NY: Putnam, 1855. 1st ed, 1st issue. Grn cl. (Sig tp, fep; lt worn, faded), o/w Fine. BAL 13667. *Cummins.* $1,000/£625

MELVILLE, HERMAN. Journal up the Straits. October 11, 1856-May 5, 1857. Raymond Weaver (ed). NY: The Colophon, 1935. 1st ed. Paper bds, leather spine label (lacks edge, not affecting print). VG. BAL 13690. *Second Life.* $125/£78

MELVILLE, HERMAN. Mardi: And a Voyage Thither. NY, 1849. 1st Amer ed. 2 vols. Pub's gilt-lettered purple cl. (Ex-lib, ink stamps; backstrips faded.) BAL 13658. *Swann*.* $373/£233

MELVILLE, HERMAN. Mardi: and a Voyage Thither. NY, 1849. 1st US ed. Clipped sig removed from scrapbook laid in. 2 vols. Orig purple cl. (Spines faded, spine tops chipped), o/w VG set. BAL 13658. *Kane*.* $2,700/£1,688

MELVILLE, HERMAN. Moby Dick. Berkeley: Univ of CA, (1981). One of 750 ptd. Folio. Blue cl, silver-lettered spine. Fine in slipcase. *Pacific*.* $63/£39

MELVILLE, HERMAN. Moby Dick. NY: Random House, 1930. Aeg. Pict blue morocco, gilt. (Spine sunned, ends sl scuffed), else VG. *Pacific*.* $75/£47

MELVILLE, HERMAN. Moby Dick. NY: Random House, 1930. 1st trade ed w/these illus. Rockwell Kent (illus). Black pict cl stamped in silver. Clean (bkpl; spine sl rubbed) in complete pict dj (spine sl worn, chipped, sl dusty, handled, few sm edge-tears). *Baltimore*.* $90/£56

MELVILLE, HERMAN. Moby Dick. Chicago, 1930. One of 1000 sets. 4to. Rockwell Kent (illus). 3 vols. Aluminum slipcase. *Swann*.* $1,610/£1,006

MELVILLE, HERMAN. Moby Dick. Chicago: Lakeside Press, 1930. One of 1000. 3 vols. 4to. Uncut, partly unopened. Stamped cl. Metal slipcase. Mint. *Argosy.* $2,200/£1,375

MELVILLE, HERMAN. Moby Dick. LEC, 1943. Ltd to 1500 numbered, signed by Boardman Robinson (illus). 2 vols. Fine in slipcase. *Swann*.* $287/£179

MELVILLE, HERMAN. Moby Dick. (NY): Artist's Ltd Ed, 1975. Ltd to 1500 numbered. Preface signed by Jacques-Yves Cousteau. Color serigraph frontis signed by LeRoy Neiman (illus); 12 dbl-pg color plts. Full brn morocco, gilt. Fine in pub's matching slipcase. *Karmiole.* $1,000/£625

MELVILLE, HERMAN. Moby Dick. SF: Arion, 1979. One of 265. Folio. Barry Moser wood engrs. Prospectus laid in. Full blue morocco, silver spine title. VF in slipcase (lt faded). *Bromer.* $4,000/£2,500

MELVILLE, HERMAN. Moby-Dick. NY: Harper, 1851. 1st Amer ed, 1st binding w/pub's circular device to cvrs, brn/orange eps. xxiii,(1),634,(2) + (6)ads pp. Orig drab purple-brn cl, gilt. (Ink name, dated 1851, feps; tp lt foxed; corners showing, spine ends, joints expertly repaired, tender, spine sl creased), else VG. BAL 13664. *Pacific*.* $7,475/£4,672

MELVILLE, HERMAN. Narrative of a Four Months' Residence. London: John Murray, 1846. 1st ed, 1st issue, 1st bk. W/reading 'Pomarea' on p19 line 1. 8vo. xvi,285pp; map. Mod 3/4 calf, marbled bds, gilt extra, leather label. Nice. BAL 13655. *Hartfield.* $1,500/£938

MELVILLE, HERMAN. Omoo. John Murray, 1847. Pub's cat; map. Sprinkled edges. Mod 1/4 leather, cl, raised bands. VG. *Tiger.* $512/£320

MELVILLE, HERMAN. Omoo. NY: Harper, 1847. 1st Amer ed. 16pp undated ads (in addition to the 9pp integral 'Publishers' Advertisement' ads, numbered [xv]-xxiii). Orig blindstamped gray-grn cl, gilt: the so-called 'green TB' cl, w/the orig marbled eps. NF (foxed; spine foot sl worn, sm 1/4-inch stain fr cvr) in VG morocco-backed slipcase. *Sumner & Stillman.* $3,750/£2,344

MELVILLE, HERMAN. Omoo. NY: Dodd, Mead, 1924. 1st illus ed. Black cl, gilt. Fine. *Pacific*.* $138/£86

MELVILLE, HERMAN. Omoo. LEC, 1961. Ltd to 1500 numbered, signed by Reynolds Stone (illus). Fine in slipcase. *Swann*.* $126/£79

MELVILLE, HERMAN. The Piazza Tales. NY: Elf, 1929. Ltd to 750 numbered. Color frontis, 5 b/w plts. Vellum-like spine, purple bds (spine lt soiled). *Karmiole.* $75/£47

MELVILLE, HERMAN. Typee. LEC, 1935. Ltd to 1500 numbered, signed by Miguel Covarrubias (illus). Fine in slipcase. *Swann*.* $138/£86

MELVILLE, HERMAN. Typee: A Peep at Polynesian Life...Revised Edition, with a Sequel. London: Routledge, 1850. Pub's cl (spine ends frayed, joints starting). 1/4 sheep fldg case. *Swann*.* $69/£43

MELVILLE, HERMAN. White Jacket; or, The World in a Man-of-War. London: Richard Bentley, 1850. 1st ed. One of 1000 sets. 2 vols. Mod calf, marbled bds, gilt labels. Good (finger soiling, corner creases). BAL 13661. *Reese.* $3,250/£2,031

MELVILLE, HERMAN. White-Jacket; or the World in a Man-of-War. NY: Harper, 1850. 1st Amer ed, later ptg. 465,(1)pp. Orig blind-stamped brn cl, gilt. (Corners rubbed, spine ends frayed), else VG. *Pacific*.* $46/£29

MELVILLE, JAMES. The Chrysanthemum Chain. Secker, 1980. 1st UK ed. NF in dj. *Williams.* $32/£20

MELVILLE, JAMES. The Death Ceremony. Secker, 1985. 1st UK ed. Fine in dj. *Williams.* $29/£18

MELVILLE, JAMES. Death of a Daimyo. Secker, 1984. 1st UK ed. NF in dj (laminate sl creased). *Williams*. $40/£25

MELVILLE, JAMES. Kimono for a Corpse. Secker, 1987. 1st UK ed. NF in Fine dj. *Williams*. $29/£18

MELVILLE, JAMES. The Wages of Zen. Secker, 1979. 1st UK ed, 1st bk. NF in dj. *Williams*. $64/£40

MELVILLE, LEWIS. Brighton: Its History, Its Follies and Its Fashions. London, 1909. 1st ed. (Bkpl; spine sl faded, head sl chipped.) *Edwards*. $61/£38

MELVILLE, LEWIS. The London Scene. Faber & Gwyer, 1926. 1st Eng ed. 15 half-tone plts. Unopened. VG (inscrip, feps partly browned; spine ends sl bumped) in dj (dusty, rubbed, chipped, torn). *Ulysses*. $72/£45

MELVILLE, ROBERT. The Legend of Ned Kelly. NY: Viking, (1964). 1st Amer ed. 27 color plts. Fine in dj. *Turtle Island*. $40/£25

Memoir of James Jackson, Jr. M.D. (By J. Jackson.) Boston, 1835. Signed presentation. 444pp. Contemp cl, paper label. (Eps foxed, bkpl), o/w VG. *Whitehart*. $288/£180

Memoir of Lieut. Edward Lewis Mitchell. NY: Pub for the Metropolitan Fair for the US Sanitary Commission, 1864. 1st ed. 52pp. Stamped blue cl. VG (sl spotted, spine ends, corners sl worn). *Chapel Hill*. $150/£94

Memoir of William Cookworthy, Formerly of Plymouth, Devonshire. By His Grandson. London: William & Frederick G. Cash, 1854. 1st ed. (iv),207pp + 4 ads. (Edges, spine faded.) *Young*. $88/£55

Memoirs of a Forty-Niner. (By Katie E. Blood.) New Haven, CT, 1907. 1st ed. VG + in wrappers, tied w/orig string. Howes B544. *Sagebrush*. $300/£188

Memoirs of a Fox-Hunting Man. (By Siegfried Sassoon.) NY: Coward-McCann, 1929. 1st US ed. Red cl stamped in black. NF in pict dj (1-inch snag loss in spine panel). *Reese*. $125/£78

Memoirs of an Infantry Officer. (By Siegfried Sassoon.) London: Faber & Faber, (1930). 1st ed, trade issue. Signed. Pub's leaflet laid in. Gilt blue cl. (Spine sl sunned, foxed through dj), o/w Nice in NF dj (sm closed tears at spine crown). *Reese*. $225/£141

Memoirs of an Infantry Officer. (By Siegfried Sassoon.) NY: Coward McCann, 1930. 1st US ed. Red cl stamped in black. VF in dj. *Reese*. $150/£94

Memoirs of an Infantry Officer. (By Siegfried Sassoon.) Faber, 1930. 1st ed. One of 750 signed. Teg, rest untrimmed. Mid-blue buckram, gilt. Good (spine faded, 5 sm areas of spotting to cvrs). *Blackwell's*. $240/£150

Memoirs of Extraordinary Popular Delusions and the Madness of Crowds. (By Charles Mackay.) London: Office of Nat'l Illus Library, 1852. 1st illus ed. 2 vols. Frontispieces, extra engr tps. Brn blind-stamped cl, gilt. (Lt foxed, ink inscrip; neatly recased w/new eps), o/w VG set. *Reese*. $125/£78

Memoirs of Literature. Containing a Large Account of Many Valuable Books, Letters and Dissertations Upon Several Subjects, Miscellaneous Observations, &c. (By Michael de la Roches.) London, 1722. 2nd ed. 8 vols. Contemp calf (rubbed, spines worn, dried; browned, foxed). *Oinonen**. $110/£69

Memoirs of Major Robert Stobo of the Virginia Regiment. Pittsburgh: John Davidson, 1854. 1st Amer ed. (6),92pp. VG (backstrip expertly repaired). *Cullen*. $350/£219

Memoirs of Other Fronts. (By John Rodker.) London: Putnam, (1932). 1st ed. Brn linen. (Eps lt foxed), o/w VG in pict dj (sl tanned, nicked, sl loss at spine crown internally reinforced). *Reese*. $150/£94

Memoirs of the Gloucester Fox Hunting Club, New Philadelphia. (By William Milnor.) NY: Derrydale, 1927. One of 375 numbered. Mtd frontis, port. Uncut. Pink bds, paper labels. (Sl worn, spine tip chipped, cvrs spotted.) *Oinonen**. $50/£31

Memoirs of the Life of Catherine Phillips. (By Catherine Phillips.) Phila: Robert Johnson, 1798. 1st Amer ed. 384pp. Full leather (fr joint broken, spine worn). Fair (tp torn). *Book Broker*. $300/£188

Memoirs of the Life of the Late John Mytton, Esq. (By Charles J. Apperley.) London, 1837. 2nd ed. Aeg. Pub's gilt-pict cl. (Sl worn, sl foxed, etc, 2 sigs sprung; spine tips sl frayed.) Protective cl solander case provided. *Oinonen**. $275/£172

Memoirs of the Life of the Late John Mytton, Esq. (By Charles Apperley.) London, 1837. 2nd ed, 1st issue, containing 6 more plts than 1st ed, w/8pp of Ackerman's ads at rear. 8vo. Engr tp. Later polished calf, gilt extra, by Riviere (orig cvr, spine bound in at rear). *Swann**. $546/£341

Memorial and Biographical History of the Counties of Fresno, Tulare and Kern, California. Chicago: Lewis Pub Co, (c. 1892). 1st ed. 822pp; 19 plts. Aeg. Orig full morocco, gilt. VG + (tp creased; hinges expertly reinforced; extrems sl worn). *Harrington*. $450/£281

Memorial of George Brown Goode, Together with a Selection of His Papers on Museums and on the History of Science in America. Washington: GPO, 1901. Frontisport, 109 full-pg ports. (Few cvr spots), else VG. *Glaser*. $100/£63

Memorial of Margaret E. Breckinridge. Phila: Lippincott, 1865. 1st ed. Orig albumen photo frontisport, 103pp. Teg. Dk brn cl (lt worn; lacks spine portion, rmdr nearly detached), gilt. Very Clean. *Baltimore**. $95/£59

Men and Manners in America. (By Thomas Hamilton.) Phila: Carey, Lea & Blanchard, 1833. 2nd Amer ed. 2 vols. (Fep cracked vol 1.) Orig cl-backed bds (spines faded), paper labels. Howes H138. *Mott*. $75/£47

Men and Manners in America. (By Thomas Hamilton.) Edinburgh: W. Blackwood, 1833. 1st ed. Inscribed. 2 vols. ix,383,(1) blank,(2) ads; (6),402pp. Uncut. Orig grn cl (old repair fr inner hinge vol 1), paper labels. Howes H138. *Mott*. $300/£188

MENCKEN, H. L. The American Language: A Preliminary Inquiry into the Development of English in the United States. NY: Knopf, 1919. 1st trade ed. One of 1500 numbered. Top edge stained dk blue; untrimmed. Black buckram. (May 1919 sig; cvrs sl warped.) Text VG in plain ptd dj w/red lettering (spine, edges sun-browned, sl worn, chipped, sig). *Baltimore**. $330/£206

MENCKEN, H. L. The Artist. Boston: John W. Luce, 1912. 1st ed. Pict bds. NF (spine sl dknd, extrems lt rubbed). *Heritage*. $300/£188

MENCKEN, H. L. A Book of Prefaces. NY, 1917. 1st ed. Dj (tips, corners sl worn). *Swann**. $488/£305

MENCKEN, H. L. Christmas Story. NY, 1946. 1st ed. (Binding lt faded, spotted.) Dj. *Woolson*. $25/£16

MENCKEN, H. L. The Eminent Physician. (Berkeley: Gillick Press, 1940.) One of 529. Pamphlet. 7pp. Wraps. Fine in ptd yellow dj. *Agvent*. $300/£188

MENCKEN, H. L. The Gist of Nietzsche. Boston: John W. Luce, 1910. 1st ed. VG (sl worn). *Lenz*. $125/£78

MENCKEN, H. L. Menckeniana: A Schimpflexikon. NY: Knopf, 1928. 1st ed. Signed. 1/4 cl, paper spine/cvr labels. (Soiled, esp spine, lacks piece of cvr label), else VG. *Pacific**. $138/£86

MENCKEN, H. L. Menckeniana: A Schimpflexikon. NY: Knopf, 1928. 1st ltd ed. One of 230 numbered, signed. Black eps; untrimmed. Yellow buckram, red bds, gilt paper labels. (Spine sl dknd, label lettering faded.) Internally VF in black paper-cvrd board slipcase (sl rubbed, dusty, spine dented, partial crack, few tears to paper surface) w/mtd paper label. *Baltimore**. $300/£188

MENCKEN, H. L. Notes on Democracy. NY: Knopf, (1926). 1st ed. One of 200. Signed. 1/2 cl, paper spine label. (Extrems sunned), else VG. *Pacific**. $184/£115

MENCKEN, H. L. Prejudices, Third Series. NY: Knopf, (1922). 1st ed. VF in navy cl. Dj (extrems sl toned). *Bromer*. $475/£297

MENCKEN, H. L. et al. Europe After 8:15. NY: John Lane, 1914. 1st ed. VG+ in dj (lt soiled, upper extrems worn). *Lame Duck*. $500/£313

MENCKEN, H. L. et al. Europe After 8:15. NY: John Lane, 1914. 1st ed. Thomas Hart Benton (illus). NF (sigs) in orange pict cl (lt worn, spine ends dknd). Dj (lt stained, spine dknd, sig). *Bromer*. $525/£328

MENDEL, LAFAYETTE. Nutrition: the Chemistry of Life. New Haven, 1923. 1st ed. *Fye*. $75/£47

MENDELSSOHN, SIDNEY. South African Bibliography. Cambridge, MA, 1993. Rpt of 1910 ed. One of 175 sets. 2 vols. New in red cl. *Adelson*. $145/£91

MENDENHALL, WALTER C. Some Desert Watering Places in Southeastern California and Southwestern Nevada. Washington: GPO, 1909. 1st ed. VG (lacks pocket map). *Book Market*. $45/£28

MENGEL, WILLI. Ottmar Mergenthaler and the Printing Revolution. Brooklyn, NY, 1954. 1st ed. Port. Vellum backed bds. (Corners bumped, spine dull.) *King*. $22/£14

MENJOU, ADOLPHE and M. M. MUSSELMAN. It Took Nine Tailors. NY, (1948). 1st Amer ed. Signed by Menjou, 1948. NF (sl rubbed, traces of removed scotch tape) in dj (chips, rubbed, mended w/scotch tape). *Polyanthos*. $30/£19

MENPES, DOROTHY and MORTIMER. Brittany. London: A&C Black, 1905. One of 350 signed by Mortimer Menpes. W/add'l inscrip. 75 color repro plts. Cream cl, gilt. *Marlborough*. $240/£150

MENPES, DOROTHY. Venice. A&C Black, 1912. 75 color plts, guards. Teg. Blue dec cl, gilt. VG. *Cox*. $32/£20

MENPES, MORTIMER. Venice. A&C Black, 1904. 1st ed. 100 full-pg color illus. Marbled eps; all edges marbled. Full tree calf, contemp prize binding, gilt, raised bands. VG (bkpl). *Sotheran*. $312/£195

MENZEL, DOROTHY. Pottery Style and Society in Ancient Peru. Berkeley: Univ of CA, (1976). 64 plts. Fine in dj. *Archaeologia*. $85/£53

MENZHAUSEN, J. The Green Vaults. Leipzig, c1968. Leipzig ed. Fine in dj, cardbd slipcase. *Blake*. $150/£94

MERA, H. P. Navajo Textile Arts. Santa Fe, (1947). Paper-cvrd bds. (Bkpl; spine faded, head worn), else VG. *Dumont*. $150/£94

MERA, H. P. Pueblo Indian Embroidery. Santa Fe, 1943. 26 plts (2 color). (Cvrs soiled, hinges reinforced), else VG in wraps. *Dumont*. $200/£125

MERA, H. P. The Rain Bird. Santa Fe, 1937. 48 plts. Stiff paper wraps. VG in dj (stained). *Dumont*. $225/£141

MERCER, A. S. The Banditti of the Plains. Norman: Univ of OK, (1955). Good in dj (sl worn). *Lien*. $17/£11

MERCER, ERIC. Furniture 700-1700. London, 1969. 16 color plts. (Lib ink stamp fep.) Dj (spine faded). *Edwards*. $29/£18

MERCER, F. A. Gardens and Gardening 1950. London: Studio, 1950. (Browned, ink inscrip; corners bumped), else VG. *Fair Meadow*. $30/£19

MERCER, F. A. Gardens and Gardening, 1937. London, 1937. 3 color tipped-on plts. (Ex-lib.) *Larry Price*. $25/£16

MERCER, HENRY C. Ancient Carpenters' Tools Illustrated and Explained Together with the Implements of the Lumberman.... Doylestown, PA, 1929. (Sl worn.) *Oinonen**. $130/£81

MERCER, HENRY C. The Hill-Caves of Yucatan. Norman: Univ of OK, (1975). (Sig.) Dj. *Archaeologia*. $35/£22

MERCIER, CHARLES. Criminal Responsibility. NY, 1926. Red, tooled cl. (Corners worn), o/w NF. *Doctor's Library*. $40/£25

MEREDITH, EDGAR. Our Stranger. London: Grayson & Grayson, (1936). 1st ed. Gilt black cl. (Fore-edge sl dusty), o/w VG in VG- dj (old mends to sm closed tear top of fr panel, longer mend in rear panel). *Reese*. $65/£41

MEREDITH, GEORGE. Letters of George Meredith. Constable, 1912. 2 vols. Frontisports. Teg. Good (pencil sigs, fore-edges spotted; spines bumped, sunned, sl splash mks to cvrs). *Tiger*. $45/£28

MEREDITH, GEORGE. Lord Ormont and His Aminta. London, 1894. 1st ed. One of 1500. 3 vols. Olive grn cl, gilt. (Sl foxed, spine sl rubbed.) *Kane**. $28/£18

MEREDITH, GEORGE. The Shaving of Shagpat. LEC, 1955. Ltd to 1500 numbered, signed by Honore Guilbeau (illus). Fine in slipcase. *Swann**. $57/£36

MEREDITH, GEORGE. The Works of George Meredith. NY: Scribner, 1909-12. Memorial ed. 37 vols. Photogravure frontispieces. Grn cl, gilt, glassine. (Glassine chipped), else Fine set. *Pacific**. $259/£162

MEREDITH, MRS. CHARLES. Notes and Sketches of New South Wales. London: John Murray, 1844. 1st ed. 1/2-title, xi,(i)blank,164pp. Maroon pebble cl, gilt. VG (sm ink lib stamps; spine ends rubbed, faded). *Morrell*. $80/£50

MEREDITH, ROY (ed). Mr. Lincoln's General. U.S. Grant. NY: Dutton, 1959. 1st ed. Blue bds, navy cl spine. (Lt soiled), else NF in dj. *Chapel Hill*. $35/£22

MEREDITH, WILLIAM. The Cheer. NY, 1980. 1st Amer ed. Fine in Fine dj. *Polyanthos*. $25/£16

MERIMEE, PROSPER. Carmen. LEC, 1941. Ltd to 1500 numbered, signed by Jean Charlot (illus). Fine in slipcase. *Swann**. $172/£108

MERINGTON, MARGUERITE (ed). The Custer Story. NY: Devin-Adair, 1950. 1st ed. The true 1st state's dj has a navy blue background and the cl cvr is dk blue shade. Dk blue cl. NF in dk blue dj. *Labordo*. $125/£78

MERKIN, RICHARD. Velvet Eden: The Richard Merkin Collection of Erotic Photography. NY: Methuen, 1979. 1st Amer ed. Illus eps. Fine in NF illus dj. *Cahan*. $85/£53

MERKLEY, CHRISTOPHER. Biography of Christopher Merkley. Salt Lake City: J.H. Parry, 1887. 1-46pp. Il. Orig pink ptd wrapper (spine faded, worn, lt soiled). Howes M537. *Parmer*. $125/£78

MERLE D'AUBIGNE, J. H. Germany, England and Scotland. London: Simpkin Marshall, 1848. xvi,506pp, 1f. 1/2 calf. *Marlborough*. $192/£120

MERRIAM, C. HART and LEONARD STEJNEGER. Results of a Biological Survey of the San Francisco Mountain Region and Desert of the Little Colorado, Arizona. Washington: GPO, 1890. 136pp + 13 full-pg plts, 5 dbl-pg maps at rear. Gray wraps. VG+ (lt worn, soiled). *Five Quail*. $125/£78

MERRIAM, J. C. The Fauna of Rancho La Brea. Berkeley: Univ of CA, 1911-1912. 1st ed. 2 vols. 14 plts; map. Partly uncut. (Edges several pp stained), else VG in wraps. *Mikesh*. $45/£28

MERRICK, GEORGE BYRON. Old Times on the Upper Mississippi: The Recollections of a Steamboat Pilot from 1854 to 1863. Cleveland: A.H. Clark, 1909. 1st ed. Map. Teg. Blue cl, gilt. (Rubberstamp; spine damp-stained, corners lt bumped), else VG. Howes M539. *Pacific**. $98/£61

MERRICK, GORDON. One for the Gods. (NY): Bernard Geis, (1974). 1st ed. (One corner bumped), else Fine in Fine dj (lt rubbed). *Between The Covers*. $75/£47

MERRICK, L. Conrad in Quest of His Youth. Richards, 1903. 1st ed. (Fore-edge lt foxed), else VG. *Fine Books*. $175/£109

MERRIHEW, S. WALLIS. The Quest of the Davis Cup. Amer Lawn Tennis, 1928. 1st ed. VG in Good dj. *Plapinger*. $75/£47

MERRILL, G. The Non-Metallic Minerals. NY: Wiley, c1904. 1st ed. Good. *Blake*. $45/£28

MERRILL, JAMES. The Country of a Thousand Years of Peace and Other Poems. NY: Knopf, 1959. 1st ed. Fine in dj. *Reese.* $125/£78

MERRILL, JAMES. Divine Comedies. NY: Atheneum, 1976. 1st ed. Fine in dj (rear edges sl creased). *Dermont.* $35/£22

MERRILL, JAMES. The Firescreen. NY: Atheneum, 1969. 1st ed. Apparent pb orig. VG + . *Pharos.* $45/£28

MERRILL, JAMES. The Firescreen. London: C&W, 1970. 1st Eng ed. Fine in dj. *Pharos.* $85/£53

MERRILL, JAMES. First Poems. NY: Knopf, 1951. 1st ed. One of 990 numbered. Fine in NF dj (edges lt tanned). *Reese.* $175/£109

MERRILL, JAMES. Jim's Book. NY: Privately ptd, 1942. 1st ed, 1st bk. Tall 8vo. 1/4 cl, gilt-lettered bds (sl bowed; eps, pastedowns lt foxed). *Swann*.* $1,265/£791

MERRILL, JAMES. Mirabell: Books of Number. NY: Atheneum, 1978. 1st ed. Signed. Fine in dj. *Pharos.* $250/£156

MERRILL, JAMES. Peter. (Old Deerfield/Dublin): Deerfield/Gallery, (1982). One of 300 signed. VF in dj. *Pharos.* $95/£59

MERRILL, JAMES. Samos. Hollywood: Sylvester & Orphanos, 1980. Ltd to 330 signed. Fine dec cl. *Truepenny.* $100/£63

MERRILL, JAMES. Scripts for the Pageant. NY: Atheneum, 1980. 1st ed. Signed. Fine in dj. *Pharos.* $250/£156

MERRILL, JAMES. Souvenirs. (NY): Nadja, (1984). Ltd to 220 signed, numbered. Fine in ptd warppers. *Black Sun.* $45/£28

MERRILL, JAMES. Water Street. NY: Atheneum, 1962. 1st ed. VG (ink name; spine ends sunned) in VG- dj (edgeworn, chips, tears). *Reese.* $75/£47

MERRILL, JAMES. The Yellow Pages. Cambridge: Temple Bar Bookshop, 1974. One of 800 in wraps (of 850). NF in wraps. *Agvent.* $60/£38

MERRILL, MARION. The Animated Pinocchio. NY: Citadel, 1945. 23x29 cm. 3 tab-operated plts. Glazed pict bds (sm spine tear). Internally Fine in dj (few chips at extrems). *Bookfinders.* $200/£125

MERRIMAN, HENRY SETON and S. G. TALLENTYRE. The Money-Spinner and Other Character Notes. London: Smith, Elder, 1896. 1st ed, 1st issue. 8vo. 12 half-tone plts by Arthur Rackham. Red cl, gilt. (Ink stamps, ink stains to pp viii and [ix]; extrems lt rubbed.) *Christie's*.* $442/£276

MERRIMAN, HENRY SETON. Flotsam: The Study of a Life. Bernhard Tauchnitz, 1896. Copyright ed. Sprinkled edges. Contemp 1/2 leather over cl. VG (spine sl sunned). *Tiger.* $26/£16

MERRITT, A. and HANNES BOK. The Black Wheel. NY: New Collectors Group, 1947. 1st ed. One of 1000. Shiny black pebbled cl, gilt, this has the title ptd in 3 lines on fr cvr. Fine. *Pacific*.* $81/£51

MERRITT, A. and HANNES BOK. The Fox Woman/The Blue Pagoda. NY: New Collectors Group, 1947. 1st ed. One of 1000. Of 2 states, issued simultaneously, this w/picture of nude man on p(19). Black pebbled cl, gilt. Fine. *Pacific*.* $104/£65

MERRITT, ARTHUR H. Periodontal Diseases, Diagnosis and Treatment. NY, 1934. VG. *Doctor's Library.* $65/£41

MERRITT, W. W., SR. A History of the County of Montgomery from the Earliest Days to 1906. Red Oak, IA, 1906. 1st ed. Frontisport. VG (hinges repaired, cl bugged). *Sagebrush.* $65/£41

Merry Christmas ABC. NY: McLoughlin Bros, 1900. 8vo. Good in full color pict wrappers (lt worn). *Reisler.* $120/£75

Merry Times Pleasant Pages for Every One with Illustrations in Color and Photogravure. Boston: De Wolfe Fiske, (ca 1890). 4to. 7 full-pg color plts. Cl-backed color illus bds (edges sl rubbed). Pict dj (chipped, tape repairs). *Reisler.* $400/£250

MERRY, THOMAS B. The American Thoroughbred. L.A.: Commercial Ptg House, 1905. 1st ed. Sheep, morocco spine labels. (Spine head lacks leather piece), else VG. *Pacific*.* $92/£58

MERRYMAN, JOHN HENRY and ALBERT E. ELSEN. Law, Ethics, and the Visual Arts. Univ of PA, 1987. 2 vols. Djs. *Edwards.* $40/£25

MERRYMAN, WILLIAM N. Yankee Caballero. NY: Robert M. McBride, 1940. 1st ed. Frontis, 13 photo plts. (Sl insect nibbles feps, few spots, spine sl faded), else VG. *Connolly.* $17/£11

MERRYWEATHER, F. S. Bibliomania in the Middle Ages. H. B. and W. A. Copinger (eds). London: Woodstock, 1933. New, rev ed. Ltd to 750. Later black cl. *Maggs.* $45/£28

MERTON, THOMAS. Disputed Questions. Hollis & Carter, 1961. 1st ed. NF in dj (fr flap creased, edges sl rubbed). *Ulysses.* $40/£25

MERTON, THOMAS. Elected Silence. London: Hollis & Carter, 1949. 1st Eng ed. VG in black cl. Dj. *Maggs.* $72/£45

MERTON, THOMAS. Original Child Bomb. (NY: New Directions, 1961). 1st ed. (Sl rubbed), else VF issued w/o dj. *Between The Covers.* $85/£53

MERTON, THOMAS. Seeds of Contemplation. (Norfolk, CT): New Directions, (1949). 1st ed. VF in burlap-cvrd bds. Dj. *Bromer.* $300/£188

MERTON, THOMAS. The Tears of the Blind Lions. (NY): New Directions, (1949). 1st ed. Fine in wrappers, dj (sl dknd). *Lenz.* $75/£47

MERTON, THOMAS. The Tower of Babel. (Norfolk: New Directions, 1957.) 1st ed. One of 250 numbered, signed by Merton & Gerhard Marcks (illus). Folio. 1/4 vellum, Fabriano over bds. (Sm owner stamp; bds sl rubbed), o/w Fine in slipcase w/paper label (sl dust-soiled). *Reese.* $1,500/£938

MERWIN, SAMUEL. Old Concord Seen Through Western Spectacles. Boston/NY: Houghton Mifflin, 1926. 1st ed. Black cl spine, ptd blue bds. VG in dj (sl nicked). *Lucas.* $20/£13

MERWIN, W. S. Feathers from the Hill. Iowa City: Windhover, (1978). One of 278 signed. Color frontis. VF. *Pharos.* $125/£78

MERWIN, W. S. Japanese Figures. Santa Barbara: Unicorn, 1971. One of 250 (of 375) numbered, signed. (Rear cvr lt soiled), else Fine in hand-sewn wraps. *Lame Duck.* $65/£41

MERWIN, W. S. Mary. (Brooklyn: Davies, 1976.) One of 176 numbered, signed. Cl-backed patterned bds. VG + . *Pharos.* $100/£63

MERWIN, W. S. The Rain in the Trees. NY: Knopf, 1988. 1st ed. Signed. Fine in illus dj. *Cahan.* $40/£25

MERWIN, W. S. Robert the Devil. Iowa City: Windhover, 1981. One of 260 (of 310). This copy signed. Paper spine label. VF. *Pharos.* $200/£125

MERYMAN, RICHARD. Andrew Wyeth. Boston, 1968. (Lt foxed throughout.) Dj (tattered). *Oinonen*.* $50/£31

MERYMAN, RICHARD. Andrew Wyeth. Boston: Houghton Mifflin, 1968. 1st ed. Lg obl folio. Dk brn/tan cl. VG (lt rubbed, shelfworn) in pict dj (worn, sl chipped, sm old stain spine bottom). *Baltimore*.* $80/£50

MESERVE, FREDERICK HILL and CARL SANDBURG. The Photographs of Abraham Lincoln. NY, (1944). 1st ed. VG in VG dj. *Wantagh.* $75/£47

Message of the President. (By Jefferson Davis.) (Montgomery, AL, April 29, 1861.) 1st ed. 24pp. (Marginal chips), else VG in mod marbled wrappers. *Pacific*.* $173/£108

MESSENT, JAN. Designing for Embroidery from Ancient and Primitive Sources. Macmillan, 1976. 1st US ed. Fine in Fine dj. *Whittle.* $22/£14

METALIOUS, GRACE. The Tight White Collar. NY: Messner, (1960). 1st ed. VF in Fine black dj (sl rubbed). *Between The Covers.* $85/£53

METCALF, PAUL. Apalache. Berkeley: Turtle Island Foundation, 1976. 1st ed. Signed. Pict bds. Fine in dj. *Pharos.* $35/£22

METCALFE, FREDERICK. The Oxonian in Iceland. London: Longman, Green, 1861. 1st ed. xvi,424pp; fldg engr map, 4 engr plts. Contemp 1/2-calf, raised bands, black labels, gilt, marbled bds. VG (sl rubbed). *Morrell.* $272/£170

METCALFE, W. M. (trans). Ancient Lives of Scottish Saints. Paisley: Alexander Gardner, 1895. Ltd to 220. xxiii,373pp (1/2-title, rep sl browned). Untrimmed. Paper spine label. *Hollett.* $72/£45

METCHNIKOFF, ELIE. Immunity in Infective Diseases. Cambridge, 1905. 1st ed in English. (Fr bd corner bent.) *Fye.* $250/£156

METCHNIKOFF, ELIE. The Prolongation of Life. NY, 1908. 1st Amer ed. *Fye.* $75/£47

METHUEN, LORD. Normandy Diary. London: Robert Hale, (1952). Orig ed. Color frontis, 5 color plts. Nice. *Turtle Island.* $90/£56

METHVIN, J. J. Andele, or The Mexican-Kiowa Captive. Louisville, KY: Pentecostal Herald Press, 1899. 184pp. Good (foxed, worn). Howes M564. *Dumont.* $125/£78

METZ, LEON C. Fort Bliss, an Illustrated History. El Paso, 1981. 1st ed. NF in dj. *Baade.* $40/£25

METZ, LEON C. John Selman, Texas Gunfighter. NY: Hastings House, 1966. 1st ed. Fine in dj. *Labordo.* $55/£34

METZGAR, JUDSON D. Adventures in Japanese Prints: A Story of Oriental Print Collecting in the Early Years of the Present Century.... L.A.: Dawson's Bookshop, n.d. 1st ed. One of 300 ptd. Old receipt from David Magee laid in. 1/4 cl, dec bds, paper spine label. (Sm chip to label), else VG. *Pacific*.* $150/£94

METZGER, D. G. et al. Geohydrology of the Parker-Blythe-Cibola Area, Arizona and California. Washington: GPO, 1973. 6 plts in rear pocket. VG. *Five Quail.* $35/£22

MEWSHAW, MICHAEL. Man in Motion. NY: Random House, 1970. 1st ed. VG + in dj. *Lame Duck.* $75/£47

MEYER, ADOLF. The Collected Papers of Adolf Meyer. Volume II (Psychiatry). Balt: Johns Hopkins Univ, 1951. 1st ed. (Lib mks.) NF Blue buckram, gilt. *Beasley.* $50/£31

MEYER, ERNST H. English Chamber Music. Lawrence & Wishart, 1946. 1st ed. VG in dj (top edge sl torn). *Hollett.* $32/£20

MEYER, FRANZ. A Handbook of Ornament. London, 1896. 3rd Eng ed. xvi,548pp; 300 plts. Teg. (Bkpl, margins lt browned; edges sl rubbed.) *Edwards.* $48/£30

MEYER, FRANZ. Marc Chagall. NY: Harry N. Abrams, (c. 1963). 1st ed. VG in dj (spine head, upper extrems chipped). *Pacific*.* $63/£39

MEYER, SAMUEL A. 50 Golden Years. A History of the City of Newport Beach, 1906-1956. Newport Harbor Pub, 1957. 1st ed. 72 plts. Gilt-emb blue cl (edgeworn). VG. *Connolly.* $55/£34

MEYER, W. and V. SCHMIEDEN. Bier's Hyperemic Treatment in Surgery, Medicine, and the Specialties. Phila, 1908. (Eps sl foxed; spine sl worn), o/w VG. *Whitehart.* $40/£25

MEYERS, WILLIAM H. Journal of a Cruise to California and the Sandwich Islands in the United States Sloop-of-War Cyane. John Haskell Kemble (ed). SF: Book Club of CA, 1955. One of 400 ptd. Frontis map, 10 color plts. 1/2 red morocco, tan linen, gilt. Fine. *Pacific*.* $138/£86

MEYERS, WILLIAM H. Journal of a Cruise to California and the Sandwich Islands. SF: Bk Club of CA, 1955. One of 400 ptd by Grabhorn Press. Folio. *Swann*.* $201/£126

MEYERS, WILLIAM H. Naval Sketches of the War in California. NY: Random House, 1939. One of 1000 ptd. Folio. Marbled bds, full white pigskin spine. (Spine lt rubbed), else Fine. *Turtle Island.* $325/£203

MEYERS, WILLIAM H. Naval Sketches of the War in California...Made in 1846-47 by William H. Meyers, Gunner of the U.S. Sloop-of-War Dale. Dudley W. Knox (text). NY: Random House, 1939. One of 1000 ptd. Folio. Uncut. White leather spine, marbled bds, red morocco spine label, gilt. (Spine sl soiled, scuffed), else Fine. *Argonaut.* $350/£219

MEYERS, WILLIAM H. Sketches of California and Hawaii. SF: Bk Club of CA, 1970. One of 450 ptd by Grabhorn Press. Sm folio. *Swann*.* $57/£36

MEYNELL, ALICE. A Father of Women and Other Poems. London, 1917. Orig wrappers (lt foxed). *Swann*.* $57/£36

MEYNELL, ALICE. The Last Poems of.... London, 1923. 1st ed. (Spine head torn, rubbed.) *King.* $12/£8

MEYNELL, ALICE. Later Poems. London/NY, 1902. 1st ed. (Extrems worn.) *King.* $20/£13

MEYNELL, ALICE. Later Poems. London/NY: John Lane, 1902. 1st ed. Black cl, gilt. Fine. *Sumner & Stillman.* $95/£59

MEYNELL, ALICE. The Wares of Autolycus. London: OUP, 1965. 1st ed. Frontis. VG in dj (sl defective). *Hollett.* $32/£20

MEYNELL, VIOLA (ed). Friends of a Lifetime. London: Cape, 1940. 1st ed. 16 plts. (Labels roughly removed from feps; sl stained, rubbed.) *Hollett.* $40/£25

MEYNELL, WILFRID. Halt! Who Goes There? Toronto: McClelland, Goodchild & Stewart, (1916). 1st Canadian ed. Tan bds. Fine in NF dj (corners sl frayed). *Reese.* $35/£22

Meynellian Science. NY: Derrydale, 1926. Frontis, guard. White cl backed over grn paper-cvrd bds, ptd paper label. Fine. *Biscotti.* $175/£109

MEYRICK, SAMUEL RUSH. A Critical Inquiry into Antient Armour, as It Existed in Europe.... London, 1824. 1st ed. Lg 4to. 3 vols. Uncolored engr add'l tps; 70 hand-colored aquatint plts, 10 uncolored etched plts. Contemp 1/2 black morocco, gilt. (Prelims heavily foxed), o/w internally Clean. *Swann*.* $1,495/£934

MEYSEY-THOMPSON, R. F. A Fishing Catechism. London: Edward Arnold, 1905. 1st ed. Teg. Grn cl, gilt. Fine. *Pacific*.* $23/£14

MEZZROW, MILTON MEZZ and BERNARD WOLFE. Really the Blues. NY: Random House, 1946. 1st ed. NF (spine dull). *Beasley.* $25/£16

MICHAELS, BARBARA. Prince of Darkness. NY, 1969. 1st Amer ed. NF in VG dj. *Polyanthos.* $35/£22

MICHALOWSKI, KAZIMIERZ. Art of Ancient Egypt. NY: Abrams, (1968). 1st ed. 15 maps and charts. Brn cl, mtd color illus fr cvr. Good in dj. *Karmiole.* $150/£94

MICHALS, DUANE. Real Dreams. Danbury, NH: Addison House, 1976. 1st ed. Stiff wrappers (lt worn), else VG. *Cahan.* $75/£47

MICHALS, DUANE. Real Dreams. Danbury: Addison House, 1976. 1st ed. Fine in dj. *Smith.* $200/£125

MICHAUD, JOSEPH FRANCOIS. The History of the Crusades. W. Robson (trans). NY: Redfield, 1853. 3 vols. 3 fldg maps. 3/4 brn morocco over marbled bds, gilt paneled spines, raised bands, marbled edges. Fine set (ex-lib stamps). *Appelfeld.* $150/£94

MICHAUX, FRANCOIS-ANDRE. The North American Sylva. Paris/Phila, 1819-18-19. 1st ed in English. 3 vols. Lg 8vo. 156 stipple-engr plts, ptd in color and hand-finished. Errata slip vol 1. Mid-19th-cent navy calf (extrems worn; text variously foxed, plts lt offset w/occasional spotting, bkpl), gilt. *Swann*.* $1,725/£1,078

MICHAUX, FRANCOIS. Travels to the Westward of the Allegany Mountains, in the States of the Ohio, Kentucky, and Tennessee. London, 1805. 1st Eng ed. Engr fldg map (browned, foxed). Orig bds (lacks backstrip). Howes M579. *Swann*.* $287/£179

MICHAUX, HENRI. Light Through Darkness. Explorations Among Drugs. Bodley Head, 1964. 1st UK ed. VG+ in dj (sl torn). *Sclanders.* $26/£16

MICHAUX, HENRI. The Major Ordeals of the Mind and the Countless Minor Ones. Richard Howard (trans). NY: HBJ, 1974. 1st US ed. NF in dj. *Sclanders.* $29/£18

MICHAUX, HENRI. Miserable Miracle. SF: City Lights, 1963. Ltd ed. NF in wraps. *Beasley.* $35/£22

MICHEL, EMILE. Rembrandt. London: Heinemann, 1894. 2 vols. 76 plts. (Sl worn, vol 2 spine ends frayed.) *Ars Artis.* $120/£75

MICHEL, EMILE. Rubens. His Life, His Work, and His Time. London/NY: Heinemann/Scribner, 1899. 2 vols. xx,292 (waterstain last leaf); xii,323pp; 40 color plts, 40 photogravures. Dec cl (sl worn). *Ars Artis.* $120/£75

MICHELET, J. Woman. NY: Rudd & Carleton, 1860. 1st ed. 284pp + ads. Mod cream linen, black spine label. (Sm stain to bottom of prelims), o/w Very Nice. *Beasley.* $75/£47

MICHENER, JAMES A. Caravans. NY: Random House, 1963. 1st ed. Fine in Fine dj. *Unger.* $125/£78

MICHENER, JAMES A. Centennial. NY, (1974). 1st ed. One of 500 numbered, signed, add'lly stamped w/his 'chop.' Slipcase. *Swann*.* $316/£198

MICHENER, JAMES A. Centennial. NY: Random House, 1974. 1st ed. Fine in NF dj. *Beasley.* $65/£41

MICHENER, JAMES A. Centennial. NY: Random House, 1974. 1st ed. Fine in NF dj. *Beasley.* $65/£41

MICHENER, JAMES A. Chesapeake. NY: Random House, (1978). Presentation ed. Blue cl, gilt. NF in slipcase. *Pacific*.* $63/£39

MICHENER, JAMES A. Chesapeake. NY: Random House, (1978). 1st ed. Signed. Fine in Fine dj. *Lenz.* $85/£53

MICHENER, JAMES A. The Covenant. NY: Random House, (1980). 1st ed. Signed. Yellow cl. NF (spine sl rubbed) in dj (spine extrems sl creased). *Heritage.* $150/£94

MICHENER, JAMES A. The Drifters. NY: Random House, 1971. One of 500 numbered, signed. Fine in NF slipcase. *Smith.* $275/£172

MICHENER, JAMES A. The Eagle and the Raven. Austin, TX: State House Press, (1990). One of 350 signed by Michener & illus. 1/4 faux leather, cream cl, gilt. Fine in cream cl open-end slipcase. *Heritage.* $125/£78

MICHENER, JAMES A. The Fires of Spring. R-H, 1949. 1st ed. NF in NF dj. *Fine Books.* $325/£203

MICHENER, JAMES A. The Floating World. NY: Random House, (1954). 1st ed. Fine. *Pacific*.* $374/£234

MICHENER, JAMES A. Hawaii. NY: Random House, (1959). 1st ed. NF in dj (spine head sl chipped, rear panel lacks piece). *Pacific*.* $63/£39

MICHENER, JAMES A. Iberia, Spanish Travels and Reflections. NY, (1968). 1st ed. (Ink name), else VG in dj (edges torn). *King.* $35/£22

MICHENER, JAMES A. Japanese Prints from the Early Masters to the Modern. Tokyo/Rutland, VT: Tuttle, 1959. 1st ed. VG in dj (sl torn). *Worldwide.* $85/£53

MICHENER, JAMES A. Poland. NY: Random House, (1983). One of 500 numbered, signed. Fine in slipcase. *Antic Hay.* $225/£141

MICHENER, JAMES A. Poland. NY: Random House, 1983. 1st ed. One of 500 numbered, signed. Fine in Fine slipcase. *Unger.* $250/£156

MICHENER, JAMES A. The Quality of Life. London: Secker & Warburg, (1971). 1st Eng ed. Fine in dj. *Jaffe.* $150/£94

MICHENER, JAMES A. The Quality of Life. N.p.: Girard Bank, 1970. 1st ed. Cvr label. (Spine lettering rubbed), else VG in slipcase. *Pacific*.* $35/£22

MICHENER, JAMES A. Return to Paradise. NY: Random House, (1951). 1st ed. VG in dj (spine ends rubbed; sm tears, creases to extrems; sm tear, rubbing to mid-rear joint; tape repairs to verso; price-clipped). *Pacific*.* $127/£79

MICHENER, JAMES A. Sayonara. NY: Random House, 1954. 1st ed. NF (sl discoloration spine foot) in dj (lt used). *Beasley.* $125/£78

MICHENER, JAMES A. Sayonara. NY: Random House, 1954. 1st ed. NF (pg edges sl dknd) in NF dj (nicks, scrapes). *Unger.* $150/£94

MICHENER, JAMES A. Sayonara. (NY: Random House, 1954.) 1st ed. 1/4 black cl, brn bds. VG (lt browned; spine ends sl rubbed) in dj (laminated, browned, flap edges chipped). *Heritage.* $150/£94

MICHENER, JAMES A. Space. NY: Random House, (1982). 1st ed. Signed. NF (extrems sl faded) in VG dj (price-clipped, sl dampstained). *Between The Covers.* $125/£78

MICHENER, JAMES A. Space. NY: Random House, 1982. 1st ed. Fine in Fine dj (price-clipped). *Unger.* $50/£31

MICHENER, JAMES A. Texas. NY: Random House, (1985). 1st ed. Fine in Fine dj. *Sadlon.* $25/£16

MICHENER, JAMES A. Texas. NY: Random House, (1985). 1st ed. Blue cl, gilt. Dj (sticker rear flap, spine extrems chipped). *Heritage.* $50/£31

MICHENER, JAMES A. Texas. NY: Random House, (1985). 1st ed. One of 1000. Signed. Fine in slipcase. *Pacific*.* $184/£115

MICHENER, JAMES A. Texas. Austin: Univ of TX, (1986). 1st Univ of TX ed. 2 vols. Folio. Fine in slipcase as issued. *Between The Covers.* $150/£94

MICHENER, JAMES A. Ventures in Editing. Huntington Beach: James Cahill, 1995. Proof copy of 26 deluxe copies. Signed w/his red stamp. Silver-lettered rose cl. As New in slipcase. *Pacific*.* $196/£123

Michigan Almanac 1883. The Detroit News. 80pp. Ptd wraps (chipped, rear cvr lacks lg piece, worn). *King.* $20/£13

Microcosm of London, or London in Miniature. London: Ptd for R. Ackermann, 1808-1810. 1st ed. Woodcut tps, engr tps in 1st state (Tooley). 3 vols. 4to. 104 color acquatint plts by Bloch, et al. Old brn calf bds (expertly rebacked, extrems worn), raised bands, maroon leather labels. Fine (1st few pp, some plts vol 1 margins sl spotted; few sl tears; sl offsetting, guards foxed). *Appelfeld.* $8,000/£5,000

MIDDAGH, JOHN. Frontier Newspaper: The El Paso Times. El Paso: Texas Western, 1958. VG in dj. *Dumont.* $35/£22

MIDDIMAN, SAMUEL. Select Views in Great Britain. London: Boydell, (1812). 53 engr plts. Contemp 3/4 calf (rebacked, rubbed, spine dried, corroded; foxed, sl stained, soiled). Internally Sound. *Oinonen*.* $300/£188

MIDDLEBROOK, LOUIS F. Maritime Connecticut During the American Revolution. 1775-1783. Salem: Essex Inst, 1925. 1st ed. 2 vols. Teg. Dk blue cl. Fine in djs (spines faded). *Parmer.* $200/£125

MIDDLEMASS, KEITH. Antique Coloured Glass. Ferndale Editions, 1979. VG in dj. *Hollett.* $32/£20

MIDDLETON, J. H. Illuminated Manuscripts in Classical and Mediaeval Times, Their Art and Their Technique. Cambridge: CUP, 1892. Frontis, xxiv,270pp. Blue cl (bumped, rubbed, sl shaken), gilt. *Maggs.* $72/£45

MIDDLETON, RICHARD. Letters to Henry Savage. London: Mandrake, 1929. One of 750. Port, facs. Uncut. Cl over beveled bds (rubbed, lettering dull). *Hollett.* $104/£65

MIDDLETON-WAKE, CHARLES H. The Invention of Printing. A Series of Four Lectures...1897. Privately ptd by John Murray, 1897. 1st ed. Frontis, 16 plts. Teg, uncut. *Forest.* $72/£45

MIERS, EARL SCHENCK and RICHARD A. BROWN (eds). Gettysburg. New Brunswick, (1948). 3rd ptg. VG. *Pratt.* $17/£11

MIERS, EARL SCHENCK. The Great Rebellion. Cleveland, (1958). 1st ed. VG in VG dj. *Pratt*. $27/£17

MIERS, EARL SCHENCK. The Web of Victory. NY: Knopf, 1955. 1st ed. Red cl. Fine in NF dj (spine faded). *Chapel Hill*. $45/£28

MIERTSCHING, JOHANN. Frozen Ships. L. H. Neatby (trans). NY: St. Martin's, 1967. Fine in dj. *High Latitude*. $25/£16

MIERTSCHING, JOHANN. Frozen Ships: The Arctic Diary...1850-1854. L. H. Neatby (trans). Toronto: Macmillan of Canada, 1967. 2 maps. VG (bkpl) in dj (worn). *Explorer*. $19/£12

Might and Right; by a Rhode Islander. (By Frances H.W.G. MacDougall.) Providence, (RI): A.H. Stillwell, 1844. 1st ed. Frontis, 345,(1)pp (frontis, tp becoming loose), errata leaf. Orig cl (spine faded, chipped). *M & S*. $125/£78

MIJATOVICS, ELODIE LAWTON. The History of Modern Serbia. London, 1872. Gilt-pict cl. (Bkpl.) *Swann**. $80/£50

MILBANK, KITTY. The Flighty Prince. NY: Privately ptd, 1963. Frontis. Aeg. Vellum backed over grn paper-cvrd bds. Fine in Fine slipcase. *Biscotti*. $125/£78

MILBURN, WILLIAM HENRY. The Rifle, Axe and Saddlebags, and Other Pleasures. NY: Derby & Jackson, 1857. 1st ed. Frontis port, 309pp. Blind-stamped beige cl (sl worn). VG. *Connolly*. $75/£47

MILCH, HENRY. Osteotomy of the Long Bones. Springfield, 1947. 1st ed. Blue cl. VG (inscrip, bkpl; extrems sl worn). *Doctor's Library*. $45/£28

MILES, ALFRED H. Five Hundred Fascinating Animal Stories. NY: Christian Herald, (1907). 1st ed. Grn cl, gilt, pict cvr label. NF. *Pacific**. $40/£25

MILES, CHARLES and PIERRE BOVIS. American Indian and Eskimo Basketry. SF: Pierre Bovis, (1969). 1st, deluxe ed. Ltd to 1000 numbered, signed by both. Brn cl. Fine in color pict dj. *Argonaut*. $50/£31

MILES, DIONE. Something in Common—An IWW Bibliography. Detroit, 1986. VG. *Dumont*. $50/£31

MILES, HENRY DOWNES (ed). The Book of Field Sports, and Library of Veterinary Knowledge. Volume II (of 2). London: Henry Lea, n.d. (1863). Full polished calf stamped in blind/gilt. (Sl soiled, foxed; rubbed; lacks vol I.) *Oinonen**. $90/£56

MILES, NELSON A. Personal Recollections and Observations of General Nelson A. Miles.... Chicago: Werner Co, 1896. 1st ed, 1st issue. Frontis port, (vi),590pp. Brn pict cl. (Bkpl, inner hinges repaired; tips, spine ends lt worn.) Howes M599. *Dawson*. $175/£109

MILES, NELSON A. Personal Recollections and Observations of General Nelson A. Miles.... Chicago: Werner, 1896. 1st ed, 1st issue. Frontisport, (6),590pp. (Sm flaw to rear cvr cl, edges rubbed), else NF. *Pacific**. $207/£129

MILES, NELSON A. Personal Recollections and Observations of General Nelson A. Miles.... Chicago, 1896. 1st ed, 1st issue. Full leather, gilt, marbled edges. VG (cvrs lt worn). Howes M595. *Baade*. $300/£188

MILES, NELSON A. Personal Recollections and Observations of General Nelson A. Miles.... Chicago: Werner, 1897. 2nd ed. (8),591pp. (Dampstain to fore-edge fr cvr), else VG. Howes M595. *Pacific**. $150/£94

MILHAUD, DARIUS. Notes Without Music. Rollo H. Myers (ed). Donald Evans (trans). Dennis Dobson, 1952. 1st English ed. Frontis. VG in dj. *Hollett*. $40/£25

MILL, HUGH R. The Siege of the South Pole. London: Alston Rivers, 1905. 1st ed. Lg fldg color map, 2 fldg charts, 61 plts (incl frontis). Grn cl, gilt. VG (lt foxed, sm tear to map). *Morrell*. $176/£110

MILL, HUGH R. The Siege of the South Pole: The Story of Antarctic Exploration. London: Alston Rivers, 1905. Lg fldg map laid down on linen at rear. Lib cl. Good (lib stamps on plt versos). *Explorer*. $48/£30

MILL, HUGH R. The Siege of the South Pole: The Story of Antarctic Exploration. London: Alston Rivers, 1905. 3 fldg maps. Dec grn cl. VG (bkpl). *Explorer*. $152/£95

MILL, JOHN STUART. Autobiography. Longmans, Green, Reader, & Dyer, 1873. 1st ed. Half-title. Contemp 1/2 calf, gilt. *Sotheby's**. $147/£92

MILL, JOHN STUART. Autobiography. London: Longmans, Green, Reader & Dyer, 1873. 1st ed. vi,313,(5)pp; w/final leaf of ads. Grn cl (extrems sl frayed). *Karmiole*. $250/£156

MILL, JOHN STUART. Autobiography. Longmans, Green, Reader, et al, 1878. Ad leaf. Good (spine bumped, fr cvr sl mkd). *Tiger*. $96/£60

MILL, JOHN STUART. An Examination of Sir William Hamilton's Philosophy and of the Principal Philosophical Questions Discussed in His Writings. Boston: William V. Spencer, 1865. 1st Amer ed. 2 vols. (3),330,(4); 354,(4)pp. Panelled mauve cl. NF set (spines sl flecked). *Gach*. $200/£125

MILL, JOHN STUART. A System of Logic Ratiocinative and Inductive. Longmans et al, 1868. 7th ed. 2 vols. xviii,541; xv,555pp. Full calf, gilt, prize bindings. (Few spots to feps; corner 1 bd sl worn, 1 vol neatly recased), o/w VF set. *Hollett*. $240/£150

MILLAIS, J. G. British Deer and Their Horns. London: Henry Sotheran, 1897. 1st ed. Folio. Color litho frontis, guards. Pict cl. (Spine cl cracked, extrems dknd, glue to joints, spine), else VG. *Pacific**. $184/£115

MILLAIS, J. G. Game Birds and Shooting-Sketches. London: Henry Sotheran, 1892. Folio. 34 plts, 15 color lithos. Orig 1/2 morocco, gilt. (Lt foxed, sl edgeworn.) *Metropolitan**. $632/£395

MILLAIS, J. G. et al. The Gun at Home and Abroad. British Deer and Ground Game, Dogs, Guns and Rifles. London, 1913. One of 950 numbered. Teg, uncut. Gilt-lettered morocco (rubbed). *Oinonen**. $400/£250

MILLAIS, J. G. The Mammals of Great Britain and Ireland. London: Longmans & Green, 1904-06. 1st ed. Ltd to 1025. 273 plts, 62 color plts. Teg. (Some plts lt spotted; spines faded, lt worn.) *Christie's**. $258/£161

MILLAIS, J. G. The Mammals of Great Britain and Ireland. London, 1904-06. Ltd to 1025. 3 vols. 4to. 62 color, 62 photogravure plts. 125 plts from photos. 1/2 blue buckram, gilt. (Sl foxed.) *Henly*. $616/£385

MILLAIS, J. G. The Mammals of Great Britain and Ireland. Longmans, Green, 1904-1906. One of 1025. 3 vols. Folio. 31 color plts. Teg. *Sotheby's**. $275/£172

MILLAIS, J. G. The Natural History of British Surface-Feeding Ducks. Longmans, Green, 1902. One of 600. Folio. 41 color, 25 uncolored plts, 6 photogravures. (Sl spotted; corners rubbed.) *Sotheby's**. $699/£437

MILLAIS, J. G. Newfoundland and Its Untrodden Ways. London, 1907. 1st ed. 6 photogravure plts, 6 color plts. Teg. (Feps lt foxed; sm chip fr joint, spine faded, sl rubbed.) *Edwards*. $104/£65

MILLAIS, J. G. Newfoundland and Its Untrodden Ways. London, 1907. Pub's gilt-pict cl. (Bkpl.) *Swann**. $115/£72

MILLAIS, J. G. Rhododendrons. London, 1917-24. Each vol ltd to 550 numbered. 2 vols (1st & 2nd Series). Folio. 34 color, 28 collotype plts. (Pp tanned, bkpls; vol 1 spine ends chipped.) *Sutton*. $1,650/£1,031

MILLAR, A. H. Traditions and Stories of Scottish Castles. Sands, 1927. 24 plts. (Few ll w/heavy pencil notes.) *Hollett*. $24/£15

MILLAR, J. Observations on the Prevailing Diseases in Great Britain. London, 1770. vi,385pp (lib label, tp foxed, ink sig, lt foxed). New 1/2 calf, marbled bds. *Whitehart.* $544/£340

MILLAR, JOHN FITZHUGH. The Architects of the American Colonies or Vitruvius Americanus. Barre, 1968. Folio. (Lt worn.) Dj. *Oinonen*.* $80/£50

MILLAR, KENNETH. Blue City. NY, 1947. 1st ed. Dj (spine extrems, tips lt rubbed). *Swann*.* $258/£161

MILLAR, R. Clinical Lectures on the Contagious Typhus Epidemic in Glasgow, and the Vicinity During the Years 1831 and 1832. Glasgow, 1833. 144pp. Mod grey paper-cvrd bds. VG. *Whitehart.* $64/£40

MILLARD, BAILEY. History of the San Francisco Bay Region. Chicago: American Hist Soc, 1924. 1st ed. 3 vols. 3 frontispieces (2 color), 116 plts, map. Marbled edges. Dk blue cl, gilt. VF set. *Argonaut.* $225/£141

MILLARD, DAVID. A Journal of Travels in Egypt, Arabia, Petrae, and the Holy Land, During 1841-2. NY: H. Ludwig, 1847. 3rd ed. 348pp. Full leather. (Sl foxed, spotted, mainly marginally; rubbed, edges frayed, fr cvr detached, spine ends chipped), o/w VG. *Worldwide.* $65/£41

MILLAY, EDNA ST. VINCENT. Conversation at Midnight. NY, 1937. 1st ed. 1/2 cl. VG in dj (edges torn, frayed). *King.* $35/£22

MILLAY, EDNA ST. VINCENT. Conversation at Midnight. NY: Harper, 1937. 1st ed. One of 615 signed. 1/4 cream cl, blue bds, ptd paper spine label. Fine (label lt browned) in pub's cardboard open-end slipcase w/ptd paper label (lt worn). *Heritage.* $350/£219

MILLAY, EDNA ST. VINCENT. Fatal Interview. NY: Harper, 1931. Signed 1st ed. Ltd to 479. Uncut. Linen-backed, paper-cvrd bds. Fine in glassine wrapper (lt chipped), NF pub's slipcase. *Hermitage.* $350/£219

MILLAY, EDNA ST. VINCENT. Fear. NY, 1929. 1st separate ed. Single sheet folded once to make 4pp. VG + . *Pharos.* $150/£94

MILLAY, EDNA ST. VINCENT. The Harp-Weaver and Other Poems. NY: Harper, 1923. 1st ed. Fine (sl sunned) in dj (chipped). *Beasley.* $60/£38

MILLAY, EDNA ST. VINCENT. The Harp-Weaver and Other Poems. NY: Harper, 1923. 1st ed. Signed in full by the author. Good in dj (defective). *Holmes.* $250/£156

MILLAY, EDNA ST. VINCENT. Huntsman, What Quarry? NY: Harper, 1929. 1st ed. (Fep corner clipped), else VF in VF dj. *Between The Covers.* $100/£63

MILLAY, EDNA ST. VINCENT. The King's Henchman. NY: Harper, 1927. Artist's ed. One of 158. Signed. (Spine label rubbed, upper cvrs dknd, joints rubbed), else VG in Poor slipcase (broken). *Pacific*.* $40/£25

MILLAY, EDNA ST. VINCENT. Mine the Harvest. NY: Harper, (1954). 1st ed. VF in VF silver foil dj (sm tear). *Between The Covers.* $85/£53

MILLAY, EDNA ST. VINCENT. The Murder of Lidice. NY/London: Harper, 1942. 1st ed, prepub rev copy w/pub's rev slip laid in, official pub date, price stamped in red (October 20, 1942), and a statement. VF in gray/blue wrappers. *Argonaut.* $150/£94

MILLAY, EDNA ST. VINCENT. Renascence. NY: Mitchell Kennedy, 1917. 1st ed, 2nd state w/MBM watermark, 1st bk. Black cl, gilt. Fine. *Macdonnell.* $75/£47

MILLAY, EDNA ST. VINCENT. Wine from These Grapes. NY: Harper, 1934. One of 299 (of 335) numbered, signed. 2 vols. (Spines sl tanned), else NF in 1/4 cl, paper-cvrd bds. VG paper-cvrd slipcase. *Lame Duck.* $150/£94

MILLEDGE, JOHN. Correspondence of John Milledge, Governor of Georgia 1802-1806. Harriet Milledge Salley (ed). Columbia, SC: Mrs. Alexander S. Salley, 1949. 1st ed. Inscribed by ed. Frontisport, 4 plts. Red cl. (Bkpl), else Fine in VG dj. *Chapel Hill.* $50/£31

Millennium, a Poem. To which is added Hymns and Songs on Various Subjects.... (By Parley Parker Pratt.) Boston: Parley P. Pratt, 1835. 1st ed. 12mo. 52pp (lt waterstained last few ll; 1835 pencil inscrip fep). Contemp plain stiff wraps (neatly re-backed). *M & S.* $15,000/£9,375

Miller and His Golden Dream. (By Eliza Lucy Leonard.) London: Wellington, Salop, 1827. Sq 12mo. Full-pg frontis, tissue guard, 30pp; 5 hand-colored copper engrs. Marbled eps. Mod mottled leather, 2 raised bands, gilt spine. Excellent (spine creases sl worn). *Hobbyhorse.* $250/£156

MILLER, ALDEN and ROBERT STEBBINS. Lives of Desert Animals in Joshua Tree National Monument. Berkeley: Univ of CA, 1964. VG + . *Book Market.* $50/£31

MILLER, ARTHUR. After the Fall. NY: Viking, (1964). 1st ltd ed. One of 999 signed. Top edge stained red, untrimmed. Lt brn buckram, gilt. Fine in orig plain glassine dj (spine sun-dknd, torn, chipped), orig plain bd slipcase (sunned). *Baltimore*.* $80/£50

MILLER, ARTHUR. The Crucible. Cresset, 1956. 1st UK ed. VG + in dj (sl dusty). *Williams.* $64/£40

MILLER, ARTHUR. Death of a Salesman. NY, (1981). One of 500 numbered, signed. Slipcase. *Swann*.* $149/£93

MILLER, ARTHUR. Death of a Salesman. NY: Viking, 1949. 1st ed. VG in dj (spine head chipped, extrems sl rubbed). *Pacific*.* $184/£115

MILLER, ARTHUR. Death of a Salesman. LEC, 1984. Ltd to 1500 numbered, signed by Miller and Leonard Baskin (illus). Fine in slipcase. *Swann*.* $402/£251

MILLER, ARTHUR. I Don't Need You Anymore. NY, 1967. 1st Amer ed. Signed. Fine in dj (sm mended spine tear). *Polyanthos.* $35/£22

MILLER, ARTHUR. The Price. NY, (1985). Penguin pb ed. Signed. *Argosy.* $25/£16

MILLER, ARTHUR. The Price. NY: Viking, 1968. 1st ed. (Reps offset from news clippings), else NF in dj (spine sl tanned). *Lame Duck.* $65/£41

MILLER, ARTHUR. A View from the Bridge. NY: Viking, 1955. 1st ed. VG (corners sl bumped) in dj (edgeworn). *My Bookhouse.* $32/£20

MILLER, B. and J. SINGEWALD. The Mineral Deposits of South America. NY: McGraw-Hill, c1919. 1st ed, 2nd imp. VG. *Blake.* $150/£94

MILLER, C. WILLIAM. Benjamin Franklin's Philadelphia Printing, 1728-1766. Phila, 1974. (Lt worn.) Dj. *Oinonen*.* $70/£44

MILLER, CELESTE J. The Newest Way Round the World. NY: Calkins, 1908. 1st ed. 69 plts. (Sl rubbed), o/w VG. *Worldwide.* $25/£16

MILLER, CHARLES CONRAD. Cosmetic Surgery: the Correction of Featural Imperfections. Phila: F.A. Davis, 1924. 1st ed. Fine in red cl stamped in blind, gilt spine. *Weber.* $250/£156

MILLER, CHARLES. Raggedy Ann's Joyful Songs. NY: Miller Music, 1937. Obl 4to. Johnny Gruelle (illus). 48pp. Color pict paper cvrs. *Reisler.* $110/£69

MILLER, DARLIS A. Soldiers and Settlers. Albuquerque: Univ of NM, (1989). 1st ed. 2 maps. Gray cl. VF in pict dj. *Argonaut.* $60/£38

MILLER, DAVID HUMPHREYS. Custer's Fall—The Indian Side of the Story. NY: Duell, Sloan and Pearce, (1957). 1st ed. VG in dj. *Perier.* $50/£31

MILLER, EDWARD. Prince of Librarians. Andre Deutsch, 1967. 1st ed. Dj. *Forest.* $40/£25

MILLER, EDWARD. Prince of Librarians...Antonio Panizzi of the British Museum. Athens: OH Univ, (1967). 1st ed. Dj. *Dawson.* $35/£22

MILLER, EDWARD. That Noble Cabinet. London: Andre Deutsch, 1973. 16 plts. Blue cl. Dj. *Maggs.* $22/£14

MILLER, EDWIN J. The Adventures of Ned Minton. Machias: A.R. Forbush, 1904. 1st ed. (Lt aging, foxed; lacks rep.) Blue cl, mtd illus fr cvr. Cvrs Good (sl old wear). *Baltimore**. $15/£9

MILLER, ELIZABETH C. Young Trajan. Doubleday/Junior Literary Guide, 1931. Stated 1st ed. Maud & Miska Petersham (illus). 23pp. Black cl w/orange stamped pict. Good + . *Price*. $18/£11

MILLER, FLOYD. Bill Tilghman, Marshal of the Last Frontier. GC: Doubleday, 1968. 1st ed. Fine in dj. *Labordo*. $55/£34

MILLER, FRANCIS TREVELYAN (ed). The Photographic History of the Civil War. NY, 1911. 10 vols. Sm 4to. Pub's cl. As New. *Swann**. $805/£503

MILLER, GENEVIEVE (ed). A Bibliography of the Writings of Henry E. Sigerist. Montreal, 1966. 1st ed. As New in dj. *Doctor's Library*. $30/£19

MILLER, HARRY G. and LEROY HAFEN. Bent's Fort on the Arkansas. Denver: State Hist Soc of CO, 1954. Pamphlet. NF. *Dumont*. $25/£16

MILLER, HENRY. Big Sur and The Oranges of Hieronymus Bosch. (NY): New Directions, (1957). 1st ed. Fine in dj (sl worn). *Lenz*. $225/£141

MILLER, HENRY. Book of Friends. Santa Barbara, 1976. 1st trade ed. VG in dj (rubbed, one tear). *King*. $25/£16

MILLER, HENRY. The Colossus of Maroussi. Norfolk, CT: New Directions, (1941). Later ed. Inscribed, dated. Black cl. (Bkpl.) *Cummins*. $400/£250

MILLER, HENRY. My Bike and Other Friends. Santa Barbara: Capra, 1978. 1st trade ed. Signed. Orange eps. Black cl. Fine in dj. *Heritage*. $75/£47

MILLER, HENRY. Nexus. NY: Grove, 1965. 1st Amer ed. NF (few sm spots at top edge) in NF white dj (lt rubbed). *Warren*. $50/£31

MILLER, HENRY. Notes on Aaron's Rod. Santa Barbara: Black Sparrow, 1980. One of 250 numbered, signed. Fine in acetate dj. *Smith*. $150/£94

MILLER, HENRY. Opus Pistorum. NY, 1983. 1st Amer ed. NF in dj. *Polyanthos*. $25/£16

MILLER, HENRY. Patchen: Man of Anger and Light with A Letter to God by Kenneth Patchen. (NY: Padell, 1946). 1st ed. VF in wrappers in dj. *Between The Covers*. $100/£63

MILLER, HENRY. Plexus. Paris: Olympia, 1953. One of 2000. 2 vols. VG in orig wrappers. *Williams*. $160/£100

MILLER, HENRY. Reflections. Capra, 1981. 1st Amer ed. NF in pict wraps. *Polyanthos*. $25/£16

MILLER, HENRY. Reflexions of the Death of Mishima. Santa Barbara, 1972. 1st ed. One of 200 numbered, signed. Add'l full-pg inscription. 1/4 cl, pict bds. *Swann**. $287/£179

MILLER, HENRY. The Rosy Crucifixion. NY: Grove, (1965). 1st Amer eds. 3 vols. VF in VF djs in Fine cardbd slipcase as issued. *Between The Covers*. $225/£141

MILLER, HENRY. The Time of the Assassins. Neville Spearman, 1956. 1st ed. NF (eps browned) in dj (nicked, sl torn, creased, dusty). *Ulysses*. $120/£75

MILLER, HENRY. To Paint Is to Love Again. NY: Grossman, 1968. 1st ed. Fine in white dj (lt soiled). *Captain's Bookshelf*. $75/£47

MILLER, HENRY. Tropic of Cancer. NY: Grove, 1961. 1st Amer ed. NF in NF dj (lt rubbed). *Warren*. $60/£38

MILLER, HENRY. Tropic of Capricorn. Paris: Obelisk, (1939). 1st ed. One of 1000 ptd. Tipped-in errata slip. Good in pict wrappers (tape repair to spine foot, covering any price, heavily shelfworn, rubbed, sm tears). *Pacific**. $98/£61

MILLER, HENRY. Tropic of Capricorn. Paris: Obelisk, (1939). 1st ed. Inscribed, signed. One of 1000 ptd. Gilt inner dentelles. Orange morocco, gilt. Fine in Good pict wrappers (bound-in, laid on to paper w/pieces lacking, repairs). *Pacific**. $173/£108

MILLER, HENRY. Tropic of Capricorn. NY: Grove, 1961. 1st Amer ed. Fine in Fine dj (lt rubbed). *Warren*. $60/£38

MILLER, HENRY. The World of Lawrence. Santa Barbara: Capra, 1980. 1st ed. One of 250 numbered, specially bound, signed. As New, w/o dj, as issued. *Smith*. $100/£63

MILLER, HEYMAN. Central Autonomic Regulations in Health and Disease with Special Reference to the Hypothalamus. NY, 1942. 1st ed. *Fye*. $50/£31

MILLER, HUGH. First Impressions of England and Its People. Boston: Gould & Lincoln, 1851. Engr frontisport, 430pp, 13ff. ads. Blindstamped cl (spine sunned, cvrs faded). *Marlborough*. $240/£150

MILLER, JAMES KNOX POLK. The Road to Virginia City. Andrew F. Rolle (ed). Norman: Univ of OK, (1960). 1st ed. Map. Brn/tan cl. VG in dj (edge faded). *House*. $30/£19

MILLER, JAMES. The Practice of Surgery. Edinburgh: A&C Black, 1846. xxiii,688pp (sl spotted). Mod 1/2 calf, gilt. *Hollett*. $136/£85

MILLER, JAMES. The Principles of Surgery. Phil, 1852. 3rd ed. 751pp (few cut in index); 240 wood engrs. Full calf. (Ex-lib, inner hinges cracked, foxed, eps water-stained; scuffed), o/w Good. *Doctor's Library*. $75/£47

MILLER, JANET. Camel-Bells of Baghdad. Boston/NY: Houghton Mifflin (Riverside), 1934. 1st ed. 8 plts. (Sl rubbed), o/w VG.. *Worldwide*. $30/£19

MILLER, JOAQUIN. His California Diary Beginning in 1855 and Ending in 1857. John S. Richards (ed). Seattle: Dogwood, 1936. One of 700. Color frontis. Tan cl. Fine. *House*. $50/£31

MILLER, JOAQUIN. Songs of the Sun-Lands. Boston, 1873. 1st Amer ed. Teg. Pict cvrs, gilt. NF (sl rubbed). BAL 13756. *Polyanthos*. $45/£28

MILLER, JOAQUIN. Unwritten History: Life Amongst the Modocs. Hartford: Amer Pub, 1874. 1st Amer ed. 445pp. 1/4 leather (lt edge worn). VG. Howes M608. *Perier*. $150/£94

MILLER, JONATHAN and DAVID PELHAM. The Facts of Life. NY: Viking Penguin, 1984. 6 dbl-pg pop-ups by Harry Willock. Glazed pict bds. VG. *Bookfinders*. $70/£44

MILLER, JONATHAN and DAVID PELHAM. The Human Body. London: Cape, 1983. 6 dbl-pg pop-ups by Harry Willok. Glazed pict bds. VG. *Bookfinders*. $70/£44

MILLER, JOSEPH (ed). The Arizona Rangers. NY: Hastings House, 1972. NF in dj. *Dumont*. $50/£31

MILLER, JULIAN H. A Monograph of the World Species of Hypoxylon. Univ of GA, 1961. 1st ed. 75 photo plts. Grn cl. VG (lib spine #s removed). *Larry Price*. $30/£19

MILLER, LEWIS B. A Crooked Trail. Pittsburgh: Axtell-Rush, (1908). 1st ed. Ptd gray wraps (lacks bottom 1/3 of spine w/rear cvr nearly detached; edges, joints sl chipped; text lt aged). *Baltimore**. $30/£19

MILLER, MAX. The Great Trek. NY: Doubleday, 1935. 1st ed. Good (spine sl faded). *Walcot*. $22/£14

MILLER, MERLE. What Happened. NY: Harper, (1972). 1st ed. VF in VF dj. *Between The Covers*. $125/£78

MILLER, OLIVE BEAUPRE (ed). My Bookhouse. Chicago: The Book House for Children, (1937). 12 vols. 4to. Dk blue cl, gilt, w/color plt on cvr. NF. *House*. $200/£125

MILLER, OLIVE BEAUPRE (ed). My Bookhouse. Chicago: Book House for Children, 1947. 12 vols. Blue cl, lg color plt. VG (plts sl scuffed, erased pencil mks 6pp, neatly written pencil bibliography 1pg, names; corners bumped). *Price*. $60/£38

MILLER, OLIVE BEAUPRE (ed). My Bookhouse. Chicago: Bookhouse for Children, ca 1925. 6 vols. 4to. Teg. Grn/white emb cl, color paste labels. Nice set. *Reisler*. $275/£172

MILLER, OLIVE BEAUPRE (ed). My Bookhouse. In the Nursery; Up One Pair of Stairs; Through Fairy Halls; The Treasure Chest; From the Tower Window; The Latch Key. Chicago: Bookhouse for Children, (1920/27). 1st eds. 6 vols. 8vo. Pict eps; teg. Dk grn frosted cl w/onlaid pict plts to each fr cvr. (Few neatly repaired sm closed tears, vol 2 cvr lt scratched), o/w Fine set. *Sotheran*. $317/£198

MILLER, OLIVE BEAUPRE. Little Pictures of Japan. Chicago: Bookhouse for Children, c.1925. 8x11. Katherine Sturges (illus). 191pp. Blue cl w/color plt. VG (names, 1/4-inch hole fr color plt; spine, corners rubbed). *Price*. $25/£16

MILLER, OLIVE BEAUPRE. Sunny Rhymes for Happy Children. Chicago: P.F. Volland, (1917). 31st ed. 12mo. Carmen L. Browne (illus). Full color pict bds (edges sl worn). Pub's pict box (sides worn). *Reisler*. $125/£78

MILLER, PATRICK. The Natural Man. NY: Brentano's, (1924). 1st US ed. Pale grn cl stamped in brn. Fine in VG pict dj (few sm nicks, edge tears, sl flecking to spine). *Reese*. $85/£53

MILLER, PAUL EDUARD. Esquire's 1945 Jazz Book. NY: Barnes, 1945. Pb issue. Good (few mks in text) in wraps (cvrs separated). *Beasley*. $40/£25

MILLER, PAUL EDUARD. Esquire's 1945 Jazz Book. NY: Barnes, 1945. 1st ed. NF in dj (lt chipped). *Beasley*. $65/£41

MILLER, PAUL EDUARD. Esquire's 1946 Jazz Book. NY: Barnes, 1946. 1st ed. Fldg map. VG (edges dampstained) in VG dj (rear panel dampstained). *Beasley*. $50/£31

MILLER, RAUP. Silhouettes on Blue. SF: John Henry Nash, 1937. 1st ed. Beige linen over blue bds, ptd paper spine label (faded). VG. *Houle*. $50/£31

MILLER, ROY ANDREW. Masterpieces of Japanese Puppetry. Rutland, VT/Tokyo: Charles E. Tuttle, 1958. Folio. 32 tipped-in color plts. Cl, emb paper. Pict dj (bumped, sm tear at base). *Metropolitan**. $258/£161

MILLER, SAMUEL. Notes on Hospital Practice. Philadelphia and New York Hospitals. Phila, 1881. 1st ed. 3 vols in one. 141; 110; 109pp. *Fye*. $75/£47

MILLER, TOM. On the Border. NY: Harper, (1981). 1st ed. Fine in Fine dj. *Book Market*. $15/£9

MILLER, W. and E. H. STRANGE. A Centenary Bibliography of the Pickwick Papers. Argonaut, 1936. Top edge green. Good (spine bumped; lacks dj). *Tiger*. $40/£25

MILLER, WALTER M., JR. A Canticle for Leibowitz. Phila: Lippincott, 1960. 1st ed. NF (inscrip) in VG dj (few chips, tears, soiled). *Warren*. $175/£109

MILLER, WILHELM. The Charm of English Gardens. London, n.d. 8 color plts. Aeg. Full crushed grn morocco by Hatchards, gilt. (Spine faded intruding sl onto bds.) *Edwards*. $144/£90

MILLER, WILLIAM (ed). The Punishments of China. London: William Miller, 1801. 1st ed. Folio. 22 hand-colored stipple-engr plts. Aeg. Full maroon ribbed morocco, gilt. Fine (bkpls). *Pacific**. $690/£431

MILLER, WILLIAM. Scottish Nursery Songs and Other Poems. Glasgow: The Author, 1863. 1st ed, only bk. Sm 4to. viii,10-69pp. Yellow eps. Blind-stamped purple cl. VG (tp browned; spine sunned, sl rubbed). *Sotheran*. $637/£398

MILLET, SAMUEL. A Whaling Voyage in the Bark 'Willis' 1849-1850. Boston: Privately ptd, 1924. 1st ed. One of 475. VG (lt foxed). *Lefkowicz*. $150/£94

MILLHAUSER, STEVEN. Edwin Mullhouse: The Life and Death of an American Writer 1943-1954 by Jeffrey Cartwright. NY: Knopf, 1972. 1st ed, 1st bk. Fine in dj (sl rubbed). *Lenz*. $75/£47

MILLHAUSER, STEVEN. From the Realm of Morpheus. NY: Morrow, (1986). 1st ed. Fine in NF dj (lt rubbed, sm tear). *Between The Covers*. $45/£28

MILLHAUSER, STEVEN. Portrait of a Romantic. NY: Knopf, 1977. 1st ed. (Rmdr stamp bottom pg edge), else Fine in Fine dj. *Pettler*. $22/£14

MILLICAN, ALBERT. Travels and Adventures of an Orchid Hunter.... Cassell, 1891. 1st ed. Chromolitho frontis, xv,222pp + pub's bklist bound in; 19 b/w plts. Grn cl, gilt. (New eps; joints rubbed.) Internally Fine. *Sotheran*. $397/£248

MILLIER, ARTHUR. Maynard Dixon. Tucson: n.p., 1945. Frontis by Ansel Adams. (Lt worn.) Illus stiff wrappers (fr wrapper spotted, sl soiled). *Turtle Island*. $65/£41

MILLIGAN, SPIKE. The (Little) Pot Boiler. Dennis Dobson, 1963. 1st ed. VG in dj. *Green Meadow*. $19/£12

MILLIGAN, SPIKE. Puckoon. London, 1963. 1st ed. NF in dj (sl rubbed, sunned). *Polyanthos*. $20/£13

MILLS, ANNETTE. The First Muffin Song Book. Chappell, 1948. 1st ed. 4to. 22pp. (Few sm edge tears), else VG in pict wraps. *Bookmark*. $32/£20

MILLS, ANNETTE. Muffin and the Magic Hat. Univ of London, (1951). 1st ed. 8vo. 128pp; 4 color plts by Molly Blake. Orange cl. VG + . *Bookmark*. $24/£15

MILLS, ANSON. My Story. Washington: The Author, 1918. Aeg. Flexible cl, gilt. (Bkpl, another item removed fep.) *Dawson*. $125/£78

MILLS, ANSON. My Story. C. H. Claudy (ed). Washington: The Author, 1918. 1st ed. Errata slip pasted to fr pastedown. Aeg. Flexible black cl, gilt. Fine. *Pacific**. $259/£162

MILLS, CHARLES and CHARLES FRAZIER et al. Tumors of the Cerebellum. NY, 1905. 1st ed. *Fye*. $100/£63

MILLS, CLIFFORD. Where the Rainbow Ends. London: Hodder & Stoughton, (1921). 1st ed. 4to. 10 full-pg color plts by Leo Bates. Red cl, gilt. Good in color dj (edges chipped, spine lacks piece). *Reisler*. $385/£241

MILLS, ENOS A. In Beaver World. Boston: Houghton & Mifflin, (1913). VG. *Perier*. $25/£16

MILLS, ENOS A. Your National Parks. Boston/NY: Houghton Mifflin, 1917. VG (inscrip) in pict cl. *Zubal**. $45/£28

MILLS, HARRY EDWARD. Select Sunflowers. Fort Scott, KS: Sunflower, 1901. 1st ed. Frontis. Gilt-emb pict cl. (Few spots), else Fine. *Connolly*. $25/£16

MILLS, J. TRAVIS. John Bright and the Quakers. London: Methuen, 1935. 1st ed. 2 vols. 34 plts, 1 map. Excellent set (sl spotted) in djs. *Hollett*. $104/£65

MILLS, JOHN. The Flyers of the Hunt. London, 1859. 1st ed. John Leech (illus). Teg. Full red polished calf by Zaehnsdorf, spine gilt. (Orig cvr, spine bound in at end; lt rubbed.) *Oinonen**. $170/£106

MILLS, JOHN. The Life of a Foxhound. London: Philip Allan, (1921). 5th ed. Red cl, gilt. (Spine sunned), else NF. *Pacific**. $29/£18

MILLS, JOHN. Stable Secrets; or, Puffy Doodles, His Sayings and Sympathies. London, 1863. 1st ed. 3/4 red morocco by Zaehnsdorf. (Orig cvrs, spine bound in at end; sl rubbed.) *Oinonen**. $90/£56

MILLS, RANDALL V. Railroads Down the Valley: Some Short Lines of the Oregon Country. Palo Alto: Pacific Books, (1950). VG in VG dj. *Perier*. $30/£19

MILLS, RANDALL V. Stern-Wheelers Up Columbia: A Century of Steamboating in the Oregon Country. Palo Alto: Pacific Books, (1947). VG in dj. *Perier*. $25/£16

MILLS, W. JAY. Through the Gates of Old Romance. Phila: J.B. Lippincott, 1903. 1st ed. 15 b/w plts. Teg. 3/4 blue levant, gilt. VG + (lt worn). *House*. $60/£38

MILLS, WINIFRED H. and LOUISE M. DUNN. Marionettes, Masks, and Shadows. GC: Doubleday, Doran, 1931. Pict eps. Dec cl. VG. *Dramatis*. $30/£19

MILLSPAUGH, CHARLES F. Medicinal Plants. Phila: John C. Yorston, 1892. 2 vols. 4to. vii-xvpp, 99 plts + text of 2 to 6pp accompanying each plt; vi-xvpp, 91 plts + text of 2 to 6pp accompanying each plt; 180 of these plts are full-pg color. Marbled edges. 3/4 black cl w/orig red cl bds (rebound), gilt. VG. *Fair Meadow*. $800/£500

MILMAN, H. H. Annals of St. Paul's Cathedral. John Murray, 1869. 2nd ed. xii,(2),540pp; 14 plts. VG (bkpl) in contemp divinity calf, gilt, morocco label. *Cox*. $48/£30

MILMAN, H. H. The Martyr of Antioch: A Dramatic Poem. John Murray, 1822. 1st ed. vii,(i),168pp + 8pg pub's cat. Uncut. Orig bds, new paper spine, label. *Bickersteth*. $96/£60

MILNE, A. A. The Christopher Robin Birthday Book. Methuen, 1930. 1st ed. Sm 8vo. E.H. Shepard (illus). viii,215pp. Red cl, gilt. (Spine tip sl worn, spine, top edge faded), else VG + in pict dj (worn, torn). *Bookmark*. $136/£85

MILNE, A. A. The Christopher Robin Story Book. London: Methuen, 1929. 1st ed thus. 8vo. E. H. Shepard (illus). (x),171,(viii)pp. Pict eps; uncut. Lt blue cl. VG in white pict color-ptd wrapper (1 sm closed tear top edge, spine browned). *Sotheran*. $637/£398

MILNE, A. A. For the Luncheon Interval. London: Methuen, 1925. 1st ed. Fore-edges untrimmed. Fine in grn ptd wrappers. *Maggs*. $56/£35

MILNE, A. A. A Gallery of Children. London: Stanley Paul, (1925). 1st ed deluxe. Ltd to 485 numbered, signed. 4to. (iv),5-105pp; 12 full-color plts by H. Willebeek Le Mair. Teg, rest uncut. 1/2 red calf, red cl sides, gilt. (Tp sl speckled), o/w Fine. *Sotheran*. $880/£550

MILNE, A. A. A Gallery of Children. London: Stanley Paul, (1925). 1st ed. One of 500 signed. 4to. 12 color plts by H. Willebeek Lemair. Teg. White gilt-stamped linen. Fine in linen fldg box. *Appelfeld*. $1,500/£938

MILNE, A. A. The House at Pooh Corner. London: Methuen, (1928). 1st ed. 8vo. Ernest H. Shepard (illus). Teg. Salmon cl, gilt. VG in pict dj (spine sl torn). *Reisler*. $750/£469

MILNE, A. A. The House at Pooh Corner. London: Methuen, (1928). One of 350 signed by Milne & Ernest H. Shepard (illus). 8vo. xi,178pp. Unopened. Blue cl over white bds, ptd paper label fr cvr. NF (eps lt browned; top bd edges, top edge sl soiled) in dj (lt foxed, soiled). *Heritage*. $4,500/£2,813

MILNE, A. A. The House at Pooh Corner. Methuen, 1928. 1st ed. Ernest H. Shepard (illus). xi,180pp. VG (few lt finger-mks; edges, spine sl faded, corners sl bruised). *Hollett*. $152/£95

MILNE, A. A. The House at Pooh Corner. London: Methuen, 1928. 1st ed. 8vo. E. H. Shepard (illus). (xi),178pp. Pict eps; teg, rest uncut. Salmon pink cl, gilt. (Inscrip, fore-edge of bk block sl speckled; spine sl sunned), o/w Clean. *Sotheran*. $269/£168

MILNE, A. A. The House at Pooh Corner. Methuen, 1928. 1st ed. Ernest H. Shepard (illus). xi,180pp. VG (sm sl dknd strip on each fep, sm edge-tear to fep, few lt finger-mks, odd spot, crease; edges, spine sl faded) in dj (sl soiled, chipped, backstrip creased, rubbed, strengthened internally). *Hollett*. $424/£265

MILNE, A. A. The House at Pooh Corner. London: Methuen, 1928. 1st ed. 8vo. E. H. Shepard (illus). (xii),178pp. Pict eps; teg. Salmon pink cl, gilt. (Eps sl browned), o/w Fine in VG pink pict dj (sm nicks to spine ends, corners). *Sotheran*. $840/£525

MILNE, A. A. The Ivory Door. London, 1929. 1st ed. Nice in dj (rubbed). *King*. $25/£16

MILNE, A. A. The Ivory Door. London: C&W, 1929. 1st ed. Uncut. Brn cl, ptd spine label. VF in dj. *Maggs*. $120/£75

MILNE, A. A. The King's Breakfast. London: Methuen, (1925). 1st ed. 8vo. Ernest H. Shepard (illus), H. Fraser-Simson (music). Cl pict bds (sm spot, edges lt worn) w/pink background. Pict dj (mkd, spine chipped). *Reisler*. $125/£78

MILNE, A. A. The King's Breakfast. London: Methuen, 1925. 1st ed. Slim royal 8vo. Ernest Shepard (illus). Pink dec bds. (Sm brn splash upper bd), o/w VG. *Sotheran*. $125/£78

MILNE, A. A. Michael and Mary. London: C&W, 1930. 1st ed. Uncut. Brn cl, ptd spine label. Fine in dj (top edge sl crumpled). *Maggs*. $80/£50

MILNE, A. A. Michael and Mary. A Play. London: C&W, 1930. 1st ed. One of 260 signed. Teg. Grn cl. (Fore-edges, few pp foxed; spine faded), o/w Fine. *Cummins*. $150/£94

MILNE, A. A. More 'Very Young' Songs. London: Methuen, 1928. 1st ed. Slim 4to. E. H. Shepard (illus). (vi),39pp. Cl-backed gray bds, onlaid pict paper label to upper cvr. Very Nice. *Sotheran*. $141/£88

MILNE, A. A. Now We Are Six. Methuen, 1927. 1st ed. Ernest H. Shepard (illus). x,104pp. VG (odd finger-mk, final pg differentially browned; sm spine head patch faded, extrems sl rubbed) in dj (sl soiled, chipped, folds rubbed, spine dknd, ends chipped). *Hollett*. $440/£275

MILNE, A. A. Now We Are Six. Methuen, 1927. 1st ed. Crown 8vo. E. H. Shepard (illus). xi,104pp (initial, final pg partly browned). Gilt edges, rest roughtrimmed. Maroon cl, gilt. VG in dj (backstrip panel sl sunned, sm tear). *Blackwell's*. $456/£285

MILNE, A. A. Now We Are Six. London: Methuen, 1927. 1st ed. 8vo. E. H. Shepard (illus). (xii),103pp. Pict eps; teg, rest untrimmed. Crimson cl, gilt. VF in Clean dj (it dust-soiled, 2 sm closed tears to edges, professionally repaired to verso). *Sotheran*. $637/£398

MILNE, A. A. Now We Are Six. London: Methuen, 1927. 1st ed. 8vo. Ernest Shepard (illus). Full red morocco w/gilt-stamped figures on fr, rear cvrs; gilt-stamped animal motifs on spine, raised bands, aeg, by Sangorski & Sutcliffe. VF. *Appelfeld*. $650/£406

MILNE, A. A. Once Upon a Time. NY: Putnam, (1922). Color frontis by Charles Robinson. Dec red cl, gilt. (Spot to frontis; spine, ends rubbed, extrems sunned), else VG. *Pacific**. $98/£61

MILNE, A. A. Once Upon a Time. NY: Putnam, 1922. 1st ed, 2nd imp. 8vo. Color frontis, 358pp; 24 dbl-pg plts, map by Charles Robinson. Illus eps. Red cl. VG (ep reinforced; cvr lt worn). *Davidson*. $85/£53

MILNE, A. A. The Red House Mystery. Methuen, 1922. 1st UK ed. VG (spine sl dull). *Williams*. $96/£60

MILNE, A. A. The Secret and Other Stories. NY/London: Fountain Press/Methuen, 1929. One of 742 numbered, signed. Cl, paper label. Good (spine label sl tanned, sm frays at spine corners, edges). *Reese*. $55/£34

MILNE, A. A. Teddy Bear and Other Songs. Methuen, 1926. 1st UK ed. E.H. Shepard (illus). (Corners sl scuffed), o/w VG. *Martin*. $38/£24

MILNE, A. A. Those Were the Days. London: Methuen, 1929. 1st ed. One of 250 signed. Red cl, gilt. Dj (lt thumbed, spine sl faded). *Maggs*. $400/£250

MILNE, A. A. Toad of Toad Hall. London: Methuen, 1929. 1st ed. 8vo. (xviii),3-168,8pp. Teg. Mid-blue cl. Nice. *Sotheran*. $77/£48

MILNE, A. A. Toad of Toad Hall. A Play from Kenneth Grahame's 'The Wind in the Willows.' London: Methuen, 1929. 1st ed. Blue cl, gilt. Fine in dj. *Maggs*. $200/£125

MILNE, A. A. Two People. London: Methuen, 1931. 1st ed. Lt brn cl, gilt. Dj (spine sl faded). *Maggs*. $40/£25

MILNE, A. A. When I Was Very Young. NY: Fountain Press, 1930. 1st ltd ed. One of 842 numbered, signed. Ernest Shepard (illus). Slim tall 8vo. Untrimmed. Pict cl, ptd paper spine label. (Spine sl sunned.) Text Fine, cvrs Good. *Baltimore**. $150/£94

MILNE, A. A. When We Were Very Young. London: Methuen, (1925). 10th ed. 8vo. Teg. Blue cl, gilt. Nice (cl wrinkle fr cvr). *Glenn*. $100/£63

MILNE, A. A. When We Were Very Young. London: Methuen, (1928). 17th ed. 8vo. Teg. Blue cl, gilt. Fine in dj (lt soiled). *Glenn*. $125/£78

MILNE, A. A. When We Were Very Young. London: Methuen, (1930). 20th ed. 8vo. Teg. Blue cl, gilt. NF (offsetting to pict eps) in dj (lt worn). *Glenn*. $150/£94

MILNE, A. A. When We Were Very Young. Methuen, 1924. 3rd ed. Ernest H. Shepard (illus). x,100pp. VG (sl fingered, few spots; fr joint tender; sl worn). *Hollett*. $192/£120

MILNE, A. A. When We Were Very Young. London: Methuen, 1924. 1st ed. 8vo. Ernest H. Shepard (illus). Teg. Pict blue cl (spine ends lt rubbed). Dj (spine lt soiled, chipped). *Christie's**. $1,749/£1,093

MILNE, A. A. When We Were Very Young. Leipzig: Bernhard Tauchnitz, 1934. 1st ed thus. 12mo. Ernest H. Shepard (illus). 123pp. Ptd paper wrappers (spine dknd). *Reisler*. $75/£47

MILNE, A. A. Winnie-the-Pooh and Eeyore's Tail. A Pop-Up Picture Book. London: Methuen, n.d. 8vo. (10)ff; 4 pop-up scenes. (Juv inscrip), else Fine in spiral-bound illus bds (extrems lt worn). *Bromer*. $300/£188

MILNE, A. A. Winnie-the-Pooh and the Bees. NY: E.P. Dutton, (1952). 1st Amer ed. 4to. 4 dbl-pg pop-ups by E. H. Shepard. Color illus bds (corners lt worn), spiral binding. *Reisler*. $150/£94

MILNE, A. A. Winnie-the-Pooh. London: Methuen, (1926). 1st ed. 8vo. E. H. Shepard (illus). (xv),158pp. Teg. Dk grn pict cl, gilt. Fine. *Sotheran*. $477/£298

MILNE, A. A. Winnie-the-Pooh. London: Methuen, (1926). 1st ed. 8vo. E. H. Shepard (illus). (xvi),158pp. Pict eps. Teg, rest untrimmed. Dk grn cl, gilt vignettes of characters on fr cvr. VF in stunning pict wrapper. *Sotheran*. $1,920/£1,200

MILNE, A. A. Winnie-the-Pooh. (NY): E.P. Dutton, (1926). One of 200 lg paper copies signed by Milne & illus. Sq 8vo. Blue cl over pink bds, pink paper spine label. VG in dj (rear panel edges lt soiled). *Heritage*. $2,000/£1,250

MILNE, A. A. Winnie-the-Pooh. London: Methuen, (1927). 3rd ed. 8vo. Teg. Forest grn cl, gilt. Fine. *Glenn*. $175/£109

MILNE, A. A. Winnie-the-Pooh. Kenosha: John Martin's House, (1946). 1st ed thus. Lg 4to. Helen Page (illus). Color pict bds (lt worn). Color dj. *Reisler*. $85/£53

MILNE, A. A. The World of Christopher Robin. Dutton, 1958. Lg 8vo. E. H. Shepard (illus). VG in VG dj. *American Booksellers*. $25/£16

MILNE-EDWARDS, H. and J. HAIME. British Fossil Corals. London, 1850-54. lxxxv,322pp; 71 of 72 plts (missing plt 52 supplied in xerox). Good. *Henly*. $160/£100

MILNER, CLYDE A. With Good Intentions. Lincoln: Univ of NE, (1982). 1st ed. VG in dj (sl worn). *Lien*. $20/£13

MILNER, JOE E. and EARLE R. FORREST. California Joe, Noted Indian Fighter. Caldwell: Caxton Ptrs, 1935. 1st ed. Gilt-dec cl. Fine (bold sig, sm rubberstamp, few notes, newspaper clipping affixed to fep). Howes M635. *Pacific**. $86/£54

MILNER, JOE E. and EARLE E. FORREST. California Joe, Noted Scout and Indian Fighter...with an Authentic Account of Custer's Last Fight by Colonel William H.C. Bowen, Formerly of the United States Army. Caldwell, ID: Caxton, 1935. 1st ed. Grn cl, gilt. (Extrems lt rubbed), else Fine. Howes M635. *Argonaut*. $125/£78

MILNER, JOHN. The History, Civil and Ecclesiastical, and Survey of the Antiquities of Winchester.... Winchester, (1798-1801). 1st ed. 2 vols. 12 plts (6 fldg). Cl-backed bds (rubbed, worn, hinge frayed, lt soiled). *Kane**. $70/£44

MILNER, JOHN. The History, Civil and Ecclesiastical, and Survey of the Antiquities, of Winchester. Winchester: Jas. Robbins, 1798-1801. 1st ed. 2 vols. Engr tps, 12 copper plts (6 fldg). Orig cl-backed bds, morocco spine labels. (Foxed; sl stained), else VG. *Pacific**. $63/£39

MILNER, JOHN. A Treatise on the Ecclesiastical Architecture of England, During the Middle Ages. John Weale, 1835. 3rd ed. xxv,134pp + 2pp pub's ads; 10 plts. (Sl browned.) Mod 1/2 calf (rebound). *Edwards*. $72/£45

MILNER, JOHN. Vladimir Tatlin and the Russian Avant-Garde. New Haven: Yale Univ, 1984. Orig ed, 2nd ptg. NF in dj. *Turtle Island*. $65/£41

MILNES, RICHARD MONCKTON (ed). Life, Letters, and Literary Remains of John Keats. Richard Monckton Milnes (ed). Edward Moxon, 1848. 1st ed, later issue w/8-pg pub's ad dated Oct 1851 at fr of vol 1, frontis w/facs of Keats's handwriting at fr of vol 2 (no frontis vol 1). Pale yellow eps. Orig purple cl (sl faded, rubbed), gilt. *Sotheby's**. $552/£345

MILNOR, W. Memoirs of the Gloucester Fox Hunting Club. NY: Derrydale, 1927. One of 375 numbered. Engr frontis tipped-in. Pink paper-cvrd bds. VG. *Biscotti*. $175/£109

MILOSZ, CZESLAW. The Captive Mind. NY, 1953. 1st Amer ed, 1st bk. VG in VG dj. *Warren*. $40/£25

MILOSZ, CZESLAW. The Captive Mind. LEC, 1983. Ltd to 1500 numbered, signed by Milosz and Janusz Kapusta (illus). Fine in slipcase. *Swann**. $103/£64

MILTON, JOHN. Comus. London: Routledge, (1906). 1st ed illus thus. 10 Fine etched plts by Jessie M. King, guards. Teg, rest uncut. Dec brn/grn cl, gilt. (Corner fep skillfully repaired; 2 sm damp spots lower bd), o/w Fine. *Sotheran*. $237/£148

MILTON, JOHN. Comus. London: Heinemann, (1921). 1st ed illus by Arthur Rackham. 24 Fine mtd color plts, guards. Dk grn cl, gilt. Externally Fine (prelims, fore-edge of book block speckled) in pict dj (sm closed tears, edge creases, sl loss spine head). *Sotheran*. $400/£250

MILTON, JOHN. Comus. London: Heinemann, (1921). 1st trade ed. 4to. 24 mtd color plts by Arthur Rackham on tan paper. Grn pict cl, gilt. Dj (edges sl frayed, few sm tears). *Christie's**. $442/£276

MILTON, JOHN. Comus. London: Heinemann, 1921. 1st ed illus by Arthur Rackham. One of 550 signed by Rackham. 4to. 24 mtd color plts, guards. Teg, rest uncut. Orig vellum-backed cream paper-cvrd bds, gilt. Very Clean. *Sotheran*. $1,117/£698

MILTON, JOHN. L'Allegro and Il Penseroso. LEC, 1954. Ltd to 1500 numbered, signed by Bruce Rogers (designer). Fine in slipcase. *Swann**. $115/£72

MILTON, JOHN. The Mask of Comus. Bloomsbury: Nonesuch, 1937. Ltd to 950 numbered. Uncut. Parchment paper bds. (Spine head sl bumped, cvr sl soiled), else Nice. *King*. $175/£109

MILTON, JOHN. The Masque of Comus. LEC, 1954. Ltd to 1500 numbered. Edmund Dulac (illus). Fine in slipcase. *Swann**. $80/£50

MILTON, JOHN. Milton's Paradise Lost. Robert Vaughn (ed). NY/London: Cassell, ca 1880. Gustave Dore (illus). Teg. Gilt-stamped buckram. Good. *Appelfeld*. $150/£94

MILTON, JOHN. Minor Poems. London, (1926). One of 250 numbered. Untrimmed, many pp unopened. Full vellum (sl worn). Dj (tattered, stained). *Woolson*. $40/£25

MILTON, JOHN. On the Morning of Christ's Nativity. Gregynog, 1937. One of 250. Full-pg wood engr. (W/o laid-in Christmas greetings leaf, mentioned in Harrop.) VF in ptd paper wrappers (sl frayed along lower edge, lt offsetting from illus). *Pirages*. $125/£78

MILTON, JOHN. Paradise Lost and Paradise Regain'd. London: Cresset, 1931. One of 195 sets. 2 vols. 14.5x10 inches. 18 full-pg wood engrs by D. Galanis. Uncut. White linen (few smudges). *Dawson*. $750/£469

MILTON, JOHN. Paradise Lost and Paradise Regain'd. SF: LEC, 1936. One of 1500 signed by Carlotta Petrina (illus). Folio. 1/4 linen, red batik over bds, paper spine label. (Lacks slipcase), else Fine. *Pharos*. $85/£53

MILTON, JOHN. Paradise Lost and Paradise Regain'd. LEC, 1936. Ltd to 1500 numbered, signed by Carlotta Petrina (illus). Fine in slipcase. *Swann**. $115/£72

MILTON, JOHN. Paradise Lost and Paradise Regain'd. To Which Is Added Samson Agonistes: And Poems upon Several Occasions. Birmingham: Ptd by John Baskerville for J. & R. Tonson, 1758. 1st Baskerville ed. 2 vols. Tall 8vo. W/sub's list. Contemp calf (rebacked in period style), raised bands, leather labels. Nice set (name; bds worn). *Hartfield*. $895/£559

MILTON, JOHN. The Paradise Lost of Milton With Illustrations, Designed and Engraved by John Martin. Septimus Prowett, 1827. 2 vols. Colombier 8vo. 24 mezzotint plts (smaller size, 8x5.75 inches). 19th-cent grn calf, gilt. (Eps, 1/2-title of vol 1 reattached w/tape, fr hinge fragile; feps vol 2 dampstained, text, plts lt foxed; rebacked, very worn.) *Sotheby's**. $662/£414

MILTON, JOHN. Paradise Lost. A Poem, in Twelve Books. London: J.F. & C. Rivington et al, 1790. 9th ed. 2 vols. Frontis ports. Old calf, morocco spine labels. (Offset from frontispieces to tp; glue to corners, rebacked in old calf), else VG. *Pacific**. $92/£58

MILTON, JOHN. Poems in English with Illustrations by William Blake. London: Nonesuch, 1926. One of 1450 (of 2040) on Van Gelder. 2 vols. Parchment, dec bds (spines sl soiled, rear corners bruised). Internally Nice. *Reese*. $175/£109

MILTON, MEYRICK. Two Plays. London: Henry, 1895. 1st ed. Blue cl (lt soiled), gilt. *Dramatis*. $40/£25

MILUNSKY, AUBREY. The Prenatal Diagnosis of Hereditary Disorders. Springfield, 1973. 1st ed. *Fye*. $100/£63

MINARIK, ELSE HOLMELUND. Little Bear's Visit. NY: Harper, (1961). 1st ed. Maurice Sendak (illus). 8vo. Color pict bds. Good in color pict dj (sl marginal wear). *Reisler*. $175/£109

MINARIK, ELSE HOLMELUND. No Fighting, No Biting! NY: Harper & Bros, (1958). 1st ed. 8vo. Cl-backed pict bds (edges lt spotted). Color pict dj (spotted, worn, price-clipped). *Reisler*. $185/£116

MINGUS, CHARLES. Beneath the Underdog. NY, 1971. 1st ed. NF in NF dj. *Warren*. $40/£25

MINGUS, CHARLES. Beneath the Underdog. NY: Knopf, 1971. 1st ed, 1st bk. Fine in NF dj (price-clipped, sm nick, sm closed tear). *Agvent*. $85/£53

MINKOFF, GEORGE ROBERT. A Bibliography of the Black Sun Press. Great Neck, NY: G.R. Minkoff, 1970. 1st ed. One of 1250. Black cl, gilt. Fine. *Heritage*. $60/£38

MINNIGERODE, MEADE. Some Personal Letters of Herman Melville and a Bibliography. NY/New Haven/Princeton: Edmond Burne Hackett/Brick Row Book Shop, 1922. 1st ptg. Linen-backed pale blue bds. Fine in dj (sl worn, stained). *Truepenny*. $150/£94

MINNIGH, L. W. Gettysburg: What They Did Here. Gettysburg: N.A. Meligakes, 1924. 1st ed. Lg fldg map tipped in at fr. VG in pict textured wrappers (sl edgeworn). *Connolly*. $27/£17

MINOT, H. D. The Land-Birds and Game-Birds of New England with Descriptions. Salem: Nat'l Agency, 1877. 1st ed. 456pp. (Ex-lib; extrems heavily rubbed, spine crudely tape repaired), else Good + . *Mikesh*. $45/£28

Minstrel Boy and Other Stories. NY: McLoughlin Bros, 1882. 4to. 8pp full color illus by Ida Waugh. Good in full color pict wrappers (lt dusty, sm spine split). *Reisler*. $110/£69

MINTZ, LANNON W. The Trail. Albuquerque, 1987. 1st ed. VG in dj. *Dumont*. $35/£22

Minutes of the Proceedings of the Committee, Appointed on the 14th September, 1793.... Phila: Ptd by Crissy & Markly, 1848. 1st pub ed. 243pp; fldg table. Contemp marbled bds. (Lib bkpl; stamps; card pocket; worn, broken, cvrs detached), else Fair. *Brown*. $20/£13

MIRANDA, GENERAL. Original Correspondence Between Generals Dumourier, Miranda, Pache and Beurnonville... Since January, 1793. London: J. Owen, 1794. 1st ed in English. (iv),136pp. New morocco-backed bds. *Young*. $48/£30

MIRO, JOAN. Miro Lithographs II. NY: Leon Amiel, (1975). 1st ed. 11 orig lithos. Fine in orig litho dj, wrap-around band. *Pacific**. $288/£180

MIRSKY, JEANETTE. To the Arctic! NY: Viking, 1934. 1st ed. Good (cl sl faded under dj) in VG dj. *Walcot*. $35/£22

MIRSKY, JEANNETTE. To the Arctic! NY: Knopf, 1948. 1st ed thus. Lg fldg map. Dj (worn). *Lefkowicz*. $35/£22

MISCIATTELLI, PIERO. The Mystics of Siena. M. Peters-Roberts (trans). Cambridge: W. Heffer, 1929. 1st Eng ed. 20 plts. (Eps spotted; spine faded, splash-mk on lettering, sl mkd.) *Hollett*. $40/£25

MISER, HUGH D. The San Juan Canyon, Southeastern Utah. Washington: USGS, 1924. 22 plts, lg fldg map. Orange wraps (sl flaws). *Five Quail*. $55/£34

MISHIMA, YUKIO. On Hagakure. Kathryn Sparling (trans). London: Souvenir, 1977. 1st Eng ed. Fine in dj. *Ulysses*. $58/£36

MISRACH, RICHARD. Telegraph 3 A.M. Berkeley: Cornucopia Press, 1974. 1st ed. VG in dj (price-clipped). *Smith*. $75/£47

Miss Vanity's Holiday. NY: McLoughlin Bros, (ca 1880). Mother's Series. Toybook. 12mo. 8pp. Good in color pict paper wrappers (spine split). *Reisler*. $50/£31

Missionary Voyage to the Southern Pacific Ocean, Performed in the Years 1796, 1797, 1798, in the Ship Duff, Commanded by Captain James Wilson. London: Missionary Soc, 1799. 1st ed (Gosnell ed). 7 fldg maps, 6 plts (margins lt stained, offset from plts; eps renewed). Full mod leather. *Parmer*. $750/£469

Missouri. NY: Duell, Sloan & Pearce, 1941. 1st ed. VG in dj. *Labordo*. $75/£47

MITCHEL, O. W. The Planetary and Stellar Worlds: A Popular Exposition...In a Series of Ten Lectures. NY: Baker & Scribner, 1848. 1st ed, 1st bk. 336pp; 17 plts (3 fldg). *M & S*. $150/£94

Mitchell's Travellers Guide Through the United States. Phila: Mitchell & Hinman, 1836. Lg fldg map (neatly hand-colored). Orig grn leather (expertly rebacked). *Appelfeld*. $300/£188

MITCHELL, A. AUGUSTUS. Texas, Oregon and California. Oakland: Biobooks, 1948. Rpt. One of 750 ptd. Fldg facs. Red cl, gilt. Fine. Howes M685 *Pacific**. $29/£18

MITCHELL, DUGALD. Tarbert Past and Present. Dumbarton: Bennet & Thomson, 1886. xii,149pp; 4 litho views. (Few spots.) *Hollett*. $72/£45

MITCHELL, E. A. Fort Timiskaming and the Fur Trade. Toronto: Univ of Toronto, 1977. 1st ed. Fldg map in pocket. VG + . *Walcot*. $21/£13

MITCHELL, EDITH. The Other Side Book. Chicago: Reilly & Britton, (1915). Color illus bds (rubbed, lt spotted; tp w/sl separation). *Reisler*. $400/£250

MITCHELL, EVELYN. Australia's Alps. Sydney/London: Angus & Robertson, 1942. 1st ed. (Spine faded.) *Maggs*. $56/£35

MITCHELL, HORACE. Raising Game Birds. Phila: Penn, 1936. 1st ed. 8 color plts. Brn pebbled cl. Fine. *Bowman*. $30/£19

MITCHELL, JOHN. Notes from Over Sea. NY, 1845. 2 vols. 331; 358pp. (Tps dusty, old stamp.) *Marlborough*. $144/£90

MITCHELL, JOSEPH. The Bottom of the Harbor. Boston: LB, (1959). 1st ed. Fine in VG illus dj (rear panel tanned, sl nicks spine extrems). *Between The Covers*. $100/£63

MITCHELL, JOSEPH. The Bottom of the Harbor. LEC, 1991. One of 250 signed. Fine in slipcase. *Swann**. $575/£359

MITCHELL, JOSEPH. Old Mr. Flood. NY: DSP, (1948). 1st ed. Signed. NF in VG dj (sm nicks, chips). *Between The Covers*. $225/£141

MITCHELL, JOSEPH. Old Mr. Flood. NY: Duell Sloan, 1948. 1st ed. VG in VG dj (price-clipped, chipped). *Pettler.* $45/£28

MITCHELL, MARGARET. Gone With the Wind. NY: Macmillan, 1936. 1st ed, 1st issue. W/'Published May 1936' on c. pg. 1st issue dj w/rear panel headed 'Macmillan Spring Novels' listing GWTW as the 2nd title in the 2nd column. Fine in VG dj (spine ends, corners chipped, spine crease, flap creases rubbed, fr panel top chip). *Pacific**. $2,070/£1,294

MITCHELL, MARGARET. Gone With the Wind. NY, 1936. 1st ed, 1st state of dj. 8vo. Dj (lt edgeworn). *Swann**. $2,185/£1,366

MITCHELL, MARGARET. Gone with the Wind. NY, 1936. 1st ed. Signed, inscribed. Later dj (extrems chipped). *Swann**. $3,450/£2,156

MITCHELL, MARGARET. Gone with the Wind. NY, 1936. 1st ed. 1st issue dj, slipcase. *Swann**. $5,290/£3,306

MITCHELL, MARGARET. Gone with the Wind. NY: Macmillan, 1939. Motion Picture ed. VG in pict wrappers (sm tear fr wrapper, lacks bottom corner). *Pacific**. $58/£36

MITCHELL, MARGARET. Gone with the Wind. NY: Macmillan, 1939. Motion Picture ed. 12 full-pg color repros. Color pict wraps. (Lt handled.) *Baltimore**. $90/£56

MITCHELL, MARGARET. Gone with the Wind. NY: Macmillan, 1939. Ltd to 1000. 2 vols. 8vo. Fine set in slipcase (defective). *Pharos.* $950/£594

MITCHELL, MARGARET. Gone With the Wind. NY: Macmillan, 1961. Anniversary ed. 1/4 cl, dec bds. Fine in slipcase. W/booklet 'Gone with the Wind and its author, Margaret Mitchell' in wrappers. *Pacific**. $104/£65

MITCHELL, MARGARET. Gone with the Wind. NY: Macmillan, 1961. 25th Anniversary ed. Pamphlet laid in. VF in VF slipcase. *Between The Covers.* $150/£94

MITCHELL, MARGARET. Gone with the Wind. LEC, 1968. Ltd to 1500 numbered, signed by John groth (illus). 2 vols. Fine in slipcase. *Swann**. $126/£79

MITCHELL, MARGARET. Gone with the Wind. NY: LEC, 1968. One of 1500. Signed by John Groth (illus). 2 vols. Blue/gray buckram. Fine in glassine, slipcase. *Pacific**. $173/£108

MITCHELL, P. CHALMERS. Thomas Henry Huxley. NY, 1900. 1st ed. Maroon/gray cl, gilt. VG. *Larry Price.* $25/£16

MITCHELL, S. AUGUSTUS. Illinois in 1837. Phila: Mitchell, 1837. 1st ed. viii,143,(9)pp; Fine fldg map. (Foxed; rebacked), else Good. Howes M689. *Dumont.* $175/£109

MITCHELL, S. AUGUSTUS. Texas, Oregon and California. Oakland: Biobooks, 1948. Rpt. Ltd to 750. Fldg map (sm tear). Unopened. Fine. *Dumont.* $35/£22

MITCHELL, S. WEIR (ed). Five Essays by John Kearsley Mitchell, M.D. Phila, 1859. 1st ed. 371pp. (Spine rubbed w/hinges reinforced, one section starting.) *Fye.* $200/£125

MITCHELL, S. WEIR. The Autobiography of a Quack. NY: Century, 1900. 1st ed. Untrimmed. VG. BAL 14192. *Second Life.* $45/£28

MITCHELL, S. WEIR. Doctor and Patient. Phila, 1888. 1st ed. 177pp. *Fye.* $200/£125

MITCHELL, S. WEIR. Hugh Wynne. NY: Century, 1899. 1st ed thus. 2 vols. xii,306; x,261pp; 62 plts, guards. Teg, untrimmed. Gilt-blocked cl. VG (lacks 1 frontis; spine sl dknd, cvrs lt spotted). *Connolly.* $45/£28

MITCHELL, S. WEIR. Hugh Wynne. Free Quaker: Sometime Brevet Lieutenant-Colonel on the Staff of His Excellency General Washington. NY, (1899). Continental ed. 2 vols. 306; 261pp. VG + . *Pratt.* $65/£41

MITCHELL, T. L. Journal of an Expedition into the Interior of Tropical Australia. London: Longman, Brown, 1848. 1st ed. Litho frontis, xiv,(i)illus,(i)blank,437,(1)imprint; 10 litho plts, 1 engr plt, 7 maps (4 fldg). Early 20th-cent calf, marbled bds, red label, gilt. (1 map torn, repaired, laid down on thin paper, 1 plt frayed; sl browned, stained, esp margins, 2 leaves w/pencil notes.) *Morrell.* $480/£300

MITCHELL, W. H. Geographical and Statistical History of Steele County. Minneapolis: Tribune Ptg Co, 1868. Orig ptd paper wraps (spine replaced, brittle, chipped). Internally Fine. *Metropolitan**. $237/£148

MITCHELL, W. H. et al. Chechakho to Sourdough: The Story of the Forty-Fifth United States Naval Construction Battalion in Alaska, World War II. J.P. Roulett, n.d. (1944?). Good. *Rybski.* $80/£50

MITCHELL, W. R. Highland Winter. Robert Hale, 1973. 1st ed. VG in dj. *Hollett.* $32/£20

MITCHILL, SAMUEL L. and EDWARD MILLER. Medical Repository. NY, 1799. Vol 2. 478pp. Orig full calf. (Ex-lib, foxed, shaken w/loose fep, tp; tape on spine). *Doctor's Library.* $125/£78

MITCHISON, NAOMI. The Alban Goes Out. London: Raven, 1939. 1st Eng ed. VG (tp sl spotted, pp browned at inner margins) in wrappers (sl soiled, creased). *Ulysses.* $104/£65

MITFORD, BERTRAM. Fordham's Feud. London: Ward, Lock, 1897. 1st ed. Frontis. Pict grn cl, gilt. Good (foxed, ink name, initial). *Reese.* $45/£28

MITFORD, BERTRAM. The Ruby Sword, a Romance of Baluchistan. London: F.V. White, 1899. 1st ed. Frontis, 2 plts. Olive cl, gilt. VG (ink name, bksllr's blindstamp; lt rubbed). *Reese.* $45/£28

MITFORD, BERTRAM. Through the Zulu Country. London: Kegan Paul Trench, 1883. 1st ed. 1/2-title, xi,(i),323pp; 5 aquatints. Black cl. Good (sl foxed, ink lib stamp, tp mkd from tape removal, affecting 2 letters of imprint; rebacked preserving orig spine, spine lettering sl defective, restored). *Morrell.* $472/£295

MITFORD, JESSICA. The Trial of Dr. Spock. NY, 1969. 1st Amer ed. Fine in dj (price-clipped). *Polyanthos.* $25/£16

MITFORD, NANCY. Don't Tell Alfred. Hamilton, 1960. 1st UK ed. Fine (inside flap sl discolored) in Fine dj. *Martin.* $19/£12

MITFORD, T. B. The Inscriptions of Kourion. Phila: American Philosophical Soc, 1971. 1st ed. VG in dj (torn). *Worldwide.* $65/£41

MITGANG, HERBERT. The Letters of Carl Sandburg. NY, 1958. 1st ed. (Inscrip), else Fine. *Bond.* $15/£9

MITTELHOLZER, WALTER et al. By Airplane Towards the North Pole. London: Geo. Allen & Unwin, (1925). 2 fldg maps. VG (sl defect edge lower bds). *High Latitude.* $65/£41

MITTELHOLZER, WALTER. By Airplane Towards the North Pole: An Account of an Expedition to Spitzbergen in the Summer of 1923. London: George Allen & Unwin, 1925. 2 fldg maps. VG. *Explorer.* $45/£28

MITTON, G. E. (ed). The Swiss Family Robinson. London: A&C Black, (1907). 1st ed thus. Thick 8vo. 8 full-pg color plts by Harry Rountree. Lt gray cl, gilt. Good in dj (worn, few sm pieces missing). *Reisler.* $135/£84

MITZMAN, MAX E. George Baxter and the Baxter Prints. David & Charles, 1978. 1st ed. 18 color plts. Dj. *Forest.* $56/£35

MIVART, ST. GEORGE. On the Genesis of Species. NY: Appleton, 1871. 1st ed. 314pp. (Spine ends rubbed), else Good + . *Mikesh.* $35/£22

MIVART, ST. GEORGE. On the Genesis of Species. NY, 1871. 1st Amer ed. 314pp. *Fye.* $75/£47

MIX, PAUL. The Life and Legend of Tom Mix. Cranbury, NJ, 1972. 1st ed. Fine in dj. *Labordo.* $40/£25

MO, TIMOTHY. The Monkey King. London: Andre Deutsch, 1978. 1st Eng ed, 1st bk. NF (spine ends sl bumped) in dj (sl creased). *Ulysses*. $232/£145

MO, TIMOTHY. Sour Sweet. Deutsch, 1982. 1st UK ed. VG in 1st state 'Chinese' dj. *Williams*. $88/£55

MOCKLER-FERRYMAN, A. F. British West Africa, Its Rise and Progress. London: Swan Sonnenschein, 1900. 2nd ed. 9 color maps. Dec blue cl. (Ex-lib, mks.) *Karmiole*. $65/£41

MODEL, LISETTE. Lisette Model. (Millerton): Aperture, 1979. 1st ed. NF in pict dj. *Cahan*. $85/£53

MODELSKI, ANDREW M. Railroad Maps of North America. Washington, 1984. VG in dj (worn). *Dumont*. $45/£28

Modern Characters from Shakespeare, Alphabetically Arranged [and] An Essay on Musical Expression by Charles Avison. London: E. Johnson/Lockyer Davis, 1778/1775. 3rd ed. 8vo. iv,88; viii,221pp; 4 fldg plts, 1f. ad. Contemp calf, raised bands, gilt. *Marlborough*. $768/£480

Modern Traveller.... (By Josiah Conder.) London: James Duncan, 1825. 1st ed. 2 vols. vi,372; iv,324pp; fldg map, 6 plts. Contemp blue calf, marbled bds, grn/maroon morocco spine labels. Good. *Karmiole*. $150/£94

MODERSOHN-BECKER, PAULA. The Letters and Journals. Gunter Busch and Liselotte von Reinken (eds). NY: Taplinger, (1983). 1st ed. NF in dj. *Hermitage*. $40/£25

MOE, LOUIS. Tommy-Tatters and the Four Bears. NY: Longmans, Green, (1930). 1st ed. Obl 4to. 10 full-pg color illus. Blue cl (lt worn), color paste label. *Reisler*. $300/£188

MOESCHLIN, ELSA. The Red Horse. NY: Coward McCann, (1944). 4to. Color pict bds. Good in full color dj (sl edgeworn). *Reisler*. $110/£69

MOFFAT, ALFRED. Little Songs of Long Ago—'More Nursery Rhymes.' Phila: David McKay, (1912). 1st ed. 9x11. H. Willebeek Le Mair (illus). Mustard cl, gilt, pict cvr label. NF. *Pacific**. $98/£61

MOFFAT, ROBERT. Missionary Labours and Scenes in Southern Africa. John Snow, 1842. 1st ed. Color frontis, xvi,624pp; fldg map. Blind-stamped cl (extrems sl chipped, worn, edges sl bumped), gilt. Good (sl browned, fingered). *Hollett*. $264/£165

MOFFAT, ROBERT. Missionary Labours and Scenes in Southern Africa. John Snow, 1846. '14th thousand' (5th ed). Steel-engr frontis, viii,164pp; fldg map. Marbled eps. Contemp 1/2 calf, gilt, brn cl sides, raised bands, black leather label. Good (ink inscrip; spine, corners rubbed). *Sotheran*. $157/£98

MOFFAT, WILLIAM. Shetland: The Isles of Nightless Summer. Heath Cranton, 1934. 1st ed. (Spine sl faded.) *Hollett*. $64/£40

MOFFETT, CHARLES S. et al. The New Painting: Impressionism 1874-1886. Phaidon, 1986. 1st ed. Rev copy. Navy cl, gilt. Fine in Fine dj. *Whittle*. $48/£30

MOFFETT, CLEVELAND. The Seine Mystery. NY: Dodd Mead, 1925. 1st Amer ed. Fine in dj (lt soiled, sm tears). *Mordida*. $95/£59

MOFFETT, KENWORTH. Kenneth Noland. NY: Abrams, (1977). Mtd color plts. Plastic dj. *Swann**. $149/£93

MOFFIT, ELLA. The Cocker Spaniel. NY: OJ, 1947. Rev, enlgd ed, 1st ptg. VG in Good dj. *October Farm*. $25/£16

MOFFIT, ELLA. The Cocker Spaniel. NY: OJ, 1950. VG in dj (chipped). *Larry Price*. $17/£11

MOHOLY-NAGY, LASZLO. L. Moholy-Nagy. Brno: Telhor, 1936. 4to. (Sl water-damaged, foxed.) Spiral-bound ptd wrappers (worn, chipped). *Swann**. $546/£341

MOHOLY-NAGY, LASZLO. Vision in Motion. Chicago: Paul Theobald, 1969. 8th ptg. (Stamps, tape mks on eps), else VG in Good dj. *Cahan*. $40/£25

MOHOLY-NAGY, SIBYL. Moholy-Nagy, Experiment in Totality. NY, (1950). 1st ed. Good (bkpl) in dj (defective). *King*. $95/£59

MOHR, EDWARD. To the Victoria Falls of the Zambesi. N. D'Anvers (trans). London: Sampson Low, Marston, 1876. 1st Eng ed. 8vo. 1/2-title, engr frontisport, xiv,(i)list,(i)blank,462pp,(2),24pp pub's lists; 4 color lithos, 11 woodcut plts, fldg color map. Grn cl. Good (margins sl browned; recased w/neat spine repairs, sl damp-spotted). *Morrell*. $928/£580

MOHR, NICOLAUS. Excursion Through America. Ray Allen Billington (ed). Lavern J. Rippley (trans). Chicago: R.R. Donnelley, 1973. Fldg map. VG. *Lien*. $25/£16

MOHS, FREDERIC EDWARD. Chemosurgery in Cancer, Gangrene, and Infections, Featuring a New Method for the Microscopically Controlled Excision of Cancer. Springfield, IL: Charles C. Thomas, (1956). Fine in dj. *Weber*. $150/£94

MOIR, ALFRED. The Italian Followers of Caravaggio. Cambridge, 1967. 2 vols. Good. *Washton*. $285/£178

MOLESWORTH, MRS. A Christmas Child. Macmillan, 1880. 1st ed. 8vo. Frontis, ix,223pp,24pp ads; 6 b/w plts by Walter Crane. Pict-dec orange cl. VG + . *Bookmark*. $72/£45

MOLESWORTH, MRS. The Rectory Children. Macmillan, 1889. 1st ed. 8vo. Frontis, 212pp,44pp ads; 6 b/w plts by Walter Crane. Pict-dec orange cl. VG. *Bookmark*. $72/£45

MOLESWORTH, MRS. The Tapestry Room. Macmillan, 1879. 1st ed. 8vo. Frontis, 237pp,47pp ads; 6 b/w plts by Walter Crane. Pict-dec orange cl. VG (fep renewed). *Bookmark*. $88/£55

MOLESWORTH, MRS. Us, an Old Fashioned Story. Macmillan, 1885. 1st ed. 8vo. Frontis, 240pp,32pp ads; 6 b/w plts by Walter Crane. Pict-dec orange cl. (Dustmks to rear cvr, spine worn), else VG. *Bookmark*. $72/£45

MOLESWORTH, MRS. Us. Macmillan, 1885. 1st ed. vii,240,32pp; 7 illus by Walter Crane. Dec cl (sl worn, dknd, joints cracked), gilt. *Hollett*. $48/£30

MOLIERE. Tartuffe and The Would-Be Gentleman. LEC, 1963. Ltd to 1500 numbered, signed by Serge Ivanoff (illus). Fine in slipcase. *Swann**. $34/£21

MOLIERE. Tartuffe and the Would-Be Gentleman. NY: LEC, 1963. One of 1500. Signed by Serge Ivanoff (illus). Red patterned cl. Fine in slipcase. *Pacific**. $35/£22

MOLIERE. Tartuffe; or, The Hypocrite. Curtis Hidden Page (trans). Leipzig: LEC, 1930. One of 1500 signed by Hugo Steiner-Prag (illus). Folio. Linen-backed emb bds. Fine in dj, slipcase (defective). *Pharos*. $125/£78

MOLLHAUSEN, BALDWIN. Diary of a Journey from the Mississippi to the Coasts of the Pacific with a United States Government Expedition. London: Longman, Brown, et al, 1858. 1st ed in English. 2 vols. xxx,(2),352; x,(2),397pp; 11 chromolithos, 12 woodcuts, fldg map. Marbled eps. 19th-cent 3/4 morocco, marbled bds, gilt, raised bands. NF (sl dampstains to corners of some plts, sl affecting images; extrems sl worn). Howes M713. *Pacific**. $1,610/£1,006

MOLLOY, J. FITZGERALD. The Life and Adventures of Edmund Kean, Tragedian. 1787-1833. London: Ward & Downey, 1888. 1st ed. 2 vols. Gilt-dec cl. VG. *Dramatis*. $80/£50

MOLLOY, P. The Cry of the Fish Eagle. London: M. Joseph, 1957. 1st ed. Fldg map. (Spine faded), else VG + . *Mikesh*. $60/£38

MOLLOY, P. A Pennant for the Kremlin. GC: Doubleday, 1964. 1st ed. Presentation inscribed, signed, dated September 26, 1964. VG in pict dj. *Cady*. $50/£31

MOLYNEUX, EDWIN. Chrysanthemums and Their Culture. London: The Author, 1881. 1st ed. 111pp + 15pp ads. Brn cl, gilt. *Cullen*. $35/£22

MOMMSEN, THEODOR. The History of Rome. Glencoe, IL: Free Press/Falcon's Wing Press, 1950. 5 vols. Burgundy cl. *Turtle Island*. $125/£78

MONAGHAN, JAY. Civil War on the Western Border. Boston/Toronto: Little, Brown, (1955). 1st ed. Lt gray cl. (Sl sunned), else Fine in dj (lt chipped). *Glenn.* $40/£25

MONAGHAN, JAY. The Legend of Tom Horn. Indianapolis, 1946. 1st ed. Inscribed. VG in Poor dj (masking tape reinforced, price-clipped). *Baade.* $45/£28

MONAGHAN, JAY. The Overland Trail. Indianapolis: Bobbs-Merrill, (1947). 1st ed. VG in dj (edge torn). *Perier.* $30/£19

Monastery. A Romance. By the Author of 'Waverley.' (By Walter Scott.) Edinburgh: Longman, 1820. 1st ed. 3 vols. Contemp plum 1/2 calf, raised bands, gilt, morocco labels. Very Sound set (no 1/2-title vol 1; vols 2, 3 misbound after titles; sl rubbed, spotted). *Young.* $104/£65

MONCRIEFF, G. K. SCOTT. The Water Supply of Barracks and Cantonments. Chatham, 1896. Frontis, xxiv,320pp; 61 fldg plts (numbered 1-60, 40A). (Plts sl foxed, new eps; sl worn.) *Edwards.* $136/£85

MOND, ROBERT and OLIVER H. MYERS. The Bucheum. London: Milford, 1934. 1st ed. 3 vols. Folio. Fldg table vol 1, 173 plts vol 3. Cl spine. (Ex-lib; rubbed, soiled, sm spine tear vol 3, lib spine #), o/w VG. *Worldwide.* $225/£141

MONDY, ROBERT WILLIAM. Pioneers and Preachers. Chicago: Nelson-Hall, (1980). 1st ed. VG in dj. *Lien.* $20/£13

MONELLI, PAOLO. Toes Up. Orlo Williams (trans). London: Duckworth, (1930). 1st ed in English. Port. Gilt pale blue cl. (Spine crown frayed, cl sl hand-soiled), else Good. *Reese.* $25/£16

MONEY, JOHN. The History of the Campaign of 1792, Between the Armies of France...and the Allies. London, 1794. 3 hand-colored fldg maps. 1/2 calf (needs rebinding; bkpl). *Swann*.* $92/£58

MONGAN, AGNES and PAUL J. SACHS. Drawings in the Fogg Museum of Art. Cambridge, 1946. 2 vols. Folio. (Fr cvr vol 1 stained, spines dulled.) Djs (frayed). *Swann*.* $230/£144

MONGAN, AGNES and PAUL J. SACHS. Drawings in the Fogg Museum of Art. Harvard Univ, 1946. 2nd ed. 2 vols. Color frontis, 404 b/w plts. (Margins lt browned.) Djs (lt soiled, chipped; sl spine loss vol 1). *Edwards.* $288/£180

MONK, MARIA. Awful Disclosures of.... London, 1853. Later, possible 1st Eng ed. Frontis. Blind-stamped cl, gilt. *Swann*.* $115/£72

Monkey's Circus. NY: McLoughlin Bros, 1883. Lg 8vo. Internally VG. *Dramatis.* $45/£28

MONKHOUSE, PATRICK and CHARLES PLUMB (eds). Oxford Poetry 1925. Oxford: Basil Blackwell, 1925. 1st ed. Good in dk blue wrappers (label). *Maggs.* $48/£30

MONKHOUSE, W. COSMO. The Turner Gallery. NY: Appleton, ca 1880. 2 vols. Sm folio. 1/2 morocco (extrems rubbed). *Swann*.* $632/£395

MONKKONEN, ERIC H. (ed). Walking to Work: Tramps in America, 1790-1935. Univ of NE, (1984). Good in dj. *Rybski.* $30/£19

MONNIER, ADRIENNE. The Very Rich Hours of.... Richard McDougall (trans). NY: Scribner, (1976). 1st Amer ed. Fine in dj. *Reese.* $20/£13

MONRO, ALEXANDER. The Morbid Anatomy of the Human Gullet, Stomach, and Intestines. Edinburgh, 1811. 1st ed. 568pp; 12 (of 20) engrs present. Recent cl. (Ex-lib, sl foxed.) *Fye.* $200/£125

MONRO, HAROLD. Elm Angel. London: Faber & Faber, 1930. 1st ed. Lg paper issue. One of 250 signed. 2 Fine wood-engrs by Eric Ravilious. VG. *Cady.* $25/£16

MONRO, HAROLD. Trees. London: The Poetry Bookshop, 1916. One of 400. Black bds, 1st issue cvr label w/o author's name. (Lt edgeworn.) *Dermont.* $100/£63

MONROE, DEBRA. The Source of Trouble. Athens: Univ of GA, (1990). 1st ed, 1st bk. Fine in Fine dj. *Robbins.* $35/£22

MONSARRAT, NICHOLAS. Something to Hide. NY: Sloane, 1966. 1st Amer ed. VF in VF dj (sm tear). *Between The Covers.* $65/£41

MONSON-FITZJOHN, G. J. Drinking Vessels of Bygone Days. Herbert Jenkins, 1927. 1st ed. (Spine faded, 25mm tear to head.) *Hollett.* $56/£35

Monster Island. London: Hamish Hamilton Children's Books, 1981. Ron Van der Meer (illus). 5 dbl-pg pop-ups. Glazed pict bds. VG. *Bookfinders.* $50/£31

MONTAGU, GEORGE. Testacea Britannica or Natural History of British Shell, Marine, Land, and Fresh-Water. London, (1803)-1808. 3 vols, incl supp, in 1. Engr tp; 29 (of 30) engr plts. Old 1/2 calf (worn, foxed, joints broken, spine chipped). *Oinonen*.* $70/£44

MONTAGU, JENNIFER. Alessandro Algardi. New Haven/London: Yale Univ, 1985. 2 vols. Frontis vol 1; 225 plts vol 2. Uniform cl. VF set in color djs. *Europa.* $192/£120

MONTAGU, MARY WORTLEY. The Letters and Works of.... Lord Wharncliffe (ed). London: Bentley, 1837. 2nd ed, rev. 3 vols. 3/4 morocco, raised bands, (rubbed, dknd), gilt. Very Clean set. *Second Life.* $250/£156

MONTAGU, MARY WORTLEY. Letters from the Levant During the Embassy to Constantinople, 1716-18.... Joseph Rickerby, 1838. lxiii,v,283pp. Contemp grn 1/2 calf, gilt, red leather label, marbled bds. Good (sl rubbed). *Sotheran.* $120/£75

MONTAGUE, C. E. Action and Other Stories. London: C&W, 1928. 1st ed. Blue cl, paper spine label. (Lt foxed), else NF in dj. *Reese.* $25/£16

MONTAGUE, C. E. The Front Line. Hodder & Stoughton, 1917. 1st Eng ed. VG in card wrappers. *Clearwater.* $80/£50

MONTAGUE, C. E. Right Off the Map. London: C&W, 1927. 1st ed, ltd issue. One of 260 numbered, specially bound, signed. Teg. Blue cl. (Eps, edges sl foxed; spine, edges sunned), else VG. *Reese.* $60/£38

MONTAGUE, C. E. Rough Justice. London: C&W, 1926. 1st ed, trade issue. Gilt red cl. VG in Good dj (long creased tear fr panel). *Reese.* $25/£16

MONTAGUE, C. E. A Writer's Notes on His Trade. London: C&W, 1930. One of 750 lg paper copies, signed. Teg. Orange buckram-backed patterned paper bds. VG in dj (sl worn). *Cady.* $50/£31

MONTAGUE, JOHN. Forms of Exile. Dublin: Dolmen, 1958 (but 1959). 1st bk. One of 225. Card wrappers (edges sl tanned). *Clearwater.* $160/£100

MONTAGUE, JOHN. Patriotic Suite. Dublin: Dolmen, 1966. Signed. VG (lib rubberstamp) in card wrappers. *Clearwater.* $56/£35

MONTAGUE, RICHARD. Oceans, Poles and Airmen. NY: Random, 1971. 1st ed. VG + in dj. *Walcot.* $24/£15

MONTAIGNE, MICHEL. The Essays of Michel de Montaigne. LEC, 1946. Ltd to 1500 numbered, signed by T. M. Cleland (designer). 4 vols. Fine in slipcase. *Swann*.* $287/£179

MONTAIGNE, MICHEL. Essays of Montaigne. Francis Carmody (ed). (Hillsborough): L-D Allen Press, 1948. One of 200. Red brocade cl, gilt. (Spine sl sunned), else NF. *Pacific*.* $219/£137

MONTALBA, ANTHONY R. (ed). Fairy Tales from All Nations. London: Chapman & Hall, 1849. 1st ed. 8vo. 408pp (worn, foxed, 1 plt reinserted w/tape); 11 full-pg b/w plts by Richard Doyle. All edges marbled. 1/2 leather (worn) w/raised bands. *Reisler.* $1,500/£938

Montana. NY: Viking, 1939. 1st ed. VG in dj. *Labordo.* $125/£78

MONTEITH, WILLIAM (ed). Narrative of the Conquest of Finland by the Russians in the Years 1808-9. London, 1854. Lg fldg map (few tears at gutter, folds, several early repairs). 1/2 morocco. (Bkpl.) Swann*. $230/£144

MONTEITH, WILLIAM. Kars and Erzeroum: With the Campaigns of Prince Paskiewitch in 1828 and 1829. London, 1856. Lg fldg map, tinted litho plt. (Bkpl; needs rebinding.) Swann*. $92/£58

MONTESQUIEU, CHARLES DE SECONDAT. Persian Letters. London: Gibbings, 1899. 3 vols. Teg. 3/4 calf, marbled bds, gilt, morocco spine labels, bound by Root & Son. (Bkpls; spines sl sunned), else VG. Pacific*. $58/£36

MONTESSORI, MARIA. The Montessori Method. Anne E. George (trans). London: Heinemann, 1912. 1st British ed. Untrimmed. Crimson cl, gilt. (Eps foxed; sl edgeworn, rubbed.) Text Good. Baltimore*. $80/£50

MONTESSORI, MARIA. The Montessori Method. Anne E. George (trans). NY: Stokes, 1912. 1st US ed, 1st bk. VG (few ll loose). Second Life. $125/£78

MONTESSORI, MARIA. Pedagogical Anthropology. Frederic Taber (trans). NY: Stokes, 1913. 1st ed in English. Frontis photo port. Ribbed navy cl, gilt. Text Good (sl foxed, few lt pencil mks, long ink note fr pastedown, margin corner of 2 leaves lacking; sl worn, spine gilt dull). Baltimore*. $75/£47

MONTGOMERIE-FLEMING, J. B. Desultory Notes on Jamieson's Scottish Dictionary. Glasgow, 1899. 1st ed. 186pp. Teg. (Inner hinges cracked; cvrs lt worn.) King. $45/£28

MONTGOMERY, BERNARD L. The Memoirs of Field Marshal the Viscount Montgomery of Alamein, K. G. London, 1958. VG in dj (torn). Clark. $23/£14

MONTGOMERY, BERNARD L. The Memoirs. London: Collins, 1958. 1st ed. VG in dj. Hollett. $32/£20

MONTGOMERY, CHARLES F. American Furniture. The Federal Period. NY, (1966). Dj. Swann*. $115/£72

MONTGOMERY, CORA. Eagle Pass; Or, Life on the Border. NY: Putnam, 1852. 1st ed. Recent dk blue cl. (Sl foxed.) Howes C251. Sadlon. $100/£63

MONTGOMERY, FRANCES TREGO. Billy Whiskers, Jr. and His Chums. Chicago: Brewer, Barse, 1907. 1st ed. Hugo Von Hofsten (illus). (Corners bumped), o/w NF. Hermitage. $65/£41

MONTGOMERY, GEORGE and JEFFREY MILLET. The Years of George Montgomery. Dallas: Taylor Publishing, 1981. 1st ed. Signed, inscribed. 1/2 calf, cl. Fine. Pacific*. $40/£25

MONTGOMERY, L. M. The Golden Road. Boston: L.C. Page, 1913. 1st ed. 8vo. Color frontis by George Gibbs. Lt gray cl, gilt, color paste label (edges lt rubbed). Reisler. $200/£125

MONTGOMERY, MARION. Why Hawthorne Was Melancholy. LaSalle: Sherwood Sugden, (1984). 1st ed. Rev slip laid in. Fine in dj. Pharos. $35/£22

MONTGOMERY, MARION. Why Poe Drank Liquor. LaSalle: Sherwood Sugden, (1983). 1st ed. Inscribed presentation. Fine in dj. Pharos. $60/£38

MONTGOMERY, RICHARD G. The White-Headed Eagle: John McLoughlin, Builder of an Empire. NY: Macmillan, 1934. 1st ed. Signed presentation. VG in dj. Perier. $35/£22

MONTGOMERY, RUTHERFORD. Big Red, a Wild Stallion. Caxton, 1971. 1st ed. Pers Crowell (illus). 163pp. Fine in Fine dj. Price. $25/£16

MONTGOMERY, RUTHERFORD. High Country. NY: Derrydale, 1938. One of 950 numbered. Brn cl. Fine. Biscotti. $200/£125

MONTGOMERY, RUTHERFORD. In Happy Hollow. Doubleday, 1958. 1st ed. 7.2x9.5. Harold Berson (illus). 128pp. Fine in Good dj (edges chipped, torn). Price. $22/£14

MONTGOMERY, THOMAS HARRISON. A History of the University of Pennsylvania. Phila, 1900. One of 750 numbered. Teg. (Foxed, eps poor; cvrs heavily soiled.) King. $35/£22

MONTGOMERY, WALTER. American Art and American Art Collections. Boston, (1889). Pub's 1/2 morocco (worn). Swann*. $80/£50

MOODIE, J. W. Thirty-Five Days March Through Palestine, Syria, and Egypt. Glasgow: John J. Rae, n.d. (1888). 1st (and only?) ed. Engr frontis, 70pp. Yellow ptd wrappers (sl rubbed, soiled). Good. Morrell. $48/£30

MOODIE, R. L. The Coal Measures Amphibia of North America. Washington, 1916. 26 plts. (Pp dampstained, browned.) Stiff wrappers (dknd, soiled, call #s, stamp, lower corners dampstained). Sutton. $95/£59

MOODIE, SUSANNA. Roughing It in the Bush. Richard Bentley, 1857. New ed. Frontis. Sprinkled edges. Contemp 1/2 leather, marbled bds (lacks sm pieces of marbled paper). Good. Tiger. $64/£40

MOODY, CHARLES STUART. Backwoods Surgery and Medicine. NY: Macmillan, 1923. Dec cl. Connolly. $17/£11

MOODY, RALPH. Horse of a Different Color: Reminiscences of a Kansas Drover. Norton, (1968). 1st ed. (Name.) Dj. Rybski. $20/£13

MOODY, RALPH. Little Britches. NY: Norton, 1950. 8vo. Edward Shenton (illus). VG. American Booksellers. $20/£13

MOODY, RICHARD. The Astor Place Riot. Bloomington: IN Univ, 1958. VG in pict dj (sm spine tear). Dramatis. $20/£13

MOODY, WINFIELD SCOTT. The Pickwick Ladle and Other Collector's Stories. NY, 1907. 1st Amer ed. Dec cvrs, gilt. NF (name; sl bubbled). Polyanthos. $30/£19

MOOMAW, LEON A. Pioneering in the Shadow of Chimney Rock. Gering, (NE), 1966. 1st ed. Presentation copy. Fine in dj (sl edgeworn). Baade. $65/£41

Moon Rocket. An All-Action Pop-Up Picture Storybook. London: Brown Watson, 1986. 6 dbl-pg pop-ups by V. Kubasta. Glazed pict bds. VG. Bookfinders. $60/£38

MOON, GRACE. The Arrow of Tee-May. Doubleday, 1931. 1st ed. Carl Moon (illus). 284pp. VG+ (spine sl faded, ends bumped). Price. $32/£20

MOON, GRACE. Chi-Wee. Doubleday, 1925. 1st ed. Carl Moon (illus). 239pp. Brn cl. NF (spine ends bumped). Price. $40/£25

MOON, VIRGIL HOLLAND. Shock and Related Capillary Phenomena.... London/NY/Toronto: Oxford Univ, (1938). (Lib stamps, call # inked after tp; spine label; bkpl removed), else VG. Weber. $30/£19

MOONEY, JOHN. St. Magnus—Earl of Orkney. Kirkwall: W.R. Macintosh, 1935. 1st ed. (Cl sl mkd.) Hollett. $64/£40

MOORE, A. W. The Alps in 1864: A Private Journal. London, 1902. 1st trade ed. Med 8vo. xxxvi,444pp; 33 photogravure plts, 10 maps. VG (ink inscrip dated April 1902, bkpl). Ulysses. $640/£400

MOORE, ALBERT BURTON. Conscription and Conflict in the Confederacy. NY: Macmillan, 1924. 1st ed. Blue cl. VG (bkpl, resultant offsetting). Howes M755. Chapel Hill. $60/£38

MOORE, ANNE CARROLL. A Century of Kate Greenaway. Frederick Warne, 1946. 1st ed. Frontis, 2 color plts. Dec wrappers. Forest. $40/£25

MOORE, BRIAN. Black Robe. NY: Dutton, 1985. 1st US ed. Inscribed. Fine in NF dj (cvrs lt rubbed) Lame Duck. $75/£47

MOORE, BRIAN. The Great Victorian Collection. NY: FSG, 1975. 1st US ed. Inscribed. (Spine head faded), else NF in VG+ dj (few sm edge tears). Lame Duck. $85/£53

MOORE, BRIAN. Judith Hearne. (London): Andre Deutsch, (1955). 1st ed. NF (bkpl) in dj. Pacific*. $288/£180

MOORE, C. B. The Book of Wild Pets. NY, 1937. Frontis. (Tape stains to eps, marginal tear to tp, name stamp, ink inscrip, pp tanned; varnished, lower corners bumped, extrems lt worn, spine ends frayed, sm tear.) *Sutton*. $75/£47

MOORE, C. L. Shambleau and Others. NY: Gnome, (1953). 1st ed. NF in dj (rear panel soiled). *Bernard*. $150/£94

MOORE, CHARLES. Daniel H. Burnham: Architect, Planner of Cities. Boston/NY: Houghton Mifflin, 1921. 1st ed. 2 vols. 112 plts (13 color). Pub's cl, gilt. (Spine head of vol 2 sl worn), else Fine. *Cahan*. $275/£172

MOORE, CHARLES. The Mental Side of Golf. NY: Horace, Liveright, 1929. 1st ed. Inscribed, signed, dated 1930. 1/4 cl. VG (emb stamp). *Pacific**. $92/£58

MOORE, CHARLES. (ed). The Improvement of the Park System of the District of Columbia. Washington: GPO, 1902. 1st ed. Frontis. 11 maps, plans. Red cl. (Browned, 1 plt sl torn; re-bound), else VG. *Fair Meadow*. $185/£116

MOORE, CLEMENT C. The Night Before Christmas. Phila: J.B. Lippincott, (1931). 1st Amer ed. 8vo. 4 full-pg color plts by Arthur Rackham. Forest grn cl, color pict paste label. Good in full color dj (faded, worn). *Reisler*. $150/£94

MOORE, CLEMENT C. The Night Before Christmas. Phila: John C. Winston, (1942). 1st ed thus. 4to. Everett Shinn (illus). Cl-backed color pict bds. Good in full color dj (edges lt worn). *Reisler*. $85/£53

MOORE, CLEMENT C. The Night Before Christmas. Phila: Franklin Ptg, (c. 1950). Ronald V. Shutts & J. Alvin Thomas (illus). 1/4 cl, pict cvr label. (Cvrs soiled, sl offset), else VG. *Pacific**. $35/£22

MOORE, CLEMENT C. The Night Before Christmas. Newark, NJ: Charles E. Graham, (ca 1910). Lg 4to. 14pp. Good in color pict wrappers (worn). *Reisler*. $235/£147

MOORE, CLEMENT C. Visit of St. Nicholas. NY: McLoughlin Bros, ca 1900s. Aunt Louise's Big Picture Series. 4to. 6 full-pg chromolithos by Thomas Nast. VG in pict wraps (rear lacks sm piece, spine resewn). *Davidson*. $325/£203

MOORE, DANIEL. Burnt Heart. SF: City Lights, 1971. 1st ed. Fine in wraps. *Beasley*. $25/£16

MOORE, DANIEL. Log of a Twentieth Century Cowboy. Tucson, 1965(6). Map. Good in dj. *Dumont*. $25/£16

MOORE, DORIS LANGLEY. The Technique of the Love Affair. London: Rich & Cowan, 1936. Rev, enlgd ed. VG (edges, prelims spotted; spine foot sl bumped) in dj (rubbed, nicked, sl torn, creased). *Ulysses*. $56/£35

MOORE, EDWARD A. The Story of a Cannoneer Under Stonewall Jackson. NY/Washington: Neale, 1907. 1st ed. Plt, facs. Untrimmed. Grn cl. (Spine lt browned), else NF. *Chapel Hill*. $450/£281

MOORE, ELIZABETH. Maternity and Infant Care in a Rural County in Kansas. Washington: US Dept of Labor, Children's Bureau, 1917. 1st ed. VG in ptd wraps (sl worn). *Petrilla*. $17/£11

MOORE, F. J. and W. T. HALL. A History of Chemistry. NY, 1939. 3rd ed. Grn cl, gilt. VG. *Larry Price*. $25/£16

MOORE, FRANCIS. Travels into the Inland Parts of Africa. London, 1738. Map (verso repaired). Mod lib buckram. *Swann**. $316/£198

MOORE, G. W. Bones: His Anecdotes and Goaks. London: C.H. Clarke, n.d. (1868). 1st ed. Contemp blind-tooled 1/2 calf, marbled bds (joints scuffed, sl soiled). *Dramatis*. $150/£94

MOORE, GAY MONTAGUE. Seaport in Virginia: George Washington's Alexandria. Garrett & Massie, (c1949). VG in Good dj. *Book Broker*. $35/£22

MOORE, GEORGE. The Brook Kerith. A Syrian Story. London: Heinemann, 1929. 1st illus ed. One of 375 signed by Moore and Stephen Gooden (illus). 12 engrs. Top edge trimmed fore/bottom edges untrimmed; unopened. Full vellum, beveled bds, gilt. Fine. *Vandoros*. $350/£219

MOORE, GEORGE. A Flood. NY: G.C., 1930. 1st ed. One of 185 numbered, signed. Red cl, gilt. *Maggs*. $96/£60

MOORE, GEORGE. A Modern Lover. Tinsley Bros, 1883. 1st ed. 3 vols. 8vo. Pub's cat at end of vol 3. Lt blue cl. (Upper hinges broken; cl worn.) *Sotheby's**. $3,035/£1,897

MOORE, GEORGE. Notes on the History of Witchcraft in Massachusetts. Worcester, MA: C. Hamilton, 1883. Inscribed. 32pp. Unopened. VG. *Middle Earth*. $75/£47

MOORE, GEORGE. Peronnik the Fool. Harrap, 1933. One of 525 signed by Moore and Stephen Gooden (illus). NF in full vellum (sl browned) in slipcase. *Williams*. $136/£85

MOORE, GEORGE. Peronnik the Fool. London: G. Harrap, 1933. Ltd to 525 signed by Moore and Stephen Gooden (illus), bound in full vellum. Slipcase. *Cullen*. $200/£125

MOORE, HARRY. Keeping in Condition: A Handbook on Training for Older Boys. NY, 1915. 1st ed. *Fye*. $75/£47

MOORE, HARRY. Poste Restante. Berkeley: Univ of CA, 1956. 1st ed. VG in dj (spot to fr panel, price-clipped). *Smith*. $25/£16

MOORE, HENRY. Heads, Figures and Ideas. (London, 1958.) Folio. Color auto-litho by Moore laid in. Dj (sl worn). *Swann**. $201/£126

MOORE, HENRY. Henry Moore. NY: Curt Valentin, 1944. 1st ed. 14 color plts. NF in VG dj. *Turtle Island*. $200/£125

MOORE, HENRY. Henry Moore. Volume 2. Sculpture and Drawings Since 1948. London, 1955. 1st ed. (Lib ink stamps tp verso, bkpl, cellotape mks pastedowns.) Dj (sl soiled, tape mks.) *Edwards*. $64/£40

MOORE, HENRY. On Sculpture. London, 1966. 1st UK ed. Dj (edges sl soiled). *Edwards*. $80/£50

MOORE, J. G. Patent Office and Patent Laws; or, a Guide to Inventors and a Book of Reference for Judges.... Phila: Parry & M'Millan, 1855. 1st ed. 342pp. *M & S*. $125/£78

MOORE, JAMES. History of the Cooper Shop Volunteer Refreshment Saloon. Phila: Jas. B. Rodgers, 1866. 1st ed. Frontis. Gilt-dec pict grn cl. NF. *Pacific**. $127/£79

MOORE, JAMES. Two Paths to the New South: The Virginia Debt Controversy, 1870-1883. Univ of KY, (1974). VG in Good+ dj. *Book Broker*. $35/£22

MOORE, JOHN HAMILTON. The New Practical Navigator. London: B. Law/G.G. & J. Robinson, 1794. 10th ed. viii,299,(1, 206 tables)pp; port, 8 plts. Contemp calf. (Inscrip, bkpl.) *Lefkowicz*. $150/£94

MOORE, JOHN HAMILTON. The Practical Navigator, and Seaman's Daily Assistant. London: B. Law/G.G.J. & J. Robinson/The Author, 1791. 9th ed. (8),296,(197 tables, 3 ads)pp; port, 4 plts. Contemp sheep (rebacked, recornered). *Lefkowicz*. $350/£219

MOORE, JOHN ROBERT. Defoe in the Pillory and Other Studies. Bloomington, (1939). Signed. *Argosy*. $50/£31

MOORE, JOSEPH. Penicillin in Syphilis. Springfield, 1946. 1st ed. *Fye*. $100/£63

MOORE, LORRIE. Anagrams. NY: Knopf, 1986. 1st ed. Fine in dj. *Smith*. $125/£78

MOORE, LORRIE. Like Life. NY: Knopf, 1990. 1st ed. Fine in dj. *Smith*. $100/£63

MOORE, LORRIE. Self-Help. NY, 1985. 1st ed, 1st bk. Fine in Fine dj. *Warren*. $50/£31

MOORE, MARIANNE. Like a Bulwark. NY: Viking, 1956. 1st ed. NF (stamp) in dj (price-clipped). *Hermitage*. $40/£25

MOORE, MARIANNE. O to Be a Dragon. NY, 1959. 1st ed. NF in VG dj. *Warren.* $35/£22

MOORE, MARIANNE. Predilections. London: Faber and Faber, (1956). 1st Eng ed. Tipped-in errata. (Ex-lib ?, eps tape-stained; bumped), else VG in dj (lt soiled, chipped, short tear). *Blue Mountain.* $25/£16

MOORE, MARIANNE. Tell Me, Tell Me. NY, 1966. 1st ed. VF in Fine dj. *Bond.* $22/£14

MOORE, MARIANNE. What Are Years. NY: Macmillan, 1941. 1st ed. Good (paper-clip mks; blue cl lt bumped, rubbed) in dj (rubbed, chipped, short tear, clipped; ex-lib, flaps glued down, spine label removed). *Blue Mountain.* $25/£16

MOORE, N. Ancient Mineralogy. Franklin Square: Harper, c1859. 2nd ed. v,250pp + 5pp. Good (spine edges worn, cl insect-damaged). *Blake.* $300/£188

MOORE, N. HUDSON. The Lace Book. NY: Frederick A. Stokes, (1904). 1st ed. Pink cl, pict cvr label. (Spine faded), else VG. *Pacific*.* $46/£29

MOORE, N. HUDSON. Old Glass. NY: Tudor, 1946. (Sl scratched.) *Hollett.* $48/£30

MOORE, NATHANIEL FISH. Diary of a Trip from New York to the Falls of St. Anthony in 1845. Stanley Pargellis and Ruth L. Butler (eds). Chicago: Univ of Chicago, 1946. VG in dj (sl worn). *Lien.* $25/£16

MOORE, NICHOLAS. The Glass Tower. Poetry London/Nicholson & Watson, 1944. 1st Eng ed. Cl-backed pict bds (edges, corners sl bumped, chafed). Good in dj (sl frayed, chipped, tanned, price-clipped). *Clearwater.* $72/£45

MOORE, PATRICK and HEATHER COUPER. Halley's Comet Pop-Up Book. NY: Bonanza Pop Up Books, 1985. 5 dbl-pg pop-ups by Paul Doherty. Glazed pict bds. VG. *Bookfinders.* $40/£25

MOORE, PATRICK. The Space Shuttle Action Book. London: Aurum Press, 1983. 6 dbl-pg pop-ups by Tom Stimpson. Glazed pict bds. VG. *Bookfinders.* $50/£31

MOORE, RACHEL WILSON. Journal...Kept During a Tour to the West Indies and South America, in 1863-64.... Phila: T. Ellwood Zell, 1867. 1st ed. 274pp. (Spine ends faded, worn.) Internally VG. *Petrilla.* $65/£41

MOORE, RICHARD. The New-York Pocket Almanack, for the Year 1764. NY: H. Gaine, (1763). 24 leaves, interleaved w/blanks. (Frayed, sl stained, soiled, corners curled, corner chipped last leaf w/loss of few letters.) *Oinonen*.* $225/£141

MOORE, T. STURGE. A Brief Account of the Origin of the Eragny Press and a Note on the Relation of the Printed Books as a Work of Art to Life.... Eragny, 1903. One of 235 (of 241). Crown 8vo. 52,(1)pp; 15 wood engrs by Lucien Pissarro, each ptd on recto of a leaf. Untrimmed. 1/4 pale gray bds, gilt, pattern of pink/white daisies over grn bds. Good (feps browned; bds lt foxed). *Blackwell's.* $800/£500

MOORE, T. STURGE. The Centaur's Booty. London, 1903. 1st ed. NF (2 corners sl chipped) in pict wraps. *Polyanthos.* $25/£16

MOORE, T. STURGE. Danae. (London: Hacon & Ricketts, 1903.) 1st ed. Plain mod cl. Fine. *Pacific*.* $184/£115

MOORE, T. STURGE. Judas. London: Grant Richards, 1923. 1st ed. Pict bds. VG (bds sl discolored). *Maggs.* $80/£50

MOORE, T. STURGE. Roderigo of Bivar. NY, 1925. Ltd to 500. NF (sl rubbed) in glassine dj (torn). *Polyanthos.* $30/£19

MOORE, T. STURGE. Some Soldier Poets. London, 1919. 1st Eng ed. (Fep stained by bkpl; cvrs sl mkd.) *Clearwater.* $48/£30

MOORE, THOMAS. Epistles, Odes and Other Poems. James Carpenter, 1806. 1st ed. Engr frontis (browned), xi,(5),341,(3)errata pp. Aeg. Contemp full grained morocco (extrems rubbed), gilt. VG. *Cox.* $104/£65

MOORE, THOMAS. Lalla Rookh, an Oriental Romance. London, 1817. 1st ed. 1/2 calf, marbled bds, gilt. Fine (lt foxed). *Polyanthos.* $200/£125

MOORE, THOMAS. Lalla Rookh: An Oriental Romance. London: Longman, Green, Longman, & Roberts, 1861. 1st Tenniel ed. John Tenniel (illus). 8 3/4 x 6 1/4. Aeg. Period gilt-tooled crimson morocco, raised bands; bound by Hayday. (Bkpl, sigs, fr hinge sl weak; soiled, spine ends, extrems rubbed), else VG. *Pacific*.* $111/£69

MOORE, THOMAS. Moore's Irish Melodies. London/NY, (1879). 1st Amer ed. 1/2 morocco, marbled edges, gilt. Fine (edges sl rubbed, sunned). *Polyanthos.* $125/£78

MOORE, THOMAS. The Nature Printed British Ferns. London: Bradbury & Evans, 1859. Octavo ed. 2 vols. 122 color plts. Contemp 3/4 morocco (rubbed, sl foxed, cvr detached, spine labels chipped). *Oinonen*.* $250/£156

MOORE, THOMAS. The Poetical Works of.... NY: P.F. Collier, 1880. Aeg, gilt inner dentelles. Dk brn morocco, gilt. (Bkpl), else NF. *Pacific*.* $98/£61

MOORE, WINSTON and MARIAN. Out of the Frying Pan. L.A.: De Vorss, 1939. Red cl. VG (contemp news clipping laid in w/shadow to eps, foxing from paste used on feps; edges, spine faded). *Connolly.* $25/£16

MOOREHEAD, ALAN. The Blue Nile. NY, 1962. VG in dj (2 sm tears). *Typographeum.* $20/£13

MOOREHEAD, ALAN. Cooper's Creek. NY: Harper, 1963. 1st ed. Map. Black cl. VG in dj (rubbed). *Parmer.* $35/£22

MOOREHEAD, ALAN. Fatal Impact. An Account of the Invasion of the South Pacific. 1767-1840. NY: Harper, 1966. 1st ed. 4 maps. Blue cl. VG in dj. *Parmer.* $30/£19

MOOREHEAD, WARREN K. Stone Ornaments Used by Indians in the United States and Canada. Andover: Andover, 1917. 1st ed. 2 fldg diags, fldg map. Olive-grn cl, gilt. Fine (1/2-inch tear to fore-edge of 4 leaves; rear cvr sl scratched). *Argonaut.* $250/£156

MOORHEAD, MAX L. The Apache Frontier. Norman: Univ of OK, (1968). Fine in Fine dj. *Book Market.* $15/£9

MOORMAN, LEWIS J. Pioneer Doctor. Norman, 1951. 1st ed. VG (bkpl). *Doctor's Library.* $35/£22

MORA, JO. A Log of the Spanish Main. SF: Jo Mora, 1933. 1st ed. Bound w/2-hole punch. VG + . *Labordo.* $50/£31

MORA, JO. Trail Dust and Saddle Leather. NY: Scribner, 1946. Early ed. VG (bkpl) in dj (worn). *Dumont.* $85/£53

MORAGA, GABRIEL. The Diary of Ensign Gabriel Moraga's Expedition of Discovery in the Sacramento Valley, 1808. Donald C. Cutter (ed). N.p.: Glen Dawson, 1957. 1st ed. One of 300 ptd. Fldg map. Unopened. Tan bds, brn cl backstrip. Fine. *Harrington.* $35/£22

MORAN, JACK. Creating a Legend. Chicago, 1973. 1st ed. VG in VG dj. *Clark.* $35/£22

MORAN, JAMES (ed). The Fortsas Hoax. London: Arborfield, 1961. Pict cvrs. NF. *Polyanthos.* $25/£16

MORAN, JAMES. Printing Presses, History and Development from the Fifteenth Century to Modern Times. London: Faber & Faber, (1973). 1st ed. 64 plts. Fine in dj (soiled tears). *Oak Knoll.* $100/£63

MORAN, JAMES. Printing Presses; History and Development.... Faber & Faber, 1973. 1st ed. Fine in dj (sl worn). *Michael Taylor.* $77/£48

MORAN, JAMES. The Private Press at Home and Abroad. Herrin, IL: Trovillion Private Press, 1959. One of a ltd ed, signed by Hal Trovillion. VG + in ptd wraps. *Bohling.* $20/£13

MORAND, J. Memoir on Acupuncturation, Embracing a Series of Cases. Phila, 1825. 1st ed. Sheep. *Felcone.* $800/£500

MORAND, PAUL. Europe at Love. London: Knopf, 1926. 1st British ed. Red cl, gilt. (Gilt sl tarnished), o/w VG in Fine pict dj. *Reese*. $40/£25

MORANTE, ELSA. Araceli. NY: Random House, (1984). 1st ed. As New in dj. *Bernard*. $17/£11

MORANTE, ELSA. House of Liars. NY: Harcourt, Brace, (1951). 1st US ed, 1st bk. VG+ in VG dj (few sm internally mended tears, spine ends creased). *Bernard*. $45/£28

MORDAUNT, ELINOR. The Venture Book. NY/London: Century, 1926. 1st ed. VG. *Worldwide*. $30/£19

More Secret Remedies: What They Cost and What They Contain. London, 1912. 1st ed. *Fye*. $75/£47

MORE, ANTHONY. (Pseud of Edwin M. Clinton, Jr.) The Puzzle Box. Raven Court: Trover Hall, 1946 (i.e. 1947). 1st ed. One of 2000. VG+ in dj (edgeworn, spine ends lt chipped). *Other Worlds*. $45/£28

MORE, CHARLES ALBERT and COMTE DE CHEVALIER DE PONTGIBAUD. The Chevalier de Pontgibaud. Paris: Charles Carrington, 1898. 2nd ed. 209pp; port. Good+ (ink blot to worn cvr). Howes M7140. *Book Broker*. $150/£94

MORE, HANNAH. Strictures on the Modern System of Female Education. Hartford: John Babcock, 1801. 2nd Amer ed. 2 vols in 1. vi,288pp (foxed). Orig mottled calf, red spine label. *Karmiole*. $200/£125

MORE, HANNAH. Thoughts on the Importance of the Manners of the Great to General Society. T. Cadell & W. Davies, 1809. New ed. Sprinkled edges. Contemp 1/2 leather, marbled bds, raised bands, leather spine label. Good (sig; spine chipped w/sl loss at head, hinges badly rubbed, rear hinge head nicked). *Tiger*. $74/£46

MORE, HANNAH. The Works of Hannah More. London: H. Fisher, R. Fisher & P. Jackson, 1833-35. 1st ed. 6 vols. Steelplt engr frontispieces each vol. Aeg. Full burgundy morocco (joints rubbed; spines chipped vols 1, 2), gilt. VG set. *Hermitage*. $200/£125

MORE, LOUIS TRENCHARD. The Life and Works of the Honourable Robert Boyle. OUP, 1944. 1st ed. Frontisport. VG. *Glaser*. $60/£38

MORE, THOMAS. Utopia. Raphe Robinson (trans). London: William Bulmer, 1808. 1st Dibdin ed. Calf, gilt. (Joints cracked through, hinges reinforced; rebacked in calf, spine chipped, extrems rubbed), else Good. *Pacific**. $115/£72

MORE, THOMAS. Utopia. LEC, 1934. Ltd to 1500 numbered, signed by Bruce Rogers (illus). Fine in slipcase. *Swann**. $69/£43

MORELL, CHARLES (trans). Tales of the Genii; or, The Delightful Lessons of Horam, the Son of Asman. London: James Wallis, 1805. 1st ed. 2 vols. xliv,368; 432pp; 14 plts. 1/2 morocco, gilt. (Sl foxed; edges sl rubbed, hinges tender), o/w VG. *Worldwide*. $95/£59

MORENUS, RICHARD. Alaska Sourdough. NY: Rand McNally, (1956). 1st ed. VG in dj. *Perier*. $35/£22

MORETON, C. OSCAR. Old Carnations and Pinks. London: Geo. Rainbird, 1955. 1st ed. Ltd to 3000. Folio. Blue cl, illus paper over bds. NF (sl bumped) in VG- dj (dampstained). *Archer*. $90/£56

MOREY, CHARLES RUFUS. Lost Mosaics and Frescoes of Rome of the Medieval Period. Princeton, 1915. 1/2 cl, bds. Good. *Washton*. $90/£56

MOREY, CHARLES RUFUS. The Mosaics of Antioch. London, 1938. Color frontis, 24 plts. Good. *Washton*. $75/£47

MOREY, WALT (ed). North to Danger. Caldwell: Caxton, 1969. 1st ed. (Ink name), else VG in dj (worn, torn). *Perier*. $15/£9

MORF, GUSTAV. The Polish Heritage of Joseph Conrad. Sampson, Low, Marston, n.d. (1930). 1st Eng ed. VG (feps partly browned, edges sl spotted; spine ends sl dusty) in dj (sl rubbed, spine dknd). *Ulysses*. $72/£45

MORGAN, BARBARA. Martha Graham: Sixteen Dances in Photographs. Dobbs Ferry: Morgan & Morgan, (1980). 1st rev ed. Signed. NF in VG dj (price-clipped). *Baltimore**. $60/£38

MORGAN, C. L. Animal Life and Intelligence. Boston, 1891. Frontis, xvi,512pp (tanned, pencil underlining, notes, tear to tp, prelim PG; corners worn). *Sutton*. $65/£41

MORGAN, CHARLES. The Fountain. London: Macmillan, 1932. 1st ed. Gilt blue cl. Fine in NF dj. *Reese*. $40/£25

MORGAN, CHARLES. The Gunroom. London: A&C Black, 1919. 1st ed. Gilt blue pastepaper cl. Sound (used, restoration to fr inner hinge). *Reese*. $65/£41

MORGAN, CHARLES. Portrait in a Mirror. London: Macmillan, 1929. 1st ed. (Pp edges sl foxed), else VG in dj. *Cady*. $15/£9

MORGAN, CHARLES. Sparkenbroke. London: Macmillan, 1936. 1st ed. NF in dj. *Cady*. $20/£13

MORGAN, CHARLES. The Voyage. London: Macmillan, 1940. 1st ed. Fine in dj (sl worn). *Cady*. $15/£9

MORGAN, DALE L. The Humboldt. Highroad of the West. NY, (1943). 1st ed. Map. Good+ (spine lt worn). *Sagebrush*. $40/£25

MORGAN, DALE L. and CARL I. WHEAT. Jedediah Smith and His Maps of the American West. SF: CA Hist Soc, 1954. One of 530 ptd. 17x11. 6 fldg maps, 3 inserted loose in rear pocket. Red cl. NF (spine, cvr edges faded). *Pacific**. $633/£396

MORGAN, DALE L. Jedediah Smith and the Opening of the West. Indianapolis: Bobbs-Merrill, (1953). 1st ed. Signed, inscribed, dated 1953. NF. *Pacific**. $127/£79

MORGAN, DALE L. Jedediah Smith and the Opening of the West. Indianapolis/NY: Bobbs-Merrill, 1953. Stated 1st ed. Frontis. Blue cl. VG+. *Backman*. $75/£47

MORGAN, DALE L. (ed). Overland in 1846. Diaries and Letters of the California-Oregon Trail. Georgetown: Talisman, 1963. 1st ed. Ltd to 1000 sets. 2 vols. Lg fldg map in rear pocket. VF set in djs (worn). *Argonaut*. $250/£156

MORGAN, DALE L. (ed). Overland in 1846. Diaries and Letters of the California-Oregon Trail. Georgetown, CA: Talisman, 1963. 1st ed. 2 vols. VF set in djs. *Labordo*. $250/£156

MORGAN, DAN. The Complete Baseball Joke Book. Stravon, 1953. 1st ed. (Browned), o/w NF in VG dj. *Plapinger*. $75/£47

MORGAN, GEORGE. The New Complete Sportsman; or, The Town and Country Gentleman's Recreation. Containing...The Breeding and Managing Game Cocks.... London: Hogg, n.d. (ca 1785). Engr frontis, iv,302pp (sl soiled, foxed) + ad leaf (sm piece torn from margin, restored, w/sl loss). Later 3/4 red morocco (rubbed). *Oinonen**. $400/£250

MORGAN, HENRY T. The Life of Henry Bruce. (Peoria, IL), 1934. 1st ed. 23 plts. 1/2 cl, fr cvr title label. Fine. *Wantagh*. $35/£22

MORGAN, JOHN HILL and MANTLE FIELDING. The Life Portraits of Washington and Their Replicas. Phila, (1931). One of 1000. Dj. *Swann**. $201/£126

MORGAN, JOSEPH. A Complete History of Algiers. London, 1731. Contemp sheep. (Lt dampstained, browned; top edge of tp frayed; needs rebinding.) *Swann**. $460/£288

MORGAN, LEWIS HENRY. The Indian Journals 1859-62. Ann Arbor: Univ of MI, 1959. Good in dj. *Dumont*. $65/£41

MORGAN, MURRAY. Dixie Raider. NY: Dutton, 1948. 1st ed. Gray cl. Fine in VG dj (spine faded). *Chapel Hill*. $65/£41

MORGAN, MURRAY. Puget's Sound. Seattle: Univ of WA, 1979. 1st ed. 32 plts. Pict eps. Fine in VG dj. *Connolly*. $30/£19

MORGAN, NICHOLAS. Phrenology. London, 1871. 1st ed. 364pp. 3/4 leather. (Lacks frontis, inner hinges cracked; cvrs heavily scuffed.) *King.* $35/£22

MORGAN, THOMAS HUNT. A Critique of the Theory of Evolution. Princeton, 1916. 1st ed. *Fye.* $75/£47

MORGAN, THOMAS HUNT. Experimental Zoology. NY, 1917. 1st ed. Rpt. *Fye.* $75/£47

MORGAN, THOMAS HUNT. The Physical Basis of Heredity. Phila, 1919. 1st ed. *Fye.* $100/£63

MORGAN, THOMAS HUNT. The Theory of the Gene. New Haven, 1926. 1st ed. *Fye.* $200/£125

MORGAN, W. H. Personal Reminiscences of the War of 1861-5. Lynchburg, VA: J.P. Bell, 1911. 1st ed. Frontisport. Teg, partly unopened. Gray cl. Fine. *Chapel Hill.* $250/£156

MORGAN, W. SCOTT. History of the Wheel and Alliance, and the Impending Revolution. Fort Scott, KS; The Author, 1889. 1st ed. Port, 776pp + ads. (Shelfworn, rubbed, soiled), else Good. *Brown.* $75/£47

MORGAN, WILLIAM. The Homoeopathic Treatment of Indigestion, Constipation, and Haemorrhoids. A. E. Small (ed). Phila, 1854. 1st Amer ed. 166pp. Fldg frontis. *Fye.* $125/£78

MORGAN, WILLIAM. The Liver and Its Diseases, Both Functional and Organic. London, 1877. 1st ed. 244pp. Recent cl, leather label. (Foxed, stained, scattered pencil notations.) *Fye.* $125/£78

MORIER, JAMES. The Adventures of Hajji Baba of Ispahan. Richard Bentley, 1835. Frontis. Marbled edges. Orig 1/2 leather, marbled bds: pub's presentation binding, ribbon marker (sm marbled paper pieces missing from cvrs). Good. *Tiger.* $26/£16

MORIER, JAMES. The Adventures of Hajji Baba of Ispahan. NY: LEC, 1947. One of 1500. Signed by Honore Guilbeau (illus). 2 vols. 1/2 black morocco, dec bds, gilt. Fine in slipcase. *Pacific*.* $40/£25

MORISON, SAMUEL ELIOT. Admiral of the Ocean Sea: A Life of Christopher Columbus. Boston: Little, Brown, 1942. 1st ed. 2 vols. (Blindstamps; lacks slipcase), else VG in djs (spines rubbed, sl sunned). *Pacific*.* $184/£115

MORISON, SAMUEL ELIOT. Christopher Columbus, Mariner. Boston, 1955. 1st Amer ed. NF in dj (few sm nicks, spine sl sunned, price-clipped). *Polyanthos.* $25/£16

MORISON, SAMUEL ELIOT. The Maritime History of Massachusetts, 1783-1860. Boston: Houghton Mifflin, 1941. Color frontis. Teg. 3/4 grn levant morocco, gilt, raised bands. (Sl shelfworn), else NF. *Pacific*.* $46/£29

MORISON, SAMUEL ELIOT. Old Bruin. Boston: Little, Brown/Atlantic Monthly, 1967. 1st ed. Frontis port. Fine in Good dj. *Connolly.* $45/£28

MORISON, SAMUEL ELIOT. The Ropemakers of Plymouth: A History of the Plymouth Cordage Company, 1824-1949. Boston: Houghton Mifflin, 1950. 1st ed. VG in dj. *Pacific*.* $29/£18

MORISON, SAMUEL ELIOT. The Story of Mount Desert Island, Maine. Boston: Little, Brown, 1960. 1st ed. 8 plts. Pict cl, gilt. NF in Good dj. *Connolly.* $25/£16

MORISON, STANLEY and HOLBROOK JACKSON. A Brief Survey of Printing History and Practice. London: Fleuron, 1923. 1st ed. 3/4 cl over bds, paper spine label. Fine in dj (soiled; foxed). *Oak Knoll.* $55/£34

MORISON, STANLEY. The English Newspaper. CUP, 1932. 1st ed. 1 fldg repro. Red-brn cl, gilt. Text Nice (sl aged, eps foxed, 1932 ink inscrip), cvrs Good (sl worn, spine sl turned, fr hinge cracked). *Baltimore*.* $210/£131

MORISON, STANLEY. First Principles of Typography. CUP, 1936. 1st ed. Wrapper. *Forest.* $51/£32

MORISON, STANLEY. The Likeness of Thomas More. Nicolas Barker (ed). London: Burns & Oates, 1963. VG in dj. *Michael Taylor.* $64/£40

MORISON, STANLEY. The Typographic Arts. Edinburgh: James Thin, 1944. 1st ed. Good in wrappers (sl soiled). *Cox.* $29/£18

MORLEY, CHRISTOPHER. Another Letter to Lord Chesterfield. Ben Abramson, 1945. 1st ed. Signed. Dec bds. Fine. *Whiteson.* $40/£25

MORLEY, CHRISTOPHER. Another Letter to Lord Chesterfield. From Samuel Johnson and Christopher Morley. NY: Ben Abramson, Argus Bkshop, 1945. 1st ed. Fine in glassine wrapper. *Cady.* $25/£16

MORLEY, CHRISTOPHER. Ex Libris Carissimis. Univ of PA, 1932. 1st Amer ed. Fine. *Polyanthos.* $25/£16

MORLEY, CHRISTOPHER. Footnotes for a Centennial. Duschnes, 1936. 1st ed. Dec cl. Good. *Whiteson.* $32/£20

MORLEY, CHRISTOPHER. Mincie Pie: Adventures on the Sunny Side of Grub Street. Doran, 1919. 1st Amer ed. (Bds dustsoiled), else Good. *Fine Books.* $13/£8

MORLEY, CHRISTOPHER. Rudolph and Amina. NY, 1930. 1st ed. (Lacks dj), o/w VG. *Bond.* $12/£8

MORLEY, CHRISTOPHER. Seacoast of Bohemia. Hoboken, NJ: Old Rialto Theatre, 1929. 1st ed. Black cl. Fine in pict dj (rear cvr sl torn). *Maggs.* $48/£30

MORLEY, CHRISTOPHER. Tales from a Rolltop Desk. NY, 1922. 1st ed. Signed, inscribed. Frontis. Dj, 1/4 morocco slipcase. *Swann*.* $138/£86

MORLEY, CHRISTOPHER. Toulemonade. GC: Doubleday, Doran, 1928. 1st ed. One of 1250. VG. *Cady.* $20/£13

MORLEY, CHRISTOPHER. Translations from the Chinese. NY, (1922). 1st Amer ed. NF (sl rubbed). *Polyanthos.* $25/£16

MORLEY, CHRISTOPHER. Travels in Philadelphia. Phila, (1920). 1st ed. Signed, inscribed. Dj, 1/4 morocco slipcase. *Swann*.* $126/£79

MORLEY, CHRISTOPHER. Where the Blue Begins. London: Heinemann, (1925). 1st deluxe ed. Ltd to 175 numbered, signed by Arthur Rackham (illus). 4to. (xii),227pp; 4 Fine color plts. Teg, rest uncut. Black cl-backed paper-cvrd bds (sl pale speckling). VG. *Sotheran.* $1,597/£998

MORLEY, F. V. My One Contribution to Chess. NY: Huebsch, 1945. 1st ed, 1st bk. Fine in dj (chipped). *Cahan.* $50/£31

MORLEY, F. V. and J. S. HODGSON. Whaling North and South. London: Methuen, 1927. VG (sl foxed) in dj (sl frayed). *Explorer.* $80/£50

MORLEY, F. V. and J. S. HODGSON. Whaling North and South. NY: Century, c. 1926. Very Nice in dj (defective). *High Latitude.* $40/£25

MORLEY, HENRY. Memoirs of Bartholemew Fair. London: C&W, 1880. New ed. Frontis, xvi,404pp + 32pp ads. VG (exlib). *Young.* $56/£35

MORLEY, HENRY. Memoirs of Bartholomew Fair. London: C&W, 1880. xvi,404pp + (32pp) cat. Olive pict gilt cl. *Marlborough.* $120/£75

MORLEY, JOHN. The Life of William Ewart Gladstone. London/NY: Macmillan, 1905-06. 2 vols. Frontisport vol 1. Orig burgundy 1/2 morocco, emb cl sides, gilt, raised bands. (Few sm marginal tears, ll sl dknd around edges; cl edges sl faded), o/w Fine. *Pirages.* $125/£78

MORLEY, S. GRISWOLD. The Covered Bridges of California. Berkeley: Univ of CA, 1938. 1st ed. NF in dj (stained, rubbed). *Pacific*.* $46/£29

MORLEY, THOMAS. A Plain and Easy Introduction to Practical Music. R. Alec Harman (ed). Dent, 1952. 1st ed. Facs tp. VG in dj. *Hollett.* $104/£65

Morning Walk, with Other Stories for Girls and Boys. Providence: Geo. P. Daniels, 1843. 12mo. Full-pg frontis, 24pp + 1pg ad on lower wrapper. Yellow pict wrappers. Good (ink dedication fep, sm spot top corner few pp; sl spotting wrapper corners, repaired cut fr wrapper). *Hobbyhorse.* $100/£63

MORNINGSTAR, F. V. Snapshots of Portland History and the Pacific Northwest, 1792-1925. Portland: Morningstar, 1925. 1st ed. (Ink inscrip), else VG. *Perier*. $35/£22

MORPHY, HOWARD (ed). Animals into Art. London, 1989. 1st ed. *Edwards*. $29/£18

MORRELL, BENJAMIN. A Narrative of Four Voyages, to the South Sea [etc.]...from the Year 1822 to 1831. NY, 1832. 1st ed. Engr frontis port (foxed, pencil scrawls over image). Orig cl (spine faded, worn; fr joint cracked; text browned, lib stamp). *Swann**. $230/£144

MORRELL, DAVID. First Blood. NY: M. Evans, (1972). 1st ed. NF in dj. *Pacific**. $58/£36

MORRELL, REGINALD A. and FREDERICK LLOYD. New Magical Sleights and Fakes. London: Hamley Bros, 1906. Label pasted to tp. Dec ribbed cl. VG (stamp). *Dramatis*. $25/£16

MORRELL, REGINALD A. Up-to-Date Mystical Sleights and Illusions.... London: Messrs. Hamley Bros, (1900). Fine in blue stiff wrappers (spine lt worn). *Argonaut*. $60/£38

MORRELL, W. P. The Gold Rushes. London, 1940. 8 maps. (Short tears to spine, new eps.) *Henly*. $77/£48

MORRELL, W. P. (ed). Sir Joseph Banks in New Zealand. Wellington: Reed, 1958. 1st ed. NF in NF dj. *Mikesh*. $30/£19

MORRILL, CLAIRE. A Taos Mosaic. Albuquerque, 1973. VG in dj (lt chipped). *Dumont*. $95/£59

MORRIS, A. A. Digging in the Southwest. GC: Doubleday, 1933. 1st ed. Dec eps. VG. *Mikesh*. $30/£19

MORRIS, BEVERLEY R. British Game Birds and Wildfowl. Groombridge & Sons, 1855. 1st ed. Lg 4to. 60 hand-colored plts. Gilt edges. Contemp 1/2 morocco. Bkpl of Percy Lubbock. (Sl spotting; upper joint sl cracked.) *Sotheby's**. $2,115/£1,322

MORRIS, C. B. Surrealism and Spain, 1920-1936. London: CUP, 1972. 1st ed. Fine in NF dj. *Beasley*. $25/£16

MORRIS, E. H. The Temple of the Warriors. NY: Scribner, 1931. 1st ed. Color frontis. VG + . *Mikesh*. $35/£22

MORRIS, E. P. The Fore and Aft Rig in America. New Haven: Yale Univ, 1927. 1st ed. Ltd to 1000. 30 plts. VG in dj (chipped). *American Booksellers*. $70/£44

MORRIS, F. O. A History of British Birds. Groombridge & Sons, (c.1880). 8 vols. 8vo. 358 hand-colored plts. (Some pp, plts detached; joints, hinges cracked most vols; few cvrs soiled; spines faded, bumped, vol 2 spine torn.) *Sotheby's**. $570/£356

MORRIS, F. O. A History of British Birds. John C. Nimmo, 1903. 5th ed. Lg 8vo. 6 vols. 400 hand-colored plts. *Sotheby's**. $1,104/£690

MORRIS, F. O. A History of British Butterflies. John C. Nimmo, 1870. 3rd ed. 159,24pp; 72 hand-colored, 2 engr plts. Blind-stamped cl (backstrip faded, ends frayed, corners sl worn), gilt. *Hollett*. $280/£175

MORRIS, F. O. A History of British Butterflies. John C. Nimmo, 1895. 8th ed. 79 hand-colored plts. Teg. Contemp red 1/2 morocco, gilt. (Orig wrappers bound in.) *Sotheby's**. $331/£207

MORRIS, F. O. A History of British Moths. London, 1896. 5th ed. 4 vols. 132 hand-colored plts. Pict gilt cl. *Henly*. $211/£132

MORRIS, F. O. and E. A. EAMES. Our Wild Orchids. NY: Scribner, 1929. 1st ed. VG in dj. *Archer*. $75/£47

MORRIS, F. O. A Series of Picturesque Views of Seats of the Noblemen and Gentlemen of Great Britain and Ireland. Volumes I-VI, with Volume of Autographs. London: Mackenzie, n.d. 240 color plts. Gilt-stamped red morocco (spines dried, corroded). Internally Sound. *Oinonen**. $275/£172

MORRIS, GEORGE FORD. Portraitures of Horses. New Jersey, 1952. (Margins lt browned) in dj (chipped). *Edwards*. $56/£35

MORRIS, HENRY. Surgical Diseases of the Kidney and Ureter Including Injuries, Malformations, and Misplacements. London, 1901. 1st ed. 2 vols. 682; 670pp. (One illus taped), o/w Fine set. *Fye*. $200/£125

MORRIS, IRA K. Morris's Memorial History of Staten Island, New York. NY: Memorial Pub Co, (1898-1900). 1st ed. 2 vols. (16),416; (16),542pp; 9 full-pg ports. Orig brn calf (scuffed, corners rubbed). *Karmiole*. $125/£78

MORRIS, JAMES. As I Saw the U.S.A. (London): Pantheon, (1956). 1st ed. (Sl spotted.) Dj. *Mott*. $20/£13

MORRIS, JAN. Conundrum. London, 1974. VG in dj. *Typographeum*. $25/£16

MORRIS, R. O. Contrapuntal Technique in the Sixteenth Century. Oxford: Clarendon, 1922. 1st ed. (Spine sl faded.) *Hollett*. $56/£35

MORRIS, ROBERT T. Fifty Years a Surgeon. NY, 1938. VG in Good dj. *Doctor's Library*. $20/£13

MORRIS, W. F. Bretherton: Khaki or Field-Grey? London: Geoffrey Bles, (1929). 1st ed. Pale blue cl stamped in black. (Edges sl foxed), o/w NF in pict dj. *Reese*. $65/£41

MORRIS, WILLIAM (trans). The History of Over Sea. NY: R.H. Russell, 1902. 1st ed thus. Dec bds. (Spine lettered in later hand, extrems rubbed), else VG-. *Pacific**. $69/£43

MORRIS, WILLIAM. An Address Delivered by William Morris at the Distribution of Prizes to Students of the Birmingham Municipal School of Art on Feb. 21, 1894. London: Chiswick, April 1898. 1st ed. Pub's prospectus loosely inserted. Uncut. Linen-backed blue paper bds. VG. *Maggs*. $120/£75

MORRIS, WILLIAM. An Address Delivered by William Morris at the Distribution of Prizes to Students...Feb. 21, 1894. Longmans, 1898. Unopened. VG (feps lt browned; cvrs sl dusty, spotted, spine faded, corners sl rubbed). *Ulysses*. $152/£95

MORRIS, WILLIAM. An Address Delivered by William Morris...Birmingham Municipal School of Art on Feb 21, 1894. London: Chiswick, 1898. 25pp. Unopened. (Cvr sl soiled), o/w VF. *Europa*. $104/£65

MORRIS, WILLIAM. Architecture and History and Westminster Abbey. Longmans, 1900. 1st Eng ed. Cl-backed paper bds. VG (top corner p33 torn, no loss; fep browned; cvrs sl spotted, spine faded). *Ulysses*. $152/£95

MORRIS, WILLIAM. Architecture and History. London: Longmans, 1900. 1st ed. Pub's ads loosely inserted. Uncut, unopened. Linen-backed pale blue paper bds. Fine. *Maggs*. $120/£75

MORRIS, WILLIAM. Art and its Producers, and the Arts and Crafts of Today. Two Addresses.... London: Chiswick, 1901. 47pp. Cl-backed ptd bds. VG. *Europa*. $112/£70

MORRIS, WILLIAM. Art and the Beauty of the Earth. London: Chiswick, 1898. 1st ed. Uncut. Blue cl. Good (sl browned). *Maggs*. $88/£55

MORRIS, WILLIAM. Art and the Beauty of the Earth. Longmans, 1898. 1st Eng ed. Unopened. Cl-backed paper bds. VG (1st/last blanks sl browned; cvrs sl spotted, spine faded). *Ulysses*. $152/£95

MORRIS, WILLIAM. Art and the Beauty of the Earth. A Lecture...October 13, 1881. London: Chiswick, 1898. 31pp. VF. *Europa*. $99/£62

MORRIS, WILLIAM. The Doom of King Acrisius. NY: R.H. Russell, 1902. White cl, gilt. (Cl soiled), else VG. *Pacific**. $63/£39

MORRIS, WILLIAM. Early Poems of William Morris. London: Blackie & Son, 1914. 1st ed. 4to. Florence Harrison (illus). Teg. Lt blue cl, gilt. (Prelims, fore-edge lt foxed.) Pict pub's box (edge-worn, browned). *Reisler*. $500/£313

MORRIS, WILLIAM. Gothic Architecture: A Lecture for the Arts and Crafts Exhibition Society. (Hammersmith: Kelmscott, 1893.) 1st ed. 3/4 morocco, marbled bds, raised bands, morocco spine label. Fine (orig wrappers bound in). *Pacific**. $173/£108

MORRIS, WILLIAM. Report upon the Customs District, Public Service, and Resources of Alaska Territory. Washington: GPO, 1879. 163pp; 11 plts, incl fldg map. VF. *High Latitude*. $90/£56

MORRIS, WILLIAM. Some Hints on Pattern-Designing. A Lecture...December 10, 1881. London: Chiswick, 1899. 45pp. Cl-backed ptd bds. VF (ex-libris). *Europa*. $96/£60

MORRIS, WILLIE. North Toward Home. Boston: Houghton Mifflin, 1967. 1st ed, 1st bk. VG in dj. *Cady*. $30/£19

MORRIS, WRIGHT. Cause for Wonder. NY: Atheneum, 1963. 1st ed. Fine in dj (sl worn). *Lenz*. $45/£28

MORRIS, WRIGHT. The Field of Vision. NY: Harcourt Brace, (1956). 1st ed. Fine in dj (sl worn). *Lenz*. $60/£38

MORRIS, WRIGHT. God's Country and My People. NY: Harper & Row, (1968). 1st ed. NF in dj (spine, lower extrems sl sunned). *Pacific**. $46/£29

MORRIS, WRIGHT. The Home Place. NY: Scribner, 1948. 1st ed. (Spine, part of rear cvr sl sunned), else VG. *Pacific**. $46/£29

MORRIS, WRIGHT. In Orbit. NY: NAL, (1967). 1st ed. Fine in Fine dj (extrems rubbed). *Between The Covers*. $65/£41

MORRIS, WRIGHT. The Inhabitants. NY, 1946. 1st ed. VG in dj (frayed, chipped). *King*. $100/£63

MORRIS, WRIGHT. Love Among the Cannibals. NY: Harcourt, Brace, (1957). 1st ed. Fine in dj (extrems worn). *Bromer*. $100/£63

MORRIS, WRIGHT. Man and Boy. NY: Knopf, 1951. 1st ed. NF in dj (sl worn). *Lenz*. $100/£63

MORRIS, WRIGHT. One Day. NY: Atheneum, 1965. 1st ed. Fine in dj (sl worn). *Lenz*. $40/£25

MORRIS, WRIGHT. The Territory Ahead. (NY): Harcourt Brace, (1958). 1st ed. Fine in dj (sl worn). *Lenz*. $60/£38

MORRISON, ARTHUR. The Hole in the Wall. Methuen, 1902. Pub's cat dated August 1902 (1 pg torn w/loss). Good (fore-edge lt spotted; spine bumped, cvr sl mkd, hinges sl rubbed). *Tiger*. $72/£45

MORRISON, ARTHUR. The Painters of Japan. NY, (1911). 2 vols. Folio. (Spines sl faded, ends worn, fr cvr blistered.) Slipcase. *Swann**. $126/£79

MORRISON, ARTHUR. The Red Triangle. Boston, 1903. 1st Amer ed. Uncut. Pict cvrs. NF (sl rubbed, soiled). *Polyanthos*. $30/£19

MORRISON, ARTHUR. Tales of Mean Streets. London: Methuen, 1894. 1st ed, 1st bk. Inscribed, 1900. (6),304pp. Contemp 3/4 morocco (sl rubbed). *Karmiole*. $350/£219

MORRISON, GEORGE ERNEST. An Australian in China. London: Horace Cox, 1895. 2nd ed. 1/2-title, frontis, xii,299pp; fldg map, fldg facs map, 25 plts. Teg. Maroon dec cl, gilt. (Sm lib stamp, few ll foxed; faded.) *Morrell*. $48/£30

MORRISON, HUGH A. Preliminary Check List of American Almanacs, 1639-1800. Washington: GPO, 1907. 1st ed. Crimson ribbed cl, gilt. (Lt aged, some pp w/written, mtd notes; ink inscrip; lib paper spine label, bkpl, sm blindstamp tp; edgeworn.) *Baltimore**. $25/£16

MORRISON, J. S. and R. T. WILLIAMS. Greek Oared Ships, 900-322 B.C. Cambridge: CUP, 1968. 31 plts. Dj. *Archaeologia*. $150/£94

MORRISON, JAMES. The Elements of Book Keeping, by Single and Double Entry. London: Longman, Rees, Brown & Green, (1825). New ed. Engr tp, viii,269pp. 1/4 calf (rebacked, title label fr cvr; name excised fr blank). *Young*. $192/£120

MORRISON, JIM. The Lords and The New Creatures. NY: S&S, (1970). 1st ed. Fine in Fine dj. *Lenz*. $125/£78

MORRISON, PEGGY. Cosy Chair Stories. London: Collins' Clear Type Press, (1924). 1st ed. Lg 4to. 48pp (corners of pp sl nicked); 6 full-pg color plts. Cl-backed color pict bds. VG. *Reisler*. $450/£281

MORRISON, TONI. Beloved. London, (1987). 1st ed. NF in NF dj. *Polyanthos*. $35/£22

MORRISON, TONI. Beloved. Knopf, 1987. 1st US ed. Fine in dj. *Williams*. $40/£25

MORRISON, TONI. Jazz. NY, 1992. 1st Amer ed. Fine in Fine dj. *Polyanthos*. $35/£22

MORRISON, TONI. Jazz. NY: Knopf, 1992. 1st ed. Signed. Fine in Fine dj. *Agvent*. $125/£78

MORRISON, TONI. Jazz. NY: Knopf, 1992. 1st ed. Signed, inscribed. Fine in dj. *Pacific**. $138/£86

MORRISON, TONI. Playing in the Dark. Cambridge: Harvard Univ, 1992. 1st ed. Fine in dj. *Smith*. $30/£19

MORRISON, TONI. Song of Solomon. NY, 1977. 1st ed. Fine in NF dj (price-clipped, sm tear, nick top fr panel; evenly sunned). *Warren*. $75/£47

MORRISON, TONI. Song of Solomon. NY: Knopf, 1977. 1st ed. Signed. Fine in Fine dj. *Lenz*. $225/£141

MORRISON, TONI. Sula. (London): Allen Lane, (1974). 1st British ed. NF in dj (spine foot rubbed). *Pacific**. $196/£123

MORRISON, TONI. Tar Baby. NY, 1981. 1st trade ed. VG in dj (sl creased, dknd). *King*. $35/£22

MORRISON, TONI. Tar Baby. NY: Knopf, 1981. 1st ed. Fine in Fine dj. *Agvent*. $75/£47

MORRISON, TONI. Tar Baby. NY: Knopf, 1981. 1st trade ed. Top edge stained blue. Cream cl, gilt. Fine in dj (lt soiled, sm scratch fr panel). *Heritage*. $125/£78

MORSE, EDWARD S. Japanese Homes and Their Surroundings. Boston: Ticknor, 1886. 1st ed. Teg. Dec blue cl, gilt. (Hinges starting, cl, spine head torn, foot rubbed), else VG. *Pacific**. $288/£180

MORSE, FRANCES CLARY. Furniture of the Olden Time. NY: Macmillan, 1905. Ribbed cl (sl rubbed, fr joint cracking), gilt. *Hollett*. $48/£30

MORSE, H. G. Robert Louis Stevenson as I Found Him. (London?: n.p., n.d. 1902.) 1st ed. Fine in blue ptd wrappers. *Macdonnell*. $45/£28

MORSE, H. K. Gardening in the Shade. NY: Scribner, 1939. 1st ed. (Browned; spine sunned), else VG. *Fair Meadow*. $25/£16

MORSE, JEDIDIAH. The American Gazeteer...on the American Continent, Also of the West-India Islands. Boston, 1797. 1st ed. 7 engr maps (part of 1 torn away). Contemp Amer calf, gilt spine. (Foxed, few maps split, repaired; rubbed.) Howes M839. *Oinonen**. $275/£172

MORSE, KATHARINE. The Pig That Danced a Jig. NY: E.P. Dutton, 1938. 1st ed. Obl 4to. Winifred Bromhall (illus). Yellow bds (lower edge sl dknd). Color pict dj (dusty, sl marginal tears). *Reisler*. $100/£63

MORSE, PETER. Jean Charlot's Prints: A Catalogue Raisonne. Honolulu, (1976). Signed etching by Charlot laid in rear pocket. 1/4 imitation leather. Slipcase. *Swann**. $201/£126

MORSE, PETER. John Sloan's Prints, Catalogue Raisonne. New Haven, 1969. Folio. (Lt worn.) Dj. *Oinonen**. $125/£78

MORSE, PETER. John Sloan's Prints: A Catalogue Raisonne of the Etchings, Lithographs and Posters. New Haven: Yale Univ, 1969. 1st ed. One of 150. Proof of prev. unpub'd plt signed by Helen Farr Sloan for John Sloan. Fine in slipcase. *Pacific**. $316/£198

MORSE, PETER. John Sloan's Prints: A Catalogue Raisonne. New Haven, 1969. One of 150 numbered w/proof of a previously unpublished etching. Folio. Slipcase. *Swann**. $460/£288

MORTENSEN, WILLIAM. Monsters and Madonnas. SF, (1943). Spiral-bound ptd wrappers (sl worn, age-dknd). *Swann**. $258/£161

MORTENSEN, WILLIAM. Monsters and Madonnas. SF: Camera Craft Pub, 1936. 1st ed. Fine in spiral bound illus wrappers, orig tissue dj (corner bumped, sm chip). *Smith*. $400/£250

MORTENSEN, WILLIAM. Monsters and Madonnas. SF: Camera Craft Pub, 1946. 3rd ptg. Rev copy, pub's slip glued to fep. NF (3 sm spots to cvr, corners worn) in photo illus wrappers, spiral bound. *Smith*. $225/£141

MORTENSEN, WILLIAM. Monsters and Madonnas. SF: Camera Craft Pub, 1948. 2nd ed, 4th ptg. 20 b/w photos. Spiral bound illus stiff wrappers. (Lt worn), else NF. *Cahan*. $150/£94

MORTENSEN, WILLIAM. Pictorial Lighting [and] Projection Control. SF: Camera Craft, (1935/1934). Pict 1st ed. 2 vols. (Eps, pastedowns age-dknd; sl worn.) Dj vol 1 (soiled, chipped). *Swann**. $69/£43

MORTIMER, J. R. Forty Years' Researches in British and Saxon Burial Mounds of East Yorkshire. A. Brown & Sons, 1905. 1st ed. Color frontis, color fldg plan, 125 plts. Teg. Orig 1/4 morocco, gilt extra. Fine (bkpl; fore-edge lt spotted). *Hollett*. $400/£250

MORTIMER, JOHN. Titmuss Regained. Viking, 1990. 1st UK ed. Signed. Fine in dj. *Williams*. $29/£18

MORTIMER, JOHN. Two Stars for Comfort. Methuen, 1962. 1st UK ed. Fine in VG+ dj. *Williams*. $48/£30

MORTON, ANTHONY. (Pseud of John Creasy.) A Branch for the Baron. London: Hodder & Stoughton, 1961. 1st ed. NF in dj (price-clipped, edges lt worn, soiled). *Murder*. $50/£31

MORTON, DESMOND and REGINALD H. ROY (eds). Telegrams of the North-West Campaign, 1885. Toronto: Champlain Soc, 1972. 1st ed. Ltd to 1000. Port, 5 maps. Red cl, gilt. Fine. *Argonaut*. $150/£94

MORTON, HENRY H. Genito-Urinary Diseases and Syphilis. Phila, 1908. 2nd ed. 158 1/2-tone & photo-engrs; 7 full pg color plts. (Inner hinges cracked, sl yellowed; extrems worn), o/w Good. *Doctor's Library*. $45/£28

MORTON, J. B. Captain Foulenough and Company. Macmillan, 1944. 1st ed. Signed presentation. (Spine sl mkd), else VG+ in Good+ dj (worn). *Any Amount*. $32/£20

MORTON, J. K. West African Lilies and Orchids. London, 1961. 1st ed. 20 color plts. VG. *Larry Price*. $17/£11

MORTON, JAMES ST. C. Memoir on American Fortification Submitted to the Hon. John B. Floyd, Secretary of War. Washington: William A. Harris, Ptr, 1859. 91pp, plt. Orig warps. (Old tape repairs to spine, chipped), else Good. *Brown*. $50/£31

MORTON, JOHN C. (ed). A Cyclopedia of Agriculture. London: Blackie, 1855. 2 vols. xliv,1022pp; 1172pp; 50 (of 51); (lacks plt 42). Full gilt edged diced calf, leather spine labels. (Sl spotted; edges sl rubbed.) *Edwards*. $120/£75

MORTON, SAMUEL GEORGE. Illustrations of Pulmonary Consumption, Its Anatomical Characters, Causes, Symptoms and Treatment. Phila: Key & Biddle, 1834. 1st ed. 13,(1),(9)-183pp (foxed); 12 color litho plts. Old calf (loose, scuffed). *M & S*. $400/£250

MORWOOD, WILLIAM. Traveller in a Vanished Landscape. Gentry Books, 1973. VG in dj. *Hadley*. $29/£18

MORWOOD, WILLIAM. Traveller in a Vanished Landscape. London: Gentry, 1973. 1st ed. VG+ in dj. *Archer*. $35/£22

MORYSON, FYNES. An Itinerary Containing His Ten Yeeres Travell Through the Twelve Dominions of Germany, [et al]. Glasgow, 1907. One of 1000 sets. 4 vols. Gilt-pict cl. *Swann**. $69/£43

MOSBY, JOHN S. Mosby's War Reminiscences and Stuart's Cavalry Campaigns. Boston: Geo. A. Jones, 1887. 1st ed. Frontisports, 256pp. Dk maroon cl. (Edges of frontisports foxed, sig, few sigs sl pulled), else NF. *Chapel Hill*. $375/£234

MOSBY, JOHN S. Stuart's Cavalry in the Gettysburg Campaign. NY: Moffat, Yard, 1908. 1st ed. Complete w/frontisport, port, fldg map. Blue cl. (Sig; sm dent top edge fr cvr), else Nice. *Chapel Hill*. $350/£219

MOSELEY, SYDNEY and H. J. BARTON CHAPPLE. Television To-Day and Tomorrow. NY: Pitman, 1930. 1st Amer ed. Frontisport, 46 plts. (Extrems sl worn), else NF. *Glaser*. $200/£125

MOSELEY, SYDNEY. John Baird. The Romance and Tragedy of the Pioneer of Television. London: Odhams, n.d. 1st ed. 11 plts. VG in dj. *Hollett*. $40/£25

MOSELY, MARTIN E. The Dry-Fly Fisherman's Entomology. Being a Supplement to Frederic M. Halford's The Dry-Fly Man's Handbook. London, 1921. 1st ed. 16 hand-colored plts. Flexible cl (lt worn) w/wallet flap. *Oinonen**. $170/£106

MOSES, BERNARD. Spain's Declining Power in South America, 1730-1806. Berkeley: Univ of CA, 1919. 1st ed. Blue cl, gilt. Fine. *Argonaut*. $75/£47

MOSGROVE, GEORGE DALLAS. Kentucky Cavaliers in Dixie. Bell Irvin Wiley (ed). Jackson, TN: McCowat-Mercer, 1957. 1st ed thus. Tan cl. Fine in VG dj. Howes M857. *Chapel Hill*. $45/£28

MOSKOWITZ, IRA. Great Drawings of All Time. NY: Shorewood, 1962. 4 vols. Folio. (Lt worn.) Slipcases. *Oinonen**. $180/£113

MOSLEY, NICHOLAS. The Assassination of Trotsky. Michael Joseph, 1972. 1st UK ed. VG in dj (price-clipped). *Williams*. $40/£25

MOSLEY, WALTER. A Red Death. NY, 1991. 1st ed. Fine in Fine dj. *Warren*. $40/£25

MOSLEY, WALTER. A Red Death. NY: Norton, 1991. 1st ed. Signed. Fine in dj. *Lame Duck*. $75/£47

MOSS, LEMUEL. Annals of the United States Christian Commission. Phila: Lippincott, 1868. 1st ed. Frontisport, 752pp. Maroon cl, gilt. (Sl worn, fr hinge very cracked; fr joint split), o/w Good. *Baltimore**. $50/£31

MOSSMAN, ISAAC. A Pony Expressman's Recollections. (Portland): Champoeg, 1955. 1st bk ed. One of 500 ptd. Tipped-in frontisport, fldg map. Red pict cl. Fine. *Harrington*. $65/£41

MOSSMAN, ISAAC. A Pony Expressman's Recollections. (Portland, OR): Champoeg, 1955. 1st ed. Ltd to 500 ptd. Tipped-on 1/2-tone port, 4 facs plts, fldg map. Uncut. Pict red cl, gilt. (Corner sl jammed), else VF. *Argonaut*. $75/£47

MOSTEL, ZERO. Zero by Mostel. NY: Horizon, 1965. 1st ed. Max Waldman (photos). VG in dj. *Cahan*. $40/£25

MOSZKOWSKI, ALEXANDER. Einstein the Searcher. Henry Brose (trans). London: Methuen, (1921). 1st Eng ed. Purple cl. (Extrems, spine sunned), else VG. *Pacific**. $46/£29

MOTH, AXEL. Technical Terms Used in Bibliographies and by the Book and Printing Trade. Boston: Boston Book Co, 1915. 1st ed. *Forest*. $32/£20

Mother Goose Jingles. (Saafield's Muslin Books.) Akron, OH: Saalfield, 1904. 4to. 16pp. Color pict cl (margins lt worn, dknd). Fine. *Reisler*. $125/£78

Mother Goose Movies. NY: Frederick A. Stokes, (1917). 1st ed. Alice Beard (illus). 12 1/2 x 10. Cl-backed pict bds. (Inscrip; extrems rubbed), else VG. *Pacific**. $81/£51

Mother Goose Nursery Rhymes. (Wee Book.) Phila: Henry Altemus, (1904). 16mo. 92pp, incl 58 illus by John R. Neill. Cl-backed color pict bds. Good in color dj (worn, chipped). *Reisler*. $75/£47

Mother Goose Old Style. NY: McLoughlin Bros, (ca 1850s-60s). 5x4. (Lacks sm spine piece), else VG in pict wrappers. *Pacific**. $46/£29

Mother Goose or the Old Nursery Rhymes. London: Routledge, (1881). 1st ed, 1st issue, binding B (Schuster). Kate Greenaway (illus). 12mo. Turquoise pict cl w/gold box around title. VG (spine sl dknd). *Reisler*. $750/£469

Mother Goose Picture Book. NY: Sam'l Gabriel Sons, (1939). Lg 4to. Elsie Deane (illus). 121pp. Wine-red cl, full color paste label. Good in color illus dj (marginal tears, few spine chips). *Reisler*. $175/£109

Mother Goose Rhymes. NY: McLoughlin Bros, (c. 1915). 8 1/4 x 6 1/2. Cl-backed chromolitho bds. (Extrems sl rubbed), else NF. *Pacific**. $63/£39

Mother Goose's Melodies. Springfield: McLoughlin Bros, ca 1925. 4to. F. Schuyler Mathews (illus). Cl-backed color pict bds (edges rubbed, worn, hinges weak). *Reisler*. $225/£141

Mother Goose's Melodies. Containing All That Have Ever Come to Light. NY: James Miller, (1869). 12mo. 96pp. Blind-stamped maroon cl mtd on stiff paper wrappers, gilt. Good. *Reisler*. $275/£172

Mother Goose's Nursery Rhymes and Nursery Songs. Set to Music by J. W. Elliott. NY: McLoughlin Bros, n.d. (ca 1900). 8vo. Full-pg engr frontis, ii,111pp; all engr done by Dalziel. Blue marbled eps. 3/4 brn sand grain w/corners, on bds (spine, corners rubbed). (Sm repaired chipped corner last pg), else Internally Fine. *Hobbyhorse*. $125/£78

Mother Goose's Nursery Rhymes. NY: Graham & Matlack, (c. 1900). 9x6.5. Red cl, gilt, chromolitho cvr label. VG. *Pacific**. $46/£29

Mother Goose's Nursery Rhymes. NY: McLoughlin Bros, (c. 1909). 9x6.5. Chromolitho frontis. Pict cl, gilt. (Shelfworn), else VG. *Pacific**. $52/£33

Mother Goose. London: Heinemann, (1913). 1st Rackham ed. One of 1130 signed by Arthur Rackham (illus). 4to. 13 mtd color plts. Teg. Full gilt-stamped white linen (sl soiled). Fine. *Appelfeld*. $1,500/£938

Mother Goose. Springfield: McLoughlin Bros, (c. 1900). 9.75x7.75. Cl-backed chromolitho bds. VG. *Pacific**. $69/£43

Mother Goose. NY: McLoughlin Bros, ca 1895. Shapebook. 15 1/2 x 7 1/4. 14pp. Illus wraps. VG (ink Christmas 1896 inscrip). *Davidson*. $225/£141

Mother Goose. If Wishes Were Horses and Other Rhymes. NY: E.P. Dutton, (1979). 1st ed. Sq 4to. Color pict bds. Fine in color dj. *Reisler*. $50/£31

Mother Goose. The Old Nursery Rhymes. NY: Century, (1913). 1st Amer ed. One of 150. Signed by Rackham. 11.25x8.75. 13 tipped-in color plts by Arthur Rackham; ptd tissue guards. Teg. Pict white cl, gilt. (Bkpl; sl soiled, spine stain), else VG. *Pacific**. $1,380/£863

Mother Goose: A Unique Version with Animated Illustrations by Julian Wehr. NY: G&D, (1942). Obl 4to. 4 tab-activated moveable plts. Color pict bds (spine lt worn), spiral binding. Color pict dj (lt edgeworn; wrapper fastened to bk w/Christmas stickers). *Reisler*. $200/£125

Mother Hubbard. NY: Raphael Tuck & Sons, (ca 1890). Father Tuck's Tiny Toddlers Series. Toybook. 4to. 8pp + 4 full-pg color plts. Good in full color pict paper wrappers (worn, spine chipped). *Reisler*. $85/£53

MOTHERWELL, ROBERT and AL REINHARDT (eds). Modern Artists in America. First Series (all published). NY, (1951). Pict bds (rubbed). *Swann**. $126/£79

MOTHERWELL, ROBERT (ed). The Dada Painters and Poets: An Anthology. NY, (1951). (Spine faded.) Dj. *Swann**. $258/£161

MOTION, ANDREW. Goodnestone. Workshop, 1972. 1st ed, 1st bk. VG (bottom of pg edges sl creased; bkpl mtd inside fr cvr, sl spotted, sl creased). *Ulysses*. $136/£85

MOTION, ANDREW. Love in a Life. London: Faber & Faber, (1991). 1st ed. Fine in Fine dj. *Dermont*. $20/£13

MOTLEY, JOHN L. The Complete Works of.... NY, (1902). 14 vols. Frontispieces. Teg. 1/2 red morocco, gilt. (Few crowns lt worn.) *Swann**. $287/£179

MOTLEY, JOHN L. History of the United Netherlands.... John Murray, 1875. New ed. 4 vols. xii,503pp, 1 fldg plt; vii,533; x,563; viii,580pp. Marbled eps; all edges marbled. Contemp red burgundy 1/2 calf, marbled bds, raised bands, gilt, grn leather labels. (Pencil notes vol 1; upper spine compartment vol 3 sl rubbed), o/w VG set. *Sotheran*. $240/£150

MOTLEY, WILLARD. We Fished All Night. NY: Appleton-Century-Crofts, (1951). 1st ed. Good (eps written on) in ptd dj (chipped). *Petrilla*. $35/£22

MOTTO, SYTHA. Old Houses of New Mexico and the People Who Built Them. Albuquerque, 1972. Sm folio. VG in dj. *Dumont*. $75/£47

MOTTRAM, ERIC. Inside the Whale. London: Writers Forum, 1970. 1st ed. NF in wraps. *Polyanthos*. $25/£16

MOTTRAM, J. C. Fly-Fishing: Some New Arts and Mysteries. London: Field, (1921). 2nd ed. *Petersfield*. $56/£35

MOTTRAM, R. H. The Crime at Vanderlynden's. London: C&W, 1926. 1st ed. Red cl, gilt. NF in dj. *Reese*. $55/£34

MOTTRAM, R. H. The Glories of Norwich Cathedral. London, n.d. (c. 1952). VG. *Gretton*. $10/£6

MOTTRAM, R. H. Journey to the Western Front. London: G. Bell, 1936. 1st ed. Red-orange cl. (Lt foxed early/late, and edges), o/w Nice. *Reese*. $25/£16

MOTTRAM, R. H. Poems New and Old. London: Duckworth, 1930. 1st ed. Gilt grn cl. (Cl lt sunned through dj), o/w NF in VG dj (spine ends sl discolored). *Reese*. $35/£22

MOTTRAM, R. H. The Spanish Farm. London: C&W, 1924. 1st ed. Red cl, gilt. VG in dj (spine lt tanned, few sm nicks). *Reese*. $125/£78

MOTTRAM, R. H. et al. Three Personal Records of the War. London: Scholartis, 1929. 1st ed. Frontis map. Black cl, gilt. VG- (eps, edges sl foxed; sl bowed) in dj (tanned, few rubs, snag rear panel). *Reese*. $60/£38

MOTTRAM, R. H. et al. Three Personal Records of the War. London, 1929. One of 100 signed. (Sm hole to backstrip; no dj.) *Typographeum*. $75/£47

MOUHOT, HENRI. Travels in the Central Parts of Indo-China. London: John Murray, 1864. 1st Eng ed. 2 vols. 8vo. 1/2-title, frontis, 303pp, port; 1/2-title, frontis, viii,301,(3)blanks,32 pub's list dated March 1863; 16 engr plts (15 fldg). Grn cl, gilt. Good (ex-lib, 2 plts repaired at folds, lib stamps, soiled, lib plts removed; sl rubbed, spines carefully repaired). *Morrell*. $608/£380

MOUNTAINE, WILLIAM. The Seaman's Vade-Mecum and Defensive War by Sea. London, 1783. This ed appears to have been issued w/o plts. Later 1/2 calf. (Sm emb lib stamp; needs rebinding.) *Swann**. $488/£305

MOUNTENEY-JEPHSON, A. J. Emin Pasha and the Rebellion at the Equator. NY: Scribner, 1890. xxiv,490,2 ads; 22 plts, fldg map, facs letter. Pict cl (lt rubbed, spine foot starting). *Adelson*. $185/£116

MOURELLE, FRANCISCO ANTONIO. Voyage of the Sonora in the Second Bucareli Expedition to Explore the Northwest Coast.... Daines Barrington (trans). SF: Thomas C. Russell, 1920. 1st Amer ed. One of 230. Frontisport, 2 fldg maps. 1/2 cl, paper spine label. Fine. Howes M438. *Pacific**. $219/£137

MOURELLE, FRANCISCO ANTONIO. Voyage of the Sonora in the Second Bucareli Expedition to Explore the Northwest Coast.... SF: Thomas C. Russell, 1920. One of 230. Signed by Russell. Frontisport, 2 maps (1 fldg). Dec lt blue paper over bds, lt blue cl spine. NF (sl worn, lt soiled). *Parmer*. $300/£188

MOURLOT, FERNAND. Art in Posters. NY: George Braziller, (1959). 1st Amer ed. NF in dj. *Pacific**. $109/£68

MOURLOT, FERNAND. Bernard Buffet: Lithographs, 1952-1966. NY, (1968). 4to. 10 color lithos. Stiff pict wrappers, slipcase. *Swann**. $517/£323

MOURLOT, FERNAND. The Lithographs of Chagall, 1957-1962. Monte Carlo/Boston: Andre Sauret/Boston Book & Art Shop, (1963). 1st ed in English. 12.5x9.5. 11 orig lithos. VG in litho dj (extrms sl rubbed). *Pacific**. $633/£396

MOUTOUSSAMY-ASHE, JEANNE. Viewfinders: Black Women Photographers. NY: Dodd, Mead, (1986). Rev copy w/publicity sheet, photo, rev slip laid in. Fine (corner bumped) in dj (sl worn; sm chip). *Hermitage*. $50/£31

MOWAT, FARLEY. Never Cry Wolf. Toronto: McClelland & Stewart, (1963). 1st ed. (Inscrip), else Fine in 2 variant djs, one NF (sm spine stain, sm tear), one Fine. *Between The Covers*. $250/£156

MOWBRAY, JAY HENRY. Thrilling Achievements of 'Bird Men' with Flying Machines. N.p., (1911). Color frontis, vi,256pp. Red cl, mtd color illus fr cvr. Good (lt aged, sl foxed; sl edge-worn, spine lettering lost). *Baltimore**. $30/£19

MOWRY, JESS. Way Past Cool. NY: FSG, 1992. 1st ed. Fine in dj. *Smith*. $25/£16

MOYER, J. W. Trophy Heads. NY: Ronald, 1962. 1st ed. VG+ in VG dj. *Mikesh*. $150/£94

MOYER, WILLIAM. The Witchery of Sleep. NY: Ostermoor, 1903. 1st ed. Inscribed, signed. Teg. (Yellowish spotting to cvrs), else VG. *Pacific**. $81/£51

MOYNIHAN, B. Abdominal Operations. Phila, 1906. 2nd ed. *Fye*. $75/£47

MOYNIHAN, B. Abdominal Operations. Phila, 1918. 3rd ed. 2 vols. Fine (foxed). *Doctor's Library*. $100/£63

MOYNIHAN, B. The Spleen and Some of Its Diseases. London, 1921. 1st ed. *Fye*. $100/£63

MOZINO, JOSE MARIANO. Noticias de Nutka. Seattle, 1970. *Dumont*. $30/£19

Mr. Facey Romford's Hounds. (By Robert Smith Surtees.) London, 1865. 1st bk ed. 24 hand-colored plts by John Leech and Hablot K. Browne. Full grn polished calf. (Sl soiled, foxed; rubbed.) *Oinonen**. $70/£44

Mr. Facey Romford's Hounds. (By Robert Smith Surtees.) London, 1865. 1st ed in bk form. 24 hand-colored plts by John Leech and Hablot K. Browne. Teg. Full red morocco by Tout, spine gilt. (Orig wrappers, ads from parts bound in at end; lt rubbed; sl foxed, soiled; corner sl chewed.) *Oinonen**. $200/£125

Mr. Pickwick. Pages from the Pickwick Papers. (By Charles Dickens.) London: Hodder & Stoughton, (1910). Ltd to 350 signed by Frank Reynolds (illus). 4to. 25 mtd color plts. Teg. Orig pict vellum (sl stained, sm hole to spine, lacks ties), gilt. *Christie's**. $101/£63

Mr. Sponge's Sporting Tour. (By Robert Smith Surtees.) London: Bradbury, Agnew, (1899). 2 vols. 13 hand-colored plts by John Leech. Teg. 3/4 red morocco, spines gilt. (Tips, edges worn.) *Oinonen**. $120/£75

Mr. Sponge's Sporting Tour. London, 1853. 1st ed in bk form, w/half-title. 13 hand-colored steel-engr plts. Orig cl (rebacked, retaining orig backstrip; spine, fr cvr blistered; offsetting from plts, bkpl removed). *Swann**. $103/£64

MRABET, MOHAMMED. The Lemon. Paul Bowles (trans). NY: McGraw-Hill, (1969). 1st Amer ed. Top edge stained black. Yellow cl. Fine in dj. *Heritage*. $50/£31

Mrs. Leicester's School. London: M.J. Godwin, 1820. 7th ed. Engr frontis, 180pp. Contemp calf (rubbed, hinges worn). VG. *Second Life*. $225/£141

Mrs. Perkins's Ball. (By William Makepeace Thackeray.) London, (1847). 1st ed. 22 color plts, incl fldg frontis (backed w/linen). 19th-cent 1/2 grn morocco (extrms rubbed, orig wrappers bound in), gilt. *Swann**. $80/£50

MUDD, SAMUEL A. The Life of Dr. Samuel A. Mudd. Nettie Mudd (ed). NY/Washington: Neale, 1906. 1st ed. Frontisport. Teg. Red buckram. NF (sig, notes on 2 text pp). Howes M871. *Chapel Hill*. $375/£234

MUDGE, JEAN McCLURE. Chinese Export Porcelain for the American Trade, 1785-1835. (Newark): Univ of DE, 1962. Orig ed. Color frontis. VG. *Turtle Island*. $35/£22

MUELLER, RALPH. Report After Action: The Story of 103rd Infantry Division. Innsbruck, 1945. 1st ed. VG in dj (torn). *Clark*. $75/£47

MUGGERIDGE, MALCOLM. The Sun Never Sets. NY: Random House, (1940). 1st ed. Fine in NF dj (internally repaired). *Captain's Bookshelf*. $75/£47

MUHAMMAD, ELIJAH. Message to the Black Man. Chicago: Mosque of Islam No. 2, (1965). 1st ed, 1st bk. Dj (sm chips). *Swann**. $172/£108

MUHLBACH, L. Works. Akron: New Werner Co, (1893). Werner ed. 16 vols. Teg. 3/4 morocco, marbled bds, gilt spines. NF. *Pacific**. $138/£86

MUIR, AUGUSTUS (ed). The Intimate Thoughts of John Baxter, Bookseller. Methuen, 1942. 1st ed. Dj. *Forest*. $26/£16

MUIR, EDWIN. An Autobiography. London: Hogarth, 1954. 1st Eng ed. NF (bkpl, feps partly browned; spine ends sl bumped) in dj (sl rubbed, torn, repaired, patches of tape-dkng). *Ulysses*. $48/£30

MUIR, EDWIN. The Three Brothers. Heinemann, 1931. 1st ed. VG (top edge dusty; ep, spine edges sl browned, ends, 1 corner sl bumped) in dj (nicked, rubbed, chipped, dusty, spine, edges browned, spine head lacks few sm pieces). *Ulysses*. $880/£550

MUIR, JOHN (ed). Picturesque California and the Region West of the Rocky Mountains from Alaska to Mexico. NY/SF: J. Dewing, (1888). 15.5x11.5. (4),204pp; 60 plts, tissue guards, 3 photo-etchings, 48 photogravures, 1 unspecified plt. Marbled eps; aeg. Gray-blue pict cl, gilt. (Extrms sl worn, gilt dull), o/w NF. *Pacific**. $575/£359

MUIR, JOHN (ed). Picturesque California: The Rocky Mountains and the Pacific Slope.... SF: J. Dewing, 1888. Deluxe ed. One of 750. 10 vols. 20.25x15.5. Internally Nice set (bkpls) in pict wrappers (spines detached). Each set in pict silk cl folder (worn, spines perished so each is in 2 parts). *Pacific**. $1,150/£719

MUIR, JOHN. John of the Mountains: The Unpublished Journals of John Muir. Linnie Marsh Wolfe (ed). Boston: Houghton Mifflin, (1938). 1st ed. Frontisport, 7 plts. Lt gray cl. (Corners sl bumped), o/w Fine in pict dj (price-clipped, sl edgeworn). *Pacific**. $40/£25

MUIR, JOHN. Letters to a Friend: Written to Mrs. Ezra S. Carr 1866-1879. Boston/NY: Houghton Mifflin, 1915. Ltd to 300. Uncut. Grn paper-cvrd bds, paper spine label. (Rear cvr scuffed, stained; spine ends sl rubbed; lower corner fr cvr sl bumped), o/w NF. *Pacific**. $345/£216

MUIR, JOHN. The Mountains of California. NY: Century, 1894. 1st ed. Tan cl. VG+ (pp lt foxed; cvrs sl worn). *Labordo*. $425/£266

MUIR, JOHN. The Mountains of California. NY, 1894. 1st ed, 1st bk. 381pp. Teg. Fine. *Truepenny*. $500/£313

MUIR, JOHN. The Mountains of California. NY: Century, 1894. 1st ed, 1st issue w/folio I below the text on pg 1. 7.5x5.25. Frontis. Teg. Tan cl, gilt. (Fr hinge neatly repaired; sl mar rear cvr), else NF. *Pacific**. $748/£468

MUIR, JOHN. The Mountains of California. NY: Century, 1903. Frontis. Teg. Tan cl, gilt. (Name crudely overwritten, sl insect damage fr cvr), o/w Fine. *Pacific**. $40/£25

MUIR, JOHN. The Mountains of California. Boston/NY: Houghton Mifflin, n.d. (last c. on tp verso is 1916). 2 vols. 14 plts, 2 fldg maps. Grn cl, gilt spines. Fine in pict djs (sl edge-worn). *Pacific*.* $92/£58

MUIR, JOHN. My First Summer in the Sierra. Boston, (1911). Frontis, guard. (Traces of erasures on eps, tp; several pg edges sl marginally water-stained, no loss to text), o/w VG. *Sagebrush.* $75/£47

MUIR, JOHN. My First Summer in the Sierra. SF: Sierra Club, (1988). 12 plts. Gray linen. Fine in pict dj. *Pacific*.* $29/£18

MUIR, JOHN. My First Summer in the Sierra. Boston/NY: Houghton Mifflin, 1911. 1st ed. 12 plts. Teg. Dk grn cl, gilt. (Extrems sl worn, neat repair fr hinge), o/w Fine. *Pacific*.* $173/£108

MUIR, JOHN. Our National Parks. Boston/NY: Houghton Mifflin, 1901. 1st ed, 1st ptg, w/tipped-in tp. Entire text on laid paper; tipped-in single pg title leaf, 2nd sig 8pp, next 23 are 16pp, last is 2pp. 1st ptg, according to pub's records, was 992 copies, w/3 add'l ptgs the same year of almost 1500 copies, all w/24 text sigs, all 16pp. (ix),370pp; 1 map, 11 photo plts incl frontis (all inserted). Teg. Olive cl, gilt. (Sl aged, fr hinge sl cracked; spine ends sl frayed, nicked, spine gilt partly rubbed.) BAL 14752. *Baltimore*.* $120/£75

MUIR, JOHN. Our National Parks. Boston: Houghton Mifflin, 1909. New, enlgd ed. 32 plts, dbl-pg map. Teg. Blue pict cl, gilt. (Pencil underlinings, marginal notes; spine ends sl worn), o/w NF. *Pacific*.* $58/£36

MUIR, JOHN. South of Yosemite. Frederic R. Grunsky (ed). GC: Natural History Press, (1968). 1st ed. 2-color cl, gilt. Fine in pict dj. *Pacific*.* $35/£22

MUIR, JOHN. Steep Trails. Boston, 1918. 1st ed. Frontis. Untrimmed. Ptd photo on cl. Good+ (feps lt water-stained, no text loss, some pg edges roughly opened; fr panel illus lt worn). *Sagebrush.* $85/£53

MUIR, JOHN. Steep Trails. Boston/NY: Houghton Mifflin, n.d. 6 plts. Pale grn cl. Fine. *Pacific*.* $23/£14

MUIR, JOHN. Stickeen, the Story of a Dog. Boston/NY: Houghton Mifflin, 1909. 1st ed, 1st ptg. 7.5x4.5. Tan cl. Fine (sl offset to eps) in ptd dj (torn, skillfully restored). *Pacific*.* $1,725/£1,078

MUIR, JOHN. A Thousand-Mile Walk to the Gulf. William Frederick Bade (ed). Boston/NY: Houghton Mifflin, 1916. Lg paper ed. One of 550. Frontisport, map, 10 plts. Uncut. Grn cl-backed bds, gilt-stamped morocco spine label. (Label rubbed), o/w NF. *Pacific*.* $219/£137

MUIR, JOHN. Travels in Alaska. Boston: Houghton Mifflin, 1915. 1st ed. (Exterior soiled), else Good. *Perier.* $125/£78

MUIR, JOHN. Travels in Alaska. Boston/NY: Houghton Mifflin, 1915. 1st trade ed. 12 plts. Partly unopened, teg. Gray cl, mtd cvr illus. (Bkpl; spine dull, ends sl rubbed), o/w NF. *Pacific*.* $127/£79

MUIR, JOHN. Two Essays on the Sights and Sounds of the Sierra Nevada. Shirley Sargent (ed). Ashland: Lewis Osborn, 1973. Ltd to 1000. 14 illus. Grn buckram, gilt. Fine in plain dj. *Pacific*.* $29/£18

MUIR, JOHN. The Yosemite. NY: Century, 1912. 1st ed. 34 plts, fldg map. Teg. Black cl, gilt. (Ink inscrip; cvrs sl rubbed), o/w NF. *Pacific*.* $219/£137

MUIR, JOHN. The Yosemite. NY, 1920. Frontis. Pict cl. VG (stamps erased from feps, tp; sl scuffed). *Sagebrush.* $65/£41

MUIR, PERCY. Catnachery. SF: Book Club of CA, 1955. One of 325 ptd. 5 fldg facs. Cl-backed dec bds, paper spine label. Fine. *Harrington.* $85/£53

MUIR, PERCY. English Children's Books 1600 to 1900. London: Batsford, (1954). 1st ed. Blue linen. Dj. *Appelfeld.* $125/£78

MUIR, PERCY. English Children's Books 1600 to 1900. London: Batsford, 1969. 2nd imp. Full color frontis. Blue linen, gilt. Fine in pict color dj (edges sl worn, spine top tattered). *Hobbyhorse.* $125/£78

MUIR, PERCY. Minding My Own Business. London: C&W, 1956. 1st ed. Frontisport. (Bkpl.) Dj. *Dawson.* $35/£22

MUIR, PERCY. Victorian Illustrated Books. NY/Washington: Praeger, (1971). 1st US ed. 5 color, 91 b/w repros. Black eps. Orange cl, gilt. (Top cvr edges sl discolored.) Text Fine in dj (lt rubbed). *Baltimore*.* $40/£25

MUIR, PERCY. Victorian Illustrated Books. London: Batsford, 1971. 1st ed. VG in dj. *Michael Taylor.* $32/£20

MUIR, WILLIAM. The Caliphate: Its Rise, Decline and Fall. T. H. Weir (ed). Edinburgh: John Grant, 1924. 1st ed. (Bkpls; spine ends rubbed), else VG. *Pacific*.* $40/£25

MUIRA, K. My World of Bibliophile Binding. Univ of CA, 1984. Fine in pict slipcase. *Moss.* $192/£120

MUIRHEAD, W. A. Practical Tropical Sanitation: A Manual for Sanitary Inspectors and Others. NY, 1915. 1st ed. *Fye.* $50/£31

MUKERJI, DHAN GOPAL. Gayneck. NY, (1927). One of 1000 signed by Mukerji & Boris Artzybasheff (illus). 1/2 parchment, pink patterned bds. (Lt aged, hinges weak; back, edges sunned, worn, spine ends sl frayed.) *King.* $95/£59

MULDOON, J. MALACHI. The Red Redeeming Dawn. Dublin: James Duffy, 1920. 1st ed. VG in ptd wraps (edges frayed, faded). *Dramatis.* $15/£9

MULFORD, AMI FRANK. Fighting Indians in the 7th United States Cavalry. Corning, NY: Paul Lindsley Mulford, (c.1930). 2nd ed. Orig wrappers bound in cl. Fine. Howes M88. *Pacific*.* $63/£39

MULFORD, ISSAC S. A Civil and Political History of New Jersey. Phila, 1851. 6,500pp,1pg ad. (Rebound.) *Heinoldt.* $60/£38

MULHOLLAND, JOHN. Story of Magic. NY: Loring & Mussey, (1935). (Edges faded, bkpl, traces of bkpl removal.) Dj (worn, chipped). *Glenn.* $35/£22

MULHOLLAND, ROSA. Our Sister Maisie. Blackie, 1907. 1st ed. Lg 8vo. 383pp; 8 mono plts by G. Demain Hammond. Teg. Pict cl, gilt. (Spine sl faded), else VG. *Bookmark.* $32/£20

MULLAN, JOHN. Miners and Travellers' Guide to Oregon, Washington, Idaho, Montana, Wyoming, and Colorado.... NY: Wm. M. Franklin, 1865. 1st ed. 7.25x4.75. 163pp; lg fldg color litho map. (Tape-repaired tears to map; spine faded), else NF. Howes M885. *Pacific*.* $1,035/£647

MULLEN, STANLEY. Kinsmen of the Dragon. Chicago: Shasta, (1951). 1st ed. Subscriber copy, signed. Fine in dj. *Pacific*.* $127/£79

MULLER, CHARLES G. The Proudest Day. NY, (1960). 1st ed. (Bkpl partly torn out, some residue), o/w Fine in dj (sl worn). *Pratt.* $20/£13

MULLER, MARCIA. Edwin of the Iron Shoes. NY: David McKay/Ives Washburn, 1977. 1st ed. Signed. Fine in dj. *Mordida.* $150/£94

MUMBY, FRANK A. The Romance of Bookselling. Chapman & Hall, 1910. 1st ed. Frontis. Uncut. (Spine faded, sm nick to head.) *Forest.* $61/£38

MUMEY, NOLIE. Calamity Jane, 1852-1903. Denver, CO: Range, 1950. 1st ed. One of 200 signed. Bds, leather, pict label pasted on. VF in glassine dj. Howes M888. *Labordo.* $450/£281

MUMEY, NOLIE. Creede. Denver, CO: Artcraft, 1949. 1st ed. One of 500 numbered, signed. Pict cl. NF in dj. Howes M890. *Labordo.* $135/£84

MUMEY, NOLIE. Early Mining Laws of Buckskin Joe—1859. Boulder, CO, 1961. One of 500 signed. Fine. *Wantagh.* $25/£16

MUMEY, NOLIE. John Williams Gunnison. Denver: Artcraft, 1955. One of 500 numbered. Signed, inscribed. Fldg map. (Lt worn, soiled), else VG. *Dumont.* $100/£63

MUMEY, NOLIE. Legends of Images. Denver: Range, 1980. One of 100 signed, numbered. Wraps bound w/leather tie. (Blemish to rear wrap, lt soiled), else NF. *Dumont.* $100/£63

MUMEY, NOLIE. March of the First Dragoons to the Rocky Mountains in 1835. Denver: Eames Bros, 1957. One of 350 signed, numbered. Sm folio. Lg fldg map. VG (bkpl; binding fragile, shelfworn). *Dumont.* $125/£78

MUMEY, NOLIE. Nathan Addison Baker (1843-1934) Pioneer Journalist, Teacher, Printer, Stockman, Founder of Early Journalism in Wyoming.... Denver: Old West, 1965. 1st ed. One of 500 signed. 5 facs in rear pocket. Cream cl, brn leather lettering pieces. Fine. *House.* $55/£34

MUMEY, NOLIE. Poker Alice, Alice Ivers, Duffield, Tubbs, Huckert (1851-1930). Denver, CO: Artcraft, 1951. 1st ed. One of 500 numbered, signed. Pict bds. NF in glassine dj. *Labordo.* $250/£156

MUMEY, NOLIE. Professor Oscar J. Goldrick and His Denver. Denver: Sage Books, (1959). VG in wraps. *Perier.* $15/£9

MUMEY, NOLIE. The Saga of 'Auntie' Stone and Her Cabin. Boulder: Johnson Pub Co, 1964. One of 500. Signed. 22 plts (1 fldg). Unopened. Full linen, spine/cvr labels. Fine. *Pacific*.* $75/£47

MUMEY, NOLIE. Wyoming Bullwhacker. Denver, 1976. 1st ed. Ltd to 150 numbered, signed. Fine in dj (tattered). *Woolson.* $75/£47

MUMFORD, LEWIS. The Culture of Cities. Secker & Warburg, 1938. 1st Eng ed. 32 b/w photo plts. Pub's cl. *Sotheran.* $80/£50

MUMMERY, A. F. My Climbs in the Alps and Caucasus. T. Fisher Unwin, 1908. 2nd ed, 4th imp. 11 plts. Leather spine labels. (Fr joint cracked, labels sl rubbed), o/w Very Nice. *Hollett.* $296/£185

MUNARI, BRUNO. Animals for Sale. NY: World, 1957. 1st Amer ed. Lg 4to. Cl-backed color pict bds. (Few mks), o/w Clean. *Reisler.* $150/£94

MUNARI, BRUNO. The Birthday Present. Cleveland: World, 1959. 1st Amer ed. Lg 4to. Cl-backed color illus bds (few mks). *Reisler.* $125/£78

MUNARI, BRUNO. Bruno Munari's Zoo. Cleveland: World, 1963. 1st ed. 8.75x11. 48pp. Fine. *Cattermole.* $60/£38

MUNDE, PAUL F. Minor Surgical Gynecology: A Manual of Uterine Diagnosis and Lesser Technicalities of Gynecologic.... NY, 1880. 381pp. (Lt cvr spotting) o/w VG. *Doctor's Library.* $100/£63

MUNDY, GODFREY CHARLES. Our Antipodes. London: Richard Bentley, 1852. 1st ed. 3 vols. 8vo. 15 plts. (Marginal browning to plts, text; feps browned, bkpl.) 1/2 calf, marbled bds (sl worn, spines cracking). *Edwards.* $560/£350

MUNDY, GODFREY CHARLES. Our Antipodes. London, 1855. 3rd ed. vii,637pp; 8 sepia plts. Blind-emb cl. (Marginal stains to plts, shaken, several sigs tender; cl worn, stained.) *Edwards.* $80/£50

MUNDY, RODNEY. Narrative of Events in Borneo and Celebes, down to the Occupation of Labuan. London, 1848. 2 vols. Frontisport, 5 maps, 17 plts. Early 1/2 calf. (Sm lib stamps; needs rebinding.) *Swann*.* $373/£233

MUNDY, RODNEY. Narrative of Events in Borneo and Celebes, down to the Occupation of Labuan: From the Journal of James Brooke. John Murray, 1848. 2 vols. Engr frontisport, 5 fldg engr maps (1 colored), 5 tinted litho plts. (Sl discolored.) Partly uncut. Recent cl. *Sotheby's*.* $368/£230

MUNDY, TALBOT. Cock O' the North. Indianapolis, (1929). 1st ed. Fine in VG dj (soiled). *Mcclintock.* $165/£103

MUNDY, TALBOT. The Gunga Sahib. NY: D. Appleton, 1934. 1st ed, 1st ptg w/(1) at bottom of p303. (Spine sl dknd), else VG in dj (sl foxed, spine stained, ends chipped, flap creases dknd). *Pacific*.* $69/£43

MUNDY, TALBOT. Gup Bahadur. Hutchinson, 1930. 1st ed. VG- (lt soiled). *Fine Books.* $50/£31

MUNDY, TALBOT. Jimgrim and Allah's Peace. NY: D. Appleton-Century, 1936. 1st ed. Variant pub's binding of brn cl, spine panel stained in black, gold lettering. NF in dj (spine head chipped). *Pacific*.* $58/£36

MUNDY, TALBOT. King—of the Khyber Rifles. Indianapolis: Bobbs Merrill, (1916). 1st ed. Frontis. Gilt olive cl. VG (extrems sl rubbed). *Reese.* $85/£53

MUNDY, TALBOT. Om: The Secret of Ahbor Valley. Indianapolis: Bobbs-Merrill, (1924). 1st ed. (Extrems sl torn), else Fine in VG dj (2 tears, few extrem chips). *Pacific*.* $115/£72

MUNDY, TALBOT. Purple Pirate. Hicksville: Gnome, (1959). 1st ed thus. NF in VG+ dj (sm chip to cpine corner). *Other Worlds.* $40/£25

MUNDY, TALBOT. Tros of Samothrace. Hicksville: Gnome, (1958). 1st ed thus. NF in VG+ dj (lt edgeworn). *Other Worlds.* $60/£38

MUNDY, TALBOT. The Winds of the World. Indianapolis, (1917). 1st ed. (Fep removed), else VG. *Mcclintock.* $22/£14

MUNDY, TALBOT. The Winds of the World. Cassell, 1916. 1st ed. VG+. *Fine Books.* $60/£38

MUNK, JOSEPH A. Arizona Sketches. NY: Grafton, 1905. 1st ed. Pict cl (sm stain). VG. *Labordo.* $100/£63

MUNK, JOSEPH A. History of Arizona Literature. N.p., 1925. (Lt browned, worn), else VG. *Dumont.* $50/£31

MUNK, JOSEPH A. Story of the Munk Library of Arizoniana. L.A.: Times-Mirror, 1927. Inscribed. 5 full-pg photo illus. (News clipping taped fep; spot on fr cvr.) *Dawson.* $35/£22

MUNK, JOSEPH A. Story of the Munk Library of Arizoniana. L.A.: Times-Mirror, 1927. 1st ed. NF in glassine dj, housed in a box. *Labordo.* $65/£41

MUNKACSI, MARTIN. Nudes. NY: Greenberg, 1951. 1st ed. NF in dj (extrems sl rubbed). *Smith.* $200/£125

MUNNINGS, A. J. Pictures of Horses and English Life. London: Eyre & Spottiswoode, 1927. 1st ed. 28 mtd color plts, guards. Teg. (Names, hinge cracking in middle w/some pp loose; sl soiled), else VG. *Pacific*.* $230/£144

MUNNINGS, A. J. Pictures of Horses and English Life. London, 1927. Lg 4to. Mtd color plts, guards. Aeg. (Sl worn.) *Oinonen*.* $550/£344

MUNRO, ALICE. Friend of My Youth. NY, 1980. 1st ed. Fine in Fine dj. *Warren.* $40/£25

MUNRO, GEORGE C. Birds of Hawaii. Honolulu, 1944. 1st ed. 20 color plts. Grn cl, pict bds (edgeworn). VG. *Larry Price.* $95/£59

MUNRO, HECTOR H. The Rise of the Russian Empire. Grant Richards, 1900. 1st Eng ed, 1st bk. 3 maps. Teg. VG (eps browned, top edge dusty; fr cvr sl soiled, cvrs dusty, sl mkd, edges rubbed). *Ulysses.* $312/£195

MUNROE, KIRK. The Golden Days of '49. NY: Dodd, Mead, (1889). Silver-dec pict cl. (Cvrs sl faded), else VG. *Pacific*.* $138/£86

MUNSELL, A. H. A Grammar of Color. Mittineague, MA: Strathmore Paper, 1921. 1st ed. 19 fld-out color sheets. Cl spine, paper bds. (2 bkpls; spine dull, sl worn; bds lt soiled), else Very Nice. *Turtle Island.* $100/£63

MUNSON, EDWARD. The Principles of Sanitary Tactics: A Handbook.... Ft Leavenworth, KS, 1911. 1st ed. 2 lg fldg maps in pockets. *Fye.* $75/£47

MUNSON, JOHN W. Reminiscences of a Mosby Guerrilla. NY: Moffat, Yard, 1906. 1st ed. Frontisport. Grn cl. (Inscrip dated 1920; spine sl faded), else VG. *Chapel Hill.* $175/£109

MUNSON, MYRON. 1637-1887: The Munson Record. New Haven, 1895. 1st ed. 2 vols. 1235pp. Fine set. *New Hampshire**. $80/£50

MUNZ, LUDWIG. Bruegel. The Drawings. London, 1961. Complete ed. Good+ in dj. *Washton.* $85/£53

MUNZ, LUDWIG. A Critical Catalogue of Rembrandt's Etchings. Vol 2 only (of 2). Phaidon, 1952. 1st ed. (Ex-lib, few stamps.) *Hollett.* $80/£50

MURCHINSON, R. I. The Silurian System, Founded on Geological Researches in the Countries of Salop, Hereford...with Description of the Coal-Fields and Overlying Formations. London, 1839. 2 parts, 1 vol. Roy 4to. xxxii,768pp; 14 litho plts (3 hand-colored, 2 fldg); 31 plts, 9 horizontal sections, hand-colored, fldg; 3 plain maps. Lg hand-colored map in 3 sections of the Silurian Region, linen backed in separate slip case. Recent 1/2-calf. Good. *Henly.* $3,168/£1,980

MURCHISON, CHARLES. Clinical Lectures on Diseases of the Liver, Jaundice and Abdominal Dropsy. NY, 1877. 2nd ed. 644pp. *Fye.* $150/£94

MURCHISON, CHARLES. A Treatise on the Continued Fevers of Great Britain. London, 1873. 2nd ed. 729pp. (Lacks feps, two stamps erased from tp w/thinning of paper and a small perforation.) *Fye.* $150/£94

MURCHISON, R. Figures of the Silurian Fossils. London: John Murray, 1872. 5th ed. 41 plts, fldg color map. Good (edge-worn). *Blake.* $75/£47

MURDOCH, IRIS. An Accidental Man. Chatto, 1971. 1st UK ed. Signed. NF in dj (price-clipped). *Williams.* $56/£35

MURDOCH, IRIS. The Bell. Chatto, 1958. 1st UK ed. Signed. VG in dj (browned, spine sl worn). *Williams.* $120/£75

MURDOCH, IRIS. Bruno's Dream. Chatto, 1969. 1st UK ed. Signed. Fine in NF dj (price-clipped). *Williams.* $72/£45

MURDOCH, IRIS. A Fairly Honourable Defeat. London, 1970. 1st Eng ed. Very Nice in dj. *Clearwater.* $40/£25

MURDOCH, IRIS. The Good Apprentice. London, 1985. 1st Eng ed. Signed. Nice (spine sl creased, sl rubbed) in dj. *Clearwater.* $64/£40

MURDOCH, IRIS. The Message to the Planet. London, 1989. 1st Eng ed. Signed. NF in dj. *Clearwater.* $72/£45

MURDOCH, IRIS. Nuns and Soldiers. Chatto, 1980. 1st ed. Signed, inscribed presentation. (Spine sl creased), else NF in dj. *Any Amount.* $64/£40

MURDOCH, IRIS. The Sacred and Profane Love Machine. London, 1974. 1st Eng ed. Nice (spine sl creased) in dj. *Clearwater.* $40/£25

MURDOCH, IRIS. Sartre. Bowes & Bowes, 1953. 1st UK ed, 1st bk. Signed. Fine in VG dj. *Williams.* $216/£135

MURDOCH, IRIS. Something Special. Helsinki: Eurographica, 1990. One of 350 numbered, signed. Fine in dj. *Ulysses.* $104/£65

MURDOCH, IRIS. The Time of the Angels. London, 1966. 1st Eng ed. Very Nice (fr cvr sl bumped) in dj (1 flap sl creased). *Clearwater.* $40/£25

MURDOCH, IRIS. Under the Net. Viking, 1954. 1st ed. (Corners sl bumped), else Fine in NF dj (spine extrems lt worn). *Fine Books.* $225/£141

MURDOCH, IRIS. The Unicorn. London: C&W, 1963. 1st ed. Fine in dj. *Hermitage.* $50/£31

MURDOCH, J. Microscopical Determination of the Opaque Minerals. NY: Wiley, c1916. 1st ed, 1st thousand. VG. *Blake.* $55/£34

MURDOCH, W. G. BURN. From Edinburgh to the Antarctic. London, 1894. 1st ed. 8vo. vii,366pp; 2 maps (1 fldg). Silvered pict cl. VF. *Maggs.* $1,200/£750

MURDOCH, W. G. BURN. Modern Whaling and Bear-Hunting. London: Seeley, Service, 1917. VG. *High Latitude.* $100/£63

MURDOCK, A. Light Without a Wick. A Century of Gas-Lighting, 1792-1892. Glasgow: Ptd at University Press, 1892. 1st ed. Frontis, 64pp. Blue/black cl (extrems sl rubbed), gilt. *Young.* $67/£42

MURO, AMADO. The Collected Stories of Amado Muro. Austin: Thorp Springs, 1979. 1st ed. Fine in dj. *Lame Duck.* $45/£28

MURPHY, BAILEY SCOTT. English and Scottish Wrought Iron-work. Edinburgh, 1904. Folio. 80 plts. (Shelfworn.) *Oinonen**. $160/£100

MURPHY, D. F. Presidential Election, 1864. NY: Baker & Godwin, 1864. 1st ed. 94pp (emb stamp tp, spot). Sewn (lacking wrappers?). *M & S.* $250/£156

MURPHY, JOHN McLEOD and W. N. JEFERS, JR. Nautical Routine and Stowage. NY: Spear, 1849. 1st ed. Brn gilt-dec cl. VG (corners bumped). *American Booksellers.* $155/£97

MURPHY, P. C. Shadows of the Gallows. Caldwell: Caxton, 1928. 1st ed. Pict cl. Good- (extrems quite worn, fr hinge starting following blank prelim). *Baade.* $65/£41

MURPHY, ROBERT CUSHMAN. Logbook for Grace. Whaling Brig Daisy, 1912-1913. London: Robert Hale, 1948. Map. VG in dj (ragged). *Explorer.* $40/£25

MURPHY, STANLEY. Martha's Vineyard Decoys. Boston: Godine, 1978. 1st ed. Fine in dj. *Bowman.* $150/£94

MURPHY, THOMAS D. On Sunset Highways. Boston: Page, 1915. 1st ed. Fine. *Book Market.* $60/£38

MURPHY, THOMAS D. Three Wonderlands of the American West. Boston: L.C. Page, 1912. 1st ed. 16 color plts, 32 duogravure plts, 3 maps. Grn pict cl, gilt. (Extrems sl rubbed), else NF. *Pacific**. $52/£33

MURPHY, THOMAS D. Three Wonderlands of the American West. Boston, 1913. 2nd imp. Teg, untrimmed. Brn cl, gilt. (Spine ends sl rubbed), else VG+. *Five Quail.* $50/£31

MURPHY, WILLIAM. Anemia in Practice, Pernicious Anemia. Phila, 1939. 1st ed. *Fye.* $150/£94

Murray's Adventures in the Adirondacks. Boston: Fields, Osgood, (1869). 1st ed. Fldg map, ad brochure in fr pocket; lg fldg Colton's Map in rear pocket. Orange cl. (Soiled), else VG. *Pacific**. $138/£86

Murray's Ireland. London, 1912. 8th ed. Clean (lacks 1 sectional map). *Gretton.* $48/£30

Murray's Northern Cathedrals Part 1: York, Ripon, Carlisle. London, 1869. 1st ed. Good+ (cl sl spotted). *Gretton.* $11/£7

Murray's Scotland. London, 1903. 8th ed. VG. *Gretton.* $48/£30

MURRAY, ALBERT. Train Whistle Guitar. NY: McGraw-Hill, 1973. 1st ed, 1st bk. Fine in dj (spine corners sl worn). *Else Fine.* $60/£38

MURRAY, AMELIA M. Letters from the United States, Cuba and Canada. NY: Putnam, 1856. 1st Amer ed. 2 vols in 1. 402pp. NF. Howes M914. *Mott.* $200/£125

MURRAY, CHARLES AUGUSTUS. Travels in North America...1834, 1835, and 1836. NY: Harper, 1839. 1st Amer ed. 2 vols. 324; 247pp. Fair (spine ends worn). Howes M913. *Lien.* $150/£94

MURRAY, DAVID. The Cockney Columbus. London, 1898. 1st ed. xiv,292pp. (Spine faded.) *Mott.* $75/£47

MURRAY, DAVID. Some Letters of Robert Foulis. Glasgow: James Maclehose & Sons, 1917. 1 plt. Uncut. Orig ptd wrappers bound in. *Forest.* $48/£30

MURRAY, F. E. A Bibliography of Austin Dobson. Murray, 1900. Unopened. (Cvrs sl stained), o/w Very Clean. *Moss.* $29/£18

MURRAY, FLORENCE. The Negro Handbook. 1944. NY, 1944. 1st ptg. (Contemp inscrip.) *Swann*.* $69/£43

MURRAY, GEORGE GILBERT AIME. Greek Comic Verse. Oxford: B.H. Blackwell, 1886. 1st ed. 9,(1)pp. Untrimmed (few edges sl soiled). Ptd gray wrappers (sl soiled, foxed). *Blackwell's.* $64/£40

MURRAY, HUGH. Historical Account of Discoveries and Travels in Asia. Edinburgh, 1820. 3 engr maps. Mod lib buckram. (Ink lib stamps.) *Swann*.* $80/£50

MURRAY, HUGH. Historical Account of Discoveries and Travels in Asia. Edinburgh: Constable/Longman, Hurst, Rees, Orme, & Brown, 1820. 1st ed. 3 vols. xvi,518; viii,526; viii,546pp; 4 lg fldg maps. Later 19th-cent black pebbled calf, grn marbled bds (sl scuffed). *Karmiole.* $350/£219

MURRAY, HUGH. Historical Account of Discoveries and Travels in North America. London: Longman, Rees et al, 1829. 2 vols. xi,530; vii,556pp (lacks 1/2-titles); fldg map (folds repaired). Full contemp calf (spine heads chipped). Howes M914. *Adelson.* $375/£234

MURRAY, J. OGDEN. The Immortal Six Hundred. Roanoke, VA: Stone Ptg, 1911. 2nd ed. Frontisport. Lt blue cl. VG (bkpl, sig; lt soiled). *Chapel Hill.* $150/£94

MURRAY, JAMES and GEORGE MARSTON. Antarctic Days: Sketches of the Homely Side of Polar Life by Two of Shackleton's Men. London: Andrew Melrose, 1913. Trade ed. Good+ (sl foxed; spine sl browned). *Explorer.* $480/£300

MURRAY, JAMES (ed). A New English Dictionary. Oxford: Clarendon, 1888-1933. 13 vols. Folio. Teg. Pub's 1/2 roan, gilt spines. (Bkpl.) *Sotheby's*.* $1,104/£690

MURRAY, JAMES ERSKINE. A Summer in the Pyrenees. John Macrone, 1837. 2nd ed. 2 vols. xii,341; viii,312pp; 12 engr plts. Orig grn pub's cl, blind-stamped/gilt. (Later eps, few plts lt browned), o/w Good set. *Sotheran.* $317/£198

MURRAY, JOHN TUCKER. English Dramatic Companies, 1558-1642. London: Constable, 1910. 1st ed. 2 vols. Teg. Fine in VG-djs (spines, extrems browned, spine ends chipped). *Pacific*.* $75/£47

MURRAY, LIEUTENANT. Fanny Campbell, the Female Pirate Captain. Boston: F. Gleason, 1845. 1st ed. (5)-100pp; 4 woodcut plts. Orig hand-colored ptd wrappers. Fine in morocco-backed clamshell box. *Lefkowicz.* $350/£219

MURRAY, LINDLEY. Introduction to the English Reader. Georgetown, DC: Joseph Milligan, 1812. 1st Amer ed. xviii,19-212pp + 4pp ads (lacks fep, paper tanned, closed tears, lt damp mks, ink drops). Full leather (chipped, affecting morocco label; worn, section at rear showing through to bds). *Connolly.* $50/£31

MURRAY, LOIS L. Incidents of Frontier Life. Goshen, IN: Ev. United Mennonite Pub House, 1880. 274pp; 2 ports. Grn cl, gilt. Good (etched, frayed, foxed). Howes M918. *Bohling.* $250/£156

MURRAY, R. The Gypsies of the Border. Galashiels: Ronald C. Hodges, 1983. One of 200. Orig wrappers. VG. *Hollett.* $32/£20

MURRAY, ROBERT A. The Army on the Powder River. (Bellevue, NE: Old Army Press, 1969.) 1st collected ed. One of 200 signed by Murray & pub. Blue cl. Fine. *Harrington.* $50/£31

MURRAY, ROBERT A. Military Posts in the Powder River Country of Wyoming 1865-1894. Lincoln, (1969). 2nd ptg. VG+ in dj. *Pratt.* $45/£28

MURRAY, ROBERT A. (ed). Fort Laramie: 'Visions of a Grand Old Post.' (Ft. Collins, CO): Old Army, (1974). 1st ed. One of 250. Signed by Murray, Merrill J. Mattes & Gordon S. Chappell (contributors). Fine in dj. *Pacific*.* $69/£43

MURRAY, ROBERT H. Science and Scientists in the Nineteenth Century. London: Sheldon Press, 1925. VG (sl worn). *Bookcell.* $30/£19

MURRAY, THOMAS. The Literary History of Galloway. Edinburgh: Waugh & Innes, 1832. 2nd ed. vii,348pp (few spots, mks, stamps). Orig cl (sl mkd, neatly rebacked, retains most of orig paper label). *Hollett.* $104/£65

MURRAY, THOMAS. Pitcairn. London, (1853). 1st ed. Frontis, xiv,414,(4)ads pp; chart, 16 plts. Pict cl, gilt. (Dust soiled.) *Maggs.* $280/£175

MURRAY, W. H. The Companion Guide to the West Highlands of Scotland. Collins, 1972. VG in dj. *Hollett.* $32/£20

MURRAY, W. H. The Hebrides. Heinemann, 1975. 18 plts, 15 maps. VG in dj. *Hollett.* $40/£25

MURRAY, W. H. Mountaineering in Scotland. Dent, 1947. 1st ed. (Edges worn.) *Hollett.* $48/£30

MURRAY, W. H. Rock Climbs—Glencoe and Ardgour. Edinburgh, 1949. 1st ed. 22 maps, diagrams. (Cl sl faded.) *Hollett.* $19/£12

MURRAY, W. H. The Story of Everest. J.M. Dent, 1953. 24 plts, 14 maps. (Extrems sl rubbed.) *Hollett.* $48/£30

MURRAY, W. H. H. The Perfect Horse. Boston: Osgood, 1873. 1st ed. 480pp; 14 full-pg engrs. Pict, gilt cl. VG. *Mikesh.* $60/£38

MURRAY, W. H. H. The Perfect Horse. Boston, 1873. 1st ed. 480pp. (Name label; 1/2-inch tear spine top), else VG. *King.* $75/£47

MURRAY-OLIVER, ANTHONY (comp). Captain Cook's Artists in the Pacific, 1769-1779. (Christchurch, NZ): Avon Fine Prints Ltd, 1969. One of 2000. 3/4 leather, cl. Fine in slipcase (faded). *Pacific*.* $150/£94

MURRELL, WILLIAM. A History of American Graphic Humor. Volume I, 1747-1865. NY: Whitney Museum of American Art, 1933. 1st ed. White bds, tan buckram. Good (edges sl rubbed) in dj (sl worn, few sm tears, sl dusty, chipped). *Baltimore*.* $25/£16

MURRELL, WILLIAM. Nitro-Glycerine as a Remedy for Angina Pectoris. Detroit, 1882. 1st Amer ed. 78pp. *Fye.* $300/£188

MURRELL, WILLIAM. What to Do in Cases of Poisoning. NY, 1884. 2nd ed. 108pp. (Sl marginal notations, underlining.) *Fye.* $50/£31

MURRY, JOHN MIDDLETON. Wrap Me Up in My Aubusson Carpet. NY, 1924. One of 500. NF. *Polyanthos.* $25/£16

MUSCATINE, DORIS et al (eds). The University of California/Sotheby Book of California Wines. Univ of CA, 1990. 1st ed. Fine in dj. *Book Market.* $70/£44

MUSE, BEN. The Memoirs of a Swine in the Land of Kultur, or, How It Felt to Be a Prisoner of War. Durham: Seeman Printery, 1919. Frontis. Good in ptd wrappers (soiled, worn). *Brown.* $30/£19

MUSES, C. A. (ed). Aspects of the Theory of Artificial Intelligence. NY: Plenum, 1962. 1st ed. Fine in dj. *Glaser.* $100/£63

MUSGRAVE, GEORGE C. To Kumassi with Scott. London: Wightman, 1896. 1st ed. Frontis, vi,216,(6)ads pp; map, 17 plts. Red pebble cl, gilt. VG (sl soiled, loose). *Morrell.* $200/£125

MUSIL, ROBERT. Five Women. NY: Delacorte, 1966. 1st ed. NF (lt soiled) in NF dj (stain visible on verso). *Beasley.* $85/£53

MUSIL, ROBERT. The Man Without Qualities. Eithne Wilkins & Ernst Kaiser (trans). London: Martin Secker & Warburg, 1953-1960. 1st Eng ed. 3 vols. VG set (top edges sl spotted; spine ends sl bumped) in djs (sl nicked, mkd). *Ulysses.* $400/£250

MUSTARDE, JOHN CLARK (ed). Plastic Surgery in Infancy and Childhood. Phila: W.B. Saunders, 1971. (Sig.) *Weber.* $100/£63

MUYBRIDGE, EADWEARD. The Human Figure in Motion. NY, 1955. 196 plts. Dj. *Fye.* $75/£47

My Book of Mother Goose Nursery Rhymes. London: Raphael Tuck & Sons, (1927). 1st ed. 4to. 12 full-pg color plts by Jennie Harbour. Cl-backed color pict bds (edgeworn, rubbed, sm repaired spine tear). *Reisler.* $385/£241

My Dog Friends. London: Hodder & Stoughton, (1913). 1st ed. 8vo. (xix),3-326pp; 12 mtd color plts by Maud Earl. Dk blue cl, gilt, onlaid pict label to upper cvr. *Sotheran.* $205/£128

My First Alphabet. (Little Folk Series.) NY: McLoughlin Bros, (ca 1870). 12mo. 6pp + alphabet. Good in color paper wrappers (margins worn, sm spine split). *Reisler.* $55/£34

My Pets Pop-Up Pictures. London: Juvenile Productions, n.d. (1948). 19x25 cm. 4 dbl-pg pop-ups. VG. *Bookfinders.* $45/£28

My Picture Scrap Book. London: Ernest Nister, ca 1880. Sm folio. 60pp (few sigs loose). Cl-backed pict chromolitho bds (edges scuffed, sl worn, soiled). Good. *Baltimore*.* $100/£63

My Pop-Out Book of Little Red Riding Hood. London: Purnell, 1970. 4 dbl-pg pop-ups. Glazed pict bds. VG. *Bookfinders.* $40/£25

MYDANS, CARL. Carl Mydans, Photojournalist. NY: Harry N. Abrams, 1985. 1st ed. Fine in dj. *Cahan.* $50/£31

MYER, JESSE. Life and Letters of Dr. William Beaumont. St. Louis, 1939. VG in dj (soiled). *Doctor's Library.* $75/£47

MYERS, BERNARD S. (ed). McGraw-Hill Dictionary of Art. NY, (1970). 5 vols. (Sl worn.) Slipcase. *Oinonen*.* $130/£81

MYERS, CHARLES E. Memoirs of a Hunter. Davenport, WA: The Author, (1948). 1st ed. Fine in dj (worn, torn). *Perier.* $60/£38

MYERS, FRANK. Soldiering in Dakota, Among the Indians, in 1863-4-5. Pierre, SD: State Hist Soc, 1936. Rpt. Sheet inserted. VG in ptd wraps. Howes M929. *Bohling.* $45/£28

MYERS, JOHN BERNARD (ed). The Poets of the New York School. (NY: Univ of PA, 1969.) 1st ed. NF in dj. *Pacific*.* $29/£18

MYERS, JOHN. The Alamo. NY: E.P. Dutton, 1948. 1st ed. Signed. NF in dj. *Labordo.* $65/£41

MYERS, JOHN. The Death of the Bravos. Boston, (1962). 1st ed. Blind-stamped cl. NF in VG + dj. *Sagebrush.* $40/£25

MYERS, JOHN. The Death of the Bravos. Boston: little, Brown, 1962. 1st ed. NF in VG dj. *Connolly.* $35/£22

MYERS, JOHN. Doc Holliday. Boston: Little, Brown, 1955. 1st ed. NF in dj (creased). *Labordo.* $55/£34

MYERS, JOHN. Print in a Wild Land. GC, 1967. Good in dj. *Dumont.* $25/£16

MYERS, MAX. Ours to Hold It High. Washington, 1947. 1st ed. VG. *Clark.* $125/£78

MYERS, ROBERT M. (ed). The Children of Pride: a True Story of Georgia and the Civil War. New Haven: Yale, 1972. 1st ed. VG in dj. *Woolman.* $60/£38

MYERS, VIRGINIA. This Land I Hold. Indianapolis, (1950). 1st ed. VG in Good + dj (edges chipped, torn). *Sagebrush.* $40/£25

MYERS, WALTER DEAN. Fallen Angels. NY: Scholastic, (1988). 1st ed. Fine in Fine dj. *Agvent.* $75/£47

MYERSON, JOEL. Ralph Waldo Emerson: A Descriptive Bibliography. Pittsburgh: Univ of Pittsburgh, 1982. 1st ed. Navy cl, gilt. NF (sl rubbed). *Baltimore*.* $70/£44

MYLNE, ROBERT SCOTT. The Master Masons to the Crown of Scotland. Edinburgh: Scott & Ferguson/Burness, 1893. Folio. Color frontis, xviii,308pp. Teg. Orig buckram, beveled bds (sl rubbed, faded, rear bd lt creased), gilt. VG (joints cracking). *Hollett.* $200/£125

MYLONAS, GEORGE E. Ancient Mycenae, the Capital City of Agamemnon. Princeton: Princeton Univ, 1957. (Bottom edge sl spotted.) Dj. *Archaeologia.* $50/£31

MYRICK, DAVID F. Railroads of Nevada and Eastern California. Berkeley, CA, 1962/1963. 1st ed. 2 vols. Fldg map vol 1. Pict eps. NF in VG + djs. *Sagebrush.* $160/£100

MYRICK, HERBERT. Cache la Poudre, the Romance of a Tenderfoot in the Days of Custer. NY, 1915. 1st trade ed. Dec cvrs. (Blindstamp, #; rear hinge reinforced, cvr spotted.) *Heinoldt.* $50/£31

MYRICK, HERBERT. Cache la Poudre. NY: OJ, 1905. One of 500 bound in 'Indian smoke tanned buckskin' w/a fringe. (Some tipped-in illus corners creased), else NF. Howes M935. *Dumont.* $550/£344

Myrtilla Miner. A Memoir. (By Ellen M. O'Connor.) Boston/NY: Houghton, Mifflin, 1885. 1st ed. 129pp; port. (Ex-lib.) *M & S.* $225/£141

N

NABOKOV, PETER. Tijerina and the Court House Raid. Albuquerque, 1970. 2nd ed, rev. Good in dj. *Dumont.* $35/£22

NABOKOV, VLADIMIR (trans). The Song of Igor's Campaign. NY: Vintage Books, (1960). Pb orig. NF in wrappers. *Between The Covers.* $125/£78

NABOKOV, VLADIMIR. The Annotated Lolita. Alfred Appel, Jr. (ed). NY: McGraw-Hill, (1970). 1st ed. Fine in dj. *Jaffe.* $150/£94

NABOKOV, VLADIMIR. Bend Sinister. NY: Henry Holt, (1947). 1st ed. Fine in dj (sm nick). *Captain's Bookshelf.* $250/£156

NABOKOV, VLADIMIR. Despair. NY, (1966). 1st Amer ed. Dj (price-clipped, few sm tears). *Swann*.* $149/£93

NABOKOV, VLADIMIR. The Eye. NY, 1965. 1st Amer ed. Fine in dj (sm tear). *Polyanthos.* $35/£22

NABOKOV, VLADIMIR. The Gift. NY: Putnam, 1963. 1st ed in English. NF in VG + dj. *Lame Duck.* $85/£53

NABOKOV, VLADIMIR. Lolita. NY: Putnam, (1955). 1st Amer ed. VG in dj (soiled, extrems sl chipped). *Pacific*.* $138/£86

NABOKOV, VLADIMIR. Lolita. Paris: Olympia, (1955). 1st ed, 1st issue w/price of '900 Francs.' 2 vols. Fine set in orig grn ptd wrappers (spines sl sunned). *Bromer.* $3,000/£1,875

NABOKOV, VLADIMIR. Lolita. London: Weidenfeld & Nicholson, (1959). 1st Eng ed. NF in dj (lt worn, spine top chipped). *Glenn.* $120/£75

NABOKOV, VLADIMIR. Lolita. London: Weidenfeld & Nicolson, 1959. 1st Eng ed. Fine in dj (sl nicked, rubbed). *Ulysses.* $152/£95

NABOKOV, VLADIMIR. Nabokov's Quartet. (NY): Phaedra, 1966. 1st ed. Mottled lt brn cl. Fine in dj (lt rubbed, worn, sm edge-tears). *Baltimore*.* $15/£9

NABOKOV, VLADIMIR. Nikolai Gogol. London: Editions Poetry London, 1947. 1st Eng ed. (Prelims foxed, paper sl acid, tanned; cvrs spotted.) Dj (foxed, sl torn). *Clearwater.* $128/£80

NABOKOV, VLADIMIR. Pale Fire. Weidenfeld, 1962. 1st UK ed. (Name; spine sl rolled), o/w VG + in VG dj (edges nicked, sl soiled). *Any Amount.* $48/£30

NABOKOV, VLADIMIR. Poems and Problems. NY: McGraw Hill, (1970). 1st ed. Fine in NF dj. *Robbins.* $45/£28

NABOKOV, VLADIMIR. The Real Life of Sebastian Knight. Norfolk: New Directions, (1941). 1st US ed, 2nd binding. Smooth red cl, ptd paper labels. Good (sl rubbed, top edge sl dusty). *Baltimore*.* $40/£25

NABOKOV, VLADIMIR. The Real Life of Sebastian Knight. London: Editions Poetry, 1945. 1st British ed. VG + in VG dj (shallow loss to spine head, 1-inch fr panel tear). *Lame Duck.* $175/£109

NADEAU, MAURICE. The History of Surrealism. NY: Macmillan, (1965). 1st ed in English. Fine in dj. *Turtle Island.* $45/£28

NADEAU, REMI. City-Makers. NY: Doubleday, 1948. 1st ed. Signed. Fine in VG dj. *Book Market.* $65/£41

NADEAU, REMI. Ghost Towns and Mining Camps of California. L.A.: Ward Ritchie, 1965. 1st ed. Yellow pict cl. (Inscrip), else VG in dj. *Parmer.* $35/£22

NADEAU, REMI. The Water Seekers. GC, 1950. 1st ed. Frontis, tp map. Pict eps. NF in VG dj. *Sagebrush.* $100/£63

NADEL, HENRI. Down the Red Lane. Blair Taylor (trans). Indianapolis: Bobbs-Merrill, (1930). 1st US ed. Blue cl. (Paper lt tanned), else NF in pict dj (long closed creased tear down lower joint, across spine). *Reese.* $50/£31

NAEF, WESTON J. The Collection of Alfred Stieglitz. NY: MMA/Viking, 1978. 1st ed. Frontis. VG in dj. *Cahan.* $100/£63

NAEGELE, FRANZ CARL. The Obliquely Contracted Pelvis, Containing Also an Appendix of the Most Important Defects of the Female Pelvis. NY: (Pynson Printers), 1939. Centennial ed. 16 litho plts. Cl-backed marbled bds, paper cvr label. (Spine ends, extrems sl rubbed), else VG. *Pacific*.* $46/£29

NAIPAUL, SHIVA. Beyond the Dragon's Mouth. Hamish Hamilton, 1984. 1st ed. Fine in dj. *Any Amount.* $29/£18

NAIPAUL, SHIVA. The Chip-Chip Gatherers. NY: Knopf, 1973. 1st ed. Fine in dj (sl rubbed). *Lenz.* $60/£38

NAIPAUL, SHIVA. The Chip-Chip Gatherers. London; Deutsch, 1973. 1st ed. VG in VG dj (top edge sl browned, sm closed tear at spine foot). *Virgo.* $88/£55

NAIPAUL, SHIVA. The Chip-Chip Gatherers. Deutsch, 1973. 1st UK ed. Fine in dj. *Williams.* $104/£65

NAIPAUL, SHIVA. Fireflies. (London): Deutsch, (1970). 1st ed, 1st bk. Fine in Fine dj. *Lenz.* $185/£116

NAIPAUL, SHIVA. Fireflies. Deutsch, 1970. 1st UK ed, 1st bk. VG in dj (price-clipped). *Williams.* $112/£70

NAIPAUL, SHIVA. Fireflies. NY: Knopf, 1971. 1st ed, 1st bk. Fine in dj (sl worn). *Lenz.* $85/£53

NAIPAUL, V. S. An Area of Darkness. Deutsch, 1964. 1st ed. Signed. NF in VG dj (sl rubbed, 2 closed tears, top edge sl creased). *Any Amount.* $176/£110

NAIPAUL, V. S. A Bend in the River. Deutsch, 1979. 1st ed. Fine in dj. *Any Amount.* $32/£20

NAIPAUL, V. S. A Congo Diary. Hollywood: Sylvester & Orphanos, 1980. Ltd to 330 signed. Fine dec cl. *Truepenny.* $100/£63

NAIPAUL, V. S. Guerillas. Deutsch, 1975. 1st UK ed. NF in dj (price-clipped). *Williams.* $35/£22

NAIPAUL, V. S. In a Free State. London, 1971. 1st Eng ed. Fine in dj. *Clearwater.* $72/£45

NAIPAUL, V. S. The Loss of El Dorado. NY, 1970. 1st Amer ed. (Blindstamp), else VG in dj. *King.* $30/£19

NAIPAUL, V. S. Miguel Street. Deutsch, 1959. 1st UK ed. VG in dj (spine sl faded). *Williams.* $456/£285

NAIPAUL, V. S. The Mystic Masseur. NY: Vanguard, 1959. 1st Amer ed. NF in VG + dj. *Warren.* $150/£94

NAIRN, J. A. Classical Hand-List. B. H. Blackwell (ed). Oxford: B.H. Blackwell, 1939. 2nd ed. (Hinges torn.) *Forest.* $48/£30

NAIRNE, SANDY (preface). Robert Mapplethorpe, 1970-1983. (London): Institute of Contemp Arts, 1983. 1st ed. 57 b/w photos. (Corner sl creased), else Fine in pict stiff wrappers. *Cahan.* $60/£38

NAITEH, STEVEN. Gene Davis. NY: Art Publishers, 1982. Folio. Fine in dj. *Metropolitan*.* $23/£14

NAITO, HATSUHO. Thunder Gods. Tokyo, (1982). 1st Amer ed. VG + in VG + dj. *Pratt.* $20/£13

NAKAMURA, TANIO. Contemporary Japanese-Style Painting. Mikio Ito (trans). NY, 1969. 1st US ed. Dj (lt soiled, chipped). *Edwards.* $40/£25

NAMORA, FERNANDO. Fields of Fate. NY: Crown, 1970. 1st ed in English. Fine in VG + dj (spine foot worn, verso dampstained). *Lame Duck.* $45/£28

NANSEN, FRIDTJOF. Farthest North. NY, 1897. 2 vols. 4 VG fldg maps in pockets vol 1. Dec cl (extrems sl worn). Contents VG. *New Hampshire*.* $80/£50

NANSEN, FRIDTJOF. Farthest North. Westminster, 1897. 1st ed. 2 vols. 16 color, 113 b/w plts, 4 fldg maps. Gilt dec cl (lt worn). *Kane*.* $120/£75

NANSEN, FRIDTJOF. Farthest North. Constable, 1897. 1st Eng ed. 2 vols. xiii,510; xiii,671pp; 4 fldg maps. Gilt-dec cl. VG. *Walcot.* $144/£90

NANSEN, FRIDTJOF. Farthest North. London: Constable, 1897. 1st ed. 2 vols. 4 fldg maps at rear. Blue pict cl (sl dampstained). Djs (worn, torn w/loss). *Christie's*.* $197/£123

NANSEN, FRIDTJOF. Farthest North. London: George Newnes, 1898. 2 vols in 1. xv,480;viii,456pp; color plt, fldg map. Contemp 1/2 calf (worn). VG. *Explorer.* $96/£60

NANSEN, FRIDTJOF. Farthest North. George Newnes, 1898. 2nd Eng ed. 2 vols. xv,480; viii,456pp. Marbled eps. Contemp dk blue 1/2 morocco, blue cl bds, raised bands, gilt. Good (spines sl rubbed). *Sotheran.* $205/£128

NANSEN, FRIDTJOF. The First Crossing of Greenland. H. M. Gepp (trans). Longmans, Green, 1910. Map. VG in 1/2 calf prize binding, gilt, morocco label. *Cox.* $40/£25

NANSEN, FRIDTJOF. Hunting and Adventure in the Arctic. London, 1925. (Lt foxed; tips, spine edges rubbed.) *Oinonen*.* $50/£31

NANTON, PAUL. Arctic Breakthrough. Toronto/Vancouver, Clarke, Irwin, 1970. Signed. Fldg map. Fine in dj. *Explorer.* $29/£18

NAOUM, PHOKION P. Nitroglycerine and Nitroglycerine Explosives. E.M. Symmes (trans). Balt: Williams & Wilkins, 1928. Navy blue cl. (Lt waterstain to outer margins 1st 100pp; fr hinge cracked, cvr lt soiled), else VG. *Weber.* $165/£103

Napa City and County Portfolio and Directory. Napa: H.A. Darms, (1908). 1st ed. 3/4 leather, red cl, gilt. (Spine worn, few chips), o/w VG. *Pacific*.* $489/£306

NAPIER, J. R. and P. H. Old World Monkeys. NY: Academic, 1970. 1st ed. Fine in VG dj. *Mikesh.* $60/£38

NAPPER, JOHN. The Sunlight Dialogues:...An Additional Set of Illustrations to the Novel by John Gardner. N.p.: Larcada Editions, 1972. 1st ed. One of 100. Numbered, titled, & signed on each litho. 13 orig lithos. Loose in cl portfolio, string ties. Fine. *Pacific*.* $115/£72

NARKISS, BEZALEL (ed). Armenian Art Treasures of Jerusalem. London, 1980. Good in dj. *Washton.* $75/£47

Narrative of the Campaigns of the British Army at Washington and New Orleans...in the Years 1814 and 1815.... (By George R. Gleig.) London, 1826. 2nd ed. Orig bds (rubbed, spine chipped). *Kane*.* $80/£50

Narrative of the Captivity and Sufferings of Benjamin Gilbert and His Family. Rptd & sold by James Phillips, 1790. 2nd Eng ed. 124pp (final ll sl spotted, sm label on tp verso). Old 1/2 calf (sm label wrapped over spine), gilt. *Hollett.* $224/£140

Narrative of the Sufferings of Massy Harbison, from Indian Barbarity...during the Years 1790, '91, '92, '93, '94. Communicated by Herself. (By Massy Harbison.) Pittsburgh, (PA): S. Engles, 1825. 1st ed. 18mo. 66pp (uniformly foxed, browned). Contemp calf-backed paper-cvrd bds (nearly detached). Hard cl tray case. Howes H179. *M & S.* $1,500/£938

NASATIR, A. P. (ed). Before Lewis and Clark: Documents Illustrating the History of Missouri, 1785-1804. St. Louis, 1952. 1st ed. 5 maps. 2 vols. Djs. *Ginsberg.* $250/£156

NASH, CHARLES EDWARD. Biographical Sketches of Gen. Pat Cleburne and Gen T. C. Hindman. Little Rock, AR: Tunnah & Pittard, 1898. 1st ed. 8vo. Frontis, 300pp. Black cl. (Cvrs sl spotted), else VG + . *Chapel Hill.* $575/£359

NASH, JAY ROBERT. Hustlers and Con Men. NY: Evans, 1976. 1st ed. Good in Good dj. *Connolly.* $22/£14

NASH, JOHN R. Mr. Cobden-Sanderson's Two-Handed Engine. (Leominster): Nine Elms Press, 1994. One of 350 signed. VF in blue-mauve dec wrappers. *Maggs.* $40/£25

NASH, JOHN. Poisonous Plants. Dr. A. W. Hill (ed). London: Frederick Etchells & Hugh MacDonald, 1927. One of 350 numbered. Folio. Uncut. Cl-backed bds, gilt. Fine (plts sl offset). *Maggs.* $520/£325

NASH, JOSEPH. Characteristics of British Palaces in the Olden Time. London: Nattali, n.d. (ca 1850?). Folio. 12 color litho plts, extra color pict tp. (Foxing.) Pub's cl (worn, soiled), later leather back. *Oinonen*.* $80/£50

NASH, JOSEPH. The Mansions of England in the Olden Time. Charles Holme (ed). Studio, 1934. New ed. VG in dec red cl. *Hadley.* $45/£28

NASH, JOSEPH. The Mansions of England in the Olden Time. J. Corbet Anderson (ed). London: Henry Sotheran, 1869-72. 2nd ed. 4 vols. Folio. 100 plts. Mod cl, gilt. (Lib #s on tp verso, bkpl, upper hinges tender, tps sl chipped, repaired, spotting; accession #s.) *Edwards.* $360/£225

NASH, OGDEN. Family Reunion. Boston: LB, 1951. 1st ed. VF in VF dj (lt pencil # rear cvr). *Between The Covers.* $125/£78

NASH, OGDEN. Good Intentions. Boston: LB, 1942. 1st ed. (Fep top corner clipped), else Fine in VF dj. *Between The Covers.* $125/£78

NASH, OGDEN. Parents Keep Out: Elderly Poems for Youngerly Readers. Boston: LB, 1951. 1st ed. VF in dj (manufacturing flaw, coating of dj unglazed bottom 1/2 inch), o/w VF. *Between The Covers.* $85/£53

NASH, OGDEN. The Private Dining Room. Boston: Little Brown, (1953). 1st ed. VF in VF dj. *Between The Covers.* $125/£78

NASH, OGDEN. Versus. Boston: LB, 1949. 1st ed. VF in VF dj. *Between The Covers.* $125/£78

NASH, PAUL. Outline: An Autobiography and Other Writings. London: Faber & Faber, 1949. 1st Eng ed. 2 color plts. VG (feps partly browned; fr cvr soiled, rear cvr sl mkd, cvrs sl bowed, spine ends sl bumped) in dj (chipped, rubbed, dusty, sl torn, creased, sl dknd). *Ulysses.* $104/£65

NASH, RAY. American Writing Masters and Copybooks. Boston, 1959. Uncut. (Text sl damp-wrinkled; lt worn, lt cvr stains.) Slipcase. *Oinonen*.* $40/£25

NASH, RAY. Printing as an Art: A History of the Society of Printers, Boston, 1905-1955. Cambridge: Harvard Univ, 1955. One of 1500. Fine in dj. *Truepenny.* $65/£41

NASMYTH, JAMES. James Nasmyth, Engineer. Samuel Smiles (ed). London: John Murray, 1885. xx,450pp; port. Old 1/2 calf, gilt (edges sl scraped; upper joint cracked). *Hollett.* $56/£35

NASON, LEONARD. Among the Trumpets. Boston/NY: Houghton Mifflin, 1932. 1st ed. Red cl. Nice (pencil erasure fep) in pict dj (spine sunned, sm tear top edge fr panel). *Reese.* $35/£22

NASON, LEONARD. A Corporal Once. GC: Doubleday, Doran, 1930. 1st ed. Brn cl. Fine in pict dj (old inner mend spine crown). *Reese.* $40/£25

NASON, LEONARD. The Man in the White Slicker. GC: Doubleday, Doran, 1929. 1st ed. Orange cl. NF in VG pict dj (sm creased edge tears, nicks). *Reese.* $35/£22

NASR, SEYYED HOSSEIN. Islamic Science: An Illustrated Study. London: World of Islam Festival, 1976. 1st ed. Folio. NF in dj. *Worldwide.* $95/£59

NASSAU, ROBERT HAMILL. Fetichism in West Africa. NY: Scribner, 1904. 1st ed. Black cl, gilt. VG. *Beasley.* $75/£47

National American Kennel Club Stud Book. Vol I—1878. St. Louis, 1879. *Swann*.* $126/£79

National Gallery Catalogues. London: National Gallery, 1958. 2 vols. Folio. 410 full-pg b/w plts, 24 color plts. Good + in djs (sl worn). *Washton.* $165/£103

Natural History of Birds. Concord, NH: Rufus Merrill, 1851. Merrill's Toys series. 12mo. 24pp + 1pg ad on rear cvr; 12 Fine wood engrs. Yellow pict paper wrappers. Good (ink sig fr cvr, pencil sig tp; lt cracking along spine, cvrs sl rubbed). *Hobbyhorse.* $100/£63

Natural History of British Birds. Alnwick: W. Davison, n.d. (ca 1815). 12mo. Frontis, 36pp; 34 VF engrs. Pict brn paper wrappers (sm chips at 2 edges); cvr reads: 32 engrs on wood. Fine. *Hobbyhorse.* $115/£72

Natural History of the Robin-Red-Breast to Which Is Added A Selection of Complimentary Verses, Addressed to His Serene Littleness.... (By Benjamin Tabart.) London: B. Tabart, 1808. 1st ed. 3.5x5.5. Hand-colored engr frontis, 54pp. Good in blue ptd paper wrappers (lt dusty). *Reisler.* $475/£297

Naturalist's Note Book for 1868. London: Reeves & Turner, 1868. Frontis, iv,382pp. Uncut. Emb cl, gilt. (Lib ink stamps, tp almost detached, lt browned, hinges cracked, upper hinge almost detached; joint splitting, spine head sl chipped.) *Edwards.* $32/£20

Nature's Own Book. (By Asenath Nicholson.) NY: Wilbur & Whipple, 1835. 1st ed. 12mo. 84pp (upper blank corner stained). Orig cl (faded, soiled). VG. *M & S.* $650/£406

NAUGHTON, BILL. One Small Boy. London: MacGibbon & Kee, 1957. 1st Eng ed. NF (edges sl spotted) in dj (sl dusty, creased; spine sl dknd, sm label remains rear panel). *Ulysses.* $72/£45

NAUGHTON. Kings of the Queensberry Realm...and an Account of the Invasion of Australian Boxers. Chicago: Continental, (1902). 1st ed. Pict cvr label. (Name; spine ends rubbed, spine lettering worn off, fr cvr sl stained), else VG. *Pacific*.* $75/£47

Naughty Boys (Aunt Oddamadodd Series). NY: McLoughlin Bros, (ca 1855). 8vo. 8pp (2pp w/marginal notes). Color pict wrappers (sig; spine resewn, dusty). *Reisler.* $225/£141

NAUMBURG, MARGARET. Psychoneurotic Art. NY: Grune & Stratton, 1953. Color frontis. (Cvr worn, lt soiled), else Sound. *Turtle Island.* $65/£41

NAUMBURG, MARGARET. Schizophrenic Art. NY: Grune & Stratton, 1950. 63 plts (9 color). VG in dj. *Turtle Island.* $55/£34

NAVILLE, EDOUARD. Ahnas el Medineh.... London: Kegan Paul, Trench, Trubner, Quaritch, 1894. 1st ed. Folio. (12),40,viii,35pp; 28 plts (8 fldg). Cl spine. (Ex-lib; edges rubbed, lib spine #), o/w VG. *Worldwide.* $65/£41

NAVILLE, EDOUARD. Bubastis (1887-1889). London: Kegan Paul, Trench, Trubner, Quaritch, 1891. 1st ed. Folio. vii,71pp; 54 plts (2 fldg). Cl spine. (Ex-lib; rubbed, sl shaken, spine ends frayed, lib spine #), o/w VG. *Worldwide.* $75/£47

NAVILLE, EDOUARD. The Festival-Hall of Osorkon II in the Great Temple of Bubastis (1887-1889). London: Kegan Paul, Trench, Trubner, 1892. 1st ed. Folio. viii,40pp; 39 plts (19 fldg). Cl spine. (Ex-lib; edges rubbed, spine ends frayed, lib spine #), o/w VG. *Worldwide.* $95/£59

NAVILLE, EDOUARD. The Shrine of Saft el Henneh and the Land of Goshen (1885). London: Trubner, 1887. 1st ed. Folio. (viii),26pp; 10 plts (6 fldg). (Rubbed, corners chewed, spine ends, edges frayed), o/w VG. *Worldwide.* $65/£41

NAYLOR, GLORIA. Bailey's Cafe. NY: Harcourt, Brace, 1992. 1st ed. Signed. Fine in Fine dj. *Unger.* $50/£31

NAYLOR, GLORIA. Linden Hills. NY, 1985. 1st ed. NF in NF dj. *Warren.* $40/£25

NAYLOR, GLORIA. Linden Hills. NY: Ticknor, 1985. 1st ed. Fine in Fine dj (sl rubbed). *Unger.* $75/£47

NAYLOR, GLORIA. The Women of Brewster Place. NY: Viking, 1982. 1st ed, 1st bk. NF (names) in NF dj (sm tear). *Unger.* $300/£188

NAYLOR, ROBERT and JOHN. From John O'Groats to Land's End. Caxton, 1916. Photogravure frontis. (Extrems sl worn.) *Hollett.* $240/£150

NAZAROFF, P. S. Hunted Through Central Asia. Malcolm Burr (trans). Edinburgh: Wm. Blackwood, 1932. 1st ed. 1/2-title, frontis. Maroon cl. (Sl foxed; spine head chipped.) *Morrell.* $56/£35

NEALE, FREDERICK ARTHUR. Narrative of a Residence in Siam. London: Office of the Nat'l Illus Library, 1852. Fronntis port, xiv,280pp + 4pp ads, add'l engr tp, map. Dec red cl (faded, spine extrems sl frayed). *Karmiole.* $100/£63

NEALE, JOHN PRESTON and EDWARD WEDLAKE BRAYLEY. The History and Antiquities of the Abbey Church of St. Peter, Westminster. Ptd for Hurst, Robinson, 1823. Lg paper copy. 2 vols. Folio. 2 engr add'l tps, 59 engr plts. Gilt edges. Contemp 1/2 morocco, gilt. (Sl spotting; sl rubbed.) *Sotheby's*. $368/£230

NEALE, R. The Medical Digest or Busy Practitioner's Vade-Me-cum. London, 1882. 2nd ed. (xi),643,lxxxiipp. Blind-stamped cl. (Ink inscrip; sl worn, spine sl torn, inner hinge sl cracked), o/w VG. *Whitehart.* $61/£38

NEALE, W. T. Cacti and Other Succulents. New Haven/Sussex, 1935. Red buckram. Fine. *Brooks.* $29/£18

NEARING, SCOTT. Black America. NY: Vanguard, 1929. 1st ed. VG + . *Beasley.* $100/£63

NEARING, SCOTT. War: Organized Destruction and Mass Murder by Civilized Nations. NY: Vanguard, (1931). 1st ed. Silver cl stamped in red. (Heavy offsetting from clipping to prelim), o/w VG in dec dj (lt dust-dknd, sm closed tear). *Reese.* $50/£31

NEBENZAHL, KENNETH. A Bibliography of Printed Battle Plans of the American Revolution. Chicago, 1975. Good in dj. *Dumont.* $25/£16

NEBENZAHL, KENNETH. A Bibliography of the Printed Battle Plans of the American Revolution, 1775-1795. Chicago: Univ of Chicago, (1975). 1st ed. VG in dj. *Pacific*. $75/£47

Nebraska. NY: Viking, 1939. 1st ed. NF in dj. *Labordo.* $75/£47

NECKER, CLAIRE. Four Centuries of Cat Books: a Bibliography, 1570 to 1970. Metuchen, NJ: Scarecrow, 1972. 1st ed. Grn cl. *Biscotti.* $125/£78

NEEDHAM, VIOLET. Adventures at Windsor Castle. Lutterworth, 1957. 1st ed. 8vo. David Walsh (illus). Blue bds. VG. *Bookmark.* $51/£32

NEEDHAM, VIOLET. Adventures at Windsor Castle. Lutterworth, 1957. 1st ed. VG in dj (sl worn). *Green Meadow.* $88/£55

NEEDHAM, VIOLET. The House of the Paladin. Collins, 1945. 1st ed. 8vo. Joyce Bruce (illus). 256pp. VG in pict dj. *Bookmark.* $42/£26

NEEDHAM, VIOLET. The Woods of Windri. Collins, 1944. 1st ed. 8vo. Joyce Bruce (illus). 255pp. Yellow cl. (Spine sl dusty), else VG in pict dj (tear, lacks piece from base). *Bookmark.* $38/£24

NEFF, BOSS. Some Experiences of Boss Neff in the Texas and Oklahoma Panhandle. (N.p.), 1968. 2nd ed. Fine in pict wraps. *Baade.* $85/£53

NEGRO ACTORS GUILD OF AMERICA. A Tribute to Marian Anderson. N.p.: The Guild, 1966. 1st ed. Port. VG + (stamp rear cvr) in spiral bound pict stiff-wraps. *Petrilla.* $35/£22

Negro Question. Attitude of the Progressive Party Toward the Colored Race. Colonel Roosevelt's Reply to a Query at the Progressive National Convention.... (NY: Mail & Express Job Print/Stoddard-Sutherland Press, 1912. 1st ed. Pamphlet. 8vo. 15pp. Orig ptd wrappers (sl discolored, old vertical fold). *M & S.* $600/£375

NEIDER, CHARLES. The Authentic Death of Hendry Jones. NY: Harper, 1956. 1st ed. Signed. NF in NF dj (edge-rubbed). *Unger.* $225/£141

NEIDER, CHARLES. Edge of the World. NY: Doubleday, 1974. Inscribed. Fine in dj. *Explorer.* $40/£25

Neighborhood Cookbook. Portland, OR: Council of Jewish Women, 1914. 2nd ed. (Old name, notes; spine ends sl rubbed), else VG. *Pacific*. $46/£29

NEIHARDT, JOHN G. Black Elk Speaks. NY: William Morrow, 1932. 1st ed. Inscribed presentation. (Sl soiled, spine ends frayed, corners rubbed), else VG. *Pacific*. $150/£94

NEIHARDT, JOHN G. Eagle Voice: An Authentic Tale of the Sioux Indians. London: Andrew Melrose, (1953). 1st British ed. NF in VG dj (corners chipped). *Authors Of The West.* $75/£47

NEIHARDT, JOHN G. The Lonesome Trail. NY, 1907. 1st ed. Frontis. Pict olive-grn cl (rear cvr w/ripples, signs of dampstain). *Swann*. $115/£72

NEIHARDT, JOHN G. The Song of the Indian Wars. NY: Macmillan, 1925. 1st ltd ed. One of 500. Signed. Fine in slipcase (top edge cracked, worn). *Labordo.* $185/£116

NEIHARDT, JOHN G. The Song of the Indian Wars. NY, 1928. Signed. (Spine dull, cvrs rubbed.) *King.* $22/£14

NEIHARDT, JOHN G. The Splendid Wayfaring. NY: Macmillan, 1920. 1st ed. Forest grn cl. (Name), else VG. *Five Quail.* $55/£34

NEILL, EDWARD D. Memoir of Rev. Patrick Copeland. Scribner, 1871. Inscribed w/als laid in. 93pp. Stiff paper cvr. Good. *Book Broker.* $75/£47

NEILL, JOHN R. Lucky Bucky in Oz. Chicago, (1942). 1st ed, 1st ptg in 16pp gatherings, in lt orange-tan cl w/monogram 'OZ' on spine. (Feps sl rubbed; spine tear.) *Kane*. $90/£56

NEILL, JOHN R. Lucky Bucky in Oz. Chicago: Reilly & Lee, (1942). 1st ed, 1st state. Spine title ptd in plain, unserified letters w/'OZ' as a stylized device; pub's spine imprint in semi-script, 'fancy' letters. 8.75x6.5. 289pp. B/w pict eps. Blue cl, pict cvr label. (Later hand-coloring to design on fep; spine sl faded), else NF. *Pacific*. $161/£101

NEILL, JOHN R. Lucky Bucky in Oz. London: Hutchinson's Books for Young People, (1945). 1st British ed. 8vo. 128pp. Red cl, black lettering. (Prelims foxed, clip in rep; sm spine tear.) Color pict dj (spine base chipped, sm spine tear.) *Reisler.* $350/£219

NEILL, JOHN R. The Scalawagons of Oz. Chicago: Reilly & Lee, (1941). 1st ed, 1st state, in 16-pg gatherings; title on spine ptd diagonally, w/the 'Scalawagons' hyphenated on 2 lines & w/'OZ' ptd as a stylized device. 8.75x6.5. 309pp. B/w pict eps. Lt grn cl, pict cvr label. (Name, dated 1941), else NF. *Pacific*. $219/£137

NEILL, JOHN R. The Scalawagons of Oz. Chicago, (1941). 1st ed, 1st ptg, in brick-red cl w/'Scala-Wagons' on spine hyphenated & on 2 lines. 1st issue dj (sm tear) w/'Scalawagons' misprinted 'Scallywagons' in list of titles on back flap. *Kane*. $400/£250

NEILL, JOHN R. The Wonder City of Oz. Chicago: Reilly & Lee, (1940). 1st ed. 16pg gatherings; the running titles on pp306-318 have the chapter # on the versos, the bk title on the rectos; the dbl-pg picture on pp(292)-(293) is ptd correctly. The later dj lists titles through 'The Hidden Valley of Oz' (1951) and is sl smaller than the bk. 8.75x6.5. 318pp. B/w pict eps. Red cl, pict cvr label. (Spine ends sl rubbed, rear hinge cracked), else VG. *Pacific*. $259/£162

NEILL, JOHN R. The Wonder City of Oz. Chicago: Reilly & Lee, (1940). 1st ed, mixed state (the running text at the top of pp306-318 is reversed but the dbl-pg illus at p292 is correctly placed). 4to. Brick red cl, color paste label. Nice. *Reisler.* $300/£188

NEILL, JOHN. Outlines of the Arteries: with Short Descriptions. Phila, 1852. 2nd ed. 28pp + 7 colored plts. *Fye.* $100/£63

NEILL, W. T. The Last of the Ruling Reptiles. NY: Columbia, 1971. 1st ed. Pict cl (few pen notes; sm edge nick rear bd), else VG + in VG + dj. *Mikesh.* $95/£59

NEILSON, CHARLES. An Original, Compiled and Corrected Account of Burgoyne's Campaign.... Albany, 1844. 1st ed. Lg fldg map at rear. (Spine head lt worn.) *Kane*.* $70/£44

NEISON, EDMUND. The Moon and the Condition and Configurations of Its Surface. London: Longmans, Green, 1876. 1st ed. xviii,576pp; 30 maps, plts and dwgs, 1 fldg. (Joints cracked, eps spotted; cl sl soiled, rubbed, spine ends worn.) *Hollett.* $120/£75

NELLA. Prince Babillon. London: T. Sealey Clark, (1907). 1st ed. 8vo. Charles Robinson (illus). xii,14-131,(v)pp. Teg, rest uncut. Gray cl, gilt. Very Clean. *Sotheran.* $205/£128

NELSON, BATTLING. Life, Battles and Career of Battling Nelson, Lightweight Champion of the World. Hegewisch, 1909. 1st ed. Inscribed, signed. Pict cl. NF. *Pacific*.* $288/£180

NELSON, BRUCE. Land of the Dacotahs. Minneapolis, (1946). 1st ed. VG in dj (lacks piece). *Woolson.* $40/£25

NELSON, BRUCE. Land of the Dacotahs. Minneapolis, 1946. 1st ed. Pict cl. (Sig; bindery crease upper corner 3pp), o/w Fine in dj (sl edgeworn). *Baade.* $45/£28

NELSON, BYRON. The Byron Nelson Story. (Cincinnati: Old Golf Shop, 1980.) 1st ed. One of 600. Signed. Gilt-ruled/blind-tooled calf. Fine. *Pacific*.* $138/£86

NELSON, BYRON. How I Played the Game. Dallas: Taylor Pub, (1993). 1st ed. One of 500. Signed. As New in VG slipcase. *Pacific*.* $161/£101

NELSON, BYRON. Winning Golf. NY: A.S. Barnes, (1946). 1st ed. Signed, dated 1996. VG in dj. *Pacific*.* $92/£58

NELSON, JOHN LOUW. Rhythm for Rain. Boston: Houghton Mifflin, 1937. 1st ed. Black cl, gilt. Fine. *Argonaut.* $45/£28

NELSON, KLONDY and CORY FORD. Daughter of the Gold Rush. NY: Random, 1958. 1st ed. NF in Good + dj. *Connolly.* $20/£13

NELSON, LOWRY. The Mormon Village. Salt Lake City: Univ of UT, 1952. 1st ed. VG in dj. *Lien.* $35/£22

NELSON, MAIDEE THOMAS. California Land of Promise. Caldwell, ID: Caxton, 1962. 1st ed. Orange cl. Fine in VG + dj (lt soiled). *House.* $25/£16

NELSON, OLIVER. The Cowman's Southwest. Angie Debo (ed). Glendale: A.H. Clark, 1953. 1st ed. Frontis map. Teg; uncut, unopened. Red cl. *Dawson.* $100/£63

NELSON, P. Ancient Painted Glass in England 1170-1500. Methuen, 1913. 33 plts. Sound (eps spotted; upper joint sl split). *Peter Taylor.* $29/£18

NELSON, R. Asiatic Cholera: Its Origin and Spread in Asia, Africa, and Europe, Introduction into America Through Canada.... NY, 1866. 1st ed. 206pp. *Fye.* $150/£94

NELSON, RAPHAEL. Cries and Criers of Old London. London/Glasgow: W. Collins Sons, 1941. Inscribed presentation. 4to. 31 unnumbered leaves; 31 VF full-pg linocuts. Linen on bds. VG in Fair pict dj (chipped). *Hobbyhorse.* $125/£78

NELSON, THOMAS AND SONS. Oban, Staffa, and Iona. T. Nelson & Sons, 1859. 106,16pp (old scrap remains on fep, corner torn off, hinges sl cracked); 11 blue-tinted chromolithos (1 dbl-pg). Blind-stamped cl (rubbed, faded), gilt. *Hollett.* $192/£120

NELSON, W. The Office and Authority of a Justice of Peace. London: E. & R. Nutt/R. Gosling et al, 1726. 9th ed. Contemp calf (sl rubbed). *Boswell.* $450/£281

NELSON, W. H. Alluring Arizona. SF, 1927. 1st ed. Brick red cl, gilt. VG (name) in dj. *Five Quail.* $22/£14

NELSON, W. H. Alluring Arizona. SF: The Author, 1938. 4th ed. Inscribed, signed, dated. Signed tls w/response stapled to it. Frontis, guard, 9 photo plts. Pict cl, gilt. Fine in dj (chipped). *Connolly.* $37/£23

NEMES, SYLVESTER. The Soft-Hackled Fly Addict. Chicago: The Author, (1981). One of 276 numbered, signed, and w/an actual blue dun soft-hackled fly tied by Nemes affixed to limitation pg. Full gilt-stamped leatherette (lt worn). Slipcase. *Oinonen*.* $110/£69

NEQUATEWA, EDMUND. Truth of a Hopi and Other Clan Stories of Shung-Opovi. Flagstaff: Museum of Northern AZ, 1936. One of 600. Frontis. Mostly unopened. (Bds soiled), else VG. *Dumont.* $95/£59

NERMAN, EINAR. Fairy Tales from the North. NY: Knopf, 1946. 1st ed. 4to. 8 full-pg color plts. Grn cl, maroon decs. Good in full color illus dj (spine lt worn). *Reisler.* $75/£47

NERUDA, PABLO. Fully Empowered. Alastair Reid (trans). NY: FSG, 1975. 1st ed. NF in dj. *Lame Duck.* $45/£28

NERUDA, PABLO. The Heights of Macchu Picchu. Nathaniel Tarn (trans). London: Jonathan Cape, 1966. 1st ed in English. (Ink inscrip), else NF in dj (price-clipped). *Lame Duck.* $100/£63

NERUDA, PABLO. Let the Rail Splitter Awake. NY: Masses & Mainstream, 1951. Wraps issue. VG + in wraps. *Lame Duck.* $55/£34

NERUDA, PABLO. Memoirs. NY: FSG, 1977. 1st US ed. VG + in dj. *Lame Duck.* $35/£22

NERUDA, PABLO. Memoirs. London: Souvenir, 1977. 1st British ed. Fine in dj. *Lame Duck.* $55/£34

NERUDA, PABLO. New Poems (1968-1970). NY: Grove, 1972. 1st ed. Bilingual ed. Rev copy w/publicity sheets laid in. Fine in dj. *Lame Duck.* $75/£47

NERUDA, PABLO. Residence on Earth. NY: New Directions, 1946. 1st ed. (Bkpl), else VG in dj (front flap chipped, spine dknd). *Lame Duck.* $100/£63

NERUDA, PABLO. Splendor and Death of Joaquin Murieta. NY: FSG, 1972. 1st US ed. Fine in dj. *Lame Duck.* $45/£28

NERUDA, PABLO. Toward the Splendid City. NY: FSG, 1974. 1st US ed. Rev copy w/slip laid in. Fine in dj. *Lame Duck.* $50/£31

NESBIT, E. Ballads and Lyrics of Socialism 1883-1908. Fabian Soc, 1908. Wrappered issue. VG (address stamp on 1/2-title, bkpl, edges dusty; cvrs rubbed, mkd, spine faded). *Ulysses.* $72/£45

NESBIT, E. Children's Stories from Shakespeare. London: R. Tuck, c. 1913. Royal 8vo. J.H. Bacon, H. Copping, et al (illus). Aeg. Beveled edges (backstrip torn). *Petersfield.* $61/£38

NESBIT, E. The Enchanted Castle. London: T. Fisher Unwin, 1907. 1st ed. 8vo. 47 illus by H. R. Millar. Teg. Red cl (spine worn, faded, few mks rear cvr), gilt. *Reisler.* $150/£94

NESBIT, E. The House of Arden. London: T. Fisher Unwin, 1908. 1st ed. 8vo. H.R. Millar (illus). Teg. Red cl (spine sl faded), gilt. Nice. *Reisler.* $250/£156

NESBIT, E. Long Ago When I Was Young. Macdonald, 1974. 1st ed thus. Lg 8vo. Pict tp, 126pp; 13 b/w chapter-head, 12 b/w illus by Edward Ardizzone. VG + (crease on rep) in pict dj (chipped). *Bookmark.* $27/£17

NESBIT, E. The Phoenix and the Carpet. London: George Newnes, (1904). 1st ed. 8vo. H. R. Millar (illus). Teg. Blue-grn cl (edges, corners worn), gilt. *Reisler.* $200/£125

NESBIT, E. Pug Peter. NY: Frederick A. Stokes, 1906. 1st Amer ed. 4to. 28 full-pg color plts by Harry Rountree, vignettes by J. Hassall. Cl-backed pict bds (spine ends, corners lt worn; fr hinge sl weak). *Reisler.* $675/£422

NESBIT, E. The Railway Children. Wells Gardner, Darton, c.1906. 5th ed. viii,309,(x)pp; 20 illus by C. E. Brock. Pict cl (sl worn, mkd). *Hollett*. $40/£25

NESBIT, E. The Story of the Amulet. Dutton, 1907. 1st Amer ed. (Spine lettering flaked), else VG. *Fine Books*. $100/£63

NESBIT, E. The Story of the Five Rebellious Dolls. London: Ernest Nister, (1904). 1st ed. Obl sm folio. 8 full-pg color plts by E. Stuart Hardy. Cl-backed color illus bds (edges lt rubbed). VG. *Reisler*. $650/£406

NESBIT, E. The Would-Be-Goods. T. Fisher Unwin, January 1911. 7th imp. 8vo. 331pp; 18 mono plts by Arthur Buckland. Teg. Pict scarlet cl, gilt. NF in orig illus dj (sl worn, chipped). *Bookmark*. $88/£55

NESBIT, E. et al. Tick Tock: Tales of the Clock. London: Raphael Tuck, (c. 1895). 9.75x7. Helen Jackson et al (illus). Cl-backed chromolitho bds. (Outer extrems of plts sl stained), else VG. *Pacific**. $52/£33

NESBITT, L. M. Desert and Forest. London, 1934. 2nd imp. Fldg map. (Fr hinge sl split, cl sl worn.) *Edwards*. $40/£25

NESFIELD, W. EDEN. Specimens of Mediaeval Architecture. (London), 1862. Folio. 100 plts (1 color). Leather-backed pict cl. (Lt soil mks.) *Kane**. $150/£94

NESS, EVALINE. Sam, Bangs and Moonshine. NY: Holt, 1966. 1st ed. 7.75x10. 36pp. Fine in dj. *Cattermole*. $100/£63

NETTEL, REGINALD. Music in the Five Towns 1840-1914. OUP, 1944. 1st ed. 4 plts. VG in dj. *Hollett*. $56/£35

NETTEL, REGINALD. The Orchestra in England. Cape, 1946. VG in dj. *Hollett*. $32/£20

NETTEL, REGINALD. Ordeal by Music. OUP, 1945. 1st ed. 4 plts. VG in dj (top edge chipped, torn). *Hollett*. $32/£20

NETTLE, RICHARD. The Salmon Fisheries of the St. Lawrence and Its Tributaries. Montreal: John Lovell, 1857. 1st ed. 12mo. 144pp (lib stamp, bkpl). Copyright slip pasted to tp verso. Very Nice. *M & S*. $550/£344

NEUBAUER, C. and J. VOGEL. A Guide to the Qualitative and Quantitative Analysis of the Urine. London, 1863. 1st ed in English. 439pp. *Fye*. $100/£63

NEUHAUS, EUGEN. The Art of the Exposition. SF: Paul Elder, (1915). 2nd ed. Uncut. NF (spine sl sunned). *Polyanthos*. $30/£19

NEUHOF, HAROLD and SAMUEL HIRSHFIELD. The Transplantation of Tissues. NY/London: D. Appleton, 1923. 1st ed. Color frontis. Black cl, gilt. Fine. *Weber*. $200/£125

NEUHOF, HAROLD. Venous Thrombosis and Pulmonary Embolism. NY, 1948. 1st ed. VG (cl bds lt faded). *Doctor's Library*. $75/£47

NEUMANN, ARTHUR H. Elephant Hunting in East Equatorial Africa. London: Rowland Ward, 1898. 1st ed. 8vo. Frontis, xix,455,(8)ads pp; fldg map in rear pocket, color plt. Red cl (sl crazed, corners sl bumped). *Maggs*. $2,240/£1,400

NEUMANN, DAISY. Now That Aprils There. Phila: Lippincott, (1945). 1st ed. Fine in NF dj (spine sl faded, few sl tears). *Between The Covers*. $50/£31

NEURDENBURG, ELISABETH and BERNARD RACKHAM. Old Dutch Pottery and Tiles. NY, 1923. *Swann**. $126/£79

NEUTRA, RICHARD. Survival Through Design. NY: OUP, 1954. NF in dj. *Smith*. $40/£25

NEUTRA, RICHARD. World and Dwelling. NY: Universe Books, (1962). 1st Amer ed. NF in illus dj. *Cahan*. $75/£47

Nevada Brand Book. Reno, 1946. 1st ed. Tall cl-backed stapled wraps. VG- (lt stain on part of text, 'Brand' on tp is missing 'd', fr wrap w/diagonal crease toward bottom corner). *Baade*. $150/£94

Nevada. Binfords & Mort, 1940. 1st ed. NF in dj. *Labordo*. $65/£41

NEVE, RICHARD. The City and Country Purchaser, and Builder's Dictionary; or, The Compleat Builders Guide. London, 1726. 2nd ed. Calf. *Felcone*. $600/£375

NEVERS, JO ANN. Wa She Shu: A Washo Tribal History. Reno: Inter-Tribal Council of NV, 1976. (Lt worn), else VG. *Dumont*. $25/£16

NEVILL, RALPH. British Military Prints. London, 1909. 88 plts (24 color). *Kane**. $45/£28

NEVILL, RALPH. Old English Sporting Books. London, 1924. (Lt foxed.) *Swann**. $57/£36

NEVILL, RALPH. Old English Sporting Prints and Their History. London, 1923. One of 1500 numbered. (Sl worn, spine sunned.) *Oinonen**. $110/£69

NEVILLE, A. W. The Red River Valley Then and Now. Paris, TX: North TX Pub, 1948. One of 2000. Signed by Neville and Carl Hertzog (ptr). VG in dj. *Dumont*. $150/£94

NEVILLE, RICHARD. Play Power. Cape, 1970. 1st ed. Fldg 'Headopoly' poster/game in rear pocket. Yellow cl (extrems sl soiled). NF (name) in VG + dj. *Any Amount*. $72/£45

NEVINS, ALLAN (ed). The Diary of Philip Hone, 1828-1851. NY, 1927. One of 150. 2 vols. Vellum, paper over bds. (Bkpls; extrems worn, vol 1 spine discolored, spotted.) Contents VG. *Woolson*. $50/£31

NEVINS, ALLAN et al (eds). Civil War Books. Baton Rouge, 1970. 2 vols. VG in djs. *Dumont*. $150/£94

NEVINSON, C. R. W. The Great War, Fourth Year. London: Grant Richards, 1918. 1st ed. Color frontis. Grn cl-backed gray bds, paper label. (Lt foxed), o/w VG in dj (spine chip, tape mks on flaps). *Reese*. $100/£63

NEVINSON, HENRY W. The Dardanelles Campaign. London: Nisbet, (1918). (Binding stained.) *Petersfield*. $32/£20

NEVIUS, HELEN S. C. Our Life in China. NY: Carter & Bros, 1869. Frontis, vi,504pp; 2 plts. (Ex-lib; spine sl faded, sl rubbed), o/w VG. *Worldwide*. $35/£22

New and Accurate Description of the Principal Great Roads and Principal Cross Roads of England and Wales.... R. & J. Dodsley, 1756. (viii),168,lxiv pp; fldg map (sm handling tear to inner margin). Contemp mid-brn sprinkled calf (upper joint split but firm), raised bands, gilt red morocco label (dulled). Good. *Blackwell's*. $144/£90

New and Complete History of Essex. (By Peter Muilman.) Chelmsford: Ptd and sold by Lionel Hassell, 1770-1772. 2nd ed. 6 vols. 52 engr plts, 3 fldg engr maps. Contemp calf. (Lacks add'l engr tps, list of subs; spines sl chipped, vol 6 w/sl loss at head.) *Sotheby's**. $368/£230

New and General Biographical Dictionary.... London: Robinson, Johnson, Nichols et al, 1798. New ed. 15 vols. Tall 8vo. 3/4 calf, marbled bds, raised bands, gilt. (Worn.) Text VG. *Hartfield*. $950/£594

New Book of Sports. London: Richard Bentley, 1885. 396pp. Pub's cl (sl mottled). *Marlborough*. $88/£55

New Directions 12. (NY): New Directions, (1950). 1st ed. VF in VF dj. *Between The Covers*. $125/£78

New Directions 14. (NY: New Directions, 1953). 1st ed. VF in VF dj (rear cvr sl soiled). *Between The Covers*. $100/£63

New Directions 16. (NY): New Directions, (1957). 1st ed. (Pp sl dknd), else VF in VF dj. *Between The Covers*. $100/£63

New Guide to Montreal and Its Environs. Montreal: Armour & Ramsay, 1851. 1st ed. 57pp + (3)pp ads; lg fldg map at rear (sm closed tears along folds). Brn cl (sunned). VG. *Chapel Hill*. $150/£94

New Hampshire Register, Farmer's Almanac, and Business Directory, for 1889. White River Junction, VT: White River Paper Co. Fldg map, 236,34pp + ads. Wrappers. (Sl worn, rubbed), else Good. *Brown*. $15/£9

New Mexico, The Last Great West. Chicago, 1917. Good (worn). *Dumont.* $150/£94

New Mexico. NY: Hastings House, 1940. 1st ed. VG+ in dj (spine ends chipped). *Labordo.* $75/£47

New Mexico: A Guide to the Colorful State. NY: Hastings House, 1953. VG in dj (sl worn). *Dumont.* $30/£19

New Mexico: Its Resources, Climate, Geography, Geology, History, Statistics, Present Condition and Future Prospects. Santa Fe: New Mexican Ptg, 1890. 216pp; 2 VG fldg maps. (Interior browned). Pict wraps (chipped). *Dumont.* $500/£313

New Purchase: Or, Seven and a Half Years in the Far West. NY, 1843. 1st ed, 1st bk. Ads at end of vol 2 are not present. 2 vols. (12),300; (8),316pp (lt foxed). Contemp calf, marbled bds (rubbed). 1/4 morocco slipcase. Howes H48. *M & S.* $150/£94

New Roman History, from the Foundation of Rome to the End of the Common-Wealth. London: E. Newbery, 1784. 12mo. VF full-pg engr frontis signed Royce, vi,136pp; 5pp copper engrs. Mottled full leather, glt, red leather spine label, cvr edges gilt. (Lt browned along cvr edges, eps, frontis, tp; dated sig; spine sl rubbed), else Fine. *Hobbyhorse.* $215/£134

New System of Agriculture; or, a Plain, Easy, and Demonstrative Method of Speedily Growing Rich...By a Country Gentleman. Dublin: George Faulkner & Peter Wilson, 1755. 1st ed. 111pp. Mod buckram. VG. *Glaser.* $450/£281

New System of Fortification. London: J. Millan, 1770. 1st ed. 12mo. (iv),ii,18pp; fldg copper plt. Old style 1/4 calf. *Maggs.* $800/£500

New System of Military Discipline, Founded upon Principle. By a General Officer. (By Richard Lambart.) Phila, 1776. Contemp sheep. *Felcone.* $2,400/£1,500

NEW YORK BOTANICAL GARDEN. Journal of the New York Botanical Garden. Volume IV. Daniel Trembly MacDougal (ed). NY: NYBG, 1903. 1st ed. 8 b/w plts. 1/2 leather, marbled paper. (Shelf-worn), else VG. *Fair Meadow.* $40/£25

New York Expositor; or, Fifth Book. NY: Samuel Wood & Sons, n.d., ca 1830. 305pp. Contemp calf, leather label. Good. *Brown.* $15/£9

NEWBERRY, CLARE TURLAY. April's Kittens. Harper, 1940. 1st ed. 9.2x10.7. Unpaginated. Good+ (stamps, pocket remnants; finger wrinkles in lib cl, bumped; corners, spine tips worn, spine #). *Price.* $22/£14

NEWBERRY, CLARE TURLAY. Cats, a Portfolio. NY: Harper & Bros, 1943. Folio. 16 plts in portfolio w/cat image pastedown. *Metropolitan*.* $28/£18

NEWBERRY, CLARE TURLAY. Cats: A Portfolio. NY: Harper, (1943). Slim lg folio. Plain thin board portfolio w/inner flaps, mtd color pict label fr cvr; text loose as issued: ptd title leaf, 13 loose plts. (Sl worn, spotted.) Text Good (lt handled). *Baltimore*.* $65/£41

NEWBERRY, CLARE TURLAY. Pandora. NY: Harper, 1944. 1st ed. Folio. Unpaginated. VG in VG dj. *Davidson.* $135/£84

NEWBERRY, PERCY E. Egyptian Antiquities, Scarabs. London: Archibald Constable, 1906. 1st ed. 44 plts (1 color). Teg. (Sm bkpl; lt rubbed.) *Archaeologia.* $275/£172

NEWBOLT, HENRY. The Story of the Oxfordshire and Buckinghamshire Light Infantry. London, (1915). 1st Eng ed. VG (spine, edges faded). *Clearwater.* $48/£30

NEWBY, ERIC. Great Ascents. London: Newton Abbot, 1977. 1st Eng ed. Very Nice in dj. *Clearwater.* $56/£35

NEWBY, ERIC. Love and War in the Apennines. Hodder, 1971. 1st UK ed. Fine in Fine dj (sm crease, tear). *Martin.* $29/£18

NEWBY, ERIC. A Short Walk: A Preposterous Adventure. GC: Doubleday, 1959. 1st US ed. Fine in VG dj (sl shelfworn, spine panel dull). *Any Amount.* $64/£40

NEWBY, ERIC. Slowly Down the Ganges. London, 1966. 1st Eng ed. Very Nice (cvrs sl bumped) in dj (sl rubbed). *Clearwater.* $56/£35

NEWBY, ERIC. Slowly Down the Ganges. London: Hodder & Stoughton, 1966. 1st Eng ed. NF (spine ends sl bumped) in dj (edges rubbed, laminate starting to lift). *Ulysses.* $72/£45

NEWBY, P. H. Something to Answer For. Faber, 1968. 1st UK ed. NF in NF dj. *Martin.* $45/£28

NEWCOMB, FRANC JOHNSON. Navajo Omens and Taboos. Santa Fe: Rydal, (1940). 1st ed. Inscribed, signed, numbered 121, indicating a limitation of some sort. Dbl-pg color repro. Paper cvr/spine labels. (Spine label sl sunned, sm chip), else NF. *Pacific*.* $173/£108

NEWCOMB, REXFORD. The Franciscan Mission Architecture of Alta California. NY: Architectural Book Pub, 1916. Folio. 41 plts. (Bds unevenly faded.) Internally VG. *Dumont.* $275/£172

NEWCOMB, REXFORD. Old Kentucky Architecture. NY: William Helburn, 1940. 1st ed. Frontis, 130 plts. Blue cl. Good. *Karmiole.* $60/£38

NEWCOMB, REXFORD. The Old Mission Churches and Historic Houses of California. Phila/London: Lippincott, 1925. 1st ed. Teg, untrimmed. Navy buckram (lt stain lower cvr), gilt. Cvrs Nice in gilt-ptd dj (spine sunned, edges chipped, lower panel worn, lower flap fold torn). *Baltimore*.* $75/£47

NEWCOMB, REXFORD. The Old Mission Churches and Historic Houses of California. Phila: J.B. Lippincott, 1925. 1st ed. Color frontis. Teg. Blue cl, gilt. (Old ink inscrip; spine sl faded), else NF. *Pacific*.* $75/£47

NEWCOMB, REXFORD. The Old Mission Churches and Historic Houses of California. Phila: Lippincott, 1925. 1st ed. Grn cl (old waterstains top edge rear cvr, spine bottom). Internally Fine; dj (chipped). *Karmiole.* $100/£63

NEWCOMB, REXFORD. Spanish-Colonial Architecture in the United States. NY, 1937. Sm folio. 130 plts. Good in dj (worn). *Dumont.* $175/£109

NEWELL, C. History of the Revolution in Texas. NY: Wiley & Putnam, 1838. x,215pp; fldg map. Good (sl foxed; rebacked). Howes N115. *Dumont.* $750/£469

NEWELL, FRANKLIN S. Cesarean Section NY, 1923. 1st ed. (Extrems worn), o/w Good. *Doctor's Library.* $60/£38

NEWELL, J. T. Hog Hunting in the East and Other Sports. London: Tinsley Bros, 1867. 466pp (p79 plt margin damaged). 3/4 calf over linen-cvrd bds (extrems rubbed), gilt. *Cullen.* $175/£109

NEWELL, PETER. The Hole Book. NY: Harper, (1908). 1st ed. Sm 4to. Pict label over bl cl (label soiled, eps spotted). *Appelfeld.* $175/£109

NEWELL, PETER. Jungle-Jangle. NY: Peter Newell, 1909. 8vo. 4 illus. Good in orange/black ptd self wrappers (lt dusty, resewn spine). *Reisler.* $875/£547

NEWELL, PETER. The Slant Book. NY: Harper, (1910). 1st ed. Slant 4to. Pict bds over blue cl spine (extrems worn). Good. *Appelfeld.* $250/£156

NEWELL, ROBERT. Robert Newell's Memoranda: Travles in the Teritory of Missourie; Travle to the Kayuse War.... Dorothy O. Johansen (ed). (Portland, OR): Champoeg, 1959. One of 1000 ptd. Frontis, facs map. Fine. *Pacific*.* $52/£33

NEWHALL, BEAUMONT and NANCY NEWHALL (eds). Masters of Photography. NY: George Braziller, 1958. 1st ed. (Dusty), else NF in VG dj. *Cahan.* $50/£31

NEWHALL, BEAUMONT and DIANA EDKINS. William H. Jackson. Dobbs Ferry, (1974). 1st ed. (Sl worn.) Dj (price-clipped, rubbed, extrems age-dknd). *Swann*.* $115/£72

NEWHALL, BEAUMONT and DIANA EDKINS. William H. Jackson. Ft. Worth, 1974. 1st ed. Fine in dj. *Baade.* $40/£25

NEWHALL, BEAUMONT (ed). Photography: Essays and Images. NY: MOMA, 1980. 1st ed. Fine. *Cahan.* $75/£47

NEWHALL, BEAUMONT. Beaumont Newhall: In Plain Sight. Salt Lake City: Gibbs Smith, 1983. 1st ed. Inscribed in 1985. VG in dj (sl rubbed, price-clipped). *Smith.* $85/£53

NEWHALL, BEAUMONT. Photographer of the Southwest. Ruth Mahood (ed). NY: Bonanza Books, (n.d.). 1st ed thus. 91 plts. Fine in dj. *Smith.* $65/£41

NEWHALL, BEAUMONT. Photography at Mid-Century. Rochester, NY: George Eastman House, (1959). 1st ed. 93 b/w photos. VG in ptd stiff wrappers (sl soiled). *Cahan.* $50/£31

NEWHALL, CHARLES. The Vines of Northeastern America. NY: Putnam, 1897. 1st ed. Pict bds. VG (ex-lib). *Archer.* $35/£22

NEWHALL, NANCY (ed). Edward Weston, Photographer; The Flame of Recognition. Rochester, NY: Aperture, (n.d.). 1st ed. (Fr pastedown browned, eps, rear pastedown lt foxed; lt soiled.) Dj (age-dknd, sm tears, soiled). *Swann*.* $57/£36

NEWHOUSE, EDWARD. You Can't Sleep Here. NY: Macaulay, (1934). 1st ed, 1st bk. Inscribed, signed. Good (edge shelfworn, spine lt frayed) in pict dj (sm losses at spine ends). *Reese.* $350/£219

NEWLAND, HENRY. Forest Life in Norway and Sweden: Being Extracts from the Journal of a Fisherman. London: Routledge, 1858. New ed. vi,418pp (sl foxed, soiled). Contemp 3/4 grn polished calf (rubbed). *Oinonen*.* $60/£38

NEWLANDS, JAMES. The Carpenter and Joiner's Assistant. Blackie, n.d. (c. 1867). 254pp; 100 full-pg engr plts. Red cl, gilt. Good (soil, worn). *Whittle.* $120/£75

NEWMAN, A. Rondeaux of Boyhood. London, 1923. 1st ed. One of 250. VG (no dj). *Typographeum.* $135/£84

NEWMAN, BERNARD. Spy. London: Gollancz, 1935. 1st ed. Black cl. (Edges lt foxed), o/w VG in house-style dj. *Reese.* $50/£31

NEWMAN, ERNEST. Hugo Wolf. Methuen, 1907. 1st ed. 13 plts. VG. *Hollett.* $48/£30

NEWMAN, ERNEST. The Man Liszt. Cassell, 1934. 1st ed. 8 plts. VG. *Hollett.* $48/£30

NEWMAN, G. et al. Prize Essays on Leprosy. New Sydenham Soc, 1895. vi,228 + 38pp (prelims foxed); fldg map. *Whitehart.* $40/£25

NEWMAN, HAROLD. Veilleuses: A Collector's Guide. NY/London, 1987. Enlgd, rev ed. 32 color plts. (Corners sl bumped.) Dj (sl chipped). *Edwards.* $48/£30

NEWMAN, ISIDORA. Fairy Flowers. London: Humphrey Milford, (1926). 1st ed. 4to. (xii),160pp; 15 mtd color plts, 15 full-pg line dwgs, by Willy Pogany. Dec eps. White cl-backed yellow dec bds. (Upper corners knocked), o/w Bright. *Sotheran.* $269/£168

NEWMAN, JOHN P. The Thrones and Palaces of Babylon and Nineveh from Sea to Sea. NY: Harper, 1876. 1st ed. 455,12pp. (Sl rubbed, sm nick, spine ends sl frayed), o/w VG. *Worldwide.* $125/£78

NEWMARK, HARRIS. Sixty Years in Southern California 1853-1913. Maurice H. and Marco R. Newmark (eds). NY: Knickerbocker, 1916. 1st ed. 65 plts. Teg. Red cl, gilt spine. Fine. *Pacific*.* $104/£65

NEWMARK, HARRIS. Sixty Years in Southern California 1853-1913. Maurice H. and Marco R. Newmark (eds). L.A.: Zeitlin & Ver Brugge, 1970. 4th ed. Ltd to 1250. Fine in Fine dj. *Book Market.* $50/£31

NEWMARK, HARRIS. Sixty Years in Southern California, 1853-1913. Maurice H. and Marco R. Newmark (eds). NY: Knickerbocker, 1926. 2nd ed. 73 plts. Teg. Red cl, gilt spine. (Extrems sl worn), o/w Fine. *Pacific*.* $40/£25

NEWSOM, J. A. The Life and Practice of the Wild and Modern Indian. Oklahoma City: J.A. Newsom, 1923. 1st ed. VG in pict wrappers. Howes N124. *Labordo.* $150/£94

NEWTON, A. EDWARD. Bibliography and Pseudo-Bibliography. Phila: Univ of PA, 1936. 1st ptg. VG in dj (spine sl stained). *Truepenny.* $35/£22

NEWTON, A. EDWARD. Books and Business. N.p.: Apellicon, 1930. 1st ed. One of 325 ptd. Signed. Paper spine/cvr labels. Fine in VG dbl slipcase. *Pacific*.* $112/£70

NEWTON, A. EDWARD. Doctor Johnson, a Play. Boston, 1923. 1st ed. Ltd to 585 numbered, signed. (Spine label sl rubbed), else VG in slipcase (frayed). *King.* $60/£38

NEWTON, A. EDWARD. Newton on Blackstone. Phila: Univ of PA, 1937. 1st ed. One of 2000. Signed. Frontisport. Fine in dj (rubbed, sunned). *Pacific*.* $29/£18

NEWTON, A. EDWARD. This Book-Collecting Game. Boston: Little, Brown, 1928. Lg paper ed. One of 990. Signed. Teg. 1/2 cl, paper spine label. (Spine sl sunned, soiled), else VG in slipcase (lt shelfworn). *Pacific*.* $58/£36

NEWTON, C. T. Travels and Discoveries in the Levant. Day & Son, 1865. 1st ed. 2 vols. 8vo. xiv,(ii),360; xiv,(ii),275pp; 11 mtd plts, 9 maps, plans (3 dbl-pg, 2 fldg), 21 plts. (Several plts w/lt water staining to edges; sl browned, bkpl.) Marbled eps, edges. 1/2 calf, marbled bds (sl worn, spine heads sl chipped, corners sl rubbed), gilt, raised bands w/morocco inlays, leather labels. *Edwards.* $960/£600

NEWTON, FRANCES E. Fifty Years in Palestine. London/Brussels: Coldharbour Press, 1948. 1st ed. Grn cl, gilt. (Spine faded, sl tilted.) Dj. *Maggs.* $160/£100

NEWTON, ISAAC. Principia: The Mathematical Principles of Natural Philosophy. NY: Ivison & Phinney, (1846). 1st US ed, variant publisher. Engr frontisport, 581pp. Contemp full sheep, black leather spine label. (Sl aged, lt foxed, fr hinge recently repaired, bkpl partly removed; edges sl worn, rubbed, joints repaired w/wide black cl tape, spine crackled, ends chipped.) *Baltimore*.* $190/£119

NEWTON, ISAAC. Sir Isaac Newton's Principia, Reprinted for Sir William Thomson...and Hugh Blackburn. Glasgow: James Maclehose, 1871. Marbled eps; teg. Levant grn morocco, gilt, raised bands; bound by Spottiswode. Fine. *Pacific*.* $196/£123

NEWTON, ISAAC. A Treatise of the Method of Fluxions and Infinite Series, with Its Applications to the Geometry of Curve Lines. London: T. Woodman, 1737. Internally Fine (foxed; rear bd, spine dampstained). *Metropolitan*.* $373/£233

NEWTON, LILY. A Handbook of the British Seaweeds. London: British Museum, 1931. 1st ed. (Sl worn.) *Edwards.* $48/£30

NEWTON, W. DOUGLAS. War. London, 1914. 1st Eng ed. Good. *Clearwater.* $32/£20

Nibelungenlied. LEC, 1960. Ltd to 1500 numbered, signed by Edy Legrand (illus). Fine in slipcase. *Swann*.* $80/£50

NICHOL, J. P. The Phenomena and Order of the Solar System. Edinburgh: William Tait, 1838. (ii, ads),241pp; complete w/21 engr plts. Orig cl gilt (faded, spine top torn, repaired, base sl chipped). *Hollett.* $120/£75

Nicholas Thomas's Jolly Pop-Ups. (Somerset)/London: Purnell & Sons, n.d. (195?). 3 dbl-pg pop-ups. Glazed pict bds. VG-. *Bookfinders.* $30/£19

NICHOLAS, A. X. (ed). Woke Up This Mornin': Poetry of the Blues. NY: Bantam Books, (1973). 1st ed. Discography. VG in pict stiff wraps. *Petrilla.* $15/£9

NICHOLAS, DAVID. The Metamorphosis of a Medieval City. Lincoln/London: Univ of NE, 1987. 2 maps. *Turtle Island.* $30/£19

NICHOLAS, DONALD. The Young Adventurer. Batchworth, 1949. 1st ed. 18 plts. (Edges sl spotted.) Dj (sl spotted). *Hollett.* $48/£30

NICHOLL, EDITH M. Observations of a Ranch Woman in New Mexico. Cincinnati: Editor Pub, 1901. 1st Amer ed. (Sl spotted.) Internally Clean. *Dumont.* $150/£94

NICHOLL, EDITH M. Observations of a Ranchwoman in New Mexico. London: Macmillan, 1898. (Extrems worn, sl cocked.) Internally Good. *Dumont.* $250/£156

NICHOLLS, ROBERT (comp). Ten Generations of a Potting Family. London: Percy Lund, n.d. Frontis, xxvi,135pp; 53 plts, fldg family tree. (Eps lt spotted; cl sl stained.) Dj (browned, chipped). *Edwards.* $58/£36

NICHOLS, ALICE. Bleeding Kansas. NY, 1954. 2nd ptg. VG+ in VG+ dj. *Pratt.* $25/£16

NICHOLS, BEVERLEY. Down the Garden Path. GC: Doubleday, Doran, 1932. 1st Amer ed. (Inked inscrip; bds sunned w/rear spotted), else VG. *Fair Meadow.* $30/£19

NICHOLS, BEVERLEY. No Man's Street. NY, 1954. 1st ed. NF in VG+ dj. *Warren.* $35/£22

NICHOLS, FRANCIS H. Through Hidden Shensi. NY: Scribner, 1902. 1st ed. 47 plts, fldg map. (Lib spine #; edges rubbed), o/w VG. *Worldwide.* $30/£19

NICHOLS, FRANCIS H. Through Hidden Shensi. London, 1902. 1st UK ed. Frontisport, fldg map. 2-tone cl, gilt. (Feps lt browned; spine lt dknd.) *Edwards.* $120/£75

NICHOLS, FREDERICK DOVETON and RALPH E. GRISWOLD. Thomas Jefferson Landscape Architect. Univ of VA, (c1978). 1st ed. VG in VG- dj. *Book Broker.* $45/£28

NICHOLS, J. B. Account of the Royal Hospital and Collegiate Church of Saint Katharine, Near the Tower of London. London: Nichols, 1824. Tp, 1f., 61pp; fldg engr frontis, 5 plts. Orig patterned grn cl (sm tear spine bottom). *Marlborough.* $136/£85

NICHOLS, JOHN and GEORGE STEVENS. The Genuine Works of William Hogarth. London: Longman et al, 1808-10. 3 vols (vols 1, 2 text; vol 3 plts). Frontis ports, vii,524; viii,444pp. (Lt spotting, browning, ms vol and pg #s upper margin each plt; hinges cracked.) 1/2 calf (rebacked), marbled bds (rubbed, sl worn), leather spine labels. *Edwards.* $240/£150

NICHOLS, JOHN. Keep It Simple. NY, 1992. Fine in dj. *Dumont.* $35/£22

NICHOLS, JOHN. Literary Anecdotes of the Eighteenth Century. The Author, 1812-1815. 9 vols bound in 10. 8vo. Engr ports (offset). Teg. Later 1/2 morocco, gilt, by Birdsall. *Sotheby's*.* $2,024/£1,265

NICHOLS, JOHN. The Milagro Beanfield War. NY: Holt, 1974. 1st ed. Fine in Fine dj (chip). *Unger.* $300/£188

NICHOLS, JOHN. The Nirvana Blues. NY: Holt, Rinehart & Winston, (1981). 1st ed. Signed. Blue cl over white bds, silver-lettered spine. (Spine extrems, corners lt rubbed), o/w Fine in dj (spine extrems, corners sl worn). *Heritage.* $150/£94

NICHOLS, JOHN. The Nirvana Blues. NY: Holt, Rinehart & Winston, 1981. 1st ed. (Shelfworn), else VG in dj. *Dumont.* $30/£19

NICHOLS, JOHN. On the Mesa. Salt Lake City, 1986. Signed. NF in dj. *Dumont.* $30/£19

NICHOLS, ROBERT (ed). Anthology of War Poetry 1914-1918. London: Nicholson & Watson, (1943). 1st ed. Lt grn cl. (Edges sl sunned), o/w Nice in VG dj (folds rubbed, rear lt soiled). *Reese.* $25/£16

NICHOLS, ROSE STANDISH. English Pleasure Gardens. NY: Macmillan, 1902. 1st ed. Teg. Pict cl, gilt. (Frontis guard foxed; cvrs sl soiled, sm spine crease), else VG. *Pacific*.* $58/£36

NICHOLS, ROSE STANDISH. Italian Pleasure Gardens. NY: Dodd, Mead, 1928. 1st ed. (Spine faded, shelf-worn), else VG. *Fair Meadow.* $80/£50

NICHOLS, T. A Hand-Book of the British Museum, for Every-Day Readers. Cassell, Peter & Galpin, 1870. 1st ed. Frontis. (Inner hinges shaken.) *Forest.* $56/£35

NICHOLSON, A. The Chetham Hospital and Library. Sherrat & Hughes, 1910. 16 plts. VG in dec cl. *Moss.* $48/£30

NICHOLSON, NORMAN. Five Rivers. NY, 1945. 1st Amer ed. Fine in dj (sl dust-soiled, spine sl torn). *Polyanthos.* $25/£16

NICHOLSON, NORMAN. Man and Literature. London: SCM Press, 1943. 1st ed. VG in dj. *Hollett.* $32/£20

NICHOLSON, NORMAN. The Shadow of Black Combe. London: Mid Northumberland Arts Group, 1978. 1st Eng ed. Signed. VG in wrappers (sl creased). *Ulysses.* $40/£25

NICHOLSON, NORMAN. William Cowper. London: John Lehmann, 1951. 1st ed. Frontis port. VG in dj (sl worn, lower panel spotted, price-clipped). *Hollett.* $64/£40

NICHOLSON, PETER. The Carpenter's New Guide. Phila: M. Carey & Son, June 1818. 2nd US ed, 'The Eighth Edition, from the Sixth London Edition.' 127pp; 84 copper plts. Old sheep. (Sl foxed, lt old stains also on plts, 2 plts w/sm holes, sm hole 1 text leaf margin, text separated at center; cvrs worn, detached, spine worn, chipped.) *Baltimore*.* $375/£234

NICHOLSON, PETER. The Student's Instructor in Drawing and Working the Five Orders of Architecture. London: J. Taylor, 1810. 3rd ed. viii,40pp + 2pp ads; 41 plts. Later 19th-cent calf, marbled bds. (Lacks either blank or 1/2-title.) *Karmiole.* $300/£188

NICHOLSON, REYNOLD A. A Literary History of the Arabs. London: T. Fisher Unwin, 1923. 3rd imp. Color frontis. Mod 1/2 morocco, gilt. (Lib stamp tp verso.) *Hollett.* $136/£85

NICHOLSON, WILLIAM. An Alphabet. Whittington, 1978. One of 150 sets (12 handcolored). 39 leaves (all but 4 from orig blocks), 16pp booklet (one of 300), 4pp leaflet. Drop-back box. Fine set. *Michael Taylor.* $560/£350

NICHOLSON, WILLIAM. Clever Bill. NY: Doubleday, Page, (1926). 1st Amer ed. Obl 4to. 23pp (sl erasure mks to 2pp). Yellow illus bds (sl edgeworn). Pict dj (sl worn). *Reisler.* $1,400/£875

NICHOLSON, WILLIAM. The Poetical Works. Castle-Douglas: Samuel Gordon, 1878. 3rd ed. Tinted litho frontisport, add'l tp, vi,231pp. Blind-stamped cl (sl rubbed), gilt. *Hollett.* $48/£30

NICOL, THOMAS. By Mountain, Moor and Loch. Stirling: Eneas Mackay, 1931. 1st ed. 50 plts. (Spine faded.) *Hollett.* $40/£25

NICOL, WALTER. The Gardener's Kalendar. London, 1812. 2nd ed. xxi,646,2 ads. Contemp straight-grained 1/2 morocco, gilt. (Lt browned, margins sl waterstained.) *Henly.* $192/£120

NICOL, WALTER. The Planter's Kalendar. Edinburgh: Archibald Constable, 1820. 2nd ed. xxiv,589pp; 3 engr tinted plts. Orig bds (rebacked, chipped label relaid). *Young.* $152/£95

NICOLA, TOUFICK. Atlas of Surgical Approaches to Bones and Joints. NY, 1945. 1st ed. (Ex-lib w/bkpl; extrems worn, cvr gilt lettering faded, marginal waterstain), o/w Good. *Doctor's Library.* $45/£28

NICOLAY, HELEN. Personal Traits of Abraham Lincoln. NY, 1912. 1st ed. Teg, sides uncut. VG (bkpl). *Wantagh.* $45/£28

NICOLAY, JOHN G. and JOHN HAY (eds). Complete Works of Abraham Lincoln. NY, (1905). New, enlgd ed. 12 vols. (3 vols stained, others less stained.) Internally Fine. *Woolman.* $100/£63

NICOLL, ALLARDYCE. The Development of the Theatre. London: Harrap, 1927. 1st ed. (Sm stain fr cvr), o/w Fine in ptd dj (sl worn). *Europa.* $56/£35

NICOLL, WILLIAM ROBERTSON and THOMAS J. WISE (eds). Literary Anecdotes of the Nineteenth Century. London/NY: Hodder & Stoughton/Dodd, Mead, 1895. 1st ed. 2 vols. Frontis, 12,634; 16,495pp. Very Nice (lib stamps, spines sunned). *M & S.* $300/£188

NICOLL, WILLIAM ROBERTSON. Dickens's Own Story. London: Chapman & Hall, 1923. 1st ed. Port. (Badly damped.) Dj (sl worn). *Hollett.* $24/£15

NICOLS, A. Zoological Notes on the Structure, Affinities, Habits and Mental Faculties of Wild and Domestic Animals. London: L.U. Gill, 1883. 1st ed. 370pp. Pict cl, gilt, dec bds. (Cvr loose), else VG. *Mikesh*. $75/£47

NICOLS, LOWELL W. (ed). An Annotated Catalog of the Alexander C. Robinson Collection of Western Pennsylvania. Sewickley: Library Soc of Sewickley, PA, 1940. Paper wrappers. (Extrems lt rubbed), else VG +. *Zubal**. $15/£9

NICOLSON, BENEDICT. Hendrick Terbrugghen. London: Lund Humpries, 1958. (Spine rubbed, faded.) *Christie's**. $405/£253

NICOLSON, BENEDICT. The International Caravaggesque Movement. Oxford: Phaidon, 1979. VF in dj. *Europa*. $112/£70

NICOLSON, BENEDICT. Joseph Wright of Derby Painter of Light. London/NY, 1968. 2 vols. (Sl sunned, corners sl bumped.) *Washton*. $225/£141

NICOLSON, HAROLD. The Desire to Please. London: Constable, 1943. 1st Eng ed. VG (spine ends sl bumped) in dj (chipped, rubbed, extensively torn, spine dknd). *Ulysses*. $56/£35

NICOLSON, JAMES R. Shetland. David & Charles, 1972. 1st ed. 2 maps. VG in dj. *Hollett*. $32/£20

NIEDECKER, LORINE. North Central. London: Fulcrum, (1968). 1st trade ed. VF in dj. *Captain's Bookshelf*. $150/£94

NIEDECKER, LORINE. North Central. London: Fulcrum, 1968. 1st ed. Fine in dj (sl rubbed). *Dermont*. $75/£47

NIELSEN, HELEN. Borrow the Night. Morrow, 1956. 1st ed. (Edges lt worn, lt remains at ep), else VG in dj (lt worn, couple chips). *Murder*. $30/£19

NIETZ, JOHN A. Old Textbooks: Spelling, Grammar, Reading, Arithmetic.... Univ of Pittsburgh, (1961). 1st ed. Red cl. Good (sl handling). *Baltimore**. $30/£19

NIETZSCHE, FRIEDRICH. Thus Spake Zarathustra. LEC, 1964. Ltd to 1500 numbered. Fine in slipcase. *Swann**. $57/£36

NIETZSCHE, FRIEDRICH. Thus Spake Zarathustra. Thomas Common (trans). NY: LEC, 1964. One of 1500. 1/2 white vellum, blue bds, gilt. Fine in glassine, slipcase. *Pacific**. $86/£54

NIGGLI, JOSEFINA. A Miracle for Mexico. NYGS, 1964. 1st ed. 4to. Alejandro Rangel Hidalgo (illus). 179pp. VG (ex-lib) in VG dj. *Price*. $30/£19

NIGGLI, P. Ore Deposits of Magmatic Origin. London: Murby, 1929. (Ex-lib; spine faded), else VG. *Blake*. $65/£41

Night Before Christmas. (NY): Duenewald Ptg Corp, 1949. 8vo. 4 tab-activated moveables by Julian Wehr. Color illus bds (lt edgewear), spiral binding. *Reisler*. $150/£94

NIGHTINGALE, FLORENCE. Notes on Nursing. Harrison, 1860. New ed. Presentation copy. 8vo. Teg. Later 1/2 vellum by Birdsall & Son. *Sotheby's**. $1,563/£977

Nightingale, or Ladies Vocal Companion. Albany: Packard & Co, 1807. 12mo. Copper engr tp, 121pp + 5pp contents. Full leather on bds, gilt. (3-pg ink poem titled 'Legacy' written on feps; lt browning, foxing on text; 3pp, reps w/repaired tears, few pg edges chipped; cvrs, spine lt rubbed, gilt partly faded.) *Hobbyhorse*. $75/£47

Nile Notes. By a Traveller. (By William George Curtis.) London: Richard Bentley, 1851. 1st ed. vi,310pp. Blue wavy cl, gilt. VG (1st, last few ll sl foxed; hinges cracked, bkpl). *Morrell*. $152/£95

NILES, BLAIR. The James. Farrar & Rinehart, (c1939). VG in VG-dj. *Book Broker*. $35/£22

NILES, BLAIR. Martha's Husband: An Informal Portrait of George Washington. NY: McGraw-Hill, 1951. 1st ed. Frontis port. VG in Fair dj. *Connolly*. $25/£16

NILES, JOHN J. The Ballad Book of John Jacob Niles. Boston: Houghton, Mifflin, 1961. 1st ed. Grn cl. VG in dj (edge chipped). *House*. $45/£28

NILES, JOHN M. The Life of Oliver Hazard Perry. Hartford: Oliver D. Cooke, 1821. 2nd ed. 384pp; 5 plts incl fldg view w/tipped-in key. Contemp calf. VG (lacks rep). Howes N157. *Lefkowicz*. $165/£103

NILSSON, STEN. European Architecture in India 1750-1850. (NY): Taplinger, 1969. 1st Amer ed. NF in dj. *Hadley*. $56/£35

NIMROD. (Pseud of Charles J. Apperley.) The Chase, the Turf, and the Road. London, 1837. 1st ed. Uncut. Orig gilt-pict cl (shelfworn, foxed, sl stained, soiled). *Oinonen**. $60/£38

NIMROD. (Pseud of Charles J. Apperley.) Hunting Reminiscences: Comprising Memoirs of Masters of Hounds; Notices of the Crack Riders; and the Characteristics of the Hunting Countries of England. London, 1943. 1st ed. Orig cl (shelfworn, expertly recased, sl foxed). *Oinonen**. $80/£50

NIMROD. (Pseud of Charles J. Apperley.) The Life of a Sportsman. London, 1842. 1st ed, 1st issue, w/4 plts mtd, etc. 8vo. Pict tp, 35 hand-colored plts. Aeg. Full red morocco by Morrell. (Sl rubbed.) *Oinonen**. $750/£469

NIMROD. (Pseud of Charles J. Apperley.) Nimrod's Northern Tour, Descriptive of the Principal Hunts in Scotland and the North of England. London: Spiers, 1838. 1st ed. Pub's cl (shelfworn). *Oinonen**. $130/£81

NIMROD. (Pseud of Charles J. Apperley.) Remarks on the Condition of Hunters, the Choice of Horses, and Their Management. London, 1831. 1st ed. Steel-engr frontis. Contemp marbled bds, calf back and tips. (Shelfworn, cvr soil, sl foxing, etc.) *Oinonen**. $90/£56

NIN, ANAIS. D. H. Lawrence. Paris: Edward W. Titus, 1932. 1st ed, 1st bk. One of 550 numbered. NF in NF dj (sm chip on bottom of fr panel). *Smith*. $400/£250

NIN, ANAIS. The Four-Chambered Heart. NY: Duell, Sloan & Pearce, (1950). 1st ed. Blue cl, gilt. Good (lt dampstaining to pastedowns, margins of 1st/last few ll; eps lt browned; spine extrems rubbed) in dj (chipped, flap folds dampstained). *Heritage*. $100/£63

NIN, ANAIS. Ladders to Fire. NY: Dutton, 1946. 1st US ed. Inscribed. VG + in dj (few chips, tears). *Lame Duck*. $125/£78

NIN, ANAIS. Realism and Reality. NY: Alicat Bookshop, 1946. One of 750. (Pp sl dknd), else NF in stapled illus wraps. *Lame Duck*. $25/£16

Ninepenny Piece, and the Little Basket Maker. Providence: George P. Daniels, 1845. Later ed. 23pp. VG in orig ptd wrappers. *Brown*. $50/£31

Nineteenth Century Type Displayed in 18 Fonts Cast by United States Founders Now in the Cases of the Grabhorn Press. SF: David Magee, 1959. One of 300 ptd. 1/2 cl, patterned bds, leather spine label. Fine. *Pacific**. $104/£65

NIVEN, DAVID. Go Slowly, Come Back Quickly. GC: Doubleday, 1981. 1st ed. Signed on tipped-in leaf. Fine in Fine dj. *Beasley*. $65/£41

NIX, EVETT DUMAS. Oklahombres, Particularly the Wilder Ones. St. Louis, 1929. 1st ed. VG in dj (worn). *Labordo*. $125/£78

NIXON, HOWARD M. Five Centuries of English Bookbinding. London: Scolar, 1978. 1st ed. Fine in dj. *Michael Taylor*. $64/£40

NIXON, HOWARD M. Five Centuries of English Bookbinding. Scolar, 1978. 1st ed. 100 plts. Dj. *Forest*. $72/£45

NIXON, RICHARD. Leaders. NY: Warner, 1982. 1st ed. Signed. Fine in NF dj. *Beasley*. $150/£94

NIXON, RICHARD. The Real War. (NY): Warner, (1980). 1st ed. Inscribed. Fine in NF dj (sm hole, rear panel lt scratched). *Between The Covers*. $200/£125

NIXON, RICHARD. Six Crises. GC: Doubleday, 1962. 1st ed, later ptg. Inscribed. Good (discoloration spots to cvr; lacks dj). *Agvent*. $300/£188

NIXON, STUART. Redwood Empire. NY, 1966. 1st ed. Color frontis, map. NF in VG + dj. *Sagebrush.* $60/£38

NIZAMI. The Poems of Nizami. Laurence Binyon (described by). Studio, 1928. 16 color plts. (Sl soiled, sm spine labels.) *Edwards.* $56/£35

NIZER, LOUIS. Between You and Me: A Biography of Spare Time. NY, (1948). Signed presentation. Dj. *Argosy.* $40/£25

Noah's Ark. Dundee: Valentine & Sons, n.d. Shapebook. 6 1/4 x 3 1/2. 23pp. Pict paper wraps. VG (1918 inscrip). *Davidson.* $95/£59

NOAKES, AUBREY. The World of Henry Alken. London: Witherby, 1952. 1st ed. VG in Fair dj. *October Farm.* $45/£28

NOAKES, VIVIEN. Edward Lear. Boston: Houghton Mifflin, (1968). 1st ed, 2nd ptg. NF in dj. *Turtle Island.* $45/£28

NOBEL, E. et al. The Nutrition of Healthy and Sick Infants and Children. Phila, 1929. 1st ed in English. *Fye.* $100/£63

NOBILI, RICCARDO. The Gentle Art of Faking. London, 1922. 22 plts hors texte. 1/2 cl (sl stained). *Washton.* $35/£22

NOBILI, RICCARDO. The Gentle Art of Faking. London, 1922. 1st ed. Buckram (rebound), title label. NF. *Polyanthos.* $35/£22

NOBLE, L. F. The Shinumo Quadrangle: Grand Canyon District, Arizona. Washington: USGS, 1914. 18 plts, map in rear pocket, full-color foldout. Good + . *Five Quail.* $45/£28

NOCK, ALBERT JAY. Journal of Forgotten Days, 1934-1935. Hinsdale, IL: Regnery, 1948. 1st ed. NF in NF dj (spine dknd). *Agvent.* $35/£22

NOE, COTTON. The Legend of the Silver Band. Louisville: John P. Morton, 1932. 1st ed. Signed. VG in Good dj. *Connolly.* $30/£19

NOEL, THEOPHILUS. Autobiography and Reminiscences of Theophilus Noel. Chicago: Theo. Noel Co Print, 1904. 1st ed. Frontisport. Blind-stamped dk red cl, gilt. VG (3 torn pp archivally repaired; hinges sl tender). *Chapel Hill.* $350/£219

NOGUCHI, YONE. Hiroshige. NY, 1921. One of 750. 20 plts, incl mtd color frontis. Japanese-style wrappers (cvrs spotted). Cl sleeve w/ivory clasps (sl worn). *Swann*.* $69/£43

NOGUCHI, YONE. Korin. London, 1922. One of 450. Tipped-in color frontis. Japanese-style wrappers. Cl sleeve w/ivory clasps (spine faded). *Swann*.* $172/£108

NOGUCHI, YONE. Lafcadio Hearn in Japan. NY, (1911). Inscribed by Hearn's great-grandson, Bon Koizumi. Silk string-tied flexible pict bds. (Bkpl.) Slipcase (defective). *Swann*.* $258/£161

NOGUERES, HENRI. Munich: The Phoney Peace. Patrick O'Brian (trans). Weidenfeld, 1965. 1st UK ed. VG + in dj (spine sl faded, sm closed tear). *Williams.* $77/£48

NOLAN, EDWARD HENRY. The Illustrated History of the British Empire in India and the East. London, late 1850s. 2 vols in 8; in orig pub's bound parts, w/tps and prelims bound at rear of last part. Gilt-pict cl. (Ex-lib, labels; spine ends frayed.) *Swann*.* $201/£126

NOLAN, FREDERICK W. (ed). The Life and Death of John Henry Tunstall. Albuquerque: Univ of NM, (1965). 1st ed. VG in dj. *Lien.* $50/£31

NOLAN, FREDERICK W. (ed). The Life and Death of John Henry Tunstall. Albuquerque, 1965. 1st ed. Fine in dj (price-clipped). *Baade.* $47/£29

NOLAN, JEANNETTE COVERT. The Story of Clara Barton of the Red Cross. NY, 1941. 1st ed. VG (extrems sl worn). *Doctor's Library.* $30/£19

NOMA, SEIROKU. Japanese Costume and Textile Arts. NY/Tokyo: Weatherhill/Heibonsha, (1974). 1st ed in English. Dec bds. Fine in dj. *Turtle Island.* $50/£31

NORBURY, JAMES. Traditional Knitting Patterns. Batsford, 1962. 1st ed. VG in dj (sl worn, repaired). *Whittle.* $40/£25

NORDAN, LEWIS. Wolf Whistle. Chapel Hill: Algonquin Books, 1993. 1st ed. Fine in Fine dj. *Pettler.* $25/£16

NORDEN, FRIDERIK LUDWIG. Travels in Egypt and Nubia. London: Lockyer Davis & Charles Reymers, 1757. 1st sm-format ed in English. 2 vols in 1. 7 fldg plts. Contemp calf. (Old lib stamps; rear joint cracked.) *Swann*.* $460/£288

NORDEN, HERMANN. Byways of the Tropic Seas. Phila: Macrae, Smith, n.d. (ca 1920). 1st ed. 2 fldg maps. (Sl rubbed, sl foxed), o/w VG. *Worldwide.* $35/£22

NORDENSKJOLD, A. E. The Voyage of the Vega Round Asia and Europe.... London: Macmillan, 1883. Rpt. 2 vols. xxv,524; xviii,413pp + ads; 2 maps. Good + (sl rubbed, spine head tear). *Walcot.* $48/£30

NORDHOFF, CHARLES and JAMES NORMAN HALL. Falcons of France. Boston: Little, Brown, 1929. 1st ed. Color frontis. Blue cl stamped in red. (Eps sl tanned), else VF in dj (few sl edge nicks). *Reese.* $275/£172

NORDHOFF, CHARLES and JAMES NORMAN HALL. The Hurricane. Boston: Little, Brown, 1936. 1st ed. (Cl lt faded), else Fine in N. C. Wyeth pict dj (extrems lt worn). Pub's ad on wraparound strip. *Bromer.* $200/£125

NORDHOFF, CHARLES and JAMES NORMAN HALL. Mutiny on the Bounty. Boston: Little, Brown, 1932. 1st ed. VG in dj (spine area dknd, ends chipped). *Pacific*.* $40/£25

NORDHOFF, CHARLES and JAMES NORMAN HALL. Mutiny on the Bounty. LEC, 1974. Ltd to 1500 numbered, signed by Fletcher Martin (illus). Fine in slipcase. *Swann*.* $126/£79

NORDHOFF, CHARLES and JAMES NORMAN HALL. Pitcairn's Island. Boston: Little, Brown, 1934. 1st ed. VF in red-brown cl. Illus dj (extrems lt worn). *Bromer.* $250/£156

NORDHOFF, CHARLES. California: A Book for Travellers and Settlers for Health, Pleasure, and Residence. NY: Harper, 1873. 225pp. VG (lacks rep, hinges worn). *Book Market.* $85/£53

NORDHOFF, CHARLES. California: For Health, Pleasure, and Residence. NY: Harper, 1873. 1st ed. 255pp + 4pp pub's ads at rear; 3 full-pg maps. Orig red-brn cl, gilt, black trim stamped in black. (Sl aged, lt foxed, few smudges, ink handstamps; sl dusty, worn, lt spotting along spine, edges.) *Baltimore*.* $60/£38

NORDHOFF, CHARLES. The Derelict. Boston: Little, Brown, 1928. 1st ed. Blue cl stamped in black. Fine in NF pict dj (creased closed tear top edge fr panel). *Reese.* $275/£172

NORDHOFF, CHARLES. Man-of-War Life. NY: Dodd, Mead, (1895). 286pp. Sound (dampstained). *Lefkowicz.* $30/£19

NORDHOFF, CHARLES. Peninsular California. NY: Harper, 1888. 1st ed. 130pp. VF. *Book Market.* $200/£125

NORDON, PIERRE. Conan Doyle: A Biography. NY: Holt, Rinehart & Winston, (1967). 1st ed. Rev slip laid in. NF in VG dj. *Gravesend.* $55/£34

NORDYKE, LEWIS. Cattle Empire. NY: William Morrow, 1949. 1st ed. Good (spine ends rubbed). *Lien.* $30/£19

NORDYKE, LEWIS. Cattle Empire. NY: William Morrow, 1949. 1st ed. VG + in dj (chipped, worn). *Labordo.* $55/£34

NORELLI, MARTINA R. American Wildlife Painting. Watson-Guptill, (1975). 1st ptg. Good in dj (repaired). *Rybski.* $65/£41

NORFOLK, HORATIO EDWARD. Gleanings in Graveyards. John Russell Smith, 1866. 3rd ed. xviii,208pp. Aeg. Contemp tree calf (neatly recased), gilt extra. *Hollett.* $120/£75

NORFOLK, LAWRENCE. Lempriere's Dictionary. S. Stevenson, 1991. One of 150 signed. 1/4 cl, marbled bds. Fine in pub's glassine (sl worn). *Any Amount.* $48/£30

NORIE, JOHN WILLIAM. The New Seaman's Guide and Coaster's Companion. London, 1821. Frontis. Later cl (fr cvr loose). *Swann*.* $103/£64

NORLING, JO and ERNEST. Pogo's Lamb: a Story of Wool. NY: Holt, (1947). 8vo. 48pp. VG (inscrip) in VG dj (extrems sl worn). *Price.* $25/£16

NORLUNDE, C. VOLMER. Letter from a Danish Typographer. Nordlundes Bogtrykkeri, 1967. One of 400. *Dawson.* $20/£13

NORMAN, A. G. (ed). Advances in Agronomy. NY: Academic, 1949-1954. 1st ed. 6 vols. (Lib sm ink spine #s), else VG. *Larry Price.* $75/£47

NORMAN, B. M. Rambles in Yucatan, Including a Visit to the Remarkable Ruins of Chi-Chen, Kabbah, Zayi, Uxmal.... NY: J. & H.G. Langley, 1843. 2nd ed. Litho frontis, 22 full-pg plts, map. Full contemp leather, gilt. (Piece torn from rep, lib jacket residue on pastedown, inner hinge weak; extrems sl worn, rubbed, bumped.) *Metropolitan*.* $258/£161

NORMAN, DOROTHY. Encounters: A Memoir. NY: Harcourt, Brace, Jovanovich, (1987). 1st ed. Summer 1987 signed presentation. Text Fine, cvrs NF (sl worn) in dj (lt rubbed). *Baltimore*.* $45/£28

NORMAN, FRANCIS MARTIN. Martello Tower in China. London: George Allen, 1902. 1st ed. Inscribed, dated 1902. 22 plts, charts (2 color), incl frontis. Grn cl, gilt. VG (lt foxed, ink inscrip; sl rubbed, stained). *Morrell.* $152/£95

NORMAN, HENRY. All the Russias. Travels and Studies.... NY: Scribner, 1902. 1st ed. 1 fldg map. Teg. (Sl rubbed), o/w VG. *Worldwide.* $65/£41

NORMAN, HOWARD. Kiss in the Hotel Joseph Conrad. NY, 1989. 1st ed. Fine in NF dj. *Warren.* $75/£47

NORMAN, L. Pioneer Shipping of Tasmania. Hobart, Tasmania: J. Walsh, 1938. 1st ed. VG in dj. *American Booksellers.* $155/£97

NORMAN, P. E. Sculpture in Wood. The Studio, 1954. 1st ed. Good+ (sl soiled). *Whittle.* $16/£10

NORMAN, PHILIP. London Signs and Inscriptions. London, 1893. Frontis, xx,237pp. Unopened. 2-tone cl, gilt medallion fr bd. (Bkpl, feps browned; soiled.) *Edwards.* $48/£30

NORMAN-NERUDA, MAY (ed). The Climbs of Norman-Neruda. T. Fisher Unwin, 1899. 1st ed. (Fep browned, sl torn, few spots; spine faded, recased, rear bd sl mkd.) *Hollett.* $280/£175

NORRIS, FRANK. The Collected Letters. Jesse Crisler (ed). SF: Book Club of CA, 1986. Ltd ed. One of 500. Patterned bds, red cl backstrip. Fine. *Harrington.* $125/£78

NORRIS, FRANK. Frank Norris of 'The Wave': Stories and Sketches from the San Francisco Weekly, 1893 to 1897. SF: Westgate, 1931. One of 500 ptd. Signed by Oscar Lewis (intro). 1/2 cl, dec bds, spine label. NF. *Pacific*.* $29/£18

NORRIS, FRANK. The Letters of Frank Norris. Franklin Walker (ed). SF: Book Club of CA, 1956. One of 350 ptd. Frontis port. Ptd spine label. Fine. *Bohling.* $120/£75

NORRIS, FRANK. The Pit. Grant Richards, 1903. 1st UK ed. Red dec cl, gilt. Good+ (pp lt foxed, tp sl creased, contents sl shaken; cl sl mkd). *Any Amount.* $48/£30

NORRIS, FRANK. The Pit. NY: Doubleday, Page, 1903. 1st ed, 2nd issue (with the J.J. Little device but without 'First Edition' on c. pg). Red cl, gilt. NF (sl askew). *Sumner & Stillman.* $75/£47

NORRIS, FRANK. The Responsibilities of the Novelist and Other Literary Essays. NY: Doubleday, Page, 1903. 1st ed. Frontisport. Grn cl (sl soiled), gilt. VG. BAL 15040. *Cummins.* $175/£109

NORRIS, GEORGE. Blood-Pressure: Its Clinical Applications. Phila, 1914. 1st ed. (Inner hinges cracked; corner bumped.) *Fye.* $100/£63

NORRIS, GEORGE. Studies in Cardiac Pathology. Phila, 1911. 1st ed. *Fye.* $200/£125

NORRIS, ISAAC. The Journal of Isaac Norris. Phila: Hawthorne Press, 1867. 1st ed. One of 80. Port, 31pp. Orig wrappers. NF. Howes N182. *Brown.* $75/£47

NORRIS, KATHLEEN. Little Ships. GC: Doubleday, Page, 1925. 1st ed. (Pencil presentation fep), else NF in dj (chip). *Hermitage.* $35/£22

NORRIS, THADDEUS. The American Angler's Book. Phila: Porter & Coates, (1865). New ed, w/supp. Grn cl, gilt. (Bkpls, fr hinge sl weak, rear hinge cracked, sig detached; spine head frayed), else VG. *Pacific*.* $58/£36

NORRIS, W. E. Adrian Vidal. Smith, Elder, 1885. 1st ed. 3 vols. Half-titles each vol. Contemp 1/4 calf, dec cl. (Bkpls; 1st, last pp lt foxed.) *Bickersteth.* $104/£65

North Dakota. NY: OUP, 1950. 2nd ed. NF in dj. *Labordo.* $25/£16

North Dakota: A Guide to the Northern Prairie State. Fargo: State Hist Soc of ND, 1938. 1st ed, 1st ptg. 3-color fldg map tipped in at rear. Grn cl, gilt. Fine in dj (chipped, losses at spine ends, tape reinforcements on verso). *Harrington.* $250/£156

NORTH, ANDREW. (Pseud of Andre Norton.) Plague Ship. NY: Gnome, (1956). 1st ed. Bkpl signed by Norton laid-in loose. 1st binding in tan bds. (Black offset from former dj protector to ep extrems, cl), else VG in NF dj. *Pacific*.* $115/£72

NORTH, ANDREW. (Pseud of Andre Norton.) Sargasso of Space. NY: Gnome, 1955. 1st ed. Inscribed, signed, both as North and Norton, dated June, 1955. 1st binding in gray cl. VG in dj (spine ends lt chipped, joints lt rubbed, spine sl sunned). *Pacific*.* $98/£61

NORTH, ARTHUR WALBRIDGE. Camp and Camino in Lower California. NY: Baker & Taylor, 1910. 1st ed. VG. *Book Market.* $50/£31

NORTH, ELISHA. A Treatise on a Malignant Epidemic, Commonly Called Spotted Fever. NY: T. & J. Swords, 1811. 1st ed. 8vo. xi,249,(1 errata),(2 ads)pp; complete w/fldg table at p60. Mod marbled bds, calf spine, red morocco label, vellum tips. Fine (bkpls). *Glaser.* $750/£469

NORTH, JOSEPH. Men in the Ranks. NY: Friends of the Abraham Lincoln Brigade, 1939. Fine in wrappers. *Heritage.* $200/£125

NORTH, MARIANNE. A Vision of Eden. NY: HRW, 1980. 1st US ed. Fine in dj (price-clipped). *Archer.* $30/£19

NORTH, MARY REMSEN. Down the Colorado River. NY, 1930. 1st ed. Pict eps. Orange cl. (Name; spine lt faded, spotting), o/w VG-. *Five Quail.* $45/£28

NORTH, ROGER. The Autobiography of the Hon. Roger North. Augustus Jessopp (ed). London: David Nutt, 1887. Dec grey cl (sl worn), gilt. *Boswell.* $125/£78

NORTHCLIFFE, ALFRED CHARLES HARMSWORTH. Motors and Motor-Driving. Longmans, Green, 1906. 4th ed. Pict cl. Nice. *Ash.* $120/£75

Northeast Passage. John Nurminen Foundation/Helsinki Univ Library, 1992. Fldg map. Mint in dj. *Explorer.* $80/£50

Northern Kensington, Survey of London, Volume XXXVII. London: Athlone Press, 1973. Fldg map in rear pocket. Cl dj. *Marlborough.* $80/£50

Northern Shepherd, Being a Report of a Committee...Upon the Diseases and Management of Sheep. Winthrop, (ME): William Noyes, 1835. 1st ed. 132pp. Contemp calf-backed bds. *M & S.* $200/£125

NORTHROP, JOHN. Crystalline Enzymes: The Chemistry of Pepsin, Trypsin, and Bacteriophage. NY, 1939. 1st ed. Signed. *Fye.* $150/£94

NORTHUP, C. S. A Bibliography of Thomas Gray. New Haven: Yale Univ, 1917. Blue cl. *Maggs.* $80/£50

NORTHWOOD, J. D. Familiar Hawaiian Birds. Honolulu: Nickerson, 1940. 1st ed. One of 330 signed. 11 full-pg color plts. Full leather. VG. *Mikesh.* $60/£38

NORTON, ANDRE and INGRID ZIERHUT (eds). Grand Masters' Choice. Cambridge, MA: Nesfa, 1989. 1st ed. One of 275. Signed. Fine in dj, slipcase. *Pacific*.* $81/£51

NORTON, ANDRE (ed). Space Pioneers. Cleveland: World, (1954). 1st ed. VG in dj (spine head chipped, extrems sl creased, torn). *Pacific**. $92/£58

NORTON, ANDRE (ed). Space Police. Cleveland: World, (1956). 1st ed. VG in dj (spine ends, extrems chipped, price-clipped). *Pacific**. $92/£58

NORTON, ANDRE (ed). Space Service. Cleveland: World, (1953). 1st ed. VG in dj (spine sunned, foot sl rubbed, price-clipped). *Pacific**. $104/£65

NORTON, ANDRE. Android at Arms. NY: Harcourt, Brace, Jovanovich, (1971). 1st ed. Signed bkpl laid-in loose. (Sm mk upper corner fep), else NF in dj (spine ends, corners sl rubbed). *Pacific**. $81/£51

NORTON, ANDRE. At Swords' Point. NY: Harcourt, Brace, (1954). 1st ed. NF in dj (spine ends rubbed, flaps clipped). *Pacific**. $104/£65

NORTON, ANDRE. Breed to Come. NY: Viking, (1972). 1st ed. Signed bkpl laid-in loose. Fine in dj. *Pacific**. $161/£101

NORTON, ANDRE. Catseye. NY: Harcourt, Brace & World, (1961). 1st ed. VG in dj (spine ends, extrems rubbed, closed tear rear panel). *Pacific**. $35/£22

NORTON, ANDRE. Dark Piper. NY: Harcourt, Brace & World, (1968). 1st ed. NF in dj (price-clipped). *Pacific**. $40/£25

NORTON, ANDRE. Dark Piper. NY: Harcourt, Brace & World, (1968). 1st ed. Signed. Fine in dj. *Pacific**. $81/£51

NORTON, ANDRE. The Defiant Agents. Cleveland: World, (1962). 1st ed. Signed bkpl laid-in loose. VG in dj (spine ends, corners sl chipped, price-clipped, 1-inch tear, crease to lower fr joint). *Pacific**. $46/£29

NORTON, ANDRE. Dread Companion. NY: Harcourt, Brace, Jovanovich, (1970). 1st ed. Inscribed, signed. (Rmdr mk bottom edges), else Fine in dj. *Pacific**. $46/£29

NORTON, ANDRE. Forerunner Foray. NY: Viking, (1973). 1st ed. Signed. Pict reinforced binding. NF in dj. *Pacific**. $40/£25

NORTON, ANDRE. Galactic Derelict. Cleveland: World, (1959). 1st ed. Signed bkpl laid-in loose. (Name), else NF in dj (spine ends, extrems rubbed). *Pacific**. $92/£58

NORTON, ANDRE. Garan the Eternal. Alhambra: Fantasy, (1972). 1st ed. Signed. NF in dj (shorter than vol due to ptr's error). *Pacific**. $29/£18

NORTON, ANDRE. Ice Crown. NY: Viking, (1970). 1st ed. Inscribed, signed. Binding A in plain grn cl. Fine in dj. *Pacific**. $81/£51

NORTON, ANDRE. Iron Cage. NY: Viking, (1974). 1st ed. Signed. Fine in dj. *Pacific**. $52/£33

NORTON, ANDRE. Judgement on Janus. NY: Harcourt, Brace & World, (1963). 1st ed. VG in dj (spine head rubbed, tear, creasing to lower joint). *Pacific**. $40/£25

NORTON, ANDRE. Lord of Thunder. NY: Harcourt, Brace & World, (1962). 1st ed. Inscribed, signed. NF in dj (spine sl sunned, ends sl rubbed). *Pacific**. $86/£54

NORTON, ANDRE. Moon of Three Rings. NY: Viking, (1966). 1st ed. NF in dj (spine ends, extrems sl rubbed, bottom flap corner clipped). *Pacific**. $40/£25

NORTON, ANDRE. Night of Masks. NY: Harcourt, Brace & World, (1964). 1st ed. Inscribed, signed. Fine in dj. *Pacific**. $115/£72

NORTON, ANDRE. Octagon Magic. Cleveland: World, (1967). 1st ed. Inscribed, signed. NF in dj (flaps clipped, 1-inch closed tear top joint fr panel). *Pacific**. $75/£47

NORTON, ANDRE. Ordeal in Otherwhere. Cleveland: World, 1964. 1st ed. NF in dj (spine head rubbed, tear to rear panel). *Pacific**. $40/£25

NORTON, ANDRE. Ordeal in Otherwhere. Cleveland: World, 1964. 1st ed. Signed. NF in dj (spine, extrems rubbed). *Pacific**. $58/£36

NORTON, ANDRE. Postmarked the Stars. NY: Harcourt, Brace & World, (1969). 1st ed. VG in dj (extrems rubbed, sm tear spine foot). *Pacific**. $46/£29

NORTON, ANDRE. Postmarked the Stars. NY: Harcourt, Brace & World, (1969). 1st ed. Signed bkpl laid-in loose. Fine in dj. *Pacific**. $81/£51

NORTON, ANDRE. Rebel Spurs. Cleveland: World, (1962). 1st ed. Fine in dj. *Pacific**. $259/£162

NORTON, ANDRE. Ride Proud, Rebel! Cleveland: World, (1961). 1st ed. (Inscrip), else NF in dj (spine ends rubbed). *Pacific**. $345/£216

NORTON, ANDRE. Rogue Reynard. Boston: Houghton Mifflin, 1947. 1st ed. 7.3x9.7. Laura Bannon (illus). VG (top corner edgeworn 1/4-inch). *Price*. $65/£41

NORTON, ANDRE. Scarface. NY: Comet Books, (1949). 1st ed. (Sl crease to lower spine), else NF in wrappers. *Pacific**. $23/£14

NORTON, ANDRE. Sea Siege. NY: Harcourt, Brace, (1957). 1st ed. Signed bkpl laid-in loose. NF in dj (spine head sl rubbed). *Pacific**. $127/£79

NORTON, ANDRE. Stand to Horse. NY: Harcourt, Brace, (1956). 1st ed. Inscribed, signed. Fine in dj. *Pacific**. $288/£180

NORTON, ANDRE. Star Born. Cleveland: World, (1957). 1st ed. Inscribed, signed, dated May 1957. Fine in dj. *Pacific**. $489/£306

NORTON, ANDRE. Star Gate. NY: Harcourt, Brace, (1958). 1st ed. Fine in 2 djs. *Pacific**. $86/£54

NORTON, ANDRE. Star Guard. NY: Harcourt, Brace, (1955). 1st ed. NF in dj (price, flap tips clipped). *Pacific**. $98/£61

NORTON, ANDRE. The Stars Are Ours! Cleveland: World, (1954). 1st ed. (Offset to fep from ptr's glue), else VG in dj (spine ends rubbed, sm tear, price-clipped). *Pacific**. $109/£68

NORTON, ANDRE. Steel Magic. Cleveland: World, (1965). 1st ed. NF in dj (spine head rubbed). *Pacific**. $46/£29

NORTON, ANDRE. The Time Traders. Cleveland: World, (1958). 1st ed. Clipped sig of Norton at bottom of tl mtd to fep. Fine in dj. *Pacific**. $109/£68

NORTON, ANDRE. Uncharted Stars. NY: Viking, (1969). 1st ed. Signed. NF in dj (spine ends sl rubbed). *Pacific**. $69/£43

NORTON, ANDRE. Victory on Janus. NY: Harcourt, Brace, World, (1966). 1st ed. Signed. NF in dj (spine sl sunned, ends sl rubbed). *Pacific**. $63/£39

NORTON, ANDRE. Victory on the Planet Janus. NY: Harcourt Brace, 1966. 1st ed. VG+ (sl shelfworn) in dj (sl edgworn, sl rubbed). *My Bookhouse*. $77/£48

NORTON, ANDRE. Were-Wrath. (New Castle, VA): Cheap Street, (1984). 1st ed. Signed by Norton and King-Rieniers (illus). One of 175. Fine in dj. *Pacific**. $127/£79

NORTON, ANDRE. The X Factor. NY: Harcourt, Brace, (1965). 1st ed. NF in dj (spine head rubbed). *Pacific**. $40/£25

NORTON, ANDRE. The X Factor. NY: Harcourt, Brace, (1965). 1st ed. Inscribed, signed. Fine in dj. *Pacific**. $75/£47

NORTON, ANDRE. Yankee Privateer. Cleveland: World, (1955). 1st ed. Inscribed, signed, dated 1959. Leonard Vosburgh (illus). NF in dj (spine ends sl rubbed, sm tear, crease to spine foot). *Pacific**. $690/£431

NORTON, EDWARD FELIX. The Fight for Everest: 1924. NY, 1925. 1st Amer ed. (Inscrip; few lt stains fr cvr.) *Swann**. $92/£58

541

NORTON, HERMAN. Record of Facts Concerning the Persecutions at Madeira in 1843 and 1846. NY: American & Foreign Christian Union, 1849. 2nd ed. 228pp; 2 ports. Orig brn emb cl, gilt. (Foxed; cl worn, esp spine.) *Parmer*. $125/£78

NORTON, L. A. The Life and Adventures of Col. L.A. Norton, Written by Himself. Oakland: Pacific Press, 1887. 1st ed. Wood-engr frontis, 492pp. (Edges rubbed), else VG. Howes N210. *Pacific**. $58/£36

NORTON, MARY. The Borrowers Afield. Harcourt, 1955. 1st ed. Beth & Joe Krush (illus). 215pp. VG (fep sl foxed, bottom edges sl worn) in VG dj (chipped, spine ends, rear torn, scrape). *Price*. $75/£47

NORTON, MARY. The Borrowers Afloat. Harcourt, 1959. 1st ed. Beth & Joe Krush (illus). 191pp. NF in VG dj (1/4-inch chips at spine ends, spine rubbed). *Price*. $60/£38

NORTON, MARY. The Borrowers Aloft. Harcourt, 1961. 1st Amer ed. Beth & Joe Krush (illus). 193pp. NF in VG dj (sm spine chips, worn, rear browned, bkpl). *Price*. $55/£34

NORWAY, ARTHUR H. History of the Post-Office Packet Service Between the Years 1793-1815. London/NY: Macmillan, 1895. 1st ed. (x),312pp; 6 plts. (Extrems rubbed.) *Lefkowicz*. $85/£53

NOSTRADAMUS. The True Prophecies or Prognostications of Michael Nostradamus, Physician to Henry II, Francis II, and Charles IX...and One of the Best Astronomers That Ever Were. London: Thomas Ratcliffe & Nathaniel Thompson, 1672. 1st ed. Folio. Frontis port, (36),522pp. Old gilt-ruled calf, partial morocco spine label. VG (bkpl; spine severely rubbed, lacks most of spine label). *Pacific**. $2,070/£1,294

NOSTRADAMUS. The True Prophecies or Prognostications.... Theophilus de Garencieres (trans). London: Thomas Ratcliffe & Nathaniel Thompson, 1672. 1st ed in English. 18 prelim ll, 522pp (lacks frontisport, tp sl torn, chipped). Old full calf (worn, rubbed, cvrs detached, spine splitting). *Kane**. $800/£500

Not so Quiet...Stepdaughters of War. (By Helen Zenna Smith.) Albert Marriott, 1930. 1st Eng ed. VG (name; no dj). *Clearwater*. $32/£20

Note Upon Early Cambridge Binders of the Sixteenth Century. Cambridge: John P. Gray & Son, 1900. 1st ed. 2 plts. Ptd wrappers. *Forest*. $51/£32

Notes of a Journey Through France and Italy. (By William Hazlitt.) London: Hunt & Clarke, 1826. 1st ed. 8vo. New 1/2 calf over brn cl bds, black leather labels. *Maggs*. $560/£350

Notes of the Cruise of the 'Caprice' Yacht, Royal St. George's Yacht Club, to Iceland and Norway in the Summer and Autumn of 1850. Dublin: Alexander Thom, 1851. 8vo. 8 litho plts. Contemp diced calf, spine gilt in compartments, morocco label. (B. R. James inscrip.) *Christie's**. $630/£394

Notes Upon the Twelve Books of Paradise Lost. Collected from the Spectator.... (By Joseph Addison.) London: J.&R. Tonson, 1738. 1st ed thus. 144pp. Recent 1/2 calf. *Young*. $64/£40

NOTESTEIN, WALLACE. The English People on the Eve of Colonization 1603-1630. NY: Harper, (1954). 1st ed. 3 maps, 16 plts. Blue cl. Fine in VG pict dj. *House*. $15/£9

Nothing to Lose. Cassell, 1955. 1st ed. NF (edges, prelims sl spotted) in dj (edges sl rubbed). *Ulysses*. $56/£35

Nothing to Wear: An Episode of City Life. (By William Allen Butler.) NY: Rudd & Carleton, 1857. 1st ed. 68pp. Pub's list inserted. (Shelf-worn, edges, spine worn), else Good. BAL 2228. *Brown*. $15/£9

Notices and Voyages of the Famed Quebec Mission to the Pacific Northwest. Being the Correspondence, Notices, etc. of Fathers Blanchet and Demers, Together with Those of Fathers Bolduc and Langlois...1838 to 1847. (Portland): OR Historical Soc, 1957. One of 1000 ptd. Fldg map. Pict cl. Fine. *Pacific**. $58/£36

Nott's Brigade in Afghanistan 1838-1842. (By John Temple Knox.) Bombay, 1880. 1st ed. 113pp. (Sl browned, lt foxed, 2 ll crudely opened; sl worn, spine sl frayed.) *Edwards*. $136/£85

NOTT, STANLEY CHARLES. Chinese Jade Throughout the Ages. London: Batsford, (1936). 1st ed. 39 color plts. Brn dec cl. Good. *Appelfeld*. $100/£63

NOTT, STANLEY CHARLES. Chinese Jade Throughout the Ages. London, (1936). 1st ed. 148 plts (39 color). *Swann**. $103/£64

NOTT, STANLEY CHARLES. Chinese Jades in the Stanley Charles Nott Collection. West Palm Beach, 1942. 1st ed. One of 1000 numbered. Folio. Color frontisport, 118 photo plts. (Fr joint cracked.) *Swann**. $201/£126

Now-A-Days Fairy Book. London: George G. Harrap, (1926). Early rpt. Folio. (vi),7-159pp; 5 full-pg color plts by Jessie Willcox Smith. Cl-backed pict bds, plt onlaid to upper cvr. Excellent (lt speckled). *Sotheran*. $109/£68

NOWAK, R. M. and J. L. PARAQDISO. Walker's Mammals of the World. Balt: Johns Hopkins, (1983). 4th ed. 2 vols. Fine in Fine djs. *Mikesh*. $75/£47

NOWLAN, PHIL. Buck Rogers and the Depth Men of Mars. Big Little Book. Racine: Whitman, 1935. 1st ed. Pict bds. (Spine ends, joints sl rubbed), else NF. *Pacific**. $35/£22

NOYCE, WILFRID and IAN McMORRIN (eds). World Atlas of Mountaineering. NY: Macmillan, 1970. 1st Amer ed. 16 full-color photo plts, 32 maps. Fine in VG dj. *Connolly*. $40/£25

NOYES, ALFRED. The Loom of Years. Grant Richards, 1902. 1st ed, 1st bk. Uncut. Good (bkpl) in japon-backed bds (spine sl dknd). *Cox*. $32/£20

NOYES, ALFRED. Walking Shadows. NY, 1918. 1st Amer ed. NF (sl rubbed, spine sunned). *Polyanthos*. $25/£16

NOZAKI, AKIHIRO. Anno's Hat Tricks. NY: Philomel, 1985. 1st ed. 8.5x10.5. Mitsumasa Anno (illus). 44pp. Glossy bds. Fine in dj. *Cattermole*. $40/£25

NUCKEL, OTTO. Destiny: A Novel in Pictures. NY: Farrar & Rinehart, (1930). 1st US ed. 190 full-pg b/w lead-cuts. Black eps. Red cl. Cvrs VG (edges sl dusty) in dj (sl worn, edges chipped, torn). *Baltimore**. $50/£31

NUNAN, THOMAS. Diary of an Old Bohemian. SF: Harr Wagner Pub, (1927). 1st ed. Inscribed, signed presentation. Blue cl. Fine. *Argonaut*. $90/£56

NUNBERG, HERMANN and ERNST FEDERN (eds). Minutes of the Vienna Psychoanalytic Society Volumes 1-4 (1906-1918). NY: Internat'l Universities Press, (1962/1967/1974/1975). 4 vols. Olive cl. VG in djs. *Gach*. $165/£103

NUNIS, DOYCE. The Bidwell-Bartleson Party. Santa Cruz, CA, 1991. VG in dj. *Dumont*. $30/£19

NUNIS, DOYCE. Los Angeles and Its Environs in the Twentieth Century. L.A.: Ward Ritchie, 1973. 1st ed. Beige linen, gilt. Fine in ptd dj. *Pacific**. $63/£39

NUNIS, DOYCE. Southern California's Spanish Heritage. L.A.: Historical Society of Southern CA, 1992. 1st ed. Ltd to 600. Signed by Nunis, Ward Ritchie & Consulate General of Spain in L.A. Gray cl, gilt. Fine in matching cl-cvrd slipcase. *Pacific**. $23/£14

NUNIS, DOYCE. (ed). Josiah Belden, 1841 California Overland Pioneer: His Memoir and Early Letters. Georgetown, CA: Talisman, 1962. Ltd to 750. Fine in VG dj. *Book Market*. $30/£19

NUNIS, DOYCE. (ed). Southern California Local History. L.A.: Zamorano Club, 1994. 1st ed. Ltd to 150, signed by Nunis & Ritchie. Fine. *Book Market*. $60/£38

Nursery ABC. Akron, OH: Saalfield Pub, 1909. Obl 8vo. 10pp (incl inside of cvrs). Full color cl (sl dusty). *Reisler*. $50/£31

Nursery Melodies, or Pretty Rhymes in Easy Verse. NY: C.P. Huestis, n.d. (ca 1880). 12mo. Full-pg tp engr, 24pp + 1pg list on lower wrapper; 12 VF 1/2pg wood engrs. Pict paper wrappers (lt dusted). VG (pencil name tp, trace of previous stitching at gutters, rebacked w/matching color paper). *Hobbyhorse.* $100/£63

Nursery Rhyme Picture Book. (By L. Leslie Brooke.) London: Frederick Warne, ca 1913. 4to. 16 full-pg color plts. Cl-backed cream bds (rear cvr dknd; separations within) w/color illus fr cvr. *Reisler.* $225/£141

Nursery Rhymes. Fullerton, CA: Lorson's, 1985. One of 115. 12 wood engrs by Gwenda Morgan. 1/4 cl, marbled bds. Fine in slipcase. *Michael Taylor.* $77/£48

Nursery Rhymes. London: Frederick Warne, ca 1920. 4to. 14 full-pg plts (6 full color) by Gordon Robinson. Color pict bds (lt mkd). *Reisler.* $200/£125

Nursery Rhymes. With Come-To-Life Pictures. London: Raphael Tuck & Sons, n.d. (195?). A Come-To-Life Little Book. 2 dbl-pg pop-ups. Pict bds. NF. *Bookfinders.* $65/£41

NUSBAUM, AILEEN. The Seven Cities of Cibola. NY: Putnam, 1926. 1st ed. Fine. *Hermitage.* $45/£28

NUTTALL, T. An Introduction to Systematic and Physiological Botany. Boston/Cambridge: Hilliard, Gray et al/Hilliard & Brown, 1827. (Eps sl foxed, sl staining bottom of pp156, 157, 161; binding loose, cracked, dry, sl worn.) *Metropolitan*.* $143/£89

NUTTALL, T. A Manual of the Ornithology of the U.S. and Canada. Boston: Hill, Gray, (1840). 2nd rev ed. 832pp. Orig cl, leather spine label. (Fr cvr loose, spine chipped.) Internally VG+. *Mikesh.* $75/£47

NUTTALL, T. A Popular Handbook of the Birds of the United States and Canada. Boston, 1929. Rev ed. 10 plts. (Bkpl removed, fep blind-stamped; cvrs rubbed.) *King.* $60/£38

NYE, DOUG. The Story of Lotus 1961-1971. Cambridge, MA, 1972. 1st ed. VG in dj (edgeworn). *King.* $50/£31

NYE, EDGAR WILSON and JAMES WHITCOMB RILEY. Nye and Riley's Wit and Humor. Chicago: Homewood Pub, (1902). 1st ed. Pict red cl, gilt. Fine. *Pacific*.* $40/£25

NYE, ELWOOD L. Marching with Custer. Glendale: A.H. Clark, 1964. 1st ed. Ltd to 300. Frontis. VG in pict fabrikoid. *Lien.* $300/£188

NYE, STEPHEN G. Addresses and Letters of Travel. SF: Ptd by Stanley-Taylor Co, 1908. Sound (rubbed, mkd). *Boswell.* $45/£28

NYE, WILBUR S. Here Come the Rebels. Baton Rouge: LA State Univ, (1965). 1st ed. Gray cl. Fine in VG dj. *Chapel Hill.* $80/£50

O

O'BRIAN, PATRICK. The Chian Wine and Other Stories. Collins, 1974. 1st Eng ed. VG (spine ends sl bumped) in dj (sl torn, nicked, creased). *Ulysses.* $200/£125

O'BRIAN, PATRICK. Clarissa Oakes. Harper Collins, 1992. 1st UK ed. Signed. Fine in dj (price-clipped). *Williams.* $200/£125

O'BRIAN, PATRICK. The Commodore. NY: Norton, 1994. 1st US ed. One of 200 numbered, signed. Fine in dj (price-clipped) in Fine illus slipcase. *Unger.* $225/£141

O'BRIAN, PATRICK. Desolation Island. Collins, 1978. 1st UK ed. Fine (bkpl) in dj (price-clipped). *Williams.* $424/£265

O'BRIAN, PATRICK. Desolation Island. Collins, 1978. 1st ed. Pale gray bds, gilt. Fine in dj. *Blackwell's.* $480/£300

O'BRIAN, PATRICK. The Fortune of War. Collins, 1979. 1st UK ed. NF (ink name) in dj. *Williams.* $360/£225

O'BRIAN, PATRICK. The Frozen Flame. Rupert Hart-Davis, 1953. 1st ed. VG (top edge sl dusty, bottom edge sl mkd, corner sl bumped) in Robert Medley dj (nicked, sl rubbed, creased, mkd, dusty, sl torn, spine, edges dknd). *Ulysses.* $880/£550

O'BRIAN, PATRICK. H. M. S. Surprise. NY, 1973. 1st Amer ed. Fine in NF dj (top fr, rear panel creased, sm tears). *Warren.* $175/£109

O'BRIAN, PATRICK. H. M. S. Surprise. Collins, 1973. 1st UK ed. VG+ (sm flaw/hole in fep) in dj. *Williams.* $464/£290

O'BRIAN, PATRICK. The Ionian Mission. Collins, 1981. 1st UK ed. NF in dj. *Williams.* $480/£300

O'BRIAN, PATRICK. The Letter of Marque. Collins, 1988. 1st UK ed. Fine in dj. *Williams.* $160/£100

O'BRIAN, PATRICK. Master and Commander. Collins, 1970. 1st UK ed. VG (ink inscrip) in dj (closed tear to fr fore-edge, rear sl strengthened w/tape). *Williams.* $480/£300

O'BRIAN, PATRICK. Master and Commander. Collins, 1970. 1st ed. Post 8vo. VG in laminated dj (lt sunned, fr panel sl mkd). *Ash.* $632/£395

O'BRIAN, PATRICK. The Mauritius Command. Collins, 1977. 1st UK ed. NF in dj (spine sl faded). *Williams.* $520/£325

O'BRIAN, PATRICK. The Nutmeg of Consolation. Collins, 1991. 1st UK ed. Fine in dj. *Williams.* $192/£120

O'BRIAN, PATRICK. Post Captain. London: Collins, 1972. 1st Eng ed. VG (feps partly browned; spine ends sl bumped) in dj (edges sl rubbed). *Ulysses.* $600/£375

O'BRIAN, PATRICK. The Reverse of the Medal. Collins, 1986. 1st UK ed. NF (rmdr mk to top edge, spine sl creased) in Fine dj. *Williams.* $200/£125

O'BRIAN, PATRICK. Richard Temple. London: Macmillan, 1962. 1st Eng ed. VG (spine ends sl bumped) in dj (rubbed, chipped, torn, creased). *Ulysses.* $400/£250

O'BRIAN, PATRICK. Treason's Harbour. Collins, 1983. 1st UK ed. NF in dj. *Williams.* $456/£285

O'BRIAN, PATRICK. The Unknown Shore. London: Rupert Hart-Davis, 1959. 1st Eng ed. VG (edges sl spotted; spine ends, corner sl bumped) in dj (sl rubbed, spine faded). *Ulysses.* $520/£325

O'BRIEN, DONOUGH. Miniatures in the XVIIIth and XIXth Centuries. London: Batsford, (1951). 1st ed. Signed presentation. Color frontis, 136 plts. Good in dj. *Karmiole.* $85/£53

O'BRIEN, EDNA. August Is a Wicked Month. NY: S&S, (1965). 1st Amer ed. (Eps offset), else VF in VF dj (brittle). *Between The Covers.* $85/£53

O'BRIEN, FLANN. (Pseud of Brian O'Nolan.) The Best of Myles. Kevin O. Nolan (ed). NY: Walker, 1968. 1st US ed. Fine in NF dj. *Pettler.* $40/£25

O'BRIEN, FLANN. (Pseud of Brian O'Nolan.) The Dalkey Archive. Macmillan, 1965. 1st US ed. NF in dj. *Williams.* $72/£45

O'BRIEN, FLANN. (Pseud of Brian O'Nolan.) Stories and Plays. London: Hart-Davis MacGibbon, 1973. 1st ed. Brn flecked bds. Fine in dj. *Maggs.* $88/£55

O'BRIEN, FLANN. (Pseud of Brian O'Nolan.) The Third Policeman. NY: Walker, 1967. 1st US ed. (Name), o/w Fine in NF dj. *Beasley.* $45/£28

O'BRIEN, HARRIET E. (comp.) Paul Revere's Own Story. (Boston): Privately ptd, 1929. 1st ed. One of 500 numbered. Frontisport. Teg, untrimmed. Tan cl, blue-gray bds (few lt spots rear cvr), gilt. Text Fine. *Baltimore*.* $30/£19

O'BRIEN, JACK. The Return of Silver Chief. Winston, 1943. Apparent 1st ed. Kurt Wiese (illus). 211pp. VG (1944 inscrip) in Good dj (edges chipped, torn). *Price.* $25/£16

O'BRIEN, JOHN S. By Dog Sled for Byrd. Chicago: Rockwell, 1931. 1st ed. VG. *High Latitude.* $50/£31

O'BRIEN, JOHN. Leaving Las Vegas. Wichita: Watermark, 1990. 1st ed. Signed. Fine in dj. *Lame Duck.* $350/£219

O'BRIEN, MARY LOUISE. Netsuke: A Guide for Collectors. Rutland, VT/Tokyo, (1965). 1st ed. Dj. *Argosy.* $60/£38

O'BRIEN, TIM. Going After Cacciato. (NY): Delacorte, (1978). 1st ed. Signed. Fine in Fine dj. *Lenz.* $225/£141

O'BRIEN, TIM. If I Die in a Combat Zone. London: Calder & Boyers, 1973. 1st ed. Fine in dj. *Smith.* $150/£94

O'CALLAGHAN, JOHN CORNELIUS. History of the Irish Brigades in the Service of France, from the Revolution in Great Britain and Ireland Under James II, to the Revolution in France Under Louis XVI. Glasgow: Cameron & Ferguson, 1870. 1st ed. Frontisport, xiii,649,6pp; 1 dbl-pg illus. Grn cl, gilt. VG (eps renewed; rubbed, corners lt worn, sm scar to center of fr cvr). Internally Fine. *Argonaut.* $250/£156

O'CASEY, SEAN. Blasts and Benedictions. Ronald Ayling (ed). Macmillan/St. Martin's, 1967. Good in dj (price-clipped, chipped). *Tiger.* $19/£12

O'CASEY, SEAN. Cock-a-Doodle Dandy. London: Macmillan, 1949. 1st ed w/Advanced Review Copy Special Notice Slip laid in. Fine in dj (soiled, few sm closed tears). *Metropolitan*.* $86/£54

O'CASEY, SEAN. Collected Plays. London: Macmillan, 1949. 1st ed. 2 vols. Maroon cl, gilt. (Extrems sl rubbed), o/w Fine set in djs (lt soiled, spines browned, extrems chipped). *Heritage.* $150/£94

O'CASEY, SEAN. The Silver Tassie. London, 1928. 1st Eng ed. (No dj.) *Clearwater.* $56/£35

O'CASEY, SEAN. The Silver Tassie. London: Macmillan, 1928. 1st ed. Port. Paper labels. NF in white dj (sl tanned, few sm edge tears). *Reese.* $125/£78

O'CASEY, SEAN. Windfalls. Macmillan, 1934. 1st ed. VG (spotted, feps lt browned; sl mkd, spine creased) in dj (nicked, rubbed, sl mkd, soiled, dusty, spine, edges browned, lacks sm piece). *Ulysses.* $72/£45

O'CONNOR, DANIEL. The Peter Pan Picture Book. NY: Macmillan, 1924. 1st ed. Alice Woodward (illus). Orange cl. VG. *Pacific*.* $58/£36

O'CONNOR, FLANNERY. Everything That Rises Must Converge. NY: FSG, (1965). 1st ed. Frontisport. Fine in dj. *Jaffe.* $250/£156

O'CONNOR, FLANNERY. A Good Man Is Hard to Find and Other Stories. NY: Harcourt, Brace, (1955). 1st ed. VG in dj (spine ends sl chipped, spine sunned, sm tears, creases to fr panel). *Pacific*.* $288/£180

O'CONNOR, FLANNERY. The Habit of Being. Sally Fitzgerald (ed). NY: FSG, 1979. Fine (lt tape mks feps) in dj (sl creased). *Ulysses.* $88/£55

O'CONNOR, FRANCIS V. and EUGENE V. THAW. Jackson Pollock: A Catalogue Raisonne of Paintings, Drawings, and Other Works. New Haven, 1978. 4 vols. Slipcase. *Swann*.* $1,495/£934

O'CONNOR, JACK. The Best Of Jack O'Connor. Clinton: Amwell, (1977). One of 1000 numbered, signed by O'Connor & Jim Rikhoff (foreword). Slipcase. *Swann*.* $230/£144

O'CONNOR, JACK. The Big Game Animals of North America. NY, (1961). Folio. *Swann*.* $57/£36

O'CONNOR, JACK. The Big Game Rifle. NY: Knopf, 1952. Stated 1st ed. One of 3607 ptd. VG (spine dknd, lt soiled). *Backman.* $55/£34

O'CONNOR, JACK. Hunting in the Rockies. NY: Knopf/Borzoi, 1947. 1st ed. VG + in dj. *Bowman.* $135/£84

O'CONNOR, JACK. Hunting in the Southwest. NY: Knopf/Borzoi, 1945. 1st ed. VG + in dj. *Bowman.* $175/£109

O'CONNOR, JACK. Sheep and Sheep Hunting. NY: Winch., 1974. 1st ed. Dec eps. NF in VG + dj. *Mikesh.* $137/£86

O'CONNOR, R. An Introduction to the Field Sports of France, Being a Practical View.... London/Paris: John Murray/Stassin et Xavier, 1846. 1st ed. Orig cl, gilt, blindstamping. (Spine sl sunned, ends rubbed), else NF. *Pacific*.* $58/£36

O'CONNOR, RICHARD. Bat Masterson. GC: Doubleday, 1957. 1st ed. VG in dj (sl worn). *Lien.* $25/£16

O'CONNOR, RICHARD. Bat Masterson. GC, 1957. 1st ed. Fine in dj (price-clipped, edgeworn). *Baade.* $40/£25

O'CONNOR, RICHARD. Hood: Cavalier General. NY: Prentice-Hall, 1949. 1st ed. Gray cl. NF in dj (sl worn). *Chapel Hill.* $80/£50

O'CONNOR, V. C. SCOTT. The Charm of Kashmir. London, 1920. 1st ed. 16 tipped-in color plts. Teg. (Edges chipped; discolored, sl soiled, sm split w/loss to fr joint.) *Edwards.* $96/£60

O'CONNOR, V. C. SCOTT. The Silken East. London: Hutchinson, 1904. 1st ed. 2 vols. Med 8vo. xx,xvi,842pp; 21 color plts, fldg panorama, fldg map. VG set (fep vol 1 joint sl cracked; cvrs sl rubbed) in blue cl, gilt. *Ulysses.* $880/£550

O'CROULEY, PEDRO ALONSO. A Description of the Kingdom of New Spain. Sean Galvin (trans). SF: John Howell Books, 1972. 1st ed. Pocket map. Fine. *Book Market.* $40/£25

O'DAY, EDWARD F. An Appreciation of James Wood Coffroth. SF: (Privately ptd), 1926. 1st ed. One of 250 ptd. Frontisport. Unopened. Marbled bds, white vellum backstrip, corners, blue leather spine label. Fine. *Harrington.* $60/£38

O'DONNELL, T. C. The Ladder of Rickety Rungs. Chicago: P.F. Volland, (1923). 1st ed. 9x6. Jane Laura Scott (illus). Pict bds. Fine in VG orig pict box (lacks piece). *Pacific*.* $75/£47

O'DONOGHUE, EDWARD GEOFFREY. Bridewell Hospital. London, 1923. 1st ed. 2 vols. (Lt spotting, vol 1 feps browned, vol 2 hinges cracked; vol 2 edges, spine lt faded.) *Edwards.* $120/£75

O'DONOVAN, EDMOND. The Merv Oasis. London: Smith, Elder, 1882. 1st ed. 2 vols. Steel-engr frontis, xx,502,(2); xvi,500pp; 11 facs, 4 maps, lg fldg map in rear pocket. Brn pebbled cl. (Ep foxed.) *Karmiole.* $350/£219

O'DRISCOLL, W. JUSTIN. Memoir of Daniel Maclise. London, 1871. Frontisport, xiv,264pp. Paper spine label. (Ex-lib, rep taped to pastedown, upper margin lt waterstained; edges sl rubbed, spine head sl chipped.) *Edwards.* $40/£25

O'FAOLAIN, EILEEN. Children of the Salmon and Other Irish Folktales. Boston: Little, Brown, (1965). 1st ed. Fine in dj (spine sl sunned, head chipped). *Pacific*.* $29/£18

O'FAOLAIN, SEAN. Bird Alone. London, (1936). 1st ed. (Spine foot sl stained), else Good in dj (spine faded, sl stained). *King.* $25/£16

O'FAOLAIN, SEAN. The Born Genius. Detroit, 1936. 1st ed. Ltd to 250 numbered, signed. (Sl cocked, spine sl discolored), else Good in slipcase (soiled). *King.* $100/£63

O'FAOLAIN, SEAN. The Born Genius. Detroit: Schuman's, 1936. 1st ed. One of 250 signed, this copy not numbered. Paper labels. (Spine sl sunned), else NF in slipcase (lt rubbed). *Reese.* $165/£103

O'FAOLAIN, SEAN. A Purse of Coppers. London, (1937). 1st ed. (Extrems, spine sl dknd), else Good in dj (edges frayed, sl chipped). *King.* $35/£22

O'FERRALL, CHARLES T. Forty Years of Active Service.... NY/Washington: Neale, 1904. 1st ed. Frontisport. Grn cl. VG (bkpl, blindstamp, pencil notes). *Chapel Hill.* $125/£78

O'FLAHERTY, DANIEL. General Jo Shelby. Chapel Hill: Univ of NC, 1954. 1st ed. Frontisport. Gray cl. VG in dj (edges chipped, ink on fr panel). *Chapel Hill.* $85/£53

O'FLAHERTY, LIAM. The Assassin. Cape, 1928. 1st ed. VG in dj (dull, sl rubbed). *Whiteson.* $40/£25

O'FLAHERTY, LIAM. The Fairy Goose and Two Other Stories. NY: Crosby Gaige, 1927. 1st ed. One of 1,190 signed. NF in NF dj. *Warren*. $75/£47

O'FLAHERTY, LIAM. I Went to Russia. London: Jonathan Cape, (1931). 1st ed. Signed. Fine in dj (spine head chipped, flaps clipped). *Pacific**. $81/£51

O'FLAHERTY, LIAM. The Informer. Cape, 1925. 1st ed. VG (ep gutters browned; sl cocked, top edge dusty, spine sl faded) in dj (nicked, rubbed, dusty, spine, edges browned). *Ulysses*. $440/£275

O'FLAHERTY, LIAM. Joseph Conrad. London, (1930). VG in orig wraps. *Edrich*. $26/£16

O'FLAHERTY, LIAM. A Tourist's Guide to Ireland. London: Mandrake, n.d. (1929). Dj. *Marlborough*. $96/£60

O'FLAHERTY, LIAM. The Wild Swan and Other Stories. London: William Jackson, 1932. 1st ed. One of 550. Signed. Frontis. Fine. *Pacific**. $63/£39

O'GORMAN, EDITH. Trials and Persecutions of Miss Edith O'Gorman. Hartford, CT, (1871). 264pp; port. (Lacks spine pieces; cvrs stained, worn.) *King*. $25/£16

O'HARA, DAVID. What the Dark Room Revealed. NY: G&D, 1939. Jimmie Drury #2; lists to itself. 5x7.5. F. E. Warren (illus). 204pp + ads. VG (corners sl bumped) in dj (edgeworn, spine sl faded). *My Bookhouse*. $25/£16

O'HARA, FRANK. In Memory of My Feelings. NY, (1967). Contents loose as issued in cl-backed bd sleeve; cl slipcase (lt soiled). *Swann**. $201/£126

O'HARA, FRANK. Lunch Poems. SF: City Lights, 1964. One of 1500. Fine in wraps. *Beasley*. $175/£109

O'HARA, FRANK. Poems. LEC, 1988. One of 550 signed in facs by William De Kooning (illus). Fine in slipcase. *Swann**. $1,955/£1,222

O'HARA, FRANK. Two Pieces. London: Long Hair Books, 1969. 1st ed. Fine in wraps. *Beasley*. $30/£19

O'HARA, JOHN. And Other Stories. NY: Random House, (1968). One of 300 numbered, signed. Grn cl. (Spine uniformly faded), o/w NF in slipcase. *Pharos*. $250/£156

O'HARA, JOHN. Appointment in Samarra. NY, (1934). 1st ed, 1st issue w/the errata slip tipped in and 'Recent Fiction' on rear panel. (Date stamp fep.) Dj (spine extrems, tips worn, rear panel soiled). *Swann**. $431/£269

O'HARA, JOHN. Appointment in Samarra. NY: Harcourt, Brace, 1934. 1st ed. Errata slip present. Black cl, gilt. (Few faint spots.) *Macdonnell*. $125/£78

O'HARA, JOHN. Assembly. Cresset Press, 1962. 1st Eng ed. Fine in dj (sl rubbed, price-clipped, edges sl creased). *Ulysses*. $72/£45

O'HARA, JOHN. The Big Laugh. Cresset Press, 1962. 1st Eng ed. Fine in dj (price-clipped). *Ulysses*. $56/£35

O'HARA, JOHN. Elizabeth Appleton. Cresset Press, 1963. 1st Eng ed. Fine (spine head sl bumped) in dj (spine head sl creased). *Ulysses*. $56/£35

O'HARA, JOHN. The Farmer's Hotel. NY: Random House, (1951). 1st ed. Fine in dj (sl worn). *Cummins*. $100/£63

O'HARA, JOHN. From the Terrace. NY: Random House, (1958). 1st ed. Dk blue cl, gilt. (Extrems sl faded, bottom edge sl soiled), o/w NF in dj (lt chipped). *Heritage*. $50/£31

O'HARA, JOHN. From the Terrace. NY: Random House, (1958). 1st ed. VG in dj (sl worn). *Cummins*. $75/£47

O'HARA, JOHN. Sermons and Soda-Water. London: Cresset, 1961. One of 525 sets signed. 3 vols. Top edges stained grn. 1/4 parchment, marbled bds, gilt. Fine set in pub's cardboard slipcase (worn). *Heritage*. $150/£94

O'HARA, KANE. Tom Thumb; a Burletta.... London: Joseph Thomas, 1837. Later ptg. 5 plts by George Cruikshank. Marbled eps; teg. Later dk grn calf, marbled bds by Zaehnsdorf, gilt. (Lt aged; sl shelfworn.) *Baltimore**. $45/£28

O'HARA, MARY. Green Grass of Wyoming. Phila: Lippincott, 1946. 1st ed. Inscribed. NF in NF pict dj. *Unger*. $125/£78

O'LEARY, N. and P. PAULET. African Wildlife. NY: Viking, 1964. 1st ed. Pict cl. Fine in Fine dj. *Mikesh*. $30/£19

O'LEARY, PETER. Travels and Experiences in Canada, the Red River Territory and the United States. London: John B. Day, (1877). Only ed. pp vii,226,(4) ads. Grn cl. *Mott*. $150/£94

O'MALLEY, AUSTIN. The Ethics of Medical Homicide and Mutilation. NY, 1919. 1st ed. (Fr inner hinge cracked; extrems worn), o/w Good. *Doctor's Library*. $50/£31

O'MEARA, BARRY. Napoleon at St. Helena. London: Richard Bentley & Son, 1888. 2 vols. Teg. 3/4 calf, marbled bds, gilt, morocco spine labels; bound by MacDonald. NF (bkpls). *Pacific**. $127/£79

O'MEARA, BARRY. Napoleon in Exile. London: Simpkin, 1822. 2 vols. 2 ports. Contemp 1/2 morocco, marbled bds (sl rubbed). *Stewart*. $200/£125

O'NEAL, BILL. Encyclopedia of Western Gun-Fighters. Norman: Univ of OK, 1983. Fine in Fine dj. *Connolly*. $25/£16

O'NEAL, BILL. Henry Brown, the Outlaw-Marshall. College Station, TX: Early West, (1980). 1st ed. Ltd to 1500. Fine in Fine dj. *Book Market*. $18/£11

O'NEAL, HANK. Berenice Abbott, American Photographer. NY, (1982). 1st ed. Signed by Abbott. Folio. Red cl. Dj (sl yellowed, soiled). *Swann**. $287/£179

O'NEAL, WILLIAM B. Primitive Into Painter: Life and Letters of John Toole. Univ of VA, 1960. VG in Good dj. *Book Broker*. $50/£31

O'NEALE, LILA. Textiles of the Early Nazca Period. Chicago: Field Museum of Natural Hist, 1937. Sm folio. 36 b/w, 2 color plts. VG in ptd wrappers. *Turtle Island*. $75/£47

O'NEILL, CHARLES. Wild Train, the Story of the Andrew Raiders. NY, (1956). Civil War Book Club ed. Signed. VG + in VG + dj. *Pratt*. $50/£31

O'NEILL, EUGENE. Ah, Wilderness! NY: Random House, (1933). 1st ed. Pict eps, top edge stained blue. Blue cl, gilt. VG (spine lt browned, edges sl rubbed) in dj (lt soiled, spine dknd, edges lt chipped). *Heritage*. $125/£78

O'NEILL, EUGENE. Ah, Wilderness! NY: LEC, 1972. One of 1500 ptd. Signed by Shannon Stirnweis (illus). 1/2 cl, dec bds. Fine in glassine, slipcase. *Pacific**. $29/£18

O'NEILL, EUGENE. Ah, Wilderness!. NY, 1933. 1st ed. One of 325 numbered, signed. Blue calf (spine extrems lt rubbed). *Swann**. $201/£126

O'NEILL, EUGENE. Anna Christie and The Emperor Jones and The Hairy Ape. NY: Modern Library, (1937). 1st Mod Lib ed. (Top corner fep sl clipped), else VF in Fine dj (fr spine edge sl rubbed). *Between The Covers*. $50/£31

O'NEILL, EUGENE. Anna Christie. NY, 1930. 1st Amer, 1st illus ed. One of 775 numbered, signed. Alexander King (illus). 1/4 cl. Slipcase (defective). *Swann**. $287/£179

O'NEILL, EUGENE. Before Breakfast: A Play in One Act. NY: Shay, 1916. 1st ed, only ptg. One of 500. NF (bkpl) in gray wrappers. Protective blue chemise, slipcase. *Bromer*. $850/£531

O'NEILL, EUGENE. The Complete Works (Plays). NY: Boni & Liveright, 1924. 1st ed. One of 1200 signed. 2 vols. Grey bds over blue linen spines. Good. *Appelfeld*. $250/£156

O'NEILL, EUGENE. Days Without End. NY: Random House, 1934. 1st ed. VG in illus dj (rubbed, closed tears). *Cahan*. $45/£28

O'NEILL, EUGENE. Dynamo. NY: Liveright, 1929. One of 775. Signed. Full mottled blue vellum, gilt, spine label. (Offset from glue of former bkpl to fr pastedown; spine label faded, cvrs bowed), else VG. *Pacific**. $69/£43

O'NEILL, EUGENE. The Emperor Jones, Diff'rent, The Straw. NY, (1921). 1st issue. NF (spine sl rubbed). *Polyanthos*. $60/£38

O'NEILL, EUGENE. The Emperor Jones. NY: B&L, 1928. 1st ltd ed. One of 775 numbered, signed. Fine in dj (sm spine chip), Good slipcase. *Agvent*. $425/£266

O'NEILL, EUGENE. Gold: A Play in Four Acts. NY: Boni & Liveright, 1920. 1st ed. Inscribed, dated 1938. (Eps lt foxed, sig; spine ends sl rubbed), else Fine. *Bromer*. $750/£469

O'NEILL, EUGENE. The Hairy Ape. NY, 1929. 1st illus ed. One of 775 numbered, signed. Alexander King (illus). 1/4 cl. Slipcase. *Swann**. $230/£144

O'NEILL, EUGENE. The Iceman Cometh. LEC, 1982. One of 2000 signed by Leonard Baskin (illus). Fine in slipcase. *Swann**. $126/£79

O'NEILL, EUGENE. Lazarus Laughed. NY: Boni & Liveright, 1927. 1st ed. One of 775 signed. Marbled bds over parchment spine, paper label. Fine. *Appelfeld*. $200/£125

O'NEILL, EUGENE. Long Day's Journey into Night. New Haven: Yale Univ, 1956. 1st ed. VG in dj (1.5-inch tear, crease to lower fr panel; extrems, spine head sl chipped). *Pacific**. $35/£22

O'NEILL, EUGENE. Lost Plays of.... NY: New Fathoms Publication, 1950. 1st ed, binding A. Unauthorized rpt. Gray cl. NF in VG- dj (clean crack 1 fold, sm chips). *Reese*. $75/£47

O'NEILL, EUGENE. Lost Plays.... NY: Citadel, (1958). 1st Citadel ed. VF in Fine dj (sl rubbed). *Between The Covers*. $85/£53

O'NEILL, EUGENE. Marco Millions. NY: Boni & Liveright, 1927. 1st ed. One of 450 signed. Marbled bds over parchment spine, paper label. Nice (spine sl soiled) w/wax wrapper. *Appelfeld*. $250/£156

O'NEILL, EUGENE. A Moon for the Misbegotten. NY: Random House, (1952). 1st ed. Top edge stained dk blue. Brn cl, blue/gray bds. (Cvr edges sl browned, soiled), o/w NF in dj (price-clipped, lt soiled, few sm tears). *Heritage*. $75/£47

O'NEILL, EUGENE. A Moon for the Misbegotten. NY: Random House, (1952). 1st ed. Fine in dj (sl dknd, price-clipped). *Reese*. $75/£47

O'NEILL, EUGENE. Mourning Becomes Electra. NY, (1931). 1st ed. One of 500 numbered, signed. Vellum. Slipcase (defective). *Swann**. $287/£179

O'NEILL, EUGENE. The Plays.... NY: Scribner, (1934). Wilderness ed. One of 770 numbered sets, signed. 12 vols. 8vo. Teg. Red buckram, gilt. Fine set in glassine wrappers, orig cardboard slipcases. *Heritage*. $2,000/£1,250

O'NEILL, EUGENE. Strange Interlude. NY: Boni & Liveright, 1928. 1st ed. (Few lt spots to cl), else NF in blue paper dj (spine ends chipped). *Bromer*. $150/£94

O'NEILL, EUGENE. Strange Interlude. NY, 1928. 1st ed. Dj (sm internal tape repair). *Swann**. $161/£101

O'NEILL, EUGENE. Strange Interlude. NY: Boni & Liveright, 1928. One of 750 (of 775) signed. Unopened. Vellum. (Evenly speckled), o/w Fine. *Pharos*. $350/£219

O'NEILL, EUGENE. Thirst and Other One-Act Plays. Boston: Gorham, 1914. 1st ed, 1st bk. VG (sl worn). *Lenz*. $300/£188

O'NEILL, EUGENE. A Touch of the Poet. New Haven: Yale Univ, 1957. 1st ed. Grn cl, gilt. Fine in dj (price-clipped, sm section fr panel scraped, spine top chipped). *Heritage*. $75/£47

O'NEILL, ROSE. The Master Mistress. NY: Knopf, 1922. 1st ed. VG (tp sl foxed; bd edges sunned, paper spine label lt tanned; lacks dj). *Between The Covers*. $85/£53

O'NEILL, T. The Irish Hand. Dolmen, 1984. Fine in dj. *Moss*. $64/£40

O'REILLY, BERNARD. Greenland, the Adjacent Seas, and the North-West Passage to the Pacific Ocean. London: Baldwin, Cradock, & Joy, 1818. 1st ed. Full-pg frontis, vi,(ii),293pp; 2 fldg engr maps, 17 (of 18) b/w aquatint plts. Early lt brn calf, marbled bds, ribbed spine, gilt, dk brn leather spine label. (Sl foxed, aged, some foxing to plts; scuffed, worn, label sl chipped, hinges w/later cl reinforcement.) *Baltimore**. $130/£81

O'REILLY, BERNARD. Greenland, the Adjacent Seas, and the North-West Passage. London: Baldwin, Cradock & Joy, 1818. 1st ed. 4to. 18 uncolored aquatint plts, 3 maps (few plts lt spotted; inscrip). Contemp 1/2 calf, drab bds (fr joints split but cords holding, extrems rubbed). *Christie's**. $648/£405

O'REILLY, HARRINGTON. Fifty Years on the Trail. Norman: Univ of OK, (1963). VG. *Lien*. $17/£11

O'REILLY, JOHN. The Anatomy and Physiology of the Placenta. NY: Hall, Clayton & Co, 1860. 1st Amer ed. Signed presentation. 111pp. Aeg. Emb cl, gilt. NF. *Glaser*. $225/£141

O'REILLY, JOHN. The Glob. NY: Viking, 1952. 1st ed. Fine in VG + dj (tear). *Other Worlds*. $125/£78

O'RELL, MAX and JACK ALLYN. Jonathan and His Continent. Madame Paul Blouet (trans). NY: Cassell, 1889. 1st ed. x,313pp + ads. Teg. Pict 2-tone cl, gilt. (Spine ends, corners worn, cl spotted), else Good. *Connolly*. $35/£22

O'ROURKE, P. J. Modern Manners, an Etiquette Book for Rude People. NY: Atlantic Monthly, 1989. 1st ed. Signed. Fine in Fine dj. *Unger*. $75/£47

O'SHAUGHNESSY, M. M. Hetch Hetchy: Its Origin and History. SF, 1934. 1st ed. One of 1000. Color frontis, map. Fine. *Pacific**. $98/£61

O'SULLIVAN, LAWRENCE. The Miscreant. NY: HRW, (1969). 1st ed. As New in dj. *Between The Covers*. $100/£63

O'SULLIVAN, PADRIEC SUEMUS. Weep Not My Children. N.p., (c.1950's). 1st ed. Signed. (Smoke damage rear cvr), else VG in pict wrappers (spine chipped). *Pacific**. $40/£25

OAKES, CLIFFORD. The Birds of Lancashire. Oliver & Boyd, 1953. 1st ed. Untrimmed. Grn ribbed cl, gilt. (Few spots to foreedge), o/w Fine. *Hollett*. $104/£65

OAKES, VANYA. Footprints of the Dragon. Phila: Winston, (1949). 1st ed. Fine in Fine dj. *Book Market*. $25/£16

OAKESHOTT, W. The Artists of the Winchester Bible. London: Faber & Faber, 1945. 44 plts. Newspaper cuttings loosely inserted. Dj (sl worn). *Maggs*. $32/£20

OATES, JOYCE CAROL. Miracle Play. Santa Barbara: Black Sparrow, 1974. One of 350. Signed. 1/4 cl, dec bds. Fine. *Pacific**. $69/£43

OATES, JOYCE CAROL. Night-Side. NY, (1977). 1st ed. Inscribed in year of pub. Dj. *Swann**. $80/£50

OATES, JOYCE CAROL. Night-Side. NY: Vanguard, 1977. 1st ed. Signed. NF in dj. *Smith*. $75/£47

OATES, JOYCE CAROL. Sentimental Education. Hollywood: Sylvester & Orphanos, 1978. Ltd to 330 signed. Belgian linen. *Truepenny*. $100/£63

OATES, JOYCE CAROL. The Triumph of the Spider Monkey. Santa Barbara: Black Sparrow, 1976. 1st published, 1st hb ed, ltd issue. One of 350 numbered, signed. Cl-backed dec bds, paper label. Fine in mylar dj, as issued. *Hermitage*. $100/£63

OATES, JOYCE CAROL. What I Lived For. NY, 1994. 1st Amer ed. Signed. Mint in Mint dj. *Polyanthos*. $35/£22

OATES, JOYCE CAROL. Zombie. NY, 1995. 1st Amer ed. Signed. Fine in Fine dj. *Polyanthos*. $35/£22

OBERMAIER, HUGO. Fossil Man in Spain. New Haven: Yale Univ Press, 1925. Color frontis, 23 plts. (Spine sl faded.) *Hollett*. $104/£65

OBERT, PETER G. Obert's System of Nature: or, Infidelity Exposed.... NY: Joseph M. Marsh, 1837. 1st ed. 148pp; port inserted on yellow paper. Contemp calf (scuffed), leather label. *M & S.* $225/£141

OBREGON, MAURICO. The Columbus Papers: The Barcelona Letter of 1493, the Landfall Controversy, and the Indian Guides. NY: Macmillan, (1991). 1st ed. 13 color plts. Red leather backed tan buckram. Fine in maroon cl slipcase w/sleeve. *House.* $80/£50

OBREITER, JOHN. The Seventy-Seventh Pennsylvania at Shiloh. (Harrisburg: Harrisburg), 1905. 1st ed. 2 Good lg fldg maps (1 mis-folded). Brn cl, gilt. (Ex-lib, ink stamp; fr hinge partly split; sl worn, dusty, spotted; spine label removed, gilt dull.) Cvrs Good. *Baltimore*.* $35/£22

Occasional Reflections Upon Several Subjects. (By Robert Boyle.) London: Henry Herringman, 1665. 1st ed. Sm 8vo. (40),80,161-264,230,(10)pp; early port of Boyle tipped in on imprimatur leaf. Contemp calf (rebacked, orig spine laid down). VG (sig). *Glaser.* $950/£594

OCHSNER, ALBERT and NELSON PERCYN. A New Manual of Surgery: Civil and Military. Chicago, 1917. 6th ed. Grn cl. Good (fep loose, fr inner hinge cracked; extrems worn). *Doctor's Library.* $40/£25

OCKLEY, SIMON. The History of the Saracens.... London, 1718. 2nd ed. 2 vols. Mod lib buckram. (Browned, ink lib stamps.) *Swann*.* $138/£86

ODENS, PETER. Picacho. Yuma: Privately ptd, (1973). 1st ed. Signed. VG + in wraps. *Book Market.* $20/£13

Odes upon Cash, Corn, Catholics and Other Matters. Selected from the Columns of the Times Journal. Longman et al, 1828. 1st ed. Frontisport (browned, spotted, crease, sm closed tear in fore-edge), vi,183,(1)pp (1/2-title creased w/tear at gutter margin, tp lt browned). Marbled eps. Mid 19th-cent 1/2 brn morocco, gilt, raised bands, morocco-grain purple cl on sides (faded). Good. *Blackwell's.* $96/£60

ODETS, CLIFFORD. Clash by Night. NY: Random House, 1942. 1st ed. NF in VG dj (soiled). *Unger.* $75/£47

ODUM, HOWARD W. and GUY B. JOHNSON. The Negro and His Songs. Chapel Hill: UNC Press, 1925. 1st ed. Dk blue cl. Fine. *Chapel Hill.* $225/£141

ODUM, HOWARD W. and GUY B. JOHNSON. Negro Workaday Songs. Chapel Hill: UNC Press, 1926. 1st ed. Black cl. NF (few pg corners creased). *Chapel Hill.* $200/£125

ODUM, HOWARD. Wings on My Feet. Indianapolis: Bobbs-Merrill, (1929). 1st ed. Pict eps. Blue cl. VG (cl faded at edges, spine through dj) in pict dj (lt rubbed, nicked). *Reese.* $50/£31

OE, KENZABURO. Nip the Buds, Shoot the Kids. NY: Marion Boyars, 1995. 1st ed in English. Signed. Fine in dj. *Lame Duck.* $65/£41

OE, KENZABURO. A Personal Matter. NY: Grove, 1968. 1st Amer ed. NF in VG + dj. *Warren.* $35/£22

OE, KENZABURO. A Personal Matter. NY: Grove, 1968. 1st ed. NF in VG + dj. *Lame Duck.* $50/£31

OE, KENZABURO. The Pinch Runner Memorandum. NY: Sharpe, 1994. 1st Amer ed. Fine in blue bds w/o dj as issued. *Warren.* $25/£16

OE, KENZABURO. The Silent Eye. NY: Kodansha Internat'l, 1974. 1st US ed. NF in dj (price-clipped). *Lame Duck.* $45/£28

OELGART, ISAAC. Falconry and Hawking Treatises. Newburyport, MA: New Mews, 1976. Ltd to 400 numbered. NF in wraps. *Biscotti.* $50/£31

OELLRICHS, INEZ H. Murder Helps. NY: David McKay, 1947. 1st ed. (Stamp), o/w VG in dj (sm spine chips, tears, fr panel rubbed). *Mordida.* $45/£28

OERTEL, HORST. The Anatomic Histological Processes of Bright's Disease and Their Relation to the Functional Changes. Phila, 1910. 1st ed. *Fye.* $125/£78

Of the Use annd Abuse of Parliaments; in Two Historical Discourses...from the Year 1660. (By James Ralph.) London, 1744. 1st ed. 2 vols. Orig bds cvrd in later paper, paper spine labels. VG. *Pacific*.* $75/£47

OFFENBACH, JACQUES. Offenbach in America. NY: G.W. Carleton, 1877. 1st ed. pp211,4 ads. (Bkpl w/black crayon.) Grn cl (sl spotted, corner rubbed). *Mott.* $50/£31

Official Catalogue of World's Columbian Exposition. Parts I-XVII. Chicago: W.B. Conkey, 1893. B/w halftone photo illus between sections. Edges stained red. Brn limp cl, gilt. (Sl aged, chipped at bottom corner last several sections; worn, cl rippled on spine, rear cvr.) Cvrs Good. *Baltimore*.* $140/£88

Official Guide Book of the World's Fair of 1934. Chicago: A Century of Progress Internat'l Exposition, 1934. Fldg diag, map. Pict ptd wrappers (extrems lt rubbed, edges creased). *Sadlon.* $15/£9

Official Guide to the Klondyke Country and the Gold Fields of Alaska. Chicago: W.B. Conkey, 1897. 1st ed. 296pp; 7 maps at fr. Orig color pict wraps, fr cvr w/lg design of goldpanner, pair of circular insets. (Text browned, lt aged; wraps sl worn, extrems sl chipped.) *Baltimore*.* $180/£113

Official Records of the Union and Confederate Navies in the War of the Rebellion. Series I, Volumes 1-27, and Series II, Volumes 1-3. Washington: GPO, 1894-1922. Navy cl, gilt. Nice set (sl rubbed, shelfworn). Internally Good. *Baltimore*.* $375/£234

OFFNER, RICHARD. Italian Primitives at Yale University. New Haven, 1927. 1/2 cl, bds. Good. *Washton.* $45/£28

OFFNER, RICHARD. The Works of Bernardo Daddi. NY, 1930. One of 250 numbered. Folio. Wrappers. (Clean tear in 1/2-title, tp; spine ends chipped.) *Swann*.* $92/£58

OGDEN, ADELE. The California Sea Otter Trade, 1784-1848. Berkeley/L.A.: Univ of CA, 1941. 1st ed. Frontis; 1 plt. Ptd wrappers (spine lt sunned). *Dawson.* $50/£31

OGDEN, ADELE. The California Sea Otter Trade, 1784-1848. Berkeley: Univ of CA, 1941. 1st ed. Blue cl (edges sl soiled, faded, spine dknd). VG + . *Harrington.* $80/£50

OGILVIE, WILLIAM. Early Days on the Yukon and the Story of Its Gold Finds. London: John Lane, et al, 1913. VG (few spots, spine faded). *High Latitude.* $120/£75

OGILVY, JAMES S. A Pilgrimage in Surrey. Routledge, 1914. 1st ed. 2 vols. Teg. Nice set (sl shaken, sl spotted; sl worn). *Ash.* $200/£125

OGILVY, JAMES S. Relics and Memorials of London City. London, 1910. 64 color plts. Teg. (Lt marginal browning, fep lacks corner; sl worn.) *Edwards.* $56/£35

Oh, How Pretty! NY: Cassell, (ca 1892). Obl 8vo. 20 mtd chromolithos. 11 panels ptd on stiff bds, hinged w/cl (1 hinge worn, cvrs rubbed). *Reisler.* $485/£303

OHLGREN, THOMAS H. (ed). Insular and Anglo-Saxon Illuminated Manuscripts. NY/London: Garland Pub, 1986. NF. *Zubal*.* $25/£16

OKIE, HOWARD PITCHER. Old Silver and Old Sheffield Plate. NY, 1936. 1st Amer ed. 12 full-pg illus. Teg. Fine. *Polyanthos.* $35/£22

OKITA, YOSHIHIRO and J. LELAND HOLLENBERG. The Miniature Palms of Japan. NY/Tokyo: Weatherhill, 1981. 1st ed. Fine. *Fair Meadow.* $30/£19

Oklahoma: A Guide to the Sooner State. Norman, 1945. 2nd ed. Fldg map in rear pocket. Fine in dj (worn, backstrip faded). *Baade.* $37/£23

OKRENT, DANIEL and HARRIS LEWINE (eds). The Ultimate Baseball Book. Houghton-Mifflin, 1979. 1st ed. Fine in Fine dj. *Plapinger.* $100/£63

OKRI, BEN. Stars of the New Curfew. London: Secker & Warburg, 1988. 1st Eng ed. Fine (spine foot sl bumped) in dj (price-clipped). *Ulysses*. $88/£55

Old Ballads. London: T. Evans, 1784. 1st collected ed. 4 vols. Full tree calf (sl worn), gilt. Text VG. *Hartfield*. $495/£309

Old Dutch Nursery Rhymes. London: Augener, (1917). 1st ed, ptd by Edmund Evans. Obl 4to. H. Willebeek Le Mair (illus). (ii),31,(ii)pp. Dk blue cl, gilt, onlaid pict label to upper cvr. (Lower corner bumped), o/w Fine. *Sotheran*. $237/£148

Old Fairy Tales. London: Frederick Warne, ca 1915. 4to. H.M. Brock (illus). 2 color paste labels. (Edges worn.) *Reisler*. $150/£94

Old Man's Rambles. London: Rivington, 1852. 2nd ed. Engr frontis, 404pp + 8 ads dated 1856. Blind-stamped straight-grained cl. Good. *Young*. $67/£42

Old Mother Bantry (No. 1 in Uncle Toby's Series). NY: McLoughlin Bros, (ca 1870). 12mo. 10pp; 4 full-pg color plts. Good in color pict wrappers (worn, spine splitting). *Reisler*. $110/£69

Old Nursery Rhymes. London: Thomas Nelson & Sons, (1942). 4to. (vii),9-142pp; 24 full color plts by Lawson Wood. Yellow pict bds. NF w/fr wrap of orig dj slipped in at fr. *Sotheran*. $157/£98

Old Old Tales Retold: Eight Best-Loved Folk Stories for Children. (By Frederick Richardson.) Chicago: P.F. Volland, (1922). 1st ed. Obl 4to. Blue emb cl, gilt, full color paste label. Fine. *Reisler*. $250/£156

Old Testament. NY: Doubleday, (1959, 1960). 1st ed. Sm folio. Marguerite de Angeli (illus). Tan cl. Good in full color dj (margins lt worn). *Reisler*. $75/£47

Old Time Ships of Salem. Salem: Essex Inst, 1922. 2nd ed. (Shelfworn, edges worn), else Good in plain paper dj. *Brown*. $30/£19

Old Woman and Her Pig. NY: McLoughlin, (1890). Little Pig Series. Unpaginated. Good (soil, spotting; 1/2 corner missing on wrap). *Davidson*. $40/£25

OLD, R. O. Colorado: United States of America.... London: British & CO Mining Bureau, (1869). 1st ed. 8.25x5. 64pp; fldg map. Mod 1/2 buckram, marbled bds. (Paper dknd, sl brittle, sm chip to corner of tp), else VG + in ptd wrappers (2 sm chips to fr). Howes O58. *Pacific**. $1,150/£719

OLDBERG, OSCAR. 1500 Prescriptions of All Kinds, Right and Wrong.... Chicago, 1898. 244pp. (Inner hinges cracked, soiled fep w/name, sm tear bottom of tp). *Doctor's Library*. $35/£22

OLDENBURG, CLAES. Notes in Hand. (NY): Petersburg, 1971. 1st ed. 50 color plts. (Neat stamp), else Fine in illus stiff wrappers. *Cahan*. $50/£31

OLDENBURG, CLAES. Proposals for Monuments and Buildings 1966-69. Chicago: Big Table Pub, (1969). Fine in NF dj. *Turtle Island*. $75/£47

OLDFIELD, OTIS. A Pictorial Journal of a Voyage Aboard the Three Masted Schooner Louise, Last of the Sailing Codfishermen out of San Francisco. SF: Grabhorn/Hoyem, 1969. 1st ed. One of 400. 19 color plts. 1/2 morocco. Fine. *Harrington*. $200/£125

OLDHAM, J. BASIL. Blind Panels of English Binders. Cambridge, 1958. 1st ed. Folio. 67 plts. Leather spine label. (Lt worn.) *Oinonen**. $90/£56

OLDROYD, HAROLD. The Natural History of Flies. London, 1964. 32 plts. Dj (torn). *Petersfield*. $29/£18

OLIN, STEPHEN. Travels in Egypt, Arabia Petraea, and the Holy Land. NY: Harper, 1843. 1st ed. 2 vols. 3 engr maps, 2 fldg, 12 engr plts. Brn cl. (Browned, spotted; cl, text dampstained.) *Christie's**. $331/£207

OLIN, STEPHEN. Travels in Egypt, Arabia Petraea, and the Holy Land. NY: Harper, 1843. 1st ed. 2 vols in 1. 3 engr maps, 12 plts. 19th-cent 1/2 calf. *Sotheby's**. $442/£276

OLIPHANT, J. ORIN (ed). On the Arkansas Route to California in 1849: The Journal of Robert B. Green of Lewisburg, Pennsylvania. Lewisburg: Bucknell Univ, 1955. 1st ed. Signed. NF. *Pacific**. $98/£61

OLIPHANT, LAURENCE. Haifa or Life in Modern Palestine. Edinburgh: William Blackwood, 1887. 1st Eng ed. 1/2-title, (ii),vi,(ii),369pp. Brn cl-backed bds. Sound (sl soiled; hinges splitting, corners worn, sl rubbed w/spine label removed). *Morrell*. $136/£85

OLIPHANT, LAURENCE. The Land of Gilead. Edinburgh: William Blackwood, 1880. 1st ed. 1/2-title, xxxvii,(i)blank,538,4 ads pp; 2 maps (1 fldg), 4 plts (incl frontis). Blue cl, gilt. Good (sm tear to fldg map, brown stain to tp, frontis; margins sl soiled, sm ink lib stamp, lib plt; rubbed, sl loose). *Morrell*. $192/£120

OLIPHANT, LAURENCE. Piccadilly, a Fragment of Contemporary Biography. Edinburgh/London: Blackwood, 1870. Frontis, vi,328pp; 7 plts. 1/2 calf (spine sl scuffed). *Marlborough*. $80/£50

OLIPHANT, LAURENCE. The Russian Shores of the Black Sea in the Autumn of 1852 with a Voyage Down the Volga, and a Tour Through the Country of the Don Cossacks. NY: Redfield, 1854. 1st US ed. 266pp; 2 maps (1 fldg). (Ex-lib; sl rubbed), o/w VG. *Worldwide*. $50/£31

OLIPHANT, MRS. Annals of a Publishing House. Blackwood, 1897. 1st ed. 2 vols. xiv,522; viii,514pp. VG in blue cl (sl worn). *Moss*. $96/£60

OLIPHANT, MRS. The Literary History of England in the End of the Eighteenth and Beginning of the Nineteenth Century. Macmillan, 1882. 3 vols. Blank before 1/2-title vols 2, 3; viii,395,(i blank); (2),(vi),392; (2),vi,405,(i erratum),(ii)pp. Top/fore-edges uncut, lower edges trimmed; vols 2, 3 unopened. Dk grn buckram, gilt. (Sm wormhole through cl of rear joint vol 3), o/w Good. *Temple*. $136/£85

OLIVER, JEAN. Architecture of the Kidney in Chronic Bright's Disease. NY, 1939. 1st ed. *Fye*. $100/£63

OLIVER, PAUL. Blues Fell This Morning: The Meaning of the Blues. NY: Horizon, (1960). 1st US ed. VG in pict dj. *Petrilla*. $40/£25

OLIVER, STEPHEN. Scenes and Recollections of Fly-Fishing, in Northumberland, Cumberland, and Westmoreland. London, 1834. 1st ed. (2)leaves; 212pp. 3/4 morocco (rubbed, sl soiled, foxed). *Oinonen**. $150/£94

OLIVER, WADE W. The Man Who Lived for Tomorrow: A Biography of William Hallock Park, M.D. NY, 1941. 1st ed. VG in Good dj. *Doctor's Library*. $30/£19

OLIVIER, CHARLES P. Comets. Balt: Williams & Wilkins, 1930. VG (spine, bd edges faded) in dj (nick). *Bookcell*. $25/£16

OLIVIER, EDITH. Four Victorian Ladies of Wiltshire, with an Essay on Those Leisured Ladies. London, 1945. 1st ed. Fine in dj (torn). *Petersfield*. $16/£10

OLLIVANT, ALFRED. Bob, Son of Battle. NY: Doubleday & McClure, 1898. 1st ed, 1st bk. NF (eps lt browned; spine, cvr edges sl faded) in dj (browned, sl chipped). *Heritage*. $450/£281

OLMSTED, FRANCIS ALLYN. Incidents of a Whaling Voyage. NY: Bell Pub, (1969). Rpt ed. Fine in dj. Howes O75. *Perier*. $35/£22

OLMSTED, FRANCIS LAW. The Cotton Kingdom. NY: Mason Bros, 1862. 2nd ed. 2 vols. Grn cl. (Frontis fldg map torn in 1/2 but repairable, old lib stamps, bkpl; spine head vol 1 chipped), else VG. *Pacific**. $69/£43

OLMSTED, FREDERICK LAW. A Journey in the Back Country. NY: Mason Bros, 1860. 1st ed. 492pp. Purple cl. VG (contemp inscrip; spine faded, cvrs spotted). Howes O77. *Chapel Hill*. $300/£188

OLMSTED, FREDERICK LAW. A Journey in the Seaboard Slave States, with Remarks on Their Economy. NY: Dix & Edwards, 1856. 1st ed. xv,723pp + ivpp ads. Brn cl. (Sig; spine sl sunned), else NF. Howes O78. *Chapel Hill.* $375/£234

OLMSTED, FREDERICK LAW. Journey Through Texas. Time-Life Classic, 1980. Facs rpt of 1857 1st ed. Frontis, fldg map. Marbled eps; aeg; ribbon markers. Emb leather, gilt. VF. *Connolly.* $30/£19

OLSEN, JACK. Silence on Monte Sole. NY, 1968. VG in Good dj. *Clark.* $28/£18

OLSEN, TILLIE. Tell Me a Riddle. (NY): Delacorte, (1978). One of 100 signed. Natural linen. Fine in Fine pub's slipcase. *Hermitage.* $200/£125

OLSEN, TILLIE. Tell Me a Riddle. Faber, 1964. 1st UK ed, 1st bk. Fine in VG + dj (sl rubbed, soiled, edgeworn). *Any Amount.* $72/£45

OLSON, ALBERT. The Flip-Flop Folks. Chicago: L.W. Walter, 1907. Obl 4to. Cl-backed pict wrappers (upper edge lt dknd). Nice. *Reisler.* $385/£241

OLSON, B. G. and MIKE MILLER. Blood on the Arctic Snow and 17 Other True Tales of Far North Adventure from the Alaska Sportsman. Seattle: Superior, (1956). 1st ed. VG in dj. *Perier.* $47/£29

OLSON, CHARLES and ROBERT CREELEY. Charles Olson and Robert Creeley: The Complete Correspondence. George F. Butterick (ed). Santa Barbara: Black Sparrow, 1980-82. 1st ed. 4 vols. Each one of 250. Each vol signed. Cl-backed pict bds. NF. *Pacific*.* $150/£94

OLSON, CHARLES. Mayan Letters. Robert Creeley (ed). Palma de Mallorca: Divers, 1953. 1st ed. Fine in wrappers. *Lenz.* $225/£141

OLUFSEN, O. The Emir of Bokhara and His Country Journeys and Studies in Bokhara. Copenhagen, 1911. 1st Eng ed. 8vo. Lg fldg map. *Maggs.* $1,080/£675

OMAN, CAROLA. The Menin Road and Other Poems. London, 1919. 1st Eng ed. VG in dj. *Clearwater.* $88/£55

OMAN, CHARLES. Castles. London, 1926. 67 dwgs, 5 plans, 2 color plts, map in back pocket. Good. *Washton.* $40/£25

OMURA, BUNJI. The Last Genro: Prince Saionji, the Man Who Westernized Japan. Phila/NY: Lippincott, 1938. 1st ed. Frontis. (Sl rubbed), o/w VG. *Worldwide.* $24/£15

OMWAKE, JOHN. The Conestoga Six-Horse Bell Teams. Cincinnati, 1939. (Edges lt worn), else VG. Howes O88. *Dumont.* $125/£78

On the Barricades. Journal for the Protection of All Beings, No. 2. SF: City Lights/Beach, 1968. 1st ed. Fine in wraps. *Beasley.* $25/£16

On the Morning of Christ's Nativity: Milton's Hymn. Whittington/Angscot, 1981. One of 325 (of 350), this copy unnumbered. 7 tipped-in color plts by William Blake. Fine in 1/4 vellum, buckram bds. Fine in slipcase. *Michael Taylor.* $192/£120

On the Nursery Stairs. Akron: Saalfield, 1906. 1st ed. 5.75x8.5. Pict muslin throughout. (Soiled), else VG. *Pacific*.* $52/£33

On the Road from Mons with an Army Service Corps Train. London, 1916. 1st Eng ed. Frontis map (torn). (Hinges cracked, cvrs mkd.) *Clearwater.* $40/£25

On the Warpath. Dundee: Valentine & Sons, (ca 1913). Lg 8vo shapebook. 12pp + 12 full-pg black/red illus. Stiff bds w/full color image, hinged at top. Nice (lt edgeworn). *Reisler.* $150/£94

ONDAATJE, MICHAEL. The Collected Works of Billy the Kid. NY: Norton, (1974). 1st Amer ed. NF in NF dj (lower flap clipped, lt soiled). *Agvent.* $90/£56

ONDAATJE, MICHAEL. The Collected Works of Billy the Kid. (Toronto): Anasi Press, 1970. 1st ed. Fine in dec wrappers. *Pacific*.* $104/£65

ONDAATJE, MICHAEL. Coming Through Slaughter. Toronto: Anasi, (1976). True 1st ed. Signed. Fine in dj. *Between The Covers.* $475/£297

ONDAATJE, MICHAEL. The Dainty Monsters. (Toronto: Coach House, 1967.) 2nd ed. One of 5000. Signed. NF in dec wrappers. *Pacific*.* $127/£79

ONDAATJE, MICHAEL. The English Patient. London: Bloomsbury, (1992). Uncorrected proof of true 1st ed. NF in wrappers. *Pacific*.* $104/£65

ONDAATJE, MICHAEL. The English Patient. London: Bloomsbury, 1992. True 1st ed. Fine in dj. *Lame Duck.* $125/£78

ONDAATJE, MICHAEL. Running in the Family. Gollancz, 1983. 1st UK ed. VG + in dj (price-clipped, spine ends sl pushed). *Williams.* $56/£35

ONETTI, JUAN CARLOS. Body Snatcher. NY: Pantheon, 1991. 1st ed in English. Fine in dj. *Lame Duck.* $45/£28

ONETTI, JUAN CARLOS. A Brief Life. NY: Grossman, 1976. 1st US ed. Fine in dj. *Lame Duck.* $100/£63

ONETTI, JUAN CARLOS. The Shipyard. NY: Scribner, 1968. 1st US ed. NF in dj (sm abrasion near fore-edge of fr flap-fld). *Lame Duck.* $175/£109

OPIE, AMELIA. Simple Tales. London: Longman, Hurst, Rees & Orme, 1806. 1st ed. 4 vols. (Ink initials tp each vol.) Marbled eps. Contemp speckled calf (joints, edges rubbed; worn), gilt, black leather labels. VG set. *Hermitage.* $175/£109

OPIE, IONA and PETER. The Lore and Language of Schoolchildren. Oxford: Clarendon, 1959. 1st ed. 417pp. VG. *Price.* $25/£16

OPIE, IONA and PETER. The Lore and Language of Schoolchildren. OUP, 1959. 1st Eng ed. NF (spine head sl bumped) in dj (sl nicked, rubbed, mkd, price-clipped). *Ulysses.* $104/£65

OPPE, A. P. Alexander and John Robert Cozens. A&C Black, 1952. 1st ed. 49 plts. VG in dj. *Hollett.* $64/£40

OPPE, A. P. English Drawings, Stuart and Georgian Periods in the Collection...at Windsor Castle. London/Oxford: Phaidon, 1950. Frontis, 117 plts. VF in dj. *Europa.* $61/£38

OPPE, A. P. The Water-Colours of Turner, Cox and de Wint. London/NY, 1925. 34 tipped-in color plts. Teg. (Feps sl browned; fore-edge of bds sl damp-stained.) *Edwards.* $40/£25

OPPEN, GEORGE. The Collected Poems of George Oppen. New Directions, (1975). 1st ed. VG in dj (sl used, discolored). *King.* $25/£16

OPPENHEIM, E. PHILLIPS. The Battle of Basinghall Street. Boston, 1935. 1st ed. VG. *Bond.* $12/£8

OPPENHEIM, E. PHILLIPS. The Yellow Crayon. NY: Dodd, Mead, 1903. 1st ed. Black/yellow cl. (Names, hinges cracking), else VG. *Pacific*.* $29/£18

OPPENHEIM, JAMES. Songs for the New Age. Grant Richards, 1915. 1st UK ed. VG + (final index leaf, rep sl nicked; corner sl bumped). *Any Amount.* $26/£16

OPPENHEIMER, JOEL. The Great American Desert. NY: Grove, 1966. 1st ed. Inscribed. NF in illus stapled wraps. *Lame Duck.* $125/£78

OPPENHEIMER, JOEL. The Love Bit. NY: Totem/Corinth, (1962). 1st ed. Signed. Fine in stapled wrappers. *Between The Covers.* $150/£94

OPPENHEIMER, JOEL. Pan's Eyes. Amherst, MA: Mulch, 1974. 1st ed. Rev copy w/slip laid in. Inscribed. NF in blue ptd wraps. *Lame Duck.* $85/£53

OPPENHEIMER, SEYMOUR. The Surgical Treatment of Chronic Suppuration of the Middle Ear and Mastoid. Phila, 1906. 1st ed. *Fye.* $200/£125

ORAM, H. K. Ready for Sea. London, 1974. 1st ed. VG + in dj. *Pratt.* $22/£14

ORCUTT, WILLIAM DANA. The Book in Italy During the Fifteenth and Sixteenth Centuries Shown in Facsimile Reproductions.... NY: Harper, 1928. Ltd to 750. 1/4 cl, bd sides. VG (portion of browning tp; tips rubbed). *Zubal*.* $55/£34

ORCUTT, WILLIAM DANA. From My Library Walls. John Murray, 1946. 1st ed. Good. *Moss.* $10/£6

ORCUTT, WILLIAM DANA. In Quest of the Perfect Book. Boston: Little, Brown, (1926). 1st ed. Fine in dj. *Oak Knoll.* $45/£28

ORCUTT, WILLIAM DANA. In Quest of the Perfect Book. Boston: Little, Brown, 1926. Inscribed. Color frontis. Brn cl (spine sl faded). *Maggs.* $32/£20

ORCUTT, WILLIAM DANA. The Kingdom of Books. Boston: Little, Brown, 1927. 1st ed. Gilt-stamped cl. Fine in dj (sl chipped). *Oak Knoll.* $40/£25

ORCUTT, WILLIAM DANA. The Kingdom of Books. Boston: Little, Brown, 1927. 1st ed. One of 475. Signed. Teg. 3/4 vellum, gilt. (Spine foxed), else VG. *Pacific*.* $63/£39

ORCUTT, WILLIAM DANA. The Magic of the Book, More Reminiscences.... Boston: Little, Brown, 1930. 1st ed. Gilt-stamped cl. Fine in dj. *Oak Knoll.* $45/£28

ORCZY, BARONESS. The Bronze Eagle. H&S, 1915. 1st ed. NF. *Fine Books.* $55/£34

ORCZY, BARONESS. The Elusive Pimpernel. London, 1908. 1st ed. (Ink sig fr cvr, binding sl skewed.) *Swann*.* $57/£36

ORD, EDWARD O. The City of the Angels and the City of the Saints or a Trip to Los Angeles and San Bernardino in 1856. L.a.: Zamorano Club, 1978. 1st ed. Ltd to 200. Fine in Fine dj. *Book Market.* $60/£38

ORDE, CUTHBERT. Pilots of Fighter Command. George G. Harrap, 1942. 1st ed. 64 plts. 2-tone cl. VG. *Hollett.* $64/£40

ORDEMAN, JOHN T. Frank W. Benson, Master of the Sporting Print. Brooklandville, MD: Privately ptd, 1983. 1st ed. Ltd to 1000 signed, numbered. Tan buckram. VF in VF ptd dj. *Biscotti.* $110/£69

ORDINAIRE, CLAUDE NICHOLAS. The Natural History of Volcanoes. London: T. Cadell/Jun.&W.Davies, 1801. 1st ed. xxiv,328pp (few contemp marginal notes). Contemp calf (rehinged). VG. *Glaser.* $450/£281

ORDRONAUX, JOHN. The Jurisprudence of Medicine in Its Relations to the Law...with a Supplement on the Liabilities of Vendors of Drugs. Phila, 1869. 1st ed. 310pp. *Fye.* $350/£219

Ore Deposits of the Western States. NY, 1933. 1st ed. Good (bottom corner few pp sl dampstained). *Blake.* $60/£38

ORFILA, P. M. Practical Chemistry. John Redman Coxe (trans). Phila: Thomas Dobson, 1818. xv,355,lxxxvi pp; 8 copper plts. Contemp sheep. (Lib bkpl, stamps, text lt toned; worn, rubbed, joints weak), else Good. *Brown.* $50/£31

ORGILL, D. The Gothic Line. London, 1967. 1st ed. VG in VG dj. *Clark.* $21/£13

ORIAS, OSCAR and EDWARDO BRAUN-MENENDEX. The Heart-Sounds in Normal and Pathological Conditions. London, 1939. 1st ed. *Fye.* $50/£31

Oriental Carpets, Runners and Rugs and Some Jacquard Reproductions. (By Sydney Humphries.) London: A&C Black, 1910. 24 color plts. Teg. (Lib ink stamp tp verso, margins sl browned; blindstamp margins of illus; bkpl, hinges cracked; sl soiled, spine browned, #s.) *Edwards.* $80/£50

ORIEUX, JEAN. Talleyrand. The Art of Survival. P. Wolf (trans). London: Secker & Warburg, (1974). Good. *Stewart.* $48/£30

Origin of Printing: In Two Essays. (By William Bowyer and J. Nichols.) W. Bowyer & J. Nichols, 1774. 1st ed. xvi,144pp + 2pp pub's ads. Contemp calf (rebacked). *Forest.* $360/£225

Original Poems, for Infant Minds. By the Taylor Family. Phila: Leary, Getz, 1860. 12mo. Full-pg engr frontis, 178pp + 2pp contents + 24pp ads. Brn emb cl, gilt spine. (Poem in pencil on back of fr cvr, ep; rubbed, corners chipped, cracked along spine.) Internally VG. *Hobbyhorse.* $70/£44

ORIGO, I. The Merchant of Prato, Francesco di Marco Datini. London: Cape, 1957. Color frontis, 25 plts. Red cl. Dj (sl worn). *Maggs.* $45/£28

ORIGO, I. The Vagabond Path. NY, 1972. 1st ed. As New in dj. *Bond.* $30/£19

ORIOLI, G. Adventures of a Bookseller. NY, 1938. 1st Amer ed. Frontisport. NF (sl rubbed) in dj (spine sl sunned, few sm chips). *Polyanthos.* $30/£19

ORIOLI, G. Adventures of a Bookseller. London: C&W, 1938. Frontisport. Red cl (sl soiled, sl bumped; bkseller's label), blue/gilt spine label. *Maggs.* $32/£20

ORMES, ROBERT M. Railroads and the Rockies. Denver: Sage Books, (1963). 1st ed. Fine in dj. *Argonaut.* $25/£16

ORMSBY, JOHN. Autumn Rambles in North Africa. London: Longman, Green, 1864. 1st ed. 1/2-title, engr frontis, ix,(iii),298pp; 3 engr plts. Gilt edges. Grn moire cl, gilt. (Margins lt browned, lib plt removed; rubbed, hinges broken.) *Morrell.* $40/£25

ORMSBY, WATERMAN L. The Butterfield Overland Mail. Lyle H. Wright and Josephine M. Bynum (ed). San Marino: Huntington Library, 1942. Centennial (3rd) ptg. Fldg facs. VF in ptd dj. *Argonaut.* $40/£25

ORNDUFF, DONALD. The Hereford in America. Kansas City: Privately ptd, 1957. 1st ed. VG. *October Farm.* $40/£25

ORNDUFF, DONALD. The Hereford in America. Kansas City: Hereford History Press, 1969. 3rd ed. Dj (sl rubbed). *Edwards.* $48/£30

OROZCO, JOSE CLEMENTE. The Orozco Frescoes at Dartmouth. Hanover, NH: Dartmouth College, (1934). Ptd wrappers. *Turtle Island.* $25/£16

ORR, MRS. SUTHERLAND. Life and Letters of Robert Browning. London: Smith, Elder, 1891. 1st ed. xiii,451pp; 2 plts (1 photo, 1 steel-engr). (Sl spotted.) *Hollett.* $40/£25

ORRELL, JOHN. The Theatres of Inigo Jones and John Webb. Cambridge: CUP, (1985). VG in pict dj. *Dramatis.* $35/£22

ORTIZ-VARGAS, A. The Towers of Manhattan. Albuquerque: Univ of NM, 1944. 1st ed in English. (Lib stamps, fore-edge lt foxed), else VG + in illus cl. *Lame Duck.* $35/£22

ORTLOFF, HENRY STUART. A Garden Bluebook of Annuals and Biennials. Doubleday, Doran, c. 1924/1931. 23 half-tone plts. (Sl foxed, browned), else VG. *Fair Meadow.* $18/£11

ORTON, J. The Andes and the Amazon. NY: Harper, (1871). 356pp; fldg map. (Spine ends, corners rubbed), else VG. *Mikesh.* $75/£47

ORVIS, CHARLES F. and A. NELSON CHENEY. Fishing with the Fly: Sketches by Lovers of the Art. Manchester, VT: C.F. Orvis, 1883. 1st ed. Gilt-lettered pict brn cl. (Fr, middle hinges cracked in a few places, sigs detaching; spine ends chipped), else VG. *Pacific*.* $316/£198

ORWELL, GEORGE and REGINALD REYNOLDS (eds). British Pamphleteers from the Sixteenth Century to the Nineteen-Thirties. Wingate, 1948-51. 1st eds. 2 vols. 21 facs (19 full-pg). Mid-brn cl, vol 2 maroon bds, gilt. VG (feps sl browned) in djs. *Blackwell's.* $152/£95

ORWELL, GEORGE and REGINALD REYNOLDS (eds). British Pamphleteers Volume I. Wingate, 1948. 1st UK ed. VG in dj (edges sl worn). *Williams.* $72/£45

ORWELL, GEORGE and REGINALD REYNOLDS. British Pamphleteers. London: Allan Wingate, 1948. 1st ed. Brn cl. Fine in dj (top edge sl worn). *Maggs.* $80/£50

ORWELL, GEORGE (ed). Talking to India. George Allen & Unwin, 1943. 1st UK ed. VG in Good dj (edges worn, torn, grubby). *Williams.* $216/£135

ORWELL, GEORGE. The Animal Farm Letters to His Agent, Leonard Moore. Michael Shelden (ed). Bloomington, IN: Fredric Bower for the Friends of Lilly Library, 1984. One of 200 numbered. Fine in dj (sl rubbed, mkd, dusty, sl faded). *Ulysses.* $200/£125

ORWELL, GEORGE. Animal Farm. NY: Harcourt, Brace, (1946). 1st Amer ed. VG in dj (spine ends, corners lack sm pieces; extrems rubbed; flaps clipped). *Pacific*.* $92/£58

ORWELL, GEORGE. Animal Farm. NY, (1946). 1st Amer ed. Advance rev copy. Ptd gray wrappers (spine tanned). *Swann*.* $172/£108

ORWELL, GEORGE. Animal Farm. Secker & Warburg, 1945. 1st ed. Crown 8vo. Apple-grn cl. VG (cvrs, backstrip foot faded) in blue 'Searchlight' dj (sl rubbed, fingersoiled at folds). *Blackwell's.* $720/£450

ORWELL, GEORGE. Animal Farm. Secker & Warburg, 1945. 1st UK ed. VG+ in VG dj (couple sm nicks, spine sl rubbed). *Williams.* $1,040/£650

ORWELL, GEORGE. The Clergyman's Daughter. NY: Harper, 1936. 1st US ed. One of 500 ptd. VG+ in dj (professionally restored). *Lame Duck.* $850/£531

ORWELL, GEORGE. The Collected Essays, Journalism and Letters of George Orwell. London: Secker & Warburg, (1968). 1st ed. 4 vols. Fine in djs. *Pacific*.* $150/£94

ORWELL, GEORGE. Coming Up for Air. Dublin: Gollancz, 1939. 1st ed. 8vo. Label of Greene & Co. (Cl sl faded.) Dj (sl defective). *Sotheby's*.* $10,120/£6,325

ORWELL, GEORGE. Down and Out in Paris and London. NY, 1933. 1st Amer ed. *Swann*.* $103/£64

ORWELL, GEORGE. Down and Out in Paris and London. Gollancz, 1933. 1st ed, 1st bk. 8vo. *Sotheby's*.* $699/£437

ORWELL, GEORGE. England Your England. London: Secker & Warburg, 1953. 1st ed. Pale grn cl. VG in dj (top edge sl chipped). *Maggs.* $120/£75

ORWELL, GEORGE. The English People. Collins, 1947. 1st ed. 8 color plts. Ptd grn bds. VG (feps sl browned) in dj. *Blackwell's.* $80/£50

ORWELL, GEORGE. The English People. London, 1947. 1st ed. Dj. *Swann*.* $103/£64

ORWELL, GEORGE. The English People. London: Collins, 1947. 1st ed. 8 color plts. NF in grn bds. Dj. *Maggs.* $104/£65

ORWELL, GEORGE. James Burnham and the Managerial Revolution. London: Socialist Book Centre, 1946. 1st ed. 8vo. Ptd wrappers (sm tear to fore-edge, sl stained around staples; text browned). *Maggs.* $960/£600

ORWELL, GEORGE. Keep the Aspidistra Flying. Gollancz, 1936. 1st UK ed. VG- (fep sl scuffed; bds sl dull). *Williams.* $256/£160

ORWELL, GEORGE. Keep the Aspidistra Flying. Gollancz, 1936. 1st ed. 8vo. Dj (sl defective). *Sotheby's*.* $1,104/£690

ORWELL, GEORGE. Nineteen Eighty-Four. NY, (1949). 1st Amer ed. NF (name) in dj (sl rubbed, sm tear, sm chip, spine sl sunned). *Polyanthos.* $60/£38

ORWELL, GEORGE. Nineteen Eighty-Four. NY: Harcourt, Brace, (1949). 1st Amer ed. NF in dj (spine ends sl chipped, extrems sl sunned). *Pacific*.* $98/£61

ORWELL, GEORGE. Nineteen Eighty-Four. NY: Harcourt, Brace, (1949). 1st Amer ed. (Cl sl foxed), o/w Fine in 2nd state blue dj (worn). *Glenn.* $145/£91

ORWELL, GEORGE. Nineteen Eighty-Four. Secker, 1949. 1st UK ed. NF in purple dj (spine lt faded, sl scuffed; couple sm closed tears, sm chip spine head). *Williams.* $952/£595

ORWELL, GEORGE. Nineteen Eighty-Four. Secker & Warburg, 1949. 1st ed. 8vo. Secker & Warburg flyer loosely inserted. Fine in pink dj (sm tears). *Sotheby's*.* $1,195/£747

ORWELL, GEORGE. Shooting an Elephant and Other Essays. NY: Harcourt, Brace, (1950). 1st Collected Amer ed. NF in dj. *Pacific*.* $35/£22

OSBALDESTON, GEORGE. Squire Osbaldeston: His Autobiography. E. D. Cuming (ed). London, (1926). (Sl foxed, soiled; shelfworn.) *Oinonen*.* $30/£19

OSBECK, PETER. A Voyage to China and the East Indies. London: Benjamin White, 1771. 1st Eng ed. 2 vols. 8vo. xx,396; (i),367pp + (xix) + (i)errata; 13 plts. (Vol 2 pp288-305 foxed, pp243-6 lack portion of corner; bkpl.) Later 1/2 calf, cl bds, leather spine labels, raised bands. (Joints cracked, vol 1 spine lacks part of tail, sl surface loss to spines.) *Edwards.* $1,280/£800

OSBECK, PETER. A Voyage to China and the East Indies. London, 1771. 1st ed in English. 2 vols. 13 engr plts. Contemp calf. *Felcone.* $1,800/£1,125

OSBORN, ALBERT. Questioned Documents. Rochester, NY, 1910. 1st ed. Incl orig 16pp 4 x 9.25 prospectus, 12pp bklet w/reviewers comments. VF. *Bond.* $75/£47

OSBORN, CAMPBELL. Let Freedom Ring. Tokyo(?), 1954. (Lt watermk 1st 2 ll), else Good in dj. *Dumont.* $65/£41

OSBORN, E. B. The Muse in Arms. London: John Murray, 1917. 1st ed. Blind-dec grn cl, gilt. (1917 ink inscrip), o/w VG in dj (few sm tears, chips). *Reese.* $85/£53

OSBORN, H. Meadow and Pasture Insects. Columbus, 1939. (Pp tanned.) *Sutton.* $36/£23

OSBORN, H. Practical Manual of Minerals, Mines, and Mining. Phila: Baird, c1895. 2nd ed. xxiv, 369pp. VG. *Blake.* $75/£47

OSBORN, H. F. The Age of Mammals in Europe, Asia and North America. NY: Macmillan, 1910. 1st ed. Pict cl, gilt. (Bkpl; fr hinge cracked), else VG. *Mikesh.* $75/£47

OSBORN, HENRY S. Plants of the Holy Land with Their Fruits and Flowers. Phila: Lippincott, 1861. 174pp; 6 Good color litho plts. Aeg. Orig blind-dotted brn cl later recased w/most of gilt-dec spine laid down. (Sl foxed, paper of plts browned, ink stamps; edgeworn, spine gilt faded, fr hinge cracked.) Text Good. *Baltimore*.* $100/£63

OSBORNE, CHARLES C. Jubal. Chapel Hill: Algonquin, 1992. Advance uncorrected proof. 2 copies of 4pp pub's prospectus laid in. Fine in ptd gray wraps. *Chapel Hill.* $40/£25

OSBORNE, JOHN. A Bond Honoured, a Play. London, 1966. 1st ed. Fine in dj. *Petersfield.* $40/£25

OSBORNE, JOHN. The Entertainer. NY, (1958). 1st Amer ed. Fine in dj (2 sm tears, sl creased). *Polyanthos.* $30/£19

OSBORNE, JOHN. Luther. NY: Criterion, (1962). 1st Amer ed. VF in VF dj (sl rubbed). *Between The Covers.* $125/£78

OSBORNE, JOHN. The World of Paul Slickey. London: Faber & Faber, 1959. 1st ed. Brn cl. Good in dj. *Maggs.* $64/£40

OSBOURNE, KATHARINE D. Robert Louis Stevenson in California. Chicago: A.C. McClurg, 1911. 1st ed. Frontis. Emb ship; spine label. Fine. *Parmer.* $60/£38

OSGOOD, ERNEST S. The Day of the Cattleman. Minneapolis: Univ of MN, 1929. 1st ed. Frontis, 9 plts, 5 maps (1 dbl-pg). Tan cl. Fine in dj (tape repairs to verso). Howes O130. *Argonaut.* $225/£141

OSGOOD, ERNEST S. The Day of the Cattleman. Minneapolis: Univ of MN, 1929. 1st ed. Fine in dj (chipped, torn). Howes O130. *Labordo.* $225/£141

OSGOOD, ERNEST S. (ed). The Field Notes of Captain William Clark, 1803-1805. New Haven: Yale Univ, 1964. 1st ed. VG+ in Good dj (well worn, chipped). *Labordo.* $275/£172

OSGOOD, FRANCES (ed). The Poetry of Flowers...to Which is Added a Simple Treatise on Botany. NY: J.C. Riker, 1841. 13 hand-colored plts. Contemp gilt-stamped red morocco, edges gilt. Fine. *Appelfeld*. $150/£94

OSGOOD, HENRY O. So This Is Jazz. Boston: Little, Brown, 1926. 1st ed. Fine in NF dj (spine sl faded). *Beasley*. $175/£109

OSLER, E. B. The Man Who Had to Hang: Louis Riel. Toronto, 1961. Good in dj (sl worn). *Dumont*. $50/£31

OSLER, EDWARD. The Life of Admiral Viscount Exmouth. Smith, Elder, 1835. 1st ed. xvi,448pp (sig dated Nov 19, 1835, marginal notes, few contemp press cuttings laid down); complete w/5 engr plts, fldg engr plan. Old diced calf (edges sl rubbed, rebacked in matching gilt calf), gilt. *Hollett*. $224/£140

OSLER, WILLIAM. Aequanimitas with Other Addresses. Phila, 1904. 1st ed, 1st ptg. *Fye*. $250/£156

OSLER, WILLIAM. An Alabama Student and Other Biographical Essays. NY, 1908. 1st ed, 1st ptg. *Fye*. $225/£141

OSLER, WILLIAM. An Alabama Student. Balt, 1896. 1st ed. 19pp. Wrappers. *Fye*. $75/£47

OSLER, WILLIAM. Bibliotheca Osleriana. Oxford, 1929. 1st ed. Recent cl (fore-edge ink stains). *Fye*. $450/£281

OSLER, WILLIAM. Bibliotheca Osleriana: A Catalogue of Books Illustrating the History of Medicine and Science.... Montreal/London: McGill-Queen's Univ, 1969. 2nd ed. Red buckram, gilt. (Sl dusty, rubbed.) Text NF. *Baltimore**. $275/£172

OSLER, WILLIAM. Cancer of the Stomach: A Clinical Study. Phila, 1900. 1st ed. *Fye*. $400/£250

OSLER, WILLIAM. Doctor and Nurse. Balt: John Murphy, 1891. 1st ed. 11pp. Orig ptd wraps (brittle, separated, chipped). Text Good (sm dent at center of ll). *Baltimore**. $110/£69

OSLER, WILLIAM. The Evolution of Modern Medicine. New Haven, 1943. 1st ed, 6th ptg. *Fye*. $60/£38

OSLER, WILLIAM. Incunabula Medica: A Study of the Earliest Printed Medical Books, 1467-1480. Oxford, 1923. 1st ed. 15 plts. (Lib stamps tp, verso of plts). Fine. *Fye*. $500/£313

OSLER, WILLIAM. Lectures on Angina Pectoris and Allied States. NY, 1897. 1st ed. 160pp. *Fye*. $450/£281

OSLER, WILLIAM. Men and Books. Collected and Reprinted from the Canadian Medical Association Journal.... Pasadena, 1959. 1st ed. Signed by Earl F. Nation (intro). Ltd to 200. *Fye*. $150/£94

OSLER, WILLIAM. The Old Humanities and the New Science. Boston, 1920. *Fye*. $100/£63

OSLER, WILLIAM. On Chorea and Choreiform Affections. Phila, 1894. 1st ed. 125pp. (1/2-inch of fr bd edge stained), else Fine. *Fye*. $1,200/£750

OSLER, WILLIAM. The Principles and Practice of Medicine. NY, 1892. 1st ed, 2nd ptg. 1079pp. Orig 1/2 morocco (sl rubbed). *Fye*. $1,250/£781

OSLER, WILLIAM. The Principles and Practice of Medicine. NY: Appleton, 1893. 1st ed, later issue. 1st issue published in 1892, w/incorrect spelling 'Georgias' on leaf preceding table of contents, and ads dated March 1892; this copy w/corrected spelling, ads dated Sept 1893. xvii,1079pp + ads at rear. Orig dk brn sheep, brn cl, gilt spine. (Lt aged; eps, 1st few pp foxed; worn, scraped, partial split along top of upper joint, spine top chipped.) Text Good. *Baltimore**. $250/£156

OSLER, WILLIAM. The Principles and Practice of Medicine. NY, 1896. 2nd ed. 1143pp. 1/2 leather. VF. *Fye*. $350/£219

OSLER, WILLIAM. The Principles and Practice of Medicine. NY, 1902. 4th ed. (Inner hinges cracked; rubbed, spine tears.) *Fye*. $75/£47

OSLER, WILLIAM. The Principles and Practice of Medicine. NY, 1903. 5th ed. 1/2 leather (rebacked w/new eps; lacks final index leaf). *Fye*. $40/£25

OSLER, WILLIAM. The Principles and Practice of Medicine. NY/London: Appleton, 1904. 5th ed. Crimson sheep, cranberry cl, gilt. (Lt aged, foxed, extensive pencil underlines, marginal mks; sl worn, scuffed, chunk missing from spine bottom.) Cvrs Good. *Baltimore**. $70/£44

OSLER, WILLIAM. The Principles and Practice of Medicine. NY, 1906. 6th ed. 1/2 leather (rubbed, worn, corners bumped, torn). VG internally. *Fye*. $50/£31

OSLER, WILLIAM. The Principles and Practice of Medicine. NY, 1909. 7th ed. (Fr inner hinge cracked; 1/2-inch cl lower fr cover missing), o/w Fine. *Fye*. $150/£94

OSLER, WILLIAM. The Principles and Practice of Medicine. NY, 1912. 8th ed. (Inner hinges cracked; shaken.) *Fye*. $75/£47

OSLER, WILLIAM. The Principles and Practice of Medicine. Henry A. Christian (ed). NY, 1942. 14th ed. *Fye*. $50/£31

OSLER, WILLIAM. The Problem of Typhoid Fever in the United States. Balt, 1899. 1st ed. 13pp. Wrappers. *Fye*. $50/£31

OSLER, WILLIAM. Science and Immortality. Boston: Houghton, Mifflin, 1904. 1st ed. Presentation copy. Card reading 'With The Compliments Of The Author' pasted to fep. Blue cl. VG (spine top chipped). *House*. $100/£63

OSLER, WILLIAM. Science and Immortality. Boston, 1905. 1st ed, rptd. *Fye*. $80/£50

OSLER, WILLIAM. Science and War. Oxford, 1915. 1st ed. Wrappers. *Fye*. $100/£63

OSLER, WILLIAM. Selected Writings of Sir William Osler. 12 July 1849 to 29 December 1919. A.W. Franklin (ed). London, 1951. Frontisport; 4 plts. (Plts sl discolored; fr inner hinge cracked), o/w VG. *Whitehart*. $40/£25

OSLER, WILLIAM. Selected Writings, 12 July 1849 to 29 December 1919. G. L. Keynes (intro). London: OUP, 1951. 1st ed thus. NF in dj. *Glaser*. $60/£38

OSLER, WILLIAM. The Student Life and Other Essays. Boston, 1931. 1st Amer ed. *Fye*. $75/£47

OSLER, WILLIAM. Thomas Linacre. Cambridge, 1908. 1st ed. *Fye*. $225/£141

OSLER, WILLIAM. What the Public Can Do in the Fight Against Tuberculosis. Oxford, 1909. Wrappers. *Fye*. $30/£19

OSLEY, A. S. Mercator. London: Faber & Faber, (1969). (Sl rippled from dampness), else VG in dj (sl soiled, few sm tears, sl rippled). *Pacific**. $86/£54

OSLEY, A. S. Scribes and Sources, Handbook of Chancery Hand in the 16th Century. London/Boston: Faber & Faber, 1980. 1st ed. Fine in dj (sl soiled). *Michael Taylor*. $32/£20

OSLEY, A. S. Scribes and Sources. Handbook of the Chancery Hand in the Sixteenth Century. Boston, 1980. 22 plts. Good in dj. *Washton*. $50/£31

OSMAN, A. H. Pigeons in the Great War. London: Racing Pigeon Pub Co, (n.d. but 1929). 1st ed. Pict wrappers ptd in blue. (Sm chip spine crown, soft crease 1 corner), else VG. *Reese*. $85/£53

OSMOND, PERCY H. Paolo Veronesi: His Life and Work. Sheldon, 1927. (Bkpl), else Very Nice. *Hadley*. $45/£28

OSSIAN. The Poems of Ossian. James Macpherson (trans). Edinburgh: John Grant, 1926. 1st Eng ed. Patterned eps; teg. NF (spine ends sl bumped, rubbed) in dj (dusty, sl rubbed, mkd, browned). *Ulysses*. $136/£85

OSSMAN, DAVID (ed). The Sullen Art. NY: Corinth, 1963. 1st ed. NF in wraps. *Beasley*. $35/£22

OSTERHOUT, W. J. V. Cell Studies I. Spindle Formation to Agave. SF: CA Academy of Sciences, 1902. 4 fldg color plts. Unopened. (Fore-edge worn, dknd.) Wrappers. *Brooks*. $32/£20

OSUMI, TAMEZO. Printed Cottons of Asia. The Romance of Trade Textiles. Tokyo/Rutland, (1963). Folio. 103 mtd color plts. Cl-backed patterned bds. Dj. *Swann**. $201/£126

OSWALD, ARTHUR. Country Houses of Dorset. Country Life, 1935. 1st ed. Mod cl-backed marbled bds. (Sl spotted.) *Hollett.* $136/£85

OSWALD, JOHN CLYDE. A History of Printing, Its Development Through Five Hundred Years. NY: D. Appleton, 1928. 1st ed. Fine in dj (pieces missing). *Oak Knoll.* $65/£41

OTERO, MIGUEL ANTONIO. My Life on the Frontier 1864-1882. NY, 1935. 1st ed. VG (sm ink note margin pg 1; back-strip lt faded). Howes O141. *Baade.* $65/£41

OTERO, MIGUEL ANTONIO. My Life on the Frontier, 1864-1882. NY: Press of the Pioneers, 1935. 1st ed. Fine in b/w dj (sl chipped). *Labordo.* $125/£78

OTERO, MIGUEL ANTONIO. The Real Billy the Kid. NY, 1936. 1st ed. Fine. Howes O142. *Baade.* $95/£59

Other Merchants and Sea Captains of Old Boston.... Boston: State Street Trust, 1919. Errata laid in. Wraps (chipped, separating at spine head). *Parmer.* $30/£19

OTIS, CHARLES. Michigan Trees. Ann Arbor: Univ of MI, 1913. 2nd ed. Grn cl. NF. *Archer.* $25/£16

OTLEY, JONATHAN. A Concise Description of the English Lakes, and Adjacent Mountains: With General Directions to Tourists.... Keswick: The Author, 1837. 6th ed. viii,184pp (stamp); fldg map. Orig grn buckram, paper title label. *Young.* $104/£65

OTT, ISAAC. The Action of Medicines. Phila, 1878. 1st ed. 168pp. *Fye.* $150/£94

Ottawa: Old and New. Ottawa, IL, 1912-1914. 1st ed. Folio. (Cvrs lt worn, stained.) *Ginsberg.* $100/£63

OTTER, WILLIAM. The Life and Remains of Edward Daniel Clarke. London, 1825. 2 vols. (vi),500pp; (iv),486pp. (Frontis-port spotted, offset). 1/2 calf w/marbled bds, leather spine labels. (Sl spotted, bkpl; corners sl worn, fr joint head vol 2 sl cracked, spine heads sl chipped.) *Edwards.* $136/£85

OTTLEY, G. A Bibliography of British Railway History. HMSO, 1983. Fine in dj. *Moss.* $72/£45

OTTLEY, WILLIAM YOUNG. An Inquiry into the Origin and Early History of Engraving upon Copper and in Wood.... London: John & Arthur Arch, 1816. 1st ed. 2 vols. 4to. Contemp calf (rebacked, corners repaired, scuffed, worn; bkpls, bkseller cat descrip glued to fr pastedown vol 1). *Glenn.* $600/£375

OTTLEY, WILLIAM YOUNG. The Italian School of Design. London: The Author, 1823. Folio. (viii),72pp + (iv)pp index; 84 plts. Mod cl (rebound), gilt. (Sm lib ink stamps, sl spotted, margins sl thumbed.) *Edwards.* $880/£550

OTTO, A. F. and T. S. HOLBROOK. Mythological Japan, or the Symbolisms of Mythology in Relation to Japanese Art. Phila: Biddle, n.d. (ca 1902). 1st ed. (Cl worn, edges frayed, padding showing.) Internally VG. *Worldwide.* $100/£63

OTTO, WHITNEY. How to Make an American Quilt. NY: Villard, (1991). 1st ed. Signed. Fine in dj. *Between The Covers.* $100/£63

OTWAY, THOMAS. The Works in Two Volumes.... D. Browne et al, 1722. 3rd ed. 2 vols. 418,(2); 396pp. Contemp sprinkled calf (backstrip heads sl worn, corner bumped), gilt, red morocco labels (renewed). VG. *Cox.* $152/£95

OUGHTON, FREDERICK. The History and Practice of Wood-carving. London, 1969. 1st ed. (Lib ink stamp.) Dj. *Edwards.* $40/£25

OUIDA. (Pseud of Marie Louise de la Ramee.) An Altruist. T. Fisher Unwin, 1897. Pub's cat dated 1897. Teg. Good (leading edges of ll tanned; fr joint cracked, spine bumped, hinges, corners rubbed). *Tiger.* $51/£32

OUIDA. (Pseud of Marie Louise de la Ramee.) A Village Commune. C&W, 1882. New ed. Pub's cat dated June 1882. Good (fore-edge lt spotted; spine bumped, ink mk fr cvr). *Tiger.* $22/£14

OUIMET, FRANCIS. A Game of Golf: A Book of Reminiscence. Boston: Houghton Mifflin, 1932. 1st ed. One of 550 ptd. Signed. Fine (emb stamp) in glassine, slipcase. *Pacific**. $1,610/£1,006

OULIE, MARTHE. Charcot of the Antarctic. London: John Murray, 1938. Errata slip, 3 maps. VG in dj (chipped). *Explorer.* $43/£27

Our Four-Footed Friends. NY: McLoughlin Bros, (ca 1890). Sm folio. 16pp; full-pg color illus mtd on linen. Color pict wrappers (spine worn, offsetting). Good. *Houle.* $150/£94

Our Little Folk's First Book. London: E. Nister, (c. 1900). 9.25x7.5. E. Lance et al (illus). Cl-backed pict bds. Fine. *Pacific**. $52/£33

Our Little Ones' ABC. London: F. Warne & Co, (ca 1900). Lg 4to. Stiff paper wrappers (resewn; worn). *Reisler.* $225/£141

OUTCAULT, R. F. Buddy Tucker Visits the House That Jack Built. NY: Cupples & Leon, 1907. Sq 8vo. 30pp of color panels. Color pict bds (few rubbed spots fr edge). VG. *Reisler.* $225/£141

OUTERBRIDGE, PAUL. Photographing in Color. NY, (1940). 1st ed. (Foxed, eps age-dknd; worn, sl soiled.) *Swann**. $92/£58

OUTHWAITE, IDA RENTOUL. Fairyland of Ida Rentoul Outhwaite. Melbourne: Ramsay Pub, 1926. Ltd to 1000 signed. Folio. 51 mtd plts (19 color). Teg. Blue cl, gilt. Good. *Reisler.* $4,000/£2,500

OVED, M. For the Sake of the Days. Faber, 1940. 1st ed. Presentation copy. (Sl dusty), else Good in dj (dull, torn). *Whiteson.* $32/£20

OVED, M. Out of Chaos. London, 1918. 1st ed. Gilt-dec leather. (Sl rubbed), else Good. *Whiteson.* $29/£18

Over the Hills. NY: McLoughlin Bros, (1882). 4to. Ida Waugh (illus). Color illus bds (edges, spine worn). Clean. *Reisler.* $200/£125

OVERMAN, F. Practical Mineralogy, Assaying and Mining. Phila: Lindsay & Blakiston, 1858. 4th ed. x,230pp. 1/4 cl, marbled paper over bds. (Lt foxed; spine top cl chipped), else Good. *Blake.* $85/£53

OVERTON, GRANT. Portrait of a Publisher. NY: D. Appleton, 1925. 1st ed. Frontis port. Partly unopened. Parchment over paper-cvrd bds, gilt. (Spine ends, corners worn), else VG. *Connolly.* $35/£22

OVERTON, RICHARD C. Gulf to Rockies. Austin, 1953. Good in dj (soiled, chipped). *Dumont.* $50/£31

OVID. The Art of Love. LEC, 1971. Ltd to 1500 numbered, signed by Eric Fraser (illus). Fine in slipcase. *Swann**. $34/£21

OVID. Hys Book of Metamorphose, Books X-XV. William Caxton (trans). Oxford: Basil Blackwell, 1924. One of 375 numbered. Sm folio. Untrimmed. Tan cl, blue-grn bds, ptd paper labels. (Stain at top of spine extending to cvrs, edges sl worn.) Text Clean. *Baltimore**. $60/£38

OVID. The Metamorphoses of Ovid. LEC, 1958. Ltd to 1500 numbered, signed by Hans Erni (illus) and Giovanni Mardersteig (designer). Fine in slipcase. *Swann**. $201/£126

OVID. Ovid's Metamorphoses in Fifteen Books. Verona: LEC, 1958. One of 1500 ptd. Signed by Hans Erni (illus) and Mardersteig (ptr). 1/2 tan cl, patterned bds. Fine in dj, slipcase. *Pacific**. $138/£86

OVID. A Translation of the First Book of Ovid's Tristia.... By Francis Arden. NY: (C.S. Van Winkle), 1821. Uncut. Orig bluish-gray bds, white paper spine (worn, lacks 2 sm pieces), orig paper spine label. Sound (binder's ticket). *Book Block.* $275/£172

OVIEDO, GONZALO. The Conquest and the Settlement of the Island of Boriquen, or Puerto Rico. LEC, 1975. Ltd to 1500 numbered, signed by Jack and Irene Delano (illus). Fine in slipcase. *Swann**. $80/£50

OVINGTON, MARY WHITE. The Shadow. NY, 1920. 1st ed. (Sig, bkpl.) *Swann**. $103/£64

OVINGTON, MARY WHITE. The Walls Came Tumbling Down. NY: Harcourt, Brace, (1947). 1st ed. (Name stamp.) *Petrilla*. $20/£13

OVITT, MABLE. Golden Treasure. Dillon: Privately ptd, 1954. Later ptg. Pict cl. Fine. *Baade*. $35/£22

OWEN, CATHERINE. Choice Cookery. NY, 1889. 1st ed. (Crayon scribbles; rear cvr heavily spotted; fr hinge loose.) *King*. $50/£31

OWEN, DAVID DALE. Report of a Geological Survey of Wisconsin, Iowa, and Minnesota. Phila: Lippincott, Grambo, 1852. 1st ed. 638pp; 27 plts, 4 maps, incl lg fldg map, 16 fldg sections. W/atlas volume bound in. (Ex-lib, bkpl, 1 map chipped, separated at fold; worn, scuffed, rubbed, dust-soiled), else Good. *Brown*. $175/£109

OWEN, FLORA. Book of Fairy Poetry. Longmans, Green, (1920). 1st ed. 4to. (x),180pp; 16 mtd color plts (2 plts sl creased at corner), guards. Uncut. Gray cl. *Sotheran*. $269/£168

OWEN, H. COLLINSON. Salonica and After, the Sideshow That Ended the War. London: Hodder, 1919. (Foxed throughout.) *Petersfield*. $19/£12

OWEN, J. A. (ed). The Wild-Fowl and Sea-Fowl of Great Britain. (By Jordan Denham.) London: Chapman and Hall, 1895. Pict cl (2 fr cvr string mks; tp sl foxed). *Petersfield*. $29/£18

OWEN, JOHN. The History of the Origin and First Ten Years of the British and Foreign Bible Society. London, 1816. 3 vols. Marbled eps, edges. 1/2 calf, marbled bds (rubbed), gilt, leather spine labels. (Ex-lib, sl spotted.) *Edwards*. $200/£125

OWEN, R. A History of British Fossil Mammals, and Birds. Van Voorst, 1846. xlvi,560pp. Partly unopened, uncut. Fine w/wide margins. *Henly*. $157/£98

OWEN, R. B. Leaves from a Greenland Diary. NY: Dodd, Mead, 1935. 1st ed. Good+. *Walcot*. $29/£18

OWEN, RICHARD. A History of British Fossil Reptiles. London: Cassell, 1849-84. One of 170 sets. 4 vols. 4to. 286 litho plts. Buckram, gilt. Excellent set (bds sl damped in places, all vols neatly recased). *Hollett*. $1,360/£850

OWEN, RICHARD. Palaeontology, or A Systematic Summary of Extinct Animals and Their Geological Relations. Edinburgh: A&C Black, 1860. 1st ed. xv,420pp; fldg table. Blind-stamped cl, gilt. VG (1 leaf sl dusty, sl fingering; neatly recased). *Hollett*. $152/£95

OWEN, ROBERT DALE. Moral Physiology; or, a Brief and Plain Treatise on the Population Question. Boston: J.P. Mendum, 1875. 88,(1)pp; 2 plts. *M & S*. $75/£47

OWEN, RUSSELL. South of the Sun. NY: John Day, c. 1934. 2nd ptg. Inscribed, signed. VG in VG dj. *High Latitude*. $35/£22

OWEN, THOMAS M. (comp). Revolutionary Soldiers in Alabama. (Montgomery, AL): State of AL, Dept of Archives & History, 1911. 1st ed. Unopened. (Rubbed, sm splits along spine), o/w VG in ptd wrappers. *Cahan*. $50/£31

OWEN, WILFRED. Collected Letters. Harold Owen and John Bell (eds). OUP, 1967. 1st Eng ed. Buckram. NF (spine ends sl bumped) in dj (sl rubbed, nicked, creased). *Ulysses*. $152/£95

OWEN, WILFRED. The Collected Poems of Wilfred Owen. C. Day-Lewis (ed). London: C&W, 1963. 1st Eng ed. VG (fep notes; spine ends, corner sl bumped) in dj (nicked, sl mkd, torn, creased, dusty, spine faded, rear panel edge lacks sm piece). *Ulysses*. $72/£45

OWEN, WILFRED. The Poems of Wilfred Owen. Edmund Blunden (ed). London: C&W, 1931. Expanded ed, trade issue, 1st ptg. Port. Plum cl, gilt. Fine in NF cream dj (lt dust-soiled). *Reese*. $175/£109

OWENS, BILL. Our Kind of People. SF: Straight Arrow Books, 1975. 1st ed. Fine in dj. *Smith*. $85/£53

OWENS, BILL. Working (I Do It for the Money). NY: S&S, 1977. 1st ed. VG in wrappers. *Smith*. $50/£31

OWENS, WILLIAM A. Look to the River. NY: Atheneum, 1963. 1st ed. Fine in dj. *Reese*. $35/£22

Owl and the Pussy Cat. NY: Whitehall, 1946. 8 moveables by Eoina. VG in wraps. *Davidson*. $60/£38

OXENDEN, A. The Pathway of Safety. SPCK, 1909. VG. *Walcot*. $32/£20

OXENHAM, E. J. The Song of the Abbey. Collins, 1954. 1st ed. VG in VG dj. *Green Meadow*. $48/£30

Oxford English Dictionary. Compact Edition. NY, (1987). 3 vols. Orig casing, w/magnifying glass. (Lt worn.) *Oinonen**. $150/£94

Oxford English Prize Essays. Oxford: D.A. Talboys, 1830. 1st ed. 4 vols. Half-titles, ix,(i),317,(1); (vi),326; (vi),294; (vi),294pp. Orig grn glazed calico. Sound (vol 1 shaken; all spine heads chipped, split, lower joint vol 1 split along 1/2 its length and across back, ptd back labels all rubbed, 1 bd damp-mkd). Contents Good. *Blackwell's*. $480/£300

Oxonians; A Glance at Society. (By Samuel Beazley.) London: Henry Colburn/Richard Bentley, 1830. 1st ed. 3 vols. Orig bds (rebacked w/new labels, ends of 1 joint partly split). *Young*. $152/£95

OZ, AMOS. Fima. NY: Harcourt, 1993. 1st ed. Inscribed. Fine in Fine dj. *Beasley*. $40/£25

OZ, AMOS. Where the Jackals Howl and Other Stories. NY, 1981. 1st Amer ed. Fine in Fine dj. *Polyanthos*. $25/£16

OZENFANT, AMEDEE. Journey Through Life. Helen Beauclerk and Violet MacDonald (trans). NY: Macmillan, 1939. 1st Amer ed. Frontisport. *Turtle Island*. $45/£28

P

PACHECO, JOSE EMILIO. Don't Ask Me How the Time Goes By. NY: Columbia, 1978. 1st ed in English. Fine in NF dj (spinal extrems worn). *Lame Duck*. $50/£31

PACK, GEORGE (ed). Tumors of the Hands and Feet. St. Louis, 1939. 1st ed. *Fye*. $100/£63

PACK, GEORGE T. and EDWARD M. LIVINGSTON (eds). Treatment of Cancer and Allied Diseases. NY/London: Paul B. Hoeber, (1940). 3 vols. Red cl. (Stamps on fore-edges, 1st few ll folded; spine label removed.) *Weber*. $200/£125

PACK, R. W. and G. SHERBURNE ROGERS. The Sunset-Midway Oil Field, California. Washington: GPO, 1919-20. 25 plts, 17 fldg plans and diags, 20 fldg maps in rear pocket. Old 1/2 calf, gilt. (Sm hole in tp, 1st few ll; worn.) *Hollett*. $136/£85

PACKARD, A. S. and F. W. PUTNAM. The Mammoth Cave and Its Inhabitants. Salem, 1872. 1st ed. 62pp; 2 engr plts. Gilt-pict cl (sl worn). *Oinonen**. $80/£50

PACKARD, FRANCIS R. Life and Times of Ambroise Pare.... NY: Paul B. Hoeber, 1926. 2nd ed. Add'l port, 3 illus neatly laid in. VG (spine dull). *Glaser*. $75/£47

PACKARD, JOSEPH. Recollections of a Long Life. Byron S. Adams, 1902. Good-. *Book Broker*. $35/£22

PADEN, IRENE D. and MARGARET SCHLICHTMANN. The Big Oak Flat Road. SF: (Emil P. Schlichtmann), 1955. 1st ed. One of 1000 ptd. 2 fldg maps. Unopened. Blue cl. Fine. *Harrington.* $90/£56

PADEN, IRENE D. and MARGARET E. SCHLICHTMANN. The Big Oak Flat Road: An Account of Freighting from Stockton to Yosemite Valley. SF: Ptd by Lawton Kennedy, 1955. 1st ed. One of 1000. Inscribed, signed presentation by both. Frontis, 4 photo plts, 7 maps, plans (2 fldg). Mostly uncut. Blue cl, gilt. VF. *Argonaut.* $125/£78

PADEN, IRENE D. The Wake of the Prairie Schooner. NY: Macmillan, 1943. 1st ed. VG in dj (tattered). *Lien.* $30/£19

PADEN, IRENE D. The Wake of the Prairie Schooner. NY: Macmillan, 1943. 1st ed. Signed, dated Oct 19, 1943. NF in dj (spine head chipped, price-clipped). *Pacific*.* $35/£22

PADGETT, LEWIS. Mutant. NY: Gnome, (1953). 1st ed. (Sl damp-stained), else Good in dj (edges chipped). *King.* $95/£59

PADGETT, LEWIS. Tomorrow and Tomorrow and The Fairy Chessmen. NY: Gnome, (1951). 1st ed. (Bkpl), else VG in dj (rubbed, sl soiled). *King.* $100/£63

PADILLA, HEBERTO. Sent Off the Field. London: Andre Deutsch, 1972. 1st ed. Fine in dj. *Lame Duck.* $65/£41

PAGANO, JO. The Condemned. NY: Prentice-Hall, (1947). 1st ed. VG in dj (edges sl worn). *Bernard.* $40/£25

PAGE, ELIZABETH. Wild Horses and Gold. NY, (1932). Fldg map. (Sl worn, backstrip faded), else VG. *Woolson.* $20/£13

PAGE, HARRY S. Between the Flags: the Recollections of a Gentleman Rider. NY: Derrydale, 1929. One of 850. Red cl. Fine in slipcase. *Biscotti.* $100/£63

PAGE, LEO. For Magistrates and Others. London: Faber & Faber, 1939. *Boswell.* $25/£16

PAGE, MARGARET. In Childhood Land. Akron: Saalfield, 1907. 1st ed. Katharine H. Greenland (illus). 11 x 8 3/4. Cl-backed pict bds. (Creases to feps, 1/2-title; corners rubbed), else VG. *Pacific*.* $58/£36

PAGE, THOMAS NELSON. Robert E. Lee. NY: Scribner, 1911. 1st ed. Frontisport, 2 fldg maps. Teg. Red cl. (Bkpl; sl edge-worn), else NF. BAL 15414. *Chapel Hill.* $75/£47

PAGE, THOMAS NELSON. Santa Claus's Partner. NY: Scribner, 1899. 1st ed. 8vo. Frontis, tp,(viii),176,(1)pp; 7 plts by W. Glackens. Teg, deckle-edged. Red cl, gilt. VG (bumped, cocked, lt soiled, spine sl faded). *Blue Mountain.* $25/£16

PAGE, THOMAS NELSON. Social Life in Old Virginia Before the War. NY, 1897. 1st ed. 109pp. Fine. BAL 15378. *Truepenny.* $60/£38

PAGE, THOMAS NELSON. Two Little Confederates. NY: Scribner, 1932. 1st ed thus. John W. Thomason (illus). Sm 4to. Color frontis, 189pp. Black cl, round pict paste-on. NF. *Davidson.* $85/£53

PAGE, THOMAS NELSON. The Works of.... NY, 1906-1912. Ltd to 230 numbered w/author's signed port in vol 1. 18 vols. 8x5 inches. Teg. Finely bound in 3/4 red gilt-stamped leather w/raised bands, stamped leaves w/berries pattern. (Bkpl), else VG set. *King.* $1,750/£1,094

PAGE, VICTOR W. The Model T Ford Car. London: Morris, Russell, 1915. Frontis (4-pg concertina-fold ad leaflet tipped onto rear). Pict blue cl. Excellent (stamp dated 1916). *Hollett.* $136/£85

PAGET, GEORGE EVELYN and JANE PENRICE HOW. English and Scottish Silver Spoons, Medieval to Late Stuart, and Pre-Elizabethan Hall-Marks on English Plate. Privately ptd, 1952-7. One of 550. 3 vols. Folio. Near Mint set in Clean djs (1 w/tear neatly repaired). *Europa.* $800/£500

PAGET, GERALD. The Lineage and Ancestry of H. R. H. Prince Charles, Prince of Wales. Edinburgh/London, 1977. 2 vols. Tipped-in color frontisports. *Edwards.* $120/£75

PAGET, JAMES. Clinical Lectures and Essays. NY, 1875. 1st Amer ed. 428pp. Recent cl (new eps). (Perforated lib stamp tp), o/w Fine. *Fye.* $100/£63

PAGET, JAMES. Lectures on Surgical Pathology. Phila, 1854. 1st Amer ed. 699pp. Full leather (backstrip worn, torn, label missing). VG internally. *Fye.* $50/£31

PAGET, JOHN. Hungary and Transylvania.... John Murray, 1855. New ed. 2 vols. Engr frontispieces, xxiv,560; xii,553pp; 2 fldg color maps. All edges marbled. Contemp dk blue full calf, raised bands, contrasting leather labels. (Spines rubbed, head of vol 2 sl chipped, bds sl faded), o/w Good set. *Sotheran.* $317/£198

PAGET, STEPHEN (ed). Memoirs and Letters of Sir James Paget. London, 1901. Frontisport, 2 photogravure ports. Uncut. (Lt spotted fr hinge sl tender; sl rubbed; edges, spine faded; spine ends chipped w/sl loss.) *Edwards.* $72/£45

PAHER, STANLEY W. Nevada: An Annotated Bibliography. Las Vegas, 1980. Fine. *Dumont.* $95/£59

PAIJKULL, CARL WILHELM. A Summer in Iceland. London, 1868. Frontis. (Hinges cracked, ink lib #s on backstrip, spine ends frayed.) *Swann*.* $161/£101

PAIN, C. ERNEST. Fifty Years on the Test. London: Allan, 1934. 1st ed. Pale grn cl. (Cl soiled), else VG. *Bowman.* $45/£28

PAIN, WILLIAM. The Practical Builder; or, Workman's General Assistant.... London, 1774. 1st ed. 4to. 83 engr plts. Period-style calf. *Felcone.* $950/£594

PAINE, ALBERT BIGELOW. Mark Twain. A Biography. NY, 1912. 1st Amer ed. 4 vols. Teg, uncut. Fine set (spines sl sunned). *Polyanthos.* $100/£63

PAINE, LAURAN. Texas Ben Thompson. L.A.: Westernlore, 1966. 1st ed. Fine in dj. *Labordo.* $50/£31

PAINE, MARTYN. The Institutes of Medicine. NY, 1847. 1st ed. 826pp. Leather. *Fye.* $150/£94

PAINE, MARTYN. Letters on the Cholera Asphyxia, as It Has Appeared in the City of New-York. NY, 1832. 1st ed. 160pp. *Fye.* $150/£94

PAINE, RALPH D. Joshua Barney, a Forgotten Hero of Blue Water. NY, (1924). 1st ed. Pict cvr. VG +. *Pratt.* $20/£13

PAINE, RALPH D. Privateers of '76. Phila: Penn, 1923. 1st ed. Lg 8vo. 316pp; color frontis, 5 b/w plts by Frank E. Schoonover. Black cl, gilt. VG (lt bumped, spine faded, sm stains, fr cvr illus sl rubbed). *Blue Mountain.* $25/£16

PAINE, RALPH D. The Ships and Sailors of Old Salem. Boston: Charles E. Lauriat, 1924. Rev ed. Teg. (Shelfworn, edges worn, spine lt rubbed), else Good. *Brown.* $25/£16

PAINE, THOMAS. The American Crisis. London: W.T. Sherwin, 1817. Tp, 196pp (1st few pp sl dusty). Uncut. Blue wrappers. *Marlborough.* $88/£55

PAINE, THOMAS. An Examination of the Passages in the New Testament...to Which Is Prefixed an Essay on Dream. Boston: J.Q. Adams, 1834. Orig cl. (Exterior wear), else Lovely. *Metropolitan*.* $103/£64

PAINE, THOMAS. Life and Writings. Daniel Wheeler (ed). NY, (1908). One of 1550 numbered sets signed by Wheeler. 10 vols. (Several hinges cracked.) *Swann*.* $126/£79

PAINE, THOMAS. Rights of Man. Lunenberg, VT: Stinehour Press for LEC, 1961. Ltd to 1500 numbered, signed by Lynd Ward (illus). Red gilt-stamped cl, marbled paper doublures. Good in slipcase. *Karmiole.* $100/£63

PAINE, THOMAS. Rights of Man. LEC, 1961. Ltd to 1500 numbered, signed by Lynd Ward (illus). Fine in slipcase. *Swann*.* $126/£79

PAINE, THOMAS. Writings of.... Moncure Daniel Conway (ed). NY, 1894-99. 4 vols. Teg. Maroon cl. (Bkpls; vol 1 corners bumped, cvrs dknd, scuffed, spotted.) *King.* $95/£59

PAINTER, C. C. The Condition of Affairs in Indian Territory and California. Phila: Office of the Indian Rights Assoc, 1888. 114pp. Good in wrappers (very chipped, rear wrap fregmentary). *Brown*. $35/£22

PAINTER, GEORGE D. Proust: The Early Years and Proust: The Later Years. Boston/Toronto: Little, Brown, (1959/1965). Vol 1, 1st ed; vol 2, 2nd ptg. 2 vols. Fine in NF djs (sl rubbed). *Bernard*. $25/£16

Painting in Italy in the Eighteenth Century: Rococo to Romanticism. Chicago: Art Inst, 1970. Good in wrappers. *Washton*. $75/£47

Paintings of George Bellows. NY, 1929. One of 2000 numbered. (Bklabel.) *Swann**. $115/£72

PALEOLOGUE, MAURICE. The Tragic Empress. H. Miles (trans). London: Thornton Butterworth, n.d. (ca 1910). Frontisport. Good. *Stewart*. $64/£40

PALEY, WILLIAM. The Principles of Moral and Political Philosophy. London: R. Faulder, 1785. 1st ed. xxi,(i),vi,657pp (lower margin last few ll lt dampstained, sm bkpls, marginal tear). Mod calf-backed bds. *Young*. $336/£210

PALGRAVE, FRANCIS T. A Golden Treasury of Songs and Lyrics. NY: Duffield, 1911. 1st ed w/illus by Maxfield Parrish. Sm 4to. 8 VG color plts, guards. Pict eps; untrimmed. Dk navy cl, gilt, mtd color pict label fr cvr. Text Good (lt aged; sl worn, scuffed, bottom corner rear cvr rounded, lt old stain cvr corners). *Baltimore**. $70/£44

PALGRAVE, FRANCIS T. Lyrical Poems. Macmillan, 1871. 1st ed. Grn cl, gilt. (Spine sl bumped, ends rubbed, corners sl bumped), o/w VG + . *Any Amount*. $56/£35

PALGRAVE, FRANCIS T. Palgrave's Golden Treasury. London: J.M. Dent, 1907. 1st ed illus thus. 8vo. xvi,366pp; 25 color plts by Robert Anning Bell. Teg, rest uncut. Pale grn cl, gilt. Very Clean. *Sotheran*. $205/£128

PALGRAVE, FRANCIS T. (ed). The Golden Treasury. Cambridge: Macmillan, 1861. 1st ed. The 1/2-title is ptd in plain capitals in 3 lines, the 1st pg of the Preface has 33 lines, p314 reads 'Louis XIV' on line 21, and p323 has only 17 lines. 1st binding: orig grn cl, gilt; the binding has the price ('4/6') at the bottom of the spine, and the top edge is not gilt. VG (foxed; corners sl shelfworn). *Sumner & Stillman*. $250/£156

PALGRAVE, WILLIAM G. Dutch Guiana. London, 1876. 1st ed. Fldg map. (Pencil underlining, notes.) *Kane**. $120/£75

PALGRAVE, WILLIAM G. Essays on Eastern Questions. London: Macmillan, 1872. 1st ed. vii,349pp. (Rebacked, edges rubbed, lib spine sticker), o/w VG. *Worldwide*. $85/£53

PALGRAVE, WILLIAM G. Narrative of a Journey Through Central and Eastern Arabia (1862-63). London, 1865. 1st ed. 2 vols. 8vo. xiii,466,(2)ads; (vii),398,(2)ads, 22 ads pp; fldg map, frontisport, 4 fldg plans. New glazed eps. Pict cl, gilt. (Sm lib stamp in plt margins, some text margins.) *Maggs*. $1,000/£625

PALGRAVE, WILLIAM G. Narrative of a Year's Journey Through Central and Eastern Arabia (1862-1863). London: Macmillan, 1865. 1st ed. 2 vols. Demy 8vo. xiii,466; (v),398pp; engr port, 4 fldg plans, color fldg map. Fine set in later 1/4 calf, marbled paper bds, leather title labels, raised bands, gilt, panels blind-emb. *Ulysses*. $1,272/£795

PALGRAVE, WILLIAM G. Narrative of a Year's Journey Through Central and Eastern Arabia (1862-63). London: Macmillan, 1865. 2nd ed. 2 vols. xii,(ii),466; 1/2-title, frontisport (sl stained), (vi),398,(2)ads; fldg map (colored in outline and mtd on linen), 4 fldg plans. 19th-cent grn 1/2-calf, gilt. Good (sl spotted; corners, joints rubbed). *Morrell*. $368/£230

PALGRAVE, WILLIAM G. Narrative of a Year's Journey Through Central and Eastern Arabia (1862-63).... London, 1866. 3rd ed. 2 vols. Frontis, 5 maps. Gilt-lettered cl. (1 map cellotape-repaired; several hinges reinforced, rest are cracked.) *Swann**. $402/£251

PALINURUS. (Pseud of Cyril Connolly.) The Unquiet Grave. London: Horizon, 1944. 1st ed. Ltd to 1000. Wrappers over card cvrs. (Sl soiled, sm splits spine ends), else VG. *Virgo*. $80/£50

PALINURUS. (Pseud of Cyril Connolly.) The Unquiet Grave. Hamish Hamilton, 1945. Rev ed. NF (ink namestamp; spine tail sl bumped) in dj (sl rubbed, spine sl faded, sm chip). *Ulysses*. $56/£35

PALLADIO, ANDREA. The Four Books of Architecture.... Isaac Ware (trans). London: For R. Ware, 1755. 2nd ed. Tp ptd in black/red, 4 engr titles, 212 engr plts. Later calf-backed bds (worn; bkpl). *Christie's**. $1,080/£675

PALLEY, REESE. The Porcelain Art of Edward Marshall Boehm. NY, 1988. Dj. *Edwards*. $48/£30

PALLIS, MARCO. Peaks and Lamas. NY: Knopf, 1949. 3rd ed. 73 plts, 3 maps. (Sl faded), o/w VG. *Worldwide*. $40/£25

PALLIS, MARCO. Peaks and Lamas. Woburn Books, 1974. 4th ed. 67 plts, 4 maps. (New fep, lib stamp tp.) Dj. *Hollett*. $56/£35

PALLISER, CHARLES. The Quincunx. Canongate, 1989. 1st UK ed. Fine in dj. *Williams*. $64/£40

PALLISER, CHARLES. The Quincunx. Canongate, 1989. 1st ed, 1st bk. Fine in dj. *Any Amount*. $72/£45

PALLISER, MRS. BURY. History of Lace. NY, 1902. Frontis. Aeg. (Hinges sl cracked; worn, spine faded.) *Edwards*. $112/£70

PALM, ANDREW J. The Death Penalty, a Consideration of the Objections to Capital Punishment, with a Chapter on War. NY: Putnam, 1891. Brn cl (stained, fr hinge cracked). Usable. *Boswell*. $75/£47

PALMA DI CESNOLA, LUIGI. Cyprus: Its Ancient Cities, Tombs, and Temples. NY, 1878. Pict cl (lib shelf #s on backstrip, spine ends frayed). *Swann**. $69/£43

PALMER, A. B. A Treatise on Epidemic Cholera and Allied Diseases. Ann Arbor, 1885. 1st ed. 224pp. *Fye*. $100/£63

PALMER, A. H. The Life of Joseph Wolf, Animal Painter. London: Longmans, 1895. *Petersfield*. $120/£75

PALMER, ARNOLD (ed). Recording Britain. OUP, 1946-1949. 1st ed. 4 vols. Djs (sl soiled, ragged). *Edwards*. $56/£35

PALMER, EDWIN O. History of Hollywood. Hollywood, CA: Arthur H. Cawston, 1937. 1st ed. 2 vols. Leather. Fine set. *Labordo*. $375/£234

PALMER, EDWIN O. History of Hollywood. Hollywood: Edwin O. Palmer, 1938. 2nd ed. Red fabricoid, gilt. Dj (sl edgeworn, sm spot of wear spine head). *Dawson*. $300/£188

PALMER, FREDERICK. Newton D. Barker: America at War Based on the Personal Papers of the Secretary of War in the World War.... NY: Dodd, Mead, 1931. 1st ed, ltd issue. One of 996 numbered sets, specially ptd and bound, signed by Palmer and Barker. 2 vols. Teg. Full dk blue pub's morocco, gilt. Fine set in glassine (chipped), slipcase (broken). *Reese*. $100/£63

PALMER, FREDERICK. With Kuroki in Manchuria. NY, 1904. 3 maps. (Prelims blindstamped, bkpl remains; fr bd corner discolored, softened; spine sl faded.) *Edwards*. $96/£60

PALMER, GEORGE. Kidnapping in the South Seas. Being a Narrative of a Three Months' Cruise of H. M. Ship Rosario. Edinburgh: Edmonston & Douglas, 1871. 1st ed. xii,234pp; 6 photogravures, 4 color lithos. Brn cl, gilt. Fine (bkpl removed from inner cvr). *Argonaut*. $600/£375

PALMER, H. MARION. The Three Caballeros. NY: Random House, (1944). 1st ed. 11x8.25. Pict bds. (Spine head, corners rubbed), else VG. *Pacific**. $63/£39

PALMER, HARRY CLAY. Athletic Sports in America, England and Australia. Phila: Hubbard Bros, (1889). 1st ed. 711pp; 4 Fine color plts, tissue guards. Lt brn cl, beveled bds, gilt. (Sm ink handstamps; extrems sl worn, spine dknd, lettering dull; recently recased, new eps.) Cvrs Good. *Baltimore**. $290/£181

PALMER, HERBERT. The Judgment of Francois Villon. London: Hogarth, 1927. Ltd to 400, this copy being mkd 'out of series' in Virginia Woolf's hand w/her purple ink. Teg. Parchment-backed cl. NF (eps, prelims lt spotted; spine foot, 2 corners sl bumped) in dj (price-clipped, sl dknd). *Ulysses*. $200/£125

PALMER, J. FREDERICK. Kodiak Bear Hunt: Stalking the Giant Bears of Alaska. NY: Exposition Press, (1958). 1st ed. Fine in dj (torn). *Perier*. $50/£31

PALMER, JOE. Recollections of a Boxing Referee. London: John Lane, (1927). 1st ed. NF. *Pacific**. $58/£36

PALMER, L. J. Raising Reindeer in Alaska. Washington: US Dept of Agriculture, 1934. Good (sm stain at rear). *Walcot*. $19/£12

PALMER, ROBERT. Deep Blues. NY: Viking, 1981. 1st ed. Fine in Fine dj. *Beasley*. $35/£22

PALMER, ROSE A. The North American Indians. Washington: Smithsonian Inst, 1943. Full-color frontis, 85 plts, map. Gilt-dec pebbled red cl. Fine. *Connolly*. $45/£28

PALMER, SAMUEL. The Letters of Samuel Palmer. Raymond Lister (ed). OUP, 1974. 1st Eng ed. 2 vols. Fine set in djs (sl creased, 1 price-clipped). *Ulysses*. $152/£95

PALMER, T. S. (ed). Place Names of the Death Valley Region in California and Nevada. (N.p.), 1948. 1st ed. Fine in orig ptd wrappers (spine sl dknd). *Argonaut*. $175/£109

PALMER, W. T. The Complete Hill Walker, Rock Climber and Cave Explorer. Pitman, 1934. 1st ed. 30 plts. VG. *Hollett*. $88/£55

PALMQUIST, PETER E. Redwood and Lumbering in California Forests. Yolla Bolly, 1983. One of 600. *Dawson*. $50/£31

PALOU, FRANCISCO. The Expedition into California of the Venerable Padre Fray Junipero Serra and His Companions in the Year 1769.... Douglas S. Watson (trans). SF: Nueva CA Press, 1934. One of 400. This copy not numbered or signed. Frontisport, fldg facs map. Unopened. 1/2 vellum. Fine in dj (soiled, few tears, spine head chipped). *Pacific**. $69/£43

PALOU, FRANCISCO. The Founding of the First California Missions, Under the Spiritual Guidance of the Venerable Padre Fray Junipero Serra.... Douglas S. Watson (trans). SF: Nueva CA Press, 1934. One of 1000. Paper spine/cvr labels. VG in dj (lt soiled, few chips, tears, sm piece cut out from rear panel, tape repairs on verso). *Pacific**. $52/£33

PALOU, FRANCISCO. Historical Memoirs of New California. Herbert Eugene Bolton (ed). Berkeley: Univ of CA, 1926. 1st ed in English. 4 vols. Blue cl, gilt. VG +. Howes P55. *Pacific**. $316/£198

PALOU, FRANCISCO. Life and Apostolic Labors of the Venerable Father Junipero Serra. C. Scott Williams (trans). Pasadena: George Wharton James, 1913. 1st complete ed in English. VG +. *Labordo*. $85/£53

PALOU, FRANCISCO. Palou's Life of Fray Junipero Serra. Maynard J. Geiger (trans). Washington: Academy of American Franciscan History, 1955. 1st ed thus. Frontisport, 5 plts, maps. Blue cl, gilt. VF. *Argonaut*. $145/£91

PALTOCK, ROBERT. The Life and Adventures of Peter Wilkins, a Cornish Man. London: Dulau, 1925. 1st ed thus. Linen spine, bds, paper label. VG. *Brown*. $50/£31

PALTOCK, ROBERT. The Life and Adventures of Peter Wilkins. NY: J.M. Dent, 1928. Amer issue w/Amer pub's name at spine foot and on dj. 5 full-pg, 4 dbl-pg color illus. Color eps. Dec cl, gilt. VG (feps partly browned; spine ends, corners sl bumped) in dj (severely torn, creased, mkd, heavily repaired w/sellotape). *Ulysses*. $192/£120

PALUKA, FRANK. Iowa Authors. A Bio-Bibliography of Sixty Native Writers. Iowa City, 1967. 1st Amer ed. NF in ptd wraps. *Polyanthos*. $25/£16

PAMMEL, L. H. et al. Honey Plants of Iowa: Iowa Geological Survey. Bulletin #7. Des Moines, 1930. Good. *Rybski*. $25/£16

Pan Pipes, a Book of Old Songs. London: George Routledge & Sons, (1885). 2nd ed. Obl 4to. Walter Crane (illus). Frontis, (viii),9-51pp. Brn eps. Cl-backed grn pict bds (rebacked). Excellent (corners sl rubbed). *Sotheran*. $205/£128

PANGBORN, J. G. The New Rocky Mountain Tourist, Arkansas Valley and San Juan Guide. Chicago, 1878. 3rd ed. 2 sm maps. Pict wrappers (sl chipped, soiled). *Dumont*. $375/£234

PANNASSIE, HUGUES and MADELEINE GAUTIER. Dictionary of Jazz. London: Jazz Book Club, 1959. Ptd bds. VG in dj (sl chipped, tanned). *Petrilla*. $45/£28

PANNASSIE, HUGUES. Hot Jazz: A Guide to Swing Music. NY: Witmark, 1934. 1st ed. VG (few mks). *Beasley*. $75/£47

PANOFSKY, ERWIN. Early Netherlandish Painting. Cambridge, 1953. 2 vols. *Swann**. $138/£86

Panorama of the East. Concord: Rufus Merrill, n.d. (ca 1850). Merrill's Pictorial Gallery. 8vo. Engr tp, 24pp + 1pg list on lower wrapper; 21 Superb wood engrs. Pict yellow paper wrappers. (Ink dedication tp; lt spots fr wrapper), else Fine. *Hobbyhorse*. $135/£84

PAPE, RICHARD. Poles Apart. London: Odhams Press, 1960. VG in dj. *Explorer*. $14/£9

PAPWORTH, JOHN BUONAROTI. Select Views of London: With Historical and Descriptive Sketches of Some of the Most Interesting Public Buildings. London: R. Ackermann, 1816. 1st ed. 4to. 76 Fine hand-colored engrs (5 fldg). Full red morocco, gilt mitre lines on cvrs, richly gilt paneled spine, raised bands, gilt top. Fine. *Appelfeld*. $3,500/£2,188

Parallel Bible [cover title]. The Holy Bible, Containing the King James Version and the Revised Versions of the Old and New Testaments.... NY: Gately & Williams, (1889). Aeg. Pub's presentation binding, deeply emb in gilt; silver clasps. *Swann**. $103/£64

PARAMORE, EDWARD E., JR. The Ballad of Yukon Jake. NY: Coward-McCann, (1928). VG in dj. *Perier*. $40/£25

PARDEE, HAROLD E. B. Clinical Aspects of the Electrocardiogram, Including The Cardiac Arrhythmias. NY, 1941. 4th ed. (Foxed), o/w Fine. *Doctor's Library*. $75/£47

PARDO-CASTELLO, V. Diseases of the Nails. Springfield, 1941. 2nd ed. *Fye*. $75/£47

PARDOE, F. E. John Baskerville of Birmingham. London, 1975. 1st ed. Fine (2 corner creases) in NF dj. *Polyanthos*. $25/£16

PARDOE, JULIA and WILLIAM BEATTIE. The Beauties of the Bosphorus: The Danube. Virtue, n.d. 8 vols. 4to. 2 engr frontisports, 2 engr tps, 3 engr maps, 165 engr plts. Gilt edges. Pub's cl (spines sl faded), gilt. *Sotheby's**. $957/£598

PARDON, GEORGE FRED. The Faces in the Fire. London: James Blackwood, 1856. 1st ed. Hand-colored frontis, tp, viii,9-270pp + 2 hand-colored plts. Stamped bds, gilt. VG (lacks fep). *Connolly*. $65/£41

PARE, AMBROISE. The Apologie and Treatise of Ambroise Pare. Geoffrey Keynes (ed). London: Falcon Books, 1951. 1st ed thus. 4 plts. VG in dj. *Hollett*. $48/£30

PARE, RICHARD (ed). Court House: a Photographic Document. NY: Horizon, 1978. 1st ed. Folio. 358 plts. Lewis Baltz, et al (photos). Fine in dj (edges lt rubbed). *Cahan*. $200/£125

PARETSKY, SARA. Burn Marks. London: Delacorte, March 1990. 1st ed. 1/4 deep yellow cl. Fine in dj. *Temple*. $32/£20

PARETSKY, SARA. Indemnity Only. Gollancz, 1982. 1st British ed. Signed. VG in dj. *Ash*. $312/£195

PARETSKY, SARA. V.I. for Short. Hamilton, 1995. 1st UK ed. Signed presentation, dated 10/95. Mint in Mint dj. *Martin*. $29/£18

PARGETER, EDITH (trans). Tales of the Little Quarter. Heinemann, 1957. 1st ed. VG (sl browned, spine ends bumped, edges sl spotted) in dj (nicked, sl rubbed, creased, dusty). *Ulysses*. $72/£45

PARGETER, EDITH. The Assize of the Dying. London: Heine-mann, 1958. 1st ed, uncorrected proof. VG (sl leaned, fore-edge lt foxed) in wrappers. *Janus.* $125/£78

PARGETER, EDITH. By This Strange Fire. NY: Reynal & Hitch-cock, 1948. 1st US ed. NF (bds lt stained) in VG+ dj. *Janus.* $50/£31

PARGETER, EDITH. The Soldier at the Door. Heinemann, 1954. 1st ed. VG (feps lt browned; sl bowed, top edge sl dusty, edges spotted, spine ends, corners sl bumped) in dj (nicked, sl rubbed, mkd, creased, spotted, edges, inside flaps browned, rear panel soiled). *Ulysses.* $120/£75

PARIS, J. A. A Treatise on Diet. London: Thomas & George Un-derwood, 1828. 3rd ed, corrected, enlgd. vii,439pp + [i]pg pub's ads. Early 1/2 morocco, cl bds, gilt. (Sl foxed; spine cor-ners, head sl rubbed, spine faded w/sl intrusion onto bds.) *Ed-wards.* $200/£125

PARK, EDGAR. The Merry Adventures of Robin Hood and Santa Claus. Boston: Houghton Mifflin, (1922). 1st ed. W. H. Montgomery (illus). 12mo. Color pict bds (corners bumped). Color pict slipcase (lt edgeworn). *Reisler.* $125/£78

PARK, FRANCIS E. Grey Sprite, the Silver Knight. Boston: Lothrop, Lee & Shepard, (1926). 1st ed. 8vo. 222pp; 8 color plts by Elizabeth Warren. Pict eps. Black pict blue cl (spine faded). VG in color pict dj (spine ends chipped). *House.* $45/£28

PARK, LAWRENCE. Gilbert Stuart: An Illustrated Descriptive List of His Works. NY, 1926. 4 vols. Folio. (Cl rubbed, shaken.) *Swann*.* $373/£233

PARK, LAWRENCE. Gilbert Stuart: An Illustrated Descriptive List of His Works. NY: William Edwin Rudge, 1926. 1st ed. 4 vols. Teg. Dk navy buckram, gilt. NF in orig buckram-cvrd bd box (lt worn). *Baltimore*.* $425/£266

PARK, MUNGO. Travels in the Interior Districts of Africa. Lon-don: W. Bulmer, 1799. 2nd ed. Frontisport, xxviii,372pp,xcii,(ii),(ii)music + (viii)pp subscribers; 1 fldg map (lacks map of North Africa), fldg chart, 4 plts. Early tree calf (rubbed, sl worn, corners rubbed w/loss to calf), rebacked in morocco (spine rubbed w/sm split to fr joint). (Lt browned, fep detached.) *Edwards.* $200/£125

PARK, MUNGO. Travels in the Interior of Africa. London: Crosby & Letterman, 1800. 2nd abridged ed. Engr frontis, half-ti-tle, tp, dedn., vii-xvi,218pp, 3ff., ads. Later 1/4 calf. (Paper aged, frontis stained.) *Marlborough.* $400/£250

PARK, MUNGO. Travels in the Interior of Africa. A&C Black, 1878. xviii,392pp; fldg map. All edges marbled. Contemp full calf prize binding (neatly rebacked), gilt. Nice (map sl foxed; corners rubbed). *Sotheran.* $157/£98

PARK, WILLIAM, JR. The Art of Putting. Edinburgh: J. & J. Gray, 1920. 1st ed. Grn cl, gilt. (Spine sl faded, sm bump to head, up-per fr cvr extrems sl spotted), else VG. *Pacific*.* $1,380/£863

PARK, WILLIAM, JR. The Game of Golf. London: Longmans, Green, 1896. 2nd ed. Pict cl. (Emb stamp, old pencil name, old ink date; joints, spine ends, cvr dec rubbed), else VG. *Pacific*.* $489/£306

PARKE, THOMAS HEAZLE. My Personal Experiences in Equato-rial Africa. London: Sampson Low, Marston, 1891. 1st ed. Fron-tisport, xxvi,(ii),526,(2)blanks,32 pub's list; 16 engr plts, lg fldg color map loose in rear pocket. Olive cl (rubbed). Internally VG (bkpl, few thumb mks, map repaired w/adhesive tape w/o loss, lib plt removed). *Morrell.* $296/£185

PARKER, ARNOLD. Ping-Pong: The Game of Parlor Tennis and How to Play It. NY: R.F. Fenno, 1902. 1st ed. Pict cl. Fine. *Pa-cific*.* $40/£25

PARKER, B. The A's and the K's or Twice Three Is Six. London: W. & R. Chambers, ca 1920. Obl lg 4to. 12 full color dbl-pg il-lus by N. Parker.Color pict bds (edges worn, sm spots to cvr). *Reisler.* $685/£428

PARKER, B. Lays of the Grays. London: W. & R. Chambers, (1909). Obl 8.75x12.5. N. Parker (illus). Chromolitho bds. (Spine ends, corners rubbed), else VG. *Pacific*.* $259/£162

PARKER, DOROTHY. The Viking Portable Library Dorothy Parker. NY: Viking, 1944. 1st ed. (Fep top corner clipped), else VF in VF dj. *Between The Covers.* $100/£63

PARKER, DOROTHY. The Viking Portable Library: Dorothy Parker. NY: Viking, 1944. Omnibus ed. Fine in NF dj (2 sm tears). *Between The Covers.* $55/£34

PARKER, DOUGLAS BURNETT. Synopsis of Traumatic Injuries of the Face and Jaws. St. Louis: C.V. Mosby, 1942. 1 fldg plt. Fine in dk grn cl. *Weber.* $45/£28

PARKER, ERIC et al. Fine Angling for Coarse Fish. Phila: Lippin-cott, n.d. Fine in dj (spine ends, extrems chipped; lacks sm pieces) w/pict cvr label. *Pacific*.* $40/£25

PARKER, ERIC. Colonel Hawker's Shooting Diaries. NY: Derry-dale, 1931. One of 250 (presumed). Red cl. NF in NF ptd dj. *Biscotti.* $175/£109

PARKER, J. J. and W. A. HASWELL. A Text-Book of Zoology. Lon-don: Macmillan, 1897. 2 vols. 779; 683pp. Grn cl. VG. *Sa-vona.* $45/£28

PARKER, J. M. An Aged Wanderer. San Angelo, TX: Elkhorn Wagon Yard, n.d. 1st ed, 1st state. NF in pict wrappers. Howes P78. *Labordo.* $800/£500

PARKER, JAMES A. The Western Highlands. Edinburgh: S.M.C., 1947. 3rd ed. Map. (Edges sl spotted), o/w VG. *Hollett.* $48/£30

PARKER, K. T. The Drawings of Antoine Canaletto in the Collec-tion of His Majesty the King at Windsor Castle. London: Phai-don, 1948. 4 fldg plts. Dj (lt soiled). *Edwards.* $48/£30

PARKER, K. T. The Drawings of Hans Holbein in the Collection of His Majesty the King at Windsor Castle. London, 1945. 2nd ed. 85 plts. VG (ex-lib). *Washton.* $45/£28

PARKER, NATHAN H. The Missouri Hand-Book. St. Louis: P.M. Pinckard, 1865. Only ed. x,11-162pp + 5pp ads; 2 fldg maps. Orig stamped bds. (Sl foxed; gilt titles sl rubbed, bottom edges repaired), else NF. Howes P86. *Dumont.* $475/£297

PARKER, OLIVIA. Under the Looking Glass. Boston: NYGS/Little, Brown, 1983. 1st ed. 43 full-pg color plts. Fine in illus dj (spine, top edge faded). *Cahan.* $100/£63

PARKER, ROBERT B. The Godwulf Manuscript. Boston: Houghton Mifflin, 1974. 1st ed. Fine in NF dj (closed tear inter-nally mended at top of fr panel). *Reese.* $275/£172

PARKER, ROBERT B. The Judas Goat. Boston: Houghton Mifflin, 1978. 1st ed. Signed. Fine in Fine dj. *Lenz.* $100/£63

PARKER, ROBERT B. Looking for Rachel Wallace. Piatkus, 1982. 1st UK ed. Fine in dj. *Williams.* $24/£15

PARKER, ROBERT B. Pale Kings and Princes. NY: Delacorte, (1987). 1st ed. (Bkseller's stamp), o/w Fine in dj. *Second Life.* $35/£22

PARKER, ROBERT B. A Savage Place. (NY): Delacorte, (1981). 1st ed. Signed. Fine in Fine dj. *Lenz.* $60/£38

PARKER, ROBERT B. Stardust. NY, 1990. 1st ed. Signed. Fine in Fine dj. *Warren.* $30/£19

PARKER, ROBERT B. Taming a Sea-Horse. NY: Delacorte, (1986). 1st ed. (Bkpl part adhered to fep), o/w Fine in dj. *Sec-ond Life.* $35/£22

PARKER, ROBERT B. Walking Shadow. NY: Putnam, (1994). 1st ed. Fine in dj. *Second Life.* $35/£22

PARKER, ROBERT B. The Widening Gyre. NY: Delacorte, 1983. 1st ed. NF in dj (lt used). *Beasley.* $30/£19

PARKER, ROBERT. A Yankee Saint, John Humphrey Noyes and the Oneida Community. NY, 1935. 1st ed. (Spine ends worn.) *Heinoldt.* $25/£16

PARKER, SAMUEL. Journal of an Exploring Tour Beyond the Rocky Mountains.... Ithaca, NY: The Author, 1838. 1st ed. xii,371pp; 1 plt. NF (lacks map; rebound). Howes P89. *Argonaut.* $250/£156

PARKER, SAMUEL. Journal of an Exploring Tour Beyond the Rocky Mountains.... Ithaca: Andrus, Woodruff, & Gauntlett, 1844. 4th ed. 416pp; fldg map, plt. Orig cl. (Map torn, repaired w/archival tissue; spotted; worn, extrems chipped), else Good. Howes P89. *Brown.* $225/£141

PARKER, SAMUEL. Journal of an Exploring Tour Beyond the Rocky Mountains...in the Years 1835-1837. Ithaca: The Author, 1840. Lg fldg frontis map (2 repaired tears, foxed), 400pp; plt. Orig blind-stamped brn cl (rebacked w/most of orig spine laid-down). Howes P89. *House.* $220/£138

PARKER, SAMUEL. Parker's Exploring Tour Beyond the Rocky Mountains, with a Map of the Oregon Territory. Minneapolis: Ross & Haines, 1967. Rpt of orig 1838 ed. One of 2000. Fldg facs map. VG in dj. Howes P89. *Brown.* $25/£16

PARKER, WATSON. Gold in the Black Hills. Norman: Univ of OK, (1966). 1st ed. Fine in dj (sl worn). *Lien.* $30/£19

PARKES, EDMUND. The Composition of the Urine in Health and Disease, and Under the Action of Remedies. London, 1860. 1st ed. 404pp. (Ex-lib.) *Fye.* $100/£63

PARKINSON, C. NORTHCOTE. Always a Fusilier. The War History of the Royal Fusiliers (City of London Regiment) 1939-1945. London: Sampson Low, 1949. Color frontis. *Petersfield.* $19/£12

PARKINSON, C. NORTHCOTE. The Law and the Profits. London: John Murray, 1960. 1st ed. Gray cl. (Sm mk on lower edges), o/w Fine in dj (sl frayed, dusty, sl chipped, spine sl faded). *Temple.* $16/£10

PARKINSON, SARAH WOODS. Memories of Carlisle's Old Graveyard. Carlisle: Mary Kirtley Lamberton, 1930. VG. *Brown.* $25/£16

PARKINSON, SYDNEY. A Journal of a Voyage to the South Seas, in His Majesty's Ship, The Endeavor. London: Stanfield Parkinson et al, 1773. 1st ed, lg paper issue. Lg 4to. Frontisport, xxiii,212pp, errata leaf; 28 copper-engr plts, map. Mod full-panelled calf in 18th-cent style, raised spine bands, morocco label. Very Nice (soil to frontis, tp; offset from plts, sl foxing, spots to pp157-8, marginal repair to frontis, lacks final blank). *Pacific*.* $4,600/£2,875

PARKINSON, THOMAS (ed). A Casebook on the Beat. NY: Crowell, 1961. 1st ed. VG (prelims excised prior to tp, some ll roughly opened) in wraps. *Beasley.* $25/£16

PARKMAN, FRANCIS. The Journals of Francis Parkman. Mason Wade (ed). NY: Harper, 1947. 1st ed. 2 vols. Blue cl. Fine in NF djs (spine sl dknd, closed tear). *Harrington.* $60/£38

PARKMAN, FRANCIS. The Oregon Trail. Boston: Little, Brown, 1892. 1st ed w/these illus, 2nd ptg, w/list of illus. 10 full-pg tinted plts by Frederic Remington. Teg. Orig pict full lt brn calf. (Ink presentation; partial cracks along fr joint w/later repairs, sl edgeworn, extrems sl dknd.) Text Clean. BAL 15484. Howes P97. *Baltimore*.* $90/£56

PARKMAN, FRANCIS. The Oregon Trail. LEC, 1943. Ltd to 1500 numbered, signed by Maynard Dixon (illus). Fine in slipcase. *Swann*.* $103/£64

PARKMAN, FRANCIS. The Oregon Trail. E. N. Feltskog (ed). Madison, WI: Univ of WI, 1969. 1st ed thus. Fine in dj. Howes P97. *Labordo.* $55/£34

PARKMAN, FRANCIS. The Works of Francis Parkman. Boston: Little, Brown, 1897-98. Champlain ed. One of 1200. 20 vols. Teg. 3/4 red morocco, cl, gilt. (Spine ends sl scuffed), else NF set. *Pacific*.* $863/£539

PARKS, GORDON. Camera Portraits: the Techniques and Principles.... NY: Franklin Watts, 1948. 1st ed. 44 full-pg plts. VG in dj (edge-chipped). *Cahan.* $175/£109

PARKS, GORDON. In Love. Phila, 1971. 1st ed. (Ink inscrip, edges sl spotted), else Good in dj (price-clipped, cellophane peeling). *King.* $35/£22

PARKYNS, G. J. Monastic and Baronial Remains.... London: Longman, Hurst, Rees et al, 1816. 1st ed. 2 vols. xii,120; iv,165pp; 99 VG b/w aquatint plts. Calls for 100 plts, but some were not ready at time of publication and issued later. No evidence of any plts removed. Aeg. Later full straight-grain dk brn morocco, raised bands, gilt. Good (few hinges cracked, sl browned, few ll and plts once detached and restored w/edges sl chipping, sl offsetting from plts, lt pencil underlining most pp; sl worn, scuffed). *Baltimore*.* $140/£88

PARKYNS, MANSFIELD. Life in Abyssinia. London: John Murray, 1853. 1st ed. 2 vols. Engr frontis, xv,(i)blank,425,(1)imprint; engr frontis, iv,432pp; 16 engr plts, fldg map (sl torn at folds, sm hole w/o loss). Early 20th-cent maroon lib cl. Good (lt browned, lt waterstain affecting few top margins of plts, lib plts). *Morrell.* $336/£210

PARMACHENEE CLUB. Constitution, By-Laws, Rules and List of Officers and Members 1916. NY, (1916). Sidney A. Kirkman's bkpl. Uncut. Paper label. (Shelfworn.) *Oinonen*.* $375/£234

PARMELIN, HELENE. Picasso Says. Christine Trollope (trans). NY: A.S. Barnes, (1969). 1st Amer ed. Fine in dj. *Turtle Island.* $30/£19

PARMELIN, HELENE. Picasso: Women, Cannes and Mougins, 1954-1963. Paris/Amsterdam, (1964). 99 tipped-in color plts. VG in dj. *Cullen.* $125/£78

PARRISH, ANNE. Floating Island. NY: Harper, (1935). 6th ed. 8vo. x,265pp; 13 b/w plts. Pict eps. Black cl, w/color plt on cvr. NF in Good+ color pict dj (edges chipped). *House.* $50/£31

PARRISH, J. M. and JOHN R. CROSSLAND (eds). The Mammoth Book of Thrillers, Ghosts and Mysteries. Odhams, 1936. 1st ed. Frontis. Complete w/unbroken seal on the last 9 stories. VG. *Hollett.* $64/£40

PARRY, EDWARD ABBOTT. Butterscotia or a Cheap Trip to Fairy Land. London: David Nutt, 1896. 1st ed. Archie MacGregor (illus). 8vo. Pict cl. Nice (feps browned, stamp). *Glenn.* $200/£125

PARRY, EDWARD. The Persecution of Mary Stewart. Cassell, 1931. 1st ed. 8 plts. VG. *Hollett.* $48/£30

PARRY, EDWARD. Royal Visits and Progresses to Wales. Edward Parry, 1850. Frontisport (stained, offset), xvii,(iii),496pp + (iv) pub's list. (Marginal browning; faded, corners rubbed w/cl loss, joints cracked through, spine chipped.) *Edwards.* $120/£75

PARRY, EDWIN S. Betsy Ross, Quaker Rebel. Phila, 1932. 3rd ptg. Fine in dj (sl worn). *Pratt.* $20/£13

PARRY, JUDGE (retold by). Don Quixote of the Mancha. NY: John Lane, 1900. 4to. xii,245pp; 11 full-pg color lithos by Walter Crane. Pict cl. VG (tear at fore-edge p195 professionally repaired; edges, spine crown rubbed). *Hobbyhorse.* $225/£141

PARRY, JUDGE (retold by). Don Quixote. London: Blackie & Son, 1900. 1st ed illus by Walter Crane. 8vo. (xii),245,(ii); 11 full-pg color plts. Edges uncut. Brick red pict cl. *Sotheran.* $205/£128

PARRY, WILLIAM EDWARD. Journal of a Voyage for the Discovery of a North-West Passage from the Atlantic to the Pacific [with] Journal of a Second Voyage... [with] Journal of a Third Voyage.... London: John Murray, 1821-1826. 1st eds. 3 vols. Crown 4to. (viii),xxix,310,clxxiixpp,14 plts, 6 charts (4 fldg), w/tipped-in errata leaf; (viii),xxx,571pp, errata pg, 29 plts, 2 plans, 4 fldg charts, 4 fldg panoramas; xxviii,187,151pp, errata leaf, 6 plts, 2 surveys, 2 charts (1 fldg), fldg panorama. Contemp 1/2 leather, marbled paper bds (recently rebacked w/new eps, old labels). VG set (sl foxed). *Ulysses.* $2,400/£1,500

PARRY, WILLIAM EDWARD. Journal of a Voyage for the Discovery of a North-West Passage From the Atlantic to the Pacific.... London: John Murray, 1821. 1st ed. 4 to. (8),xxix(3),310(2),clxxixpp; 20 plts, maps. Marbled eps, edges. Contemp full diced calf (rebacked). VG. *High Latitude*. $700/£438

PARRY, WILLIAM. Welsh Hillside Saints. Manchester, 1896. 1st ed. Dec eps. (Spotted, spine chipped, rubbed.) *Edwards*. $29/£18

PARSONS, C. S. M. and F. H. CURL. China Mending and Restoration. London: Faber, 1963. 78 plts. Dj (sl chipped, rubbed). *Edwards*. $64/£40

PARSONS, CLERE. Poems. Faber & Faber, 1932. 1st Eng ed. Wrappers. VG (edges nicked, chipped, sl torn, spine worn; ends, corners bumped). *Ulysses*. $120/£75

PARSONS, ELSIE CLEWS. Isleta Paintings. Esther S. Goldfrank (ed). Washington: Smithsonian Inst, 1962. Orig ed. Color frontis. (Bkpl, call # traces, stamps.) *Turtle Island*. $35/£22

PARSONS, ELSIE CLEWS. Isleta Paintings. Esther S. Goldfrank (ed). Washington: Smithsonian Inst, 1962. 150 plts. Fine in dj. *Pacific**. $46/£29

PARSONS, ELSIE CLEWS. Taos Pueblo. Menasha, WI, 1936. 1st ed. 13 photo plts, fldg map. NF. *Dumont*. $295/£184

PARSONS, EUGENE. A Guide Book to Colorado. Boston: Little Brown, (1911). Good (burn mk fr cvr). *Perier*. $25/£16

PARSONS, GEORGE F. The Life and Adventures of James W. Marshall. SF: George Fields, 1935. Rpt of 1870 1st ed. One of 450. Port, fldg color plt, fldg tinted plt, fldg color map. 2 orig Gold Rush documents tipped in. Uncut. Grn bds, ptd paper spine label, ptd pict pastedown on fr cvr. VF. *Argonaut*. $300/£188

PARSONS, JAMES. A Mechanical and Critical Enquiry into the Nature of Hermaphrodites. London: J. Walthoe, 1741. Tp, dedication, liv,[ii],156pp; 3 fldg plts at rear. (Mainly maringal sporadic spoting, few margins sl thumbed, upper margin pp xiii-xvi torn w/sl loss to tp, corner pp 1-2 sl chipped.) Mod calf, leather label. *Edwards*. $480/£300

PARSONS, JOHN E. First Winchester: The Story of the 1866 Repeating Rifle. William Morrow, 1955. 1st ed. Good in dj (chipped, repaired). *Rybski*. $55/£34

PARSONS, JOHN E. Henry Deringer's Pocket Pistol. NY: William Morrow, 1952. 1st ed. VG in dj. *Labordo*. $85/£53

PARSONS, JOHN E. The Peacemaker and Its Rivals. NY: William Morrow, 1950. 1st ed. NF in dj (sl faded). *Labordo*. $85/£53

PARSONS, JOHN E. Smith and Wesson Revolvers. NY: William Morrow, 1957. 1st ed. NF in dj. *Labordo*. $85/£53

PARSONS, TALCOTT et al (eds). Theories of Society. NY: Free Press of Glencoe, (1961). 2 vols. Cl-backed blue buckram. Slipcase (shelfworn). *Gach*. $50/£31

PARSONS, W. L. E. Salle, the Story of a Norfolk Parish. London, 1937. 1st ed. VG in dj. *Gretton*. $43/£27

PARSONS, WILLIAM B. Engineers and Engineering in the Renaissance. Balt: Williams & Wilkins, 1939. 1st ed. Navy ribbed cl, gilt. (Edges sl aged; sl rubbed.) Text Clean, cvrs VG. *Baltimore**. $35/£22

PARTINGTON, J. R. A History of Greek Fire and Gunpowder. Cambridge: Heffer, (1960). 1st ed. Frontis. Fine in dj. *Glaser*. $185/£116

PARTINGTON, J. R. A Short History of Chemistry. London: Macmillan, 1937. Fine in dj (lt worn). *Weber*. $40/£25

PARTINGTON, WILFRED. Forging Ahead. NY: Putnam, 1939. Dj (spine dknd, margins lt chipped). *Zubal**. $35/£22

PARTINGTON, WILFRED. Thomas J. Wise in the Original Cloth. London: Hale, 1946. 1st ed. Frontis port. VG in dj (edges chipped, lacks piece fr panel). *Hollett*. $120/£75

PARTON, JAMES. Smoking and Drinking. Boston, 1868. 1st ed. 151pp. *Fye*. $100/£63

PARTON, JAMES. Triumphs of Enterprise, Ingenuity, and Public Spirit. Illustrated. Hartford: A.S. Hale, 1871. 677pp. (Lt age-spotted; spine lightened, extrems rubbed.) *Zubal**. $30/£19

PARTRIDGE, BELLAMY. A Pretty Pickle. NY, 1930. 1st Amer ed. NF (sl rubbed, sl soiled) in VG dj. *Polyanthos*. $25/£16

PARTRIDGE, ERIC. A Charm of Words. NY, 1961. 1st Amer ed. NF in dj (spine sunned, 3 sm tears). *Polyanthos*. $25/£16

PARTSCH, SUSAN. Klimt: Life and Work. London: Bracken Books, (1989). 96 color plts. (Top edge sunned), else Fine in illus dj (bumped, creased). *Metropolitan**. $57/£36

PARVIS, MERRILL M. and ALLEN P. WIKGREN (eds). New Testament Manuscript Studies. Chicago, 1950. 32 plts. Good in wrappers (sl worn). *Washton*. $125/£78

PASCAL, BLAISE. Les Pensees. LEC, 1971. Ltd to 1500 numbered, signed by Ismar David (illus). Fine in slipcase. *Swann**. $103/£64

PASOLINI, PIER PAOLO. The Raguzzi. NY: Grove, 1968. 1st Amer ed. NF in NF dj. *Warren*. $35/£22

PASTERNACK, BORIS. My Sister-Life. LEC, 1991. One of 250 signed by Yuri Kuper (illus). Fine in slipcase. *Swann**. $373/£233

PASTERNAK, BORIS. Doctor Zhivago. Collins & Harvill, 1958. 1st UK ed. Fine in VG dj (lt stained). *Williams*. $104/£65

PASTERNAK, BORIS. Doctor Zhivago. London, 1958. 1st UK ed. Dj (several short closed tears, 2 sm nicks spine head). *Swann**. $201/£126

PASTERNAK, BORIS. Three Letters from Pasternak. NY, 1967. Ltd ed. Fine in tissue dj. *Warren*. $30/£19

PASTEUR, LOUIS. Correspondence of Pasteur and Thuillier Concerning Anthrax and Swine Fever Vaccinations. Robert M. Frank and Denise Wrotnowska (eds). Univ of AL, (1968). 1st ed. 16 plts. Fine in dj. *Glaser*. $40/£25

PASTEUR, LOUIS. Studies on Fermentation. London, 1879. 1st ed in English. 12 plts. (Fr inner hinge starting; worn, rubbed.) *Kane**. $100/£63

PASTEUR, LOUIS. Studies on Fermentation: The Diseases of Beer, Their Causes, and the Means of Preventing Them. London, 1879. 1st ed in English. 418pp. (Inner hinges cracked, backstrip torn.) *Fye*. $150/£94

PASZTORY, ESTER. Aztec Art. NY: Abrams, (1983). As New in pict dj. *Metropolitan**. $51/£32

PATCH, JOSEPH DORST. The Battle of Ball's Bluff. Leesburg, VA: Potomac, (1958). 1st ed. (Sig), else NF in ptd wraps. *Chapel Hill*. $75/£47

PATCHEN, KENNETH. An Astonished Eye Looks Out of the Air. Waldport, OR: Untied, (1945). 2nd imp. VF in wrappers. *Between The Covers*. $150/£94

PATCHEN, KENNETH. An Astonished Eye Looks Out of the Air. Waldport: Untied, 1944. 1st ed. NF in wraps (sl spine wear, tape repair). *Beasley*. $85/£53

PATCHEN, KENNETH. Because It Is. NY: New Directions, (1960). 1st ed. Perfectbound wrappers. VF. *Between The Covers*. $65/£41

PATCHEN, KENNETH. CCCLXXIV Poems. (NY: Padell, 1948). Tipped-in label noting one of 126 numbered signed. White linen (variant). VF in VF dj. *Between The Covers*. $850/£531

PATCHEN, KENNETH. Fables and Other Little Tales. Karlsruhe/Baden: Jonathan Williams, 1953. One of 450. Self wrappers as issued. (Fep price-clipped), else VF. *Between The Covers*. $200/£125

PATCHEN, KENNETH. The Famous Boating Party and Other Poems in Prose. (NY): New Directions, (1954). 1st ed. Fine in dj (flaps clipped). *Pacific**. $40/£25

PATCHEN, KENNETH. The Famous Boating Party. NY: New Directions, (1954). 1st ed. VF in VF dj. *Between The Covers.* $250/£156

PATCHEN, KENNETH. First Will and Testament. (NY: Padell, 1948). 2nd ed. VF in VF dj. *Between The Covers.* $150/£94

PATCHEN, KENNETH. Hurrah for Anything. Highlands, (NC): Jonathan Williams, 1957. 1st ed. Stiff wrappers, dj. As New. *Between The Covers.* $250/£156

PATCHEN, KENNETH. The Love Poems of Kenneth Patchen. SF: City Lights Books, (1960). 1st ed. One of 300 ptd. (Name; fore-edges, upper cvr edges sl dampstained), else VG. *Pacific*.* $58/£36

PATCHEN, KENNETH. Memoirs of a Shy Pornographer. NY: New Directions, (1945). 2nd imp w/black tp. VF in VF red-orange dj. *Between The Covers.* $125/£78

PATCHEN, KENNETH. Orchards, Thrones, and Caravans. (SF): The Print Workshop, (1952). One of 120 numbered signed. Stiff wrappers in selfwrappers. VF. *Between The Covers.* $850/£531

PATCHEN, KENNETH. Outlaw of the Lowest Planet. Grey Walls, 1946. 1st ed. Fine in VG dj (few grease spots). *Any Amount.* $64/£40

PATCHEN, KENNETH. Panels for the Walls of Heaven. (Berkeley): Bern Porter, 1946. 1st ed. One of 750. VF in VF- dj (sm spine hole, sm smudge mks). *Between The Covers.* $350/£219

PATCHEN, KENNETH. Pictures of Life and of Death. NY: Padell, 1946. 1st ed. Fine in wrappers, dj (sl worn). *Lenz.* $50/£31

PATCHEN, KENNETH. Pictures of Life and of Death. NY: Padell, 1946. 1st ed. Wraps. Fine in NF dj (few sm spine chips). *Beasley.* $100/£63

PATCHEN, KENNETH. Red Wine and Yellow Hair. NY: New Directions, (1949). 1st ed. VF in VF dj. *Between The Covers.* $275/£172

PATCHEN, KENNETH. See You in the Morning. NY: Padell, (1947). 1st ed. VF in Fine dj (sl soiled, internal brn paper repair). *Between The Covers.* $175/£109

PATCHEN, KENNETH. See You in the Morning. NY: Padell, (1947). 1st ed, 1st issue. VF in VF white dj (rear cvr sl soiled). *Between The Covers.* $300/£188

PATCHEN, KENNETH. Selected Poems. (NY): New Directions, (1946). 1st ed. VF in VF dj. *Between The Covers.* $100/£63

PATCHEN, KENNETH. Sleepers Awake. (NY: Padell, 1946). 1st ed. VF in VF dj. *Between The Covers.* $350/£219

PATCHEN, KENNETH. The Teeth of the Lion. Norfolk: New Directions, 1942. 1st ed. Wraps. Fine in Fine dj. *Beasley.* $75/£47

PATCHEN, KENNETH. They Keep Riding Down All the Time. NY: Padell, 1946. 1st ed. Wraps. Fine in dj (lt soiled, few sm edge tears). *Beasley.* $85/£53

PATCHEN, KENNETH. To Say If You Love Someone. Prairie City, IL: Prairie, (1948). 1st issue in off-yellow cl w/black lettering ruled in purple on fr bd. Variant blue dj lettered in gold/black. As New in dj. *Between The Covers.* $3,500/£2,188

PATENCIO, FRANCISCO. Stories and Legends of the Palm Springs Indians. Palm Springs: Desert Museum, (1943). 1st ed. Fine in wraps. *Book Market.* $30/£19

Patents for Inventions. Abridgements of Specifications. Class 139. Watches, Clocks, and Other Timekeepers. 1855-1930. London, 1905-1934. 2 vols. (Lib buckram; stamped; sl soiled), else VG. *King.* $100/£63

PATER, WALTER. Appreciations. London, 1889. 1st ed. NF (sl rubbed, spine sunned). *Polyanthos.* $75/£47

PATER, WALTER. An Imaginary Portrait. Oxford: Ptd by H. Daniel, 1894. 1st ed. One of 250. VG in ptd wrappers (sl soiled). *Maggs.* $240/£150

PATER, WALTER. Plato and Platonism. NY, 1893. 1st Amer ed. NF (sl rubbed, sm nick). *Polyanthos.* $35/£22

PATER, WALTER. The Renaissance. LEC, 1976. One of 2000 signed by Martino Mardersteig (designer). Fine in slipcase. *Swann*.* $103/£64

PATER, WALTER. Sebastian Van Stork. London: John Lane, 1927. Ltd ed w/one plt signed in pencil by Alastair (illus). Large 4to. Beige dec linen. *Appelfeld.* $425/£266

PATER, WALTER. The Works of.... London/NY: Macmillan, 1900-01. 9 vols. 8vo. Frontis vol 1. Teg. Full dk blue morocco by Riviere & Son, gilt. (Lt foxed, joints lt rubbed), o/w Fine. *Cummins.* $1,750/£1,094

PATERSON, A. B. Waltzing Matilda. HRW, (1970). 1st Amer ed. 10.5x8.5 oblong. Desmond Digby (illus). Unpaginated. VG in Good full color illus dj (edges rubbed, extrems worn, 1/2-inch chips to spine ends, award seal). *Price.* $20/£13

PATERSON, DANIEL. A New and Accurate Description of All the Direct and Principal Cross Roads in England and Wales.... London: Longman, 1808. 14th ed. xvi,64,528pp; lg fldg map. Uncut. Orig bds. (Several ll holed, repaired, some w/loss of text; new eps, recent cl rebacked.) *Marlborough.* $120/£75

Pathfinder; or, The Inland Sea. (By James Fenimore Cooper.) Phila, 1840. 1st ed, earliest state. 2 vols. Orig grn muslin, ptd paper spine labels. *Felcone.* $1,100/£688

PATMORE, COVENTRY. The Children's Garland. Macmillan, 1862. 1st ed. Half-title, xvi,344,(iv) ads dated Nov 1862. (Sl worn, neatly recased, new eps.) *Hollett.* $208/£130

PATON, ALAN. Cry, the Beloved Country. PA: Franklin Library, 1978. 1st Amer ed. Signed. Aeg. Full leather, gilt. Fine. *Polyanthos.* $45/£28

PATON, ALAN. Too Late the Phalarope. NY: Scribner, 1953. 1st ed. Grayish-blue cl. VG (eps lt foxed; cvrs spotted, spine ends sl rubbed) in dj (browned, chipped). *Heritage.* $50/£31

PATON, DAVID. Animals of Ancient Egypt. Princeton: Princeton Univ, 1925. Folio. (Materials for a 'Sign List' of Egyptian Hieroglyphs 'E' only; corner bumped, bds stained.) *Archaeologia.* $175/£109

PATON, E. RICHMOND and OLIVER G. PIKE. The Birds of Ayrshire. Witherby, 1929. 1st ed. Color frontis, 24 plts, fldg map. Blue cl, gilt. VG. *Hollett.* $120/£75

PATON, JAMES (ed). The Story of John G. Paton Told for Young Folks.... NY/London: Hodder & Stoughton, n.d. (ca 1895). 304pp. (Sl rubbed, soiled), o/w VG. *Worldwide.* $30/£19

PATON, JOHN G. John G. Paton: Missionary to the New Hebrides. NY: Revell, 1889. 2 vols. Brn cl. VG set. *American Booksellers.* $75/£47

PATON, JOHN G. John G. Paton: Missionary to the New Hebrides. NY et al: Revell, 1907. New, complete illus ed. 2 vols in 1. 14 plts, map. (Sl rubbed, soiled), o/w VG. *Worldwide.* $45/£28

PATRICK, JOHN. The Teahouse of the Autumn Moon. NY: Putnam, (1952). 1st ed. VF in VF dj. *Between The Covers.* $300/£188

PATRICK, MARSENA RUDOLPH. Inside Lincoln's Army. David S. Sparks (ed). NY, (1964). 1st ed. VG+ in dj (piece torn from spine head). *Pratt.* $40/£25

PATRICK, MILLAR. Four Centuries of Scottish Psalmody. OUP, 1949. 1st ed. 13 plts. VG in dj. *Hollett.* $72/£45

PATTEN, BRIAN. Little Johnny's Confession. Allen & Unwin, 1967. 1st ed, 1st bk. VG in dj (sl chipped). *Whiteson.* $38/£24

PATTEN, BRIAN. Notes to the Hurrying Man. Allen & Unwin, 1969. 1st ed. VG in VG dj. *Whiteson.* $24/£15

PATTERSON, ADA. Maude Adams. NY, (1907). 1st Amer ed. Pict cvrs, gilt. NF. *Polyanthos.* $25/£16

PATTERSON, ARTHUR HENRY. In Norfolk Bird Haunts in A.D. 1755. Norfolk: Holt, 1930. Rpt. (Sl foxed.) *Petersfield.* $72/£45

PATTERSON, AUGUSTA OWEN. American Homes of To-Day. NY: Macmillan, 1924. 1st ed. Black cl (sl worn, spotted), gilt. Text VG (sl aged). *Baltimore**. $80/£50

PATTERSON, EDMUND DeWITT. Yankee Rebel. John G. Barrett (ed). Chapel Hill: Univ of NC, (1966). 1st ed. Port. Tan cl. Fine in dj (rear panel lt soiled). *Chapel Hill*. $95/£59

PATTERSON, H. ORLANDO. An Absence of Ruins. London: Hutchinson, 1967. 1st Eng ed. VG (spine ends sl bumped) in dj (sl rubbed, spine sl faded). *Ulysses*. $72/£45

PATTERSON, H. ORLANDO. The Children of Sisyphus. London: Hutchinson, 1964. 1st Eng ed, 1st bk. VG (spine ends sl bumped) in dj (rubbed, nicked, torn, spine head defective). *Ulysses*. $88/£55

PATTERSON, HAYWOOD and EARL CONRAD. Scottsboro Boy. GC: Doubleday, 1950. 1st ed. Fine in NF dj (spine tips sl worn). *Agvent*. $150/£94

PATTERSON, J. B. (ed). Autobiography of Ma-Ka-Tai-Me-She-Kia-Kiak, or Black Hawk.... Oquawka: Patterson, 1882. Frontis port, 208pp; 2 plts. Lt brn blind pebbled cl, gilt. Text Very Clean (lt aged), cvrs VG (sl edgeworn). Howes P120. *Baltimore**. $70/£44

PATTERSON, J. H. The Man-Eaters of Tsavo and Other East African Adventures. London, 1908. 1st ed, later issue. Map. Pict cl, gilt. Fine. *Maggs*. $192/£120

PATTERSON, JAMES. Black Market. NY, 1986. 1st ed. VG+ in VG+ dj. *Warren*. $30/£19

PATTERSON, R. L. The Sage Grouse in Wyoming. Denver: Sage, 1952. 1st ed. Signed. Pict cl, gilt. NF in NF dj. *Mikesh*. $67/£42

PATTERSON, TOM. Landmarks of Riverside and the Stories Behind Them. Riverside: Press-Enterprise, 1964. 1st ed. Fine in Fine dj. *Book Market*. $35/£22

PATTILLO, R. Moose-Hunting, Salmon-Fishing and Other Sketches of Sport. Toronto: Wm. Briggs, 1902. 1st ed. Signed, inscribed. Red cl, gilt. (Bkpls), else VG. *Pacific**. $98/£61

PATTON, ANNALEONE D. California Mormons by Sail and Trail. Salt Lake City, 1961. (Fep sl water-damaged), o/w VG. *Benchmark*. $22/£14

PAUL, ELLIOT and JAY ALLEN. All the Brave. NY: Modern Age Books, (1939). 1st trade ed. (Backstrip edges sl chipped, worn), else Good in pict stiff wrappers. *Holmes*. $50/£31

PAUL, ELLIOT. The Amazon. NY: Horace Liveright, 1930. 1st ed. Grn cl stamped in gilt/blue. (Sl offset fep), o/w Fine in dj. *Reese*. $85/£53

PAUL, ELLIOT. The Black and the Red. NY: Random House, 1956. 1st ed. VG (shelfworn) in dj (sl dingy, chipped). *My Bookhouse*. $27/£17

PAUL, JAMES BALFOUR. An Ordinary of Arms. Edinburgh: William Green & Sons, 1893. xvii,263pp (feps lt spotted). Teg. Orig 1/4 morocco (rebacked in matching levant morocco), gilt. *Hollett*. $192/£120

PAUL, RODMAN. The California Gold Discovery. Georgetown, CA: Talisman, 1966. Special ed. One of 100. Signed. 1/2 morocco, marbled bds, gilt. Fine in dbl slipcase (outer slipcase extrems rubbed). *Pacific**. $98/£61

PAUL, WILLIAM. The Cultivation of Roses in Pots. London: Simpkin, Marshall, Hamilton, Kent, n.d. (1899). 8th ed. 88pp + 2pp ads. (Inner hinge cracked, prelims browned.) *Quest*. $45/£28

PAULLIN, CHARLES OSCAR. Commodore John Rodgers, Captain, Commodore and Senior Officer of American Navy. Cleveland: Clark, 1910. 1st ed. (2 labels removed inside fr cvr.) *Heinoldt*. $60/£38

PAULSEN, MARTHA. Follow Me Animal Book. Akron: Saalfield, 1945. 1st ed. 7.75x10. 8 animations by Vivienne Blake. Pict bds. VG in dj (tear along fr joint). *Pacific**. $58/£36

PAULSEN, MARTHA. Toyland. Akron: Saalfield, 1944. 1st ed. Julian Wehr (animator). 7 3/4 x 10. Pict bds. NF. *Pacific**. $46/£29

PAUSE, WALTER. Salute the Mountains. Ruth Michaelis-Jena & Arthur Ratcliff (trans). Harrap, 1962. 1st Eng ed. 100 plts, each w/map. Very Nice in dj. *Hollett*. $136/£85

PAVESE, CESARE. The Harvesters. London: Peter Owen Ltd, 1961. 1st Eng ed. VG (top edge sl dusty; spine ends sl bumped) in dj (sl creased, spine faded). *Ulysses*. $72/£45

PAVESE, CESARE. The Moon and the Bonfire. Louise Sinclair (trans). John Lehmann, 1952. 1st ed. NF (feps lt browned; top edge sl dusty, spine gilt sl oxidised, ends sl bumped) in dj (nicked, sl creased, dusty). *Ulysses*. $120/£75

PAVIERE, SYDNEY H. A Dictionary of British Sporting Painters. Leigh-on-Sea, England: F. Lewis Pub, 1965. Color frontis tipped-in. Blue cl. Fine in Fine ptd dj. *Biscotti*. $165/£103

PAVITT, W. and K. The Book of Talismans, Amulets and Zodiacal Gems. London: Rider, 1914. VG (lt foxed; spine sl faded). *Blake*. $125/£78

PAVLOV, I. Conditioned Reflexes. G. V. Anrep (ed). (London): Oxford Univ, 1927. 1st Eng ed. NF in black buckram (sl rubbed). *Weber*. $200/£125

PAVLOV, I. Conditioned Reflexes: An Investigation of the Physiological Activity of the Cerebral Cortex. G.V. Anrep (ed). Oxford, 1927. 1st ed in English. (Ex-lib.) *Fye*. $150/£94

PAXTON, JOHN A. An Alphabetical List of All the Wards, Streets...in the City and Suburbs of Philadelphia. (Phila, 1810.) Lg fldg map, hand-colored in outline (100mm tear from gutter into map). Mod 1/4 cl; orig pub's price label mtd to fr pastedown. *Swann**. $230/£144

PAXTON, PHILIP. (Pseud of Samuel Hammett.) A Stray Yankee in Texas. NY: Redfield, 1853. 416,(8)pp (lacks frontis, foxed; fr bd almost off). Howes H140. *Dumont*. $125/£78

PAYER, JULIUS. New Lands Within the Arctic Circle. NY: D. Appleton, 1877. 1st ed. Color ptd frontis, xiv,400 + 6pp ads; 2 dbl-pg maps. Dec blue cl (sm waterstains fr cvr, reps), gilt. *Karmiole*. $250/£156

PAYER, JULIUS. New Lands Within the Arctic Circle. Narrative of the Discoveries of the Austrian Ship 'Tegetthoff' in the Years 1872-1874. London: Macmillan, 1876. 1st ed in English. 2 vols. 2 frontispieces (1 chromolitho), xxxi,(1),335,(1); xiv,303,(1)pp; 22 full-pg illus, 2 dbl-pg maps. Blue cl, gilt. VG set (new eps; worn, spine sl faded, ends, corners lt worn). Internally Fine. *Argonaut*. $250/£156

PAYER, JULIUS. New Lands Within the Arctic Circle. Narrative of the Discoveries of the Austrian Ship 'Tegetthoff' in the Years 1872-1874. Macmillan, 1876. 1st ed. 2 vols. xxi,(i),335; xiv,303pp; 24 plts (1 chromolitho), fldg map. Teg. Recent speckled 1/2 calf, raised bands, gilt, contrasting leather labels, marbled bds. VG. *Sotheran*. $480/£300

PAYETTE, B. C. The Northwest. Montreal: Payette Radio Radio, 1964. Fine. *Perier*. $45/£28

PAYETTE, B. C. The Oregon Country Under the Union Jack. Montreal: Payette Radio Radio, 1962. Postscript ed. VG. *Perier*. $45/£28

PAYNE, BLANCHE. History of Costume. NY: Harper & Row, (1965). Orig ed. NF in VG dj. *Turtle Island*. $65/£41

PAYNE, DORIS PALMER. Captain Jack: Modoc Renegade. Portland: Binford & Mort, (1938). 1st ed. VG in dj. *Perier*. $35/£22

PAYNE, HUMFRY and GERARD MACKWORTH-YOUNG. Archaic Marble Sculpture from the Acropolis. London, 1950. 2nd ed. Frontis, 140 plts. (Ink stamp, lib labels; faded, corners sl bumped.) *Edwards*. $72/£45

PAYNE, ROBERT. The Blue Negro. NY: Avon 373, 1951. 1st ed. Fine in wraps. *Beasley*. $35/£22

PAYNE, ROBERT. The Splendors of Asia. India, Thailand, Japan. NY: Viking, 1965. 1st ed. VG in dj (torn). *Worldwide.* $25/£16

PAYNE-GALLWEY, RALPH. Letters to Young Shooters. Longmans, Green, 1892-1896. 4th, 1st & 1st eds. 3 vols. xii,274,(xviii); (xiv),524; (xxx),630,(ii)pp. Good+ set (1 ep cracking, few mks, spotted; sl worn, vol 2 sl rubbed, bumped). *Ash.* $152/£95

PAYNE-GALLWEY, RALPH. Projectile-Throwing Engines of the Ancients. Longmans, Green, 1907. 1st ed. (Feps sl spotted, bkpl; sl faded, spine head sl bowed.) *Hollett.* $288/£180

PAYNE-GALLWEY, RALPH. The Scaffold 'George' of Charles I. London: E. Arnold, 1908. 16 plts. Cream cl. *Marlborough.* $56/£35

PAYTON, CHARLES A. Days of a Knight. London: Hutchinson, 1924. 16 plts. (Spine faded.) *Hollett.* $72/£45

PAZ, IRENEO. Life and Adventures of the Celebrated Bandit, Joaquin Murrieta (sic): His Exploits in the State of California. Francis P. Belle (trans). Chicago: Chas T. Powner, 1937. 2nd ed in English. Brn cl. Fine in NF dj. *Harrington.* $35/£22

PAZ, OCTAVIO (comp). An Anthology of Mexican Poetry. Samuel Beckett (trans). London: Thames & Hudson, (1958). 1st Eng ed. NF in dj (spine head tape-mended). *Pharos.* $75/£47

PAZ, OCTAVIO. Alternating Current. London: Wildwood House, 1974. 1st British ed. (Pp sl browned), else Fine in dj (price-clipped). *Lame Duck.* $65/£41

PAZ, OCTAVIO. The Bow and the Lyre. Austin: Univ of TX, 1973. 1st US ed. NF in VG+ dj (spine faded). *Lame Duck.* $75/£47

PAZ, OCTAVIO. Marcel Duchamp. NY: Viking/Richard Seaver, (1978). 1st ed. Fine in dj. *Turtle Island.* $75/£47

PAZ, OCTAVIO. The Monkey Grammarian. NY: Seaver, 1981. 1st US ed. Fine in dj. *Lame Duck.* $50/£31

PEABODY, ELIZABETH P. Key to History. Boston: Marsh, Capen & Lyon, 1833. 1st ed. (6),156pp. Contemp cl-backed bds, paper label. Very Nice. *M & S.* $300/£188

PEABODY, ELIZABETH P. Reminiscences of Rev. Wm. Ellery Channing, D.D. Boston: Roberts Bros, 1880. 1st ed. 459pp. Brn cl. Good (news clipping pasted to blank fep; sl worn, rubbed). *Lucas.* $95/£59

PEACH, B. N. and J. HORNE. The Silurian Rocks of Britain. Vol 1. Scotland. Glasgow, 1899. xviii,749pp; fldg color map, 27 plts. (Short tears in map repaired, rear cvr sl dampstained.) *Henly.* $192/£120

Peacock at Home. (By Catherine Ann Dorset.) London: J. Harris, 1808. Sq 12mo. Full-pg frontis, tp water-mkd 1807, 16pp; 5 VF copper-engr plts. Full red leather on bds, gilt. Fine (tp w/sm repaired tear) in marbled stiff paper wrappers. *Hobbyhorse.* $250/£156

PEACOCK, PRIMROSE. Buttons for the Collector. London: Newton Abbot, 1972. 1st ed. 53 plts (6 color). Dj (sl rubbed, chipped). *Edwards.* $26/£16

PEACOCK, THOMAS LOVE. Crotchet Castle. T. Hookham, 1831. 1st ed, w/o ad leaf. Contemp 1/2 calf. (Sl spotted; worn, crayon mks fr cvr.) *Sotheby's*.* $459/£287

PEACOCK, THOMAS LOVE. Maid Marian. T. Hookham et al, 1822. 1st ed. Contemp calf, gilt spine. (Sl foxed, spotted, bkpl.) *Sotheby's*.* $368/£230

PEACOCK, THOMAS LOVE. Nightmare Abbey. T. Hookham & Baldwin, Craddock, & Joy, 1818. 1st ed, w/o half-title. Inner edges gilt. 19th-cent 1/2 calf. (Sl spotted; rebacked, worn, hinges cracked.) *Sotheby's*.* $459/£287

PEACOCK, THOMAS LOVE. Palmyra and Other Poems. T. Bensley for W.J. & J. Richardson, 1806. 1st ed. Engr frontis. Mottled calf, gilt. (Offsetting; lower joint chipped.) *Sotheby's*.* $331/£207

PEACOCK, THOMAS LOVE. Rhododaphne: Or the Thassalian Spell. T. Hookham & Craddock, Baldwin & Joy, 1818. 1st ed. Half-title. Inner edges gilt. 19th-cent straight-grained purple morocco. *Sotheby's*.* $405/£253

PEAK, HOWARD W. A Ranger of Commerce or 52 Years on the Road. San Antonio: Naylor Ptg, (1929). 1st ed. Frontisport, 3 plts. Leatherette, emb cvr illus, gilt. (Inner fr cvr sl rubbed from erased name), else Fine. *Argonaut.* $125/£78

PEAKE, MERVYN. Figures of Speech. Gollancz, 1954. 1st UK ed. VG in dj (browned, edges sl worn). *Williams.* $72/£45

PEAKE, MERVYN. The Glassblowers. Eyre & Spottiswoode, 1950. 1st UK ed. NF in VG dj (edges sl worn). *Williams.* $56/£35

PEAKE, MERVYN. A Reverie of Bone. Rota, 1967. One of 320 numbered. Thin plain white card. Fine in pict dj. *Any Amount.* $96/£60

PEAKE, MERVYN. Selected Poems. London: Faber & Faber, 1972. 1st Eng ed. Fine in dj (sl nicked, mkd, spine sl dknd). *Ulysses.* $40/£25

PEAKE, MERVYN. Titus Groan. NY, (1946). 1st Amer ed, 1st bk. Good in dj (edges chipped, frayed; spotted). *King.* $75/£47

PEAKE, ORA BROOKS. The Colorado Range Cattle Industry. Glendale, CA: A.H. Clark, 1937. 1st ed. Fine. *Labordo.* $175/£109

PEARCE, CHARLES WILLIAM. Notes on Old London City Churches. Vincent Music Co, (c. 1909). (Spine faded.) *Hollett.* $72/£45

PEARCE, F. SAVARY. A Practical Treatise on Nervous Diseases for the Medical Student and General Practitioner. NY, 1904. 1st ed. Color fep. Author photo laid-in. (Inner hinges cracked, fr bkplt/inscrip). VG. *Doctor's Library.* $50/£31

PEARCE, HAYWOOD J., JR. Benjamin H. Hill. Chicago: Univ of Chicago, (1928). 1st ed. Blue cl. (Sl spotted), else VG in dj (price-clipped, few sm tears). *Chapel Hill.* $45/£28

PEARCE, RICHARD. The Spleen and Anaemia Experimental and Clinical Studies. Phila, 1918. 1st ed. *Fye.* $125/£78

PEARE, C. O. A Scientist of Two Worlds. Phila: Lippincott, 1958. 1st ed. Photo frontis. Fine in VG dj. *Mikesh.* $30/£19

PEARL, M. L. William Cobbett: A Bibliographical Account of His Life and Times. London: Geoffrey Cumberlege, 1953. Grn cl (headcaps sl bumped). Dj (sl defective). *Maggs.* $136/£85

PEARSALL, RONALD. Victorian Sheet Music Covers. Newton Abbot: David & Charles, 1972. 1st ed. VG in dj. *Hollett.* $32/£20

PEARSON, F. K. Isle of Man Tramways. Newton Abbot, (1970). Grn bds. VG+ in dj. *Bohling.* $30/£19

PEARSON, HESKETH. Conan Doyle. NY: Walker, (1961). 1st Amer ed. VG in VG dj (sm discoloration where price lable removed). *Gravesend.* $35/£22

PEARSON, HESKETH. Iron Rations. (London): Cecil Palmer, (1928). 1st ed. Mustard cl. (Bkpl, eps tanned), else VG in dj (lt nicked, rubbed). *Reese.* $50/£31

PEARSON, HESKETH. The Smith of Smiths. London: Hamish Hamilton, 1934. Frontis port. (Spine sl faded.) *Hollett.* $32/£20

PEARSON, JOHN. James Bond: The Authorized Biography of 007. Morrow, 1973. 1st Amer ed. (Pp edges lt soiled), else NF in dj. *Murder.* $35/£22

PEARSON, JOHN. Observations on the Effects of Various Articles of the Materia Medica, in the Cure of Lues Venerea: Illustrated with Cases. London, 1800. 1st ed. 188pp. 1/2 leather (rubbed). *Fye.* $250/£156

PEARSON, MARGARET M. Poppet and Pete. Sydney: Australasian Pub, (1943). 1st ed. Obl 4to. Color pict bds (corners lt worn). *Reisler.* $200/£125

PEARSON, T. R. A Short History of a Small Place. NY: Linden, 1985. 1st ed, 1st bk. Fine in Fine dj (sl rubbed). *Pettler*. $45/£28

PEARY, ROBERT E. The North Pole. London: Hodder & Stoughton, 1910. 4 photogravure plts, 16 special plts, lg fldg color map. VG (spine sl dknd). *Explorer*. $224/£140

PEARY, ROBERT E. Northward Over the 'Great Ice': A Narrative of Life and Work Along the Shores and Upon the Interior Ice-Cap of Northern Greenland in the Years 1886 and 1891-1897. London: Methuen, 1898. 2 vols. lxxx,521; xiv,625pp; 2 fldg maps. Fine (sig). *Explorer*. $352/£220

PEARY, ROBERT E. Secrets of Polar Travel. NY, 1917. Dj (top edge sl worn, paper label over price on spine). *Swann**. $230/£144

PEASE, ALFRED E. The Book of the Lion. London: Murray, 1913. 1st ed. Teg. Gilt-dec red cl. VG + . *Bowman*. $250/£156

PEASE, ALFRED E. Travel and Sport in Africa. London: Arthur L. Humphries, 1902. 1st ed. 3 vols. 4to. Teg. Orig blue cl backed in buckram (spines browned; bkpls, inscrip). *Christie's**. $1,710/£1,069

PEASLEE, E. RANDOLPH. Ovarian Tumors: Their Pathology, Diagnosis and Treatment, Especially by Ovariotomy. NY, 1872. 1st ed. 551pp. (Frontis port tears; 2-inch outer hinge tear.) Fine internally. *Fye*. $400/£250

PEAT, FERN BISEL. Calico Pets. Akron, OH: Saalfield, 1931. Lg 4to. 14pp. Good in full color pict paper wrappers. *Reisler*. $55/£34

PEAT, HAROLD R. Private Peat. Indianapolis: Bobbs-Merrill, (1917). 1st ed. Frontisport. Brn cl. (Spine lettering sl flaked), o/w VG in pict dj (2 sm edge tears, long creased tear, chip rear panel). *Reese*. $35/£22

PEATTIE, DONALD CULROSS. An Almanac for Moderns. LEC, 1938. Ltd to 1500 numbered, signed by Asa Cheffetz (illus). Fine in slipcase. *Swann**. $34/£21

PEATTIE, DONALD CULROSS. Audubon's America. Boston, 1940. 15 full-pg color litho repros. (Spine faded), else VG. *Dumont*. $55/£34

PEATTIE, DONALD CULROSS. A Natural History of Western Trees. Boston: Houghton Mifflin, 1953. 1st ed. 35 full-pg illus. VG in dj (chipped). *Fair Meadow*. $35/£22

PEATTIE, RODERICK (ed). The Black Hills. NY: Vanguard, 1952. 1st ed. Fine in dj. *Labordo*. $50/£31

PEATTIE, RODERICK (ed). The Pacific Coast Ranges. NY: Vanguard, (1946). 1st ed. 18 b/w photo plts, 4 maps. Tan cl. Fine in VG pict dj. *House*. $25/£16

PEATTIE, RODERICK (ed). The Sierra Nevada: The Range of Light. NY: Vanguard, (1947). 1st ed. 26 b/w photo plts, fldg map (crease tear). Tan cl. VG in dj (chipped). *House*. $25/£16

PEATTIE, RODERICK. Rambles in Europe. NY: American Book Co, 1934. 1st ed. Pict cl. Fine. *Connolly*. $30/£19

PECK, CHARLES. Annual Report of the State Botanist of the State of New York. Albany: NY State, 1896. 1st ed. 241pp; 43 plts. Grn cl. Good. *Archer*. $125/£78

PECK, FRANCIS. Desiderata Curiosa; or, A Collection of Divers Scarce and Curious Pieces Relating Chiefly to Matters of English History. London: Thomas Evans, 1779. 2 vols in 1. Marbled edges. Gilt-ruled caramel calf, morocco spine label, raised bands; bound by James Toovey. (Fr joint sl worn), else NF. *Pacific**. $316/£198

PECK, GEORGE. Peck's Bad Boy with the Circus. Chicago: Thompson & Thomas, (1906). 1st ed. C. Frink (illus). Sq 8vo. Dk grn pict cl. (Sl aged, fr hinge lt cracked, rear hinge repaired, rep lacks top corner, which is adhered to pastedown; sl edgeworn.) Cvrs VG. *Baltimore**. $35/£22

PECK, GEORGE. Wyoming; Its History, Stirring Incidents, and Romantic Adventures. NY: Harper, 1858. 1st ed. 12 plts. (Rubbed, gilt dull.) *Sadlon*. $125/£78

PECK, J. M. A Gazeteer of Illinois, in Three Parts. Phila: Grigg & Elliot, 1837. 2nd ed. Fldg map colored in outline, xi,328pp. Orig muslin bds, paper label. (Spine gone, fr cvr detached but present), o/w VG. Howes P170. *Brown*. $450/£281

PECK, J. M. A Guide for Emigrants, Containing Sketches of Illinois, Missouri, and the Adjacent Parts. Boston, 1831. Hand-colored fldg map frontis. Pub's cl, paper spine label. (Ex-lib, emb stamp on tp, fep adhering to remnants of lib label on pastedown.) Howes P171. *Swann**. $258/£161

PECK, MORTON E. A Manual of the Higher Plants of Oregon. Portland, 1941. 1st ed. Grn cl. VG. *Larry Price*. $45/£28

PEDDIE, R. A. The History of Printing Together with Printing in Colours. London: Students of Saint Bride Foundation Printing School, 1917. Circulation slip present. Paper spine label. (Exlib.) *Oak Knoll*. $30/£19

PEEL, C. V. A. The Polar Bear Hunt. London: Old Royalty Book Pub, 1928. Map. Good (binding sl soiled, spotted). *High Latitude*. $65/£41

PEEL, MICHAEL. The Camera Never Lies. Surrey, England: Circle, 1979. 1st ed. One of 300 signed. 16 mtd photos, captioned, laid in. C type color print, signed, numbered. Full maroon morocco, gilt. Fine in clamshell cl box. *Cahan*. $375/£234

PEELE, R. Mining Engineers' Handbook. NY: Wiley, c1927. 2nd ed. VG. *Blake*. $50/£31

Peeps into Fairy Land. A Panorama Picture Book of Fairy Stories. London: Ernest Nister, (1896). Obl, sm folio. 6 3-D scenes. (Marginal tears.) Cl-backed color illus bds (worn). *Reisler*. $850/£531

PEER, FRANK SHERMAN. Cross Country with Horse and Hound. NY: Scribner, 1902. Teg. 3/4 morocco (rubbed). *Oinonen**. $70/£44

PEER, FRANK SHERMAN. The Hunting Field with Horse and Hound in America, the British Isles and France. NY: Mitchell Kennerley, 1910. Teg, uncut. Pict cvr label. (Sl worn.) *Oinonen**. $60/£38

PEET, CREIGHTON. Dude Ranch. Chicago: Albert Whitman, 1939. VG in dj (sl worn). *Lien*. $15/£9

PEGUY, CHARLES. Men and Saints. London, 1947. Fine in dj (sl rubbed). *Polyanthos*. $25/£16

PEICH, MICHAEL. The First Ten: A Penmaen Bibliography. Lincoln: Penmaen, 1978. 1st ed. One of 100. Signed by Peich et al. Woodcut, signed by McCurdy (illus). Prospectus laid in. Blind-stamped blue cl, gilt. Fine in slipcase. *Pacific**. $46/£29

PEIRCE, A. C. A Man from Corpus Christi. NY, 1894. 1st ed. 257pp + ads. Fine. *Truepenny*. $250/£156

PEIRSON, ERMA. The Mojave River and Its Valley. Glendale: A.H. Clark, 1970. 1st ed. Fine in Fine dj. *Book Market*. $30/£19

PEIRSON, ERMA. The Mojave River and Its Valley. Glendale, CA, 1970. 1st ed. Ltd to 2500. NF in NF dj. *Sagebrush*. $40/£25

PEIRSON, LYDIA JANE. Forest Minstrel.... B. S. Schneck (ed). Phila: Moore, Harrisburg, Hickok, 1846. 1st ed. 264pp. Dec cl (spine ends lt repaired). *Ginsberg*. $125/£78

PEIXOTTO, ERNEST. Our Hispanic Southwest. NY: Scribner, 1916. 1st ed. (Spine faded; shaken.) Internally Clean. *Dumont*. $45/£28

Pelayo: A Story of the Goth. (By W.G. Simms.) NY, 1838. 1st ed. 2 vols. Orig cl, ptd paper labels. VG set (foxed; rubbed, spines faded, hinges sl cracked). BAL 18063. *M & S*. $350/£219

PELHAM, CAMDEN. The Chronicles of Crime; or The New Newgate Calendar. London: T. Miles, (1841). 2 vols. xii,592; viii,636pp; 52 etchings. Pebbled ruled blue cl, gilt. (Spine ends frayed, 3cm tear upper rear joint 2nd vol), else VG. *Gach*. $85/£53

PELHAM, CAMDEN. The Chronicles of Crime; or The New Newgate Calendar. London: Reeves & Turner, 1886. 2 vols. Phiz (illus). Teg. Bound by Whitman Bennett. 3/4 tan calf, marbled bds, red morocco spine labels. (Joints, extrems sl rubbed, spine ends scuffed), else VG. *Pacific**. $138/£86

PELLEGRIN, PIERRE. Aristotle's Classification of Animals. Anthony Preus (trans). Univ of CA, (1986). 1st Amer ed. Fine in dj. *Glaser*. $35/£22

PELTER, JEROME. Warbonnets and Epaulets. Montreal: Payette Radio Ltd, (1971). Fine. *Perier*. $60/£38

PELZER, LOUIS. The Cattlemen's Frontier. Glendale, CA: A.H. Clark, 1936. 1st ed. (Spine faded), o/w VG + . Howes P187. *Labordo*. $195/£122

PEMBERTON, CHRISTOPHER. A Practical Treatise on Various Diseases of the Abdominal Viscera. Worcester, 1815. 1st Amer ed. 201pp; 2 plts. Full tree calf, red label. (Text browned; cvrs rubbed.) *King*. $150/£94

PEMBERTON, EBENEZER. A Funeral Sermon on the Death of That Learned and Excellent Divine the Reverend Mr. Samuel Willard...to which is Annexed, a Poem...by the Reverend Mr. Benjamin Colman. Boston: Benj. Eliot, 1707. 1st ed. 18mo. (16),80,(2),14pp (leaf w/short marginal replacement; tp, few ll cleaned, professionally inserted from other copy). Contemp calf (rebacked). *M & S*. $2,250/£1,406

PEMBERTON, H. The Dispensatory of the Royal College of Physicians, London.... London, 1748. 2nd ed. x,414pp. Contemp calf, gilt, morocco label. (Corners worn), o/w VG. *Whitehart*. $216/£135

PENCE, MARY LOU and LOLA M. HOMSHER. The Ghost Towns of Wyoming. NY, 1956. 1st ed. Signed by Pence & Homsher. (Sl faded to backstrip), else NF in dj (chipped, price-clipped). *Baade*. $50/£31

PENCE, MARY LOU. Boswell. Laramie: Privately ptd, 1978. 1st ed. Inscribed. Fine in dj. *Baade*. $45/£28

PENDER, WILLIAM DORSEY. The General to His Lady. William W. Hassler (ed). Chapel Hill: Univ of NC, (1965). 1st ed. Gray cl. (Bkpl, newspaper rev affixed to rear pastedown), else Fine in VG dj. *Chapel Hill*. $60/£38

PENFIELD, WILDER and THEODORE RASMUSSEN. The Cerebral Cortex of Man. NY: Macmillan, 1950. 1st ed. (Lib stamps, sl signs of plt removal), else Fine. *Beasley*. $85/£53

Penicillin: Its Properties, Uses and Preparations. London, 1946. 1st ed. *Fye*. $150/£94

PENINGTON, JOHN. Footprints: or, Fugitive Poems. Phila: The Author, 1843. 1st ed. 92pp. Orig bds. (Spine worn, paper label missing), else Good. *Brown*. $30/£19

PENINOU, ERNEST P. and SIDNEY S. GREENLEAF. A Directory of California Wine Growers and Wine Makers in 1860. Berkeley: Tamalpias, 1967. 1st ed. One of 450. Signed by both, initialed by Roger Levenson (pt Grn cl. Fine in glassine. *Pacific**. $81/£51

PENN, ARTHUR. The Home Library. NY, 1883. 1st ed. 154pp. Dec cl. (Bkpl; sl worn.) *King*. $25/£16

PENN, IRVING. Inventive Paris Clothes, 1909-1939. Text by Diana Vreeland. NY: Viking, 1977. 1st ed. Inscribed by Penn. Fine in dj. *Smith*. $300/£188

PENN, IRVING. Moments Preserved. Text by Alexander Liberman and Rosemary Blackmon. NY: S&S, 1960. 1st ed. Folio. Fine in NF dj (spine sl browned), NF slipcase. *Smith*. $600/£375

PENN, IRVING. Moments Preserved: Eight Essays in Photographs and Words. Text by Alexander Liberman and Rosemary Blackmon. NY, (1960). 1st ed. Signed. Folio. (Fep sl soiled, fr hinge partly split; sm tear at foot of spine panel.) Dj (age-dknd, sm tear spine panel foot). Slipcase (worn, soiled). *Swann**. $1,035/£647

PENN, IRVING. Worlds in a Small Room. NY, (1974). 1st ed. (Eps foxed, pencil note rep; sl soiled.) Dj (stained, rubbed). *Swann**. $80/£50

PENN, IRVING. Worlds in a Small Room. NY: Grossman, 1974. 1st ed. 76 b/w photos. Fine in pict dj. *Cahan*. $150/£94

PENN, J. For Readers Only. London: Chapman & Hall, 1936. VG (extrems rubbed). *Zubal**. $28/£18

PENN, WILLIAM. A Brief Account of the Rise and Progress of the People Called Quakers. Dublin: Robert Jackson, 1776. 8th ed. Period calf. (Old name; joints starting), else VG. *Pacific**. $104/£65

PENN, WILLIAM. The Papers of William Penn. Mary Maples Dunn and Richard S. Dunn (eds). Phila: Univ of PA, 1981-1987. 5 vols. VG set. *Brown*. $240/£150

PENN, WILLIAM. Some Fruits of Solitude, in Reflexions and Maxims, Relating to the Conduct of Human Life. (London: Edward Arnold, 1901.) One of 250. Vellum, yapp edges. (Bkpl, cvrs soiled), else VG. *Pacific**. $184/£115

PENNANT, THOMAS. The Literary Life of the Late Thomas Pennant, Esq. by Himself. London, 1793. (5),144pp (fep corner missing, margins soiled); port (soiled), plt (soiled). Contemp bds (worn, soiled, backstrip partly perished, fr hinge tender). *Sutton*. $225/£141

PENNANT, THOMAS. The Literary Life of the Late.... London, 1793. Frontisport, 144pp; plt (as called for, but w/o add'l fldg frontis and 2 ports which are sometimes present). 1/2 calf (rebound), marbled bds. (Plts browned; rubbed.) *Edwards*. $120/£75

PENNANT, THOMAS. Some Account of London. J. Faulder et al, 1813. 5th ed. Extra engr tp, viii,660pp; lg fldg engr map, 14 plts (1 fldg). VG (stamp, bkpl) in contemp full calf (sl rubbed), gilt, morocco label. *Cox*. $112/£70

PENNANT, THOMAS. A Tour in Scotland, and A Voyage to the Hebrides. London: Benj. White, 1776. 2nd ed. 3 vols. Tall thick 4to. 400; 439; 481pp + 34pp of Additions to the Tour, index to each vol; 133 engr, full-pg, fldg illus. Full speckled calf (nicely rebacked), raised bands, gilt, red leather labels. VG set (worn). *Hartfield*. $1,095/£684

PENNANT, THOMAS. Tours in Wales. Wilkie & Robinson et al, 1810. Posthumous ed. 3 vols. 44 engr plts. Orig tree calf, gilt. Externally Sound (lacks labels). *Bickersteth*. $176/£110

PENNECUIK, ALEXANDER. An Historical Account of the Blue Blanket: Or, Crafts-Mens Banner. Edinburgh: John Mosman, 1722. 1st ed. (viii),(ii),x,140pp. Recent contemp-style calf, raised bands, red morocco label. *Young*. $368/£230

PENNELL, ELIZABETH ROBINS. Nights. Phila, 1916. 1st Amer ed. Teg, uncut. Gilt-dec cvrs. Fine. *Polyanthos*. $35/£22

PENNELL, H. CHOLMONDELEY. Pegasus Re-Saddled. Phila, 1878. 1st Amer ed. 120pp. Aeg. (Cvrs rubbed, spine ends frayed.) *King*. $35/£22

PENNELL, JOSEPH. The Adventures of an Illustrator. Boston, 1925. Ltd ed for subs, signed. Signed etching. 1/4 calf (spine dknd, joints rubbed). *Swann**. $103/£64

PENNELL, JOSEPH. The Adventures of an Illustrator. Boston: Little, Brown, 1925. 1st ed. Fine in dj (lt worn). *Glenn*. $150/£94

PENNELL, JOSEPH. The Glory of New York. NY, 1926. One of 355 numbered. Inscribed by Elizabeth Pennell. Folio. 24 mtd color plts. (Spotted, sl discolored.) *Swann**. $230/£144

PENNELL, JOSEPH. Pen Drawing and Pen Draughtsmen. London, 1889. Folio. (Lt foxed; sl worn.) *Swann**. $69/£43

PENNELL, JOSEPH. Pen Drawing and Pen Draughtsmen. London, 1921. 10 plts. Lib cl. (Bkpl, ink stamp tp verso; rebound, lib #, soiling.) *Edwards*. $64/£40

PENNELL, JOSEPH. San Francisco. London/Edinburgh: T.N. Foulis, 1913. 1st Eng ed. VG (eps, prelims sl spotted) in card wrappers (dusty, mkd; yapp edges, spine creased). *Ulysses*. $72/£45

PENNINGTON, CAMPBEL W. The Tepehuan of Chihuahua, Their Material Culture. Salt Lake City: Univ of UT, (1969). 1st ed. Fine in Fine dj. *Book Market*. $30/£19

PENNINGTON, PATIENCE. (Pseud of Elizabeth A. A. Pringle.) A Woman Rice Planter. Macmillan, 1928. VG-. *Book Broker*. $35/£22

Pennsylvania. A Guide to the Keystone State. American Guide Series. NY: OUP, (1947). Lg fldg map in rear pocket. Blue cl. VG in pict dj (chipped, worn). *House*. $45/£28

PENROSE, CHARLES B. The Rustler Business. Douglas, WY, (1959). 1st ed thus. NF in pict wraps. *Baade*. $75/£47

PENROSE, MATT R. Pots o' Gold. Reno, NV: A. Carlisle, 1935. 1st ed. (Lg bkpl), o/w NF. *Labordo*. $175/£109

PENROSE, ROLAND. Scrap Book 1900-1981. NY: Rizzoli, (1981). Fine in dj. *Turtle Island*. $65/£41

PENROSE, ROLAND. The Sculpture of Picasso. NY: MOMA, (1967). Orig ed. Ptd wrappers (soiled). *Turtle Island*. $45/£28

PENZEL, FREDERICK. Theatre Lighting Before Electricity. Middletown: Weslyan Univ, (1978). 50 plts. VG in dec dj. *Dramatis*. $40/£25

PENZER, N. M. The Harem: An Account of the Institution.... Spring Bks, 1965. Fldg plan. Red bds, gilt. VG in dj (worn). *Whittle*. $24/£15

PENZER, N. M. Paul Storr. The Last of the Goldsmiths. London: Batsford, (1954). 1st ed. Frontis, 81 plts. Red cl. Fine in dj (lt chipped). *Karmiole*. $150/£94

PENZER, N. M. Poison-Damsels, and Other Essays in Folklore and Anthropology. London: Chas. J. Sawyer, 1952. 1st ed. Red cl, gilt. Good in dj. *Karmiole*. $65/£41

PEPLER, DOUGLAS. The Devil's Devices. Hampshire Workshops, 1915. 1st ed. One of 1500 ptd. Eric Gill (illus). (Pp browned, name; cvrs sl rubbed, soiled), o/w VG. W/o dj, as issued. *Virgo*. $128/£80

PEPOON, H. S. An Annotated Flora of the Chicago Area. Chicago: Chicago Acad. Sci., 1927. 1st ed. Grn cl. NF. *Archer*. $80/£50

PEPPE, RODNEY. Run Rabbit, Run. NY: Delacorte, 1982. 2 dbl-pg pop-ups. Glazed pict bds. VG. *Bookfinders*. $30/£19

PEPPER, WILLIAM. A System of Practical Medicine by American Authors. Phila, 1885. 1st ed. 5 vols. Full leather. *Fye*. $250/£156

PEPPIN, B. and L. MICKLETHWAIT. Dictionary of British Book Illustrators. The Twentieth Century. London: John Murray, 1983. Black cl. Dj. *Maggs*. $24/£15

PEPYS, SAMUEL, JR. (Pseud of R. M. Freeman & R. A. Bennett.) A Last Diary of the Great Warr.... London: John Lane, Bodley Head, 1919. 1st ed. Gilt brn linen, bds. (Edges lt foxed), else VG in pict dj (lt edgeworn, nicked). *Reese*. $60/£38

PEPYS, SAMUEL. Diary and Correspondence of Samuel Pepys, F.R.S., Secretary to the Admiralty in the Reigns of Charles II and James II. Phila: Lippincott, 1856. 1st Amer ed from the 5th London ed. 2 steel-engr frontis ports. Mod 1/2 morocco, marbled bds, gilt, raised bands. (Margins sl dknd), else NF. *Pacific**. $173/£108

PEPYS, SAMUEL. The Diary of Samuel Pepys. LEC, 1942. Ltd to 1500 numbered, signed by William Sharp (illus). 10 vols. Fine in slipcase. *Swann**. $126/£79

PEPYS, SAMUEL. The Diary of Samuel Pepys. Henry B. Wheatley (ed). NY: Walpole Ptg Office, 1942. 10 vols. 1/2 blue linen, gilt-stamped w/floriated lettering, blue paper sides. Fine in box. *Appelfeld*. $250/£156

PEPYS, SAMUEL. The Diary of Samuel Pepys. Henry Wheatley (ed). London/NY, (1899). 9 vols. Engr frontispieces. Teg. 1/2 brn morocco, gilt spines, raised bands. (Spine extrems lt worn.) *Swann**. $230/£144

PEPYS, SAMUEL. Memoires Relating to the State of the Royal Navy of England. London: Ben. Griffin for Sam. Keble, 1690. 1st ed, issue w/Griffin-Keble imprint. W/sigs and signed leaf of notes of Benjamin William Page. (2),214,(17)pp; fldg table. Later 19th-cent cl, red leather spine label. (Tp soiled, damp-stained; lacks port.) *Swann**. $402/£251

PERCIVAL, A. BLAYLEY. A Game Ranger's Note Book. E. D. Cuming (ed). London, 1924. 1st ed. Fldg map. (Feps lt browned; spine dknd, sl chipped, sm split to fr joint.) *Edwards*. $64/£40

PERCIVAL, OLIVE. Mexico City. Chicago: Herbert S. Stone, 1901. 1st ed. Frontis, 7 plts. Mostly unopened. Pict cl. (Fep corner clipped), else VG. *Connolly*. $35/£22

PERCIVAL, ROBERT. An Account of the Island of Ceylon.... London: C. & R. Baldwin, 1803. x,420pp; 4 fldg maps (lt foxed). New 1/2 cl, marbled bds. *Adelson*. $425/£266

PERCY, BISHOP. Bishop Percy's Folio Manuscript: Ballads and Romances. John W. Hales and Frederick J. Furnivall (ed). London: N. Trubner, 1867. 1st ed. 3 vols. Teg. 3/4 red morocco, gilt, bound by Morrell. (Spine ends rubbed), else VG. *Pacific**. $104/£65

PERCY, SHOLTO and REUBEN. Pastime. NY: W.B. Gilley, 1822. Engr frontisport. Marbled eps. 1/2 morocco (rubbed), marbled bds. VG. *Dramatis*. $40/£25

PERCY, WALKER. Lancelot. NY: Farrar, (1977). 1st ed. Fine in NF dj. *Reese*. $30/£19

PERCY, WALKER. Lancelot. NY: FSG, 1977. 1st ed. Top edge stained red. Orange cl, gilt. Fine in dj. *Heritage*. $60/£38

PERCY, WALKER. The Last Gentleman. NY: FSG, 1966. 1st ed. (Sm chip to spine head), else VG in dj (spine sl sunned). *Pacific**. $58/£36

PERCY, WALKER. Love in the Ruins. NY, (1971). 1st ed. (Sm erasure mk, edge soiled), else VG in dj (sl used, dknd). *King*. $45/£28

PERCY, WALKER. Love in the Ruins. NY: FSG, (1971). 1st ed. Orange eps. Black cl, gilt. Fine in dj. *Heritage*. $85/£53

PERCY, WALKER. The Moviegoer. NY: Knopf, 1961. 1st ed. Fine in NF dj (lt rubbed, sm tear fr panel). *Between The Covers*. $2,000/£1,250

PERCY, WALKER. The Second Coming. NY, (1980). 1st ed. One of 450 numbered, signed. Slipcase. *Swann**. $172/£108

PEREC, GEORGES. W or the Memory of Childhood. Boston, 1988. 1st Amer ed. Advance rev copy w/slip laid in. Fine in Fine dj. *Warren*. $25/£16

PERELMAN, S. J. Chicken Inspector No. 23. NY: S&S, (1966). 1st ed. Top edge stained red. Yellow cl over orange bds. Fine in dj (price-clipped, lt soiled, spine sl faded). *Heritage*. $60/£38

PERELMAN, S. J. Dawn Ginsbergh's Revenge. NY: Horace Liveright, (1929). 1st ed, 1st bk, 2nd binding. Clean. *Dermont*. $500/£313

PERELMAN, S. J. The Dream Department. NY: Random House, 1943. 1st ed. Fine (spine head sun spot) in dj (lt used, spine head chip, wrinkled tear to fr panel head). *Beasley*. $125/£78

PERELMAN, S. J. and Q. J. REYNOLDS. Parlor, Bedlam and Bath. NY: Horace Liveright, 1930. 1st Amer ed. VG + (lacks dj) in orange bds. *Warren*. $175/£109

PERELMAN, S. J. The Rising Gorge. NY: S&S, 1961. 1st ed. White cl over orange bds. (Spine ends bumped), o/w Fine in dj (soiled). *Heritage*. $60/£38

PERELMAN, S. J. The Road to Miltown; or, Under the Spreading Atrophy. NY: S&S, 1957. 1st ed. Top edge stained red. Yellow cl over red bds. VG (spine sl browned, extrems lt rubbed) in dj (lt chipped, soiled). *Heritage*. $50/£31

PERERIA, JONATHAN. A Treatise on Food and Diet: With Observations on the Dietetical Regimen Suited for Disordered States of the Digestive Organs.... NY, 1843. 1st Amer ed. 318pp. *Fye*. $125/£78

PEREZ-TIBI, DORA. Dufy. Abrams, (1989). Good in dj. *Rybski*. $85/£53

Perfection Fireless Cook Book. Caro, MI: Johnston-Slocum, n.d. 4th ed. VG. *Perier*. $35/£22

Perilous Adventures of Quintin Harewood and His Brother Brian, in Asia, Africa, and America. NY/Boston: C.S. Francis, 1854. Sq 8vo. Full-pg frontis w/guard, 254pp + 10pp list. Brn eps. Tooled blue cl on bds, gilt spine. VG (sm chip spine top). *Hobbyhorse*. $110/£69

PERKINS, CHARLES E. The Pinto Horse. Santa Barbara, CA, 1927. 1st ed. Color frontis, 16 full-pg b/w plts. (Rebound w/fr cvr transposed.) *Heinoldt*. $45/£28

PERKINS, CHARLES E. The Pinto Horse. Santa Barbara, 1927. 1st ed. (Bds very bowed.) Internally Good in dj (soiled, torn). *Dumont*. $135/£84

PERKINS, J. R. Trails, Rails and War. Indianapolis, 1929. 1st ed. VG (sig, bkpl). *Baade*. $45/£28

PERKINS, JOCELYN. Westminster Abbey. London/Oxford: OUP, 1938-40. 2 vols. Uncut. (Eps sl spotted.) *Edwards*. $64/£40

PERKINS, JOHN B. History of Hyde County South Dakota.... N.p., 1908. 1st ed (?). Cl, gilt w/stapled text. Good (hinges broken, cvrs lt spotted). *Baade*. $100/£63

PERKINS, JUSTIN. A Residence of Eight Years in Persia, Among the Nestorian Christians. Andover, 1843. Fldg map, 27 litho plts (23 hand-colored). (Extrems worn.) *Swann**. $172/£108

PERKINS, LUCY FITCH. The Pickaninny Twins. Boston: Houghton Mifflin, 1931. 1st ed. 8vo. 153pp. Tan pict cl. Good in full color dj (rear lacks piece, margins worn). *Reisler*. $285/£178

PERKINS, SIMEON. The Diary of Simeon Perkins, 1780-1812. D. C. Harvey (ed). Toronto: Champlain Soc, 1958, 1961, 1967, 1978. 1st, ltd eds. 4 vols. 3 maps. Red cl, gilt. (2 frontis ll in 2nd vol w/tape stains at gutter, repaired), else Fine set. *Argonaut*. $350/£219

PERRAULT, CHARLES. Beauty and the Beast. Star & Elephant Bk (Green Tiger Press), 1980. 1st ed. 74pp; 18 mtd color plts by Michael Hague. Paper wraps, emb title. VG. *Davidson*. $85/£53

PERRAULT, CHARLES. Perrault's Popular Tales. Andrew Lang (ed). Oxford: Clarendon, 1888. 1st ed. Teg. 1/4 vellum, maroon cl, gilt. (Sl soiled), else NF. *Pacific**. $104/£65

PERRAULT, CHARLES. The Sleeping Beauty. London: Heinemann, 1919. 1st ed. One of 625 numbered, signed by Arthur Rackham (illus). White bds, vellum back. VG (edgeworn) in VG slipcase. *Davidson*. $1,500/£938

PERRIN, MRS. I. S. British Flowering Plants.... Bernard Quaritch, 1914. 1st, only ed. One of 1000. 4 vols. Royal 4to. 300 color plts. Teg, unopened. Cream cl, gilt. (Bindings sl age-dknd), o/w Fine. *Sotheran*. $720/£450

PERROT, GEORGES and CHARLES CHIPIEZ. A History of Art in Chaldaea and Assyria. Walter Armstrong (ed). London, 1884. 2 vols. xiii,398; xii,420pp; 14 plts (4 chromolithos). Teg. (Ink stamps, bkpls; lib spine #s, blind stamps; spines faded, chipped, w/loss to heads.) *Edwards*. $96/£60

PERROT, GEORGES and CHARLES CHIPIEZ. History of Art in Phoenicia and Its Dependencies. London, 1885. 2 vols. 10 plts. Pict cl. *Argosy*. $100/£63

PERRY, BLISS. Fishing with a Worm. Boston: Houghton Mifflin, 1916. 1st separate ed. One of 1044. Grn bds, paper cvr label. Fine. *Pacific**. $40/£25

PERRY, GEORGE SESSIONS. Hackberry Cavalier. NY: Viking, 1944. 1st ed. Signed. VG in dj. *Dumont*. $50/£31

PERRY, GILLIAN. Paula Modersohn-Becker. NY: Harper & Row, 1979. NF in dj. *Turtle Island*. $35/£22

PERRY, JOHN. The State of Russia, Under the Present Czar. London: Benjamin Tooke, 1716. 1st ed. (8),280pp; fldg map. Mod paneled calf, morocco spine label, new eps. Fine. *Pacific**. $316/£198

PERRY, MARIA PHILLIPS. Snowflake, Our Own Kitty's Story. Cambridge: Riverside, 1919. 1st ed. Sq 12mo. Helen Irene Fitton (illus). 45pp. Cl-backed bds, color pict emblem. Fine in glassine dj, pub's box (edges sl worn) w/same emblem. *Reisler*. $100/£63

PERRY, MATTHEW C. Narrative of the Expedition of an American Squadron to the China Seas and Japan. Washington, 1856. 3 vols. 4to. Contains the bathing plt. Orig cl (extrems rubbed, cl along 1 joint splitting; lacks 1 fep). *Swann**. $2,070/£1,294

PERRY, MATTHEW C. Narrative of the Expedition of an American Squadron to the China Seas and Japan...1852, 1853 and 1854.... Washington: Nicholson, 1856. 1st ed. 3 vols. 4to. xviii,537; (8),414,xi; xliii,705pp; 86 tinted, 3 color plts (2 fldg), 6 maps (2 fldg) to vol 1; 'Bathing plate' which is not called for is present; 27 plts (18 handcolored, 4 tinted), 16 fldg maps, 17 charts to vol 2; 352 plts to vol 3. Orig cl, but cl of vol 2 does not match. Overall VG (sl foxed, few fldg maps vol 2 sl frayed, vol 1 sl shaken; edges rubbed, spine ends frayed, spine tears vols 1, 2). *Worldwide*. $1,800/£1,125

PERRY, MILTON F. Infernal Machines. (Baton Rouge): LA State Univ, (1965). 1st ed. Red cl. Fine in dj. *Chapel Hill*. $95/£59

PERRY, R. I Went a'Shepherding. Lindsay Drummond, 1948. VG in dj (edges sl creased, chipped). *Hollett*. $24/£15

PERRY, R. Montgomery's Children. NY, 1984. 1st ed. NF in NF dj. *Warren*. $35/£22

PERRY, R. A Naturalist on Lindisfarne. London: L. Drummond, 1946. 1st ed. Fldg map. Pict cl, gilt. NF in VG dj. *Mikesh*. $155/£97

PERRY, R. The World of the Giant Panda. London: Cassell, 1969. 1st ed. NF in NF dj. *Mikesh*. $25/£16

PERRY, THOMAS. Metzger's Dog. NY, 1983. 1st ed. NF in Fine dj. *Warren*. $40/£25

PERRY, W. A. et al. American Game Fishes: Their Habits, Habitat, and Peculiarities. Chicago: Rand McNally, 1892. 1st ed. Chromolitho frontis. Gilt-lettered pict beveled blue cl. NF. *Pacific**. $207/£129

PERSE, ST. JOHN. Anabasis. London: Faber & Faber, 1930. 1st ed. Ltd to 350 numbered, signed by T. S. Eliot (trans). NF in slipcase (worn, sl chipped). *Black Sun*. $450/£281

PERSE, ST. JOHN. Anabasis. London: Faber & Faber, 1930. One of 350 signed by T. S. Eliot (trans). Grn cl, gilt. Fine (spine ends sl rubbed) in pub's open-end cardboard slipcase. *Heritage*. $500/£313

PERSHING, JOHN J. My Experiences in the World War. NY: Frederick A. Stokes, 1931. 1st ed, trade issue. 2 vols. Teg. Gilt blue cl. Fine in djs (lt sunned, few sm nicks). *Reese*. $75/£47

PERTCHIK, B. and H. Flowering Trees of the Caribbean. NY: Rinehart, 1951. 1st ed. NF in VG dj (rubbed). *Archer*. $30/£19

PESMAN, M. WALTER. Meet Flora Mexicana. Globe, AZ, 1962. Rev copy. Color fldg map. Fine in 3 color washable vinyl cl on bds. *Brooks*. $39/£24

PETAIN, HENRI PHILIPPE. Verdun. Margaret MacVeagh (trans). London: Elkin Mathews & Marrot, 1930. 1st British ed. Port. Orange cl. (Eps sl foxed; edges, cl sl dusty), o/w Nice in dj (spine tanned) w/pub's price reduction sticker on spine. *Reese.* $35/£22

Peter Parley's Book of the United States. (By Samuel Griswold Goodrich.) Boston: Charles J. Hendee, 1837. 8vo. Engr frontis, 208pp + 1pg list lower cvr; 6 copper engr maps. Pict paper on bds, brn roan spine, gilt. VG (foxed, ink dated sig fep; scuff, repaired tear at frontis; cvrs lt rubbed, soiled, corners rounded). *Hobbyhorse.* $200/£125

Peter Parley's Method of Telling about Geography to Children. (By S.G. Goodrich.) Boston/Hartford: Carter & Hendee/H. & F.J. Huntington, 1830. 1st ed (?). 7 maps (6 hand-colored), 75 engrs. (Stained, soiled.) Orig ptd bds, calf shelf back (worn). *M & S.* $200/£125

Peter Parley's Universal History, on the Basis of Geography. (By Nathaniel Hawthorne.) Boston: American Stationers' Co/John B. Russell, 1837. 1st ed, 2nd state, w/vol # at bottom of 1st pg of each sig. 2 vols. Orig yellow eps. Orig gilt-dec blind-stamped blue-gray cl. The cvrs have Blanck's 'A' design, a 'rococo frame' surrounding a gilt lyre that includes the name of the binder, B. Bradley. Each spine includes a vignette illus of Peter Parley in gilt. F. H. Goodyear bkpl to each vol. Fine (early inscrip, early cat description affixed to 1 pastedown; few sm nicks to spine ends) in cl clamshell case, leather label. *Sumner & Stillman.* $3,250/£2,031

Peter Rabbit and Jimmy Chipmunk. Chicago: Saalfield, (1918). 8vo. Virginia Albert (illus). Color pict bds. Color illus dj (dusty, mkd). *Reisler.* $90/£56

Peter Rabbit Goes to School. Akron: Saalfield, (1917). 4to. Albert (illus). 12pp. Linentex surface to cvrs, pp. (Cvrs lt worn.) Stiff paper wrappers. *Reisler.* $75/£47

Peter Rabbit Story Book. NY: Platt & Munk, (1943). 1st combined ed. 4to. Bess Goe Willis (illus). 64pp (sm spot where paper stuck, lifted). Orange cl. VG in full color dj. *Reisler.* $150/£94

Peter Rabbit. A Honey Bear Giant Pop-Up Book. NY: Modern Promotions, 1983. Rpt. 4 dbl-pg pop-ups. Glazed pict bds. VG. *Bookfinders.* $20/£13

PETER, JOHN. Aluminum in Modern Architecture. (KY): Reynolds Metal, 1956. 2 vols. VG in dec cl. Slipcase (worn). *Hadley.* $96/£60

PETERKIN, JULIA. Black April. Indianapolis: BM, (1927). 1st ed, 1st issue. NF (cl sl dust-spotted) in VG dj (sl edgeworn, lg chip not affecting lettering). *Agvent.* $200/£125

PETERKIN, JULIA. Roll, Jordan, Roll. NY, (1933). 1st ed. (Pencil sig; worn, faded.) *Swann*.* $201/£126

PETERMANN, AUGUSTUS. An Account of the Progress of the Expedition to Central Africa.... London: For the Author by E. Stanford, 1854. Color litho frontis incorporating map and 4 ports, 2 hand-colored litho maps, 1 fldg. (Emb lib stamp tp, hole in prelim blank, bkpl.) Orig cl stamped in gilt/blind (lt scuffed, spine rubbed). *Christie's*.* $1,981/£1,238

PETERS, CHARLES. The Autobiography of Charles Peters. Sacramento: LaGrave, n.d. (ca 1915). 1st ed. Frontis photos. VG in ptd wrappers. *Connolly.* $45/£28

PETERS, ELLIS. Dead Man's Ransom. Macmillan, 1984. 1st UK ed. VG + (sm label) in dj. *Williams.* $80/£50

PETERS, ELLIS. Death to the Landlords. Macmillan, 1972. 1st UK ed. VG in dj (sm nicks). *Williams.* $45/£28

PETERS, ELLIS. The Devil's Novice. Macmillan, 1983. 1st UK ed. Fine (sm label removed) in dj. *Williams.* $120/£75

PETERS, ELLIS. The Devil's Novice. London: Macmillan, 1983. 1st ed. VF in dj. *Mordida.* $175/£109

PETERS, ELLIS. Monk's-Hood. Macmillan, 1980. 1st UK ed. NF in dj. *Williams.* $240/£150

PETERS, ELLIS. A Nice Derangement of Epitaphs. London: CCC, 1965. 1st ed. (Name), o/w Fine in dj. *Mordida.* $200/£125

PETERS, FRED J. (comp). Railroad, Indian and Pioneer Prints by N. Currier and Currier and Ives. NY: Antique Bulletin Pub Co, 1930. Red pict cl. Fine in VG dj (spine dknd, ends sl stained), slipcase (worn, stained). *Harrington.* $100/£63

PETERS, H. S. and T. D. BURLEIGH. Birds of Newfoundland. Boston: Houghton Mifflin, 1951. 1st ed. 32 full-pg color plts. Pict cl. Fine in VG dj. *Mikesh.* $75/£47

PETERS, HARRY T. America on Stone. GC: Arno Press, (1976). (Sl worn, cvr soiled.) *Oinonen*.* $130/£81

PETERS, HARRY T. America on Stone. GC, 1931. 1st ed. One of 751 numbered (this one out of series). 18 color, 136 b/w plts. VG in dj (torn, rubbed), slipcase (tattered). *King.* $495/£309

PETERS, HARRY T. America on Stone. (NY, 1931.) One of 751 numbered. Thick 4to. Dj, slipcase. *Swann*.* $517/£323

PETERS, HARRY T. California on Stone. GC: Doubleday, Doran, 1935. 1st ed. One of 501. Sm folio. VG + in dj. *Bohling.* $400/£250

PETERS, HARRY T. California on Stone. GC: Doubleday Doran, 1935. Ltd to 501. 112 plts, 3 mtd photo ports. Beige linen. Good in heavy gray paper dj (soiled), pub's slipcase. *Karmiole.* $500/£313

PETERS, HARRY T. California on Stone. NY: Doubleday, 1935. 1st ed. Ltd to 501 numbered. 112 plts on 99 leaves. Glazed linen stamped on fr cvr, spine in black/gold. VF in dj (spine faded), pub's slipcase (lt worn). *Argonaut.* $600/£375

PETERS, HARRY T. Currier and Ives. GC, 1929. One of 501 numbered. (Shelfworn, inner joints broken, spine sl chewed.) *Oinonen*.* $120/£75

PETERS, HARRY T. Currier and Ives. NY: Doubleday, Doran, 1942. 192 plts (32 color). Pict cl (stained, especially bottom edge), gilt. *Hollett.* $192/£120

PETERS, HERMAN. Pictorial History of Ancient Pharmacy. Chicago: G.F. Englehard, 1899. 2nd ed. xiv,184pp. Brn cl. Good. *Karmiole.* $85/£53

PETERS, HERMAN. Pictorial History of Ancient Pharmacy; with Sketches of Early Medical Practice. William Netter (ed). Chicago: G.P. Engelhard, 1889. 1st ed in English. Teg. Gilt-dec cl. (Bkpl removed from fr pastedown; spine ends rubbed), else VG. *Pacific*.* $98/£61

PETERS, JOHN. Body Water, The Exchange of Fluids in Man. Springfield, 1935. 1st ed. *Fye.* $50/£31

PETERSEN, JEAN. Pranks of Peter Pig. Springfield, MA: McLoughlin Bros, (1936). 4to. Norma Whiting (illus). Cl-backed color pict bds (edges, corners rubbed). *Reisler.* $100/£63

PETERSEN, KAREN DANIELS. Plains Indian Art from Fort Marion. Norman: Univ of OK, 1971. 1st ed. Internally VG in dj (chipped, short tears). *Dumont.* $65/£41

PETERSEN, WILLIAM FERDINAND. Hippocratic Wisdom for Him Who Wishes to Pursue Properly the Science of Medicine. Springfield, IL: Charles C. Thomas, 1946. (Dj w/short tear), else Fine. *Weber.* $50/£31

PETERSEN, WILLIAM J. A Reference Guide to Iowa History. Iowa City, IA, 1942. NF in wraps. *Dumont.* $20/£13

PETERSEN, WILLIAM J. Steamboating on the Upper Mississippi. Iowa City: State Hist Soc of IA, 1937. 1st ed. Dec grn cl, gilt. VG (few water spots to cvrs). Howes P263. *House.* $50/£31

PETERSEN, WILLIAM J. Steamboating on the Upper Mississippi. Iowa City: State Hist Soc of IA, 1937. 1st ed. *Heinoldt.* $85/£53

PETERSHAM, MAUD and MISKA. Get-A-Way and Hary Janos. NY: Viking, 1933. 1st ed. 4to. Cl-backed color pict bds. Good in full color dj (lt dusty, marginal tears). *Reisler.* $185/£116

PETERSHAM, MAUD and MISKA. Gold. Chicago: Winston, 1935. 8vo. VG in VG dj. *American Booksellers.* $35/£22

PETERSHAM, MAUD and MISKA. Miki. NY: Doubleday, 1929. 1st ed. 8.5x10. 56pp. Cl spine, pict bds. Good. *Cattermole.* $100/£63

PETERSHAM, MAUD and MISKA. The Rooster Crows. NY: Macmillan, 1945. 1st ed. Slim 4to. Lt brn cl. VG (spine sl flattened) in color pict dj (fr panel, fr flap heavily chipped, torn). *Baltimore**. $20/£13

PETERSHAM, MAUD and MISKA. Stories from the Old Testament. Chicago: Winston, 1938. 1st ed. 7x9. Unpaginated. (Old price; sl shelfworn), else VG + in dj (edgeworn). *My Bookhouse.* $42/£26

PETERSHAM, MAUD and MISKA. Stories from the Old Testament. Winston, 1938. 1st ed. 7.3x9.5. c.120pp. VG (edgeworn, sm chips) in VG- dj. *Price.* $45/£28

PETERSHAM, MAUD and MISKA. The Story Book of Houses. Chicago: Winston, 1933. 8vo. Good. *American Booksellers.* $25/£16

PETERSON, CHARLES S. Take Up Your Mission. Tucson: Univ of AZ, 1973. Brn cl. VG + in dj. *Five Quail.* $25/£16

PETERSON, CYRUS and JOSEPH HANSON. Pilot Knob, the Thermopylae of the West. NY/Washington: Neale, 1914. 1st ed. Blue cl. NF. *Chapel Hill.* $250/£156

PETERSON, H. C. Propaganda for War: The Campaign Against American Neutrality, 1914-1917. Norman: Univ of OK, 1939. 3rd imp. Tan cl. VG in dj (tattered). *Reese.* $20/£13

PETERSON, HAROLD L. Notes on Ordnance of the American Civil War 1861-1865. Washington: American Ordnance Assoc, 1959. 2nd ptg. NF in ptd plum wraps. *Chapel Hill.* $50/£31

PETERSON, J. Shetland. Lindsay Drummond, 1948. 1st ed. (Inscrip.) *Hollett.* $32/£20

PETERSON, LARS P. One Man's Story of Pioneer Days. N.p.: Maverick, (1980). 1st ed. Fine in dj. *Perier.* $15/£9

PETERSON, ROBERT. Only the Ball Was White. Prentice-Hall, 1970. Later ptg. VG + in VG dj. *Plapinger.* $85/£53

PETERSON, ROGER TORY and VIRGINIA MARIE. Audubon's Birds of America. NY, (1981). 1st trade ed. Folio. Dj. *Swann**. $80/£50

PETERSON, VIRGIL (ed). The Westerners Brand Book 1946. Twelve Original Papers Pertaining to the History of the West. Denver: Denver Posse, 1947. Ltd to 500. VG. *Perier.* $65/£41

PETHICK, DERECK. S.S. Beaver: The Ship That Saved the West. Vancouver, B.C.: Mitchell, 1970. VG in dj. *American Booksellers.* $50/£31

PETIS DE LA CROIX. The Thousand and One Days: Persian Tales. Mr. Philips (trans). London: Harrison, 1783. 3 vols in 1. 306pp; 6 copper engr plts. Recent morocco signed at tail by 'G.M.'. (Sl foxed, sig), o/w VG. *Worldwide.* $225/£141

PETO, S. MORTON. The Resources and Prospects of America Ascertained During a Visit to the States in the Autumn of 1865. London: Alexander Strahan, 1866. 1st ed. 2 tinted frontispieces, xv,428pp. Grn cl. (Frontispieces, tp lt foxed), o/w Fine. *Mott.* $125/£78

PETO, S. MORTON. The Resources and Prospects of America. London: Alexander Strahan, 1866. 1st ed. xvi,428pp; 2 color litho plts. 19th-cent polished calf, marbled bds, gilt, red morocco label. (Bkpl, sig, sm gouge outer margin pp401-420; corners, hinge extrems sl scuffed.) *Karmiole.* $250/£156

PETRARCH. The Sonnets of Petrarch. LEC, 1965. Ltd to 1500 numbered, signed by Aldo Salvadori (illus) and Giovanni Mardersteig (designer). Fine in slipcase. *Swann**. $92/£58

PETRE, F. LORAINE. The History of the Norfolk Regiment 1914-1918. Volume 2. London, 1922. 1st ed. Red cl. VG-. *Gretton.* $136/£85

PETREMENT, SIMONE. Simone Weil: A Life. Raymond Rosenthal (trans). NY: Pantheon Books, (1976). 1st Amer ed. VG in dj (stained, lt worn). *Hermitage.* $30/£19

PETRIE, CHARLES. The Jacobite Movement. The Last Phase, 1716-1807. Eyre & Spottiswoode, 1950. 1st ed. Frontisport, 14 plts. (Edges sl spotted.) Dj. *Hollett.* $40/£25

PETRIE, W. M. FLINDERS and F. GRIFFITH. Deshasheh. London: Kegan Paul, Trench, Trubner, Quaritch, 1898. 1st ed. Folio. Frontis, 52pp; 37 plts (1 color, 6 dbl-pg, 2 fldg). Cl spine. (Ex-lib; edges rubbed, lib spine #), o/w VG. *Worldwide.* $65/£41

PETRIE, W. M. FLINDERS. Historical Scarabs: A Series of Drawings from the Principal Collections. London: D. Nutt, 1889. 14pp; 15 lg fldg plts. (Spine worn.) *Archaeologia.* $450/£281

PETRIE, W. M. FLINDERS. Hyksos and Israelite Cities. London: BSAE, 1906. Folio. 40 plts (1 color). 3/4 cl. (2 corners lt bumped, bds stained.) *Archaeologia.* $85/£53

PETRIE, W. M. FLINDERS. Social Life in Ancient Egypt. London: Constable, 1923. 1 color plt. (News article pasted in on fr bd; spine worn, fr bd spotted.) *Archaeologia.* $25/£16

PETRIE, W. M. FLINDERS. Tanis. London: Kegan Paul, Trench, Trubner, 1889, 1888. Part 1, 2nd ed; Part 2, 1st ed. Folio. viii,64; 44,viii,116pp; 81 plts (2 fldg). Cl spine. (Ex-lib; sl worn, rear cvr part 2 detached, spine ends frayed, lib spine #), o/w VG. *Worldwide.* $140/£88

PETRIE, W. M. FLINDERS. Ten Years' Digging in Egypt, 1881-1891. London: Religious Tract Soc, 1893. 2nd ed. Frontis, 201pp. (Ex-lib, sig; shelfwear.) Sig of Ambrose Lansing. *Archaeologia.* $45/£28

PETROFF, IVAN Report on the Population, Industries, and Resources of Alaska. (Washington: GPO, 1884). vi,189pp; 8 color plts, 6 maps (2 fldg in pocket). VG (rebound). *High Latitude.* $200/£125

PETROFF, IVAN. Report on the Population, Industries, and Resources of Alaska. (Washington, 1884.) 187pp; 8 color plts, 2 lg maps. Black antique cl (rebound). Fine. *Perier.* $225/£141

PETROFF, PETER and IRMA. The Secret of Hitler's Victory. London: Hogarth, 1934. 1st ed. VG (name) in dj (soiled, sl nicked). *Virgo.* $64/£40

PETRONIUS. The Satyricon of Petronius. NY: LEC, 1964. One of 1500. Signed by Antonio Sotomayor (illus). 1/2 velum, gilt-dec cl. Fine in glassine, slipcase. *Pacific**. $40/£25

PETRY, ANN. Country Place. Boston: Houghton Mifflin, 1947. 1st ed. Top edge stained red. Gray cl. (Ink sig; spine ends sl rubbed), o/w NF in dj (lt browned, price-clipped, few sm edge tears). *Heritage.* $85/£53

PETRY, ANN. Harriet Tubman: Conductor on the Underground Railroad. NY: Thomas Y. Crowell, (1955). VG in pict dj (lt chipped). *Petrilla.* $35/£22

PETRY, ANN. The Narrows. Boston: Houghton Mifflin, 1953. 1st ed. NF in VG + dj (extrems lt worn). *Pettler.* $100/£63

PETRY, ANN. Tituba of Salem Village. NY: Crowell, 1964. 1st ed. (Bkpl), else VG + in VG dj (spine head, fr panel chipped). *Pettler.* $45/£28

PETTENGILL, RAY W. (ed). Letters from America, 1776-1779. Boston: Houghton, 1924. 1st ed. One of 450 ptd. Paper spine label. Orig box, ptd paper spine label. Howes L293. *Ginsberg.* $150/£94

PETTER, HELEN MARY. The Oxford Almanacks. OUP, 1974. 1st ed. Dj. *Forest.* $40/£25

PETTIGREW, THOMAS JOSEPH. A History of Egyptian Mummies, and an Account of the Worship and Embalming of the Sacred Animals by the Egyptians. London: Longman, Rees, Orme et al, 1834. 1st ed. xxi,264,(1)pp; 13 plts (3 hand-colored), hand-colored engr plt, 2 plain lithos. Orig bds, ptd paper cvr label, blue cl spine (later?). (Sl foxed, aged, new eps; edges worn, corners retouched, cvr label chipped), else VG. Pacific*. $374/£234

PETTIGREW, THOMAS JOSEPH. On Superstitions Connected with the History and Practice of Medicine and Surgery. Phila: Ed. Barrington, 1844. 1st ed. Orig cl, gilt. (Foxed; spine foot rubbed), else VG. Pacific*. $150/£94

PETTIJOHN, F. J. Sedimentary Rocks. NY: Harper, 1949. 1st ed. 40 plts. VG in dj (spine head chipped). Hollett. $48/£30

PEUGNET, EUGENE. The Nature of Gunshot Wounds of the Abdomen, and Their Treatment: Based on a Review of the Case of the Late James Fisk, Jr., in Its Medico-Legal Aspects. NY, 1874. 1st ed. 96pp. 1/4 leather (backstrip worn, partially missing). VG internally. Fye. $200/£125

PEVSNER, NIKOLAUS. Pioneers of Modern Design from William Morris to Walter Gropius. NY: MOMA, 1949. Rev, enlgd ed. VG (sl mk fr cvr, spine ends sl bumped) in dj (rubbed, nicked, sl creased, price-clipped, dknd). Ulysses. $136/£85

PEVSNER, NIKOLAUS. Pioneers of Modern Design from William Morris to Walter Gropius. (NY): MOMA, 1957. Rpt of 1949 rev ed. VG in dec cl. Hadley. $29/£18

PEYTON, JOHN ROWZEE. 3 Letters from St. Louis. Denver: Libros Escogidos, 1958. One of 300 numbered. NF. Dumont. $125/£78

PFEFFERKORN, IGNAZ. Sonora: A Description of the Province. Theodore E. Treutlein (trans). Albuquerque: Univ of NM, 1949. Facs frontis, 5 plts, fldg map. Fine in dj (dknd, sl worn). Pacific*. $63/£39

PFISTER, HAROLD FRANCIS. Facing the Light: Historic American Portrait Daguerreotypes. Washington: Nat'l Portrait Gallery, 1978. 1st ed. (Prelims sl foxed; crown sl bumped), else VG in dj (worn). Cahan. $75/£47

PFISTER, OSKAR. Expressionism in Art. London: Kegan Paul, 1922. 1st ed. VG (ex-lib). Beasley. $40/£25

PFISTER, OSKAR. Love in Children. London: George Allen & Unwin, 1924. 1st ed in English. VG (lib stamps; spine frayed). Beasley. $50/£31

PHAIR, CHARLES. Atlantic Salmon Fishing. NY: Derrydale, (1937). One of 950. Teg, uncut. (Shelfworn, spine tips frayed.) Oinonen*. $375/£234

PHAIR, CHARLES. Atlantic Salmon Fishing. NY: Derrydale, (1937). Ltd to 950. Teg. Gilt-stamped cl. (Extrems worn, corners sl bumped), else VG. King. $400/£250

Phantom Flowers. A Treatise on the Art of Producing Skeleton Leaves. Boston: Tilton, 1868. 6 plts. (Rep pieces torn away.) Pub's cl (shelfworn, sl soiled). Oinonen*. $60/£38

PHARES, ROSS. Bible in Pocket, Gun in Hand. GC: Doubleday, 1964. 1st ed. Fine in dj. Labordo. $55/£34

PHARES, ROSS. Texas Tradition. NY: Henry Holt, 1954. 1st ed. 2-tone cl. Fine in dj. Labordo. $40/£25

Pharmacopoeia of the United States of America. Boston, 1828. 2nd ed. 272pp. Untrimmed, uncut. Orig bds w/paper label (minor waterstain lower margin some ll, 2 lib stamps). Fye. $200/£125

PHAYRE, ARTHUR P. History of Burma. London: Trubner, 1883. 1st ed. Inscribed, dated 1883. 1/2-title, xvi ads,xii,311pp; lg fldg map loose in rear pocket, 2 plans (1 fldg). Beige dec cl, gilt. VG (few ll lt foxed; upper hinge cracking, lt soiled). Morrell. $232/£145

PHELPS, NOAH A. History of Simsbury, Granby, and Canton, from 1842 to 1845. Hartford: Case, 1845. Enlgd ed. 176pp. Contemp cl. Howes P288. Ginsberg. $150/£94

PHIFER, LINCOLN. The Dramas of Kansas. Chicago: John F. Higgins, Ptr, 1915. 1st ed. Port. (Cl soiled), o/w Good. Brown. $50/£31

PHILBY, H. ST. J. B. Arabian Days. London, 1948. 1st ed. Frontisport. Maggs. $160/£100

PHILBY, H. ST. J. B. Harun al Rashid. N.p.: Peter Davies, 1933. 1st ed. Frontis. Cvrs Fine. Maggs. $80/£50

PHILBY, H. ST. J. B. The Heart of Arabia. NY: Putnam, 1923. 1st US ed. 2 vols. Demy 8vo. xxiii,386; vii,354pp; 48 plts, 2 fldg maps, plan. Grn cl (sl bubbled). VG set. Ulysses. $1,584/£990

Philip Leslie and His Robin with Surprise Pictures. Transformation Book. London: Dean & Son, (ca 1880). Sq 8vo. 4 full-pg color pp w/4 fold-over lifting sections. Good in stiff color pict wrappers (spine, edges worn). Reisler. $975/£609

PHILIP, A. P. W. A Treatise on Indigestion and Its Consequences Called Nervous and Bilious Complaints. London, 1828. 6th ed. xxviii,416pp (ink sig, foxed). Old bds (worn, rebacked), paper label. Whitehart. $144/£90

PHILIPPART, JOHN. Northern Campaigns, from the Commencement of the War in 1812, to the Armistice Signed and Ratified June 4, 1813. London: Patrick Martin, 1813. 2 vols. xvi,324; viii,443pp; 2 ports, 5 maps. New 1/2 morocco, marbled bds. VF set. Adelson. $385/£241

PHILIPS, JOHN. Poems Attempted in the Style of Milton. London: J. & R. Tonson & T. Lownds, 1762. 1st ed. 176pp. Period calf, gilt, morocco spine label. VG (bkpls, old entries mtd to fep). Pacific*. $127/£79

PHILIPS, SHINE. Big Spring. NY: Prentice-Hall, 1942. 1st ed. VG in dj (sl worn). Lien. $40/£25

PHILLIPPO, JAMES M. Jamaica: Its Past and Present State. London: John Snow, 1843. 1st ed. 1/2-title (sl repaired), xvi,487,(1)errata; 10 engr plts. Orig dk grn blind-stamped cl. VG (sl foxed; recased w/new eps). Morrell. $256/£160

PHILLIPPS-WOLLEY, CLIVE et al. Big Game Shooting. London, 1894. 2 vols. xvi,453pp + (ii)pub's ads; x,443pp. Dec eps. Illus cl. (Rep vol 1 detached, eps lt browned, hinges cracked; edges bumped, corners rubbed w/sl cl loss, spines sl rubbed, sm stain fore-edge fr bd vol 1.) Edwards. $120/£75

PHILLIPS, CATHERINE COFFIN. Cornelius Cole: California Pioneer and United States Senator. SF: John Henry Nash, 1929. 1st ed. One of 250. Signed, dated 1929. Frontis. Marbled cl, leather spine label. (Spine faded), else VG in slipcase (rubbed). Pacific*. $63/£39

PHILLIPS, CATHERINE COFFIN. Coulterville Chronicle: The Annals of a Mother Lode Mining Town. SF: Grabhorn, 1942. 1st ed. One of 500. 1/2 cl, patterned bds, paper spine label. (Spine ends sl rubbed), else NF. Pacific*. $75/£47

PHILLIPS, CATHERINE COFFIN. Jessie Benton Fremont: A Woman Who Made History. SF: John Henry Nash, 1935. 1st ed. Paper spine label. NF in VG dj (sm corner tears). Howes P310. Pacific*. $46/£29

PHILLIPS, CATHERINE COFFIN. Portsmouth Plaza: The Cradle of San Francisco. SF: John Henry Nash, 1932. 1st ed. Signed, inscribed. 1/2 vellum, marbled bds, gilt spine. (Lacks blank fep; 1 corner vellum dknd), o/w Fine in slipcase (sl worn). Howes P311. Pacific*. $109/£68

PHILLIPS, CATHERINE COFFIN. Portsmouth Plaza: The Cradle of the San Francisco. SF: John Henry Nash, 1932. 1st ed. 1/2 vellum, marbled bds, gilt. (Lib #s to tp, emb stamp), else VG. Howes P311. Pacific*. $46/£29

PHILLIPS, CHRISTOPHER. Steichen at War. NY, (1981). 1st ed. (Shaken, sl soiled; sl scuffed.) Dj (rubbed, soiled, spine panel discolored). Swann*. $80/£50

PHILLIPS, ELLIS L. Alaska Summer 1938. Glen Head, NY: Privately ptd, 1938. One of 500 numbered. Frontis. Ptd bds. VG. High Latitude. $25/£16

PHILLIPS, G. F. A Practical Treatise on Drawing and on Painting in Water-Colours.... London: Baily, 1839. 48pp; color chart, 20 aquatint plts. (Tidemark few plts; cl worn, loose.) *Ars Artis.* $312/£195

PHILLIPS, H. Pomarium Britannicum. London, 1823. 3rd ed. ix,372pp; 3 hand-colored plts. Straight-grained morocco (sl rubbed). (Plts sl foxed, bkpl.) *Henly.* $192/£120

PHILLIPS, H. RANDALL. The Book of Bungalows. Country Life, 1922. 2nd ed. Ptd label. (1 opening pulled), o/w NF. *Whittle.* $29/£18

PHILLIPS, HUGH. The Thames, About 1750. London: Collins, 1951. 1st ed. 258 plts. Good in dj w/mtd color illus. *Karmiole.* $75/£47

PHILLIPS, ISAAC N. The Union Volunteers. N.p., (1902). Wraps. (Stamped, cvr sl discolored.) *King.* $22/£14

PHILLIPS, J. Illustrations of the Geology of Yorkshire. Part 1. The Yorkshire Coast. R. Etheridge (ed). London: John Murray, 1875. 3rd ed. xii,354pp; color litho map, 28 litho plts (7 hand-colored). J. E. Marr's sig. (New eps; corners sl bumped, neatly recased.) *Hollett.* $352/£220

PHILLIPS, J. The Rivers, Mountains and Sea-Coast of Yorkshire. London: John Murray, 1853. 1st ed. xv,302pp; 35 engr plts and maps (1 hand-colored), fldg diag. Blind-stamped cl, gilt. (Foxing, esp to fep, frontis, some plts, 1st index leaf; spine, edges faded, fr bd sl mkd.) *Hollett.* $152/£95

PHILLIPS, JAYNE ANNE. Black Tickets. (NY): Delacorte, (1979). 1st ed. Signed. Fine in Fine dj. *Lenz.* $185/£116

PHILLIPS, JAYNE ANNE. The Secret Country. Palaemon, (1982). One of 100 numbered, signed. Cl, dec paper-cvrd bds. New. *Dermont.* $75/£47

PHILLIPS, JOHN C. and FREDERICK C. LINCOLN. American Waterfowl. Boston, 1930. 1st ed. (Binding sl worn.) Dj (sm tears, chips, sl discolored). *Woolson.* $50/£31

PHILLIPS, JOHN C. and LEWIS WEBB HILL (eds). Classics of the American Shooting Field. Boston, 1930. Color frontis. (Spine dknd, top frayed.) *Swann*.* $69/£43

PHILLIPS, JOHN C. Wenham Great Pond. Salem: Peabody Museum, 1938. One of 400. Uncut. (Lt worn.) *Oinonen*.* $80/£50

PHILLIPS, LANCE. Yonder Comes the Train. NY: Barnes, 1965. VG + (sl shelfworn) in dj (tears at folds). *My Bookhouse.* $32/£20

PHILLIPS, PAUL CHRISLER. The Fur Trade. Norman: Univ of OK, (1961). 1st ed. 2 vols. VG (ex-lib, mks). *Pacific*.* $86/£54

PHILLIPS, PAUL CHRISLER. The Fur Trade. Norman, (1961). 1st ed. 2 vols. (Backstrips sl rubbed, discolored) in slipcase (sl worn). *Woolson.* $150/£94

PHILLIPS, PAUL CHRISLER. The Fur Trade. Norman: Univ of OK, 1961. 1st ed. 2 vols. Fine set in slipcase. *Labordo.* $195/£122

PHILLIPS, PHILIP LEE. A List of Maps of America in the Library of Congress. Wash, 1901. (Lib mks; shelfworn, spine head repaired.) Internally Sound. *Oinonen*.* $80/£50

PHILLIPS, PHILIP. The Forth Bridge in Its Various Stages of Construction. Edinburgh: R. Grant, ca 1889. 2nd ed (so stated). Obl folio. (xii)pp and 303 numbered columns; 55 plts. Brn cl (sl rubbed, dusty). Text Clean, cvrs VG. *Baltimore*.* $425/£266

PHILLIPS, W. S. Indian Tales for Little Folks. NY: Platt & Munk, (1928). Obl, 8.5x11. 11 color plts. NF in dj (tears, chips). *Pacific*.* $58/£36

PHILLPOTTS, EDEN. A Dish of Apples. London: Hodder & Stoughton, (1921). 1st ed. One of 500. Signed by Phillpotts & Rackham. 10x7.5. 3 tipped-in color plts by Arthur Rackham; tissue guards. Teg. Pict cl, gilt. (Sl soiled), else NF in later chemise, 1/2 morocco slipcase. *Pacific*.* $748/£468

PHILLPOTTS, EDEN. A Dish of Apples. London/NY: Hodder & Stoughton, n.d. (1921). 3 tipped-in color plts, 7 full-pg b/w plts by Arthur Rackham. Illus eps. Pict cl. Fine in dj (chipped, lacks spine top). *Cullen.* $120/£75

PHILLPOTTS, EDEN. Plain Song 1914-1916. London: Heinemann, (1917). 1st ed. Tan paper bds, paper spine label. VG in dj (few sm nicks). *Reese.* $75/£47

Philosophical Dictionary, for the Pocket. (By Francois Marie Arouet de Voltaire.) Catskill/NY: Creswell/Duyckinck, 1796. Tp port. Paneled calf. (Lib stamp, perf initials at tp foot, browned.) *Rostenberg & Stern.* $130/£81

Philosophical Rambler; or, The Observations and Adventures of a Pedestrian Tourist Through France and Italy. (By George Hume Weatherhead.) London: Simpkin & Marshall, 1834. 1st ed. viii,448pp (eps foxed). 19th-cent calf, marbled bds (extrems scuffed; 2 bkpls). *Karmiole.* $125/£78

PHINNEY, H. F. (comp). The Water Cure in America. NY: Fowler & Wells, 1856. Enlgd ed. 380pp. *M & S.* $125/£78

PHINNEY, MARY ALLEN. Allen-Isham Genealogy: Jirah Isham Allen...During Four Years of Indian Warfare...1839 to 1929. Rutland, VT: Tuttle, (1946). One of 200. Inscribed, signed presentation, dated Seattle 1949. Fine. *Pacific*.* $431/£269

PHIPSON, T. Phosphorescence. London: L. Reeve, 1870. xv,210pp. Good (ll outside edges sl dampstained; spine ends chipped). *Blake.* $175/£109

PHOENIX, DAVID. Geology of the Lee's Ferry Area, Coconino County, Arizona. Washington: USGS, 1963. 3 plts (maps in rear pocket). VG + . *Five Quail.* $45/£28

PHOENIX, JOHN. (Pseud of George Horatio Derby.) Phoenixiana; or, Sketches and Burlesques. NY: D. Appleton, 1856. 1st ed. 274pp + (14)pp ads. Blindstamped cl, gilt. (Staining to contents, fr hinge repaired, lacks rep; cvr faded, extrems worn), else Good + . *Pacific*.* $52/£33

PHOENIX, JOHN. (Pseud of George Horatio Derby.) Phoenixiana; or, Sketches and Burlesques. NY: D. Appleton, 1873. Frontisport, 274pp + (14)pp ads. Red cl, gilt. (Bklabel; sl worn, extrems rubbed), else NF. *Pacific*.* $138/£86

Photographer of the Southwest: Adam Clark Vroman, 1856-1916. L.A.: Ward Ritchie, 1961. 1st ed. Fine in VG glassine dj. *Book Market.* $60/£38

Photographs from the Julien Levy Collection. NY: Witkin Gallery, 1977. Photo-pict wrappers (lt soiled), spiral bound. *Swann*.* $92/£58

Photography 1839-1937. NY: MOMA, (1937). 1st ed. One of 3000 ptd. (Eps, prelims age-dknd; sl worn.) *Swann*.* $161/£101

PHYSICK, JOHN. Catalogue of the Engraved Work of Eric Gill. V. & A., 1963. Good in dj. *Ars Artis.* $72/£45

PHYSICK, JOHN. Designs for English Sculpture 1680-1860. 1969. 151 plts. Good in dj. *Washton.* $95/£59

PHYSICK, JOHN. The Victoria and Albert Museum. Phaidon/Christies, 1982. VG in dj. *Hadley.* $51/£32

PIAF, EDITH. The Wheel of Fortune. Phila: Chilton, (1965). 1st ed. VF in VF dj (sm rubbed spot). *Between The Covers.* $200/£125

PIAGET, JEAN and PAUL FRAISSE. History and Method. Experimental Psychology: Its Scope and Method. Judith Chambers (trans). NY: Basic Books, (1968). 1st US ed. Brn cl. VG in dj. *Gach.* $25/£16

PIAGET, JEAN. The Child's Conception of Number. London: Routledge/Kegan Paul, (1952). 1st ed in English. Blue cl. Fine in Good ptd dj (edge chipped, reinforced w/tape). *House.* $75/£47

PIASSETSKY, P. Russian Travellers in Mongolia and China. J. Gordon-Cumming (trans). London: Chapman & Hall, 1884. 1st Eng ed. 2 vols. 1/2-title, vi,321; 1/2-title, vi,315pp. Grn dec cl, gilt (damp-spotted, spines worn, vol 2 edges worn), gilt. Internally VG (sl browned, owner ticket tipped to 1st pg vol 2). Morrell. $368/£230

PIATT, DONN. Memories of the Men Who Saved the Union. NY: Belford, 1887. 1st ed. 302pp. Ginsberg. $75/£47

PIATTI, CELESTINO. The Happy Owls. Atheneum, 1964. 1st US ed. 12x8.5 oblong. Unpaginated. VG in Good+ dj (edgeworn, spine head chipped, soiled). Price. $75/£47

PICASSO, PABLO. Desire. NY: Philosophical Lib, (1948). 1st Amer ed. VF in VF dj (sl rubbed). Between The Covers. $150/£94

PICASSO, PABLO. Hunk of Skin. Paul Blackburn (trans). SF: City Lights, 1968. 1st ed. Fine in wraps. Beasley. $25/£16

PICASSO, PABLO. Linoleum Cuts. NY: Abrams, (1962). Obl folio. 45 color linoleum block plts, tissue guards. Pict bd box. Argosy. $300/£188

Picayune Creole Cook Book. New Orleans: Times-Picayune, (1916). 5th ed. Frontis. (Fep removed), o/w VG. Petrilla. $30/£19

PICCOLOPASSO, CIPRIANO. The Three Books of the Potter's Art. Bernard Rackham & Alfred Van de Put (trans). London, 1934. One of 750. Sm folio. 80 collotype plts. (Sl soiled.) Washton. $200/£125

PICCOLPASSO, CIPRIANO. The Three Books of the Potter's Art. Bernard Rackham & Albert Van de Put (trans). London, Victoria & Albert Museum, 1934. Ltd to 750. Folio. 80 b/w plts. Dj (soiled, chipped, sl loss). Edwards. $240/£150

PICKARD, KATE E. R. The Kidnapped and the Ransomed. N.p.: Negro Publication Soc of Amer, 1941. (Cvrs, edges soiled.) King. $60/£38

PICKARD, W. BASHYR. The Adventures of Alcassim. Cape, 1936. 1st ed. 13 full-pg b/w dwgs. NF (spine ends sl bumped) in dj (nicked, sl torn, creased, rubbed, spotted, dusty, dknd). Ulysses. $120/£75

PICKERING & CHATTO. A Catalogue of Old and Rare Books. Pickering & Chatto, 1895. 257pp. Paper label. (Rear cvr spotted), o/w Very Clean. Moss. $48/£30

PICKERING, HAROLD G. Angling of the Test. NY: Derrydale, 1936. One of 297 numbered. Black cl, issued boxed. VG. Biscotti. $300/£188

PICKERING, HAROLD G. Dog-Days on Trout Waters. NY: Derrydale, 1933. 1st ed. Pink bds, paper cvr/spine labels. (Fr cvr discolored, spine sunned, head chipped), else VG-. Pacific*. $173/£108

PICKERING, HAROLD G. Dog-Days on Trout Waters. NY: Derrydale, 1933. One of 199 numbered, signed. Pink bds (shelfworn), paper labels. Oinonen*. $475/£297

PICKERING, HAROLD G. Merry Xmas Mr. Williams: 20 Pine St., NY. NY: Derrydale, 1940. One of 267 numbered, signed. 8vo. Grn dec cl, silver lettering. VF. Biscotti. $600/£375

PICKERING, HAROLD G. Neighbors Have My Ducks. NY: Derrydale, 1937. One of 227 numbered, signed; also inscribed. 8vo. Maroon cl. Fine. Biscotti. $550/£344

PICKERING, JOHN. A Vocabulary. Boston, 1816. 1st ed. 206pp, errata leaf. 19th-cent (ca 1840) 3/4 leather, figured cl (fr hinge repaired). VG. M & S. $400/£250

PICKERING, W. A. Pioneering in Formosa. London: Hurst and Blackett, 1898. 1st ed. 1/2-title, frontisport, xvi,283,(1)blank,(4)ads; 23 plts, 1 map. Red cl, gilt. (Lib blindstamps, brown stain affecting margin upper fore-edge corner 2/3 of book, lib plt removed from fr pastedown; sl soiled, brown stain upper outer corner, upper hinge weak), else Good. Morrell. $48/£30

PICKETT, LASALLE CORBELL. Pickett and His Men. Atlanta, GA: Foote & Davies, 1900. 2nd ed. Frontisport. Lt blue cl. VG. Chapel Hill. $85/£53

PICKETT, M. The Fourth Physician. McClurg, 1911. 1st ed. 3 full-pg color illus. Grn bds. 1/4 leather spine. (Dust-soiled, spine sl scuffed), else VG. Fine Books. $35/£22

PICKFORD, MARY. My Rendezvous with Life. NY: H.C. Kinsey, 1935. 1st ed. Fine in dj (lt soiled). Beasley. $25/£16

PICKLE, R. William Orpen. NY: Scribner, 1923. Frontis, 34 plts. Paper bds, cl spine. VG. Turtle Island. $45/£28

PICKWELL, GAYLE. Deserts. NY: Whittlesey House, 1939. 64 full-pg photos. VG in dj (chipped). Dumont. $50/£31

PICO, DON PIO. Don Pio Pico's Historical Narrative. Martin Cole and Henry Welcome (eds). Arthur P. Botello (trans). Glendale, CA, 1973. 1st ed. Ltd to 1077. Frontisport. Pict eps. VG+. Sagebrush. $95/£59

PICTON, G. W. The Battle of Waterloo. London: R. Edwards, (1816). 3 hand-colored fldg engr plans, 9 plts, 2 engr ports. (Occasional dampstaining, browning.) 19th-cent calf gilt (joints cracked, cvrs stained). Christie's*. $235/£147

Pictorial Photography in America. Volume 5. NY: Pictorial Photographers of America at the Art Center, 1929. Folio. 58 full-pg b/w plts. Cl-backed paper, gilt, over bds. (Lt soiled, rubbed, sm bump to spine base), else VG. Cahan. $150/£94

Picture Gallery. Paintings and Drawings by Tom Lea. Boston, (1968). 1st ed. W/portfolio of 35 plts (12 color). (Sm mk back cvr from extra glue), else VG in slipcase (worn, sl stained). Woolson. $150/£94

Picture of London for 1816. London: Longman, (1816). 17th ed. Tp, xii,4ff.,340pp+12pp cat; 6 engr maps or plans. Sheep (rebacked). Marlborough. $160/£100

Picture Pages for Little Folks of All Ages. London: Ernest Nister, ca 1895. 4to. Cl-backed color pict bds (edges rubbed, hinges weak, rear cvr mkd, worn). Reisler. $350/£219

Picture Treasures for the Little Folks. London: Ernest Nister, ca 1895. 4to. E. S. Hardy et al (illus). Cl-backed color pict bds (corners lt rubbed). Reisler. $375/£234

Pictures and Stories from Natural History. NY: McLoughlin Bros, 1886. 10.75x8.25. Cl-backed chromolitho bds. (Corners rubbed), else VG. Pacific*. $35/£22

Pictures and Stories from Uncle Tom's Cabin. (By H.B. Stowe.) Boston: John P. Jewett, (1853). 1st ed. 32pp incl tp (soiled, pencil mks, last leaf w/inner marginal tears); 9 full-pg illus. Orig pict fr wrapper. M & S. $250/£156

Pictures and Stories. Providence: Geo. P. Daniels, 1847. 12mo. 8 unnumbered ll; 15 half-pg wood engrs (crudely hand-painted). Dec pink stiff paper wrappers, two 1/2pg wood engrs ptd inside each wrapper. Fine (pencil sig inside fr wrapper). Hobbyhorse. $125/£78

Picturesque Europe. Cassell, Petter & Galpin, (c. 1870). 5 vols. Engr add'l tps, 60 engr plts. Gilt edges. Contemp 1/2 morocco, spines gilt. Sotheby's*. $699/£437

Picturesque Palestine, Sinai and Egypt. NY: D. Appleton, (1883). 1st ed. 2 vols. Aeg. 3/4 morocco, gilt, raised bands. NF. Pacific*. $374/£234

Picturesque Representations of the Dress and Manners of the English. For Thomas M'Lean, (c.1827). 8vo. 50 hand-colored etched plts (plts watermarked 1827; text 1825). Uncut. Contemp maroon morocco. (1 plt w/sm marginal tear; sl soiled; worn, rebacked retaining spine.) Sotheby's*. $773/£483

Picturesque Representations of the Dress and Manners of the Russians. (By William Alexander.) T. M'Lean, (c.1825). 8vo. 64 hand-colored aquatint plts (plts watermarked 1823; text 1825). Black 1/2 morocco, orig bds. (Bkpl, sm ink mk on plt 12.) Sotheby's*. $552/£345

Picturesque Representations of the Dress and Manners of the Russians. London: James Goodwin, ca 1814. 4to. 64 hand-colored engrs. Full crimson straight-grain morocco, gilt-stamped borders, gilt paneled spine, raised bands, edges gilt. Good. *Appelfeld*. $650/£406

Picturesque Representations of the Dress and Manners of the Russians. London: James Goodwin, ca 1820. 64 color engrs. Full morocco (bds detached). *Metropolitan**. $345/£216

Picturesque Tour Through the Oberland in the Canton of Berne, Switzerland. (By Gabriel Lory.) London: R. Ackermann, 1823. 1st ed. 8vo. viii,120pp; 17 plts. Aeg. (Eps, 1st 15 leaves soiled, not affecting images; inner hinge split.) Nice in red straight-grain morocco (extrems rubbed), gilt. *Bromer*. $2,500/£1,563

PIENKOWSKI, JAN. The Haunted House. London: Heinemann, 1979. 10th ptg. 6 dbl-pg pop-ups. Glazed pict bds. VG. *Bookfinders*. $40/£25

PIERCE, BENJAMIN. A History of Harvard University, From Its Foundation in the Year 1636 to the Period of the American Revolution. Cambridge: Shattuck, 1833. 1st ed. 2 litho plts. Orig drab bds, linen spine, paper label. Fine. *Appelfeld*. $200/£125

PIERCE, BESSIE LOUISE. A History of Chicago. NY: Knopf, 1937, 1940, 1957. 1st eds. 3 vols. Blue cl. (Vol 1 sl foxed, name), else VG set. *Cahan*. $125/£78

PIERCE, FRANK C. A Brief History of the Lower Rio Grande Valley. Menasha, WI, 1917. 1st ed. 3 fldg maps. Orig bds (edge-worn). *Dumont*. $60/£38

PIERCE, GERALD S. Texas Under Arms. The Camps,...of the Republic of Texas, 1836-1846. Austin: Encino, 1969. 1st ed. VG in dj. *Perier*. $40/£25

PIERCY, MARGE. Going: Down: Fast. NY: Trident, (1969). 1st ed. Fine in dj (1-inch spine tear). *Hermitage*. $50/£31

PIEROTTI, ERMETE. Customs and Traditions of Palestine. T. G. Bonney (trans). Cambridge: Deighton, Bell, 1864. 1st ed. viii,280pp + ad leaf at rear, tipped-in errata slip. Brn coated eps. Royal blue cl, beveled bds, gilt. (Sl aged, hinges weak, bkpl removed; extrems sl worn.) *Baltimore**. $45/£28

PIERRON, PIERRE SCHRUMPF. Tobacco and Physical Efficiency. NY: Paul B. Hoeber, 1927. 1st ed. Maroon cl. Fine in VG ptd dj (edge chipped). *House*. $40/£25

PIETROWSKI, M. RUFIN. The Story of a Siberian Exile. London, 1863. Frontis, xii,321,(ii)pp. Blind-emb cl, gilt device. (Prelims lt spotted, fr hinge cracked, bkpl; cl discolored, spine faded, sl chipped.) *Edwards*. $136/£85

PIFFARD, HENRY. The Modern Treatment of Eczema. Detroit, 1890. 1st ed. 54pp. (Lt margin water stain.) *Fye*. $75/£47

PIGAFETTA, ANTONIO. Magellan's Voyage: A Narrative Account of the First Circumnavigation. R.A. Skelton (ed). New Haven: Yale Univ, 1969. 2 vols. Cream cl, red spine labels. Fine in slipcase. *Pacific**. $207/£129

PIGAFETTA, ANTONIO. The Voyage of Magellan: The Journal of Antonio Pigafetta. Englewood Cliffs, NJ: Prentice-Hall, (1969). 1st ed thus. Frontisport, 5 facs of maps. Emb cl, gilt. VG in dj. *Pacific**. $35/£22

PIGGIOT, F. T. The Music and Musical Instruments of Japan. London: Batsford, 1893. Inscribed. 1893 als tipped in. (Hinges cracked, edgeworn, sl soiled, spine label residue.) *Metropolitan**. $258/£161

PIGNATTI, TERISIO. Italian Drawings in Oxford. Phaidon, 1977. 80 color plts. Dj, slipcase (sl chipped). *Edwards*. $64/£40

PIGNATTI, TERISIO. Pietro Longhi, Complete Paintings and Drawings. London: Phaidon, 1969. 24 color plts. Fine in color dj. *Europa*. $104/£65

PIGOTT, GRENVILLE. A Manual of Scandinavian Mythology Containing a Popular Account of the Two Eddas and of the Religion of Odin. London: William Pickering, 1839. 3/4 red morocco, marbled bds, gilt. (Spine ends, joints sl worn), else VG. *Pacific**. $109/£68

PIKE, ALBERT. State or Province? Bond or Free? (Little Rock), 1861. 1st ed. 40pp. Ptd wrappers (chipped, frayed; sl worn, soiled). Howes P366. *Oinonen**. $250/£156

PIKE, G. D. The Singing Campaign for Ten Thousand Pounds. NY: American Missionary Assn, 1875. Frontis view, xiv,272pp. Pict cl (sl mottled). VG + . *Petrilla*. $50/£31

PIKE, JAMES. The Scout and Ranger.... Cincinnati, 1865. 1st issue. 12,19,394pp; 24 plts. Errata pg. 3/4 leather, beautifully bound by Kushner of Paterson, NJ. Contents VG. *Heinoldt*. $450/£281

PIKE, NICOLAS. A New and Complete System of Arithmetic, Composed for the Use of the Citizens of the United States. Newbury-Port: Mycall, 1788. 1st ed, w/tipped-in errata slip at end. 512pp (few ll loose, frayed). Contemp calf (worn, browned, sl stained, soiled). *Oinonen**. $70/£44

PIKE, NICOLAS. Sub-Tropical Rambles in the Land of the Aphanapteryx. NY, 1873. (Ex-lib.) *Argosy*. $60/£38

PIKE, NICOLAS. Sub-Tropical Rambles in the Land of the Aphanapteryx.... NY, 1873. 1st ed. 509pp + 4 color fldg maps, 7 engr plts. Brn cl, gilt. *Larry Price*. $95/£59

PIKE, NICOLAS. Sub-Tropical Rambles in the Land of the Aphanapteryx...the Island of Mauritius. NY, 1873. *Swann**. $201/£126

PIKE, ROBERT L. Bank Job. GC: Doubleday, 1974. 1st US ed. NF (top edge sl dusty, pub's stamp fep; spine ends sl bumped) in dj (nicked, sl rubbed, dusty, spine faded, edges sl dknd). *Ulysses*. $56/£35

PIKE, ZEBULON MONTGOMERY. An Account of Expeditions to the Sources of the Mississippi and Through the Western Parts of Louisiana. Ann Arbor: Readex, 1966. Facs rpt. 2 fldg maps. VG. *Dumont*. $40/£25

PILCHER, RICHARD B. (comp). The Institute of Chemistry of Great Britain and Ireland. History of the Institute: 1877-1914. London, 1914. Teg. Blue cl. (Few black spots rear cvr), else Fine. *Weber*. $50/£31

PILCHER, VELONA. The Searcher. London, 1929. One of 1000 ptd. (Rubber name stamp.) Buckram-backed bds (sl faded, spine sl rubbed; no dj). *Clearwater*. $56/£35

PILKINGTON, MATTHEW. A Dictionary of Painters. London, 1810. New ed. Contemp diced russia, gilt. (Bkpl; rear joint cracked, hinges reinforced w/cl, rebacked retaining orig backstrip.) *Swann**. $201/£126

PILKINGTON, MATTHEW. A General Dictionary of Painters. London, 1852. New ed. Engr frontis port (sl spotted), cxii,623pp (hinges cracked, sl shaken). Emb cl (lt soiled, faded, spine sl bumped), gilt. *Edwards*. $72/£45

PILKINGTON, MATTHEW. The Gentleman and Connoisseur's Dictionary of Painters. London: Walker & Robinson, 1798. xii,840pp,xxiii + glossary, index, etc. Full mottled calf, gilt. Fine (re-backed, re-cornered). *Europa*. $160/£100

Pillsbury's 100 Prize Winning Recipes. Minneapolis: Pillsbury Mills Inc, 1950. 1st ed. Booklet. (Bottom margin stained 1st 20pp), else VG. *Perier*. $70/£44

Pilot; a Tale of the Sea. By the Author of 'The Spy,' 'Pioneers,'.... (By James Fenimore Cooper.) Paris: A. & W. Galignani, 1825. 1st ed ptd at Paris. 3 vols. Contemp 1/4 calf. Good. *Young*. $128/£80

PIM, BEDFORD. The Gate of the Pacific. London: Lovell, Reeve, 1863. 1st ed. Color litho frontis, xiv,432pp; 7 maps (2 fldg), 1 b/w, 7 color litho plts. Pict cl, gilt. (Bkpl, sig, seal; inner hinges cracked, portions of margins of fldg maps soiled, stain affecting upper margins few ll, corners 2 images.) *Dawson*. $250/£156

PINART, ALPHONSE. Journey to Arizona in 1876. George H. Whitney (trans). L.A.: Zamorano Club, 1962. 1st ed in English. One of 500. Fldg map. Black cl. Fine. *Harrington.* $75/£47

PINCKARD, GEORGE. Notes on the West Indies. London: Longman, Hurst, Rees & Orme, 1806. 1st ed. 3 vols. (Lacks 1/2-titles, lt spotting.) Contemp bds (skillfully rebacked, recornered, cvrs lt rubbed.) *Christie's*.* $397/£248

PINCKNEY, DARRYL. High Cotton. NY, 1992. 1st ed, 1st bk. Signed. Fine in Fine dj. *Warren.* $50/£31

PINCKNEY, PAULINE A. American Figureheads and Their Carvers. NY, (1940). Dj (few sm chips, edge tears). *Swann*.* $57/£36

PINCKNEY, PAULINE A. Painting in Texas. Fort Worth, 1967. 1st ed. VG in dj (taped). *Dumont.* $100/£63

PINDAR. Pythian Odes. London: Nonesuch, 1928. Ltd ed. 3 copper engrs. Teg. White linen. Fine in box. *Appelfeld.* $100/£63

PINDER-WILSON, R. (ed). Paintings from Islamic Lands. Oxford: Cassirer, 1969. 1st ed. VG in dj. *Worldwide.* $45/£28

PINERO, ARTHUR W. The Benefit of Doubt. London: Heinemann, 1896. Rebound in 1/2 leather, morocco labels, gilt, marbled bds, eps, edges. VG. *Dramatis.* $30/£19

PINERO, ARTHUR W. The Times. Heinemann, 1891. Presentation copy inscribed on 1/2 title: 'Annie Hill/ from/ Arthur W. Pinero.' Aeg. Orig full leather (spine sunned, sl rubbed). Good. *Tiger.* $35/£22

PINKERTON, ALLAN. The Detective and the Somnambulist. The Murderer and the Fortune Teller. Chicago: W.B. Keene, Cooke, 1875. 1st ed. Grn cl, gilt. (Sl shelfworn), else VG. *Pacific*.* $57/£36

PINKERTON, JOHN. Modern Geography. A Description of the Empires, Kingdoms, States, and Colonies. London, 1802. 2 vols. Contemp calf. (Worn, broken; foxed.) *Oinonen*.* $200/£125

PINKERTON, JOHN. Russia; or, Miscellaneous Observations on the Past and Present State of That Country and Its Inhabitants. London, 1833. W/the half-title. 8 hand-colored aquatint plts. Contemp calf. (Lt foxed; skillfully rebacked.) *Swann*.* $172/£108

PINKLEY, EDNA TOWNSLEY. Casa Grande. The Greatest Valley Pueblo of Arizona. AZ Archaeological Soc, 1926. VG in wraps. *Perier.* $10/£6

PINKNEY, LIEUTENANT-COLONEL. Travels Through the South of France, and in the Interior of the Provinces of Provence and Languedoc, in the Years 1807 and 1808.... London, 1814. 2nd ed. Fldg map hand-colored in outline. Orig bds (needs rebinding). *Swann*.* $69/£43

PINKS, WILLIAM J. The History of Clerkenwell. London: Charles Herbert, 1880. 2nd ed. x,800pp (prelims misbound); lg fldg map. Patterned cl. (Hinges strained.) *Marlborough.* $144/£90

PINKWATER, DANIEL M. Alan Mendelsohn. The Boy from Mars. Dutton, 1979. 1st ed. 248pp. NF in Good+ illus dj (rubbed, edges creased, sl chipped). *Price.* $95/£59

Pinocchio's Adventures. London: Brown Watson, 1974. J. Pavlin & G. Seda (illus). 6 pop-ups. Glazed pict bds. VG. *Bookfinders.* $45/£28

Pinocchio. NY: Random House, 1946. 4to. Lois Lenski (illus), Newman-Rudolph (lithos). VG. *American Booksellers.* $25/£16

PINON, NELIDA. The Republic of Dreams. NY: Knopf, 1989. 1st Amer ed. Fine in Fine dj. *Agvent.* $30/£19

PINTER, HAROLD. Betrayal. Eyre Methuen, 1978. 1st UK ed. NF in dj. *Williams.* $32/£20

PINTER, HAROLD. The Birthday Party and Other Plays. London: Methuen, (1960). 1st ed. (Spine sl cocked), o/w Fine in dj (sl rubbed). *Jaffe.* $150/£94

PINTER, HAROLD. The Caretaker. London: Encore, (1960). 1st ed. NF in stapled wrappers. *Pharos.* $150/£94

PINTER, HAROLD. The French Lieutenant's Woman, a Screenplay. Boston, (1981). 1st ed. One of 360 numbered, signed by Pinter and John Fowles. Slipcase. *Swann*.* $126/£79

PINTER, HAROLD. Old Times. London: Karnac Books, (1971). One of 150 signed, numbered. VF in acetate. *Pharos.* $200/£125

PINTER, HAROLD. The Proust Screenplay. Eyre Methuen, 1978. 1st ed. Fine in Fine dj. *Whiteson.* $40/£25

PINTER, HAROLD. The Screenplay of the French Lieutenant's Woman.... London: Cape, (1981). 1st (British) trade ed. Fine in dj. *Reese.* $35/£22

PINTO, V. DE SOLA. Rochester: Portrait of a Restoration Poet. London: John Lane, Bodley Head, 1935. 1st Eng ed. 5 b/w plts. VG (prelims, edges spotted, feps sl browned; spine ends, corners sl bumped) in dj (nicked, rubbed, mkd, dusty, sl creased, browned, snag fr panel). *Ulysses.* $88/£55

Pioneers of the Sacramento: A Group of Letters by and about Johann Augustus Sutter, James W. Marshall and John Bidwell. SF: Book Club of CA, 1953. One of 400 ptd. Fldg map, plt. B/w marbled bds, black cl backstrip, paper spine label. Fine. *Harrington.* $125/£78

PIOZZI, HESTER LYNCH. Anecdotes of the Late Samuel Johnson, During the Last Twenty Years of His Life. S. C. Roberts (ed). Cambridge, 1925. Frontis. Good in cl-backed dec bds (rubbed), paper label. *Cox.* $24/£15

PIPER, CHARLES V. and RUSSELL A. OAKLEY. Turf for Golf Courses. NY: Macmillan, 1929. Dk grn cl, gilt. (Emb stamp, corner fep clipped, old name; fr hinge starting, spine rubbed), else VG-. *Pacific*.* $58/£36

PIPER, HUGH. Poultry: A Practical Guide.... Groombridge, 1883. 3rd ed. vii,(i),152,(8)pub's cat; 8 color plts. Cream chalked eps. Sand-grain brn cl, gilt. Good (letterpress sl browned, stitching shaken; cl dull). *Blackwell's.* $104/£65

PIPER, JOHN. Oxfordshire—A Shell Guide. Faber & Faber, 1953. New ed. VG (spine tail sl bumped) in dj (sl rubbed, spotted, creased, spine sl dknd). *Ulysses.* $88/£55

PIPER, MYFANWY (ed). Sea Poems. Frederick Muller, 1944. 1st Eng ed. Signed. 16 color lithos. Color pict cl. VG (edges sl spotted) in dj (sl chipped, rubbed, spotted, spine sl dknd). *Ulysses.* $88/£55

PIPER, WATTY (retold by). The Little Engine That Could. NY: Platt & Munk, 1984. 4 pop-ups by Richard Walz. Glazed pict bds. VG. *Bookfinders.* $30/£19

PIPER, WATTY. The Little Engine That Could from The Pony Engine by Mabel C. Bragg. NY: Platt & Munk, (1930). 1st ed. Lois Lenski (illus). 8vo. Red cl, color paste label. Good in full color dj (dusty, edges chipped). *Reisler.* $100/£63

Piratical Barberity: or The Female Captive. (By George G. Parker.) NY: S. Walker, 1826. 1st ed. 36pp. 1/2 grn morocco. (Sl stained, creased.) *Maggs.* $480/£300

PIRSIG, ROBERT M. Zen and the Art of Motorcycle Maintenance. NY, 1974. 1st ed. Fine (sl worn) in Fine dj (faint remnants of 2 paperclips top fr panel). *Warren.* $95/£59

PIRSIG, ROBERT M. Zen and the Art of Motorcycle Maintenance. NY, 1974. 1st ed. Signed. NF in NF dj (2-inch closed spine tear). *Warren.* $350/£219

PIRSSON, LOUIS V. Fly-Fishing Days or The Reminiscences of an Angler. Waldron Faulkner (ed). Washington: Privately ptd, 1946. 1st ed. Faulkner calling card laid in. Cl-backed marbled bds, gilt. (Corners, spine ends rubbed), else VG. *Pacific*.* $207/£129

PISSARO, CAMILLE. Letters to His Son Lucien. John Rewald (ed). NY: Pantheon Books, (1943). 1st ed. VG in dj (worn). *Turtle Island.* $30/£19

PITEZEL, JOHN H. Lights and Shades of Missionary Life: Containing Travels, Sketches, Incidents, and Missionary Reports, During Nine Years Spent in the Region of Lake Superior. Cincinnati: Western Book Concern, 1860. Rpt of the 1857. 431pp + (1)ad pg; 4 wood-engr plts. Blindstamped cl. (Bkpl, lt stained, lacks 1 fep, another coming loose; rubbed, extrems worn, spine sunned), else Good. *Pacific*. $29/£18

PITMAN, BENN. The Trials for Treason at Indianapolis, Disclosing the Plans for Establishing a North-Western Confederacy. Cincinnati, 1865. Frontis. Contemp sheep (worn). Howes P394. *Swann**. $57/£36

PITMAN, C. R. S. A Game Warden Takes Stock. London, 1942. (Spine faded.) *Grayling*. $40/£25

PITTENGER, WILLIAM. Daring and Suffering: A History of the Great Railroad Adventure. Phila: J.W. Daughaday, 1863. 1st ed. Mezzotint frontisport (partly detached), 288pp (sl aging, foxed; pencil sigs). Blind dotted brn cl (fr hinge split; edges worn), gilt (dull). Text Good. *Baltimore**. $55/£34

Pity's Gift: A Collection of Interesting Tales, to Excite the Compassion of Youth for the Animal Creation. London: Longman, Newbery, 1798. 12mo. John Bewick (illus). viii,147pp. 19th-cent 3/4 morocco, marbled bds. (Pg 19 torn w/some loss of paper, affecting text but no images; extrems lt rubbed), else Fine. *Bromer*. $300/£188

PIZZETTI, IPPOLITO and HENRY COCKER. Flowers: A Guide for Your Garden. (NY): Abrams, 1975. 2 vols. 297 color plts. VG set in VG djs. *Hadley*. $96/£60

PLANCHE, J. R. A Corner of Kent. Robert Hardwicke, 1864. 1st ed. Frontis (sl spotted), xxiii,413pp; 13 litho plts. 1/2 calf, gilt backstrip, label, marbled bds. VG. *Hollett*. $224/£140

PLANCHE, J. R. The Pursuivant of Arms. London, 1852. xi,207pp. Uncut. (Lt spotted; lt soiled, corners rubbed, spine worn w/loss, joints cracked.) *Edwards*. $61/£38

PLANCK, MAX. Where Is Science Going? James Murphy (ed). London: Allen & Unwin, 1933. 1st ed. Frontis port. Bkpl of Arthur Raistrick. (Lower corner of pastedowns, 1st few ll sl dampstained; cl bubbled.) *Hollett*. $64/£40

PLANT, MARJORIE. The English Book Trade. George Allen & Unwin, 1939. 1st Eng ed. VG (spine ends, corners sl bumped) in dj (nicked, creased, sl rubbed, spine sl dknd). *Ulysses*. $88/£55

PLANTE, DAVID. The Ghost of Henry James. Boston: Gambit, 1970. 1st US ed, 1st bk. Fine in Fine dj (edge sl rubbed). *Pettler*. $85/£53

Planter: Or, Thirteen Years in the South. By a Northern Man. (By David Brown.) Phila: H. Hooker, 1853. 1st ed. 275pp, (1)pg ads. Dk blue cl. (Bkpl, blindstamp; spine sl faded), else VG. Howes B834. *Chapel Hill*. $200/£125

PLARR, VICTOR. Ernest Dowson 1888-1897. London: Elkin Mathews, 1914. 1st Eng ed. VG (spine dknd, spine ends, corners sl bumped, sm mk fr cvr). *Ulysses*. $136/£85

PLATE, ROBERT. Palette and Tomahawk. NY: David McKay, 1962. 1st ed. VG in dj (sl worn). *Lien*. $20/£13

PLATH, SYLVIA. The Bell Jar. NY: Harper, (1971). 1st Amer ed. (Sm crescent mk fep; sl rubbed), else Fine in Fine dj. *Between The Covers*. $100/£63

PLATH, SYLVIA. The Bell Jar. London: Heinemann, 1963. 1st Eng ed. VG (sm ink mk fep, lg mk fr pastedown; spine ends sl bumped) in dj (sl creased, rubbed). *Ulysses*. $1,272/£795

PLATH, SYLVIA. Letters Home. Aurelia Schober Plath (ed). NY: Harper & Row, 1975. 1st ed. NF in dj (price-clipped). *Smith*. $30/£19

PLATH, SYLVIA. Lyonnesse. London: Rainbow Press, 1971. One of 400. 1/4 calf, dec bds, gilt. Fine. *Heritage*. $200/£125

PLATH, SYLVIA. Winter Trees. NY, 1972. 1st US ed. (Inscrip), o/w Mint in dj. *Bond*. $30/£19

PLATO. Lysis, or Friendship; The Symposium; Phaedrus. (Mt. Vernon, NY): LEC, 1968. One of 1500. Signed by Eugene Karlin (illus). 1/2 vellum, bds, leather spine label. Fine in glassine, slipcase. *Pacific**. $58/£36

PLATO. The Republic of Plato. LEC, 1944. Ltd to 1500 numbered, signed by Fritz Kredel (illus) and Bruce Rogers (designer). 2 vols. Fine in slipcase. *Swann**. $201/£126

PLATO. The Republic. NY: William E. Rudge's Sons, 1944. Signed by Bruce Rogers (designer) and Fritz Kredel (illus). 2 vols. 1/4 black morocco, gilt, brn paper sides. Fine in box. *Appelfeld*. $250/£156

PLATO. Symposium or Supper. Francis Birrell & Shane Leslie (trans). (London): Nonesuch, (1924). Untrimmed. Nice. *Second Life*. $85/£53

PLATO. Three Dialogues of Plato: Lysis, the Symposium and Phaedrus. LEC, 1968. Ltd to 1500 numbered, signed by Eugene Karlin (illus). Fine in slipcase. *Swann**. $92/£58

PLATO. The Trial and Death of Socrates. LEC, 1962. Ltd to 1500 numbered, signed by Hans Erni (illus) and Giovanni Mardersteig (designer). Fine in slipcase. *Swann**. $115/£72

PLATO. The Works of Plato, Abrig'd. London: A. Bell et al, 1720. 2nd ed. 2 vols. Frontisports. Paneled calf, morocco spine labels. (Old name; spine ends rubbed, vol 2 sm spine piece replaced), else VG. *Pacific**. $230/£144

PLATT, P. L. and N. SLATER. Traveler's Guide Across the Plains Upon the Overland Route to California. SF: John Howell-Books, 1963. Rpt. Ltd to 475. Mtd facs of orig 1852 tp, fldg facs map. 1/2 cl, facs map on cvrs, paper spine label. Fine. *Pacific**. $63/£39

PLATT, P. L. and N. SLATER. Travelers' Guide Across the Plains upon the Overland Route to California. (SF): John Howell, 1963. 2nd ed. One of 475 ptd by Barbara Holman, signed by her. Tipped-in facs of orig tp; fldg map. Cl spine w/paper label, black bds. Fine. Howes P417. *Harrington*. $110/£69

PLATTES, GABRIEL. A Discovery of Infinite Treasure, Hidden Since the World's Beginning. George Hutton, 1639. 1st ed. 4to. Errata leaf at end. Mod 1/2 morocco (spine head sl rubbed; 1 letter of tp shaved). *Sotheby's**. $846/£529

PLAUT, J. S. (ed). Oskar Kokoschka. Boston/London: Inst Contemporary Art/Parrish, n.d. (1948). 56 plts (8 color), 2 lithos. (Lib stamps, spine #), else Good. *Ars Artis*. $400/£250

Play Time in Action. Newton, MA: Walter P. Phillips, 1949. 25x20 cm. 5 dbl-pg pop-ups by William Kemp Tilley. VG in pict wraps. *Bookfinders*. $80/£50

PLAYFAIR, JOHN. Elements of Geometry. NY: Collins & Hannay, Collins, 1830. xvi,333pp (lt foxed). Leather (worn). Good + . *Bookcell*. $60/£38

PLAYFAIR, R. L. The Scourge of Christendom. London: Smith Elder, 1884. 1st ed. xiv,327pp; fldg map, 6 plts. Uncut. Fine. *Maggs*. $192/£120

PLAYFAIR, R. L. Travels in the Footsteps of Bruce in Algeria and Tunis. London: C. Kegan Paul, 1877. 1st ed. 1/2-title, frontis, x,300 + (1)ads; 28 lithos, fldg map (colored in outlin). Gilt edges. Grn pict cl, gilt. VG (1st few ll creased at lower corner; spine foot rubbed). *Morrell*. $336/£210

PLAYFAIR, W. S. A Treatise on the Science and Practice of Midwifery. Phila, 1893. 6th Amer ed. 697pp. 5 plts. (Binding worn). *Doctor's Library*. $60/£38

Playful Fairyland Pop-Ups. Londen (sic): Bairns Books, n.d. (196?). 4 dbl-pg pop-ups. Glazed pict bds (lt worn). Internally VG. *Bookfinders*. $40/£25

Playtime Book. London: Dean's Rag Book Co, (ca 1920). Herouard (illus). 4to. 14pp; each pg is doubled-over material w/illus and text. Color cl, pinking shear edges (sm fold rear cvr). Dean Ragbook brochure laid in. *Reisler*. $175/£109

Plea for Polygamy. NY: Panurge, (1929). One of 1010. Frontis. Teg. Black cl, gilt. NF. *Pacific**. $173/£108

PLEASANTS, HENRY. Serious Music—and All That Jazz! NY: S&S, (1969). 1st ed. VG in ptd dj. *Petrilla*. $25/£16

PLEASONTON, A. J. The Influence of the Blue Ray of the Sun Light and of the Blue Colour of the Sky, In Developing Animal and Vegetable Life.... Phila, 1876. 1st ed. 185pp. (Ex-lib.) *Fye*. $100/£63

PLEDGE, H. T. Science Since 1500. A Short History of Mathematics, Physics, Chemistry, Biology. London: HMSO, 1939. 15 plts. Navy blue cl. Fine. *Weber*. $50/£31

PLENDERLEITH, H. J. The Conservation of Antiquities and Works of Art. OUP, 1956. 1st ed. Color frontis, 55 plts. *Forest*. $56/£35

PLENDERLEITH, H. J. The Preservation of Leather Bookbindings. British Museum, 1950. Limp cl. *Forest*. $16/£10

PLENDERLEITH, H. J. The Preservation of Leather Bookbindings. British Museum, 1957. VG. *Moss*. $19/£12

PLINY THE YOUNGER. The Letters of Pliny the Consul: With Occasional Remarks. By William Melmoth, Esq. London: J. Dodsley, 1796. 9th ed. 2 vols. (viii),368,(1)errata; (ii),322,(7)(index and errata)pp. Full sprinkled calf (rubbed, dull, joint extrems splitting). *Zubal**. $40/£25

PLIVIER, THEODOR. The Kaiser Goes: The Generals Remain. A. W. Wheen (trans). NY: Macmillan, 1933. 1st US ed. Khaki cl stamped in red. Fine in dj (few sm tears, sl edge chips, spine sunned). *Reese*. $65/£41

PLIVIER, THEODOR. The Kaiser's Coolies. Margaret Green (trans). NY: Knopf, 1931. 1st US ed. Orange cl stamped in black. VG in pict dj (chipped, inner mends, tear along 1 joint). *Reese*. $65/£41

PLOMER, HENRY R. A Short History of English Printing 1476.... Alfred Pollard (ed). Kegan Paul, Trench, Trubner, 1900. 1st ed. Frontis, 3 plts. Teg, uncut. Buckram. *Forest*. $56/£35

PLOMER, HENRY R. William Caxton (1424-1491). Leonard Parsons, 1925. 1st ed. Frontis. *Forest*. $26/£16

PLOMER, WILLIAM. Address Given at the Memorial Service for Ian Fleming. London, Sept 15, 1964. 1st Eng ed. One of 50 of hb issue. Paper title-label on fr cvr. Fine (sm spot rep) in dj (sl chipped). *Ulysses*. $472/£295

PLOMER, WILLIAM. The Fivefold Screen. Hogarth, 1932. One of 450 signed. Good (fr cvr mkd; spine ends, 2 corners sl bumped, rubbed). *Ulysses*. $104/£65

PLOMER, WILLIAM. Museum Pieces. NY: Noonday, (1954). 1st Amer ed. Adv rev copy, slip laid in. (Pg edges sl dknd), else Fine in VG+ dj (lt worn). *Between The Covers*. $75/£47

PLOMER, WILLIAM. Turbott Wolfe. London: Hogarth, 1925. 1st Eng ed, 1st bk. One of 1000. Very Nice (pencil inscrip). *Clearwater*. $96/£60

PLOT, ROBERT. The Natural History of Oxford-Shire. Oxford: For Charles Brome & John Nicholson, 1705. 2nd ed. 16 engr plts. Contemp calf. (Contents leaf detached, faulty at margins; prelims sl stained, tatty; lacks map; extrems worn.) *Christie's**. $35/£22

PLOWDEN, FRANCIS. Jura Anglorum: The Rights of Englishmen. Dublin: George Bonham, 1792. xii,620,(8)pp. Calf, morocco spine label. NF (lib bkpls). *Pacific**. $138/£86

PLUCKNETT, THEODORE F. T. A Concise History of the Common Law. Boston: Little, Brown, 1956. 5th ed. (Ink mks), else Good. *Boswell*. $35/£22

PLUES, MARGARET. Rambles in Search of Flowerless Plants. Heulston & Wright, 1864. 1st ed. viii,316,(4)index, ad leaf pp; 20 color-ptd litho plts w/add'l hand-coloring. Uncut. Good (bkpl) in grn cl (sides cockled, edges sl rubbed). *Cox*. $72/£45

PLUMMER, F. G. Forest Conditions in the Black Mesa Forest Reserve, Arizona. Washington: GPO, 1904. VG+. *Five Quail*. $35/£22

PLUMMER, WILLIAM. The Holy Goof. NY, 1981. 1st ed. Inscribed, dated. Fine in NF dj. *Warren*. $40/£25

PLUMMER, WILLIAM. The Holy-Goof: a Biography of Neal Cassady. Englewood Cliffs, NJ: Prentice-Hall, (1981). 1st ed. Brn bds, gilt in pict dj (top edge sl torn). NF. *Blue Mountain*. $45/£28

PLUNKETT, GRACE. Doctors Recommend It. Dublin: The Subscribers, 1930. One of 500. Obl folio. 12 plts. Rough linen bds, ptd cvr label. (Bds sl bowed), o/w Fine. *Maggs*. $320/£200

PLUTARCH. Lives and Writings. A.H. Clough and William W. Goodwin (eds). NY: Colonial, 1905. Connoisseurs ed. One of 200 sets. Teg. Red cl (cvrs partly discolored), ptd paper spine labels. *Kane**. $55/£34

PLUTARCH. The Lives of the Noble Grecians and Romans. LEC, 1941. Ltd to 1500 numbered, signed by W. A. Dwiggins (designer). 8 vols. Fine in slipcase. *Swann**. $161/£101

PLUTARCH. Plutarch's Lives. John and William Langhorne (trans). London: Dilly, 1770. 1st ed. 6 vols. Engr frontis each vol. Full early polished calf (professionally rebacked, w/orig spines laid down), red leather labels, gilt. VG set. *Hartfield*. $450/£281

PLUTARCH. Plutarch's Lives. Phila: James Crissey, 1825. 4 vols. Period calf, gilt. NF. *Pacific**. $115/£72

PLUTARCH. Plutarch's Lives. J. Langhorne (trans). London, 1826. 6 vols. Later 1/2 polished tan calf, gilt extra, red/grn labels. *Swann**. $316/£198

POAGUE, WILLIAM THOMAS. Gunner with Stonewall. Monroe F. Cockrell (ed). Jackson, TN: McCowat-Mercer, 1957. 1st ed. Frontisport, fldg map. Blue cl. Fine in NF dj. *Chapel Hill*. $150/£94

POCHE, EMANUEL. Bohemian Porcelain. Richard K. White (trans). London: Spring Books, n.d. 70pp; 160 b/w, 16 color plts, 2pp of marks. (Lower corner of plts, cl edges sl waterstained; cl lt faded.) Dj (water-stained, sl chipped, wrinkled). *Edwards*. $48/£30

POCHIN, W. F. Angling and Hunting in British Columbia. Vancouver, BC: Sun Directories, 1946. VG in dj (edgeworn). *Perier*. $25/£16

PODESCHI, JOHN. Books on the Horse and Horsemanship. Tate Gallery, 1981. (Lt worn.) Dj. *Oinonen**. $80/£50

PODMORE, FRANK. The Newer Spiritualism. London: T. Fisher Unwin, (1911). 2nd ptg. Ptd pebbled russet cl. VG (neat early pencilling). *Gach*. $40/£25

PODOLSKY, EDWARD. Encyclopedia of Aberrations, a Psychiatric Handbook. NY, 1953. 1st ed. 550pp. *Fye*. $50/£31

POE, DAVID. Personal Reminiscences of the Civil War. Charleston, WV: News-Mail Pub, 1908. 1st ed. Author's name corrected from 'John' to 'David' by rubberstamp, as called for by Dornbusch. 8vo. VG- in ptd wraps (spine tape-repaired in 3 places, edgeworn). *Chapel Hill*. $750/£469

POE, EDGAR ALLAN. Collected Works. Thomas O. Mabbott (ed). Cambridge, MA: Belknap Press, 1969-1978. 1st collected ed. 3 vols. Frontis each vol. Maroon cl, gilt. Good set in djs (vol I lacks dj). *Maggs*. $120/£75

POE, EDGAR ALLAN. The Fall of the House of Usher. (NY): LEC, 1985. One of 1500 ptd. Signed by Raphael Soyer (afterword). 2 color lithos, color etching. Hand-marbled bds, burgundy niger spine, fore-edges. Fine in black cl box lined w/red velvet, gilt-lettered scarlet niger cvr label. *Pacific**. $403/£252

POE, EDGAR ALLAN. The Fall of the House of Usher. LEC, 1985. One of undetermined # signed by Raphael Soyer and Alice Neel (illus). Fine in slipcase. *Swann**. $632/£395

POE, EDGAR ALLAN. Lenore. Boston: Estes & Lauriat, 1886. One of 280 numbered. 13 mtd India proof engrs. Patterned eps w/cl-reinforced hinges; aeg. Orig dk brn sheep, relief central oval port fr cvr, gilt. (Sl offsetting; scuffed.) Text Clean. *Baltimore**. $50/£31

POE, EDGAR ALLAN. The Literati. NY/Boston: J.S. Redfield/B.B. Mussey, 1850. 1st ed, 1st ptg, w/the wrong signature number ('2*') at the bottom of p9. Blanck's binding 'F': orig blindstamped dk blue cl. VG (extrems sl shelfworn). *Sumner & Stillman.* $475/£297

POE, EDGAR ALLAN. The Murders in the Rue Morgue. Antibes: Allen, (1958). One of 150. Prospectus laid in. Fine. *Pacific*.* $161/£101

POE, EDGAR ALLAN. The Narrative of Arthur Gordon Pym. NY: LEC, 1930. One of 1500 numbered, signed by Rene Clarke (illus). Cl, paper-parchment back. (Sl worn.) Slipcase. *Oinonen*.* $30/£19

POE, EDGAR ALLAN. The Poems of Edgar Allan Poe. LEC, 1944. Ltd to 1500 numbered, signed by Hugo Steiner-Prag (illus). Fine in slipcase. *Swann*.* $149/£93

POE, EDGAR ALLAN. Poems. NY: Charles Breyner, 1950. 1st US ed w/these illus. One of 999 numbered. J. G. Daragnes (illus). 12 full-pg wood engrs. Marbled eps; untrimmed, teg. Prospectus laid in. Dk blue sheep, marbled bds, gilt spine. (Joints, edges scuffed.) *Baltimore*.* $60/£38

POE, EDGAR ALLAN. The Poetical Works. London: Hodder & Stoughton, (1921). 1st ed illus by Edmund Dulac. 28 color plts, guards. (Bkpl, spot to top edges of several pp; spine sl dull), else VG. *Pacific*.* $207/£129

POE, EDGAR ALLAN. The Poetical Works. London: Addey, 1853. 1st ed. Blindstamped olive grn cl. NF (spine sunned, ends sl chipped). *Sumner & Stillman.* $675/£422

POE, EDGAR ALLAN. The Purloined Letter, from Chambers' Edinburgh Magazine November 1844. London: Ulysses Bookshop, 1931. One of 325. Ptd paper wrappers (faded). *Petersfield.* $19/£12

POE, EDGAR ALLAN. Tales of Mystery and Imagination. London: George G. Harrap, 1919. Ltd to 170 signed. Thick 4to. 24 b/w full-pg line dwgs by Harry Clarke, 10 dec tailpieces. Teg. White vellum, gilt. Good. *Reisler.* $6,500/£4,063

POE, EDGAR ALLAN. Tales of Mystery and Imagination. London: George C. Harrap, 1935. 1st trade ed. 4to. 12 color plts by Arthur Rackham. Orig dk blue leatherette, gilt. Fine in dj. *Christie's*.* $515/£322

POE, EDGAR ALLAN. Tales of Mystery and Imagination. London: Tudor Pub Co, 1939. 8 mtd color plts by Harry Clarke. Deckled edges. Black cl w/onlaid label to upper cvr. NF. *Sotheran.* $317/£198

POE, EDGAR ALLAN. Tales of Mystery and Imagination. LEC, 1941. Ltd to 1500 numbered, signed by William Sharp (illus). Fine in slipcase. *Swann*.* $126/£79

POE, EDGAR ALLAN. The Works. N.P. Willis et al (notes). NY: J.S. Redfield, 1850. 1st Collected ed. 1st ptg: in Vol 1 the last pg of ads includes the line 'Was Published on the First of April,' and in Vol 2, p46, the 'r' of 'choir' is lacking in the 1st line of the 3rd stanza. 2 vols. 4pp ads vol 1. Orig blindstamped bluegray cl: primary binding, w/gilt rule under the vol # on each spine. VG set (foxed; 1 spine foot sl shelfworn, 1 sm scrape on other vol's rear cvr, few sl cvr spots). *Sumner & Stillman.* $1,475/£922

POE, EDGAR ALLAN. The Works. London: Routledge, 1896. 6 vols. 8vo. Engr port. Teg. 3/4 blue morocco, raised bands. VG set. *Appelfeld.* $550/£344

POE, SOPHIE A. Buckboard Days. Caldwell, ID: Caxton Ptrs, 1936. 1st ed. VG + in dj (chipped). *Labordo.* $95/£59

POE, SOPHIE A. Buckboard Days. Eugene Cunningham (ed). Caldwell, 1936. 1st ed. (Cvr faded, sl spotted), else Fine. *Baade.* $67/£42

Poems by Two Brothers. (By Alfred Tennyson.) Macmillan, 1893. (2nd ed.) Half-title present, facs of 1st ed tp, xix,(i),251pp. Unopened. Fine bead-grain grn cl, gilt. Good (eps foxed, bkpl). *Blackwell's.* $96/£60

Poems on Several Occasions. (By Matthew Prior.) London: Jacob Tonson, 1709. 1st Authorized ed. 8vo. Engr frontis, xxiv,(iv),328pp. Orig full chestnut polished calf (rebacked in period style), morocco/gilt label. VG. *Hartfield.* $395/£247

Poems. (By Charlotte, Emily and Anne Bronte.) Smith, Elder, 1846 (1848). 1st ed, 2nd issue. 8vo. Ads for 'Prose Fictions' facing tp, incl 3rd ed of Jane Eyre, 16pp ads at end dated May 1848. Orig grn cl, gilt. Bkpls of Maurice Baring and Eric Quayle. (Tp stamped w/initials, some pp sl foxed, lacks errata slip; spine gilt chipped, worn.) *Sotheby's*.* $1,803/£1,127

Poems. MDCCCXXX. MDCCCXXXIII. (By Alfred Tennyson.) Privately ptd, 1862. Pirated rpt of 1830, 1833 vols. viii,112pp. Unopened. VG in blue wrappers, stab-sewn. *Blackwell's.* $400/£250

POESCH, JESSIE. Titian Ramsay Peale 1799-1855 and His Journals of the Wilkes Expedition. Phila: Amer Philosophical Soc, 1961. 1st ed. Pict cl. NF in matching dj (lt soiled). *House.* $30/£19

Poet and the Painter; or, Gems of Art and Song. NY: D. Appleton, 1869. 1st ed. 11 x 7 3/4. Aeg. Emb brn morocco, gilt, raised bands. (Fr joint cracking), else VG. *Pacific*.* $58/£36

Poetical Tributes to the Memory of Abraham Lincoln. Phila, 1865. 1st Amer ed. Frontisport. Teg. Pict cvrs, gilt. NF (fep sl chipped; rubbed). *Polyanthos.* $35/£22

Poetry Made Familiar and Easy...Being the Fourth Volume of the Circle of the Sciences, &c. London: T. Carnan & F. Newbery, 1776. 4th ed. 24mo. 281pp + 3pp pub's list. Ivory vellum, ptd spine label (rubbed), off-white bds (mkd, rubbed, worn). *Reisler.* $450/£281

POGANY, NANDOR. The Hungarian Fairy Book. NY: Frederick A. Stokes, (1913). 1st Amer ed. 8vo. 21 full-pg illus + color frontis by Willy Pogany. Blue pict cl, gilt. Good. *Reisler.* $150/£94

POGANY, WILLY and ELAINE. Peterkin. Phila: David McKay, 1940. 1st ed. 4to. 15 full-pg color plts. Cl-backed bds, color illus fr cvr. Good in full color dj (sl wear to rear). *Reisler.* $225/£141

POGANY, WILLY. Willy Pogany's Mother Goose. NY: Thomas Nelson, 1928. 1st ed. Royal 8vo. Color frontis, (152)pp. Teg. Bright blue cl, gilt. NF (spine sl rubbed). *Sotheran.* $352/£220

POGUE, J. The Turquoise. Part II. Third Memoir. Washington, 1915. Color frontis; 22 plts (1 color). As issued w/the Second Memoir by C. Adams on the Snails of the Genus IO. 184pp; 61 plts. Color frontis; 22 plts (1 color). Later maroon buckram. VG (ex-lib, bkpl) *Blake.* $200/£125

POGZEBA, WOLFGANG. Ranchos de Taos; San Francisco de Asis Church. Kansas City, 1981. Fine in dj. *Dumont.* $40/£25

POHL, FREDERIK. The Annals of the Heechee. NY: Ballantine, (1987). 1st ed. Fine in NF dj. *Antic Hay.* $20/£13

POHL, FREDERIK. The Way the Future Was: A Memoir. NY, (1978). 1st ed. Presentation copy. Inscribed, signed. (Extrems sl worn), else VG in dj (edges worn). *King.* $25/£16

POINGDESTRE, JOHN EDMUND. Nevada County Mining and Business Directory, 1895. Oakland: Pacific Press, (1895). 1st ed. 196pp + (12)pp ads; fldg map. Black cl, gilt, leather spine. (Sm tape-repaired tear to map; 3x4-inch piece of cl gone from fr cvr, joints cracked, rear split w/leather lifting), o/w VG. *Pacific*.* $196/£123

Points and Pickings of Information About the Chinese. (By George Mogridge.) London: Grant & Griffith, 1844. 2nd ed. xii,316pp; 8 engr plts (incl frontis). Contemp diced calf, gilt, black label. VG (1 plt sl foxed). *Morrell.* $128/£80

POLACK, J. S. Manners and Customs of the New Zealanders. London: James Madden, 1840. 2 vols. 8vo. xxxiv,288; xviii,304pp; fldg map, 3 plts. Orig cl (rebacked), leather labels. *Adelson.* $585/£366

POLACK, J. S. New Zealand. London: Richard Bentley, 1838. 1st ed. 2 vols. xii,403; vi,441pp; 6 plts, fldg map. (W/o list of plts; lt spotted, pp207/8 vol 2 repaired w/cellotape.) Cl-backed bds (extrems worn), spine labels (chipped). *Edwards.* $480/£300

POLE, HELEN. The Aristocrats: Being the Impressions of...During Her Sojourn in the Great North Woods.... Leipzig: Bernhard Tauchnitz, 1901. Copyright ed. *Mott.* $20/£13

POLIAKOFF, NICOLAI. Coco the Clown. London: J.M. Dent, 1940. 1st ed. (Few dampstains.) Dj (torn, creased, w/sl loss). *Hollett.* $32/£20

Political Debates Between Hon. Abraham Lincoln and Hon. Stephen A. Douglas. Columbus: Follett, Foster, 1860. 1st ed, 2nd issue. iv,268pp (sl foxed). Blind brn cl (spine ends chipped; edges sl worn), gilt. VG. Howes L338. *Baltimore*.* $100/£63

Political Mirror; or, Review of Jacksonism. NY: J.P. Peaslee, 1835. 1st ed. xvi,316pp (lt aged, sl foxed). Orig grn cl (sl worn), gilt. Text Clean, cvrs VG. Howes P440. *Baltimore*.* $50/£31

POLK, DORA BEALE. The Island of California: A History of the Myth. Spokane: A.H. Clark, 1991. 1st ed. Fine in dj. *Pacific*.* $86/£54

POLK, JAMES K. The Diary of James K. Polk During His Presidency, 1845-1849. Milo M. Quaife (ed). Chicago: McClurg, 1910. One of 500 sets. 4 vols. Untrimmed. Cl spines, paper over bds, paper labels. (Extrems sl worn, spines sl discolored, spotted; sl foxed.) Howes P445. *Woolson.* $100/£63

POLK, JAMES K. The Diary of James K. Polk, During His Presidency, 1845 to 1849. Milo M. Quaife (ed). Chicago: A.C. McClurg, 1910. Ltd to 500 sets. 4 vols. 4 plts, 2-pg facs. Blue bds, linen spines w/paper labels. Fine set. Howes P445. *Karmiole.* $150/£94

POLK, R. L. Baltimore City Business Directory, 1887-'88. Washington: Polk, 1887. 1st ed. (iv),(3)-474pp + 14pp ads. Dk brn cl, gilt. Good (sl handled). *Baltimore*.* $140/£88

POLK, RALPH W. Elementary Platen Presswork. Peoria, IL: Chas. A. Bennett, (1965). (Bkpl.) *Oak Knoll.* $45/£28

POLK, RALPH W. The Practice of Printing. Peoria, IL: Manual Arts Press, (1945). Rpt. Fine. *Oak Knoll.* $45/£28

POLLARD, A. W. Fine Books. Methuen, 1912. 1st ed. Frontis, 40 plts. Teg, uncut. (Inner hinge shaken; spine head torn, stuck down.) *Forest.* $56/£35

POLLARD, A. W. Fine Books. London: Methuen, 1912. 40 plts. Red cl (fr cvr rt side rubbed), gilt. *Maggs.* $80/£50

POLLARD, A. W. Italian Book Illustrations Chiefly of the 15th Century. Seeley, 1894. 80pp; 9 full-pg engrs. Red dec cl (sl worn, hinges partly split). *Moss.* $38/£24

POLLARD, A. W. The Romance of King Arthur and His Knights of the Round Table. London: Macmillan, 1917. Ltd to 500 signed. Thick 4to. 509pp; 16 full-pg mtd color plts, 70 b/w dwgs by Arthur Rackham. Teg. White vellum, gilt. (Lt dusty, few mats spotted.) Overall VG. *Reisler.* $2,250/£1,406

POLLARD, A. W. Shakespeare's Fight with the Pirates and the Problems of the Transmission of His Text. London: Alexander Moring, 1917. 1st ed. 1/4 cl, paper spine label. (Extrems dknd), else VG. *Pacific*.* $46/£29

POLLARD, A. W. and G. R. REDGRAVE. Short-Title Catalogue of Books Printed in England, Scotland, and Ireland 1475-1640. London, 1950. (Worn.) *Oinonen*.* $50/£31

POLLARD, A. W. and G. R. REDGRAVE. A Short-Title Catalogue of Books Printed in England, Scotland, and Ireland. London: Bibliographical Society, 1948. 2nd ed, 2nd ptg. Tan cl, bds, black spine lettering. (Edges scuffed, worn.) Text Good (lt pencil notes). *Baltimore*.* $130/£81

POLLARD, A. W. (ed). The Travels of Sir John Mandeville. The Version of the Cotton Manuscript in Modern Spelling. London: Macmillan, 1900. Red cl (worn), gilt. *Maggs.* $29/£18

POLLARD, EDWARD A. Echoes from the South. NY: E.B. Treat, 1866. 1st ed. vi,(7)-211pp + 4pp pubs ads. Good (foxed, lacks fep; backstrip worn, faded). *Connolly.* $45/£28

POLLARD, EDWARD A. The First Year of the War. Richmond: West & Johnson, 1862. 2nd ed, Corrected and Improved Edition. (iii),389pp (ink sig; lt aging, sl foxed); 4 steel-engr port plts (lt foxed), guards. Dk grn blind cl (sl worn, spine chipped). VG. Howes P449. *Baltimore*.* $70/£44

POLLARD, EDWARD A. The Lost Cause; a New Southern History of the War of the Confederates...etc. NY: E.B. Treat, 1867. Enlgd, expanded ed. Lg hand-colored fldg map, 6 steel engr ports. 3/4 brn calf over marbled bds. Fine. Howes P455. *Appelfeld.* $125/£78

POLLARD, EDWARD A. The Second Year of the War. NY: Charles B. Richardson, 1863. 386pp. Gilt-dec cl. VG (foxed, lower edge very shelfworn). *My Bookhouse.* $87/£54

POLLARD, H. B. C. The Secret Societies of Ireland. London, 1922. 1st ed. (1st/last few ll lt browned; cl lt dampspotted, corners sl bumped.) *Edwards.* $64/£40

POLLARD, HENRY ROBINSON. Memoirs and Sketches of the Life of Henry Robinson Pollard. Richmond: Lewis Ptg, (1923). 1st ed. Frontisport. Red cl. VG +. *Chapel Hill.* $50/£31

POLLEN, MRS. JOHN HUNGERFORD. Seven Centuries of Lace. Heinemann, 1908. 120 Fine full-pg plts. Teg. Pict cl, gilt. (Blind-stamp, sm lib stamp; sl rubbed, sm label removed from spine.) *Hollett.* $152/£95

POLLEY, J. B. A Soldier's Letters to Charming Nellie. NY: Neale, 1908. 1st ed. 8vo. Frontisport. Teg. Red cl. NF (traces bkpl removal on pastedowns, ink stamp). *Chapel Hill.* $550/£344

POLLOCK, M. Light and Water, Study of Reflexion and Colour in River, Lake and Sea. London: Bell, 1903. 39plts. (2 sm spots fr cvr.) *Ars Artis.* $29/£18

POLLOCK, WALTER H. et al. Fencing. Longmans, Green, 1889. 1st ed. (xvi),304pp. Pict cl. VG (spotted, mostly to prelims, edges; sl shaken). *Ash.* $136/£85

Polonius: A Collection of Wise Saws and Modern Instances. (By Edward FitzGerald.) William Pickering, 1852. 1st ed. Grn cl (spine, edges faded; sl foxed). *Sotheby's*.* $442/£276

POLYAK, STEPHEN. The Vertebrate Visual System. Chicago, 1957. 1st ed. *Fye.* $250/£156

Polyanthea: or, A Collection of Interesting Fragments, in Prose and Verse.... (By Charles Henry Wilson.) London: J. Budd, 1804. 1st ed. 2 vols. Teg. 3/4 red morocco, marbled bds, gilt. (Vol 1 lacks sm pieces from tops of prelims, cat entry mtd to fep verso; spine sl dknd), else VG. *Pacific*.* $58/£36

POMERANZ, GARY. Out at Home. Boston, 1985. 1st ed, 1st bk. VG in dj. *King.* $20/£13

POMEROY, LAURENCE. The Grand Prix Car. Volume 2. (London, 1960.) 3rd imp. VG in dj (price-clipped, torn). *King.* $395/£247

POMEROY, SETH. The Journals and Papers of.... Louis Effingham DeForest (ed). New Haven, 1926. 1st ed. *Ginsberg.* $50/£31

POMMER, RICHARD. Eighteenth-Century Architecture in Piedmont. NY/London, 1967. Good. *Washton.* $125/£78

PONDER, H. W. Java Pageant. Phila: Lippincott, n.d. (ca 1935). 2nd ed. Dbl-pg map. (Sl rubbed), o/w VG. *Worldwide.* $30/£19

PONENTE, NELLO. The Structures of the Modern World 1850-1900. Skira, 1965. Dj, in cl slipcase as issued. *Edwards.* $56/£35

PONGE, FRANCIS et al. G. Braque. NY: Abrams, (1971). Dj. *Swann*.* $92/£58

PONICSAN, DARRYL. Cinderella Liberty. NY, (1973). 1st ed. (Ink inscrip), else Good in dj (sl used). *King.* $17/£11

PONSONBY, ARTHUR (ed). English Diaries.... [and] More English Diaries.... Methuen, 1923-1927. 1st eds. 1st vol bears pub's 'Presentation Copy' stamp. 2 vols. Later 1/4 morocco. VG set (pencil notes, underlining, sl browned, spotted). *Ash.* $160/£100

PONSONBY, FREDERICK. The Grenadier Guards in the Great War of 1914-1918. London: Macmillan, 1920. 1st ed. 3 vols. 17 plts, 18 maps. Tan cl over gray bds (spines lt soiled). *Karmiole.* $100/£63

PONSONBY, FREDERICK. The Grenadier Guards in the Great War of 1914-1918. London, 1920. 1st Eng ed. 3 vols. (Rubbed, chafed, some corners sl bumped.) *Clearwater.* $192/£120

PONSONBY, MONTAGUE VERNON. The Preposterous Yankee. London: Limpus, Baker, 1903. 1st ed. Pict cl (rep cracked). *Mott.* $30/£19

PONTING, HERBERT G. The Great White South. Duckworth, 1921. 1st ed. Good. *Walcot.* $176/£110

PONTING, HERBERT G. The Great White South. London: Duckworth, 1930. 6th imp. VG (lt foxed; cl sl faded). *Explorer.* $16/£10

PONTING, HERBERT G. In Lotus-Land Japan. Macmillan, 1922. New ed. 88 plts (8 color). Blue pict cl, gilt. (Ink inscrips), o/w Fine. *Sotheran.* $157/£98

PONTOPPIDAN, ERICH. The Natural History of Norway. London: A. Linde, 1755. 1st ed in English. 2 parts in 1 vol. 28 engr plts, 1 fldg map. (1 plt mtd on newly supplied leaf, lacks leaf KK2 in part II, text lt spotted; lower hinge cracked.) Contemp calf (extrems rubbed), spine gilt, contrasting lettering piece. *Christie's*.* $576/£360

PONTOPPIDAN, ERICH. The Natural History of Norway. London, 1755. 2 parts in 1. Folio. xxiv,206; viii,291,(12)pp (lt foxed, spotted, pp tanned; rear inner joint open); lg fldg engr map (hand-colored in outline), 28 engr plts. Contemp 1/2 calf (worn, rebacked). *Sutton.* $1,650/£1,031

POOL, RAYMOND T. Flowers and Flowering Plants. McGraw-Hill, 1929. 4th ptg. (Tape mks, name; shelf-worn), else Good. *Fair Meadow.* $15/£9

POOLE, ERNEST. Blind: A Story of These Times. NY: Macmillan, 1920. 1st ed. Gilt blue cl. Fine in NF dj (few sm nicks, sm chip). *Reese.* $125/£78

Poor Little Edith Freeman. The Pocasset Fanatics. Phila, (1879). Orig pict wrappers. (Ink stamps; sl dampstained.) *Swann*.* $230/£144

Poor's Manual of the Railroads of the United States. 1888-1915. 28 vols. Thick 8vos. Orig grn cl (1888 vol rebound in lib buckram). (Ex-lib, 1889, 1896 vols worn, shabby.) *Kane*.* $2,700/£1,688

POOR, CHARLES L. Men Against the Rule. NY: Derrydale, 1937. One of 950 numbered. Dk blue cl backed over lt blue cl-cvrd bds. Fine. *Biscotti.* $100/£63

POOR, CHARLES L. Men Against the Rule: A Century of Progress in Yacht Design. NY: Derrydale, (1937). One of 950. (Lt spots fr cvr, rear cvr extrems stained), else VG. *Pacific*.* $69/£43

POORE, BEN PERLEY. The Life and Public Services of Ambrose E. Burnside, Soldier-Citizen-Statesman. Providence, RI: J.A. & R.A. Reid, 1882. 1st ed. One of 300. Frontisport, 448,(6)pp. Aeg. Orig blind-tooled full morocco, gilt, raised bands. (Lt rubbed), else NF. *Chapel Hill.* $375/£234

POORTVLIET, RIEN and WIL HUYGEN (adapted by). The Pop-Up Book of Gnomes. London: Kestrel, 1979. Tor Lokvig (engineer). 5 dbl-pg pop-ups. Glazed pict bds. VG. *Bookfinders.* $50/£31

Pop-Up Airport. London: Bancroft, 1963. Pop-Up Model Book N. 509. 2 dbl-pg pop-ups. VG in pict wraps. *Bookfinders.* $30/£19

Pop-Up Book of Cars. NY: Random House, 1976. 4 dbl-pg pop-ups by Renzo Barto. Glazed pict bds. VG. *Bookfinders.* $55/£34

Pop-Up Book of the Circus. NY: Random House, 1979. 4 dbl-pg pop-ups by Loretta Lustig. Glazed pict bds. VG. *Bookfinders.* $45/£28

Pop-Up Mother Goose. NY: Blue Ribbon, (1934). 1st ed. 9.25x8. 3 pop-ups by Harold B. Lentz. Pict bds. (Lower 3 inches of spine chipped, cracked), else VG. *Pacific*.* $104/£65

Pop-Up Mother Goose. NY: Blue Ribbon, 1934. 20x24 cm. 3 dbl-pg pop-ups (1st repaired, last repasted) by Harold Lentz. Pict bds (sl bumped; new fr hinge, new cl on spine). VG. *Bookfinders.* $150/£94

Pop-Up Picture Nursery Rhymes. London: Juvenile Productions, n.d. (1953). 5 dbl-pg pop-ups by Rene Coke. Internally VG in illus wraps (lt worn). *Bookfinders.* $80/£50

Pop-Up Puss in Boots. NY: Blue Ribbon Books, (1934). 1st ed. 9.25x7.75. 3 pop-ups by C. Carey & Harold B. Lentz. Pict bds. (Rear pop-up sl lazy), else NF. *Pacific*.* $137/£86

Pop-Up Sound Alikes. NY: Random House, 1967. 18pp tab-operated mechanicals. Glazed pict bds (spine lt worn). *Bookfinders.* $55/£34

POPE, ALEXANDER. Essay on Man. Phila: B. Buzby, 1818. Fairly early Amer ed. Orig leather-backed bds. Good (sig; foxed, stained). *Agvent.* $75/£47

POPE, ALEXANDER. Letters of Mr. Pope, and Several Eminent Persons. From the Year 1705 to 1735. London: Ptd by Booksellers of London & Westminster, 1735. 1st ed. Engr frontisport, vi,7-266,22pp. Old calf (neatly rebacked), raised bands, gilt. *Young.* $192/£120

POPE, ALEXANDER. Of the Use of Riches. London: Lawton Gilliver, 1732. 1st ed, 1st issue. Folio. 20pp. Uncut. Mod marbled bds, ribbon ties, paper label. Good (sm defect in inner margins of 1st few ll, not affecting text). *Hartfield.* $295/£184

POPE, ALEXANDER. Pope's Own Miscellany. Norman Ault (ed). Nonesuch, 1935. One of 750. Grn buckram, gilt. VG (spine sl sunned, tip of 1 corner sl bumped; no dj). *Clearwater.* $112/£70

POPE, ALEXANDER. The Works of.... London: B. Lintot et al, 1736. 4 vols. Frontisport. Period calf. VG set (bkpls). *Pacific*.* $288/£180

POPE, ALEXANDER. The Works of.... London, 1776. 6 vols. Contemp full sheep, flat spines, red labels. (Few joints tender.) *Swann*.* $201/£126

POPE, ARTHUR. An Introduction to the Language of Drawing and Painting. Cambridge: Harvard Univ, 1929. Orig ed. 2 vols. 53 b/w plts vol 2. VG set. *Turtle Island.* $50/£31

POPE, C. H. Amphibians and Reptiles of the Chicago Area. Chicago, 1947. (Name.) 12 plts (6 color). Wrappers (name). *Sutton.* $30/£19

POPE, C. H. The Reptiles of China. NY, 1935. 27 plts, fldg table. (Pp browned, ink note, name; varnished, soiled, spine sunned, sm tears to spine head.) *Sutton.* $385/£241

POPE, C. H. Turtles of the U.S. and Canada. NY: Knopf, (1946). VG in Good+ dj. *Mikesh.* $37/£23

POPE, CHARLES HENRY (ed). The Plymouth Scrap Book. Boston: C.E. Goodspeed, 1918. 1st ed. 14 photo plts. Grn linen, gilt. Good. *Karmiole.* $75/£47

POPE, DUDLEY. Admiral. Secker, 1982. 1st UK ed. NF in dj. *Williams.* $26/£16

POPE, DUDLEY. The Black Ship. Phila/NY: Lippincott, 1964. Map. Grn cl. VG in dj. *Parmer.* $45/£28

POPE, JESSIE. Babes and Beasts. NY: H.M. Caldwell, (1912). 1st Amer ed. 12mo. Charles Robinson (illus). Cl-backed color pict bds (soiled, corners rubbed). *Reisler.* $250/£156

POPE, JESSIE. The Doll Town Day. NY: Dodge, (ca 1910). 8vo. G. F. Christie (illus). Dk brn bds (spine sl shelfworn, sm fold of frontis at spine). Nice. *Reisler.* $485/£303

POPE, JESSIE. The Teddy Bear Scouts. London: Blackie & Son, (ca 1910). Charles Robinson (illus). 5.5x2.5 inches. Cl-backed color pict bds (rebacked). *Reisler.* $750/£469

POPE, JOHN ALEXANDER. Chinese Porcelains from the Ardebil Shrine. Washington: Freer Gallery of Art, 1956. Inscribed, signed. 142 plts. Good in dj (worn). *Rybski.* $100/£63

POPE-HENNESSY, JAMES. America Is an Atmosphere. Home & Van Thal, 1947. 1st Eng ed. VG (spine ends sl bumped) in dj (rubbed, nicked, sl chipped, price-clipped). *Ulysses.* $58/£36

POPE-HENNESSY, JOHN. The Complete Work of Paolo Uccello. London: Phaidon, 1950. Color frontis, 108 plts. Fine. *Europa.* $61/£38

POPE-HENNESSY, JOHN. The Drawings of Domenichino in the Collection...at Windsor Castle. London/Oxford: Phaidon, 1948. 69 plts. (Spine sl faded), o/w Fine. *Europa.* $112/£70

POPE-HENNESSY, JOHN. Fra Angelico. London: Phaidon, 1974. 2nd ed. Good in dj. *Ars Artis.* $168/£105

POPE-HENNESSY, JOHN. An Introduction to Italian Sculpture. Oxford: Phaidon, 1986. 3rd ed. 3 vols. VF set in uniform stiff dec wrappers. *Europa.* $80/£50

POPE-HENNESSY, JOHN. The Portrait in the Renaissance. NY: Pantheon Books, (1966). NF in dj. *Turtle Island.* $50/£31

POPE-HENNESSY, JOHN. The Portrait in the Renaissance. NY, 1966. Good. *Washton.* $45/£28

Popeye the Sailor Man. NY: G&D, (1937). 4to. Blue color pict bds (lt edgeworn, sl bowed). Full color dj (few marginal tears). *Reisler.* $385/£241

POPHAM, A. E. Catalogue of the Drawings of Parmigianino. New Haven, 1971. 3 vols. Folio. Slipcase. *Swann*.* $747/£467

POPHAM, A. E. The Drawings of Leonardo da Vinci. Cape, 1946. 1st ed. Buckram, gilt. VG in dj (sl worn). *Hollett.* $64/£40

POPHAM, A. E. and K. M. FENWICK. European Drawings (and Two Asian Drawings) in the Collection of the National Gallery of Canada. Toronto, 1965. Good in dj. *Washton.* $65/£41

POPPER, HANS and F. SCHAFFNER. Liver: Structure and Function. NY, 1957. 1st ed. *Fye.* $100/£63

Popul Vuh, the Book of the People. LEC, 1955. Ltd to 1500 numbered, signed by Everett Gee Jackson (illus). Fine in slipcase. *Swann*.* $46/£29

Popular Pastimes for Field and Fireside. (By Caroline Smith.) Springfield: Milton Bradley, 1867. Patterned cl (extrems sl worn; 1 sig loose), gilt. *Dramatis.* $90/£56

Popular Songs of the A.E.F. Compiled for Use in the Huts of the Knights of Columbus. Paris: Editions Francis Salabert, 1918. 1st ed. Folio. Blind-stamped brn cl, gilt. (Paper uniformly tanned, sl shaken, lt discoloration top edge, few marginal tears), else Sound. *Reese.* $25/£16

PORCELAIN, SIDNEY E. The Purple Pony Murders. NY: Phoenix, 1944. 1st ed, 1st bk. Signed. (Name; corners bumped), else NF in purple dj (spine lt sunned to blue, sl worn). *Murder.* $75/£47

PORCHIA, ANTONIO. Voices. W.S. Merwin (trans). Chicago: Big Table, 1969. 1st ed. NF in dj (price-clipped, spine lt rubbed). *Lame Duck.* $45/£28

PORGES, IRWIN. Edgar Rice Burroughs: The Man Who Created Tarzan. Provo: Brigham Young Univ, (1975). 1st ed. VG in dj (extrems chipped). *Pacific*.* $29/£18

PORNY. The Elements of Heraldry. London: Thomas Carnan, 1787. 4th ed. 24 copper plts. Calf, morocco spine label. VG. *Pacific*.* $230/£144

PORSILD, A. E. Botony of Southwestern Yukon, Adjacent to the Canol Road. Ottawa, 1951. 34 plts. (Pp yellowed.) Wrappers (name). *Sutton.* $55/£34

PORTER, BURTON B. One of the People: His Own Story. (N.p): The Author, (1907). 1st ed. Frontisport. Grn ribbed cl. VG (lt shelf wear, rear hinge sl loose). *House.* $60/£38

PORTER, CLYDE and MAE REED PORTER. Matt Field on the Santa Fe Trail. Norman, 1960. Map. VG in dj. *Dumont.* $45/£28

PORTER, COLE. Red Hot and Blue. NY: Random House, 1936. 1st ed. One of 300 numbered, signed. Silk (discolored, rubbed). VG. *Lame Duck.* $2,850/£1,781

PORTER, DAVID. Journal of a Cruise Made to the Pacific Ocean...in the United States Frigate Essex, in the Years 1812, 1813, and 1814. Phila, 1815. 1st ed. 2 vols in 1. 13 plts, fldg map. Mod 1/2 calf. *Felcone.* $2,000/£1,250

PORTER, DAVID. A Voyage in the South Seas, in the Years 1812, 1813, and 1814, with Particular Details of the Gallipagos and Washington Islands. London, 1823. Map, 2 plts. Mod 1/4 cl. *Swann*.* $161/£101

PORTER, DOROTHY B. The Negro in the United States. Washington, 1970. (Bds lt soiled), else VG. *Dumont.* $20/£13

PORTER, ELIOT. Down the Colorado. Dutton, 1969. 1st ed. Folio. Off-white woven cl. Fine in Fine coated dj. *Five Quail.* $70/£44

PORTER, ELIOT. Forever Wild: The Adirondacks. Blue Mountain Lake, NY: Adirondack Museum/Harper & Row, 1966. 1st ed. Folio. (1st, last few pp foxed), else VG in dj. *Cahan.* $60/£38

PORTER, ELIOT. Galapagos. SF: n.d. (ca 1968). 1st ed. 2 vols. 138 color plts. Djs (sl chipped w/sl loss to spine foot of vol 1). Cl slipcase (frayed, sl worn). *Edwards.* $200/£125

PORTER, ELIOT. Intimate Landscapes. NY: MMA/Dutton, 1979. 1st ed. Hb issue. Folio. Fine. *Smith.* $100/£63

PORTER, EUGENE O. San Elezario, a History. Austin, 1973. Signed by Jose Cisneros (illus). Map. NF. *Dumont.* $35/£22

PORTER, GENE STRATTON. See STRATTON-PORTER, GENE

PORTER, JAMES A. Modern Negro Art. NY: Dryden Press, 1943. 1st ed. (Bkpl; spine extrems worn.) *Swann*.* $201/£126

PORTER, JANE. The Scottish Chiefs. NY: Scribner, 1921. 4to. N.C. Wyeth (illus). VG. *American Booksellers.* $80/£50

PORTER, JANE. The Scottish Chiefs. NY: Scribner, 1923. Early rpt. Royal 8vo. (xviii),503pp; 10 color plts by N. C. Wyeth. Deckled edges. Black cl, onlaid pict label. Very Bright (ink mk to ep which is sl offset to 1/2-title). *Sotheran.* $125/£78

PORTER, JANE. The Scottish Chiefs. Kate Douglas Wiggin and Nora Smith (eds). NY: Scribner, 1921. 1st ed. 14 color plts by N. C. Wyeth. Pict cvr label. (Label discolored, spine faded), else VG in VG dj (few sm extrem tears). *Pacific*.* $575/£359

PORTER, JOHN W. H. Record of Events in Norfolk County, Virginia, from April 19th, 1861, to May 10th, 1862. Portsmouth, VA: W.A. Fiske, Ptr & Bookbinder, 1892. Only ed. 366pp + (6)pp ads. Purple cl. VG (rear hinge starting internally). *Chapel Hill.* $300/£188

PORTER, JOSIAH LESLIE. Five Years in Damascus.... John Murray, 1855. 1st ed. 2 vols. 8vo. 2 fldg maps (1 hand-colored in outline), 10 plts, 32-pg ad at end vol 2. Pub's orange cl, gilt. *Sotheby's*.* $662/£414

PORTER, KATHERINE ANNE. A Christmas Story. NY: Delacorte, (1967). 1st ed. One of 500 w/special frontis by Shahn. Signed by Shahn, twice by Porter. (Spine gilt faded), else NF in slipcase (sl faded). *Pacific*.* $75/£47

PORTER, KATHERINE ANNE. The Collected Essays and Occasional Writings of.... NY: Delacorte, (1970). One of 250 signed. Color photo frontis. Teg. 1/4 grn leather, marbled bds, gilt. Fine in cardboard open-end slipcase. *Heritage.* $125/£78

PORTER, KATHERINE ANNE. Flowering Judas. NY: Harcourt, Brace, (1930). 1st ed. Ltd to 500. VF in cl-backed paper bds. 1/2 morocco book-style drop-back box. *Bromer.* $625/£391

PORTER, KATHERINE ANNE. Hacienda. (NY): Harrison of Paris, (1934). One of 895. Red cl, gilt spine. Fine in Good slipcase (lacks piece of spine). *Pacific*.* $58/£36

PORTER, KATHERINE ANNE. Hacienda. A Story of Mexico. NY: Harrison of Paris, 1934. 1st ed. Ltd to 895 numbered. As New in pub's slipcase, paper title label. *Black Sun.* $75/£47

PORTER, KATHERINE ANNE. The Leaning Tower and Other Stories. NY: Harcourt, (1944). 1st ed. NF in VG dj (few internal mends). *Reese.* $55/£34

PORTER, KATHERINE ANNE. The Leaning Tower and Other Stories. NY: Harcourt Brace, 1944. 1st ed. VG + in VG dj (price-clipped, pencil writing on rear panel). *Pettler.* $30/£19

PORTER, KATHERINE ANNE. Pale Horse, Pale Rider. NY: Harcourt, Brace, (1939). 1st ed. Fine in NF dj (lt toned). *Bromer.* $235/£147

PORTER, KATHERINE ANNE. Ship of Fools. Boston: Atlantic-Little Brown, 1962. 1st ed. NF in VG dj. *Pettler.* $35/£22

PORTER, LUTHER H. Cycling for Health and Pleasure. NY: Dodd, Mead, 1896. Rev ed. Pict cl. VG. *Pacific*.* $75/£47

PORTER, ROBERT KER. A Narrative of the Campaign in Russia, During the Year 1812. Hartford, 1814. 379pp (sl browned); port, 2 fldg maps. Old tree calf, red spine label. Nice. *King.* $125/£78

PORTER, RUFUS. Aerial Navigation. SF: Lawton R. Kennedy, 1935. One of 200. 3 color lithos (2 fldg), 1 plt. Orange bds, brn cl backstrip. Fine. *Harrington.* $100/£63

PORTER-MEEHAN, JEANNETTE. Life and Letters of Gene Stratton-Porter. London: Hutchinson, 1927. 1st Eng ed. 4 plts. (Feps sl browned; spine lettering faded.) *Hollett.* $40/£25

PORTLAND, DUKE OF. Memories of Racing and Hunting. NY, 1935. Errata slip. Untrimmed, some pp unopened. (Fr inner hinge cracking; spine ends, corners worn.) *Woolson.* $50/£31

PORTOGHESI, PAOLO. The History of an Architectonic Culture. Cambridge, MA, (1970). Folio. (Lt worn.) Dj. *Oinonen*.* $70/£44

Ports, Harbours, Watering Places, and Coast Scenery of Great Britain. (By W. H. Beattie.) London: Virtue, ca 1848. 2 vols. 4to. 2 engr tps; 142 plts by W. H. Bartlett, et al. 3/4 19th-cent morocco over marbled bds (extrems sl worn), edges gilt. Sound. *Appelfeld.* $650/£406

POSNER, DAVID. The Dialogues. Santa Barbara: Black Sparrow, 1969. One of 150 signed. Frontisport. Hessian-backed color dec paper bds. Fine in glassine. *Any Amount.* $35/£22

POSNER, DONALD. Annibale Carracci. A Study in the Reform of Italian Painting Around 1590. Volume 2: Catalogue and Plates. London: Phaidon, 1971. Vol 2 only. 5 color plts. (Sm lib stamps; sl worn.) *Ars Artis.* $800/£500

POST, CHARLES CLEMENT. Ten Years a Cowboy. Chicago: Rhodes & McClure, 1887. Rpt ed. Pict cl. VG. Howes P500. *Labordo.* $55/£34

POST, DAN R. (ed). The Classic Cord. Arcadia, CA, (1954). 2nd ed. Pict wraps (rubbed, soiled). *King.* $50/£31

POST, MELVILLE DAVISSON. The Corrector of Destinies.... NY: Edw. J. Clode, (1908). 1st ed. Brick-red cl. (Part of fly-title torn w/loss of 1 letter; white coloring gone from spine vignette.) *Kane*.* $50/£31

POST, MELVILLE DAVISSON. The Man of Last Resort. NY, 1897. Orig ptd wraps (sigs, sl soiled, spine lacks lower 3/4-inch). *Kane*.* $65/£41

POSTGATE, R. W. et al. A Workers' History of the Great Strike. Plebs League, 1927. 1st Eng ed. Wrappers. VG (sig; title written on spine, cvrs sl rubbed, partly faded). *Ulysses.* $72/£45

Posthumous Works of the Author of a Vindication of the Rights of Woman. (By Mary Wollstonecraft.) Ptd for J. Johnson, 1798. 1st ed. 4 vols. 8vo. Contemp calf. (No 1/2-titles; joints sl cracked.) *Sotheby's*.* $2,115/£1,322

POSTLETHWAITE, JOHN. The Geology of the English lake Dirict.... Carlisle: G. & T. Coward, 1906. 2nd ed. Color fldg map (sl repaired, tipped in), 7 plts (1 hand-colored), 1 section. Orig dec bds (rebacked). *Hollett.* $136/£85

POSTLETHWAITE, JOHN. Mines and Mining in the Lake District. Leeds: Samuel Moxon, 1889. 2nd ed. x,(i),101,(xi)pp; fldg map. Grn cl (rear bd sl cockled). *Hollett.* $192/£120

POTE, WILLIAM, JR. Journal of Captain William Pote, Jr. During His Captivity in the French and Indian War from May, 1745, to August. 1747. (By William Pote.) NY: Dodd, Mead, 1896. Ltd to 350. Fldg map. Orig morocco-backed bds. *Christie's*.* $72/£45

POTOCKI OF MONTALK, COUNT. Snobbery with Violence. Wishart, 1932. 1st Eng ed. VG in wrappers (sl creased, mkd, spine sl faded). *Ulysses.* $40/£25

POTOCKI OF MONTALK, GEOFFREY. Surprising Songs. Columbia Press, 1930. 1st Eng ed. Good (spine faded, label chipped, ends bumped). *Ulysses.* $56/£35

POTOK, CHAIM. The Name Is Asher Lev. NY: Knopf, 1972. 1st ed. (Eps sl foxed), else Fine in Fine dj. *Between The Covers.* $45/£28

POTOUS, P. L. My Enemy, the Crocodile. NY: Funk, 1957. 1st ed. NF in VG dj. *Mikesh.* $30/£19

POTTER, ALONZO and GEORGE B. EMERSON. The School and the Schoolmaster. NY: Harper, 1842. 1st ed. 2 vols in 1. (12),264; (265)-552pp; 12 woodcut plts, plans. Contemp black calf over black cl. (Foxed; sl rubbed.) *Karmiole.* $175/£109

POTTER, BEATRIX. Beatrix Potter's Journal. London: Warne, 1986. 1st ed thus. 13 plts. VG in dj. *Hollett.* $32/£20

POTTER, BEATRIX. Cecily Parsley's Nursery Rhymes. London: Frederick Warne, (1922). 1st ed. 53pp; 14 full-pg color plts. Correct eps, identifying bk as 1st ed. Red bds, white lettering, blind-stamped box surrounding full color paste label fr cvr. Good in ptd glassine dj (marginal tears, long tear rear cvr), ptd flaps; rear cvr lists Cecily Parsley's Nursery Rhymes. *Reisler.* $2,000/£1,250

POTTER, BEATRIX. The Fairy Caravan. Phila: David McKay, (1929). 1st Amer ed. Sm 4to. 225pp; 6 full-pg color illus. Dk grn cl, pict label. VG (spine top rubbed). *Davidson.* $450/£281

POTTER, BEATRIX. The Fairy Caravan. Phila: David McKay, (1929). 1st ed. 8vo. Grn cl, pict color paste label. Good in full color dj (edges lt dusty, few marginal tears). *Reisler.* $750/£469

POTTER, BEATRIX. Ginger and Pickles. London: Frederick Warne, 1909. 1st ed. Sq 8vo. 51pp. Pict eps. Beige paper-cvrd bds, onlaid pict label to fr bd. Clean. *Sotheran.* $589/£368

POTTER, BEATRIX. The Jemima Puddleduck Pop-Up Book. England: Frederick Warne, 1985. 3 dbl-pg pop-ups, 2 single pop-ups by Colin Twinn. Glazed pict bds. VG. *Bookfinders.* $50/£31

POTTER, BEATRIX. Peter Rabbit's Almanac for 1929. NY: Frederick Warne, 1928. 1st Amer ed. 16mo. Buff bds (edges sl rubbed), brn lettering, color paste label. *Reisler.* $485/£303

POTTER, BEATRIX. Peter Rabbit's Painting Book. NY: Frederick Warne, (ca 1910s). 8.25x7. Pict bds. (Spine perishing, cvrs sl insect-damaged), else VG. *Pacific*.* $86/£54

POTTER, BEATRIX. Peter Rabbit. Chicago: Hall & McCreary, (1918). 12mo. Florence Nosworthy (illus). 32pp. Pict cl (lt worn), mtd on paper. *Reisler.* $85/£53

POTTER, BEATRIX. Peter Rabbit. Racine: Whitman, 1936. Lg 4to. 14 full-pg color illus by Jo Musial. Good in linen-like paper wrappers (cvr lt mkd, spine sl worn), full color illus. *Reisler.* $100/£63

POTTER, BEATRIX. The Roly-Poly Pudding. London: Frederick Warne, 1908. 1st ed, 1st issue. Sq 8vo. (viii),69pp (thumbed, 1-inch neat triangle lower corner 1 pg expertly restored). Red grained cl, gilt. *Sotheran.* $637/£398

POTTER, BEATRIX. The Story of Miss Moppet. London: Frederick Warne, (1913). 1st ed in bk form. 12mo. (vii),8-52pp. Gray paper-cvrd bds, round pict label to upper cvr. Very Clean (2-cm closed tear to fore-edge margin 1 leaf; spine sl browned). *Sotheran.* $637/£398

POTTER, BEATRIX. The Story of Peter Rabbit. Racine: Whitman, (1934). 12mo. Nina, R. Jordan (illus). Color pict bds. Good. *Reisler.* $75/£47

POTTER, BEATRIX. The Tailor of Gloucester. NY: Frederick Warne, 1903. 5 1/2 x 4. Steel blue bds, pict cvr label. (Sm spot fr cvr), else VG. *Pacific*.* $109/£68

POTTER, BEATRIX. The Tailor of Gloucester. London: Frederick Warne, 1903. Deluxe ed. 1st ed sheets (bound w/4 copies of single pg eps) bound in a deluxe cl binding. 16mo. Art fabric, flower patterned cl (spine faded, rear hinge sl weak; sl mkd internally), gilt. *Reisler.* $2,500/£1,563

POTTER, BEATRIX. The Tailor of Gloucester. NY: Frederick Warne, 1968. Ltd to 1500 numbered. 8vo. 12 color illus. Black cl, gilt. VG in full color pict slipcase (edges worn). *Reisler.* $100/£63

POTTER, BEATRIX. The Tailor of Gloucester. Warne, 1970. 1st ed. 7x9. 64pp. VG (bkpl) in Good dj. *Price.* $25/£16

POTTER, BEATRIX. The Tailor of Gloucester. London: Strangeways & Sons Ptrs, (Privately Published), December 1902. 1st ed. Ltd to 500. 16mo. Color frontis, 15 plts. (Eps, few pp lt spotted.) Pink paper bds (few lt spots). *Christie's*.* $3,680/£2,300

POTTER, BEATRIX. The Tale of Ginger and Pickles. London: Frederick Warne, (ca 1945). 16mo. Orig paper-cvrd bds, color pict pastedown. Fine in dj (lt worn). *Glenn.* $40/£25

POTTER, BEATRIX. The Tale of Johnny Town Mouse. London: Frederick Warne, (1918). 1st ed. 16mo. (viii),9-84pp. Teg. 1/2 dk grn calf (newly rebound), spine w/5 raised bands, gilt. Orig cvr, pict eps bound in at rear. *Sotheran.* $317/£198

POTTER, BEATRIX. The Tale of Little Pig Robinson. Phila: David McKay, (1930). 1st Amer ed. 8vo. 141pp; 6 color plts. Pict eps. Grn cl (spine faded). VG. *Davidson.* $350/£219

POTTER, BEATRIX. The Tale of Mr. Jeremy Fisher. London: Frederick Warne, (ca 1945). 16mo. Orig paper-cvrd bds, color pict pastedown. Fine in dj (lt worn). *Glenn.* $40/£25

POTTER, BEATRIX. The Tale of Mr. Jeremy Fisher. London: Frederick Warne, 1906. 1st ed, 1st or 2nd ptg. Color frontis, 26 plts. Gray-grn paper bds. Good. *Christie's*.* $883/£552

POTTER, BEATRIX. The Tale of Mrs. Tiggy-Winkle. London: Frederick Warne, (ca 1945). 16mo. Orig paper-cvrd bds, pict pastedown. Fine in dj (lt worn). *Glenn.* $40/£25

POTTER, BEATRIX. The Tale of Mrs. Tiggy-Winkle. London: Frederick Warne, 1905. 1st ed, 1st or 2nd ptg. 16mo. Color frontis, 26 plts. Brn paper bds (outer margin of fr cvr lt damp-stained, sm stain to rear cvr; inscrip). *Christie's*.* $478/£299

POTTER, BEATRIX. The Tale of Mrs. Tiggy-Winkle. London: Frederick Warne, 1905. 24mo. Brn bds, pict paste label. Clean. *Reisler.* $750/£469

POTTER, BEATRIX. The Tale of Mrs. Tittlemouse. London: Frederick Warne, (1912). 1st ed. 12mo. (vii),8-84pp. Cream bds, pict label to upper cvr. VG in ptd glassine wrapper (tears, loss) *Sotheran.* $269/£168

POTTER, BEATRIX. The Tale of Mrs. Tittlemouse. London: Frederick Warne, 1910. 1st ed, early ptg. 16mo. Color frontis, 26 plts (lt soiled). Blue-gray paper bds (lower joints cracked, spine chipped, 2 sm wormholes to fr cvr). *Christie's*.* $64/£40

POTTER, BEATRIX. The Tale of Peter Rabbit. London: Frederick Warne, (1902). 1st trade ed. 16mo. Silver-gray floral eps. Dk gray bds (spine ends repaired), full color paste label (chip to lower edge). *Reisler.* $3,000/£1,875

POTTER, BEATRIX. The Tale of Peter Rabbit. London: Frederick Warne, (1902). 1st ed. 16mo. Dk gray bds, white lettering, color pict vignette of Peter Rabbit running to the right set in blind-stamped area on fr cvr; letters O have dot in center. VG (1902 inscrip; invisibly recased). *Reisler.* $4,000/£2,500

POTTER, BEATRIX. The Tale of Peter Rabbit. London: Frederick Warne, (October-December 1902). 1st Warne ed, early ptg, w/'wept big tears' on p51 and leaf-pattern eps. 16mo. Color frontis, 30 color plts. (Lt soiled, sl ink mks to pp8, 9; blue pencil doodles reps.) Lt brn cl w/red lettering, mtd pict label fr cvr (lt rubbed, upper joint broken). *Christie's*.* $1,104/£690

POTTER, BEATRIX. The Tale of Peter Rabbit. Phila: Henry Altemus, 1904. Pict cl. VG. *Pacific*.* $316/£198

POTTER, BEATRIX. The Tale of Peter Rabbit. London: Strangeways & Sons Ptrs, (Privately Published), February 1902. 1st ed, 2nd ptg. Ltd to 200. 16mo. Color frontis. (Lacks prelim blank, upper stitching of gathering B loose, lt spotting at beginning; inscrip to frontis verso.) Olive-grn paper bds, rounded back (spine, extrems lt faded, fr cvr lt spotted). *Christie's*.* $5,152/£3,220

POTTER, BEATRIX. The Tale of Pigling Bland. London: Frederick Warne, 1913. 1st ed. 12mo. (vi),7-93pp. Pinkish bds, onlaid pict plt to upper cvr. (Sl lightened, rubbed.) *Sotheran.* $560/£350

POTTER, BEATRIX. The Tale of the Faithful Dove. NY: Frederick Warne, (1956). 1st ed. 12mo. Wheat cl, blue lettering. Good in illus dj (lt dusty). *Reisler.* $175/£109

POTTER, BEATRIX. The Tale of the Faithful Dove. NY: Frederick Warne, (1970). 1st ed illus by Marie Angel. 12mo. Blue pict bds. VG in full color dj (sl line fr cvr). *Reisler.* $100/£63

POTTER, BEATRIX. The Tale of the Flopsy Bunnies. London: Frederick Warne, 1909. 1st ed. 16mo. (vii),8-84pp. Greenish-gray paper-cvrd bds, onlaid pict vignette. Excellent (sm spine bruise, sm splits). *Sotheran.* $560/£350

POTTER, BEATRIX. The Tale of the Pie and the Patty Pan. London: Frederick Warne, (ca 1945). 16mo. Orig paper-cvrd bds, color pict pastedown. Fine in dj (lt worn). *Glenn.* $40/£25

POTTER, BEATRIX. The Tale of Timmy Tiptoes. London: Frederick Warne, 1911. 1st ed. 16mo. (vii),8-84pp. Pict eps. Lt brn paper-cvrd bds, onlaid paper label to upper cvr. Very Nice (spine sl rubbed). *Sotheran.* $520/£325

POTTER, BEATRIX. The Tale of Tom Kitten. London: Frederick Warne, 1907. 1st ed. 16mo. Gray-blue bds, color paste label. Good. *Reisler.* $675/£422

POTTER, BEATRIX. The Tale of Tom Kitten. London: Frederick Warne, 1907. 1st ed. 12mo. (vii),8-84pp. Greenish-brn paper-cvrd bds, onlaid pict label. VG (sl lightened near spine, sm strip upper edge). *Sotheran.* $680/£425

POTTER, BEATRIX. The Tale of Tuppenny. NY: Frederick Warne, (1973). 1st ed thus. 12mo. 40pp; 19 full color illus by Marie Angel. Illus grn cl. Good. *Reisler.* $85/£53

POTTER, BEATRIX. Wag-by-Wall. Boston: Horn Book, 1944. 1st ed. J. J. Lankes (illus). 6 1/4 x 4 1/2. Tipped-in frontisport. Pict cvr label. VG in dj (lacks pieces from spine, corners). *Pacific*.* $109/£68

POTTER, DENNIS. Blackeyes. Faber, 1987. 1st ed. (Edges sl yellowed), else NF in NF dj. *Any Amount.* $38/£24

POTTER, DENNIS. Potter on Potter. G. Fuller (ed). Faber, 1993. 1st ed. Fine in Fine dj. *Whiteson.* $24/£15

POTTER, DENNIS. Son of Man. Deutsch, 1970. 1st ed. NF in VG + dj (rear panel sl soiled, sm closed tear). *Any Amount.* $45/£28

POTTER, DENNIS. Ticket to Ride. Faber, 1986. 1st ed. Potter's signature tipped in. Fine in Fine dj. *Whiteson.* $64/£40

POTTER, DONALD. My Time with Eric Gill: A Memoir. Kenilworth: Walter Ritchie, 1980. 1st ed. One of 500. Dec cl. Fine. *Maggs.* $40/£25

POTTER, JACK M. Cattle Trails of the Old West. Clayton, NM: Laura Krehbiel, 1939. 2nd ed. VG in wrappers. Howes P512. *Labordo.* $125/£78

POTTER, JOHN. Archaeologia Graeca, or the Antiquities of Greece. Edinburgh: Stirling & Slade, 1820. New ed. 2 vols. xv,527,(16)index; vi,422,112 (appendix),(24)indexes and errata pp; fldg map (top margin shaved barely touching border). 1/2 calf (worn, spine chipped, needs rebacking). *Zubal**. $50/£31

POTTER, STEPHEN. D. H. Lawrence. Jonathan Cape, 1930. 1st ed. 3 plts. Good (inscrip). *Cox.* $24/£15

POTTINGER, GEORGE. Muirfield and the Honourable Company. Edinburgh: Scottish Academic, 1972. 1st ed. Frontis. NF (emb stamp) in dj. *Pacific**. $86/£54

POTTLE, FREDERICK A. Boswell and the Girl from Botany Bay. NY, 1937. One of 500 numbered. Cl-backed patterned bds. VG (name) in slipcase (sl rubbed). *Clearwater.* $104/£65

POTTOR, SAMUEL. Handbook of Materia Medica, Pharmacy, and Therapeutics. Phila, 1897. 6th ed. 900pp. Full leather. *Fye.* $50/£31

POTTS, JEAN. The Trash Stealer. Scribner, 1967. 1st ed. (Edges lt worn), else NF in dj (lt used). *Murder.* $45/£28

POTTS, JOHN FAULKNER. Letters from America. London: James Spelrs, 1880. Only ed. pp viii,303,(8) ads. Pict cl. *Mott.* $25/£16

POUCHER, W. A. Escape to the Hills. Country Life, 1943. 1st ed. (Feps lt spotted.) *Hollett.* $40/£25

POUCHER, W. A. The Magic of Skye. Chapman & Hall, 1949. 1st ed. Fine in dj (price-clipped). *Hollett.* $152/£95

POUCHER, W. A. The Scottish Peaks. Constable, 1974. 4th ed. 32 maps. VG in dj. *Hollett.* $24/£15

POUCHER, W. A. Wanderings in Wales. Country Life, 1949. 1st ed. VG in dj (worn, torn, sl loss, neatly repaired). *Hollett.* $64/£40

POULIK, JOSEF. Prehistoric Art. F. Finlayson Samsour (trans). London: Spring Books, n.d. Orig ed in English. 189 monochrome photo plts (22 full color). Pict cl. Fine in dj, pub's slipcase (worn). *Turtle Island.* $60/£38

POULSEN, FREDERIK. Greek and Roman Portraits in English Country Houses. Oxford: Clarendon, 1923. Frontis, 112 plts. Emb cl, gilt. (Sm spine tears, sl shelfworn), o/w Fine. *Archaeologia.* $350/£219

POULSOM, NEVILLE. The White Ribbon: A Medallic Record of British Polar Exploration. London: B.A. Seaby, 1968. Fine in dj. *Explorer.* $96/£60

POULTON, HELEN J. Index to History of Nevada, 1881. Reno: Univ of NV, 1966. 1st ed. Orange wrappers (spotted, rubbed). NF. *Harrington.* $50/£31

POUND, D. J. The Drawing-Room Portrait Gallery of Eminent Personages. London: John Tallis, 1860. 1st ed. Folio. 40 steel-engr ports. Aeg. Grn cl, gilt. (Corners rubbed, spine ends chipped, fr joint cracked through), else VG-. *Pacific**. $40/£25

POUND, EZRA and E. FENOLLOSA. The Chinese Written Character as a Medium for Poetry. Nott, 1936. 1st ed. NF in VG dj (lt soiled). *Fine Books.* $235/£147

POUND, EZRA. Canto CX. (Paris: Herne, 1967.) 1st ed thus. One of 224. Fine in wrappers. *Pacific**. $63/£39

POUND, EZRA. The Cantos. NY: New Directions, 1948. 1st collected ed. NF in VG + dj (spine sl tanned, few sm chips). *Lame Duck.* $200/£125

POUND, EZRA. Canzoni of Ezra Pound. London: Elkin Matthews, 1911. 1st ed. Brn bds, gilt. VG (bkpl, sl foxed; spine top chipped, spine, joints, edges worn). *Heritage.* $500/£313

POUND, EZRA. Cathay. London: Elkin Mathews, 1915. 1st ed. (Sl soil), else NF in ptd wrappers. *Pacific**. $207/£129

POUND, EZRA. Cathay. LEC, 1992. One of 300 signed by Francesco Clemente (illus). Fine in slipcase. *Swann**. $1,265/£791

POUND, EZRA. The Classic Anthology Defined by Confucius. Cambridge: Harvard Univ, 1954. 1st Amer ed. Fine (spine, edge lt sunned, sm spine chip). *Polyanthos.* $25/£16

POUND, EZRA. Drafts and Fragments of Cantos CX-CXVII. (NY): New Directions/Stone Wall, (1968). One of 310 signed. Folio. Fine in pub's slipcase. *Felcone.* $600/£375

POUND, EZRA. Homage to Sextus Propertius. London: Faber & Faber, 1934. 1st separate, sl rev ed. (Feps offset), else NF in VG + dj (1-inch edge tear). *Lame Duck.* $350/£219

POUND, EZRA. How to Read. London: Desmond Harmsworth, (1931). 1st ed. Fine in dj (sm interior mend, chip spine head). *Pharos.* $250/£156

POUND, EZRA. The Letters of Ezra Pound, 1907-1941. D. D. Paige (ed). NY: Harcourt, Brace, (1950). 1st ed, w/advance copy slip affixed to fep. Top edge stained yellow. Brn cl, gilt. (Spine ends sl rubbed), o/w Fine in dj (edges sl creased). *Heritage.* $150/£94

POUND, EZRA. Lustra. London, 1916. 1st ed, 2nd imp. Tan cl lettered in blue. *Swann**. $103/£64

POUND, EZRA. Lustra. NY: Knopf, 1917. 1st Amer trade ed. Yellow ptd bds. (Spine crown chipped, sl soiled), else Fine. *Macdonnell.* $150/£94

POUND, EZRA. Lustra. NY: Knopf, 1917. 1st Amer ed, 2nd imp. Yellow bds (sl soiled), lettered in blue. Cl fldg case, leather title label. *Black Sun.* $450/£281

POUND, EZRA. Personae. London: Elkin Mathews, 1909. 1st ed. VF in moth-brn bds, gilt. *Bromer.* $750/£469

POUND, EZRA. The Pisan Cantos. (NY): New Directions, (1948). 1st ed. Black cl. NF in fiber-type dj (edges lt tanned, 2 sm chips). *Reese.* $275/£172

POUND, EZRA. Poems 1918-21. NY: Boni & Liveright, (1921). 1st ed. (Initials; cvrs soiled, aged; lacks dj), else VG. *Pharos.* $125/£78

POUND, EZRA. Pound/Joyce: Letters of Ezra Pound to James Joyce.... NY: ND, (1967). 1st ed. One of 2900. VG (sig) in Good dj (soiled, worn). *Agvent.* $50/£31

POUND, EZRA. Pound/Joyce: The Letters of Ezra Pound to James Joyce, with Pound's Essays on Joyce. Forrest Read (ed). London: Faber & Faber, 1968. 1st Eng ed. NF (spine ends sl bumped) in dj (sl rubbed, edges sl creased). *Ulysses.* $72/£45

POUND, EZRA. Quia Pauper Amavi. London: Egoist, (1919). 1st ed. One of 500 ptd. 1/2 cl, paper spine label. Good (corners rubbed, spine ends chipped, label rubbed). *Pacific**. $109/£68

POUND, EZRA. A Quinzaine for This Yule. (Charlottesville, 1984.) 1st authorized Amer rpt. One of 500. VG + in sewn wraps. *Pharos.* $20/£13

POUND, REGINALD. The Strand Magazine 1891-1950. Heinemann, 1966. 1st ed. Frontis. (Ex-lib.) Dj. *Forest.* $29/£18

POURADE, RICHARD F. The History of San Diego. Volume One: The Explorers. San Diego: Union-Tribune, 1960. Special ed. Signed by Pourade & James Copley (pub). Tan linen, gilt. Fine in pict slipcase. *Pacific**. $23/£14

POURADE, RICHARD F. The History of San Diego. Volume Six: The Rising Tide. San Diego: Union-Tribune, (1967). Special ed. Signed by Pourade & James Copley (pub). Tan linen, gilt. Fine in pict slipcase. *Pacific**. $23/£14

POURADE, RICHARD F. The History of San Diego. Volume Two: Time of the Bells. San Diego: Union-Tribune, 1960. 1st ed. Tan linen, gilt. Fine in pict dj. *Pacific**. $23/£14

POWELL, ANTHONY. Agents and Patients. Duckworth, 1936. 1st UK ed. Good (bkpl; cvrs worn, faded, mkd, spine hinge repaired, spine extrems sl frayed). *Williams.* $136/£85

POWELL, ANTHONY. At Lady Molly's. Boston, 1957. 1st Amer ed. NF in NF dj. *Warren.* $35/£22

POWELL, ANTHONY. Books Do Furnish a Room. London, 1971. 1st ed. Fine in Fine dj. *Polyanthos.* $40/£25

POWELL, ANTHONY. Casanova's Chinese Restaurant. Heinemann, 1960. 1st UK ed. VG in dj. *Williams.* $88/£55

POWELL, ANTHONY. Dance to the Music of Time. Heinemann, 1951-1975. 1st UK ed. 12 vols. Vol 1 is NF in VG dj (closed tear to fr panel). Other vols NF in dj. *Williams.* $4,000/£2,500

POWELL, ANTHONY. Hearing Secret Harmonies. Boston: Little Brown, 1975. 1st US ed. Fine in Fine dj. *Pettler.* $20/£13

POWELL, ANTHONY. Hearing Secret Harmonies. London, 1975. 1st ed. Fine in dj (sm tear, price-clipped). *Polyanthos.* $35/£22

POWELL, ANTHONY. Hearing Secret Harmonies. London: Heinemann, 1975. 1st ed. Signed. (Spine lettering off-register), o/w NF in dj (coffee cup ring on verso fr panel). *Lame Duck.* $250/£156

POWELL, ANTHONY. John Aubrey and His Friends. London, 1948. 1st Eng ed. Nice (inscrip) in dj (sl torn, chipped, rubbed). *Clearwater.* $120/£75

POWELL, ANTHONY. The Kindly Ones. Boston: Little, Brown, (1962). 1st US ed. (Sm sticker mk ep), else Fine in VG white dj (lt dust-mkd, ink price inner flap). *Reese.* $35/£22

POWELL, ANTHONY. The Kindly Ones. London: Heinemann, (1962). 1st ed. Fine in dj (price-clipped, sm closed tear spine head). *Agvent.* $125/£78

POWELL, ANTHONY. The Military Philosophers. London, 1968. 1st ed. Fine (spine sl creased) in dj (spine sl sunned, creased, price-clipped). *Polyanthos.* $50/£31

POWELL, ANTHONY. The Military Philosophers. Heinemann, 1968. 1st UK ed. Fine in NF dj. *Williams.* $64/£40

POWELL, ANTHONY. The Military Philosophers. London: Heinemann, 1968. 1st ed. Inscribed, signed. Fine in dj. *Lame Duck.* $275/£172

POWELL, ANTHONY. The Soldier's Art. Heinemann, 1966. 1st UK ed. Fine in dj. *Williams.* $77/£48

POWELL, ANTHONY. Temporary Kings. London, 1973. 1st ed. Fine in Fine dj. *Polyanthos.* $40/£25

POWELL, ANTHONY. Temporary Kings. Heinemann, 1973. 1st UK ed. NF in dj. *Williams.* $48/£30

POWELL, ANTHONY. The Valley of Bones. Heinemann, 1964. 1st UK ed. Fine in VG + dj (price-clipped, spine ends sl worn). *Williams.* $96/£60

POWELL, COLIN and JOSEPH E. PERSICO. My American Journey. NY: Random House, 1995. 1st ed. Signed by Powell. VF in VF dj. *Unger.* $125/£78

POWELL, CUTHBERT. Twenty Years of Kansas City's Live Stock Trade and Traders. Kansas City, MO: Pearl Ptg, 1893. 1st ed, 2nd state. Fine. Howes P523. *Labordo.* $450/£281

POWELL, DAWN. A Cage for Lovers. London: W.H. Allen, 1958. 1st Eng ed. Fine in VG + dj (lt worn, few sm tears, sl rubbed). *Between The Covers.* $125/£78

POWELL, DAWN. The Golden Spur. NY: Viking, 1962. 1st ed. Fine in Fine dj. *Beasley.* $50/£31

POWELL, DAWN. The Locusts Have No King. NY: Scribner, 1948. 1st ed. Fine in NF dj (spine sl faded, sl rubbed). *Between The Covers.* $275/£172

POWELL, DAWN. A Time to Be Born. NY: Scribner, 1942. 1st ed. NF in VG dj (chipped). *Warren.* $50/£31

POWELL, DILYS. Descent from Parnassus. Cresset, 1934. 1st ed, 1st bk. Inscribed. Brn cl. (Spine, edges faded), else VG. *Any Amount.* $26/£16

POWELL, E. ALEXANDER. Fighting in Flanders. NY: Scribner, 1914. 1st ed. Frontis. Straw cl stamped in red/black. Fine in pict dj (sm chip spine crown, sm creased edge tear top rear panel). *Reese.* $65/£41

POWELL, G. HAROLD. Letters from the Orange Empire. L.A.: Hist Soc of Southern CA, 1990. Ltd to 100 signed by L. C. Powell. Fine. *Book Market.* $40/£25

POWELL, HORACE B. The Original Had This Signature—W. K. Kellogg. Englewood Cliffs, NJ, (1956). 1st ed. Color frontis. NF. *Sagebrush.* $35/£22

POWELL, JOHN J. The Golden State and Its Resources. SF: Bacon, 1874. 1st ed. xi,(2),14-219,(1),(2,ads)pp. Purple cl, gilt. Fine (sig; spine faded, ends, corners sl rubbed). *Argonaut.* $125/£78

POWELL, JOHN WESLEY and ELIOT PORTER. Down the Colorado. NY, 1969. Rpt. Folio. VG in dj. *Dumont.* $65/£41

POWELL, JOHN WESLEY. Exploration of the Colorado River of the West. Washington, 1875. xi,291pp; fldg map, fldg profile in rear pocket. (Sl browned; rebound), else VG. Howes P525. *Dumont.* $450/£281

POWELL, JOHN WESLEY. Report on the Lands of the Arid Region of the United States. Wallace Stegner (ed). Cambridge, 1962. 2 fldg maps. VG in dj (sl used, lt stained). *King.* $35/£22

POWELL, JOHN WESLEY. Report on the Lands of the Arid Region of the United States.... Wallace Stegner (ed). Cambridge: Harvard Univ, 1962. 1st ed thus. VG in dj (sl dampstaining upper corners). *Pacific**. $86/£54

POWELL, LAWRENCE CLARK. Bookman's Progress. L.A.: Ward Ritchie, 1958. Signed. VG in dj (clipped). *Dumont.* $55/£34

POWELL, LAWRENCE CLARK. Books West Southwest. L.A.: Ward Ritchie, 1957. (Sl cocked), else VG. *Dumont.* $55/£34

POWELL, LAWRENCE CLARK. Heart of the Southwest: A Selective Bibliography.... L.A.: Dawson's Book Shop, 1955. Ptd bds, cl spine. Dj, glassine. *Dawson.* $150/£94

POWELL, LAWRENCE CLARK. A Passion for Books. Cleveland: World, (1958). 1st ed. One of 975. Cl-backed bds. NF in glassine, slipcase. *Pacific**. $58/£36

POWELL, LAWRENCE CLARK. The Southwest of the Bookman. L.A., 1959. Inscribed by a contributor. VG. *Dumont.* $75/£47

POWELL, LYMAN P. Historic Towns of the Southern States. Putnam, 1900. VG-. *Book Broker.* $35/£22

POWELL, NICOLAS. From Baroque to Rococo. London: Faber & Faber, 1959. 4 color plts, 2 maps, 9 plans. (Feps lt browned.) Dj (chipped, browned). *Edwards.* $48/£30

POWELL, PADGETT. Edisto. NY: FSG, (1984). 1st ed, 1st bk. Fine in Fine dj. *Dermont.* $35/£22

POWELL, PADGETT. A Woman Named Drown. NY, (1987). 1st ed. VG in dj. *King.* $15/£9

POWER, D'ARCY (ed). A System of Syphilis. London, 1908. 1st ed. 6 vols. VG set (lib stamps, spine #). *Fye.* $300/£188

POWER, H. et al (eds). A Biennial Retrospect of Medicine, Surgery, and Their Allied Sciences, for 1873-74. New Sydenham Soc, 1875. vi,557pp. Blind-stamped cl. (Label removed, sm lib stamps; spine top sl defective), o/w VG. *Whitehart.* $40/£25

POWER, JOHN. A Handy-Book About Books, for Book-Lovers, Book-Buyers, and Book-Sellers. John Wilson, 1870. 1st ed. Half-title present, xiv,(ii),217,(1)blank,(16),(1)pp; 8 litho facs plts, errata leaf present, slip ptd in black/red tipped in. Grn chalked eps. Grn cl-backed color/gold litho bds. Good (cl dulled, sm string-mk on fore-edge of rear bd). *Blackwell's.* $144/£90

POWER, W. TYRONE. Impressions of America, During the Years 1833, 1834, and 1835. London: Richard Bentley, 1836. 1st ed. 2 vols. 2 engr plts. Orig brn bds (expertly rebacked, eps renewed). *Appelfeld*. $250/£156

POWER, W. TYRONE. Sketches in New Zealand, with Pen and Pencil. London: Longman, Brown et al, 1849. xlviii,290pp (lib stamp); 8 tinted plts. New 1/2 calf, marbled bds, red label. *Adelson*. $385/£241

POWERS, ALFRED (ed). Buffalo Adventures on the Western Plains. Portland: Binfords & Mort, 1945. 1st ed. (Bkpl), else Fine in VG dj. *Perier*. $30/£19

POWERS, ALFRED. Early Printing in the Oregon Country. (1933). Ltd to 500. VG. *Perier*. $45/£28

POWERS, BOB. North Fork Country. L.A.: Westernlore, 1974. 1st ed. Signed. *Book Market*. $40/£25

POWERS, BOB. South Fork Country. L.A.: Westernlore, 1971. 1st ed. Signed. *Book Market*. $40/£25

POWERS, RICHARD. The Gold Bug Variation. London: Scribner, 1991. 1st ed. Fine in dj. *Smith*. $60/£38

POWERS, RICHARD. Operation Wandering Soul. NY: William Morrow, 1993. 1st ed. Fine in NF dj. *Lame Duck*. $75/£47

POWERS, STEPHEN. Afoot and Alone. Hartford, CT: Columbian Book Co, 1872. 1st ed. VG (spine top tender). Howes P537. *Labordo*. $200/£125

POWERS, STEPHEN. Afoot and Alone; A Walk from Sea to Sea. Hartford, CT: Columbian Book Co, 1872. 1st ed. 327pp. (Worn, sl cocked), else Good. Howes P537. *Dumont*. $195/£122

POWERS, STEPHEN. Tribes of California. U.S. Geographical and Geological Survey of the Rocky Mountain Region. Vol III. Washington: GPO, 1877. 1st ed. 635pp; lg fldg color map in rear pocket. VG (spine ends expertly repaired). *House*. $220/£138

POWERS, TIM. An Epitaph in Rust. Cambridge: NESFA Press, 1989. One of 225 numbered, signed by Powers, Tom Whitmore (preface), and Jim Gurney (dj). (Sl worn.) Dj, slipcase. *Oinonen**. $50/£31

POWERS, TIM. On Stranger Tides. NY, (1987). One of 150 numbered, signed. 1/2 citron morocco by Denis Gouey as issued. (Sl worn.) *Oinonen**. $50/£31

POWICKE, M. The Thirteenth Century 1216-1307. Oxford: Clarendon, 1953. Blue cl (sl bumped). Dj (edge sl chipped). *Maggs*. $35/£22

POWYS, JOHN COWPER. Atlantis. London: Macdonald, (1954). 1st UK ed. (Fep lt foxed), o/w Fine in VG dj. *Bernard*. $95/£59

POWYS, JOHN COWPER. Dostoievsky. Bodley Head, 1946. 1st ed. Red cl, gilt. VG (eps partly browned) in dj (backstrip panel browned). *Blackwell's*. $80/£50

POWYS, JOHN COWPER. In Defence of Sensuality. Gollancz, 1930. 1st ed. VG (prelims, eps spotted; spine ends, corners sl bumped) in dj (nicked, sl rubbed, mkd, dusty, spine, edges sl browned). *Ulysses*. $120/£75

POWYS, JOHN COWPER. Obstinate Cymric. Essays 1935-47. Carmarthen: Druid, 1947. 1st ed. Inscribed. Red cl (waterstained, spine faded), gilt. *Blackwell's*. $216/£135

POWYS, JOHN COWPER. The War and Culture: A Reply to Professor Munsterberg. NY: G. Arnold Shaw, 1914. 1st ed. Fine. *Reese*. $125/£78

POWYS, LAURENCE. At the Harlot's Burial. (London): Lahr, 1930. 1st ed, 1st bk. Wraps. Fine in orig glassine (lt worn). *Agvent*. $75/£47

POWYS, LITTLE C. The Powys Family. Yeovil, (1952). 1st Eng ed. Signed. Card wrappers. *Clearwater*. $40/£25

POWYS, LLEWELLYN and JOHN C. Confessions of Two Brothers. Rochester: Manas Press, 1916. 1st ed, 1st bk. Blue cl. Ptd paper labels. (Spine label sl worn), o/w Fine. *Reese*. $100/£63

POWYS, LLEWELYN. Henry Hudson. NY: Harper & Bros, 1928. 7 plts. VG. *High Latitude*. $30/£19

POWYS, LLEWELYN. The Letters of Gamel Woolsey to Llewelyn Powys, 1930-1939. Kenneth Hopkins (ed). North Walsham: Warren House, 1983. Fine (name sticker) in dj. *Clearwater*. $40/£25

POWYS, T. F. Black Bryony. London: C&W, 1923. 1st ed. 5 woodcuts. Fine in patterned blue-grn cl. Dj (lt smudged). *Bromer*. $125/£78

POWYS, T. F. Christ in the Cupboard. London: E. Lahr, 1930. 1st ed. One of 500 numbered, signed. Frontis. Untrimmed. Fine in ptd wrappers. *Maggs*. $40/£25

POWYS, T. F. The Dewpond. Woburn Books, 1928. One of 530 signed. Patterned bds. VG (1 corner sl bumped) in dj. *Clearwater*. $88/£55

POWYS, T. F. Fables. Chatto, 1929. 1st ed. Ltd to 750 signed. Teg. Good in dj (dull, sl mkd). *Whiteson*. $112/£70

POWYS, T. F. Feed My Swine. London: E. Archer, 1926. 1st ed. One of 100 numbered, signed. Fine in marbled wrappers. *Maggs*. $136/£85

POWYS, T. F. Goat Green or the Better Gift. (London): Golden Cockerel, 1937. Unltd ed. Grn cl. Fine. *Maggs*. $40/£25

POWYS, T. F. Goat Green.... Golden Cockerel, 1937. 1st ed. Ltd to 150 signed. Leather spine. (Sl faded), else VG. *Whiteson*. $144/£90

POWYS, T. F. Kindness in a Corner. Chatto, 1930. 1st UK ed. VG + (spine lt faded) in dj (sl worn, browned, sm spine loss). *Williams*. $58/£36

POWYS, T. F. Mr. Trasker's Gods. London: C&W, 1925. 1st Eng ed. VG. *Cady*. $25/£16

POWYS, T. F. The Only Penitent. London: C&W, 1931. 1st ed. One of 160 numbered, signed. Teg, rest untrimmed. 1/4 buckram over blue patterned bds. VG. *Maggs*. $56/£35

POWYS, T. F. The Rival Pastors. London: E. Archer, 1927. 1st ed. One of 100 numbered, signed. Wrappers, paper label. (Spine sl dusty), else Fine. *Maggs*. $128/£80

POWYS, T. F. Uncle Dottery, a Christmas Story. Cleverdon, 1930 (but published 1931). 1st ed. One of 300 (of 350) signed. Crown 8vo. 24pp; 2 wood engrs by Eric Gill. Untrimmed. 1/4 dk grn buckram, gilt, patterned bottle-grn/white bds. VG (feps browned). *Blackwell's*. $240/£150

POWYS, T. F. Uriah on the Hill. Cambridge: Minority Press, 1930. 1st trade ed. NF in gray wrappers. *Maggs*. $48/£30

POWYS, T. F. Uriah on the Hill. Cambridge: Minority, 1930. 1st ed. One of 85 numbered, signed. Gray-grn cl, gilt. Fine. *Maggs*. $120/£75

POWYS, T. F. The White Paternoster. Chatto, 1930. 1st ed. Ltd to 310 signed. Teg. Internally Good (binding dull, discolored). *Whiteson*. $64/£40

POYNDER, F. S. The 9th Gurkha Rifles 1817-1936. London: Royal United Service Inst, 1937-1953. 1st eds. 2 vols. Super royal 8vo. xviii,275pp, 16 illus, 17 maps; xiii,355, 5 illus, 12 maps (1 full color, 3 fldg). (Prelims, fore-edge vol 1 sl foxed; top edges dusty, bkpls inside fr cvrs), o/w VG in grn cl, backed in black cl w/titles blocked in silver, silver cvr vignette. *Ulysses*. $800/£500

POYNTON, F. J. and A. PAINE. Researches on Rheumatism. NY, 1914. 1st Amer ed. *Fye*. $150/£94

POZZI, S. Treatise on Gynaecology, Medical and Surgical. NY, 1891-1892. 1st ed in English. 2 vols. 581; 583pp; 2 plts. Full leather. VF. *Fye*. $250/£156

POZZO, ANDREA. Rules and Examples of Perspective Proper for Painters and Architects. London, 1707. 1st ed in English. Folio. 2 engr tps, 102 plts, full-pg illus, engr sub's list. Early 19th-cent 1/2 diced russia (covers detached, marginal soiling). Swann*. $1,092/£683

Practical Fisherman: Dealing with the Natural History, the Legendary Lore, and the Capture of British Freshwater Fish. Parts II and III. London: The Bazaar, (c. 1880). 1st ed. 2 vols. Pict wrappers. NF. Pacific*. $58/£36

PRADA, RENATO. The Breach. GC: Doubleday, 1971. 1st ed in Eng. NF in VG dj. Lame Duck. $35/£22

PRAEGER, R. L. Irish Topographical Botany. Dublin, 1901. 6 fldg color maps. Teg. Near Mint. Henly. $218/£136

PRAEGER, S. ROSAMUND. The Adventures of the Three Bold Babies. London: Longmans, Green, 1897. 1st ed. Obl 8vo. (48)pp. Pale pink pict bds backed w/red cl (lt soiled, corners knocked, ring mk upper cvr). Nice. Sotheran. $205/£128

PRAIN, ERIC. The Oxford and Cambridge Golfing Society, 1898-1948. London: Eyre & Spottiswoode, (1949). 1st ed. Blue cl, gilt. (Rubberstamp), else NF in VG dj (extrems sl torn, spine ends chipped). Pacific*. $196/£123

Prairie Crusoe; or, Adventures in the Far West. Boston: Lee & Shepard, 1869. Later ed. 277pp, 6 pp ads. (Shelfworn, edges worn), else Good. Brown. $15/£9

PRASAD, KUNWAR JAGDISH. Monograph on Carpet Making in the United Provinces. Allahabad, 1907. (Lib ink stamps, margins lt browned, sl thumbed; hinges repaired; worn, rebacked, orig spine laid down.) Edwards. $72/£45

PRASSE, LEONA. Lyonel Feininger: A Definitive Catalogue.... Cleveland, (1972). Dj. Swann*. $316/£198

PRASSEL, FRANK RICHARD. The Great American Outlaw. Norman: Univ of OK, (1993). 1st ed. Fine in dj. Lien. $30/£19

PRATCHETT, TERRY. Lords and Ladies. Gollancz, 1992. 1st UK ed. Signed. NF (ink inscrip) in dj. Williams. $22/£14

PRATCHETT, TERRY. Pyramids. Gollancz, 1989. 1st UK ed. Signed. Fine in dj. Williams. $58/£36

PRATCHETT, TERRY. Reaper Man. Gollancz, 1991. 1st UK ed. Fine in dj. Williams. $24/£15

PRATCHETT, TERRY. Truckers. Doubleday, 1989. 1st UK ed. Fine in dj. Williams. $35/£22

PRATT, A. E. To the Snows of Tibet Through China. London: Longmans, Green, 1892. 1st ed. Frontisport, xviii,268pp; 28 full-pg illus, 4 plts, fldg map. (Lt browned; spine sl dknd, chipped w/loss.) Edwards. $352/£220

PRATT, ANNE. The Ferns of Great Britain, and Their Allies. London, n.d. c.(1862). 2nd ed. iv,164pp; 41 color plts. (Sl browned; sl dampstained, spine sl faded, sm split fr joint.) Edwards. $72/£45

PRATT, CLYDE H. The Automobile Instructor. NY: Barse & Hopkins, (1912). 1st ed. Grn cl, gilt. (Fep lacks sm piece), else VG. Pacific*. $40/£25

PRATT, DAVIS (intro). Newly Re-Created: Photographic Printing Processes Revived. (Cambridge): Fogg Art Museum, 1973. 1st ed. 10 b/w photos. (Stamp), else NF in ptd stiff wrappers. Cahan. $30/£19

PRATT, ENOCH. A Comprehensive History, Ecclesiastical and Civil, of Eastham, Welfleet and Orleans, County of Barnstable, Mass. from 1644 to 1844. Yarmouth: W.S. Fisher, 1844. 1st ed. 180pp. Brn cl (worn, esp spine; spine label chipped; foxed). Good. Lucas. $250/£156

PRATT, FLETCHER and L. SPRAGUE DE CAMP. The Incomplete Enchanter. NY, (1941). 1st ed. Fine in dj. Swann*. $149/£93

PRATT, FLETCHER and L. SPRAGUE DE CAMP. Land of Unreason. NY, (1942). 1st ed. Pict dj. Swann*. $172/£108

PRATT, HARRY E. The Personal Finances of Abraham Lincoln. Springfield, IL, 1943. 1st ed. Frontis. Good+. Wantagh. $35/£22

PRATT, PARLEY P. A Voice of Warning and Instruction to All People, or an Introduction to the Faith and Doctrine of the Church of Jesus Christ, of Latter-Day-Saints. Plano, IL: Reorganized Church of Jesus Christ, of Latter-Day-Saints, 1863. Rev ed. 256pp. Period 1/2 cl, mottled bds (1st 8 pp, dampstined, incl tp; rubbed, edgeworn), else Good. Pacific*. $98/£61

PRATT, RICHARD. The Picture Garden Book. NY: Howell, Soskin, 1942. 1st ed. VG in dj (lacks chip, extrems sl rubbed). Smith. $45/£28

PRATT, THEODORE. Perils in Provence. NY: DSP, (1944). 1st ed. Fine in Fine dj (sl worn, lt rubbed, torn, sl loss at crown). Between The Covers. $75/£47

PRATT, WALTER MERRIAM. Adventure in Vermont. Cambridge: CUP, 1943. 1st ed. Inscribed. Frontis. Paper spine label, pict paper label on cvr. Fine in dj (sl chipped). Connolly. $35/£22

PRATT, WALTER MERRIAM. The House of Edward Winslow, Built in the Eighteenth Century at Plymouth Massachusetts. Cambridge, MA, 1949. Only ed. Fine. Bond. $18/£11

Prayers for Children. Little Golden Book. NY: S&S, (1945). 7th ed. 7x8. Rachel Taft Dixon (illus). 38pp. VG (shelfworn) in dj (edgeworn, spine chipped). My Bookhouse. $52/£33

PRAZ, MARIO. Conversation Pieces. London: University Park, 1971. Good+ in dj (sl worn). Washton. $75/£47

PRAZ, MARIO. The House of Life. Angus Davidson (trans). London: Methuen, 1964. 1st Eng ed. (Name), else NF in VG dj (edges sl rubbed). Virgo. $64/£40

PRAZ, MARIO. An Illustrated History of Interior Decoration. Thames & Hudson, 1964. 1st ed. Fine in dj (sl nicked). Ulysses. $152/£95

Precaution, a Novel. (By James Fenimore Cooper.) NY: A.T. Goodrich, 1820. 1st ed. 2 vols. 286; 340pp. Contemp calf. (Tp vol 1 in facs, brnd, toned, 2 leaves vol 2 w/marginal defects affecting text, ink marginalia; worn, vol 2 cvrs detached, spines worn), else Fair. BAL 3825. Brown. $150/£94

PRELINGER, ELIZABETH. Edvard Munch. NY: W. W. Norton, (1983). 115 b/w, 18 color plts. Fine in dj. Turtle Island. $50/£31

PRENTICE, E. PARMALEE. American Dairy Cattle: Their Past and Future. Harper, 1942. Good. Rybski. $50/£31

PRESCOTT, HARRIET ELIZABETH. Axarian: An Episode. Boston: Ticknor & Fields, 1864. 1st ed. 251pp. VG in pub's cl (sl worn). Second Life. $45/£28

PRESCOTT, KENNETH W. The Complete Graphic Works of Ben Shahn. NY: Quadrangle Books, (1973). Orig ed. Nice in dj. Turtle Island. $125/£78

PRESCOTT, PHILANDER. The Recollections of Philander Prescott, Frontiersman of the Old Northwest, 1819-1862. Donald Dean Parker (ed). Lincoln: Univ of NE, 1966. 1st ed. Map. VF in NF dj. Connolly. $37/£23

PRESCOTT, WILLIAM H. History of the Conquest of Mexico. London: Richard Bentley, 1843. 1st Eng ed. 3 vols. Frontis port each vol, xxx,442; xvi,440; xvi,456pp; 2 fldg maps, facs. Teg. 1/2 polished red calf over maroon cl (extrems sl rubbed), gilt, raised bands; bindings signed by 'L. Broca.' Karmiole. $400/£250

PRESCOTT, WILLIAM H. History of the Conquest of Mexico. NY: Harper, 1852. Rpt. 3 vols. 488; 480; 524pp. VG set (foxed; hinges, corners worn). Book Market. $80/£50

PRESCOTT, WILLIAM H. History of the Conquest of Peru. London: Richard Bentley, 1847. 1st ed. 2 vols. Engr frontis ports, xxxvi,480; xx,490pp; map, plt. 1/2 polished maroon calf over pebbled bds, by L. Broca, gilt spines (lt faded), grn morocco labels. Karmiole. $200/£125

PRESCOTT, WILLIAM H. History of the Conquest of Peru. NY: Harper, 1847. 1st ed. 2 vols. Frontisport each vol; map vol 1, facs vol 2. Blind-stamped cl (tips, spine ends worn; few spots on cvrs; lt foxed, tps browned). *Dawson.* $250/£156

PRESCOTT, WILLIAM H. History of the Conquest of Peru. LEC, 1957. Ltd to 1500 numbered, signed by Everett Gee Jackson (illus) and Harry Block (designer). Fine in slipcase. *Swann*.* $57/£36

PRESCOTT, WILLIAM H. History of the Conquest of Peru. Mexico City: LEC, 1957. One of 1500. Signed by Everett Gee Jackson (illus) & Harry Block (Full marbled sheepskin, raised bands, 3 red leather spine labels. Fine in slipcase. *Pacific*.* $69/£43

PRESCOTT, WILLIAM H. History of the Reign of Ferdinand and Isabella, the Catholic of Spain. London: Richard Bentley, 1838. 1st Eng ed. 3 vols. Frontis port each vol, xxviii,460; xxii,562; xx,616pp. Teg. 1/2 polished red calf over maroon cl (extrems sl rubbed), bindings signed 'L. Broca,' gilt spines w/raised bands. *Karmiole.* $350/£219

PRESCOTT, WILLIAM H. History of the Reign of Ferdinand and Isabella. NY: LEC, 1967. One of 1500. Signed by Lima de Freitas (illus). Full leather, gilt-lettered morocco spine labels. Fine in glassine, slipcase. *Pacific*.* $58/£36

Present State of the West-Indies: Containing an Accurate Description of What Parts Are Possessed by the Several Powers in Europe.... London, 1778. 4to. Fldg map, partly colored. Calf. *Felcone.* $1,500/£938

PRESTON, JOHN. Every Man His Own Teacher. Albany, (NY): The Author, 1817. 1st ed. Royal 8vo. 520,(2)pp. Full contemp tree calf, leather label. Fine (hinges cracking). *M & S.* $850/£531

PRESTON, NORMAN (ed). Cricketers' Almanack 1955. Wisden, 1955. (Lib bkpl; upper bd sl creased, sl soiled.) *Edwards.* $29/£18

PRESTON, PAUL. The Fireside Magician. NY: Dick & Fitzgerald, (1870). VG in color pict wraps (lacks rear wrap, corners upper cvr, spine ends chipped). *Dramatis.* $70/£44

PRESTON, RICHARD. Rocky Mountain Trees. Ames: IA State College, 1947. 2nd ed. Fine in dj (dampstained). *Archer.* $25/£16

PRESTWICH, J. Geology: Chemical, Physical and Stratigraphical. London, 1886-88. 2 vols. 5 fldg colored maps, 3 sections, 16 plts. (Skillfully rebacked preserving spines; plts waterstained.) *Henly.* $90/£56

PRETORIUS, P. J. Jungle Man. NY: Dutton, (1948). Good+ in VG dj. *Mikesh.* $25/£16

Pretty ABC. NY: Sheldon & Co, (c. 1861). 7x7. Pict orange/red wrappers. (Name, date; spine rubbed), o/w VG. *Pacific*.* $46/£29

PREUSS, CHARLES. Exploring with Fremont. Norman, 1958. 1st ed. Map. VG in dj. *Dumont.* $40/£25

PRICE, A. GRENFELL. White Settlers in the Tropics. NY: Nat'l Geographic Soc, 1939. Special pub #23. 1st ed. (Lib spine #; sl rubbed), o/w VG. *Worldwide.* $30/£19

PRICE, ALFRED. Rail Life. Toronto: Thomas Allen, (1925). 1st ed. VG in dj. *Lien.* $25/£16

PRICE, CON. Trails I Rode. Pasadena, CA: Trails End, 1947. 1st ed. VF in dj. *Labordo.* $95/£59

PRICE, DOUGHBELLY. Short Stirrups. L.A., 1960. Typed letter laid in. Photo, news stories tipped onto eps. Good in dj (taped). *Dumont.* $45/£28

PRICE, DOUGHBELLY. Short Stirrups: The Story of Doughbelly Price. L.A., 1960. 1st ed. VG in dj (sl worn). *Woolson.* $30/£19

PRICE, LAKE. Interiors and Exteriors in Venice.... (London): T. McLean, 1843. Tinted litho tp, 25 plts by Joseph Nash after Price. (Tp spotted, occasional lt spotting, mainly marginal browning, few short tears.) Orig morocco-backed bds (lacks spine, rubbed). *Christie's*.* $1,080/£675

PRICE, M. PHILIPS. America After Sixty Years. London: George Allen & Unwin, (1936). 1st ed. 2 plts. Dj. *Mott.* $40/£25

PRICE, REYNOLDS. The Annual Heron. NY: Albondocani, 1980. One of 300 numbered, signed. Fine in sewn marbled wrappers. *Dermont.* $60/£38

PRICE, REYNOLDS. Clear Pictures. NY, 1989. 1st Amer ed. Fine in Fine dj. *Polyanthos.* $25/£16

PRICE, REYNOLDS. Lessons Learned: Seven Poems. NY: Albondocani, 1977. 1st ed. One of 226 ptd. Signed, add'lly inscribed, signed. Holograph postcard of Billy Carter, signed, dated 1978 laid-in loose. Fine in stiff marbled wrapper, paper cvr label. *Pacific*.* $63/£39

PRICE, REYNOLDS. The Use of Fire. NY: Atheneum, 1990. 1st ed. Fine in Fine dj. *Dermont.* $20/£13

PRICE, RICHARD. The Wanderers. Boston: Houghton Mifflin, 1974. 1st ed, 1st bk. Fine in dj. *Reese.* $50/£31

PRICE, ROBIN. An Annotated Catalogue of Medical Americana in the Library of the Wellcome Institute for the History of Medicine. Wellcome Institute, 1983. 1st ed. Frontis, 29 facs. *Forest.* $56/£35

PRICE, ROSE LAMBERT. A Summer on the Rockies. London: Sampson, Low, Marston, 1898. 1st ed. Frontisport, x,279pp; fldg map, photo plt. Red cl. (Sl flecked), o/w Fine. Howes P587. *Mott.* $150/£94

PRICE, S. GOODALE. Black Hills the Land of Legend. L.A., 1935. 1st ed. (Extrems lt worn), else Good. *Dumont.* $40/£25

PRICE, T. A Narrative of the Adventures and Escape of Moses Roper, from American Slavery. Phila: Merrihew & Gunn, 1838. 72pp. Wraps (lacks most of spine, edges sl worn, foxed). *Metropolitan*.* $230/£144

PRICE, THOMAS. The Literary Remains of.... Llandovery, 1854-5. 2 vols. Mtd photo frontisports, xvi,400; xii,420pp. Blue blind-emb cl, gilt. (Lt sporadic soil, hinges cracked vol 2; spines chipped w/loss, sm splits vol 2 joints, corners rubbed w/sl cl loss.) *Edwards.* $200/£125

PRICHARD, H. HESKETH. Hunting Camps in Wood and Wilderness. London, 1910. Frontisport. Teg. (Lt marginal browning, fr hinge cracked; spine sl rubbed, faded.) *Edwards.* $80/£50

PRICHARD, H. HESKETH. Through the Heart of Patagonia. NY: D. Appleton, 1902. 1st Amer ed. Fldg map. Red cl, gilt. Fine. *Appelfeld.* $100/£63

PRICHARD, H. HESKETH. Through Trackless Labrador. London: Heinemann, 1911. 54 plts, map. Teg. Dec cl. VG (Sl faded, worn). *High Latitude.* $125/£78

PRIDEAUX, HUMPHREY. The Old and New Testament Connected in the History of the Jews and Neighbouring Nations... London: R. Knaplock & J. Tonson, 1718. 5th ed. 2 vols. 5 maps (4 dbl-pg), dbl-pg plan. Full paneled calf. (Feps loose; worn, rubbed.) *Kane*.* $325/£203

PRIDEAUX, S. T. An Historical Sketch of Bookbinding. Lawrence & Bullen, 1893. 1st ed. Frontis. Uncut. *Forest.* $104/£65

PRIDGEN, TIM. Courage: The Story of Modern Cockfighting. Boston: Little, Brown, 1938. 1st ed. (Spine sunned), else VG. *Pacific*.* $75/£47

PRIEST, ALAN. Aspects of Chinese Painting. NY: Macmillan, 1954. 1st ptg. VG in dj (torn). *Worldwide.* $45/£28

PRIEST, ALAN. The Sculpture of Joseph Coletti. London/NY: Macmillan, 1968. 132 plts. (Sl worn.) *Ars Artis.* $56/£35

PRIEST, JOSIAH. American Antiquities, and Discoveries in the West. Albany: Ptd by Packard, Hoffman, & White, 1833. 1st ed. Lg fldg frontis, viii,(9)-400pp (2 leaves w/sm stain, vertical tear in top of 1 leaf, no loss of text; lt dampstained, few pencil mks). Orig marbled paper sides (worn, crudely rebacked w/black cl, orig red morocco spine label glued inside fr cvr). Howes P592. *Pirages.* $250/£156

PRIESTLEY, J. B. Angel Pavement. Heinemann, 1930. One of 1025 signed. Fine in orig glassine dj w/paper flaps. *Williams.* $128/£80

PRIESTLEY, J. B. The English Comic Characters. London, 1925. 1st Eng ed. Very Nice in dj (sl frayed). *Clearwater.* $72/£45

PRIESTLEY, J. B. I for One. London, 1923. 1st Eng ed. Very Nice in dj (sl nicked, dusty). *Clearwater.* $72/£45

PRIESTLEY, J. B. Jenny Villiers. Heinemann, 1947. 1st UK ed. NF in VG dj. *Martin.* $14/£9

PRIESTLEY, J. B. Midnight on the Desert. London: Heinemann, (1937). 1st ed. Errata slip. Blue cl. Fine. *Mott.* $30/£19

PRIESTLEY, J. B. Thomas Love Peacock. London: Macmillan, 1927. 1st Eng ed. VG (feps partly browned; extrems rubbed, spine ends bumped) in dj (nicked, rubbed, sl torn, mkd, browned). *Ulysses.* $72/£45

PRIESTLEY, J. B. Three Men in New Suits. Heinemann, 1945. 1st UK ed. NF in VG dj. *Martin.* $14/£9

PRIESTLEY, J. B. The Town Major of Miraucourt. London: Heinemann, 1930. 1st ed. One of 525 signed. Teg. Full vellum, gilt. Fine in orig bd slipcase. *Cummins.* $100/£63

PRIESTLEY, JOSEPH. Experiments and Observations on Different Kinds of Air, and Other Branches of Natural Philosophy, Connected with the Subject. Birmingham, 1790. 1st ed thus. 3 vols. 411; 472; 574pp; 9 engr plts. (Hinges weak, one bd detached, spine worn, labels missing). VG internally. *Fye.* $400/£250

PRIESTLEY, JOSEPH. Historical Account of the Navigable Rivers, Canals and Railways of Great Britain.... London: Longman, Rees et al, 1831. 1st ed. Fldg frontis map, xiv,702,viiipp (final index margin neatly repaired); fldg hand-colored section (sm repair to end margin, not affecting surface). Mod 1/2 blue levant morocco, gilt, raised bands, contrasting spine label. *Hollett.* $560/£350

PRIESTLEY, JOSEPH. The History and Present State of Discoveries Relating to Vision, Light, and Colours. London: J. Johnson, 1772. 1st ed. 2 vols in 1, bound w/o vol 2 tp. 4to. 25 fldg engr plts. Early calf (rebacked; tp offset). 1/4 morocco slipcase. Bkpls of John Patrick Crichton Stuart and E.N. da C. Andrade. *Swann*.* $1,265/£791

PRIESTLEY, JOSEPH. The History and Present State of Electricity, with Original Experiments. London: J. Dodsley, J. Johnson & B. Davenport, & T. Cadell, 1767. 1st ed. 4to. (4),31,(1),736,(2),(4)pp; 6 (of 7) fldg plts. Contemp calf (rubbed, hinges tender). VG. *M & S.* $1,350/£844

PRIESTLEY, JOSEPH. The History and Present State of Electricity, with Original Experiments. London: J. Dodsley et al, 1767. 1st ed. 4to. 8 engr plts, incl specimen chart, all but 1 fldg. (Some plts and ll spotted, sl offsetting, sl worming upper outer margin, upper margins pp182-183 ink-stained, stain upper margin about 30 leaves; inscrip.) Sprinkled edges. Contemp calf (rebacked, scuffed). *Christie's*.* $2,160/£1,350

PRIETO, GUILLERMO. San Francisco in the Seventies. Edwin S. Morby (ed). SF: Ptd by John Henry Nash, 1938. 1st ed in English. Ltd to 650. Port. Cl-backed marbled bds, paper spine label. VF in dj. *Argonaut.* $90/£56

PRIME, ALFRED COXE. The Arts and Crafts in Philadelphia, Maryland and South Carolina. 1721-1800. N.p.: Walpole Soc, 1929-1932. One of 500 sets. 2 vols. (Top edge spotted; lt worn.) *Oinonen*.* $160/£100

PRIME, NATHANIEL S. A History of Long Island, From Its First Settlement by Europeans, to the Year 1845.... NY: Robert Carter, 1845. 1st ed. Fldg map frontis (sl offset), xii,420pp + 8pp ads. Black blind dec cl, gilt (rebacked w/orig spine laid down). Internally Clean. Howes P608. *House.* $200/£125

PRIME, SAMUEL I. Under the Trees. NY: Harper, 1874. 1st ed. Brick red cl, gilt. NF. *Pacific*.* $86/£54

PRIME, W. C. I Go A-Fishing. NY: Harper, 1873. 1st ed. Signed, inscribed. 3/4 red morocco, marbled bds, gilt. (Joints, extrems rubbed), else VG. *Pacific*.* $127/£79

PRIME, WENDELL. Fifteenth Century Bibles. NY: Anson D.F. Randolph, 1898. 1st ed. Inscribed. 94,viiipp. Black linen. Good. *Karmiole.* $100/£63

Prince Darling, a Tale. Wellington: Houlston & Son, n.d. (ca 1810). 3rd ed. 16mo. Full-pg frontis, 48pp; 5 full-pg engrs. Stiff yellow paper cvr, dec title label. VG (ink inscrips; glue spots inside cvrs; cvr lt soiled). *Hobbyhorse.* $170/£106

Prince of Abissinia. (By Samuel Johnson.) London: F. & C. Rivington, 1798. 10th ed. viii,304pp (name excised from blank tp margin). Old calf (rebacked). *Young.* $96/£60

PRINCE, F. T. Poems. London: Faber & Faber, 1938. 1st Eng ed, 1st bk. VG (sig; spine ends sl bumped) in dj (sl rubbed, frayed, spine faded). *Ulysses.* $72/£45

PRINCE, L. BRADFORD. A Concise History of New Mexico. Cedar Rapids: Torch, 1912. (Spine neatly taped), else Good. *Dumont.* $100/£63

PRINCE, L. BRADFORD. Historical Sketches of New Mexico. Kansas City: Leggat Bros, 1883. 2nd ed. 327pp. (Lt worn), else NF. *Dumont.* $135/£84

PRINCE, MORTON. The Psychology of the Kaiser. Boston: Badger, 1915. 1st ed. VG (spine dknd). *Beasley.* $60/£38

PRINCE, NORMAN. Roentgen Technique (Diagnostic). St. Louis, 1917. 1st ed. (Margins sl damp wrinkled.) *Fye.* $75/£47

PRINCE, OLIVER H. A Digest of the Laws of the State of Georgia.... Milledgeville: Grantland & Orme, 1822. 669pp (browned, soiled, stained, frayed). Contemp calf (neatly rebacked, rubbed). *Oinonen*.* $110/£69

PRINGLE, A. Practical Photo-Micrography. London: Iliffe, 1902. 3rd ed. VG. *Savona.* $45/£28

PRINSEP, HENRY THOBY. History of the Political and Military Transactions in India During the Administration of the Marquess of Hastings 1813-1823. London, 1825. 2 vols. Contemp 1/2 sheep (extrems worn; hinges reinforced, several maps w/clean tears from gutter into image). *Swann*.* $258/£161

Prints from the Mourlot Press. N.p., (1964). One of 2000. 18 color lithos by Fernand Mourlot (incl outer wrapper). Stiff wrappers, pict outer wrapper. *Swann*.* $316/£198

PRINZING, FRIEDRICH. Epidemics Resulting from Wars. Oxford, 1916. 1st ed. (Ex-lib.) *Fye.* $150/£94

PRIOR, BEATRIX. Lota of the Little Trees. Suttonhouse, 1936. 1st ed. 8vo. Grace Mallon (illus). 136pp. Blue cl. Good + (sl leaning; edges, spine faded). *Price.* $30/£19

PRIOR, JAMES. A Voyage Along the Eastern Coast of Africa, to Mozambique Johanna, and Quiloa. London: Richard Phillips, 1819. 114pp; plt, 2 fldg maps. Mod cl, leather label. VG. *Adelson.* $425/£266

PRIOR, MATTHEW. Poems on Several Occasions. London, 1754. 2 vols. Engr frontispieces. Aeg. Later 1/2 red crushed morocco, gilt. *Swann*.* $115/£72

PRITCHARD, JAMES A. The Overland Diary of, from Kentucky to California in 1849.... Dale L. Morgan (ed). Denver, 1959. 1st ed. Good + in dj. *Wantagh.* $100/£63

PRITCHETT, V. S. George Meredith and English Comedy. London: C&W, 1970. 1st Eng ed. Fine in dj (sl rubbed, nick). *Ulysses.* $72/£45

PRITCHETT, V. S. The Turn of the Years. NY: Random House, (1982). One of 500 numbered, signed. Grn cl. Fine in slipcase. *Antic Hay.* $50/£31

PRITT, THOMAS EVAN. North-Country Flies. London, 1886. 2nd ed. 12 plts (11 hand-colored). Gilt-pict cl (lt worn). *Oinonen*.* $275/£172

PRITT, THOMAS EVAN. Yorkshire Trout Flies. Leeds, 1885. 1st ed. One of 200 ptd. 8vo. 63pp; 11 hand-colored plts, 1 b/w plt. 3/4 morocco (neatly rebacked preserving orig spine, rubbed). *Oinonen**. $600/£375

Proceedings of the Association for Promoting the Discovery of the Interior Part of Africa. London: T. Cadell, 1791. 2nd ed. xvi,351pp,(1)blank + 16pp pub's list; lg fldg map (sl torn). Contemp 1/2 calf, marbled bds. (Lib stamps; rebacked w/grn label, bds sl rubbed.) *Morrell*. $432/£270

PROCTER, ALEXANDER P. Sculptor in Buckskin, an Autobiography. Norman: Univ of OK, (1971). 1st ed. Obl folio. Boxed. *Heinoldt*. $50/£31

PROCTER, MAURICE. The Pennycross Murders. Harper, 1951. 1st Amer ed. NF in dj (piece out at spine head, lt chipped). *Murder*. $27/£17

PROCTOR, HENRY HUGH. Between Black and White. Boston: Pilgrim, 1925. 1st ed. Port. (Binding rubbed, soiled), else Good. *Brown*. $95/£59

PROCTOR, L. B. The Bench and Bar of New York. NY: Diossy, 1870. Brn pebbled cl (spine faded; ex-lib). Sound. *Boswell*. $175/£109

PROCTOR, MOLLY G. Victorian Canvas Work: Berlin Wool Work. Batsford, 1972. 1st ed. 4 color plts. VG + in dj (sl torn). *Whittle*. $32/£20

PROCTOR, RICHARD A. Our Place Among Infinities. NY: Appleton, 1876. 1st ed. x,323pp. VG + . *Middle Earth*. $95/£59

PROCTOR, ROBERT. An Index to the Early Printed Books in the British Museum: Part II. MDI-MDXX Section I. Germany. Kegan Paul, Trench, Trubner, 1903. 1st ed. Uncut. Ptd wrappers (spine chipped). *Forest*. $77/£48

PROCTOR, ROBERT. The Printing of Greek in the Fifteenth Century. Illustrated Monographs No. VIII. Oxford: Bibliographical Soc, 1900. 1st ed. 24 facs plts. Uncut, unopened. Ptd wrappers. *Forest*. $152/£95

PROEHL, CARL. The Fourth Marine Division in World War II. Washington, 1946. 1st ed. VG. *Clark*. $125/£78

Professor; a Tale. (By Charlotte Bronte.) Smith, Elder, 1857. 1st ed. 2 vols. Half-titles, 1 leaf ads at end vol 1; 8pp ads, 16pg pub's cat dated June 1857 at end of vol 2, w/ orig auction purchase record, exhibition details, and other ephemera pasted in. Gray-purple cl, gilt. (Bkpls; faded, bumped; fr hinge vol 1 cracked.) *Sotheby's**. $1,067/£667

Progressive Men of the State of Montana. Chicago: A.W. Bowen, n.d. 1st ed. Full leather. VG. *Labordo*. $950/£594

PROKOFIEV, SERGEI. Peter and the Wolf. NY: Viking Penguin, 1985. Barbara Cooney (illus). Opens up to fold down 5 perfect pop-ups (3 w/movement, 2 sl hard to work). Ties w/ribbon. VG-. *Bookfinders*. $30/£19

PROKOSCH, FREDERIC. Age of Thunder. NY: Harper, (1945). 1st ed, trade issue. Dec eps. Fine in dj. *Reese*. $30/£19

PROKOSCH, FREDERIC. America, My Wilderness. NY: FSG, (1972). 1st ed. (Sm ink mk fr cvr), else VF in VF dj. *Between The Covers*. $85/£53

PROKOSCH, FREDERIC. The Assassins. NY: Harpers, 1936. 1st ed. (Fep lt clipped), else As New in As New dj. *Between The Covers*. $200/£125

PROKOSCH, FREDERIC. The Carnival. NY: Harpers, 1938. 1st ed. (Fep lt clipped), else As New in As New dj. *Between The Covers*. $125/£78

PROKOSCH, FREDERIC. Chosen Poems. GC: Doubleday, 1947. 1st ed. VF in VF dj (sl soiled). *Between The Covers*. $150/£94

PROKOSCH, FREDERIC. The Conspirators. NY: Harper, 1943. 1st ed. (Fep corner lt clipped), else VF in VF dj. *Between The Covers*. $100/£63

PROKOSCH, FREDERIC. Death at Sea. NY: Harpers, 1940. 1st ed. (Fep lt clipped), else As New in As New dj. *Between The Covers*. $125/£78

PROKOSCH, FREDERIC. Night of the Poor. NY: Harpers, 1939. 1st ed. VF in VF dj (few wrinkles). *Between The Covers*. $150/£94

PROKOSCH, FREDERIC. The Seven Who Fled. NY: Harper, 1937. 1st ed, trade issue. Fine in VG dj (sm corner chip). *Reese*. $30/£19

PROKOSCH, FREDERIC. The Skies of Europe. NY: Harpers, 1941. 1st ed. (Fep corner lt clipped), else VF in VF dj (rear cvr sl soiled). *Between The Covers*. $125/£78

PROKOSCH, FREDERIC. Sunburned Ulysses. Lisbon, 1941. 1st ed. One of 22 'printed by the author for his friends.' Inscribed. (Few soft creases to text), o/w NF in marbled wrappers, ptd label fr cvr. *Maggs*. $192/£120

PROKOSCH, FREDERIC. A Tale for Midnight. Boston: LB, (1955). 1st ed. VF in VF dj. *Between The Covers*. $100/£63

PROLIX, PEREGRINE. (Pseud of Philip H. Nicklin.) A Pleasant Peregrination Through the Prettiest Parts of Pennsylvania. Phila: Grigg & Elliott, 1836. 1st ed. 148pp. Orig cl, paper label. (Sm portion of fep missing; cl worn, esp spine ends), else Good. Howes N149. *Brown*. $75/£47

Propaganda for Reform in Proprietary Medicines. Chicago, 1916. 9th ed. *Fye*. $75/£47

PROPERT, JOHN LUMSDEN. A History of Miniature Art. Macmillan, 1887. One of 125. Folio. xvi,285pp (prelims, eps sl foxed; cl sl mkd); 23 plts. Untrimmed. *Hollett*. $288/£180

PROPERT, JOHN LUMSDEN. A History of Miniature Art. London, 1887. Folio. 23 plts. Orig vellum. (Fr hinge cracked.) *Swann**. $316/£198

PROUD, ROBERT. The History of Pennsylvania in North America. Phila: Zachariah Poulson, Jr, 1797-1798. 1st ed. 2 vols. 8vo. Frontisport, tp (offset), 508; 373,(146)pp; fldg map (offset). Later 3/4 grn calf, marbled bds (edges lt worn), gilt. VG set. Howes P639. *House*. $750/£469

PROULX, E. ANNIE. Postcards. NY: Scribner, 1992. 1st ed. Signed. Fine in dj. *Lame Duck*. $450/£281

PROULX, E. ANNIE. Postcards. 4th Estate, 1993. 1st UK ed. Fine in Fine dj. *Martin*. $54/£34

PROULX, E. ANNIE. The Shipping News. NY: Scribner, (1993). 1st ed. NF in Fine dj. *Bernard*. $200/£125

PROULX, E. ANNIE. The Shipping News. NY: Scribner, 1993. 1st ed. Signed. Fine in dj. *Lame Duck*. $250/£156

PROULX, E. ANNIE. The Shipping News. 4th Estate, 1994. 1st UK ed. Mint in Mint dj. *Martin*. $45/£28

PROUST, MARCEL. Marcel Proust, Selected Letters 1880-1903. GC: Doubleday, 1983. 1st ed. Fine in dj. *Bernard*. $20/£13

PROUST, MARCEL. The Past Recaptured. NY: A&C Boni, 1932. 1st Amer ed. (Sl rubbed), else Fine in NF dj (lt worn). *Between The Covers*. $125/£78

PROUST, MARCEL. Swann's Way. NY: LEC, 1954. One of 1500. Signed by Bernard Lamotte (illus). Patterned gray cl. NF in slipcase. *Pacific**. $52/£33

PROUST, MARCEL. Time Regained. Stephen Hudson (Pseud of Sidney Schiff), (trans). London: C&W, 1931. 1st British ed. One of 1300. Blue-gray cl, gilt. Good (eps foxed; spine sl rubbed). *Reese*. $40/£25

PROUT, SAMUEL. Hints on Light and Shadow. James Rimmell & Son, 1876. New ed. Lg paper copy. Folio. Complete w/20 ll of tinted litho plts. Blindstamped cl (extrems sl rubbed), gilt. VG (sl spotted). *Hollett*. $240/£150

PROUT, SAMUEL. Illustrations of the Rhine, Drawn from Nature. London: E. Gambart, 1853. Tinted litho tp, 30 plts by Hullmandel & Walton after Prout. (Frontis, tp spotted, occasional mainly marginal spotting, lib stamp tp verso, bkpl.) Contemp 1/2 morocco (very rubbed), gilt. *Christie's**. $576/£360

PROUT, WILLIAM. On the Nature and Treatment of Stomach and Urinary Diseases.... London, 1840. 3rd ed. 483pp. (Inner hinge cracked.) *Fye*. $150/£94

PROVENSEN, ALICE and MARTIN. The Year at Maple Hill Farm. Atheneum, 1978. 1st ed. 9.5x12.5. Unpaginated. Fine in Fine dj. *Price*. $60/£38

Proverbs Exemplified, and Illustrated by Pictures from Real Life. London: J. Trusler, 1790. 12mo. viii,196pp; 50 woodcuts by John Bewick. 19th-cent full mottled calf, gilt. (Bkpls; extrems lt rubbed), else Fine. *Bromer*. $850/£531

PRUCHA, FRANCIS PAUL (ed). Army Life on the Western Frontier. Selections from the Official Reports Made Between 1826 and 1845 by Colonel George Croghan. Norman, (1958). 1st ed. Map. Postal stamp affixed to tp. VG (name, bkpl) in VG dj. *Sagebrush*. $40/£25

PRUDDEN, T. MITCHELL. Dust and Its Dangers. NY: Putnam, 1904. 4 plts. Grn cl, gilt. (Sm dent fr cvr), o/w Fine. *House*. $35/£22

PRUDDEN, T. MITCHELL. On the Great American Plateau. NY: Putnam, 1906. VG. *Dumont*. $45/£28

PRUNIER, MADAME. Prunier's: The Story of a Great Restaurant. NY: Alfred Knopf, 1957. 1st ed. VG in dj (edge worn). *Perier*. $25/£16

PRUSSING, EUGENE E. George Washington in Love and Otherwise. Covic, 1925. One of 1000. (Cvrs waterstained.) *Book Broker*. $50/£31

PRYCE-TANNATT, T. E. How to Dress Salmon Flies: A Handbook for Amateurs. London: A&C Black, 1914. 1st ed. 12 color plts, guards. Grn cl, gilt. (Spine cl torn, repaired along joints), else VG. *Pacific**. $115/£72

PRYCE-TANNATT, T. E. How to Dress Salmon Flies: A Handbook for Amateurs. London, 1948. 2nd ed. 12 plts (8 color). Dj (badly torn). *Petersfield*. $56/£35

PRYDE, DUNCAN. Nunaga: Ten Years of Eskimo Life. NY: Walker, 1971. 1st ed. Gray cl. Fine in NF dj. *Connolly*. $20/£13

PRYER, MRS. W. B. A Decade in Borneo. London: Hutchinson, 1893. 1st ed. Inscribed, dated Aug 3, 1896. 1/2-title, (vi),iii,(i)blank,iv,199,(1)blank,v index,(i)blank,x ads. Beige cl. Good (some ll w/pencil underlining; stained, sl rubbed). *Morrell*. $144/£90

PRYNNE, J. H. Down Where Changed. Ferry, 1979. 1st ed. NF (cvrs sl mkd) in wrappers. *Ulysses*. $56/£35

PSEUDOMAN, AKKAD. (Pseud of Edwin F. Northrup.) Zero to Eighty. NY, 1937. 1st ed. Color frontis. Fine in VG dj (lt rubbed). *Mcclintock*. $50/£31

Publications of the Gratz College. Phila: Gratz College, 1897. 1st ed. Frontisport vol 1, guard. (Spine head chipped), else VG. *Pacific**. $104/£65

PUCCINI, GIACOMO. Letters of Giacomo Puccini. Guiseppe Adami (ed). Ena Makin (trans). Harrap, 1931. 1st ed. 5 plts. VG. *Hollett*. $48/£30

PUFENDORF, SAMUEL. The Compleat History of Sweden. London, 1702. Contemp 1/2 sheep. (Final text leaf lacks corner, about 10 words; needs rebinding.) *Swann**. $161/£101

PUFENDORF, SAMUEL. An Introduction to the History of the Kingdoms and States of Asia, Africa and America, Both Ancient and Modern. London: R.J., 1705. (24),621,(11)pp. Period paneled calf, gilt, morocco spine label. (Joints, spine head rubbed), else VG. *Pacific**. $207/£129

Pug's Tour Through Europe; or, The Travell'd Monkey. London: John Harris, n.d. (ca 1827). #42 from list of the Harris' Cabinet of Amusement & Instruction. 12mo. 17pp + 1pg list; 16 half-pg hand-colored wood engrs. Watermarked 1827. Orig buff pict stiff paper wrappers ptd w/Harris seal on lower wrapper. (Faded spot at outer edge of tp, dampstain throughout inner lower corners of hinges; wrappers sl soiled, chipped, spine reinforced; ink dedication verso of fr wrapper, ink name top edge of cvr.) Text, engrs Fine. *Hobbyhorse*. $450/£281

PUGH, P. D. GORDON. Naval Ceramics. Newport: Ceramic Book, 1971. 12 color, 118 monochrome plts. Fine. *Explorer*. $120/£75

PUGIN, A. and AUGUSTUS WELBY. Examples of Gothic Architecture Selected from Various Ancient Edifices in England. London/Edinburgh, 1850/1895. 3 vols. (Dampstain in corners vol 1, affecting plts; cl worn.) *Swann**. $115/£72

PUGIN, A. Modern Furniture. London: M.A. Nattali, 1823. Sq lg 8vo. 44 hand-colored engrs. Aeg. Full leather, emb dec border, gilt. (Worn, corners bumped, hinge weak; sl soiled, foxed.) *Metropolitan**. $603/£377

PUGIN, A. and C. HEATH. Paris and Its Environs. London, 1831. 2 vols. Sm folio. (Lt foxed; needs rebinding.) *Swann**. $230/£144

PUGIN, A. Specimens of the Architecture of Normandy from the XIth to the XVIth Century.... Richard Phene Spiers (ed). London, 1874. New ed. 78 engr plts, incl frontis. Later cl. *Swann**. $69/£43

PUGSLEY, WILLIAM and ROY W. HANKEY. Bunker Hill. Corona del Mar: Trans-Anglo Books, (1977). 1st ed. Fabricoid. Dj (top edge worn). *Dawson*. $75/£47

PUIG, MANUEL. Betrayed by Rita Hayworth. NY: Dutton, 1971. 1st US ed. NF in dj. *Lame Duck*. $85/£53

PUIG, MANUEL. Blood of Requited Love. NY: Random House, 1984. 1st US ed. Inscribed. Fine in self-wraps. *Lame Duck*. $100/£63

PUIG, MANUEL. Eternal Curses on the Reader of These Pages. NY: Random House, 1982. 1st US ed. NF in dj. *Lame Duck*. $45/£28

PUIG, MANUEL. Heartbreak Tango. NY: Dutton, (1973). 1st Amer ed. Fine in NF dj (lt scratch). *Agvent*. $125/£78

PUIG, MANUEL. Heartbreak Tango: A Serial. NY: Dutton, 1973. 1st US ed. (Pp top edges foxed, feps offset), else NF in NF dj. *Lame Duck*. $75/£47

PUIG, MANUEL. Kiss of the Spider Woman. NY, 1979. 1st Amer ed. Fine in Fine dj. *Warren*. $40/£25

PUIG, MANUEL. Kiss of the Spider Woman. NY: Knopf, 1979. 1st US ed. Signed. Fine in dj. *Lame Duck*. $250/£156

PULLAN, MRS. The Lady's Manual of Fancy-Work: A Complete Instuctor in Every Variety of Ornamental Needlework. NY: Dick & Fitzgerald, 1859. 8 fldg color plts. Blind-stamped cl, gilt. (Marginal dampstain; hinges cracked; facing to cvrs), else VG. *Pacific**. $69/£43

PULLEN, JOHN J. A Shower of Stars. Phila, (1966). 1st ed. Fine in Fine dj. *Pratt*. $35/£22

PULMAN, GEORGE P. R. The Vade-Mecum of Fly-Fishing for Trout. London, 1851. 3rd ed. xii,186pp + ad leaf. (Shelfworn.) *Oinonen**. $100/£63

PULSZKY, FRANCIS and THERESA. White, Red, Black: Sketches of American Society in the United States During the Visit of Their Guests. NY: Redfield, 1853. 1st US ed. 2 vols. (iv)-xii,331pp + 4pg pub's cat; 342pp + 6pg pub's cat. Grn cl, gilt. (Sl aged, lt foxed, sm spot stains; spine ends frayed, sl worn, cvrs spotted.) Texts Good. Howes P647. *Baltimore**. $70/£44

PULTENEY, WILLIAM and BEATRIX BRICE. The Immortal Salient. Ypres League, 1925. 3rd ed. Stiff card cvrs (spine sl stained from tape). Good. *Clearwater*. $48/£30

PUMPELLY, RAPHAEL. My Reminiscences. NY: Holt, 1918. 1st ed. 2 vols. 64 plts, 13 maps (6 fldg, 1 color). Teg. (Notes, 5 ll cut off, rehinged w/scotch tape; sl rubbed, faded), o/w Good. *Worldwide.* $35/£22

PUMPELLY, RAPHAEL. My Reminiscences. NY: Holt, 1918. 1st ed thus. 2 vols. VG. Howes P650. *New Hampshire**. $70/£44

PUNCEY, PHILIP and J. A. GERE. Italian Drawings in the Department of Prints and Drawings in the British Museum. London, 1962. 2 vols. 278 plts. Good+ in djs. *Washton.* $145/£91

Punch and Judy. LEC, 1937. Ltd to 1500 numbered. George Cruikshank (illus). Fine in slipcase. *Swann**. $126/£79

Punch and Judy. NY: LEC, 1937. 1st ed thus. 8vo. George Cruikshank (illus). Stamped leather. Good in glassine dj (lacks sm piece), cardbd chemise, slipcase (lt worn). *Reisler.* $200/£125

PUNNETT, R. C. Mendelism. London, 1911. 3rd ed. Frontis port, 6 plts (5 color). (Lower hinge cracked, fep browned; cl lt soiled, joints sl rubbed, spine sl discolored.) *Edwards.* $24/£15

Puppy Dog's ABC. London: Raphael Tuck & Sons, (ca 1890). Tall, narrow shapebook cut around head & sides in a dog's image. 14pp (4 color, rest in sepia). VG stiff color pict wrappers. *Reisler.* $125/£78

PURCELL, LESLIE HARPER. Miracle in Mississippi: Laurence C. Jones of Piney Woods. NY: Comet, (1956). 1st ed. Presentation copy. VG+. *Petrilla.* $40/£25

PURCELL, WILLIAM. Onward Christian Soldier. London: Longmans, Green, 1957. 1st ed. 8 plts. (Spine lettering dull.) *Hollett.* $32/£20

PURCELL, WILLIAM. Onward Christian Soldier. Longmans, Green, 1957. 1st Eng ed. 8 b/w plts. VG (top edge dusty; spine ends, top corners bumped) in dj (rubbed, creased, dusty, browned). *Ulysses.* $43/£27

PURCHAS, SAMUEL. Hakluytus Posthumus; or, Purchas His Pilgrimes. Glasgow, 1905-07. One of 1000 sets. Inscribed by publisher. 20 vols. 8vo. Orig 1/4 vellum, gilt. *Swann**. $920/£575

PURCHAS, SAMUEL. Hakluytus Posthumus; or, Purchas His Pilgrimes.... Glasgow: MacLehose, 1905. One of 1000. 8 vols (of 20). 16 plts (5 fldg), 36 fldg maps. All edges marbled. 1/2 morocco, marbled bds. (Sl rubbed, hinges tender, 3 cvrs detached, 1 spine w/missing labels), o/w VG. *Worldwide.* $375/£234

PURDOM, C. B. (ed). Everyman at War. London/Toronto: J.M. Dent, (1930). 1st ed. Blind-stamped red cl, gilt. (Edges lt foxed), else NF (w/o dj). *Reese.* $45/£28

PURDY, CHARLES W. Practical Urinalysis and Urinary Diagnosis: A Manual for the Use of Physicians, Surgeons, and Students. Phila, 1899. 4th ed. 365pp. (Fr inner hinge cracked; extrems worn). Good. *Doctor's Library.* $50/£31

PURDY, HELEN THROOP. San Francisco: As It Was—As It Is—and How to See It. SF: Paul Elder, 1912. 1st ed. Buckram spine, bds, pict pastedown fr cvr. Fine (spine sl dknd). *Argonaut.* $75/£47

PURDY, JAMES. Eustace Chisholm and His Works. NY: FSG, (1967). 1st ed. VF in VF dj (two sm rubbed spots). *Between The Covers.* $100/£63

PURDY, JAMES. Lessons and Complaints. (NY): Nadja, (1978). One of 525 signed. (8)pp. Unopened. Fine in stiff wrappers. *Heritage.* $50/£31

PURDY, JAMES. Scrap of Paper and The Berry Picker. Hollywood: Sylvester & Orphanos, 1981. Ltd to 330 signed. Fine dec cl. *Truepenny.* $100/£63

PURSER, PHILIP. Where Is He Now? The Extraordinary Works of Edward James. London, 1978. 1st Eng ed. Fine in dj. *Clearwater.* $40/£25

PURVES-STEWART, JAMES. Intracranial Tumours and Some Errors in Their Diagnosis. Oxford Medical Publications, 1927. (Sm spine tear.) *Bickersteth.* $38/£24

PUSHKIN, ALEXANDER. The Captain's Daughter and Other Stories. LEC, 1971. Ltd to 1500 numbered, signed by Charles Mozley (illus). Fine in slipcase. *Swann**. $34/£21

PUSHKIN, ALEXANDER. Eugene Onegin. LEC, 1943. Ltd to 1500 numbered, signed by Fritz Eichenberg (illus). Fine in slipcase. *Swann**. $103/£64

PUSHKIN, ALEXANDER. Gabriel: A Poem in One Song. Max Eastman (trans). NY: Covici Friede, 1929. One of 750. Rockwell Kent (illus). Unopened. Gilt-stamped flexible vellum. Fine in glassine. *Pacific**. $150/£94

PUSHKIN, ALEXANDER. The Golden Cockerel. NY: LEC, (1949). One of 1500. Signed by Edmund Dulac (illus). Gilt-stamped cl, dec bds. Fine in chemise. *Pacific**. $196/£123

PUSHKIN, ALEXANDER. The Golden Cockerel. LEC, 1950. Ltd to 1500 numbered, signed by Edmund Dulac (illus). Fine in slipcase. *Swann**. $126/£79

Puss in Boots. NY: Blue Ribbon Press, (1934). C. Carey Cloud & Harold B. Lentz (illus). 4to. 20pp incl 3 dbl-pg pop-ups, all in Fine working order. Color illus bds. Good. *Reisler.* $225/£141

Puss in Boots. NY: Duenewald Ptg Co, 1944. 1st ed thus. 8vo. 6 moveables by Julian Wehr. Spiral paper pict bds. VG (tp sl dknd) in VG dj. *Davidson.* $200/£125

Puss in Boots. An All-Action Treasure Hour Pop-Up Illus. England: Brown Watson, 1981. 6 dbl-pg pop-ups by V. Kubasta. Glazed pict bds. VG. *Bookfinders.* $45/£28

Put's Golden Songster Containing the Largest and Most Popular Collection of California Songs Ever Published. (By John A. Stone.) SF: D. Appleton, (1858). (2),3-64pp. VG in pict wrappers. *Pacific**. $98/£61

PUTNAM, GEORGE HAVEN. Books and Their Makers During the Middle Ages. NY, 1962. Rpt of 1896-1897 ed. 2 vols. Good in slipcase. *Washton.* $95/£59

PUTNAM, GEORGE HAVEN. A Prisoner of War in Virginia, 1864-5. NY/London: Putnam, 1912. 1st ed. Frontisport. Blue cl. (Sm ink stamp), else VG. *Chapel Hill.* $45/£28

PUTNAM, GEORGE PALMER. Death Valley and Its Country. NY: Duell, Sloan & Pearce, 1946. 1st ed. NF in Good+ dj. *Connolly.* $35/£22

PUTNAM, GEORGE PALMER. Death Valley Handbook. NY, (1947). 1st ed. NF (ink stamp, name) in VG dj. *Sagebrush.* $25/£16

PUTNAM, GEORGE PALMER. Hickory Shirt. NY, (1949). 1st ed. VG in VG dj. *Sagebrush.* $25/£16

PUTNAM, GEORGE PALMER. Hickory Shirt: A Novel.... NY: Duell, Sloan & Pearce, (1949). 1st ed. Red cl, gilt. Dj. *Dawson.* $50/£31

PUTNAM, GEORGE R. Sentinel of the Coasts. NY: Norton, 1937. 1st ed. Blue cl. Good (ex-lib). *American Booksellers.* $35/£22

PUTNAM, MRS. WILLIAM LOWELL. The Happiness of Our Garden. NY, 1926. 1st Amer ed. Fine (sl rubbed). *Polyanthos.* $30/£19

PUTNAM, NINA WILCOX. Sunny Bunny. Chicago: P.F. Volland, (1918). 38th ed. 12mo. Full color pict bds (edges worn). *Reisler.* $110/£69

PUZO, MARIO. The Godfather. London: Heinemann, 1969. 1st ed. VG (lt foxed) in VG white dj. *Smith.* $75/£47

PUZO, MARIO. The Godfather. NY: Putnam, 1969. 1st ed. VG in VG dj (edge chipped, interior clear tape reinforcement). *Pettler.* $100/£63

PUZO, MARIO. The Runaway Summer of Davie Shaw. NY: Platt & Munk, (1966). 1st ed. NF (name, eps sl foxed) in dj (fr flap bottom clipped). *Between The Covers.* $85/£53

Puzzle for a Curious Girl. (By Elizabeth Kilner.) London: Richard Phillips, 1810. 3rd ed. 12mo. VF full-pg copper-engr frontis w/Tabart & Co. imprint dated Oct 9, 1804; 124pp; twelve 2/3pg copper engrs. Marbled paper on bds, 3/4 grn roan spine, gilt. VF (sm color drawing, ink dedication loose inside fr cvr; sm repaired hole at center of p105/6 w/loss of 2 or 3 letters; sl shelfworn, lib label inside fr cvr). *Hobbyhorse.* $350/£219

Puzzledom. An Original Collection of Charades, Conundrums, Puzzles, and Games. Phila: Willis P. Hazard, 1854. 1st ed. Sq slim 8vo. 128pp (sl foxed). Lt yellow eps. Dk brn grained cl (spine, edges lt worn, spine lt sunned), gilt. Text Nice. *Baltimore**. $25/£16

PYCRAFT, W. P. Birds in Flight. London, 1922. 1st ed. 12 color tipped-in, 8 b/w plts. Dj (ragged w/loss). *Edwards.* $40/£25

PYCROFT, JAMES. Twenty Years in the Church. London: L. Booth, 1861. 4th ed. viii,280pp. Mod 1/2 levant morocco, gilt. VG. *Hollett.* $120/£75

PYLE, HOWARD. Howard Pyle's Book of the American Spirit: The Romance of American History. Francis J. Dowd (ed). NY: Harper, 1923. 1st ed. 1/2 cl, bds, color pict cvr label, gilt spine. (Corners lt bumped), else NF in dj (few sm edgetears, wear). *Pacific**. $150/£94

PYLE, HOWARD. The Merry Adventures of Robin Hood. Scribner, 1909. 4to. 296pp. VG + . *Price.* $40/£25

PYLE, HOWARD. The Merry Adventures of Robin Hood. NY: Scribner, 1923. 9 x 6 3/4. Dec cl. (Name, adhesion residue from former bkpl; spine head rubbed), else VG. *Pacific**. $35/£22

PYLE, HOWARD. The Merry Adventures of Robin Hood. Scribner, 1929. 4to. 296pp. VG + . *Price.* $40/£25

PYLE, HOWARD. Pepper and Salt for Young Folk. London: Sampson Low et al, 1888. 1st Eng ed. 4to. Frontis, xiii,121pp. Brn dec cl. *Sotheran.* $477/£298

PYLE, HOWARD. The Ruby of Kishmoor. NY, 1908. 1st Amer ed. 10 color plts. Teg, uncut. Pict cvrs, gilt. Fine (bkpl). *Polyanthos.* $65/£41

PYLE, HOWARD. Stolen Treasure. NY: Harper, 1907. 1st ed. Frontis, guards, 8 plts. Pict cvr label. NF in Fair dj (lacks lg pieces, incl most of spine; insect-damage). *Pacific**. $150/£94

PYLE, HOWARD. The Story of Champions of the Round Table. NY: Scribner, 1905. 1st ed. 4to. Brn cl (hinges starting). *Reisler.* $175/£109

PYLE, HOWARD. The Story of Sir Launcelot and His Companions. NY: Scribner, 1907. 1st ed. 4to. Brn cl. Good. *Reisler.* $225/£141

PYM, BARBARA. Crampton Hodnet. NY: Dutton, 1985. 1st US ed. Fine in Fine dj. *Pettler.* $20/£13

PYNCHON, THOMAS. The Crying of Lot 49. Phila: Lippincott, 1966. 1st ed. Fine in NF dj (1/8-inch trimmed fore-edge of fr flap). *Beasley.* $125/£78

PYNCHON, THOMAS. The Crying of Lot 49. London: Cape, 1967. 1st Eng ed. Fine (spine foot sl bumped) in dj (spine head sl rubbed). *Ulysses.* $472/£295

PYNCHON, THOMAS. Gravity's Rainbow. NY: Viking, (1973). 1st ed. NF in NF 1st issue dj (rear corners dampstained). *Agvent.* $450/£281

PYNCHON, THOMAS. Gravity's Rainbow. NY, 1973. Pb ed. Fine (sl rubbed, sm crease) in pict wraps. *Polyanthos.* $40/£25

PYNCHON, THOMAS. Gravity's Rainbow. NY, 1973. 1st ed. Fine in NF dj. *Warren.* $450/£281

PYNCHON, THOMAS. Slow Learner. London: Cape, 1984. 1st ed. Fine in dj. *Smith.* $60/£38

PYNCHON, THOMAS. V. Cape, 1963. 1st UK ed. Fine in NF dj. *Any Amount.* $272/£170

PYNCHON, THOMAS. V. Cape, 1963. 1st ed. Fine (spine foot sl bumped) in dj (sl rubbed, edges mkd). *Ulysses.* $440/£275

PYNCHON, THOMAS. V. London: Cape, 1963. 1st ed, 1st bk. VF in dj. *Smith.* $850/£531

PYNCHON, THOMAS. V. Phila: Lippincott, 1963. 1st ed, 1st bk. 8vo. Mustard eps, top edge stained blue. Purple cl. (Extrems sl rubbed, faded), o/w Fine in dj (lt edgeworn). *Heritage.* $850/£531

PYNCHON, THOMAS. Vineland. Boston, 1990. 1st ed. Fine in NF dj. *Warren.* $25/£16

PYNCHON, THOMAS. Vineland. London: Secker & Warburg, 1990. 1st UK ed. Fine in Fine dj. *Beasley.* $60/£38

PYNE, W. H. The Costume of Great Britain. London: William Miller, (1819). Folio. 14x10. 60 hand-colored litho plts, hand-colored tp. Aeg. Full maroon ribbed morocco, gilt. Fine (bkpls). *Pacific**. $920/£575

PYNE, WILLIAM HENRY. The History of the Royal Residences of Windsor Castle, St. James's Palace...and Frogmore. London, 1919. 3 vols. Tall 4to. 100 Fine hand-colored plts. Contemp calf (worn, broken, spines corroded; sl soiled, stained, foxed). Internally Clean. *Oinonen**. $4,100/£2,563

Q

Q. (Pseud of Arthur T. Quiller-Couch.) The Astonishing History of Troy Town. Cassell, 1888. 2nd ed. Orig pict cl (spine bumped, sl chipped; sl spotted, pencil sig). Good. *Tiger.* $19/£12

QUACKENBOS, JOHN D. Geological Ancestors of the Brook Trout and Recent Saibling Forms from Which It Evolved. NY: Angler's Club of NY, 1916. 1st ed. One of 300 numbered. Signed, inscribed presentation. 6 color plts. Uncut. Gilt-lettered leather (rubbed; joints, spine tips worn), pict cvr label. *Oinonen**. $200/£125

QUACKENBOS, JOHN D. Hypnotism in Mental and Moral Culture. NY/London, 1903. (Few margins sl thumbed; cl sl soiled.) *Edwards.* $32/£20

QUAIFE, MILO M. The Attainment of Statehood. Madison: State Hist Soc of WI, (1928). 1st ed. Ltd to 2000. VG. *Sadlon.* $50/£31

QUAIFE, MILO M. Checagou: From Indian Wigwam to Modern City 1673-1835. Chicago: Univ of Chicago, 1933. 1st ed. Frontis map. NF in Good+ dj. *Connolly.* $30/£19

QUAIFE, MILO M. Chicago and the Old Northwest 1673-1835. Chicago: Univ of Chicago, 1913. 1st ed. Frontis, 10 plts (1 fldg). (Scrape mks along fore-edge cl of fr bd, 1 sm spot exposed), else Fine. Howes Q1. *Cahan.* $125/£78

QUAIFE, MILO M. The Struggle over Ratification 1846-47. Madison: State Hist Soc of WI, 1920. 1st ed. Ltd to 1500. (Cvrs sl spotted.) *Sadlon.* $50/£31

QUAIFE, MILO M. (ed). Army Life in Dakota. Chicago, 1941. Lakeside Classics ed. (Sl worn.) *Woolson.* $20/£13

QUAIFE, MILO M. (ed). The John Askin Papers. Detroit Lib Commission, 1928-1929. One of 1000 ptd. 2 vols. VG. Howes A359. *Lien.* $350/£219

QUARITCH, BERNARD. A Catalogue of Books in English History and Literature from the Earliest Times to the End of the Seventeenth Century [with Index]. Catalogue No. 369. Bernard Quaritch, 1922. Fldg frontis, 120 facs. Orig ptd wrappers bound in. *Forest.* $40/£25

QUARITCH, BERNARD. Catalogue of Books on the History, Geography and of the Philosophy of America, Australasia, Asia, Africa. Quaritch, 1886. 416 + 62pp index. Maroon cl (newly rebound). *Moss.* $48/£30

QUARITCH, BERNARD. A Catalogue of Books, Arranged in Classes.... [with] Valuable English and Foreign Books. Bernard Quaritch, 1864. 557,16pp. (Upper cvr detached.) *Forest.* $40/£25

QUARITCH, BERNARD. Catalogue of the Monuments of the Early Printers in All Countries. Bernard Quaritch, 1886-87. Contemp 1/2 calf. *Forest.* $48/£30

QUARLES, BENJAMIN. The Negro in the Civil War. Boston: Little, Brown, (1953). 1st ed. Blue cl. NF in VG dj. *Chapel Hill.* $65/£41

QUARTERMAIN, LESLIE B. South to the Pole: The Early History of the Ross Sea Sector, Antarctica. London/Wellington, Melbourne: OUP, 1967. Fldg map. NF in dj (worn). *Explorer.* $88/£55

QUARTERMAIN, LESLIE B. Two Huts in the Antarctic. New Zealand: R.E. Owen, 1963. 1st ed. Pict card cvrs. VG. *Explorer.* $40/£25

Quarto-Millenary: The First 250 Publications and the First 25 Years, 1929-1954, of the Limited Editions Club. NY: LEC, 1959. One of 2250. 1/2 black morocco, red cl, emb black morocco medallion fr cvr. Fine in slipcase. *Pacific*.* $345/£216

QUAYLE, ERIC. Ballantyne the Brave. London: Hart-Davis, 1967. 1st ed. Inscribed presentation. 9 plts. VG in dj. *Hollett.* $48/£30

QUAYLE, ERIC. Early Children's Books. David & Charles, 1983. 1st ed. Fine in dj. *Moss.* $29/£18

QUEAL, WILLIAM G. The Overthrow of American Slavery. NY/Cincinnati: Phillips & Hunt/Cranston & Stowe, 1885. 1st ed. Presentation from Queal's daughter. 275pp. (Sl worn), o/w VG. *Brown.* $100/£63

Queen Victoria's Jubilee Garland. London: Routledge, 1887. Only ed. Thin obl 12mo. 4 full-pg color friezes, upper cvr illus by Kate Greenaway. Pict card cvrs, orig crimson silk ribbon tie. Excellent (sl rubbed). *Sotheran.* $472/£295

Queen's Beasts. Newman Neame, n.d. (1953). 1st ed. Folio. 56pp; 6 color plts by Edward Bawden; 5 color plts by Cecil Keeling. Pict bds. VG + . *Bookmark.* $32/£20

QUEEN, ELLERY (ed). The Misadventures of Sherlock Holmes. Boston: Little, Brown, 1944. 1st ed. Black cl. Fine in VG dj (spine ends chipped). *Sumner & Stillman.* $350/£219

QUEEN, ELLERY. The Chinese Orange Mystery. London: Gollancz, 1934. 1st ed. Black linen. (Tape mks on eps, edges sl foxed), o/w NF. *Temple.* $64/£40

QUEEN, ELLERY. The Chinese Orange Mystery. Gollancz, 1934. 1st UK ed. VG + (sl bumped) in dj (edges worn; faded, sl chipped, hinges split, strengthened to rear). *Williams.* $176/£110

QUEEN, ELLERY. The Dragon's Teeth. London: Gollancz, 1939. 1st ed. Black glazed cl. (Lg stain affecting prelims, lower margins of 1st/last sigs; cvrs worn.) Reading Copy. *Temple.* $11/£7

QUEEN, ELLERY. Ellery Queen's The Tragedy of X. NY: Frederick A. Stokes, 1940. 1st ed thus. Signed by 'Ellery Queen.' (Name), else VG in dj (spine ends, extrems chipped, sm tears). *Pacific*.* $63/£39

QUEEN, ELLERY. Half-Way House. London: Gollancz, 1936. 1st ed. Black linen. (Tape mks on eps, edges sl foxed), o/w NF. *Temple.* $64/£40

QUEEN, ELLERY. The Murderer Is a Fox. Boston: Little, Brown, 1945. 1st Amer ed. Yellow cl. VG (eps lt browned, spine ends rubbed) in dj (price-clipped, sl chipped, soiled). *Heritage.* $100/£63

QUEEN, ELLERY. The Spanish Cape Mystery. London: Gollancz, 1935. 1st ed. Black linen. (Tape mks on eps, edges lt foxed), o/w Fine. *Temple.* $64/£40

QUEEN, ELLERY. Ten Days' Wonder. London: Gollancz, 1948. 1st ed. Sky-blue cl. (Spine, cvr edges sl faded; gilt oxidized), o/w Fine in dj (faded). *Temple.* $26/£16

QUEEN, ELLERY. Ten Days' Wonder. Boston: Little Brown, 1948. 1st ed. Fine in dj (sm tear, spine ends sl worn). *Mordida.* $100/£63

QUEENY, EDGAR M. Cheechako—The Story of an Alaskan Bear Hunt. NY: Scribner, 1941. 1st ed. Ltd to 1200. VG. *Perier.* $135/£84

QUENNELL, PETER. A Letter to Mrs. Virginia Woolf. London: Hogarth, 1932. Orig wraps. *Edrich.* $19/£12

QUENNELL, PETER. A Letter to Mrs. Virginia Woolf. London: Hogarth, 1932. 1st ed. VG wrappers (sl soiled). *Virgo.* $40/£25

QUICK, ARMAND. The Hemorrhagic Diseases and the Physiology of Hemostasis. Springfield, 1942. 1st ed. *Fye.* $100/£63

QUICK, ARMAND. The Physiology and Pathology of Hemostasis. Phila, 1951. 1st ed. *Fye.* $75/£47

QUIGLEY, HUGH. Passchendaele and the Somme: A Diary of 1917. London: Methuen, (1928). 1st ed. Red cl stamped in gilt/blind. (Few fox mks at fore-edge; spine sl sunned), o/w VG. *Reese.* $100/£63

QUIGLEY, JOSEPH. The Slogan. T.S. Dickson (ed). Dunoon, (1916). 1st Eng ed. Stiff card cvrs (spine very worn, fr bd partly detached). *Clearwater.* $32/£20

QUILLER-COUCH, ARTHUR (ed). In Powder and Crinoline. London: Hodder & Stoughton, (1913). 1st ed. Lg paper copy, ptd on fine quality paper, w/2 extra plts which do not appear in the ordinary trade ed. 4to. (xii),14-163; 26 Fine mtd color plts, guards. Teg, uncut. Buckram-backed lt gray bds (recently, expertly rebound, matching orig binding, w/ptd labels preserved). *Sotheran.* $2,880/£1,800

QUILLER-COUCH, ARTHUR (ed). In Powder and Crinoline. (London): Hodder & Stoughton, (1913). 1st ed. One of 500. Signed by Kay Nielson (illus). 12.25x9.5. 26 tipped-in color plts, guards. Teg. Pict grn vellum, gilt, string ties. (Extrems sl rubbed), else NF. *Pacific*.* $4,313/£2,696

QUILLER-COUCH, ARTHUR (ed). The Sleeping Beauty and Other Fairy Tales. London: Hodder & Stoughton, (1910). 1st ed illus thus. 4to. (xviii),128pp; 30 mtd color plts by Edmund Dulac, guards. Brn cl, gilt w/rococo designs. (Sl shaken; sl knock to lower corner; spine ends, corners sl rubbed.) *Sotheran.* $520/£325

QUILLER-COUCH, ARTHUR (ed). The Sleeping Beauty and Other Fairy Tales. London: Hodder & Stoughton, (1910). 1st ed. 4to. 129pp; 30 tipped-in color plts by Edmund Dulac. Aeg. Full morocco (rebound), raised bands. Fine. *Davidson.* $750/£469

QUILLER-COUCH, ARTHUR (ed). Sleeping Beauty and Other Fairy Tales. NY: Doran, n.d. 6.25 x 9 inches. 16 tipped-in color illus by Edmund Dulac. Gilt-pict red cl. Fine. *American Booksellers.* $150/£94

QUILLER-COUCH, ARTHUR. Foe-Farrell. NY: Macmillan, 1918. 1st US ed. Frontis. Gilt red cl. Fine in VG pict dj (lt worn, nicked). *Reese.* $50/£31

QUILLER-COUCH, ARTHUR. The Westcotes. J.W. Arrowsmith, 1902. 1st ed. VG + . *Fine Books.* $60/£38

QUIN, E. R. W. Notes on Irish Architecture. London, 1875. 1st ed. 2 vols. Folio. 125 mtd Autotype plts (incl 5 double-pg); errata slip in vol 2. Orig cl, gilt. (Plt mts warped, sl foxed generally not affecting photo plts; spines, extrems worn, few sm binding repairs.) *Swann*.* $3,450/£2,156

QUIN, JAMES. The Life of Mr. James Quin, Comedian. London, 1887. 1st ed. 107pp. (Rebound.) *Heinoldt.* $15/£9

QUIN, MICHAEL J. A Visit to Spain. London: Hurst, Robinson, 1823. 1st ed. iv,359,(1)blank,xxiv pp. Marbled edges. Contemp marbled calf, gilt, red label. Good (foxed; joints, spine ends well repaired). *Morrell.* $120/£75

QUINBY, JANE (comp). Catalogue of Botanical Books in the Collection of Rachel McMasters Miller Hunt. Pittsburgh, 1958-61. One of 750 sets. 2 vols in 3. (Sl worn.) *Oinonen*.* $400/£250

QUINCY, J. Medicina Statica: Being the Aphorisms of Sanctorius.... London, 1728. 4th ed. 463pp + index. Contemp full leather, rebacked w/new eps. (1 plt taped w/sl loss, foxed.) *Fye*. $500/£313

QUINCY, J. Pharmacopoeia Officinalis and Extemporanea...in Two Parts, Theoretic and Practical. London, 1761. 13th ed. xxiv,704pp + index. Old leather. (Eps detached, torn, ink notes, pg edges discolored; sl worn, no title label), o/w Good. *Whitehart*. $192/£120

QUINN, CHARLES and ELENA (eds). Edward H. Davis and the Indians of the Southwest United States and Northwest Mexico. Downey, CA: Elena Quinn, 1965. 1st ed. Ltd to 500. Fine. *Book Market*. $50/£31

QUINN, DAVID B. North America From Earliest Discovery to First Settlements. The Norse Voyages to 1612. NY: Harper & Row, (1977). 1st ed. 16 plts. Blue cl. Fine in dj. *House*. $15/£9

QUINN, P. T. Pear Culture for Profit. NY: OJ, 1869. 136pp. Fine. *Book Market*. $10/£6

R

RAAEN, AAGOT. Grass of the Earth: Immigrant Life in the Dakota Country. Northfield, MN: Norwegian-American Hist Assoc, 1950. 1st ed. Fine in NF dj. *Connolly*. $30/£19

RABAUT DE SAINT-ETIENNE, JEAN-PAUL. An Impartial History of the Late Revolution in France. Phila: Carey, 1794. 2 vols in 1. Pub's ads at fr. Calf (very scuffed). *Rostenberg & Stern*. $175/£109

Rabbit Book: (The Stump Book). London: Anthony Treherne, (ca 1905). 2nd ed. Obl 16mo. Mary Tourtell (illus). Color pict cl (spine tightened, sl worn) w/bone handle, clasp. *Reisler*. $285/£178

RABELAIS, FRANCOIS. The Complete Works. London: John Lane, 1927. One of 4300 sets. 2 vols. 24 engr plts. Pict cl. Wrappers (sl worn). *Marlborough*. $120/£75

RABELAIS, FRANCOIS. Gargantua and Pantagruel. NY: LEC, 1936. One of 1500 numbered sets, signed by W. A. Dwiggins (illus). 5 vols. Prospectus, ephemera laid in. Paper spine labels. (Lt worn.) Slipcase (scuffed). *Oinonen**. $90/£56

RABELAIS, FRANCOIS. Gargantua and Pantagruel. LEC, 1936. Ltd to 1500 numbered, signed by W. A. Dwiggins (designer). 5 vols. Fine in slipcase. *Swann**. $149/£93

RABELAIS, FRANCOIS. The Works. Thomas Urquhart & Peter Motteux (trans). London, (1927). Ltd ed. 2 vols. Black cl, gilt. *Argosy*. $125/£78

RABELAIS, FRANCOIS. The Works. Thomas Urquhart & Peter Motteux (trans). London: Gibbings, 1901. 5 vols. Teg. 3/4 red straight-grain morocco, tooled spines, raised bands. Fine. *Appelfeld*. $300/£188

RACKHAM, ARTHUR. The Allies' Fairy Book. Phila: Lippincott, (1916). 1st Amer ed. 8vo. Red cl, gilt. NF (spine lettering sl rubbed). *Glenn*. $150/£94

RACKHAM, ARTHUR. Arthur Rackham's Book of Pictures. London: Heinemann, 1913. 1st ed. Royal 8vo. (vi),7-43pp; 44 mtd color plts, guards. Gray cl, gilt. *Sotheran*. $637/£398

RACKHAM, BERNARD The Three Books of the Potter's Art. Albert Van de Put (trans). London: Victoria & Albert Museum, 1934. One of 750. Folio. 80 b/w plts. Dj (soiled, chipped, sl loss). *Edwards*. $240/£150

RACKHAM, BERNARD. The Ancient Glass of Canterbury Cathedral. London, 1949. 101 plts hors texte (21 color). Good. *Washton*. $200/£125

RACKHAM, BERNARD. A Book of Porcelain: Fine Examples in the Victoria and Albert Museum. London: A&C Black, 1910. 1st ed. Pict grn cl, gilt. (Lt foxed), else VG. *Pacific**. $46/£29

RACKHAM, BERNARD. Catalogue of the Glaisher Collection of Pottery and Porcelain in the Fitzwilliam Museum, Cambridge. Cambridge, 1935. 2 vols. Folio. 302 plts (36 color). 1/2 leather (spines faded), gilt. VG set (ex-lib). *Swann**. $460/£288

RACKHAM, BERNARD. Early Netherlands Maiolica. London, (1926). 56 plts. Dj (chips, tears), glassine outer wrapper. *Swann**. $115/£72

RACKHAM, BERNARD. Guide to Italian Maiolica. London, 1933. 48 b/w plts at rear. (Cl sl soiled, spine ends sl worn w/loss.) *Edwards*. $56/£35

RADCLIFFE, WILLIAM. Fishing from the Earliest Times. London: John Murray, 1921. 1st ed. 1/2 cl, bds, paper spine label. Fine. *Pacific**. $207/£129

RADCLYFFE, C. E. Big Game Shooting in Alaska. London: Rowland Ward, 1904. 1st ed. Fldg map in rear pocket. Grn cl, gilt. VG (corners, extrems sl discolored). *House*. $450/£281

RADCLYFFE-HALL, MARGUERITE. The Forgotten Island. Chapman & Hall, 1915. 1st Eng ed. VG (edges, prelims, eps spotted; lt foxing; spine ends, 2 corners sl bumped). *Ulysses*. $136/£85

RADCLYFFE-HALL, MARGUERITE. Poems of the Past and Present. Chapman & Hall, 1910. 1st Eng ed. VG (fep sl mkd, sm label rep; edges rubbed, spine tail bumped). *Ulysses*. $152/£95

RADEN, WOLDEMAR. Switzerland; Its Mountains and Valleys. Bickers & Son, 1878. 1st ed. Lg 4to. xiv,487pp; 418 wood-engr illus. Contemp 1/2 morocco, raised bands, gilt, marbled bds. (Ink inscrip; spine ends sl worn, 4 sm worm holes to fr bd morocco), o/w Good. *Sotheran*. $797/£498

RADER, DOTSON. Tennessee: Cry of the Heart. GC: Doubleday, 1985. 1st ed. Fine in dj. *Antic Hay*. $25/£16

RADER, JESSE L. South of Forty. Norman, 1947. (Extrems worn.) Internally Good. *Dumont*. $90/£56

RADFORD, J. History of Woodford County. Peoria, IL: Ptd by W.T. Dowdall, 1877. 1st ed. Signed presentation in pencil, dated Dec. 26, 1914. 78pp. Black cl (spine, extrems worn), gilt. Good + . Howes R3. *Wantagh*. $750/£469

RADISSON, PIERRE ESPRIT. The Explorations of Pierre Esprit Radisson, from the Original Manuscript in Bodleian Library and the British Museum. Arthur T. Adams (ed). Minneapolis: Ross & Haines, 1961. 1st ed thus. VF in Perfect dj. *Argonaut*. $60/£38

RADZINOWICZ, LEON. A History of English Criminal Law and Its Administration from 1750. London: Stevens & Sons, 1948-1956. 3 vols. *Boswell*. $225/£141

RAE, EDWARD. The White Sea Peninsula. London: John Murray, 1881. 1st, only ed. Inscribed. 1/2 title, xviii,347pp; fldg map loose in rear pocket, 27 plts (incl frontis). Grn cl, gilt, beveled edges (spine mkd, cvr pocket torn). Internally Good (lib blindstamps, plt, ink stamps). *Morrell*. $160/£100

RAE, JOHN. John Rae's Correspondence with the Hudson's Bay Company on Arctic Exploration. E. E. Rich (ed). London: Hudson's Bay Record Soc, 1953. 1st ltd ed. Fine. *Perier*. $95/£59

RAE, W. F. Austrian Health Resorts and the Bitter Waters of Hungary. London, 1888. 292pp. VG (extrems sl worn). *Doctor's Library*. $90/£56

RAE, W. F. Columbia and Canada; Notes on the Great Republic and the New Dominion. London: Daldy, Isbister, 1877. 1st ed. viii,316pp. (Spine sl worn.) *Mott*. $50/£31

RAE, W. F. Westward by Rail: The New Route to the East. London: Longmans, Green, 1870. 1st ed. Pub's presentation blindstamp on tp. Frontis map, xiv,391pp. (Fr joint cracked, fep detached, few pencil mks to tp, bkseller's entry laid on fr pastedown; cvrs worn), else Good. *Pacific**. $138/£86

RAE, W. F. Westward by Rail: The New Route to the East. NY: D. Appleton, 1871. 1st Amer ed. Frontis map, pp xiv,391,(2) ads. (Spine sunned.) *Mott.* $75/£47

RAEBURN, HAROLD. Mountaineering Art. NY: Frederick A. Stokes, (1920). 1st Amer ed. Grn cl. Good (top corner 1st few ll creased; bumped, spine quite rubbed). *Blue Mountain.* $75/£47

RAFFALD, ELIZABETH. The Experienced English Housekeeper, for the Use and Ease of Ladies, Housekeepers, Cooks, &c. A. Millar et al, 1795. New ed. Engr frontisport (frontis, 1st few pp dampstained at upper margin, sl wormed), 3 fldg engr plts (2 w/sm tears at lower margin). Contemp calf (rubbed, rebacked). *Sotheby's*.* $275/£172

RAFFLES, THOMAS S. The History of Java. Kuala Lumpur/London/NY: OUP, 1965. Photo rpt of 1817 orig ed. 2 vols. Dk grn buckram, gilt. Fine set in clear plastic djs (lt rubbed), bd slipcase (sl worn, dusty, 1 edge split). *Baltimore*.* $65/£41

RAFINESQUE, C. S. The Complete Writings...on Recent and Fossil Conchology. Wm G. Binney and George W. Tryon, Jr (eds). NY/London: Bailliere Bros, 1864. 1st ed. 96,7pp; 3 plts. Orig ptd wrappers. *M & S.* $300/£188

RAFINESQUE, C. S. Florula Ludoviciana; or, A Flora of the State of Louisiana. NY: C. Wiley, 1817. Sm 8vo. Leather, marbled paper-cvrd bds. (Tp professionally restored, other pp restored, foxed.) *Metropolitan*.* $1,955/£1,222

RAFINESQUE, C. S. Medical Flora; or, Manual of the Medical Botany of the United States of North America. Phila: Atkinson & Alexander, (1828/1830). 2 vols bound together. 8vo. 99 (of 100) color plts. Old leather. (Hinges split; dampstained, foxed, name cut out tp vol 1, affecting text; vol 1 lacks p221-224 and plt 43.) *Metropolitan*.* $575/£359

RAGG, LAURA M. The Women Artists of Bologna. London: Methuen, 1907. Frontis, 18 plts, map. Fine. *Europa.* $80/£50

RAGON, MICHEL. The Space of Death: A Study of Funerary Architecture: Decoration and Urbanism. Alan Sheridan (trans). VA Univ, 1983. Fine in dj. *Hadley.* $40/£25

Rags and Tatters. A Magic Action Story. Racine, WI: Whitman, 1936. 20x18 cm. 15pp (sl browned); 3 dbl-pg pop-ups. Pict wraps (extrems lt worn). *Bookfinders.* $100/£63

RAGUET, CONDY. A Treatise on Currency and Banking. Phila: Grigg & Elliott, 1839. 1st ed. 16,264pp (lt foxed, emb stamp). Orig cl (rebacked w/lib buckram). *M & S.* $325/£203

RAHT, CARLYSLE GRAHAM. The Romance of David Mountains and Big Bend Country. El Paso: Rahtbooks, (1919). 1st ed. Frontisport, 13 plts w/images on both sides, dbl-pg map. Gilt-dec cl. (Ink name, hinge cracked before tp; extrems worn), else Good+. *Pacific*.* $150/£94

RAHT, CARLYSLE GRAHAM. The Romance of David Mountains and Big Bend Country. El Paso, 1919. 1st ed. Pict cl (extrems sl worn), else VG. Howes R16. *Baade.* $55/£34

RAIKES, DAVID. The Poems of David Raikes. Eynsham, Oxford: Fantasy Press, 1954. Fine (feps sl spotted) in dj (spine sl dknd). *Ulysses.* $72/£45

Railway Economics. Chicago, 1912. (Shelfworn, hinges starting.) *Dumont.* $65/£41

Railway Economics: A Collective Catalogue of Books in Fourteen American Libraries. Chicago: Bureau of Railway Economics, (1912). 1st ed. Dk grn buckram, gilt. VG (sl rubbed, worn). *Baltimore*.* $55/£34

RAINE, CRAIG. A Free Translation. Edinburgh, 1981. 1st Eng ed. One of 1000 ptd. This copy one of 200 hb. Fine in dj (sl faded). *Clearwater.* $72/£45

RAINE, KATHLEEN. Berkeley, Blake and the New Age. Ipswich: Golgonooza, 1977. 1st Eng ed. VG (spine ends, corners sl rubbed) in wrappers. *Ulysses.* $48/£30

RAINE, KATHLEEN. Living in Time. London: Editions Poetry/Nicholson & Watson, 1946. 1st ed. Unopened. VG (fep sl creased; spine head sl bumped) in dj (nicked, sl rubbed, mkd, chipped, spine, edges browned). *Ulysses.* $88/£55

RAINE, KATHLEEN. The Pythoness. Hamish Hamilton, 1949. 1st ed. VG (top edge sl spotted, spine foot, top corners sl bumped) in dj (worn). *Ulysses.* $58/£36

RAINE, WILLIAM MACLEOD and WILL C. BARNES. Cattle. GC: Doubleday, Doran, 1930. 1st ed. Fine in dj. Howes R17. *Labordo.* $95/£59

RAINE, WILLIAM MACLEOD. Famous Sheriffs and Western Outlaws. GC: Doubleday, Doran, 1929. Stated 1st ed. (Few lib stamps), else Good. *Dumont.* $45/£28

RAINE, WILLIAM MACLEOD. Famous Sheriffs and Western Outlaws. GC: Doubleday, Doran, 1929. 1st ed. Fine in dj (tape-repaired). *Labordo.* $95/£59

RAINE, WILLIAM MACLEOD. Guns of the Frontier. Boston: Houghton Mifflin, 1940. 1st ed. Maroon cl. (Top edge foxed), o/w Fine in Good dj (spine dknd, chipped), mylar cvr. *Harrington.* $45/£28

RAINES, C. W. A Bibliography of Texas. Austin, 1896. 1st ed. Frontis, xvi,268pp. (Extrems worn.) Internally Good. *Dumont.* $150/£94

RAINIER, P. Green Fire. NY: Random House, c1942. 1st ptg. Good (sm dampstain bottom outside edge of text). *Blake.* $50/£31

RAINSFORD, MARCUS. An Historical Account of the Black Empire of Hayti. London: James Cundee, 1805. 1st ed. Engr frontis, 8 (of 9) engr plts, fldg map, fldg plan, 3-pg facs letter. (Some plts, text ll lt spotted; bkpls, lib stamps.) Contemp 1/2 calf, marbled bds (extrems rubbed). *Christie's*.* $576/£360

RAISOR, GARY. Less Than Human. Woodstock: Overlook Connection, (1993). One of 300 numbered, signed by Raisor and Guy Aitchison (illus). Pict cl (sl worn). Wooden velvet-lined coffin-shaped protective case as issued. *Oinonen*.* $150/£94

RAISTRICK, ARTHUR. Quakers in Science and Industry. David & Charles, 1968. 2nd ed. 16 plts. VG in dj (sl rubbed). *Hollett.* $72/£45

RALEIGH, WALTER and H. A. JONES. The War in the Air. Oxford: Clarendon, 1922-28. 1st ed. 2 vols. Black buckram, gilt. (Bkpls, eps sl foxed, offset), o/w VG set in VG djs (edgeworn). *Reese.* $150/£94

RALEIGH, WALTER. The History of the World, in Five Books. G. Conyers, J.J. & P. Knapton, D. Midwinter et al, 1736. 11th ed. Folio. 5 parts in 2 vols. Engr frontisport, 8 fldg maps. Contemp paneled calf. (Browned; worn.) *Sotheby's*.* $442/£276

RALEIGH, WALTER. Works...Together with His Letters and Poems.... London, 1751. 1st ed. 2 vols. Frontis vol 1. Full calf (worn, rubbed, fr cvr vol 1 detached). *Kane*.* $275/£172

RALLING, CHRISTOPHER. Shackleton: His Antarctic Writings. London: BBC, 1983. Fine in dj (chipped). *Explorer.* $24/£15

RALPH, JULIAN. Dixie. NY: Harper, 1896. xiv,412pp. NF. *Connolly.* $45/£28

RALPH, JULIAN. On Canada's Frontier: Sketches of History, Sport, and Adventure and of the Indians, Missionaries, Fur-Traders, and Newer Settlers of Western Canada. NY: Harper, 1892. 1st ed. Brn cl, gilt. (Ink name; spine ends, corners lt rubbed), else NF. *Pacific*.* $130/£81

RAMADGE, FRANCIS. Consumption Curable: and the Manner in Which Nature as well as Remedial Art Operates in Effecting a Healing Process in Cases of Consumption. NY, 1839. 1st Amer ed. 160pp. (Ex-lib.) *Fye.* $75/£47

RAMAL, WALTER. (Pseud of Walter de la Mare.) Songs of Childhood. Longmans, Green, 1902. 1st ed. 8vo. Photo frontis, vii,106pp. Teg, rest uncut. Parchment-backed lt blue cl, gilt. Near Mint. *Sotheran.* $720/£450

RAMALEY, FRANCIS. Wild Flowers and Trees of Colorado. Boulder: Greenman, 1909. 1st ed. VG (ex-lib, sl mkd). *Archer.* $25/£16

RAMEY, W. SANFORD. Kings of the Battlefield.... Phila, 1887. Pict cvr. (Sl worn), o/w VG. *Pratt.* $15/£9

RAMIREZ VAZQUEZ, PEDRO. The National Museum of Anthropology, Mexico. NY: Abrams, (1968). 54 color plts tipped-in. Fine in dj. *Turtle Island.* $65/£41

RAMOS, GRACILIANO. Anguish. NY: Knopf, 1946. 1st US ed. VG + (sm bump top edge of fr bd, eps sl offset, sticker) in VG dj (extrems sl chipped). *Lame Duck.* $85/£53

RAMOS, GRACILIANO. Childhood. London: Peter Owen, 1979. 1st ed. (Eps offset), else NF in dj. *Lame Duck.* $35/£22

RAMPLING, ANNE. (Pseud of Anne Rice.) Exit to Eden. NY, 1985. Advance reading copy. NF (1/2-inch ink line at fore-edge). *Warren.* $95/£59

RAMSAY, ANDREW CROMBIE. The Glaciers of Switzerland and North Wales. London: Longman, 1860. 1st ed. (vi),116pp; fldg map, 8 plts. Blind-stamped grn cl, gilt. Good. *Young.* $96/£60

RAMSAY, DAVID. The History of the American Revolution. Dublin: William Jones, 1795. 2nd Dublin ed. 2 vols in 1. 319,320-640pp. Contemp full polished flame calf, morocco spine label. VG (hinges tender, cvrs lt worn). Howes R35. *Chapel Hill.* $150/£94

RAMSAY, EDWARD BANNERMAN BURNETT. Reminiscences of Scottish Life and Character. Gall & Inglis, n.d. xlix,259pp. Aeg. Early 20th-cent 1/2 crushed morocco, gilt. VG. *Hollett.* $48/£30

RAMSAY, W. M. The Church in the Roman Empire Before A.D. 170. London: Hodder & Stoughton, 1907. 9th ed. 2 maps. Grn cl. *Turtle Island.* $35/£22

RAMSBOTHAM, FRANCIS H. The Principles and Practice of Obstetric Medicine and Surgery, in Reference to the Process of Parturition. John Churchill, 1845. 2nd ed. xxiii,(i),732pp + pub's cat; 90 litho plts (lt spotted, 1 plt loose, margins chipped). Orig cl (dull, slits in cl at joints). *Bickersteth.* $240/£150

RAMSDELL, CHARLES. San Antonio: A Historical and Pictorial Guide. Austin: Univ of TX, (1959). 1st ed. Signed. Fine in NF dj. *Sadlon.* $40/£25

RAMSEY, FREDERIC JR. Been Here and Gone. New Brunswick: Rutgers Univ, (1960). 1st ed. VG in pict dj. *Petrilla.* $30/£19

RAMSEY, ROBERT H. Men and Mines of Newmont. NY, 1973. 1st ed. Good +. *Wantagh.* $20/£13

RAMSEY, ROBERT H. Men and Mines of Newmont. NY: Octagon, 1973. 1st ed. 10 photo plts. Fine in Fine dj. *Connolly.* $35/£22

Ranch Life in California. (By Evelyn M. Hertslet.) London, 1886. 1st ed. iv,172pp; 2 plts. Pub's cl (sl worn, sl stained). Howes H445. *Oinonen*.* $140/£88

Rand McNally Guide to San Francisco, Oakland, Berkeley and Environs of the Bay Cities. NY: Rand McNally, (1927). Lg fldg color map. Grn cl. Fine. *House.* $25/£16

Rand McNally Ideal Atlas of the World. Chicago, 1915. Color map. VG. *King.* $85/£53

RAND, AUSTIN L. Stray Feathers from a Bird Man's Desk. Doubleday, 1955. Good in dj. *Rybski.* $25/£16

RAND, AYN. Atlas Shrugged. NY: Random House, (1957). 1st ed. Grn cl, gilt. (Tp corner torn away, no loss; spine sl faded), o/w VG in dj (price-clipped, tape-reinforced to verso, edge-worn). *Heritage.* $225/£141

RAND, AYN. The Fountainhead. Indianapolis, ca 1948. Later ed. Inscribed. 8vo. Grn cl (stained). Dj (worn). *Swann*.* $632/£395

RAND, CHRISTOPHER. A Nostalgia for Camels. Boston/Toronto: Little, Brown, 1957. 1st ed. 2-tone cl. VG in dj (torn). *Worldwide.* $25/£16

RANDALL, DAVID A. Dukedom Large Enough. NY: Random House, (1960). 1st ed. Fine in Fine dj. *Harrington.* $40/£25

RANDALL, DAVID A. Dukedom Large Enough. NY, 1969. 1st Amer ed. Fine in NF dj. *Polyanthos.* $25/£16

RANDALL, L. W. Footprints Along the Yellowstone. San Antonio: Naylor, (1961). VG in dj. *Perier.* $35/£22

RANDALL, LILIAN M. C. Images in the Margins of Gothic Manuscripts. Berkeley/LA, 1966. 158 plts. 1/2 cl, bds. Good in dj. *Washton.* $175/£109

RANDOLPH, EDMUND. Hell Among the Yearlings. Chicago: R.R. Donnelley, 1978. Frontis. VG. *Lien.* $30/£19

RANDOLPH, MARY. The Virginia Housewife. Balt: Plaskitt & Cugle, (1828). Stereotype ed. Calf. (Fr joint cvr detached), else VG-. *Pacific*.* $184/£115

RANDOLPH, MARY. The Virginia Housewife. Washington: P. Thompson, 1830. 4th ed. Calf. (Foxed, dknd; hinges cracked, spine worn, corners rounded), else VG-. *Pacific*.* $127/£79

RANK, BENJAMIN KEITH and A. R. WAKEFIELD. Surgery of Repair as Applied to Hand Injuries. Edinburgh/London: E. & S. Livingstone, 1953. 1st ed. Fine. *Weber.* $145/£91

RANKE, HERMANN. Masterpieces of Egyptian Art. London: Allen & Unwin, (1951). Folio. Color frontis, 64 plts. (Extrems lt rubbed.) *Archaeologia.* $25/£16

RANKE, LEOPOLD. The Ecclesiastical and Political History of the Popes of Rome During the Sixteenth and Seventeenth Centuries. Sarah Austin (trans). London: John Murray, 1840. 3 vols. 3/4 dk blue morocco, mottled bds, gilt, raised bands. (Bkpls), else VG. *Pacific*.* $58/£36

RANKIN, IAN. The Flood. Edinburgh: Polygon, 1986. 1st ed, 1st bk. NF (spine ends sl bumped) in dj (sl creased, mkd, dusty, price-clipped). *Ulysses.* $88/£55

RANSOM, JOHN CROWE. Chills and Fever. NY: Knopf, 1924. 1st ed, 1st bk. 1/4 cl, striped bds, label. Fine. *Macdonnell.* $150/£94

RANSOM, JOHN CROWE. Grace After Meat. London: Hogarth, 1924. 1st ed. Ltd to 400. (Corner lt bumped), else VF in patterned bds, cvr label. *Bromer.* $650/£406

RANSOM, P. J. G. The Archaeology of the Transport Revolution 1750-1850. World's Work, 1984. 1st ed. Frontis. Dj. *Forest.* $32/£20

RANSOM, WILL. Little Dutchy Nursery Songs from Holland. London: George G. Harrap, (1925). 1st ed. 4to. Color frontis, (iv),5-79pp; 12 mtd color plts by Rie Cramer. Blue cl-backed pict bds. (Feps browned), o/w Fine in pict wrapper (lacks section of lower edge, sm closed tears, sm nicks). *Sotheran.* $269/£168

RANSOME, ARTHUR. Aladdin in Rhyme. Nisbet, (1919). 1st ed. 4to. Unpaginated. Complete w/12 tissue-guarded color plts by Thomas Blakeley Mackenzie tipped on to black card. B/w eps. Dec cl. VF (sl dust-soiled). *Hollett.* $560/£350

RANSOME, ARTHUR. Aladdin in Rhyme. London: Nisbit, (1919). Ltd to 250 signed. Lg 4to. 12 mtd color plts by Thomas Mackenzie. Teg. White cl (lt dusty), gilt. VG. *Reisler.* $2,250/£1,406

RANSOME, ARTHUR. The Big Six. Cape, 1940. 1st ed. VG. *Green Meadow.* $72/£45

RANSOME, ARTHUR. Great Northern? Cape, 1947. 1st ed. VG. *Green Meadow.* $72/£45

RANSOME, ARTHUR. The Picts and the Martyrs. Cape, 1943. 1st ed. VG. *Green Meadow.* $56/£35

RANSOME, ARTHUR. Six Weeks in Russia in 1919. London: George Allen & Unwin, 1919. 1st ed. (Binding soiled, backstrip chipped.) Brn ptd paper wrappers (fr wrapper nearly detached). *Maggs.* $88/£55

RANSOME, FREDERICK LESLIE. Notes on Some Mining Districts in Humboldt County, Nevada. Washington, 1909. 1st ed. Fldg map. NF in wrappers. *Sagebrush.* $65/£41

RAPER, ARTHUR F. Preface to Peasantry: A Tale of Two Black Belt Counties. Chapel Hill: UNC Press, 1936. 1st ed. VG in dj. *Cahan.* $150/£94

RAPER, ARTHUR F. Tenants of the Almighty. NY: Macmillan, 1943. 1st ed. 79 photo plts by Jack Delano. VG (single word of text corrected in ink) in dj (edges chipped). *Cahan.* $165/£103

RAPHAEL, FREDERIC. Obbligato. London, 1956. 1st Eng ed, 1st bk. Nice (sm tear fore-edge of tp, next leaf; spine sl bumped) in dj (sl torn, nicked). *Clearwater.* $80/£50

RAPHAEL, SAMUEL. Advanced Fur Craftsmanship. NY: Fur Craftsmanship, (1948). (Cvr lettering worn off, several stamps.) *Perier.* $45/£28

RASCOE, BURTON. Belle Starr, 'The Bandit Queen.' NY: Random House, 1941. 1st ed. Fine in dj. *Labordo.* $75/£47

RASCOE, BURTON. Belle Starr: 'The Bandit Queen'. NY, 1941. 1st ptg. VG (sig, address; cvr sl dull). *Baade.* $35/£22

RASCOVICH, MARK. The Bedford Incident. NY: Atheneum, 1963. 1st ed. Fine in dj (price-clipped). *Bernard.* $20/£13

RASHDALL, HASTINGS. The Universities of Europe in the Middle Ages. F. M. Powicke and A. B. Emden (eds). Oxford: Clarendon, 1936. New ed. 3 vols. 2 frontispieces, fldg map. Blue buckram, gilt. Good (spines faded, sl mks). *Blackwell's.* $176/£110

RASKY, FRANK. The North Pole or Bust. Toronto: McGraw-Hill Ryerson, (1977). Map. Fine in dj. *Explorer.* $24/£15

RASMO, N. Michael Pacher. London: Phaidon, 1971. 20 mtd color plts. Good in dj. *Ars Artis.* $72/£45

RASMUSSEN, KNUD. Across Arctic America. Putnam, 1927. 1st ed. Good (inner hinges strengthened w/black tape; dusty, dull). *Walcot.* $61/£38

RASPE, RUDOLPH. The Singular Adventures of Baron Munchausen. LEC, 1952. Ltd to 1500 numbered, signed by Fritz Kredel (illus). Fine in slipcase. *Swann*.* $80/£50

RASPUTIN, MARIA. My Father. London: Cassell, (1934). 1st ed in English. Frontis photo port. Black cl. (Ink sig, edges sl dusty.) Plain dj (sl worn, fold nicked). *Baltimore*.* $90/£56

RASWAN, CARL R. Black Tents of Arabia. Boston, 1935. 1st ed. Signed, dated. (Cvrs heavily dknd, worn.) *King.* $50/£31

RATCLIFF, ARTHUR JAMES JOHN. A History of Dreams. Boston: Small, Maynard, (1923). 1st Amer ed. Ptd ruled grn cl. *Gach.* $35/£22

RATCLIFF, J. D. Yellow Magic. NY: Random House, (1945). 1st ed. 8 photo plts. Black cl. Fine in VG dj (edge chipped). *House.* $40/£25

RATCLIFF, J. D. Yellow Magic: The Story of Penicillin. NY, 1945. 1st ed. VG in dj (worn). *Doctor's Library.* $30/£19

RATHBONE, BASIL. In and Out of Character. GC, 1962. 1st ed. Inscribed. Dj. *Argosy.* $200/£125

RATHBONE, BELINDA (ed). One of a Kind: Recent Polaroid Color Photography. Boston: David R. Godine, (1979). 1st ed. 72 color photos. (Stamp), else NF in VG dj. *Cahan.* $75/£47

RATHBONE, HANNAH MARY. Letters of Richard Reynolds. London: Charles Gilpin, 1852. 1st ed. vii,310,12pp; engr port. Blind-stamped cl, gilt. (Pencil notes lower pastedown), o/w Very Nice. *Hollett.* $104/£65

RATHENAU, ERNEST. Oskar Kokoschka Drawings, 1906-1965. Coral Gables, FL: Univ of Miami, (1970). Fine in dj. *Metropolitan*.* $28/£18

RATHER, L. J. Addison and the White Corpuscles: An Aspect of Nineteenth-Century Biology. London: Wellcome Inst, 1972. 1st ed. Fine in dj. *Glaser.* $30/£19

RATTENBURY, RICHARD C. Packing Iron. Millwood, NY: Zon International Pub, (1993). Fine in dj. *Lien.* $45/£28

RATTIGAN, TERENCE. Ross: a Dramatic Portrait. NY: Random House, (1962). 1st Amer ed. VF in VF dj (4 tiny pinpricks). *Between The Covers.* $150/£94

RATTIGAN, TERENCE. Ross: A Dramatic Portrait. (London: Lowe & Brydone), 1960. 1st ed. Frontisport. 12pp incl wrappers. Fine in ptd wrappers. *Maggs.* $48/£30

RATTIGAN, TERENCE. Separate Tables. NY: Random House, (1955). 1st Amer ed. Fine (sl rubbed) in NF dj (few sm tears). *Between The Covers.* $85/£53

RATTLEBRAIN. Sir Guy de Guy: A Stirring Romannt. London: Routledge, Warne & Routledge, 1864. 1st ed. Phiz (illus). Aeg. Pict blue cl, gilt. (Foxed), else VG. *Pacific*.* $40/£25

RATTRAY, ALEXANDER. Vancouver Island and British Columbia. London: Smith, Elder, 1862. 1st ed. 1/2-title, viii,182,16 pub's list; 4 tinted lithos (incl frontis), fldg map (sm piece torn away w/loss), fldg chart. Blue blindstamped cl. (Plts foxed, offsetting from plts, lt frontis stain; upper joint splitting but firm.) *Morrell.* $208/£130

RATTRAY, R. F. Poets in the Flesh. London, 1961. Orig wraps. *Edrich.* $19/£12

RAUCH, FREDERICK A. Psychology; or, a View of the Human Soul: Including Anthropology. NY: M.W. Dodd, 1840. 1st ed. 388pp (foxed, stained). Orig cl (stained). VG. *M & S.* $175/£109

RAUH, WERNER. The Wonderful World of Succulents. Washington, 1984. 2nd ed. 96 plts (62 color), 2 maps. VG in dj. *Brooks.* $75/£47

RAUM, JOAN O. History of City of Trenton. Trenton, NJ, 1871. 1st ed. Fldg frontis map (repaired), 12,448pp. (Rebound.) *Heinoldt.* $35/£22

RAVEN, SIMON. Before the Cock Crow. London: Muller, Blond, & White, 1986. 1st Eng ed. NF (spine head sl bumped) in dj (sl creased). *Ulysses.* $40/£25

RAVEN, SIMON. Doctors Wear Scarlet. Blond, 1960. 1st ed. Signed presentation. VG. *Any Amount.* $56/£35

RAVEN, SIMON. The Face of the Waters. London: Anthony Blond, 1985. 1st Eng ed. NF (spine ends sl bumped) in dj (sl creased). *Ulysses.* $40/£25

RAVEN, SIMON. Fielding Gray. Blond, 1967. 1st UK ed. Fine in dj. *Williams.* $48/£30

RAVEN, SIMON. Morning Star. London: Blond & Briggs, 1984. 1st Eng ed. NF (spine head sl bumped) in dj (sl creased). *Ulysses.* $40/£25

RAVEN, SIMON. The Sabre Squadron. Blond, 1966. 1st UK ed. Fine in dj. *Williams.* $48/£30

RAVENEL, BEATRICE ST. JULIEN. Architects of Charleston. Charleston: Carolina Art Assoc, 1945. 1st ed. Fine in dj. *Cahan.* $150/£94

RAVILIOUS, ERIC. English Wits, Their Lives and Jests. Leonard Russell (ed). London: Hutchinson, 1940. 1st ed. Red cl. Dj (spine browned). *Maggs.* $64/£40

RAWLINGS, CHARLES. In Our Neck o' the Woods. Memoirs of a Pioneer Banker. (Sheridan: Rangeland Photo & News, 1972). Fine in dj (edge torn). *Perier.* $50/£31

RAWLINGS, MARJORIE KINNAN. Cross Creek Cookery. NY, 1942. 1st ed. Pict cl (Ink inscrip; sl worn.) *King.* $35/£22

RAWLINGS, MARJORIE KINNAN. Cross Creek Cookery. NY: Scribner, 1942. 1st ed, 1st ptg. Pict cl. VG (sl shelfworn) in dj (edgeworn). *My Bookhouse.* $77/£48

RAWLINGS, MARJORIE KINNAN. Cross Creek. Scribner, 1942. True 1st ed w/both Scribner 'A' and Scribner Seal on c. pg. (Spine lettering flaked), else VG + in NF dj (sl rubbed). *Fine Books.* $90/£56

RAWLINGS, MARJORIE KINNAN. The Marjorie Rawlings Reader. Julia Scribner Bigham (ed). NY: Scribner, 1956. 1st ed. NF in VG dj (edges chipped). *Pettler.* $40/£25

RAWLINGS, MARJORIE KINNAN. South Moon Under. NY, 1933. 1st Amer ed, 1st bk. NF (sl rubbed, spine sunned). *Polyanthos.* $50/£31

RAWLINGS, MARJORIE KINNAN. When the Whippoorwill. NY: Scribner, 1940. 1st ed. VG + in dj. *Lame Duck.* $475/£297

RAWLINGS, MARJORIE KINNAN. The Yearling. NY: Scribner, 1938. 1st ed. (Top stain sl faded), else NF in VG + dj (extrems sl chipped). *Lame Duck.* $350/£219

RAWLINGS, MARY. The Albemarle of Other Days. Michie, 1925. Map. VG-. *Book Broker.* $35/£22

RAWLINSON, GEORGE. History of Ancient Egypt. NY: Dodd, Mead, 1882. 2 vols. xx,570; xiv,576pp. (Edges rubbed, spine ends frayed or chipped), o/w Good. *Worldwide.* $45/£28

RAWLINSON, GEORGE. The Seventh Great Oriental Monarchy. London: Longmans, Green, 1876. 1st ed. Chromolitho frontis, (4),xxii,692pp; 18 full-pg plts, engr fldg map outlined by hand in blue/pink. Dk brn cl (spine top sl chipped). *Karmiole.* $100/£63

RAWLINSON, GEORGE. The Sixth Great Oriental Monarchy or the Geography, History, and Antiquities of Parthia. London/NY: Longman/Scribner, 1872. 1st ed. Hand colored frontis, xvi,458pp; 2 fldg maps. Lib buckram. (Ex-lib; sl rubbed, lib spine #), o/w Good. *Worldwide.* $45/£28

RAWORTH, TOM. The Big Green Day. London: Trigram, 1968. 1st ed. Translucent frontis. NF in ptd illus wrappers. *Turtle Island.* $50/£31

RAWSON, GEOFFREY. Bligh of the 'Bounty.' London: Philip Allan, 1930. 1st ed. 8 plts, 1 map. (Fore-edge spotted; extrems sl worn.) *Hollett.* $88/£55

RAWSON, MARION NICHOLL. Little Old Mills. Dutton, (1935). 1st ed. Good in dj (worn). *Rybski.* $40/£25

RAWSTORNE, LAWRENCE. Gamonia; or, The Art of Preserving Game. London, 1837. 1st ed, w/half-title and errata slip. 15 hand-colored aquatint plts. Orig brn morocco, gilt. (Bkpl, few sigs loose.) *Swann*.* $460/£288

RAY, ANTHONY. English Delftware Pottery in the Robert Hall Warren Collection, Ashmolean Museum, Oxford. Boston: Boston Book & Art Shop, (1968). 1st Amer ed. 8 color plts, 104 add'l plts. Red cl, gilt. Good in dj. *Karmiole.* $65/£41

RAY, EDWARD. Golf Clubs and How to Use Them. NY: Robert McBride, 1922. 1st ed. Pict spine label. (Soiled, spine foot lacks sm piece), else VG. *Pacific*.* $75/£47

RAY, EDWARD. Inland Golf. London: T. Werner Laurie, (c.1914). 1st ed. Red cl, gilt. (Emb stamp, sig; sm nick to spine), else Fine. *Pacific*.* $46/£29

RAY, GORDON N. The Illustrator and the Book in England from 1790 to 1914. (NY/Oxford): J.P. Morgan Library/OUP, (1976). 1st ed. Color frontis. Fine. *Pacific*.* $92/£58

RAY, MAN. Alphabet for Adults. Beverly Hills: Copley Galleries, 1948. One of 500. 39 repros of dwgs by Ray, incl tp. 1/4 cl, pict bds. *Swann*.* $402/£251

RAY, MAN. Photographies 1920-1934 Paris. Hartford, n.d. Folio. Plastic multi-ring binder, color photo-pict bds (extrems worn; sl soiled, offsetting). *Swann*.* $1,725/£1,078

RAY, MAN. Self-Portrait. Boston/Toronto, (1963). 1st ed. (Eps lt soiled; spotted, soiled.) Dj (torn, rubbed). *Swann*.* $46/£29

RAY, MILTON S. The Farallones, the Painted World and Other Poems of California.... SF: John Henry Nash, 1934. 1st ed. One of 2000. 2 vols. 1/2 vellum, gilt. Fine in slipcase (sl worn). *Pacific*.* $46/£29

RAY, OPHELIA. Daughter of the Tejas. Greenwich: NYGS, (1965). 1st ed, 2nd issue dj in white. Fine in dj. *Pacific*.* $46/£29

RAY, ROBERT J. Cage of Mirrors. Lippincott, 1980. 1st ed, 1st bk. NF in dj. *Murder.* $75/£47

RAY, WILLIAM. Horrors of Slavery. Troy, (NY): Oliver Lyon, 1808. 1st ed. 298pp. Contemp calf. Good (inscrips; few ll torn, one w/loss of several words; worn). *Lefkowicz.* $200/£125

RAY, WILLIAMS. Horrors of Slavery: Or The American Tars in Tripoli. Troy: Oliver Lyon, 1808. 296pp. Copyright slip on tp verso. Orig full calf. Good. *Cullen.* $225/£141

RAY-JONES, TONY. A Day Off. Boston: NYGS, (1977). 1st US ed. 120 full-pg b/w photo plts. (1st, last ll lt foxed), else VG in pict stiff wrappers. *Cahan.* $60/£38

RAYLEIGH, LORD and WILLIAM RAMSAY. Argon, a New Constituent of the Atmosphere. Washington: Smithsonian Inst, 1896. 1st ed. (iv),43pp. Fine. *Bickersteth.* $104/£65

RAYMOND, ALEX. Flash Gordon in the Water World of Mongo. Big Little Book. Racine: Whitman, 1937. Pict bds. (Bds sl faded), else NF. *Pacific*.* $35/£22

RAYMOND, ALEX. Flash Gordon: The Tournament of Death. Chicago: Pleasure Books, (1935). 3 color pop-ups. Pict bds. (Spine soiled, rubbed, chipped), else VG. *Pacific*.* $316/£198

RAYMOND, DANIEL. Thoughts on Political Economy. Balt, 1820. 1st ed. Uncut. Orig bds (backstrip chipped, cvrs detached; browned, lib stamp tp). *Swann*.* $287/£179

RAYMOND, DORA. Captain Lee Hall of Texas. Norman: Univ of OK, 1940. 1st ed. NF in dj (chipped). Howes R83. *Labordo.* $135/£84

RAYMOND, ELEANOR. Early Domestic Architecture of Pennsylvania. NY: William Helburn, 1931. 1st ed. One of 1100. 159 plts. Plum cl, gilt. VG (spine lt faded, extrems lt worn). *House.* $225/£141

RAYMOND, ERNEST. The Jesting Army. NY: D. Appleton, 1931. 1st US ed. Blue cl. VG + (ink name; cl sl sunned at edges) in dj (lt edgeworn). *Reese.* $45/£28

RAYMOND, JOHN. Simenon in Court. London: Hamish Hamilton, 1968. 1st ed. Fine in Fine dj. *Janus.* $45/£28

RAYMOND, OLIVER. The Art of Fishing on the Principle of Avoiding Cruelty, with Approved Rules for Fishing. London: Longmans, Green, 1866. 1st ed. Unopened. Grn cl, gilt. NF (bkpl). *Pacific*.* $115/£72

RAYMOND, ROSSITER W. Camp and Cabin. NY: Fords, Howard, & Hulbert, 1880. 1st ed. Wood-engr frontis, 243pp. Brn coated eps, edges stained red. Dk brn cl, gilt. (Contemp ink inscrip; extrems sl rubbed.) Cvrs VG. *Baltimore*.* $90/£56

RAYMOND, THOMAS L. Stephen Crane. Newark: Carteret Book Club, 1923. 1st ed. One of 250 ptd. NF. *Pacific*.* $23/£14

RAYNAL, MAURICE. Modern French Painters. NY, (1928). 1st Amer ed. Fine (sl rubbed). *Polyanthos.* $30/£19

RAYNAL, PAUL. The Unknown Warrior: A Tragedy in Three Acts. Cecil Lewis (trans). NY/London: Century, (1928). 1st US ed. Black cl, multi-colored moire over bds. VG (ink name, date; corners sl rubbed). *Reese.* $30/£19

RAYNER, D. H. and J. E. HEMINGWAY (eds). The Geology and Mineral Resources of Yorkshire. London: Yorkshire Geological Soc, 1974. 1st ed. Color frontis, fldg color map. Mint in dj. *Hollett.* $152/£95

RAYNER, J. L. and G. T. CROOK (eds). The Complete Newgate Calendar. London: Privately ptd for the Navarre Soc Ltd, 1926. 1st ed. 5 vols. 26 plts. Panelled dk gray cl, gilt. VG set (sl scuffed, rubbed). *Gach.* $125/£78

RAYNER, RICHARD. The Elephant. London: Jonathan Cape, (1991). Signed. Fine in Fine dj. *Dermont.* $50/£31

RAYNOLDS, W. F. Report of the Exploration of the Yellowstone River. Washington, 1868. 1st ed. Fldg map (tear, breaks at folds). *Kane*.* $150/£94

REA, ELLA M. Mutiny on the Long Trail and King Chinook. Portland: Metropolitan, 1933. 1st ed. VG. *Perier.* $32./£20

REACH, ANGUS B. Clement Lorimer; or, The Book with the Iron Clasps. London: David Bogue, 1849. (8),280pp; 12 etched plts (incl frontis) by George Cruikshank. Marbled eps; teg. Full polished tan calf, gilt, morocco labels. Bound by Riviere. (Spine, edges sl dknd, lt rubbed), else NF. *Pacific*.* $207/£129

READ, GARDNER. Thesaurus of Orchestral Devices. Pitman, 1953. 1st ed. VG in dj (chipped, defective). *Hollett.* $72/£45

READ, HERBERT and LESLIE MARTIN. Gabo. Cambridge, (1957). 10 stereoscopic repros; 3-D glasses in rear cvr pocket. *Swann*.* $69/£43

READ, HERBERT. A Coat of Many Colours: Occasional Essays. London: Routledge, (1945). 1st ed. Frontis. Gilt red cl. VG. *Reese.* $25/£16

READ, HERBERT. The End of a War. (London): Faber & Faber, (1933). 1st ed. Ptd bds (Top edge dust-spotted), else Nice in dj (closed creased tear bottom edge fr panel). *Reese.* $50/£31

READ, HERBERT. The End of a War. London, 1933. 1st ed. Fine in dj. *Petersfield.* $29/£18

READ, HERBERT. English Stained Glass. London/NY, 1926. 69 plts. (Sl foxed; spine sl sunned.) *Washton.* $95/£59

READ, HERBERT. The Green Child. Grey Walls, 1945. 1st ed thus. Ltd ed. 8vo. 137pp; 4 color plts by Felix Kelly. NF (eps lt foxed) in dj (sl frayed). *Bookmark.* $48/£30

READ, HERBERT. The Green Child. London: Eyre & Spottiswoode, 1947. Fine in dj (spine sl dknd, edges sl rubbed). *Ulysses.* $88/£55

READ, HERBERT. In Retreat. London: Hogarth, 1925. 1st ed. Fldg map. Pict stiff wrappers. (Eps foxed; wrappers lt soiled), else VG. *Reese.* $85/£53

READ, HERBERT. In Retreat. London: Leonard & Virginia Woolf, 1925. 1st ed. Fine in pale gray dec wrappers. *Maggs.* $104/£65

READ, HERBERT. Poems, 1914-34. London, 1935. 1st ed. (Eps sl foxed.) Dj (faded). *Petersfield.* $56/£35

READ, HERBERT. A World Within a War. London, 1944. 1st ed. (Eps, tp, prelims spotted.) Dj. *Petersfield.* $24/£15

READ, PIERS PAUL. The Junkers. NY, 1969. 1st ed. VG in dj (repaired). *Typographeum.* $16/£10

READ, PIERS PAUL. The Junkers. NY: Knopf, 1969. 1st Amer ed. Fine in NF white dj (sl dknd). *Between The Covers.* $45/£28

READE, BRIAN. Ballet Designs and Illustrations 1581-1940. A Catalogue Raisonne. London: HMSO, 1967. Folio. Purple cl. VG in pict dj. *Dramatis.* $100/£63

READE, BRIAN. Edward Lear's Parrots. Duckworth, 1949. 1st ed. 12 Fine color plts. Cl-backed pict bds. VG in dj (edges sl dusty). *Hollett.* $48/£30

READE, BRIAN. Regency Antiques. Batsford, 1953. 1st ed. Color frontis, 181 plts. VG in dj (price-clipped). *Hollett.* $72/£45

READING, PETER. Fiction. Martin Secker & Warburg, 1979. 1st ed. Signed. NF (spine ends, corners sl bumped) in dj (sl rubbed, mkd, clipped, later price sticker fr flap). *Ulysses.* $120/£75

READING, PETER. Water and Waste. Walton-on-Thames: Outposts, 1970. 1st ed, 1st bk. VG (erased inscrip; sl mkd, creased) in wrappers. *Ulysses.* $136/£85

READING, ROBERT S. Arrows over Texas. San Antonio: Naylor, (1960). 1st ed. Fine in NF dj. *Sadlon.* $25/£16

READY, OLIVER G. Life and Sport in China. London, 1903. 1st ed. 13 plts. (Feps lt browned; corners rubbed w/sl loss, lower edges lt dampspotted; sm wormholes.) *Edwards.* $256/£160

REAGAN, NANCY. My Turn, the Memoirs of.... NY, (1989). 1st trade ed. Signed. (Sm stain to fore-edge), else Good in dj (price-clipped). *King.* $75/£47

Real Mother Goose. Chicago: Rand McNally, (1916). 1st ed. 12x9.5. Blanche Fisher Wright (illus). Pict cvr label. VG- (lacks fep, sm tears to few pp, last pp sl dampstained). *Pacific*.* $46/£29

REATH, NANCY ANDREWS. The Weaves of Hand-Loom Fabrics. Phila: PA Museum, 1927. 1st ed. Blue cl, paper label. Mylar cvr. *Hermitage.* $35/£22

REBREANU, LIVIU. The Forest of the Hanged. A. V. Wise (trans). London: George Allen & Unwin, (1930). 1st British ed. Pub's dated rev slip laid in. Black cl stamped in red. Fine in VG pict dj (nicks, corner chips). *Reese.* $85/£53

REBUFFAT, GASTON. Between Heaven and Earth. Eleanor Brockett (trans). Nicholas Vane, 1965. 1st Eng ed. (Sm stain top of fr bd.) *Hollett.* $48/£30

REBUFFAT, GASTON. Starlight and Storm. Wilfrid Noyce and John Hunt (trans). Dent, 1956. 1st Eng ed. 37pp plts. VG. *Hollett.* $48/£30

Recent Expeditions to Eastern Polar Seas. T. Nelson & Sons, 1882. 1st ed. (144)pp. Contemp full prize calf, banded, gilt. Nice (sl mkd, lacks fep). *Ash.* $104/£65

RECHY, JOHN. City of Night. NY, 1963. 1st Amer ed, 1st bk. Fine (sl rubbed) in dj (rear panel sl soiled). *Polyanthos.* $35/£22

RECHY, JOHN. Numbers. NY: Grove, (1967). 1st ed. VF in VF dj. *Between The Covers.* $100/£63

RECHY, JOHN. The Sexual Outlaw: A Documentary. NY: Grove, (1977). 1st ed. VF in VF dj. *Between The Covers.* $65/£41

RECHY, JOHN. This Day's Death. NY: Grove, (1969). 1st ed, 1st bk. Advance rev copy w/pub's material. NF in NF dj. *Agvent.* $45/£28

RECHY, JOHN. This Day's Death. NY: Grove, 1969. 1st ed. Fine in Fine dj. *Beasley.* $35/£22

RECK, FRANKLIN M. Sergeant Pinky. NY: Dodd Mead, 1931. 1st ed. Pict stamped brn cl. Fine in NF pict dj (sm sticker abrasion fr panel). *Reese.* $45/£28

Recollections of an Excursion to the Monasteries of Alcobaca and Batalha. (By William Beckford.) London: Richard Bentley, 1835. 1st ed. Frontis port. Marbled edges. Contemp 3/4 brn calf, marbled bds. (Inscrip.) *Appelfeld.* $325/£203

Reconnaissance Report on the Potential Development of Water Resources in the Territory of Alaska. House Exec Doc No. 197. Washington: USDI, 1952. Good (edgeworn). *Perier.* $45/£28

Record of a School: Exemplifying the General Principles of Spiritual Culture. (By Elizabeth P. Peabody.) Boston/NY, 1836. 2nd ed. Old leather, marbled bds. VG. *M & S.* $475/£297

Record of Service of the Forty-Fourth Massachusetts Volunteer Militia in North Carolina, August 1862 to May 1863. Boston: Privately ptd, 1887. 364pp + index. Unbound, uncut, unopened. (Ends chipped, soiled.) *King.* $125/£78

Record of the Court at Upland, in Pennsylvania 1676 to 1681 [and one other work]. Phila: Historical Soc of PA, 1860. 1st ptg. Emb cl (very worn, chipped). Usable. *Boswell.* $125/£78

Record of the Federal Dead Buried from Libby, Belle Isle, Danville and Camp Lawton Prisons, and at City Point, and in the Field Before Petersburg and Richmond. Phila: Ptd by Jas. B. Rodgers, 1865. 1st ed. 168pp. VG in ptd wraps (sl chipped, spine worn). *Chapel Hill.* $95/£59

Record of the Proceedings of a Court of Inquiry Convened at the Navy Department...to Investigate the Circumstances of the Loss of the Exploring Steamer Jeannette.... (Washington: GPO, 1883). (ii),lll,(3)-363pp; 12 fldg maps, 3 fldg plans. VG (recent cl). *High Latitude.* $175/£109

Records of North American Big Game. NY, 1964. (Sl worn.) Dj (fraying, sl edge tears). *Oinonen*.* $100/£63

Records of the Past, Being English Translations of the Assyrian and Egyptian Monuments.... London: Bagster, 1873-88. 13 vols. Dec cl. *Petersfield.* $61/£38

Records of the Town of Newark, NJ, from Its Settlement in 1666 to Its Incorporation as a City in 1836. Newark, 1864. 1st ed. 294pp; lg fldg map. (Rebound.) *Heinoldt.* $15/£9

RECTO, CLARO M. Three Years of Enemy Occupation: The Issue of Political Collaboration in the Philippines. Manila: People's Publishers, 1946. 1st ed. Good in pict wraps (extrems sl worn). *Brown.* $20/£13

Red Riding Hood. Northampton: W.F. Graham, (ca 1950). 4to. 16pp (4 w/full-pg illus). Willy Schermele (illus). Color pict bds. Good. *Reisler.* $55/£34

Red Riding Hood. London: Bancroft, 1961. V. Kubasta (illus). 8 dbl-pg pop-ups, pull-tabs, incl fr cvr. Glazed pict bds. VG-. *Bookfinders.* $100/£63

RED, GEORGE PLUNKETT. The Medicine Man in Texas. (Houston: Standard Ptg & Litho, 1930.) 1st ed. Blue cl (extrems sl worn). NF. *Harrington.* $175/£109

REDFERN, W. B. Royal and Historic Gloves and Shoes. London: Methuen, (1904). 1st ed. 79 Good plts. Teg, untrimmed. Crimson buckram, gilt. (Lt worn; spine bottom, corners lt frayed; fr cvr lt spotted, edge bumped.) Internally Good (lt shaken, hinges cracked; lib ink spine # neatly removed, ink handstamps). *Baltimore*.* $90/£56

REDFIELD, JAMES. The Celestine Prophecy. NY, 1994. 1st ed thus. Fine in Fine dj. *Warren.* $75/£47

REDGROVE, H. Alchemy: Ancient and Modern. London: William Rider, 1922. 2nd ed. VG. *Blake.* $50/£31

REDMAN, BEN RAY. Down in Flames. NY: Payson & Clarke, 1930. 1st ed. Blue cl stamped in red. NF in cream dj (sl tanned). *Reese.* $65/£41

REDPATH, JAMES. Echoes of Harper's Ferry. Boston: Thayer & Eldridge, 1860. 1st ed. Bkpl of Carroll Wilson. (Spine, extrems sl dknd, sm spine tear), else VG-. *Pacific*.* $104/£65

REDPATH, JAMES. Echoes of Harper's Ferry. Boston: Thayer & Eldridge, 1860. Ads at end. (Cl faded.) BAL 143. *Rostenberg & Stern.* $300/£188

REDPATH, JAMES. The Public Life of Capt. John Brown...with an Autobiography of His Childhood and Youth. Boston: Thayer & Eldridge, 1860. 1st ed, early ptg. Frontis, (408)pp. Brn cl. Good (sl foxed, sl worn). *Lucas.* $50/£31

REECE, BENNY. A Bibliography of First Appearances of the Writings by A. Conan Doyle. Greenville, SC, 1975. 1st ed. Signed. Wrappers. As New. *Bond.* $22/£14

REECE, BENNY. A Bibliography of First Appearances of the Writings by A. Conan Doyle. (Greenville, SC): Furman Univ, 1975. 1st ed. Ltd to 300 numbered. VG in ptd wrappers. *Gravesend.* $25/£16

REECE, R. The Medical Guide. London, 1817. 12th ed. xx,418pp (lt foxed). Contemp bds (mkd, sl stained), cl spine, paper label. *Whitehart.* $128/£80

REED, C. W. and LOUIS K. HARLOW. Bits of Camp Life. Munich/NY: Obpacher Bros, 1888. 1st ed. Toned litho tp, chromolitho leaf, 6 ll toned lithos; 6 VG chromolitho plts. Patterned eps. Brn cl, cream finished bds (lt worn, dustsoiled, stains); chromolitho pict title fr cvr. Internally VG (sl aging; all pp once stuck together, now separated w/adhesions at all fore-edge margins). *Baltimore*.* $30/£19

REED, E. T. Mr. Punch's Prehistoric Peeps. London: Bradbury Agnew, (1896). Obl 4to. 26 full-pg cartoons, guards. Aeg. Red cl-backed grn pict bds, gilt. Fine. *Sotheran.* $205/£128

REED, F. W. A Bibliography of Alexandre Dumas Pere. J.A. Neuhuys, 1933. 1st ed. One of 300 numbered. Teg. *Forest.* $152/£95

REED, HENRY M. The A. B. Frost Book. Rutland: Charles E. Tuttle, (1967). 1st ed. 4to. 149pp; 70 plts (44 color). Natural linen. NF in color pict dj (extrems sl chipped). *House.* $200/£125

REED, HENRY M. The A. B. Frost Book. Rutland, VT: Charles E. Tuttle, 1967. 1st ed. Tan buckram. Fine. *Biscotti.* $80/£50

REED, HENRY. A Map of Verona. London: Cape, (1946). 1st ed, 1st bk. Grn cl. Fine in dj (sl rubbed). *Jaffe.* $250/£156

REED, HENRY. The Novel Since 1939. London: British Council, (1946). 1st ed. Ptd wrappers. (Wraps lt sunned), o/w NF. *Reese.* $30/£19

REED, IRVING McKENNY. Boyhood in the Nome Gold Camp. Mineral Ind. Research Lab/Univ of AK, (1969). 1st ed. VG in wraps. *Perier.* $20/£13

REED, ISHMAEL. Conjure. Selected Poems 1963-1970. Amherst: Univ of MA, 1972. 1st ed. Fine in dj. *Smith.* $125/£78

REED, ISHMAEL. The Last Days of Louisiana Red. NY: Random House, (1974). 1st ed. Red cl, gilt. Fine in dj (price-clipped). *Heritage.* $50/£31

REED, ISHMAEL. The Terrible Twos. NY: St. Martin's/Marek, (1982). 1st ed. Blue bds, gilt spine. Fine in dj. *Heritage.* $60/£38

REED, JOHN. The Day in Bohemia, or, Life Among the Artists.... NY, 1913. One of 500. Stiff ptd wraps. Slipcase (worn, pieces missing lower edge). *Kane*.* $150/£94

REED, JOHN. Ten Days That Shook the World. NY: Boni & Liveright, 1919. 1st ed. Port. Good+ (fr inner hinge sl cracking, offset few pp from clippings, sl damp discoloration and rippling top edge of text block; cl sl soiled). *Reese.* $125/£78

REED, JOHN. The War in Eastern Europe. NY: Scribner, 1916. 1st ed. Frontis. Tan cl stamped in black/red. VG (spine, edges sl dknd). *Reese.* $125/£78

REED, LEAR B. Human Wolves. 17 Years of War on Crime. Kansas: BWL, 1941. 1st ed. Signed presentation. VG+. *Any Amount.* $32/£20

REED, S. G. A History of the Texas Railroads. Houston, TX: St. Clair Pub, (1941). 1st ed. One of 2500 signed. Blue cl. (Spine sl sunned), o/w NF. *Chapel Hill.* $350/£219

REED, TALBOT BAINES. A History of the Old English Letter Foudries. Dawson, 1974. New ed. Fine in black cl. *Michael Taylor.* $40/£25

REEDSTROM, ERNEST LISLE. Bugles, Banners and War Bonnets. Caldwell, ID: Caxton Ptrs, 1977. 1st ed. Blue fabricoid. Fine in NF dj. *Harrington.* $70/£44

REEMAN, DOUGLAS. Badge of Glory. Hutchinson, 1982. 1st ed. NF (spine head sl bumped) in dj (spine head sl creased). *Ulysses.* $40/£25

REEP, THOMAS P. Lincoln at New Salem. (Petersburg, IL): Old Salem Lincoln League, 1927. (Lib mks; extrems worn), else Good. *King.* $35/£22

REES, DIANA and MARJORIE G. CAWLEY. A Pictorial Encyclopaedia of Goss China. Newport, 1970. 1st ed. Color frontis, 63 plts. (Lower bd soiled, spine faded.) *Edwards.* $56/£35

REES, GARETH. Early Railway Prints. Phaidon, 1980. 1st ed. Dj. *Forest.* $40/£25

REES, J. ROGERS. The Brotherhood of Letters. Elliot Stock, 1889. Beveled bds. Good (bkpl, lt spotted; spine bumped). *Tiger.* $19/£12

REES, JONATHAN. Memoirs of Evan Rees. London: Jonathan Rees, 1853. 1st ed. viii,115pp. Blind-stamped cl (spine, edges faded). *Young.* $120/£75

REES, LESLIE. Kurri Kurri the Kookaburra. Sydney: Sands, (1950). 7x10. Margaret Senior (illus). 42pp. NF (paper yellowed) in VG dj (edgeworn). *Price.* $35/£22

REES, THOMAS D. and DONALD WOOD-SMITH. Cosmetic Facial Surgery. Phila: W.B. Saunders, 1973. 1st ed. (Sig.) *Weber.* $100/£63

REESE, A. M. The Alligator and Its Allies. NY, 1915. Color frontis, 28 plts. (Pp yellowed; corners worn.) *Sutton.* $95/£59

REESE, GUSTAVE. Music in the Middle Ages. Dent, 1941. 1st Eng ed. 8 plts. VG in dj. *Hollett.* $72/£45

REESE, LISLE (ed). A South Dakota Guide. (Pierre): State of SD, 1938. 1st ed, 1st ptg. 64 plts on 32 sheets; fldg map in rear pocket. Red fabricoid. (Spine head sl worn), o/w Fine in dj (chipped, sl loss spine ends). Howes R141. *Harrington.* $250/£156

REESE, M. M. The Royal Office of Master of the Horse. London, (1976). VG in dj. *Woolson.* $40/£25

REEVE, ARTHUR B. The Gold of the Gods. Toronto: McClelland, Goodchild & Stewart, 1915. 1st Canadian ed. Fine in VG dj (nicks, sm hole in spine, torn). *Mordida.* $150/£94

REEVE, J. STANLEY. Foxhunting Formalities. NY: Derrydale, 1930. One of 990. Brn mottled paper over bds. NF. *Biscotti.* $150/£94

REEVE, J. STANLEY. Red Coats in Chester County. NY: Derrydale, (1940). One of 570 numbered. Signed, inscribed presentation. Gilt-dec cl. (Sl worn.) *Oinonen*.* $180/£113

REEVES, BRUCE DOUGLAS. The Night Action. NY: NAL, (1966). 1st ed. VF in Fine black dj (sl rubbed). *Between The Covers.* $65/£41

REEVES, JAMES. The Blackbird in the Lilac. OUP, 1952. 1st ed. Edward Ardizzone (illus). xi,96pp (inscrip). *Hollett.* $48/£30

REEVES, JAMES. History of the Twenty-Fourth Regiment, New Jersey Volunteers. Camden: Reunion Soc of the Twenty-Fourth Regiment, 1889. 1st ed. 45pp. Internally Fine (lt aging) in ptd buff wraps (lt sunned, dusty). *Baltimore*.* $90/£56

REEVES, JAMES. The Natural Need. London: Seizin Press/Deya Majorca/Constable, 1935. 1st ed. Errata slip tipped to contents leaf. Brn cl, gilt. (Margins spotted.) Dj (spine chipped, dusty). Julian Symons' copy w/sig. *Maggs.* $120/£75

REEVES, RICHARD STONE and PATRICK ROBINSON. Classic Lines: A Gallery of the Great Thoroughbreds. Birmingham, (1975). Signed by both authors. Obl folio. 1/2 leather. Dj. *Swann*.* $57/£36

REEVES, RICHARD STONE and PATRICK ROBINSON. The Golden Post. (NY, 1985.) Signed by both authors. Obl folio. Brn leather, gilt-emb port fr cvr. Cl slipcase. *Swann*.* $57/£36

Reform Medical Practice: with a History of Medicine, from the Earliest Period Until, the Present Time.... Macon, GA: M.S. Thomson, 1857. 1st ed. Thick 8vo. 15,1120pp (sl foxed, ink name). Contemp calf, leather label. *M & S.* $500/£313

REGAN, LOUIS. Medical Malpractice. St. Louis, 1943. 1st ed. *Fye.* $75/£47

Register of All Officers and Agents, Civil, Military, and Naval, in the Service of the United States, on the Thirtieth of September, 1839. Washington: Garrett Anderson, 1839. viii,311pp. Orig cl (fr cvr loose, dampstained). *Lefkowicz.* $95/£59

Register of the Commissioned, Warrant, and Volunteer Officers of the Navy of the United States...1862. Washington: GPO, 1863. 110pp. Ptd wrappers (loose). *Lefkowicz.* $75/£47

Regulations for the Army of the Confederate States 1862. Richmond: J.W. Randolph, 1862. Rebound in 1/4 leather. (Browned), else Good. *Dumont.* $450/£281

REICH, SHELDON. John Marin: A Stylistic Analysis and Catalogue Raisonne. Tucson, (1970). 2 vols. Djs, slipcase. *Swann*.* $373/£233

REICHARD, GLADYS A. Dezba, Woman of the Desert. NY: J.J. Augustin, (1939). 1st ed. Frontis. Fine in pict dj (spine dknd). *Argonaut.* $125/£78

REICHARD, GLADYS A. Navajo Shepherd and Weaver. NY: J.J. Augustin, (1936). 2nd ptg. Tan buckram. Fine in Good- dj (rubbed, chipped, closed tears), mylar cvr. *Harrington.* $75/£47

REICHARD, GLADYS A. Navajo Shepherd and Weaver. NY: J.J. Augustin, (1936). 1st ed. Burlap. Fine (spine sl sunned). *Pacific*.* $150/£94

REICHARD, GLADYS A. Navajo Shepherd and Weaver. NY, 1936. 1st ed. 15 photo plts. Ptd burlap-cvrd bds (spine faded). *Dumont.* $100/£63

REICHEL, WILLIAM C. A History of the Rise, Progress, and Present Condition of the Bethlehem Female Seminary. With a Catalogue of Its Pupils. 1785-1858. Phila, 1858. 1st ed. 468pp. Pub's cl. (Shelfworn, spotted; sl foxed, soiled.) *Oinonen*.* $30/£19

REICHERT, IRVING FREDERICK. Judaism and the American Jew: Selected Sermons and Addresses. SF: Grabhorn, 1953. One of 1500. Tan/red cl, ptd spine label. Fine. *Bohling.* $60/£38

REICHL, ERNST. Legibility: A Typographic Book of Etiquette. Brooklyn, (1949). VG + . *Truepenny.* $20/£13

REID, DAVID BOSWELL. Elements of Practical Chemistry, Comprising a Systematic Series of Experiments.... Edinburgh: Maclachan & Stewart, 1831. 2nd ed. xliii,555pp. Orig cl (neatly rehinged). *Young.* $72/£45

REID, DOUGLAS A. Soldier-Surgeon. Joseph O. Baylen and Alan Conwauy (eds). Knoxville, (1968). 1st ed. Map. VG + in VG + dj. *Pratt.* $30/£19

REID, ED. Las Vegas, City Without Clocks. Englewood Cliffs: Prentice Hall, (1961). (Ink name), else Fine in dj. *Perier.* $25/£16

REID, FORREST. A Garden by the Sea. Dublin/London: Talbot/T. Fisher Unwin, 1918. 1st Eng ed. Buckram-backed bds. Good (ep edges browned, fep mkd; fr cvr sl creased, cvrs rubbed, sl mkd; spine label browned, worn). *Ulysses.* $248/£155

REID, H. The Virginian Railway. Milwaukee: Kalmbach, 1961. VG + (spine bumped, sl shelfworn) in dj (sl edgeworn). *My Bookhouse.* $42/£26

REID, HARVEY. Biographical Sketch of Enoch Long: An Illinois Pioneer. Volume II. Chicago Hist Soc Colls, 1884. 134 pp. Uncut. Good in early dj (soiled). *Rybski.* $55/£34

REID, IRA DEA. Adult Education Among Negroes. Washington, 1936. 1st Amer ed. Fine in dec wraps. *Polyanthos.* $20/£13

REID, MAYNE. The Headless Horseman: A Strange Tale of Texas. Richard Bentley, 1866. Contemp 1/2 leather, cl (spine chipped, rear hinge repaired, corners rubbed; lt spotted). Good. *Tiger.* $128/£80

REID, SAMUEL C. The Scouting Expeditions of McCulloch's Texas Rangers. Phila: J.W. Bradley, 1859. Frontis, 251pp + ads; map. (Text lt browned; spine sunned, worn, shelfworn), else Good. Howes R175. *Brown.* $95/£59

REID, WILLIAM. Golfing Reminiscences: The Growth of the Game, 1887-1925. Edinburgh: J. & J. Gray, (1925). 1st ed. Blue cl, gilt. NF (museum bkpl). *Pacific*.* $546/£341

REIGART, J. FRANKLIN. The Life of Robert Fulton.... Phila: C.G. Henderson, 1856. 1st ed. 297pp; 26 plts. Blind-stamped brn cl, gilt. VG (pg 113-114 w/expertly repaired tear; extrems sl worn). Howes R178. *House.* $250/£156

REIGER, BARBARA and GEORGE. The Zany Grey Cookbook. Englewood Cliffs: Prentice-Hall, (1976). 1st ed. VF in dj. *Perier.* $25/£16

REIGER, GEORGE. The Bonefish. Stone Harbor: Meadow Run, (1994). One of 100 numbered, signed by Reiger and Peter Corbin (illus). Paper spine label (lt worn). Slipcase. *Oinonen*.* $140/£88

REIGER, JOHN F. The Passing of the Great West: Selected Papers of George Bird Grinnell. NY: Winchester, 1972. Blue buckram. Fine in NF pict dj. *Biscotti.* $50/£31

REILLEY, E. B. The Amateur's Vademecum: A Practical Treatise on the Art of Dancing. Phila: J. Nicholas, 1870. 1st ed. Frontis, 232pp; plt. Purple cl (faded). *Karmiole.* $100/£63

REILLY, JOSEPH J. James Russell Lowell as a Critic. NY/London: Putnam, 1915. 1st ed. Blue cl. *Lucas.* $40/£25

REIN, J. J. The Industries of Japan. London, 1889. xii,570pp; 23 (of 24) plts, 3 fldg maps. (Lib ink stamps throughout incl on plts; pp353-4, 365-8 repaired w/tape, pp321-2 w/sm corner portion lacking.) Gilt-edged calf-backed cl (rebound), raised bands, spine label. *Edwards.* $280/£175

REIN, J. J. The Industries of Japan. London, 1889. 1st ed. 3 maps. Pict cl, gilt. *Swann*.* $431/£269

REINAECKER, VICTOR. The Paintings and Drawings of J. B. C. Corot. London/NY, 1929. Tipped-in color frontis, 7 tipped-in color, 71 b/w plts. Teg, rest uncut. (Lt faded, spine sl chipped.) *Edwards.* $88/£55

REINHARDT, AD. Art as Art. Barbara Rose (ed). NY: Viking, (1975). 1st ed. NF in VG dj (price-clipped). *Turtle Island.* $100/£63

REINIKKA, MERLE. A History of the Orchid. Coral Gables, 1972. 1st ed. VG (ex-lib) in dj (sunned). *Archer.* $30/£19

REISS, LIONEL S. My Models Were Jews: A Painter's Pilgrimage to Many Lands. NY: Gordon, 1938. 1st ed. One of 1200. Signed. NF. *Pacific*.* $150/£94

REISS, STEPHEN. Aelbert Cuyp. London: Zwemmer, 1975. 1st ed. 12 color plts. (Ex-lib, stamp, fep sl mkd), o/w Fine. *Europa.* $77/£48

REIT, SEYMOUR. Those Fabulous Flying Machines. NY: Macmillan, 1985. Randy Weidner & Frank Ossmann (illus). 6 dbl-pg pop-ups, model in rear pocket. Glazed pict bds. VG. *Bookfinders.* $32/£20

REITLINGER, GERALD. The Economics of Taste. NY: Holt, Rinehart, and Winston, (1963). 1st ed. NF in VG dj. *Turtle Island.* $65/£41

REITMAN, FRANCIS. Psychotic Art. NY: International Universities, 1951. Color frontis, 16 plts. NF in dj (worn). *Turtle Island.* $50/£31

Remarkable History of Five Little Pigs. Boston: Brown, Taggard & Chase, 1857. 12mo. 32pp (1 pg marginally ragged). Color pict wrappers (rebacked). *Reisler.* $110/£69

REMARQUE, ERICH MARIA. All Quiet on the Western Front. A. W. Wheen (trans). London: Putnam, (1929). 1st ed in English. Tan cl stamped in grn. (Lt tape shadows on eps), o/w NF in NF dj (nicks to spine crown). *Reese.* $200/£125

REMARQUE, ERICH MARIA. All Quiet on the Western Front. A.W. Wheen (trans). Boston: Little, Brown, 1929. 1st US ed. Fine in VG+ pict dj (sl nicked). *Reese.* $125/£78

REMARQUE, ERICH MARIA. All Quiet on the Western Front. A.W. Wheen (trans). London, 1929. 1st Eng ed. Nice (feps lt spotted; sl tanned) in dj (frayed, worn). *Clearwater.* $200/£125

REMARQUE, ERICH MARIA. All Quiet on the Western Front. LEC, 1969. Ltd to 1500 numbered, signed by John Groth (illus). Fine in slipcase. *Swann*.* $57/£36

REMARQUE, ERICH MARIA. The Road Back. A. W. Wheen (trans). London: Putnam, (1931). 1st British ed. Tan cl stamped in grn. Fine in dj (few sm closed edge tears). *Reese.* $85/£53

REMARQUE, ERICH MARIA. The Road Back. Boston: Little, Brown, 1931. 1st US ed. Tan cl stamped in black/red. Fine in NF pict dj. *Reese.* $85/£53

REMINGTON, FREDERIC. Crooked Trails. NY: Harper, 1898. 1st ed. 49 plts. Pict cl. (Ink name to back of frontis, dated Oct '98; spine sl sunned), else NF. Howes R203. *Pacific*.* $196/£123

REMINGTON, FREDERIC. Done in the Open. NY, 1902. 1st ed, 1st issue, w/'Frederick' on fr cvr, 'Caught in the Circle' in red/blue. Folio. Pict bds, cl back. (Worn, spotted, soiled; sl foxed.) Howes R204. *Oinonen*.* $375/£234

REMINGTON, FREDERIC. Done in the Open. NY: Collier, 1903. Slim folio. 1 dbl-pg color print. Tan buckram, bds. (Pp sl aged, handled; cl worn, stained, old spotting.) Text VG. *Baltimore*.* $70/£44

REMINGTON, FREDERIC. Done in the Open: Drawings. NY: Collier, 1904. 1/2 cl, color pict bds. (Fr hinge split; soiled, rubbed), else VG. Howes R204. *Pacific*.* $92/£58

REMINGTON, FREDERIC. Men with the Bark On. NY: Harper, 1900. 1st ed, 1st issue, ptd on thinner paper. 32 plts. Pict cl, gilt. (Spine insect-damaged), else VG. *Pacific*.* $63/£39

REMINGTON, FREDERIC. Pony Tracks. NY: Harper, 1895. 1st ed. VG. Howes R207. *Labordo.* $400/£250

REMINGTON, FREDERIC. Sundown Leflare. NY: Harper, 1899. 1st ed. Frontis, viii,116pp + 4pp ads; 11 plts. Dec brn linen. Good. *Karmiole.* $125/£78

REMINGTON, JOSEPH and HORATIO WOOD, JR. The Dispensatory of the United States of America. Phila, 1918. 20th ed. (Sm tear tp.) *Fye.* $75/£47

Reminiscences of America in 1869. By Two Englishmen. (By Alexander Rivington & W. A. Harris.) London, 1870. 2nd ed. (20),332,(32)pp. (Emb private lib stamp, bkpl.) *Ginsberg.* $175/£109

REMISE, JAC and JEAN FONDIN. The Golden Age of Toys. D. B. Tubbs (trans). Greenwich: Edita Lausanne, (1967). 1st ed in English. Fine in dj, slipcase. *Pacific*.* $86/£54

REMONDINO, P. C. History of Circumcision from the Earliest Times to the Present. Phila: F. A. Davis, 1891. 1st ed. VG+ (lib stamp, rear pocket). *Beasley.* $75/£47

REMSBURG, JOHN E. and GEORGE J. Charley Reynolds: Soldier, Hunter, Scout and Guide. Kansas City, MO: H.M. Sender, 1931. One of 175. Frontisport. Fine. Howes R209. *Pacific*.* $161/£101

REMSBURG, JOHN E. and GEORGE J. Charley Reynolds: Soldier, Hunter, Scout and Guide. John M. Carroll (ed). Bryan, TX: Guidon, (1978). New ed, rpt of 1931 ed. One of 200. Fine in wrappers. *Pacific*.* $40/£25

RENARD, JULES. Carrots. G.W. Stonier (trans). London, 1946. VG in dj (frayed). *Typographeum.* $18/£11

RENARD, MAURICE. New Bodies for Old. NY, (1923). 1st ed in English. VF in VF dj. *Kane*.* $110/£69

RENAULT, MARY. The Charioteer. NY: Pantheon, (1959). 1st Amer ed. As New in dj. *Between The Covers.* $100/£63

RENAULT, MARY. Fire from Heaven. NY: Pantheon, (1969). 1st ed. Fine in NF dj (sl rubbed). *Between The Covers.* $45/£28

RENAULT, MARY. Funeral Games. NY, 1981. 1st ed. VG in dj. *Typographeum.* $18/£11

RENAULT, MARY. The King Must Die. NY: Pantheon, 1958. 1st ed. Fine in NF dj (sm tear). *Beasley.* $45/£28

RENAULT, MARY. The Lion in the Gateway. London: Longmans, 1964. 1st Eng ed. NF (spine head sl bumped) in dj (edges sl creased, spine sl dknd). *Ulysses.* $48/£30

RENAULT, MARY. The Mask of Apollo. Longmans, 1966. 1st UK ed. Fine in dj. *Williams.* $24/£15

RENAULT, MARY. Return to Night. London: Longmans, Green, 1947. 1st Eng ed. VG (spine head sl bumped) in dj (sl chipped, rubbed, mkd, one short tear). *Ulysses.* $56/£35

RENDELL, RUTH. The Copper Peacock. Hutchinson, 1991. 1st UK ed. Signed. Fine in Fine dj. *Martin.* $22/£14

RENDELL, RUTH. The Crocodile Bird. Hutchinson, 1993. 1st UK ed. Signed. Fine in Fine dj. *Martin.* $19/£12

RENDELL, RUTH. A Guilty Thing Surprised. Hutchinson, 1970. 1st UK ed. Signed. VG (sl bumped, sm chip to rep, creased) in Good dj (rubbed, creased, worn). *Williams.* $152/£95

RENDELL, RUTH. Kissing the Gunner's Daughter. Hutchinson, 1992. 1st UK ed. Signed. Fine in Fine dj. *Martin.* $19/£12

RENDELL, RUTH. A New Lease of Death. John Long, 1967. 1st UK ed. Signed. VG (fep sl torn) in dj (sl rubbed, edges sl worn, few short closed tears). *Williams.* $312/£195

RENDELL, RUTH. One Across, Two Down. Hutchinson, 1971. 1st UK ed. Signed. VG in dj. *Williams.* $312/£195

RENDELL, RUTH. A Sleeping Life. NY, 1978. 1st Amer ed. Fine in NF dj. *Warren.* $40/£25

RENDELL, RUTH. The Tree of Hands. London: Hutchinson, 1984. 1st ed. Black bds. Fine in dj. *Temple.* $32/£20

RENDELL, RUTH. Vanity Dies Hard. London: John Long, 1966. 1st Eng ed. Fine in dj (sl nicked, creased). *Ulysses.* $920/£575

RENDELL, RUTH. Wolf to the Slaughter. John Long, 1967. 1st UK ed. Signed. VG (sm pinhole to spine) in dj (edges rubbed, sl ring-mks to fr panel). *Williams.* $952/£595

RENDELL, VERNON. Wild Flowers in Literature. London: Scholartis, 1934. (Sm color photo on fep), else NF in dj. *Quest.* $65/£41

RENN, LUDWIG. (Pseud of Arnold F. V. von Golssenau.) After War. Willa & Edwin Muir (trans). London: Martin Secker, 1931. 1st British ed. Blue cl stamped in black. VG in dj (lt rubbed, smudged). *Reese.* $60/£38

RENN, LUDWIG. (Pseud of Arnold F. V. von Golssenau.) Death Without Battle. London: Martin Secker & Warburg, 1937. 1st British ed. Gray linen. Sound (foxed, spine rubbed). *Reese.* $18/£11

RENN, LUDWIG. (Pseud of Arnold F.V. von Golssenau.) War. Willa & Edwin Muir (trans). London, 1929. 1st Eng ed. Good (no dj). *Clearwater.* $56/£35

RENN, LUDWIG. (Pseud of Arnold F. V. von Golssenau.) War. Willa & Edwin Muir (trans). London: Martin Secker, 1929. 1st British ed. Tan linen stamped in gray. (Eps sl foxed), o/w VG in dj. *Reese.* $100/£63

RENNER, FREDERIC. Charles M. Russell: Paintings, Drawings, and Sculpture in the Amon Carter Museum. Austin: Univ of TX, (1966). 1st ed. Fine in pict dj (sl chipped). *Argonaut.* $75/£47

RENNER, FREDERIC. Charles M. Russell: Paintings, Drawings, and Sculpture in the Amon G. Carter Collection. Ft. Worth, (1966). One of 250 numbered, signed. Slipcase. *Swann*.* $149/£93

RENNERT, JACK and ALAIN WEILL. Alphonse Mucha: The Complete Posters and Panels. Boston, (1984). Folio. Dj (price-clipped). *Swann*.* $103/£64

RENNIE, JAMES. Alphabet of Scientific Angling, for the Use of Beginners. London: William Orr, 1833. 1st ed. Later plain brn wrappers. (Name stamp), else VG. *Pacific*.* $58/£36

RENNIE, R. Essays on the Natural History and Origin of Peat Moss. Edinburgh: Archibald Constable/John Murray, 1807. 1st ed. viii,233,(i)pp (prelims sl damped in lower margins). Orig cl (sl mkd), gilt. VF (pencil note on tp). *Hollett.* $192/£120

Renowned History of Primrose Prettyface, Who, by Her Sweetness of Temper and Love of Learning, Was Raised from Being the Daughter of a Poor Cottager, to Great Riches.... York: Ptd by T. Wilson & R. Spence, 1804. 1st ed thus w/Thomas Bewick cuts. 4.5x3.25. Woodcut frontis, 36 cuts within. VG in plain pink paper wrappers. *Reisler.* $600/£375

RENSCH, HERO EUGENE and ETHEL GRACE. Historic Spots in California. Stanford: University Press, 1932. Fine in VG dj. *Book Market.* $60/£38

RENWICK, ROBERT et al. History of Glasgow. Glasgow, 1921-34. 3 vols. 2 fldg maps. (Cl sl discolored.) *Edwards.* $200/£125

Report of the Commissioner of Agriculture for the Year 1868. GPO, 1969. (Foxed; stained, worn.) *Rybski.* $35/£22

Report of the Commissioner of Patents for the Year, 1854, Agriculture. Washington, 1855. 520pp. (Ex-lib?, blindstamp.) *Rybski.* $50/£31

Report of the Commissioner of the General Land Office. Senate Exec Doc No 2. 1850. 144pp (foxed); 10 fldg maps. (Nicely rebound.) *Dumont.* $100/£63

Report of the Director of the Mint upon Production of the Precious Metals in the U.S. During the Calendar Year 1888. Washington: GPO, 1889. 246pp. VG (spine faded). *Bookcell.* $30/£19

Report of the Governor of Washington Territory Made to the Secretary of the Interior for the Year 1879. Washington: GPO, 1879. 8pp. (Text dampstained), o/w Good in wrappers (extrems worn). *Brown.* $30/£19

Report of the Judge Advocate General of the 'Order of the American Knights' alias 'The Sons of Liberty,' a Western Conspiracy in Aid of the Southern Rebellion. (By Joseph Holt.) Washington: Daily Chronicle, 1864. 16pp. Ptd wraps. *Cullen.* $175/£109

Report of the Select Committee of the Senate of the United States on the Sickness and Mortality on Board Emigrant Ships. Washington, 1854. 1st ed. 147pp. (Foxed; cvrs, backstrip worn, torn, stained.) *Fye.* $125/£78

Report of the Trial of Arthur Hodge...for the Murder of His Negro Man Slave Named Prosper. Middletown: Tertius Dunning, 1812. 1st ed. 8vo. 186pp. Orig bds. Good (lt stained throughout, closed tear to 1 pg, bottom gutter of tp torn w/marginal loss; lacks backstrip, rear bd holding by cords). *Agvent.* $750/£469

Report of the Watering Committee of the Select and Common Councils of Philadelphia, Relative to the Termination of the Columbia and Philadelphia Rail Road. Phila: Lydia Bailey, 1830. 1st ed. 18pp. VG in contemp gray sewn wrappers. *Glaser.* $60/£38

Report on the Big Trees of California. Washington: US Dept of Ag, 1900. Later issue. 2 fldg maps. Black cl, gilt. (Marginal dust-soiling 2 ll.) *Dawson.* $100/£63

Report on the Collections of Natural History Made in the Antarctic Regions During the Voyage of the 'Southern Cross.' (By E. Ray Lankester & Jeffrey Bell.) London: British Museum (Natural History), 1902. 8vo. 53 plts (9 color lithos). Dk grn cl, gilt. NF (plts sl foxed). *Explorer.* $784/£490

Report on the Resurvey of the Maryland-Pennsylvania Boundary Part of the Mason and Dixon Line. Harrisburg: State Ptg Office, 1909. 1st ed. 82 plts, 2 fldg maps, lg fldg facs map in rear pocket. Black cl. Sound (2 lib stamps not affecting any plts; repairs to joints, spine ends). *House.* $200/£125

Report on Vaccination and Its Results, Based on the Evidence Taken by the Royal Commission During the Years 1889-1897. Volume I. London, 1898. 1st ed. 493pp. *Fye.* $100/£63

Report Upon the U.S. Geographical Surveys West of the One Hundreth Meridian, etc. Volume VII-Archaeology. Washington: GPO, 1879. 1st ed. 20 plts, 1 map. 3/4 brn morocco, raised bands, marbled edges. Fine. *Appelfeld.* $300/£188

Reports of Explorations and Surveys to Ascertain the Most Practicable and Economical Route for a Railroad from the Mississippi River to the Pacific Ocean.... Washington, 1855-9. Senate issue. Vols 1-4, 5-11. 4to. Tan buckram. (Ex-lib, blindstamps, few plts lt foxed, vol 11 maps brittle, chips, few repairs, maps weak at folds.) *Kane*.* $800/£500

Reports of Explorations and Surveys, to Ascertain...a Route for a Railroad from the Mississippi River to the Pacific Ocean, 1853-54. House Exec Doc No 91. Washington: Ptd by A.O.P. Nicholson, 1855. Vol I of US Pacific Railroad Survey. viii,134,vii,651pp, index. Contemp calf-backed marbled bds (scuffed). VG. Howes P3. *House.* $175/£109

Reports of Explorations and Surveys...1853-4. House Exec Doc No 91. Washington: Ptd by O.P. Nicholson, 1855. Vol II of US Pacific Railroad Survey. 128,132,45,187,50,22pp, index; lg fldg map, fldg chart, 13 tinted litho plts, 24 engr plts. Contemp calf-backed marbled bds (spine gilt dull). VG. Howes P3. *House.* $250/£156

Reports of Explorations and Surveys...1853-4. Senate Exec Doc No 78. Washington: Beverley Tucker, 1855. Vol II of US Pacific Railroad Survey. 128,132,45,187,50,28,22pp, index; lg fldg map, fldg chart, 13 tinted litho plts, 24 engr plts. Orig blind-stamped black cl, gilt. VG (some plts lt foxed; spine ends lt chipped). Howes P3. *House.* $250/£156

Reports on the Progress of Zoology and Botany 1841, 1842. Edinburgh, 1845. 1st pub of the Ray Soc. vii,348,104,xixpp. Contemp 3/4 leather (rubbed). *Oinonen*.* $110/£69

Repository of Arts, Literature, Fashions, Manufactures, &c. London: R. Ackermann, Jan 1809-Dec 1815. Volumes I, III, V, VIII-XIV only (of 14). 1st series. 8vo. 10 engr tps, 383 plts, mtd cl samples. (Lt spotting, offsetting; lacks few cl samples.) 19th-cent 1/2 crimson morocco by Morrell, spines gilt. *Christie's*.* $2,520/£1,575

Repository of Arts, Literature, Fashions, Manufactures, &c. Volumes I-XII. London: R. Ackermann, Jan 1, 1823-Dec 1, 1828. 3rd series. 12 vols. 8vo. 12 engr tps, 428 plts. (1 plt torn not affecting image, 2 plts torn and repaired, 1 plt detached; lt spotting, offsetting.) 19th-cent 1/2 crimson morocco by Morrell, spines gilt. *Christie's*.* $2,880/£1,800

Repository of Arts, Literature, Fashions, Manufactures, &c. Volumes I-XIV. London: R. Ackermann, Jan 1, 1816-Dec 1, 1822. 2nd series. 14 vols. 8vo. 509 plts. (Vol III lacks fldg litho, part of 1 fldg plt detached, 1 plt torn and repaired, few short marginal tears, occasional lt spotting or offsetting.) 19th-cent 1/2 crimson morocco by Morrell, spines gilt. *Christie's*.* $3,421/£2,138

Representative New Mexicans. Denver: C.S. Peterson, 1912. 1/2 leather. VG in later slipcase. *Dumont.* $300/£188

Reproduction of Thomson and West's History of Sacramento California with Illustrations. Berkeley: Howell-North, 1960. Facs rpt of 1880 ed. Black cl, gilt. Fine in dj (torn, chipped, lacks piece). *Pacific*.* $92/£58

REPTON, HUMPHREY. The Art of Landscape Gardening. John Nolen (ed). Boston: Houghton Mifflin, 1907. Color frontis, 22 b/w plts (9 w/overlays to show scenes before, after). (Spine sl scuffed, label worn), else VG. *Fair Meadow.* $185/£116

RERESBY, JOHN. The Travels and Memoirs of Sir John Reresby, Bart...Exhibiting a View of the Governments and Society in the Principal States and Courts of Europe.... London: Edward Jeffery, 1813. xii,414,(32)pp; 40 engr plts. Aeg. Period full calf, gilt-dec borders. VG (rebacked w/orig spine strip laid on). *Pacific*.* $219/£137

RESNICK, MARCIA. Re-Visions. Toronto: Coach House, 1978. 1st ed. 47 full-pg b/w photos. (Lt rubbed), else NF in pict stiff wrappers. *Cahan.* $85/£53

REUBEN, DAVID. Everything You Always Wanted to Know About Sex But Were Afraid to Ask. NY: McKay, (1969). 1st ed. VF in VF dj. *Between The Covers.* $300/£188

REUSSWIG, WILLIAM. A Picture Report of the Custer Fight. NY: Hastings House, (1967). 1st ed. Signed. 1 dbl-pg spread. Brn cl. Fine in Fine dj. *Harrington.* $50/£31

REVERE, JOSEPH W. A Tour of Duty in California; Including a Description of the Gold Region: And an Account of the Voyage Around Cape Horn.... NY: C.S. Francis, 1849. 1st ed. (12),305,(1)pp + (6)pp ads; 6 litho plts, fldg map. Orig blind-stamped dk grn cl. (Margins sl damp-stained, sm stub tear to map; lt stained, extrems worn, stabhole to spine), else VG. Howes R222. *Pacific*.* $230/£144

REWALD, JOHN. Paul Cezanne: The Watercolors. Boston, (1983). Folio. Slipcase. *Swann*.* $138/£86

REWALD, JOHN. Works in Sculpture. A Complete Catalogue. London, 1944. 112 plts. Relevant news clipping loosely inserted. 2-tone cl, gilt. (Margins lt browned, bkpl; sl rubbed.) *Edwards.* $96/£60

REXROTH, KENNETH. The Signature of All Things. (NY): New Directions, (1949). 1st ed. Cl-backed dec bds. Fine in dj. *Pacific*.* $46/£29

REY, GUIDO. Peaks and Precipices. Fisher Unwin, 1914. 1st Eng ed. Pict cl, gilt. VG (lt spotted; sl faded, scratched, neatly re-cased). *Hollett.* $192/£120

REY, H. A. Anybody at Home? London: C&W, 1939. 1st UK ed. 7 3/4 x 9 1/2. 12pp; flap lifts up on each pg. Good in pict wraps. *Cattermole.* $250/£156

REY, H. A. Feed the Animals. Boston: Houghton Mifflin, 1944. 1st ed. 4.5x4.75. (1 pg bound upside-down), else VG in cl-backed pict wrappers. *Pacific*.* $92/£58

REY, H. A. Feed the Animals. Boston: Houghton Mifflin, 1944. 1st ed. Lg sq 8vo. (20)pp; 11 full-color plts, fldg flaps covering 1/2 of picture. Cl-backed pict paper wraps. *Sotheran.* $125/£78

REY, H. A. How Do You Get There? London: Folding Books, n.d. (1951). 1st UK ed. 6 1/4 x 5 1/2. 11pp; a lift-the-flap bk. Comb binding. VG. *Cattermole.* $50/£31

REY, H. A. Where's My Baby? Boston: Houghton, Mifflin, 1943. 1st ed. 9 1/2 x 8 1/4. 24pp. VG in wraps. *Cattermole.* $75/£47

REY, H. A. Zebrology. London: C&W, 1937. 3rd ed. 9x7. 8pp. VG in wraps. *Cattermole.* $60/£38

Reynard the Fox, a Poem in Twelve Cantos. E. W. Holloway (trans). Dresden/Leipzig/London: A.H. Payne/W. French, (1852). 4to. Frontis, engr add'l tp, xiv,81,(1)pp; 37 steel engrs, 35 plts (browned, foxed). Marbled eps, edges. Contemp 1/2 grn morocco (extrems rubbed), gilt, raised bands, morocco-grain dk grn cl sides. Good. *Blackwell's.* $192/£120

REYNARDSON, C. T. S. BIRCH. Down the Road, or Reminiscences of a Gentleman Coachman. London, 1875. 3/4 morocco by Larkins. (Sl foxed; rubbed.) *Oinonen*.* $180/£113

REYNOLDS, E. W. The True Story of the Barons of the South. Boston: Walker, Wise, 1862. 1st ed. xii,(ix)-240 + 4pp pub's ads. Blind lt brn wavy-ribbed cl (lt worn, rubbed), gilt. Internally Good (lt aging). *Baltimore*.* $20/£13

REYNOLDS, FREDERICK. The Rage. Dublin: P. Wogan, 1795. 1st Dublin ed. (vii),73,(1)pp. Calf-backed bds. *Young.* $104/£65

REYNOLDS, GRAHAM. The Later Paintings and Drawings of John Constable. Yale Univ, 1984. 1st ed. 2 vols. 1087 plts (250 color). Djs. *Edwards.* $128/£80

REYNOLDS, GRAHAM. Painters of the Victorian Scene. London: Batsford, (1953). 113 plts (4 color). Nice in dj. *Turtle Island.* $50/£31

REYNOLDS, HELEN BAKER. Gold, Rawhide and Iron. The Biography of Dorsey Syng Baker. Palo Alto: Pacific Books, (1955). 1st ed. Fine in VG dj. *Perier.* $20/£13

REYNOLDS, HELEN WILKINSON. Dutch Houses in the Hudson Valley Before 1776. NY, 1929. One of 250 numbered. 2-toned cl (soiled, lt worn). *Oinonen*.* $140/£88

REYNOLDS, HELEN WILKINSON. Dutchess County Doorways and Other Examples of Period-Work in Wood 1730-1830. NY, 1931. (Lt worn.) *Oinonen*.* $80/£50

REYNOLDS, J. RUSSELL. Lectures on the Clinical Uses of Electricity. Phila, 1872. 1st Amer ed. 112pp. *Fye.* $125/£78

REYNOLDS, J. RUSSELL. A System of Medicine. Phila, 1880. 1st Amer ed. 3 vols. 1127; 935; 990pp. Full leather. *Fye.* $200/£125

REYNOLDS, JAMES. Andrea Palladio and the Winged Device.... NY: Creative Age, (1948). 1st ed. Color pict eps. White cl. VG in dj (price-clipped, spine sunned, sl worn, chipped). *Baltimore*.* $30/£19

REYNOLDS, JOHN. My Own Times, Embracing Also, the History of My Life. Belleville, IL, 1855. 1st ed. One of 400. 1-600,xxii pp. Later 1/2 leather, marbled bds. (Lacks port, last pg index; fr cvr detached but present), else Good. Howes R236. *Brown.* $200/£125

REYNOLDS, JOHN. My Own Times: Embracing Also the History of My Life. Chicago Hist Soc, 1879. 2nd ed. 395pp. Nice (spine label sl chipped). Howes R236. *Rybski.* $110/£69

REYNOLDS, JOHN. Pacific and Indian Oceans; or, The South Sea Surveying and Exploring Expedition. NY, 1841. Orig cl (spine faded; foxed throughout). Swann*. $373/£233

REYNOLDS, JOHN. The Pioneer History of Illinois. Belleville, IL, 1852. Lib buckram. (Lib stamp tp.) Howes R237. Swann*. $201/£126

REYNOLDS, PAUL. The Writing Trade. Boston, 1949. 1st ed, 1st bk. VF. Bond. $15/£9

REYNOLDS, QUENTIN. They Fought for the Sky. NY: Rinehart, (1957). 1st ed. Black cl, pale blue bds. (Ink stamp, heavy offset from clipping on tp), o/w VG in pict dj (lt edgeworn). Reese. $30/£19

REYNOLDS, REGINALD. My Life and Crimes. London: Jarrolds, 1956. 1st ed. VG in dj (sl chipped). Hollett. $32/£20

REYNOLDS, STEPHEN. The Voyage of the New Hazard to the Northwest Coast, Hawaii and China, 1810-13.... F. H. Howay (ed). Salem: Peabody Museum, 1938. One of 500. 12 plts. Teg. VG (ex-lib) in dj. High Latitude. $60/£38

REZANOV, NIKOLAI PETROVICH. The Rezanov Voyage to Nueva California in 1806. Thomas C. Russell (ed). SF: Thomas C. Russell, 1926. 1st ed in English. One of 260. 5 plts, guards. 1/2 cl, paper spine label. Fine in dj (spine sl faded, rubbed). Howes R244. Pacific*. $196/£123

REZNIKOFF, CHARLES and NATHAN. Early History of a Sewing-Machine Operator. NY: Charles Reznikoff, 1936. 1st ed. (Bd edges faded), else NF in dj (1-inch tear). Lame Duck. $150/£94

REZNIKOFF, CHARLES. Going To and Fro and Walking Up and Down. NY: Charles Reznikoff, 1941. 1st ed. (Top edges soiled), else VG + in dj (spine faded). Lame Duck. $125/£78

REZNIKOFF, CHARLES. Inscriptions: 1944-1956. NY: N.p., 1959. 1st ed. NF in NF dj (spine faded). Lame Duck. $85/£53

RHEAD, G. WOOLLISCROFT. History of the Fan. 1910. One of 450. Folio. Sm group of ephemera loosely inserted. (Spotted, fr hinge split.) Sotheby's*. $275/£172

RHEAD, LOUIS. Bold Robin Hood and His Outlaw Band. NY, 1912. 1st Amer ed. Pict cvrs. NF (spine sl sunned). Polyanthos. $30/£19

RHIND, WILLIAM. A History of the Vegetable Kingdom. London, 1855. 3rd ed. xii,720pp, w/addt'l engr tp, vignette; port, 20 (of 22) hand-colored plts, 19 plain plts. 1/2 calf, gilt. Henly. $179/£112

RHIND, WILLIAM. A History of the Vegetable Kingdom. Glasgow/London, n.d. c.(1860). Frontis port, x,711pp; 12 plts. Marbled eps, edges. 1/2 morocco, marbled bds, gilt. (Sl ink mk to frontis not affecting illus; edges, spine sl rubbed.) Edwards. $56/£35

RHODE, ELEANOUR SINCLAIR. The Old English Herbals. NY: Longmans, Green, 1922. 1st ed. 18 plts. Tan linen, gilt. (Bkpl.) Karmiole. $150/£94

RHODE, JOHN. Death in Wellington Road. Bles, 1952. 1st UK ed. NF (lg stamp) in dj (sl nicked). Williams. $72/£45

RHODE, JOHN. The Lake House. London: Geoffrey Bles, 1946. 1st ed. Yellow cl. (Cvrs lt dusty, foxed), o/w Nice. Temple. $38/£24

RHODE, JOHN. The Secret Meeting. Bles, 1951. 1st UK ed. VG + in dj. Williams. $72/£45

RHODE, JOHN. The Venner Crime. London: Odhams Press, 1933. 1st ed. Dk red cl. (Spine sl faded, gilt oxidized), o/w Fine in dj (2 sm chips). Temple. $19/£12

RHODES, DANIEL. Tamba Pottery. Palo Alto/Tokyo: Kodansha, (1970). 1st ptg. Fine in dj. Turtle Island. $45/£28

RHODES, EUGENE MANLOVE. Beyond the Desert. Boston: Houghton Mifflin, 1934. 1st ed. VG + (bkpl) in dj (spine stained, extrems lt worn). Pacific*. $29/£18

RHODES, EUGENE MANLOVE. Bransford in Arcadia or The Little Eohippus. Henry Holt, 1914. 1st ed. Frontis. VG. Authors Of The West. $100/£63

RHODES, EUGENE MANLOVE. The Little World Waddies. Chico, CA: William Hutchinson, (1946). 1st ed. One of 1000 ptd. Photo frontisport. Pict cl. Fine (sm bkpl) in dj (sm tears, chips). Pacific*. $161/£101

RHODES, EUGENE MANLOVE. Once in the Saddle and Paso por Aqui. Boston: Houghton Mifflin, 1927. 1st ed. (Clipping tipped to fep; shelfworn), else Clean. Dumont. $85/£53

RHODES, EUGENE MANLOVE. Once in the Saddle. Boston: Houghton Mifflin, 1927. 1st ed. Fine (sm bkpl) in dj (spine stained, fr panel lt rubbed). Pacific*. $69/£43

RHODES, EUGENE MANLOVE. Penalosa. Santa Fe: Writer's Editions, 1934. Ltd to 500 signed, numbered. (Bkpl; spine sl faded), else NF. Dumont. $225/£141

RHODES, EUGENE MANLOVE. Say Now, Shibboleth. Chicago: Bookfellows, 1921. 1st ed. One of 400. 1/2 cl, paper spine/cvr labels. (Few sl stains to fr cvr), else VG + . Pacific*. $46/£29

RHODES, EUGENE MANLOVE. The Trusty Knaves. Boston: Houghton Mifflin, 1933. 1st ed. VG (sm bkpl) in dj (spine sl rubbed, dknd, sl worn). Pacific*. $29/£18

RHODES, EUGENE MANLOVE. West is West. NY: H.K. Fly, 1917. 1st ed. Frontis. (Sticker remnants to fep, lt worn; shelfworn), else Clean. Dumont. $85/£53

RHODES, JOHN. The Surprising Adventures and Sufferings of John Rhodes.... NY, 1798. Contemp sheep. (Browned, lacks feps.) Swann*. $230/£144

RHODES, MAY D. The Hired Man on Horseback. Boston, 1938. 1st ed. VG in dj (sl worn). Woolson. $65/£41

RHODES, MAY D. The Hired Man on Horseback. Boston: Houghton Mifflin, 1938. 1st ed. Fine in dj (chipped). Labordo. $65/£41

RHODES, R. C. The Plays and Poems of Richard Brinsley Sheridan. Oxford: Basil Blackwell, 1928. 3 vols. Frontisport, 2 plts. Blue cl (extrems sl rubbed). Maggs. $160/£100

RHODES, RICHARD S. The Audiphone, and How to Use It in Hearing Through the Teeth. Chicago: Rhodes & McClure, 1895. Apparent 1st ed. 1 plt. Aeg. (Corners, spine lt worn, few wrinkles to rear cvr), o/w Fine. Pirages. $100/£63

RHODES, S. A. Gerard de Nerval 1808-1855. London, (1952). Frontis. NF in dj (rubbed, sm tear; spine sunned). Polyanthos. $25/£16

RHODES, WILLIAM BARNES. Bombastes Furioso: A Burlesque Tragic Opera. Thomas Rodd, et al & T. Griffiths, 1830. 1st Cruikshank ed. George Cruikshank (illus). 36pp; 7 full-pg woodcuts. Inner dentelles, aeg, by Riviere. Full mottled calf, gilt borders to sides, spine lettered in gilt. (Pp10-18 foxed), o/w VG. Sotheran. $477/£298

RHODIUS, APOLLONIUS. Argonautica, or The Quest of Jason for the Golden Fleece. Athens: LEC, 1957. One of 1500 ptd. Signed by A. Tassos (illus). NF in VG- slipcase (insect damage). Pacific*. $52/£33

RHOIDIS, EMMANUEL. Pope Joan. Charles Hastings Collette (trans). George Redway, 1886. 1st ed in English. 96pp + 2pp ads. Good (feps browned, edges sl browned; sl mkd, top edges dusty, spine browned, ends sl bumped, edges faded). Ulysses. $120/£75

Rhymes for the Nursery. By the Authors of 'Original Poems.' (By Ann and Jane Taylor.) London: Darton, Harvey, & Darton, 1810. 4th ed. Tall 16mo. Copperplt engr frontis dated Sept 1st, 1807; 95pp + 4pp pub's list (pg edges roughly cut, sm piece of paper transferred from tp to frontis, not affecting image). Leather-backed bds (worn), gilt. VG. Reisler. $450/£281

RHYS, HORTON. A Theatrical Trip for a Wager! Through Canada and the United States. London: Charles Dudley, 1861. 1st ed. 8vo. Frontisport, 3 prelim ll, (3)-140(i.e.144)pp; 3 color plts. Blue cl (sl rubbed, bubbled), gilt. Howes R245. *Mott.* $600/£375

RIBOUD, MARC. Face of North Vietnam. Text by Philippe Devillers. NY: Holt, Rinehart and Winston, 1970. 1st ed. NF in VG+ dj (extrms rubbed). *Smith.* $150/£94

RICARDO, DAVID. On the Principles of Political Economy, and Taxation. London: John Murray, 1817. 1st ed. 8vo. viii,589,(i),(xiii)pp; Trimmed. Later 19th-cent brn calf, marbled bds, brn leather spine labels. (Lt foxed, lt pencil mks few ll, ink sig, bkpl; lacks 1/2-title, 8pp of pub's ads; later cl-tape reinforcement to hinges; edges lt worn, spine rubbed, gilt sl flaked.) *Baltimore*. $6,200/£3,875

RICARDO, DAVID. On the Principles of Political Economy, and Taxation. Georgetown, DC: Joseph Milligan, 1819. 1st Amer ed. 8vo. viii,448,(8)pp. Recent 1/4 calf, marbled bds. (Text browned, last few pp lt dampstained; rebound), o/w Good. *Brown.* $950/£594

RICARDO, DAVID. On the Principles of Political Economy, and Taxation. John Murray, 1819. 2nd ed. 8vo. 1 ad leaf at end. Contemp calf. (Tp sl discolored.) *Sotheby's*. $1,472/£920

RICCI, C. Pintoricchio (Bernardino di Betto of Perugia). London/Phila: Heinemann/Lippincott, 1902. 6 photogravure, 15 color plts. (Sl loose; sl worn, spine ends frayed.) *Ars Artis.* $240/£150

RICCI, CORRADO. Baroque Architecture and Sculpture in Italy. Stuttgart, 1926. 1st Eng ed. Fine in dj (sl nicked, neatly repaired). *Clearwater.* $144/£90

RICCIUTI, ITALO WILLIAM. New Orleans and Its Environs. NY: William Helburn, 1938. Folio. (Lt worn.) *Oinonen*. $80/£50

RICCIUTI, ITALO WILLIAM. New Orleans and Its Environs: The Domestic Architecture, 1727-1870. NY, (1938). 135 b/w plts. (Cvrs soiled.) *Swann*. $92/£58

RICE, ANNE. Cry to Heaven. NY, 1982. 1st ed. Signed. NF in NF dj. *Warren.* $75/£47

RICE, ANNE. Cry to Heaven. NY: Knopf, 1982. 1st ed. NF in dj. *Pacific*. $75/£47

RICE, ANNE. Cry to Heaven. NY: Knopf, 1982. 1st ed. Inscribed, signed. Fine in dj. *Pacific*. $98/£61

RICE, ANNE. The Feast of All Saints. NY: S&S, (1979). 1st ed. (Label), else NF in dj (fr panel lacks sm piece). *Pacific*. $46/£29

RICE, ANNE. The Feast of All Saints. NY: S&S, (1979). Uncorrected proof. NF in ptd wrappers (spine soiled). *Pacific*. $58/£36

RICE, ANNE. The Feast of All Saints. NY: S&S, (1979). 1st ed. Fine in dj. *Pacific*. $81/£51

RICE, ANNE. The Feast of All Saints. NY, 1979. 1st ed. NF in Fine dj. *Warren.* $75/£47

RICE, ANNE. Interview with the Vampire. NY: Knopf, 1976. 1st ed. (Lower extrems sl faded), else VG in dj (spine head chipped, foot rubbed, sm tear, scratches, scrape fr panel). *Pacific*. $316/£198

RICE, ANNE. Interview with the Vampire. Knopf, 1976. 1st US ed (true 1st) ed. VG+ in VG metallic dj (sl creased). *Williams.* $520/£325

RICE, ANNE. The Mummy; or, Ramses the Damned. London: C&W, (1989). 1st hb ed. Fine in Fine dj. *Other Worlds.* $125/£78

RICE, ANNE. The Queen of the Damned. NY: Knopf, 1988. 1st ed. Inscribed, signed. Fine in dj. *Pacific*. $52/£33

RICE, ANNE. The Queen of the Damned. NY, 1988. One of 124 numbered, signed. Uncut. Leather-backed bds (lt worn). *Oinonen*. $80/£50

RICE, ANNE. The Vampire Lestat. NY, 1985. 1st ed. Orig prospectus, card laid in. Uncut. (Lt worn.) Dj. *Oinonen*. $50/£31

RICE, ANNE. The Vampire Lestat. NY: Knopf, 1985. 1st ed. NF in dj. *Pacific*. $104/£65

RICE, ANNE. The Vampire Lestat. NY, 1985. 1st ed. Signed. Fine in NF dj. *Warren.* $125/£78

RICE, ANNE. The Vampire Lestat. NY: Knopf, 1985. 1st ed. Signed. Fine in dj. *Pacific*. $161/£101

RICE, ANNE. The Vampire Lestat. NY: Knopf, 1985. Uncorrected proof. Fine in ptd wrappers. *Pacific*. $230/£144

RICE, DAVID TALBOT. The Art of Byzantium. London, 1959. 44 tipped-in color, 196 b/w plts. Good in dj. *Washton.* $85/£53

RICE, EDWARD LE ROY. Monarchs of Minstrelsy, from 'Daddy' Rice to Date. NY: Kenny Pub, (1911). 1st ed. Frontis port. Teg. (Ex-lib; sl shelfworn.) *Dramatis.* $70/£44

RICE, ELMER. Cue for Passion. NY: Dramatists Play Service, (1959). 1st ed. VF in VF dj. *Between The Covers.* $150/£94

RICE, ELMER. The Grand Tour. NY: Dramatists Play Service, (1952). 1st ed. VF in dj (1/16 inch short). *Between The Covers.* $125/£78

RICE, ELMER. The Show Must Go On. NY: Viking, 1949. 1st ed. (Sm edge tear 2 pp), else VF in VF dj (sl rubbed). *Between The Covers.* $100/£63

RICE, GRANTLAND et al (eds). Golfers 1938 Yearbook. Nat'l Golf Review, 1938. 1st ed. Good (cvrs worn). *Plapinger.* $45/£28

RICE, GRANTLAND. Base-Ball Ballads. Tennessean, 1910. 1st ed. VG. *Plapinger.* $400/£250

RICE, GRANTLAND. The Bobby Jones Story, from the Writings of O. B. Keeler. Atlanta: Tupper & Love, (1953). 1st ed. (Emb stamp), else VG in Nice dj (spine sl dknd, ends sl rubbed). *Pacific*. $127/£79

RICE, HOWARD C., JR. and ANNE S. K. BROWN. The American Campaigns of Rochambeau's Army 1780, 1781, 1782, 1783. Princeton/Providence: Princeton Univ/Brown Univ, 1972. 1st ed. 2 vols. Black cl. Fine in djs, slipcase (sl worn). *Parmer.* $150/£94

RICE, HOWARD C., JR. The Rittenhouse Orrery; Princeton's Eighteenth-Century Planetarium, 1767-1954. Princeton: Univ Library, 1954. 1st ed. 16 plts. VG. *Weber.* $50/£31

RICE, JOSIAH M. A Cannoneer in Navajo Country. Journal of Private Josiah M. Rice, 1851. Richard H. Dillon (ed). (Denver): Denver Public Library, 1970. 1st ed. One of 1500. Frontis map. Brn cl. Fine in pict dj (chipped, torn). *Argonaut.* $60/£38

RICE, STANLEY. Life of Sayaji Rao III. Maharaja of Baroda. OUP, 1931. 1st ed. 2 vols. 8 plts. (Sl worn.) *Edwards.* $48/£30

RICE, WILLIAM B. The Los Angeles Star, 1851-1864. Berkeley: Univ of CA, 1947. 1st ed. Grn cl. Fine in dj. *Argonaut.* $60/£38

RICH, BARBARA. (Pseud of Robert Graves and Laura Riding.) No Decency Left. Cape, 1932. 1st ed. 8vo. Fine in John Aldridge dj (3 sm defects). *Sotheby's*. $2,760/£1,725

RICH, E. E. Hudson's Bay Company, 1670-1870. NY: Macmillan, (1961). 1st Amer ed. 3 vols. 6 ports (2 color), 3 fldg maps. Blue cl, gilt. VF set in ptd djs (sl stain to 1 spine head), sectioned slipcase. *Argonaut.* $350/£219

RICH, E. E. (ed). Colin Robertson's Correspondence Book, September 1817 to September 1822. London: Hudson's Bay Record Soc, 1939. 1st ltd ed. Fine. *Perier.* $85/£53

RICH, E. E. (ed). Copy Book of Letters Outward and Etc. Begins 29 May 1680, Ends 5 July 1687. London: Hudson's Bay Record Soc, 1948. 1st ltd ed. Fine. *Perier.* $60/£38

RICH, E. E. (ed). John Rae's Correspondence with the Hudson's Bay Company on Arctic Exploration 1844-1855. London: Hudson's Bay Record Soc, 1953. 3 maps (2 fldg). NF. *Explorer.* $144/£90

RICH, E. E. (ed). Minutes of the Hudson's Bay Company, 1679-1684. First Part 1679-82. London: Hudson's Bay Record Soc, 1945. 1st ltd ed. Fine. *Perier.* $85/£53

RICH, E. E. (ed). Simpson's 1828 Journey to the Columbia. Part of a Dispatch from Simpson to the Governor and Committee of the HBCo, London. London: Hudson's Bay Record Soc, 1947. 1st ltd ed. Fine. *Perier.* $100/£63

RICH, OBADIAH. Bibliotheca Americana Nova. London/NY, 1835. 1st ed. One of 250. (iv),424pp (lib stamps, foxed). Mod buckram. *Oinonen*.* $60/£38

RICH, VIRTULON. Western Life in the Stirrups. Chicago: Caxton Club, 1965. 1st ed. Frontisport, 3 plts. Orig prospectus laid in. Cl-backed marbled bds. (Sl edgeworn), o/w NF. *Harrington.* $45/£28

Richard and Rover. Phila: Amer Sunday-School Union, (1845). 12mo. Full-pg wood engr frontis, 24pp + 1pg list. Buff paper wrappers. Good (trace of glue on frontis verso, sl affecting fr wrapper). *Hobbyhorse.* $55/£34

RICHARD, MARK. The Ice at the Bottom of the World. NY: Knopf, 1989. 1st ed, 1st bk. Signed. Fine in Fine dj. *Robbins.* $60/£38

RICHARDS, A. J. (ed). The Pollination of Flowers by Insects. London: Academic Press, 1978. 1st ed. VG (bumped) in dj. *Archer.* $30/£19

RICHARDS, FRANK. Billy Bunter and the Blue Mauritius. Charles Skilton, 1952. 1st ed. VG in dj (worn). *Green Meadow.* $88/£55

RICHARDS, FRANK. Old Soldier Sahib. (NY): Harrison Smith & Robert Haas, (1936). 1st US ed. Tan cl stamped in red. Fine in VG dj (spine faded, sl tanned, sm chips, tears). *Reese.* $150/£94

RICHARDS, FRANK. Old Soldiers Never Die. London: Faber & Faber, (1933). 1st ed. Orange cl, gilt. (Sl used, nick to dj edge), o/w VF in dj. *Reese.* $850/£531

RICHARDS, G. TILGHMAN. Handbook of the Collection Illustrating Typewriters. Science Museum: HMSO, 1938. Wrappers. (Few marginal blind-stamps, accession stamp tp verso.) *Hollett.* $40/£25

RICHARDS, GRANT. Houseman 1897-1936. London, 1941. Fldg chart at rear. (Name, binding worn, faded.) *Woolson.* $20/£13

RICHARDS, GRANT. Housman 1897-1936. Oxford: OUP, 1941. 1st ed. 12 plts, fldg chart. (Edges sl damped.) *Hollett.* $40/£25

RICHARDS, J. A Treatise on the Construction and Operation of Wood-Working Machines. London: E. & F.N. Spon, 1872. 1st ed. xx,283pp; 117 plts. Cl over beveled bds (extrems worn). *Hollett.* $384/£240

RICHARDS, J. M. An Architectural Journey in Japan. Architectural Press, 1963. VG in dj (creased). *Hadley.* $32/£20

RICHARDS, J. M. High Street. London: Country Life Ltd, 1938. 1st Eng ed. 24 color lithos. Pict bds. VG (eps spotted, partly browned; spine ends, corners nicked, rubbed, sl bumped, rear cvr sl creased) in acetate dj (fragile, cellophane chipped), w/paper flaps, upper flap ptd. *Ulysses.* $1,520/£950

RICHARDS, RAYMOND. Old Cheshire Churches. Batsford, 1948-9. Deluxe ed. Rubric tp, color frontis, 3 color illus, fldg map, fldg plan. Marbled eps; teg. Full morocco, blind-edged raised bands. (Sl worn.) *Edwards.* $200/£125

RICHARDS, VYVYAN. Portrait of T. E. Lawrence. London: Jonathan Cape, 1936. 1st ed, 2nd imp. Blue cl. Fine in dj. *Maggs.* $40/£25

RICHARDS, VYVYAN. T. E. Lawrence. London: Duckworth, 1954. 1st ed, 3rd imp. Map. Red cl, gilt. Fine in illus dj. *Maggs.* $32/£20

RICHARDSON, A. E. and H. D. EBERLEIN. The Smaller English House of the Later Renaissance 1660-1830. NY/London, (1925). Inscribed, signed by Eberlein. (Corner bumped, spine ends repaired.) *Swann*.* $138/£86

RICHARDSON, A. E. and H. DONALDSON EBERLEIN. The Smaller English House of the Later Renaissance, 1660-1830. London: Batsford, 1925. 1st ed. Grn cl, gilt. (Card envelope to fr pastedown), else NF. *Pacific*.* $92/£58

RICHARDSON, B. W. The Asclepiad. London, 1884-95. 11 vols. xi,388; viii,388; viii,387; viii,400; (viii),396; (viii),400; (viii),400; viii,404; (viii),440; (viii),440; (viii),484pp. 3/4 leather, gilt. (Sm lib label, stamp; corners, edges rubbed), o/w VG set. *Whitehart.* $720/£450

RICHARDSON, CHARLES JAMES. Studies from Old English Mansions....Series I-IV. London, 1841-48. 4 vols. Folio. 1/2 leather (worn; foxed, sl soiled). Internally Sound. *Oinonen*.* $325/£203

RICHARDSON, CHARLES. Cassell's New Book of the Horse. London, 1911. 4 vols. 29 color plts, incl 3 anatomical frontispieces w/multiple superimposed flaps. *Swann*.* $126/£79

RICHARDSON, CHARLES. The Chancellorsville Campaign. NY/Washington: Neale, 1907. 1st ed. Grn cl. VG (sm spot rear cvr, spine sunfaded). *Chapel Hill.* $250/£156

RICHARDSON, DOROTHY. Deadlock. London: Duckworth, (1921). 1st ed, 1st issue. Signed. Blue cl w/pub's device ptd on rear cvr. Fine in pict dj (sl chipped). *Pharos.* $400/£250

RICHARDSON, DOROTHY. Deadlock. Duckworth, 1921. 1st ed. Pale blue cl (backstrip lt faded). VG (rubberstamp, feps lt browned) in dj. *Blackwell's.* $240/£150

RICHARDSON, DOROTHY. The Trap. Duckworth, 1925. 1st ed. NF in VG dj (lt soiled, chipped). *Fine Books.* $185/£116

RICHARDSON, E. RAMSAY. Little Aleck. A Life of Alexander H. Stephens. Indianapolis, (1932). 1st ed. (Bkpl, sl worn, dirty.) *Woolman.* $15/£9

RICHARDSON, EDWIN HAUTENVILLE. Forty Years with Dogs. London, c. 1925. (Sl foxed.) *Petersfield.* $48/£30

RICHARDSON, FREDERICK. Frederick Richardson's Book for Children. Chicago: M.A. Donohue, (1938). 1st ed. 8.75x11.25. Pict cvr label. (Spine ends, corners rubbed), else VG. *Pacific*.* $63/£39

RICHARDSON, GEORGE. Journal of the Gospel Labours of George Richardson.... London: Alfred Bennett, 1864. 1st ed. xxiii,363pp. Blind-stamped cl. Fine. *Young.* $88/£55

RICHARDSON, GEORGE. A Treatise on the Five Orders of Architecture.... London, 1787. Folio. 22 plts. Old calf-backed bds (worn, spine corroded; foxed). Internally Sound. *Oinonen*.* $450/£281

RICHARDSON, JAMES. A Compilation of the Messages and Papers of the Confederacy. Nashville: US Pub, 1906. 2nd ed. 2 vols. Frontispieces. Teg. Orig 1/2 red morocco. (Ink stamps), else NF set. *Chapel Hill.* $275/£172

RICHARDSON, JAMES. Wonders of the Yellowstone Region. London, 1874. 1st Eng ed. 256pp + fldg map, engr plts. Grn cl, gilt. VG. *Larry Price.* $95/£59

RICHARDSON, JOHN MUNSELL and FINCH MASON. Gentleman Riders Past and Present. London: Vinton, 1909. Uncut. Vellum sides, straight-grained leather back and tips. (Sl foxed, soiled; rubbed.) *Oinonen*.* $100/£63

RICHARDSON, JOHN. Arctic Searching Expedition: A Journal of a Boat Journey Through Rupert's Land and the Arctic Sea, in Search of...Sir John Franklin. London: Longman, Brown, 1851. 1st ed. 2 vols. viii,413; vii,426pp; fldg color map (1 corner repaired), 10 color litho plts. Marbled eps; all edges marbled. Contemp full grn leather (sl rubbed), highly gilt-dec spine. VG. *Walcot.* $1,408/£880

RICHARDSON, JOHN. The War of 1812. Toronto: Musson Book Co, 1902. One of 100. 15 ports (14 color), 9 plts, 2 maps, 2 facs. 1/2 black morocco. VG. *Adelson.* $285/£178

RICHARDSON, KENNETH. The British Motor Industry 1896-1939. Macmillan, 1977. 1st ed. VG in dj. *Hollett.* $40/£25

RICHARDSON, M. A. The Local Historian's Table Book. Newcastle-upon-Tyne, 1841-46. 8 vols. Contemp rose 1/2 calf. (Inner hinges sl weak; spines faded, extrems lt rubbed.) *Christie's*.* $341/£213

RICHARDSON, MARVIN M. The Whitman Mission: The Third Station on the Oregon Trail. Walla Walla, WA: Whitman Pub Co, (1940). Signed. VG in dj (worn). *Perier.* $40/£25

RICHARDSON, MARY E. The Life of a Great Sportsman (John Maunsell Richardson). London: Vinton, 1919. Uncut. Pict cl. (Sl foxed, lt dampstains; sl worn.) *Oinonen*.* $70/£44

RICHARDSON, OWEN WILLANS. The Electron Theory of Matter. Cambridge: CUP, 1914. 1st ed. Grn cl. Fine. *Weber.* $100/£63

RICHARDSON, SAMUEL. The Works. Henry Sotheran, 1883. One of 750. 12 vols. 8vo. Engr frontis. 19th-cent tree calf by Riviere, gilt. (Bkpl; vol 4 spine sl rubbed.) *Sotheby's*.* $1,011/£632

RICHERAND, A. Elements of Physiology. Phila, 1825. 447pp. Cvrs quite good. (Heavily foxed, brnd). Good. *Doctor's Library.* $75/£47

RICHIE, DONALD. Design and Craftsmanship of Japan. NY: Abrams, (1964). Folio. 1 fldg chart. Fine in dj. *Turtle Island.* $125/£78

RICHIE, DONALD. The Japanese Movie. Tokyo/Palo Alto: Kodansha Internat'l, 1966. 1st ed, 2nd ptg. VG in dj (sl soiled, torn). *Worldwide.* $45/£28

RICHINGS, G. F. Evidences of Progress Among Colored People. Phila: Geo. S. Ferguson, 1896. 1st ed. (Spine ends, joints rubbed), else VG. *Pacific*.* $63/£39

RICHLER, MORDECAI. The Acrobats. A. Deutsch, 1954. 1st ed, 1st bk. NF in VG + dj (lt dust-soiled). *Fine Books.* $195/£122

RICHLER, MORDECAI. Jacob Two-Two Meets the Hooded Fang. Knopf, 1975. 1st ed. Fritz Wegner (illus). 84pp. NF (spine head bumped) in VG dj (top spine edge chipped, sl edgeworn). *Price.* $45/£28

RICHMOND, W. The Grammar of Lithography. Wyman & Sons, 1886. 254pp. Blind-stamped cl. VG. *Moss.* $96/£60

RICHTER, A. G. Medical and Surgical Observations. T. Spens (trans). Edinburgh, 1794. xx,334pp. Contemp bds, paper-cvrd spine. (Ink inscrip, few pp sl discolored; worn, no title label, sm lib label), o/w Good. *Whitehart.* $256/£160

RICHTER, CONRAD. Early Americana and Other Stories. NY, 1936. 1st ed. (Bkpl), else VG in dj (repaired w/papertape from inside). *Woolson.* $35/£22

RICHTER, CONRAD. The Lady. NY: Knopf, 1957. 1st ed. VG in dj (lt worn). *Dumont.* $60/£38

RICHTER, ED. Making of a Big League Pitcher. Chilton, 1963. 1st ed. VG + in VG dj. *Plapinger.* $45/£28

RICHTER, FRANCIS C. How the White Sox Won the World's Championship for 1907. (N.p.): The Author, 1907. 1st ed. 16-pg pamphlet. Fine in stapled pict wrappers. *Between The Covers.* $950/£594

RICHTER, GISELA. The Archaic Gravestones of Attica. London: Phaidon, 1961. 1st ed. Folio. (Corner lt bumped.) Dj (tattered). *Archaeologia.* $125/£78

RICHTER, GISELA. Greek Art, Handbook. London: Phaidon, 1963. 3rd ed. Fine in dj. *Petersfield.* $29/£18

RICHTER, GISELA. The Sculpture and Sculptors of the Greeks. New Haven: Yale Univ, (1967). New rev ed. Fine in dj. *Archaeologia.* $100/£63

RICKARD, T. A. Journeys of Observations. SF: Dewey Publishing, 1907. 1st ed. VG. *Book Market.* $100/£63

RICKARD, T. A. Through the Yukon and Alaska. SF: Mining & Scientific, 1909. VG (sticker, rubber stamps; dec cl sl mkd) *High Latitude.* $110/£69

RICKARDS, MAURICE. Posters of the First World War. Walker, (1968). Good. *Rybski.* $40/£25

RICKETTS, CHARLES. Oscar Wilde: Recollections by 'Jean Paul Raymond.' Nonesuch, 1932. One of 800. Teg on the rough, rest untrimmed, partly unopened. White buckram, gilt. Fine (feps sl browned) in dj (sl internal tape repair, spine head lacks sm piece). *Blackwell's.* $480/£300

RICKETTS, CHARLES. Unrecorded Histories. Martin Secker, 1933. 1st ed. Ltd to 950. 6 full-pg silhouette illus. Teg, others uncut. Good in sand buckram, gilt. Bkpl, acquisition note of Lord Kenyon. *Cox.* $104/£65

RICKETTS, W. P. 50 Years in the Saddle. Sheridan, WY: Star, 1942. Stated 1st ed. NF. Howes R279. *Cullen.* $550/£344

RICKEY, DON, JR. History of Custer Battlefield. (Billings, MT, 1967.) 1st ed. (Title inked on sl faded spine), else Fine in wrappers. *Pacific*.* $63/£39

RICKMAN, THOMAS CLIO. The Life of Thomas Paine. London, 1819. 1st ed. 277pp; port. Later bds. (Text spotted, eps browned, inner hinges badly cracked; spine heavily frayed.) Howes R278. *King.* $95/£59

RICORD, PHILIPPE. A Practical Treatise on Venereal Diseases; or, Critical and Experimental Researches on Inoculation, Applied to the Study of These Affections. NY, 1842. 1st Amer ed. 339pp. *Fye.* $200/£125

RIDDELL, J. S. A Manual of Ambulance. London, 1897. 3rd ed. xvi,214pp. (Cl sl mkd), o/w VG. *Whitehart.* $56/£35

RIDDLE, A. G. Alice Brand. NY: D. Appleton, 1875. 1st ed. Dec reddish-brn cl. NF. *Sumner & Stillman.* $95/£59

Ride a Cock-Horse and Other Nursery Rhymes. C&W, 1940. 1st ed. 4to. B/w frontis, 14 rhymes, each accompanied by a full-pg illus by Mervyn Peake (10 hand-colored). Hand-colored pict paper bds. VG (eps lt spotted; spine ends, corners sl bumped) in hand-colored dj (sl chipped, nicked, mkd, dusty, spine sl dknd, tail lacks piece). *Ulysses.* $840/£525

RIDGE, JOHN R. A Trumpet of Our Own. Black Stone, 1981. One of 650. *Dawson.* $40/£25

RIDGELY, ANNA. A Girl in the Sixties. Octavia Roberts Corneau (ed). (Springfield, IL, 1929.) Port. Uncut. (Cvrs soiled, frayed.) Wraps. *King.* $22/£14

RIDGELY, LAURENCE BUTLER. Santa Francesca, Our Lady of the Golden Gate. SF: (The Author), 1935. Ltd ed. One of 250 ptd. Parchment-backed plum bds. Fine. *Harrington.* $30/£19

RIDGELY, MABEL L. The Ridgelys of Delaware and Their Circle...Letters 1751-1890. Portland, ME: Anthoensen, (1949). 1st ed. Signed presentation. Sm folio. 32 plts. *Heinoldt.* $40/£25

RIDGWAY, MARION V. Night-Night. NY: Howell, Soskin, 1944. 19x15 cm. Marjorie Thompson (illus). 11pp (5 fold-out). Pict bds. VG. *Bookfinders.* $45/£28

RIDING, LAURA. Americans. (L.A.): Primavera Press, 1934. One of 200. Patterned bds, cl spine, paper spine label (faded, 2 sm chips). *Dawson.* $350/£219

RIDING, LAURA. Contemporaries and Snobs. London: Jonathan Cape, 1928. 1st ed. Fair in beige cl (spine lettering faded). Julian Symons' copy w/sig. *Maggs.* $64/£40

RIDING, LAURA. Poet: a Lying Word. London, 1933. 1st Eng ed. (Name; one cvr edge sl nicked, sl mkd; lacks dj.) *Clearwater.* $104/£65

RIDING, LAURA. Twenty Poems Less. Paris: Hours Press, 1930. 1st ed. Folio. Uncut. Dec bds, morocco spine (ends sl worn). *Maggs.* $480/£300

RIDINGS, SAM P. The Chisholm Trail. Guthrie, OK: Co-Operative Pub, (1936). 1st ed. Fldg map. VG in dj. Howes R281. *Lien*. $200/£125

RIDINGS, SAM P. The Chisholm Trail. Guthrie, OK: Co-Operative Pub Co, (1936). 1st ed. Fldg map. Black pict cl. Fine in dj (lt chipped, soiled). Howes R281. *Glenn*. $250/£156

RIDINGS, SAM P. The Chisholm Trail. Guthrie, OK: Co-Operative Pub, 1936. 1st ed. Fine in dj (chipped, lt soiled, sm tape repair). Howes R281. *Labordo*. $250/£156

RIDLEY, BROMFIELD L. Battles and Sketches of the Army of Tennessee. Mexico, MO: MO Ptg & Pub, 1906. 1st ed. Frontis, errata slip. Rust cl. (Sl marginal dampstaining to last 50 or so pp, not affecting text), else VG. Howes R282. *Chapel Hill*. $325/£203

RIDPATH, JOHN CLARK. Beyond the Sierras. Oakland: Biobooks, (1963). 1st CA ed. Ltd to 650. Fine. *Book Market*. $35/£22

RIEFENSTAHL, LENI. Coral Gardens. NY: Harper & Row, 1978. 1st US ed. (Stamp lower edge), else Fine in dj (price-clipped). *Cahan*. $85/£53

RIEFSTAHL, ELIZABETH. Ancient Egyptian Glass and Glazes in the Brooklyn Museum. Brooklyn: Brooklyn Museum, (1968). 13 color plts. *Archaeologia*. $150/£94

RIEFSTAHL, ELIZABETH. Toilet Articles from Ancient Egypt from the Charles Edwin Wilbour Memorial Collection.... Brooklyn: Brooklyn Museum, 1943. Wraps, dj. *Archaeologia*. $25/£16

RIEFSTAHL, R. MEYER. The Parish-Watson Collection of Mohammadan Potteries. NY, 1922. Folio. (Spine dknd.) *Swann**. $345/£216

RIEGEL, O. W. Crown of Glory. New Haven: Yale Univ, 1935. 1st ed. Frontis. VG in dj (sl worn). *Lien*. $50/£31

RIENACKER, VICTOR. John Sell Cotman 1782-1842. Leigh-on-Sea: F. Lewis, 1953. One of 500. 4 tipped-in color illus. VG in dj. *Hollett*. $152/£95

RIESENBERG, FELIX. The Golden Road. NY: McGraw-Hill, (1962). 1st ed. Black cl. Fine in NF dj. *Harrington*. $30/£19

Rifle and Infantry Tactics. Mobile: S.H. Goetzel, First Year of the Confederacy (1861). Vol 1 (of 2). 31 plts. (Browned; worn), else Good. *Dumont*. $250/£156

RIGGS, LYNN. Green Grow the Lilacs. LEC, 1954. Ltd to 1500 numbered, signed by Thomas Hart Benton (illus). Fine in slipcase. *Swann**. $402/£251

RIGGS, STEPHEN R. Mary and I. 40 Years with the Sioux. Boston, (1887). 2nd ed. 437pp. (Spine ends worn.) Slipcase. *Heinoldt*. $50/£31

RIIS, JACOB A. Is There a Santa Claus? Macmillan, 1904. 1st ed. Sm 8vo. 29pp. Teg. Blue cl, gilt-stamped. VG (name; corners bumped). *Price*. $35/£22

RIIS, JACOB A. The Making of an American. NY: Macmillan, 1901. 3rd ptg. VG in red cl, gilt. *Smith*. $30/£19

RIIS, JACOB A. The Making of an American. NY: Macmillan, 1901. 1st ed. Blue cl, gilt. Good. *Karmiole*. $100/£63

RIIS, JACOB A. The Making of an American. NY: Macmillan, 1902. 1st ed, 6th ptg. Signed presentation on frontisport. Teg, untrimmed. Ribbed navy cl, gilt. (Frontis verso foxed; bkpl; fr hinge lt cracked, sm spots fr cvr; sl worn.) Text Clean. *Baltimore**. $60/£38

RILEY, CARROLL L. The Frontier People. Albuquerque, 1987. Fine in dj. *Dumont*. $35/£22

RILEY, ELIHU S. Stonewall Jackson. Annapolis, MD, 1920. 1st ed. Frontisport. Gray cl. (Sigs; soiled, faded, sm hole in cl of rear cvr.) *Chapel Hill*. $375/£234

RILEY, FREDERIC. The Ribble from Its Source to the Sea. Settle: J.W. Lambert, 1914. 1st ed. 21 plts, 4 maps. Pict cl (lettering on fr bd flaked), gilt. *Hollett*. $112/£70

RILEY, JAMES A. All Time All Stars of Black Baseball. TK Pubs, 1983. 1st ed. (Occasional mks), o/w VG +. *Plapinger*. $60/£38

RILEY, JAMES WHITCOMB. All the Year Round. Indianapolis: Bobbs Merrill, (1912). 1st Gustave Baumann ed. Blue/white cl, gilt. NF. *Pacific**. $173/£108

RILEY, JAMES WHITCOMB. Armazindy. Indianapolis: Bobbs-Merrill, 1894. 1st ed, likely 2nd ptg. Inscribed, signed. Grn cl. (Bkpl; spine dull, ends chipped), else VG. BAL 16602. *Pacific**. $98/£61

RILEY, JAMES WHITCOMB. A Child-World. Indianapolis: Bowen-Merrill, 1897. 1st ed, later ptg, w/'London' on tp. 209pp. Red cl, gilt. VG (sl shelfworn). *My Bookhouse*. $62/£39

RILEY, JAMES WHITCOMB. The Complete Works of.... Edmund Henry Eitel (ed). Indianapolis: Bobbs-Merrill, (1913). Biographical ed. 6 vols. Teg. Dk brn morocco, gilt. (Spines, extrems sunned), else VG set. *Pacific**. $98/£61

RILEY, JAMES WHITCOMB. The Flying Islands of the Night. Indianapolis: Bobbs-Merrill, (1913). 1st illus ed. Franklin Booth (illus). 1/2 cl, dec bds. Fine in VG dj (spine ends chipped, sm chip lower edge fr panel, spine, extrems dknd). *Pacific**. $218/£136

RILEY, JAMES WHITCOMB. Old School Day Romances. Indianapolis: Bobbs-Merrill, (1909). 8.75x6.25. E. Stetson Crawford (illus). Dec cvr label. (Sl soiled), else NF. *Pacific**. $40/£25

RILEY, JAMES WHITCOMB. Riley Child Verse. Indianapolis: Bobbs-Merrill, (1906). 1st ed thus. 9.5x6.75. Ethel Franklin Betts (illus). Pict cvr label. (Spine head sl water-damaged, soiled), else VG. *Pacific**. $40/£25

RILEY, JAMES WHITCOMB. Riley Roses. Indianapolis: Bobbs Merrill, (1909). 1st ed. Grn linen, gilt. Fine. *Karmiole*. $100/£63

RILEY, JAMES WHITCOMB. When She Was About Sixteen. (Indianapolis): Bobbs-Merrill, (1911). Lg 8vo. Howard Chandler Christy (illus). Dk grn cl, color pict label fr cvr. VG (fr cvr lt soiled). *House*. $75/£47

RILEY, JAMES WHITCOMB. While the Heart Beats Young. Indianapolis: Bobbs-Merrill, (1906). 1st Betts ed. Ethel Franklin Betts (illus). Pict cvr label. (Rear hinge starting; spine ends, corners rubbed), else VG. *Pacific**. $46/£29

RILEY, JAMES. Loss of the American Brig Commerce. London: John Murray, 1817. 1st London ed. xvi,618pp; fldg map. Orig 1/4 calf. Good (scuffed, spine repaired). *Cullen*. $375/£234

RILKE, RAINER MARIA. Duineser Elegien—Elegies from the Castle of Duino. V. & Edward Sackville-West (trans). London: Hogarth, 1931. 1st Eng ed. One of 230 numbered, signed by trans. Initials engr in wood by Eric Gill. Teg. 1/4 vellum. Fine (edges sl spotted; sm dent top edge fr cvr; lacks slipcase) in unptd dj (spine dknd, sl frayed). *Ulysses*. $1,680/£1,050

RILKE, RAINER MARIA. The Life of the Virgin Mary. Stephen Spender (trans). (London): Vision, 1951. 1st ed thus. Nice in dj (shelf worn, yellowed). *King*. $22/£14

RILKE, RAINER MARIA. The Notebooks of Malte Laurids Brigge. LEC, 1987. One of 2000. Fine in slipcase. *Swann**. $92/£58

RILKE, RAINER MARIA. Requiem and Other Poems. J. B. Leishman (trans). London: Hogarth, 1935. 1st ed. One of 1075. Brn cl cvrs (sl soiled, speckled, spine rubbed, gilt dull; pp browned, eps, prelims spotted). Good (lacks dj). *Virgo*. $16/£10

RILKE, RAINER MARIA. Selected Poems of Rainer Maria Rilke. LEC, 1981. Ltd to 1500 numbered, signed by Robert Kipness (illus). Fine in slipcase. *Swann**. $103/£64

RILKE, RAINER MARIA. Wartime Letters of...1914-1921. M. D. Herter Norton (trans). NY: W.W. Norton, (1940). 1st US ed. Gilt grn cl. VG in dj (sm tear spine foot). *Reese*. $50/£31

RIMBAUD, ARTHUR. Complete Works, Selected Letters. Wallace Fowlie (ed). Chicago/London: Univ of Chicago, 1966. VG (top edge sl dusty; spine ends sl bumped, spine sl dknd) in dj (nicked, rubbed, sl mkd, browned). *Ulysses*. $58/£36

RIMBAUD, ARTHUR. A Season in Hell. Delmore Schwartz (trans). Norfolk, CT: New Directions, (1939). Ltd to 780. Beige linen over purple bds, ptd label fr cvr. Good. *Karmiole.* $150/£94

RIMBAUD, ARTHUR. A Season in Hell. LEC, 1986. One of 1000 signed by Paul Schmidt (trans) and Robert Mapplethorpe (photos). Fine in slipcase. *Swann*.* $1,150/£719

RIMMEL, EUGENE. The Book of Perfumes. London: Chapman & Hall, 1871. 7th ed. Inscribed presentation. xx,266,(ii)pp. Aeg. (Spine faded.) *Hollett.* $80/£50

RINEHART, FRANK A. The Face of Courage: The Indian Photographs of Frank A. Rinehart. (Ft. Collins, CO): Old Army, (1972). 1st ed. Signed by Royal Sutton (intro). One of 100 bound w/3 orig photos loose in accompanying linen sleeve, as issued. Linen eps; gilt inner dentelles. Full leather, gilt. Fine in slipcase. *Pacific*.* $196/£123

RINEHART, FRANK A. Rinehart's Indians (cover title). (Omaha: F.A. Rinehart, 1899.) 1st ed. Color frontis, (4); 46 b/w, 3 color plts. Pict red cl, stamped in white, black inks. VG (sm area where plt shows surface damage from sticking to another leaf, lt finger-worn, mkd; fr cvr sl dampstained). *Cahan.* $950/£594

RINEHART, MARY ROBERTS. 23 1/2 Hours Leave. NY: George H. Doran, (1918). 1st ed. Frontis. Tan bds pict stamped in blue/black. (Sm slip w/ink name affixed to 1/2-title), o/w VG in dj. *Reese.* $45/£28

RINEHART, MARY ROBERTS. The Amazing Interlude. NY: George H. Doran, (1918). 1st ed. Frontis. Gray cl. (Ink inscrip, foxed early/late; cl rubbed), else Good in pict dj (lt chipped, sl rubbed, soiled). *Reese.* $45/£28

RINEHART, MARY ROBERTS. The Case of Jennie Brice. Indianapolis, (1913). 1st ed. Fine in VG dj (lacks strip along spine foot, edges lt worn, rubbed; nicked, spot on fr panel). *Mcclintock.* $145/£91

RINEHART, MARY ROBERTS. Dangerous Days. NY: George H. Doran, (1919). 1st ed. Gray cl (few spots, rubs). Good. *Reese.* $25/£16

RINEHART, MARY ROBERTS. Kings, Queens and Pawns: An American Woman at the Front. NY: George H. Doran, (1915). 1st ed. Red cl pict stamped in black/gilt. NF. *Reese.* $45/£28

RINEHART, MARY ROBERTS. The Man in Lower Ten. Indianapolis, (1909). 1st ed. VG. *Mcclintock.* $20/£13

RINEHART, MARY ROBERTS. The Street of Seven Stars. Boston: Houghton Mifflin, 1914. 1st ed. VG (cvr spotted, shelfworn). *My Bookhouse.* $27/£17

RINEHART, MARY ROBERTS. Through Glacier Park. Boston: Houghton Mifflin, 1916. 1st ed. VG in pict cl. *Mikesh.* $30/£19

RINHART, FLOYD and MARION. American Daguerreian Art. NY, 1967. 1st ed. (Inscrip; worn.) *Swann*.* $69/£43

RINHART, FLOYD and MARION. The American Daguerreotype. Athens: Univ of GA, (1981). 1st ed. Dj (worn, scuffed). *Baltimore*.* $80/£50

RINK, EVALD. Technical Americana: A Checklist...Before 1832. Milwood, 1981. (Lt worn.) *Oinonen*.* $70/£44

Rip Van Winkle. NY: McLoughlin Bros, n.d. ca 1880. 4to. 6 full-pg chromolithos by Thomas Nast. VG in pict wraps (edges worn, lt soil). *Davidson.* $285/£178

RIPLEY, A. LASSELL. Sporting Etchings. Barre, MA: Barre Pub, 1970. 1st ed. Grn buckram. Fine in Fine pict dj. *Biscotti.* $100/£63

RIPLEY, ROBERT L. Believe It or Not! NY: S&S, (1929). 4th ptg. Inscribed presentation. 1-pg tls affixed to rep, dated Feb 26, 1929. Top edge stained red. Grn cl. Good (2.5-inch chip half-title; cvrs lt worn). *Heritage.* $250/£156

RIPLEY, SHERMAN. The Raggedies in Fairyland. Chicago: Rand McNally, (1930). 1st ed. 4to. 2 full-pg color plts by Harrison Cady. Black cl, turquoise lettering, color paste label. (Lib stamps, 1pg sl marginal tear.) *Reisler.* $165/£103

RIPPEY, SARAH CORY. The Sunny-Sulky Book. Chicago: Rand McNally, (1927). Blanche Fisher Wright & Mary L. Spoor (illus). Pict cvr label. NF. *Pacific*.* $46/£29

RISCH, ERNA. Supplying Washington's Army. Military Hist US Army, 1981. 1st ed. Good. *Rybski.* $45/£28

RISCHBIETER, HENNING. Art and the Stage in the 20th Century, Painters and Sculptors Work for the Theater. Greenwich, CT: NYGS, (1970). 2nd ptg. Obl folio. Red cl bds. Fine in illus dj (discolored, rubbed, bumped). *Metropolitan*.* $46/£29

Rise and Progress of Australia, Tasmania, and New Zealand. (By Daniel Puseley.) London, 1857. 2nd ed. xvi,496pp + 18pp pub's ads (1/2-title torn). Emb cl (joints splitting, spine torn w/loss). *Edwards.* $136/£85

RISTER, CARL COKE. Border Captives: The Traffic in Prisoners by Southern Plains Indians, 1835-1875. Norman: Univ of OK, 1940. 1st ed. Fine in dj (creased, chipped). *Labordo.* $150/£94

RISTER, CARL COKE. No Man's Land. Norman: Univ of OK, 1948. 1st ed. Fine in dj (chipped). *Labordo.* $45/£28

RISTER, CARL COKE. No Man's Land. Norman, 1948. 1st ed. Map. (Ink name, date), o/w VG + in VG dj (edges worn). *Sagebrush.* $50/£31

RISTER, CARL COKE. Southern Plainsmen. Norman: Univ of OK, 1938. 1st ed. Fldg map. Good in dj (price-clipped, chipped). Howes R316. *Dumont.* $95/£59

RITCH, JOHNNY. Shorty's Saloon. Z-Bar Network, 1940?. Fine in wraps. *Perier.* $35/£22

RITCHIE, ANN THACKERAY. Alfred, Lord Tennyson and His Friends. London: T. Fisher Unwin, 1893. 1st ed. One of 400 numbered. Lg folio. Frontis, 16pp text; 25 full-pg photogravure ports, tissue guards. Lt grn coated eps; aeg. Brn linen, gilt. (Margins lt dusty, aged; sl worn, partial discoloration, hinges cracked or splitting.) Text VG. *Baltimore*.* $900/£563

RITCHIE, GEORGE T. A List of Lincolniana in the Library of Congress. Washington: GPO, 1906. Rev ed. Good (bkpl; spine heel, corners bumped). *Wantagh.* $45/£28

RITCHIE, J. EWING. East Anglia, Personal Reflections and Historical Associations. London, 1893. 2nd enlgd ed. *Gretton.* $35/£22

RITCHIE, JAMES. The Influence of Man on Animal Life in Scotland. Cambridge: CUP, 1920. 1st ed. 8 maps. VG in dj. *Hollett.* $136/£85

RITCHIE, LEITCH. A History of the Indian Empire, and the East India Company, from the Earliest Times to the Present. London: W.H. Allen, 1848. 2 vols. xv,500; xi,512pp. Orig cl (faded, rubbed, hinges sl repaired). *Adelson.* $275/£172

RITCHIE, LEITCH. Ireland, Picturesque and Romantic. London: Longman, Rees, Orme, Brown, Green & Longman, 1837. vi,264pp; 20 engr plts. Aeg. Emb velvet. (Plts lt browned; spine sl faded.) *Edwards.* $136/£85

RITCHIE, LEITCH. Versailles. London: Longman et al, 1839. 1st ed. vii,256pp; 20 steel-engr plts incl extra pict tp. Marbled eps; aeg. Contemp dk grn morocco, marbled bds, raised bands, gilt. Contents Good. (Lt aged, sl foxed; scuffed, hinges recently repaired.) *Baltimore*.* $30/£19

RITCHIE, LEITCH. Wanderings by the Seine. London: Longman, Rees, 1835. 1st ed. Engr frontis, (iii),(i)blank,258,(1)list; 19 engr plts. Gilt edges. Contemp grn roan, gilt. (Margins, frontis foxed; spine, edges worn, hinges strengthened.) *Morrell.* $144/£90

RITCHIE, NEIL. Harold Acton, a Bibliography. Florence: Privately ptd, 1984. One of 500. Color frontisport. Fine in dj (sl rubbed, partly faded). *Ulysses.* $72/£45

RITCHIE, WARD. Art Deco: The Books of Francois-Louis Schmied. Ward Ritchie, 1987. One of 550. *Dawson.* $100/£63

RITSON, JOSEPH. An Essay on Abstinence from Animal Food, as a Moral Duty. London: Richard Phillips, 1802. 1st ed. 8vo. (3),236pp. Fldg satirical engr of Ritson tipped in. Marbled edges. Mod 1/4 calf over marbled bds, black morocco spine label. Fine. *Glaser.* $950/£594

RITTENHOUSE, JACK. American Horse Drawn Vehicles. L.A.: Jack D. Rittenhouse, 1948. One of 1000 numbered. (Edges browned), else NF in dj. *Dumont.* $225/£141

RITTENHOUSE, JACK. Carriage Hundred. Houston: Stagecoach, 1961. One of 450. NF in dj (sl faded). *Dumont.* $85/£53

RITTENHOUSE, JACK. New Mexico Civil War Bibliography. Houston: Stagecoach, 1961. One of 400. Fine in dj. *Dumont.* $175/£109

RITTENHOUSE, JACK. The Santa Fe Trail. Albuquerque, 1971. 1st ed. Signed. VG in dj (lt worn). *Dumont.* $100/£63

RITTER, CARL. The Comparative Geography of Palestine and the Sinaitic Peninsula. William L. Gage (trans). Edinburgh: Clark, 1866. 1st ed. 4 vols. xvi,451; viii,418; viii,396; viii,410pp. (Exlib; sl rubbed, spines defective.) Internally VG. *Worldwide.* $85/£53

RITTER, LAWRENCE. The Glory of Their Times. MacMillan, 1966. 1st ed, 1st ptg. VG + in VG dj. *Plapinger.* $85/£53

RITTER, MARY BENNETT. More Than Gold in California 1849-1933. Berkeley: Professional Press, 1933. 1st ed. Fine in dj (worn). *Parmer.* $95/£59

RITTNER, GEORGE H. Impressions of Japan.... London: John Murray, 1904. 1st ed. Photogravure frontis, 32 other photogravure plts. Maroon cl, gilt. (Lt foxed; sl rubbed, faded.) *Morrell.* $56/£35

RITZ, CHARLES. A Fly Fisher's Life. Humphrey Hare (trans). NY: Henry Holt, (1959). 1st Amer ed. One of 250. Signed. Blue morocco, morocco spine label. Fine in slipcase. *Pacific*.* $196/£123

Rival Crusoes; or, the Shipwreck. John Harris, 1836. 4th ed. Frontis, 209pp(fep renewed),(7)pp pub's cat. Brn vertical ribbed cl (sl rubbed, soiled). *Cox.* $32/£20

RIVAZ, C. A. G. Indian Small-Game Shooting for Novices. London, 1912. Dj (dknd, torn, chipped). *Swann*.* $69/£43

RIVERS, HENRY. Accidents: Popular Directions for Their Immediate Treatment; with Observations on Poisons and Their Antidotes. Boston, 1845. 1st ed. 108pp. *Fye.* $150/£94

RIVES, REGINALD W. The Coaching Club. Its History, Records and Activities. NY: Derrydale, 1935. One of 300 numbered, privately ptd for the Coaching Club. Gilt-stamped 2-tone cl. (Lt worn.) *Oinonen*.* $350/£219

RIVOIRA, G. T. Lombardic Architecture. G. Rushford (trans). London, 1910. 1st ed. 2 vols. Marbled edges. Mod cl. (Lib ink stamps, sm blind stamps; margins lt browned.) *Edwards.* $184/£115

RIZZI, ALDO. The Etchings of the Tiepolos. (NY, 1979?) *Swann*.* $126/£79

ROA BASTOS, AUGUSTO. I the Supreme. NY: Knopf, 1986. NF in dj. *Lame Duck.* $45/£28

ROA BASTOS, AUGUSTO. Son of Man. London: Victor Gollancz, 1965. 1st ed in English. VG + (few multi-colored patches of paper to fep, feps offset, lt foxed) in dj (sm extrem tears). *Lame Duck.* $150/£94

Roanoke Stud 1795-1833. (By Fairfax Harrison.) Richmond: Privately ptd at Old Dominion Press, 1930. Uncut. Paper spine label. (Sl worn.) *Oinonen*.* $90/£56

ROBACK, A. A. Jewish Influences on Modern Thought. Cambridge: Sci-Art, 1929. 1st ed. Good (spine worn). *Beasley.* $30/£19

ROBACK, C. W. The Mysteries of Astrology and the Wonders of Magic.... Boston: C.W. Roback, 1854. 1st ed. Blind-stamped cl, gilt. (Cvrs, joints insect-damaged), else VG. *Pacific*.* $58/£36

ROBARTS, HENRY. A Most Friendly Farewell to Sir Francis Drake. Cambridge: Harvard Univ, 1924. Rpt of 1585 pamphlet. One of 755 ptd. Unopened. Red bds, tan cl backstrip, paper spine label. VG + (corners worn, sunned, water spot fr bd). Internally Fine. *Harrington.* $35/£22

ROBB, DAVID M. The Art of the Illuminated Manuscript. NY, 1973. Good in dj. *Washton.* $65/£41

Robber Bridegroom: A Fairy Tale from Grimm. London: A&C Black, 1922. 1st ed thus. 4to. 8 mtd color plts by H. S. Owen. Blue cl, color paste label. (Label, cl worn.) *Reisler.* $150/£94

ROBBINS, ROLAND WELLS. Discovery at Walden. (Stoneham, MA: George R. Barnstead, 1947.) 1st ed. Inscribed presentation dated Oct 21, 1947. Gray cl (lt flecked). Good. *Lucas.* $45/£28

ROBBINS, TOM. Another Roadside Attraction. GC: Doubleday, 1971. 1st ed, 1st bk. Fine (touched-up rubbed spots) in Fine dj. *Between The Covers.* $750/£469

ROBBINS, TOM. Even Cowgirls Get the Blues. Boston: Houghton Mifflin, 1976. Uncorrected proofs. Ptd lt blue wraps. Good (1st few pp corners sl creased; soiled, sl stained, sm piece out fr cvr bottom rt corner, top corner creased; sm tear fr joint head). *Blue Mountain.* $250/£156

ROBBINS, TOM. Jitterbug Perfume. NY, 1984. 1st ed. NF in NF dj. *Warren.* $30/£19

ROBBINS, TOM. Still Life with Woodpecker. NY: Bantam, (1980). 1st ed. Signed. Fine in Fine dj. *Lenz.* $100/£63

ROBERT-HOUDIN. The Secrets of Conjuring and Magic. Professor Hoffmann (ed). London: Routledge, n.d. (c. 1890). 2nd ed. Pict reddish cl (lt soiled, spine ends scuffed), gilt. *Dramatis.* $80/£50

ROBERTS, BRIAN B. Antarctic Ornithological Observations Made During Bellingshausen's Voyage of Circumnavigation in 1819-1821. London: The Ibis, 1939. Pamphlet. 1 photo plt. VG in ptd paper wrapper. *Explorer.* $19/£12

ROBERTS, C. G. D. More Kindred of the Wild. Ward-Lock, 1911. 1st Eng ed. NF in VG dj (lt chipped). *Fine Books.* $125/£78

ROBERTS, CHARLES V. H. Louvain: A Tragedy in Three Acts. NY/Cedar Rapids/London: Torch Press, 1917. 1st ed. Blue-gray bds (lt dust-soiled), paper labels (tanned). VG. *Reese.* $50/£31

ROBERTS, DAVID. The Holy Land, Syria, Idumea, Arabia, Egypt and Nubia. London: Day & Son, 1855-56. 6 vols in 3. 4to. 6 tinted litho tps, 2 maps, 242 plts (marginal dampstaining). Aeg. Contemp 1/2 morocco, gilt, raised bands. (Spine foot vol 1 bumped, extrems rubbed; bkpl.) *Christie's*.* $3,600/£2,250

ROBERTS, EDITH A. and E. REHMANN. American Plants for American Gardens. NY, 1929. 1st ed. 11 photo plts. Maroon cl, gilt. VG in dj (torn). *Larry Price.* $23/£14

ROBERTS, EMMA. Views in India. China and on the Shores of the Red Sea. London: H. Fisher, R. Fisher & P. Jackson, 1835. 2 vols bound in 1. 2 engr frontispieces, 2 engr tps, 60 engr plts (few lt spotted). Marbled edges. Later 1/2 calf, marbled bds (orig spine relaid, cvrs scuffed), gilt. *Christie's*.* $541/£338

ROBERTS, F. J. and J. H. PEARSON (eds). The Wipers Times. London: Eveleigh Nash & Grayson, (1930). 2nd imp this ed. Khaki cl stamped in black. VG. *Reese.* $55/£34

ROBERTS, FLORENCE. Fifteen Years with the Outcast. Anderson, IN: Gospel Trumpet Co, 1912. 1st ed. Port. Later cl (rebound). VG. *Brown.* $45/£28

ROBERTS, HENRY (ed). The Green Book of Golf...a Record of Tournaments Held.... SF: Ellis & Roberts, 1925-26. 3rd ed. Grn cl, gilt. VG-(dampstained, margins lt stuck together; spine extrems chipped, torn). *Pacific*.* $230/£144

ROBERTS, HENRY. A History of the Royal Pavilion, Brighton. Country Life, 1939. 1st ed. 96 plts, 20 maps, plans, text illus. VG in dj (sl chipped). *Hollett.* $136/£85

ROBERTS, JACK. The Amazing Adventures of Lord Gore. Silverton, CO: Sundance Books, 1977. Ltd ed, signed, numbered. VG. *Dumont.* $40/£25

ROBERTS, JACK. The Wonderful Adventures of Ludo the Little Green Duck. London: A. Tolmer or the Poetry Bookshop, 1924. 1st Eng ed. Sq 8vo. Color pict bds (dusty). *Reisler.* $225/£141

ROBERTS, JIM. Roy Rogers and the South-Paw Bandit. Paulton: Purnell & Sons, ca 1958. Obl 4to. 5 dbl-pg full color pop-ups. Full color pict bds. *Reisler.* $200/£125

ROBERTS, JOHN BINGHAM. War Surgery of the Face. NY: William Wood, 1919. 1st ed. Deep red cl. NF. *Weber.* $500/£313

ROBERTS, KENNETH G. and PHILLIP SHACKLETON. The Canoe: A History of the Craft from Panama to the Arctic. Camden: Intl. Marine, 1983. Obl folio. VG in dj. *American Booksellers.* $65/£41

ROBERTS, KENNETH. Lydia Bailey. GC: Doubleday, 1947. 1st ed. One of 1050 signed, w/typewritten pg from working ms tipped in, w/corrections in pencil. Frontis. Teg. Beige cl, gilt. Fine (frontis offset to tp) in pub's cardboard slipcase (lt soiled). *Heritage.* $175/£109

ROBERTS, KENNETH. Lydia Bailey. GC: Doubleday, 1947. 1st ed. Ltd to 1050 signed. Pg from working ms tipped in w/corrections in Roberts' hand. Teg. (Spine sl dknd), else VF in gray-grn linen. Glassine dj, slipcase (chips, joint split). *Bromer.* $250/£156

ROBERTS, KENNETH. Trending into Maine. Boston: Little, Brown, 1938. 1st ed. One of 1075 signed by Roberts & N. C. Wyeth (illus). Royal 8vo. 14 full-pg color plts. Pict eps. Cream buckram, blue cl, gilt-lettered black morocco spine label. (Cvrs sl faded), o/w Fine in pub's cardboard slipcase (soiled). *Heritage.* $600/£375

ROBERTS, KENNETH. Why Europe Leaves Home. (NY): Bobbs-Merrill, (1922). 1st ed. Inscribed. (Spine faded), else Fine. *Bromer.* $650/£406

ROBERTS, LESLIE. When the Gods Laughed. NY: Sears Pub Co, 1931. 1st US ed. Grn cl. (Sl nick fore-edge of few ll), o/w NF in pict dj (spine sunned, lt edgeworn, price-clipped). *Reese.* $40/£25

ROBERTS, MICHAEL. Poems. London: Cape, 1936. 1st Eng ed. NF in dj (sl nicked, dusty, faint tape-mks). *Ulysses.* $104/£65

ROBERTS, MORLEY. A Humble Fisherman: Being Simple, Autobiographic Essays.... London: Grayson & Grayson, (1932). 1st ed. Frontis. Grn cl, gilt. Fine. *Pacific*.* $35/£22

ROBERTS, MORLEY. W. H. Hudson, a Portrait. NY: E.P. Dutton, (1924). 1st US ed. Ltd to 1500 (of 1550). NF in dj (spine edge top sl chipped). *Bernard.* $30/£19

ROBERTS, NED. The Muzzle-Loading Cap Lock Rifle. Harrisburg: Stackpole, 1958. 5th ptg. VG (shelfworn) in dj (sl edgeworn, rubbed, brn spots). *My Bookhouse.* $47/£29

ROBERTS, OLIVER AYER. The California Pilgrimage of Boston Commandery Knight Templars, August 4-September 4, 1883. Boston: Alfred Mudge, 1884. 1st ed. xv,400,(1)pp; 2 steel-engr ports incl frontis. Aeg. Dec brn cl. (Fr joint neatly reglued, other sl wear), else VG. *Pacific*.* $98/£61

ROBERTS, RANDAL. The River's Side; or, The Trout and Grayling, and How to Take Them. London: Horace Cox, 1866. 1st ed thus. Grn cl, gilt. (Bkpls), else VG. *Pacific*.* $58/£36

ROBERTS, S. C. The Charm of Cambridge. A&C Black, 1927. 24 plts. Pict eps. Pict cl (sl rubbed, joints sl split; hinges sl tender). *Edwards.* $56/£35

ROBERTS, W. The Book-Hunter in London. Elliot Stock, 1895. 1st ed. Frontis. Teg, uncut. Dec cl. (Upper cvr sl stained), o/w Nice. *Forest.* $104/£65

ROBERTS, W. Printers' Marks. George Bell & Sons, 1893. 1st ed. Frontis. Teg, uncut. (Inner hinges shaken; cl worn, hinges torn.) *Forest.* $48/£30

ROBERTS, W. J. Mary Russell Mitford: The Tragedy of a Blue Stocking. Andrew Melrose, 1913. Good (fore-edge lt spotted, sig; spine bumped). *Tiger.* $42/£26

ROBERTSON, A. J. A History of Alresford. London: Winchester, (1937). (Binding faded, browned.) *Petersfield.* $26/£16

ROBERTSON, ALEXANDER F. Alexander Hugh Holmes Stuart, 1807-1891. Wm. Byrd, (c1925). Good+ (sl cocked, insect damage). *Book Broker.* $45/£28

ROBERTSON, ARCHIBALD. A Topographical Survey of the Great Road from London to Bath and Bristol. London: The Author, 1792. 1st ed. 2 parts in 2 vols. 8vo. (iv),xv,(i)index,154pp; vii,190pp + (i) errata; half-title vol 1; 11 plans (10 dbl-pg fldg), 65 aquatint plts. Marbled eps. Early gilt-edged morocco. (Ex-lib; staining, surface loss esp to spine.) *Edwards.* $800/£500

ROBERTSON, BRYAN. Jackson Pollock. NY: Abrams, ca 1960. Dj. *Swann*.* $287/£179

ROBERTSON, DAVID. A Tour through the Isle of Man, to Which Is Subjoined a Review of the Manks History. The Author, 1794. 1st ed. 8 aquatint plts. (Margins discolored.) Uncut. Orig bds (rebacked). *Sotheby's*.* $294/£184

ROBERTSON, E. GRAEME and JOAN. Cast Iron Decoration. London, 1977. Dj. *Edwards.* $64/£40

ROBERTSON, FRANK C. and BETH KAY HARRIS. Soapy Smith, King of the Frontier Con Men. NY: Hastings House, 1962. 1st ed. NF in dj. *Labordo.* $50/£31

ROBERTSON, GEORGE. Chitral, the Story of a Minor Siege (1895). London, 1898. 1st ed. Fldg map. (Cvrs worn.) *Gretton.* $19/£12

ROBERTSON, HEATHER (ed). A Gentleman Adventurer: The Arctic Diaries of R.H.G. Bonnycastle. Lester & Orpen Dennys, (1984). Map. Fine in dj. *Explorer.* $19/£12

ROBERTSON, HENRY. A General View of the Natural History of the Atmosphere, and of Its Connection with the Sciences of Medicine and Agriculture. Edinburgh: Laing et al, 1808. 1st ed. 2 vols. xvi,403; vii,406pp. Later 3/4 calf, marbled bds, red morocco spine labels. Fine. *Glaser.* $400/£250

ROBERTSON, HENRY. A Handbook of Bankers' Law. Edinburgh: Bell & Bradfute, 1901. 6th ed. Blue cl (worn, spotted). Sound. *Boswell.* $50/£31

ROBERTSON, JOHN W. Francis Drake and Other Early Explorers Along the Pacific Coast. SF: Grabhorn, 1927. One of 1000. Inscribed, signed presentation. 1/2 vellum, gilt. (Spine sl rubbed), else Fine in slipcase (neat repair spine foot). *Pacific*.* $259/£162

ROBERTSON, JOHN. The Elements of Navigation.... London, 1764. 2nd ed. 2 vols. 16 engr fldg maps, charts. Contemp sheep (needs rebinding). *Swann*.* $201/£126

ROBERTSON, JOHN. The Elements of Navigation.... London, 1786. 5th ed. 2 vols. 16 fldg engr maps and diags. Contemp sheep. (Foxed, lib stamps; spines dknd, worn, joints cracked.) *Swann*.* $103/£64

ROBERTSON, M. Futility. M.F. Mansfield, 1898. 1st ed. Pict orange cl. (Dust-soiled), else VG. *Fine Books.* $500/£313

ROBERTSON, MERLE GREENE. The Sculpture of Palenque. Volumes 1-3. Princeton, (1983-85). (Lt worn.) Djs. *Oinonen*.* $250/£156

ROBERTSON, THOMAS A. A Southwestern Utopia. L.A.: Ward Ritchie, 1947. 1st ed. Brn cl, paper spine label. NF in Good dj (chipped), mylar cvr. *Harrington.* $35/£22

ROBERTSON, WILLIAM. The History of America. London: Strahan, Cadell & Balfour, 1788. 5th ed. 3 vols. 3/4 calf, marbled bds, morocco spine labels. (Spine ends of vol 1 sl worn), else NF set. Howes R359. *Pacific**. $316/£198

ROBERTSON, WILLIAM. The History of America. London: A. Strahan et al, 1796. 7th ed of 1st 3 vols, 1st ed of last vol. 4 vols. 4 fldg copper-engr maps, fldg plt. Period tree calf, gilt. (Bkpls, 1st spine head chipped, rear joint cracked w/cvr nearly detached), o/w VG set. Howes R493. *Pacific**. $127/£79

ROBERTSON, WILLIAM. The History of the Reign of the Emperor Charles V.... London: W. & W. Strahan, 1769. 1st ed. 3 vols. Folios. Frontisports. 19th-cent gilt-ruled tree calf, morocco spine labels. (Lib bkpls; 1 vols lacks spine label, another chipped, glue to spine heads), else VG set. *Pacific**. $161/£101

ROBESON, GEORGE M. and JOSEPH HENRY. Instructions for the Expedition Toward the North Pole.... Washington: GPO, 1871. Presentation on title from Henry. 36pp. New 1/4 leather, ptd fr wrapper bound in. VG. *High Latitude*. $80/£50

ROBESON, KENNETH. The Land of Terror. NY: Street & Smith, (1933). 1st ed. Pict bds. (Spine ends sl rubbed), else NF. *Pacific**. $63/£39

ROBESON, KENNETH. The Man of Bronze. NY: Street & Smith, (1933). 1st ed. Pict bds. (Yellow stains to feps, tp; fr hinge starting; spine ends sl rubbed), else VG. *Pacific**. $58/£36

ROBESON, KENNETH. Quest of the Spider. NY: Street & Smith, (1933). 1st ed. Pict bds. (Rear cvr irregularly faded, corners sl bumped), else NF. *Pacific**. $58/£36

ROBICSEK, FRANCIS. The Smoking Gods. Tobacco in Maya Art, History, and Religion. Norman: Univ of OK, (1978). 1st ed. Dec blue cl. (Fep foxed), else VF in pict dj. *Argonaut*. $125/£78

Robin Hood and Little John. NY: McLoughlin Bros, (ca 1870s). 8vo. 8pp. Nice in red/black paper wrappers (spine split, chipped). *Reisler*. $110/£69

Robin Hood. London: George G. Harrap, (1921). 1st Eng ed illus by N. C. Wyeth. 8vo. (iv),5-289pp; 8 color plts. Uncut. Grn cl, lg pict plt upper cvr, gilt. Very Nice (inscrip). *Sotheran*. $205/£128

Robin Hood. Phila: David McKay, 1917. 1st ed. 4to. 8 full-pg color plts by N. C. Wyeth. Teg. Grn cl, gilt, color paste label. Good. *Reisler*. $200/£125

ROBINS, W. P. Etching Craft. London, 1922. 1st ed. NF. *Polyanthos*. $75/£47

Robinson Crusoe. London: George G. Harrap, (ca 1915). Sq 12mo. Panorama w/expanding panels ptd on both sides. 14pp text, 16 panels of color illus by Willy Pogany. Color illus bds (edges rubbed). *Reisler*. $350/£219

ROBINSON, A. H. W. Marine Cartography in Britain. A History of the Sea Chart to 1855. Leicester Univ, 1962. 1st ed. Dbl-pg color plt, 42 half-tones. VG in dj. *Cox*. $88/£55

ROBINSON, ALVARETTA and DAISY GILLINS (eds). They Answered the Call. Minersville: Minersville Centennial Committee, 1962. 1st ed. Blue cl, gilt. Fine. *Argonaut*. $35/£22

ROBINSON, ARMIN L. (ed). The Ten Commandments: Ten Short Novels of Hitler's War Against the Moral Code. NY: S&S, 1943. 1st ed. (Fep corner lt clipped), else VF in VF dj. *Between The Covers*. $125/£78

ROBINSON, B. W. The Baur Collection: Japanese Sword-Fittings and Associated Metalwork. (Geneva, 1980.) One of 1600 numbered. Dj, slipcase. *Swann**. $201/£126

ROBINSON, B. W. A Descriptive Catalogue of the Persian Paintings in the Bodleian Library. Oxford, 1938. Color frontis. Dj. *Petersfield*. $51/£32

ROBINSON, BEVERLEY. With Shotgun and Rifle in North American Game Fields. Shooting and Hunting Experiences and Methods of the Chase of Large and Small Game. NY: D. Appleton, 1925. 1st ed. 17 plts. Grn cl. VG. *House*. $40/£25

ROBINSON, BRADLEY. Dark Companion. London: Hodder & Stoughton, 1948. VG in dj. *Explorer*. $32/£20

ROBINSON, CHANDLER A. J. Evetts Haley and the Passing of the Old West. Austin, 1978. Frontis. VG. *Dumont*. $45/£28

ROBINSON, CHARLES N. The British Tar in Fact and Fiction. Harper, 1909. 1st ed. Color frontis. Teg. Recent 1/2 blue morocco, banded, gilt. (Rear margins lt stained, sm tear to 1 plt), o/w VG. *Ash*. $200/£125

ROBINSON, CHARLES N. Celebrities of the Army. George Newnes, 1900. 72 full-pg color ports. Orig leather-backed cl (backstrip rubbed, scraped, edges dknd), gilt. *Hollett*. $120/£75

ROBINSON, CHARLES N. Old Naval Prints: Their Artists and Engravers. London: The Studio, 1924. One of 1500 numbered. 96 plts. *Swann**. $172/£108

ROBINSON, DOANE. A History of the Dakota or Sioux Indians from Their Earliest Traditions and First Contact with White Men to the Final Settlement of the Last of Them.... Aberdeen, SD: News Ptg, 1904. 1st ed. Possibly one of 500. 1/2 cl. (Pp63-78 bound upside-down and backwards, bkpl; worn), else VG. *Pacific**. $288/£180

ROBINSON, DOUGLAS H. The Dangerous Sky. A History of Aviation Medicine. Seattle: Univ of WA, (1973). 1st ed. Fine in dj. *Glaser*. $85/£53

ROBINSON, EDWIN ARLINGTON. Modred, a Fragment. NY: Edward Byrne Hackett/Brick Row Bookshop, 1929. 1st ed. One of 250 numbered, signed. VG (eps lt foxed; extrems sl rubbed). *Reese*. $60/£38

ROBINSON, EDWIN ARLINGTON. Roman Bartholow. NY: Macmillan, 1923. One of 750 signed. Teg. Beige cl over brn bds. (3 leather bkpls, offsetting to facing pg; spine dknd), o/w Fine in pub's cardboard slipcase (falling apart). *Heritage*. $50/£31

ROBINSON, EDWIN ARLINGTON. The Torrent and the Night Before. NY/New Haven/Princeton: Edmond Byrne Hackett, 1928. Ltd ed. One of 110 numbered, signed. Untrimmed. Black cl, dk grn bds, ptd paper spine label. VG (spine, edges sl dusty) in portions of orig plain glassine dj. *Baltimore**. $130/£81

ROBINSON, GIL. Old Wagon Show Days. Cincinnati: Brockwell, (1925). Frontis. *Dramatis*. $30/£19

ROBINSON, H. M. The Great Fur Land or Sketches of Life in the Hudson's Bay Territory. NY: Putnam, 1882. xi,348pp. All edges yellow. 3/4 lt brn morocco, marbled bds, gilt. VG+ (few lt scuffs). *House*. $120/£75

ROBINSON, H. W. and T. M. BUCHANAN. Fishes of Arkansas. Fayetteville, 1984. Dj. *Sutton*. $54/£34

ROBINSON, HENRY CRABB. Diary, Reminiscences and Correspondence of Henry Crabb Robinson, Barrister-at-Law. Thomas Sadler (ed). NY: Hurd & Houghton, 1877. 2 vols in 1. xxvi,496,555pp. Paper spine label (rubbed). (Edges, spine faded, damped, holes to upper hinge.) *Hollett*. $56/£35

ROBINSON, HENRY CRABBE. Diary, Reminiscences, and Correspondence of Henry Crabbe Robinson, Barrister-at-Law. Macmillan, 1869. 3 vols. Extra-illus, 69 engr ports/plts, those added inlaid to size. Teg. Contemp calf, gilt. *Sotheby's**. $459/£287

ROBINSON, J. A. and M. R. JAMES. The Manuscripts of Westminster Abbey. Cambridge: CUP, 1909. (Bklabel.) Black cl, gilt. *Maggs*. $96/£60

ROBINSON, JAMES H. Road Without Turning: An Autobiography. NY: Farrar, Straus, (1950). 1st ed. Inscribed, signed. VG in pict dj (chipped). *Petrilla*. $40/£25

ROBINSON, JOHN and GEORGE FRANCIS DOW. The Sailing Ships of New England. Series Two. Salem, MA: Marine Research Soc, 1924. 1st ed. Blue linen. Good. *Karmiole*. $85/£53

ROBINSON, JOHN BELL. Pictures of Slavery and Anti-Slavery. Phila, 1863. 1st ed. 388pp. (Shelfworn, rubbed, soiled), o/w Good. *Brown*. $150/£94

ROBINSON, JOHN MARTIN. The Latest Country Houses. Bodley Head, 1984. VG in dj. *Hadley*. $24/£15

ROBINSON, JOHN W. The San Gabriels Southern California Mountain Country. San Marino: Golden West, (1977). 1st ed. Fine in Fine dj. *Book Market*. $75/£47

ROBINSON, M. L. Runner of the Mountain Tops. NY, 1939. 8 color plts. (Eps browned, pp tanned.) *Sutton*. $40/£25

ROBINSON, MARILYNNE. Housekeeping. NY: FSG, (1980). 1st ed. Fine in dj. *Hermitage*. $75/£47

ROBINSON, MARILYNNE. Housekeeping. NY: FSG, 1980. 1st ed, 1st book. Fine in Fine dj. *Smith*. $75/£47

ROBINSON, MATTHEW. The New Family Herbal and Botanic Physician. London: William Nicholson & sons, n.d. Litho frontis and tp. (Cl sl worn.) *Hollett*. $48/£30

ROBINSON, MRS. Memoirs of the Late Mrs. Robinson...with Some Posthumous Pieces. London: Phillips, 1801. 1st ed. 4 vols. Frontisport. Contemp mottled calf, gilt, dbl lettering pieces. VG (edgeworn, few spine ends lt chipped). *House*. $300/£188

ROBINSON, P. F. Designs for Ornamental Villas. London: Carpenter, 1827. 2nd ed. Tp, 96 plts by Hullmandel. Mod bds, eps. (Margin stain 1 plt of Design no 8), o/w Fine set. *Europa*. $280/£175

ROBINSON, PHIL. The Poets and Nature: Reptiles, Fishes, and Insects. London: C&W, 1893. 1st ed. Gray pict cl, gilt. (Soiled), else Fine. *Pacific**. $40/£25

ROBINSON, SUGAR RAY with DAVE ANDERSON. Sugar Ray. NY: Viking, (1970). 1st ed. Inscribed, signed by Robinson, dated 1970. VG in dj (sl discolored). *Pacific**. $138/£86

ROBINSON, TOM. Greylock and the Robins. NY: Junior Literary Guild/Viking, 1946. 1st ed. Robert Lawson (illus). 4to. Blue dec cl. Good in full color dj (spine ends, edges lt chipped). *Reisler*. $100/£63

ROBINSON, TOM. In and Out. Viking, 1943. 1st ed. 6.5x9.5. Marguerite deAngeli (illus). 140pp. Blue cl, stamped. Good + (few lt wrinkles). *Price*. $40/£25

ROBINSON, W. W. Land in California. Berkeley: Univ of CA, 1948. 1st ed. Signed. Tan cl. VG + . *House*. $20/£13

ROBINSON, W. W. Lawyers of Los Angeles. (L.A.): L.A. Bar Assoc, 1959. 1st ed. Fine in Fine dj. *Book Market*. $40/£25

ROBINSON, W. W. Lawyers of Los Angeles. L.A.: Los Angeles Bar Assoc, 1959. (Lt shelfworn), else NF. *Dumont*. $75/£47

ROBINSON, W. W. and LAWRENCE CLARK POWELL. The Malibu. L.A.: Dawson's Book Shop, 1958. One of 320. Signed by Saul and Lillian Marks, Irene and W. W. Robinson, and by L. C. P. Patterned bds, cl spine, paper spine label. Orig glassine. *Dawson*. $600/£375

ROBINSON, W. W. Ranchos Become Cities. Pasadena: San Pasqual Press, 1939. 1st ed. NF in dj (sl edgeworn). *Pacific**. $52/£33

ROBINSON, WILL H. Under Turquoise Skies. NY: Macmillan, 1928. 1st ed. Signed. (Sl shelf-worn), o/w VG. *Brown*. $35/£22

ROBINSON, WILL H. Under Turquoise Skies. NY: Macmillan, 1928. 1st ed. Frontis. Red cl, gilt. Fine. *Argonaut*. $50/£31

ROBINSON, WILLIAM. Alpine Flowers for Gardens. John Murray, 1903. 3rd ed. Teg, rest uncut. Good in blue cl, gilt. *Cox*. $24/£15

ROBINSON, WILLIAM. Alpine Flowers for Gardens. London: John Murray, 1910. 4th ed. (Inner hinge cracked but holding), else VG. *Quest*. $95/£59

ROBINSON, WILLIAM. The English Flower Garden and Home Grounds. London: John Murray, 1905. 9th ed. Dec blue cl, gilt. (Eps foxed; corners bumped), else VG. *Fair Meadow*. $95/£59

ROBINSON, WILLIAM. The English Flower Garden and Home Grounds.... London, 1933. 15th ed. Color frontis; 17 plts. (Tp lt foxed, new eps; cl rebacked, corners worn.) *Brooks*. $49/£31

ROBINSON, WILLIAM. The English Flower Garden. London, 1883. 1st ed. Inscribed. cxxiv, 332pp; 274 plts. (Rebacked, sl worn). Generally Good. *Henly*. $104/£65

ROBINSON, WILLIAM. The English Flower Garden: And Home Grounds of Hardy Trees and Flowers Only. J. Murray, 1932. 15th ed. 16 plts. Textured grn cl, ptd label. (Lacks fep; rebound), o/w Good + . *Whittle*. $24/£15

ROBINSON, WILLIAM. The Garden Beautiful. London: John Murray, 1907. 1st ed. Uncut, many unopened. Paper-cvrd bds, linen spine, paper labels (worn). *Quest*. $125/£78

ROBINSON, WILLIAM. The Wild Garden. London: John Murray, 1894. 4th ed. (x)-xx,304pp. Teg. Grn cl. (Foxed, browned, name; scuffed, spine lt worn), else VG. *Fair Meadow*. $80/£50

ROBINSON, W. HEATH. See HEATH ROBINSON, W.

ROBLEY, MAJOR-GENERAL. Moko. Wellington: Reed, (1969). Facs rpt. Pict cl. Fine in Fine dj, slipcase. *Mikesh*. $150/£94

ROBOTHAM, W. A. Silver Ghosts and Silver Dawn. Constable, (1970). Good in dj. *Rybski*. $25/£16

ROBSON, A. W. MAYO. Cancer of the Stomach. NY, 1907. 1st Amer ed. *Fye*. $100/£63

ROBSON, E. R. School Architecture. Leicester Univ, 1972. Reissue. Fine in dj. *Hadley*. $29/£18

ROBSON, ISABEL SUART. Two Lady Missionaries in Tibet. London: S.W. Partridge, n.d. (1909). 1st ed. Frontis. Red pict cl, gilt. Good (margins browned; bkpl, sl mkd, sl loose). *Morrell*. $104/£65

ROBSON, JOHN S. How a One-Legged Rebel Lives. Charlottesville, VA: Chronicle Steam Ptg House, 1888. 2nd ed. 146pp. (Sm oval stamp), else VG in blue wraps (worn). *Chapel Hill*. $325/£203

ROCHLIN, HARRIET and FRED. Pioneer Jews. Boston: Houghton Mifflin, 1984. 1st ed. Frontisport. Yellow cl. VF in pict dj. *Argonaut*. $75/£47

Rocket. NY: Amer Tract Soc, n.d. (ca 1860). 12mo. 118pp (dated ink sig fep). Blind-tooled cl on bds, gilt spine. VG (lt discoloration at spine, corners sl rounded). *Hobbyhorse*. $70/£44

ROCKWELL, CHARLES. Sketches of Foreign Travel and Life at Sea. Boston: Tappan & Dennet, 1842. 1st ed. 2 vols. Frontis. (Sl foxed, stained; shelfworn.) *Oinonen**. $90/£56

ROCKWELL, NORMAN. Norman Rockwell: My Adventures as an Illustrator. GC: Doubleday, 1960. 1st ed. Signed. (Name), else VG. *Pacific**. $75/£47

ROCKWELL, WILSON (ed). Memoirs of a Lawman. Denver, 1962. 1st ed. Fine in dj (lt soiled). *Baade*. $47/£29

ROCKWOOD, ROY. Bomba the Jungle Boy and the Hostile Chieftain. NY: Cupples & Leon, 1934. Bomba #16; lists to #17 on dj flap. 5x7.5. 212pp. VG in dj (edgeworn). *My Bookhouse*. $47/£29

ROCKWOOD, ROY. Bomba the Jungle Boy at the Giant Cataract. NY: Cupples & Leon, 1926. Bomba #3; lits to #6 at rear of bk. Earliest state dj w/wraparound spine. 5x7.5. 204pp + ads. VG in dj (extrems worn, soiled, reinforced w/brn tape). *My Bookhouse*. $32/£20

ROCKWOOD, ROY. Bomba the Jungle Boy in a Strange Land. NY: Cupples & Leon, 1931. Bomba #11; lists to #17 on dj flap. 5x7.5. 209pp + ads. VG (shelfworn) in dj (sl edgeworn). *My Bookhouse*. $42/£26

ROCKWOOD, ROY. By Air Express to Venus. NY: Cupples & Leon, 1929. The Great Marvel Series #8; lists to this title. 5x7.5. 248pp + ads. VG + (eps browned, carelessly opened at tp; sl shelfworn) in dj (edgeworn, sm chips). *My Bookhouse*. $87/£54

Rocky Mountain Directory and Colorado Gazetteer for 1871.... Denver: S.S. Wallihan, (1870). 1st ed. (6)ad,442 + (58)pp ads. (Fr hinge cracked, few sigs sprung; cvrs faded, stained, extrems worn), else VG. Howes C611. *Pacific**. $690/£431

ROCQ, MARGARET M. (ed). California Local History. Stanford: Stanford Univ, 1970. 2nd ed. VF in ptd yellow dj. *Argonaut.* $60/£38

ROCQ, MARGARET M. (ed). California Local History. Stanford: University Press, 1970. 2nd ed. Fine in Fine dj. *Book Market.* $65/£41

RODAHL, KAARE. The Last Few. NY: Harper & Row, (1963). 1st ed. VG in dj. *Perier.* $25/£16

RODD, RENNEL. Rose Leaf and Apple Leaf. Phila, 1882. 1st, deluxe ed. 8vo. Apple-grn inter-leaves; uncut. Parchment. *Sotheby's*.* $552/£345

RODDENBERRY, GENE. Star Trek: The Motion Picture. NY: S&S, (1979). 1st ed. (Name), else Fine in dj. *Pacific*.* $29/£18

RODGER, ALEXANDER. Poems and Songs, Humorous and Satirical. Glasgow: David Robertson, 1838. 1st ed. (ii),x,362pp. Yellow chalked eps. Orig vertical-ribbed grn cl (lifting, browned, stitching strained, loose), gilt. *Blackwell's.* $120/£75

RODGERS, BRUCE. The Queen's Vernacular. A Gay Lexicon. Blond, 1972. 1st UK ed. VG + in wraps. *Any Amount.* $26/£16

RODGERS, H. J. Twenty-Three Years Under a Sky-Light, or Life and Experiences of a Photographer. Hartford: H.J. Rodgers, 1872. 1st ed. Frontis, guard, 235pp, errata leaf. (Lt foxed, fep dampstained, name; rubbed, soiled.) *Cahan.* $200/£125

RODGERS, JOSEPH. The Scenery of Sherwood Forest. London, 1908. Frontisport. Teg. (Lt browned; spine lt faded.) *Edwards.* $72/£45

RODGERS, RICHARD and OSCAR HAMMERSTEIN, 2nd. Me and Juliet. NY: Random House, (1953). 1st ed. VF in VF dj. *Between The Covers.* $350/£219

RODGERS, RICHARD and OSCAR HAMMERSTEIN, 2nd. Six Plays by Rodgers and Hammerstein. NY: Random House, (1955). 1st ed. VF in VF dj (sl soiled). *Between The Covers.* $175/£109

RODITI, EDOUARD. Oscar Wilde. Norfolk: New Directions, (1947). 1st ed. VF in VF dj. *Between The Covers.* $85/£53

RODKER, J. Adolpe 1920. Aquila, 1929. 1st ed thus. Ltd to 850. White buckram (sl mkd, dull). Internally Good. *Whiteson.* $42/£26

RODMAN, JOHN STEWART. History of the American Board of Surgery, 1937-1952. Phila: Lippincott, (1956). Fldg plt. NF in dj. *Weber.* $40/£25

RODMAN, SELDEN. Horace Pippin, a Negro Painter in America. NY, 1947. 1st ed. 4 mtd color plts. Dj (chipped, tape-repaired). *Swann*.* $230/£144

RODNEY, GEORGE BRYDGES. As a Cavalryman Remembers. Caldwell: Caxton Ptrs, 1944. 1st ed. Frontis. Blue cl. Fine (spine ends sl rubbed) in dj (sl chipped). *Argonaut.* $125/£78

RODNEY, WALTER. A History of the Upper Guinea Coast 1545-1800. OUP, 1970. 1st ed. 5 maps. Dj. *Edwards.* $48/£30

RODOCANACHI, C. P. Between the Woods and the Water. London, 1986. 1st Eng ed. Signed. Fine in dj. *Clearwater.* $72/£45

RODOCANACHI, C. P. Forever Ulysses. Patrick Leigh-Fermor (trans). NY, 1938. 1st Amer ed. VG (rubberstamp) in dj (sl rubbed, nicked). *Clearwater.* $240/£150

RODOCANACHI, C. P. Mani. London, 1958. 1st Eng ed. Frontis. Fine in dj (neatly repaired in 1 place). *Clearwater.* $64/£40

RODOCANACHI, C. P. Roumeli. London, 1966. 1st Eng ed. Fine (cvr edges sl faded) in dj (price-clipped). *Clearwater.* $88/£55

RODOCANACHI, C. P. Three Letters from the Andes. London, 1991. 1st Eng ed. Signed. Fine in dj. *Clearwater.* $48/£30

RODOCANCHI, C. P. A Time of Gifts. London, 1977. 1st Eng ed. Fine (bkpl) in dj. *Clearwater.* $80/£50

RODRIGUEZ, JOSE (ed). Music and Dance in California. Hollywood: Bureau of Musical Research, 1940. 1st ed. Pict cl. (Name; repaired tear spine, ends rubbed, lower extrems sl dknd), else VG. *Pacific*.* $58/£36

ROE, F. GORDON. Sea Painters of Britain. Leigh-On-Sea: Lewis, 1947-48. Vol 1: #163/500; vol 2: #326/500. 2 vols. 40 plts horstexte (8 color); 47 plts hors-texte (8 color). Uncut except on top, deckle edges. Uniform blue buckram, gilt. (Spine vol 1 sl sunned), o/w VF set. *Europa.* $144/£90

ROE, F. GORDON. Windsor Chairs. Phoenix House, 1953. 1st ed. 54 plts. VG in dj. *Hollett.* $56/£35

ROE, FRANCES M. A. Army Letters from an Officer's Wife 1871-1888. NY, 1909. (Edges sl worn), else VG. Howes R404. *Dumont.* $150/£94

ROE, FRANCES M. A. Army Letters from an Officer's Wife, 1871-1888. NY: D. Appleton, 1909. 1st ed. Photo frontisport. Teg. (Ep hinges repaired, inscrips; rubbed), else VG. Howes R403. *Pacific*.* $92/£58

ROE, FRANK GILBERT. The Indian and the Horse. Norman: Univ of OK, 1955. Fldg map. VG in dj (lt worn). *Dumont.* $55/£34

ROE, FRED. A History of Oak Furniture. London, 1920. 76 plts. Good. *Washton.* $75/£47

ROE, HENRY. West African Sketches. London: Elliot Stock, 1874. 1st ed. Engr frontis (lt browned), vi,(ii),215,(1)ads; 5 engr plts. Grn dec cl, gilt. VG (string mk fr cvr). *Morrell.* $48/£30

ROEDIGER, VIRGINIA MORE. Ceremonial Costumes of the Pueblo Indians. Berkeley: Univ of CA, 1941. 1st ed. (Glassine chipped, tape across edges), else NF in VG glassine. *Pacific*.* $161/£101

ROETHKE, THEODORE. The Lost Son and Other Poems. GC: Doubleday, 1948. 1st ed. Signed leaf tipped iin. Black cl, gilt. (Few lt cvr scratches), o/w Fine in dj (sl soiled, edgeworn). *Heritage.* $350/£219

ROGERS, ARCHIBALD et al. Hunting. NY: Scribner, 1896. 1st ed. Inscribed (fading). Frontis, vii,327pp. VG + (edges worn; bkpl). *Backman.* $60/£38

ROGERS, BRUCE. Paragraphs on Printing, Elicited from Bruce Rogers in Talks with James Hendrickson on the Functions of the Book Designer. NY: William Edwin Rudge, 1943. 1st ed. Frontis photogravure port. NF. *Pacific*.* $63/£39

ROGERS, CAMERON. The Magnificent Idler. NY, 1926. 1st Amer ed. NF (sl rubbed). *Polyanthos.* $25/£16

ROGERS, FRED B. Soldiers of the Overland. SF: Grabhorn Press, 1938. 1st ed thus. Ltd to 1000. Frontisport, 2 fldg maps. Buckram-backed bds, spine label. Fine. *Sagebrush.* $95/£59

ROGERS, FRED B. Soldiers of the Overland. SF: Grabhorn, 1938. 1st ed. One of 1000. 2 fldg maps. Linen-backed dec bds, paper spine label. Fine (bd edges sl faded). *Harrington.* $100/£63

ROGERS, FRED B. William Brown Ide: Bear Flagger. SF: John Howell Books, 1962. One of 750. Fine. *Pacific*.* $29/£18

ROGERS, HENRY DARWIN. The Geology of Pennsylvania. Phila: J.B. Lippincott, 1858. 2 vols. Color frontispieces, xxvii,586, 23 plts; xxiv,1045pp, 40 plts (1 color), 2 maps (1 color). (Lacks 2 lg maps; worn, rubbed, scuffed, dust-soiled, cvrs detached vol 2 but present), else Good set. *Brown.* $150/£94

ROGERS, J. M. The Topkapi Saray Museum. Carpets. Boston: Little Brown, 1987. 1st ed. Folio. 98 color plts. NF in dj, protective cardbd slipcase. *Worldwide.* $95/£59

ROGERS, J. M. The Topkapi Saray Museum. Costumes, Embroideries and Other Textiles. Boston: Little Brown/NYGS, 1986. 1st US ed. NF in dj. *Worldwide.* $95/£59

ROGERS, JOHN WILLIAMS. Finding Literature on the Texas Plains. Dallas: Southwest, (1931). 1st ed. Frontis. 1/2 cl, gilt. (Frontis, pp5-8 neatly detached but present; corners, spine ends sl rubbed), else VG. *Pacific*.* $40/£25

ROGERS, JOHN WILLIAMS. The Lusty Texans of Dallas. NY: Dutton, 1951. 1st ed. Frontis. VG in dj (worn). *Lien*. $30/£19

ROGERS, JULIA. Little Red Riding Hood. Rochester: Stecher Litho, 1929. 10.5x10. Frances Brundage (illus). NF in chromolitho wrappers. *Pacific**. $52/£33

ROGERS, JULIA. The Tree Book. NY: Doubleday, Page, 1905. 1st ed. 16 color, 160 b/w plts. (Shelf-worn), else VG. *Fair Meadow*. $30/£19

ROGERS, MEYRIC R. Carl Milles. An Interpretation of His Work. New Haven, 1940. One of 2000. Folio. 163 plts. Good. *Washton*. $85/£53

ROGERS, SAMUEL. The Pleasures of Memory. Dublin: Ptd by William Porter, 1802. Dublin ed (?). vi,7-62pp; 2 unsigned engr plts. Contemp mottled-calf, red morocco label (fr joint cracked but firm). *Young*. $88/£55

ROGERS, THOMAS H. Bee's Wax and Gold. Portland, OR: Gill, 1929. 1st ed. Signed presentation. Brn pict cl. VG. *American Booksellers*. $60/£38

ROGERS, W. G. Wise Men Fish Here: The Story of Frances Steloff and the Gotham Book Mart. NY: Harcourt, Brace & World, (1965). 1st ed. NF in dj (worn). *Hermitage*. $30/£19

ROGERS, W. G. Wise Men Fish Here: The Story of Frances Steloff and the Gotham Book Mart. NY: HBW, (1965). 1st ed. VF in VF dj (rear cvr sl rubbed). *Between The Covers*. $85/£53

ROGERS, WILL. Ether and Me. NY: Putnam, (1929). 1st ed. White bds. VG (eps lt browned; bds lt soiled, extrems sl rubbed) in dj (soiled, lt chipped). *Heritage*. $125/£78

ROGERS, WILL. How We Elect Our Presidents. Boston: Little, Brown, (1952). 1st ed. Signed by Donald Day (ed). Grn cl. (Spine sl faded), o/w Fine in dj (edges lt chipped). *Heritage*. $125/£78

ROGERS, WILL. The Illiterate Digest. NY: Albert & Charles Boni, 1924. 1st ed. One of 250. Inscribed, signed. Paper spine label. (Residue from removed bkpl to fr pastedown; spine sl soiled), else VG. *Pacific**. $288/£180

ROGERS, WILL. Letters of a Self-Made Diplomat to His President. NY: Albert & Charles Boni, 1926. 1st ed. Brn cl. (Spine ends bumped), o/w NF in dj (lt soiled, sl chipped). *Heritage*. $250/£156

ROGERS, WILL. Twelve Radio Talks Delivered by Will Rogers. E.R. Squibb & Sons, (1930). 1st Amer ed. NF in ptd wraps. *Polyanthos*. $25/£16

ROGERSON, SYDNEY and CHARLES TUNNICLIFFE. Our Bird Book. London, 1947. 1st ed. Dj (lt foxed, chipped). *Edwards*. $56/£35

ROGERSON, SYDNEY. Our Bird Book. Collins, 1947. 1st ed. Lg 4to. 128-pp; 32 color plts by Charles Tunnicliffe. Pink cl. VG. *Bookmark*. $72/£45

ROGET, PETER MARK (comp). Thesaurus of English Words.... Boston: Gould & Lincoln, 1854. 1st Amer ed. 468pp. Early 1/4 calf, marbled bds, orig spine label. *M & S*. $275/£172

ROHAN, JACK. Yankee Arms Maker. NY: Harper, (1948). Rev ed. VG in dj (chipped). *Lien*. $20/£13

ROHDE, ELEANOR SINCLAIR. The Old English Gardening Books. London: New Aldine Library, 1924. 16 plts, 8 plans. Uncut. Canvas-backed bds, paper labels. *Maggs*. $120/£75

ROHDE, ELEANOR SINCLAIR. Oxford's College Gardens. Herbert Jenkins, 1932. 1st ed. 24 color plts. Blue cl, gilt. Fine. *Hollett*. $136/£85

ROHDE, ELEANOUR SINCLAIR. The Scented Garden. London: Medici, 1948. Fldg chart. Fine in dj (lt worn). *Quest*. $40/£25

ROHMER, SAX. Bimbashi Baruk of Egypt. NY: Robert M. McBride, 1944. 1st ed. Blue cl, gilt. VG (spine ends bumped, extrems lt rubbed) in dj (price-clipped, edgeworn, soiled). *Heritage*. $100/£63

ROHMER, SAX. The Day the World Ended. GC: DCC, 1945. 1st ed. Black cl. VG (lt foxed; extrems rubbed) in dj (spine top, fr panel chipped, loss to 3 letters). *Heritage*. $150/£94

ROHMER, SAX. The Drums of Fu Manchu. (GC): DCC, 1939. 1st ed. Black cl. (Label; spine extrems lt rubbed), o/w Fine in dj (lt edgeworn). *Heritage*. $250/£156

ROHMER, SAX. Emperor Fu Manchu. London: Herbert Jenkins, (1959). 1st ed. Red bds. Fine in dj (lt soiled). *Heritage*. $75/£47

ROHMER, SAX. The Island of Fu Manchu. GC: DCC, 1941. 1st ed. Orange cl. VG (eps browned; spine ends rubbed) in dj (price-clipped, lt chipped, soiled). *Heritage*. $250/£156

ROHMER, SAX. Slaves of Sumuru. London: Herbert Jenkins, (1952). 1st Eng ed. Red cl. VG (1st/last few ll lt foxed; ink inscrip) in dj (lt soiled, edgeworn). *Heritage*. $75/£47

ROHMER, SAX. The Trails of Fu Manchu. GC: DCC, 1934. 1st ed. Black cl. VG (ink inscrip, spine ends bumped) in dj (lt chipped, soiled). *Heritage*. $250/£156

ROJAS, MANUEL. Born Guilty. NY: Library Pub, 1955. 1st ed. NF in VG + dj (spine residue from sticker). *Lame Duck*. $45/£28

ROLAND, GEORGE. An Introductory Course of Fencing. Edinburgh: The Author, (c1820). 2nd ed. 41pp; 5 full-pg plts. Orig cl (extrems faded). *Young*. $144/£90

ROLAND, GEORGE. An Introductory Course of Fencing. Edinburgh: The Author, 1837. 41pp; 5 litho plts. (Grubby, lt foxed.) *Marlborough*. $480/£300

ROLFE, FREDERICK. The Armed Hands. London: Cecil & Amelia Woolf, 1974. Ltd to 200 numbered. VG in slipcase. *King*. $100/£63

ROLFE, FREDERICK. Ballade of Boys Bathing. Holburn, 1972. Ltd to 200 numbered. VG in orig env. *King*. $35/£22

ROLFE, FREDERICK. Collected Poems. London: Cecil & Amelia Woolf, 1974. 1st Eng ed. Fine in dj (sl mkd, top edge sl creased). *Ulysses*. $40/£25

ROLFE, FREDERICK. The Desire and Pursuit of the Whole. London: Cassell, 1953. 1st 'Auden' ed, 2nd imp. Good in dk grn cl, gilt. Dj (top edge chipped, hole in spine middle). *Maggs*. $48/£30

ROLFE, FREDERICK. The Desire and Pursuit of the Whole. (NY): New Directions, 1953. 1st Amer ed. Blue-grn cl, silver lettering. Pict dj (edges chipped, soiled). *Maggs*. $64/£40

ROLFE, FREDERICK. Don Tarquinio, a Kataleptic Phantasmatic Romance. London: C&W, 1957. One of 2000. Pub's slip loosely inserted. Fine in blue cl, gilt. Dj. *Maggs*. $32/£20

ROLFE, FREDERICK. Letters to C. H. C. Pirie-Gordon. Cecil Woolf (ed). London: Nicholas Vane, 1959. 1st ed. One of 30 (of 330) unnumbered out of series. Teg, rest untrimmed. Good in 1/4 white buckram, gilt, orange buckram sides. *Maggs*. $88/£55

ROLFE, FREDERICK. Nicholas Crabbe. London, 1958. VG in dj (sl frayed). *Typographeum*. $65/£41

ROLFE, R. A. and C. C. HURST. The Orchid Stud-Book. Kew, 1909. Frontis. (Marginal pencil mks, sm tear lower margin of 8pp, pp tanned, ex-lib, 2 inner joints cracked; extrems worn.) *Sutton*. $150/£94

ROLLAND, ROMAIN. Above the Battle. C. K. Ogden (trans). Chicago: Open Court, 1916. 1st US ptg. Teg. Blue-gray cl, gilt. (Few sl spots at edges), o/w Fine in dj. *Reese*. $40/£25

ROLLAND, ROMAIN. Beethoven the Creator. Ernest Newman (trans). Gollancz, 1929. 1st Eng ed. 30 plts. Leather spine label (sl chipped). *Hollett*. $72/£45

ROLLAND, ROMAIN. Mother and Son.... Van Wyck Brooks (trans). NY: Henry Holt, (1927). 1st US ed. Gilt blue cl. Nice in VG dj (spine faded, sl loss at spine ends). *Reese*. $45/£28

ROLLESTON, C. W. Parsifal, or the Legend of the Holy Grail. NY: Crowell, (1912). Willy Pogany (illus). Teg. Gilt-stamped maroon cl. *Appelfeld.* $250/£156

ROLLESTON, GEORGE. Scientific Papers and Addresses by George Rolleston. W. Turner and E. B. Tylor (eds). Oxford, 1884. 2 vols. Frontisport, lxxvi,944pp. Good. *Whitehart.* $144/£90

ROLLESTON, T. W. The Tale of Lohengrin. London: G.G. Harrap, (ca 1912). 1st ed. Willy Pogany (illus). 4to. Blind-stamped gilt-dec brn cl. Good in illus cardbd slipcase (worn, dusty). *Reisler.* $450/£281

ROLLIN, CHARLES. The Ancient History of the Egyptians, Carthaginians, Assyrians, Babylonians, Medes and Persians, Grecians and Macedonias. London: J. Rivington, 1768. 5th ed. 7 vols. 19 plts (5 fldg), 14 fldg maps. Contemp calf. (Sl foxed; sl rubbed, scuffed, few spines chipped), o/w Good. *Worldwide.* $125/£78

ROLLINS, CARL P. Off the Dead Bank. Yale Univ, 1949. One of 675. *Dawson.* $25/£16

ROLLINS, CARL P. Some Trifles Which Make for Perfection. Brooklyn, 1949. Fine. *Truepenny.* $30/£19

ROLLO, W. KEITH. The Art of Fly Fishing: Practical Hints.... London: H.F. & G. Witherby, (1933). 2nd ed. (Sl soiled), else VG. *Pacific*.* $40/£25

ROLLS, S. C. Steel Chariots in the Desert. London, 1937. 1st Eng ed. Good (spine foot sl snagged; no dj). *Clearwater.* $120/£75

ROLT, L. T. C. Alec's Adventures in Railwayland. London: Ian Allan, 1964. 1st Eng ed. VG in wrappers (sl rubbed, rear creased, staples rusting). *Ulysses.* $72/£45

ROLT, L. T. C. Narrow Boat. London: Eyre & Spottiswoode, (1945). Rpt. (Edges sl foxed.) *Petersfield.* $13/£8

ROMAINS, JULES. (Pseud of Louis Farigoule.) Death of a World. Gerard Hopkins (trans). NY: Knopf, 1938. 1st US ed. Purple cl stamped in gilt/black. Fine in NF dj (price-clipped). *Reese.* $50/£31

ROMAINS, JULES. (Pseud of Louis Farigoule.) Verdun. Gerard Hopkins (trans). NY: Knopf, 1939. 1st US ed. Fldg map. Blue cl stamped in black/gilt. Fine in dj. *Reese.* $50/£31

Romance of Tristan and Iseult. NY: LEC, 1960. One of 1500. Signed by Serge Ivanoff (illus). 1/2 red morocco, gilt-stamped bds. Fine in glassine, slipcase. *Pacific*.* $52/£33

ROMANES, G. J. An Examination of Weismannism. Chicago: Open Court, (1899). 2nd ed. Frontisport, 221pp + ads. Teg. VG. *Mikesh.* $45/£28

ROMANES, G. J. Mental Evolution in Animals (with) a Posthumous Essay on Instinct by Charles Darwin. London: Kegan et al, 1885. 1st ed. Fldg frontis chart, 411pp. Dec leather. VG. *Mikesh.* $150/£94

ROMIG, EMILY CRAIG. A Pioneer Woman in Alaska. Caldwell, ID: Caxton, 1948. 1st trade ed. Fine in dj. *High Latitude.* $45/£28

RONALDS, ALFRED. The Fly-Fisher's Entomology, with Coloured Representations of the Natural and Artificial Insect.... London: Longmans, Green, 1901. 10th ed. 20 hand-colored copper plts. Fine. *Pacific*.* $184/£115

RONALDS, ALFRED. The Fly-Fisher's Entomology, with Directions for Making the Artificial Representations of Each Fly. Liverpool: Henry Young & Sons, 1913. 11th ed. One of 250 numbered sets, signed by pubs. 2 vols. 4to. 48 artificial flies in sunken mounts. Uncut. Orig 1/2 morocco, gilt spines. Superb (rubbed, lt foxed). *Oinonen*.* $1,900/£1,188

RONALDS, ALFRED. The Fly-Fisher's Entomology, with Directions for Making the Artificial Representations of Each Fly. Liverpool: Henry Young, 1913. 11th ed. One of 250 numbered. 2 vols. 4to. 48 artificial flies in sunken mounts. Uncut. Orig 1/2 morocco (rubbed), spines gilt. Excellent set (sl foxed). *Oinonen*.* $2,500/£1,563

RONALDS, FRANCIS (comp). Catalogue of Books and Papers Relating to Electricity, Magnetism, the Electric Telegraph.... Alfred J. Frost (ed). London/NY: E. & F.N. Spon, 1880. 1st ed. xxvii,564pp. Later red cl, gilt. *Weber.* $400/£250

RONALDSHAY, EARL OF. A Wandering Student in the Far East. William Blackwood & Sons, 1908. 1st ed. 2 vols. 60 photo plts, fldg map. (Fore-edges sl spotted), o/w Fine set. *Hollett.* $192/£120

RONNE, FINN. Antarctic Command. NY: Bobbs-Merrill, (1961). Map. VG in dj (chipped). *Explorer.* $26/£16

RONNE, FINN. Antarctic Conquest. NY: Putnam, c. 1949. VG in dj. *High Latitude.* $27/£17

ROOKE, LEON. The Broad Back of the Angel. NY: Fiction Collective, (1977). 1st ed. As New in dj. *Bernard.* $20/£13

ROOME, WILLIAM J. W. Tramping Through Africa. London: A&C Black, 1930. 1st ed. 32 plts. Brn cl. (Lt foxed, presentation plt; edge sl stained), o/w VG in ptd dj (sl torn). *Morrell.* $32/£20

ROONEY, ANDY and BUD HUTTON. The Story of the Stars and Stripes: A Paper for Joe. NY: F&R, (1946). 1st ed. (Rear bd sl soiled), else Fine in VG dj (price-clipped, spine extrems rubbed, sl chipped). *Between The Covers.* $85/£53

ROOS, FRANK J., JR. Bibliography of Early American Architecture. Urbana: Univ of IL, 1968. 1st rev ed. Brn cl stamped in black. VF in dj (price-clipped, sl rubbed). *Baltimore*.* $40/£25

ROOSES, MAX (ed). Dutch Painters of the Nineteenth Century. F. Knowles (trans). NY/London, 1898-1901. 4 vols. 4to. 238; 258; 253; 247pp. Gilt-dec cl (soiled). VG set (lt foxed, few plt edges stained; few hinges weak). *Washton.* $750/£469

Roosevelt Hospital, 1871-1957. NY, 1957. 1st ed. Red cl. VG (extrems sl worn). *Doctor's Library.* $45/£28

ROOSEVELT, ELLIOT. Murder at Hobcaw Barony. St. Martins, 1986. 1st ed. Fine in dj. *Murder.* $25/£16

ROOSEVELT, FRANKLIN D. The Roosevelt Letters. Elliott Roosevelt (ed). London: George Harrap, 1949-52. 1st ed. 3 vols. (Few spots to fore-edges), o/w Fine set in djs. *Hollett.* $72/£45

ROOSEVELT, R. BARNWELL and SETH GREEN. Fish Hatching, and Fish Catching. Rochester: Union & Advertiser, 1879. 1st ed. Grn cl, gilt. NF. *Pacific*.* $81/£51

ROOSEVELT, THEODORE and GEORGE BIRD GRINNELL. American Big-Game Hunting. NY: Forest & Stream, (1983). Facs of orig 1893 ed. One of 450. Membership list. Maroon cl. Fine in ptd dj. *House.* $50/£31

ROOSEVELT, THEODORE and GEORGE BIRD GRINNELL. Hunting in Many Lands. NY, 1895. Silver-gilt pict cl. (Sl worn, rear inner joint broken.) *Oinonen*.* $100/£63

ROOSEVELT, THEODORE. African Game Trails. NY/London: Syndicate Pub, (1910). Pict lt brn cl (sl worn). Text Nice, cvrs Clean. *Baltimore*.* $30/£19

ROOSEVELT, THEODORE. African Game Trails. NY, 1910. 1st ed. 1/2 morocco (extrems lt rubbed). *Swann*.* $201/£126

ROOSEVELT, THEODORE. An Autobiography. NY, 1913. 1st ed. Port. Teg. (Extrems worn.) *King.* $40/£25

ROOSEVELT, THEODORE. Big Game Hunting in the Rockies and on the Great Plains. NY, 1899. Lg paper ed. Ltd to 1000 numbered, signed. 11x8 inches. 476pp + index. Port. Teg. 3/4 leather; marbled bds, eps. (Worn; cvrs, spine detached), else Good. *King.* $850/£531

ROOSEVELT, THEODORE. Fear God and Take Your Own Part. NY: George H. Doran, (1916). Unspecified later ptg. Tan cl. (Ink name dated 1926), else VG in dj. *Reese.* $22/£14

ROOSEVELT, THEODORE. Hoofs, Claws and Antlers of the Rocky Mountains, by the Camera. Denver: Frank S. Thayer, 1894. One of 1000. Gilt-lettered pict bds. (Rebacked w/red tape, ex-lib w/mks), else VG. *Pacific*.* $127/£79

ROOSEVELT, THEODORE. Hunting Trips of a Ranchman. NY: Putnam, 1895. xvi,347pp + (4)ads. Natural buckram, gilt. VG (lt soiled, spine browned). Howes R430. *House.* $120/£75

ROOSEVELT, THEODORE. Outdoor Pastimes of an American Hunter. NY: Scribner, 1905. 1st ed. Gravure frontisport. Teg. (Ink name; spine faded), else VG + . *Pacific*.* $71/£44

ROOSEVELT, THEODORE. Outdoor Pastimes of an American Hunter. NY, 1905. One of 260 numbered, signed. This add'lly inscribed, signed on leaf mtd to fep. Thick 8vo. 1/2 pigskin (extrems rubbed). *Swann*.* $2,070/£1,294

ROOSEVELT, THEODORE. Outdoor Pastimes of an American Hunter. NY: Scribner, 1908. 2nd enlgd ed. Frontisport, 54 photogravure plts. Brn cl (spine, edges faded, sl sprung w/hinge cracking). Sound. *Morrell.* $48/£30

ROOSEVELT, THEODORE. Outdoor Pastimes of an American Hunter. NY: Scribner, October 1905. 1st ed. Teg. Pict cl, gilt. VG. *Mikesh.* $95/£59

ROOSEVELT, THEODORE. Ranch Life and the Hunting-Trail. London, (1888). 1st Eng ed. Pict cl (worn; hinges cracked). *Swann*.* $69/£43

ROOSEVELT, THEODORE. Ranch Life and the Hunting-Trail. NY, (1888). 1st ed. Pub's gilt-pict cl (extrems rubbed, backstrip dknd, ends frayed). *Swann*.* $201/£126

ROOSEVELT, THEODORE. Ranch Life and the Hunting-Trail. NY: Century, (1888). 1st ed, 2nd binding. Frederick Remington (illus). (10),186,(187)pp, vignette. Aeg. Brn linen, gilt. VG (p131 creased; extrems worn, spine foot lacks sm piece). Howes R432. *House.* $250/£156

ROOSEVELT, THEODORE. The Rough Riders. NY: Scribner, 1899. 1st ed. xii,298pp. Teg, untrimmed. Olive cl, gilt. (Fr hinge lt cracked, tp loosened along upper portion; sl worn, spine lt sunned, splash stain across fr cvr top.) Text Clean. *Baltimore*.* $40/£25

ROOSEVELT, THEODORE. Through the Brazilian Wilderness. London, 1914. 1st ed. 2 maps (1 fldg). (Fr hinge cracked; lib bkpl, cardholder, ink stamp; shaken, joints splitting, spine faded.) *Edwards.* $48/£30

ROOSEVELT, THEODORE. Through the Brazilian Wilderness. London: Murray, 1914. 1st ed. 2 fldg maps. Teg. 3/4 leather, cl. (Spine sl dknd), else VG + . *Mikesh.* $75/£47

ROOSEVELT, THEODORE. The Works of.... NY: Scribner, 1923-26. One of 1050 sets. Signed by Edith Kermit Roosevelt. 24 vols. Fine in slipcases. *Pacific*.* $920/£575

ROOT, A. I. and E. R. The ABC and XYZ of Bee Culture. OH: A.I. Root, 1917. 161st thousand. Color frontis. VG (joints sl strained). *Hollett.* $72/£45

ROOT, EDWARD W. Philip Hooker. NY, 1929. One of 750 numbered. Folio. Dj (top, bottom edges reinforced w/cellotape). *Swann*.* $80/£50

ROOT, FRANK A. and WILLIAM E. CONNELLEY. The Overland Stage to California. Topeka: The Authors, 1901. 1st ed. Fldg map. Brn pict cl (lt edgeworn, soiled). Howes R434. *Glenn.* $200/£125

ROOT, WAVERLEY. The Paris Edition. The Autobiography of Waverley Root 1927-1934. Samuel Abt (ed). SF: North Point, 1987. 1st ed. NF in dj. *Any Amount.* $24/£15

ROOTH, SIGNE ALICE (ed). Seeress of the Northland. Frederika Bremer's American Journey 1849-1851. Phila: Amer Swedish Hist Foundation, (1955). 1st ed. Inscribed by ed. Blue cl. VG in dj. *House.* $25/£16

ROPER, F. C. S. Catalogue of Works on the Microscope and Those Referring to Microscopical Subjects.... London, 1865. vii,102pp. (Lib binding, stamp.) *Henly.* $77/£48

ROPER, LANNING. The Gardens in the Royal Park at Windsor. London: C&W, 1961. 2nd ptg. Signed. 45 color, 59 b/w plts. VG in dj (chipped). *Fair Meadow.* $50/£31

ROPER, LANNING. The Gardens of Anglesey Abbey Cambridgeshire. London: Faber & Faber, 1964. Ltd to 600. VG in dj (lt worn). *Fair Meadow.* $125/£78

ROPER, LANNING. On Gardens and Gardening. NY: Harper & Row, 1969. 1st Amer ed. VG in dj. *Fair Meadow.* $45/£28

ROQUELAURE, A. N. (Pseud of Anne Rice.) Beauty's Punishment. NY: Dutton, (1984). 1st ed, hb issue. Fine in NF dj. *Reese.* $125/£78

ROQUELAURE, A. N. (Pseud of Anne Rice.) Beauty's Punishment. NY: E.P. Dutton, (1984). 1st ed. Fine in dj (fr flap crease). *Pacific*.* $138/£86

ROQUELAURE, A. N. (Pseud of Anne Rice.) Beauty's Release. NY: E.P. Dutton, (1985). 1st ed. Fine in dj. *Pacific*.* $115/£72

ROQUELAURE, A. N. (Pseud of Anne Rice.) Beauty's Release. NY, 1985. 1st ed. (Red rmdr dot to top edge), o/w Fine in Fine dj. *Warren.* $75/£47

ROQUELAURE, A. N. (Pseud of Anne Rice.) The Claiming of Sleeping Beauty. NY: Dutton, (1983). 1st ed, wrapper issue. Fine in pict stiff wrappers. *Reese.* $30/£19

ROQUELAURE, A. N. (Pseud of Anne Rice.) The Claiming of Sleeping Beauty. NY: E.P. Dutton, (1983). 1st ed. Signed by Rice as both names. Fine in dj. *Pacific*.* $288/£180

ROREM, NED. The New York Diary. NY: Braziller, (1967). 1st ed. VF in VF dj. *Between The Covers.* $85/£53

ROREM, NED. The Paris Diary of Ned Rorem. NY: Braziller, (1966). 1st ed. VF in Fine white dj (sm sticker shadow rear cvr). *Between The Covers.* $85/£53

RORIE, DAVID. A Medico's Luck in the War. Aberdeen, 1929. 1st Eng ed. (Faded, mkd, spine head sl chafed.) *Clearwater.* $96/£60

ROSA, JOAO GUIMARAES. The Devil to Pay in the Backlands. NY: Knopf, 1963. 1st US ed. Fine in NF dj (few tears). *Lame Duck.* $150/£94

ROSA, JOAO GUIMARAES. Sagarana. Harriet de Onis (trans). NY: Knopf, 1966. 1st US ed. Fine in NF dj (sm spine nick). *Reese.* $45/£28

ROSA, JOSEPH G. The Gunfighter, Man or Myth? Norman: Univ of OK, 1969. 1st ed. Fine in dj. *Labordo.* $60/£38

ROSA, JOSEPH G. They Called Him Wild Bill. Norman: Univ of OK, 1964. 1st ed. Fine in dj. *Labordo.* $85/£53

ROSA, RODRIGO REY. The Path Doubles Back. Paul Bowles (trans). (NY: Red Ozier, 1982.) 1st ed thus. One of 185 numbered, signed by Rosa, Bowles & David Craven (illus). Dec bds. Fine. *Reese.* $175/£109

ROSCOE, HENRY. Eminent British Lawyers. London: Longman, Rees, Orme et al, 1830. Purple cl (spine very faded; foxed). Sound. *Boswell.* $150/£94

ROSCOE, THOMAS. Wanderings and Excursions in South Wales. London, 1854. xi,336pp; add'l engr tp, 2 fldg plans, fldg map, 46 engr plts. Marbled eps; all edges marbled. Mod gilt-ruled full calf, morocco label, raised bands. (Pp15/6 w/taped fore-edge, sl sporadic browning, bkpl; sm spine stains.) *Edwards.* $160/£100

ROSCOE, THOMAS. Wanderings and Excursions in South Wales; Including the Scenery of the River Wye. London, (1837). 48 engr plts. Morocco (extrems sl worn), gilt extra. *Swann*.* $258/£161

ROSCOE, WILLIAM. The Life of Lorenzo De' Medici, Called the Magnificent. London: Strahan, Cadell & Davies, 1797. 3rd ed. 2 vols. Engr stipple port, full-pg plt. Mod bds. (Stamps, lower blank portion of 1st half-title restored.) *Rostenberg & Stern.* $250/£156

ROSE, BARBARA. Claes Oldenburg. NY: MOMA, (1970). 1st ed. Signed. Obl sm folio. Laminated flexible white plastic wraps lettered in grn (lt sunned, dusty). Text Good (few pp rubbed at edges). *Baltimore*.* $110/£69

ROSE, BARBARA. Frankenthaler. NY, ca 1970. Pict cl. Plastic dj (soiled). *Swann**. $138/£86

ROSE, D. MURRAY. Historical Notes and Essays on the '15 and '45. Edinburgh: William Brown, 1897. Ltd to 150. xii,198pp (bkpl); 2 ports, 10 facs. Buckram, gilt. *Hollett*. $104/£65

ROSE, FRANCIS. The White Cow and Other Chinese Fairy Tales. Lutterworth, 1945. 1st Eng ed. VG (spine tail sl bumped) in dj (rubbed, chipped, torn, creased, sl spotted). *Ulysses*. $58/£36

ROSE, HUGH. The Elements of Botany.... London: T. Cadell, 1775. 13 (of 14) plts. Old calf bds. (Sig, hinges weak, foxed.) *Metropolitan**. $86/£54

ROSE, JAMES C. Creative Gardens. NY: Reinhold, 1958. (Sm spot rear cvr), else Fine in dj (worn). *Quest*. $50/£31

ROSE, T. The Metallurgy of Gold. London, 1896. 2nd ed. 495pp. Maroon cl, gilt. (Edgeworn), else Good+. *Larry Price*. $150/£94

ROSE, T. The Metallurgy of Gold. London: Charles Griffin, 1902. 4th ed. VG. *Blake*. $135/£84

ROSE, VICTOR M. The Life and Services of Gen. Ben McCulloch. Phila: Pictorial Bureau of the Press, 1888. 1st ed. 8vo. 260pp; 2 ports. Stamped dk brn cl. VG (edgeworn). Howes R443. *Chapel Hill*. $3,500/£2,188

ROSE, VICTOR M. Ross' Texas Brigade.... Continental Book, 1960. Facs of 1881 Louisville Courrier-Journal ed. VG. *Book Broker*. $45/£28

Rose-Bud: A Flower in the Juvenile Garland. London: Baldwin & Cradock, 1834. 4th ed. Sm 12mo. 68pp+4pp ads+2pp contents. Marbled paper on bd. Fine (lt rubbed, spine sl chipped). *Hobbyhorse*. $200/£125

ROSE-TROUP, FRANCES. The Western Rebellion of 1549. Smith Elder, 1913. 1st ed. 6 plts. (Bkpl; edges sl spotted; spine sl faded.) *Hollett*. $72/£45

ROSEN, PETER. Pa-Ha-Sa-Pa; or, the Black Hills of South Dakota. St. Louis, MO: Nixon-Jones Ptg, 1895. 1st ed. Good+ (pp dknd; cvrs faded, spine head worn). Howes R446. *Labordo*. $285/£178

ROSEN, R. D. Strike Three You're Dead. Walker, 1984. 1st ed. Fine in Fine dj. *Plapinger*. $150/£94

ROSENAU, HELEN. Social Purpose in Architecture; Paris and London Compared, 1760-1800. London: Studio Vista, 1970. Pub's cl. Fine in dj (frayed). *Europa*. $56/£35

ROSENAU, M. J. (ed). Proceedings of the International Congress on Health Problems in Tropical America. Boston, 1924. 1st ed. *Fye*. $75/£47

ROSENAU, MILTON. Preventive Medicine and Hygiene. NY, 1913. 1st ed. *Fye*. $200/£125

ROSENBACH CO. Catalogue 16: Rare and Important Books and Manuscripts Relating to America. Phila: Rosenbach Co, 1913. Good in ptd cvrs. *Moss*. $38/£24

ROSENBACH, A. S. W. The All-Embracing Doctor Franklin. Phila: Privately ptd, 1932. One of 198, this copy not numbered, ptd by Fred Anthoensen. Frontis port. Uncut. Morocco-backed bds (sl rubbed). *Oinonen**. $80/£50

ROSENBACH, A. S. W. A Book Hunter's Holiday. Boston/NY, 1936. VG in dj. *Truepenny*. $65/£41

ROSENBACH, A. S. W. Books and Bidders. Boston, 1927. 1st Amer ed. Signed. Teg. Fine (name; spine lt sunned; sl rubbed). *Polyanthos*. $50/£31

ROSENBACH, A. S. W. Books and Bidders. Boston: Little, Brown, 1927. 1st ltd ed. One of 785 numbered, signed on tipped-in limitation leaf. Teg; untrimmed, partly unopened. Dk brn buckram, lt brn bds, ptd paper spine label. (Spine, edges lt rubbed.) Text Good (fr hinge cracked, tp lt foxed). Bd slipcase (edges chipped, worn, several splits). *Baltimore**. $50/£31

ROSENBACH, A. S. W. Books and Bidders. Boston: Little, Brown, 1928. 1st ed, lg paper ed. One of 785. Signed. Teg. 1/2 cl, paper spine label. Fine in slipcase (splitting). *Pacific**. $75/£47

ROSENBACH, A. S. W. The Unpublishable Memoirs. NY: Mitchell Kennerley, 1917. 1st ed. Inscribed. *Dawson*. $100/£63

ROSENBERG, FRANTZ. Big Game Shooting in British Columbia and Norway. London: Hopkinson, 1928. 1st ed. VF. *Bowman*. $100/£63

ROSENBERG, HAROLD. De Kooning. NY: Abrams, ca 1973. Dj. *Swann**. $431/£269

ROSENBERG, HAROLD. Willem de Kooning. NY: Abrams, n.d. Obl folio. 65 color plts. Dj (sl soiled). *Swann**. $546/£341

ROSENBERG, ISAAC. The Collected Poems. Gordon Bottomley and Denys Harding (eds). London: C&W, 1949. Rev & definitive ed. (Soft crease to few ll), o/w Fine in NF dj (few sm nicks). *Reese*. $60/£38

ROSENBERG, ISAAC. The Collected Works of.... Ian Parsons (ed). NY: OUP, 1979. 1st ed. Gray cl, gilt. Fine in dj. *Reese*. $45/£28

ROSENBERG, ISAAC. The Collected Works. Ian Parsons (ed). NY: OUP, 1979. 1st Amer ed. Fine (spine sl rubbed) in Fine dj. *Polyanthos*. $25/£16

ROSENBERG, ISAAC. Poems. Gordon Bottomley (ed). London, 1922. 1st ed. Nice (bkpl, feps renewed; spine label, 2 corners sl rubbed). *Clearwater*. $88/£55

ROSENBERG, ISAAC. Poems. Gordon Bottomley (ed). London: Heinemann, 1922. 1st ed. Port. Black cl, paper spine label. NF in VG+ dj (few mks, smudges). *Reese*. $350/£219

ROSENBERG, SAMUEL. Naked Is the Best Disguise. Indianapolis: Bobbs-Merrill, (1974). 1st ptg. VG in VG dj. *Gravesend*. $30/£19

ROSENBLUM, NAOMI. A World History of Photography. NY: Abbeville, 1984. 1st ed. (Sm tear on fep), else Fine. *Cahan*. $50/£31

ROSENTHAL, IRVING. Sheeper. NY: Grove, 1967. 1st ed. Fine in Fine dj (price-clipped). *Warren*. $45/£28

ROSENTHAL, MICHAEL. Constable. The Painter and His Landscape. Yale Univ, 1983. 1st ed. Dj. *Edwards*. $48/£30

ROSEVEAR, D. R. The Rodents of West Africa. London, 1969. 11 color plts. (Paint streak along backstrip edge.) Dj (lacks sm piece). *Sutton*. $100/£63

ROSMAN, ABRAHAM and PAULA G. RUBEL. Feasting with Mine Enemy. NY: Columbia Univ, 1971. VG in dj. *Perier*. $45/£28

ROSS, ALAN Time Was Away. Lehmann, 1948. 1st Eng ed. VG (bkpl) in dj (creased, repaired, rubbed). *Clearwater*. $184/£115

ROSS, ALAN. African Negatives. London: Eyre & Spottiswoode, 1962. 1st Eng ed. NF (spine foot bumped) in dj (sl creased, spine sl faded). *Ulysses*. $40/£25

ROSS, ALAN. The Taj Express. London: Magazine Editions, 1973. 1st Eng ed. Fine in dj (sl faded). *Clearwater*. $40/£25

ROSS, ALAN. Time Was Away. John Lehmann, 1948. 1st ed. 8 color plts. Dec buckram, gilt. VG (bkpl, spotted; sl mkd, spine foot, top corners sl bumped) in dj (nicked, chipped, creased, rubbed, sl torn, spotted, internally repaired, spine, edges dknd). *Ulysses*. $360/£225

ROSS, ALEXANDER. Adventures of the First Settlers on the Oregon or Columbia River. Milo Milton Quaife (ed). NY: Citadel, (1969). 1st ptg. Frontis map. Red cl. NF in dj (lt soiled). Howes R448. *House*. $20/£13

ROSS, ALEXANDER. Adventures of the First Settlers on the Oregon or Columbia River. Milo Quaife (ed). NY: Citadel, (1969). Fine. Howes R448. *Perier*. $32/£20

ROSS, ALEXANDER. Adventures of the First Settlers on the Oregon or Columbia River. Reuben Gold Thwaites (ed). Cleveland: A.H. Clark, 1904. 1st ed. VG +. Howes R448. *Labordo.* $175/£109

ROSS, CLYDE P. Routes to Desert Watering Places in the Lower Gila Region, Arizona. Washington, 1922. 3 fldg maps in rear pocket. (Wraps worn, chipped, lt watermks to bottom fore-edge), else Good. *Dumont.* $45/£28

ROSS, DUDLEY T. Devil on Horseback. Fresno, 1975. Good in dj. *Dumont.* $25/£16

ROSS, FITZGERALD. A Visit to the Cities and Camps of the Confederate States. Edinburgh/London: William Blackwood & Sons, 1865. 1st ed. 300pp + (2)pp ads; fldg map. Maroon cl. (Spine faded, ends bumped), else VG. Howes R453. *Chapel Hill.* $450/£281

ROSS, FREDERICK. The Ruined Abbeys of Britain. London, n.d. c.(1883). 2 vols. viii,288pp; 12 color plts. Aeg. (Hinges tender; corners rubbed w/sl cl loss; corners, spines chipped w/loss.) *Edwards.* $256/£160

ROSS, HUGH. Induced Cell-Reproduction and Cancer. Phila, 1911. 1st ed. *Fye.* $150/£94

ROSS, ISHBEL. Rebel Rose, Life of Rose O'Neal Grenhow, Confederate Spy. NY, (1954). Rpt. VG in VG dj. *Pratt.* $27/£17

ROSS, JAMES CLARK. A Voyage of Discovery and Research in the Southern and Antarctic Regions During the Years 1839-43. London: John Murray, 1847. 1st ed. 2 vols. lii,366; x,447pp. Marbled eps. 19th-cent full calf, gilt. VG. *Walcot.* $1,592/£995

ROSS, JAMES CLARK. A Voyage of Discovery and Research in the Southern and Antarctic Regions, During the Years 1839-43. London: John Murray, 1847. 2 vols. 8vo. lii,(iii),366; x,(iii),447pp + 16 ads. Full leather (orig cvrs laid in). Fine. *Explorer.* $2,400/£1,500

ROSS, JOHN D. Scottish Poets in America. NY: Pagan & Ross, 1889. Frontisport, 218,(ii)pp. (Fep stuck to ep, stamps; extrems sl worn, sm label spine base.) *Hollett.* $104/£65

ROSS, JOHN. Narrative of a Second Voyage in Search of a North-West Passage and of a Residence in the Arctic Regions During the Years 1829, 1830, 1831, 1832, 1833. London: A.W. Webster, 1835. 1st ed. 4to. xxxiii,740pp; 31 plts, charts (10 color). Mod 1/2 calf; gilt, raised bands to spine. VG (sl foxed). *Walcot.* $560/£350

ROSS, JOHN. Narrative of a Second Voyage in Search of a North-West Passage and of a Residence...During the Years 1829, 1830, 1831, 1832, 1833. London: A.W. Webster, 1835. 1st ed. 2 vols. Med 4to. (viii),xxxiv,740; xii,120,clxiv,ciipp + errata leaf; 50 plts (16 hand-colored), 5 charts. Uncut. (2 plts professionally repaired; foxed), o/w VG set in orig blue figured cl (vol 1 rebacked w/orig spine laid on). *Ulysses.* $3,360/£2,100

ROSS, JOHN. Narrative of a Second Voyage in Search of a North-West Passage, and of a Residence in the Arctic Regions, 1829-1833. Phila, 1835. 1st Amer ed. Fldg map (wrinkled, gutter tear neatly repaired). Uncut. Contemp cl-backed bds (shelfworn; lacks fep), remnant of ptd spine label. *Oinonen*.* $275/£172

ROSS, JOHN. Narrative of a Second Voyage in Search of a North-West Passage, and of a Residence in the Arctic Regions.... Paris: Baudry's European Library, 1835. Pirated ed. xvi(17)-475pp; 2 plts, lg fldg map. (Sl foxed; recent cl-backed bds), else VG. *High Latitude.* $95/£59

ROSS, JOHN. Narrative of a Second Voyage in Search of a North-West Passage. London, 1835. 12.5x10 inches. 740pp; fldg map, 30 plts (10 color). Recent 1/2 calf, marbled bds. (New eps, inked out inscrip; tp, frontis foxed, other sl foxed, offset), else Nice. *King.* $600/£375

ROSS, JOHN. Narrative of a Second Voyage in Search of a North-West Passage.... London: A.W. Webster, 1835. 4 to., (i), ad (i), errata (i),xxxiii, plts for binder (i), 740pp; 30 plts & maps incl 9 color and 1 fldg. Blue cl (rubbed). VG (map strengthened on fold, sl foxed, sl edge stain on several plts). *Explorer.* $544/£340

ROSS, JOHN. Narrative of a Second Voyage in Search of a North-west Passage.... London: A.W. Webster, 1835. Vol 1 only (of 2). 30 plts, maps, charts (9 hand-colored), lg fldg map. Orig bds. (Foxed, prelim pp loose; inner gutter split, worn, rubbed.) *Kane*.* $250/£156

ROSS, JOHN. Narrative of a Voyage in Search of a North-West Passage. London: A.W. Webster, 1835. 4to. 25 plts, incl 9 partly hand-colored lithos and mezzotints, 6 engr and litho maps, 1 fldg and color. Errata leaf. (Occasional lt staining, bkpl.) Contemp blue 1/2 calf, spine gilt, red morocco label. W/o Appendix vol published separately. *Christie's*.* $901/£563

ROSS, LEONARD Q. The Education of Hyman Caplan. Constable, 1937. 1st UK ed. Dec bds. Fine in VG dj (sl rubbed, 5cm closed tear to spine hinge). *Williams.* $77/£48

ROSS, LILLIAN. Picture: A Story About Hollywood. NY: Rinehart, (1952). 1st ed. VG (pg edges browned, lt stain top edge, lt crease fr fly) in VG + dj (nicks, wear). *Between The Covers.* $75/£47

ROSS, M. The Art of Karl Faberge and His Contemparies. Norman: Univ of OK, c1965. 75 color plts. Fine in dj. *Blake.* $350/£219

ROSS, M. J. Polar Pioneers: John Ross and James Clark Ross. Montreal: McGill-Queen's Univ, 1994. Fine in dj. *Explorer.* $38/£24

ROSS, M. J. Ross in the Antarctic: The Voyages of James Clark Ross in Her Majesty's Ships Erebus and Terror 1839-1843. Whitby: Caedmon, 1982. 2 fldg maps. Fine in dj. *Explorer.* $26/£16

ROSS, ROBERT. Friend of Friends. Margery Ross (ed). London, 1952. 1st Eng ed. VG in dj (sl rubbed). *Clearwater.* $88/£55

ROSS, RONALD. Mosquito Brigades and How to Organise Them. London, 1902. (Ex-lib, ink stamps; sl dknd, spine chipped w/loss to head.) *Edwards.* $24/£15

ROSS, WALTER. The Immortal. NY: S&S, 1958. 1st ed. VF in VF black dj (sl rubbed). *Between The Covers.* $100/£63

ROSSETTI, CHRISTINA. Goblin Market. London: George Harrap, (1933). 1st Rackham ed. One of 410 signed by Arthur Rackham (illus). 8vo. 4 color plts. Teg. Full limp vellum gilt. Fine. *Appelfeld.* $650/£406

ROSSETTI, CHRISTINA. Goblin Market. London: George G. Harrap, 1933. 1st ed illus by Arthur Rackham. 4 color plts. Dec card wraps (sl soiled). Pict wrapper. *Sotheran.* $205/£128

ROSSETTI, DANTE GABRIEL. Ballads and Narrative Poems. Kelmscott Press, 1893. One of 310. 8vo. Uncut; silk ties. Orig limp vellum. *Sotheby's*.* $1,011/£632

ROSSETTI, DANTE GABRIEL. The Collected Works. William M. Rossetti (ed). London: Ellis & Elvey, 1888. 1st collected ed. 2 vols. Dk grn gilt-stamped cl. Fine (sig). *Appelfeld.* $250/£156

ROSSETTI, DANTE GABRIEL. Hand and Soul. (Hammersmith/Chicago: Kelmscott/Sold by Way & Williams, 1895.) 1st ed. One of 300 ptd. 16mo. Full vellum, gilt. (2 bkpls.) *Kane*.* $300/£188

ROSSETTI, DANTE GABRIEL. Letters to William Allingham, 1854-1870. George Birkbeck Hill (ed). Fisher Unwin, 1897. 1st Eng ed. (Lib labels removed; cvrs sl scratched, mkd, fr hinge weak.) *Clearwater.* $112/£70

ROSSETTI, DANTE GABRIEL. Sonnets and Lyrical Poems. Kelmscott Press, 1894. One of 310. 8vo. Uncut; silk ties. Orig limp vellum. *Sotheby's*.* $1,067/£667

ROSSETTI, W. M. Bibliography of the Works of Dante Gabriel Rossetti. Ellis, 1905. One of 250. Fine in wrappers (sl creased, torn at overlapping edges). *Clearwater.* $136/£85

ROSSETTI, W. M. Letters of William Michael Rossetti Concerning Whitman, Blake, and Shelley. Anne and Herbert Gilchrist (eds). Durham, NC: Duke Univ, 1934. 1st ed. Grn cl. Fine in NF dj. *Macdonnell.* $75/£47

ROSSETTI, W. M. Life of John Keats. London: Walter Scott, 1887. 1st ed. Teg. Maroon cl, gilt. Fine. *Macdonnell*. $75/£47

Rosso Fiorentino. Washington: National Gallery of Art, 1987. Good+ in wrappers. *Washton*. $65/£41

ROSTAND, EDMOND. Cyrano de Bergerac. LEC, 1954. Ltd to 1500 numbered, signed by Pierre Brissaud (illus). Fine in slipcase. *Swann**. $69/£43

ROSTENBERG, LEONA and MADELEINE B. STERN. Old and Rare. NY, 1974. VG in dj. *Dumont*. $28/£18

ROSTENBERG, LEONA. Bibliately. State College, PA: American Philatelic Soc, 1978. Dec cvrs. *Rostenberg & Stern*. $30/£19

ROSTENBERG, LEONA. The Minority Press and the English Crown. Nieuwkoop: De Graaf, 1971. *Rostenberg & Stern*. $75/£47

ROSTLUND, ERHARD. Freshwater Fish and Fishing in Native North America. Berkeley/L.A.: Univ of CA, 1952. 1st ed. (Corners sl curled), else Fine in orig ptd wrappers. *Argonaut*. $125/£78

ROSTOVTZEFF, M. A History of the Ancient World. J.D. Duff (trans). Oxford: Clarendon, 1930, 1927. Vol 1, 2nd ed; vol 2, 1st ed. 2 vols. 188 plts, 7 fldg maps. (Ex-lib; rubbed, vol 2 spine torn, lib spine #), o/w Good. *Worldwide*. $145/£91

ROTERS, EBERHARD. Painters of the Bauhaus. London, 1969. 1st UK ed. 32 color plts. (Ink stamps, fr hinge tender.) Dj (lib spine #s). *Edwards*. $72/£45

ROTH, ARTHUR. Eiger: Wall of Death. London: Victor Gollancz, 1982. 1st ed. Frontis. Red cl. Fine in dj. *Argonaut*. $50/£31

ROTH, B. The Treatment of Lateral Curvature of the Spine. London, 1899. 141pp. (Stamps, ink sig; spine ends sl worn), o/w VG. *Whitehart*. $56/£35

ROTH, H. LING. The Natives of Sarawak and British North Borneo.... Truslove & Hanson, 1896. Ltd to 700. 2 vols. 8vo. Pict add'l tp, fldg map, sub's list. Teg. Pub's grn cl (sl rubbed), gilt. *Sotheby's**. $1,011/£632

ROTH, H. LING. Oriental Silverwork. Truslove & Hanson, 1910. 1st ed. Teg. Beveled bds. (Feps sl spotted), o/w VF. *Hollett*. $280/£175

ROTH, HENRY. Nature's First Green. NY: Targ Editions, 1979. One of 350 numbered, signed. Fine in dj. *Dermont*. $60/£38

ROTH, IRVING. Cardiac Arrhythmias, Clinical Features and Mechanism of the Irregular Heart. NY, 1928. 1st ed. *Fye*. $200/£125

ROTH, JOSEPH. Job, the Story of a Simple Man. Dorothy Thompson (trans). London: Heinemann, (1932). 1st British ed. Purple-brn cl, gilt. (Sl discoloration lower corner last few ll; sl wrinkle in cl of fr cvr), o/w VG in pict dj (sl used, price reduction sticker on spine). *Reese*. $175/£109

ROTH, LELAND. A Monograph of the Works of McKim Mead and White 1879-1915. NY, 1973. Facs of 1915 ed. 4 vols in 1. Frontis port; 399 plts. Pict cl. *Edwards*. $77/£48

ROTH, PHILIP. The Breast. NY: Holt, Rinehart & Winston, 1972. 1st ed. Inscribed. Fine in dj. *Lame Duck*. $75/£47

ROTH, PHILIP. The Great American Novel. NY: Holt, Rinehart & Winston, 1973. Rev copy. Rev slip, publicity photo laid in. (Sm stain to pp edges), else Fine in NF dj. *Lame Duck*. $75/£47

ROTH, PHILIP. Novotny's Pain. Hollywood: Sylvester & Orphanos, 1980. Ltd to 330 signed. Fine debossed cl. *Truepenny*. $100/£63

ROTH, PHILIP. Our Gang. NY: Random House, (1971). 1st ed. Fine in dj. *Between The Covers*. $75/£47

ROTH, PHILIP. Portnoy's Complaint. Cape, 1969. 1st UK ed. Fine in dj. *Williams*. $48/£30

ROTH, PHILIP. Portnoy's Complaint. NY: Random House, 1969. 1st ed. Inscribed. NF in VG+ dj (spine soiled, price-clipped, extrems lt worn). *Lame Duck*. $200/£125

ROTH, SAMUEL. Europe: A Book for America. NY: Boni & Liveright, 1919. 1st ed. Gilt gray bds. (Few lt spots to bds), else VG. *Reese*. $35/£22

ROTHENBERG, BENO. God's Wilderness: Discoveries in Sinai. London: Thames & Hudson, (1961). Folio. (Bkpl removed; corner bumped.) *Archaeologia*. $45/£28

ROTHENSTEIN, JOHN. Brave Day Hideous Night. London: Hamish Hamilton, 1966. 1st ed. VG in dj. *Hollett*. $24/£15

ROTHENSTEIN, JOHN. British Art Since 1900. London: Phaidon, 1962. Dj (spine, upper wrap lt faded). *Edwards*. $32/£20

ROTHENSTEIN, WILLIAM. Men and Memories: Recollections of...1900-1922. London: Faber & Faber, (1934). 1st imp this format. Gilt red cl (Fore-edge sl foxed), o/w NF in NF dj (spine sunned, price-clipped). *Reese*. $30/£19

ROTHLISBERGER, MARCEL. Claude Lorraine. The Paintings. New Haven: Yale Univ, 1961. 2 vols. Pub's cl. VF set. Salloch bkpl. *Europa*. $456/£285

ROTHSCHILD, FRITZ. The Lost Tradition in Music. A&C Black, 1953. 1st ed. VG in dj (spine sl faded). *Hollett*. $72/£45

ROTHWELL, RICHARD P. The Mineral Industry, Its Statistics, Technology and Trade, in the United States and Other Countries from the Earliest Times to the End of 1892-3. NY: Scientific, 1894. 1st ed. 2 vols. Brn cl, gilt. VG. *Pacific**. $98/£61

ROUGHEAD, WILLIAM. The Murderer's Companion. NY: W.W. Norton, (1968). 1st ptg this ed. VG in VG dj (lt worn). *Gravesend*. $35/£22

ROULIN, DOM E. A. Vestments and Vesture: A Manual of Liturgical Art. London, 1933. 2nd imp. Teg. Silk marker. (Corner cut from fep), o/w VG+ in dj (worn). *Whittle*. $72/£45

ROUMAIN, JACQUES. Masters of the Dew. Langston Hughes and Mercer Cook (trans). NY, (1947). 1st ed. Later issue w/Liberty Book Club on spine, dj but Reynal & Hitchcock sheets. (Offset on fep, text browned), else Good in dj (sl stained, edges worn). *King*. $65/£41

ROUMAIN, JACQUES. Masters of the Dew. Langston Hughes and Mercer Cook (trans). NY: Reynal & Hitchcock, (1947). 1st ed. Blue cl. (Feps sl browned; spine faded, extrems sl rubbed), o/w Fine in dj (chipped, spine sl faded). *Heritage*. $75/£47

ROURKE, CONSTANCE. Troupers of the Gold Coast. NY: Harcourt Brace, (1928). 1st ed. VG in pict dj (sl worn). *Dramatis*. $40/£25

ROUSE, HUNTER and SIMON INCE. History of Hydraulics. State Univ of IA, 1957. 1st ed. VG. *Glaser*. $85/£53

ROUSE, W. H. D. The Giant Crab. London: David Nutt, 1897. 1st ed. 8vo. Charles Robinson (illus). x,119pp + (xii) pub's cat. Uncut. Blue pict cl. (Tp vignette neatly hand-colored by owner), o/w Very Nice. *Sotheran*. $141/£88

ROUSE, W. H. D. (ed). The Arabian Nights. London: Ernest Nister, (1907). 1st ed illus by Walter Paget. 8vo. (v),6-328pp; 6 Fine chromolitho plts. Aeg. Dk grn pict cl (spine strip sunned), gilt. *Sotheran*. $141/£88

ROUSSEAU, JEAN-JACQUES. The Confessions of Jean-Jacques Rousseau. UK: Privately ptd, 1904. 15 etchings by Ed Hedouin, 2 ports. Uncut, unopened. Fine (sm corner crease). *Polyanthos*. $60/£38

ROUSSEAU, JEAN-JACQUES. The Confessions of Jean-Jacques Rousseau. LEC, 1955. Ltd to 1500 numbered, signed by William Sharp (illus). Fine in slipcase. *Swann**. $34/£21

ROUSSEL, RAYMOND. Impressions of Africa. Lindy Foord and Rayner Heppenstall (trans). Calder & Boyars, 1966. 1st UK ed. (Edges sl faded), o/w NF in dj (sl rubbed, spotted, spine sl dknd). *Sclanders*. $32/£20

ROUSSELET, LOUIS. India and Its Native Princes. Lieut-Col. Buckle (ed). London, 1876. 6 maps. 1/2 morocco (rebacked w/orig backstrip replaced; margin corners stained 1st 20pp). Good. *Petersfield*. $320/£200

ROUSSELET, LOUIS. India and Its Native Princes: Travels in Central India. NY, 1876. 1st Amer ed. Sm thick folio. Mod gilt-pict cl. *Swann**. $230/£144

ROUSSIN, ANDRE. The Little Hut. Nancy Mitford (adapter). NY: Random House, (1953). 1st Amer ed. VF in VF dj. *Between The Covers*. $150/£94

ROWAN, RICHARD W. The Pinkertons, a Detective Dynasty. Boston, 1931. 1st ed. 6 plts. *Heinoldt*. $20/£13

ROWAN, THOMAS. Coal. Spontaneous Combustion and Explosions Occurring in Coal Cargoes. London: E. & F.N. Spon, 1882. 1st ed. xi,45,lxviipp. VG. *Hollett*. $72/£45

ROWE, A. L. and O. P. MEDSGER. Rambling in the Valley of Jacobs Creek. Smithton: A.L. Rowe, n.d. ca 193?. Pamphlet. Good in wrappers (browned, chipped). *Brown*. $25/£16

ROWE, JOHN. Long Live the King. NY, 1984. 1st Amer ed. NF in NF dj. *Polyanthos*. $25/£16

ROWE, N. L. and H. C. KILLEY. Fractures of the Facial Skeleton. Edinburgh: E.& S. Livingstone, 1955. 1st ed. VG (rear inner hinge cracked, bkpl). *Weber*. $75/£47

ROWE, R. P. P. and C. M. PITMAN. Rowing. Longmans, Green, 1898. 1st ed. xvi,(352)pp. Partly unopened. Pict cl. Nice (spotted, sl shaken). *Ash*. $152/£95

ROWE, THOMAS L. (ed). Notes from a Chinese Dictionary. Anthony Blond, (1957). Ltd to 100. Fine in box (sl rubbed). *Polyanthos*. $35/£22

ROWLAND, BENJAMIN. The Art and Architecture of India. Buddhist, Hindu, Jain. Balt: Penguin, 1956. 2nd ed. 190 plts, 1 map. (Sl rubbed), o/w VG. *Worldwide*. $65/£41

ROWLAND, BENJAMIN. The Wall-Paintings of India, Central Asia and Ceylon. Boston: Merrymount Press, 1938. One of 500 numbered. Folio. 30 color plts. Text booklet, unbound plts in cl portfolio (sl worn), as issued. *Swann**. $230/£144

ROWLAND, MRS. DUNBAR (ed). Life, Letters and Papers of William Dunbar of Elgin, Morayshire, Scotland, and Natchez, Mississippi. Jackson, MS, 1930. 1st ed. VG (few spine flecks). *Wantagh*. $35/£22

ROWLANDSON, THOMAS. The English Dance of Death. London: Ackerman, 1816. 1st ed. 2 vols. Tall 8vo. Engr tps, 72 aquatint plts. Later full calf (worn, cvrs off). *Swann**. $977/£611

ROWLANDSON, THOMAS. Loyal Volunteers of London and Environs, Infantry and Cavalry, in Their Respective Uniforms.... (London: R. Ackermann, 1798-99.) 1st ed, early imp. Complete w/86 plts; 2 further dbl-pg plts not present in this copy. 4to. Hand-colored etched tp. Gilt-paneled red levant by Morrell. Cl fldg case. Bkpls of David Lionel Salomons and Robert M. Rosenbaum. *Swann**. $7,475/£4,672

ROWLEY, C. D. Aboriginal Policy and Practice. Australian Nat'l Univ, 1971. 3 vols. (Sl pencil underlining, pg waviness vol 3.) *Rybski*. $100/£63

ROWNTREE, B. SEEBOHM and G. R. LAVERS. English Life and Leisure. Longman, Green, 1951. 1st ed. (Eps lt spotted.) Dj (chipped, spotted). *Hollett*. $48/£30

ROWSE, A. L. Poems Chiefly Cornish. London, 1944. 1st ed. Fine in dj (faded). *Petersfield*. $32/£20

ROWSE, A. L. Poems of a Decade 1931-1941. London, 1941. 1st ed. Fine in dj (sl worn). *Petersfield*. $19/£12

ROWSON. Charlotte Temple: A Tale of Truth. Harrisburg: John Wyeth for Matthew Carey, 1801. 4th Amer ed. 2 vols in 1. Period calf. (Names, lacks fep), else VG-. *Pacific**. $115/£72

Roy Rogers Jump-Up Book. (Somerset)/London: Purnell & Sons, n.d. (195?). Authorised ed. 5 dbl-pg pop-ups. Glazed pict bds. VG. *Bookfinders*. $70/£44

ROY, RENE. The Night's Candle. Homer White (trans). NY: Macmillan, 1931. 1st US ed. Black cl stamped in white. Fine in NF pict dj. *Reese*. $50/£31

ROY, WILLIAM. The Military Antiquities of the Romans in Britain. London: W. Bulmer, 1793. 1st ed. Lg folio. (10),xvi,206,(6)pp; 51 engr maps, plts (3 dbl-pg, 1 lg fldg). Brn buckram (rebacked), orig gilt calf spine (sl chipped), laid down, old marbled bds. *Karmiole*. $750/£469

Royal Artillery War Commemoration Book. London: G. Bell & Sons, 1920. Photogravure frontis. Teg, gilt-inner dentelles. Levant navy blue morocco, gilt, raised bands, bound by Zaehnsdorf. Fine. *Pacific**. $161/£101

Royal Illuminated Book of Legends. Narrated in Ancient Ballad Form with Appropriate Music. Edinburgh: William P. Nimmo, (ca 1880). Obl 4to. Brn cl (sl shelfworn, hinges weak), 2-color paste labels, gilt. *Reisler*. $350/£219

ROYCE, JOSIAH. The Feud of Oakfield Creek: A Novel of California Life. Boston: Houghton Mifflin, 1887. 1st ed. Inscribed. Mustard cl. Good (sig; sl soiled, corners bumped, spine rubbed, cocked). *Reese*. $100/£63

RUARK, ROBERT. Grenadine Etching. GC: Doubleday, 1947. 1st ed, 1st bk. Fine in NF dj (spine sl faded, sm tear, chip). *Between The Covers*. $150/£94

RUARK, ROBERT. The Honey Badger. NY, 1965. 1st Amer ed. Fine (spine sl rubbed) in dj (2 sm tears). *Polyanthos*. $35/£22

RUARK, ROBERT. The Honey Badger. NY: McGraw-Hill, 1965. 1st ed. VF in dj. *Bowman*. $35/£22

RUARK, ROBERT. The Old Man's Boy Grows Older. NY: Holt, Rinehart & Winston, (1961). 1st ed. Brn cl. (Ink inscrip), o/w NF in dj (lt soiled, spine sl dknd). *Heritage*. $75/£47

RUARK, ROBERT. Something of Value. GC: Doubleday, 1955. 1st ed. VG + . *Bowman*. $20/£13

RUARK, ROBERT. Use Enough Gun. Stuart Rose (ed). NY: NAL, (1966). 1st ed. Fine in dj. *Captain's Bookshelf*. $100/£63

RUBIN, JERRY. Do It: Scenarios of the Revolution. NY: S&S, 1970. 1st ed. Fine in dj (lt used, chip rear panel). *Captain's Bookshelf*. $75/£47

RUBIN, WILLIAM (ed). Cezanne. The Late Work. London: Thames & Hudson, 1978. Dj (spine faded). *Edwards*. $56/£35

RUBIN, WILLIAM (ed). Primitivism in 20th Century Art. NY: MOMA/NYGS, (1984). 2 vols. Fine set in djs, slipcase. *Turtle Island*. $75/£47

RUBY, ROBERT H. and JOHN A. BROWN. The Chinook Indians: Traders of the Lower Columbia River. Norman: Univ of OK, (1976). 1st ed. (Ink name), else Fine in dj. *Perier*. $45/£28

RUDA, JEFFREY. Fra Filippo Lippi: Life and Work with a Complete Catalogue. (NY, 1993.) Dj. *Swann**. $69/£43

Rudiments of Conchology. (By Mary Ann Venning.) London: Harvey & Darton, 1826. 1st ed. 8vo. vii,103pp; 10 engr plts. Orig red roan-backed marbled bds. VG. *Young*. $208/£130

RUDISILL, RICHARD. Mirror Image: The Influence of the Daguerreotype on American Society. Albuquerque: Univ of NM, 1971. 1st ed. 202 plts. Fine in illus dj (sl rubbed). *Cahan*. $225/£141

RUDOLPH, MARGUERITA. Masha the Little Goose Girl. Macmillan, 1939. 1st ed. Emma Brock (illus). 64pp. VG in Good dj (1 tear, 1 chip). *Price*. $40/£25

RUFFHEAD, OWEN. The Life of Alexander Pope. London: C. Bathhurst, 1769. 1st 8vo ed. Engr frontis, (vi),578pp. Contemp calf (expertly rebacked), raised bands, red morocco label. Nice. *Young*. $112/£70

RUHEN, OLAF. Tangaroa's Godchild. Boston: Little, Brown, 1962. 1st ed. Blue cl. VG in dj (worn). *Parmer*. $25/£16

RUKEYSER, MURIEL. The Green Wave. NY: Doubleday, 1948. 1st ed. VG in dj (sl chipped). *Second Life*. $100/£63

RUKEYSER, MURIEL. U.S. 1. NY: Covici, Friede, (1938). 1st ed. NF in dj (clean tear fr panel, internally mended at early date). *Pharos*. $125/£78

RULFO, JUAN. Pedro Paramo. NY: Grove, 1959. 1st US ed. NF in dj. *Lame Duck*. $450/£281

RULHIERE, CLAUDE. A History, or Anecdotes of the Revolution in Russia, in the Year 1762. Boston: Nancrede, 1798. Frontisport; pub's ads at end. Orig calf (detached, but present; bkpl, long note). *Rostenberg & Stern*. $225/£141

RUMBELOW, DONALD. The Complete Jack the Ripper. Boston: NYGS, 1975. 1st US ed. Fine in dj (sl edgeworn). *Janus*. $65/£41

RUNDALL, L. B. The Ibex of Sha-Ping and Other Himalayan Studies. London, 1915. VG in dj. *Petersfield*. $120/£75

RUNYON, DAMON. Guys and Dolls. Jarrolds, 1932. 1st UK ed. VG (lacks dj). *Williams*. $216/£135

RUNYON, DAMON. Short Takes. Constable, 1948. 1st UK ed. VG (ink name) in dj (price-clipped). *Williams*. $56/£35

RUNYON, DAMON. Take It Easy. NY, 1938. 1st ed. Dj (spine head lt rubbed). *Swann**. $345/£216

Rupert and the Magic Pyramid. (Somerset): Purnell & Sons, 1970. 3 dbl-pg pop-ups by Peter Adby. Glazed pict bds. VG. *Bookfinders*. $30/£19

Rupert and the Ruined Garden. (Somerset)/London: Purnell, 1975. 3 dbl-pg pop-ups. Glazed pict bds (spine sl rubbed). *Bookfinders*. $30/£19

RUPERT, CHARLES G. Apostle Spoons. OUP, 1929. 1st ed. 23 plts. Uncut. Buckram, gilt. VG. *Hollett*. $240/£150

RUPORT, ARCH. The Art of Cockfighting. NY: Devin-Adair, 1949. 1st ed. NF (sl shelfworn) in dj (sl edgeworn). *My Bookhouse*. $67/£42

RUPP, I. DANIEL. History of the Counties of Berks and Lebanon: Containing a Brief Account of the Indians.... Lancaster, PA: G. Hills, 1844. 1st ed. 516pp + index, subscriber's list. 3 litho plts. Contemp mottled calf w/red leather lettering piece. VG (foxed, tear to p.429 w/no loss of text; edges lt worn). Howes R512. *House*. $120/£75

Rural Felicity; or, The History of Tommy and Sally. (By Richard Johnson.) Phila: Francis Bailey, 1793. 1st Amer ed. Chapbook. 16mo. 12 woodcuts. Orig wrappers (very worn; lt stains, heavy soiling, foxing, contemp sigs). Cl-backed bd folder. *Swann**. $6,210/£3,881

RUSCHA, EDWARD. Edward Ruscha (ed-werd rew-shay) Young Artist. Minneapolis, 1972. One of 2000. Ruscha's business card laid in. (Fep, following pg detached but present; rubbed, joints starting.) *Swann**. $287/£179

RUSCHA, EDWARD. Guacamole Airlines and Other Drawings. NY: Abrams, 1980. Fine in dj. *Turtle Island*. $65/£41

RUSCHA, EDWARD. Guacamole Airlines and Other Drawings. NY: Abrams, 1980. 1st ed. Fine in ptd tissue wrapper. *Smith*. $65/£41

RUSCHA, EDWARD. Some Los Angeles Apartments. L.A.: N.p., (1970). 2nd ed. Fine in orig glassine dj, ptd wrappers. *Turtle Island*. $150/£94

RUSCHA, EDWARD. Various Small Fires and Milk. L.A.: N.p., (1970). 2nd ed. Fine in orig glassine, ptd stiff wrappers. *Turtle Island*. $150/£94

RUSH, ALFRED C. Death and Burial in Christian Antiquity. Catholic Univ, 1941. 1st ed. (Name; spine lettering dull.) *Rybski*. $35/£22

RUSH, BENJAMIN. The Letters of Benjamin Rush. L.H. Butterfield (ed). Princeton: Princeton Univ, 1951. 1st Amer ed. 2 vols. NF in djs (rear panel vol 2 torn). *Glenn*. $25/£16

RUSH, BENJAMIN. Medical Inquiries and Observations Upon the Diseases of the Mind. Phila, 1827. 3rd ed. 365pp. Full leather. (Lib stamp; hinges reinforced.) *Fye*. $200/£125

RUSH, BENJAMIN. Medical Inquiries and Observations. Five Volumes. Phila, 1794-1798. Vols 4,5: 1st ed; Vols 1,2,3: 2nd ed. Orig leather. (Water stain prelims vol 3, 1/2 ll vol 4, foxed; cracked outer hinges 3 vols, spine chip 3 vols.) *Fye*. $1,500/£938

RUSH, BENJAMIN. The Selected Writings.... Dagobert D. Runes (ed). NY: Philosophical Library, (1947). 1st ed. Frontisport, 1 plt. VG. *Glaser*. $40/£25

RUSH, BENJAMIN. Sixteen Introductory Lectures to Courses of Lectures upon the Institutes and Practice of Medicine.... Phila: Bradford & Innskeep, 1811. 1st ed. viii,455pp (sig of Isaac Hays, 1814). Old full calf (rubbed, worn, spine eroded, pieces gone, outer hinges cracked). *Kane**. $275/£172

RUSH, BENJAMIN. The Works of Thomas Sydenham, M.D. on Acute and Chronic Diseases. Phila, 1815. 2nd ed. 513,(9)pp (bkpl). Full contemp tree calf (spine worn). *M & S*. $85/£53

RUSH, JACOB. Charges and Extracts of Charges, on Moral and Religious Subjects.... Phila: Geo. Forman, May 1804. (5)-183pp. Contemp calf, leather label. *M & S*. $175/£109

RUSH, JAMES. The Philosophy of the Human Voice. Phila: Lippincott, 1859. 5th ed. 677pp. (Spine, corners worn.) *M & S*. $100/£63

RUSH, LESLIE V. Atlas of Rush Pin Technics: A System of Fracture Treatment. Meridian, MS: 1955. Black, gold ptd cvr, spine. (Sl worn, soiled). NF. *Doctor's Library*. $100/£63

RUSH, N. ORWIN. The Banditti of the Plains. NY: Westerners NY Posse, 1960. 1st ed. NF in wrappers. *Labordo*. $50/£31

RUSH, PHILIP S. Some Old Ranchos and Adobes. (San Diego, 1964.) 2nd ed. VG. *Perier*. $20/£13

RUSH, RICHARD. A Residence at the Court of London. London, 1833. 1st Eng ed. 420pp. 1/2 leather. (Eps spotted; cvrs worn, spine split at fr hinge.) *King*. $200/£125

RUSH, RICHARD. Washington in Domestic Life. Phila: Lippincott, 1857. 85pp. (Lib bkpl, stamps, spine #; worn), else Good. *Brown*. $20/£13

RUSHDIE, SALMAN. East, West. London: Jonathan Cape, (1994). 1st ed. Signed, dated in month of pub. Fine in dj. *Pacific**. $86/£54

RUSHDIE, SALMAN. Grimus. Gollancz, 1975. 1st UK ed, 1st bk. Fine in dj. *Williams*. $240/£150

RUSHDIE, SALMAN. Grimus. Woodstock: Overlook Press, 1979. 1st US ed, 1st bk. (Rmdr line bottom edge), else Fine in Fine dj. *Beasley*. $85/£53

RUSHDIE, SALMAN. Midnight's Children. NY: Knopf, 1981. 1st US ed. (Name, foxed), else Fair in dj (worn, edges chipped, spine sunned). *Pettler*. $35/£22

RUSHDIE, SALMAN. Midnight's Children. NY: Knopf, 1981. 1st ed. Fine in dj (sl used). *Dermont*. $175/£109

RUSHDIE, SALMAN. The Moor's Last Sigh. London: Jonathan Cape, (1995). 1st ed. One of 200. Signed. Blue cl, gilt. Fine in slipcase. *Pacific**. $127/£79

RUSHDIE, SALMAN. The Satanic Verses. NY: Viking, (1988). 1st Amer ed. Signed, dated 1989. (Sm smudge lower fr joint), else NF. *Pacific**. $104/£65

RUSHDIE, SALMAN. The Satanic Verses. Viking, 1988. 1st ed. VG in dj (price-clipped). *Cox*. $40/£25

RUSHDIE, SALMAN. The Satanic Verses. Viking, 1988. 1st UK ed. NF in dj. *Williams*. $96/£60

RUSHDIE, SALMAN. Shame. London: Cape, (1983). 1st ed. Fine in Fine dj. *Lenz*. $125/£78

RUSHDIE, SALMAN. Shame. Cape, 1983. 1st UK ed. Signed. Fine in dj. *Williams*. $128/£80

RUSK, C. E. Tales of a Western Mountaineer. Boston: Houghton Mifflin, 1924. 1st ed. Signed. Fine. *Book Market*. $35/£22

RUSK, RALPH LESLIE. The Literature of the Middle Western Frontier. NY, 1925. 2 vols. VG (soiled) in plain brn paper djs (chipped). *Dumont.* $125/£78

RUSKIN, ARIANE. Spy for Liberty. NY, (1965). 1st ed. VG + in VG + dj. *Pratt.* $20/£13

RUSKIN, JOHN. The Art of England. Orpington: George Allen, 1884. 1st ed. 272,20(index)pp. Marbled eps; aeg. Full black polished morocco (professionally rehinged), raised bands, blind/gilt spine. VG. *Hartfield.* $265/£166

RUSKIN, JOHN. The Lamp of Beauty. Joan Evans (ed). London, 1959. Good+ in dj. *Washton.* $50/£31

RUSKIN, JOHN. Letters upon Subjects of General Interest from John Ruskin to Various Correspondents. Privately ptd, 1892. 1st ed. VG + . *Fine Books.* $250/£156

RUSKIN, JOHN. Modern Painters. George Allen, 1888. Complete ed. 6 vols. Uncut. Grn cl, gilt. (Inscrip, fore-edge of 1 plt sl dusty, chipped), o/w VG set. *Hollett.* $240/£150

RUSKIN, JOHN. Modern Painters. Orpington: George Allen, 1888. Complete ed, lg paper copy. 6 vols incl index. 90 engr plts. Uncut. Contemp grn cl (spine ends bumped). *Sotheby's*.* $331/£207

RUSKIN, JOHN. Notes on the Construction of Sheepfolds. Smith, Elder, 1851. 1st ed. Ad leaf at end. Contemp speckled calf, gilt, by Mansell. (Tp soiled, sl torn.) *Sotheby's*.* $405/£253

RUSKIN, JOHN. Of Queens Gardens. (London: George Allen, 1902.) 1st ed. Orig gilt vellum (lacks fore-edge ties). *Karmiole.* $125/£78

RUSKIN, JOHN. Praeterita. London: Rupert Hart-Davis, 1949. VG in dj. *Hollett.* $120/£75

RUSKIN, JOHN. The Seven Lamps of Architecture. Smith, Elder, 1855. 2nd ed. xv,(iv),206,(ii)pp; 14 engr plts. Blind-stamped cl. VG (few neat marginal lines, notes). *Hollett.* $192/£120

RUSKIN, JOHN. The Two Paths: Being Lectures on Art.... London: Smith, Elder, 1859. 1st ed. 2 steel-engr b/w plts; 24-pg May 1859 pub's cat at rear. Untrimmed. Dk maroon cl, gilt. Cvrs VG (lt edgeworn, spine lt sunned, sm chip top edge; text sl aged, lt foxed). *Baltimore*.* $45/£28

RUSKIN, JOHN. Verona and Other Lectures. W.G.C. (ed). London: George Allen, Sunnyside, Orpington, 1894. Photolitho frontis, tissue guard, 10 monochrome plts in photogravure, 1 plan, tissue guards; (x),168pp. Top edge uncut, rest rough trimmed. Dk grn fine crushed morocco cl, gilt. (Spine sl dull), o/w Good. *Temple.* $48/£30

RUSSELL, A. A Tour Through the Australian Colonies in 1839. Glasgow, 1840. 1st ed. (viii),332pp. Orig blindstamped cl (re-cased), gilt. *Maggs.* $440/£275

RUSSELL, ALEXANDER. The Natural History of Aleppo, and Parts Adjacent.... London: A. Millar, 1856 (i.e., 1756). 1st ed. viii,266,(10)pp (old stamps); 13 (of 17) fldg engr plts. Contemp calf (spine dknd, cvrs detached). *Swann*.* $431/£269

RUSSELL, CHARLES EDWARD. The Greatest Trust in the World. NY: Ridgeway-Thayer, 1905. 1st ed. VG + . *Labordo.* $100/£63

RUSSELL, CHARLES M. Rawhide Rawlins Stories. Pasadena: Trail's End, 1946. 1st rev ed. Pict cl. Fine in dj (extrems sl worn). Howes R530. *Pacific*.* $58/£36

RUSSELL, CHARLES M. Rawhide Rawlins Stories. Pasadena: Trail's End Pub Co, 1946. 1st rev ed. Pict eps. Beige pict cl. Fine in NF red pict dj (sl chipped). Howes R530. *Harrington.* $70/£44

RUSSELL, CHARLES M. Rawhide Rawlins Stories. Pasadena, CA: Trails End, 1946. Rev ed. (Sm nick near spine), o/w VG + in dj (chipped). Howes R530. *Labordo.* $75/£47

RUSSELL, CHARLES M. Trails Plowed Under. GC: Doubleday, Page, 1927. 10 plts. Terracotta cl, gilt. Fine. *Pacific*.* $86/£54

RUSSELL, CHARLES M. Trails Plowed Under. GC: Doubleday, Doran, 1935. VG. Howes R532. *Lien.* $50/£31

RUSSELL, CHARLES M. Trails Plowed Under. NY, 1944. Pict cl. (Sig, date, inner hinge starting), o/w VG in dj (sl soiled, chipped). Howes R532. *Baade.* $30/£19

RUSSELL, FRANK. Explorations in the Far North: Being the Report of an Expedition Under the Auspices of the University of Iowa During the Years 1892, '93, and '94. (IA): Univ of IA, 1898. 1st ed. Presentation slip of Dr. C. W. Richmond tipped-in at fr. vii,(2),290pp; 21 photo plts, fldg map. Largely unopened. Fine in ptd wrappers (chipped, spine repaired w/archival tape). *Pacific*.* $127/£79

RUSSELL, FRED. Ventriloquism and Allied Arts. (London): Keith, Prowse, n.d. (1898). Frontisport. Patterned-paper over bds (spine sunned, sl shaken). *Dramatis.* $65/£41

RUSSELL, J. H. Cattle on the Conejo. (L.A.), 1957. 1st ed. Inscribed. Dec bds, cl. NF in dj (backstrip faded). *Baade.* $65/£41

RUSSELL, JAMES ANDERSON. The Book of Galloway. Dunfries: Blacklock Farries & Sons, 1973. Rev ed. VG in dj. *Hollett.* $32/£20

RUSSELL, JERRY and RENNY. On the Loose. SF, 1967. 1st ed. As New in dj, slipcase. *Bond.* $20/£13

RUSSELL, JESSE LEWIS. Behind These Ozark Hills. NY: Hobson Book Press, 1947. 1st ed. VG. *Labordo.* $150/£94

RUSSELL, JOHN. Don Carlos; or, Persecution. Longman, Hurst et al, 1822. 1st ed. xvi,119pp. Marbled eps. Contemp 1/2 polished calf, marbled paper bds, gilt stamp. *Cox.* $64/£40

RUSSELL, JOHN. Max Ernst: Life and Work. NY: Abrams, (1967). 1st US ed. 49 tipped-in color plts. Color pict eps. Yellow cl stamped in black. (Sl shelfworn.) Dj (several inch-long tears, lacks pieces at edges). *Baltimore*.* $40/£25

RUSSELL, K. F. British Anatomy 1525-1800. Melbourne Univ, 1963. 1st ed. Ltd to 750 signed, numbered. Frontis, 52 plts. *Forest.* $56/£35

RUSSELL, LEONARD (ed). English Wits. London: Hutchinson, 1940. 1st ed. Eric Ravilious (illus). VG in dj (edges rubbed, spine base lacks piece). *Hollett.* $40/£25

RUSSELL, N. A Bibliography of William Cowper to 1837. Oxford: Oxford Bib Soc, 1963. Frontisport, 12 plts. Cl-backed blue bds. *Maggs.* $56/£35

RUSSELL, OSBORNE. Journal of a Trapper. Aubrey L. Haines (ed). (Portland): OR Hist Soc, 1955. 3rd ed. One of 750. Frontis, 10 maps (2 fldg). Unopened. Blue cl, gilt, pict inset on fr cvr. Fine. Howes R537. *Harrington.* $100/£63

RUSSELL, OSBORNE. Osborne Russell's Journal of a Trapper. Portland, OR: OR Hist Soc, 1955. 3rd ed. Ltd to 750 ptd. VF. Howes R537. *Labordo.* $150/£94

RUSSELL, RACHEL. Letters of...from the Manuscript in the Library at Woburn Abbey...To Which Is Added, the Trial of Lord William Russell for High Treason. Extracted from the State Trials. London: C. Dilly, 1793. 5th ed. ccxxxi,235-589pp; 3 engr plts (spotted). New eps; marbled edges. Contemp diced calf (neatly rebacked), gilt. *Young.* $80/£50

RUSSELL, RACHEL. Letters. Longman, Brown et al, 1852. 2 vols. 2 engr frontispieces, 2 engr tps, xii,289; viii,231pp. Paper spine labels. (Bkpls; extrems sl frayed, labels worn.) *Hollett.* $104/£65

RUSSELL, ROGER W. (ed). Frontiers in Psychological Psychology. NY: Academic, 1966. 1st ed. Black cl. Fine in VG dj (rubbed). *House.* $45/£28

RUSSELL, RONALD. Guide to British Topographical Prints. David & Charles, 1979. 1st ed. Dj. *Forest.* $56/£35

RUSSELL, ROSS. Jazz Style in Kansas City and the Southwest. Berkeley: Univ of CA, 1971. 1st ed. NF in VG- dj (holes to rear panel, rumpled). *Beasley.* $30/£19

RUSSELL, ROSS. The Sound. NY: Dutton, (1961). 1st ed, 1st bk. VG in pict dj. *Petrilla.* $30/£19

RUSSELL, VIRGIL Y. Indian Artifacts of the Rockies. Douglas, WY, 1945. Good in dj (soiled). *Dumont.* $45/£28

RUSSELL, W. CLARK. The Copsford Mystery. NY, 1896. 1st US ed. 8 full-pg plts. Teg. Maroon cl, gilt. Fine. *Kane**. $35/£22

RUSSELL, W. CLARK. Representative Actors. London: Frederick Warne, n.d. (1875). Engr frontis. Contemp 1/2 calf (extrems rubbed), marbled bds, spine gilt, morocco label. (Tp sl offset.) *Dramatis*. $45/£28

RUSSELL, W. CLARK. A Voyage to the Cape. London: C&W, 1886. 1/2-title not called for; (viii),360pp, pub's inserted 32-pg cat at end dated May 1886 (not listing this title). Top edge uncut, eps coated dk chocolate. Ribbed lt gray-grn cl. (Eps sl cracked, 3 prelims, last leaf of cat foxed; spine faded), o/w Good. *Temple*. $35/£22

RUSSELL, W. CLARK. What Cheer! Cassell, 1896. Pub's cat dated 6G-8.96. Teg. Good (sigs, fore-edge sl spotted; spine bumped). *Tiger*. $45/£28

RUSSELL, W. H. The British Expedition to the Crimea. Routledge, 1858. Rev ed. vii,629pp; 13 plts, fldg plans (some sl torn, lacks port). Old 1/2 calf (sl rubbed), gilt, w/raised bands, spine label. *Hollett*. $192/£120

RUSSELL, W. H. My Diary North and South. Boston: T.O.H.P. Burnham, 1863. 1st Amer ed. 602pp. Brn cl. VG. Howes R540. *Chapel Hill*. $150/£94

RUSSELL, W. H. My Diary North and South. London: Bradbury & Evans, 1863. 1st ed. 2 vols. 424; 442pp; fldg map. Emb blue cl. Good (lib bkpls, blindstamps, fldg map crudely repaired on verso; hinges broken). Howes R540. *Chapel Hill*. $200/£125

RUSSELL, W. H. My Diary North and South. London: Bradbury & Evans, 1863. 1st ed. 2 vols. xvi,424,16 inserted ads, fldg map (clean tear, no loss); xi,442,(l)pp. Blue cl (rubbed, hinges cracked). Good. *Mott*. $200/£125

RUSSELL, W. H. My Diary, North and South. London: Bradbury & Evans, 1863. 1st ed. 2 vols. Lg fldg map (torn, no loss). Blindstamped blue cl (extrems worn, spine ends chipped). Good. *Cullen*. $125/£78

RUSSELL, WILLIAM R. The Civil War in America. Boston: Gardner A. Fuller, August 1861. 1st ed. 189pp. Orig ptd fr wrapper (lacks rear wrapper). *Mott*. $90/£56

RUSSELL, WILLIAM S. Pilgrim Memorials, and Guide for Visitors to Plymouth Village. Boston: The Author, 1851. viii,148pp; fldg map. (Portions dknd, 1 map edge tattered; extrems rubbed.) *Zubal**. $20/£13

RUSSELL, WILLIAM. The History of Ancient Europe with a View of the Revolutions in Asia and Africa. Phila: Maxwell, 1801. 2 vols. iv,491; 492pp. Contemp calf. (Sl rubbed, hinges tender), o/w VG. *Worldwide*. $65/£41

Russians in California. SF: CA Hist Soc, 1933. 1st ed. 2 plts (1 color, 1 duotone), sketch, view; fldg facs map laid in loose. Red buckram, paper cvr label, gilt spine. (Glue residue fr pastedown; extrems rubbed), else VG. *Pacific**. $58/£36

RUSSO, ANTHONY J. and DOROTHY R. A Bibliography of James Whitcomb Riley. Indianapolis, 1944. 1st ed. Teg. 2-tone cl. VG. *King*. $45/£28

RUSSO, JOHN P. The Desert Bighorn Sheep in Arizona. Phoenix, AZ, 1956. 1st ed. VG (pg edges taped) in wrappers. *Sagebrush*. $35/£22

RUSTAD, WILLIAM H. The Recurrent Laryngeal Nerves in Thyroid Surgery. Springfield, IL: Charles C. Thomas, (1956). 1st ed. Fine in dj. *Weber*. $75/£47

Rustic Rhymes. (By Sidney George Fisher.) Phila: Parry & McMillan, 1859. 1st ed. 113pp. VG (sl shelfworn). *Brown*. $15/£9

RUTH, GEORGE HERMAN. Babe Ruth's Own Book of Baseball. Putnam, 1928. 1st ed. Good+ (occasional underlining, marginal notes). *Plapinger*. $85/£53

RUTH, GEORGE HERMAN. Babe Ruth's Own Book of Baseball. NY, 1928. One of 1000 numbered, signed. 8vo. (Prelim sl soiled, ex-lib, worn, extensively repaired w/brn paper tape.) Dj. *Swann**. $747/£467

RUTHERFORD, EDWARD. (Pseud of Francis Wintle.) Sarum. Century, 1987. 1st ed. Signed presentation. Fine in NF dj (price-clipped). *Any Amount*. $64/£40

RUTHERFORD, ERNEST. Radio-Activity. Cambridge: CUP, 1904. 1st ed. 1/2-tone plt. Dk grn cl. (Eps lt foxed; rubbed), else VG. *Weber*. $500/£313

RUTHERFORD, ERNEST. Radio-Activity. Cambridge: CUP, 1905. 2nd ed. 1 plt. Grn cl. (Sig, inner hinges lt cracked; extrems rubbed, corners sl bumped.) *Weber*. $275/£172

RUTHERFORD, ERNEST. Radioactive Substances and Their Radiations. Cambridge: CUP, 1913. 1st ed. 5 plts. Grn cl. (Lacks rep), o/w Fine. *Weber*. $300/£188

RUTHERFORD, ERNEST. Radioactive Transformations. London: Archibald Constable, 1906. 1st ed. Navy blue cl. Fine. *Weber*. $275/£172

RUTHVEN, A. G. et al. The Herpetology of Michigan. Ann Arbor, 1928. 19 plts. (Pp tanned.) Wrappers (worn, spine dknd, lt soiled, fr corner creased, name). C. F. Kauffeld's copy. *Sutton*. $65/£41

RUTT, JOHN TOWILL. Life and Correspondence of Joseph Priestley. R. Hunter, 1831. 1st ed. 2 vols. xii,424; xv,(i),552pp. Untrimmed. Orig buff bds (vol 1 backstrip worn w/loss at head, vol 2 backstrip chipped at tail), ptd paper labels (rubbed). Good (cancelled lib bkpls, early sig; corners, edge worn). *Blackwell's*. $200/£125

RUTTER, OWEN. The Court-Martial of the 'Bounty' Mutineers. William Hodge, 1931. 1st ed. 10 plts. (Spine sl dull.) *Hollett*. $104/£65

RUTTLEDGE, HUGH. Everest: The Unfinished Adventure. (London): Hodder & Stoughton, (1937). 1st ed. 63 plts, 2 fldg maps. Blue cl, gilt. Fine (spine ends, corners sl worn). *Argonaut*. $175/£109

RUXTON, GEORGE F. Adventures in Mexico and the Rocky Mountains. London: J. Murray, 1847. 1st ed. viii,332,16pp. Red cl, gilt. VG+ (lib ink stamp; cl sl rubbed, spine ends just showing, spine sl dknd, pinhole). Howes R553. *Harrington*. $275/£172

RUXTON, GEORGE F. Adventures in Mexico and the Rocky Mountains. NY: Harper, 1848. 1st Amer ed. 312pp. Orig cl. (Dampstained, old lib bkpl; stained, spine rubbed, ends, corners worn), else Good. *Pacific**. $86/£54

RUXTON, GEORGE F. Life in the Far West. Norman: Univ of OK, 1951. Rpt ed. VG in dj. Howes R554. *Labordo*. $50/£31

RUXTON, GEORGE F. Life in the Far West. Leroy Hafen (ed). Norman, 1951. 1st ed. (Bkpl; bottom corners bumped), o/w VG- in dj (sl worn, price-clipped). Howes R554. *Baade*. $50/£31

RUXTON, GEORGE F. Life in the Far West. LeRoy R. Hafen (ed). Norman: Univ of OK, (1951). 1st ed by this pub. 12 plts. VF in pict dj. *Argonaut*. $90/£56

RUYLE, JOHN. D Is for Doyle. CA: Pequod, 1981. 1st ed. Ltd to 242. Ptd wrappers. *Gravesend*. $40/£25

RYAN, ALAN. Cast a Cold Eye. Niles: Dark Harvest, 1984. One of 200 numbered, signed by Ryan and Jill Bauman (illus). (Sl worn.) Dj, slipcase. *Oinonen**. $30/£19

RYAN, MARAH ELLIS. The Flute of the Gods. NY: F.A. Stokes, (1909). 1st ed. Fair in pict cl. *Lien*. $50/£31

RYAN, WILLIAM REDMOND. Personal Adventures in Upper and Lower California in 1848-9. London: William Shoberl, 1850. 1st ed. 2 vols. 4pp ads, vi,92),(vii)-x,347,(1),(4)ads; vi,413pp; 23 plts, incl 3 duotone lithos. Mod cl, gilt leather spine labels. (Foxing, marginal staining, pp309-10 w/top corner torn off; rebound), else VG. Howes R558. *Pacific**. $316/£198

RYDER, DAVID WARREN. Memories of the Mendocino Coast. SF: Privately ptd, 1948. 1st ed. Brn buckram. Fine. *Harrington*. $45/£28

RYDER, JOHN. Printing For Pleasure. London: Phoenix House, (1955). 1st ed. Fine in dj. *Oak Knoll.* $25/£16

RYDER, JOHN. Printing for Pleasure. Phoenix House, 1955. 1st ed. VG in dj. *Moss.* $24/£15

RYDER, LILLIAN. A Child's Story of the Circus in Living Pictures. London: World Distributors (Manchester), n.d. (195?). 4 dbl-pg pop-ups by Walter Howarth. Spiral bound. VG in illus wraps. *Bookfinders.* $50/£31

RYLAND, ELIZABETH HAWES (comp). King William County, Virginia from Old Newspapers and Files. Deitz, 1955. VG (ex-lib). *Book Broker.* $35/£22

RYLANDS, GEORGE. Poems. London: Hogarth, 1931. One of 350 numbered, signed. Patttered paper bds. VG (some pp sl spotted, top edge dusty; spine browned, ends bumped; cvrs sl dusty, edges sl rubbed). *Ulysses.* $232/£145

RYLEY, E. All About Kitty Cat. NY: Cupples & Leon, (1927). 16mo. M. Morris (illus). 48pp. Grn bds (corners sl worn), full color paste label. Full color dj (margins torn, worn). *Reisler.* $110/£69

RYMILL, JOHN R. Southern Lights: The Official Account of the British Graham Land Expedition 1934-1937. London: C&W, 1938. 4 unlisted maps. Grn cl. Clean (sig). *Explorer.* $192/£120

RYMILL, JOHN R. Southern Lights: The Official Account of the British Graham Land Expedition 1934-1937. Malvern: Knell, 1986. Fldg map. Mint in dj. *Explorer.* $24/£15

RYNNING, THOMAS HARBO. Gun Notches. NY: Frederick A. Stokes, 1931. 1st ed. Inscribed, signed. Fine in dj. *Labordo.* $150/£94

RYUS, WILLIAM H. The Second William Penn. Kansas City, MO: Frank T. Riley, 1913. 1st ed. Port. (Some pp lt damp-stained), else Good in pict wraps (worn, corners bumped). *Brown.* $30/£19

RYUS, WILLIAM H. The Second William Penn. Kansas City: Frank T. Riley, 1913. VG + in paper wrappers. *Zubal*.* $40/£25

RYWELL, MARTIN. Judah Benjamin: Unsung Rebel Prince. Stephens, 1948. Inscribed presentation. Good (cvr badly water-stained). *Book Broker.* $45/£28

S

S., W. (W. S. Stebbing.) Outlines. Oxford: Daniel, 1899. 1st ed. One of 150. Uncut. VG in vellum wrappers (overlapping wrappers sl crumpled). *Maggs.* $136/£85

SABARTES, JAIME. Picasso: Toreros. NY/Monte Carlo: George Braziller/Andre Sauret, (1961). Orig ed. 4 orig lithos. Fine in dj. *Turtle Island.* $450/£281

SABATINI, RAFAEL. The Hounds of God. Boston: Houghton Mifflin, 1928. 1st ed. NF in wrap-around pict dj (folds worn, spine ends chipped). *Else Fine.* $85/£53

SABATINI, RAFAEL. The King's Minion. Toronto: McClelland & Stewart, 1930. 1st Canadian ed. Fine in dj (corners sl worn). *Else Fine.* $65/£41

SABATINI, RAFAEL. The Sea-Hawk. NY: Grosset, n.d. Photoplay ed. Fine in Fine pict dj (lt rubbed). *Unger.* $125/£78

SABATINI, RAFAEL. Sinner, Saint and Jester. London: Hutchinson, 1954. 1st ed. Fine in pict dj (sl chipped). *Else Fine.* $50/£31

SABATO, ERNESTO. On Heroes and Tombs. Boston: Godine, 1981. 1st US ed. NF in VG + dj. *Lame Duck.* $45/£28

SABATO, ERNESTO. The Outsider. NY: Knopf, 1950. 1st US ed. VG + in dj. *Lame Duck.* $375/£234

SABIN, EDWIN L. Kit Carson Days (1809-1868). Chicago: A.C. McClurg, 1914. 1st ed. Fine in dj (chipped). Howes S1. *Labordo.* $250/£156

SABIN, EDWIN L. Kit Carson Days (1809-1868). NY: Press of the Pioneers, 1935. 3rd ed. 2 vols. Fine set. *Labordo.* $150/£94

SABIN, EDWIN L. Kit Carson Days, 1809-1868. NY: Press of the Pioneers, 1935. Rev ed. 2 vols. 20 full-pg dwgs. Grn buckram, gilt. Fine (ink inscrip) in slipcase (nearly broken). Howes S1. *Truepenny.* $125/£78

SABIN, EDWIN L. On the Plains with Custer. Phila, 1913. 1st ed. Pict cl. (Bkpl; cvrs rubbed.) *King.* $35/£22

SABIN, EDWIN L. Wild Men of the Wild West. NY: Thomas Crowell, (1929). 1st ed. Frontis. Pict cl. (Inscrip; spine ends rubbed), else VG. *Pacific*.* $46/£29

SABIN, EDWIN L. Wild Men of the Wild West. NY: Thomas Y. Crowell, 1929. 1st ed. NF in dj (chipped). *Labordo.* $150/£94

SABIN, FRANK T. A Catalogue of Old English Sporting Prints. V.P. Savin (comp). London, 1933. 58 engrs (2 color). Red buckram w/orig wraps bound in. *Edrich.* $40/£25

SABINE, LORENZO. Notes on Duels and Duelling.... Boston, 1856. 2nd ed. Mod purple morocco (spine faded), gilt. Cl slipcase. *Swann*.* $172/£108

SABINE, WALLACE CLEMENT. Collected Papers on Acoustics. Cambridge: Harvard Univ, 1923. 1st ed. Presentation from author's widow. Frontis port. Untrimmed. VG. *Hollett.* $104/£65

SABRETACHE. (Pseud of Albert Stewart Barrow.) Shires and Provinces. London, 1926. Folio. Uncut, teg. (Sl worn.) *Oinonen*.* $275/£172

SACCHERI, GIROLAMO. Euclides Vindicatus. George Bruce Halsted (ed). Chicago: Open Court, 1920. 1st ed in English. Fine. *Glaser.* $125/£78

SACHS, B. A Treatise on the Nervous Diseases of Children. NY: William Wood, 1905. 2nd ed. VG (rep excised, ex-lib). *Beasley.* $75/£47

SACHS, EDWIN T. Sleight-of-Hand: A Practical Manual of Leger-demain for Amateurs and Others. Fleming, 1946. Good. *Rybski.* $40/£25

SACHS, ERNEST. The Diagnosis and Treatment of Brain Tumors. St. Louis, 1931. 1st ed. *Fye.* $150/£94

SACHS, MAURICE. Witches' Sabbath. Cape, 1965. 1st UK ed. VG in dj (sl nicked, edges worn). *Williams.* $32/£20

SACHS, SAMUEL. Fakes and Forgeries. Minneapolis: Minneapolis Inst of Arts, July 11-September 29, 1973. Fine in VG dj. *Turtle Island.* $50/£31

SACKETT, CARL L. (ed). Big Horn Pioneers. Big Horn, WY, 1961. 1st rev ed. Good + in pict wraps. *Wantagh.* $25/£16

SACKETT, WILLIAM. Modern Battles of Trenton Being a History of New Jersey's Politics and Legislation from 1868 to 1894. Trenton, 1895. 1st ed. 501pp. (Rebound, orig spine transposed.) *Heinoldt.* $15/£9

SACKETT, WILLIAM. Modern Battles of Trenton, Being a History of New Jersey's Politics...1868 to the Year 1894. Trenton: John L. Murphy, Ptr, 1895. 501pp. VG + . *Zubal*.* $25/£16

SACKS, B. Be It Enacted. Phoenix, 1964. 2 fldg maps, 1 fldg document in rear pocket. Unopened. NF in dj (sl browned). *Dumont.* $75/£47

SACKS, B. Be It Enacted: The Creation of the Territory of Arizona. Phoenix: AZ Hist Foundation, 1964. 1st bk ed. 14 maps, incl 2 fldg maps & 1 facs in rear pocket. Blue cl. Fine in NF dj (spine sl dknd). *Harrington.* $65/£41

SACKS, OLIVER. Seeing Voices. Berkeley: Univ of CA, 1989. 1st ed. Signed. Fine in NF dj. *Lame Duck.* $65/£41

SACKVILLE-WEST, VITA. Daughter of France. NY: Doubleday, 1959. 1st US ed. VG in dj. *Second Life.* $75/£47

SACKVILLE-WEST, VITA. The Eagle and the Dove. GC: Doubleday, 1944. 1st US ed. Fine in dj (sl chipped). *Second Life.* $75/£47

SACKVILLE-WEST, VITA. English Country Houses. Britain in Pictures, (1941). 1st UK ed. Variant lt grn binding w/no mention of pubs Collins on tp. VG + in dj. *Williams.* $45/£28

SACKVILLE-WEST, VITA. The Garden. London: Michael Joseph, (1946). 1st ed. Nice (bkpl) in dj (sl chipped). *Second Life.* $135/£84

SACKVILLE-WEST, VITA. In Your Garden. London: Michael Joseph, 1952. 3rd imp. VG in dj (worn). *Fair Meadow.* $70/£44

SACKVILLE-WEST, VITA. Knole and the Sackvilles. London, 1934. Cheaper ed. White cl. VG. *Gretton.* $19/£12

SACKVILLE-WEST, VITA. Knoll and the Sackvilles. NY: Doran, n.d. (1922?). 1st Amer ed from British sheets w/cancel tp. Pict cl, Doran imprint at spine foot, pub's device rear cvr. Fine. *Pharos.* $250/£156

SACKVILLE-WEST, VITA. The Land. London: Heinemann, 1926. 1st Eng ed. Spare title label. VG (top edge dusty; cvrs sl bowed; spine foot, corners sl bumped, rubbed) in dj (nicked, rubbed, sl torn, creased, browned). *Ulysses.* $136/£85

SACKVILLE-WEST, VITA. Nursery Rhymes. London, 1947. 1st ed. One of 550 numbered. Dj (lt rubbed). *Swann*.* $115/£72

SACKVILLE-WEST, VITA. Selected Poems. London: Hogarth, (1941). 1st ed. Red paper bds. Fine in dj (spine dknd). *Cummins.* $75/£47

Sacramento Guide Book. Sacramento Bee, (1939). Fldg map. Fine. *Perier.* $40/£25

Sacramento Illustrated: A Reprint of the Original Edition Issue by Barber and Baker in 1855. Sacramento: Sacramento Book Collectors Club, 1950. One of 300 ptd. Fine. Howes B127. *Pacific*.* $185/£116

Sad Fate of Poor Robin. NY: McLoughlin Bros, n.d. (ca 1865). Susie Sunshine's Series. Sm 8vo. 8 leaves + 1pg list rear wrapper; 7 half-pg chromolithos. Pict paper wrappers. VG (sm scuff fr corner,, lower part of inner wrapper fold reinforced). *Hobbyhorse.* $95/£59

SADDLEBAGS, JEREMIAH. (Pseud of James A. Read and D. F. Read.) Journey to the Gold Diggins. NY: Stringer & Townsend, 1849. 2nd ed. Orig lt grn ptd wraps w/illus on fr cvr, pub's ads on rear. (Wraps detached, sl worn, chipped, fr cvr lacks 1-1/2 x 1/2-inch piece upper left corner; sl foxed, few pp lack margin corners, edges sl worn, sl shaken.) Text Good. Howes R92. *Baltimore*.* $400/£250

SADLEIR, MICHAEL. Daumier. The Man and the Artist. London, 1924. Tipped-in color frontis, 91 plts. Teg, rest uncut. (Few margins sl thumbed; edges sl rubbed, spine sl bumped; #s.) *Edwards.* $56/£35

SADLEIR, MICHAEL. XIX Century Fiction. Cambridge: CUP, 1951. One of 1025 ptd. 2 vols. Maroon cl (headcaps bumped, sl rubbed). Vol 2 w/dj (sl torn). *Maggs.* $480/£300

SADLEIR, THOMAS U. and PAGE L. DICKINSON. Georgian Mansions in Ireland. Dublin: The Authors, 1915. One of 700, this copy not numbered. 80 plts. (Lt worn.) *Oinonen*.* $250/£156

SADLER, ELIZABETH HATCHER. The Bloom of Monticello. The Author, (c1925). Stiff paper cvrs. VG. *Book Broker.* $12/£8

SAFARI CLUB. Record Book of Trophy Animals. Tucson, 1982. One of 2500. (Lt worn.) *Oinonen*.* $30/£19

SAFFORD, WILLIAM H. Life of Harman Blennerhassett. Cincinnati, 1859. 239pp. Buckram (rebound; lt foxed). *Heinoldt.* $18/£11

SAGAN, FRANCOISE. Bonjour Tristesse. NY: Dutton, 1955. 1st Amer ed, 1st bk. Fine in NF dj (few sm tears). *Between The Covers.* $75/£47

SAGAN, FRANCOISE. Toxique. N.p.: Dutton, (1964). 1st Amer ed. VG in wraps (sl sunned, spine torn), mylar cvr. *Hermitage.* $40/£25

SAGAN, FRANCOISE. The Wonderful Clouds. NY: Dutton, 1962. 1st Amer ed. VF in VF dj. *Between The Covers.* $75/£47

SAGE, LEE. The Last Rustler. Boston, 1930. 1st ed. (Backstrip sl worn, faded.) *Woolson.* $40/£25

SAGE, LEE. The Last Rustler: The Autobiography of Lee Sage. Boston: Little, Brown, 1930. 1st ed. Signed, inscribed presentation. VG. *Pacific*.* $40/£25

SAGENDORPH, KENT. Radium Island. NY: Cupples & Leon, (1938). 1st ed. Blue cl. Pict dj (lt worn). *Cullen.* $45/£28

SAGENDORPH, ROBB. America and Her Almanacs: Wit, Wisdom and Weather 1639-1970. Dublin, NH/Boston: Yankee/Little, Brown, 1970. 1st ed. Fine in dj (few closed tears). *Sadlon.* $30/£19

Sagittarius: His Book. John S. Fass, 1951. One of 640. *Dawson.* $15/£9

Sailing Ships. Viking Penguin, 1984. 6 dbl-pg pop-ups by Borge Svensson. Glazed pict bds. VG. *Bookfinders.* $35/£22

SAINSBURY, ETHEL BRUCE. A Calendar of the Court Minutes Etc. of the East India Company 1664-1679. OUP, 1925-1938. Vols 1-5 (of 7). Djs (vol 2 lacks dj; sl worn, vol 3 sl browned). *Edwards.* $720/£450

SAINT-GERMAIN, COMTE. Practical Palmistry. Chicago: Laird & Lee, 1897. 284pp. VG-. *Middle Earth.* $75/£47

SAINT-MANDE, WILFRED. Sons of Cain. NY: Coward-McCann, (1931). 1st US ed. Tan cl ptd in red. Fine in pict dj (lt rubbed, closed edge tear). *Reese.* $95/£59

SAINT-MANDE, WILFRED. War, Wine and Women. London (etc): Cassell, (1931). 1st ed. Red cl. (Lt foxed; spine very faded), else Good. *Reese.* $30/£19

SAINT-SAENS, CAMILLE. Musical Memories. Edwin Gile Rich (trans). John Murray, 1921. 1st Eng ed. 12 plts. Untrimmed. VG. *Hollett.* $48/£30

SAINT-SIMON. The Memoirs of Louis de Rouvroy Duc de Saint-Simon Covering the Years 1691-1723. Desmond Flower (ed). (NY): LEC, 1959. One of 1500. Signed by Pierre Brissaud (illus). 2 vols. Crimson buckram, gilt. Fine in glassine, slipcase. *Pacific*.* $29/£18

SAISSY, JEAN A. An Essay on the Diseases of the Internal Ear. Nathan R. Smith (trans). Balt: Hatch & Dunning, 1829. 1st US ed. 228pp; fldg b/w litho plt at fr. Orig full sheep, red leather spine label. (Pp lt rippled, sl foxed, aged, old stain at bottom margin throughout; sl edgeworn.) Internally Good. *Baltimore*.* $120/£75

SAJER, GUY. The Forgotten Soldier. NY, 1971. 1st Amer ed. VG in VG dj. *Warren.* $50/£31

SAKURAI, TADAYOSHI. Human Bullets. Alice Mabel Bacon (ed). Boston/NY: Houghton Mifflin, 1907. 1st ed. Color frontis. (Edges sl rubbed, spine ends sl frayed), o/w VG. *Worldwide.* $30/£19

SALA, GEORGE AUGUSTUS. America Revisited: From the Bay of New York.... London: Vizetelly, 1882. 1st ed. 2 vols. Pict cl (sl shelfworn, hinges cracked), gilt. William West bkpls. *Mott.* $50/£31

SALA, GEORGE AUGUSTUS. London up to Date. London: A&C Black, 1894. Blank before 1/2-title; integral ad leaf at end; (2),xiv,378,(ii)pp. Glazed white eps. Dull turquoise art linen. (Inscrips, prelims lt foxed), o/w Fine. *Temple.* $64/£40

SALA, GEORGE AUGUSTUS. Make Your Game; or, The Adventures of the Stout Gentleman, the Slim Gentleman, and the Man with the Iron Chest. Ward & Lock, 1860. Fldg frontis. Sprinkled edges. Contemp 1/2 leather, marbled bds (re-spined, shelf-worn). VG. *Tiger.* $128/£80

SALA, GEORGE AUGUSTUS. William Hogarth: Painter, Engraver, and Philosopher. London: Smith, Elder, 1866. 1st ed. (ii),318,(ii)pp. Dec cl, gilt, beveled bds (sl worn, neatly recased; sm lib label, stamp, few marginal blind stamps). *Hollett.* $104/£65

SALAMAN, MALCOLM C. Shakespeare in Pictorial Art. Charles Holme (ed). London: Studio, 1916. 1st ed. Beveled edges. (Text sl browned; extrems sl rubbed, spine sl sunned.) *Dramatis.* $75/£47

SALAS, FLOYD. Tattoo the Wicked Cross. NY: Grove, 1967. 1st Amer ed, 1st bk. Fine in NF dj. *Polyanthos.* $20/£13

SALE, EDITH TUNIS. Old Time Belles and Cavaliers. Lippincott, 1912. 1st ed. Color frontis. Good+ (binding weak). Howes S51. *Book Broker.* $65/£41

SALE, RICHARD. The Oscar. NY: S&S, (1963). 1st ed. VF in VF dj (1/16 inch shorter than bk). *Between The Covers.* $85/£53

SALE, WILLIAM MERRITT. Samuel Richardson. A Bibliographical Record. New Haven: Yale, 1936. (Lt worn.) *Oinonen*.* $60/£38

SALES, LUIS. Observations on California, 1772-1790. Charles N. Rudkin (ed). L.A.: Glen Dawson, 1956. 1st ed in English. One of 300 ptd. Paper-cvrd bds. (Name), else Fine. Howes S52. *Argonaut.* $75/£47

SALINGER, J. D. The Catcher in the Rye. Boston, 1951. 1st ed. Dj (few internal archival tape repairs). *Swann*.* $1,092/£683

SALINGER, J. D. For Esme—with Love and Squalor and Other Stories. Hamilton, 1953. 1st Eng ed. Pale blue bds, gilt (somewhat tarnished). Good in dj (sl frayed, dust-soiled). *Blackwell's.* $96/£60

SALINGER, J. D. The Kit Book for Soldiers, Sailors and Marines. R. M. Barrows (ed). Chicago: Consolidated Book Pubs, 1943. 1st ed, 2nd state. (Corners sl worn, pp acidic), else NF in VG box (sl scuffed). *My Bookhouse.* $175/£109

SALINGER, J. D. Nine Stories. Boston, (1953). 1st Amer ed. Fine (spine sl bumped). *Polyanthos.* $75/£47

SALINGER, J. D. Nine Stories. Boston: Little, Brown, (1953). 1st ed. Ltd to 4995, according to pub's records. This copy w/text ptd on 2 different batches of paper, w/half of sigs sl browned at edges. Black cl (neatly recased), gilt spine (partial flaking). Dj (spine sunned, sl worn; edges, folds dusty; sl chipped, lt creases). *Baltimore*.* $275/£172

SALINGER, J. D. Raise High the Roof Beam, Carpenters and Seymour, an Introduction. Boston, 1963. 1st ed, 3rd issue. NF in NF dj. *Warren.* $60/£38

SALINGER, J. D. Raise High the Roof Beam, Carpenters, and Seymour: An Introduction. Boston: little, Brown, (1963). 1st ed, 3rd state, w/dedication after tp. Gray cl, gilt. VG (spine faded) in dj (price-clipped, spine faded, edgeworn, tape-reinforced in 2 places on verso). *Heritage.* $75/£47

SALISBURY, ALBERT and JANE. Here Rolled the Covered Wagons. Seattle: Superior, 1948. 1st ltd ed. Ltd to 2050. NF in dj. *Labordo.* $65/£41

SALISBURY, E. J. The Living Garden. London: G. Bell, 1936. 3rd imp. Grn cl, gilt. VG in dj (torn). *Fair Meadow.* $40/£25

SALISBURY, JESSE. A Glossary of Words Used in S.E. Worcestershire. London: (The Author), 1893. 1st ed. 92pp. Recent buckram. *Marlborough.* $104/£65

SALMI, MARIO. Drawings of Michelangelo. NY: Braziller, (1965). Thick folio. 103 dwgs in facs, tissue guards. 1/2 calf. *Argosy.* $250/£156

SALMI, MARIO. Italian Miniatures. NY: Abrams, (1964). (Lt worn.) Dj. *Oinonen*.* $120/£75

SALMON, F. A Practical Essay on the Stricture of the Rectum. London, 1828. xi,188pp. Old marbled bds, paper label. (Eps lt foxed, ink, perforated lib stamps; spine worn, torn), o/w Good. *Whitehart.* $112/£70

SALMON, F. et al. Collected Papers of St. Mark's Hospital, London. London, 1935. (Frontisport sl detached; cl spotted, corners knocked.) *Whitehart.* $56/£35

SALMON, RICHARD. Fly Fishing for Trout. NY, (1952). 1st ed. (Ink name, extrems sunned), else VG in dj (chipped, frayed). *King.* $50/£31

SALMOND, J. B. The Story of the R. and A., Being the History of the First Two Hundred Years of the Royal and Ancient Golf Club of St. Andrews. London: Macmillan, 1956. 1st ed. VG in dj (rubbed, sl torn). *Pacific*.* $150/£94

Salmonia; or, Days of Fly Fishing. (By Humphry Davy.) Phila, 1832. 1st Amer ed. 3 engr plts (offsetting onto facing pp). Orig cl. (Ex-lib; spine faded, paper label worn.) *Swann*.* $201/£126

SALMONY, ALFRED. Carved Jade of Ancient China. Berkeley, 1938. 1st ed. Folio. 72 plts. (Lt worn.) *Swann*.* $172/£108

SALMONY, ALFRED. Sculpture in Siam. London: Ernest Benn, 1925. (Foxed; worn.) *Metropolitan*.* $57/£36

SALOMON, JULIAN HARRIS. The Book of Indian Crafts and Indian Lore. NY/Evanston: Harper & Row, (1928). 1st ed. Pict cream cl. NF (1 sm abrasion). *Sadlon.* $25/£16

SALSBURY, CORA B. Forty Years in the Desert: A History of Ganado Mission 1901-1941. Chicago: Physicians Record Co, 1948. 3rd ptg. VG in stiff pict wraps. *Brown.* $20/£13

SALT, HENRY. A Plea for Vegetarianism, and Other Essays. Manchester, 1886. 1st ed. 115pp. *Fye.* $100/£63

SALT, SIDNEY. Thirty Pieces. Majorco: Caravel, 1934. 1st bk. One of 500 numbered. (Cvrs sl rubbed), else Fine. *Pharos.* $60/£38

SALTEN, FELIX. Bambi. A Life in the Woods. NY, 1928. 1st Amer ed. NF (name; sl rubbed, spine sl sunned). *Polyanthos.* $50/£31

SALTER, J. W. A Catalogue of the Collection of Camrian and Silurian Fossils.... London, 1873. xlvi,204pp; port. New cl, gilt. (Lib stamps.) *Henly.* $88/£55

SALTER, JAMES. Solo Faces. Boston: Little Brown, 1979. 1st ed. VG in dj (extrems sl worn). *Smith.* $45/£28

SALTER, JAMES. A Sport and a Pastime. NY: Doubleday, 1967. Black cl over blue cl, gilt. (Spine cocked, extrems sl rubbed), o/w Fine in dj (price-clipped, sl edgeworn). *Heritage.* $125/£78

SALTER, T. F. The Angler's Guide, Being a Complete Practical Treatise on Angling. London, 1815. 3rd ed. Uncut, top edge red. Vellumized bds (shelfworn, joints cracked, spine sl soiled, chipped, stained; browned, soiled). *Oinonen*.* $50/£31

SALTER, T. F. The Angler's Guide, Being a Complete Practical Treatise on Angling. London, 1815. 2nd ed. Uncut. Mod 3/4 leather. (Sl foxed.) *Oinonen*.* $225/£141

SALTER, T. F. The Angler's Guide, Being a Plain and Complete Practical Treatise on the Art of Angling.... London: R. Carpenter & Son, (1823). 5th ed. 2 frontis aquatint plts, copper-engr frontisport, tp, xii,(8),378pp; 4 plts, inserted plt. Mod 1/2 morocco, marbled bds. (New eps), else VG. *Pacific*.* $115/£72

SALTER, T. F. The Angler's Guide, Being a Plain and Complete Practical Treatise on the Art of Angling.... London: John Wicksteed, 1833. 8th ed. Copper-engr frontisport, tp, xii,(8),378pp; fldg map, 4 plts, inserted plt. 19th-cent 3/4 morocco, marbled bds, gilt. (Bkpls, sl crack top of fr joint, pp sl trimmed), else NF. *Pacific*.* $161/£101

SALTER, T. F. The Angler's Guide, Being a Plain and Complete Treatise on the Art of Angling for Sea, River and Pond Fish. London: J. Maynard, 1841. 9th ed. 6 plts. 1/2 blue calf (sl faded), backstrip gilt. *Petersfield.* $104/£65

SALTER, T. F. The Troller's Guide, a New and Complete Practical Treatise on the Art of Trolling or Fishing for Jack and Pike. London: Carpenter & Son, 1820. 1st ed. Contemp 3/4 calf, marbled bds. (Fr cvr detached, rear cvr nearly so, spine calf perished), else VG-. *Pacific*.* $173/£108

SALTER, TOM. Carnaby Street. (Surrey: Hobbs, 1970.) 1st ed. Fine in Fine dj. *Between The Covers.* $100/£63

SALZMAN, L. F. English Life in the Middle Ages. London: Humphrey Milford, 1926. Frontis. Blue cl (rubbed, extrems sl bumped). *Maggs.* $19/£12

SAMARAS, LUCAS. Photo-Transformations. Constance W. Glenn (ed). Long Beach, CA/NY: CA State Univ/E.P. Dutton, 1975. 1st ed. 40 full-pg color plts. VG (stamp; corner bumped, lt rubbed). *Cahan.* $25/£16

Sammy Tickletooth (Aunt Grumble's Series). NY: McLoughlin Bros, (ca 1870). 12mo. 7pp. Good in 2-color pict wrappers. *Reisler.* $85/£53

Sammy Tickletooth (Little Slovenly Peter Series). NY: McLoughlin Bros, (ca 1880). 12mo. 8pp. Good in color pict wrappers. *Reisler.* $125/£78

Samples. A Collection of Stories.... (By F. Scott Fitzgerald.) NY: Boni & Liveright, (1927). 1st ed. Dj (spine sl dknd, ends worn). *Swann*.* $258/£161

Samson and Delilah, from the Book of Judges According to the Authorised Version. Golden Cockerel, 1925. One of 325. 4to. 7 wood engrs (2 full-pg). Untrimmed. White buckram, gilt. VG (eps sl browned). *Blackwell's.* $560/£350

SAMSON, JACK. The Grizzly Book. Clinton: Amwell, (1981). One of 1000 numbered, signed by Samson, Gene Hill (foreword), & Al Barker (illus). Slipcase. *Swann*.* $92/£58

SAMSON, JACK. Hunting the Southwest. Clinton, NJ: Amwell, 1985. 1st ed. Ltd to 1000 numbered, signed. Brn bonded leather. Slipcase. *Biscotti.* $65/£41

SAMUEL, MAURICE (trans). Schlump. The Story of an Unknown Soldier. London, 1929. 1st Eng ed. Nice (edges sl faded, corner sl bumped) in pict dj (sl torn, rubbed). *Clearwater.* $120/£75

SAMUEL, MAURICE (trans). Schlump: The Story of a German Soldier Told by Himself. NY: Harcourt, Brace, (1929). 1st US ed. Gray cl stamped in black. (Fore-edge sl dusty), o/w NF in NF pict dj. *Reese.* $55/£34

SAMUELS, ADELAIDE F. On the Wave; or Dick Travers Aboard the Happy Jack. NY: Lee & Shepard, 1874. 12mo. Grn pict cl, gilt. VG. *American Booksellers.* $25/£16

SAMUELS, EDWARD A. With Fly-Rod and Camera. NY: Field & Stream, 1890. 1st ed. 150 plts. Teg. Pict grn cl, gilt. Fine. *Pacific*.* $161/£101

SAMUELS, EDWARD A. With Rod and Gun in New England and the Maritime Provinces. Boston: Samuels & Kimball, 1897. 1st ed. Aeg. Fine. *Pacific*.* $104/£65

SAMWELL, DAVID. Captain Cook and Hawaii. SF: David Magee, 1957. One of 750 ptd. Fldg plt, facs of orig tp. Unopened. Red cl, gilt, silhouette fr cvr. Fine. *Pacific*.* $98/£61

San Francisco Directory for the Year Commencing April, 1871. SF: Henry G. Langley, 1871. 8 7/8x6 1/8 inches. civ,904,51pp; fldg map. Ptd bds, new leather spine. *Dawson.* $450/£281

San Francisco Directory for the Year Commencing July, 1860. SF: Henry G. Langley, 1860. 8 7/8x5 5/8 inches. xxxii,519pp. Ptd bds, new leather spine. *Dawson.* $500/£313

San Francisco Municipal Reports, 1859-60. SF: Towne & Bacon, 1860. 1st ed. iv,(1),186pp. Full law calf, gilt-stamped morocco spine labels. (Bkpl; lt foxed; leather lt worn), o/w VG. *Pacific*.* $150/£94

San Francisco Municipal Reports, for the Fiscal Year 1867-8.... SF: John H. Carmany, 1868. 1st ed. Presentation binding in gilt-ruled/lettered morocco to Henry H. Haight. (Bkpl; rebacked, orig spine laid on, extrems scuffed), else VG. *Pacific*.* $63/£39

San Francisco Vigilance Committee of 1856. L.A.: Westerners Silver Anniversary Pub, (1971). 1st ed. Ltd to 500. Fine. *Book Market.* $85/£53

SANBORN, F. B. and WILLIAM T. HARRIS. A. Bronson Alcott, His Life and Philosophy. Boston: Roberts Bros, 1893. 1st ed. 2 vols. Frontis, 354; frontis, (355)-679pp. Red cl (spine ends sl worn). Good. *Lucas.* $100/£63

SANBORN, F. B. (ed). Thoreau the Poet Naturalist. Boston: Goodspeed, 1902. New ed. One of 250. Uncut, unopened. Ptd leather label. (Foxed; sl worn, soiled.) *M & S.* $250/£156

SANCHEZ, THOMAS. Zoot-Suit Murders. NY, (1978). 1st ed. Presentation copy. Inscribed, signed. Good in dj (sl worn, sunned). *King.* $45/£28

SAND, GEORGES. Tales of a Grandmother. Margaret Bloom (trans). Phila: Lippincott, 1930. 1st ed. 7.3x9.3. 304pp; 12 color plts by Harold Hess. Grn cl, stamped. VG (corner bumped, spine head rolled; sl faded). *Price.* $30/£19

SANDBURG, CARL. Abraham Lincoln: The Prairie Years. NY: Harcourt, Brace, (1927). 7th ptg. Signed. 2 vols in 1. Dk grn cl (lt rubbed, fr hinge cracked; sm spine nick), gilt (sl flaked). Internally Good (sl foxed). *Baltimore*.* $45/£28

SANDBURG, CARL. Abraham Lincoln: The War Years. NY: Harcourt, Brace, (1939). 1st trade ed. 4 vols. NF. *Sadlon.* $100/£63

SANDBURG, CARL. Always the Young Strangers. NY, 1953. 1st ed. One of 600 numbered, signed. Mylar dj, slipcase. *Swann*.* $161/£101

SANDBURG, CARL. A Carl Sandburg Miscellany. Valley Stream, NY: Appletree Books, 1977. One of 290. Fine in yellow wrappers. *Heritage.* $50/£31

SANDBURG, CARL. Complete Poems. NY: Harcourt, Brace, (1950). One of unspecified number, signed on tipped-in leaf. Untrimmed. Dk blue-grn cl, gilt. Very Clean in dj (lt worn, sl chipped, few sm edgetears). *Baltimore*.* $125/£78

SANDBURG, CARL. Good Morning America. NY: Crosby Gaige, 1928. One of 811 signed. One of approx 10 ptd throughout on blue paper. 8vo. Teg. Red cl, gilt. VG (bkpl; spine sunned, gilt flaked). *Heritage.* $850/£531

SANDBURG, CARL. A Lincoln and Whitman Miscellany. Chicago: Holiday Press, 1938. 1st ed. One of 250 for private distribution. 1/4 cl, wrap-around leather label. *Swann*.* $161/£101

SANDBURG, CARL. Lincoln Collector. NY, 1949. 1st ed. Ltd to 2425 numbered, signed. VG in slipcase (sl used). *King.* $150/£94

SANDBURG, CARL. Lincoln Collector: The Story of Oliver R. Barrett's Great Private Collection. NY: Harcourt, Brace, 1949. 1st ed. One of 2425. Signed. Fine in slipcase. *Pacific*.* $138/£86

SANDBURG, CARL. The People, Yes. NY: Harcourt, Brace, 1936. 1st ed. Inscribed, 1936. Blue cl (spine faded). Dj (tattered). *Cummins.* $150/£94

SANDBURG, CARL. Remembrance Rock. NY, (1948). 1st trade ed. Signed. VG in dj (chipped, torn). *King.* $100/£63

SANDBURG, CARL. Remembrance Rock. NY: Harcourt, Brace, (1948). 1st ed. One of 1000. 2 vols. Blue buckram w/paper spine labels. *Cummins.* $200/£125

SANDBURG, CARL. Remembrance Rock. NY: Harcourt, Brace, 1948. 1st ed. One of 1000 numbered, signed vol 1. 2 vols. Blue cl. Fine in acetate djs, pub's slipcase (flaked). *Unger.* $200/£125

SANDBURG, CARL. Steichen the Photographer. NY, (1929). Ltd to 925 signed by Steichen and Sandburg. Folio. (Inscrip; sl rubbed.) *Swann*.* $1,380/£863

SANDBURG, CARL. Steichen the Photographer. NY: Harcourt, Brace, (1929). 1st ed. One of 925 (this out-of-series) signed by Sandburg & Steichen. 4to. Frontis, 48 full-pg b/w photos. (Sm bkpl, eps sl foxed; sm mks to cl), else NF. *Cahan.* $1,500/£938

SANDBURG, CARL. Steichen the Photographer. NY, (1929). 1st ed. One of 925 signed by Sandburg and Edward Steichen. 4to. Black cl. Fine. *Appelfeld.* $1,500/£938

SANDEMAN, FRASER. Angling Travels in Norway. London: Chapman & Hall, 1895. 1st ed, lg paper copy. 4 plts. 1/4 bds, cl, paper spine label. Fair (hinges cracked; cvrs lack cl, rubbed). *Pacific**. $230/£144

SANDER, AUGUST. Men Without Masks, Faces of Germany 1910-1938. Greenwich, 1973. 1st Amer ed. (Handstamp eps.) Dj (creased, torn). *Swann**. $201/£126

SANDER, ELLEN. Trips: Rock Life in the Sixties. NY: Scribner, 1973. 1st ed. (Lower corner bumped), o/w NF in dj (sl torn, lt creased). *Sclanders*. $32/£20

SANDER, GUNTHER. August Sander: Photographer Extraordinary. London: Thames & Hudson, 1973. 1st Eng ed. Mtd frontis port, 275 b/w photos. Fine in pict dj. *Cahan*. $300/£188

SANDERS, ALVIN H. At the Sign of the Stock Yard Inn.... Chicago: Ptd by Breeders Gazette, 1915. Frontis. Good in wrappers (spine sl dknd, worn, cvrs lt soiled). *Brown*. $25/£16

SANDERS, ALVIN H. Red White and Roan.... American Shorthorn Breeders' Assoc, 1936. Good. *Rybski*. $65/£41

SANDERS, ALVIN H. Short-Horn Cattle. Chicago: Sanders Pub, 1916. 2nd ed. Grn cl, gilt, photo illus pasted to fr cvr, as issued. Fine. *Argonaut*. $50/£31

SANDERS, ED. The Family. The Story of Charles Manson's Dune Buggy Attack Battalion. NY: E.P. Dutton, 1971. 1st ed. Fine in dj. *Sclanders*. $40/£25

SANDERS, F. K. (ed). The Biological Replication of Macromolecules. Cambridge: CUP, 1958. 1st ed. Grn cl. Fine in ptd dj. *House*. $50/£31

SANDERS, HELEN FITZGERALD (ed). X. Beidler, Vigilante. Norman: Univ of OK, (1957). 1st ed. VG in dj (sl worn). *Lien*. $20/£13

SANDERS, WILBUR E. et al. Mine Timbering. NY, 1907. 1st ed thus. (Old ink price fep; few spots on cvr, binding sl cocked), o/w VG. *Baade*. $50/£31

SANDERS, WILLIAM BLISS. Examples of Carved Oak Woodwork in the Houses and Furniture of the 16th and 17th Centuries. London, 1883. Folio. Unpaginated. 25 plts. (Lib ink stamps, bkpl; dampstained, bumped, rubbed.) *Edwards*. $64/£40

SANDERSON, G. P. Thirteen Years Among the Wild Beasts of India, Their Haunts and Habits from Personal Observation. Edinburgh: J. Grant, (1907). 6th ed. Teg. Pict cl, gilt. (Bottom corners rubbed), else VG. *Mikesh*. $95/£59

SANDERSON, G. P. Thirteen Years Among the Wild Beasts of India. London, 1878. 1st ed. Hand-colored frontis. 1/2 calf (rubbed). *Grayling*. $72/£45

SANDERSON, J. An Ocean Cruise and Deep Water Regatta of the Pacific Yacht Club, July, 1884. SF: H.S. Crocker, 1884. 1st ed. 4to. 55pp; 8 full-pg color litho plts. Grn cl, gilt. Fine (some plts lt foxed). *Argonaut*. $2,500/£1,563

SANDHAM, ELIZABETH. The History of William Selwyn. London: J. Harris, 1815. 1st ed. 8vo. Engr frontis, vii,205pp. Old sheep (rebacked). *Young*. $144/£90

SANDLER, LUCY FREEMAN. The Psalter of Robert de Lisle in the British Library. London, 1983. One of 1000. Good. *Washton*. $195/£122

SANDOZ, MARI. The Buffalo Hunters. NY: Hastings House, (1954). 1st ed. Map. Brn cl. VG in pict dj. *House*. $50/£31

SANDOZ, MARI. The Buffalo Hunters. NY: Hastings House, 1954. VG in dj (price-clipped, chipped). *Dumont*. $45/£28

SANDOZ, MARI. Capital City. Boston, 1939. 1st ed. Buckram. NF in VG + dj. *Sagebrush*. $50/£31

SANDOZ, MARI. The Cattlemen. NY: Hastings House, (1958). 1st ed. Good. *Lien*. $35/£22

SANDOZ, MARI. Crazy Horse. NY, (1942). 1st ed. Fldg map. VG + . *Pratt*. $115/£72

SANDOZ, MARI. Crazy Horse. NY: Knopf, 1942. 1st ed. Fine. *Labordo*. $85/£53

SANDOZ, MARI. The Maze. GC: Doubleday, 1945. 1st Amer ed. Salvador Dali (illus). (Offset to eps), else VG- in dj (lacks spine piece, offset to flaps). *Pacific**. $46/£29

SANDOZ, MAURICE. The Crystal Salt Cellar. Guilford, 1954. 1st Eng ed. VG (feps partly browned; cvr extrems faded) in dj (rubbed, soiled, sm edge tears). *Ulysses*. $58/£36

SANDOZ, MAURICE. The Maze. GC: Doubleday, 1945. 1st ed. (Fep lt clipped), else VF in VF dj. *Between The Covers*. $150/£94

SANDWEISS, MARTHA A. Laura Gilpin: An Enduring Grace. Fort Worth: Amon Carter Museum, (1986). 1st ed. 126 photo plts by Laura Gilpin. Fine in dj. *Pacific**. $63/£39

SANDWICH, EARL OF. The Sandwich Papers...Volumes LXIX, LXXI, LXXV and LXXVIII. G. R. Barnes and J. H. Owen (eds). London: The Society, 1932-38. 4 vols. 4 ports. VG set. *Hollett*. $136/£85

SANDWITH, HUMPHRY. A Narrative of the Siege of Kars.... London, 1856. 3rd ed. Frontis, 2 maps. Contemp calf (backstrip faded), gilt. *Swann**. $103/£64

SANFORD, GEORGE B. Fighting Rebels and Redskins. E. R. Hagemann (ed). Norman: Univ of OK, (1969). 1st ed. Inscribed by Hagemann. Frontisport. 2-toned cl. Fine in NF dj. *Chapel Hill*. $55/£34

SANFORD, HERB. Tommy and Jimmy: The Dorsey Years. New Rochelle: Arlington House, (1972). VG in pict dj. *Petrilla*. $30/£19

SANFORD, MOLLIE DORSEY. Mollie: The Journal of Mollie Dorsey Sanford in Nebraska and Colorado Territories, 1857-1866. Univ of NE, 1959. 1st ed. VG in dj (sl worn). *Lien*. $25/£16

SANSON, HENRY (ed). Memoirs of the Sansons. Chatto, 1876. 1st Eng ed. 2 vols. 1/2 dk grn morocco (faded), marbled sides. VG. *Clearwater*. $144/£90

Santa Claus in Toyland. Harry Doehla Co, (1951). 4to. 4 moveables, 1 pop-up. Spiral-bound paper pict bds. VG. *Davidson*. $85/£53

SANTA MARIA, VICENTE. The First Spanish Entry into San Francisco Bay, 1775. John Galvin (ed). SF: John Howell Books, 1971. One of 5000 ptd. 4 maps. Blue cl, gilt. Fine in dj (spine sunned). *Pacific**. $52/£33

SANTANGELO, ANTONINO. A Treasury of Great Italian Textiles. NY, (1964). Dj. *Swann**. $138/£86

SANTAYANA, GEORGE. Lucifer of the Heavenly Truce. Cambridge, MA: Dunster House, 1924. One of 450 ptd at Southworth Press. Folio. Uncut. (Sl worn.) *Oinonen**. $40/£25

SANTAYANA, GEORGE. The Works of George Santayana. NY: Scribner, 1936-40. Triton ed. One of 940 sets. Signed. 14 (of 15) vols. Frontisport. Teg. Cl-backed bds, paper spine labels. (Glassine sl chipped), else Fine in slipcases, orig packing boxes (stained). *Pacific**. $431/£269

SANTAYANA, GEORGE. The Works.... NY: Triton Editions, 1936-40. One of 940 signed sets. 15 vols. Fine in slipcases, boxes (sl weak). *Metropolitan**. $345/£216

SANTEE, ROSS. Apache Land. NY, 1947. 1st ed. Good in dj (soiled). *Dumont*. $65/£41

SANTEE, ROSS. The Bar X Golf Course. NY: Farrar Rinehart, 1933. 1st ed. Golf score card laid in loose. NF in dj. *Labordo*. $175/£109

SANTEE, ROSS. Dog Days. NY: Scribner, 1955. 1st ed. Fine in dj. *Labordo*. $45/£28

SANTEE, ROSS. Lost Pony Tracks. NY: Scribner, 1953. 1st ed. VG in dj. *Lien*. $50/£31

SANTEE, ROSS. Lost Pony Tracks. NY: Scribner, 1953. 1st ed. NF in dj (chipped). *Labordo*. $65/£41

SANTEE, ROSS. Men and Horses. NY: Century, 1926. 1st ed, 1st bk. NF in dj (sl worn). *Labordo.* $250/£156

SANTINI, PIER CARLO. Modern Landscape Painting. Phaidon, 1972. 1st UK ed. 245 plts (52 color). (Fr hinge cracked.) Dj (spine head sl torn, fr wrap sl wrinkled). *Edwards.* $48/£30

SANTMYER, HELEN HOOVER. Ohio Town. (N.p.): OH State Univ, (1962). 1st ed. (Edges sl rubbed), else NF in VG dj (lt soiled, sl loss at crown). *Between The Covers.* $150/£94

SAPIO, VICTOR A. Pennsylvania and the War of 1812. Univ of KY, (1970). Good in dj (worn). *Rybski.* $37/£23

SAPPER. (Pseud of H. C. MacNeile.) No Man's Land. London/NY/Toronto: Hodder & Stoughton, 1917. 1st ed. Plum cl. (Eps lt foxed, edges; bound w/o free endsheets), else VG. *Reese.* $30/£19

SAPPER. (Pseud of H. C. MacNeile.) Sergeant Michael Cassidy, R.E. London/NY/Toronto: Hodder & Stoughton, 1915. 1st ed. Pict-stamped lt grn cl. Good (fr inner hinge cracking; spine dknd, sl worn) in dj (sl chipped, old mends to closed tears on verso). *Reese.* $35/£22

SAPPHO. The Songs of Sappho. Marion Mills Miller & David Moore Robinson (trans). NY: Frank-Maurice, 1925. One of 750. 10 plts. 1/4 vellum, gilt. Fine. *Pacific*.* $104/£65

SAPPINGTON, JOHN. The Theory and Treatment of Fevers. Arrow Rock, MO: The Author, 1844. 1st ed. Blue cl, black leather spine labels. (Sl foxed throughout.) *Glenn.* $350/£219

SARAMAGO, JOSE. Baltasar and Blimunda. San Diego: Harcourt Brace Jovanovich, 1987. 1st US ed. Fine in NF dj. *Lame Duck.* $50/£31

SARDUY, SEVERO. Cobra. NY: Dutton, 1972. NF in dj. *Lame Duck.* $75/£47

SARETT, LEW. Many Many Moons. A Book of Wilderness Poems. NY: Henry Holt, 1920. 1st ed. Inscribed. Gilt-dec cl. NF. *Sadlon.* $20/£13

SARETT, LEW. Slow Smoke. NY: Henry Holt, 1925. 1st ed. Inscribed. Dec cl (spine ends, corners sl rubbed). *Sadlon.* $15/£9

SARG, TONY. Tony Sarg's Book of Tricks. N.p.: Greenberg, n.d. Likely 1st ed. 11x7.5. Cl-backed pict bds. VG (bkpl, 2-inch tear to upper 1/2-title, rep tear, lacks 1/2 of rear pastedown, ink spot to upper edges of last pp; cvrs sl scratched, extrems rubbed). *Pacific*.* $29/£18

SARG, TONY. Where Is Tommy? NY: Greenberg, (1932). 1st ed. Obl 8vo. 6 full-pg plts w/flaps. Cl-backed color illus bds (dusty). *Reisler.* $100/£63

SARGANT, E. and B. WHISHAW. A Guide Book to Books. H. Frowde, 1891. 344pp. VG. *Moss.* $22/£14

SARGENT, CHARLES SPRAGUE. Manual of the Trees of North America. Boston: HM, 1933. Ltr ptg. VG + (spine rubbed). *Archer.* $50/£31

SARGENT, CHARLES SPRAGUE. The Silva of North America. Boston/NY, 1891-1902. 14 vols. Folio. 740 plts. (Pp tanned, lt browned, brn marginal spots to few plts; dknd, edges chipped, worn, bumped; soiled, spotted, stained; spine ends chipped, sm tears; sm paper split to outer hinge, spine labels chipped; tear to backstrip vol 1, fr hinge partly split, reinforced internally w/cl tape.) *Sutton.* $2,400/£1,500

SARGENT, EPES et al. The Life and Public Services of Henry Clay, Down to 1848. Horace Greeley (ed). NY/Auburn: Miller, Orton & Mulligan, 1856. New, enlgd ed. 627,(5)pp. VG + . *Zubal*.* $24/£15

SARGENT, EPES. Velasco. NY: Harper, 1839. 1st published ed. (8),(13)-110pp (foxed, lacks fep). Orig patterned cl (faded). BAL 17201. *M & S.* $125/£78

SARGENT, GEORGE H. A Busted Bibliophile and His Books. Boston, 1928. Ltd to 600. Cl-backed marbled bds. VG (bkpl, lt scuffed). *Truepenny.* $75/£47

SARGENT, SHIRLEY (ed). Seeking the Elephant, 1849. Glendale: A.H. Clark, 1980. 1st ed. Ltd to 750 ptd. Signed, inscribed. Frontisport, 1 full-pg illus. Uncut. Red cl, gilt. Fine in plain dj. *Pacific*.* $92/£58

SARGENT, SHIRLEY. Yosemite and Its Innkeepers. Yosemite: Flying Spur Press, (1975). 1st ed. Red cl, gilt spine. Fine in pict dj. *Pacific*.* $29/£18

SARGENT, SHIRLEY. Yosemite and Its Innkeepers. Yosemite: Flying Spur, (1975). 1st ed. Inscribed by Sargent and Horace M. Albright (foreword). (Bkpl.) Dj (lt worn). *Dawson.* $40/£25

SARGESON, FRANK. That Summer and Other Stories. Lehmann, 1946. 1st Eng ed. VG (spine sl sunned) in VG dj. *Clearwater.* $64/£40

SAROYAN, WILLIAM. The Cave Dwellers. S. French, 1958. 1st ed. VG + in wraps (lt soiled). *Fine Books.* $25/£16

SAROYAN, WILLIAM. The Daring Young Man on the Flying Trapeze and Other Stories. Faber, 1935. 1st Eng ed, 1st bk. Red cl, dec spine. VG. *Whiteson.* $38/£24

SAROYAN, WILLIAM. Inhale and Exhale. NY: Random House, (1936). 1st ed. Pale gray cl. (Sm chip 1 leaf; spine, cvr edges lt foxed), o/w Fine in dj (rear panel sl soiled). *Heritage.* $200/£125

SAROYAN, WILLIAM. Inhale and Exhale. R-H, 1936. 1st ed. VG. *Fine Books.* $25/£16

SAROYAN, WILLIAM. Morris Hirshfield. Franco Maria Ricci, 1976. 1st ed. One of 3000 signed. Folio. 44 tipped-in color plts numbered, signed. Dec eps. Mtd color illus. Pub's box. *Metropolitan*.* $69/£43

SAROYAN, WILLIAM. Peace, It's Wonderful. NY: Starling, (1939). 1st ed. Mauve cl. VG (eps browned; spine ends sl rubbed) in dj (spine, rear cvr sl soiled; corners, spine extrems chipped). *Heritage.* $175/£109

SAROYAN, WILLIAM. Peace, It's Wonderful. Modern Age, 1939. 1st ed. Fine in wraps. *Fine Books.* $25/£16

SAROYAN, WILLIAM. Razzle-Dazzle. NY: Harcourt, Brace, (1942). 1st ed. Grn cl. (Few lt cvr spots), o/w Fine in dj (rear panel lt soiled). *Heritage.* $225/£141

SAROYAN, WILLIAM. The Saroyan Special. NY: Harcourt, Brace, (1948). 1st ed. Natural cl. Dj (spine sl browned, extrems sl rubbed). *Heritage.* $175/£109

SAROYAN, WILLIAM. Saroyan's Fables. (NY): Harcourt, Brace, 1941. 1st ed. One of 1000 signed. Top edges stained yellow. Grn cl, gilt. (Eps, spine lt browned), o/w Fine in pub's cardboard open-end slipcase (lt worn). *Heritage.* $175/£109

SARRIS, ANDREW. The Films of Josef von Sternberg. NY: MOMA, (1966). 1st ed. VF in VF dj (sm, neat ink price fep). *Between The Covers.* $100/£63

SARTON, MAY. The Birth of a Grandfather. London: Gollancz, 1958. 1st Eng ed. Fine (sm label fep) in dj (sl rubbed, spotted, spine sl dknd). *Ulysses.* $72/£45

SARTON, MAY. Faithful Are the Wounds. NY: Rinehart, (1955). 1st ed. Fine in dj (sl worn). *Second Life.* $75/£47

SARTON, MAY. The House by the Sea. Norton, 1977. 1st ed. Signed presentation. Fine in NF dj (sl creased, top edges frayed). *Any Amount.* $88/£55

SARTON, MAY. In Time Like Air. NY: Rinehart, (1958). 1st ed. (Edges sunned), else Fine in dj. *Hermitage.* $40/£25

SARTON, MAY. In Time Like Air. NY, (1958). 1st ed. Fine in dj. *Second Life.* $75/£47

SARTON, MAY. Kinds of Love. NY: Norton, (1970). 1st ed. (Name), o/w VG in dj (chipped). *Second Life.* $45/£28

SARTON, MAY. The Leaves of the Tree. Mt. Vernon, IA: Cornell Cottage Chapbooks, 1950. 1st ed. One of 300. Signed presentation. VG in pale blue self wraps (edges sunned). *Any Amount.* $96/£60

SARTON, MAY. The Poet and the Donkey. NY: Norton, (1969). 1st ed. Signed. Fine in NF dj (price-clipped). *Reese*. $50/£31

SARTON, MAY. A Shower of Summer Days. NY: Rinehart, (1952). 1st ed. VG in VG dj (price-clipped, sm stain rt corner of fr cvr). *Second Life*. $75/£47

SARTRE, JEAN-PAUL. The Age of Reason. H. Hamilton, 1947. 1st Eng ed. (Sl discolored), else Good in dj (worn, dull). *Whiteson*. $26/£16

SARTRE, JEAN-PAUL. Being and Nothingness. NY: Philosophical Library, 1956. 1st ed. Fine in Fine dj. *Beasley*. $50/£31

SARTRE, JEAN-PAUL. The Chips Are Down. Louise Varese (trans). London: Rider, 1951. 1st Eng ed. NF (1 spot to fore-edge) in dj (sl rubbed). *Ulysses*. $77/£48

SARTRE, JEAN-PAUL. The Diary of Antoine Roquentin. Lloyd Alexander (trans). London: John Lehmann, 1949. 1st Eng ed. VG (eps browned; spine ends sl bumped) in dj (dusty, nicked, spine sl dknd). *Ulysses*. $88/£55

SARTRE, JEAN-PAUL. Intimacy and Other Stories. Lloyd Alexander (trans). London: Peter Nevill, 1949. 1st Eng ed. VG (feps sl spotted) in dj (sl frayed, nicked, rubbed). *Ulysses*. $88/£55

SARTRE, JEAN-PAUL. Kean, or Disorder and Genius. Kitty Black (trans). London: Hamish Hamilton, 1954. 1st Eng ed. NF (spine ends sl bumped) in dj (sl mkd, spine sl dknd, edges rubbed). *Ulysses*. $56/£35

SARTRE, JEAN-PAUL. Portrait of the Anti-Semite. Erik de Mauny (trans). London: Secker & Warburg/Lindsay Drummond, 1948. 1st Eng ed. VG (eps sl spotted, fep creased; spine foot sl bumped) in dj (nicked, chipped, sl torn, rubbed, spotted, creased). *Ulysses*. $56/£35

SARTRE, JEAN-PAUL. Situations. NY: George Braziller, 1958. 1st ed. Fine in NF dj (spine dknd, rear panel sl creased w/tear). *Beasley*. $35/£22

SARTRE, JEAN-PAUL. The Wall and Other Stories. Lloyd Alexander (trans). (NY): New Directions, (1948). Ltd ed. (Spine sunned), else VG in slipcase (broken). *Pacific**. $63/£39

SARTRE, JEAN-PAUL. Words. Irene Clephane (trans). London: Hamish Hamilton, 1964. 1st Eng ed. NF (spine foot sl bumped) in dj (sl rubbed). *Ulysses*. $56/£35

SARYCHEV, GAVRILA ANDREEVICH. Account of a Voyage of Discovery to the North-East of Siberia, the Frozen Ocean, and the North-East Sea. London, 1806-07. 2 vols in 1. 8vo. 5 engr plts (2 hand-colored). 19th-cent 1/2 calf (spine ends frayed). Howes S115. *Swann**. $517/£323

SASOWSKY, NORMAN. The Prints of Reginald Marsh. NY: Potter, (1976). 1st ed. Black cl, gilt. (Edges sl dusty.) Text VG in dj (price-clipped, sl worn). *Baltimore**. $40/£25

SASOWSKY, NORMAN. The Prints of Reginald Marsh. NY: Potter, 1976. Good. *Ars Artis*. $80/£50

SASSOON, SIEGFRIED. Counter-Attack and Other Poems. Heinemann, 1918. 1st ed. Fine in red/orange ptd wrappers, pale blue cl chemise, matching cl slipcase, gilt. *Blackwell's*. $280/£175

SASSOON, SIEGFRIED. The Heart's Journey. NY/London: Crosby Gaige/Heinemann, 1927. 1st ed. One of 590 (of 599) signed. Cl, blue bds, gilt label. (Sm bkpl stain on pastedown; spine crown, lower tips sl worn), o/w VG. *Reese*. $200/£125

SASSOON, SIEGFRIED. In Sicily. London: Faber & Faber, 1930. One of 400 signed. Grn bds, gilt. Good (spine splitting, chipped). *Heritage*. $50/£31

SASSOON, SIEGFRIED. In Sicily. Ariel Poems, 1930. One of 400 signed copies on lg paper. NF (spine sl chafed). *Clearwater*. $120/£75

SASSOON, SIEGFRIED. Memoirs of a Fox-Hunting Man. Faber, 1929. 1st Eng illus ed. 8 plts. Untrimmed. White cl. Good (feps lt browned, bkpl). *Blackwell's*. $160/£100

SASSOON, SIEGFRIED. Memoirs of a Fox-Hunting Man. LEC, 1977. One of 1600 signed by Paul Hogarth (illus). Fine in slipcase. *Swann**. $34/£21

SASSOON, SIEGFRIED. Memoirs of an Infantry Officer. London: Faber & Faber, (1931). 1st Eng illus ed. Pict eps. VG (bkpl) in pict cl. *Maggs*. $216/£135

SASSOON, SIEGFRIED. Memoirs of an Infantry Officer. London, 1930. 1st ed. One of 300 numbered, signed. Unopened. (Spine sl faded.) *Swann**. $287/£179

SASSOON, SIEGFRIED. Nativity. London: Ariel Poems, (1927). 1st Eng ed. Fine in pict card wrappers. *Clearwater*. $40/£25

SASSOON, SIEGFRIED. The Old Century and Seven More Years. London, 1938. 1st Eng ed. Reynolds Stone (illus). VG (bkpl) in dj (sl nicked). *Clearwater*. $72/£45

SASSOON, SIEGFRIED. The Old Huntsman and Other Poems. NY: Dutton, (1920). 2nd ptd of 1st ed ptd in US. Unopened. Linen, bds, ptd spine label. (Eps sl offset from dj flaps), o/w Fine in NF dj (sm chip). *Reese*. $45/£28

SASSOON, SIEGFRIED. The Old Huntsman and Other Poems. London, 1917. One of 1000 ptd. Errata slip. (Inscrip; sl tanned, faded, lt mkd, corner chafed.) *Clearwater*. $240/£150

SASSOON, SIEGFRIED. Poems Newly Selected 1916-1935. London: Faber, (1940). 1st ed. Ptd bds. NF in yellow dj (spine lt tanned), wraparound band. *Reese*. $75/£47

SASSOON, SIEGFRIED. Rhymed Ruminations. London, 1940. 1st ed. Fine in dj. *Petersfield*. $38/£24

SASSOON, SIEGFRIED. The Road to Ruin. London, 1933. 1st Eng ed. (Sl dknd, spine head, 2 corners sl bumped.) Dj (sl nicked, dust-mkd). *Clearwater*. $96/£60

SASSOON, SIEGFRIED. Sherston's Progress. London: Faber & Faber, (1936). 1st ed, trade issue. Gilt blue cl. VG in dj (sl nicked, frayed), wraparound band intact. *Reese*. $65/£41

SASSOON, SIEGFRIED. Sherston's Progress. London, (1936). 1st ed. One of 300 numbered, signed. *Swann**. $230/£144

SASSOON, SIEGFRIED. Sherston's Progress. London, 1936. 1st ed. VG in Fair dj. *Typographeum*. $60/£38

SASSOON, SIEGFRIED. Sherston's Progress. Faber, 1936. 1st UK ed. NF in dj. *Williams*. $77/£48

SASSOON, SIEGFRIED. Sherston's Progress. GC: Doubleday, Doran, 1936. 1st US ed. Pict-stamped tan cl. (Early ink inscrip), o/w NF in pict dj (few mks rear panel, sm tear 1 corner). *Reese*. $85/£53

SASSOON, SIEGFRIED. Sherston's Progress. Faber, 1936. 1st ed. One of 300 signed. Teg, rest untrimmed, partly unopened. Mid blue buckram, gilt backstrip (faded). Good (feps lt browned). *Blackwell's*. $200/£125

SASSOON, SIEGFRIED. Siegfried's Journey 1916-1920. London: Faber & Faber, (1945). 1st ed. Port. Tp cut by Reynolds Stone. Gilt pink cl. Fine in NF dj (price-clipped). *Reese*. $55/£34

SASSOON, SIEGFRIED. Something About Myself. (Worcester: Stanbrook Abbey Press, 1966.) 1st ed. White wrappers (lt soiled), else Fine. *Bromer*. $250/£156

SASSOON, SIEGFRIED. To My Mother. London: Ariel Poems, (1928). 1st Eng ed. Pict card wrappers (edges sl faded). *Clearwater*. $40/£25

SASSOON, SIEGFRIED. To My Mother. London, 1928. 1st ed. One of 500 lg paper copies numbered, signed. Brick-red bds. *Swann**. $201/£126

SASSOON, SIEGFRIED. To My Mother. Ariel Poem No. 14. Faber, 1928. 1st ed. One of 500 signed. 2 full-pg illus (1 color-ptd). Untrimmed. Salmon-pink bds, gilt. VF. *Blackwell's*. $144/£90

SASSOON, SIEGFRIED. To the Red Rose. London: Ariel Poems, (1931). 1st Eng ed. Pict card wrappers (sl creased). *Clearwater*. $40/£25

SASSOON, SIEGFRIED. Vigils. Heinemann, 1935. 1st trade ed. Fine in VG dj. *Williams.* $77/£48

SASSOON, SIEGFRIED. The War Poems of Siegfried Sassoon. London: Heinemann, (1919). 1st ed. Red cl, ptd labels. (Sm ink name, few fox mks at fore-edge, few sl bumps), o/w NF in dj (spine sl tanned). *Reese.* $350/£219

SATCHELL, W. The Greenstone Door. NY, 1914. 1st ed. (Sl dull), else Good. *Whiteson.* $24/£15

SATO, SHOZO. The Art of Arranging Flowers, a Complete Guide to Japanese Ikebana. NY: Abrams, n.d. Folio. Mtd color illus on cl. Fine. *Metropolitan*.* $57/£36

SATTERFIELD, ARCHIE. Alaska Bush Pilots in the Float Country. Seattle: Superior, (1969). 1st ed. VG in dj. *Perier.* $40/£25

SATTERTHWAIT, WALTER. Miss Lizzie. NY: St. Martin's, 1989. 1st ed. Signed. Fine in Fine dj. *Unger.* $300/£188

Saturday Evening Post Stories, 1950. NY: Random House, (1950). 1st ed. Fine in Fine dj (2 sm tears). *Between The Covers.* $75/£47

SAUDEK, ROBERT. The Psychology of Handwriting. London: George Allen & Unwin, 1925. 1st UK ed. Fore-edge uncut. Supplement in rear pocket w/48 plts. (1st few pp sl spotted; spine lt faded.) *Edwards.* $56/£35

SAUER, MARTIN. An Account of a Geographical and Astronomical Expedition to the Northern Parts of Russia. London, 1802. 4to. xxvi,errata,332pp + 58pp appendix, half-title; lg fldg map, 14 engr plts. Marbled eps. Contemp gilt-ruled calf. (Offsetting to plts, lt foxing; worn, rebacked.) *Edwards.* $1,200/£750

SAUERLANDT, MAX. Emil Nolde. Munchen, 1921. Folio. Buckram. (Sl foxed, sl wear.) *Oinonen*.* $90/£56

SAULNIER, TONY. Headhunters of Papua. NY: Crown, 1963. 1st ed. 2 maps. VG in dj. *Worldwide.* $45/£28

SAUM, LEWIS O. The Fur Trader and the Indian. Seattle: Univ of WA, (1965). 1st ed. Frontis, map. Tan cl. Fine in dj. *Argonaut.* $50/£31

SAUNDBY, ROBERT. Lectures on Bright's Disease. London, 1889. 1st ed. 290pp. *Fye.* $125/£78

SAUNDERS, CHARLES FRANCIS. The Southern Sierras of California. Boston/NY: Houghton Mifflin, 1923. 1st ed. 32 plts. Olive-grn cl, gilt. (Inscrip; spine faded), else NF. *Pacific*.* $69/£43

SAUNDERS, CHARLES FRANCIS. Under the Sky in California. NY, 1913. 1st ed. Pict cl. (Cvr lt soiled, rubbed.) *King.* $35/£22

SAUNDERS, CHARLES FRANCIS. Under the Sky in California. NY: McBride, Nast, 1913. 1st ed. 48 plts. Olive-grn pict cl, gilt. NF. *Pacific*.* $81/£51

SAUNDERS, LOUISE. The Knave of Hearts. Racine, WI: Artists and Writers Guild, (1925). 4to. Dec tp, 22 color illus by Maxfield Parrish. Pict wrappers, wire spiral binding. (Pg sl nicked), else Fine. *Appelfeld.* $600/£375

SAUNDERS, LYLE. A Guide to Materials Bearing on Cultural Relations in New Mexico. Albuquerque, 1944. Good in dj (sl worn, sm hole in cvr). *Dumont.* $100/£63

SAUNDERS, R. CROMBIE. A Guide to the Fishing Inns of Scotland. Nicholas Kaye, 1951. 1st ed. 12 plts. VG in dj. *Hollett.* $24/£15

SAUNDERS, RICHARD WEST. Skallagrim (Grim the Bald). Privately ptd, 1925. Ltd to 500. Dec cvrs, vellum spine. NF (spine sl sunned). *Polyanthos.* $40/£25

SAUNDERS, WILLIAM. A Treatise on the Structure, Economy, and Diseases of the Liver; Together with an Inquiry into the Properties and Component Parts of the Bile and Biliary Concretions. London, 1793. 1st ed. 232pp. Recent 1/4 leather, marbled bds. (Worm hole affecting margins of 25 ll), o/w Fine. *Fye.* $400/£250

SAUNDERSON, NICHOLAS. The Elements of Algebra. Cambridge: CUP, 1740. 1st ed. 2 vols. Engr frontis port, engr plt, 8 fldg engr plts. Mod panelled calf. (Lt spotted, lib stamp, lacks add'l tp vol I.) *Christie's*.* $306/£191

SAUNIER, CLAUDIUS. Treatise on Modern Horology.... London: A. Fischer, (1882). 2nd ed. xvi,844pp; 21 dbl-pg color plts. Orig 1/2 leather, gilt. (Accession stamp tp verso; few marginal blind stamps; rebacked lib style.) *Hollett.* $288/£180

Savage Club Papers. London: Hutchinson, 1897. 1st, only ed. Dec eps; plain edges. Beige pict cl. VG (fep speckled; spine sl dknd, cvrs sl rubbed). *Sotheran.* $125/£78

SAVAGE, C. The Mandarin Duck. London: Blackie, 1952. 1st ed. Color frontis repro. VG+ in Good+ dj. *Mikesh.* $47/£29

SAVAGE, CHARLES C. Architecture of the Private Streets of St. Louis: The Architects and the Houses They Designed. Univ of MO, 1987. VG in dj. *Hadley.* $29/£18

SAVAGE, D. S. The Autumn World. London: Fortune Press, (1939?). Frontisport. Grn cl, gilt. Dj (sl soiled). *Maggs.* $40/£25

SAVAGE, E. A. Old English Libraries. London: Methuen, 1911. Frontis, 35 plts. Red cl (sl worn, shaken; inscrip), gilt. *Maggs.* $40/£25

SAVAGE, GEORGE. Seventeenth and Eighteenth Century French Porcelain. London: Barrie & Rockliff, 1960. 1st ed. Color frontis, 3 color plts, 96 b/w plts. (Upper bd, spine tail lt faded.) Dj (spine loss). *Edwards.* $40/£25

SAVAGE, HENRY (ed). The Harleian Miscellany: An Entertaining Selection. (By Harley Edward.) Cecil Palmer, 1924. Good (spotted, prize plt, sl dusty; spine bumped, chipped, sunned, cvrs unevenly sunned; lacks dj). *Tiger.* $16/£10

SAVAGE, HENRY, JR. Discovering America 1700-1875. NY: Harper & Row, (1979). 1st ed. 4 maps, 32 plts. Blue cl. Fine in pict dj. *House.* $15/£9

SAVAGE, MARGARET E. Jack Horner Pop-Up. Percy Graves (ed). UK: Burnley, n.d. (194?). No. 1 in the Candlelight Pop-Up Series. 18x24 cm. Dbl-pg pop-up by J. Walmsley Heap. VG (some pencil, color fill-ins worked) in dj. *Bookfinders.* $120/£75

SAVAGE, MARMION. The Bachelor of the Albany. London: Elkin Mathews & Marrot, 1927. VG. *Cady.* $20/£13

SAVAGE, TOM. Precipice. Little, Brown, 1994. 1st ed, 1st bk. Fine in dj. *Murder.* $27/£17

SAVAGE, WILLIAM W., JR. Singing Cowboys and All That Jazz. Norman: Univ of OK, (1983). 1st ed. Signed. Fine in dj. *Lien.* $25/£16

SAVAGE-LANDOR, A. HENRY. Across Coveted Lands, or, A Journey from Flushing (Holland) to Calcutta Overland. NY: Scribner, 1903. 1st ed. 2 vols. 124 plts, 2 fldg maps. (Ex-lib; edges rubbed, lib spine #), o/w VG. *Worldwide.* $125/£78

SAVAGE-LANDOR, A. HENRY. Across Coveted Lands, or, A Journey from Flushing (Holland) to Calcutta, Overland. London: Macmillan, 1902. 1st ed. 2 vols. vii,461; viii,459pp. Red cl (spine sl faded). VG set. *Young.* $136/£85

SAVAGE-LANDOR, A. HENRY. Across Unknown South America. London: Hodder, (1913). 2 vols. 2 maps, 8 color plts. (Sl foxed throughout.) *Petersfield.* $104/£65

SAVAGE-LANDOR, A. HENRY. Everywhere, the Memoirs of an Explorer. London, 1924. VG. *Petersfield.* $61/£38

SAVAGE-LANDOR, A. HENRY. The Gems of the East. London: Macmillan, 1904. 1st ed. 2 vols. 1/2-titles, xii,328pp; xi,(i)blank,460pp; fldg color map, fldg table, 51 plts. Red dec cl. (Lib stamps, plts, ink mks; hinges, joints cracked, new eps vol 2, loose.) Internally Clean. *Morrell.* $48/£30

SAVAGE-LANDOR, A. HENRY. The Gems of the East. London: Macmillan, 1904. 1st ed. 2 vols. 49 plts, fldg color map. VG (sl worn, edges rubbed, spine tears). *Worldwide.* $140/£88

SAVAGE-LANDOR, A. HENRY. In the Forbidden Land. NY/London: Harper, 1899. 1st ed. 2 vols. Gravure frontis, xvii,307; xiii,250pp; 8 color plts, 50 full-pg illus, lg fldg map rear vol 2. Teg, untrimmed. Grn pict cl. VG set (fore-edge rep vol 2 lt chipped). *Baltimore**. $130/£81

SAVAGE-LANDOR, A. HENRY. In the Forbidden Land. Heinemann, 1899. 1st 1-vol ed. Frontisport, xxvii,(i),501pp; fldg map (lt soiled, frayed in blank fore-margin). Grn cl, gilt. Good (eps sl foxed). *Blackwell's*. $200/£125

SAVAGE-LANDOR, A. HENRY. Tibet and Nepal, Painted and Described. London: A. & C. Black, 1905. 75 color plts, dec cl. *Petersfield*. $115/£72

SAVAGE-LANDOR, A. HENRY. Tibet and Nepal. London: A&C Black, (1905). 1st ed. 75 full-pg repros, guards, fldg dwg. Teg. Lt blue cl. (Sl foxed; spine top heavily spotted.) Text Clean. *Baltimore**. $90/£56

SAVILE, GEORGE. A Character of King Charles the Second. London: Tonson & Draper, 1750. 1st ed. Calf (rebacked; bkpl), gilt. *Rostenberg & Stern*. $150/£94

SAVILE, LORD. Illustrated Catalogue of Classical Antiquities from the Site of the Temple of Diana, Nemi, Italy, Discovered During Excavations Undertaken by Lord Savile. Nottingham: Nottingham Castle Museum, (c. 1900). 1st ed. 3/4 calf, gilt, morocco spine label, sl raised bands. (Bkpl), else VG. *Pacific**. $86/£54

SAVILLE, MALCOLM. The Gay Dolphin Adventure. Newnes, 1945. 1st ed. VG + in dj (sl worn). *Green Meadow*. $104/£65

SAVILLE, MALCOLM. The Long Passage. Evans, 1954. 1st ed. VG + in Fine dj. *Green Meadow*. $56/£35

SAVILLE, MALCOLM. Marston - Master Spy. Heinemann, 1978. 1st ed. VG in dj. *Green Meadow*. $88/£55

SAVILLE, MALCOLM. The Riddle of the Painted Box. Noel Carrington, 1947. 1st ed. VG in Fine dj. *Green Meadow*. $48/£30

SAVILLE, MALCOLM. Spring Comes to Nettleford. H&S, 1954. 1st ed. Joan Kiddell Monroe (illus). VG in dj. *Green Meadow*. $40/£25

SAVORY, ISOBEL. A Sportswoman in India. London, 1900. Port. Gilt-dec cl. (Ep removed; sl mkd.) *Petersfield*. $72/£45

SAVORY, THEODORE H. The Spiders and Allied Orders of the British Isles. London, 1945. 2nd ed. (Sl worn.) *Edwards*. $32/£20

SAVOURS, ANN (ed). Scott's Last Voyage Through the Antarctic Camera of Herbert Ponting. NY/Washington: Praeger, 1975. Fine in dj. *Explorer*. $35/£22

SAWATZKY, HARRY. They Sought a Country: Mennonite Colonization in Mexico. Berkeley: Univ of CA, 1971. 1st ed. Fine in Fine dj. *Book Market*. $20/£13

SAWYER, ARTHUR ROBERT. Miscellaneous Accidents in Mines. London, 1889. Presentation copy. 280pp. (Feps soiled; joints splitting, spine sl chipped, faded.) *Edwards*. $64/£40

SAWYER, C. W. Our Rifles. Boston, 1944. Dj. *Hallam*. $24/£15

SAWYER, CHARLES J. and F. J. DARTON. English Books 1475-1900. Sawyer, 1927. 2 vols. Teg, uncut. (Inscrips vol 1), o/w Good. *Moss*. $120/£75

SAWYER, CHARLES J. and F. J. DARTON. English Books, 1475-1900. A Signpost for Collectors. Volume II (only): Gray to Kipling. Westminster: Chas. J. Sawyer, 1927. VG + in dj. *Zubal**. $50/£31

SAWYER, EUGENE T. History of Santa Clara County, California, with Biographical Sketches.... L.A.: Historic Record Co, 1922. 1st ed. Orig 3/4 morocco, gilt spine. (Joints cracked, spine strip split through at fr joint), else VG. *Pacific**. $109/£68

SAWYER, EUGENE T. The Life and Career of Tiburcio Vasquez, the California Stage Robber. Oakland, CA: Biobooks, 1944. Ltd to 500. 4 plts (1 fldg). Red cl over marbled bds, paper spine label. Good. *Karmiole*. $125/£78

SAWYER, EUGENE T. The Life and Career of Tiburcio Vasquez, the California Stage Robber. Oakland, CA: Biobooks, 1944. Rpt ed. Ltd to 500 ptd. Silk-screened bkpl of R. F. McGraw. Fine. *Labordo*. $150/£94

SAWYER, LORENZO. Way Sketches Containing Incidents of Travel Across the Plains, from St. Joseph to California in 1850. NY: Edward Eberstadt, 1926. One of 35 lg paper copies. Frontisport from engr. 1/2 parchment, gilt. (Spine sl dknd, shelfwear, soil), else NF. Howes S133. *Pacific**. $288/£180

SAWYER, ROBERT and EDWIN H. PERKINS. Water Gardens and Goldfish. NY: De La Mare, 1928. 1st ed. VG. *Fair Meadow*. $15/£9

SAWYER, RUTH. The Christmas Anna Angel. NY: Viking, 1944. 1st ed. Kate Seredy (illus). Sm sq 8vo. 48pp. VG in dj (worn). *Davidson*. $75/£47

SAY, THOMAS. American Entomology, or Descriptions of the Insects of North America. Phila: Samuel Augustus Mitchell, 1824-25, 1828. 1st ed. 3 vols. Tall 8vo. Extra engr tp vol 1; 54 hand-colored engr plts, guards. Untrimmed, uncut. Orig pink bds (rebacked in grn paper bds replicating orig), orig grn pict label fr cvr vol 1, orig pink spine label vol 2. Lovely set (bkpl, lt foxed, sl spotted) in black cl clamshell box w/morocco spine label. *Glaser*. $3,000/£1,875

SAYCE, A. H. The Archaeology of the Cuneiform Inscriptions. London: SPCK, 1908. (Spine faded.) *Archaeologia*. $45/£28

SAYCE, A. H. Monument Facts and Higher Critical Fancies. London: Religious Tract Soc, 1904. Frontisport. *Archaeologia*. $35/£22

SAYCE, A. H. Records of the Past, Being English Translations of the Ancient Monuments of Egypt and Western Asia. London: Samuel Bagster & Sons, n.d. New ed. 6 vols. (Ex-lib, mks), else VG. *Pacific**. $52/£33

SAYER, OLIVER M. (ed). Max Reinhardt and His Theatre. NY: Brentano's, (1924). 1st ed. 57 color plts. Black gilt-stamped cl. Fine. *Appelfeld*. $100/£63

SAYERS, DOROTHY L. Busman's Honeymoon. NY: Harcourt, Brace, (1937). 1st US ed. VG + in VG dj (spine sl faded, edges, folds lt worn). *Bernard*. $250/£156

SAYERS, DOROTHY L. Creed or Chaos. Hodder, 1940. 1st UK ed. Pb. NF (ink name). *Williams*. $24/£15

SAYERS, DOROTHY L. Gaudy Night. NY: Harcourt, Brace, (1936). 1st US ed. Black cl (bottom edges lt discolored). Text Clean. Dj (lt worn, chipped, fr panel wrinkled, several long tears, narrow vertical loss of 1-inch fr corner). *Baltimore**. $90/£56

SAYERS, DOROTHY L. Hangman's Holiday. NY, (1933). 1st Amer ed. (Sig.) Dj (lt rubbed, sl edgeworn). *Swann**. $103/£64

SAYERS, DOROTHY L. In the Teeth of the Evidence and Other Stories. London: Gollancz, 1939. 1st ed. Black buckram. Nice. *Temple*. $80/£50

SAYERS, DOROTHY L. In the Teeth of the Evidence. Gollancz, 1939. 1st UK ed. NF in VG + dj (few closed tears to rear panel). *Williams*. $520/£325

SAYERS, DOROTHY L. Lord Peter Views the Body. London: Gollancz, 1928. 1st Eng ed. Good (feps browned; edges rubbed, spine faded, bumped). *Ulysses*. $88/£55

SAYERS, DOROTHY L. Op. 1. Oxford: B.H. Blackwell, 1916. 1st ed, 1st bk. One of 350 ptd. Uncut. (1st pg torn out), o/w Good in drab wrappers (fr wrapper cleanly detached), ptd label fr cvr. *Maggs*. $160/£100

SAYERS, DOROTHY L. Whose Body? NY: Boni & Liveright, 1923. 1st ed, 1st issue, w/o 'Inc.' after pub's name on tp. Gray cl. (Spine sl faded), else Fine. *Cummins*. $350/£219

SAYERS, FRANCES CLARKE. Mr. Tidy Paws. NY: Viking, 1935. 1st ed. 7.25x9.25. Zhena Gay (illus). 64pp. Cl spine, pict bds. Fine in dj. *Cattermole*. $50/£31

SAYERS, FRANCES CLARKE. Tag-Along TooLoo. Viking, 1941. 1st ed. Helen Sewell (illus). 87pp. VG- (inscrip; spine, bds faded). *Price*. $30/£19

SAYLER, OLIVER. Inside the Moscow Art Theatre. NY: Brentano's, (1925). 1st ed. Signed by 19 members of the Moscow Art Theatre. Fldg color frontis (loose), fldg plt. (3 other sigs; soiled, rubbed.) *Dramatis*. $200/£125

SAYLES, JOHN. Pride of the Bimbos. Little Brown, 1975. 1st ed. VG + (name) in VG + dj. *Plapinger*. $150/£94

SAYLES, JOHN. Union Dues. Boston: Little, Brown, (1977). 1st ed. Signed, inscribed. Fine in dj. *Pacific**. $52/£33

SAYLOR, DAVID J. Jackson Hole, Wyoming. Norman, 1970. VG in dj. *Dumont*. $25/£16

SCAMMELL, G. V. The World Encompassed: The First European Maritime Empires, c.800-1650. London/NY: Methuen, (1981). 1st Amer ed. Fine in dj. *Pacific**. $40/£25

SCAMMON, CHARLES M. The Marine Mammals of the North-Western Coast of North America and the American Whale Fishery. Riverside: Manessier, (1969). Facs ed. Grn cl, gilt. Fine. *Pacific**. $58/£36

SCAMMON, CHARLES M. The Marine Mammals of the North-western Coast of North America and the American Whale Fishery. Riverside, CA: Manessier Pub Co, (1969). Facs ed. 27 facs plts (6 dbl-pg), 3 charts on 2 sheets in rear pocket. Grn cl, gilt. Fine. Howes S136. *Harrington*. $150/£94

SCAMMON, JAMES. Culpepper's Family Physician. Exeter, (NH): James Scammon, 1824. 1st ed. 360pp. Contemp calf (warped). *M & S*. $175/£109

SCAMMON, RICHARD E. and LEROY CALKINS. The Development and Growth of the External Dimensions of the Human Body in the Fetal Period. Minneapolis, 1929. 1st ed. (Extrems sl worn), o/w VG. *Doctor's Library*. $65/£41

SCAMUZZI, ERNEST. Egyptian Art in the Museum of Turin. NY: Abrams Turin, n.d. (ca 1965). 1st US ed. Folio. 114 plts. VG. *Worldwide*. $95/£59

SCANLON, WILLIAM T. God Have Mercy on Us! A Story of 1918. Boston/NY: Houghton Mifflin, 1929. 1st ed. Crimson cl, gilt. Fine in VG pict dj (sl rubs, sm chips spine crown). *Reese*. $65/£41

SCARBOROUGH, JOHN. Roman Medicine. Ithaca: Cornell Univ, (1969). 1st ed. 49 plts. Fine in dj. *Glaser*. $50/£31

SCATTERGOOD, THOMAS. Memoirs of Thomas Scattergood. London: Charles Gilpin, 1845. 1st ed. xii,464,(iv)pp. Orig blind-stamped cl (neatly recased), gilt. *Hollett*. $120/£75

Scenic Resources of the Tennessee Valley. A Descriptive and Pictorial Inventory. Knoxville: TN Valley Authority, (1938). 1st ed. 7 lg color fldg maps. Brn cl (few scuffs to cvrs, fr hinge weak). Good + . *House*. $40/£25

SCHAAF, LARRY J. Sun Gardens: Victorian Photograms by Anna Atkins. NY: Aperture, 1985. 1st ed. Frontis. Fine in dj. *Cahan*. $85/£53

SCHABACKER, R. W. Stock Market Theory and Practice. NY: B.C. Forbes Pub Co, (1930). 1st ed, 2nd ptg. (Partly removed ink sig; cvrs sl worn.) *Glenn*. $50/£31

SCHACHNER, NAT. Space Lawyer. NY: Gnome, (1953). 1st ed. VG + in NF dj (rear panel soiled). *Other Worlds*. $50/£31

SCHACHNER, NATHAN. Aaron Burr. NY: Frederick A. Stokes, 1937. 31 plts. Uncut, unopened, unstitched. (Spine sl faded.) Supplied loose in cl case. *Hollett*. $40/£25

SCHAEFER, JACK. The Great Endurance Horse Race. Santa Fe, 1963. Ltd to 750. Fine in dj. *Baade*. $100/£63

SCHAEFER, JACK. Heroes Without Glory. Boston: HMC, 1965. 1st ed. Fine in NF dj (edges sl rubbed). *Unger*. $100/£63

SCHAEFER, JACK. Heroes Without Glory. London: Deutsch, 1966. 1st Eng ed. Fine in NF dj (price-clipped, sl faded). *Unger*. $75/£47

SCHAEFER, JACK. Monte Walsh. Boston: HMC, 1963. 1st ed. NF in VG + dj (chipped). *Unger*. $325/£203

SCHAEFER, JACK. The Pioneers. Boston: HMC, 1954. 1st ed. NF in VG + dj (edges chipped). *Unger*. $150/£94

SCHAEFER, JACK. Shane. Boston: HMC, 1954. 1st illus ed. VG in VG dj (scuffed, few tears). *Unger*. $275/£172

SCHAEFFER, L. M. Sketches of Travel in South America, Mexico and California. NY, 1860. 1st ed. (vi),247pp. Blindstamped cl. (Bkseller stamp, sm lib stamp; head/tail caps repaired), o/w VG. *Maggs*. $192/£120

SCHAEFFER, L. M. Sketches of Travels in South America, Mexico and California. NY: James Egbert, 1860. 1st ed. 247pp. Blind-stamped cl. (Spine, cvr edges faded, spine head lt rubbed), else Fine. *Argonaut*. $175/£109

SCHAFER, JOSEPH (ed). Memoirs of Jeremiah Curtin. Madison: State Hist Soc of WI, 1940. 1st ed. (Ink marginal notes; shelfworn, lt dust-soiled), else Good. *Brown*. $15/£9

SCHAFFNER, VAL. The Algonquin Cat. NY: Delacorte, (1980). 1st ed stated. Hilary Knight (illus). 4to. 133pp. VG in VG dj. *Davidson*. $45/£28

SCHALDACH, WILLIAM J. Fish by Schaldach. Phila, 1937. One of 1500 numbered. Folio. 60 plts. (Sl soiling, stains along cvr edges.) *Swann**. $138/£86

SCHALDACH, WILLIAM J. The Wind on Your Check or More Chips from the Log of an Artist Sportsman. Rockville Centre, (1972). One of 200 numbered. Orig etching signed by Schaldach. Leather back. (Lt worn.) Slipcase. *Oinonen**. $160/£100

SCHAPIRO, MEYER. Modern Art—19th and 20th Centuries. NY: George Braziller, (1978). 1st ed. 11 color, 91 b/w plts. Fine in dj. *Turtle Island*. $40/£25

SCHAPIRO, MEYER. Romanesque Art. NY: George Braziller, (1977). 1st ed. Fine in dj. *Turtle Island*. $45/£28

SCHARF, J. THOMAS. History of the Confederate States Navy. Hartford: Rogers & Sherwood, 1887. 1st ed. 824pp (bkpl; marginal pencil mks). Grn cl (worn, frayed; joints puckered; hinges very cracked), gilt. Text Clean. Howes S147. *Baltimore**. $90/£56

SCHARF, J. THOMAS. History of the Confederate States Navy. NY: Rogers & Sherwood, 1887. 1st ed. 824pp; 42 b/w plts, ports. Untrimmed. Plain bds (general ed issued in grn cl; this version to be sold to those planning to have vol rebound in leather), ptd paper spine label. (Lt aging; lt worn, chipped.) Text VG. Howes S147. *Baltimore**. $140/£88

SCHARF, J. THOMAS. History of the Confederate States Navy.... Albany, 1894. 2nd ed. Frontis, 44 inserted plts. (Fep chipped, loose; inner hinges opening; cl soiled, spine label chipped.) *Kane**. $160/£100

SCHARY, DORE. The Devil's Advocate. NY: Morrow, 1961. 1st ed. VF in dj (price-clipped w/new price stamped by pub?; sl rubbed, rear cvr sl wrinkled), o/w Fine. *Between The Covers*. $225/£141

SCHAUWECKER, FRANZ. The Fiery Way. T. W. H. Holland (trans). NY: Dutton, (1929). 1st ed in English, US issue. Red cl stamped in black. NF in VG pict dj (sm chips spine, rear). *Reese*. $75/£47

SCHAUWECKER, FRANZ. The Furnace. R. T. Clark (trans). London: Methuen, (1930). 1st British ed. Yellow cl stamped in black. Fine in orange dj (sunned, sl spots spine, few chips top edge). *Reese*. $60/£38

SCHAUWECKER, FRANZ. The Furnace. R. T. Clark (trans). Methuen, 1930. 1st ed. VG (bkpl, feps browned; spotted, sl mkd, soiled, top edge dusty, spine faded). *Ulysses*. $51/£32

SCHEFFAUER, H. Drake in California. Ballads and Poems. London: A.C. Fifield, 1912. 1st collected ed. Grn cl, gilt. Fine. *Argonaut*. $35/£22

SCHENCK, DAVID. North Carolina, 1780-81, Being a History of Invasion of the Carolinas by British Army Under Lord Cornwallis in 1780-81. Raleigh, NC, 1884. 1st ed. Signed presentation. 498pp. (Lacks 1 map; spine ends worn.) *Heinoldt.* $30/£19

SCHERY, ROBERT. Plants for Man. Englewood Cliffs: P-H, 1972. 2nd ed. NF in Good dj. *Archer.* $22/£14

SCHEVILL, JAMES. Selected Poems 1945-1959. N.p. (SF): Bern Porter Books, 1960. 1st Eng ed. VG (sig; spine sl dknd) in wrappers. *Ulysses.* $40/£25

SCHIEL, JAMES. The Land Between. L.A.: Westernlore, 1957. VG in dj. *Dumont.* $35/£22

SCHILLER, FRANCIS. Paul Broca: Founder of French Anthropology, Explorer of the Brain. 1979. As New. *Doctor's Library.* $35/£22

SCHILLER, FREDERICK. Schiller's Works. Phila: George Barrie, (1883). 4 vols. Aeg. 3/4 black morocco, textured cl, gilt. (Bkpls; spines sl sunned), else NF. *Pacific*.* $74/£46

SCHILLING, T. Tigerman of Anai. London: A. & U., 1957. 1st ed. Fine in VG dj. *Mikesh.* $37/£23

SCHINDEL, BAYARD. Golden Pilgrimage. GC: Doubleday, Doran, 1929. 1st ed. Pict eps. Brn cl stamped in black. NF in Good pict dj (sm chips, spine sunned, internally mended creased tears). *Reese.* $50/£31

SCHINDLER, RUDOLF. Gastroscopy, the Endoscopic Study of Gastric Pathology. Chicago, 1937. 1st ed in English. Buckram. (Ex-lib.) *Fye.* $100/£63

SCHLES, KEN. Invisible City. CA: Twelvetrees, 1986. 1st ed. As New, sealed in plastic. *Warren.* $200/£125

SCHLESINGER, KATHLEEN. The Greek Aulos. London: Methuen, 1939. (Backstrip faded.) *Petersfield.* $29/£18

SCHLEY, WINFIELD S. and J. R. SOLEY. The Rescue of Greely. NY: Scribner, 1885. vii,277pp; 14 plts, 5 fldg maps. Good (cl sl spotted, worn). *High Latitude.* $85/£53

SCHLIEMANN, HENRY. Troy and Its Remains; a Narrative of Researches and Discoveries Made on the Site of Ilium, and in the Trojan Plain. Philip Smith (ed). NY: Scribner, Welford & Armstrong, 1876. lv,392pp. Teg. Orig cl. (Rebacked, sl rubbed, corners frayed), o/w VG. *Worldwide.* $125/£78

SCHMALENBACH, WEMER. Kurt Schwitters. NY: Abrams, (1967). 1st US ed. 54 tipped-in color plts. NF in dj. *Cahan.* $185/£116

SCHMALENBACH, WERNER. Kurt Schwitters. NY: Abrams, (1967). Color mtd repros. Dj. *Swann*.* $345/£216

SCHMECKEBIER, L. G. Catalogue and Index of the Publications of the Hayden, King, Powell, and Wheeler Surveys. Washington, 1904. (Underlining; spine strengthened.) Wraps (fr chipped). *Dumont.* $65/£41

SCHMECKEBIER, LAURANCE E. Modern Mexican Art. Minneapolis: Univ of MN, (1939). Orig ed. 216 b/w plts. Nice. *Turtle Island.* $50/£31

SCHMIDT, ERICH F. and WILTON MARION KROGMAN. The Alishar Huyuk. Seasons of 1928 and 1929. Part 2. Chicago: Univ of Chicago, 1933. 1st ed. Color frontis, 11 plts, 2 fldg tables, 2-tone cl. (Edges sl rubbed), o/w NF. *Worldwide.* $135/£84

SCHMIDT, ERICH F. The Treasury of Persepolis and Other Discoveries in the Homeland of the Achaemenians. Chicago: Univ of Chicago, (1939). Frontis. Wraps. *Archaeologia.* $125/£78

SCHMIDT, FRANZ. A Hangman's Diary. Albrecht Keller (ed). London, 1929. 2nd imp. VG (fep sl torn) in dj (sl chipped). *Clearwater.* $40/£25

SCHMIT, ROBERT. Eugene Boudin, 1824-1898. Paris, 1973. One of 2000 numbered sets. 3 vols. 4to. *Swann*.* $2,070/£1,294

SCHMITT, MARTIN F. and DEE BROWN. Fighting Indians of the West. NY: Scribner, 1948. 1st ed. Good+ (spine, cvr margins faded, corners bumped, showing) in dj (worn, heavily repaired w/tape, price-clipped). *Pacific*.* $58/£36

SCHMITZ, JAMES A. Agent of Vega. Hicksville: Gnome, (1960). 1st ed, 1st binding, 1st bk. (Lt shelfworn), else NF in dj (browned, lt edgeworn). *Other Worlds.* $25/£16

SCHMITZ, JAMES H. The Witches of Karres. Phila/NY, (1966). 1st ed. Fine in NF dj (edges lt shelf-worn). *Mcclintock.* $495/£309

SCHNEIDDR, R. C. Crafts of the North American Indians. NY: Van Nostrand, 1972. 1st ed. (Spine ends rubbed), else VG in color pict wrappers. *Mikesh.* $25/£16

SCHNEIDER, GEORGE A. (ed). The Freeman Journal: The Infantry in the Sioux Campaign of 1876. San Rafael, CA: Presidio Press, (1977). 1st ed. One of 1000. Als tipped in. Brn cl. Fine in Fine dj. *Harrington.* $50/£31

SCHNEIDER, PIERRE. Matisse. NY, (1984). Folio. Dj. *Swann*.* $172/£108

SCHOBERL, FREDERICK. The World in Miniature....Austria. London, ca 1823. 2 vols. 32 hand-colored engr plts. Later 1/2 morocco. *Swann*.* $316/£198

SCHOENBERG, WILFRED P. Jesuit Mission Presses in the Pacific Northwest. (Portland): Champoeg, 1957. Ltd to 804. Tipped-in frontis; first part of 'a Catechism of the Christian Doctrine,' 1880, laid in. Good. *Karmiole.* $75/£47

SCHOENBERG, WILFRED P. Jesuit Mission Presses in the Pacific Northwest: A History and Bibliography of Imprints, 1876-1899. Portland, OR: Champoeg, 1977. 1st ed. One of 804 ptd. Tipped-in frontisport. Orig 1880 imprint laid in loose (lacks top corner). Red cl, gilt. Fine. *Pacific*.* $40/£25

SCHOENBERGER, DALE T. The Gunfighters. Caldwell, ID: Caxton Ptrs, 1971. 1st ed. VF in dj. *Labordo.* $75/£47

SCHOENHERR, ALLAN S. A Natural History of California. Berkeley: Univ of CA, (1992). 1st ed. Fine in Fine dj. *Book Market.* $40/£25

SCHOENSTEIN, LOUIS J. Memoirs of a San Francisco Organ Builder. (SF: Cue Publications, 1977.) 1st ed. Signed, inscribed. Fine in wrappers. *Pacific*.* $35/£22

SCHOLES, ARTHUR. Fourteen Men: The Story of the Australian Antarctic Expedition to Heard Island. London: George Allen & Unwin, 1951. Fine in dj. *Explorer.* $29/£18

SCHOLES, PERCY A. The Mirror of Music 1844-1944. Novello/OUP, 1947. 1st ed. 2 vols. 118 plts. VG in djs (1 panel torn, spine heads frayed). *Hollett.* $96/£60

SCHOMBURGK, ROBERT H. Ichthyology: The Fishes of British Guiana. Edinburgh: W.H. Lizars, 1852. 2 vols. 66 hand-colored plts, guards. Teg. Gilt-lettered red cl. (Spine ends, fr joint part I chipped), else VG. *Pacific*.* $219/£137

SCHOOLCRAFT, HENRY R. Algic Researches...Indian Tales and Legends. NY, 1839. 1st ed. 2 vols. Pub's cl, paper spine labels. (Lib bkpl, ink stamp.) Howes S180. *Swann*.* $161/£101

SCHOOLCRAFT, HENRY R. Historical and Statistical Information Respecting the History, Condition, and Prospects of the Indian Tribes of the United States. (NY: Historical American Indian, 1969.) Facs repro. 6 vols. Vol 2: color map, Vol 3: 4 maps, plts, Vol 4: 2 maps, plts, Vol 5: fldg map, color plt. (Sl shelfworn, soiled), else NF set in slipcase. *Dumont.* $1,400/£875

SCHOOLCRAFT, HENRY R. Letter from Sec. of War, Transmitting Report of Schoolcraft's Expedition Among the Northwestern Indians. House of Reps. March 2, 1833. Washington, 1833. 16pp. Mod cl. VG. *Adelson.* $150/£94

SCHOOLCRAFT, HENRY R. Narrative Journal of Travels Through the Northwestern Regions of the United States Extending from Detroit Through the Great Chain of American Lakes.... Albany: E. & E. Hosford, 1821. 8vo. Engr tp, xvi,17-419,4pp, errata; fldg map, 7 plts. Orig 1/4 calf, marbled bds (rebacked, rubbed, lt foxed). Howes S186. *Adelson.* $685/£428

SCHOOLCRAFT, HENRY R. New York Historical Society. Semi-Centennial Celebration. Nov. 20, 1854. NY: The Society, 1854. Signed. 96pp. 1/2 morocco (rubbed). *Adelson.* $120/£75

SCHOOLCRAFT, HENRY R. Notes on the Iroquois. Albany: Erastus H. Pease, 1847. xv,498,2,12 ads; 2 color plts. Orig pict brn cl (spine ends chipped). Howes S191. *Adelson.* $425/£266

SCHOOLCRAFT, HENRY R. Notes on the Iroquois. Senate Document 24. NY: Bartlett & Welford, 1846. 283pp. Good (exlib; pp239,240 xeroxed). *Lien.* $85/£53

SCHOOLCRAFT, HENRY R. Report of the Sec. of Interior Communicating a Report by H.R. Schoolcraft on the State of Indian Statistics. Senate, Dec. 27, 1854. Washington, 1854. 11pp. Mod cl. VG. *Adelson.* $100/£63

SCHOOLING, WILLIAM. The Gouvenor and Company of Adventurers of England Trading into Hudson's Bay...1670-1920. London: Hudson's Bay, 1920. Fldg plt, fldg map. (Stiff white wrapper soiled), else VG. *High Latitude.* $35/£22

SCHOONOVER, CORTLANDT. Frank Schoonover, Illustrator of the North American Frontier. NY: Watson-Guptill, 1976. 1st ed. Fine in dj. *Labordo.* $75/£47

SCHOONOVER, T. J. The Life and Times of Gen'l John A. Sutter. Sacramento: D. Johnston, 1895. 1st ed. Frontisport, (8),2-136pp. Brn cl, gilt. Fine. Howes S196. *Pacific*.* $52/£33

SCHORR, MARK. Red Diamond, Private Eye. St. Martins, 1983. 1st ed, 1st bk. Fine in dj. *Murder.* $40/£25

SCHOTTER, H. W. The Growth and Development of the Pennsylvania Railroad Company 1846-1926. 1927. Gilt edges. Full leather. VG (spine edgeworn). *Bookcell.* $30/£19

SCHRADER, DEL and JESSE JAMES III. Jesse James Was One of His Names. Arcadia, 1975. 1st ptg. Inscribed. Fine. *Baade.* $50/£31

SCHREINER, OLIVE. The Story of an African Farm. (Westerham, Kent): Westerham Press, 1961. One of 1500. Signed by Paul Hogarth (illus). Bark-cl, morocco spine label. Fine in glassine, slipcase. *Pacific*.* $40/£25

SCHREINER, OLIVE. The Story of an African Farm. LEC, 1961. One of 1500. Signed by Paul Hogarth (illus). Fine in Fine box. *Polyanthos.* $75/£47

SCHREINER, OLIVE. Trooper Peter Halket of Mashonaland. London: T. Fisher Unwin, 1897. 1st Eng ed. Frontis photo. Teg. VG (inscrip, eps lt browned; spine ends, corners sl bumped). *Ulysses.* $152/£95

SCHRETLEN, M. J. Dutch and Flemish Woodcuts of the Fifteenth Century. Boston, 1925. Folio. *Swann*.* $80/£50

SCHREYVOGEL, CHARLES. My Bunkie and Others. NY, 1909. Lg obl folio. Pict dec cl. VG. Howes S199. *Ginsberg.* $1,500/£938

SCHRODER, TIMOTHY B. The Gilbert Collection of Gold and Silver. (L.A., 1988.) Dj. *Swann*.* $92/£58

SCHROEDER, FRANCIS. Shores of the Mediterranean. NY: Harper, 1846. 1st ed. 2 vols in 1. 2 engr frontispieces, xii,270; viii,304pp; 11 engr plts. Aeg. Contemp purple morocco. (Foxed; spine scuffed, faded.) *Karmiole.* $300/£188

SCHROEDER, HENRY ALFRED and LAURENCE A. PETERS. Shirt-Tail and Pigtail. NY: Minton, Batch, 1930. 1st ed. (Sl rubbed, spine faded), o/w VG. *Worldwide.* $35/£22

SCHROEDER, R. and F. NEWMYER. Gamebird Taxidermy with Frank Newmyer. Harris: Stackpole, 1989. 1st ed. NF in NF dj. *Mikesh.* $30/£19

SCHULBE, ERNEST. Advanced Piping and Modelling. Manchester: Sherratt & Hughes, 1921. 2nd ed. Ribbed cl, gilt. VG. *Hollett.* $64/£40

SCHULBE, ERNEST. Cake Decoration. Maclaren & Sons, n.d. (1920s?). 9th ed. Sound (lt waterstain to gutter margin; cl lt rubbed, mkd). *Cox.* $48/£30

SCHULBERG, BUDD. A Face in the Crowd: a Play for the Screen. NY: Random House, (1957). 1st ed. VF in VF dj (sl rubbed). *Between The Covers.* $250/£156

SCHULBERG, BUDD. Waterfront. NY: Random House, (1955). 1st ed. VF in VF dj (lamination sl bubbled). *Between The Covers.* $250/£156

SCHULBERG, BUDD. What Makes Sammy Run? NY, (1941). 1st ed. Dj. *Swann*.* $431/£269

SCHULLIAN, DOROTHY M. and FRANCIS E. SOMMER. A Catalogue of Incunabula and Manuscripts in the Army Medical Library. NY: Henry Schuman, (1948). 1st ed. Black buckram, gilt. (Sl rubbed, dusty.) *Baltimore*.* $25/£16

SCHULMAN, EDMUND. Tree-Ring Hydrology of the Colorado River Basin. Univ of AZ, Oct 1, 1945. Lg foldout. VG. *Five Quail.* $30/£19

SCHULTES, RICHARD EVANS and ALBERT HOFMANN. The Botany and Chemistry of Hallucinogens. Springfield, IL: Charles C. Thomas, 1980. Rev, enlgd 2nd ed. Blue cl. NF. *Sclanders.* $40/£25

SCHULTHESS, EMIL. The Amazon. NY: S&S, 1960. 1st ed. Oblong folio. 162 plts. (Sm sticker; few scratches), else NF. *Cahan.* $65/£41

SCHULTZ, J. W. Sinopah the Indian Boy. Boston: Houghton Mifflin, (1913). 4 full-pg dwgs. VG in pict cl. *Mikesh.* $60/£38

SCHULTZ, JACKSON S. The Leather Manufacture in the United States. NY, 1876. 1st ed. 3/4 leather (rubbed; sl foxed, soiled). *Oinonen*.* $50/£31

SCHULTZ, JAMES WILLARD. Bird Woman, the Guide of Lewis and Clark. Boston: Houghton & Mifflin, 1918. 1st ed. (Spine faded), else Good. *Perier.* $75/£47

SCHULTZ, JAMES WILLARD. Blackfeet and Buffalo, Memories of Life Among the Indians. Norman, 1962. 1st ed. Fine in dj (sl worn). *Baade.* $60/£38

SCHULTZ, JAMES WILLARD. Questers of the Desert. Boston: Houghton Mifflin, 1925. 1st ed. 4 plts. (Spine faded, extrems worn), else VG. *Pacific*.* $81/£51

SCHULTZ, JAMES WILLARD. Questers of the Desert. Boston: Houghton Mifflin, 1925. 1st ed. 4 plts. Brn cl. VG (extrems sl worn, sl leaning, spine sl faded). *Harrington.* $90/£56

SCHULTZ, JAMES WILLARD. The War-Trail Fort. Further Adventures of Thomas Fox Pitamakan. Boston: Houghton & Mifflin, 1921. 1st ed. (1/2-inch square gone from tp corner), else VG. *Perier.* $65/£41

SCHULTZ, JAMES WILLARD. William Jackson, Indian Scout. Boston: Houghton Mifflin, 1926. 1st ed. 4 plts. Brn cl. NF (sl foxed, extrems lt worn) in later slipcase. Howes S204. *Harrington.* $175/£109

SCHULTZ, JAMES WILLARD. William Jackson, Indian Scout. Boston: Houghton Mifflin, 1926. 1st ed. Frontis, 3 full-pg illus. Orange-stamped cl. Dj (lt edgeworn). *Dawson.* $200/£125

SCHULTZ, JAMES WILLARD. William Jackson, Indian Scout: His True Story Told by His Friend. Boston: Houghton, Mifflin, 1926. 1st ed. 4 plts. (Sl shelfworn), else Fine. *Pacific*.* $69/£43

SCHUMACHER, GENNY (ed). Deepest Valley Guide to Owens Valley and Its Mountain Lakes, Roadsides and Trails. SF: Sierra Club, (1962). 1st ed. Signed. Fine in Fine dj. *Book Market.* $50/£31

Schumann Album of Children's Pieces for Piano. London: Augener, (1915). 4to. Henriette Willebeek Le Mair (illus). Gray cl-backed bds, color pict paste label, gilt. Good in ptd dj (spine head lt worn), w/color paste label. *Reisler.* $200/£125

SCHUYLER, EUGENE. Turkistan. NY: Scribner Armstrong, 1876. 1st Amer ed. 2 vols. Demy 8vo. xii,411; x,463pp + 21 woodcut plts, 3 fldg maps. (Prelims vol 1 lt stained; extrems sl bruised, rubbed), o/w Fine set in brn cl, gilt. *Ulysses.* $1,040/£650

SCHUYLER, JAMES. Freely Espousing. Poems. GC: Doubleday/Paris Review Editions, 1969. 1st ed. Fine in NF dj (tips lt worn). *Reese.* $85/£53

SCHWARTZ, DELMORE. In Dreams Begin Responsibilities. Norfolk: New Directions, (1938). 1st ed, 1st bk. One of 1000. Black cl, gilt. Fine in VG- dj (top edge chipped, folds rubbed). *Reese.* $100/£63

SCHWARTZ, DELMORE. Shenandoah. Norfolk: New Directions/Poet of the Month, (1941). 1st ed. Fine in wrappers (spine sl faded). *Pharos.* $125/£78

SCHWARTZ, G. Rembrandt: All the Etchings Reproduced in True Size. London: Oresko Books, 1977. 399 repros. 3 outside sheets in pocket inside rear cvr. Good in dj (sl torn). *Ars Artis.* $56/£35

SCHWARTZ, JACOB. The Writings of Alfred Edgar Coppard. London: Ulysses Bookshop, 1931. 1st Eng ed. One of 650 signed by Coppard. Very Nice (eps tanned). *Clearwater.* $80/£50

SCHWARTZ, SEYMOUR I. and RALPH EHRENBERG. The Mapping of America. NY: Abrams, 1980. 1st ed. VF in dj, pub's shipping box. *Labordo.* $125/£78

SCHWARZ, ARTURO. Man Ray: The Rigour of Imagination. NY, (1977). Dj. *Swann*.* $126/£79

SCHWARZER, MITCHELL. German Architectural Theory and the Search for Modern Identity. CUP, 1995. 1st ed. Dj. *Edwards.* $35/£22

SCHWARZKOPF, NORMAN and PETER PETRE. It Doesn't Take a Hero. NY, (1992). Signed by Schwarzkopf. Fine in dj. *Argosy.* $75/£47

SCHWATKA, FREDERICK. Along Alaska's Great River. NY: Cassell, (1885). 360pp; 3 maps, 2 fldg, 1 of which is loose in fep pocket. Grn cl, gilt. (Bkpl, fr hinge cracking at eps; extrems sl rubbed), else NF. *Pacific*.* $138/£86

SCHWATKA, FREDERICK. A Summer in Alaska. St. Louis, 1892. Aeg. 1/4 leather. (Shelfworn), else Good. *Dumont.* $65/£41

SCHWATKA, FREDERICK. A Summer in Alaska. St. Louis: J.W. Henry, 1894. Frontis, 418pp; map. VG. *High Latitude.* $50/£31

SCHWATKA, FREDERICK. Wonderland: Or, Alaska and the Inland Passage. St. Paul: Chas. S. Fee, 1886. (Upper corner fr cvr chipped, creased, repaired), else VG in pict wrappers. *Pacific*.* $58/£36

SCHWEITZER, ALBERT. My Life and Thought. C. T. Campion (trans). London: Allen & Unwin, 1933. Inscribed presentation. 10 plts. VG. *Hollett.* $40/£25

SCHWIEBERT, ERNEST. Death of a Riverkeeper. NY: E.P. Dutton, 1980. Stated 1st ed. Fine in VG + dj. *Backman.* $25/£16

SCHWIEBERT, ERNEST. Matching the Hatch: A Practical Guide to Imitationn of Insects Found on Eastern and Western Trout Rivers. NY: Macmillan, 1955. 1st ed. Signed, inscribed. VG in dj (sm tears dj extrems). *Pacific*.* $161/£101

SCHWIEBERT, ERNEST. Trout. NY, (1978). 1st ed. Each vol signed. 2 vols. (Lt worn.) Slipcase. *Oinonen*.* $130/£81

SCHWIEBERT, ERNEST. Trout. NY, (1978). 1st ed. One of 750 numbered, signed, w/an artificial fly tied by Schwiebert inside sunken mount. 2 vols. (Lt worn.) Cl slipcase (sl scuffed, sunned). *Oinonen*.* $275/£172

SCIDMORE, ELIZA RUHAMAH. Appleton's Guide Book to Alaska and the Northwest Coast. NY: D. Appleton, 1898. New ed. 167pp. NF. *Perier.* $275/£172

SCLATER, PHILIP LUTLEY (ed). Nitzsch's Pterylography. London: Robert Hardwicke, 1867. 1st Eng ed. Folio. 10 copper-engr plts. Teg. 3/4 morocco, marbled bds, gilt. (Bkpl; fr cvr almost detached), else NF. *Pacific*.* $184/£115

SCOBEE, BARRY. The Steer Branded Murder. Houston: Frontier, 1952. 1st ed. Fine (tipped-in index not present) in wrappers. *Labordo.* $60/£38

SCOBIE, A. Animal Heaven. London: Cassell, (1954). 2nd ed. VG + in VG dj. *Mikesh.* $25/£16

SCOFIELD, SAMUEL. A Practical Treatise on Vaccinia or Cowpock. NY, 1810. 1st ed. 139pp. Full leather. (Lacks plt), o/w Fine. *Fye.* $200/£125

SCORER, A. G. The Entomologist's Log-Book. London, 1913. (Lt foxed, sm tears spine heel, sl stains fr cvr.) *Sutton.* $45/£28

SCORESBY, WILLIAM. An Account of the Arctic Regions with a Description of the Northern Whale-Fishery. London: David & Charles, 1969. Facs rpt. 2 vols. VG. *Explorer.* $112/£70

SCORESBY, WILLIAM. Journal of a Voyage to the Northern Whale-Fishery. Caedmon, 1980. xliii,472pp; 4 fldg maps. Fine in dj. *Explorer.* $51/£32

SCORESBY, WILLIAM. The Story of Dr. Scoresby. London: T. Nelson, 1890. Frontis, 120pp. Full prize navy blue calf. VG. *Hollett.* $72/£45

SCORZA, MANUEL. Drums for Rancas. NY: Harper & Row, 1970. 1st US ed. Fine in dj. *Lame Duck.* $75/£47

SCOTT MONCRIEFF, J. M. and L. W. LUNN (eds). Memories and Letters. Chapman & Hall, 1931. 1st ed. Good (pg edges browned, 1/2-title, last text pg browned; hinges cracked, spine head nicked, ends, corners bumped, bruised, cvrs sl mkd). *Ulysses.* $120/£75

SCOTT, ANNA M. A Year with the Fairies. Chicago: P.F. Volland, (1914). 1st ed. 4to. 47 full-pg color plts by M. T. Ross. Cl-backed color pict bds (edges rubbed). *Reisler.* $285/£178

SCOTT, DOUGLAS D. et al. Archaeological Perspectives on the Battle of the Little Bighorn. Norman: Univ of OK, (1989). 1st ed. VG in dj. *Lien.* $35/£22

SCOTT, EDWARD B. The Saga of Lake Tahoe. Lake Tahoe: Sierra-Tahoe Pub, 1964. Fldg map. Grn cl, gilt. VG in dj (chipped, worn). *Parmer.* $50/£31

SCOTT, EVELYN. The Wave. NY: Cape & Smith, (1929). 1st ed. NF in VG dj (sm chips to joints). *Reese.* $125/£78

SCOTT, EVERETT. Third Base Thatcher. Dodd Mead, 1923. 1st ed. Good + . *Plapinger.* $50/£31

SCOTT, G. FIRTH. From Franklin to Nansen. London: James Bowden, 1899. 296pp, map. Blue dec cl. VG. *Explorer.* $42/£26

SCOTT, GENIO. Fishing in American Waters. NY: OJ, (1875). New ed. Brick-red cl, gilt. (Ex-lib, bkpl, emb stamp tp, #s on eps, tp lacks corner; spine ends chipped), else VG. *Pacific*.* $58/£36

SCOTT, GENIO. Fishing in American Waters. NY, 1869. 1st ed. Pub's gilt-pict cl (worn, spine ends frayed). *Swann*.* $69/£43

SCOTT, GEORGE GILBERT. Gleanings from Westminster Abbey. Oxford/London: J.H. & Jas. Parker, 1861. 1st ed. Dbl-pg aquatint. Teg. 3/4 crushed red morocco, cl, gilt, raised bands. (Lt foxed, joints sl rubbed), else NF. *Pacific*.* $86/£54

SCOTT, HARVEY W. History of the Oregon Country. Cambridge: Riverside, 1924. One of 500 sets. Signed by Leslie M. Scott. 6 vols. Gilt-lettered red cl. Fine in djs (dknd, chipped, lg pieces missing vol 1 dj). *Pacific*.* $230/£144

SCOTT, HUGH. In the High Yemen. London: John Murray, 1947. 2nd ed. 66 plts (2 fldg), 4 maps (1 fldg). (Sl foxed), o/w VG in dj (sl torn). *Worldwide.* $45/£28

SCOTT, J. E. A Bibliography of the Works of Sir Henry Rider Haggard 1856-1925. Bishop's Stortford, 1947. Ltd to 500. Frontisport, 5 plts. Grn cl (sl rubbed). *Maggs.* $40/£25

SCOTT, J. E. A Bibliography of the Works of Sir Henry Rider Haggard 1856-1925. Takeley: Elkin Mathews, 1947. 1st ed. One of 500. Frontis, 7 plts. (Hinges sl worn.) *Forest.* $80/£50

SCOTT, J. M. The Land That God Gave to Cain. London: C&W, 1933. Fldg map. VG in dj (chipped, worn, stained). *High Latitude.* $65/£41

SCOTT, JACK DENTON. Forests of the Night. NY: Rinehart, 1959. 1st ed. VG + in VG dj (edges sl chipped). *Backman.* $30/£19

SCOTT, JEAN. A Visit to Paris in 1814.... Longman, Hurst, Rees, et al, 1816. 4th ed. Orig bds. Good (sig, sl spotted; re-spined, shelfworn). *Tiger.* $40/£25

SCOTT, JOB. A Journal of the Life, Travels, and Gospel Labours, of That Faithful Servant an Minister of Christ. NY/London: Ptd by James Phillips & Son, 1797. 1st Eng ed. xii,(ii),354,(2) ads pp. Contemp sheep (joints sl cracking). *Young.* $96/£60

SCOTT, JOB. A Journal of the Life, Travels, and Gospel Labours, of That Faithful Servant and Minister of Christ. NY: Isaac Collins, 1797. 1st ed. xiv,360pp. Old calf, leather spine label. (Sl browned, foxed, few pp sprung, lacks fep w/later blank inserted; worn, scuffed.) Text Good. Howes S228. *Baltimore*.* $140/£88

SCOTT, JOB. A Journal of the Life, Travels, and Gospel Labours, of That Faithful Servant and Minister of Christ. William Phillips & W. Alexander, 1815. xix,(iii),388pp. Old 1/2 calf (neatly recased), gilt. *Hollett.* $104/£65

SCOTT, JOCK (ed). Greased Line Fishing for Salmon, Compiled from the Fishing Papers of the Late A.H.E. Wood, of Lassel. London: Seeley Service, 1935. 1st ed. Color frontis. Grn cl, gilt. (Spine sl sunned), else VG. *Pacific*.* $35/£22

SCOTT, JOCK. Spinning Up to Date, Trout, Salmon and Pike. London, (1937). 1st ed. Color frontis, 12 plts. *Petersfield.* $34/£21

SCOTT, JOHN. Paris Revisited in 1815.... London: Longman, et al, 1816. Uncut. Orig paper spine over bds (upper joint cracked, rather worn). *Stewart.* $128/£80

SCOTT, JOHN. A Visit to Paris in 1814.... London, 1816. 5th ed. Early calf (cvrs loose; bkpl). *Swann*.* $57/£36

SCOTT, JOSEPH FREDERICK. The Scientific Work of Rene Descartes (1596-1650). (London: Taylor & Francis, 1952.) Frontisport. VG in dj (price-clipped, extrems lt worn). *Weber.* $75/£47

SCOTT, JOSEPH. A Geographical Dictionary; of the United States of North America. Phila, 1805. Enlgd ed. Fldg map (sm gutter tear). Contemp calf (rubbed, spine dknd, dried; foxed, browned). Howes S237. *Oinonen*.* $100/£63

SCOTT, MARY HURLBURT. The Oregon Trail Through Wyoming. Aurora, CO: Powder River, 1958. One of 750 numbered. 2 fldg maps. (Name, lt worn), else VG. *Dumont.* $125/£78

SCOTT, MARY MONICA MAXWELL. Abbotsford. The Personal Relics and Antiquarian Treasures of Sir Walter Scott. London: A&C Black, 1893. xvi,66pp; 26 chromolitho plts. Teg. (Edges sl worn, sm spine nick.) *Hollett.* $72/£45

SCOTT, MEL. The San Francisco Bay Area, a Metropolis in Perspective. Berkeley: Univ of CA, 1959. 1st ed. NF in dj (chipped, faded), mylar cvr. *Harrington.* $40/£25

SCOTT, MICHAEL. Tom Cringle's Log. NY: Dodd Mead, 1927. 1st Schaeffer ed. 9 1/4 x 6 3/4. 7 color plts by Mead Schaeffer. Fine in dj (chipped, torn). *Pacific*.* $46/£29

SCOTT, PAUL. The Birds of Paradise. Eyre, 1962. 1st UK ed. VG in dj. *Williams.* $40/£25

SCOTT, PAUL. The Chinese Love Pavilion. Eyre & Spottiswoode, 1960. 1st UK ed. NF in dj (sl browned). *Williams.* $45/£28

SCOTT, PAUL. Staying On. London, 1977. 1st Eng ed. VG in dj. *Clearwater.* $72/£45

SCOTT, PETER. Portrait Drawings. Country Life, 1949. 1st ed. Signed. (Prelims sl spotted.) 42 monochrome plts. Oatmeal canvas, gilt. Dj (sl chipped, repaired tear to verso, inner flap sl spotted). *Hollett.* $136/£85

SCOTT, PETER. Wild Chorus. Country Life, 1938. 1st ed. One of 1250 signed. 24 color-ptd, 65 other plts. Teg, rest untrimmed. Mid-blue buckram, gilt. Good (sm band of sl fading to fr cvr head, sm stain fr joint). *Blackwell's.* $376/£235

SCOTT, R. L. Between the Elephants Eyes. London, 1955. 1st Eng ed. (Lt rubbed.) *Grayling.* $24/£15

SCOTT, RALPH. A Soldier's Diary. London, (1923). 1st Eng ed. (Mkd, handled, corners sl chafed.) *Clearwater.* $48/£30

SCOTT, ROBERT F. Scott's Last Expedition. London: Smith, Elder, 1914. 5th and final ed. 2 vols. 10 color plts, 2 fldg panoramas, 2 fldg maps; 8 color plts, 8 fldg maps. Good + set (lt foxed rear hinge vol 1 worn). *Explorer.* $120/£75

SCOTT, ROBERT F. Scott's Last Expedition. London: John Murray, 1914. 1st Murray ed. 2 vols. 10 color plts, 2 fldg panoramas, 2 fldg maps; 8 color plts, 8 fldg maps. VG set (inscrip; spines sunned). *Explorer.* $240/£150

SCOTT, ROBERT F. Scott's Last Expedition. London: John Murray, 1935. 2 vols. 2 fldg maps. Add'l map tipped-in to vol 2. VG set (bkpl, sl dusty) in dj. *Explorer.* $80/£50

SCOTT, ROBERT F. Scott's Last Expedition. London: John Murray, 1947. Cheaper ed. 2 vols. Fldg map each vol. VG set. *Explorer.* $40/£25

SCOTT, ROBERT F. Scott's Last Expedition. Folio Soc, 1968. VG in slipcase. *Walcot.* $19/£12

SCOTT, ROBERT F. The Voyage of the 'Discovery.' Smith, Elder, 1905. 1st ed. 2 vols. 2 fldg maps in rear pockets. VG- (sl worn). *Walcot.* $400/£250

SCOTT, SUTTON SELWYN. Southbooke. Columbus, GA: Ptd by Thos. Gilbert, 1880. 1st ed. (18),259,(11)pp. (Shelf-worn, lt soiled, rubbed), else Good. *Brown.* $50/£31

SCOTT, WALTER. The Abbot. Edinburgh: Longman, Hurst, Rees et al, 1820. 1st ed. 3 vols. Period 3/4 calf, marbled bds, gilt. NF. *Pacific*.* $184/£115

SCOTT, WALTER. The Border Antiquities of England and Scotland. London: For Longman, Hurst et al, 1814. 1st ed. 2 vols. Engr frontispieces, tps, 91 plts. Gilt edges. Contemp grn morocco, gilt. (Lt spotted; rubbed; inscrips.) *Christie's*.* $238/£149

SCOTT, WALTER. The Fortunes of Nigel. Edinburgh: Constable, 1822. 1st ed. 3 vols. 1/2 polished calf, marbled bds, smooth backs, gilt, leather lettering pieces. VG (bds lt rubbed). *House.* $180/£113

SCOTT, WALTER. Ivanhoe. NY: LEC, 1940. One of 1500 signed by Allen Lewis (illus). 2 vols. Chain mail buckram. Fine set in box. *Appelfeld.* $125/£78

SCOTT, WALTER. Ivanhoe. LEC, 1951. Ltd to 1500 numbered, signed by Edward A. Wilson (illus). 2 vols. Fine in slipcase. *Swann*.* $34/£21

SCOTT, WALTER. The Journals of Sir Walter Scott [with] Familiar Letters of Sir Walter Scott 1797-1825. London, 1891/1894. 1st eds. 4 vols. 416; 518; 446; 436pp; map vol 1, port, fldg map vol 2. Pub's uniform brn cl. VG. *Gretton.* $64/£40

SCOTT, WALTER. Kenilworth; a Romance. Edinburgh: Constable, 1821. 1st ed. 3 vols. 2 prelim ads vol 1; 3pp ads vol 3. Cream-backed drab paper over bds (rebound), paper spine labels. Nice (hinges repaired w/binder's cl). *Glenn.* $350/£219

SCOTT, WALTER. Letters on Demonology and Witchcraft, Addressed to J. G. Lockhart, Esq. John Murray, 1831. 2nd ed. Frontis; ads dated January 1831. Orig cl (spine bumped, rear hinge head nicked, rear cvr water-stained). Good. *Tiger.* $58/£36

SCOTT, WALTER. The Life of Napoleon Buonaparte, Emperor of the French. Edinburgh: Longman, Rees et al, 1827. 1st ed. 9 vols. Contemp 1/2 calf (spines evenly faded, sl rubbed, scuffed), gilt. Good set (eps stained). *Hollett.* $240/£150

SCOTT, WALTER. Lives of the Novelists. Paris: A. & W. Galignani, 1825. Pirated ed. 2 vols. (i),268; (i),256pp. Contemp 1/2 calf (sl rubbed), gilt. *Hollett.* $240/£150

SCOTT, WALTER. The Lord of the Isles. Edinburgh: Constable, 1815. 1st ed. 3/4 old brn calf, marbled bds (extrems worn, hinges rubbed), raised bands, maroon leather label. *Appelfeld.* $200/£125

SCOTT, WALTER. Memoirs of the Life of Sir Water Scott. Edinburgh: Robert Cadell, 1837. 1st ed. 7 vols. 7.5x4.5. Frontisport. Diced calf, gilt, morocco spine labels. NF. *Pacific*.* $748/£468

SCOTT, WALTER. The Poetical Works of.... Edinburgh: James Nichol, 1857. 3 vols. Calf, gilt, morocco spine labels. (Lacks 2 spine labels, others chipped), else VG set. *Pacific*.* $46/£29

SCOTT, WALTER. Quentin Durward. Edinburgh: Archibald Constable, 1823. 1st ed. 3 vols. Period 3/4 calf, marbled bds, gilt. NF. *Pacific*.* $161/£101

SCOTT, WALTER. Redgauntlet, a Tale of the Eighteenth Century. Edinburgh: Archibald Constable, 1824. 1st ed. 3 vols. Period 3/4 calf, marbled bds, gilt. NF. *Pacific*.* $161/£101

SCOTT, WALTER. Rokeby; a Poem. Edinburgh: John Ballantyne, 1813. 1st ed. Full contemp brn calf, gilt paneled spine, raised bands, marbled edges. Fine. *Appelfeld.* $300/£188

SCOTT, WALTER. Rokeby; a Poem. London: Tilt & Bogue, 1841. Illus ed. 303pp; 8 engr plts (margins spotted). Aeg. Contemp dk plum coarse-grained morocco, gilt. *Young.* $72/£45

SCOTT, WALTER. Some Unpublished Letters of Walter Scott. Oxford: Basil Blackwell, 1932. 1st ed. 14 plts, 4 facs. Prospectus, compliments slip signed and dated by editor loosely inserted. Uncut. Fine in dj. *Hollett.* $136/£85

SCOTT, WALTER. St. Ronan's Well. Edinburgh: Constable, 1824. 1st ed. 3 vols. Contemp polished calf, marbled bds, smooth backs, gilt. VG set (1 lettering piece edge sl chipped, few sm scuffs). *House.* $180/£113

SCOTT, WALTER. Tales of a Grandfather. Phila: Carey & Lea, 1831. Inscribed. 12mo. 232pp. Fair (sl browned, last pg, bd waterdamaged, hole; fr bd loose, joint separating; edges, corners very worn). *Price.* $55/£34

SCOTT, WALTER. Walter Scott's Works. London: Merrill & Baker, (c. 1900). Edition des Amateurs. One of 250. 9x6. 33 vols. Hand-colored frontispieces each vol, guards. Teg. 3/4 marbled morocco, marbled bds, gilt-tooled spines, raised bands. Fine set. *Pacific*.* $920/£575

SCOTT, WALTER. Waverley Novels. Edinburgh: Cadell, 1829-1833. 48 vols. 12mo. Engr frontispieces, tps. 19th-cent 1/2 morocco, gilt spines. (Some vols sl rubbed, sl browned; vol 14 rebound.) *Sotheby's*.* $662/£414

SCOTT, WALTER. The Waverley Novels. Edinburgh: Robert Cadell, 1842-1847. Abbotsford ed. Als tipped in. 12 vols. 4to. Edges gilt. Orig 1/2 morocco, gilt. (Spotting; sl rubbed.) *Sotheby's*.* $662/£414

SCOTT, WALTER. The Waverly Novels. NY, (ca 1900). 12 vols. 8vo. 1/2 polished tan calf, gilt, red/grn labels. Fine set. *Swann*.* $747/£467

SCOTT, WALTER. Woodstock; or, The Cavalier. Edinburgh: Archibald Constable, 1826. 1st ed. 3 vols. Period 3/4 dk grn morocco, pink bds, gilt, sl raised bands. (Bkpls, lt foxed; bds sl soiled), else VG set. *Pacific*.* $138/£86

SCOTT, WALTER. Works. Edinburgh: A&C Black, 1871. Centenary ed. 25 vols. 8vo. Contemp crimson 1/2 morocco. *Sotheby's*.* $552/£345

SCOTT, WILLIAM STUART. Marie Corelli: The Story of a Friendship. Hutchinson, 1955. Good (cello tape mks to pastedown; spine bumped) in dj (chipped, lacks sm pieces). *Tiger.* $22/£14

SCOTT-HERON, GIL. Small Talk at 125th and Lenox. NY, 1970. 1st ed. Fine in NF dj. *Warren.* $75/£47

SCOTT-JAMES, ANNE and OSBERT LANCASTER. The Pleasure Garden. John Murray, 1977. 1st ed. NF in dj. *Hadley.* $24/£15

SCOTT-JAMES, ANNE and OSBERT LANCASTER. The Pleasure Garden. Ipswich: Gambit, 1977. 1st Amer ed. VG. *Fair Meadow.* $25/£16

SCOTT-JAMES, ANNE. Sissinghurst: The Making of a Garden. Joseph, 1974. VG in dj. *Hadley.* $24/£15

SCOTT-MONCRIEFF, GEORGE. The Scottish Islands. Batsford, 1952. 1st ed. Color frontis. VG in dj (top edges sl worn, price-clipped). *Hollett.* $32/£20

SCOURSE, NICOLETTE. The Victorians and Their Flowers. Croom Helm, 1983. VG in dj. *Hadley.* $24/£15

SCRIPTURE, E. W. Thinking, Feeling, Doing. NY, 1895. 1st ed. 304pp. NF. *Doctor's Library.* $50/£31

SCROPE, G. P. The Geology and Extinct Volcanoes of Central France. London, 1858. 2nd ed. xvii,258pp; 17 plts (8 fldg, 1 color), 2 color fldg maps in pockets. (Lib stamps, inner joints repaired.) *Henly.* $144/£90

SCROPE, WILLIAM. Days and Nights of Salmon Fishing in the Tweed. London, 1843. 1st ed. 13 tinted litho plts (1 hand-colored). Mod 3/4 leather, preserving orig gilt-pict cl sides. (Foxed, sl stained, soiled.) *Oinonen*.* $450/£281

SCROPE, WILLIAM. Days and Nights of Salmon Fishing in the Tweed. London: John Murray, 1843. 1st ed. Hand-colored litho frontis (detached), litho tp vignette, 11 tinted litho plts. (Browned, spotted, mainly at margins; bkpl.) Orig grn cl (lt stained, rubbed), gilt. *Christie's*.* $469/£293

SCROPE, WILLIAM. Days and Nights of Salmon Fishing in the Tweed. London, 1843. 8vo. Litho add'l tp. Early 1/2 morocco (backstrip secured w/cl tape). *Swann*.* $546/£341

SCROPE, WILLIAM. Days and Nights of Salmon Fishing in the Tweed. London: John Murray, 1843. 1st ed. Tall 8vo. 12 litho plts. Mod navy blue 1/2 morocco, gilt spine. *Glenn.* $850/£531

SCRUTATOR. (Pseud of K. W. Horlock.) Lord Fitzwarine. London, 1860. 1st ed. 3 vols. Frontis each vol. Pub's cl (shelfworn, spine tips sl frayed; sl foxed). *Oinonen*.* $90/£56

SCRUTATOR. (Pseud of K. W. Horlock.) Recollections of a Fox-Hunter. London, 1861. 1st ed. Frontis. Teg. Full blue polished calf by Riviere, spine gilt. (Lt rubbed.) *Oinonen*.* $100/£63

SCUDAMORE, FRANK IVES. The Day Dreams of a Sleepless Man. London: Griffith & Farran, 1875. viii,264pp. Eps coated gray-chocolate. Ribbed brn cl. Good. *Temple.* $22/£14

SCUDDER, CHARLES LOCKE. The Treatment of Fractures, with Note Upon a Few Common Dislocations. Phila, 1926. 10th ed. (Stamped), o/w VG. *Doctor's Library.* $50/£31

SCUDDER, RALPH E. Custer Country. Portland: Binfords & Mort, 1963. 1st ed. Photo-pict cl. Fine. *Harrington.* $35/£22

SCUDDER, SAMUEL HUBBARD. The Butterflies of the Eastern United States and Canada. Cambridge, MA: The Author, 1889. 1st ed in orig 12 parts. 12 vols. 4to. 3 litho ports, 3 litho fldg maps, 89 litho plts. (Pp149, 457 cropped at margin, pp629, 1569 w/section cut away at top corner, pg1775 w/section cut away at corner affecting pg #s.) Teg. Contemp 1/2 morocco (rubbed, spines browned). *Christie's*.* $720/£450

SCULL, E. MARSHALL. Hunting in the Arctic and Alaska. Phila: John C. Winston, 1914. 1st ed. VG-. *Walcot.* $120/£75

SCULL, E. MARSHALL. Hunting in the Arctic and Alaska. Phila: John C. Winston, 1915. 72 plts, 11 maps. VG (Spine sl worn). *Explorer.* $112/£70

Sea, the Ship and the Sailor. Tales of Adventure From Log Books and Original Narratives. Salem: Marine Research Soc, 1925. 1st ed. 33 plts, maps. Blue cl, gilt. NF. *House.* $85/£53

SEABURY, GEORGE J. An Ode to Lake Bass. (NY): Privately ptd, (1890). 1st ed. Pict color cl, gilt. (Bkpl; corners, spine ends sl rubbed), else NF. *Pacific**. $127/£79

SEALE, BOBBY et al. Contempt: Transcript of the Contempt Citations, Sentences, and Responses of the Chicago Conspiracy 10. Chicago: Swallow, (1970). 1st ed. (Sm adhesive remnant on fep), o/w Fine in NF dj (lt rubbed). *Agvent*. $125/£78

SEALE, BOBBY. Seize the Time: The Story of the Black Panther Party and Huey P. Newton. NY: RH, (1970). 1st ed, 1st bk. NF in VG dj (lt edgeworn, sl soiled). *Agvent*. $50/£31

SEALE, WILLIAM. Texas Riverman: The Life and Times of Captain Andrew Smyth. Austin: Univ of TX, (1966). 1st ed. Blue cl. Fine in Fine dj. *Harrington*. $35/£22

SEAMAN, OWEN. War-Time Verses. London: Constable, 1915. 1st ed. Ptd wrapper over stiff wrappers. NF. *Reese*. $30/£19

SEAMON, W. H. (ed). Albemarle County: A Handbook. Wm. H. Prout, 1888. 108pp. Paper cvrs (some torn). *Book Broker*. $65/£41

SEARINGEN, ESTELLE MARGARET. Pickaninny. NY: Duffield, 1925. 1st ed. 8vo. 132pp; 6 full-pg b/w illus by E. W. Kemble. Orange-yellow cl. Good in dj (dusty, lacks 2 pieces from spine, rear cvr). *Reisler*. $185/£116

SEARLE, MARK. Turnpikes and Toll-Bars in Two Volumes.... London, n.d. Ltd to 500 numbered. Vol 1: #345/500; Vol 2: #401/500. 12 color plts. (Inner hinges broken, 1st sig vol 2 starting.) *October Farm*. $795/£497

SEARLE, RONALD. Which Way Did He Go? (London): Perpetua Books, (1961). 1st ed. Black cl, gilt. NF (eps lt foxed, extrems sl rubbed) in dj (spine sl dknd, sl edgeworn). *Heritage*. $100/£63

SEARLES, HAROLD F. Collected Papers on Schizophrenia and Related Subjects. NY: Internat'l Universities Press, 1965. 1st collected ed. Fine (sigs) in dj (edges sl frayed). *Glaser*. $45/£28

SEARLS, NILES. The Diary of a Pioneer and Other Papers. (SF: Robert M. Searls, 1940.) Signed. Pict tan bds (bottom tips bumped). *Dawson*. $350/£219

SEARS, JULIAN D. Geology of Comb Ridge and Vicinity North of San Juan River, San Juan County, UT. Washington: USGS, 1956. 4 plts (1 pocket foldout). VG. *Five Quail*. $12/£8

SEARS, W. H. Notes from a Cowboy's Diary. Lawrence, KS, (ca 1915). 1st ed. NF in ptd blue wraps. *Chapel Hill*. $50/£31

SEARS, W. H. Notes from a Cowboy's Diary. Lawrence, KS, n.d. 1st ed. Fine in wrappers. *Labordo*. $65/£41

SEAVER, GEORGE. Edward Wilson of the Antarctic. London: Murray, (1934). Color frontis; 3 maps. VG. *Mikesh*. $30/£19

SEAVER, GEORGE. The Faith of Edward Wilson. London: Murray, 1948. 1st ed. Frontis. VG in dj (chipped). *Explorer*. $19/£12

SEAVER, GEORGE. Scott of the Antarctic: A Study in Character. London: John Murray, 1940. 1st ed. Nice (sig) in dj. *Explorer*. $35/£22

SEAVER, JAMES E. A Narrative of the Life of Mrs. Mary Jemison, Who Was Taken by the Indians in the Year 1755.... Canadaigua: J. D. Bemis, 1824. 1st ed. 16mo. 189pp. Orig bds. (Lacks last pg, but supplied in copy, browned; spine w/old cl reinforcement.) Howes S268. *Dumont*. $725/£453

SEAWARD, A. C. Plant Life Through the Ages, a Geological and Botanical Retrospect. Cambridge, 1931. (Bkpl.) *Henly*. $67/£42

SEAWELL, M. ELLIOT. Decatur and Somers. NY: D. Appleton, 1894. 1st ed. (4)-169pp,(1 blank,4 ads)pp; 6 plts. (Fep, attached blank loose, margins lt dampstained; cvr sl worn.) *Lefkowicz*. $45/£28

SEBASTIAN, TIM. The Spy in Question. Delacorte, 1988. 1st Amer ed, 1st bk. Fine in dj. *Murder*. $30/£19

SECCOMBE, JOSEPH. A Discourse Utter'd in Part at Ammaus-keeg-Falls in the Fishing-Season, 1739. Barre: Barre Publishers, 1971. One of 1000 ptd. Signed by Michael McCurdy (engrs). 1/4 calf, dec bds, gilt. Fine in glassine, slipcase. *Pacific**. $46/£29

SECCOMBE, T. S. Comic Sketches from English History. W.H. Allen, 1884. Obl lg 8vo. 55pp; 12 full-pg color plts. Cl-backed pict bds (corners worn, sl chipped, lt soiled, fr joint cracked). *Hollett*. $56/£35

Second Biennial Report of the California State Board of Forestry for the Year 1887-88, to Governor R. W. Waterman. Sacramento: State Office, 1888. 182pp; 24 collotype plts, 6 fldg color litho maps. VG (fr hinge cracked). *Pacific**. $40/£25

SECOY, FRANK RAYMOND. Changing Military Patterns of the Great Plains. Locust Valley, NY, (1953). Map. (Spine faded), o/w Fine. *Pratt*. $15/£9

Secret History; or, the Horrors of St. Domingo.... (By Leonora Sansay.) Phila, 1808. 1st ed. Ink presentation by Peter S. Du Ponceau. 12mo. Contemp calf (rebacked). *M & S*. $650/£406

Secret Out. (By W. H. Cremer, Jr.) NY: Dick & Fitzgerald, (1859). Apparent 1st ed. 398pp + 10pp pub's ads. Lt yellow coated eps. Blind brn cl, gilt. Good (sl aged, foxed, few sigs lt sprung, pencil note; spine lt sunned, head sl frayed). *Baltimore**. $70/£44

SEDGWICK, MABEL CABOT. The Garden Month by Month. NY: Frederick A. Stokes, 1907. (Leading edge of chart frayed, sl browned, foxed; rebound, sl scuff mks), else VG. *Fair Meadow*. $40/£25

SEDGWICK, MABEL CABOT. The Garden Month by Month. NY: GC, 1907. 1st ed. Fldg chart. VF. *Quest*. $60/£38

SEDGWICK, MRS. WILLIAM T. Acoma, the Sky City. Cambridge: Harvard Univ, 1927. 2nd ptg. Teg; unopened. 1/2 cl. (Top corner of fr cvr sl bumped), else Fine. *Pacific**. $35/£22

SEE, R. P. M. Masquerier and His Circle. London, 1922. *Swann**. $57/£36

SEEBOHM, FREDERIC. The Tribal System in Wales. London, 1904. 2nd ed. (Lt marginal browning; spine wrinkled, sl dknd.) *Edwards*. $77/£48

SEEBOHM, HENRY. Siberia in Europe. London: John Murray, 1880. 1st ed. 1/2-title, xviii,304pp; fldg color map. Pale blue cl (hinges cracked, spine, extrems rubbed, chipped, rear cvr stained). Internally Clean. *Morrell*. $120/£75

SEEBOLD, HERMAN DE BACHELLE. Old Louisiana Plantation Homes and Family Trees. New Orleans, (1941). 2 vols. (Vol 2 sl foxed; bindings sl faded.) Slipcase (worn, torn). *Woolson*. $150/£94

SEEGER, ALAN. Letters and Diary. London, 1917. 1st Eng ed. (Bkpl; mkd, edges sl faded.) *Clearwater*. $56/£35

SEEGER, ALAN. Poems. London: Constable, 1917. 1st British ed. Untrimmed. Pale rose bds ptd in grn. (Ink name dated 1919, sl foxed), o/w VG in dj (heavy internal reinforcements to spine, few sm chips). *Reese*. $100/£63

SEELER, KATHERINE and EDGAR. Nantucket Lightship Baskets. Nantucket: Deer Mouse, 1972. 2nd ed. Color frontis. Pict white cl. VG. *American Booksellers*. $40/£25

SEELY, JOHN E. B. Fear, and Be Slain. London: Hodder & Stoughton, (1931). 1st ed. Photogravure frontis. Gilt red cl. (Spine soiled), o/w VG in NF dj. *Reese*. $40/£25

SEGALE, BLANDINA. At the End of the Santa Fe Trail. Columbia, OH: Columbia Press, 1932. 1st ed. Author's signature is rubber-stamped on half-title. Pict red cl. (2 sm nicks to cvrs, some silver-fishing), o/w VG + . *Labordo*. $95/£59

SEGAR, CHARLES (ed). Official History of the National League. Jay, 1951. 1st ed. Issued to commemorate league's 75th anniversary. VG + in Good + dj. *Plapinger*. $50/£31

SEGAR, E. C. Popeye with the Hag of the 7 Seas. Chicago: Pleasure Book Inc, (1935). Sq 4to. 3 dbl-pg pop-ups. Pict bds. Very Nice. *Davidson*. $500/£313

SEGARD, W. and F. TESTARD. Picturesque Views of Public Edifices in Paris. London, 1814. 20 aquatint plts. Contemp 1/2 sheep (needs rebinding; ink notes several plts, ink lib stamps verso each plt). *Swann**. $287/£179

SEGER, JOHN. Early Days Among the Cheyenne and Arapahoe Indians. Stanley Vestal (ed). Norman: Univ of OK, 1934. 1st ed thus. Fine in dj. *Labordo*. $50/£31

SEGUIN, E. C. Medical Thermometry and Human Temperature. NY, 1876. 1st ed. 446pp. *Fye*. $200/£125

SEGUIN, LISBETH GOOCH. Rural England. London, ca 1880. One of 300 numbered. Thick folio. Gilt-/color-stamped paper-vellum (soiled). *Swann**. $230/£144

SEIBERT, JERRY. Sacajawea, Guide to Lewis and Clark. Boston: Houghton & Mifflin, (1960). (Corner worn), else VG. *Perier*. $20/£13

SEILER, CARL. Handbook of the Diagnosis and Treatment of Diseases of the Throat, Nose, and Naso-Pharynx. Phila, 1883. 2nd ed. 295pp. VG. *Doctor's Library*. $60/£38

SEIMS, CHARLES. Trolley Days in Pasadena. San Marino, CA: Golden West Books, 1982. 1st ed. Fine in dj. *Labordo*. $35/£22

SEKON, G. A. (Pseud of George Augustus Nokes.) A History of the Great Western Railway, Being the Story of the Broad Gauge. London, 1895. 2nd ed. xvi,373pp. (Ex-lib, sl worn.) *Bohling*. $65/£41

SELBY, HUBERT, JR. Last Exit to Brooklyn. NY: Grove, (1964). 1st ed. Black cl, red bds, gilt. Fine in dj (rear panel lt stained red). *Heritage*. $250/£156

SELBY, HUBERT, JR. Last Exit to Brooklyn. NY: Grove, (1964). 1st ed, 1st bk. VF in VF dj. *Bromer*. $300/£188

SELBY, HUBERT, JR. Last Exit to Brooklyn. Calder & Boyars, 1966. 1st UK ed. VG in dj. *Williams*. $40/£25

SELBY, JOHN. Over the Sea to Skye. History Book Club, 1973. 60 plts (10 color), 6 maps. VG in dj. *Hollett*. $48/£30

SELBY-LOWNDES, JOAN. Bronze Eagles. Collins, 1946. 1st ed. 8vo. 192pp. VG in pict dj (lt worn). *Bookmark*. $24/£15

Select Lessons for Every Month of the Year. Concord, (NH): J.B. Moore, 1827. 12mo. 12pp + 1pg ad on lower wrapper. Pict buff paper wrappers (sl spotting, spine tender). VG. *Hobbyhorse*. $215/£134

Select Views in London and Westminster. London: Colnaghi & Co, (1800). 17 engr plts. (Occasional mainly marginal soiling.) Contemp morocco-backed bds (rubbed, lt stained). *Christie's**. $307/£192

Select Views of London and Its Environs. London: Vernor & Hood et al, 1804-05. 2 vols. 4to. 1/2-title vol 1; 62 engr plts (some spotted, marginal dampstaining to 1). Aeg. Contemp red morocco, gilt (extrems lt rubbed.) *Christie's**. $630/£394

Selection from the Harleian Miscellany of Tracts, which Principally Regard the English History.... London: C.& G. Kearsley, 1793. Mod full morocco, gilt paneled spine, raised bands. *Appelfeld*. $250/£156

SELF, WILL. Cock and Bull. Bloomsbury, 1992. 1st UK ed. Signed. Mint in Mint dj. *Martin*. $29/£18

SELF, WILL. Cock and Bull. NY, 1992. 1st Amer ed. Signed. Fine in Fine dj. *Warren*. $45/£28

SELF, WILL. The Quantity Theory of Insanity. Bloomsbury, 1991. 1st UK ed, 1st state, 1st bk. Fine in wraps as issued. *Martin*. $54/£34

SELF, WILL. The Quantity Theory of Insanity. London: Bloomsbury, 1991. True 1st ed, 1st bk. VG + . *Warren*. $75/£47

SELF, WILL. The Quantity Theory of Insanity. London: Bloomsbury, 1991. Correct 1st ed, 1st bk. Signed. Fine in illus wraps. *Lame Duck*. $150/£94

SELFRIDGE, THOMAS O. Trial of Thomas O. Selfridge, Attorney at Law.... Boston, (1807). 1st ed. 168pp; (3)leaves; 1 plt (sm piece torn from corner). Contemp bds (spine rebacked w/binder's tape, shelfworn, soiled; fep removed). *Oinonen**. $50/£31

SELIGMAN, GERMAIN. Roger de la Fresnaye, with a Catalogue Raisonne. (Greenwich); NYGS, (1969). One of 900 numbered. Dj. *Swann**. $172/£108

SELIGMANN, CHARLES GABRIEL. The Melanesians of British New Guinea. Cambridge: CUP, 1910. Half-title, fldg map. (Spotting.) Pub's grn cl (stained), gilt. *Sotheby's**. $184/£115

SELL, HENRY B. and VICTOR WEYBRIGHT. Buffalo Bill and the Wild West. NY, 1955. Inscribed. Good in dj (sl soiled). *Dumont*. $65/£41

SELOUS, EDMUND. The Bird Watcher in the Shetlands. J.M. Dent, 1905. 1st ed. Photogravure frontis. Teg, uncut. (Feps sl browned; sm spot fr bd, rear corner sl bumped), o/w VG. *Hollett*. $136/£85

SELOUS, EDMUND. Realities of Bird Life. London, 1927. *Petersfield*. $19/£12

SELOUS, FREDERICK C. A Hunter's Wandering in Africa. London, 1895. 4th ed. Frontis, xviii,455pp; 7 plts. Dec eps. (Lt browned; lt faded, hinges cracked, joint corners, edges rubbed w/sl loss, spine chipped.) *Edwards*. $80/£50

SELOUS, FREDERICK C. Recent Hunting Trips in British North America. London, 1907. Gilt-pict cl. (Lt foxing.) *Swann**. $149/£93

SELOUS, FREDERICK C. Sunshine and Storm in Rhodesia. London, 1896. Map. Buckram (faded, discolored). Internally VG. *Petersfield*. $128/£80

SELOUS, FREDERICK C. Sunshine and Storm in Rhodesia. Rowland Ward, 1896. 2nd ed. xxvii,290,(x)pp; 17 plts, fldg map. Striped fur design eps w/matching bookmark. Buckram (spine, edges dknd). VG (feps, fore-edge spotted). *Hollett*. $288/£180

SELOUS, PERCY and HENRY A. BRYDEN. Travel and Big Game. NY: Longmans, Green, 1897. 8,195pp; 6 plts. Pict cl (lt rubbed). *Adelson*. $285/£178

SELPH, FANNIE EOLINE. The South in American Life and History. Nashville, TN: McQuiddy Ptg, 1928. 1st ed. Signed. Frontisport. VG + (contemp inscrip; lt spotted). *Chapel Hill*. $85/£53

SELSAM, MILLICENT E. Seeds and More Seeds. NY: Harper & Bros, (1959). 1st ed. Review copy, slip laid in. 8vo. 60pp. Cl-backed color pict bds (edges lt rubbed). Color dj (spine dknd, chip). *Reisler*. $110/£69

SELTZER, DAVID. Omen. Arthur Barker, 1976. 1st UK ed. Fine in dj. *Williams*. $45/£28

SELVON, SAMUEL. The Housing Lark. London: MacGibbon & Kee, 1965. 1st ed. Adv rev copy. VG in dj. *Virgo*. $26/£16

SELWAY, N. C. The Regency Road. Faber, 1957. 1st ed. Port, 66 color plts. (Ex-lib, neat labels on and removed from feps, sm shelf-#s.) *Hollett*. $96/£60

SELZ, PETER. Sam Francis. NY, (1975). Dj. *Swann**. $126/£79

SEMPLE, DAISY with GENEVIEVE RIELY. Tommy and Jane and the Birds. Akron: Saalfield, (1929). 1st ed. 8vo. Fern Bisel Peat (illus). Cl-backed color illus bds (edges sl rubbed). Full color dj (lacks spine piece, marginal wear). *Reisler*. $100/£63

SEMPLE, MISS. The Costume of the Netherlands, Displayed in Thirty Coloured Engravings. R. Ackermann, 1817. Half-title, engr tp, 30 hand-colored aquatint plts (watermks dated 1818). Orig pink bds (worn; sl dust-soiled), pub's letter-press label fr cvr, dated 1819. *Sotheby's**. $368/£230

SENAN, JOSE. The Letters of Jose Senan, O.F.M.: Mission San Buenaventura, 1796-1823. SF: John Howell-Books, 1962. 1st ed. One of 1000 ptd. Frontis, fldg map. Fine. *Harrington*. $45/£28

SENDAK, MAURICE. Atomics for the Millions. NY: McGraw-Hill, (1947). 1st ed, 1st issue, 1st bk. 8vo. Blue cl, gilt (spine lettering sl faded). *Reisler*. $225/£141

SENDAK, MAURICE. Hector Protector. Harper & Row, (1965). 1st ed. Obl 8vo. Fine in Fine dj, price $4.25. *Davidson*. $150/£94

SENDAK, MAURICE. In the Night Kitchen. Harper & Row, 1970. Obl 4to. Fine in Fine dj. *American Booksellers*. $50/£31

SENDAK, MAURICE. In the Night Kitchen. Bodley Head, 1970. 1st ed. VG in VG dj. *Green Meadow*. $72/£45

SENDAK, MAURICE. Where the Wild Things Are. Harper, Row, 1963. Obl 4to. VG (bumped corners). *American Booksellers*. $45/£28

SENECA, LUCIUS ANNAEUS. Seneca's Morals by Way of Abstract. Roger L'Estrange (trans). London: G. Strahan et al, 1729. 13th ed. (30),475,(12)pp; 6 copper plts, incl frontis. Period calf, later morocco spine label. (Bkpl; corners sl bumped), else VG. *Pacific**. $58/£36

SENEFELDER, ALOIS. The Invention of Lithography. J. W. Muller (trans). NY: Fuchs & Lang Manufacturing, 1911. (Inside hinges cracked; cvrs rubbed w/spotting along back hinge.) *Oak Knoll*. $75/£47

SENEFELDER, ALOIS. The Invention of Lithography. NY, 1911. Litho port. (Cvrs heavily worn, dknd.) *King*. $95/£59

SENKEVITCH, ANATOLE, JR. Soviet Architecture: 1917-1962. Univ of VA, 1974. VG in red cl. *Hadley*. $40/£25

SENKEWICZ, ROBERT M. Vigilantes in Gold Rush San Francisco. Stanford, CA: Stanford Univ, 1985. 1st ed. Pict eps. Red cl. Fine in Fine dj. *Harrington*. $35/£22

SENN, EDWARD L. Wild Bill Hickok, Prince of Pistoleers. Deadwood, SD, 1939. 1st ed. Fine in wrappers. *Labordo*. $225/£141

SENN, N. Intestinal Surgery. Chicago: W.T. Keener, 1889. 1st ed. vii,269pp; 1 plt. Good (ex-lib; edges rubbed, rear hinge cracked, spine top chipped). *Glaser*. $125/£78

SENN, N. Intestinal Surgery. Chicago, 1889. 1st ed. 269pp. *Fye*. $250/£156

SENN, N. Medico-Surgical Aspects of the Spanish American War. Chicago: AMA Press, 1900. (Ex-lib, perf on tp; spine #s, spine ends frayed.) *Glaser*. $95/£59

SENN, N. The Pathology and Surgical Treatment of Tumors. Phila, 1895. 1st ed. 709pp. 515 Fine engr plts. Full leather. Fine. *Fye*. $200/£125

SENN, N. Principles of Surgery. Phila: F.A. Davis, 1895. 2nd ed. xvi,656,(2 ads),14(ads)pp; 5 plts. Fine. *Glaser*. $125/£78

SENN, N. Surgical Bacteriology. Phila: Lea Bros, 1889. 1st ed. (7),(17)-270,32(ads)pp; 13 plts (11 color). Good (ex-lib, tp detached but present; rear joint started, extrems lt worn). *Glaser*. $95/£59

SERLING, ROD. The Season to Be Wary. Boston/Toronto: Little, Brown, (1967). 1st ed. NF in dj (price-clipped, sm tear). *Bernard*. $65/£41

SERLING, ROD. The Season to be Wary. Boston, (1967). 1st ed. Inscribed, signed. (Cvrs sl damp-stained.) *Argosy*. $125/£78

Sermon on the Mount. (SF: Grabhorn, 1924.) One of 190. 1/2 gray cl, grn bds, pict cvr label. (Spine foxed), else NF. *Pacific**. $69/£43

Sermon on the Mount. LEC, 1977. One of 1600. Fine in slipcase. *Swann**. $92/£58

SERRA, JUNIPERO. Writings of Junipero Serra. Antonine Tibesar (ed). Washington: Academy of American Franciscan Hist, 1965-1966. 4 vols. Buckram, gilt (spotted). *Dawson*. $125/£78

SERVEN, JAMES and CARL METZGER. Colt Percussion Pistols. Dallas: Carl Metzger, 1947. 1st ed. Signed by Serven. NF in wrappers. *Labordo*. $40/£25

SERVEN, JAMES E. Colt Firearms, 1836-1954. Santa Ana, CA: The Author, 1954. 1st ed. Signed. Grn fabricoid. Fine in NF dj. *Harrington*. $100/£63

SERVEN, JAMES E. (ed). Colt Percussion Pistols. Santa Ana: Foundation, 1947. 1st ed. (1st pg sl foxed), else Fine in ptd wrappers. *Argonaut*. $50/£31

SERVICE, ROBERT W. Rhymes of a Red Cross Man. NY: Barse & Hopkins, (1916). 1st US ed. Grn cl, gilt. VG (sm ink stamp; extrems sl rubbed) in dj (chipped, reinforced w/tape on verso). *Heritage*. $100/£63

SERVICE, ROBERT W. Rhymes of a Red Cross Man. Toronto: William Briggs, 1916. 1st ed. Grn cl, gilt. (Pencil erasure fep), o/w VG. *Reese*. $100/£63

SERVICE, ROBERT W. Rhymes of a Rolling Stone. London, 1913. 1st ed. Dec cvrs, gilt. NF (name). *Polyanthos*. $50/£31

SERVICE, ROBERT W. The Spell of the Yukon and Other Verses. NY, (1907). 1st Amer ed. Suede cvrs, gilt. NF (sunned, sl frayed). *Polyanthos*. $25/£16

SERVICE, ROBERT W. The Trail of '98. NY: G&D, (1910). Early rpt. 4 b/w plts. Tan cl. VG (ink inscrip; extrems rubbed) in dj (lt chipped, soiled). *Heritage*. $75/£47

SERVISS, GARRETT P. Edison's Conquer of Mars. L.A.: Carcosa House, 1947. 1st ed. One of 1500. VG in Good dj (spine lacks piece, tape repairs to verso). *Pacific**. $69/£43

SETH, VIKRAM. All You Who Sleep Tonight. NY: Knopf, 1990. 1st ed. Fine in dj. *Any Amount*. $22/£14

SETH, VIKRAM. The Golden Gate. Faber, 1986. 1st UK ed. Signed. Fine in dj. *Williams*. $80/£50

SETH, VIKRAM. A Suitable Boy. NY, 1993. 1st Amer ed. Signed. Fine in Fine dj. *Polyanthos*. $40/£25

SETON, ERNEST THOMPSON. Lives of the Hunted. NY: Scribner, 1901. 1st US ed. Gilt-dec cvr. VG (inscrip; corners bumped, spine faded). *My Bookhouse*. $47/£29

SETON, ERNEST THOMPSON. Lives of the Hunted. NY, 1906. (Spine faded), else Good. *Dumont*. $35/£22

SETON, ERNEST THOMPSON. Monarch the Big Bear. NY: n.p., 1904. 1st ed. Good (bkpl, inscrip; bds lt worn). *Dumont*. $65/£41

SETON, ERNEST THOMPSON. Monarch, the Big Bear of Tallac. NY: Scribner, 1904. 1st ed. 7 3/4 x 5 3/4. Blue cl, gilt, pict cvr label.. (Spine sl rubbed), else VG. *Pacific**. $58/£36

SETON, ERNEST THOMPSON. Rolf in the Woods. GC, 1909. 1st ed. (Bds worn, faded), else Good. *Dumont*. $60/£38

SETON, ERNEST THOMPSON. The Trail of the Sandhill Stag. NY, 1919. 8 full-page illus. (Bds sl soiled), else Good. *Dumont*. $40/£25

SETON, ERNEST THOMPSON. Two Little Savages. NY, 1911. (Lt worn.) *Dumont*. $35/£22

SETON, ERNEST THOMPSON. Wild Animals at Home. NY, 1913. 1st ed. (Spine faded), else Good. *Dumont*. $40/£25

SETON, ERNEST THOMPSON. Wild Animals I Have Known. NY, 1916. 34th imp. *Dumont*. $35/£22

SETON, ERNEST THOMPSON. Woodmyth and Fable. NY: Century, 1905. 1st ed. Red cl. (Spine dknd, extrems rubbed, cvrs sl soiled, scratched.) *Heritage*. $100/£63

SETON, GRAHAM. Colonel Grant's To-Morrow. NY: Farrar & Rinehart, (1932). 1st US ed. Brn cl. Fine in pict dj (lt rubbed, nick). *Reese*. $50/£31

SETON-KARR, H. W. Ten Years' Wild Sports in Foreign Lands. London, 1889. 1st ed. 'From the Author, 1889' on half-title. (vi),333pp + 40pp pub's cat. (Text split between pp160-1, prelims lt stained, fr hinge sl cracked; cl sl dknd, spine sl faded, chipped.) Edwards. $144/£90

SETON-THOMPSON, ERNEST. Bird Portraits. Boston, 1901. 1st ed w/20 full-pg b/w plts after Seton-Thompson. Pict cl. (Inner hinges split, sl soiled internally, ink inscrip; cvrs worn; extrems soiled, frayed; color flaking from cvrs.) King. $45/£28

SETON-THOMPSON, ERNEST. Trail of an Artist-Naturalist; the Autobiography.... London: Hodder & Stoughton, 1951. 1st Eng ed. Frontisport. Red cl. Fine in ptd dj (chipped). Biscotti. $40/£25

SETON-THOMPSON, ERNEST. The Wild Animal Play for Children. Phila/NY, (1900). 1st ed. Pict cl. Good. Pacific*. $63/£39

SETON-THOMPSON, GRACE GALLATIN. A Woman Tenderfoot. NY: Doubleday, Page, 1900. 1st ed. Grn pict cl. NF (corners sl bumped, sl edgeworn). Harrington. $75/£47

SETTLE, MARY LEE. Blood Tie. Boston: Houghton Mifflin, 1977. 1st ed. Fine in NF dj. Pettler. $22/£14

SETTLE, MARY LEE. Fight Night on a Sweet Saturday. NY: Viking, 1964. 1st ed. (Ink price), else Fine in VG + dj. Pettler. $35/£22

SETTLE, MARY LEE. The Love Eaters. NY: Harper, 1954. 1st US ed, 1st bk. NF in VG + dj (soiled, rubbed, price partly clipped). Lame Duck. $150/£94

SETTLE, RAYMOND W. and MARY LUND. Empire on Wheels. Stanford: Stanford Univ, (1949). 1st ed. Yellow cl. Fine in dj (lt worn). Glenn. $25/£16

SETTLE, RAYMOND W. and MARY LUND. Empire on Wheels. Stanford: Stanford Univ, (1949). Fine in VG dj. Perier. $40/£25

SETTLE, RAYMOND W. and MARY LUND (eds). Overland Days to Montana in 1865. Glendale: A.H. Clark, 1971. 1st collected ed. Fldg map. Red cl. Fine. Harrington. $55/£34

SETTLE, RAYMOND W. and MARY LUND (eds). Overland Days to Montana in 1865: The Diary of Sarah Raymond and Journal of Dr. Waid Howard. Glendale: A.H. Clark, 1971. 1st ed. Fldg map. Red cl, gilt. Fine. Pacific*. $40/£25

SETTLE, RAYMOND W. and MARY LUND. Saddles and Spurs. The Pony Express Saga. Harrisburg, PA, (1955). 1st ed. VG in VG dj. Woolson. $35/£22

SETTLE, WILLIAM A., JR. Jesse James Was His Name. Columbia, MO: Univ of MO, 1966. 1st ed. VG + in dj. Labordo. $125/£78

SEUSS, DR. (Pseud of Theodore Seuss Geisel.) The 500 Hats of Bartholomew Cubbins. NY: Vanguard, (1938). 1st ed(?). 11x8. Pict bds. (Sl bleeding from red cl to lower 1st few pp; corners lt rubbed, bds sl warped), else VG. Pacific*. $138/£86

SEUSS, DR. (Pseud of Theodore Seuss Geisel.) And to Think That I Saw It on Mulberry Street. NY, (1937). 12th ptg. Signed. 11x8. Unpaginated. Pict bds (worn, cvrs creased, spine torn). King. $175/£109

SEUSS, DR. (Pseud of Theodore Seuss Geisel.) The Butter Battle Book. NY: Random House, (1984). 1st ed. 4to. Color pict bds. Good. Reisler. $125/£78

SEUSS, DR. (Pseud of Theodore Seuss Geisel.) The Cat in the Hat Comes Back. NY: Beginner Books, (1958). 1st ed. 8vo. Color pict bds. Good in color pict dj (lt marginal wear). Reisler. $485/£303

SEUSS, DR. (Pseud of Theodore Seuss Geisel.) Horton Hears a Who! NY: Random House, (1954). 1st ed. 11x8. Pict bds. Lists title through Scrambled Eggs Super! at fr. NF in dj (spine sunned, ends, extrems rubbed). Pacific*. $863/£539

SEUSS, DR. (Pseud of Theodore Seuss Geisel.) I Had Trouble in Getting to Solla Sollew. NY: Random House, (1965). 1st ed. 4to. Color illus bds (edges lt worn). Full color dj (sm spine chip, marginal wear, tears). Reisler. $275/£172

SEUSS, DR. (Pseud of Theodore Seuss Geisel.) If I Ran the Circus. NY: Random House, (1956). 1st ed. Signed, inscribed. 11x8. Pict bds. Lists title through If I Ran the Circus on rear dj panel. NF in dj (spine sl sunned, 1-inch closed tear fr panel top). Pacific*. $1,035/£647

SEUSS, DR. (Pseud of Theodore Seuss Geisel.) The Seven Lady Godivas. NY: Random House, (1939). 1st ed. VF in dj (3 sm chips). Bromer. $475/£297

SEUSS, DR. (Pseud of Theodore Seuss Geisel.) Yertle the Turtle and Other Stories. NY: Random House, (1958). 1st ed, w/price to fr dj flap, rear list of bks beginning w/'And to Think That I Saw It on Mulberry Street' and ending w/'How the Grinch Stole Christmas.' Pictures of previous Seuss bks on rear dj panel. 11x8. Pict bds. Fine in dj. Pacific*. $288/£180

SEUSS, DR. (Pseud of Theodore Seuss Geisel.) You're Only Old Once. NY, (1986). 1st ed. One of 500 numbered, signed. Slipcase. Swann*. $230/£144

Seven Little Sisters Who Live on the Round Ball That Floats in the Air. (By Jane Andrews.) Boston: Ticknor & Fields, 1861. 1st ed. Sm 8vo. 1/2-title, full-pg wood engr dec tp w/plt guard, vi,127pp + 1pg ad; 7 full-pg VF wood engrs by S. S. Kilburn. Blind emb brn cl on bds (edges lt soiled, rubbed), gilt. Fine. Hobbyhorse. $325/£203

SEVERIN, TIMOTHY. Explorers of the Mississippi. NY: Knopf, 1968. Map. Good in dj. Dumont. $20/£13

SEVERN, J. MILLOTT. The Life Story and Experiences of a Phrenologist. London, 1929. Presentation copy. Frontis port. (Spine lt faded.) Edwards. $56/£35

SEVERN, MARK. (Pseud of Franklin Lushington.) The Gambardier. London: Ernest Benn, (1930). 1st ed. Tan cl stamped in black. (Few lt fox mks at fore-edge), o/w VG in pict dj. Reese. $150/£94

SEVERSON, THOR. Sacramento: An Illustrated History, 1839 to 1874. SF: CA Hist Soc, (1973). 1st ed. Dec eps. Brn linen, gilt. Fine in pict dj. Pacific*. $29/£18

SEWALL, RICHARD B. The Life of Emily Dickinson. NY, (1974). 1st ptg. 2 vols. VG in slipcase. Woolson. $40/£25

SEWARD, A. C. Plant Life Through the Ages. CUP, 1933. 2nd ed. Inscribed. Frontis (back sl spotted). VG (ex-lib, labels) in dj. Hollett. $120/£75

SEWARD, OLIVE RISLEY. William H. Sewards' Travels Around the World. NY: Appleton, 1873. 730pp; fldg map. Teg. Full brn leather. VG. American Booksellers. $110/£69

SEWARD, WILLIAM WENMAN. The Hibernian Gazetteer, Being a Description...Roads, Market, Post and Fair Towns, in Ireland. Dublin, 1789. Fldg map. Tree sheep (worn). Swann*. $103/£64

SEWEL, WILLIAM. The History of the Rise, Increase and Progress of the Christian People Called Quakers. Burlington, NJ, 1774. 3rd ed. Folio. 12,812pp + index. (Foxed; rebound.) Heinoldt. $125/£78

SEWEL, WILLIAM. The History of the Rise, Increase, and Progress, of the Christian People Called Quakers.... London: J. Sowle, 1725. 2nd ed. Folio. (12),699,(17)pp. Gilt-ruled black morocco, raised bands. (Extrems sl scuffed), else VG. Pacific*. $184/£115

SEWELL, ALFRED L. The Great Calamity!...Also Some Account of...the Burning of Peshtigo, Wisconsin. Chicago: Sewell, 1871. 1st ed. Fldg frontis map, 100pp. Orig flexible cl (sl worn, spine sl chipped, frayed). Oinonen*. $50/£31

SEWELL, ANNA. Black Beauty. London: J.M. Dent & Sons, 1915. 1st ed illus thus. 8vo. 24 color plts by Lucy Kemp-Welch. Teg. 1/2 dk grn calf over grn cl sides, gilt, red leather label, center tools of a horse's head in compartments. Fine. *Sotheran*. $269/£168

SEWELL, ANNA. Black Beauty. Jarrolds, n.d. 1st ed thus. Lg 8vo. viii,291pp; 18 color plts by Cecil Aldin. Pict cl (corners sl damped), gilt. *Hollett*. $192/£120

SEWELL, ANNA. Black Beauty: His Grooms and Companions. London: Jarrold & Sons, 3, Paternoster Buildings, (1877). 1st ed, and a binding variant: the decoration to the upper cvr does not accord w/either binding A, B or C as described by Carter. Outer panel, rustic decoration, title and horse's head all ptd in black here, whereas the floral decoration and reins are gilt. Carter's A has title, horse head gilt; his B has title, panels gilt, all other stamping in black. 8vo. Engr frontis, viii,9-247pp + 7pg pub's cat. Brn eps; plain edges. Orig dk grn pict cl, stamped in black/gilt. VG (ink inscrip to frontis, speckled internally and to edges of book block, 1 gathering sl proud, but tightly sewn in; rubbed, lower corner extrem sl worn). *Sotheran*. $4,000/£2,500

SEWELL, ANNA. Black Beauty: His Grooms and Companions. Boston: George T. Angell, (1890). 1st US ed. Sm 8vo. Orig ptd stiff bds. (Top corner margin most ll lt chipped; cvrs sl dusty, spine ends sl chipped, splash spots along some edges.) *Baltimore**. $260/£163

SEWELL, ANNA. Black Beauty: His Grooms and Companions. Boston: Offices 19 Milk St., American Humane Education Soc, (1890). 1st pirated Amer ed. 8vo. (ix),10-245,(xii)pp. Fine in burnt-orange dec wrappers (expertly rebacked using matching paper, sm corner tear, sm nick). *Sotheran*. $797/£498

SEWELL, ANNA. Black Beauty: His Grooms and Companions. Boston: American Human Soc, (1900). Gray-grn pict wrappers (lt chipped). VG. *Glenn*. $85/£53

SEWELL, BROCARD (ed). Frederick Rolfe and Others. Aylesford, Kent: St. Albert's, 1961. 1st ed. One of 450 numbered. Good in white wrappers (edges sl spotted). *Maggs*. $32/£20

SEWELL, MARY. The Little Forester and His Friend. London: Jarrold & Sons, (1866). Inscribed presentation. 8vo. Engr frontis, 1/2-title, 101,2 ads pp (lt spotted). Blind/gilt-stamped grn cl over beveled bds. *Young*. $96/£60

SEWELL, ROBERT. A Forgotten Empire. London, 1900. 1st ed. 3 maps. Marbled eps, edges. 1/2 morocco, marbled bds, gilt. (Lt marginal browning; sl worn, lower joint sl rubbed.) *Edwards*. $152/£95

SEXTON, ANNE. The Book of Folly. Boston: Houghton Mifflin, 1972. 1st ed. Ltd to 500 signed. Aeg. VF in red paper bds backed in black cl, gilt. Red slipcase, ptd label. *Bromer*. $125/£78

SEXTON, ANNE. To Bedlam and Part Way Back. Boston: Hougton Mifflin, 1960. 1st ed, 1st bk. VG in dj (sl rubbed, worn). *Second Life*. $150/£94

SEYBOLD, DAVID (ed). Seasons of the Angler. NY: Weidenfeld & Nicolson, (1988). 1st ed. NF in dj (fr panel lt scratched, spine edges lt worn). *Bernard*. $40/£25

SEYD, ERNEST. California and Its Resources. London: Trubner, 1858. 1st ed. 8.5x5.5. (4),168,(1)pp; 18 plts, tissue guards, 2 fldg maps. Aeg. Black pebbled cl, gilt. VG (cvrs sl rubbed). *Pacific**. $1,495/£934

SEYMOUR, CHARLES, JR. Masterpieces of Sculpture from the National Gallery of Art. Washington, 1949. 41 plts. Good in dj (worn). *Washton*. $40/£25

SEYMOUR, DANIEL. A Loud Song. NY: Lustrum, 1971. 1st ed. VG in pict stiff wrappers (sl dusty). *Cahan*. $85/£53

SEYMOUR, E. S. Sketches of Minnesota, the New England of the West. NY, 1850. 1st ed. Fldg map (sm gutter tear). (Shelfworn; foxed.) Howes S313. *Oinonen**. $110/£69

SEYMOUR, FLORA WARREN. Indian Agents of the Old Frontier. NY, 1941. 1st ed. Good in dj (sl worn). *Dumont*. $45/£28

SEYMOUR, PETER. Frontier Town. A Panorama Pop-Up Book. NY: Holt, Rinehart & Winston, 1982. Marvin Boggs & Borge Svensson (illus). Unfolds to reveal 4 scenes. Glazed pict bds. VG. *Bookfinders*. $30/£19

SEYMOUR, PETER. The Old West. Kansas City: Hallmark, n.d. (1974). 5 dbl-pg pop-ups by Rich Rudish. Glazed pict bds. VG. *Bookfinders*. $60/£38

SEYMOUR, PETER. What's in the Cave. A Lift-the-Flap Pop-Up Book. NY: Holt, Rinehart & Winston, 1985. 6 pop-ups under flaps; dbl-pg pop-up. Glazed pict bds. VG. *Bookfinders*. $15/£9

SEYMOUR, ROBERT. Seymour's Humourous Sketches. London, 1872. 1/2 red morocco, gilt. (Orig cvr, spine bound in at rear.) *Swann**. $92/£58

SEYMOUR-SMITH, M. Robert Graves. His Life and Works. London: Hutchinson, 1982. Blue cl (headcaps sl bumped). Dj. *Maggs*. $24/£15

SHAARA, MICHAEL. The Killer Angels. NY: David McKay, (1974). 1st ed. 8vo. Blue bds. NF in dj. *Chapel Hill*. $550/£344

SHACKELFORD, GEORGE GREEN (ed). Collected Papers to Commemorate Fifty Years of the Monticello Association of the Descendants of Thomas Jefferson. Princeton Univ, 1965. Inscribed. *Book Broker*. $50/£31

SHACKLEFORD, WILLIAM YANCEY. Belle Starr, the Bandit Queen. Girard, KS: Haldemann-Julius, 1943. 1st ed. VG + in wrappers. *Labordo*. $20/£13

SHACKLEFORD, WILLIAM YANCEY. Buffalo Bill Cody, Scout and Showman. Girard, KS: Haldeman-Julius, (1944). 1st ed. VG + in fragile wraps. *Book Market*. $25/£16

SHACKLETON, ERNEST. South. The Story of Shackleton's Last Expedition 1914-1917. London, 1919. 1st ed. Tall 8vo. Lg fldg color map. Pict cl blocked in silver. *Maggs*. $600/£375

SHACKLETON, ERNEST. South. The Story of Shackleton's Last Expedition 1914-1917. NY: Macmillan, 1926. 2nd ptg. Fldg map. VG. *High Latitude*. $32/£20

SHACKLETON, ERNEST. South. The Story of Shackleton's Last Expedition 1914-1917. London: Heinemann, Dec 1919. 1st rpt of 1st ed. Color frontis, fldg map at rear. Blue cl, gilt. VG. *Explorer*. $224/£140

SHACOCHIS, BOB. The Next New World. NY: Crown, (1989) 1st ed. Fine in dj (price-clipped). *Bernard*. $20/£13

SHAFFER, ELLEN. The Garden of Health: An Account of Two Herbals. SF: Book Club of CA, 1957. One of 300 ptd. Orig tipped-in leaf. Prospectus laid in. Dec bds. Fine. *Pacific**. $207/£129

SHAFFER, PETER. Amadeus. Deutsch, 1980. 1st UK ed. Fine in dj. *Williams*. $77/£48

SHAFFER, PETER. Five Finger Exercise. H. Hamilton, 1958. 1st UK ed, 1st bk. (Sl sticky patch fep, fr flap), o/w VG + in VG dj. *Martin*. $19/£12

SHAFFER, PETER. The Private Ear and the Public Eye. Hamilton, 1962. 1st UK ed. NF in dj. *Williams*. $48/£30

SHAFFER, PETER. Shrivings. Deutsch, 1974. 1st UK ed. Fine in dj. *Williams*. $64/£40

SHAFFNER, TAL P. The War in America. London: Hamilton, Adams, (1862). 1st ed. Hand-colored fldg frontis map, 418pp. Blue cl. VG (spine dknd, lt soiled). Howes S321. *Chapel Hill*. $250/£156

SHAHN, BEN. Ben Shahn, Photographer, an Album from the Thirties. Margaret R. Weiss (ed). NY, 1973. 1st ed. (Age-dknd; extrems faded.) Dj (soiled, yellowed). *Swann**. $69/£43

SHAHN, BEN. Love and Joy About Letters. NY, 1963. 1st Amer ed. Obl folio. Fine in slipcase (rubbed). *Polyanthos*. $60/£38

SHAKESPEAR, HENRY. The Wild Sports of India: With Detailed Instructions for the Sportsman. London, 1862. 2nd ed. Port. Pub's cl. (Inner joint broken, sl soiled, foxed; sl worn.) *Oinonen**. $80/£50

Shakespeare's Comedy of Twelfth Night, Or What You Will. London: Hodder & Stoughton, (1908). 1st ed. 40 full-pg mtd color plts by W. Heath Robinson. Grn cl, gilt. (Spine edge sl spotted), o/w VG in dj (worn), color paste label. *Reisler.* $675/£422

SHAKESPEARE, WILLIAM. As You Like It. London: Hodder & Stoughton, (1909). 1st ed illus by Hugh Thomson. Deluxe ed. Ltd to 500 numbered, signed by Thomson. 4to. 40 mtd color plts, guards. Teg, rest uncut, new gold silk ties. Orig full cream vellum, gilt. (Lacks fep; spine sl speckled), o/w Very Clean. *Sotheran.* $557/£348

SHAKESPEARE, WILLIAM. As You Like It. London: Hodder & Stoughton, (c. 1915). 24 mtd color plts by Hugh Thomson, guards. Grn dec cl. Very Clean. *Sotheran.* $141/£88

SHAKESPEARE, WILLIAM. A Collection of Poems. London: Bernard Lintott, (1709). 2nd ed. (4),155pp. Contemp calf, gilt. (Few expertly repaired tears to pp; expertly rebacked), else VG in cl chemise, 1/2 morocco slipcase. *Pacific**. $2,300/£1,438

SHAKESPEARE, WILLIAM. The Comedies, Histories and Tragedies of William Shakespeare. Herbert Farjeon (ed). NY: LEC, 1939-41. One of 1950. 37 vols. (Foxing, dkng to spines), else VG set. *Pacific**. $431/£269

SHAKESPEARE, WILLIAM. The Complete Works of William Shakespeare. OUP, Henry Frowde, The World's Classics, 1910. 9 vols. Teg, rest untrimmed. VG set in dk blue buckram, ptd paper labels. *Maggs.* $120/£75

SHAKESPEARE, WILLIAM. The First Part of Henry the Fourth. SF: Grabhorn, 1961. One of 180. 1/2 cl, dec bds, paper spine label. (Extrems dknd), else VG. *Pacific**. $86/£54

SHAKESPEARE, WILLIAM. Hamlet, Prince of Denmark. London: Selwyn & Blount, ca 1920. Black dec bds, white linen spine. *Appelfeld.* $150/£94

SHAKESPEARE, WILLIAM. The Life of King Henry V. Herbert Arthur Evans (ed). NY: LEC, 1951. One of 1500. Gilt-dec cl, beveled bds. Fine in slipcase. *Pacific**. $58/£36

SHAKESPEARE, WILLIAM. The Merry Wives of Windsor. NY: Frederick A. Stokes, 1910. 1st Amer ed thus. 40 tipped-in color plts by Hugh Thomson, guards. Teg. Grn cl, gilt, pict cvr label. NF. *Pacific**. $196/£123

SHAKESPEARE, WILLIAM. The Merry Wives of Windsor. NY: Frederick A. Stokes, 1910. 1st Amer ed. 4to. 40 full-pg mtd color plts by Hugh Thomson. Teg. Grn cl, gilt, color paste label. Good. *Reisler.* $225/£141

SHAKESPEARE, WILLIAM. A Midsummer-Night's Dream. London: Heinemann, 1908. 1st Rackham trade ed, Amer issue w/secondary publisher Doubleday's imprint on spine. 40 tipped-in color plts by Arthur Rackham. 1/2 cl, gilt-pict bds. (1 plt detached, creased, frontis tissue guard detached, bkpl; sl shaken; cvrs foxed, edges worn.) Internally VG. *Pacific**. $86/£54

SHAKESPEARE, WILLIAM. A Midsummer-Night's Dream. London: Heinemann, 1908. Ltd to 1000 signed by Arthur Rackham (illus). 4to. 40 mtd color plts on brn paper. (Lt spotting.) Teg. Orig pict vellum (lt stained, lacks ties), gilt. *Christie's**. $773/£483

SHAKESPEARE, WILLIAM. A Midsummer-Night's Dream. London: Heinemann, 1920. Early ed. 4to. (vi)-134pp; 40 mtd color plts by Arthur Rackham. Lt blue cl, gilt. VG. *Sotheran.* $301/£188

SHAKESPEARE, WILLIAM. A New Variorum Edition of Shakespeare. Horace Howard Furness (ed). Phila: Lippincott, (1926). 27 vols. Teg. Rust cl, gilt. (Spines dknd, sl discoloration), else VG set. *Pacific**. $259/£162

SHAKESPEARE, WILLIAM. The Plays. Ptd by T. Bensley for Wynne & Scholey, 1803-05. Bensley ed. 10 vols. 8vo. Tissue guards present. Marbled eps; blue sprinkled edges. Contemp sprinkled tan calf, gilt, dk blue morocco label. VG (backstrips lt faded). *Blackwell's.* $2,400/£1,500

SHAKESPEARE, WILLIAM. The Plays. Pickering's Diamond Classics. William Pickering, 1825. 9 vols. Engr frontisport, 38 plts (some offsetting). Uncut. Orig cl (spines faded, labels rubbed). *Sotheby's**. $515/£322

SHAKESPEARE, WILLIAM. The Poems of William Shakespeare. LEC, 1941. Ltd to 1500 numbered, signed by Bruce Rogers (illus). 2 vols. Fine in slipcase. *Swann**. $201/£126

SHAKESPEARE, WILLIAM. Romeo and Juliet. London: Hodder & Stoughton, (1912). 1st ed illus by W. Hatherell. 22 mtd color plts, guards. Grn cl, gilt. Fine. *Sotheran.* $317/£198

SHAKESPEARE, WILLIAM. Shakespeare's Tragedy of Macbeth. London: Folio Soc, 1964. 1st Eng ed. Nice (cvrs sl faded). *Clearwater.* $64/£40

SHAKESPEARE, WILLIAM. Shakspere's Works. Edward Dowden (ed). Kegan Paul, Trench, 1882-1883. Parchment Library ed. 12 vols. Vellum. Orig parchment. Nice set (few sm mks, pencil notes). *Ash.* $312/£195

SHAKESPEARE, WILLIAM. The Stratford Shakespeare. Charles Knight (ed). NY: D. Appleton, 1881. 6 vols. Marbled edges. 3/4 calf, marbled bds, gilt, red/grn morocco spine labels. (Spine ends lt worn), else VG set. *Pacific**. $196/£123

SHAKESPEARE, WILLIAM. The Tempest. London: Hodder & Stoughton, (1908). 1st ed illus thus. 40 Fine mtd color plts by Edmund Dulac. Dk grn cl, gilt. (1/2 title speckled, text lt spotted.) *Sotheran.* $400/£250

SHAKESPEARE, WILLIAM. The Tempest. London: Heinemann, (1908). One of 500 numbered, signed by Arthur Rackham (illus). 20 tipped-in color plts. Gilt-dec white bds, 1/4 vellum, gilt. (Spine lt soiled), o/w Fine. *Cullen.* $1,150/£719

SHAKESPEARE, WILLIAM. The Tempest. London: Hodder & Stoughton, (1911). 1st ed. One of 500 signed by Edmund Dulac (illus). 4to. 40 mtd color plts. Teg. Gilt-stamped vellum. Sound (cockled, lacks ties). *Appelfeld.* $1,500/£938

SHAKESPEARE, WILLIAM. The Tempest. NY: Doubleday Page, (1926). 1st Amer ed. 4to. 20 full-pg mtd color plts by Arthur Rackham. Yellow tinted top. Gray/black cl (sl pucker to edge), gilt. VG in pict dj (faded, edgeworn). *Reisler.* $375/£234

SHAKESPEARE, WILLIAM. The Tempest. London: Heinemann, (1926). 1st trade ed. 4to. 20 mtd color plts by Arthur Rackham on cream paper. (Eps lt spotted, contemp pencil inscrip.) Dk gray pict cl, gilt. Dj (sm tear fr cvr, spine lt stained, spotted). *Christie's**. $405/£253

SHAKESPEARE, WILLIAM. The Tempest. London: Heinemann, (1926). 1st ed illus thus. 20 mtd color plts by Arthur Rackham. Black cl, gilt. Very Clean (corners sl bruised) in ptd dj (purple 4-inch-wide water stain). *Sotheran.* $429/£268

SHAKESPEARE, WILLIAM. The Tempest. London: Heinemann, (1926). 1st ed. One of 525 signed by Arthur Rackham (illus). 4to. 21 mtd color plts. Teg. White gilt-stamped bds, vellum spine. Fine in linen slipcase. *Appelfeld.* $1,500/£938

SHAKESPEARE, WILLIAM. The Tempest. London: Freemantle, 1901. 1st ed illustrated by Robert Anning Bell. Teg, rest uncut. Pict eps. Pict gray cl. Very Nice (prelims sl speckled; spine rubbed). *Sotheran.* $141/£88

SHAKESPEARE, WILLIAM. The Tempest. London: Freemantle, 1901. 1st ed. Signed by Robert Anning Bell (illus). Teg, rest uncut. Gray cl. Very Nice (spine sl rubbed, edges sl browned). *Sotheran.* $237/£148

SHAKESPEARE, WILLIAM. The Tempest. London: Freemantle, 1901. Ltd to 174 signed by Robert Anning Bell (illus). 4to. Teg. Vellum bds (sl warp), gilt. Pub's box (rubbed, chipped, lacks edge pieces). *Reisler.* $485/£303

SHAKESPEARE, WILLIAM. The Tragedie of Julius Caesar. SF: Grabhorn, 1954. One of 180. 1/2 red morocco, dec black bds, gilt. Fine in dj. *Pacific**. $92/£58

SHAKESPEARE, WILLIAM. The Tragedie of King Lear. SF: Grabhorn, 1959. One of 180 ptd. 1/2 cl, dec bds, leather spine label. (Offset from removed bkpl to fr pastedown), else NF. *Pacific**. $184/£115

SHAKESPEARE, WILLIAM. The Tragedie of Othello, the Moore of Venice. SF: Grabhorn, 1956. One of 185. 1/4 levant red morocco, dec bds, gilt. (Spine sunned), else NF. *Pacific**. $69/£43

SHAKESPEARE, WILLIAM. The Tragedy of Hamlet, Prince of Denmark. NY: LEC, 1933. One of 1500 signed. Eric Gill (illus). Full pigskin. VG in slipcase. *Clearwater*. $424/£265

SHAKESPEARE, WILLIAM. The Tragedy of Hamlet. London: Hodder & Stoughton, ca 1908. 1st ed w/these plts. 24 mtd color plts by W. G. Simmonds. 3/4 brn morocco, gilt-paneled spine, raised bands. Fine. *Appelfeld*. $300/£188

SHAKESPEARE, WILLIAM. The Tragedy of Richard the Third: With the Landing of Earle Richmond and the Battell at Boswell Field. SF: Grabhorn, 1953. One of 180. Full vellum, gilt, string ties. Fine in slipcase (sl sunned). *Pacific**. $98/£61

SHAKESPEARE, WILLIAM. Twelfth Night, or What You Will. London: Hodder & Stoughton, (1908). 1st trade ed w/illus by W. Heath Robinson. 40 tipped-in color plts on gray art paper mounts, guards. Slate eps. Grn cl (spine sl sunned), gilt. Text NF. Lt grn dj (spine sunned, heavy chipping, several long tears), mtd color illus fr panel. *Baltimore**. $150/£94

SHAKESPEARE, WILLIAM. The Works. London/NY: Virtue, (1875-76). 'Imperial Edition,' Amer issue. 2 vols. Lg thick folio. 57 full-pg steel engrs. Aeg. Full gilt-pict brn morocco. Bookbinder's ticket each vol 'J. Beacham, Bookbinder, 12 Dey St. New York.' *Swann**. $373/£233

SHAKESPEARE, WILLIAM. The Works. Alexander Pope (ed). London: Jacob Tonson, 1723-25. 1st 4to ed. 6 vols. Contemp calf (expertly rebacked), morocco spine labels. VG set. *Pacific**. $2,300/£1,438

SHAKESPEARE, WILLIAM. The Works. NY, 1847. 3 vols. Aeg. Contemp pub's deluxe binding: full gilt-pict maroon morocco. *Swann**. $345/£216

SHAKESPEARE, WILLIAM. The Works. Herbert Farjeon (ed). (London)/NY: Nonesuch, 1929-33. One of 1600 numbered sets (550 for US). 7 vols. Lg 8vo. Teg. Full tan niger morocco, raised bands. Nice set (eps offset; few sm mks; spines, few edges sl sunned). *Reese*. $1,650/£1,031

SHALER, WILLIAM. Journal of a Voyage Between China and the Northwestern Coast of America Made in 1804 by William Shaler. Claremont, CA: Saunders Private Press, 1935. One of 700. Fldg map. 1/2 cl, marbled bds. (Spine sl dull), else NF. Howes S324. *Pacific**. $150/£94

SHANAFELT, T. M. The Baptist History of South Dakota. Sioux Falls, (1899). 1st ed. (Ink inscrip; bumped, spine label.) *King*. $75/£47

SHAND, P. MORTON. The Architecture of Pleasure. Modern Theatres and Cinemas. London: Batsford, 1930. 1st ed. 128 illus hors texte. (Spine sl faded), o/w Fine. *Europa*. $86/£54

SHANGE, NTOZAKE. A Daughter's Geography. NY: St. Martin's, (1983). 1st ed. Fine in pub's slipcase. *Hermitage*. $50/£31

SHANGE, NTOZAKE. For Colored Girls Who Have Considered Suicide/When the Rainbow Is Enuf. NY: Macmillan, (1977). 1st ed. Rev copy w/slip laid in. Inscribed. Fine in dj. *Hermitage*. $150/£94

SHANGE, NTOZAKE. Nappy Edges. NY: St. Martin's, (1978). 1st ed. Fine in dj (spine faded, sl chipped). *Hermitage*. $50/£31

SHANGE, NTOZAKE. Sassafrass, Cypress and Indigo. NY: St. Martin's, (1982). 1st ed. NF in dj. *Hermitage*. $50/£31

SHANGE, NTOZAKE. Sassafrass, Cypress and Indigo. NY, 1982. 1st ed. Fine in Fine dj (lt rubbed). *Warren*. $35/£22

SHANGE, NTOZAKE. Sassafrass, Cypress and Indigo. NY: St. Martins, 1982. Advance uncorrected proof. NF in ptd blue wrappers. *Pettler*. $45/£28

SHANKS, EDWARD. Old King Cole. London: Macmillan, 1936. 1st ed. (Pg edges lt spotted), o/w Fine in dj (spine sl dknd, sm tears). *Mordida*. $85/£53

SHANKS, EDWARD. Songs. Poetry Bookshop, 1915. 1st Eng ed. Pict card wrappers. VG (foxed). *Clearwater*. $40/£25

SHANKS, EDWARD. The Universal War and the Universal State. London, 1946. One of 550. Uncut. Fine (sl rubbed). *Polyanthos*. $35/£22

SHANNON, BILL and GEORGE KALINSKY. The Ball Parks. Hawthorn, 1975. 1st ed. VG in VG dj. *Plapinger*. $175/£109

SHANNON, DELL. Extra Kill. NY, 1962. 1st ed. Nice in dj (rear sl soil rubbed). *King*. $40/£25

SHANNON, FRED ALBERT. The Organization and Administration of the Union Army. Cleveland: A.H. Clark, 1928. 1st ed. 2 vols. Frontispieces. Blue cl. VF in djs (vol 1 tattered remnants, vol 2 spine top cut away to show spine title). *Chapel Hill*. $365/£228

SHAPIRO, ARNOLD. All Kinds of Cats. A Pop-Up Book. London: World Distributors, 1976. Larry Moore (illus). 5 dbl-pg pop-ups. Glazed pict bds. VG. *Bookfinders*. $40/£25

SHAPLEY, FERN RUSK. Paintings from the Samuel H. Kress Collection. Italian Schools XIII-XV Century. London: Phaidon for Samuel H. Kress Foundation, (1966). 1st ed. 17 full-pg tipped-in color plts. Dk blue buckram. Good in dj. *Karmiole*. $100/£63

SHARP, DENNIS. Sources of Modern Architecture: A Bibliography. Lund Humphries, 1967. VG in dec wraps. *Hadley*. $16/£10

SHARP, GRANVILLE. The Law of Retribution. London: White & Dilly, 1776. 2,357,2 ads. Mod 1/4 calf, red label. VG. *Adelson*. $285/£178

SHARP, MARGERY. Miss Bianca and the Bridesmaid. Boston: Little, Brown, 1972. 1st US ed. 5x8. Erik Blegvad (illus). 123pp. VG + in dj (sl edgeworn). *My Bookhouse*. $47/£29

SHARP, MARGERY. Miss Bianca in the Salt Mines. Boston/Toronto: Little, Brown, (1966). 1st ed. 8vo. Garth Williams (illus). (vii),148pp. Yellow cl. VG (bumped, lt spotted, sm stain) in dj (soiled, lt chipped). *Blue Mountain*. $15/£9

SHARP, PAUL F. Whoop-Up Country. Helena: Historical Soc of MT, 1960. (Bkpl), else Good. *Dumont*. $40/£25

SHARPE, EDMUND A. Treatise on the Rise and Progress of Decorated Window Trachery in England. London, 1849. xii,113pp; 97 woodcuts, 6 steel engrs. Marbled eps; aeg. Orig 1/2 morocco, gilt. (Bkpl, tape-repair to pg x, sl browned, hinges cracked; rubbed.) *Edwards*. $64/£40

SHARPE, PHILIP. The Rifle in America. NY, 1938. 1st ed. Signed. Good (hinges sl loose, corner bumped, lt rubbed). *King*. $65/£41

SHARPE, PHILIP. The Rifle in America. NY, 1938. 1st ed. Signed. Dec buckram. (Plt of stamps pasted to fep, edges spotted), o/w VG + in VG dj. *Sagebrush*. $95/£59

SHARPE, PHILIP. The Rifle in America. NY: William Morrow, 1938. 1st ed. Signed. VG + in dj (worn). *Labordo*. $150/£94

SHARPE, PHILIP. The Rifle in America. NY: Funk & Wagnalls, 1947. 2nd ed. Black cl. (Lt edgeworn), else VG + . *Bowman*. $65/£41

SHARPE, SAMUEL. The History of Egypt from the Earliest Times Till the Conquest by the Arabs A.D. 640. London: Moxon, 1859. 4th ed. 2 vols. xxxii,407; xx,411,8pp. (Ex-lib; crudely rebacked, rubbed, lib spine #), o/w Good. *Worldwide*. $85/£53

SHARPE, TOM. Indecent Exposure. Secker, 1973. 1st ed. Black bds, gilt. VG (edges sl foxed) in dj (sm tear). *Blackwell's*. $96/£60

SHARPE, TOM. Porterhouse Blue. Secker, 1974. 1st ed. Red bds, gilt. Fine in dj (sl rubbed). *Blackwell's*. $120/£75

SHAUGHNESSY, JIM. Rutland Road. Howell-North Books, (1981). 2nd ed, 1st ptg. Good in dj (worn, repaired). *Rybski*. $55/£34

SHAW, ALBERT. Abraham Lincoln. NY, 1929. 2 vols. Teg. (Cvrs rubbed, sl stained.) *King*. $50/£31

SHAW, ALBERT. Abraham Lincoln. His Path to the Presidency. NY: Review of Reviews Corp, 1929. 1st ed. 2 vols. Teg. Red cl stamped in black/gold. Very Nice set in djs (sl chipped). *Karmiole*. $75/£47

SHAW, ALBERT. Abraham Lincoln: His Path to Presidency. Abraham Lincoln: The Year of His Election. NY: Review of Reviews, 1929. 1st ed. 2 vols. Pict cl, gilt. NF. *Sadlon*. $50/£31

SHAW, ANNA HOWARD. The Story of a Pioneer. NY/London: Harper, (1915). 1st ed. Teg. Port label of Shaw to fr cvr. (Spine ends sl rubbed, gilt sl dull.) *Sadlon*. $25/£16

SHAW, ARNOLD. The Street That Never Slept: New York's Fabled 52d St. NY: Coward, McCann, (1971). 1st ed. VG in pict dj. *Petrilla*. $40/£25

SHAW, C. E. and S. CAMPBELL. Snakes of the American West. NY, 1974. 1st ed. Dj (lt chipped). *Sutton*. $65/£41

SHAW, CHARLES. A Topographical and Historical Description of Boston.... Boston: Oliver Spear, 1817. 1st ed. Frontis, 311,(1)pp, errata leaf; 6 (of 8) plts. Uncut. Contemp 2-toned bds (rebacked). Howes S337. *M & S*. $150/£94

SHAW, EDWARD. Civil Architecture; or...System of Building.... Boston: Marsh, Caper & Lyon, 1832. 2nd ed. 97 b/w copper plt engrs (foxed). Full contemp calf (rubbed, bumped, fr bd nearly detached). *Metropolitan**. $115/£72

SHAW, FRED G. The Science of Fly Fishing for Trout. NY, 1925. *Swann**. $149/£93

SHAW, FREDERICK et al. Oil Lamps and Iron Ponies. SF: Bay Books, 1949. 1st deluxe ed, signed by all 3 authors. Inscribed, signed presentation by George Harlan (co-author). Dec cl, gilt. VF in dj (spine faded). *Argonaut*. $125/£78

SHAW, GEORGE A. Madagascar and France. Religious Tract Soc, 1885. 1st ed. 320pp. Contemp red 1/2 calf, raised gilt bands, black leather label, gilt. Nice (spine sl rubbed). *Sotheran*. $240/£150

SHAW, GEORGE BERNARD. Androcles and the Lion, Overruled, Pygmalion. London: Constable, 1916. 1st ed. Lt grn cl, gilt. (Sm spine indentation), else Fine in lt blue dj (price sticker remains on spine). *Bromer*. $500/£313

SHAW, GEORGE BERNARD. The Apple Cart: A Political Extravaganza. NY: Brentano's, 1931. 1st separate Amer ed. Paper spine label. (Eps foxed), else VG in VG dj (flaps foxed, few sm chips). *Reese*. $40/£25

SHAW, GEORGE BERNARD. The Author's Apology from Mrs. Warren's Profession. NY: Brentano's, 1905. VG in ptd wraps. *Dramatis*. $65/£41

SHAW, GEORGE BERNARD. Back to Methuselah. LEC, 1939. Ltd to 1500 numbered, signed by John Farleigh (illus). Fine in slipcase. *Swann**. $46/£29

SHAW, GEORGE BERNARD. The Collected Works of.... NY: W.H. Wise, 1930-32. One of 1790. 30 (of 33) vols. Teg. 1/2 cl, bds, paper spine labels. Fine. *Pacific**. $374/£234

SHAW, GEORGE BERNARD. The Doctor's Dilemma, Getting Married, and The Shewing-Up of Blanco Posnet. London: Constable, 1911. 1st ed. Lt grn cl, gilt. (Eps, spine sl dknd), else Fine in dj (chipped). *Bromer*. $500/£313

SHAW, GEORGE BERNARD. Everybody's Political What's What? London: Constable, (1944). 1st ed. Red cl, gilt. (Eps foxed), o/w NF in dj (sl foxed). *Heritage*. $75/£47

SHAW, GEORGE BERNARD. Heartbreak House, Great Catherine, and Playlets of the War. London: Constable, 1919. 1st British ed. Pale grn cl, gilt. (Eps sl offset), o/w VG in dj (lt worn, inner mend spine crown). *Reese*. $100/£63

SHAW, GEORGE BERNARD. The League of Nations. London: Fabian Soc, 1929. 1st Eng ed. VG (staple rusted causing spine spotting; cvrs sl creased) in wrappers. *Ulysses*. $48/£30

SHAW, GEORGE BERNARD. Man and Superman: The Revolutionist's Handbook. LEC, 1962. Ltd to 1500 numbered, signed by Charles Mozley (illus). Fine in slipcase. *Swann**. $69/£43

SHAW, GEORGE BERNARD. A Plan of Campaign for Labor. London: Fabian Soc, 1894. 1st Eng ed. VG (staple rusting, fr cvr sl spotted, partly dknd) in wrappers. *Ulysses*. $104/£65

SHAW, GEORGE BERNARD. Prefaces. London: Constable, (1934). 1st collective ed, ordinary binding. VG (eps foxed) in dj (chipped, tanned). *Reese*. $30/£19

SHAW, GEORGE BERNARD. Pygmalion and Candida. LEC, 1974. One of 2000 signed by Clark Hutton (illus). 2 vols. Fine in slipcase. *Swann**. $57/£36

SHAW, GEORGE BERNARD. The Quintessence of Ibsenism. London: Walter Scott, 1891. 1st ed. Indigo cl. (Spine ends lt rubbed), else Fine. *Bromer*. $300/£188

SHAW, GEORGE BERNARD. The Sanity of Art. London: New Age, 1908. 1st ed. NF (spine foot sl worn) in brn wrappers, 1st state w/3 colons following Shaw's name. *Sumner & Stillman*. $75/£47

SHAW, GEORGE BERNARD. Shaw on Stalin. (London: Russia Today Soc, 1941.) 1st ed. Pamphlet. Fine (pp toned) in wrappers (spot on fr going through to c. pg). *Bromer*. $75/£47

SHAW, GEORGE BERNARD. Sixteen Self Sketches. London: Constable, 1949. Standard ed. (Fore-edge sl spotted.) Dj (sl spotted, chipped). *Hollett*. $32/£20

SHAW, GEORGE BERNARD. Two Plays for Puritans. NY: LEC, 1966. One of 1500 ptd. Signed by George Him (illus). Red cl, gilt. Fine in slipcase. *Pacific**. $23/£14

SHAW, GEORGE BERNARD. Two Plays for Puritans. NY: LEC, 1966. One of 1500. Signed by George Him (illus). Sm folio. Fine in slipcase (soiled, 2 stickers removed from rear). *Agvent*. $40/£25

SHAW, GEORGE BERNARD. The Works of.... London: Constable, (1930). One of 1000 numbered sets. 33 vols. 8vo. Teal cl, gilt. Fine set in djs. *Heritage*. $1,750/£1,094

SHAW, GRAHAM. Printing in Calcutta to 1800. Bibliographical Society, 1981. 1st ed. VG. *Cox*. $19/£12

SHAW, HENRY. The Hand Book of Medieval Alphabets and Devices. London: William Pickering, 1853. 36 plts. Blue blind-stamped cl (extrems worn; tp spotted). *Maggs*. $56/£35

SHAW, IRWIN. Bury the Dead. NY: Random House, (1936). 1st ed, 1st bk. Red cl, gilt. VG (eps, edges lt foxed; bkseller's foil label rep) in dj (spine tanned, few nicks). *Reese*. $100/£63

SHAW, IRWIN. Paris Photographs 1935-1981 Magnum. NY: Aperture, 1981. 1st ed w/dj. *Appelfeld*. $90/£56

SHAW, IRWIN. Tip on a Dead Jockey. NY: Random House, (1957). 1st ed. Inscribed. Fine in Fine dj (sl rubbed). *Between The Covers*. $100/£63

SHAW, IRWIN. Two Weeks in Another Town. London, (1960). 1st Eng ed. (Ink name, date), else VG in dj. *King*. $20/£13

SHAW, IRWIN. Two Weeks in Another Town. NY: Random House, (1960). 1st ed. VF in VF dj. *Between The Covers*. $150/£94

SHAW, IRWIN. Voices of a Summer Day. NY: Delacorte, (1965). 1st ed. VF in VF dj. *Between The Covers*. $150/£94

SHAW, IRWIN. The Young Lions. NY: Random House, (1948). 1st ed. VF in VF dj (sl rubbed). *Between The Covers*. $400/£250

SHAW, JAMES BYAM. Drawings by Old Masters. Clarendon, 1976. Presentation copy. 2 vols. 890 plts. Djs. *Edwards.* $240/£150

SHAW, JAMES C. North from Texas. Herbert O. Brayer (ed). Evanston, IL: Branding Iron Press, 1952. Rpt ed. One of 750. VG. *Labordo.* $85/£53

SHAW, LLOYD. Cowboy Dances. Caldwell, ID: Caxton, 1949. Rev ed. Good in dj (sl worn). *Lien.* $15/£9

SHAW, LORD. The Law of the Kinsmen. London: Hodder & Stoughton, 1923? Usable (cl mkd, stained). *Boswell.* $45/£28

SHAW, LUELLA. True History of Some of the Pioneers of Colorado. Hotchkiss: W.S. Coburn, John Patterson & A.K. Shaw, 1909. 1st ed. (Corner chipped), else NF in gray paper wraps, stapled. *Hermitage.* $85/£53

SHAW, R. CUNLIFFE. The Men of the North. Leyland: Privately ptd, n.d. (c.1970). Mint in pict dj. *Hollett.* $48/£30

SHAW, ROBERT. A Card from Morocco. NY: HBW, (1969). 1st ed. VF in VF dj (sm rubbed spot). *Between The Covers.* $100/£63

SHAW, THOMAS. Travels, or Observations Relating to Several Parts of Barbary and the Levant. Oxford: Theatre, 1738. 1st ed. Folio. viii,442,60,(8 index)pp; 23 copper-engr plts, 11 maps (6 fldg). Contemp full calf, gilt. Fine (bkpls removed; spine sl rubbed, fr joint sl weak). *Sotheran.* $2,480/£1,550

SHAW, THOMAS. Travels, or Observations Relating to Several Parts of Barbary and the Levant.... London, 1757. 2nd ed. 34 (of 36) engr plts. Contemp sheep (fr cvr loose; sl marginal worming several sigs). *Swann*.* $230/£144

SHAW-SPARROW, WALTER. Angling in British Art. London: John Lane, (1923). 1st ed. Blue cl, gilt. (Spine head sl sunned, sm tear), else VG. *Pacific*.* $138/£86

SHAW-SPARROW, WALTER. Angling in British Art. London, (1923). (Backstrip, cvr edges dknd.) *Swann*.* $149/£93

SHAW-SPARROW, WALTER. Angling in British Art. London: John Lane, 1923. 1st ed. 39 color plts. Blue cl. NF. *Biscotti.* $200/£125

SHAW-SPARROW, WALTER. A Book of Sporting Painters. London/NY, (1931). Uncut. (Sl worn.) *Oinonen*.* $120/£75

SHAW-SPARROW, WALTER. A Book of Sporting Painters. London/NY, 1931. 1st ed. 136 plts (15 color). Fore/lower edge uncut. (Lt spotted.) *Edwards.* $120/£75

SHAW-SPARROW, WALTER. British Sporting Artists from Barlow to Herring. London/NY, (1922). Uncut. Gilt-pict cl. (Sl worn.) *Oinonen*.* $110/£69

SHAW-SPARROW, WALTER. George Stubbs and Ben Marshall. London, 1929. One of 250 numbered. Uncut. Gilt-lettered cl. (Sl worn.) *Oinonen*.* $170/£106

SHAW-SPARROW, WALTER. Henry Alken. London, 1927. One of 250 numbered, signed by Sir Theodore Cook (intro). Uncut. Gilt-lettered cl. (Sl worn, cvrs sl spotted, soiled.) *Oinonen*.* $180/£113

SHAW-SPARROW, WALTER. Old England. NY, 1908. 80 plts. Teg. (Lib bkpl; corners sl rubbed, sl dkng, sm spine stain.) *Edwards.* $136/£85

SHAY, FRANK (ed). Iron Men and Wooden Ships. GC: Doubleday, Page, 1924. 1st trade ed. Orig bds (badly worn). Text Good. *Zubal*.* $20/£13

SHEA, JOHN GILMARY. Discovery and Exploration of the Mississippi Valley with the Original Narratives.... Albany: Joseph McDonough, 1903. 2nd ed. One of 500. Port, fldg map. Cl spine, paper label, paper-cvrd bds. (Worn, lt rubbed), else Good. Howes S357. *Brown.* $95/£59

SHEA, JOHN GILMARY. Discovery and Exploration of the Mississippi Valley. Albany: Joseph McDonough, 1903. 2nd ed. One of 500 numbered. Lg fldg map. (Internally soiled; extrems worn), else Good. Howes S363. *Dumont.* $135/£84

SHEA, RICHARD F. Transistor Audio Amplifiers. NY/London: John Wiley & Sons/Chapman & Hall, (1955). VG in dj (worn). *Weber.* $20/£13

SHEBL, JAMES. In This Wild Water. The Suppressed Poems of Robinson Jeffers. (Pasadena: Ward Ritchie, 1976.) 1st ed. Frontis by Ansel Adams. Brn cl, gilt. VF in pict dj. *Argonaut.* $75/£47

SHECKLEY, ROBERT. Untouched by Human Hands. London: Michael Joseph, 1955. 1st ed. (Pg edges lt foxed), else NF in dj. *Lame Duck.* $125/£78

SHEEHAN, JOSEPH EASTMAN. Plastic Surgery of the Nose. NY: Paul B. Hoeber, 1925. 1st ed. 9 plts. Dk grn cl (inner hinges cracked, corners sl showing; sig). *Weber.* $300/£188

SHEEHAN, JOSEPH EASTMAN. Plastic Surgery of the Orbit. NY: Macmillan, 1927. 1st ed. Color frontis, 11 color plts. Lt olive grn cl. Fine in dj remnant (worn). *Weber.* $265/£166

SHEELER, CHARLES. Charles Sheeler: Paintings, Drawings, Photographs. NY: MOMA, 1939. 1st ed. One of 5000. Stiff wraps. (Ex-lib, sl mks, worn, cvrs spotted.) *King.* $50/£31

SHEERAN, JAMES B. Confederate Chaplain. Joseph T. Durkin (ed). Milwaukee, (WI): Bruce Pub, (1960). 1st ed. Gray cl. Fine in NF dj. *Chapel Hill.* $80/£50

SHELDON, HAROLD P. Tranquillity. NY: Derrydale, 1936. One of 950 numbered. Red cl (spine corners sl rubbed). Fine. *Biscotti.* $300/£188

SHELDON, J. Concretions from the Champlain Clays of the Connecticut Valley. Boston: The Author, c1900. 14 plts. VG. *Blake.* $75/£47

SHELFORD, V. E. Animal Communities in Temperate America. Geog Soc Chicago, 1913. 1st ed. Fldg map. Blue cl. (Ex-lib), else VG. *Larry Price.* $25/£16

SHELFORD, V. E. et al (eds). Naturalist's Guide to the Americas. Balt: Williams/Wilkins, 1926. 1st ed. 16 maps. Pict limp cl. VG + (ex-lib). *Mikesh.* $25/£16

SHELLEY, D. The Fraktor, Writings or Illuminated Manuscripts of the Pennsylvania Germans. PA German Folklore Soc, 1961. 6 color, 130 monochrome plts. VG. *Moss.* $72/£45

SHELLEY, E. Hunting Big Game with Dogs in Africa. Columbus: The Author, 1924. 1st ed. Inscribed, signed. Frontis. VG + (sl spotted; few sm rust spots to edge) in blue cl, gilt. *Backman.* $100/£63

SHELLEY, FRANCES. The Diary of Frances Lady Shelley 1787-1873. Richard Edgcumbe (ed). John Murray, 1912-1913. 2 vols. Fldg genealogical chart. Teg. Good (lt spotted; spines bumped, chipped, sunned, corners bumped, rubbed). *Tiger.* $51/£32

SHELLEY, MARY W. Frankenstein or, The Modern Prometheus. NY: Harrison Smith & Robert Haas, 1934. 1st ed. Signed by Lynd Ward (illus). 1/2 cl, dec bds, paper spine label. VG- (spine, extrems dknd, ends chipped, label w/white smudge). *Pacific*.* $81/£51

SHELLEY, MARY W. Frankenstein, or the Modern Prometheus. NY: Henry G. Daggers, 1845. 8vo. Orig ptd wraps. (Foxing, dampstaining; lg chunk out of cvr, edges curled, chips, splits.) *Metropolitan*.* $517/£323

SHELLEY, MARY W. Frankenstein, or, the Modern Prometheus. NY: G&D, n.d. 7 plts of 'Scenes from the Universal Photoplay,' 1 dbl-pg. Red cl, lettered in black. Fine in NF pict dj (sl edgeworn, sl chipped). *Pacific*.* $863/£539

SHELLEY, MARY W. Frankenstein. NY: Dodd, Mead, (1983). 1st ed thus. Ltd to 526, this one of 26 signed by Berni Wrightson (illlus), and Stephen King (intro). 4to. Pict tp; 43 full-pg, 1 dbl-pg b/w illus. Black cl, gilt. NF in VG blue paper slipcase (stained, rubbed). *Blue Mountain.* $700/£438

SHELLEY, MARY W. Frankenstein. Boston/Cambridge: Sever, Francis et al, 1869. 2nd Amer ed. 177pp. Maroon cl (spine ends, corners rubbed). VG. *Second Life.* $450/£281

SHELLEY, PERCY BYSSHE. The Dramatic/Narrative Poems. Florence, 1922/1927. 3 vols. Teg, rest uncut. Black cl (backs sl faded). *Petersfield.* $67/£42

SHELLEY, PERCY BYSSHE. The English Replicas...Adonais. NY: Payson & Clarke, 1927. One of 100 numbered. Vellum over stiff bds. NF. *Reese.* $85/£53

SHELLEY, PERCY BYSSHE. Ode to the West Wind. Florence: Allen, 1951. One of 100. (Spine, extrems sl sunned), else VG in wrappers. *Pacific*.* $75/£47

SHELLEY, PERCY BYSSHE. The Sensitive Plant. London: Heinemann, (1911). 1st ed illus by Charles Robinson, in deluxe binding. 4to. 18 mtd color plts. Teg. Full cream parchment, gilt. Fine. *Sotheran.* $840/£525

SHELLEY, PERCY BYSSHE. Shelley's Lost Letters to Harriet. Leslie Hotson (ed). Faber & Faber, 1930. Contemp newspaper cutting tipped-in. (Ex-lib, label removal fr cvr, cancellation mk lower edge; rebacked w/orig strip relaid, cvrs unevenly sunned w/sl mks, corners rubbed). *Tiger.* $13/£8

SHELLEY, PERCY BYSSHE. The Works in Verse and Prose. Harry Buxton Forman (ed). London: Reeves and Turner, 1880. 8 vols. Tall 8vo. Engr frontis each vol. Full olive green morocco, gilt mitre lines on cvrs enclosing gilt emblem of ram's head, gilt paneled spines, raised bands, inner wide gilt borders, aeg, by Morley, Oxford. (Spine colors sl faded), else Sound set. *Appelfeld.* $1,750/£1,094

SHELTON, LOUISE. Continuous Bloom in America. NY: Scribner, 1915. 1st ed. 16 plts. Dec grn cl, gilt. (Bkpl, browned), else VG. *Fair Meadow.* $40/£25

SHELTON, WILMA LOY. Checklist of New Mexico Publications. Albuquerque: Univ of NM, 1954. (Wraps sl soiled), else VG. *Dumont.* $35/£22

SHEPARD, ERNEST H. Drawn from Life. London: Methuen, 1961. 1st Eng ed. Fine (spine foot sl bumped) in dj (sl nicked, spine sl dknd). *Ulysses.* $56/£35

SHEPARD, ERNEST H. Drawn From Memory. London: Methuen, 1957. 1st Eng ed. VG (paperclip mk to top edge first few ll, feps partly browned) in dj (sl dusty, nicked, edges rubbed, spine sl faded). *Ulysses.* $56/£35

SHEPARD, ESTHER. Paul Bunyon. Seattle: McNeil, (1925). 2nd ptg. VG. *Perier.* $20/£13

SHEPARD, ISOBEL S. The Cruise of the U.S. Steamer 'Rush' in Behring Sea, Summer of 1889. SF: Bancroft, 1889. 1st ed. 257pp; fldg map. Pict cl (rubbed). Good (ex-libris). *Walcot.* $61/£38

SHEPARD, L. The History of Street Literature. Newton Abbot: David & Charles, 1973. Frontis. Brn cl. Dj. *Maggs.* $24/£15

SHEPARD, LORENZO B. The Dignity of Mechanical Labor. NY: Casper C. Childs, 1852. 1st ed. 32pp. Orig ptd wrappers. *M & S.* $125/£78

SHEPARD, LUCIUS. The Golden. Singletown, CA: Mark V. Ziesing, 1993. 1st ed. One of 500. Signed by Shepard & Arnie Fenner (illus). As New in dj, slipcase. *Pacific*.* $40/£25

SHEPARD, ODELL. Pedlar's Progress: The Life of Bronson Alcott. Boston: Little, Brown, 1937. 1st ed. One of 500 signed. Some pp unopened. Brn cl spine, tan bds. NF (lacks glassine dj, slipcase). *Lucas.* $90/£56

SHEPARD, ODELL. Thy Rod and Thy Creel. Hartford: Mitchell, 1931. 2nd ed. Fine in VG dj (verso taped). *Bowman.* $75/£47

SHEPARD, SAM. Hawk Moon. A Book of Short Stories, Poems and Monologues. L.A.: Black Sparrow, 1973. 1st ed, ltd issue. One of 200 numbered (of 226), signed. (Edges sl sunned), o/w Fine. *Reese.* $175/£109

SHEPARD, SAM. Operation Sidewinder. Indianapolis: Bobbs-Merrill, (1970). 1st ed. Gray cl. Fine (spine ends sl rubbed) in dj (sl edgeworn). *Heritage.* $100/£63

SHEPARD, SAM. The Unseen Hand and Other Plays. Indianapolis: Bobbs-Merrill, (1972). 1st ed. Black bds, gilt. (Top edge sl spotted), o/w NF in dj (price-clipped, lt edgeworn). *Heritage.* $75/£47

SHEPHERD, GORDON. Where the Lion Trod. Macmillan, 1960. 1st ed. 8vo. 177pp; 18 illus by John Verney. VG + in pict dj. *Bookmark.* $35/£22

SHEPHERD, HENRY E. Life of Robert Edward Lee. NY/Washington: Neale, 1906. 1st ed. Teg. Gray cl. VG (faded). *Chapel Hill.* $185/£116

SHEPHERD, R. H. The Bibliography of Thackeray, a Bibliographical List. London: Elliot Stock, 1880. Supp to deluxe ed. Blue cl (headcaps, corners bumped), gilt. *Maggs.* $29/£18

SHEPHERD, THOMAS. Metropolitan Improvements. London: Jones, 1829. 1st ed. 2 vols. Crown 4to. vi,ii,172; iii,160pp. Aeg, inner edge gilt dentelles. NF set (sl foxed, ep edges sl stained, tissue guards sl offset) in contemp red morocco (spine ends sl rubbed, bkpls), gilt-emb, raised bands. *Ulysses.* $2,400/£1,500

SHEPHERD, WILLIAM. Prairie Experiences in Handling Cattle and Sheep. London: Chapman & Hall, 1884. 1st ed. Pict cl. VG. Howes S389. *Labordo.* $450/£281

SHEPPARD, EDWARD. Brief Memoir of Mrs. Edward Sheppard, by Her Father. Milton-on-Thames: Ptd by James Large, 1849. Only ed. Inscribed presentation. 57pp. Orig cl (spine faded). *Young.* $120/£75

SHEPPARD, ERIC W. Bedford Forest, the Confederacy's Greatest Cavalryman. NY, 1930. (Bkpl, faded, sl worn, spine sl discolored.) *Woolman.* $125/£78

SHEPPARD, WILLIAM. The Touch-Stone of Common Assurances.... London: Ptd by W. Strahan & W. Woodfall et al, 1784. 5th ed. Mod 1/4 leather over buckram. Good. *Boswell.* $350/£219

SHERARD, ROBERT H. Child Slaves of Britain. London: Hurst & Blackett, 1905. 1st Eng ed. Teg. Buckram (spine ends sl bumped). VG. *Ulysses.* $152/£95

SHERIDAN, PHILIP H. Personal Memoirs. NY: Charles L. Webster, 1888. 1st ed. 2 vols. Dk grn cl, gilt. (Old dampstain margin of text throughout vol 1; few hinges cracked, weak; sl stains vol 1; worn.) *Baltimore*.* $60/£38

SHERIDAN, RICHARD BRINSLEY. The Critic: Or, A Tragedy Rehearsed. Dublin: Messrs Sheppard, Wilkinson, 1785. 2nd Dublin ed (?). vi,(iv),61pp (apparently lacks 1/2 title). Calf-backed bds. *Young.* $32/£20

SHERIDAN, RICHARD BRINSLEY. The Rivals. LEC, 1953. Ltd to 1500 numbered, signed by Rene Ben Sussan (illus). Fine in slipcase. *Swann*.* $34/£21

SHERIDAN, RICHARD BRINSLEY. The School for Scandal. Stratford-upon-Avon: Shakespeare Head, 1930. Ltd to 475. 1/2 vellum over patterned bds. Fine in slipcase. *Cullen.* $200/£125

SHERIDAN, RICHARD BRINSLEY. The School for Scandal. LEC, 1934. Ltd to 1500 numbered, signed by Rene Ben Sussan (illus). Fine in slipcase. *Swann*.* $40/£25

SHERIDAN, RICHARD BRINSLEY. The School for Scandal. London: Simpkin, Marshall, Hamilton, Kent, ca 1894. 1st ed illus thus. Folio. Lucius Rossi (illus). (vi),35pp. Dec eps; aeg. Gray cl, gilt, w/onlaid pict labels. VG (sl shaken). *Sotheran.* $125/£78

SHERIDAN, SONIA LANDY. Energized Artscience. Text by Diane Kirkpatrick. Chicago: Museum of Science and Industry, 1978. 1st ed. NF in illus spiral-bound stiff wrappers. *Cahan.* $60/£38

SHERINGHAM, HUGH and JOHN C. MOORE (eds). The Book of the Fly-Rod. Boston: Houghton Mifflin, 1931. 1st ed. Grn cl, gilt. (Spine sunned), else VG in slipcase (sl cracked). *Pacific*.* $46/£29

SHERINGHAM, HUGH. An Angler's Hours. London: Macmillan, 1905. 1st ed. Grn cl, gilt. (Spine, extrems sunned), else VG. *Pacific*.* $35/£22

SHERMAN, ANDREW. In the Lowlands of Louisiana in 1863 an Address Delivered.... Morristown, NJ: Howard, 1908. Port. Flexible cl bds. (Sl worn), else Good. *Brown.* $60/£38

SHERMAN, HAROLD M. Safe! NY: G&D, 1928. 5x7.5. 308pp. VG (sl shelfworn) in dj (sm chips). *My Bookhouse.* $42/£26

SHERMAN, HENRY. The Centennial Year of the Confederacy. The United States of America. Washington: Sherman & Atlee, 1875. 1st ed. Internally Fine (spine ends, corners frayed, sm chip, bubbling, rear pastedown loose). *Sadlon.* $15/£9

SHERMAN, JAMES E. and BARBARA H. Ghost Towns of Arizona. Norman: Univ of OK, (1969). 1st ed. Black cl. Fine in NF dj. *Harrington.* $40/£25

SHERRIFF, R. C. Journey's End. NY: Brentano's, 1929. 1st US ed. Cl-backed batik bds. (Shadow of ink name eradicated from pastedown), else Fine in NF pict dj (nick spine top). *Reese.* $75/£47

SHERRIFF, R. C. Journey's End. Gollancz, 1930. One of 600 signed by Sherriff and Vernon Bartlett. 1/4 leather. No dj (as issued?). VG. *Martin.* $77/£48

SHERRILL, CHARLES HITCHCOCK. Stained Glass Tours in Germany, Austria and the Rhine Lands. London/NY, 1927. 1st ed. Color frontis. (Lt spotting; spine faded.) *Edwards.* $32/£20

SHERRILL, MILES O. A Soldier's Story: Prison Life and Other Incidents in the War of 1861-65. (Raleigh, 1904.) 1st ed. Fine in ptd wrappers. *Chapel Hill.* $300/£188

SHERRINGTON, CHARLES. The Integrative Action of the Nervous System. Cambridge, 1947. 2nd ed. *Fye.* $150/£94

SHERROD, ROBERT. History of Marine Corps Aviation in World War II. Washington, (1952). 1st ed. VG +. *Pratt.* $32/£20

SHERWIN, HENRY ALDEN. Bibliotheca Piscatoria: The Library of the Late Henry Alden Sherwin.... NY: Parke-Bernet Galleries, 1946. NF (prices realized penciled in margins). *Biscotti.* $50/£31

SHERWOOD, M. E. W. Here and There and Everywhere Reminiscences. Chicago: Herbert S. Stone, 1898. 301pp + 23pp pub's cat. Teg, rest untrimmed. (Few smudge mks in margins; sl worn.) *Woolson.* $10/£6

SHERWOOD, MARTYN. The Voyage of the Tai-Mo-Shan. London: Geoffrey Bles, n.d. (1935). 1st ed. Frontis, 15 plts. Blue cl (sl mkd, faded). *Morrell.* $16/£10

SHERWOOD, MRS. The Broken Hyacinth, or Ellen and Sophia. Phila: Amer Sunday School Union, n.d. (ca 1840). 12mo. VF full-pg copper engr frontis, 106pp. Marbled paper on bds, grn roan spine. VG (lt foxing, water spot rep; extrems chipped, rubbed). *Hobbyhorse.* $115/£72

SHERWOOD, MRS. The Re-Captured Negro. Boston: Samuel T. Armstrong, and Crocker & Brewster, 1821. 1st Amer ed. 12mo. 72pp. 3/4 black roan spine, gilt, gray paper on bds. (Pencil dedication, lacks pp53-56, lt foxing, rep restored; cvrs soiled, faded, spine sl rubbed.) *Hobbyhorse.* $100/£63

SHERWOOD, MRS. Social Tales for the Young. William Darton & Son, n.d. (1835). 1st ed. 8vo. 230pp (lacks frontis, rep). Aeg. Dk blackish-grn emb leather (hinges strained, spine ends chipped). *Bookmark.* $29/£18

SHERWOOD, ROBERT E. Idiot's Delight. NY: Scribner, 1936. 1st ed. (Offsetting to eps from flaps), else Fine in NF dj (lt rubbed). *Between The Covers.* $100/£63

SHERWOOD, ROBERT E. There Shall Be No Night. NY: Scribner, 1940. 1st ed. NF (lt soiled) in dj (lt used, rear panel sl chipped). *Beasley.* $45/£28

SHETTLES, ELIJAH L. Recollections of a Long Life. (Nashville): Blue & Gray, (1973). 1st ed. Fine. *Labordo.* $35/£22

SHIBLEY, FRED WARNER. Aspinwall Island. NY: Privately ptd, 1916. 1st ed. Uncut. Paper cvr-label. (Shelfworn.) *Oinonen*.* $130/£81

SHIEL, ROGER R. Early to Bed and Early to Rise.... Indianapolis, IN, 1909. 1st ed. Grn cl. NF. *Labordo.* $300/£188

SHIELDS, CAROL. Mary Swann. London: 4th Estate, 1990. 1st ed. Fine in dj. *Smith.* $75/£47

SHIELDS, CAROL. The Stone Diaries. NY, 1994. 1st Amer ed. Fine in Fine dj. *Warren.* $75/£47

SHIELDS, CAROL. Swann. NY, 1987. 1st Amer ed. Signed. NF in Fine dj. *Warren.* $50/£31

SHIELDS, G. O. Cruisings in the Cascades. Chicago/NY, 1889. 1st ed. 339pp + 6 leaves ads. Gilt-pict cl (shelfworn, spine ends sl frayed). *Oinonen*.* $60/£38

SHIELDS, G. O. (ed). American Game Fishes: Their Habits, Habitat, and Peculiarities. Chicago, 1892. 1/2 morocco (extrems rubbed). *Swann*.* $57/£36

SHIELS, ARCHIE W. (comp). Little Journeys Into the History of Russian America and the Purchase of Alaska. Bellingham, WA, 1949. One of 125. Signed. Blue cl, gilt. Fine. *Pacific*.* $219/£137

SHIFLET, KENNETH E. The Convenient Coward. Harrisburg, PA: Stackpole, (1961). 1st ed. VG in dj. *Lien.* $35/£22

SHIFLET, KENNETH E. The Convenient Coward. Harrisburg, PA, 1961. 1st ed. Map. Good in dj (chipped). *Dumont.* $35/£22

SHIH-HUA, TAN. A Chinese Testament: The Autobiography of Tan Shih-Hua as Told to S. Tretiakov. NY: S&S, 1934. 1st ed. (Sl soiled, spine ends sl frayed, sl foxed), o/w VG. *Worldwide.* $25/£16

SHILLITOE, THOMAS. Journal of the Life, Labours, and Travels of Thomas Shillitoe. London: Harvey & Darton, 1839. 1st ed. 2 vols. xvi,428; iv,427pp (few spots; vol 2 sl cocked). *Hollett.* $192/£120

SHILLITOE, THOMAS. Journal of the Life, Labours, and Travels of...in the Service of the Gospel of Jesus Christ. London: Harvey & Darton, 1839. 1st ed. 2 vols. xvi,428; (viii),427pp. Orig blind-stamped cl (worn). Fair. *Young.* $40/£25

Shining Clarity: God and Man in the Works of Robinson Jeffers. (Amador City): Quintessence, (1977). 1st ed. NF in dj, slipcase lined in blue felt w/brass emb cvr plt (detached). *Pacific*.* $109/£68

SHINKLE, JAMES D. Reminiscences of Roswell Pioneers. Roswell, NM, 1966. (Lt shelfworn), else VG. *Dumont.* $75/£47

SHINN, CHARLES H. Mining Camps. NY: Scribner, 1885. 1st ed. NF. Howes S416. *Labordo.* $550/£344

SHINN, CHARLES H. Mining Camps. NY: Knopf, 1948. Rpt. VG in dj (sl worn). *Dumont.* $35/£22

SHINN, CHARLES H. The Story of the Mine, As Illustrated by the Great Comstock Lode of Nevada. NY: D. Appleton, 1896. 1st ed. Fine. *Labordo.* $150/£94

SHINN, CHARLES H. The Story of the Mine. NY: D. Appleton, 1896. 1st ed. 272pp. VG in pict cl. *Lien.* $50/£31

SHIP, REUBEN. The Investigator. London: Sidgwick & Jackson, 1956. 1st Eng ed. NF (spine foot sl bumped) in dj (edges sl creased). *Ulysses.* $58/£36

SHIPLEY, WILLIAM. A True Treatise on the Art of Fly-Fishing, Trolling, Etc., as Practised on the Dove. Edward Fitzgibbon (ed). London, 1838. 1st ed, w/the List of Subscribers. Lg-paper issue. Frontis, text vignettes are mtd India proofs. xxxv,264pp. (Sl foxed; shelfworn, spine torn along rear joint.) *Oinonen*.* $120/£75

SHIPTON, CLIFFORD and JAMES MOONEY. National Index of American Imprints Through 1800. (Worcester): American Antiquarian Soc and Barre Publishers, 1969. 1st ed. 2 vols. Scarlet buckram, gilt, partly blocked in grn. (Sl rubbed.) *Baltimore*.* $110/£69

SHIPTON, CLIFFORD and JAMES MOONEY. National Index of American Imprints Through 1800: The Short-Title Evans. Worcester, 1969. 2 vols. (Lt worn.) *Oinonen*.* $90/£56

SHIPTON, ERIC. The Mount Everest Reconnaissance Expedition 1951. Hodder & Stoughton, 1952. 1st ed. (Inscrip.) Dj (piece torn from top edge affecting 1st 2 letters of title). *Hollett.* $64/£40

SHIPTON, ERIC. Mountains of Tartary. Hodder & Stoughton, (1951). 1st ed. 29 plts. VG in dj (edges chipped, sl spine loss). *Hollett.* $80/£50

SHIPTON, ERIC. Nanda Devi. London: Hodder & Stoughton, (1936). 1st ed. Frontis, 26 plts, guards. Pict eps. Black cl. NF (spine ends, corners lt worn, fr cvr sl spotted; sm ink name). Internally Fine. *Argonaut.* $225/£141

SHIPTON, ERIC. Upon That Mountain. London: Hodder & Stoughton, (1943). 1st ed. Frontis, 4 maps. Black cl. VG (sm stamp; lt worn, corners bumped). *Argonaut.* $60/£38

SHIRAZI, J. K. M. Life of Omar Al-Khayyami. Edinburgh/London: Foulis, 1905. 1st Eng ed. Highly patterned bds (sl handled, rubbed). *Clearwater.* $80/£50

SHIRCLIFFE, ARNOLD. The Edgewater Beach Hotel Salad Book. Chicago: Hotel Monthly, (1934). 5th ptg. VG. *Perier.* $35/£22

SHIRK, DAVID. The Cattle Drives of David Shirk. Martin F. Schmitt (ed). Portland, OR: Champoeg, 1956. 1st ed. Ltd to 750. VG. *Lien.* $65/£41

SHIRK, DAVID. The Cattle Drives of David Shirk...1871 and 1873 [and] His Later Experiences as a Cattleman in Eastern Oregon. (Portland): Champoeg, 1956. 1st ed. One of 750. Frontis, tipped-in photo. Fine. *Harrington.* $90/£56

SHIRLEY, GLENN. Buckskin and Spurs. NY: Hastings House, (1958). 1st ed. Fine in pict dj. *House.* $25/£16

SHIRLEY, GLENN. Guardian of the Law: The Life and Times of William Matthew Tilghman. Austin: Eakin, 1988. 1st ed. VF in dj. *Labordo.* $35/£22

SHIRLEY, GLENN. Heck Thomas, Frontier Marshall. Phila: Chilton, 1962. 1st ed. VG+ in dj. *Labordo.* $45/£28

SHIRLEY, GLENN. Henry Starr. NY: David McKay, 1965. 1st ed. Fine in dj. *Labordo.* $45/£28

SHIRLEY, GLENN. Pawnee Bill. Albuquerque, 1958. 1st ed. Good in dj. *Dumont.* $35/£22

SHIRLEY, GLENN. Red Yesterdays. Wichita Falls, TX: Nortex, 1977. VG in dj. *Dumont.* $30/£19

SHIRLEY, GLENN. Six Gun and Silver Star. Albuquerque: Univ of NM, 1955. 1st ed. Fine in dj. *Labordo.* $45/£28

SHIRLEY, GLENN. Six-Gun and Silver Star. Albuquerque: Univ of NM, 1955. 1st ed. VG in dj. *Lien.* $30/£19

SHIRLEY, GLENN. Temple Houston: Lawyer with a Gun. Norman: Univ of OK, (1980). 1st ed. VG in dj. *Lien.* $35/£22

SHIRLEY, GLENN. West of Hell's Fringe. Norman, 1978. 1st ed. NF in dj (price-clipped, rear cvr lt rubbed, soiled). *Baade.* $65/£41

SHIRLEY, RODNEY W. The Mapping of the World: Early Printed World Maps, 1472-1700. (London): Holland, (1984). VG (shelfworn) in dj. *Pacific*.* $138/£86

Shirley. (By Charlotte Bronte.) Smith, Elder, 1849. 1st ed. 3 vols. 8vo. Ads at end vol 1; ad for 3rd ed of Jane Eyre at end vol 3. Orig red cl, gilt. Bkpls of Eric S. Quayle. (Vol 1 edges sl dampstained, not affecting text; hinges neatly repaired, joints vol 1 split; spines faded.) *Sotheby's*.* $2,024/£1,265

Shirley. A Tale. (By Charlotte Bronte.) Smith, Elder, 1849. 1st ed. 3 vols. 8vo. Vol 2 p304 misnumbered 403. No ads at end of vol 1; ads at end of vol 3 advertising 3rd ed of Jane Eyre. Orig red vertically-ribbed cl (binder's ticket of Wesley & Co inside rear cvr vol 1), stamped in blind, spines lettered in gilt. The Jones-Newton-Doheny-Manney copy, w/bkpls (sl offsetting onto tps). Red cl box. *Sotheby's*.* $5,520/£3,450

SHIVE, JOHN N. The Properties, Physics, and Design of Semiconductor Devices. Princeton: Van Nostrand, (1959). 1st ed. VG. *Glaser.* $75/£47

SHIVERS, LOUISE. Here to Get My Baby Out of Jail. NY, 1983. 1st ed. Fine in Fine dj. *Warren.* $35/£22

SHLOSS, CAROL. In Visible Light. NY/Oxford: OUP, 1987. Fine in pict dj. *Cahan.* $35/£22

SHOAF, GEORGE H. Fighting for Freedom. Kansas City: Simplified Economics, n.d. 1st ed. Fine (imprint on tp sticker) in wraps. *Beasley.* $75/£47

SHOBERL, FREDERICK. Austria: Containing a Description of the Manners, Customs, Character and Costumes of the People of That Empire. Phila: C.S. Williams, 1828. 1st ed. 21 hand-colored stipple-engr plts. 3/4 red morocco, blue bds, gilt. (Offset from plts to facing pp; fr joint cracked, sm stain fr cvr), else VG. *Pacific*.* $86/£54

Shoe Book of Nursery Rhymes. NY: Capitol Pub Co, 1945. Shapebook. Dauber (illus). Spiral red metal w/red shoelace. VG. *Davidson.* $50/£31

SHOEBOTHAM, H. Anaconda, Life of Marcus Daly. Harrisburg: Stackpole, c1956. 1st ed. VG in dj. *Blake.* $45/£28

SHOEMAKER, MICHAEL MYERS. Winged Wheels in France. Knickerbocker Press, 1906. Teg. Gilt-illus cl. (Feps lt spotted; bd fore-edges lt dampstained.) *Edwards.* $72/£45

SHOLOKHOV, MIKHAIL. And Quiet Flows the Don. Stephen Garry (trans). London: Putnam, (1934). 1st British ed. Black cl, gilt. (Offset to eps, edges lt foxed), else NF in pict dj, wrap-around band intact. *Reese.* $100/£63

SHOLOKHOV, MIKHAIL. The Don Flows Home to the Sea. Stephen Garry (trans). London: Putnam, (1940). 1st British ed. Gilt dk gray cl. (Offset to eps), else NF in dj (lt edgeworn). *Reese.* $60/£38

Short Account of Algiers...with a Concise View of the Origin of the Rupture Between Algiers and the United States. Phila: Mathew Carey, Oct 20, 1794. 50,2 ads; fldg map. Mod 1/4 morocco. VG. Howes A127. *Adelson.* $325/£203

Short Account of the Big Trees of California. Washington: GPO, 1900. 15 plts, 2 fldg maps. Gray ptd wrappers. (Lib stamp on fr wrapper, map versos), o/w NF. *Pacific*.* $69/£43

Short History of Bookbinding and a Glossary of Styles and Terms Used in Binding. Chiswick, 1895. 1st ed. Color frontis, 38pp. Ptd wrappers (chipped, creased). *Forest.* $88/£55

SHORT, THOMAS. Discourses on Tea, Sugar, Milk, Made-Wines, Spirits.... London: T. Longman & A. Millar, 1750. 1st ed. vi,(iv),424pp, incl ad leaf before tp. Old milled calf, gilt. (Lt browning, spotting; rebacked, few sm worm holes in spine.) *Hollett.* $1,040/£650

SHORTHOUSE, J. H. On the Platonism of Wordsworth. UK, 1881. 1st ed. Ptd wraps. NF in NF chemise, box w/leather gilt labels. *Polyanthos.* $35/£22

SHOSTECK, ROBERT. Flowers and Plants. NY: Quadrangle, 1974. 1st ed. Fine in VG dj. *Archer.* $15/£9

SHOVE, FREDEGOND. Daybreak. Hogarth, 1922. One of 250. Errata slip loosely inserted. Patterned paper bds. Good (1st few pp sl creased, edges, inside spotted, esp rear; sl dusty, corners sl bumped, spine worn, title label on fr cvr dusty, sl mkd, spine dknd). *Ulysses.* $360/£225

SHOVE, FREDEGOND. Fredegond and Gerald Shove. Brookthorpe, Gloucester: Privately ptd for Ermengard Maitland, Colliers, 1952. 1st ed. One of 250. Cl-backed Curwen paper bds. Dj. *Maggs.* $88/£55

SHREVE, FORREST and IRA L. WIGGINS. Vegetation and Flora of the Sonoran Desert. Stanford: Stanford Univ, 1964. 1st ed. 2 vols. Fine set in VG djs. *Book Market.* $100/£63

SHUDRAKA, KING. The Little Clay Cart (Mrcchakatika). Arthur William Ryder (trans). Cambridge, MA: Harvard Univ, 1905. 1st ed. (Sl rubbed, corner sl affected by dampness), o/w VG. *Worldwide.* $25/£16

SHUFFREY, L. A. The English Fireplace. London: Batsford, (1912). 1st ed. 123 b/w photo plts. Teg. Dk grn cl, gilt. (Text split at center w/few ll partly detached, sl aged, finger smudges; sl worn, edges frayed, spine partly turned.) Baltimore*. $40/£25

SHULMAN, IRVING. The Amboy Dukes. GC: Doubleday, 1947. 1st ed. Pub's file copy stamp on fep. NF (cl sl dusty) in VG dj (sl rubbed, closed tears). Any Amount. $58/£36

SHULTZE, DAVID. Journals and Papers.... Pennsburg, 1952-3. 1st ptg. 2 vols. As New. Kane*. $70/£44

SHUMATE, ALBERT. The Life of George Henry Goddard, Artist, Architect, Surveyor and Mapmaker. Berkeley: Friends of the Bancroft Library, 1969. Lg fldg map in rear pocket. Stiff brn ptd wrappers. (Cvrs sl worn, dk streaks on rear cvr), o/w VG; text, map Fine. Pacific*. $40/£25

SHUMWAY, GEORGE et al. Conestoga Wagon, 1750-1850. York: Early American Industries Assoc/George Shumway, (1964). One of 1500. Dj (rear panel spotted). Dawson. $125/£78

SHURCLIFF, W. A. Bombs at Bikini. NY, 1947. 1st ed. VG in dj (defective). King. $25/£16

SHURE, DAVID S. Hester Bateman. W.H. Allen, 1959. 1st ed. 87 plts. (Few lt spots to feps), o/w Fine in dj. Hollett. $240/£150

SHURE, ROBERT. Twink. SF: City Lights, 1958. 1st City Lights ed. Fine in wraps. Beasley. $45/£28

SHUSTER, PHILIP et al. C & O Power: Steam and Diesel Locomotives of the Chesapeake and Ohio Railway 1900-1965. Carrollton, OH: Staufer, 1965. VG+ in dj (sl edgeworn). My Bookhouse. $62/£39

SHUSTER, W. MORGAN. The Strangling of Persia. NY: Century, 1912. 1st ed. 57 plts. Teg. (Eps sl smudged; sl rubbed), o/w VG. Worldwide. $45/£28

SHUTE, D. K. A First Book in Organic Evolution. Chicago: Open Court, (1911). 2nd ed. Color frontis. VG+. Mikesh. $25/£16

SHUTE, JOHN. The First and Chief Groundes of Architecture.... London, 1912. Ltd to 1000 unnumbered. Paper title label. (Bkpl; eps spotted; lt soiled, 2 sm spine splits, bumped.) Edwards. $136/£85

SHUTE, NEVIL. On the Beach. London, (1957). 1st ed. Fine in dj. Swann*. $287/£179

SHUTE, NEVIL. On the Beach. London, 1957. 1st Eng ed. Very Nice in dj (sl rubbed, nicked). Clearwater. $72/£45

SHUTE, NEVIL. Slide Rule. NY, 1954. 1st Amer ed. NF (spine sl sunned). Polyanthos. $25/£16

SHUTTLE, PENELOPE. All the Usual Hours of Sleeping. Calder, 1969. 1st ed. (Spine sl creased), else NF in VG+ dj (spine sl mkd). Any Amount. $32/£20

SIBELL, MURIEL V. Cloud Cities of Colorado. Boulder, 1934. (Faint water line rear wrap, ep), else VG in stiff paper wraps. Dumont. $90/£56

SIBERELL, LLOYD EMERSON. A Bibliography of the First Editions of John Cowper Powys. Cincinnati: Ailanthus, 1934. One of 350, this copy one of a sm # of out-of-series copies that had remained in sheets since 1934. Marbled card wrappers (newly rebound), paper label. Fine. Clearwater. $80/£50

SIBLEY, MARILYN McADAMS. Lone Stars and State Gazettes. College Station, 1983. 1st ed. VG in dj. Dumont. $40/£25

SIDDONS, ANNE RIVERS. The House Next Door. Atlanta, 1993. One of 450 numbered, signed by Siddons and Stephen King (foreword). (Sl worn.) Slipcase. Oinonen*. $30/£19

SIDDONS, ANNE RIVERS. John Chancellor Makes Me Cry. GC: Doubleday, 1975. 1st ed. (Rmdr spray bottom edge), else Fine in Fine dj (sl soiled, crease rear flap). Between The Covers. $150/£94

SIDDONS, SARAH KEMBLE. The Reminiscences. William Van Lennep (ed). Cambridge: Widener Library, 1942. One of 237. Fine (bkpl). Hartfield. $95/£59

SIDGWICK, MRS. ALFRED. Salt of the Earth. NY: W.J. Watt, (1917). 1st US ed. Tan cl. (Bkseller stamp, label), o/w Nice in dj (lt chipped, spine top lacks 3/4-inch). Reese. $35/£22

SIDIS, BORIS. An Experimental Study of Sleep. Boston: Badger, 1909. 1st ed. VG (ex-lib, labels; rear pocket removed, dot on spine). Beasley. $65/£41

SIDIS, BORIS. Psychopathological Researches. Studies in Mental Dissociation. NY: Stechert, 1902. 1st ed. VG (lib mks; mk on spine). Beasley. $125/£78

SIDNEY, MARGARET. Five Little Peppers Midway. Boston: D. Lothrop, (1890). 1st ed. W. L. Taylor (illus). Pict gilt-dec cl. (Spine ends, joints rubbed), else VG. Pacific*. $40/£25

SIDNEY, MARGARET. Five Little Peppers/The Stories Polly Pepper Told. Lothrop, c.1899. 66th thousand. Teal-blue cl, stamped. VG (few lt scratches to fr bd). Price. $25/£16

SIEBERT, ERNA and WERNER FORMAN. North American Indian Art. (London): Paul Hamlyn, (1967). 103 color plts. Turtle Island. $75/£47

SIEGEL, HENRY A. et al. The Derrydale Press: A Bibliography. Goshen: Angler's & Shooter's Press, 1981. 1st ed. One of 1250, this an out-of-series 'Author's Copy' w/signed presentation by Isaac Oelgart (one of the authors). Red cl, gilt. (Sl handled.) Blue bd slipcase (lt rubbed). Baltimore*. $110/£69

SIEGEL, HENRY A. et al. The Derrydale Press: A Bibliography. Goshen, CT: Angler's & Shooter's, 1981. Ltd to 1250 numbered. Red buckram. VF in VF slipcase. Biscotti. $150/£94

SIEGEL, HENRY A. et al. The Derrydale Press: A Bibliography. Goshen: Angler's & Shooter's Press, 1981. One of 1250 numbered. Bd slipcase (cracked). Swann*. $172/£108

SIENKIEWICZ, HENRYK. Quo Vadis? LEC, 1959. Ltd to 1500 numbered, signed by Salvatore Fiume (illus) and Giovanni Mardersteig (designer). Fine in slipcase. Swann*. $103/£64

SIEVEKING, L. DE G. Dressing Gowns and Glue. Paul Nash (ed). (London): Cecil Palmer & Hayward, (1919). 1st ed. Color illus paper over bds. Good (blank ep lt foxed; bds sl rubbed, dusty). Cahan. $85/£53

SIGAUD, LOUIS A. Belle Boyd, Confederate Spy. Richmond, VA: Dietz, (1944). 1st ed. Gray cl. (Sl soiled), else NF. Chapel Hill. $45/£28

SIGERIST, HENRY E. A History of Medicine. Volume 1: Primitive and Archaic Medicine. NY, 1955. 2nd ptg. (Ex-lib), o/w Good. Doctor's Library. $75/£47

Sights and Scenes in Scotland. Cassell, n.d. Sub's ed. Dec brn cl (sl dknd, mkd). Hollett. $40/£25

SILCOCK, ARNOLD. Introduction to Chinese Art and History. London: Faber & Faber, 1935. 2nd ed. 36 plts (4 color), 2 maps. VG. Worldwide. $28/£18

SILGAILIS, A. The Latvian Legion. GB, 1986. 1st ed. VG. Clark. $27/£17

SILK, W. H. Bantams and Miniature Fowl. London: Dorset, 1951. 1st ed. VG+ in Good+ dj. Mikesh. $20/£13

SILKO, LESLIE MARMON. Almanac of the Dead. NY: S&S, 1991. 1st ed. Signed. Fine in Fine dj. Unger. $75/£47

SILKO, LESLIE MARMON. Laguna Woman. Greenfield Center: Greenfield Review Press, (1974). 1st ed, 1st bk. (Sl soil), else Fine in wrappers. Pacific*. $1,265/£791

SILKO, LESLIE MARMON. Storyteller. NY: Seavers Books, (1981). 1st ed. (Fr panel dj scratched, crumpled; rear panel torn), else VG. Hermitage. $85/£53

SILKO, LESLIE MARMON. Storyteller. NY, 1981. 1st Amer ed. Fine in Fine dj. Polyanthos. $100/£63

SILKO, LESLIE MARMON. Storyteller. NY: Seaver, 1981. 1st ed. Fine in Fine dj. Unger. $150/£94

SILLIMAN, BENJAMIN. Elements of Chemistry, in the Order of the Lectures Given in Yale College. New Haven, (CT): Hezekiah Howe, 1830-31. 1st ed. 8vo. 2 vols. 3 engr plts. Full contemp calf, leather labels. VG (sl worn, rubbed). *M & S*. $650/£406

SILLITOE, ALAN and RUTH FAINLIGHT. All Citizens Are Soldiers—Fuente Ovejuna. London: Macmillan, 1969. 1st Eng ed. Signed by both. Fine (feps partly browned) in dj (edges sl rubbed). *Ulysses*. $72/£45

SILLITOE, ALAN. The Loneliness of the Long-Distance Runner. London: W.H. Allen, 1959. 1st ed. (Sl offset from flaps to feps), else NF in dj (spine ends sl rubbed, soiled, price-clipped). *Pacific**. $98/£61

SILLITOE, ALAN. The Loneliness of the Long-Distance Runner. London: W.H. Allen, 1959. 1st Eng ed. Signed. VG (feps partly browned; cvrs partly faded) in dj (sl nicked, creased, partly dknd). *Ulysses*. $280/£175

SILLITOE, ALAN. Love in the Environs of Voronezh and Other Poems. London: Macmillan, 1968. 1st Eng ed. Inscribed. Pict laminated bds. NF (spine ends sl rubbed) in dj (edges sl rubbed). *Ulysses*. $56/£35

SILLITOE, ALAN. Mountains and Caverns, Selected Essays. London, 1975. 1st ed. Fine in dj. *Typographeum*. $18/£11

Silly Riddle School. 52 Riddles with Action Surprises on Every Page. Kansas City: Hallmark, n.d. (1976). 13pp pull-tabs by Marianne Smith. Glazed pict bds. VG. *Bookfinders*. $55/£34

SILONE, IGNAZIO. Mr. Aristotle. Samuel Putnam (trans). NY: McBride, (1935). 1st Amer ed. (Heavy bleedthrough to pastedowns from binder's glue), else Fine in VG white dj (soiled, lt worn). *Between The Covers*. $85/£53

SILTZER, FRANK. The Story of British Sporting Prints. NY, 1925. (Sl foxed; sl worn.) *Oinonen**. $50/£31

SILTZER, FRANK. The Story of British Sporting Prints. Scribner, 1925. Color frontis. Uncut. (Sl worn.) *Forest*. $88/£55

SILURIENSIS, LEOLINUS. The Anatomy of Tobacco. London, 1884. 1st ed, 1st bk. Full vellum. (Browned; lettering faded.) *Mcclintock*. $495/£309

SILVEIRA DE BRAGANZA, RONALD LOUIS (ed). The Hill Collection of Pacific Voyages. San Diego: University Library, 1974/1982/1983. Ltd ed. 3 vols incl index. Copy of the Quarterly Newsletter laid in loose. Lt blue cl, gilt. Fine. *Pacific**. $920/£575

Silver Voice: A Fairy Tale, Being the Adventures of Harry's Mother, Harry's Sweetheart, and Harry Himself. London: Field & Tuer, (1887). 1st ed. Hand-colored wrappers (browned, lt chipped). *Glenn*. $125/£78

SILVER, ARTHUR P. Farm-Cottage, Camp and Canoe in Maritime Canada. London, 1907. Teg. (1/2-title lt browned; recased, spine faded, corner sl bumped.) *Edwards*. $77/£48

SILVER, NATHAN. Lost New York. NY, (1967). 1/4 cl. Dj. *Argosy*. $100/£63

SILVERBERG, ROBERT. Lord Valentine's Castle. NY, 1980. 1st ed. One of 250 specially bound, signed. Slipcase. *Swann**. $57/£36

SILVERBERG, ROBERT. Starman's Quest. Hicksville: Gnome, (1958). 1st ed, 1st state binding. Fine in Fine dj. *Other Worlds*. $30/£19

SILVERBERG, ROBERT. Starman's Quest. Hicksville, NY: Gnome, (1958). 1st ed, 1st issue. (Browned), else VG in dj (rubbed, sl soiled). *King*. $35/£22

SILVERBURG, R. Mound Builders of Ancient America. Greenwich: NYGS, 1968. 1st ed. Fine in NF dj. *Mikesh*. $47/£29

SILVERMAN, MAIDA. Dune. A Pop-Up Panorama Book. NY: G&D, 1984. Daniel Kirk (illus). 4 dbl-pg pop-ups, press outs fr & back complete. Glazed pict bds. VG. *Bookfinders*. $45/£28

SILVERSTEIN, SHEL. The Giving Tree. NY: Harper & Row, 1964. 1st ed. 7x8.75. 60pp. Pict bds. Fine in dj. *Cattermole*. $75/£47

SILVESTRO, CARLO (ed). The Living Book of the Living Theatre. CT: NYGS, 1971. 1st ed. Fine in dj (price-clipped). *Sclanders*. $48/£30

SIMENON, GEORGES. Across the Street. RKP, 1954. 1st ed. (Spine sl rolled), else Fine in NF dj (sl frayed). *Any Amount*. $29/£18

SIMENON, GEORGES. Aunt Jeanne. RKP, 1953. 1st ed in English. Fine in NF dj (sl rubbed). *Any Amount*. $32/£20

SIMENON, GEORGES. Aunt Jeanne. Rouledge & Kegan Paul, 1953. 1st UK ed. VG in dj (rubbed, torn, sl chipped). *Williams*. $40/£25

SIMENON, GEORGES. Inquest on Bouvet. Hamilton, 1958. 1st UK ed. Fine in VG dj. *Williams*. $35/£22

SIMENON, GEORGES. Maigret and the Loner. Hamilton, 1975. 1st UK ed. Fine in dj (spine sl faded). *Williams*. $26/£16

SIMENON, GEORGES. Maigret and the Man on the Boulevard. Hamilton, 1975. 1st UK ed. VG + in dj (price-clipped). *Williams*. $24/£15

SIMENON, GEORGES. Maigret and the Man on the Boulevard. London: Hamish Hamilton, 1975. 1st Eng ed. Fine in dj. *Mordida*. $50/£31

SIMENON, GEORGES. Maigret and the Old Lady. Hamish Hamilton, 1958. 1st ed. Fine in NF dj (sl soiled, rubbed). *Any Amount*. $32/£20

SIMENON, GEORGES. Maigret and the Old Lady. London: Hamish Hamilton, 1958. 1st ed in English. Red linson bds (spine sl worn). Fine in dj (sl worn). *Maggs*. $40/£25

SIMENON, GEORGES. Maigret and the Wine Merchant. Eileen Ellenbogen (trans). London: Hamish Hamilton, 1971. 1st ed in English. Fine in dj (sl edgeworn). *Janus*. $50/£31

SIMENON, GEORGES. Maigret and the Young Woman. Hamish Hamilton, 1955. 1st ed. (Ep sl offset), else Fine in NF dj (rear panel sl soiled, edges sl frayed). *Any Amount*. $35/£22

SIMENON, GEORGES. Maigret Goes to School. Hamish Hamilton, 1957. 1st ed. Fine in dj. *Any Amount*. $38/£24

SIMENON, GEORGES. Maigret Has Scruples. London: Hamish Hamilton, 1959. 1st ed in English. Blue linson bds. Fine in dj (extrems sl worn). *Maggs*. $40/£25

SIMENON, GEORGES. Maigret Loses His Temper. Hamilton, 1965. 1st UK ed. VG in dj (couple closed tears). *Williams*. $29/£18

SIMENON, GEORGES. Maigret's Failure. Hamilton, 1962. 1st UK ed. VG in dj (price-clipped). *Williams*. $32/£20

SIMENON, GEORGES. Maigret's Pipe. NY: Harcourt, Brace, Jovanovich, (1978). 1st ed. NF in dj. *Antic Hay*. $25/£16

SIMENON, GEORGES. Poisoned Relations. Routledge & Kegan Paul, 1950. 1st UK ed. VG + in dj (spine sl faded). *Williams*. $72/£45

SIMENON, GEORGES. A Sense of Guilt. Hamilton, 1955. 1st UK ed. VG in dj (worn, browned, sl chipped). *Williams*. $24/£15

SIMENON, GEORGES. The Shadow Falls. Stuart Gilbert (trans). NY: Harcourt, Brace, (1945). 1st Amer ed. Blue cl. (Spine cocked, extrems sl rubbed), o/w NF in dj (soiled, lt edgeworn). *Heritage*. $100/£63

SIMENON, GEORGES. The Shadow Falls. Routledge & Kegan Paul, 1945. 1st UK ed. VG (spine sl browned) in dj (worn, browned, sl chipped). *Williams*. $42/£26

SIMENON, GEORGES. The Stain on the Snow. RKP, 1953. 1st ed in English. Fine in NF dj (edges sl rubbed). *Any Amount*. $32/£20

SIMENON, GEORGES. The Strangers in the House. Routledge, 1951. 1st UK ed. VG + in dj. *Williams*. $77/£48

SIMENON, GEORGES. The Trial of Bebe Donge. Routledge & Kegan Paul, 1952. 1st UK ed. VG + in dj (stained, creased). *Williams.* $35/£22

SIMENON, GEORGES. The Venice Train. NY: Harcourt, Brace, Jovanovich, (1974). 1st ed. NF in dj. *Antic Hay.* $25/£16

SIMENON, GEORGES. A Wife at Sea. Routledge & Kegan Paul, 1949. 1st UK ed. NF (ink name) in dj (defective). *Williams.* $35/£22

SIMIC, CHARLES. Classic Ballroom Dances. NY: Braziller, (1980). Hb ed. Fine in Fine dj. *Agvent.* $75/£47

SIMIC, CHARLES. Somewhere Among Us a Stone Is Taking Notes. SF: Kayak, (1969). One of 1000. Signed. Fine in wraps. *Agvent.* $175/£109

SIMMONDS, PETER LUND. The Curiosities of Food.... Richard Bentley, 1859. 1st ed. xvi,372pp. Dec cl, gilt. Nice (sl shaken, loose; sm nick spine foot). *Ash.* $152/£95

SIMMONS, ALBERT D. Wing Shots. NY: Derrydale, (1936). 1st ed. One of 950. 83 plts. (Spine ends sl rubbed), else NF. *Pacific*.* $69/£43

SIMMONS, DAN. Carrion Comfort. Arlington Heights, IL: Dark Harvest, 1989. 1st ed. One of 450. Signed by Simmons & Sherman (illus). Fine in dj, slipcase. *Pacific*.* $184/£115

SIMMONS, DAN. Entropy's Bed at Midnight. Northridge: Lord John, 1990. One of 300 numbered, signed. (Sl worn.) *Oinonen*.* $120/£75

SIMMONS, DAN. Hyperion. NY: Doubleday, (1987). Uncorrected proof. (Spine sl sunned), else NF in wrappers. *Pacific*.* $127/£79

SIMMONS, DAN. Phases of Gravity. London: Headline, (1989). One of 250 numbered, signed. Aeg. Gilt-lettered leatherette (sl worn). Slipcase. *Oinonen*.* $50/£31

SIMMONS, GEORGE. Target: Arctic. Phila: Chilton, c. 1965. VG in dj. *High Latitude.* $35/£22

SIMMONS, HERBERT. Man Walking on Eggshells. Boston: Houghton Mifflin, 1962. 1st ed. Fine in dj (sl worn). *Beasley.* $35/£22

SIMMONS, MARC. Witchcraft in the Southwest. Flagstaff, 1974. 1st ed. VG in dj (worn). *Dumont.* $45/£28

SIMMONS, RALPH B. Boulder Dam and the Great Southwest. L.A., 1936. Deluxe ed. Inscribed. Frontisport, fldg panorama. VG + (extrems sl worn). *Sagebrush.* $125/£78

SIMMS, WILLIAM EMMETT. Speech of Hon. W.E. Simms, of Kentucky, on Polygamy in Utah. (Washington): Lemuel Towers, 1860. VG (1st pg sl soiled) in self wraps (removed, newly stapled along left edge). *Blue Mountain.* $150/£94

SIMMS, WILLIAM GILMORE. The Geography of South Carolina. Charleston: Babcock, 1843. 1st ed. 192pp; fldg map. Contemp calf bds, leather label. (Archival tissue repair along some flds; scuffed, worn, rebacked w/later calf), else Good. Howes S469. *Brown.* $125/£78

SIMON, ANDRE L. The Noble Grapes and the Great Wines of France. NY: McGraw-Hill, n.d. Aeg, gilt inner dentelles. Full grn morocco, gilt, raised bands, bound by Zaehnsdorf. (Ink inscrip; spine, top of fr cvr faded), else NF. *Pacific*.* $86/£54

SIMON, BARBARA ANNE. The Hope of Israel. London, 1829. Orig bds (fr cvr loose, backstrip cracked). *Swann*.* $92/£58

SIMON, HELENA. Eleven Poems. Acorn, 1978. One of 50 (this copy not numbered or signed as called for). Fine in gray stiff wrappers, title label. *Michael Taylor.* $77/£48

SIMON, HILDA. The Date Palm. NY: Dodd, Mead, 1978. 1st ed. NF in dj (price-clipped, spine sunned). *Archer.* $22/£14

SIMON, JOHN. Private Screenings: Views of the Cinema of the Sixties. NY: Macmillan, (1967). 1st ed. VF in VF dj. *Between The Covers.* $75/£47

SIMON, NEIL. Last of the Red Hot Lovers. NY, 1970. 1st ed. Fine in NF dj. *Warren.* $40/£25

SIMON, NEIL. The Odd Couple. NY: Random House, (1966). 1st ed. Fine in NF dj (fr panel bottom sl rubbed). *Between The Covers.* $200/£125

SIMON, OLIVER and HAROLD CHILD (eds). The Bibliophile's Almanack for 1928. Plaistow: Curwen, 1928. 1st ed. Plt. Uncut. Cl-backed dec bds. *Forest.* $48/£30

SIMON, OLIVER and JULIUS RODENBERG. Printing of To-Day. London/NY, 1928. Folio. 122 plts. Cl spine, ptd paper over bds (extrems sl worn). Dj (tattered, spine gone). *Woolson.* $50/£31

SIMON, OLIVER and JULIUS RODENBERG. Printing of To-Day. London/NY: Peter Davies/Harper, 1928. 122 plts. Fine in dj. *Cullen.* $85/£53

SIMON, OLIVER and JULIUS RODENBERG. Printing of To-Day. London: Peter Davies, 1928. 1st ed. Folio. Cl-backed dec bds. VG in dj (spine dknd, lacks sm piece, sl soil, sm stain). *Pacific*.* $86/£54

SIMON, OLIVER and JULIUS RODENBERG. Printing of To-Day. London: Peter Davies, 1928. 1st ed. Dec cvr label. NF in glassine. *Pacific*.* $138/£86

SIMON, OLIVER (ed). Signature: A Quadrimestrial of Typography and Graphic Arts. London: Signature, 1935-36. 1st ed. 3 vols. VG in wrappers, cl-backed bds string portfolio (extrems dknd). *Pacific*.* $127/£79

SIMOND, L. Switzerland. Boston: Wells & Lilly, 1822. 2 vols. Contemp calf. (Lib bkpl, stamps, remains of shelf labels; worn, scuffed), else Good. *Brown.* $30/£19

SIMONDS, JOHN ORMSBEE. Landscape Architecture. NY: F.W. Dodge, c. 1961. VG. *Fair Meadow.* $40/£25

SIMONIN, L. Underground Life. H. W. Bristow (ed). London: Chapman & Hall, 1869. 1st Eng ed. xix,522,(ii)pp; 10 chromolithos, 20 color maps. Orig roan-backed cl, gilt. (Lacks color frontis, spotting, foxing, few sm tears; spine sl rubbed, neatly recased.) *Hollett.* $256/£160

SIMONIN, L. Underground Life; or, Mines and Miners. H. W. Bristow (ed). London: Chapman & Hall, 1869. xix,522pp; 160 wood engrs, 20 color maps, 10 chromolitho plts. (Lib ink stamps, label, 2 pieces cut from tp head not affecting text, tp re-back and thus repaired, ppi/ii silked, repaired at corners, sm tear fore-edge pp79/80 repaired w/o loss; rebound, accession #s.) *Edwards.* $200/£125

SIMONSON, LEE. The Art of Scenic Design. NY: Harper, (1950). 1st ed. Inscribed. Black cl. Fine in dj. *Appelfeld.* $85/£53

SIMPKINSON, F. G. and E. BELCHER. H.M.S. Sulphur at California, 1837 and 1839. Castle, 1969. One of 400. *Dawson.* $25/£16

Simple Songs of Khatchik Minasian. (By William Saroyan.) SF: Colt, 1950. One of 300 ptd. Signed by Saroyan and Minasian. 1/2 red cl, dec bds. Fine. *Pacific*.* $52/£33

SIMPSON, C. J. W. North Ice. Hodder & Stoughton, 1957. 1st ed. Map. VG in dj. *Walcot.* $26/£16

SIMPSON, E. BLANTYRE. The Robert Louis Stevenson Originals. T.N. Foulis, 1912. Top edge tan. Good (fore-edge spotted; spine bumped). *Tiger.* $22/£14

SIMPSON, EVE B. The Robert Louis Stevenson Originals. London: Foulis, 1912. 1st ed. Teg, uncut. Brn cl, gilt. VF. *Macdonnell.* $50/£31

SIMPSON, GEORGE. London Correspondence Inward from Sir George Simpson, 1841-42. London: Hudson's Bay Record Soc, 1973. 1st ed. Frontisport, 2 fldg maps, fldg plan. Black cl. Fine in dj. *Argonaut.* $85/£53

SIMPSON, GEORGE. Narrative of a Voyage to California Ports in 1841-42. Thomas C. Russell (ed). SF: Private Press of Thomas C. Russell, 1930. Ltd to 250 (this copy not numbered). Fldg map. Blue cl, red cl spine, paper label. Good. *Karmiole.* $150/£94

SIMPSON, JAMES H. Navaho Expedition. Norman: Univ of OK, (1964). 1st ed. Fine in Fine dj. *Book Market.* $40/£25

SIMPSON, JAMES H. Navajo Expedition. Norman: Univ of OK, 1964. VG in dj (price-clipped). *Dumont.* $50/£31

SIMPSON, JAMES H. Report of Explorations Across the Great Basin of the Territory of Utah for a Direct Wagon-Route from Camp Floyd to Genoa, in Carson Valley, in 1859. Washington, 1876. 1st ed. 17 plts, 5 fldg charts, 3 maps. (Sm erasure to tp foot; extrems rubbed, sl frayed, hinges starting; lib # stamped to spine foot.) Howes 501. *Sadlon.* $300/£188

SIMPSON, JOHN L. A Holiday in Wartime, and Other Stories: Episodes of Occupied Belgium and France, 1915-1917. (N.p.: Privately ptd, 1956.) 1st bk ed. Frontis. Red cl, gilt. Fine. *Harrington.* $30/£19

SIMPSON, LESLEY BYRD (ed). The San Saba Papers: A Documentary Account of the Founding and Destruction of San Saba Mission. Paul D. Nathan (trans). SF: John Howell-Books, (1959). 1st ed. Fldg map in rear pocket. Fine. *Argonaut.* $75/£47

SIMPSON, MONA. Anywhere But Here. NY: Knopf, 1987. 1st ed, 1st bk. Fine in Fine dj. *Dermont.* $50/£31

SIMPSON, MONA. The Lost Father. NY, 1992. 1st ed. Signed. Fine in Fine dj. *Warren.* $30/£19

SIMPSON, W. G. The Art of Golf. Edinburgh: David Douglas, 1887. 1st ed. Calf-backed pict bds. (Name, dated 1889, emb stamp; spine head, joints scuffed, corners sl bumped), else VG. *Pacific*.* $1,150/£719

SIMPSON, WILLIAM. A Private Journal Kept During the Niger Expedition. London: John F. Shaw, 1843. 1st ed. xii,139,(1)imprint. Orig maroon blindstamped cl. Sound (lt foxed, fep torn away; faded, stained, spine head chipped, sl loose). *Morrell.* $176/£110

Sinbad the Sailor and Other Stories from the Arabian Nights. London: Hodder & Stoughton, (1911). 1st ed. 4to. 23 mtd color plts by Edmund Dulac. Brn gilt-stamped cl. Fine. *Appelfeld.* $500/£313

Sinbad the Sailor and Other Stories from the Arabian Nights. London: Hodder & Stoughton, (1914). 1st ed. Lg 4to. 23 mtd color plts by Edmund Dulac. Tan dec cl, gilt. Good. *Reisler.* $750/£469

Sinbad the Sailor. London: Octopus Books, 1979. J. Pavlin & G. Seda (illus). 6 dbl-pg pop-ups. Glazed pict bds. VG-. *Bookfinders.* $45/£28

SINCLAIR, ARTHUR. Two Years on the Alabama. London: Gay & Bird, 1896. 1st Eng ed. Frontisport, 352pp. Pict gray cl. (Eps foxed), else VG. *Chapel Hill.* $200/£125

SINCLAIR, H. M. The Work of Sir Robert McCarrison. London, 1953. 1st ed. *Fye.* $75/£47

SINCLAIR, IAIN. Flesh Eggs and Scalp Metal. London: Paladin, 1989. 1st Eng ed. NF (cvr edges sl rubbed) in wrappers. *Ulysses.* $32/£20

SINCLAIR, IAIN. Jack Elam's Other Eye. London: Hoarse Comerz, 1991. 1st Eng ed. One of 200. Fine in wrappers. *Ulysses.* $32/£20

SINCLAIR, MAY. (Pseud of Mary Amelia St. Clair Sinclair.) Arnold Waterlow. Hutchinson, n.d. (1924). (Spine bumped; lacks dj), else VG. *Tiger.* $22/£14

SINCLAIR, MAY. (Pseud of Mary Amelia St. Clair Sinclair.) The Divine Fire. Henry Holt, 1904. VG (bkpl; spine bumped). *Tiger.* $26/£16

SINCLAIR, UPTON. The Book of Life. Mind and Body. NY: Macmillan, 1921. 1st ed. NF (spine sunned). *Beasley.* $40/£25

SINCLAIR, UPTON. A Captain of Industry. Girard, KS, 1906. 1st ed. (Fr cvr lt stained, extrems rubbed, one corner sl frayed.) *King.* $50/£31

SINCLAIR, UPTON. It Happened to Didymus. NY: Sagamore Press, 1958. 1st ed. Fine in Fine dj. *Beasley.* $35/£22

SINCLAIR, UPTON. Jimmie Higgins, a Story. Pasadena: Upton Sinclair, 1919. Author's issue/ptg. Gray cl stamped in black. VG. *Reese.* $65/£41

SINCLAIR, UPTON. The Jungle. Balt: LEC, 1965. One of 1500. Signed by Sinclair & Fletcher Martin (illus). 1/2 pigskin, bds. Fine in slipcase. *Pacific*.* $104/£65

SINCLAIR, UPTON. The Millennium. Pasadena: The Author, 1929. 1st US hb ed. Fine (spine dull). *Beasley.* $30/£19

SINCLAIR, UPTON. One Clear Call. NY, 1948. 1st ed. VG in Nice dj. *King.* $25/£16

SINCLAIR, UPTON. Presidential Mission. NY: Viking, 1947. 1st ed. Fine (bkpl) in dj (lt used). *Beasley.* $40/£25

SINCLAIR, UPTON. World's End. NY: Viking, 1940. 1st ed, trade issue. Red cl stamped in silver. VG in dj (spine sl sunned). *Reese.* $40/£25

SINEL, J. The Geology of Jersey. Jersey: J.T. Bigwood, 1912. Good (ex-lib). *Blake.* $75/£47

Sing a Battle Song. Poems by Women in the Weather Underground Organization. N.p.: Red Dragon Print Collective, 1975. 1st ed. (Sm stain to fr cvr), o/w NF in saddle-stapled wraps. *Sclanders.* $40/£25

SINGER, CHARLES et al (eds). A History of Technology. NY/London: OUP, 1954-1958 (1957-1959). 1st US ed. 5 vols. 4 color frontispieces. Blue cl (sl rubbed), gilt. Clean set. *Baltimore*.* $60/£38

SINGER, CHARLES et al (eds). A History of Technology. Volume III (only). OUP, 1964. Rpt. Color frontis, 32 plts. (Ex-lib, sl mks, cardholder remains fep.) Dj. *Edwards.* $40/£25

SINGER, CHARLES. Science, Medicine and History. E. Ashworth Underwood (ed). London/NY/Toronto: Geoffrey Cumberlege/OUP, 1953. 2 vols. Lg 8vo. 106 plts. Blue cl. VF in djs. *Weber.* $675/£422

SINGER, CHARLES. A Short History of Medicine. NY: OUP, 1928. 1st Amer ed. Grn cl. VG (bkpl removed fr pastedown). *Glaser.* $45/£28

SINGER, ISAAC BASHEVIS. The Gentleman from Cracow and The Mirror. LEC, 1979. One of 2000 signed by Singer and Raphael Soyer (illus). Fine in slipcase. *Swann*.* $517/£323

SINGER, ISAAC BASHEVIS. A Little Boy in Search of God. NY, 1976. 1st ed. One of 150 signed by Singer and Ira Moscowitz (illus), w/orig etching signed by Moscowitz laid in. Slipcase. *Swann*.* $126/£79

SINGER, ISAAC BASHEVIS. Lost in America. NY, 1981. 1st ed. One of 500 signed, w/orig print signed by Rafael Soyer (illus) laid in. Slipcase. *Swann*.* $126/£79

SINGER, ISAAC BASHEVIS. The Magician of Lublin. LEC, 1984. Ltd to 1500 numbered, signed by Larry Rivers (illus). Fine in slipcase. *Swann*.* $287/£179

SINGER, ISAAC BASHEVIS. Nobel Lecture. London, 1979. VG in orig wraps. *Edrich.* $19/£12

SINGER, ISAAC BASHEVIS. Short Friday. Phila: Jewish Publication Soc, 1965. 1st ed. Fine in dj (sl worn). *Lenz.* $75/£47

SINGER, ISAAC BASHEVIS. A Tale of Three Wishes. NY: FSG, 1976. 1st ed. Irene Lieblich (illus). 12mo. 30pp. VG in VG dj. *Davidson.* $45/£28

SINGER, ISAAC BASHEVIS. Yentl, the Yeshiva Boy. NY, (1983). 1st ed. One of 450 numbered, signed by Singer and Antonio Frasconi (illus). Slipcase. *Swann*.* $138/£86

SINGER, ISAAC BASHEVIS. A Young Man in Search of Love. NY, 1978. 1st ed. One of 300 numbered, signed, w/color print signed by Rafael Soyer (illus) laid in. Slipcase. *Swann**. $126/£79

SINGER, ISAAC BASHEVIS. Zlateh the Goat. NY: Harper Row, 1966. 1st trade ed. Fine in dj w/$4.50 price. *Cattermole*. $100/£63

SINGER, ISAAC BASHEVIS. Zlateh the Goat. NY: Harper Row, 1966. Ltd ed, signed by Singer & Maurice Sendak (illus). 6 1/2 x 9 1/4. 90pp. VG (spine sl rubbed) in slipcase. *Cattermole*. $900/£563

SINGER, ROLF. Mushrooms and Truffles: Botany, Cultivation, and Utilization. London: Leonard Hill, (1961). 1st ed. (Lower fr flap clipped), else VG in dj. *Pacific**. $23/£14

SINGH, MADANJEET. Himalayan Art. Greenwich, CT: NYGS/UNESCO, (1968). Sm folio. 140 plts. Fine in dj. *Turtle Island*. $75/£47

SINGLETON, WILLIAM A. (ed). Studies in Architectural History. Saint Anthony's, 1954. VG in dj (mkd). *Hadley*. $24/£15

Singular Aesthetic, Photographs and Drawings 1921-1941. Santa Barbara, 1981. 1st ed. One of 1500. Folio. Paul Outerbridge (repros). (Spine sl worn.) Contents Clean. Ptd acetate dj (sl rubbed). *Swann**. $402/£251

SINNETT, MRS. PERCY. Hunters and Fishers; or Sketches of Primitive Races in the Lands Beyond the Sea. London: Chapman & Hall, 1846. 1st ed. 4 chromolitho plts w/add'l hand coloring. Speckled edges. Orig purple cl, gilt. Clean (lower cvr sl mkd, spine sunned). *Sotheran*. $157/£98

SIODMAK, CURT. Donovan's Brain. NY, 1943. 1st ed. Dj. *Swann**. $126/£79

SIPLEY, LOUIS WALTON. Frederick E. Ives: Photographic Inventor. Phila: Amer Museum of Photography, 1956. 1st ed. Ltd to 500 numbered. Errata slip. Fine. *Cahan*. $125/£78

SIPPRELL, CLARA. Moment of Light. NY: John Day, (1966). 1st ed. White linen-cvrd bds (sl sunned, rubbed). VG in dj (rubbed). *Hermitage*. $65/£41

Sir Gawain and the Green Knight. LEC, 1971. Ltd to 1500 numbered, signed by Cyril Satorsky (illus). Fine in slipcase. *Swann**. $92/£58

SIREN, OSVALD. Gardens of China. NY, (1949). (Inscrip.) Bd slipcase. *Swann**. $402/£251

SIRIANNI, J. E. and D. R. SWINDLER. Growth and Development of the Pigtailed Macaque. Boca Raton, 1985. (Spine rubbed.) *Sutton*. $164/£103

SIRINGO, CHARLES A. A Cowboy Detective. Chicago: (W.B. Conkey), 1912. 1st ed. Pict cl. VG- (fr hinge starting, extrems lt worn, backstrip sl faded). Howes S515. *Baade*. $275/£172

SIRINGO, CHARLES A. History of 'Billy the Kid'. Austin, 1967. Facs rpt of 1920 bk. Pict cl. (Sl soiled), else Fine. Howes S516. *Baade*. $55/£34

SIRINGO, CHARLES A. A Lone Star Cowboy. Santa Fe: Privately ptd, 1919. 1st ed. Pict cl. VG (extrems lt worn, few spots on cvrs). Howes S518. *Baade*. $125/£78

SIRINGO, CHARLES A. Riata and Spurs. Boston, 1927. New ed, 1st thus. Pict cl. Fine in dj (disintegrating w/just fr panel, part of backstrip present). Howes S517. *Baade*. $75/£47

SIRINGO, CHARLES A. Riata and Spurs. Boston: Houghton Mifflin, 1927. Rev ed. NF. *Labordo*. $85/£53

SIRINGO, CHARLES A. Riata and Spurs. Boston/NY: Houghton Mifflin, 1927. 1st ed. Pict cl. NF. Howes S517. *Sadlon*. $175/£109

SIRINGO, CHARLES A. Riata and Spurs. Boston, 1927. 1st, unexpurgated ed. Pict cl. NF (sig, bookseller label) in dj (sl chipped). Howes S517. *Baade*. $350/£219

SIRINGO, CHARLES A. Riata and Spurs. Boston: Houghton Mifflin, 1931. Frontis. (Spine faded, sl cocked), else Clean. *Dumont*. $25/£16

SIRINGO, CHARLES A. A Texas Cowboy. Chicago/NY: Rand McNally, (1886). Frontis, 8 plts, 31pg addenda (2 ad leaves neatly repaired, leaves browned). Later 1/2 tan morocco, linen-cvrd bds, gilt paneled spine, raised bands. Howes S518. *Sadlon*. $350/£219

SIRINGO, CHARLES A. A Texas Cowboy. NY: William Sloane, 1950. Rpt ed. Fine in dj. Howes S518. *Labordo*. $125/£78

SIRINGO, CHARLES A. A Texas Cowboy. NY: Time-Life, 1980. Facs of orig 1885 ed. Marbled eps. Simulated emb leather. *Heinoldt*. $35/£22

SIRINGO, CHARLES A. Two Evil Isms. Austin, 1967. Facs rpt of 1915 ed. (Sl soiled), else Fine. Howes S519. *Baade*. $55/£34

SIS, VLADIMIR and JOSEF VANIS. On the Road Through Tibet. Iris Urwin (trans). London: Spring (Artia), n.d. (ca 1948). 1st ed. 224 plts. (Ex-lib; sl rubbed, soiled, spine tears), o/w VG. *Worldwide*. $40/£25

SISKIND, AARON. Aaron Siskind, Photographer. Rochester, (1965). 1st ed. (Worn.) Dj (rubbed, soiled). *Swann**. $126/£79

SISKIND, AARON. Places. NY: Light Gallery, 1976. 1st ed. Signed. NF in dj (spine ends worn, sl dampstain to top edge). *Smith*. $150/£94

SISSON, JAMES E. and ROBERTS W. MARTENS. Jack London First Editions. Oakland, 1979. VG. *Dumont*. $50/£31

Site of the Globe Playhouse, Southwark.... (By W. W. Braines.) London: Hodder & Stoughton, 1924. 2nd ed. Frontis, fldg table, traced map w/ms notes bound in. Grn cl (sl stained), gilt. *Marlborough*. $152/£95

SITGREAVES, L. Report of an Expedition Down the Zuni and Colorado Rivers. Washington: Beverly Tucker, 1854. 2nd ed. 198pp; 79 litho plts (1 fldg), lg fldg map. Blind-stamped cl, gilt. Fine (contents sl dknd). Howes S521. *Pacific**. $489/£306

SITWELL, EDITH. Alexander Pope. London: Faber & Faber, (1930). 1st ed. One of 220. Signed. Frontisport. Teg. Yellow cl, gilt. (Spine sl dknd), else VG. *Pacific**. $40/£25

SITWELL, EDITH. Alexander Pope. London, 1930. 1st ed. Rev copy. Yellow cl. Good+. *Gretton*. $16/£10

SITWELL, EDITH. Bucolic Comedies. London: Duckworth, 1923. 1st ed. (Foxed throughout.) Patterned paper bds. *Maggs*. $48/£30

SITWELL, EDITH. English Eccentrics. NY: Vanguard, 1957. 2nd ed. NF in dj. *Cady*. $20/£13

SITWELL, EDITH. English Women. London: Collins, 1942. 1st ed. 8 color plts. VG in dj (spine sl rubbed, dknd). *Hollett*. $32/£20

SITWELL, EDITH. Five Poems. Duckworth, 1928. One of 275 numbered, signed. VG (eps browned; cvrs dented in few spots, edges sl grazed) in dj (torn). *Ulysses*. $200/£125

SITWELL, EDITH. Five Poems. London: Duckworth, 1928. 1st ed. One of 250 (of 275) signed, numbered. Uncut. Blue cl, gilt. Good (eps browned) in dj (unevenly browned). *Maggs*. $216/£135

SITWELL, EDITH. The Pleasures of Poetry. Duckworth, 1930. 1st UK ed. NF (foxed) in VG dj. *Williams*. $56/£35

SITWELL, EDITH. Poems New and Old. London: F&F, (1940). 1st ed. NF (pastedowns, eps offset) in NF dj. *Agvent*. $50/£31

SITWELL, EDITH. Poetry and Criticism. London: Hogarth, 1925. 1st ed. VG (lt soiled, worn) in stiff blue wraps. *Agvent*. $100/£63

SITWELL, EDITH. Popular Song. London: Ariel Poems, (1928). 1st Eng ed. Fine in pict card wrappers. *Clearwater*. $40/£25

SITWELL, EDITH. The Queens and the Hive. Boston: Little, Brown, (1962). 1st Amer ed. VG in dj. *Hermitage*. $45/£28

SITWELL, EDITH. Rustic Elegies. Duckworth, 1927. 1st ed. Frontis. VG in dj (sl frayed). *Cox.* $40/£25

SITWELL, EDITH. Troy Park. London: Duckworth, (1925). 1st ed. NF (sl foxed) in NF dj (spine chipped, sl sunned). *Agvent.* $125/£78

SITWELL, EDITH. Victoria of England. Faber & Faber, 1936. 1st ed. VG (inscrip, eps, edges spotted; sm mk fr cvr, spine foot sl bumped) in dj (sl rubbed, chipped, nicked, spine faded). *Ulysses.* $104/£65

SITWELL, OSBERT and MARGARET BARTON. Brighton. Boston: Houghton Mifflin, 1935. 1st Amer ed. NF in dj (lg chip spine head). *Agvent.* $50/£31

SITWELL, OSBERT. The Collected Satires and Poems of Osbert Sitwell. London: Duckworth, 1933. One of 110 numbered, signed. Unopened. Buckram. Fine. *Dermont.* $75/£47

SITWELL, OSBERT. Dumb Animal and Other Stories. London: Duckworth, 1930. One of 110 numbered, signed. Red buckram. Fine in plain dj. *Dermont.* $125/£78

SITWELL, OSBERT. The Four Continents. Macmillan, 1934. 1st ed. Signed, dated. 24 photo plts. (Spine sl bumped), o/w Fine in NF dj (2 sm chips). *Any Amount.* $38/£24

SITWELL, OSBERT. Four Songs of the Italian Earth. Banyan, 1948. One of 260 signed. NF (ink inscrip; spine sl faded) in sewn wrappers, paper label. *Pharos.* $75/£47

SITWELL, OSBERT. Left Hand, Right Hand! An Autobiography. Macmillan, 1946-1950. 5 vols. 1st eds of vols 2, 4 & 5. Good set in djs (frayed). *Cox.* $40/£25

SITWELL, OSBERT. The Man Who Lost Himself. London: Duckworth, 1929. 1st ed. Top edges orange, rest uncut. 1/4 black buckram, patterned paper bds. VG in dj (sm closed tear to spine head). *Maggs.* $72/£45

SITWELL, OSBERT. The Man Who Lost Himself. London: Duckworth, 1929. 1st ed. Cl-backed dec paper over bds. VF in dj. *Pharos.* $125/£78

SITWELL, OSBERT. Wrack at Tidesend. London, 1952. 1st ed. (Cvrs sl discolored), else Good in dj (rubbed, chipped). *King.* $25/£16

SITWELL, SACHEVERELL and WILFRED BLUNT. Great Flower Books 1700-1900. London, 1956. One of 1750. Folio. (Shelfworn.) *Oinonen*.* $200/£125

SITWELL, SACHEVERELL et al. Fine Bird Books, 1700-1900. London, 1953. 1st ed. Folio. Prospectus, specimen plt laid in. Dj (sl worn). *Swann*.* $287/£179

SITWELL, SACHEVERELL et al. Fine Bird Books, 1700-1900. NY, 1990. 1st ed thus. 52 color plts. New in dj. *Young.* $64/£40

SITWELL, SACHEVERELL et al. Old Garden Roses. Parts I and II. George Rainbird/Collins, 1955/1957. One of 160. Signed by authors and Charles Raymond (illus). 2 vols. Thin folio. 16 color plts. Illus eps; teg. 1/2 vellum, marbled bds, gilt. Cl slipcases. *Edwards.* $480/£300

SITWELL, SACHEVERELL. A Background for Domenico Scarlatti 1685-1757. Faber, 1935. 1st ed. Frontis. Uncut. Good (sl rubbed). *Cox.* $19/£12

SITWELL, SACHEVERELL. A Background for Domenico Scarlatti. Faber, 1935. 1st ed. Port. VG in dj (sm tear). *Hollett.* $48/£30

SITWELL, SACHEVERELL. Canons of Giant Art, Twenty Torsos in Heroic Landscapes. London, 1933. 1st ed. (Eps sl foxed; backstrip sl faded; lacks dj.) *Petersfield.* $26/£16

SITWELL, SACHEVERELL. The Cyder Feast and Other Poems. London, 1927. 1st ed. VF. *Bond.* $20/£13

SITWELL, SACHEVERELL. Doctor Donne and Gargantua. London: Gerald Duckworth, 1930. One of 215 signed. Blue cl, dec bds, gilt. (Spine sl faded), o/w NF. *Heritage.* $125/£78

SITWELL, SACHEVERELL. The Fair-Haired Victory. London, 1930. 1st ed. NF in dj (spine sunned). *Polyanthos.* $25/£16

SITWELL, SACHEVERELL. The Gothick North: A Study of Mediaeval Life, Art, and Thought. Boston: Houghton Mifflin, 1929. 1st Amer ed. 1/2 cl, gilt. (Sl foxed; rear cvr sunned, sl insect damage to cl), else VG. *Pacific*.* $63/£39

SITWELL, SACHEVERELL. The Hundred and One Harlequins. London: Grant Richards, 1922. 1st ed. (Spine label sl age-dknd), o/w Fine. *Pharos.* $85/£53

SITWELL, SACHEVERELL. Narrative Pictures. Batsford, 1937. 1st ed. Color frontis, 133 plts. (Feps spotted.) Brn cl, gilt. *Hollett.* $56/£35

SITWELL, SACHEVERELL. The Netherlands. Batsford, n.d. (1948). 1st Eng ed. VG (edges spotted; spine ends bumped) in dj (sl spotted, rubbed, price-clipped, spine sl dknd). *Ulysses.* $48/£30

SITWELL, SACHEVERELL. Portugal and Madeira. Batsford, 1954. 1st ed. Color frontis. NF (feps lt browned; top/fore-edge sl spotted, spine foot sl bumped) in dj (worn). *Ulysses.* $51/£32

SITWELL, SACHEVERELL. Southern Baroque Revisited. London, 1967. Color frontis. (Lib ink stamp fep.) Dj. *Edwards.* $32/£20

SITWELL, SACHEVERELL. Spain. Batsford, 1950. 1st ed. Inscribed presentation, dated April 25, 1950. 4 color plts. VG (spine foot sl bumped, cvrs sl mkd, bowed, dusty) in dj (nicked, sl creased, rubbed, chipped, internally sl mkd, spotted, spine head sl frayed). *Ulysses.* $120/£75

SITWELL, SACHEVERELL. Tropical Birds from Plates by John Gould. Batsford, (1948). 16 color plts. Good in dj. *Rybski.* $20/£13

SITWELL, SACHEVERELL. Valse de Fleurs, a Day in St. Petersburg and a Ball at the Winter Palace in 1868. London, 1941. 1st ed. Fine in dj (faded, sl chipped). *Petersfield.* $22/£14

SITWELL, SACHEVERELL. The Visit of the Gypsies. London, 1929. 1st ed. Fine (sl rubbed) in dj (spine sunned). *Polyanthos.* $25/£16

SIVIERO, RODOLFO. Jewelry and Amber of Italy. NY: McGraw-Hill, 1959. 1st ed. Tall folio. 274 plts (20 color). Blue cl. Good in dj (chipped). *Karmiole.* $150/£94

Six Months of a Newfoundland Missionary's Journal, from February to August, 1835. (By Edward Wix.) London, 1836. 1st ed. 264pp. Uncut, unopened. Orig cl-backed bds (shelfworn, loose in casing), paper spine label. *Oinonen*.* $160/£100

Sixpenny Wonderfuls. (London): C&W/Hogarth, (1985). 1st UK ed. Fine laminated pict bds. *Bernard.* $15/£9

Sixth Report of the Senate Fact-Finding Committee on Un-American Activities 1951. (Sacramento): CA Legislature, (1951). (Bkpl, sl worn.) *King.* $45/£28

SIZER, NELSON. Forty Years in Phrenology, Embracing Recollections of History, Anecdote, and Experience. NY: Fowler & Wells, 1882. 1st ed. 413pp. VG+. *Middle Earth.* $60/£38

SJOWALL, MAJ and PER WAHLOO. The Laughing Policeman. NY, 1970. 1st Amer ed. NF in NF dj. *Warren.* $45/£28

SJOWALL, MAJ and PER WAHLOO. The Laughing Policeman. NY: Pantheon, 1970. 1st Amer ed. (3pp sl dknd), o/w Fine in dj. *Mordida.* $75/£47

SKAFTE, H. Rhino Country (Sumatra). London: Hale, 1964. 1st ed. NF in VG dj. *Mikesh.* $37/£23

SKARMETA, ANTONIO. I Dreamt the Snow Was Burning. London: Readers International, 1985. 1st ed. Fine in NF dj. *Lame Duck.* $45/£28

SKEET, FRANCIS JOHN ANGUS. Stuart Papers, Pictures, Relics, Medals and Books. Leeds: John Whitehead & Son, 1930. Ltd to 375 signed. 6 tissue-guarded plts. Teg, uncut. VG. *Hollett.* $120/£75

SKELDING, SUSIE B. (ed). Flowers from Sunlight and Shade. NY, 1885. 12 color litho plts. (Name; sl worn.) *Woolson.* $60/£38

SKELTON, JOHN. Charles I. London: Goupil, 1898. 1st ed. Hand-tinted frontis. Aeg. 3/4 crushed grn morocco, gilt, raised bands. (Bkpls; spine sl sunned, cvrs smudged), else VG. *Pacific**. $86/£54

SKELTON, R. A. Decorative Printed Maps of the 15th to 18th Centuries. London: Staples, (1952). Rev ed. 84 plts. Reddish-brn cl, gilt. (Spine sl faded), else NF. *Pacific**. $58/£36

SKELTON, R. A. Decorative Printed Maps of the 15th to 18th Centuries. London, 1952. Sm follio. 84 plts. (Extrems worn.) Internally Good. *Dumont*. $85/£53

SKELTON, R. A. Explorers' Maps. London: Routledge/Kegan Paul, (1958). 1st ed. Color frontis. Mustard yellow cl. (Sm lib stamp, Amer pub's label, eps renewed), else Fine in dj (sl worn). *Argonaut*. $100/£63

SKERTCHLY, SYDNEY B. J. Our Island. Hong Kong: Kelly & Walsh, 1893. 1st ed. (vi),(ii),56,(2),xxxii list,(1)imprint; Beige cl. Good (ink sig, underlining in red/blue crayon; spine repaired, rubbed). *Morrell*. $176/£110

Sketch of the Life of Com. Robert F. Stockton. (By Samuel J. Bayard.) NY: Derby & Jackson, 1856. 1st ed. 210,131pp; port. (Lacks fep, foxed; cvrs rubbed.) Howes B259. *Lefkowicz*. $250/£156

Sketches of a New-England Village in the Last Century. (By Eliza Buckminster Lee.) Boston: Munroe, 1838. 1st ed, 1st bk. 110pp. Brn pub's patterned cl (spine extrems worn), gilt. VG. *Second Life*. $75/£47

Sketches of Mission Life Among the Indians of Oregon. NY: Carlton & Phillips, 1854. 1st ed. 229,(4)ads pp; 4 (of 5) wood-engr plts incl frontis, all incl in pagination. (Internal soil, staining, lacks 1 plt; cvrs worn, stained), else Good. Howes P230. *Pacific**. $151/£94

Sketches of Switzerland. By an American. (By James Fenimore Cooper.) Phila: Carey, Lea & Blanchard, 1836. 1st ed. 2 vols. 244; 239pp. Orig lt brn muslin, ptd paper spine labels. Good (sl foxed, few sigs lt sprung; ex-lib, label on cvrs, bkpls, ink notes feps; sl worn, spotted, labels chipped, partly scuffed). BAL 3871. *Baltimore**. $150/£94

Sketches of the War, Between the United States and the British Isles. (By Gideon Minor Davison.) Rutland, 1815. Contemp sheep (worn; ink lib stamp). *Swann**. $149/£93

SKETCHLEY, R. E. D. English Book-Illustrations of To-Day. London, 1903. 1st ed. Uncut. VG (sl rubbed). *Whittle*. $56/£35

SKETCHLEY, W. The Cocker; Containing Every Information to the Breeders and Amateurs of That Noble Bird, the Game Cock.... Burton-on-Trent, 1814. Engr frontis, 154pp. Old polished calf. (Rubbed; foxing.) *Oinonen**. $170/£106

SKEY, FREDERIC. A Practical Treatise on the Venereal Disease. London, 1840. 1st ed. 195pp; 2 lithographs. *Fye*. $125/£78

SKEYHILL, TOM. Soldier-Songs from Anzac, Written in the Firing Line. Melbourne et al, (post-1916). 1st Eng ed. (Name.) Pict card wrappers (chafed, spine partly defective). *Clearwater*. $40/£25

SKILLERN, R. H. The Catarrhal and Suppurative Diseases of Accessory Sinuses of the Nose. Phila, 1916. 2nd ed. VG (sig). *Doctor's Library*. $150/£94

SKINNER, ADA M. and ELEANOR L. A Child's Book of Country Stories. NY: Duffield, 1925. 1st ed. 4 full-pg color plts + insert on cvr. (Fold to tp.) Red cl (spine faded), gilt, color paste label (sm chip). *Reisler*. $150/£94

SKINNER, CONSTANCE LINDSAY. Pioneers of the Old Southwest. New Haven, 1919. 1st ed. Teg. Gilt-dec cl. VG (few ink notes, lt blue mk top edge) in dj (chipped). *Baade*. $65/£41

SKIPP, JOHN and CRAIG SPECTOR (eds). Book of the Dead. Williamantic: Ziesing, 1989. One of 500 numbered, signed by contributors. (Sl worn.) Dj, slipcase. *Oinonen**. $60/£38

SKIR, LEO. Boychick. NY: Winter House, 1971. 1st ed. VF in VF black dj (sl rubbed). *Between The Covers*. $85/£53

SKODA, JOSEPH. Auscultation and Percussion. W. O. Markham (trans). Phila, 1854. 1st Amer ed. 380pp. (Fr bd, prelims detached.) *Fye*. $250/£156

SKORY, EDMUND. An Extract Out of the Historie of the Last French King Henry the Fourth. London: Robert Barker, 1610. 1st ed. 4to. 16 unnumbered ll. A1 blank except for sig mkg 'A' in lg type w/in floral woodcut tailpiece on recto. Mod bds. (Lt waterstain upper edge last 2 sigs), o/w Good. *Sokol*. $600/£375

SKREBNESKI, VICTOR. Portraits, a Matter of Record. NY, (1978). 1st ed. Signed. (Pencil notes fep; fr cvr damp-wrinkled, lt soiled.) Dj (chipped, torn) w/label that reads 'autographed copy,' acetate wrapper. *Swann**. $149/£93

SKRINE, FRANCIS HENRY. Fontenoy and Great Britain's Share in the War of the Austrian Succession 1741-1748. London: William Blackwood, 1906. Frontisport, facs; 2 maps, 6 plts. Good. *Stewart*. $96/£60

SKRINE, HENRY. Two Successive Tours Throughout the Whole of Wales. London: T. Turner, 1812. 2nd ed. xii,280pp, half-title present; hand-colored fldg frontis map (sl offset onto tp). Marbled eps; teg. Later 1/2 morocco, marbled bds, gilt. (Bkpl; spine lt faded.) *Edwards*. $160/£100

SKUES, G. E. M. Itchen Memories. London: Jenkins, 1951. 1st ed. (Lower spine sunned), else VG + in dj (chipped). *Bowman*. $165/£103

SKUES, G. E. M. Minor Tactics of the Chalk Stream and Kindred Studies. London: A&C Black, 1910. 2nd ed. Frontis color plt. Grn cl, gilt. VG. *Pacific**. $127/£79

SKUES, G. E. M. Minor Tactics of the Chalk Stream and Kindred Studies. London, 1910. 1st ed. (Sl foxed; lt worn.) *Oinonen**. $250/£156

SKUES, G. E. M. Minor Tactics of the Chalk Stream. London: Black, 1910. 1st ed. Color frontis. Brn cl. (1st, last 3pp lt foxed; fr hinge strengthened), else VG. *Bowman*. $165/£103

SKUES, G. E. M. Nymph Fishing for Chalk Stream Trout. London, 1939. 1st ed. 1/2 grn crushed levant, gilt spine, by Bayntun. *Swann**. $345/£216

SKUES, G. E. M. Side-Lines, Side-Lights and Reflections. Phila: Lippincott, (c. 1932). 1st Amer ed. (Extrems irregularly dknd, fr joint cl torn), else VG. *Pacific**. $109/£68

SKUES, G. E. M. Silk, Fur and Feather. Kent: Fishing Gazette, 1950. 1st ed. VF in grn hard paper wraps. *Bowman*. $125/£78

SKUES, G. E. M. The Way of a Trout with a Fly, and Some Further Studies in Minor Tactics. London: A&C Black, 1921. 1st ed. 3 plts (2 color). Brn cl, gilt. VG. *Pacific**. $104/£65

SKVORECKY, JOSEF. Dvorak in Love. NY: Knopf, 1987. 1st US ed. As New in dj. *Bernard*. $20/£13

SLACK, H. J. Marvels of Pond-Life. London: Groombridge, 1861. Frontis, 197pp; 6 plts. VG. *Savona*. $29/£18

SLADE, B. C. Maria Edgeworth 1767-1849: A Bibliographical Tribute. London: Constable, 1937. Ltd to 250. Frontis, 9 plts. Uncut. Cl-backed marbled bds, gilt. Dj. *Maggs*. $264/£165

SLADE, DANIEL D. Diphtheria: Its Nature and Treatment. Phila: Blanchard & Lea, 1864. 2nd, rev ed. 166pp. VG. *Glaser*. $60/£38

SLADE, GURNEY. In Lawrence's Bodyguard. Warne, 1930. 1st UK ed from US sheets, w/cancel tp. Pub's file copy stamp on fep. NF (pencil note) in Good pict dj (chipped, torn). *Any Amount*. $48/£30

SLADEN, DOUGLAS. Japan in Pictures. London/NY: Newnes/Warne, 1904. 1st ed. (Sl rubbed, soiled), o/w VG. *Worldwide*. $45/£28

SLADEN, W. PERCY. A Monograph on the British Fossil Echinodermata...Volume 2: The Asteroidea. London: Palaeontographical Soc, 1891. 28pp; 8 litho plts. VG in mod grn wrappers. *Hollett*. $72/£45

SLATE, GEORGE L. Lilies for American Gardens. NY, 1939. 1st ed. 44 photo plts. VG in dj (chipped). *Larry Price*. $30/£19

SLATER, J. H. Book Collecting. London: Swan Sonnenschein, 1892. Lg paper ed. Ltd to 500 numbered. Frontis, 130pp. Blue cl (headcaps sl bumped), gilt. *Maggs*. $32/£20

SLATER, J. H. Book-Plates. Grant, 1898. 1st ed. (Spine, fr cvr top lightened), else VG. *Fine Books*. $65/£41

SLATER, J. H. The Romance of Book-Collecting. London: Elliot Stock, 1898. Frontis. (Backstrip sl faded w/sm mk), o/w Good. *Petersfield*. $32/£20

SLATER, JOHN M. El Morro, Inscription Rock, New Mexico. L.A.: Plantin, 1961. One of 500. Dj. *Dawson*. $75/£47

SLATKIN, W. Aristide Maillol in the 1890s. Univ of MI Research Press, 1982. Rev ed. 36 plts. Good. *Ars Artis*. $40/£25

SLAUGHTER, F. Surgeon's Tools and Writers Instincts. Doubleday, 1957. 1st ed. Pamphlet. Fine in wraps. *Fine Books*. $12/£8

Slavery Illustrated in Its Effects upon Woman and Domestic Society. (By George Bourne.) Boston, 1837. Orig cl-backed bds. (Lacks fep, contemp pencil notes; stained, soiled.) *Swann**. $258/£161

SLEEMAN, W. H. Rambles and Recollections of an Indian Official. London, 1844. 2 vols. Color frontispieces (sm margin stain 1st frontis); 6 only (of 32) chromolitho plts. Dec cl (backs faded.) *Petersfield*. $240/£150

SLEEMAN, W. H. Rambles and Recollections of an Indian Official. Vincent Arthur Smith (ed). Westminster, 1893. New ed. 2 vols. xxxvi,447pp; ix,368pp; fldg map. Blind-emb cl (spines sl chipped). *Edwards*. $88/£55

Sleeping Beauty. London: Bancroft, 1961. 8 dbl-pg pop-ups by V. Kubasta. VG in pict wraps. *Bookfinders*. $100/£63

Sleeping Beauty. A Peepshow Book. London: C&W, 1975. 5 fldg-out scenes by Karen Avery. Glazed pict bds. VG-. *Bookfinders*. $40/£25

SLEMMONS, ROD. Like a One-Eyed Cat: Photographs by Lee Friedlander, 1956-1987. NY: Abrams, 1989. 1st ed. 153 b/w photos. (1st few ll sl vertically creased), else Fine in pict dj. *Cahan*. $125/£78

SLEMONS, J. MORRIS. John Whitridge Williams. Balt: Johns Hopkins, 1935. 1st ed. Frontisport. Cl spine, paper label. Fine. *Glaser*. $35/£22

SLOAN, A. Wanderings in the Middle East. London: Hutchinson, n.d. (ca 1924). 1st ed. 16 plts. (Sl rubbed, unevenly faded), o/w VG. *Worldwide*. $75/£47

SLOAN, ERIC. Gremlin Americanus: A Scrapbook Collection of Gremlins. (N.p.: B.F. Jay & Co, 1943.) 1st ed. VG (few sm tide mks pg bottoms; few sm stains fr bd; lacks dj). *Between The Covers*. $400/£250

SLOAN, RICHARD E. History of Arizona. Phoenix: Record Pub, 1930. 1st ed. 4 vols. Full leather. NF set. *Labordo*. $350/£219

SLOAN, RICHARD E. Memories of an Arizona Judge. Stanford, CA: Stanford Univ, 1932. 1st ed. Gray cl. (Spine, edges sl sunned), o/w Fine. *Harrington*. $40/£25

SLOAN, SAMUEL. The Model Architect. Phila: E.S. Jones, (1852). 1st ed. Thick folio. (ii),7-100,(3)-104pp; 212 litho plts. Recent dk brn eps. Contemp dk brn morocco and cl, raised bands, gilt. (Lt aged, foxed; edgeworn, recently repaired along upper joint w/orig spine retained.) *Baltimore**. $425/£266

SLOAN, SAMUEL. Sloan's Homestead Architecture.... Phila: Lippincott, 1861. 1st ed. 355pp. (Soiled.) *M & S*. $450/£281

SLOANE, ERIC. Gremlin Americanus: A Scrap Book Collection of Gremlins. N.p.: B.F. Jay, 1942. 1st ed. Pict cl. (Faded, spine bumped), else VG. *Pacific**. $29/£18

SLOANE, ERIC. The Vanishing Landscape. NY: Funk, 1955. 1st ed. 7x9. 107pp. Fine. *Price*. $45/£28

SLOANE, JOSEPH C. French Painting Between the Past and the Present. Artists, Critics, and Traditions from 1848 to 1870. Princeton, 1951. Good in wrappers. *Washton*. $45/£28

SLOAT, JOHN DRAKE. The Life of the Late Admiral John Drake Sloat of the United States Navy Who Took Possession of California and Raised the Flag at Monterey...1846. Edward A. Sherman (comp). Oakland: Carruth & Carruth, 1902. Enlgd Monumental ed. Blue cl, gilt. NF. *Pacific**. $52/£33

SLOCUM, JOSHUA. Sailing Alone Around the World. NY: Century, 1900. 1st ed. Teg. Dec blue cl (spine extrems sl rubbed). *Karmiole*. $350/£219

SLOCUM, VICTOR. Captain Joshua Slocum. NY: Sheridan House, 1950. 1st Amer ed. VG in dj. *American Booksellers*. $40/£25

SLOVO, GILLIAN. Morbid Symptoms. London: Pluto Crime, 1984. 1st ed, 1st bk. Fine in Fine dj. *Murder*. $45/£28

SLUDER, GREENFIELD. Concerning Some Headaches and Eye Disorders of Nasal Origin. St. Louis: Mosby, 1918. 1st ed. Red cl. VG (extrems lt worn). *Glaser*. $135/£84

Sly Joe; and Other Tales. All in Words of Three Letters. London: Dean & Son, (ca 1855). 8vo. 16pp. Ptd paper wrappers (spine lt worn). Nice. *Reisler*. $225/£141

SMALL, GEORGE L. The Blue Whale. NY: Columbia Univ, 1971. 1st ed. VG in dj. *Walcot*. $22/£14

SMALL, JOE AUSTELL (ed). The Best of True West. NY: Julian Messner, (1964). 1st ed. VG in dj. *Lien*. $25/£16

SMALL, JOHN W. Ancient and Modern Furniture. Stirling, 1903. One of 250. 50 plts. Teg, rest uncut. (Few margins sl thumbed, eps spotted, feps browned; rear joint split, cl worn, sl spine loss.) *Edwards*. $104/£65

SMALL, WALTER HERBERT. Early New England Schools. Ginn, 1914. 1st ed. Nice. *Rybski*. $50/£31

SMALLEY, B. English Friars and Antiquity in the Early Fourteenth Century. Oxford: Basil Blackwell, 1960. Frontis. Red cl. Dj (sl worn). *Maggs*. $61/£38

SMALLEY, EUGENE V. History of the Northern Pacific Railroad. NY: Putnam, 1883. 1st ed, advance rev copy. xxii,(3)-437pp; fldg chart, lg fldg map in rear pocket. Advance Copy ptd slip tipped in at tp. Patterned eps ptd in grn. Beveled lt brn cl, gilt. (Sl loss of paper at bottom of hinges, sl rubbed, sl spotted.) Text Clean, cvrs VG. Howes S561. *Baltimore**. $80/£50

SMALLZRIED, KATHLEEN. The Everlasting Pleasure. NY: Appleton Century Crofts, 1956. 1st ed. VG + (sl shelfworn) in dj (edgeworn, spine faded). *My Bookhouse*. $27/£17

SMART, ADAM. Prehistoric Beasts Discovered for His Grandchildren. (SF: Grabhorn, 1937.) One of 500. Inscribed by Alfred Sutro (photos, text). 2-tone cl. *Dawson*. $100/£63

SMEATON, JOHN. A Narrative of the Building and a Description of the Construction of the Edystone Lighthouse with Stone. London: T. Davison, 1813. 2nd ed. 23 engr plts and maps. (Lt spotting, browning, emb lib stamps, bkpl.) Orig 1/2 calf (rubbed, inner hinges reinforced). *Christie's**. $541/£338

SMEDES, SUSAN DABNEY. A Southern Planter. London, 1889. 1st Eng ed. x,298pp. (Lt dust soiled.) *Maggs*. $200/£125

SMEDLEY, FRANK. Lewis Arundel; or, the Railroad of Life. London: Virtue, 1852. 1st ed. viii,663pp; 41 engr plts by Phiz. Marbled sides. Recent maroon 1/2 calf, gilt, twin blue morocco labels. Very Clean. *Young*. $80/£50

SMEE, ALFRED. Principles of the Human Mind, Deduced from Physical Laws. NY: Fowlers & Wells, 1850. 64,(6)pp (sm piece clipped from half-title). Orig ptd wrappers. *M & S*. $85/£53

SMETHAM, HENRY. History of Strood. Chatham & Rochester, 1899. 435pp + 3pp subs. Dec eps (sl browned; hinges sl tender; spine sl rubbed, faded, lt soiled). *Edwards*. $96/£60

SMILES, SAMUEL. The Huguenots. John Murray, 1868. 2nd ed. xv,534pp (feps sl spotted). All eps, edges marbled. 1/2 hard-grained morocco (spine sl rubbed), gilt, raised bands. *Hollett.* $104/£65

SMILES, SAMUEL. Life of a Scotch Naturalist. John Murray, 1884. New ed. xxxv,392pp (feps lt spotted); map. Aeg. Full grn calf (fr bd sl scratched), gilt. *Hollett.* $64/£40

SMILES, SAMUEL. Lives of Boulton and Watt. London: John Murray, 1865. 1st ed. xvi,521,(vi ads)pp; 2 engr ports. Contemp 1/2 morocco, gilt. (Bkpl, lt damp stain center of lower margins throughout.) *Hollett.* $120/£75

SMILES, SAMUEL. Lives of the Engineers, with an Account of Their Principal Works. London: John Murray, 1862. 6th thousand. 3 vols. (2),xvii,484; xiv,502; xx,(4),512pp; 7 steel-engr port plts. Blindstamped cl, gilt. (Vol 2 mostly marginally damp-stained; vol 2 w/paper remnants on cvrs, stained; all spines sl faded), else VG. *Pacific*.* $86/£54

SMILES, SAMUEL. Lives of the Engineers. London: John Murray, 1862-68. 6th thousand. 3 vols. xvi,484; xi,502; lii,542pp; 2 half-titles. All edges marbled. Full tree calf, gilt, raised bands, contrasting spine labels. (Feps spotted; spines sl dull.) *Hollett.* $240/£150

SMILES, SAMUEL. Men of Invention and Industry. John Murray, 1884. (1st ed). viii,390,10pp. Gilt (spine faded). *Hollett.* $72/£45

SMILEY, JANE. The Age of Grief. NY: Knopf, 1987. 1st ed. Signed. Fine in Fine dj. *Beasley.* $150/£94

SMILEY, JANE. Ordinary Love and Good Will. NY: Knopf, 1989. 1st ed. Inscribed. Fine in Fine dj. *Beasley.* $85/£53

SMILEY, JANE. A Thousand Acres. NY, 1991. 1st ed. Fine in Fine dj. *Warren.* $40/£25

SMIRKE, SYDNEY. Illustrations of the Architectural Ornaments and Embellishments and Painted Glass, of the Temple Church, London. London: John Weale, 1845. Paper bds (lt worn). *Oinonen*.* $80/£50

SMITH, ADAM. An Inquiry into the Nature and Causes of the Wealth of Nations. London: W. Strahan & T. Cadell, 1784. 3rd ed. 1st 8vo ed. Errata statement in 3rd ed appears only in vol 1 on verso of ad leaf at fr. viii,499; vi,518,(v); v, 465,(xlix),(i)pp incl ad at rear vol 3. Contemp full polished tree calf, gilt. (Sl browned, lt foxed, ink sigs, bkpls; spines worn, scuffed, lacks orig leather labels, cracks along most joints, fr cvr vol 2 detached w/some peeling to cvr at spine edge.) Texts VG. *Baltimore*.* $950/£594

SMITH, ADAM. An Inquiry into the Nature and Causes of the Wealth of Nations. London: Strahan & Cadell, 1793. 7th ed. 3 vols. Tall 8vo. Fine rebinding in full mottled calf, gilt, dbl leather labels. Fine set (sl foxed). *Hartfield.* $895/£559

SMITH, ADAM. An Inquiry into the Nature and Causes of the Wealth of Nations. Hartford, (CT): Oliver D. Cooke, 1804. New ed. 2 vols. 8vo. (Browned, edges ink stained, few prelim ll loose.) Contemp calf, leather labels. *M & S.* $600/£375

SMITH, ADAM. An Inquiry into the Nature and Causes of the Wealth of Nations. Edinburgh: William Creech et al, 1806. 3 vols. Period tree calf, gilt, morocco lettering pieces. (Contents aged, marginal worming to prelims vol 3, incl tp; spines, edges rubbed, scuffed, joints cracked, fr cvr detached from vol 3), else VG. *Pacific*.* $184/£115

SMITH, ADAM. The Theory of Moral Sentiments: An Essay...to Which Is Added, A Dissertation on the Origin of Languages. Phila: Anthony Finley, 1817. 1st Amer ed. vii,(1),598 + (2)ad pp. Period tree calf. (Bkpl; extrems, spine, joints cracked), else VG-. *Pacific*.* $196/£123

SMITH, ALBERT. The Adventures of Mr. Ledbury and His Friend Jack Johnson. London: Bentley, 1886. 21 steel-engr plts by John Leech. 3/4 red polished calf (rubbed, rear cvr nearly detached). *Oinonen*.* $20/£13

SMITH, ALBERT. The Natural History of 'Stuck-Up' People. London: Bogue, 1847. 4th ed. Frontis, 112pp; 8ff. ads. Pict ptd wrappers (sm loss to spine foot). *Marlborough.* $104/£65

SMITH, ALBERT. The Struggle and Adventures of Christopher Tadpole at Home and Abroad. London: Richard Bentley, 1848. 1st ed. Stipple-engr frontisport, xi,512pp; 32 etched plts by John Leech. Marbled eps; teg. Full polished tan calf, gilt, morocco labels. NF (bkpl; spine, rear cvr sunned). *Pacific*.* $86/£54

SMITH, ALEXANDER. Books and Gardens. Herrin, IL: Trovillion Private Press, 1946. One of 807 signed. Frontis. VG + . *Bohling.* $20/£13

SMITH, ALEXANDER. A Complete History of the Lives and Robberies of the Most Notorious Highwaymen. NY: Brentano's, n.d. (ca 1926). 1st ed. Frontis, 15 plts. Beige over red cl, labels. Good in dj (chipped, sl soiled). *Karmiole.* $85/£53

SMITH, ALEXANDER. Dreamthorp: A Book of Essays Written in the Country. Strahan, 1863. 1st ed. viii,296pp, pub's cat at end. Grn ribbed cl. Fine. *Bickersteth.* $88/£55

SMITH, ALEXANDER. A Summer in Skye. Sampson Low, Marston, n.d. (c.1912). 16 color plts. (Tp, fore-edge lt spotted; spine sl faded.) *Hollett.* $64/£40

SMITH, ALLAN CORSTORPHIN. The Secrets of Jujitsu: A Complete Course in Self-Defense. Columbus, OH: Stahara, (1918). 1st ed. 7 vols. Fine in illus wrappers, VG- string-clasped paper portfolio (lacks piece). *Pacific*.* $58/£36

SMITH, AMANDA. Autobiography: The Story of the Lord's Dealings with Mrs. Amanda Smith. Chicago: Meyer & Brother, 1893. 1st ed. Engr frontisport. Fine (bottom rt corner fr cvr worn). *Swann*.* $402/£251

SMITH, ANN ELIZA. Atla: A Story of the Lost Island. NY: Harper, 1886. 1st ed. 284pp + 4pp ads. Pict cl. (Sl shelfworn), else VG. *Brown.* $50/£31

SMITH, ART. Pavement's End. Pat Smith (ed). Clinton, NJ: Amwell, 1985. 1st ed. Ltd to 1000 numbered, signed. Red bonded leather. Fine in Fine slipcase. *Biscotti.* $65/£41

SMITH, ART. Water's Edge. Clinton, NJ: Amwell, 1986. 1st ed. Ltd to 1000 numbered, signed. Blue bonded leather. Fine in Fine slipcase. *Biscotti.* $65/£41

SMITH, BENJAMIN. A Fugitive From Hell. (Joplin): Privately ptd, 1935. (Extrems, fr hinge following frontis sl worn), else VG. *Baade.* $40/£25

SMITH, BENJAMIN. Private Smith's Journal. Clyde C. Walton (ed). Chicago: R.R. Donnelley, 1963. VG. *Lien.* $25/£16

SMITH, BENJAMIN. Private Smith's Journal. Clyde C. Walton (ed). Chicago, 1963. 1st ed. Gilt edge. Pict cl. Fine. *Pratt.* $35/£22

SMITH, BERTHA H. Yosemite Legends. SF: Paul Elder, (1904). 1st ed. Dec eps. Dec cl, gilt. Fine. *Pacific*.* $92/£58

SMITH, BETTY. Maggie-Now. NY: Harpers, (1958). 1st ed. Fine in NF dj (sl tanned, spine sl torn). *Between The Covers.* $75/£47

SMITH, BRADLEY and WAN-GO WENG. China: A History in Art. NY/SF/London/Evanston: Harper & Row, n.d. (ca 1972). VG in dj. *Worldwide.* $65/£41

SMITH, BRADLEY. Japan: A History in Art. NY, 1964. 1st ed, deluxe issue. Ltd to 500. Signed. Japanese silk brocade, gilt. Fine in wooden box w/ironwork corners, latch. *Truepenny.* $300/£188

SMITH, BRIDGES. The Channel Cat and the Rose. Macon: J.W. Burke, 1924. Port. VG in wraps. *Brown.* $12/£8

SMITH, C. E. From the Deep of the Sea. Macmillan, 1923. 1st US ed. 2 maps. Pict cl. VG. *Walcot.* $48/£30

SMITH, C. ROSS. Paris Nights. NY: S&S, (1965). 1st ed. VF in VF dj (sl rubbed). *Between The Covers.* $65/£41

SMITH, C. W. Thin Men of Haddam. NY: Grossman, 1973. 1st ed, 1st bk. Advance rev copy w/slip, publicity photo of Smith laid in. As New in dj. *Bernard.* $100/£63

SMITH, CHARLES W. Old Charleston. Richmond: Dale, (1933). 1st ed. One of 1550 signed. 24 full-pg plts. Pict bds. VG in pict dj (edge chipped). *House.* $55/£34

SMITH, CHARLES W. Pacific Northwest Americana. Portland, 1950. 3rd ed, rev. (Spine sl faded), else Good. *Dumont.* $75/£47

SMITH, CHARLES W. Pacific Northwest Americana. OR: Binfords & Mort, 1950. 3rd ed. Red cl, gilt. (Spot fr cvr), else Fine. *Argonaut.* $90/£56

SMITH, CHARLES. The Aberdeen Golfers: Records and Reminscences. (London): Ellesborough, (1982). Facs ed. One of 200. Signed by J.S.R. Cruikshank. Aeg. Full dk grn morocco, gilt, raised bands. (Spine sl sunned), else Fine in slipcase. *Pacific*.* $288/£180

SMITH, CLARE SYDNEY. The Golden Reign. London: Cassell, 1940. 1st ed. Signed (later). Grn cl. VG in dj (spine sl dknd). *Maggs.* $320/£200

SMITH, CLARE SYDNEY. The Golden Reign. London: Cassell, 1949. 2nd ed. Inscribed. Patterned bds. Fine in dj. *Maggs.* $48/£30

SMITH, CLARK ASHTON. Lost Worlds. Sauk City: Arkham House, 1944. 1st ed. (Cvrs sl dampstained), else Good in dj (sl rubbed, discolored). *King.* $200/£125

SMITH, CLARK ASHTON. Spells and Philtres. Sauk City, WI: Arkham House, 1958. 1st ed. Ltd to 519. VF in VF ptd dj. *Bromer.* $600/£375

SMITH, CORNELIUS C., JR. Emilio Kosterlitzky: Eagle of Sonora and the Southwest Border. Glendale: A.H. Clark, 1970. 1st ed. VG. *Lien.* $40/£25

SMITH, DAVE. In the House of the Judge. NY: Harper & Row, (1983). 1st ed. Fine in Fine dj. *Dermont.* $20/£13

SMITH, DAVID EUGENE. Rara Arithmetica: A Catalogue of the Arithmetics Written Before the Year MDCI.... NY: Chelsea, 1970. 4th ed (so stated). Navy cl, gilt. (Pencil notes in index w/mtd typed explanatory slip.) *Baltimore*.* $80/£50

SMITH, DAVID EUGENE. The Sumario Compendioso of Brother Juan Diez. Boston: Ginn, 1921. 1st ed thus. Gray bds, parchment spine. VG in slipcase (worn). *Glaser.* $75/£47

SMITH, E. BOYD. The Railroad Book: Bob and Betty's Summer on the Railroad. Boston: Houghton Mifflin, (1913). 1st ed. Obl 4to. 12 full-pg color plts. Cl-backed color illus bds (lt dusty). *Reisler.* $225/£141

SMITH, E. BOYD. The Seashore Book: Bob and Betty's Summer with Captain Hawes. Boston: Houghton Mifflin, (1912). 1st ed. 8.25x11. Cl-backed pict bds. (Soiled, stamp, hinges weak, tear to 1 plt; extrems rubbed), else VG-. *Pacific*.* $69/£43

SMITH, E. BOYD. So Long Ago. Boston: Houghton Mifflin, 1944. 1st ed. Lg 4to. Grn cl (spine sl faded). Color pict dj (tears). *Reisler.* $165/£103

SMITH, E. BOYD. The Story of Pocahontas and Captain John Smith. Boston: Houghton Mifflin, 1906. 1st ed. Obl 4to. 26 full-pg color plts (few sheets foxed). Lt blue cl (lt stained), gilt, color paste label. *Reisler.* $200/£125

SMITH, EDGAR NEWBOLD. American Naval Broadsides. NY: Phila Maritime Museum/Potter, 1974. 1st ed. Fine in dj. *American Booksellers.* $45/£28

SMITH, EDMOND REUEL. The Araucanians...A Tour Among the Indian Tribes of Southern Chili. NY, 1855. 1st ed. (Faded, spine ends worn.) *Kane*.* $180/£113

SMITH, EDMUND WARE. The Further Adventures of the One-Eyed Poacher. NY: Crown, (1947). 1st ed. One of 750. Signed. Red cl, gilt. (Ink inscrip), else NF. *Pacific*.* $75/£47

SMITH, EDMUND WARE. The Further Adventures of the One-Eyed Poacher. NY, (1947). One of 750 numbered, signed. *Swann*.* $149/£93

SMITH, EDMUND WARE. Tall Tales and Short. NY: Derrydale, 1938. One of 950 numbered. Fine. *Biscotti.* $200/£125

SMITH, EDWARD CONRAD. The Borderland in the Civil War. NY: Macmillan, 1927. 1st ed. Dk blue cl, gilt. NF in VG dj (price-clipped, spine ends, corners chipped). *Chapel Hill.* $75/£47

SMITH, EDWARD E. The Skylark of Space. (Providence: Buffalo Book, 1946.) 1st ed. Lt blue binding. (Spine ends faded), else VG- in dj (worn, torn, chipped). *Other Worlds.* $150/£94

SMITH, EDWARD E. Spacehounds of IPC. Reading: Fantasy, 1947. 1st ed. (Hinges cracked, spine head stained), else VG + in dj (worn, torn, lt chipped, spine head stained). *Other Worlds.* $45/£28

SMITH, ELEANOR. Ballerina. London: Gollancz, 1932. 1st Eng ed. VG (feps partly browned; spine foot sl bumped) in dj (sl frayed, nicked, spine sl faded). *Ulysses.* $56/£35

SMITH, ELIAS. The American Physician, and Family Assistant. Boston: R. True, 1837. 4th ed. 274pp (lacks frontis). Old calf (rebacked; inner fr hing weak, shaken). *M & S.* $125/£78

SMITH, ELIAS. A Discourse on Government and Religion; Delivered at Gray, (Maine) July Fourth, 1810. Portland, (ME): Herald Office, 1810. 1st ed. 54pp. Sewn as issued. Very Nice (few stains). *M & S.* $100/£63

SMITH, ESTHER RUTH. The History of Del Norte County, California.... Oakland: Holmes Book Co, 1953. Ltd to 350 ptd. Signed by Oscar Lewis (intro) w/1st name only. 8 plts. Prospectus laid in. Gray cl, gilt spine. Fine in ptd dj. *Pacific*.* $40/£25

SMITH, EUSTACE. Clinical Studies of Diseases in Children. Diseases of the Lungs, Acute Tuberculosis. London, 1876. 1st ed. 303pp. *Fye.* $125/£78

SMITH, F. HOPKINSON. Colonel Carter of Cartersville. Boston/NY: Houghton Mifflin, 1891. 1st ed, 1st state. (Extrems lt rubbed, spine sl dull, hinges starting.) Dk grn wrapper w/leather label. *Sadlon.* $30/£19

SMITH, F. R. Practical Leatherwork...for Students and Craft Workers. Pitman, 1930. 32 plts. VG + in dj. *Whittle.* $13/£8

SMITH, FREDERICK. My American Visit. London: Hutchinson, 1918. 1st ed. *Mott.* $30/£19

SMITH, G. BARNETT. The Romance of the South Pole. London: Nelson, 1902. 1st ed. 12 full-pg engrs. Full school prize leather, gilt. VG. *Mikesh.* $60/£38

SMITH, G. BARNETT. Sir John Franklin and the Romance of the North-West Passage. London: S.W. Partridge, (1896). 160pp,(20) ads. Color dec blue cl. VG (inscrip). *Explorer.* $40/£25

SMITH, G. ELLIOT. Elephants and Ethnologists. London: Kegan Paul, Trench, Trubner, 1924. Frontis, 52 plts. 1/2 cl. (Extrems rubbed.) *Archaeologia.* $110/£69

SMITH, G. ROYDE. The History of Bradshaw. Henry Blacklock, 1939. 1st ed. Color frontis. (Sl worn, faded.) *Forest.* $40/£25

SMITH, GARDEN. Side Lights on Golf. London: Sisley's, (c.1907). 1st ed. (Emb stamp; sl soiled, lt spotted), else VG. *Pacific*.* $288/£180

SMITH, GARDEN. The World of Golf; The Isthmian Library. London: A.D. Innes, 1898. 1st ed. Frontis. Grn cl, gilt. (Emb stamp, stain to frontis, guard), else VG. *Pacific*.* $374/£234

SMITH, GEDDES. Plague on Us. NY: Commonwealth Fund, 1941. 1st ed. VG (few pencil notes) in dj. *Glaser.* $45/£28

SMITH, GEORGE O. Nomad. Phila: Prime, (1950). 1st ed. VG in dj (chipped, extrems dull, sm tear). *Pacific*.* $23/£14

SMITH, GRAHAM. King's Cutters. The Revenue Service and the War Against Smuggling. London: Conway Maritime, 1983. VG in dj. *Parmer.* $20/£13

SMITH, GRIFFIN, JR. Forgotten Texas. (Austin): TX Monthly Press, 1983. 1st ed. Cream cl. Fine in photo dj. *House.* $20/£13

SMITH, GUSTAVUS. The Battle of Seven Pines. NY: C.G. Crawford, 1891. 1st ed. 202pp. Nice in wraps (worn), custom-made protective folder, 1/2 morocco slipcase. *Chapel Hill.* $300/£188

SMITH, H. Jewellery. NY: Putnam, 1908. 54 plts. Good (ex-libris). *Blake.* $175/£109

SMITH, H. Jewellery. London: Methuen, 1909. 2nd ed. 54 plts. Good (eps cracked, foxed). *Blake.* $150/£94

SMITH, H. ALLEN. Larks in the Popcorn. GC, 1948. 1st ed. Presentation copy. Inscribed, signed. (Bkpl; cvrs waterstained.) Dj (heavily chipped). *King.* $30/£19

SMITH, H. CLIFFORD. Buckingham Palace. Its Furniture, Decoration and History. London/NY, 1931. Frontis port, port, 3 color plts, 351 b/w plts. Teg. Dj (lt soiled, torn) w/mtd b/w plt upper wrap. *Edwards.* $64/£40

SMITH, H. M. Handbook of Lizards. Ithaca, (1946). 41 maps. (Pp tanned; fr cvr lt stained, spine ends, corners rubbed.) *Sutton.* $65/£41

SMITH, HAL H. On the Gathering of a Library. Privately ptd, 1943. Tipped-in frontis. 2-tone cl. *Dawson.* $35/£22

SMITH, HARRY B. First Nights and First Editions. Boston, 1931. 1st Amer ed. Fine (spine sl sunned). *Polyanthos.* $35/£22

SMITH, HARRY B. A Sentimental Library Comprising Books Formerly Owned by Famous Writers, Presentation Copies.... N.p.: Privately ptd, 1914. 1st ed. Signed, inscribed presentation. Uncut. 1/2 vellum (lt worn; sl foxed). Dj (frayed), slipcase (sl scuffed, soiled). *Oinonen*.* $130/£81

SMITH, HARRY B. Stage Lyrics. NY: R.H. Russell, 1900. 1st ed. 41 ports. Pict bds, gilt. (Extrems sl rubbed), else VG. *Pacific*.* $52/£33

SMITH, HARRY B. Stage Lyrics. NY: R.H. Russell, 1900. 1st ed. Color pict bds (extrems sl rubbed, bumped). VG (closed tears to head of 2 ll). Bkpl of Harry B. Smith. *Dramatis.* $95/£59

SMITH, HARRY WORCESTER. Life and Sport in Aiken and Those Who Made It. NY: Derrydale, (1935). Ltd to 950. Good (lacks dj). *Cullen.* $125/£78

SMITH, HARRY WORCESTER. A Sporting Family of the Old South. Albany, 1936. Sound (lt foxed; spine edges, tips rubbed, sl shaken). *Oinonen*.* $50/£31

SMITH, HELENA HUNTINGTON. The War on Powder River. NY: McGraw-Hill, (1966). 1st ed. Map. Brn cl. Fine in Fine dj. *Harrington.* $60/£38

SMITH, HELENA HUNTINGTON. The War on Powder River. NY, 1966. 1st ed. (Inscrip; sl cocked), else VG in dj (edgeworn, price-clipped). *Baade.* $45/£28

SMITH, HOLLAND. Coral and Brass. NY, 1949. 1st ed. VG. *Clark.* $40/£25

SMITH, HOMER W. Lectures on the Kidney. Univ of KS, (1943). 1st ed, 2nd issue. NF. *Glaser.* $60/£38

SMITH, HOPE. A True Story of a Cape Cod Kitten. East Providence, RI: Hope Smith, 1953. 1st ed. Signed. Obl 8vo. Lura Sellow (illus). Blue bds (faded, spine worn). Dj (worn, lacks few pieces). *Reisler.* $225/£141

SMITH, HORATIO DAVIS. Early History of the United States Revenue Marine Service...1789-1849. (N.p.: R.L. Polk, 1932.) 1st ed. (6),89pp; 4 plts. *Lefkowicz.* $75/£47

SMITH, HUGH. Letters to Married Women, on Nursing and the Management of Children. Phila: Matthew Carey, 1796. 2nd Amer ed. 154pp. Contemp calf (rubbed; spine top, corners sl chipped). *Karmiole.* $150/£94

SMITH, IRA L. Baseball's Famous Pitchers. Barnes, 1954. 1st ed. VG + in VG dj. *Plapinger.* $27/£17

SMITH, J. (ed). Songs and Selections from the Album of the Edinburgh Angling Club, Founded 1847. Edinburgh: David Douglas, 1900. New, enlgd ed. Frontis. Grn cl, gilt. NF. *Pacific*.* $98/£61

SMITH, J. GREIG. Abdominal Surgery. Phila, 1887. 1st Amer ed. 606pp. *Fye.* $175/£109

SMITH, J. THORNE, JR. Out O'Luck. NY: Frederick A. Stokes, (1919). 1st ed. Pict bds. Good (ink inscrips, spine ends chipped) in pict dj (spine defective, closed tear fr panel). *Reese.* $50/£31

SMITH, JACK. The Big Orange. Pasadena: Ward Ritchie, (1976). 1st ed. Signed. VG in dj. *Houle.* $75/£47

SMITH, JAMES and JAMES SOWERBY. English Botany, or Coloured Figures of British Plants. G. Bell & Sons, 1913. 3rd ed. 8vo. 13 vols. Aeg. Later full morocco, gilt. (Hinges sl cracked.) *Sotheby's*.* $957/£598

SMITH, JAMES EDWARD. The English Flora. London: Longman, Rees, Orme, et al, n.d. c.(1828-1830). 2nd ed. 4 vols. Orig cl. (Lacks feps; recased, sl soiled; spines sl faded, chipped.) *Edwards.* $120/£75

SMITH, JAMES EDWARD. An Introduction to Physiological and Systematical Botany. Boston, 1814. 1st Amer ed. 12,(9)-415pp; 16 engr plts. Uncut. Orig 2-toned bds (spine cracked, hinges weak). *M & S.* $175/£109

SMITH, JAMES EDWARD. An Introduction to Physiological and Systematical Botany. London: Longman, Hurst, Rees, et al, 1819. 4th ed. xxi,407pp + (i); 15 plts (stained). 1/2 morocco, leather label. (Foxed; label rubbed.) *Edwards.* $77/£48

SMITH, JAMES EDWARD. Plantarum Icones Hactenus Ineditae Plerumque ad Plantas in Herbario Linnaeano Conservatas Delineatae. London: J. Davis, 1789/1790/1791. 3 parts bound in 1. Folio. 75 full-pg b/w plts. Internally Nice (sl foxed, damp-stained; cl stained). *Metropolitan*.* $1,150/£719

SMITH, JAMES EDWARD. Spicilegium Botanicum...Gleanings of Botany. London: For The Author by J. Davis, 1791-92. 2 parts in 1 vol. 23 (of 24) hand-colored engr plts (lacks plt 8 in 1st part). 8 duplicate hand-colored engr plts from the work loosely inserted. Mod brn 1/2 morocco (orig wrappers bound in; spotted). *Christie's*.* $270/£169

SMITH, JEDEDIAH S. The Southwest Expedition of Jedediah S. Smith. His Personal Account...1826-1827. Glendale, CA, 1977. 2nd ptg. One of 513. Frontis, fldg map, 2 maps on single sheet. VG + (gilt dull). *Sagebrush.* $90/£56

SMITH, JEDEDIAH S. The Southwest Expedition of Jedediah S. Smith: His Personal Account...1826-1827. George R. Brooks (ed). Glendale: A.H. Clark, 1977. 2nd ptg. VG. *Labordo.* $85/£53

SMITH, JEROME V. C. Natural History of the Fishes of Massachusetts.... Boston: Allen & Ticknor, 1833. 1st ed. 7,399,(1)pp. Ptd paper label. Very Nice. *M & S.* $350/£219

SMITH, JESSIE WILCOX. A Child's Book of Old Verses. NY: Duffield, 1910. 1st ed. 4to. 10 full-pg color plts. Teg. Blue cl (edges lt rubbed), gilt, color paste label (rubbed). *Reisler.* $350/£219

SMITH, JESSIE WILCOX. Seven Ages of Childhood. Verses by Carolyn Wells. NY: Moffat, Yard, 1909. 1st ed. 10x6.75. 7 color plts. Pict cvr label. (Ink spot to margin of 1 plt, 2 plts w/marginal tears; spine dknd, soiled, red smudge to rear cvr), else VG-. *Pacific*.* $109/£68

SMITH, JOHN CHALONER. British Mezzotinto Portraits. Henry Sotheran, 1883. 4 vols. Teg. Contemp 1/2 crimson morocco. *Sotheby's*.* $552/£345

SMITH, JOHN E. Bethel. Polk County, Oregon. (Corvallis), 1941. Good (exterior soil) in wraps. *Perier.* $30/£19

SMITH, JOHN RUSSELL. Bibliotheca Cantiana. London: for John Russell Smith, 1837. Frontis, x,(iv)subs,360pp; 1 plt. Leather spine label. (Plt edges heavily browned, frontis sl fragile, index pp sl spotted, last text pg sl soiled, numerous blanks bound in at rear; rebound in cl, new eps.) *Edwards.* $80/£50

SMITH, JOHN THOMAS. Antiquities of London, and Its Environs. T. Sewell, R. Faulder et al, 1791. 1st ed. Folio. Engr frontis, 113 engr plts. Later 1/2 morocco. (Offsetting, sm tear p75; extrems rubbed.) *Sotheby's*.* $238/£149

SMITH, JOHN. A Catalogue Raisonne of the Works of the Most Eminent Dutch, Flemish, and French Painters.... London, 1829-1842. 9 vols. Sm 4to. 2 lg Alfred Beit engr bkpls in each vol. Marbled eps. Full leather, gilt. *Washton.* $600/£375

SMITH, JOHN. Curiosities of Common Water. NY/London: Fowlers & Wells/C. Donovan, 1851. 92pp + ads. Orig ptd wrappers (lt waterstained). *M & S.* $125/£78

SMITH, JOHN. Fruits and: Farinacea, the Proper Food of Man. NY: Fowler and Wells, (1854). 1st Amer ed. Hand-colored frontis. Blindstamped cl, gilt. VG. *Pacific*.* $46/£29

SMITH, JOHN. Galic Antiquities: Consisting of a History of the Druids, Particularly Those of Caledonia.... Edinburgh: T. Cadell & C. Elliot, 1780. 1st ed. viii,352pp. Mod 3/4 calf, maroon bds, morocco spine label. Fine (new eps; date on spine incorrect). *Pacific*.* $259/£162

SMITH, JOHN. The Generall Historie of Virginia, New-England, and the Summer Isles.... (Cleveland: World, 1966.) Facs ed. Full vellum, gilt, ribbon tie closures. Fine in NF fldg box w/paper label, vellum spine label. *Harrington.* $120/£75

SMITH, JOHN. Travels, and Works of Captain John Smith. Edward Arber (ed). Edinburgh: John Grant, 1910. New ed. 2 vols. Unopened. (Shelfworn), o/w Good set. *Brown.* $100/£63

SMITH, JOHN. The True Travels, Adventures, and Observations.... NY: Rimington & Hooper, 1930. Rpt. One of 377. Frontispiort, fldg plt from 1630 ed. Rose buckram w/ptd label. Fine in slipcase (sl soiled), ptd label. *House.* $65/£41

SMITH, JOSEPH FIELDING (comp). Life of Joseph F. Smith, Sixth President of the Church of Jesus Christ of Latter-Day Saints. Salt Lake City: Deseret News Press, 1938. 1st ed. (Ex-lib, rubberstamp on pastedowns, fr inner hinge cracked), o/w Good. *Brown.* $20/£13

SMITH, JOSEPH, JR. (trans). Book of Mormon. Salt Lake City: George Q. Cannon, 1871. 1st ed w/Salt Lake City imprint. 12,563pp. Aeg. Contemp full black morocco (fr cvr detached, rear hinge weak), gilt. *Kane*.* $160/£100

SMITH, JOSEPH. Bibliotheca Anti-Quakeriana; or a Catalogue of Books Adverse to the Society of Friends. London, 1873. 474pp. (Ex-lib; rebacked preserving orig spine, shelfworn.) *Oinonen*.* $120/£75

SMITH, JOSHUA TOULMIN. Journal in America, 1837-1838. Floyd Benjamin Streeter (ed). Metuchen, NJ: Charles F. Heartman, 1925. 1st ed. One of 99. Uncut, partly unopened. Paper labels. *Mott.* $125/£78

SMITH, JUSTIN H. The War with Mexico, 1846-1848. NY: Macmillan, 1919. 1st ed. 2 vols. Blue cl, gilt. VF set. Howes S636. *Argonaut.* $375/£234

SMITH, L. P. More Trivia. Constable, 1922. 1st Eng ed. VG +. *Fine Books.* $20/£13

SMITH, LEE. Family Linen. NY: Putnam, (1985). 1st ed. Fine (sl scuff fore-edge) in Fine dj. *Between The Covers.* $50/£31

SMITH, LOGAN PEARSALL. More Trivia. Constable, 1922. 1st UK ed. VG in dj (defective). *Cox.* $13/£8

SMITH, M. Diamonds, Pearls, and Precious Stones.... Boston: Smith Patterson, c1913. 1st ptg. Good. *Blake.* $40/£25

SMITH, MARIAN W. Indians of the Urban Northwest. NY: Columbia Univ, 1949. 1st ed. VG in Good dj. *Perier.* $60/£38

SMITH, MARY STUART (comp). Virginia Cookery-Book. Harper, 1885. 352pp (pp333-352 blank w/add'l recipes w/5 filled in). Rebound in mod buckram (spotted, spine frayed). Good (lacks rep, foxed, browned, pin holes due to newsclippings; hinges repaired). *Book Broker.* $165/£103

SMITH, MICHAEL A. Landscapes 1975-1979, Volume I. Revere, PA: Lodima, (1981). One of 1000 signed, numbered. 42 tipped-in duotones. (Offsetting; edgeworn, spine ends rubbed.) Plastic wrapper (heavily scratched). *Swann*.* $172/£108

SMITH, NATHAN. Medical and Surgical Memoirs. Balt, 1831. 1st ed. 374pp. Recent cl. *Fye.* $250/£156

SMITH, NATHAN. A Practical Essay on Typhous Fever. NY: Bliss & White, 1824. 1st ed. 88pp. Uncut. Orig bds (spine eroding). NF (eps foxed). *Glaser.* $500/£313

SMITH, NORA ARCHIBALD. Boys and Girls of Bookland. NY: Cosmopolitan Book Co, 1923. 1st ed. 12 x 9 1/2. 11 color plts by Jessie Wilcox Smith. Gilt-lettered cl, pict cvr label. (Spine ends, extrems rubbed), else VG. *Pacific*.* $127/£79

SMITH, O. Identification and Qualitative Chemical Analysis of Minerals. NY: Van Nostrand, c1953. 2nd ed. VG. *Blake.* $50/£31

SMITH, OLGA WRIGHT. Gold on the Desert. Albuquerque, 1956. 1st ed. (Inscrip), else VG in dj (sl worn). *Dumont.* $40/£25

SMITH, P. A. L. Boyhood Memories of Fauquier. Old Dominion, 1926. VG. *Book Broker.* $45/£28

SMITH, PATRICK MONTAGUE. The Royal Family Pop-Up Book. London: Dean's Intl, 1984. 5 dbl-pg pop-ups by Roger Payne. Glazed pict bds. VG. *Bookfinders.* $55/£34

SMITH, PATTI. Seventh Heaven. Telegraph Press, 1972. 1st ed. Signed. NF in pict wrappers. *Pacific*.* $40/£25

SMITH, PERCY J. DELF. Civic and Memorial Lettering. London: A&C Black, 1946. 1st ed. VG. *Michael Taylor.* $13/£8

SMITH, PERCY. Lettering, a Plea. London: First Edition Club, 1932. 1st separate ed. One of 400 ptd for First Edition Club. Black cl, silver label. Tissue dj. *Maggs.* $88/£55

SMITH, PETER. Houses of the Welsh Countryside. HMSO, 1988. 2nd ed. Mint in dj. *Hadley.* $128/£80

SMITH, PHILIP. New Directions in Bookbinding. London: Studio Vista, 1974. Fine (bkpl) in dj. *Michael Taylor.* $144/£90

SMITH, R. SKILBECK. A Subaltern in Macedonia and Judea, 1916-17. London, 1930. 1st Eng ed. (Cvrs scored.) Dj (sl chipped). *Clearwater.* $80/£50

SMITH, RICHARD GORDON. Ancient Tales and Folklore of Japan. London: A&C Black, 1908. 1st ed. 62 color plts, ptd tissue guards. Dec gray cl (sl soiled). *Karmiole.* $125/£78

SMITH, RICHARD. A Tour of Four Great Rivers. Francis W. Halsey (ed). NY: Scribner, 1906. One of 780 numbered. Cl-backed bds (sl worn), leather spine label (scuffed). *Oinonen*.* $50/£31

SMITH, ROBERT WAYNE. The Couer d'Alene Mining War of 1892. Corvallis, 1961. 2nd ed. (Ink stamp erased from fep), else Fine in dj (worn). *Baade.* $37/£23

SMITH, SAM B. Tennessee History, a Bibliography. Knoxville: Univ of TN, (1974). 1st ed. Fine in dj. *Sadlon.* $35/£22

SMITH, SAMUEL B. The Medical Application of Electro-Magnetism. NY, 1859. 4th ed. 96,(4)pp. Orig self-wraps, sewn. *M & S.* $125/£78

SMITH, STEVIE. A Good Time Was Had by All. (London: Jonathan Cape, 1937.) 1st ed. (Name; extrems sl dknd), else VG in dj (dknd, soiled, spine ends chipped). *Pacific*.* $86/£54

SMITH, STEVIE. Harold's Leap. Chapman & Hall, 1950. 1st UK ed. NF in VG dj (spine faded). *Williams.* $120/£75

SMITH, STEVIE. Novel on Yellow Paper or Work It Out for Yourself. London: Cape, (1936). 1st ed. VG (top edge sl dusty; spotted) in dj (worn, word 'novel' missing from spine). *Hermitage.* $300/£188

SMITH, SYDNEY. The Works. Longman, Orme et al, 1839-40. 1st eds. 4 vols. Old full speckled calf (attractively rebacked to match, w/raised bands, dbl spine labels), gilt. VF set (bkpl). *Hollett.* $312/£195

SMITH, T. C., JR. From the Memories of Men. Brownwood, TX: T.C. Smith, Jr, 1954. 1st ed. Fine in wrappers. *Labordo.* $50/£31

SMITH, THOMAS. A Topographical and Historical Account of the Parish of St. Mary-Le-Bone.... London: John Smith, 1833. 5ff., 319pp + (1 errata n.n.); lg fldg map, 6 litho plts. Pub's cl, label (foxed). *Marlborough.* $144/£90

SMITH, THORNE. Biltmore Oswald: The Diary of a Hapless Recruit. NY: Stokes, (1918). 1st ed, 1st bk. Pict bds. (Inscrip, old tape repair along spine bottom, corners sl worn; lacks dj.) *Agvent.* $95/£59

SMITH, THORNE. Topper. NY: McBride, 1926. 1st ed. Good (sm leather bkpl; soiled, rubbed; lacks dj). *Agvent.* $75/£47

SMITH, THORNE. Topper: An Improbable Adventure. NY: Robert M. McBride, 1926. 1st ed. Good dj (insect damage holes along flap creases, extrems rubbed, chipped, lower spine lacks piece). *Pacific*.* $863/£539

SMITH, TUNSTALL. James McHenry Howard: A Memoir. Balt: Privately ptd, 1916. 1st ed. 2 b/w photo port plts. (Bkpl.) Tan bds (sl sunned; sm stain fr cvr). Text Very Clean. *Baltimore*.* $30/£19

SMITH, VINCENT A. A History of Fine Art in India and Ceylon. Clarendon, 1930. 2nd ed. Color frontis, 165 plts (4 color). Fore, lower edges uncut. (Bkpl, feps lt browned, 3 sm ink spots fore-edge sl intruding onto inner margin; corners sl worn, spine lt spotted.) *Edwards.* $112/£70

SMITH, W. EUGENE and AILEEN M. SMITH. Minamata. NY: Holt, Rinehart & Winston, 1975. 1st ed. NF in stiff wrappers. *Cahan.* $85/£53

SMITH, WALLACE. Bessie Cotter. Paris: Obelisk, 1936. 1st Obelisk ptg. Pict wrappers. (Wraps sl soiled, corners nicked), else VG. *Reese.* $65/£41

SMITH, WALLACE. Oregon Sketches. NY: Putnam, 1925. 1st ed. (Wrapper spine dknd, spine head chipped, rubbed), else Good in dj. *Brown.* $25/£16

SMITH, WALLACE. Prodigal Sons. Boston, 1951. 1st ptg, 1st issue. Inscribed. VG. *Baade.* $95/£59

SMITH, WALLACE. Prodigal Sons. Boston: Christopher Pub House, 1951. 1st ed, 1st state. Signed. NF. *Labordo.* $175/£109

SMITH, WALTER H. B. Pistols and Revolvers [together with] Rifles. Volume One and Two of the N.R.A. Book of Small Arms. Washington/Harrisburg, PA: Nat'l Rifle Assoc of America/Military Service Pub, 1948. Vol 1 2nd corrected ptg, vol 2 1st ed. 2 vols. Fine set in djs (both chipped). *Labordo.* $150/£94

SMITH, WALTER PARRY HASKETT. Climbing in the British Isles. Longman, Green, 1894-95. 1st eds. 2 vols. xii,162pp + (ii)pp ads; viii,197pp. Red cl (rounded corners, spines faded, few sm mks), gilt. *Hollett.* $288/£180

SMITH, WILLIAM A. M. The History of the Province of New York. London: J. Almon, 1776. 2nd ed. viii,160,(12),161-256,(12),257-334pp. Recent 1/2 leather (rebound), label, marbled bds. (Text lt spotted, browned), else VG. Howes S703. *Brown.* $300/£188

SMITH, WILLIAM B. On Wheels and How I Came There. Joseph Gatch Bonnell (ed). NY: Hunt & Eaton, 1893. 1st ed. Photo frontis (lg ink sig verso), 338pp (lt browned, lacks fep). Lt brn (rear hinge split; spotted, sl worn). *Baltimore*.* $20/£13

SMITH, WILLIAM JAY. Laughing Time.... Boston: Little, Brown, (1955). 1st ed. Pict cl. Fine in VG dj (sl tanned, nicked). *Reese.* $35/£22

SMITH, WILLIAM JAY. Poems 1947-1957. Boston: Little, Brown, (1957). 1st ed. Nice in dj (spine sunned, sm nicks). *Reese.* $30/£19

SMITH, WILLIAM JAY. Poems. NY: Banyan, 1947. 1st ed, 1st bk. One of 500 numbered. NF w/o ptd dj, as issued. *Reese.* $85/£53

SMITH, WILLIAM R. The History of Wisconsin: In Three Parts, Historical, Documentary, and Descriptive. Volume III only (of 2). Madison: Beriah Brown, 1854. 1st ed. (Lt foxed, mainly eps; spine ends, corners rubbed, few sm splits to spine ends.) Howes S719. *Sadlon.* $50/£31

SMITH, WILLIAM. A Yorkshireman's Trip to the United States and Canada. London: Longman, Green, 1892. 1st ed. pp xvi,317,(3) ads. Red cl, gilt. *Mott.* $50/£31

SMITH, WINSTON O. The Sharps Rifle. NY: William Morrow, 1943. 1st ed. VG + in dj. *Labordo.* $85/£53

SMITHELLS, C. Tungsten. NY: Chemical, c1953. 1st Amer ed. VG in dj. *Blake.* $50/£31

SMITHERS, D. W. On the Nature of Neoplasia in Man. Edinburgh: E. & S. Livingstone, 1964. 1st ed. VG (3pp stained, pencil underlinings). *Glaser.* $25/£16

SMOLLETT, TOBIAS. The Adventures of Gil Blas. London, 1819. 1st ed thus. 3 vols. VG + set in 1/2 leather, marbled bds. *Fine Books.* $150/£94

SMOLLETT, TOBIAS. The Adventures of Peregrine Pickle. Edinburgh: Silvester Doig, 1793. 4 vols. Engr frontispieces. Aeg. 19th-cent speckled calf, gilt spines. VG set (extrems, joints rubbed; sl foxed). *Glenn.* $300/£188

SMOLLETT, TOBIAS. The Adventures of Peregrine Pickle. LEC, 1936. Ltd to 1500 numbered, signed by John Austen (illus). 2 vols. Fine in slipcase. *Swann*.* $34/£21

SMOLLETT, TOBIAS. The Adventures of Roderick Random. London: J. Osborn, 1748. 2nd ed, setting 'a' w/vol 1, p2, line 2: 'an highland seer'; p2, line 20: 'fortold'; numbers 157-168 omitted in vol 2 pagination, but w/continuous text. 2 vols. 2 engr frontispieces, xxiii,324; xii,372pp. Old calf (worn, labels gone). *Marlborough.* $160/£100

SMOLLETT, TOBIAS. Travels Through France and Italy. R. Baldwin, 1778. (4th ed.) 2 vols. Half-titles present, 291; 290pp (text sl dust-soiled, early sigs). Contemp brn sheep (fr joints cracked, held on cords, sl loss to backstrip heads, gilt dull), raised bands, red leather labels. *Blackwell's.* $136/£85

Smuggler: a Tale. (By John and Michael Banim.) Richard Bentley, 1833. Frontis. Sprinkled edges. Contemp 1/2 leather, marbled bds, raised bands. Good (sl spotted; corners rubbed). *Tiger.* $48/£30

SMYTH, A. L. John Dalton, 1766-1844. A Bibliography of Works by and About Him. Manchester Univ, (1966). 1st ed. 11 plts. VG. *Glaser.* $75/£47

SMYTH, C. PIAZZI. Life and Work at the Great Pyramid During the Months of January, February, March, and April, A.D. 1865. Edinburgh, 1867. 3 vols. (Bkpls, lt foxed throughout, several hinges cracked; vol 1 sl cocked; spines faded, ends worn, tips rubbed.) *Swann*.* $258/£161

SMYTH, H. D. A General Account of the Development of Methods of Using Atomic Energy for Military Purposes Under the Auspices of the United States Government 1940-1945. Washington: GPO, 1945. 1st pub ed, 1st issue, w/correct date on the colophon at p182. (Ink name; cvrs creased.) Ptd wrappers. *Glaser.* $475/£297

SMYTH, JAMES CARMICHAEL. The Effect of the Nitrous Vapour, in Preventing and Destroying Contagion.... Phila, 1799. 1st Amer ed. 174pp; fldg table. Old tree calf (rebacked; stained, foxed, piece torn tp corner w/loss of 2 letters, lib stamps). *Oinonen*.* $250/£156

SMYTHE, BARBARA (trans). Troubador Poets. London/NY: C&W/Duffield, 1911. Color frontis facs, added woodcut tp. Marbled eps; aeg. Contemp calf by Bumpus, signed on fr turn-in, gilt, raised bands. (Lg bkpl, few sm spots; spine evenly faded, few mks, sl evidences of adhesion to cvrs, joints sl worn.) *Pirages.* $50/£31

SMYTHE, F. S. The Adventures of a Mountaineer. J.M. Dent, 1941. 17 plts. (Spine sl rubbed, dknd.) *Hollett.* $32/£20

SMYTHE, F. S. A Camera in the Hills. A&C Black, 1939. 1st ed. (Half-title sl spotted.) Dj (edges sl chipped, worn). *Hollett.* $48/£30

SMYTHE, F. S. Camp Six. Hodder & Stoughton, 1938. Map. VG. *Hollett.* $32/£20

SMYTHE, F. S. The Spirit of the Hills. Hodder & Stoughton, 1935. 1st ed. 36 plts. (Edges sl faded.) Dj (spine dknd). *Hollett.* $48/£30

SMYTHE, F. S. The Valley of Flowers. London: Hodder & Stoughton, 1938. 1st ed. One of 250 signed. Med 8vo. xiii,322pp; 16 color, mtd illus, fldg map. Teg, rest uncut. White buckram. Fine (bkpl). *Ulysses.* $1,200/£750

SMYTHE, MRS. Ten Months in the Fiji Islands. London, 1864. 1st ed. 8vo. xviii,282pp; 4 maps (2 fldg), 4 chromolithos, 6 plts. (Frontis lt foxed, new eps, hinges repaired.) *Maggs.* $520/£325

SMYTHIES, BERTRAM E. The Birds of Burma. London, 1953. 2nd rev ed. 31 color plts; fldg map. Mod rebind in gilt-edged morocco, spine gilt. *Edwards.* $104/£65

SNAFFLES. (Pseud of Charles Johnson Payton.) More Bandobast. London, 1936. 12 color plts. Canvas. (Name; fr cvr sl spotted, sm backstrip tear.) *Petersfield.* $160/£100

SNAPE, ANDREW. The Anatomy of a Horse. London, 1683. 1st ed. 2 parts in 1 vol. Folio. 49 engr plts. Aeg. Contemp red morocco, gilt side panels w/floral corner pieces, spine gilt in 7 compartments, morocco label (chipped). There is no port, apparently not issued in all copies. (Sl stained, foxed, soiled; rubbed.) *Oinonen*.* $1,400/£875

SNEAD, SAM. Natural Golf. NY, (1953). 1st ed. (Ink name, spine top sl worn), else VG in dj (sunned, edgeworn, price-clipped). *King.* $35/£22

SNEED, WILLIAM C. A Report on the History and Mode of Management of the Kentucky Penitentiary, from Its Origin, in 1798, to March 1, 1860. Frankfort, KY, 1860. 1st ed. Frontis, 614pp. (Foxed; shelfworn.) *Oinonen*.* $80/£50

SNELL, ROY J. The Strangeland Bird Life: The Book of Antarctic Birds. Chicago: Just Right Books, (1924). 1st ed. Cobb X. Shinn (illus). Pict cvr label. NF. *Pacific*.* $81/£51

SNIDER, DENTON J. Psychology and the Psychosis Intellect. St. Louis: Sigma Co, 1896. 1st ed. VG (lib mks, pencilling). *Beasley.* $65/£41

SNODGRASS, J. J. Narrative of the Burmese War...to the Conclusion of a Treaty of Peace at Yandaboo, in February 1826. London, 1827. Fldg map (torn), 2 plts. Orig bds (backstrip defective; bkpl). *Swann*.* $103/£64

SNODGRASS, W. D. Heart's Needle. NY, 1959. 1st ed, 1st bk. Ltd to 1500. This copy inscribed. NF in dj. *Black Sun.* $225/£141

SNOOK, J. F. Gun Fodder. London: George Allen & Unwin, (1930). 1st ed. Red cl stamped in black. (Edges, eps sl foxed), o/w NF in pict dj. *Reese.* $175/£109

Snow White. Duenewald Ptg Co, 1949. 4 moveable pp by Julian Wehr. Spiral-bound. (Corners bumped), o/w VG. *Davidson.* $150/£94

Snow White. London: Brown Watson, 1982. 6 dbl-pg pop-ups by V. Kubasta. Glazed pict bds. VG-. *Bookfinders.* $40/£25

Snow White. An All-Action Treasure Hour Pop-Up Book. London: Murrays Children's Books, 1976. 6 dbl-pg pop-ups by V. Kubasta. Glazed pict bds. VG. *Bookfinders.* $90/£56

SNOW, CARMEL. The World of Carmel Snow. NY: McGraw-Hill, (1962). VG in dj. *Turtle Island.* $40/£25

SNOW, EDWARD ROWE. True Tales of Buried Treasure. NY: Dodd, Mead, 1954. Fine in dj. *American Booksellers.* $30/£19

SNOW, JACK. The Magical Mimics in Oz. Chicago, (1946). 1st ed, 1st ptg on heavier stock, book measuring 1 1/16-inch thick. Pict eps. (Ink on owner leaf; lt rubbed.) *Kane*.* $120/£75

SNOW, JACK. The Magical Mimics in Oz. Chicago: Reilly & Lee, (1946). 1st ed, 1st state w/vol 1 1/8-inch thick; ptd on white stock. 8.75x6.5. Frank Kramer (illus). 242pp. Pict eps in grn on pale yellow stock. Lt gray cl, pict cvr label. (Torn, repaired along upper fr joint), else VG. *Pacific*.* $138/£86

SNOW, JACK. The Shaggy Man of Oz. Chicago, (1949). 1st ed, 1st ptg w/black/white pict eps. (Old lt stain, lt rubbed.) *Kane*.* $75/£47

SNOW, JACK. The Shaggy Man of Oz. Chicago: Reilly & Lee, (1949). 1st ed, 1st ptg w/pict eps. 8.75x6.5. Frank Kramer (illus). 254pp. Greenish-gray cl, pict cvr label. (Sm tear spine head), else VG in dj (rubbed, sm tears, creases, few nicks). *Pacific*.* $259/£162

SNOW, JACK. The Shaggy Man of Oz. Chicago: Reilly & Lee, (1949). 1st ed. 4to. Pict eps. Gray cl w/greenish cast, color paste label, spine w/pub's name in semi-script letters. Very Nice (corner sl bumped) in full color dj (margins lt worn). *Reisler.* $500/£313

SNOW, JACK. Who's Who in Oz. Chicago, (1954). (Cvrs soiled, sl worn.) *King.* $150/£94

SNOW, JACK. Who's Who in Oz...in Collaboration with Professor H. M. Wogglebug, T. E., Dean of the Royal College of Oz. Chicago: Reilly & Lee, (1954). 1st ed. John R. Neill, Frank Kramer & 'Dirk' (illus). Fine in dj (price-clipped). *Pacific*.* $316/£198

SNOW, ROYALL H. Thomas Lovell Beddoes: Eccentric and Poet. NY, 1928. 1st ed. Good (no dj). *Clearwater.* $48/£30

SNOWMAN, A. KENNETH. Eighteenth Century Gold Boxes of Europe. Boston, (1966). Folio. Dj. *Swann*.* $69/£43

SNOWMAN, J. A Short History of Talmudic Medicine. NY: Hermon, (1974). Rpt of 1935 ed. Fine. *Glaser.* $30/£19

SNYDER, FAIRMOUNT. Rhymes for Kindly Children: Modern Mother Goose Jingles. Chicago: P.F. Volland, (1916). 38th ed. 8vo. John B. Gruelle (illus). Full color illus bds w/wraparound image carried onto eps. Good. *Reisler.* $135/£84

SNYDER, GARY. Myths and Texts. NY: Totem, (1960). 1st ed. One of 1100. Signed. (Soiled), else VG in wrappers. *Pacific*.* $52/£33

SNYDER, JOHN FRANCIS. Adam W. Snyder, and His Period in Illinois History, 1817-1842. E. Needham, 1906. 2nd rev ed. Good. *Rybski.* $110/£69

SNYDER, JOHN FRANCIS. Captain John Baptiste Saucier. (Springfield, IL, 1920.) Rpt of 1st ed. Good+. *Wantagh.* $50/£31

SNYDER, JOHN FRANCIS. Selected Writings. Clyde C. Walton (ed). Springfield, IL: State Hist Soc, 1962. 1st ed. Fine. *Sadlon.* $25/£16

SOBOLEV, LEONID. Soul of the Sea. NY: Lippincott, 1946. 1st ed. VG in dj. *American Booksellers.* $30/£19

SOBY, JAMES THRALL. The Early Chirico. NY, 1941. 1st ed of the 1st English-language monograph on Chirico. Dj (top, bottom of spine panel rubbed). *Swann*.* $258/£161

SOBY, JAMES THRALL. The Prints of Paul Klee. NY, (1947). (2nd ed.) 40 plts. Text booklet and plts loose as issued in bd fldg case (sl worn). *Swann*.* $149/£93

Social Hours with Friends. (Mary S. Wood, comp.) Phila: H. Longstreth, (1867). 315pp. (Lib mks), else VG. *Bohling.* $20/£13

SODDY, FREDERICK. The Interpretation of Radium. London: John Murray, 1909. 2nd ed. (Eps spotted; spine sl rubbed.) *Hollett.* $64/£40

SOGLOW, OTTO. Everything's Rosy. NY: Farrar & Rinehart, (1932). 1st ed. Hidden-picture bk. Originally w/red plastic filter sheet in envelope at fr pastedown (w/recent replacement sheet). Yellow cl. Cvrs VG (edges lt dusty) in pict dj (sl chipped, sm edgetears, sm tear center of fr cvr). *Baltimore*.* $40/£25

SOGLOW, OTTO. Pretty Pictures. NY: Farrar, (1931). 1st ed. Sm folio. VG in dj (nicked). *Houle.* $125/£78

SOHMER, STEPHEN. The Way It Was. NY: S&S, (1966). 1st ed, 1st bk. Fine in VG + dj (few sm tears, nicks). *Between The Covers.* $150/£94

SOKOLOFF, BORIS. The Crime of Dr. Garine. NY: Covici-Friede, 1928. 1st US ed. Red cl, paper spine label. Sound. *Reese.* $30/£19

SOLDATI, MARIO. The Commander Comes to Dine. John Lehmann, 1952. 1st ed. VG (feps lt browned; top edge sl mkd, spine head sl nicked, ends bumped, cvrs bowed) in dj (nicked, sl dusty, sl creased). *Ulysses.* $61/£38

Soldier and Brave: Indian and Military Affairs in the Transmississippi West, Including a Guide to Historic Sites and Landmarks. NY: Harper & Row, 1963. 1st ed. 4 fldg maps. Brn cl. Fine in NF dj. *Harrington.* $45/£28

Soldier's Diary of the Great War. London: Faber & Gwyer, (1929). 1st ed. Gilt red cl. (Bkpl, edges sl foxed), o/w NF in VG dj (sl nicked). *Reese.* $85/£53

Soldier's Diary. (By David Lane.) N.p. (Jackson, MI?), n.d. (1905?). 1st ed. (Inner hinges cracked, sigs loose.) *King.* $350/£219

Soldier's Story of the War; Including the Marches and Battles of the Washington Artillery, and of Other Louisiana Troops. (By Napier Bartlett.) New Orleans: Ptd by Clark & Hofeline, 1874. 1st ed. 252 (i.e. 262),13,(35)pp + (6)pp ads. Blue cl. Good (lacks frontis, bkpl; worn). *Chapel Hill.* $250/£156

SOLIS, DON ANTONIO. The History of the Conquest of Mexico by the Spaniards. Thomas Townsend (trans). London: T. Woodward, 1724. 1st ed in English. Folio. Tp, ded (ii), preface b, contents (c-d2), subs (c-c2), 163,252,152pp; frontisport (hand-colored fldg map), 2 maps, 6 plts (1 dbl-pg, 1 fldg). (Marginal browning to frontis, lt wrinkling, lt dust soil upper margin throughout.) Morocco-backed cl (rebound). *Edwards.* $880/£550

SOLIS-COHEN, EMILY. David the Giant-Killer and Other Tales of Grandma Lopez. Phila: Jewish Pub Soc of America, 1908. 1st ed. Alfred Feinberg (illus). Pict cvr label. (Soiled; hinges starting), else VG. *Pacific*.* $196/£123

SOLOMON, CARL. Mishaps, Perhaps. SF: City Lights, (1966). 1st Amer ed, 1st bk. Signed. Fine in pict wraps. *Polyanthos.* $50/£31

SOLON, M. L. The Art of the Old English Potter. London/Derby: Bemrose & Sons, 1883. Ltd to 260. Author's copy, signed by author & pub. Folio. xx,214pp; 50 etchings. Uncut. Dec cl. (Lib ink stamp, lib #s partly removed from spine; few margins sl thumbed; hinges cracked, lt soiled, worn.) *Edwards.* $280/£175

SOLON, M. L. A History and Description of Italian Majolica. Cassell, 1907. 1st ed. 72 plts (23 color). (Sl rubbed, bumped.) *Hollett.* $96/£60

SOLZHENITSYN, ALEXANDER. August 1914. M. Glenny (trans). NY, 1972. VG in dj. *Typographeum.* $18/£11

SOLZHENITSYN, ALEXANDER. One Day in the Life of Ivan Denisovich. M. Hayward and R. Hingley (trans). NY, 1963. 1st ed. VG in dj (few sm tears). *Typographeum.* $45/£28

SOLZHENITSYN, ALEXANDER. One Day in the Life of Ivan Denisovich. Ralph Parker (trans). London: Gollancz, 1963. 1st ed in English. Red bds, gilt spine. (Sl shelfworn, dusty.) Dj (sl sunned, dusty). *Baltimore*.* $70/£44

SOLZHENITSYN, ALEXANDER. One Day in the Life of Ivan Denisovich. London, 1963. 1st ed in English. Dj (price-clipped). *Swann*.* $172/£108

Some Account of the Oxford University Press 1468-1921. Oxford: Clarendon, 1922. 2nd imp. Frontis, 40 plts. Canvas-backed blue bds (extrems faded; stamp, label), paper cvr label. *Maggs.* $48/£30

Some British Ballads. London: Constable, (1918). 1st ed. 16 Fine color plts by Arthur Rackham mtd-at-lg behind tissue guards. Lt blue cl, gilt. Very Nice (spine sl rubbed, few sm nicks). *Sotheran.* $301/£188

Some British Ballads. London: Constable, (1919). Ltd to 575 signed by Arthur Rackham (illus). 16 mtd color plts. Teg. Vellum-backed pict bds, gilt. *Christie's*.* $504/£315

Some British Ballads. NY: Dodd, Mead, 1918. 1st Amer ed. 16 tipped-in color plts by Arthur Rackham. Blue cl, gilt. *Cullen.* $125/£78

Some British Ballads. London: Constable, 1918. 1st deluxe ed. Ltd to 575 numbered, signed by Arthur Rackham (illus). 4to. 16 Fine mtd color plts. Teg, rest uncut. Parchment-backed cream paper-cvrd bds, gilt. Very Clean. *Sotheran.* $1,040/£650

SOMERVELL, T. HOWARD. Knife and Life in India. London: Hodder & Stoughton, 1940. 1st ed. 9 plts, map, plan. VG in dj. *Hollett.* $72/£45

SOMERVILLE and ROSS. Dan Russell the Fox: An Episode in the Life of Miss Rowan. Methuen, 1911. Pub's cat dated Aug 1911. Good (sl spotted, fr corner last few ll lt water-stained, new fep; spine bumped, cvrs sl mkd). *Tiger.* $42/£26

SOMERVILLE and ROSS. An Enthusiast. Longmans, Green, 1921. Good (lt spotted; spine bumped, sunned; lacks dj). *Tiger.* $48/£30

SOMERVILLE and ROSS. French Leave. Heinemann, 1928. Good (fore-edge lt spotted; spine bumped, sunned, fr cvr unevenly sunned; lacks dj). *Tiger.* $45/£28

SOMERVILLE and ROSS. Further Experiences of an Irish R. M. Longmans, Green, 1908. Good (fore-edge lt spotted, new fep; spine bumped, chipped, sunned). *Tiger.* $58/£36

SOMERVILLE and ROSS. Happy Days! Essays of Sorts. Longmans, Green, 1946. New imp. Top edge grn. (Cvrs warped), else Good in dj (chipped, price-clipped). *Tiger.* $29/£18

SOMERVILLE and ROSS. In Mr. Knox's Country. Longmans, Green, 1915. 1st ed. Good (sl mkd, sl slack; sl rubbed). *Ash.* $80/£50

SOMERVILLE and ROSS. Irish Memories. Longmans, Green, 1917. Good (new fep, lt spotted; spine bumped, corners badly rubbed). *Tiger.* $64/£40

SOMERVILLE and ROSS. Maria and Some Other Dogs. Methuen, 1949. Good (new fep; lacks dj). *Tiger.* $32/£20

SOMERVILLE and ROSS. Mount Music. Longmans, Green, 1919. Good (sl spotted, new fep; spine bumped, chipped, sunned; lacks dj). *Tiger.* $45/£28

SOMERVILLE and ROSS. Sarah's Youth. Longmans, Green, 1938. Good (fore-edge lt spotted; spine bumped, creased; lacks dj). *Tiger.* $45/£28

SOMERVILLE and ROSS. The Smile and the Tear. Methuen, 1933. 2nd ed. Good (spine bumped, sunned; lacks dj). *Tiger.* $26/£16

SOMERVILLE and ROSS. Some Irish Yesterdays. Longmans, Green, 1906. Pict cl (spine bumped, chipped, hinges rubbed; fore-edge lt spotted). *Tiger.* $45/£28

SOMERVILLE and ROSS. The Sweet Cry of Hounds. Methuen, 1936. Good (sl spotted; spine bumped, sl sunned; lacks dj). *Tiger.* $48/£30

SOMERVILLE, BOYLE. Commodore Anson's Voyage into the South Seas and Around the World. London, 1934. 1st ed. Frontisport. (Fr hinge cracked.) *Edwards.* $40/£25

SOMERVILLE, E. The States Through Irish Eyes. Boston/NY: Houghton Mifflin, 1930. 8 full-pg b/w dwgs. VG (eps browned; prelims, edges, eps spotted; top edge dusty; spine ends sl bumped, head faded) in dj (nicked, chipped, rubbed, mkd, dusty, sl torn, creased, frayed, sl dknd). *Ulysses.* $152/£95

SOMERVILLE, E. O. Slipper's ABC of Fox Hunting. Longmans, Green, 1903. 1st ed. Sm folio. 20 full-pg color plts. Pict cl. VG. *Hollett*. $560/£350

SOMERVILLE, MARY. On Connexion of the Physical Sciences. John Murray, 1837. 4th ed. Frontis, xv,499pp; 4 plts. Orig cl (spine faded, sm slits top of joints; inner joints cracked). *Bickersteth*. $45/£28

SOMERVILLE, WILLIAM. The Chace. A Poem. London, 1735. 1st ed, w/the errata leaf. Engr frontis. Old calf, spine gilt, red morocco labels. (Sl foxed, soiled; rubbed.) *Oinonen**. $80/£50

SOMERVILLE, WILLIAM. The Chase. (London): Albion, 1804. 9 hand-colored engr plts. Mod mottled calf, gilt. (Fr joint weak.) *Swann**. $287/£179

SOMERVILLE, WILLIAM. The Chase. A Poem. London: Bulmer & Co, Shakespeare Ptg Office, 1796. Uncut. Contemp bds, paper spine label. (Shelfworn, spine chipped.) Internally Sound in protective cl case provided. *Oinonen**. $130/£81

SONDERGAARD, ARENSA. My First Geography of the Americas. Boston: Little, Brown, 1942. 1st ed. 10.5x13. Fritz Kredel (illus). 60pp. Fine in Good dj (edgeworn, 1/2-inch chips from spine ends). *Price*. $45/£28

SONDHEIM, STEPHEN and HUGH WHEELER. A Little Night Music. NY: Dodd Mead, (1973). 1st ed. VF in VF dj. *Between The Covers*. $350/£219

SONDHEIM, STEPHEN. Sweeney Todd: The Demon Barber of Fleet Street. NY: Dodd, Mead, 1979. 1st ed. Fine in dj (sl edgeworn). *Janus*. $100/£63

Song of Roland. Charles Scott Moncrieff (trans). NY: LEC, 1938. One of 1500 ptd. Signed by Valenti Angelo (illus). Teg. 1/2 vellum, blue bds, gilt. (Upper extrems sl sunned; lacks slipcase), else VG. *Pacific**. $58/£36

Song of Solomon. Cambridge: Rampant Lions, 1937. One of 125. 3/4 levant purple morocco, white cl, gilt. (Spine, extrems sl sunned), else VG. *Pacific**. $86/£54

Songs of the Chace; Containing an Extensive Collection Relative to the Sports of the Field.... London, 1811. 2nd ed. Aeg. Full gilt-pict calf by Thomas Gosden. (Sl soiled, foxed; calf worn.) *Oinonen**. $60/£38

Songs of the Chace; Containing an Extensive Collection Relative to the Sports of the Field.... London: Simpson, 1811. 1st ed. Extra engr tp, (vi),469pp. Teg. Full straight-grained red morocco by Taffin, spine gilt. (Sl foxed, soiled; lt rubbed.) *Oinonen**. $100/£63

SONN, ALBERT H. Early American Wrought Iron. NY, 1928. 3 vols. Folio. 320 plts. (Spines faded.) *Swann**. $126/£79

SONN, ALBERT H. Early American Wrought Iron. NY, 1928. 1st ed. 3 vols. 320 plts. *Kane**. $250/£156

SONNECK, OSCAR GEORGE THEODORE. A Bibliography of Early Secular American Music (18th Century). Washington: Library of Congress, 1945. (Lt worn.) *Oinonen**. $50/£31

SONNICHSEN, C. L. and WILLIAM V. MORRISON. Alias Billy the Kid. Albuquerque: Univ of NM, 1955. (Worn), else Good. *Dumont*. $25/£16

SONNICHSEN, C. L. Billy King's Tombstone. Caldwell, 1942. 1st ed. Pict cl (extrems frayed, cvrs soiled). *Baade*. $20/£13

SONNICHSEN, C. L. Cowboys and Cattle Kings. Norman: Univ of OK, 1950. 1st ed. NF in dj (worn). *Labordo*. $55/£34

SONNICHSEN, C. L. I'll Die Before I'll Run.... NY: Devin-Adair, 1962. Rpt ed. VF in dj. *Labordo*. $30/£19

SONNICHSEN, C. L. Outlaw Bill Mitchell Alias Baldy Russell: His Life and Times. Denver: Sage Books, (1965). 1st ed. NF in dj (top edge sl worn). *Sadlon*. $35/£22

SONNICHSEN, C. L. Roy Bean: Law West of the Pecos. NY: Macmillan, 1943. 1st ed. NF in dj. *Labordo*. $100/£63

SONNICHSEN, C. L. Tularosa; Last of the Frontier West. Greenwich, CT, 1972. (Inscrip), else Good in dj. *Dumont*. $30/£19

Sonoma County and Russian River Valley, Illustrated. SF: Bell & Heymans, (1888). 1st ed. 13.75x10.25. Color litho supp; lg fldg map. (Lt foxed), else VG in pict wrappers (foxed). *Pacific**. $546/£341

SONTAG, SUSAN. The Benefactor. NY: FS & Co, (1963). 1st ed. VF in Fine dj (sm rubbed spot). *Between The Covers*. $100/£63

SONTAG, SUSAN. Duet for Cannibals, a Screenplay. NY: FSG, (1970). 1st ed. NF in dj. *Hermitage*. $75/£47

SOPHOCLES. The Antigone of Sophocles. Dudley Fitts and Robert Fitzgerald (trans). NY: HB & Co, (1939). 1st ed. (Fep lt clipped), else VF in VF dj. *Between The Covers*. $125/£78

SOPHOCLES. Antigone. (Greenbrae): Allen, 1978. One of 130. Prospectus laid in. White bds. Fine. *Pacific**. $127/£79

SOPHOCLES. Oedipus at Colonus. Robert Fitzgerald (trans). NY: HB, (1941). 1st ed. (Fep clipped), else VF in VF dj (sm rubbed spot). *Between The Covers*. $125/£78

SOPHOCLES. Oedipus Rex. NY: HB & Co, (1949). 1st ed. VF in VF dj. *Between The Covers*. $125/£78

SOPHOCLES. Oedipus Rex. LEC, 1955. Ltd to 1500 numbered, signed by Demetrios Galanis (illus). Fine in slipcase. *Swann**. $126/£79

SOPHOCLES. Oedipus the King. Haarlem: LEC, 1955. One of 2000 ptd. Signed by Demetrios Galanis (illus). Dec cl, gilt. Fine in glassine, VG slipcase. *Pacific**. $69/£43

SORENSON, ALFRED. The Story of Omaha. Omaha, 1923. 3rd ed, rev. Reading copy. (1st few pp pencil mks on margins; fr, rear hinges, rebinding soon necessary; faded backstrip, cvrs lt worn.) Howes S765. *Baade*. $50/£31

SORGE, ERNEST. With 'Plane, Boat and Camera in Greenland. London: Hurst & Blackett, 1935. Fldg panoramic frontis. VG. *High Latitude*. $60/£38

SORIA, M. S. The Paintings of Zurbaran. London: Phaidon, 1953. Complete ed. 9 mtd color plts. (Sl faded.) *Ars Artis*. $96/£60

SORLEY, CHARLES HAMILTON. Letters. Cambridge, 1919. 1st Eng ed. VG. *Clearwater*. $152/£95

SORLIER, CHARLES. Chagall Lithographs 1969-1973. Volume IV. NY, 1974. 2 orig color lithos as frontis and dj. VG in dj. *Ars Artis*. $480/£300

SORLIER, CHARLES. Chagall's Posters: A Catalogue Raisonne. NY, (1975). Folio. Dj. *Swann**. $201/£126

SORLIER, CHARLES. The Lithographs of Chagall, 1969-1973. NY, (1974). Color litho frontis. Dj, plastic outer wrapper, slipcase (worn). *Swann**. $575/£359

SORRENTINO, GILBERT. Selected Poems: 1958-1980. Santa Barbara: Black Sparrow, 1981. 1st ed. One of 500 trade hbs. (Top edge dust-soiled), else Fine. *Other Worlds*. $35/£22

SOTHEBY, WILLIAM. Poems. London: Ptd by William Nicol, 1825. 1st ed. Inscribed. (viii),281pp. Aeg. Contemp olive-grn morocco (extrems sl rubbed), gilt. *Young*. $192/£120

SOTHERN, EDWARD ASKEW. Birds of a Feather Flock Together: or, Talks with Sothern. F. G. De Fontaine (ed). NY: G.W. Carleton, 1878. 1st ed. 250pp. Orig pict wrappers (spine worn). *Mott*. $85/£53

SOULE, FRANK et al. The Annals of San Francisco. NY: D. Appleton, 1855. 1st ed. 824pp; 6 steel-engr plts, fldg map. Aeg. Mod full morocco, gilt. (Bkpl, few sl marginal dampstains, other aging to contents), else internally VG in Fine binding. Howes S769. *Pacific**. $230/£144

SOULE, FRANK et al. The Annals of San Francisco. NY: D. Appleton, 1855. 1st ed. 824pp; 6 steel-engr plts, 2 maps (1 lg fldg w/professional repair). Marbled edges, eps. Orig full maroon morocco (rebacked w/mod morocco). NF (inner hinges reinforced). Howes S769. *Harrington*. $325/£203

SOULE, FRANK et al. The Annals of San Francisco. D.H. Huggins (comp). Palo Alto, CA, 1966. Fldg map. Fine. Howes S769. *Wantagh*. $65/£41

SOULE, JOHN et al. The Annals of San Francisco. NY: Appleton, 1855. 1st ed. 824pp; lg fldg b/w litho map (sm margin tear), 6 steel-engr ports, views, guards, 1 full-pg map. Aeg. Orig full lt brn sheep (scuffed; gouges, scrapes to spine w/some effect on lettering), gilt. Text Very Clean. Howes S769. *Baltimore**. $125/£78

SOULIE, BERNARD. Tantra: Erotic Figures in Indian Art. Miller Graphics, 1982. 1st ed. VG in dj. *Worldwide*. $28/£18

SOUSTER, RAYMOND. New Wave Canada. (Toronto: Rubicon Press, 1966.) 1st ed. NF in wrappers. *Pacific**. $29/£18

South Dakota Department of History—Report and Historical Collections. Volume XXXI. Pierre, SD: State Pub, (c.1962). Map. VG. *Lien*. $50/£31

South Dakota Historical Collections, Volume I, 1902. Aberdeen, SD, 1902. Good. *Lien*. $175/£109

South Dakota Historical Collections. Volume VI, 1912. Pierre, SD, 1912. Good. *Lien*. $125/£78

South Dakota Historical Collections. Volume XII, 1924. Pierre: Hipple Ptg, 1924. Good. *Lien*. $100/£63

South Dakota Report and Historical Collections. Volume XXVIII, 1956. Pierre, SD: South Dakota Hist Soc, 1956. Map. VG. *Lien*. $50/£31

South Dakota. NY: Hastings House, 1952. 2nd ed. NF in dj. *Labordo*. $25/£16

SOUTH, RICHARD. The Moths of the British Isles. H. M. Edelsten and D. S. Fletcher (eds). London: Warne, (1980). 2 vols. Djs. *Petersfield*. $40/£25

SOUTHARD, CHARLES ZIBEON. The Evolution of Trout and Trout Fishing in America. NY: Dutton, 1928. 1st ed. 9 color plts. Red cl. VG. *Bowman*. $80/£50

SOUTHARD, CHARLES ZIBEON. Trout Fly-Fishing in America. NY: E.P. Dutton, 1914. 1st trade ed. Teg. Red cl, gilt. (Soiled, spine sunned, ends rubbed), else VG. *Pacific**. $138/£86

SOUTHERLAND, ELLEASE. Let the Lion Eat Straw. NY: Scribner, 1979. 1st ed. Fine in NF dj (1/2-inch tear). *Lame Duck*. $45/£28

SOUTHERN, EILEEN. The Music of Black Americans: A History. NY: Norton, (1971). 1st ed. VG in illus dj. *Petrilla*. $50/£31

SOUTHERN, RICHARD. The Georgian Playhouse. London: Pleiades, 1948. 1st ed. VG in dj (worn). *Dramatis*. $40/£25

SOUTHERN, RICHARD. The Victorian Theatre. Newton Abbot: David & Charles, (1970). Color frontis. VG in pict dj. *Dramatis*. $40/£25

SOUTHERN, TERRY. Blue Movie. NY: World, 1970. 1st ed. NF in dj. *Sclanders*. $32/£20

SOUTHERN, TERRY. Blue Movie. NY: World, 1970. 1st ed. Fine in dj (sm tear rear spine fold). *Beasley*. $40/£25

SOUTHERN, TERRY. Candy. Bernard Geis, 1968. 1st UK ed. NF in dj (sl edgeworn). *Sclanders*. $24/£15

SOUTHERN, TERRY. Flash and Filigree. NY: Coward-McCann, 1958. 1st ed. Fine in dj. *Smith*. $35/£22

SOUTHERN, TERRY. The Magic Christian. Andre Deutsch, 1959. 1st ed. NF in dj (sl edgeworn). *Sclanders*. $64/£40

SOUTHERN, TERRY. The Magic Christian. London, 1959. 1st Eng ed. VG in dj (sl rubbed, dust-mkd). *Clearwater*. $80/£50

SOUTHERN, TERRY. Red Dirt Marijuana. NY: NAL, 1967. 1st ed. Fine in dj. *Smith*. $50/£31

SOUTHESK, JAMES CARNEGIE. Saskatchewan and the Rocky Mountains.... Edinburgh: Edmonston & Douglas, 1875. 1st ed. xxx,448pp. Dec cl, gilt. VG (eps rejointed, tp notes; expertly refurbished, restored). *Ash*. $312/£195

SOUTHEY, ROBERT (trans). The Chronicle of the Cid. Haarlem: LEC, 1958. One of 1500. Signed by Rene Ben Sussan (illus). Fine in glassine, slipcase. *Pacific**. $52/£33

SOUTHEY, ROBERT. Journal of a Tour in the Netherlands in the Autumn of 1815. Boston: Riverside, 1902. One of 519. Uncut, partly unopened. Marbled cvrs, leather title label. Fine. *Polyanthos*. $45/£28

SOUTHEY, ROBERT. The Life of Nelson. London: Bickers & Son, 1895. xv,351pp; 8 woodbury-type plts, 4 plans, 1pg facs. Aeg. Full crimson morocco (extrems sl rubbed), gilt. *Hollett*. $192/£120

SOUTHEY, ROBERT. Southey's Common-Place Book. London: Longman, Brown, Green & Longmans, 1849. 2nd binding. (viii),(694),(ii)pp; integral ad leaf at end. Uncut, eps coated chocolate. Lt yellow-grn fine ripple grain cl, gilt. (Spine faded, rubbed through at foot), o/w Good; internally Fine. *Temple*. $38/£24

SOUTHEY, ROBERT. A Tale of Paraguay. London: Longman, Hurst, Rees et al, 1825. 1st ed. Frontis; engr plt. Orig bds (sl worn, stained). Fine. *Cummins*. $150/£94

SOUTHWART, ELIZABETH. The Password to Fairyland. London: Simpkin Marshall, (1920). 1st ed. 4to. (xiv),15-186pp (few sm mks, fore-edge of book block sl speckled); 3 full-pg line dwgs, 8 color plts by Florence Mary Anderson. Cream cl. Externally Fine. *Sotheran*. $296/£185

SOUTHWOOD, T. and DENNIS LESTON. Land and Water Bugs of the British Isles. London: Warne, 1959. 32 color, 31 b/w plts. Fine in dj. *Petersfield*. $144/£90

SOUTHWORTH, JOHN. Pegleg to Date—and Beyond. (Privately ptd, 1975.) Fine in wraps. *Book Market*. $10/£6

SOUTHWORTH, MAY E. One Hundred and One Chafing Dish Recipes. SF: Paul Elder, (1906). Rev ed. Flexible leather, morocco onlay. (Fr pastedown tear, upper corners sl dog-eared), else VG. *Pacific**. $68/£43

Souvenir of the Fine Art Section Franco-British Exhibition 1908. (London), 1908. (Extrems rubbed.) *Swann**. $126/£79

SOWELL, A. J. Early Settlers and Indian Fighters. NY: Argosy-Antiquarian, 1964. Rpt ed. Ltd to 750. 2 vols. VG + set in slipcase. Howes S797. *Labordo*. $150/£94

SOWELL, A. J. Life of Bigfoot Wallace. Austin: Steck, 1957. Rpt ed. VG. Howes S800. *Labordo*. $40/£25

SOWELL, A. J. Rangers and Pioneers of Texas.... NY: Argosy-Antiquarian, 1964. Rpt ed. Ltd to 750. Fine. Howes S801. *Labordo*. $95/£59

SOWERBY, ARTHUR DE CARLE. A Naturalist's Holiday by the Sea. Routledge, 1923. 1st ed. VG. *Hollett*. $136/£85

SOWERBY, E. MILLICENT. Rare People and Rare Books. Constable, 1967. 1st ed. Frontis, 2 plts. Dj (torn). *Forest*. $45/£28

SOWERBY, GITHA. The Bumbletoes. London: C&W, (1907). 1st ed. 12mo. 60pp; 12 full-pg color illus by Millicent Sowerby. Cl-backed bds, raised letters. VG in pict dj. *Reisler*. $275/£172

SOWERBY, GITHA. Childhood. C&W, 1907. 12 color plts by Millicent Sowerby. (Lt spotted; fr hinge tender, edges lt soiled, rubbed.) *Edwards*. $48/£30

SOWERBY, GITHA. The Wise Book. J.M. Dent, 1906. 1st ed. Sm 8vo. Color frontis, 12 color plts by Millicent Sowerby. Pict cream bds, gilt. (Edges sl dusty), else NF. *Bookmark*. $104/£65

SOWERBY, JAMES and JAMES SMITH. English Botany. London: For C.E. Sowerby, (1832)-40. Mixed eds. 7 vols only (of 12). 1407 hand-colored engr plts (few affected by lt spotting). Later 1/2 cl. (Inner hinges each vol reinforced.) *Christie's**. $541/£338

SOWERBY, JAMES and JAMES SMITH. English Botany. London: For C.E. Sowerby, 1790-1800. 11 vols. 792 hand-colored engr plts. (Lib bkpls all vols, lib stamps affecting most plts and some text ll, severe dampstaining vols 7/8, some plts spotted.) Later lib morocco-backed cl (extrems lt rubbed). *Christie's**. $576/£360

SOWLS, L. K. Prairie Ducks. Harrisburg, 1955. Color frontis. (Name, eps browned, pp tanned; spotted, spine faded.) *Sutton.* $45/£28

SOZINSKEY, THOMAS S. Medical Symbolism. Phila: Davis, 1891. 1st ed. VG (rep shipped, lib stickers; lib spine label). *Beasley.* $40/£25

SPAETH, EDMUND BENJAMIN. Newer Methods of Ophthalmic Plastic Surgery. Phila: P. Blakiston's Son, (1925). 1st ed. Maroon cl. Fine. *Weber.* $185/£116

Spalding's New and Improved Pocket Base Ball Score Book. Chicago: A.G. Spalding, 1882. 1st ed. VG (name on paper label; bds lt rubbed, fr gutter sl torn). *Between The Covers.* $300/£188

SPALDING, VOLNEY M. Distribution and Movement of Desert Plants. Washington, 1909. 31 plts (incl 1 fldg chart). (Ex-lib.) Wrappers (chipped, dknd). *Brooks.* $45/£28

SPALLANZANI, LAZZARO. Experiments Upon the Circulation of the Blood, Throughout the Vascular System. London, 1801. 1st ed in English. Recent 1/2 antique calf w/marbled bds, new eps. (Lib stamp), o/w Fine. *Fye.* $1,000/£625

SPARK, MURIEL. The Abbess of Crewe. Macmillan, 1974. 1st UK ed. Fine in Fine dj. *Martin.* $19/£12

SPARK, MURIEL. Collected Poems: 1. NY: Knopf, 1968. 1st ed. (Faint damp line top of fep), o/w NF in NF dj (spine ends sl worn). *Beasley.* $25/£16

SPARK, MURIEL. The Mendelbaum Gate. London: Macmillan, 1965. 1st ed. (Name, sm crease fr fly), else Fine in NF dj (lt worn, price-clipped). *Between The Covers.* $65/£41

SPARK, MURIEL. The Portobello Road and Other Stories. Helsinki: Eurographica, 1990. One of 350 numbered, signed. Fine in dj, wrappers. *Ulysses.* $104/£65

SPARK, MURIEL. The Prime of Miss Jean Brodie. Phila: Lippincott, 1962. 1st Amer ed. Fine in dj (lt rubbed). *Hermitage.* $45/£28

SPARKE, EDWARD. Scintilla-Altaris, Being a Pious Reflection on Primative Devotion in the Feasts and Fasts of the Church of England. London: W.G. & R.W., 1660. 2nd ed. (54),644pp; 39 copper plts. Aeg. Contemp red morocco, gilt. (Soiled; joints expertly reinforced), else VG. *Pacific*.* $219/£137

SPARKS, EDWIN ERLE (ed). The English Settlements in the Illinois. London/Cedar Rapids, IA: Museum Book Store/Torch, 1907. One of 250. Teg, others uncut. Blue cl. Fine. *Mott.* $100/£63

SPARKS, WILLIAM. The Apache Kid, and Other True Stories of the Old West. L.A.: Skelton, 1926. 1st ed. 4 photo plts. (Sl worn, vertical creases to spine), else VG + in pict wrappers. *Pacific*.* $184/£115

SPARLING, H. The Kelmscott Press and William Morris Master-Craftsmen. London: Macmillan, 1924. Frontis, 16 plts. Uncut. Cl-backed blue bds (headcaps, corners bumped), paper spine label (worn), extra spine label inserted loose. *Maggs.* $192/£120

SPARRMAN, ANDERS. A Voyage Round the World with Captain James Cook in H.M.S. Resolution. London: Golden Cockerel, 1944. One of 350. 1st English ed. Teg, rest untrimmed. Gilt-dec grn buckram, leather spine label. (Bkpl; spine ends, corners rubbed), else VG. *Pacific*.* $403/£252

SPARROW, JOHN. Grave Epigrams and Other Verses. Cygnet, 1981. 1st ed. Fine in dj. *Cox.* $24/£15

SPARROW, JOHN. Grave Epigrams. (Bembridge: Simon Rendall, 1974.) One of 200. Uncut. Fine in orig ptd wrappers. *Cox.* $48/£30

SPARROW, WALTER SHAW. See SHAW-SPARROW, WALTER

SPATE, VIRGINIA. Orphism. Oxford: Clarendon, 1979. 8 color plts. Fine in dj. *Turtle Island.* $60/£38

SPEAKMAN, HAROLD. Mostly Mississippi. NY: Dodd, Mead, 1927. 1st ed. (Gilt sl dull.) Dj (sl edgeworn). *Sadlon.* $15/£9

SPEAR, PERCIVAL. Twilight of the Mughuls. Cambridge: CUP, 1951. 1st ed. Frontis, 4 plts, fldg map. (Lib spine #; sl rubbed), o/w VG. *Worldwide.* $30/£19

SPEAR, RICHARD E. Caravaggio and His Followers. Cleveland: Museum of Art, (1971). Fine in dj. *Turtle Island.* $55/£34

Specimens of German Romance. London: Geo. B. Whittaker, 1826. 1st ed. 3 vols. Etched frontis by George Cruikshank each vol. Teg. Uniform 3/4 dk blue levant morocco, cl, gilt. (Aging/offset; metal medallion bkpls), else Fine. *Pacific*.* $174/£109

Specimens of German Romance. London, 1826. 1st ed. 3 vols. Frontispieces by George Cruikshank. Later 1/2 polished tan calf (lt rubbed), gilt, dbl red labels. *Swann*.* $201/£126

SPECK, GORDON. Breeds and Half-Breeds. NY, 1969. 1st ed. Fine in dj (sl edgeworn, sl soiled). *Baade.* $45/£28

SPECK, GORDON. Samuel Hearne and the Northwest Passage. Caldwell, 1963. 1st ed. NF in dj (sl worn, price-clipped). *Baade.* $35/£22

SPECKTER, MARTIN K. Disquisitions on the Composing Stick. Ptd by Clarke & Way, 1971. *Dawson.* $50/£31

Spectator. London: S. Buckley & J. Tonson, 1713-1715. 2nd collected ed. 8 vols (contemp inscrip each vol). Contemp calf, red morocco spine labels (few spines sl chipped, few hinges starting). *Karmiole.* $300/£188

Speech of Hon. Chas. Sumner of Massachusetts on Cession of Russian America to U.S. Washington: Congressional Globe, 1867. 1st ed. 48pp. (Blindstamp, tp corner torn off; cvr loose.) Ptd wraps, laid in custom-made box. *Heinoldt.* $85/£53

SPEED, KELLOGG. Traumatic Injuries of the Carpus, Including Colles' Fracture. NY, 1925. 1st ed. (Bkplt; extrems sl worn), o/w VG. *Doctor's Library.* $100/£63

SPEEDY, TOM. Craigmillar and Its Environs. Selkirk: George Lewis & Son, 1892. xv,248,(ii)pp. (Edges sl dknd.) *Hollett.* $96/£60

SPEERT, HAROLD. Iconographia Gyniatrica: A Pictorial History of Gynecology and Obstetrics. Phila: F.A. Davis, (1973). 1st ed. Black cl, gilt. Fine. *Pacific*.* $81/£51

SPEERT, HAROLD. Obstetric and Gynecologic Milestones. Essays in Eponymy. NY: Macmillan, 1958. 1st ed. Fine in dj. *Glaser.* $150/£94

SPEISER, WERNER. The Art of China. George Lawrence (trans). London: Methuen, 1960. 1st ed. NF in dj, cardbd box. *Worldwide.* $45/£28

SPEISER, WERNER. Oriental Architecture in Colour. Thames & Hudson, 1965. 112 color plts, 32 plans. VG in dj. *Hadley.* $32/£20

SPEKE, JOHN HANNING. Journal of the Discovery of the Source of the Nile. William Blackwood & Sons, 1863. 1st ed. Engr frontis port, fldg map hand-colored in outline in rear pocket (frontis, tp dampstained at inner corner; sl spotted; hinges repaired, rebacked retaining orig backstrip, cvrs sl soiled). *Sotheby's*.* $478/£299

SPEKE, JOHN HANNING. Journal of the Discovery of the Source of the Nile. Edinburgh/London: William Blackwood, 1864. 1st ed. Demy 8vo. xxxi,658pp; 2 maps (1 fldg in pocket). 1/2 dk brn sheep, marbled paper bds. VG (recently recased). *Ulysses.* $1,120/£700

SPELL, HAZEL M. The Twentynine Palms Story. Privately done, 1959. 3rd ed. Fine in wraps. *Book Market.* $25/£16

SPELLMAN, FRANCIS CARDINAL. What America Means to Me and Other Poems and Prayers. NY, 1953. Inscribed, signed. *Argosy.* $45/£28

SPENCE, PERCY F. S. Australia. A&C Black, 1910. 75 color plts, fldg map. Teg. Dec cl. (Several plts detached, sl chipped, discolored; feps lt browned, sm tear w/o loss; cl dampstained to foreedge, spine sl rubbed.) *Edwards.* $80/£50

Spencer Collection of Illustrated Books. NY: NY Public Library, 1928. Rev ed. Partly unopened. Good in ptd tan wraps (lt aged). *Baltimore**. $55/£34

SPENCER, EDMUND. The Works. London: Routledge, 1865. New ed. Frontisport, add'l engr tp, lx,562pp. Aeg. Full purple morocco, gilt, raised bands. (1st few ff foxed, bkseller ticket.) *Marlborough*. $120/£75

SPENCER, HERBERT. Herbert Spencer on the Americans and the Americans on Herbert Spencer. NY: D. Appleton, 1883. 1st ed, 2nd issue w/date corrected from Nov 11 to Nov 9 on wrapper only. 96pp. Orig ptd wrappers (chipped). *Mott*. $75/£47

SPENCER, HERBERT. Illustrations of Universal Progress. NY: Appleton, 1874. 1st US ed. NF (sm cracks in finish of joints). *Beasley*. $85/£53

SPENCER, ROBERT F. The North American Eskimo. BAE Bulletin 171. Washington: Smithsonian Inst, (1969). 2nd ed. VG in dj. *Perier*. $35/£22

SPENCER, SCOTT. Reservation Hall. NY, 1976. 1st ed. Fine in NF dj. *Warren*. $50/£31

SPENCER, WALTER T. Forty Years in My Bookshop. London, 1923. 1st ed. Teg, uncut. Fine (sl rubbed). *Polyanthos*. $50/£31

SPENDER, JOHN. Therapeutic Means for the Relief of Pain. London, 1874. 1st ed. 230pp. *Fye*. $250/£156

SPENDER, STEPHEN. The Backward Son. London: Hogarth, 1940. 1st Eng ed. VG (feps partly browned, top edge dusty; spine ends, corners sl bumped, cvrs sl spotted) in dj (nicked, chipped, frayed, rubbed, mkd, sl creased, internally browned). *Ulysses*. $120/£75

SPENDER, STEPHEN. The Burning Cactus. London, 1936. 1st ed. Fine (lacks dj). *Petersfield*. $72/£45

SPENDER, STEPHEN. China Diary. London: Thames & Hudson, 1982. Ltd to 1000 signed by Spender and David Hockney (illus) w/signed 5-color litho in separate folder. Sm 4to. Red cl, red paper folder. In orig cardbd box. *Christie's**. $368/£230

SPENDER, STEPHEN. Cyril Connolly: A Memoir. Edinburgh: Tragara, 1978. One of 165. Frontisport. Cl-backed paper bds. NF. *Any Amount*. $45/£28

SPENDER, STEPHEN. Forward from Liberalism. London: Gollancz, 1937. 1st Eng ed. VG (spine ends, corners sl bumped, gilt sl oxidized) in dj (nicked, rubbed, dusty, sl mkd, creased, browned, sl frayed). *Ulysses*. $200/£125

SPENDER, STEPHEN. Journals 1939-1983. Faber, 1985. 1st ed. Signed presentation. NF in dj. *Any Amount*. $48/£30

SPENDER, STEPHEN. Life and the Poet. London: Secker & Warburg, 1942. 1st Eng ed. NF (nameplt) in wrappers (spine sl creased), dj (sl rubbed, spine sl dknd). *Ulysses*. $40/£25

SPENDER, STEPHEN. The New Realism. London: Hogarth, 1939. 1st ed. Pamphlet. NF in wraps. *Lame Duck*. $45/£28

SPENDER, STEPHEN. Poetry Since 1939. London, 1946. Orig wraps (sl frayed). *Edrich*. $19/£12

SPENDER, STEPHEN. Returning to Vienna 1947, Nine Sketches. (Pawlett): Banyan, (1947). 1st ed. One of 500 numbered, signed. Dec wrappers, ptd label. (Spine sl dknd, label sl smudged), else Fine. *Reese*. $75/£47

SPENDER, STEPHEN. Ruins and Visions. London, 1942. 1st ed. (Tp sl foxed.) Dj (faded). *Petersfield*. $42/£26

SPENDER, STEPHEN. The Still Centre, Poems. London, 1939. 1st ed. Fine in dj (top edge sl worn). *Petersfield*. $64/£40

SPENSER, EDMUND. The Faerie Queen. Cambridge: CUP, 1909. One of 350. Teg. Full vellum, gilt. (Inscrips, sl offset from tape 1/2-title vol 1, prelim vol 2; vol 1 fr hinge cracking), else NF. *Pacific**. $115/£72

SPENSER, EDMUND. The Faerie Queen. LEC, 1953. Ltd to 1500 numbered, signed by Agnes Miller Parker (illus). 2 vols. Fine in slipcase. *Swann**. $149/£93

SPENSER, EDMUND. The Shepherd's Calender. NY/London: Harper, 1898. 1st ed. 12 illus by Walter Crane. Grn pict cl. Fine. *Appelfeld*. $150/£94

SPERA, STEPHEN. Stephen Spera: Photoworks, 1976-1981. Phila: Portico Eds, n.d. VG in pict stiff wrappers (lt worn). *Cahan*. $40/£25

SPERRY, ARMSTRONG. One Day with Jambi in Sumatra. Phila: John C. Winston, (1934). 1st ed. 8vo. Red cl spine. VG (soil). *Davidson*. $35/£22

SPEWACK, SAMUEL and BELLA. Kiss Me Kate: A Musical Play. NY: Knopf, 1953. 1st trade ed. Dec bds. Fine in NF dj (spine sunned). *Reese*. $60/£38

SPEYER, EDWARD. My Life and Friends. London: Cobden Sanderson, 1937. 1st ed. 8 plts. VG. *Hollett*. $32/£20

SPEYER, LEONORA. Slow Wall. NY, 1939. 1st ed. Inscribed, signed, dated 1939. Fine. *Bond*. $20/£13

SPICER, JACK. Fifteen False Prepositions About God. SF: Manroot, 1974. 1st ed. NF in illus stapled wraps. *Lame Duck*. $65/£41

SPICER-SIMPSON, THEODORE. Men of Letters of the British Isles. NY: William Edwin Rudge, 1924. One of 520 numbered. 29 sepia-toned gravures, tissue guards. Untrimmed. Cream holland cl, red-brn bds, gilt. Very Clean in bd slipcase (broken, worn) w/inner bd liner (worn). *Baltimore**. $35/£22

SPIEGELBERG, FREDERIC. Spiritual Practices of India. (SF: Greenwood Press), 1951. One of 500. Woodblock print. Patterned bds, cl spine, paper spine label. (Glue remnants fr pastedown.) *Dawson*. $60/£38

SPIELMAN, M. H. and G. S. LAYARD. Kate Greenaway. London: A&C Black, 1905. 1st ed, 2nd imp, corrected. 52 color plts. 3/4 morocco over cl bds. *Cullen*. $160/£100

SPIELMANN, M. H. and G. S. LAYARD. Kate Greenaway. London: A&C Black, 1905. 2nd imp. 53 color plts, guards. Teg. 1/2 dk blue calf, gilt. Orig cl cvr bound in at rear. Fine. *Sotheran*. $317/£198

SPIERS, WILLIAM. Rambles and Reveries. London: Kelly, 1890. Frontis, 256pp. Dec cl. Good + . *Savona*. $40/£25

SPIES, WERNER. Max Ernst: Oeuvre-Katalog, 1906-1938. Houston/Cologne, 1975-79. Vols 1-3 (of 4). 4to. Djs. *Swann**. $920/£575

SPILLANE, MICKEY. The Deep. NY: E.P. Dutton, (1961). 1st ed. Signed, inscribed. (Spine irregularly sunned), else VG in dj. *Pacific**. $115/£72

SPILLANE, MICKEY. Tomorrow I Die. NY: Mysterious Press, (1984). 1st ed. One of 250 signed. Gray eps. Maroon cl, gilt. Fine in pict dj, maroon cl open-end slipcase. *Heritage*. $125/£78

SPILLER, BURTON L. Firelight. NY: Derrydale, 1937. One of 950 numbered. Maroon cl. Fine. *Biscotti*. $300/£188

SPILLER, BURTON L. Grouse Feathers. NY: Derrydale, 1935. One of 950 numbered. Maroon cl. Fine. *Biscotti*. $325/£203

SPILLER, BURTON L. More Grouse Feathers. NY: Derrydale, 1938. One of 950 numbered. Maroon cl. Fine. *Biscotti*. $300/£188

SPILLER, BURTON L. More Grouse Feathers. NY: Crown, 1972. 1st ed thus. Brn pebble-grain cl. Fine in VG pict dj. *Biscotti*. $25/£16

SPILLER, BURTON L. More Grouse Feathers. NY: Crown, 1972. Ltd to 750 numbered, signed. This copy signed but out of series. Brown pebble-grain cl. Fine in Fine ptd dj. *Biscotti*. $125/£78

SPILLER, ROBERT E. The Philobiblon Club of Philadelphia. The First 80 Years, 1893-1973. N.p.: Philobiblon Club, 1973. One of 275. Vellum-backed patterned bds. As New. *Kane**. $80/£50

SPILSBURY, WILLIAM HOLDEN. Lincoln's Inn Its Ancient and Modern Buildings with an Account of the Library.... William Pickering, 1850. 1st ed. Wood-engr frontis, xvi,324,4pp. Variant binding: vertical-ribbed dk blue cl, by Bone, gilt. VG (prelims, last ll lt foxed; Bone ticket). *Blackwell's.* $104/£65

SPILSBURY, WILLIAM HOLDEN. Lincoln's Inn. William Pickering, 1850. 1st ed. Frontis. (Spine head torn.) *Forest.* $45/£28

SPINGARN, JOEL ELIAS. The New Hesperides and Other Poems. NY, 1911. 1st Amer ed. VG (rubbed, sl soiled). *Polyanthos.* $25/£16

SPINK, J. G. TAYLOR. Baseball Register. St. Louis: Sporting News, 1942. Blue cl (rebound), owner's gilt name fr cvr. *Glenn.* $50/£31

SPITZKA, E. C. Insanity. Its Classification, Diagnosis and Treatment. NY: Bermingham, 1883. 1st ed. VG (spine frayed). *Beasley.* $75/£47

SPIVACK, JULIUS L. The Surgical Technic of Abdominal Operations. Chicago, 1937. (Sig; spine sl worn), o/w Fine. *Doctor's Library.* $100/£63

SPLAN, JOHN. Life with the Trotters.... Chicago, 1889. 1st ed. 450pp. (Name label, extrems worn), else VG. *King.* $75/£47

SPLITSTONE, FRED JOHN. Orcas: Gem of the San Juans. Sedro-Woolley, WA: Courier Times, 1946. 1st ed. Signed. NF. *Sadlon.* $50/£31

SPOFFORD, HARRIET PRESCOTT. A Little Book of Friends. Boston: Little, Brown, 1916. 1st ed. Presentation copy, inscribed. Dec cl. (Spine sl dull), o/w Good. BAL 18560. *Holmes.* $125/£78

SPOLANSKY, JACOB. The Communist Trail in America. NY: Macmillan, 1951. 1st ed. NF. *Beasley.* $25/£16

SPOONER, HENRY J. Motors and Motoring. NY: Dodd, Mead, 1905. 1st ed. NF. *Pacific*.* $46/£29

Sportsman's Dictionary; or, The Gentleman's Companion: For Town and Country. London, 1778. 16 engr plts. Contemp calf. (Sl foxed, soiled; rubbed, spine tips sl worn.) *Oinonen*.* $250/£156

Sportsman's Portfolio of American Field Sports. NY: Derrydale, 1929. One of 400. Brn cl backed over pict tan paper-cvrd bds. NF. *Biscotti.* $125/£78

Sportsman's Repository; Comprising a Series of Highly Finished Engravings, Representing the Horse and the Dog.... (By John Lawrence.) London: Bohn, 1845. Orig cl. (Foxed, soiled; worn, most of spine gone.) *Oinonen*.* $425/£266

SPOTA, LUIS. The Enemy Blood. London: Frederick Muller, 1961. 1st British ed. VG+ in dj (sm extrem tears). *Lame Duck.* $65/£41

SPOTA, LUIS. The Wounds of Hunger. Boston: Houghton Mifflin, 1957. 1st US ed. NF in dj (price-clipped). *Lame Duck.* $55/£34

SPOTSWOOD, J. B. An Historical Sketch of the Presbyterian Church in New Castle, Delaware. Phila: Joseph M. Wilson, 1859. 39pp. Later 1/2 leather, marbled bds. (Several pp of later ink ms notes, photos laid in; lib blind stamps, call #; text soiled; scuffed), else Good. *Brown.* $25/£16

SPOTTS, DAVID L. Campaigning with Custer and the Nineteenth Kansas Volunteer Cavalry on the Washita Campaign, 1868-69. E. A. Brininstool (ed). L.A.: Wetzel, 1928. 1st ed. One of an unstated ed of 800. Signed. Teg. Blue cl, gilt. NF (bkpl) in dj (heavily tape-repaired at folds, joints, spine; spine dknd, very chipped). Howes S843. *Pacific*.* $230/£144

SPRAGUE, DEAN. Freedom Under Lincoln. Boston, 1965. 1st ed. VG+ in dj (sl worn, 1-inch tear, 4 sm tears). *Pratt.* $17/£11

SPRAGUE, E. and C. How to Design Monograms. NY: Bodley Head/Pelham, 1927. 1st ed. VG in dj (sl torn). *Moss.* $16/£10

SPRAGUE, J. T. The Original, Progress, and Conclusion of the Florida War. NY, 1848. 1st ed, this being the issue w/o plts. Contemp 3/4 leather (rubbed, spine # remnant; lib stamp tp, lib mks, foxing). Howes S844. *Oinonen*.* $50/£31

SPRAGUE, J. T. USA: The Treachery in Texas. NY, 1862. Good+ in ptd wraps. *Wantagh.* $75/£47

SPRAGUE, MARSHALL. The Great Gates: The Story of the Rocky Mountain Passes. Boston: Little, Brown, (1964). 1st ed. Fine in VG dj. *Perier.* $35/£22

SPRATT, G. The Medico-Botanical Pocket Book, Comprising a Compendium of Vegetable Toxicology. London: John Churchill, (1836). Sm 8vo. x,118pp; 15 full-pg hand-colored plts. Orig full cl, morocco label, gilt. Good. *Cullen.* $750/£469

SPRENGEL, KURT. An Introduction to the Study of Cryptogamous Plants. London: For J. White, 1807. viii,411pp; 10 VG fldg copper plts at rear, all w/orig hand-coloring. Period calf, rose cl w/watered pattern, black leather spine label, gilt. (Lt browned, foxed, name clipped from tp across entire leaf; some plts w/old improper folds; scuffed, edgeworn.) *Baltimore*.* $210/£131

SPRENGELL, CONRAD JOACHIM (comp). The Aphorisms of Hippocrates. 1987. Facs ed. As New in dj. *Doctor's Library.* $25/£16

SPRING, AGNES WRIGHT. Caspar Collins. NY: Columbia Univ, 1927. 1st ed. Frontis, 11 full-pg illus. Blind/white-stamped cl (white spine lettering flaking). Dj (worn). *Dawson.* $60/£38

SPRING, AGNES WRIGHT. Caspar Collins: The Life and Exploits of an Indian Fighter of the Sixties. NY: Columbia Univ, 1927. 1st ed. NF. *Sadlon.* $50/£31

SPRING, AGNES WRIGHT. Cow Country Legacies. Kansas City: Lowell, 1976. 1st ed. Fine in dj. *Labordo.* $35/£22

SPRING, AGNES WRIGHT. Seventy Years, a Panoramic History of the Wyoming Stock Growers' Association.... Cheyenne, WY: WY Stock Growers' Assoc, 1942. 1st ed. NF in wrappers. Howes S850. *Labordo.* $150/£94

SPRING, GARDINER. Memoirs of the Rev. Samuel J. Mills, Late Missionary to the South Western Section of the United States. NY: NY Evangelical Missionary Soc, 1820. (1st ed.) (4),(9)-247pp. (Foxed; lacks binding bds.) Howes S851. *Bohling.* $75/£47

SPRINGSTUN, HUMPHREYS. Doctors and Juries. Phila, 1935. VG (extrems sl worn). *Doctor's Library.* $30/£19

SPRUCE, RICHARD. Notes of a Botanist on the Amazon and Andes. London, 1908. 1st ed. 2 vols. 7 maps. Teg. (Blind-stamped name; sl foxed; spine sunned, extrems rubbed.) *King.* $300/£188

SPRUNT, ALEXANDER, JR. Florida Bird Life. Coward-McCann, 1954. (1st few pp, cvr edge sl stained.) *Rybski.* $55/£34

SPRUNT, JAMES. Tales of the Cape Fear Blockade.... Cornelius M. D. Thomas (ed). Wilmington, NC: Charles Towne Preservation Trust, 1960. 1st ed. One of unspecified # signed by Thomas. Fldg map. (Few faint spots along gutters), else NF in dj. *Chapel Hill.* $75/£47

SPRY, W. J. J. The Cruise of the 'Challenger.' London: Sampson Low, Marston, Searle & Rivington, 1876. Inscribed, signed 'W.S.' dated 1876. xviii,388pp + 24pp list; fldg map. Blind-stamped, gilt-dec cl (hinges, lower extrem fr bd rubbed; spine ends sl worn). VG (sl foxed). *Explorer.* $288/£180

SPURR, HARRY A. A Cockney in Arcadia. Allen, 1899. 1st ed. 28 plts by John Hassall & Cecil Aldin, incl Hassall frontis. Pict cl. (Spine ends sl bruised, pict design sl scratched), else NF. *Any Amount.* $112/£70

SPURR, HARRY A. A Cockney in Arcadia. George Allen, 1899. 1st Eng ed. Color pict cl. VG (edges, eps spotted; spine ends bumped, corners sl rubbed, cvrs sl dusty). *Ulysses.* $152/£95

SPURR, JOSIAH EDWARD. Through the Yukon Gold Diggings. Boston: Eastern Pub, 1900. Frontis. Dec cl. VG. *High Latitude.* $160/£100

SPURR, RUSSELL. A Glorious Way to Die: The Kamikaze Mission of the Battleship Yamato, April 1945. Newmarket, (1981). 1st ed. Good in dj. *Rybski.* $30/£19

SPYRI, JOHANNA. Heidi. Helen B. Dole (trans). Boston: Ginn, (1899). 1st ed thus. 365pp. Red cl, gilt. VG (name; sl dust soiled). *Second Life.* $125/£78

SPYRI, JOHANNA. Heidi. Phila: David McKay, 1922. 1st ed. 4to. 10 full-pg color plts, color tp by Jessie Wilcox Smith. Teg. Slate blue cl, color paste label (edges of both lt rubbed; rear hinge strengthened). Full color pict dj (worn, spine chip). *Reisler.* $225/£141

ST. BARBE BAKER, RICHARD. Green Glory. London, 1948. 1st ed. 60 photo plts. Grn cl, gilt. (3-4pp ink-underlined), else VG. *Larry Price.* $25/£16

ST. CLAIRE, EMILY ENTWISLE. Beautiful and Historic Albemarle. Richmond: Appeals, 1932. VG-. *Book Broker.* $35/£22

ST. JOHN ROOSA, D. B. and EDWARD T. ELY. Ophthalmic and Otic Memoranda. NY, 1880. Rev ed. Good (corners, spine worn). *Doctor's Library.* $45/£28

ST. JOHN, CHARLES. Natural History and Sport in Moray. Edinburgh, 1863. 1st ed. Frontis, xlvii,336pp. (Names, lt foxed; worn, spine foot frayed, sm nick, shaken.) *Sutton.* $95/£59

ST. JOHN, CHARLES. Sketches of the Wild Sports and Natural History of the Highlands. John Murray, 1878. xv,338pp. Pict cl, beveled bds (extrems, spine worn, ends repaired, joints strengthened), gilt. *Hollett.* $224/£140

ST. JOHN, CHARLES. A Tour in Sutherlandshire. London, 1884. 2nd ed. 2 vols. (Lt faded, rubbed.) *Grayling.* $104/£65

ST. JOHN, CHARLES. Wild Sports and Natural History of the Highlands. London, 1893. Mod 1/2 calf. *Grayling.* $120/£75

ST. JOHN, CHARLES. Wild Sports and Natural History of the Highlands. T.N. Foulis, 1919. 50 plts (28 color). Uncut. Fine (spine sl faded). *Hollett.* $104/£65

ST. JOHN, CHRISTOPHER (ed). Ellen Terry and Bernard Shaw: A Correspondence. Constable, 1931. 2nd ed. Good (sig; spine bumped, chipped, corners rubbed; lacks dj). *Tiger.* $13/£8

ST. JOHN, J. HECTOR. Letters from an American Farmer.... Phila: Matthew Carey, March 4, 1793. 1st Amer ed. 240pp. Contemp calf. (Upper portion tp clipped, repaired later; spotted, browned, clumsily rebacked), else Good. Howes C883. *Brown.* $150/£94

ST. JOHN, JOHN. To the War with Waugh. Whittington, 1973. One of 600. Signed. Linen, title label. (Lacks dj), else VG. *Michael Taylor.* $216/£135

ST. JOHN, JUDITH. The Osborne Collection of Early Children's Books, 1566-1910. Toronto: Toronto Public Library, (1975). 2nd rev ed. 2 vols. Dk grn/blue-grn cl, gilt. (Sl handled, lt rubbed.) *Baltimore*.* $130/£81

ST. JOHN, SPENSER. Life in the Forests of the Far East; or Travels in Northern Borneo. London: Smith, Elder, 1863. 2nd ed. 2 vols. Demy 8vo. xvi,406; xi,424pp; 16 tinted litho plts, 3 fldg maps. VG set (Lt foxed, sm repair to 1 map, bkpls; hinges cracked, few sm spine end tears) in mod custom-made slipcase. *Ulysses.* $1,360/£850

ST. MARIE, COUNT. Algeria in 1845. London: Bentley, 1846. 1st ed. Frontis, vii,284pp. Orig cl. (Ex-lib, sm tear tp; worn, spine torn; lacks part of spine, rear cvr detached), o/w Good. *Worldwide.* $35/£22

St. Paul City Directory for 1874. St. Paul: Campbell & Davison, 1874. 477pp. Orig 1/2 cl, ptd bds. (Cvrs sl rubbed, worn), else VG. *Pacific*.* $86/£54

STACK, JOHN. A Short System of Optics. Dublin, 1811. 2nd ed. Tp,(ii),x,179pp (lt spotted); 6 fldg plts. Marbled edges. Mod 1/2 cl (rebound), gilt. *Edwards.* $72/£45

STACKPOLE, EDOUARD A. The Sea-Hunters. NY: Lippincott, 1953. 1st ed. VG in dj. *Walcot.* $29/£18

STACKPOLE, EDOUARD A. The Sea-Hunters. The New England Whalemen During Two Centuries 1635-1835. Phila: J.B. Lippincott, (1953). 16 plts. Gray bds. VG + in color, pict dj. *House.* $40/£25

STACKPOLE, EDWARD J. Chancellorsville: Lee's Greatest Battle. Harrisburg, PA: Stackpole, (1958). 1st ed. Pict cl. (Spine sl faded, ends lt bumped), else NF in VG dj. *Chapel Hill.* $40/£25

STADING, J. Through Siberia.... F. H. H. Guillemard (ed). Westminster: Archibald Constable, 1901. Good (rebacked, ex-lib, sl mkd). *High Latitude.* $95/£59

STAEHELIN, WALTER A. The Book of Porcelain. Michael Bullock (trans). London, 1966. 1st UK ed. 34 mtd color plts. (Lib ink stamps, bkpl, lt wrinkled.) Dj (sl chipped). *Edwards.* $88/£55

STAEL HOLSTEIN, BARONESS. Germany. NY: Eastburn, Kirk, 1814. 1st Amer ed. 3 vols in 2. Period tree calf, gilt, sm architectural devices. NF. *Pacific*.* $86/£54

STAFF, FRANK. The Picture Postcard and Its Origins. London, 1966. 1st ed. VG in dj. *Gretton.* $40/£25

STAFF, FRANK. The Valentine and its Origins. Lutterworth, 1969. 1st ed. Dj. *Forest.* $51/£32

STAFFORD, ANTHONY. The Female Glory; The Life of the Blessed Virgin. Chiswick, 1860. 1st ed thus. 8vo. xciv,(95)prelims,185pp; 7 engr plts, guards. Dec cream cl, gilt. VG (sl browned). *Bookmark.* $24/£15

STAFFORD, JEAN. A Mother in History. NY, 1966. 1st ed. NF in NF dj (sm closed tear). *Warren.* $35/£22

STAFFORD, WILLIAM. Traveling Through the Dark. NY: H&R, (1962). 1st ed. NF in NF dj. *Agvent.* $250/£156

Stage Illusions and Entertainments. London: Cassell, (1923). (Rebacked, shaken.) Pict wraps. *Dramatis.* $18/£11

STAHLMAN, JAMES. From the Shoulder. Nashville, TN, 1945-6-7. 1st eds. Vol 1 inscribed. 3 vols (complete). VF set. *Bond.* $25/£16

STALLINGS, LAURENCE (ed). The First World War: A Photographic History. NY: S&S, 1933. 1st ed. Caption brochure laid in. Black cl. (Reps tanned), o/w VG. *Reese.* $30/£19

STAMP, TERENCE. Stamp Album. Bloomsbury, 1987. 1st UK ed. Signed. Mint in Mint dj. *Martin.* $29/£18

Stan Lee Presents the Incredible Hulk. A Piccolo Pop-Up Book. London: Pan Books, 1980. Tor Lokvig (engineer). 3 dbl-pg pop-ups. Glazed pict bds. VG. *Bookfinders.* $40/£25

STANARD, MARY NEWTON. Richmond: Its People and Its Story. Lippincott, 1923. 1st ed. VG. *Book Broker.* $30/£19

STANDING BEAR, CHIEF LUTHER. My People the Sioux. E. A. Brinninstool (ed). Boston: Houghton, Mifflin, (1928). Signed, inscribed. Ephemera loosely laid in. NF (2pp dknd from inserted item) in dj (chipped). *Pacific*.* $230/£144

STANDLEY, PAUL. Plants of Glacier National Park. Washington: GPO, 1926. 1st ed. VG in wraps. *Archer.* $15/£9

Stanford's London Atlas of Universal Geography. London, 1904. 3rd, folio ed. 110 maps (mainly dbl-pg). 1/2 calf (sl rubbed). Internally Clean. *Gretton.* $136/£85

STANGER, FRANK M. Sawmills in the Redwoods...1849-1967. (San Mateo): San Mateo County Hist Assoc, 1967. 1st ed. Frontis, fldg map. Grn cl. Fine. *Argonaut.* $75/£47

STANGER, FRANK M. and ALAN K. BROWN. Who Discovered the Golden Gate? (San Mateo): San Mateo County Hist Assoc, 1969. 1st ed. Blue cl. Fine. *Argonaut.* $45/£28

STANHOPE, HESTER. Memoirs as Related by Herself in Conversations with her Physician. Henry Colburn, 1845. 1st Eng ed. 3 vols. Frontis each vol. 1/2 morocco. Internally Sound (all hinges cracked or tender; cvrs rubbed at most extrems, chafed). *Clearwater*. $400/£250

STANISLAVSKY, CONSTANTIN. Stanislavsky Produces Othello. Helen Nowak (trans). London: Geoffrey Bles, 1948. 1st Eng ed. NF (spine ends sl bumped) in dj (rubbed, nicked, sl chipped, mkd, dusty, spine dknd). *Ulysses*. $58/£36

STANLEY, ARTHUR PENRHYN. The Life and Correspondence of Thomas Arnold, D.D. London: B. Fellowes, 1852. 7th ed. Frontisport, xxiv,725pp. Marbled eps, edges. Tan calf, raised bands, red/black labels. Sound (extrems sl rubbed). *Young*. $32/£20

STANLEY, EDWIN J. Rambles in Wonderland: Or, Up the Yellowstone, and Among the Geysers, Canons, Cataracts, Forests, Lakes, Mammoth Springs, Mud Volcanoes, and Boiling Caldrons.... NY: D. Appleton, 1883. 3rd ed. Fldg frontis map, vii,(2),(7)-179pp + (8)pp ads; 12 wood-engr plts. (Lt foxed; spine ends, corners rubbed), else VG. *Pacific**. $46/£29

STANLEY, F. The Apaches of New Mexico, 1540-1940. Pampa, TX, 1962. (Spine faded), else VG in dj. *Dumont*. $85/£53

STANLEY, F. Ciudad Santa Fe. N.p.: (F. Stanley, 1958-1965). 3 vols. Vols II and III ltd to 500. Each vol signed. Yellow cl. Djs (lt edgeworn). *Dawson*. $175/£109

STANLEY, F. The Clovis, New Mexico, Story. Pampa, TX, 1966. Signed. VG in dj. *Dumont*. $50/£31

STANLEY, F. Desperadoes of New Mexico. Denver: World, 1953. 1st ed. One of 800. Signed. VG + in dj (worn). *Labordo*. $125/£78

STANLEY, F. The Duke City. Pampa, TX, 1963. Signed. (Foreedge soiled), else Good in dj. *Dumont*. $60/£38

STANLEY, F. Giant in Lilliput. Pampa, TX, 1963. Signed. Good in dj. *Dumont*. $65/£41

STANLEY, F. Jim Courtright Two Gun Marshall of Forth Worth. Denver, 1957. 2nd ptg. Good in dj (sl worn). *Dumont*. $45/£28

STANLEY, F. Jim Courtright, Two Gun Marshal of Fort Worth. Denver: World, 1957. 1st ed. One of 500. Signed. NF in dj. *Labordo*. $85/£53

STANLEY, F. The Lamy (New Mexico) Story. Pep, TX, 1966. 1st ed. Ltd to 400. Signed. Fine in wrappers. *Labordo*. $25/£16

STANLEY, F. Longhair Jim Courtright. N.p.: (F. Stanley, 1957). One of 500. Blue-stamped cl. Dj. *Dawson*. $50/£31

STANLEY, F. No Tears for Black Jack Ketchum. Denver, 1958. One of 500 numbered, signed. Wraps. (Spine sl sunned), else VG. *Dumont*. $85/£53

STANLEY, F. Notes on Joel Fowler. Pep, TX, 1963. 1st ed. Ltd to 500. Signed. Fine in stiff wrappers. *Labordo*. $25/£16

STANLEY, F. The Private War of Ike Stockton. Denver, 1959. Ltd ed. Signed. Fine in dj (sl worn, sm chip on rear). *Baade*. $55/£34

STANLEY, F. The Private War of Ike Stockton. Denver: World, 1959. 1st ed. One of ltd ed. Signed. Fine in dj. *Labordo*. $75/£47

STANLEY, F. Railroads of the Texas Panhandle. Borger, TX: Hess Pub Co, 1976. NF in dj (sl soiled, chipped). *Dumont*. $120/£75

STANLEY, F. The Shakespeare (New Mexico) Story. Pantex, TX: F. Stanley, 1961. 1st ed. Signed. NF in stiff wrappers. *Labordo*. $25/£16

STANLEY, F. The Springer (New Mexico) Story. Pantex, TX: F. Stanley, 1962. 1st ed. Signed. Fine in stiff wrappers. *Labordo*. $25/£16

STANLEY, F. The Texas Panhandle from Cattlemen to Feed Lots. Borger, TX, 1971. Signed. VG in dj. *Dumont*. $85/£53

STANLEY, HENRY M. The Congo and the Founding of Its Free State. Sampson Low, Marston, Searle, & Rivington, 1885. 1st ed. 2 vols. 8vo. xxvii,528; x,483pp; 2 lg fldg color maps. Pict grn cl, gilt. Good set (new eps, repair to outer margin of pg iv vol 2, fldg maps; extrems sl worn). *Sotheran*. $600/£375

STANLEY, HENRY M. The Congo and the Founding of Its Free State.... NY, (1885.) 2 vols. 528; 483pp + index; 2 maps. (One corner chewed, cvrs discolored, spine dull.) *King*. $125/£78

STANLEY, HENRY M. Coomassie and Magdala: The Story of Two British Campaigns in Africa. Sampson Low, Marston, Low & Searle, 1874. 1st ed. xiv,510,48ads pp; 2 fldg maps. Grn pict cl, gilt. Good (extrems sl worn, neatly repaired split upper joint). *Sotheran*. $480/£300

STANLEY, HENRY M. In Darkest Africa. London: Sampson Low, Marston, Searle & Rivington, 1890. 1st ed. 2 vols in 6. Frontis port, 4 color maps, 3 fldg. (Lt spotting, mainly to text.) Orig red pict cl gilt (lt soiled). *Christie's**. $325/£203

STANLEY, HENRY M. In Darkest Africa. Sampson Low, Marston, Searle & Rivington, 1890. 1st ed. 2 vols. xv,528; xv,472,(ii)ads pp; 2 lg fldg color maps. Partly uncut. Red pict cl, gilt. VG (neat repairs to maps; extrems sl bumped, worn). *Sotheran*. $472/£295

STANLEY, HENRY M. In Darkest Africa. NY, 1890. 1st ed. One of 250, Edition de Luxe, signed. 2 vols. 4to. 2 frontispieces, xv,529; xv,472pp; 38 plts, 5 maps (incl 2 lg color fldg; 2-inch tear to 1 map fold). Orig 1/2 morocco over vellum cvrs (soiled, edges worn, rubbed; inner hinges cracked, but solid), raised bands, gilt. *Sutton*. $1,950/£1,219

STANLEY, HENRY M. In Darkest Africa. NY: Scribner, 1891. 1st US ed. 2 vols. 2 steel-engr frontisports, guards, xiv,(ii),547; xvii,540pp; 3 fldg maps (2 lg, 1 sm) in rear pockets. Pale cream eps. Fine diaper-grain dk grn cl, gilt. Good (sl worn, split on edge which has projected from pocket, hinges strengthened). *Blackwell's*. $240/£150

STANLEY, HENRY M. In Darkest Africa. Sampson Low, Marston, Searle & Rivington, 1891. 5th ed. 2 vols. xv,529,(i); xv,472,(ii)ads pp; 2 fldg maps (sm repairs). Red pict cl, gilt. VG set (edges lt spotted, extrems sl bumped). *Sotheran*. $280/£175

STANLEY, HENRY M. My Dark Companions and Their Strange Stories. Sampson Low, Marston, 1893. 1st ed. viii,333,32ads pp. Aeg. Brn pict cl, gilt. (Spine foot sl rubbed), o/w VG. *Sotheran*. $280/£175

STANLEY, HENRY M. My Early Travels and Adventures in America and Asia. Sampson Low, Marston, 1895. 1st ed. 2 vols. xxi,301; ix,424pp; 2 maps, 2 photogravure ports. All edges uncut. Maroon cl, gilt. Nice set (bkpls; edges sl browned). *Sotheran*. $352/£220

STANLEY, HENRY M. Through the Dark Continent. Toronto: J. B. Magurn, 1878. 1st ed. 2 vols. 509; 483pp; 10 maps (1 lg fldg). Pict cl. (Lt shaken), else VG. *Mikesh*. $125/£78

STANLEY, HENRY M. Through the Dark Continent. NY: Harper, 1878. 1st Amer ed. 2 vols. 9 (of 10) maps, incl 1 fldg in rear pocket vol 1 (tearing at folds). Pict emb grn cl, gilt. (Lacks fldg map in rear pocket vol 2; ink name; ep hinges vol 2 tender; extrems sl rubbed), else VG set. *Pacific**. $259/£162

STANLEY, HENRY M. Through the Dark Continent. George Newnes, 1899. 7th ed. 2 vols. xxxii,400; xi,419pp; 1 lg fldg map. Red dec cl, gilt. VG set (sl faded, extrems sl bumped). *Sotheran*. $280/£175

STANLEY, LOUIS T. Collecting Staffordshire Pottery. London, 1963. 4 color plts. Dj (sl chipped, spine head loss). *Edwards*. $80/£50

STANSBERY, LON R. The Passing of 3-D Ranch. NY, 1966. Facs rpt of 1930 ed. NF (sm ink # upper corner rep). *Baade*. $50/£31

STANSBURY, HOWARD. Exploration and Survey of the Valley of the Great Salt Lake of Utah, Including a Reconnoissance of a New Route Through the Rocky Mountains. Phila: Lippincott, Grambo, 1852. 487pp; 57 litho plts, fldg map. (Foxed, mostly marginally dknd, ink names dated 1852, 1 plt torn, lacks 1/2; rubbed, faded), else Good. *Pacific**. $184/£115

STANSBURY, HOWARD. Exploration and Survey of the Valley of the Great Salt Lake of Utah. Phila, 1852. 1st ed. W/o separate vol containing 2 lg fldg maps. 487pp; map, 34 tinted lithos, 23 other plts. (Sm ink spot tp, lib stamp in margin; upper joint split but firm, lib label removed from spine.) Howes S884. *Maggs.* $280/£175

STANTON, FRANK L. Frank L. Stanton's 'Just from Georgia.' Marcelle Stanton Megahee (comp). Atlanta: Byrd Pub, 1927. 1st ed. Port. (Fr inner hinge starting), else Good. *Brown.* $15/£9

STANTON, G. SMITH. When the Wildwood Was in Flower, Covering the 15 Years' Experiences of a Stockman on Western Plains and His Vacation Days in the Open. NY, (1909). 1st ed. (Fep removed.) *Heinoldt.* $25/£16

STANTON, WILLIAM. The Great United States Exploring Expedition of 1838-1842. Berkeley: Univ of CA, 1975. 1st ed. Gray cl. Fine in dj. *Argonaut.* $75/£47

STANYON, ELLIS. Bibliography of Conjuring. London: Ellis Stanyon, 'School of Magic,' 1899. 24pp. (1st 7 pp foxed), else Fine in pict white wrappers (fr cvr foxed). *Argonaut.* $50/£31

STAPLEDON, OLAF. Last Men in London. London: Methuen, (1932). 1st ed. Gilt lt blue cl. VG. *Reese.* $85/£53

STAPLEDON, OLAF. Odd John. Methuen, 1935. 2nd issue w/8pp pub's ads at rear, 1st pg of which advertises this bk, w/the price 3/6 on dj. VG (ep gutters sl browned, bottom corner fep sl creased, sm mk on top edge; cvrs sl mkd) in dj (sl rubbed, nicked, dusty). *Ulysses.* $600/£375

STAPLES, HENRY LEE et al. Fall of a Railroad Empire: Brandeis and the New Haven Merger Battle. Syracuse Univ, 1947. Good. *Rybski.* $40/£25

STAPP, WILLIAM F. Robert Cornelius: Portraits from the Dawn of Photography. Washington: Nat'l Portrait Gallery, 1983. 1st ed. 32 full-pg plts. NF in illus stiff wrappers (lt rubbed). *Cahan.* $75/£47

Star Wars. Return of the Jedi. NY: Random House, 1983. 4 dbl-pg pop-ups by John Ampert. Glazed pict bds. VG. *Bookfinders.* $30/£19

STARK, FREYA. Ionia. A Quest. NY, 1954. 1st Amer ed. NF. *Polyanthos.* $25/£16

STARK, FREYA. The Lycian Shore. John Murray, 1956. 1st Eng ed. Buckram. VG (spine, bottom edge fr cvr sl faded) in dj (sl rubbed, price-clipped, spine head frayed). *Ulysses.* $80/£50

STARK, FREYA. Riding to the Tigris. John Murray, 1959. 1st Eng ed. Buckram. VG (spine ends sl bumped) in dj (price-clipped, sl rubbed). *Ulysses.* $56/£35

STARK, RICHARD. The Green Eagle Score. Greenwich: Fawcett, 1967. 1st ed. Pb orig. Fine. *Janus.* $25/£16

STARK, RICHARD. The Handle. London, 1985. 1st hb ed. Fine in Fine dj. *Warren.* $30/£19

STARK, RICHARD. The Man with the Getaway Face. Boston: Gregg, 1981. 1st ptg. Fine in Fine dj. *Warren.* $35/£22

STARK, RICHARD. The Sour Lemon Score. London, 1986. 1st hb ed. Fine in Fine dj. *Warren.* $30/£19

STARKEY, DINAH (retold by). Ghosts and Bogles. Good Reading Ltd, 1978. 1st ed. 8vo. Jan Pienkowski (illus). 123pp + Notes of sources. Pict bds. VG + . *Bookmark.* $32/£20

STARKIE, ENID. A Lady's Child. London, 1941. 1st ed. (Eps, tp sl foxed.) Dj. *Petersfield.* $16/£10

STARLING, ERNEST. The Fluids of the Body. Chicago, 1909. 1st Amer ed. 186pp. *Fye.* $175/£109

STARLING, ERNEST. Mercers' Company Lectures on Recent Advances in the Physiology of Digestion. Chicago: W.T. Keener, 1907. 1st Amer ed. Good (fep loose, hinges cracked; spine ends rubbed). *Glaser.* $75/£47

STARLING, ERNEST. Recent Advances in the Physiology of Digestion. Chicago, 1906. 1st Amer ed. *Fye.* $100/£63

STAROBIN, JOSEPH R. Eyewitness in Indo-China. NY, (1954). 1st ed. Map. VG + in dj (sm piece torn out, sl worn). *Pratt.* $27/£17

STAROKADOMSKIY, L. M. Charting the Russian Northern Route. The Arctic Ocean Hydrographic Expedition 1910-1915. William Barr (ed). Montreal/London: Arctic Inst of North America/McGill-Queen's Univ, 1976. Mint in dj. *Explorer.* $32/£20

STARR, CHESTER G. (ed). From Salerno to the Alps: A History of the Fifth Army, 1943-1945. Washington, (1948). 1st ed. Good. *Rybski.* $55/£34

STARR, FREDERICK. Hunting Bookplates in Mexico. Cedar Rapids: Torch Press, 1927. One of 100. 7 full-pg bkpl facs. (Bkpl.) Stiff pict wrappers. *Dawson.* $60/£38

STARR, HENRY. Thrilling Events. College Station, 1982. Ltd facs rpt of 1914 ed. Aeg. Full leather. Fine. Howes S901. *Baade.* $40/£25

STARR, SANDRA LEONARD. Joseph Cornell. NY: Castelli Feigen Corcoran, (1982). Fine in ptd wrappers. *Turtle Island.* $85/£53

STARR, WALTER A., JR. Guide to the John Muir Trail and the High Sierra Region. SF: Sierra Club, 1934. 1st ed. Frontis; fldg map in rear pocket. (Few mks fr cvr.) *Dawson.* $100/£63

STARR, WALTER A., JR. Guide to the John Muir Trail and the High Sierra Region. SF: Sierra Club, 1934. 1st ed. Frontisport, lg fldg map. Grn cl, gilt. Fine in ptd dj (sl dknd). *Pacific**. $259/£162

STARR, WALTER A., JR. My Adventures in the Klondike and Alaska 1898-1900. (SF): Privately ptd, 1960. Frontis; fldg map. VG. *High Latitude.* $35/£22

STARRETT, VINCENT. Books Alive. NY, 1940. 1st ed. Signed. (Cvrs soiled, sl faded), else Good. *King.* $35/£22

STARRETT, VINCENT. Late, Later and Possibly Last Essays. Michael Murphy (intro). St. Louis: Autolycus, 1973. Ltd to 500 signed by Starrett and Murphy. NF. *Zubal**. $85/£53

STARRETT, VINCENT. Murder in Peking. London: Walter Edwards, (1947). 1st Eng ed. Gray rough cl. Fine in dj (sl frayed). *Temple.* $136/£85

STARRETT, VINCENT. Penny Wise and Book Foolish. NY, 1929. 1st ed. VF in dj. *Truepenny.* $75/£47

STARRETT, VINCENT. Persons from Porlock. Chicago: Bookfellows, 1923. 1st ed. Ltd to 300 signed. Hand-sewn wrappers. *Black Sun.* $150/£94

STARRETT, VINCENT. What's O'Clock? (Ysleta, TX: Edwin B. Hill, 1930.) 1st ed. One of 100 ptd. Leaflet. Fine. *Reese.* $35/£22

State Register and Year Book of Facts: For the Year 1857. SF/Sacramento: Henry G. Langley, Samuel A. Mathews/James Queen, 1857. viii,384pp,36pp ads incl in pagination. (Rebacked w/orig spine laid down.) *Dawson.* $300/£188

Statement and Reports Concerning the Uncle Sam Senior and Gold Canon Silver Lodes, in Nevada. Boston: Alfred Mudge, 1865. 1st ed. 24,8pp. (Spine neatly reglued), else Fine in ptd wrappers. *Pacific**. $92/£58

Statement of the Quantity of Mackerel Packed from Hingham Vessels, from 1815 to 1828, Both Years Included. Hingham, (MA): Farmer & Brown, 1829. 1st ed. 16pp. Sewn, uncut. (Soiled.) *M & S.* $200/£125

STATHAM, H. H. Architecture Among the Poets. Batsford, 1898. 1st ed. (Spine sl faded), else NF. *Fine Books.* $85/£53

Statistical Account of the Shetland Isles. Blackwood & Sons, 1841. 1st ed. (iv),179 (neat underlining); color map. Orig cl (sl faded, worn), paper label. *Hollett.* $240/£150

Statistical History of John Ridgway's Vertical Revolving Battery. Boston: Prentiss & Deland, 1865. 1st ed. 30pp. VG (sm marginal ink spot at fore-edge of a few ll; spine worn) in ptd wraps. *Chapel Hill.* $125/£78

Statutes of California and Amendments to the Codes, Passed at the Thirty-Third Session of the Legislature, 1899. Sacramento: A.J. Johnson, 1899. Contemp sheep (worn, rubbed, rear joint cracked). Usable. *Boswell.* $35/£22

Statutes of California Passed at the Fifth Session of the Legislature.... Sacramento, 1854. Orig 1st ed. xiv,(ii),17-230,(ii),i-xvii,6pp. Orig full sheep, spine labels (fragmented). Good + (tp top cut away, not affecting text, spot on contents pg worn through from erasure; edges worn, chipped). *Sagebrush.* $95/£59

Statutes of California Passed at the First Session of the Legislature. Begun the 15th Day of Dec. 1849, and Ended the 22d Day of April, 1850, at the City of Pueblo de San Jose. San Jose: J. Winchester, State Ptr, 1850. 1st ed. Sm 4to. ix,(l),482pp. Teg. Later 3/4 brn morocco, gilt, raised bands. Fine (corners, spine foot lt rubbed). *Argonaut.* $750/£469

Statutes of the State of Nevada Passed at the First Session of the Legislature 1864-5.... Carson City: Ptd by John Church, 1865. One of 600. Contemp sheep (rebacked, worn, stained). Sound. *Boswell.* $350/£219

STAUFFER, DAVID McNEELY. American Engravers on Copper and Steel. NY, 1907. One of 350. 2 vols. 1/2 buckram, gilt-stamped paper labels, paper-cvrd bds. (Lt worn.) *Oinonen*.* $225/£141

STAUNTON, SCHUYLER. (Pseud of L. Frank Baum.) Daughters of Destiny. Chicago: Reilly & Britton, (1906). 1st ed, 1st binding, w/pict cvr label above gilt-stamped title and author's name. Thomas Mitchell Pierce & Harold DeLay (illus). Grn cl, gilt. (Stamps, hinges weak; spine ends, corners rubbed), else VG. *Pacific*.* $173/£108

STAUNTON, SCHUYLER. (Pseud of L. Frank Baum.) The Fate of a Crown. Chicago: Reilly & Britton, (1905, but c. 1912). 2nd ed. Frontis by Hazel Roberts. Red cl. (Old name; spine lettering worn), else VG. *Pacific*.* $104/£65

STAVERT, GEOFFREY. A Study in Southsea: The Unrevealed Life of Doctor Arthur Conan Doyle. Portsmouth: Milestone, (1987). 1st ed. VG (label to tp; sm spot to fore-edge) in VG dj (price-clipped). *Gravesend.* $50/£31

STAVIS, BARRIE. The Chain of Command. NY, (1945). 1st Amer ed, 1st bk. Pict bds. NF in dj (sl soiled). *Polyanthos.* $35/£22

STAWALL, MRS. RUDOLPH. My Days with the Fairies. London: Hodder & Stoughton, (1913). 1st ed thus. Royal 8vo. (vi),8-169pp; 8 mtd color plts, guards. Red pict cl. Fine. *Sotheran.* $477/£298

STAWELL, MRS. RUDOLPH. Fabre's Book of Insects. NY, 1936. 3rd ptg. Tipped-in color frontis, 11 tipped-in color plts by E. J. Detmold. Dec gilt cl. (Eps, some text spotted; cl sl damp-spotted.) Dj (sl chipped). *Edwards.* $72/£45

STAWELL, MRS. RUDOLPH. Fabre's Book of Insects; Retold from Alexander Teixeira de Mattos' Translation of Fabre's 'Souvenirs Entomologiques.' Hodder & Stoughton, (1921). 1st ed illus by E. J. Detmold. 4to. vii,184pp; 12 Fine mtd color plts. White cl, gilt. VF (1/2-title browned, fore-edge sl spotted). *Sotheran.* $317/£198

STEAD, PHILIP JOHN. Mr. Punch. London, 1950. 1st Eng ed. Good in dj (torn, chipped, dust-mkd, rubbed). *Clearwater.* $40/£25

STEADMAN, RALPH and MISCHA DAMJAM. The False Flamingoes. London: Dobson, (1968). 1st ed. Folio. Fine in NF dj (price inked out, sm scrape). *Between The Covers.* $100/£63

STEADMAN, RALPH. Cherrywood Cannon, Based on a Story Told to Him by Dimitri Sidjanski. NY: Paddinton, (1978). 1st ed. Signed. Dec cl. Fine in dj. *Pacific*.* $58/£36

STEADMAN, RALPH. Cherrywood Cannon. NY: Paddington, 1978. 1st ed. Fine in dj. *Smith.* $75/£47

STEADMAN, RALPH. Jones of Colorado. London: Ebury, 1995. 1st ed. Signed, dated on date of pub. Fine in dj. *Smith.* $75/£47

STEALINGWORTH, SLIM. Tom Wesselmann. NY, (1980). Acetate dj. *Swann*.* $69/£43

STEARNS, SAMUEL. Dr. Stearn's Tour from London to Paris. Dublin: W. Sleater, 1791. iv,176pp (inked-out name; foxed). Contemp calf (hinges scuffed). *Karmiole.* $150/£94

STEBBING, E. P. The Forests of India. London, 1922-6. 3 vols. 2 color fldg maps. (Lib ink/blind stamps, bkpls, cardholders, labels; sl shaken; extrems rubbed, vol 3 spine tail split, accession #s, label remains upper bds vols 1, 2.) *Edwards.* $80/£50

STEBBINS, R. C. Amphibians of Western North America. Berkeley, 1951. 64 plts. (Name, pg edges lt soiled; varnished.) *Sutton.* $55/£34

STEBBINS, THEODORE E. and NORMAN KEYES, JR. Charles Sheeler: The Photographs. Boston, (1987). 1st ed. 90 repros. Dj (sl rubbed). *Swann*.* $103/£64

STEBBINS, THEODORE E. The Life and Works of Martin Johnson Heade. New Haven, 1975. Dj (sl worn). *Swann*.* $258/£161

STECKBECK, JOHN S. Fabulous Redmen: The Carlisle Indians and Their Famous Football Teams. Harrisburg: J. Horace McFarland, 1951. 1st ed. VG in dj. *Pacific*.* $46/£29

STEDMAN, J. G. Narrative of a Five Years' Expedition Against the Revolted Negroes of Surinam in Guiana on the Wild Coast of South America from the Years 1772 to 1777.... Barre: Imprint Soc, 1971. 2 vols. Fldg map. 1/2 cl, paper spine labels. Fine in slipcase. *Pacific*.* $58/£36

STEEDMAN, CHARLES JOHN. Bucking the Sagebrush.... NY: Putnam, 1904. 1st ed. Charles M. Russell (illus). (Bkpl removed), o/w VG + . Howes S916. *Labordo.* $325/£203

Steel's Original and Correct List of the Royal Navy, and Hon. East India Company's Shipping...March 1, 1811. London: Steel, (1811). 90pp. Mod cl. *Lefkowicz.* $85/£53

Steel's Original and Correct List of the Royal Navy, and Hon. East-India Company's Shipping...February 1, 1812. London: Steel, (1812). 90pp. Mod cl. *Lefkowicz.* $85/£53

STEEL, FLORA ANNIE. English Fairy Tales. Macmillan, 1918. 1st ed. Lg 8vo. 16 color plts by Arthur Rackham, guards. Red cl, gilt. Internally VG (cl faded in streaks, patches). *Bookmark.* $136/£85

STEEL, FLORA ANNIE. The English Fairy Tales. London: Macmillan, 1922. 2nd ed. 8vo. (ix),316pp; 16 color plts by Arthur Rackham. Teg. Red cl, gilt. VG (eps browned; spine sunned, ends bruised). *Sotheran.* $221/£138

STEELE, DAN. Snow Trenches. Chicago: A.C. McClurg, 1931. 1st ed. Signed, inscribed 1941. Pict cl. (Bkpl, fore-edge dust-soiled, edges sl dknd), o/w VG in glassine dj (largely intact). *Reese.* $85/£53

STEELE, JAMES W. The Sons of the Border. Topeka, KS: Commonwealth, 1873. 1st ed. 280pp. Dec cl, gilt. (Spine faded, cvrs lt worn.) Howes S7961. *Ginsberg.* $150/£94

STEELE, MATTHEW F. American Campaigns. Washington: Adams, 1909. 1st ed. 2 vols. Mod navy cl. Fine set. *Chapel Hill.* $95/£59

STEELE, MATTHEW F. American Campaigns. Washington: US Infantry Assoc, 1935. Later ed. 2 vols. 311 full/dbl-pg maps in vol 2. Pebbled dk brn cl (sl worn, dusty), gilt. Internally Good. *Baltimore*.* $20/£13

STEELE, MAX. Debby. NY: Harper, (1950). 1st ed. Fine in VG + dj (few sm tears, lt crease, sm lt dampstain rear panel, crown sl rubbed). *Between The Covers.* $65/£41

STEELE, THOMAS J. and ROWENA A. RIVERA. Penitente Self-Government. Santa Fe, 1985. NF in dj. *Dumont.* $30/£19

STEELE, THOMAS SEDGWICK. Canoe and Camera; or, Two Hundred Miles Through the Maine Forests. NY: OJ, 1880. 1st ed. Fldg map in rear pocket. Pict grn cl, gilt. (Extrems sl rubbed), else NF. *Pacific*.* $92/£58

STEELE, W. D. Meat. Harper, 1928. 1st ed. NF in Nice dj (spine extrems, flap folds chipped). *Fine Books.* $45/£28

STEEN, RAGNA and MAGDA HENDRICKSON. Pioneer Days in Bardo, Alberta. Tofield, Alberta: Hist Soc of Beaver Hills Lake, 1944. Signed by both. (Stain top margin last few pp), else VG. *Perier.* $35/£22

STEERE, C. A. When Things Were Doing. Chicago: Charles H. Kerr, 1908. 1st ed. (Spine sl sunned), else Fine. *Beasley.* $250/£156

STEEVENS, G. W. From Capetown to Ladysmith. Vernon Blackburn (ed). Edinburgh: William Blackwood, 1900. 1st ed. 2 maps (1 fldg/partly colored). Yellow cl, gilt. (Lg map, leaf of contents torn w/out loss, repaired, few ll lt foxed; sl soiled.) *Morrell.* $64/£40

STEFANSSON, VILHJALMUR. Arctic Manual. NY: Macmillan, 1944. 1st ed. Inscribed. Fine. *High Latitude.* $75/£47

STEFANSSON, VILHJALMUR. The Friendly Arctic. NY: Macmillan, 1922. 2 fldg maps in pocket. VG (sl edge wear). *High Latitude.* $50/£31

STEFANSSON, VILHJALMUR. Greenland. NY: Doubleday, Doran, 1942. 1st ed. Inscribed, signed, 1942 (3/4 inch split head of spine), else VG. *High Latitude.* $35/£22

STEFANSSON, VILHJALMUR. Iceland: The First American Republic. GC, 1947. Inscribed. Frontis. Dj (chipped). *Argosy.* $85/£53

STEFANSSON, VILHJALMUR. My Life with the Eskimo. NY: Macmillan, 1913. 1st ed, 1st bk. VG. *Walcot.* $104/£65

STEFANSSON, VILHJALMUR. Northwest to Fortune. NY: Duell, Sloan & Pierce, 1960. 1st ed. VG in dj. *Walcot.* $24/£15

STEFANSSON, VILHJALMUR. Northwest to Fortune. London: George Allen & Unwin, 1960. Fine in dj. *Explorer.* $51/£32

STEFANSSON, VILHJALMUR. Northwest to Fortune. NY: Duell, Sloan & Pearce. c. 1958. Inscribed, signed, 1958. Fine in dj. *High Latitude.* $35/£22

STEFANSSON, VILHJALMUR. Prehistoric and Present Commerce Among the Arctic Coast Eskimo. Ottawa: Gov't Ptg Bureau, 1914. Fldg map. VG in ptd wrapper. *High Latitude.* $30/£19

STEFANSSON, VILHJALMUR. The Three Voyages of Martin Frobisher in Search of a Passage to Cathay and India by the North-West, A. D. 1576-8.... Amsterdam/NY: N. Israel/Da Capo, 1971. Facs rpt. 2 vols in one. *High Latitude.* $75/£47

STEFANSSON, VILHJALMUR. Ultima Thule. NY: Macmillan, 1940. 1st ed. VG in dj (chipped, worn). *High Latitude.* $35/£22

STEFANSSON, VILHJALMUR. Unsolved Mysteries of the Arctic. NY: Macmillan, 1939. 1st ed. Inscribed, signed. 4 maps. VG in dj. Carl Loman bkpl. *High Latitude.* $60/£38

STEFFEN, JEROME O. William Clark, Jeffersonian Man on the Frontier. Norman: Univ of OK, (1977). 1st ed. Frontisport. Fine in pict dj. *Argonaut.* $75/£47

STEFFEN, RANDY. The Horse Soldier, 1776-1943. Univ of OK, (1979). 1st ed. Good in dj (sl worn, repaired). *Rybski.* $45/£28

STEFFENS, HENRY J. The Development of Newtonian Optics in England. NY: Science History, 1977. 1st ed. VG. *Glaser.* $45/£28

STEGNER, WALLACE (ed). Report on the Lands of the Arid Region of the United States. Cambridge: Belknap Press, 1962. 2 lg fldg maps under strap inside rear cvr. Brn cl. Fine in NF dj. *Five Quail.* $75/£47

STEGNER, WALLACE. 20-20 Vision: In Celebration of the Peninsula Hills. (Palo Alto: Green Foothills Assoc, 1982.) 1st ed. Signed. Fine in pict wrappers. *Pacific*.* $81/£51

STEGNER, WALLACE. All the Little Live Things. NY: Viking, 1967. 1st ed. Signed. Fine in NF dj. *Unger.* $275/£172

STEGNER, WALLACE. Angle of Repose. London: Heinemann, 1971. 1st ed. NF in dj. *Smith.* $125/£78

STEGNER, WALLACE. Beyond the Hundredth Meridian. Boston: Houghton Mifflin, 1954 (Sept 9). 1st ed. Adv copy, pub's dated slip laid in. Map frontis. NF in NF dj (extrems sl worn, spine sl browned). *Smith.* $500/£313

STEGNER, WALLACE. Beyond the Hundredth Meridian. Boston, 1954. Lg fldg frontis, map. Brn cl. VG + . *Five Quail.* $80/£50

STEGNER, WALLACE. Beyond the Hundredth Meridian. Boston: Houghton Mifflin, 1954. 1st ed. Signed. 8vo. NF in dj (short tear to rear corners). *Smith.* $600/£375

STEGNER, WALLACE. The Big Rock Candy Mountain. NY: Duell, Sloan & Pearce, (1943). 1st ed. Crimson cl, gilt spine. (Splash spots along bulked fore-edge; edges, spine ends sl rubbed, exposed cl at pastedown edges, few sm insect holes at joints.) VG color pict dj. *Baltimore*.* $240/£150

STEGNER, WALLACE. The Big Rock Candy Mountain. NY: Duell, Sloan & Pearce, (1943). Advance copy. (Spine creased, rubbed, head chipped, extrems sl sunned, adhesion residue from tape along fr joint), else VG. *Pacific*.* $288/£180

STEGNER, WALLACE. The Big Rock Candy Mountain. NY: Duell, Sloan & Pearce, (1943). 1st ed. Signed, inscribed. VG in dj (spine, upper fr panel extrems sunned, ends sl rubbed, 2 sm tears upper fr panel). *Pacific*.* $1,265/£791

STEGNER, WALLACE. The Gathering of Zion: The Story of the Mormon Trail. NY: McGraw-Hill, (1964). 1st ed. (Sm stain fore-edge lt affecting few pp), else Fine in VG dj (spine sl dknd). *Between The Covers.* $250/£156

STEGNER, WALLACE. On the Writing of History. N.p., 1989. One of 100 ptd. Signed. Stegner 80th birthday program laid-in. Fine in ptd stiff wrappers, ptd envelope. *Pacific*.* $196/£123

STEGNER, WALLACE. Remembering Laughter. L-B, 1937. 1st ed. (Spine tips faded), else VG + in VG dj (1/8-inch chip from spine head). *Fine Books.* $275/£172

STEGNER, WALLACE. Wolf Willow. NY: Viking, (1962). 1st ed. Fine in dj. *Pacific*.* $150/£94

STEGNER, WALLACE. Wolf Willow. NY: Viking, 1962. 1st ed. NF in dj (1 chip, lt sunned). *Smith.* $200/£125

STEGNER, WALLACE. Wolf Willow. London: Heinemann, April, 1963. 1st ed. NF in VG dj (price-clipped, sticker removal remnants fr panel). *Smith.* $125/£78

STEICHEN, EDWARD. The Blue Ghost. NY: Harcourt, Brace, 1947. 1st ed. Frontis. (Name), else VG. *Cahan.* $85/£53

STEICHEN, EDWARD. A Life in Photography. NY: Doubleday, 1963. 1st ed. Black cl, gilt. Fine (inscrip) in dj. *Glenn.* $70/£44

STEIN, AUREL. Ancient Khotan: Detailed Report of Archaeological Explorations in Chinese Turkestan. NY: Hacker Art Books, 1975. Rpt of 1907 ed. 2 vols in 1. As New. *Pacific*.* $138/£86

STEIN, AUREL. Old Routes of Western Iran. London: Macmillan, 1940. 1st ed. Med 8vo. xxviii,432pp; 112 illus, 31 plts, 31 plans, sketch maps, 2 fldg maps (1 in pocket). NF in brn cl. *Ulysses.* $1,280/£800

STEIN, GERTRUDE. The Autobiography of Alice B. Toklas. (By Gertrude Stein.) NY, (1933). 1st ed. Dj (edgewear, chips). *Swann*.* $230/£144

STEIN, GERTRUDE. Everybody's Autobiography. NY: Random House, (1937). 1st ed. VG (eps, pp edges, spine sunned; lacks dj). *Hermitage.* $60/£38

STEIN, GERTRUDE. Geography and Plays. Boston: Four Seas, (1922). 1st ed, 1st issue. Dj (sm nicks spine head, tips rubbed). *Swann*.* $230/£144

STEIN, GERTRUDE. Gertrude Stein's America. Gilbert A. Harrison (ed). Washington: Robert Luce, (1965). 1st ed. VF in VF black dj (sl rubbed). *Between The Covers.* $125/£78

STEIN, GERTRUDE. In Savoy or 'Yes' is for Yes for a Very Young Man. London: Pushkin, (1946). 1st ed. ('Savoy' stamped on fep, sm wrinkle), else VF in wrappers in dj (sm wrinkle). *Between The Covers.* $150/£94

STEIN, GERTRUDE. Last Operas and Plays. NY, (1949). 1st ed. Port. (Bumped), else Good in dj (edges lt chipped; dknd). *King.* $50/£31

STEIN, GERTRUDE. Last Operas and Plays. Carl Van Vechten (ed). NY: Rinehart, (1949). 1st ed. Fine in NF dj. *Bromer.* $150/£94

STEIN, GERTRUDE. Lucy Church Amiably. Paris: Imprimerie Union, 1930. 1st ed. Blue paper over bds. VG (ink inscrip; extrems rubbed, spine sl worn, binding sl shaken) in plain brn dj (chipped, sm spine stain). *Heritage.* $250/£156

STEIN, GERTRUDE. The Making of Americans. NY: Something Else Press, 1966. 1st Something Else ed. VF in VF dj. *Between The Covers.* $200/£125

STEIN, GERTRUDE. Paris France. London: Batsford, 1940. 1st ed. Pink-red cl. Fine in dj. *Maggs.* $192/£120

STEIN, GERTRUDE. Paris France. NY: Scribners, 1940. 1st Amer ed from British sheets. VF in VF dj. *Between The Covers.* $250/£156

STEIN, GERTRUDE. Paris France. NY: Scribner, 1940. 1st Amer ed, 1st binding. 8 plts. Top edge stained blue. Rose cl. Fine in dj (sm price stamp fr flap). *Heritage.* $250/£156

STEIN, GERTRUDE. Useful Knowledge. London: John Lane, Bodley Head, (1928). 1st British ed. Top edge stained gray. Black cl. VG (ink name, eps lt browned; extrems lt rubbed, spine top sl bumped) in black dj (lt edgeworn, neat black circular hole in spine). *Heritage.* $250/£156

STEIN, GERTRUDE. Wars I Have Seen. NY: Random House, (1945). 1st ed. Paper labels. Fine in VG dj (lt edgeworn). *Reese.* $60/£38

STEIN, GERTRUDE. What Are Masterpieces. L.A.: Conference Press, (1940). 1st ed. Dj. *Dawson.* $150/£94

STEIN, LEON. The Triangle Fire. Phila: Lippincott, 1962. 1st ed. Fine in NF dj. *Beasley.* $35/£22

STEINBECK, ELAINE and ROBERT WALLSTEN. Steinbeck: A Life in Letters. NY: Viking, (1975). 1st ed. One of 1000. (Spine sunned), else NF in slipcase. *Pacific*.* $58/£36

STEINBECK, JOHN. America and Americans. NY: Viking, (1966). 1st ed. Blue/grn cl. Fine in VG dj (price-clipped, lt soiled). *House.* $50/£31

STEINBECK, JOHN. America and Americans. NY: Viking, (1966). 1st ed, 1st binding, w/lettering running down spine. Fine in dj (1-inch chip, spine sl dknd). *Cummins.* $75/£47

STEINBECK, JOHN. America and Americans. NY: Viking, (1966). 1st ed, 1st binding. VG in dj (lt worn, lacks sm piece from fr). *Agvent.* $75/£47

STEINBECK, JOHN. Bombs Away. NY, 1942. 1st ed. (Inscrip, cl lt spotted.) Dj (extrems rubbed, sm tear fr joint). *Swann*.* $57/£36

STEINBECK, JOHN. Bombs Away. NY, 1942. 1st ed. VG + (inscrip) in VG dj. *Warren.* $75/£47

STEINBECK, JOHN. Burning Bright. NY: Viking, 1950. 1st ed. Gray cl. Fine in Fine dj. *Macdonnell.* $125/£78

STEINBECK, JOHN. Burning Bright. NY: Viking, 1950. 1st ed. Top edge stained orange. Gray cl. Fine in dj (spine sl sunned, extrems lt worn). *Heritage.* $200/£125

STEINBECK, JOHN. Cannery Row. NY: Viking, 1945. 1st ed, 2nd state binding. Yellow cl lined in blue. (Spine head bumped), else VG in VG dj (spine ends sl rubbed; price, flaps clipped). *Pacific*.* $109/£68

STEINBECK, JOHN. Cannery Row. NY: Viking, 1945. 1st ed, 2nd state binding. Yellow cl lined in blue. Fine in dj. *Pacific*.* $138/£86

STEINBECK, JOHN. The Collected Poems of Amnesia Glasscock. South SF: Manroot, 1976. One of 250. Fine in ptd wrappers, plain dj. *Pacific*.* $75/£47

STEINBECK, JOHN. Cup of Gold. NY: Robert M. McBride, 1929. 1st ed, 1st issue, 1st bk. 8vo. Top edge stained blue. Orangish-yellow cl. (Eps lt browned, sm stain rep verso; spine ends sl rubbed), o/w NF in dj (price-clipped; spine faded; upper extrems chipped w/loss of letters; lt rubbed, expert minor coloring, repairs, w/adhesive residue). *Heritage.* $3,750/£2,344

STEINBECK, JOHN. Cup of Gold. NY: Covici Friede, 1936. 2nd ed. Dk blue cl. Dj w/no pub's imprint and words 'Author of/Of Mice and Men' on fr panel. Fine in dj (fr joint lacks sm piece, spine foot rubbed). *Pacific*.* $92/£58

STEINBECK, JOHN. East of Eden. NY: Viking, 1952. 1st ed. (Few pin-prick size perforations in 1st few ll), else VG in dj (edges chipped). *Cahan.* $100/£63

STEINBECK, JOHN. East of Eden. NY, 1952. 1st ed. Fine in dj. *Swann*.* $402/£251

STEINBECK, JOHN. East of Eden. NY: Viking, 1952. One of 1500 signed. (Tape stains to pastedowns, offsetting to eps), o/w Fine in glassine (lacks case). *Agvent.* $900/£563

STEINBECK, JOHN. The Grapes of Wrath. NY, (1939). 1st ed. Dj (price-clipped, rubbed, extrems worn). *Swann*.* $402/£251

STEINBECK, JOHN. The Grapes of Wrath. NY: Viking, (1939). 1st ed. (Tape repairs to verso; cl cvrs, spine foxed), else VG in dj (spine ends, extrems browned, rubbed, chipped). *Pacific*.* $403/£252

STEINBECK, JOHN. The Grapes of Wrath. Viking, (1939). 8vo. (Spine sl dknd.) Dj (sl chipped; spine sl dk, missing 1/4-inch chip). *Cummins.* $600/£375

STEINBECK, JOHN. The Grapes of Wrath. NY, (1939). 1st ed. Fine in dj. *Swann*.* $1,150/£719

STEINBECK, JOHN. The Grapes of Wrath. NY: Viking, (1939). 1st ed. VF in ptd beige cl. Pict dj (extrems lt rubbed, 3/8-inch closed tear). *Bromer.* $1,250/£781

STEINBECK, JOHN. The Grapes of Wrath. NY: LEC, 1940. One of 1146 signed by Thomas Hart Benton (illus). 2 vols. 4to. Beige sackcloth over rawhide. Fine in box (sl worn). *Appelfeld.* $600/£375

STEINBECK, JOHN. The Grapes of Wrath. LEC, 1940. One of 1146 sets signed by Thomas Hart Benton (illus). 2 vols. Fine in slipcase. *Swann*.* $690/£431

STEINBECK, JOHN. In Dubious Battle. NY, (1936). 1st ed. Dj (internal paper tape repairs, chipped). *Swann*.* $258/£161

STEINBECK, JOHN. Journal of a Novel. London: Heinemann, 1970. 1st ed. NF (fep corner creased) in dj (price-clipped). *Smith.* $35/£22

STEINBECK, JOHN. Journal of a Novel. The East of Eden Letters. NY: Viking, (1969). 1st ed, trade issue. Fine in dj. *Cummins.* $100/£63

STEINBECK, JOHN. A Letter...Explaining Why He Could Not Write an Introduction for This Book. (NY: Random House, 1964.) 1st ed. Ptd here separately for 1st and only time. Pamphlet. VF in orig wrappers, orig pub's ptd mailing envelope. *Cummins.* $500/£313

STEINBECK, JOHN. Letters to Elizabeth. SF: Book Club of CA, 1978. One of 500. Cream cl over orange bds, ptd paper spine label. Fine in gray dj (lt soiled). *Heritage*. $125/£78

STEINBECK, JOHN. Letters to Elizabeth. Florian J. Shasky and Susan F. Riggs (eds). SF: Book Club of CA, 1978. 1st ed. Ltd to 500 ptd. 1 plt. Paper spine label. VF in dj. *Argonaut*. $200/£125

STEINBECK, JOHN. The Log From the Sea of Cortez. NY: Viking, 1951. 1st ed. VG in dj (spine taped). *Smith*. $125/£78

STEINBECK, JOHN. The Moon Is Down. NY: Viking, 1942. 1st ed, 1st issue w/o ptr's name on copyright pg & w/lg period between 'talk' & 'this' on p112, line 11. VG in dj (spine head chipped, few spots fr panel, price-clipped, spine sunned). *Pacific**. $46/£29

STEINBECK, JOHN. The Moon Is Down. Heinemann, 1942. 1st UK ed. Fine in VG dj (spine head sl worn). *Williams*. $56/£35

STEINBECK, JOHN. Of Mice and Men. NY: Covici Friede, (1937). 1st ed, 1st issue, w/the bullet on p88 and the lines 'and only moved because the heavy hands were/pendula' on p9. Beige cl. VG (lt stains on eps; cvr edges, spine sl faded, lt soiled) in dj (spine dknd; corners, spine extrems sl chipped). *Heritage*. $450/£281

STEINBECK, JOHN. Of Mice and Men. Norwalk: Heritage Press, (1970). Fine in slipcase. *Pacific**. $23/£14

STEINBECK, JOHN. Of Mice and Men. LEC, 1970. Ltd to 1500 numbered, signed by Fletcher Martin (illus). Fine in slipcase. *Swann**. $92/£58

STEINBECK, JOHN. Once There Was a War. NY, 1958. 1st ed. NF in NF dj (rear panel rubbed). *Warren*. $75/£47

STEINBECK, JOHN. Once There Was a War. NY: Viking, 1958. 1st ed. 1/2 cl. Fine in glassine dj. *Pacific**. $92/£58

STEINBECK, JOHN. The Pastures of Heaven. C-F, 1932. 1st ed, 4th issue consisting of 1st ed sheets in Covici-Friede binding. NF in VG- dj (spine faded, chipped). *Fine Books*. $450/£281

STEINBECK, JOHN. The Pastures of Heaven. NY: Brewer, Warren & Putnam, 1932. 1st ed, 1st issue, w/'BREWER/WARREN/PUTNAM' on spine. 8vo. Top edge stained blue. Grn cl, gilt. VG (eps lt browned, spine faded) in dj (tape-reinforced on verso; edges, folds lt worn; sm scrape fr panel). *Heritage*. $2,750/£1,719

STEINBECK, JOHN. The Pastures of Heaven. NY: Brewer, Warren & Putnam, 1932. 1st ed, 1st issue. About 650 copies were published of 1st issue w/Brewer, Warren & Putnam imprint on tp and spine (the rest were sold to Robert O. Ballou). VG in dj (few nicks, spine top sl chipped). *Karmiole*. $3,000/£1,875

STEINBECK, JOHN. The Pearl. NY, 1947. 1st ed. (Ink name; cvr sl speckled), else Good in 2nd state dj (frayed, spine chipped). *King*. $65/£41

STEINBECK, JOHN. The Pearl. NY, 1947. 1st ed. 2nd issue dj (sm closed tear rear panel, spine lt sunned). *Swann**. $230/£144

STEINBECK, JOHN. Sea of Cortez. NY: Viking, 1941. 1st ed. 15 color plts. VG in VG- dj (internally repaired). *Warren*. $250/£156

STEINBECK, JOHN. The Sea of Cortez. NY: Viking, 1941. 1st ed, cl issue. Signed, inscribed, w/sm dwg to Gene Fowler. VG in dj (extrems rubbed, sm tears, spine foot, corners chipped). Later chemise, slipcase. *Pacific**. $3,163/£1,977

STEINBECK, JOHN. Sweet Thursday. London: Heinemann, (1954). 1st British ed. Fine in pict dj (lt worn). *Glenn*. $75/£47

STEINBECK, JOHN. Sweet Thursday. NY, 1954. 1st ed. Dj (spine extrems sl worn). *Swann**. $57/£36

STEINBECK, JOHN. Sweet Thursday. NY: Viking, 1954. 1st ed, 1st issue w/top edges stained red. Beige cl. (Extrems sl rubbed), else VG in dj (extrems sl rubbed, spine ends creased). *Pacific**. $75/£47

STEINBECK, JOHN. To a God Unknown. NY, (1935). 1st ed, 2nd issue. Dj (sl soiled, spine head lt chipped). *Swann**. $287/£179

STEINBECK, JOHN. Tortilla Flat. NY: Covici Friede, (1935). 1st ed. 8vo. Top edge stained blue. Tan cl. (Spine sl dknd), o/w Fine in dj (spine browned, 2 sm chips bottom of fr panel). *Heritage*. $2,000/£1,250

STEINBECK, JOHN. Tortilla Flat. NY: Modern Library, (1937). 1st ed thus. Fine in illus dj. *Cahan*. $100/£63

STEINBECK, JOHN. Tortilla Flat. NY: Viking, 1947. New illus ed. 1st ed thus. 17 paintings by Peggy Worthington. Grn cl. VG + in dj (lacks chip at spine top). *Smith*. $125/£78

STEINBECK, JOHN. Travels with Charlie in Search of America. NY: Viking, 1962. 1st ed. Full crimson morocco, gilt paneled spine, raised bands, aeg, by Sangorski & Sutcliffe. Fine. *Appelfeld*. $250/£156

STEINBECK, JOHN. The Wayward Bus. NY: Viking, 1947. 1st ed. Signed, add'lly inscribed, signed, dated 1948. VG in VG- dj (scrape to fr panel, price-clipped, spine ends rubbed, rear panel soiled). *Pacific**. $1,955/£1,222

STEINBERG, LEO. Michelangelo's Last Paintings. NY, 1975. Folio. 64 plts. Good + in dj. *Washton*. $75/£47

STEINBERG, SAUL. All in Line. NY: Duell, Sloan, & Pearce, (1945). 1st ed, 1st bk. NF in VG dj. *Turtle Island*. $100/£63

STEINDLER, ARTHUR. Orthopedic Operations: Indications, Techniques, and End Results. Springfield, 1947. 1st ed. VG. Dj (tattered). *Doctor's Library*. $100/£63

STEINDLER, ARTHUR. Reconstructive Surgery of the Upper Extremity. Springfield, 1923. 1st ed. (Sl yellowed, extrems worn), o/w VG. *Doctor's Library*. $175/£109

STEINDLER, ARTHUR. The Traumatic Deformities and Disabilties of the Upper Extremities. Springfield, 1946. 1st ed. (Eps yellowed, sl damaged tp by sticking to ep), o/w Good. *Doctor's Library*. $125/£78

STEINDORFF, GEORGE. Egypt. Photographed by Hoyningen-Huene. NY: J.J. Augustin, (1943). Frontis. Dj (lt torn). *Archaeologia*. $45/£28

STEINER, CHARLOTTE. Lulu. NY: Doubleday, 1939. 1st ed. Obl 4to. Illus bds. VG. *American Booksellers*. $75/£47

STEINER, GEORGE. The Death of Tragedy. NY: Knopf, 1961. 1st ed. Fine in dj (lt used, price-clipped, few sm tears). *Captain's Bookshelf*. $100/£63

STEINER, RALPH. Ralph Steiner: A Point of View. CT: Wesleyan Univ, 1979. 2nd ptg. NF in dj (lt rubbed). *Cahan*. $50/£31

STEINER, RUDOLF. The Story of My Life. H. Collison (trans). London: Anthroposophical Pub, 1928. 1st Eng ed. 4 ports. VG in dj (edges sl chipped, torn). *Hollett*. $40/£25

STEINGRABER, E. Royal Treasures. NY: Macmillan, c1968. 80 full color plts. VG. *Blake*. $85/£53

STEINMETZ, ANDREW. The Romance of Duelling.... London, 1868. 2 vols. 336; 384pp. Teg. 1/2 grn leather, raised bands, gilt, by Root & Son. (Bkpls, extrems rubbed, spines dknd), else Good set. *King*. $250/£156

STEINMETZ, CHARLES P. Theory and Calculation of Alternating Current Phenomena. NY: W.J. Johnston, 1897. 1st ed. xvii,431pp + 12pp pub's ads. Dk grn cl, gilt. Clean (sl shelfworn, rubbed). *Baltimore**. $50/£31

STEJNEGER, L. and T. BARBOUR. Check List of North American Amphibians and Reptiles. Cambridge, 1943. 5th ed. Wrappers. *Sutton*. $43/£27

STEJNEGER, LEONHARD. Georg Wilhelm Steller. Cambridge: Harvard Univ, 1936. 1st ed. Color frontis, 29 plts, fldg map. Red cl, gilt. VF in dj (sl soiled). *Argonaut*. $175/£109

STEJNEGER, LEONHARD. Georg Wilhelm Steller: The Pioneer of Alaskan Natural History. Cambridge: Harvard Univ, 1936. 1st ed. NF (corner sl bumped) in dj (sl soiled, extrms lt worn). *Pacific*. $92/£58

STELLMAN, LOUIS J. The Vanished Ruin Era: San Francisco's Classic Artistry of Ruin Depicted in Picture and Song. SF: Paul Elder, (1910). 1st ed. 27 tipped-in plts. 1/2 burlap, gilt bds, pict cvr label. (Bkpl; stained, rubbed, worn), else VG. *Pacific*. $42/£26

STEMENS, T. and W. S. MYERS. Spring Flora of Oklahoma with Key. Oklahoma City: Harlow Pub, 1929. 1st ed. Grn cl. Good. *Archer*. $45/£28

STENDHAL. The Charterhouse of Parma. LEC, 1955. Ltd to 1500 numbered, signed by Rafaello Busoni (illus). Fine in slipcase. *Swann**. $57/£36

STENDHAL. The Red and Black. LEC, 1947. Ltd to 1500 numbered, signed by Rafaello Busoni (illus). Fine in slipcase. *Swann**. $92/£58

STENDHAL. Rome, Naples and Florence. London: John Calder, 1959. 1st Eng ed. Fine (margin p371 creased by production fault; spine ends sl bumped) in dj (sl rubbed, mkd, price-clipped). *Ulysses*. $88/£55

STENHOUSE, J. R. Cracker Hash. London: Percival-Marshall, 1955. 1st ed. VG in dj. *American Booksellers*. $35/£22

STENHOUSE, MRS. T. B. H. Tell It All: The Story of a Life's Experience in Mormonism. Hartford: A.D. Worthington, 1875. 1st ed. Period calf, leather spine label. VG. *Pacific**. $40/£25

STENHOUSE, MRS. T. B. H. Tell It All: The Story of a Life's Experience in Mormonism. Hartford: A.D. Worthington, 1875. xxx,(31)-623pp. Grn cl, gilt. (Foxed, rear hinge starting; cl worn.) *Parmer*. $45/£28

STENTON, F. M. Anglo-Saxon England. Oxford: Clarendon, 1950. 2nd ed. 8 maps. Blue cl (edges sl worn, upper hinge split; inscrip). *Maggs*. $35/£22

STENZEL, A. The British Navy. London, 1898. 1st ed. VG. *Gretton*. $56/£35

STEP, EDWARD. Animal Life of the British Isles. London, 1942. 8th imp. 111 plts (48 color). (Sl warped, soiled.) *Edwards*. $24/£15

STEPHENS, ALEXANDER H. Recollections of Alexander H. Stephens. Myrta Lockett Avary (ed). NY: Doubleday, Page, 1910. 1st ed. Frontisport. Maroon cl. VG (pencil notes, bkpl, lib stamps; spine spotted, sm pinhole fr cvr). *Chapel Hill*. $85/£53

STEPHENS, C. A. The Knockabout Club in the Woods. Boston: Estes & Lauriat, 1882. 1st ed. Chromolitho bds. (Extrms rubbed), else VG. *Pacific**. $52/£33

STEPHENS, HENRY. Book of the Farm. London: William Blackwood, 1908-9. 3 vols. 60 animal ports. Orig roan-backed cl, gilt. VG set (some joints cracking). *Hollett*. $120/£75

STEPHENS, HENRY. Journeys and Experiences in Argentina, Paraguay, and Chile. NY: Knickerbocker, 1920. 1st ed. Inscribed, dated 1921. Frontisport, 3 add'l frontispieces; 2 fldg maps (1 partly colored), 3 plts. Teg. Yellow dec cl, gilt. VG. *Morrell*. $160/£100

STEPHENS, HENRY. South American Travels. NY: Knickerbocker, 1915. 1st ed. 1 fldg map. Pict red cl, gilt. (Corners sl bumped), o/w Fine. *Sotheran*. $360/£225

STEPHENS, J. F. A Systematic Catalogue of British Insects.... London: Privately ptd, 1829. 1st ed. 2 vols in 1. 416; 388pp. 1/2 leather, marbled bds. VG + (bkpl). *Mikesh*. $95/£59

STEPHENS, JAMES. Arthur Griffith, Journalist and Statesman. Dublin: Wilson, Hartnell, n.d. 1st Eng ed. B/w frontis photo. VG in wrappers (sl rubbed, mkd, dusty). *Ulysses*. $58/£36

STEPHENS, JAMES. Charwoman's Daughter. London: Macmillan, 1912. 1st ed. Fine (eps sl foxed). *Agvent*. $80/£50

STEPHENS, JAMES. The Crock of Gold. LEC, 1942. Ltd to 1500 numbered, signed by Robert Lawson (illus). Fine in slipcase. *Swann**. $40/£25

STEPHENS, JAMES. Green Branches. Dublin/London, 1916. 1st ed. Ltd to 500. (Cvrs browned, chipped.) Internally Fine in orig ptd wrappers in custom-made clamshell box. *Truepenny*. $75/£47

STEPHENS, JAMES. Irish Fairy Tales. London: Macmillan, 1920. 1st ed. One of 525 ptd on hand-made paper, signed by Arthur Rackham (illus). 4to. 16 mtd plts. Teg. Gilt-stamped bds over vellum spine. Fine. *Appelfeld*. $1,800/£1,125

STEPHENS, JAMES. Irish Fairy Tales. London: Macmillan, 1920. Ltd to 520 signed. Thick 4to. 16 full-pg mtd color plts by Arthur Rackham. Teg. Vellum-backed ivory bds, gilt. Red/beige pict dj (worn, lacks spine piece). *Reisler*. $2,800/£1,750

STEPHENS, JAMES. Kings and the Moon. Macmillan, 1938. 1st ed. VG in dj (lt rubbed). *Cox*. $35/£22

STEPHENS, JAMES. Songs from the Clay. NY, 1915. 1st Amer ed. NF (sunned). *Polyanthos*. $25/£16

STEPHENS, JOHN L. Incidents of Travel in Central America, Chiapas, and Yucatan.... London: Arthur Hall, Virtue, 1854. 4th London ed. xvi,548pp; engr map, port, 29 engr plts (incl frontis). Red blind-stamped cl (stained, faded, spine discreetly repaired), gilt. Internally Good (sl spotted, margins lt browned). *Morrell*. $304/£190

STEPHENS, JOHN L. Incidents of Travel in Egypt, Arabia Petraea, and the Holy Land, by an American. NY: Harper, 1841. 10th ed. 2 vols. 240; 286pp; 18 plts, 1 fldg map. Orig cl. (Sl foxed throughout, sl dampstained; rubbed, faded, soiled, spine ends frayed), o/w Good. *Worldwide*. $45/£28

STEPHENS, JOHN L. Incidents of Travel in Yucatan. London: J. Murray, 1843. 1st ed. 2 vols. xii,9-459; xvi,9-478,(4)pp; fldg map, 2 panoramas, 75 plts. Fine (maps, plts sl foxed). *Maggs*. $960/£600

STEPHENS, JOHN L. Incidents of Travels in the Yucatan. NY: Harper, 1843. 2 vols. Fldg frontis each vol, fldg map, all the engr plts, 74 full-pg vignettes. (Hinges weak, foxing, bkpl fr bd, bumped, worn, sunned.) *Metropolitan**. $230/£144

STEPHENS, L. DOW. Life Sketches of a Jayhawker of '49. (San Jose), 1916. 1st ed. One of 300. 6 plts. (Bold ink name w/imp visible on tp), else VG in wrappers (edges worn, spine head chipped), gilt. Howes S941. *Pacific**. $58/£36

STEPHENS, L. DOW. Life Sketches of a Jayhawker of '49. N.p.: Privately published, 1916. 1st ed. 6 plts. Brn wrappers, gilt. (Spine foot chipped, few sm tears wrapper edges), o/w VG. Howes S941. *Pacific**. $127/£79

STEPHENS, MICHAEL. The Brooklyn Book of the Dead. Normal, IL: Dalkey Archive, 1992. 1st ed. Xerox of LA Times rev laid in. Fine in dj. *Lame Duck*. $45/£28

STEPHENS, ROBERT W. Walter Durbin, Texas Ranger and Sheriff. Clarendon, TX: Clarendon, 1970. 1st ed. Fine in dj (chipped). *Labordo*. $75/£47

STEPHENSON, RICHARD W. Civil War Maps. Washington, 1989. NF. *Dumont*. $65/£41

STEPHENSON, RUSSELL. Eighty Sketches in Water Colour from Nature. London: Saint Catherine, 1926. One of 220. 13.5x11. 80 tipped-in color plts. Mottled eps; teg, rest untrimmed, gilt inner dentelles. Full red morocco, gilt, raised spine bands. (Frontis corner sl creased), else Fine. *Pacific**. $633/£396

STEPHENSON, TERRY E. The Shadows of Old Saddleback. N.p.: Fine Arts Press, 1948. 1st ed. Maroon cl, tan cl backstrip. Fine. *Harrington*. $85/£53

STERLING, GEORGE. The Caged Eagle and Other Poems. SF: A.M. Robertson, 1916. 1st ed. Inscribed, signed, dated 1916. Teg, gilt inner dentelles. Brn morocco, gilt. (Rubbed), else VG. *Pacific**. $58/£36

STERLING, GEORGE. The House of Orchids and Other Poems. SF: Robertson, 1911. 1st ed, 1st issue w/'langourous' for 'languorous' on line 10 of p31, and 'Omniponent' for 'Omnipotent' on line 12 of p48. Clipped sig of Sterling laid in. Purple cl, gilt. (Eps offset), else VF in pict dj (spine faded). *Argonaut.* $300/£188

STERLING, HELEN. Santa's Christmas Party. Polygraphic Co of America, 1951. 5 dbl-pg pop-ups by Mary Stevens. Internally VG (fr pg button missing) in illus wraps (lt worn). *Bookfinders.* $70/£44

STERLING, TOM. Autobiography of Tom Sterling. (By Tom Sterling and T. J. Heady.) (Santa Monica): Privately ptd, 1941. 1st ed. Pict cl. (Fr hinge starting where corner of fep has been removed), else VG. *Baade.* $200/£125

STERLING, WILLIAM WARREN. Trails and Trials of a Texas Ranger. N.p.: Privately ptd, 1959. 1st ed. 1/2 leather. NF in dj. *Labordo.* $150/£94

STERN, ALEC. Etchings of Yosemite by Alec Stern. San Mateo: Studio of Alec Stern, 1979. 1st ed. Ltd to 1000. Port. Vinyl-backed brn cl, gilt. Fine. *Pacific*.* $81/£51

STERN, F. C. A Chalk Garden. London: Faber & Faber, 1974. 2nd ed. Fine. *Fair Meadow.* $40/£25

STERN, F. C. A Study of the Genus Paeonia. London: Royal Horticultural Soc, 1946. Folio. 15 color plts. Gilt-dec bds (sl edgeworn). VG. *Metropolitan*.* $402/£251

STERN, JAMES. The Hidden Damage. London, 1990. VG in dj. *Typographeum.* $35/£22

STERN, MADELINE B. Imprints in History: Book Publishers and American Frontiers. IN Univ, 1956. 1st ed. Good. *Moss.* $34/£21

STERN, MADELINE B. Sherlock Holmes: Rare-Book Collector. NY: Schulte Pub, 1953. 1st ed. (Edges lt soiled), else Fine in pict wrappers. *Murder.* $35/£22

STERN, PHILIP VAN DOREN. Secret Missions of the Civil War. Chicago: Rand McNally, (1959). 1st ed. Signed on tipped-in pub's presentation leaf. Fine in pict dj (lt rubbed). *Argonaut.* $50/£31

STERNBERG, GEORGE M. Photomicrographs and How to Make Them. Boston: James R. Osgood, 1884. 1st ed. 204pp; 20 repro plts. (Fr joint partly cracked, but firm; spine ends sl chipped), else VG. *Cahan.* $125/£78

STERNBERG, GEORGE. Immunity, Protective Inoculations in Infectious Diseases and Serum-Therapy. NY, 1895. 1st ed. 325pp. *Fye.* $200/£125

STERNBERG, GEORGE. Report on the Etiology and Prevention of Yellow Fever. Washington, 1890. 1st ed. 271pp. (Eps loose, ex-lib.) *Fye.* $150/£94

STERNDALE, ROBERT ARMITAGE. Seonee, or Camp Life on the Satpura Range. London, 1877. 1st ed. xi,455pp; 4 plts, fldg map. (Sm marginal repair p445, frontis fore-edge lt stained, lt marginal browning, bkpl.) Marbled eps, edges. Full morocco (rebound), gilt, raised bands. *Edwards.* $240/£150

STERNE, LAURENCE. The Beauties of Sterne. Boston: John W. Folsom, 1793. 11th ed, 3rd Amer ed. xii,230pp. Contemp calf, spine label. Good. *Karmiole.* $85/£53

STERNE, LAURENCE. The Life and Opinions of Tristam Shandy, Gentleman. London, 1760-68. 9 vols. Vols 1 & 2 are 2nd eds, others are 1st eds. Tops of chapter I of vols 5, 7 & 9 signed as usual for c. purposes. W/initial blank in vol 5. Vol 7 is 1st state w/errata on verso of tp and w/uncorrected text. Hogarth frontis, marbled leaf vol 3. (6),179; (2),182; 202; (4),220; (6),150; (4),155, [(6),38pp]; (2),160; (2),156; (8),145pp. Early 19th-cent gilt-tooled mottled calf, morocco spine labels. (Tops of tps of vols 2, 4, 5 & 6 trimmed, not affecting text; 2 vols expertly rebacked), else VG set. *Pacific*.* $345/£216

STERNE, LAURENCE. The Life and Opinions of Tristam Shandy. London, 1775. 10th ed. 6 vols. Full-pg frontis. Full polished calf, raised spines, gilt. *Argosy.* $150/£94

STERNE, LAURENCE. The Life and Opinions of Tristram Shandy, Gent. LEC, 1935. Ltd to 1500 numbered. 2 vols. Fine in slipcase. *Swann*.* $69/£43

STERNE, LAURENCE. A Sentimental Journey Through France and Italy. Golden Cockerel, 1928. One of 500. 6 copperplt engrs. Teg, rest untrimmed. Maroon buckram (faded, rear cvr waterstained; sig), gilt. Later protective drop-down back, 1/4 dk blue gilt morocco/blue cl box. *Blackwell's.* $160/£100

STERNE, LAURENCE. A Sentimental Journey Through France and Italy. LEC, 1936. Ltd to 1500 numbered, signed by Denis Tegetmeier (illus) and Eric Gill (designer). Fine in slipcase. *Swann*.* $115/£72

STEUART, HENRY. The Planter's Guide. Edinburgh: John Murray, 1828. 2nd ed. Engr frontis, (6),xxxviii,528pp; 5 engr plts. Old calf, marbled bds (extrems sl rubbed). *Karmiole.* $300/£188

STEVENS, CHARLES W. Fly-fishing in Maine Lakes; or, Camp-Life in the Wilderness. Boston: A. Williams, 1881. 1st ed. Frontis chromolitho. Brn cl, gilt. Fine. *Pacific*.* $138/£86

STEVENS, F. L. Through Merrie England. Frederick Warne, 1928. 1st ed. 12 color plts. Color eps. Teg. VG in dj (few sl chips). *Hollett.* $120/£75

STEVENS, FRANCIS (etcher). Domestic Architecture. London, n.d. Folio. 53 etched plts. Contemp blind-emb cl. (Lt browned, lt spotted, corner few ll sl water-stained, bkpl, new eps; cl soiled, sl edgeworn; rebacked, much of orig spine laid down.) *Edwards.* $448/£280

STEVENS, FRANCIS. The Heads of Cerberus. Reading, PA: Polaris, 1952. 1st ed thus. Ltd to 1500 numbered. (Bkpl; cvrs dampstained), else Good in slipcase (rubbed, lacks dj?). *King.* $40/£25

STEVENS, FRANK E. The Black Hawk War, Including a Review of Black Hawk's Life. Chicago: Stevens, 1903. 1st ed. Signed. Frontisport. Dk grn cl, gilt, ptd paper spine label. (Lt aged, hinges cracked; sl edgeworn, sm spots fr cvr, label rubbed, chipped.) Text Clean, cvrs Nice. *Baltimore*.* $70/£44

STEVENS, FREDERIC H. Santo Tomas Internment Camp. 1942-1945. Privately ptd, (1946). VG (sm ink name). *Perier.* $75/£47

STEVENS, HENRY BAILEY. A Cry Out of the Dark. Boston: Four Seas, 1919. 1st collective ed. Gray-grn bds, paper spine label. (Edges lt foxed), else Fine in dj (spine sl dknd). *Reese.* $50/£31

STEVENS, HENRY N. and GEORGE F. BARWICK (eds). New Light on the Discovery of Australia, as Revealed by the Journal of Capt. Don Diego de Prado y Tovar. London: Hakluyt Soc, 1930. 2 lg fldg maps in rear pocket. Blue cl. *Appelfeld.* $60/£38

STEVENS, HENRY. Benjamin Franklin's Life and Writings. A Bibliographical Essay on the Stevens' Collection.... Dryden Press, 1881. 1st ed. 6 engr plts, 6 add'l engr ports. Uncut. Dec cl. *Forest.* $120/£75

STEVENS, HENRY. Who Spoils Our New English Books? Henry Newton Stevens, 1884. 1st ed. Inscribed presentation. Teg, uncut. *Forest.* $40/£25

STEVENS, J. MORGAN. Memories of Perkins County. Astoria, IL: Stevens Pub, n.d. Signed. VG in wraps. *Perier.* $15/£9

STEVENS, JAMES. Mattock. NY: Knopf, 1927. 1st ed. Brn cl stamped in black. (Spine sl cocked), o/w VG in pict dj (sm chip spine foot). *Reese.* $100/£63

STEVENS, JOHN L. and W. B. OLESON. Picturesque Hawaii: A Charming Description of Her Unique History. (Phila): Edgewood, (c.1894). Pict cl, gilt. (Sl shaken; circular stain to fr cvr), else VG. *Pacific*.* $115/£72

STEVENS, MONTAGUE. Meet Mr. Grizzly. Albuquerque: Univ of NM, 1944. 2nd ed. Frontis. VG. *Bowman.* $40/£25

STEVENS, WALLACE. The Auroras of Autumn. NY: Knopf, 1950. 1st ed. Top edge stained blue. Blue cl, gilt. Fine in dj (spine sl browned). *Heritage.* $300/£188

STEVENS, WALLACE. The Auroras of Autumn. NY: Knopf, 1950. 1st ed. Fine in dj (sl worn). *Lenz.* $400/£250

STEVENS, WALLACE. Harmonium. NY: Knopf, 1923. 1st ed, 1st bk. Paper spine label. (Name; spine ends rubbed, label chip, spine sl discolored; partial dj laid in), else VG. *Pacific*.* $138/£86

STEVENS, WALLACE. The Man with the Blue Guitar and Other Poems. NY: Knopf, 1937. 1st ed, 2nd state dj w/'conjunctions' replacing 'conjunctioning' on fr flap. Yellow cl (lt stains; dj spine sl dkned). *Cummins.* $350/£219

STEVENS, WALLACE. Notes Toward a Supreme Fiction. Cummington, MA: Cummington, (1942). 2nd ed. Ltd to 330. Fine. *Bromer.* $300/£188

STEVENS, WALLACE. The Palm at the End of the Mind. NY: Knopf, 1971. 1st ed. Fine (bd sl streaked) in dj (lt used, sm nicks top edge). *Beasley.* $75/£47

STEVENS, WALLACE. A Primitive Like an Orb. NY: Gotham Book Mart, 1948. One of 500. 2 full-pg dwgs. VG (inscrip; dusty, spine, edges browned, edges sl rubbed, creased, sm split spine foot) in wrappers. *Ulysses.* $200/£125

STEVENS, WALLACE. Selected Poems. London: Fortune, (1952). 1st ed. Partly unopened. Black cl over textured black bds, gilt. (Rear hinge over-opened), o/w Fine. *Heritage.* $125/£78

STEVENS, WALLACE. Selected Poems. London: Faber, 1953. 1st Eng ed. Very Nice in dj (sl nicked, rubbed). *Clearwater.* $160/£100

STEVENS, WALLACE. Transport to Summer. NY: Knopf, 1947. 1st ed. VG (sl worn) in dj (sl worn). *Lenz.* $475/£297

STEVENSON, ANNE. Living in America. Ann Arbor: Generation, (1965). 1st ed, 1st bk. (Edges sunned), else Fine in dj (edges lt worn, sunned). *Hermitage.* $40/£25

STEVENSON, D. ALAN. The World's Lighthouses Before 1820. OUP, 1959. VG. *Hadley.* $120/£75

STEVENSON, EDWARD LUTHER. Terrestrial and Celestial Globes. New Haven: Yale Univ, 1921. 2 vols. 8vo. Frontispieces, 143 plts. (Sl rubbed.) *Forest.* $520/£325

STEVENSON, G. D. and R. L. COX (eds). Architectural Sketches. Volume 6. Privately ptd, 1877. Folio. 1/2 morocco. (Sl spotted; sl soiled, worn, sl water-stained, spine lt faded, rubbed, sl loss.) *Edwards.* $72/£45

STEVENSON, J. B. (ed). The Species of Rhododendron. Edinburgh, 1947. 2nd ed. Blue cl, gilt. VG. *Larry Price.* $80/£50

STEVENSON, JAMES. Barbara's Birthday. NY: Greenwillow Books, 1983. 8 dbl-pg pop-ups, oversize fold-out pg. Glazed pict bds. VG. *Bookfinders.* $40/£25

STEVENSON, ROBERT LOUIS with FANNY VAN DE GRIFT STEVENSON. More New Arabian Nights. The Dynamiter. London: Longmans, Green, 1885. 1st ed. Good in orig ptd wrappers (rebacked; chipped, lt soiled), red morocco-backed case. *Cummins.* $200/£125

STEVENSON, ROBERT LOUIS and LLOYD OSBOURNE. The Wrecker. London/Paris/Melbourne: Cassell, 1892. 1st ed. 12pp undated ads at end. Blue cl (sl tilted), gilt. *Maggs.* $120/£75

STEVENSON, ROBERT LOUIS. Across the Plains with Other Memories and Essays. Chatto, 1892. 1st ed. ix,317pp. Teg, rest untrimmed. Dk blue bevel-edges buckram, gilt backstrip (lt faded). Good (inscrip, eps lt browned). *Blackwell's.* $64/£40

STEVENSON, ROBERT LOUIS. Across the Plains with Other Memories and Essays. London: C&W, 1892. One of 100 lg paper copies. Signed by R. & R. Clark. Teg. 3/4 red calf, cl, gilt, sl raised bands. (Leather rubbed, scuffed; expertly recased w/later eps; sl crease rear cl), else VG. *Pacific*.* $75/£47

STEVENSON, ROBERT LOUIS. The Beach of Falesa. LEC, 1956. Ltd to 1500 numbered, signed by Millard Sheets (illus). Fine in slipcase. *Swann*.* $46/£29

STEVENSON, ROBERT LOUIS. The Black Arrow: A Tale of the Two Roses. London/Paris/NY/Melbourne: Cassell, 1888. 1st Eng ed. 20pp ads. Red cl (sm puncture to leading joint), gilt (faded). *Maggs.* $128/£80

STEVENSON, ROBERT LOUIS. The Black Arrow: A Tale of the Two Roses. London: Cassell, 1888. 1st ed. W/ads at rear dated July 1888. 8vo. (viii),324,(20)ads pp. Teg. 1/2 dk red calf over red cl sides, gilt. Fine (orig cl cvr, spine, ep expertly bound in). *Sotheran.* $360/£225

STEVENSON, ROBERT LOUIS. A Child's Garden of Verses. London: George G. Harrap, (1931). 1st Eng ed. Obl 4to. 72pp; 12 full-pg color plts by H. Willebeek Le Mair. Cl-backed color pict bds (sl worn). VG. *Reisler.* $335/£209

STEVENSON, ROBERT LOUIS. A Child's Garden of Verses. Longmans, Green, 1885. 1st ed. 8vo. Prelim leaf w/'By the Same Author' on verso; half-title. Teg. Blue cl, fr cvr stamped in gilt w/pub's emblem, spine gilt. (Sl bumped.) *Sotheby's*.* $846/£529

STEVENSON, ROBERT LOUIS. The Child's Garden of Verses. London: John Lane, The Bodley Head, 1896. 1st illus ed. 8vo. Charles Robinson (illus). xiv,136pp + (23)pp pub's cat. Aeg. Ribbed dk grn cl, gilt. VG (fr/rear blanks lt speckled, uncut edges sl browned; narrow strip of dkng to lower edge of rear bd). *Sotheran.* $269/£168

STEVENSON, ROBERT LOUIS. A Child's Garden of Verses. London: Longmans, Green, 1905. 1st ed illus thus. Royal 8vo. (xii),124pp; 12 color plts by Jessie Willcox Smith, guards. Teg. Dk blue cl, gilt, lg onlaid pict label. Fine. *Sotheran.* $269/£168

STEVENSON, ROBERT LOUIS. A Child's Garden of Verses. C&W, 1908. 1st ed thus. Lg 8vo. 125pp; 12 color plts by Millicent Sowerby. Teg. Pict cl, gilt. (Few sm mks; spine sl dknd), else VG. *Bookmark.* $112/£70

STEVENSON, ROBERT LOUIS. A Child's Garden of Verses. Chicago: Rand McNally, 1919. 8x10.5. Ruth Mary Hallock (illus). 96pp. Blue cl w/picture paste-on. (Stamp, fingermks; shelfworn), else VG + . *My Bookhouse.* $62/£39

STEVENSON, ROBERT LOUIS. A Child's Garden of Verses. NY: Scribner, 1941. 9 1/4 x 6 3/4. 9 color plts by Jessie Wilcox Smith. Black cl, pict cvr label, gilt spine. NF. *Pacific*.* $46/£29

STEVENSON, ROBERT LOUIS. A Child's Garden of Verses. LEC, 1944. One of 1100 signed by Roger Duvoisin (illus). Fine in slipcase. *Swann*.* $46/£29

STEVENSON, ROBERT LOUIS. A Child's Garden of Verses. NY: OUP, 1947. 1st ed. 8vo. Tasha Tudor (illus). Grn cl, gilt, color paste label. Good in color dj (spine sl dknd). *Reisler.* $200/£125

STEVENSON, ROBERT LOUIS. A Child's Garden of Verses. Chicago: Rand McNally, 1985. 1st ptg. 4to. Tasha Tudor (illus). Illus bds. Fine. *American Booksellers.* $50/£31

STEVENSON, ROBERT LOUIS. Complete Works. NY: Scribner, 1921-3. The 'Vailima Edition,' Amer issue, ltd to 1030 numbered sets. 26 vols. Blue-gray cl, spine labels. NF set (spine sl faded, labels sl dknd) in 26 paper-cvrd bd slipcases (some sl worn at edges) w/spine labels. *Sumner & Stillman.* $375/£234

STEVENSON, ROBERT LOUIS. Essays in the Art of Writing. C&W, 1905. 1st Eng ed. 36pp pub's ads at rear. Teg. Buckram. VG (eps lt browned; spine sl faded, ends sl rubbed). *Ulysses.* $40/£25

STEVENSON, ROBERT LOUIS. Essays of Travel. London: C&W, 1905. 1st ed. Teg, rest untrimmed. Fine in dk blue buckram, gilt. *Maggs.* $72/£45

STEVENSON, ROBERT LOUIS. Familiar Studies of Men and Books. C&W, 1924. Florence Press ed. Teg, other uncut. VG in cl-backed bds. *Cox.* $16/£10

STEVENSON, ROBERT LOUIS. Father Damien. C&W, 1890. 1st ed. Half-title, final blank, (30),2pp. Uncut. Good in mod wrappers. *Cox.* $40/£25

STEVENSON, ROBERT LOUIS. Father Damien. Oxford: Howard Wilford Bell, 1901. 2nd Eng ed. One of 299. Frontisport. Parchment bds (spine head chipped). *Maggs.* $48/£30

STEVENSON, ROBERT LOUIS. In the South Seas Being an Account of Experiences and Observations in the Marquesas, Paumotus and Gilbert Islands in the Course of Two Cruises.... London: C&W, 1900. 1st separately pub Eng ed. Teg, fore/bottom edges untrimmed. Fine (marginal pencil notes) in black buckram, gilt. *Maggs.* $104/£65

STEVENSON, ROBERT LOUIS. Island Nights' Entertainments, Consisting of the Beach of Falesa, the Bottle Imp, the Isle of Voices. London/Paris/Melbourne: Cassell, 1893. 1st Eng ed, 2nd issue. 8vo. W/the 8 ad leaves dated '7G - 3 93.' VG in blue-grn pebbled cl, gilt. *Maggs.* $192/£120

STEVENSON, ROBERT LOUIS. Island Nights' Entertainments. London: Cassell, 1893. 1st ed, 1st issue w/price for this title corrected by hand. xi,277,(16)ads; color sketch map. Dec eps. Gilt-pict blue cl. NF (bkpl; lt worn). *House.* $250/£156

STEVENSON, ROBERT LOUIS. Kidnapped. London: Cassell, (1913). 1st Eng ed. 4to. 14 full-pg color plts, fldg map by N. C. Wyeth. Tinted top. Grn cl, color paste label. (Prelim pg, fore-edge sl foxed), o/w VG. *Reisler.* $140/£88

STEVENSON, ROBERT LOUIS. Kidnapped. Cassell, 1886. 1st UK ed, 2nd issue w/'pleasure' on pg 40, line 11, and ads dated 5.G.7.86. VG (lt foxed; cvrs sl stained, spine extrems sl worn) in grn cl. *Williams.* $200/£125

STEVENSON, ROBERT LOUIS. Kidnapped. Cassell, 1886. Fldg frontis map, facs 1/2-title; pub's cat dated 5G-7.86. Facs 1/2 title. Good (bkpl removed; joints cracked, spine bumped, sl chipped, hinges, corners rubbed, fr hinge base nicked). *Tiger.* $256/£160

STEVENSON, ROBERT LOUIS. Kidnapped. NY: Scribner, 1913. 1st ed. 4to. 14 full-pg color plts, fldg map. N. C. Wyeth (illus). Teg. Black cl (lt worn), gilt, color pict paste label (lt rubbed). *Reisler.* $275/£172

STEVENSON, ROBERT LOUIS. Kidnapped. LEC, 1938. Ltd to 1500 numbered, signed by Hans Alexander Mueller (illus). Fine in slipcase. *Swann*.* $34/£21

STEVENSON, ROBERT LOUIS. The Letters to His Family and Friends. Sidney Colvin (ed). London: Methuen, 1899. 1st ed. 2 vols. Frontis photo each vol. Teg, rest untrimmed. Red buckram (spines rubbed), ptd paper labels, spare spine labels tipped in at end of each vol. *Maggs.* $56/£35

STEVENSON, ROBERT LOUIS. The Master of Ballantrae. LEC, 1965. Ltd to 1500 numbered, signed by Lynd Ward (illus). Fine in slipcase. *Swann*.* $92/£58

STEVENSON, ROBERT LOUIS. The Master of Ballantrae: A Winter's Tale. London et al: Cassell, 1889. 1st ed. 12th thousand w/ads dated July 1889. viii,332pp + 18 ads. Red cl. Very Nice. *Young.* $208/£130

STEVENSON, ROBERT LOUIS. The Merry Men and Other Tales and Fables. C&W, 1887. 1st ed. (ix),296,32(pub's list dated Sept 1886)pp. Pale blue fine-grain cl, gilt. VG (eps lt foxed). *Blackwell's.* $200/£125

STEVENSON, ROBERT LOUIS. The Merry Men. C&W, 1887. 1st ed, 1st issue w/September ads. Dec cl. Nice (fep cracked, sl shaken; lt worn). *Ash.* $104/£65

STEVENSON, ROBERT LOUIS. The Novels and Tales/Travels and Essays of Robert Louis Stevenson. NY: Scribner, 1911. 27 vols. Frontis. Teg. Red cl, gilt. (Couple w/extrems lt damp-stained), else NF set. *Pacific*.* $161/£101

STEVENSON, ROBERT LOUIS. Poems and Ballads. NY: Scribner, 1896. 1st ed thus. Frontisport. Teg. Dec grn cl, gilt. (Spine sunned), else NF. *Pacific*.* $40/£25

STEVENSON, ROBERT LOUIS. R.L.S. to J.M. Barrie. Grabhorn, 1962. One of 475. *Dawson.* $25/£16

STEVENSON, ROBERT LOUIS. R.L.S. to J.M. Barrie. (By Robert Louis Stevenson.) SF: Book Club of CA, 1962. One of 475 ptd. Prospectus laid in loose. 1/2 linen, patterned bds, gilt-lettered spine label. Fine. *Pacific*.* $46/£29

STEVENSON, ROBERT LOUIS. Robert Louis Stevenson's Silverado Journal. John E. Jordan (ed). SF: Book Club of CA, 1954. One of 400. 2-tone cl. NF (bkpl) in plastic wrapper. *Bohling.* $100/£63

STEVENSON, ROBERT LOUIS. San Francisco, a Modern Cosmopolis. SF: Book Club of CA, 1963. Ltd to 450 ptd. Cl-backed pict bds, paper spine label. Fine. *Pacific*.* $29/£18

STEVENSON, ROBERT LOUIS. The Silverado Squatters. London: C&W, 1883. 1st ed, 1st issue, omitting 'His' on next to last line of p140 and w/ads dated October. Grn cl, sepia/gilt. NF (edges lt worn). Howes S980. *Labordo.* $550/£344

STEVENSON, ROBERT LOUIS. The Silverado Squatters. NY: Scribner, 1923. One of 380. Floral cl. Matching slipcase. *Cullen.* $150/£94

STEVENSON, ROBERT LOUIS. The Silverado Squatters. SF: Grabhorn, 1952. Ltd ed. One of 900. Frontis. Blue patterned bds, tan cl backstrip, blue paper spine label. Fine. Howes S980. *Harrington.* $75/£47

STEVENSON, ROBERT LOUIS. The Silverado Squatters. SF: Grabhorn, 1952. Fine in plain dj (dknd, sl soiled). *Bohling.* $100/£63

STEVENSON, ROBERT LOUIS. The Strange Case of Dr. Jekyll and Mr. Hyde. London: Longmans, Green, 1886. 4th ed. Salmon cl (soiled, lt worn). *Glenn.* $100/£63

STEVENSON, ROBERT LOUIS. The Strange Case of Dr. Jekyll and Mr. Hyde. London, 1886. 1st Eng ed, wrappered issue w/the date '1885' corrected by hand to '1886.' 8vo. (Sm stamp.) Orig wrappers rebound in 1/4 morocco. *Swann*.* $1,035/£647

STEVENSON, ROBERT LOUIS. The Strange Case of Dr. Jekyll and Mr. Hyde. Longmans, Green, 1886. 1st ed. 8vo. (viii),142,(1, ad)pp. Marbled eps; teg. 1/2 dk blue morocco, spine w/raised bands, lettering in gilt, marbled bd sides (rebound by Stikeman & Co; orig wrappers ptd in red/blue bound in). VG (bkpl; spine lettering sl dull). *Sotheran.* $1,040/£650

STEVENSON, ROBERT LOUIS. The Strange Case of Dr. Jekyll and Mr. Hyde. Longmans, Green, 1886. 1st ed, 2nd issue. 8vo. Half-title, 'By the Same Author' on verso, 1 pg ads at end. Salmon pink cl pict blocked in black. (Bkpl; fr cvr rubbed, some loss of color, spine bumped.) *Sotheby's*.* $1,141/£713

STEVENSON, ROBERT LOUIS. The Strange Case of Dr. Jekyll and Mr. Hyde. Longmans, Green, 1886. 1st ed. 8vo. Half-title, list of works on verso, ad leaf at end. Ptd wrappers, w/the '6' in the date having been changed by hand from '5,' ad for Longman's Magazine on inner fr wrapper, ads on inner, outer rear wrapper. Cl solander case. Bkpl of Eric S. Quayle. (Prelims dog-eared; fr wrapper sl soiled, lacks sm pieces of outer corners, spine chipped w/loss.) *Sotheby's*.* $1,931/£1,207

STEVENSON, ROBERT LOUIS. The Strange Case of Dr. Jekyll and Mr. Hyde. NY: Random House, 1929. Ltd to 1200 numbered, signed by W.A. Dwiggins (illus). Black cl, black bds, gilt. Good. *Karmiole.* $75/£47

STEVENSON, ROBERT LOUIS. The Strange Case of Dr. Jekyll and Mr. Hyde. LEC, 1952. Ltd to 1500 numbered, signed by Edward A. Wilson (illus). Fine in slipcase. *Swann*.* $115/£72

STEVENSON, ROBERT LOUIS. Travels with a Donkey in the Cevennes. LEC, 1957. Ltd to 1500 numbered, signed by Roger Duvoisin (illus). Fine in slipcase. *Swann*.* $69/£43

STEVENSON, ROBERT LOUIS. Treasure Island. London: Cassell, (1911). 1st Eng ed. 4to. 14 full-pg color plts by N. C. Wyeth. Tinted top. Grn cl, gilt, color paste label. Full color pict dj (chipped, edges, spine worn). *Reisler*. $250/£156

STEVENSON, ROBERT LOUIS. Treasure Island. NY: Geo. H. Doran, (1927). 1st Dulac ed. Tall 8vo. 12 mtd color plts by Edmund Dulac. Grn cl. Dj (nicked). *Appelfeld*. $200/£125

STEVENSON, ROBERT LOUIS. Treasure Island. Cassell, 1883. 1st ed, 1st issue. This copy has the following issue points: the ads are dated 5G-783 (i.e. July 1883); '7' is missing on p127; 'dead man's chest' on pp2, 7; 'worse' instead of 'worst' on p197; 'a' missing on p183; full-stop lacking after 'opportunity' on p 178. 8vo. Frontis map, 4pp ads at end. Pub's brn cl, gilt. (Sl foxed, sm tear lower margin of 1 leaf, sl cracked at sig H; spines sl bumped.) Bkpl of Eric S. Quayle. *Sotheby's**. $4,784/£2,990

STEVENSON, ROBERT LOUIS. Treasure Island. Boston: Roberts Bros, 1884. 1st Amer ed, 1st illus ed. 8vo. Frontis map. Floral patterned eps. Pict brn cl. (Fr hinge cracked at 1/2-title; corners, spine extrems sl worn, 3/4-inch tear rear joint top.) *Glenn*. $1,000/£625

STEVENSON, ROBERT LOUIS. Treasure Island. NY: Scribner, 1911. 1st ed. 4to. 14 full-pg color plts by N. C. Wyeth. Teg. Black cl (corner edge worn), color pict paste label (lt rubbed). *Reisler*. $335/£209

STEVENSON, ROBERT LOUIS. Treasure Island. NY: Scribner, 1932. 9 color plts by N. C. Wyeth. Black cl, pict cvr label. (Bkpl, name; sl smudge fr cvr), else VG. *Pacific**. $115/£72

STEVENSON, ROBERT LOUIS. Treasure Island. LEC, 1941. Ltd to 1500 numbered, signed by Edward A. Wilson (illus). Fine in slipcase. *Swann**. $126/£79

STEVENSON, ROBERT LOUIS. Treasure Island. London: Octopus Books, 1979. 2nd imp. J. Pavlin & G. Seda (illus). 6 dbl-pg pop-ups. Glazed pict bds. VG. *Bookfinders*. $40/£25

STEVENSON, ROBERT LOUIS. Underwoods. London: C&W, 1887. 1st UK ed. 32pp ads dated July 1887. Dk grn cl. (Spine ends sl rubbed), o/w VG + . *Bernard*. $250/£156

STEVENSON, ROBERT LOUIS. Virginibus Puerisque and Other Papers. C. Kegan Paul, 1881. 1st binding of 3, spine imprint reading 'C. Kegan Paul & Co.', 1st issue, w/earliest date of cat. 32-pg pub's inserted cat at end dated 8.80. Top/fore-edges uncut, lower edges rough trimmed; eps coated black. Beveled ribbed orange cl. VG. *Temple*. $192/£120

STEVENSON, ROBERT LOUIS. Weir of Hermiston. C&W, 1896. 1st Eng ed. 32pp pub's ads dated March 1896 at rear. Unopened; teg. Buckram. VG (eps sl spotted; spine faded, head sl bumped). *Ulysses*. $56/£35

STEVENSON, ROBERT LOUIS. The Works of.... NY: Scribner, 1916. Biographical ed. 30 vols. 6.75x4.25. Teg. 3/4 crushed pinkish-red morocco, gilt, raised bands. (Bkpls; spines sunned), else NF set. *Pacific**. $546/£341

STEVENSON, ROBERT LOUIS. The Works of.... NY: Scribner, 1921-23. One of 1030 sets. 26 vols. Paper spine labels. Fine in slipcases (sl sunned). *Pacific**. $288/£180

STEVENSON, ROBERT LOUIS. Works. Constable/(Methuen), 1894-1901. Edinburgh ed. One of 1035 sets initialed by a pub. 32 vols. Editorial statement slip tipped into vol 1. Teg, rest untrimmed. VF in red cl, ptd labels (spare labels tipped-in). *Blackwell's*. $560/£350

STEWARD, HAL. Thunderbolt: The History of the 11th Armored Division. Washington, 1948. VG (shelf worn). *Clark*. $125/£78

STEWARD, JOHN F. The Reaper: A History of the Efforts of Those Who Justly May Be Said to Have Made Bread Cheap. Greenberg, 1931. (Few sl cvr stains.) *Rybski*. $40/£25

STEWART, BASIL. Subjects Portrayed in Japanese Colour-Prints: A Collector's Guide. NY, 1922. Folio. Orig bds, later cl back. (Eps renewed, ex-lib.) *Swann**. $149/£93

STEWART, C. and R. W. REID (eds). Holden's Human Osteology. London, 1887. 7th ed. ix,356pp (ink sig, pencil notes few pp); 56 plts (some edges discolored, few detached). Blind-stamped cl (spine tear, corners sl worn, inner hinges, few sections cracked). *Whitehart*. $29/£18

STEWART, EDGAR I. Custer's Luck. Norman: Univ of OK, (1955). 1st ed. 2 fldg maps. (Fep inscrip.) Dj (lt chipped). *Dawson*. $60/£38

STEWART, ELINORE PRUITT. Letters on an Elk Hunt by a Woman Homesteader. Boston/NY: Houghton Mifflin, 1915. (Binding dknd), else VG + . *Zubal**. $45/£28

STEWART, FRANK H. Notes on Old Gloucester County, NJ. NJ Soc of PA/Gloucester County Hist Soc, 1917. 1st ed. Wraps. *Heinoldt*. $60/£38

STEWART, GEORGE R. The California Trail. NY: McGraw-Hill, (1962). 1st ed. Fine in dj. *Argonaut*. $30/£19

STEWART, GEORGE R. Committee of Vigilance. Boston: Houghton Mifflin, 1964. 1st ed. Brn cl. Fine in NF dj (spine sl dknd, sm closed tear). *Harrington*. $35/£22

STEWART, GEORGE R. Take Your Bible in Hand: The Life of William Henry Thomes.... SF: Colt, 1939. One of 750. Cl-backed dec bds. (Extrems faded, sl soiled), else VG. *Pacific**. $23/£14

STEWART, J. I. M. The Bridge at Arta and Other Stories. London: Gollancz, 1981. 1st Eng ed. Fine (spine foot sl bumped) in dj (sl creased). *Ulysses*. $40/£25

STEWART, J. I. M. A Memorial Service. London: Gollancz, 1976. 1st Eng ed. Fine (spine foot sl bumped) in dj (price-clipped). *Ulysses*. $40/£25

STEWART, J. I. M. Our England Is a Garden and Other Stories. London: Gollancz, 1979. 1st Eng ed. Fine (spine foot sl bumped) in dj (sl creased). *Ulysses*. $40/£25

STEWART, J. I. M. Parlour 4 and Other Stories. London: Gollancz, 1986. 1st Eng ed. Fine in dj. *Ulysses*. $40/£25

STEWART, J. I. M. Vanderlyn's Kingdom. London: Gollancz, 1967. 1st Eng ed. Fine (spine foot sl bumped) in dj (spine foot sl creased). *Ulysses*. $56/£35

STEWART, J. I. M. A Villa in France. London: Gollancz, 1982. 1st Eng ed. Fine in dj (sl creased). *Ulysses*. $40/£25

STEWART, JAMES LINDSAY. Golfiana Miscellanea.... London: Hamilton, Adams, 1887. 1st ed. Red cl, gilt. (Emb stamp; spine sl dull, head sl chipped, foot sl rubbed), else VG. *Pacific**. $920/£575

STEWART, JOYCE and BOB CAMPBELL. Orchids of Tropical Africa. South Brunswick/NY: A.S. Barnes, c. 1970. 45 color plts. VG in dj. *Fair Meadow*. $25/£16

STEWART, ROBERT. The American Farmer's Horse Book. Cincinnati: C.F. Vent, 1867. viii,600pp. Tooled leather. Good (lt foxed; spine damaged). *Bookcell*. $40/£25

STICKLEY, GUSTAV. More Craftsman Homes. NY, (1912). Pict bds. (Spine defective, fr cvr heavily stained, soiled.) *King*. $150/£94

STIEGLITZ, ALFRED. America and Alfred Stieglitz. Waldo Frank et al (eds). NY: Literary Guild, 1934. 1st ed. VG in VG dj (extrems chipped). *Smith*. $75/£47

STIEGLITZ, ALFRED. Georgia O'Keeffe: A Portrait. NY: MMA, 1978. 1st ed. Folio. 51 full-pg plts. Cl-backed bds, gilt. Fine in illus dj, pub's slipcase. *Cahan*. $125/£78

STIGAND, C. H. and DENNIS D. LYELL. Central African Game and Its Spoor. London: Horace Cox, 1909. 2nd ed. (1/2-title lt spotted.) Orig ochre cl. *Christie's**. $253/£158

STIGAND, C. H. The Game of British East Africa. London: Horace Cox, 1913. 2nd ed. (Tps lt spotted.) Grn cl. *Christie's**. $235/£147

STIGAND, C. H. The Game of British East Africa. Horace Cox, 1913. 2nd ed. 4to. 74 plts. Grn cl, beveled bds, gilt. (Sl spotted), o/w Fine. *Hollett.* $560/£350

STIGAND, C. H. The Land of Zinj. London: Constable, 1913. 1st ed. 21 plts, 1 fldg map in rear pocket. (Sl rubbed, soiled, spine ends sl frayed, sl faded), o/w VG. *Worldwide.* $125/£78

STIGAND, C. H. The Land of Zinj. London: Constable, 1913. 1st ed. 21 plts (incl frontis), lg fldg map loose in rear pocket. Blue cl. Sound (lt foxed; rebacked preserving orig backstrip, spine repaired, rear cvr scored, extrems nicked). *Morrell.* $288/£180

STILES, EDWARD H. Recollections and Sketches of Notable Lawyers and Public Men of Early Iowa.... Des Moines, 1916. 1st ed. (Spine faded.) *Ginsberg.* $100/£63

STILES, MARTHA BENNETT. The Strange House at Newburyport. NY: Dial, 1963. 1st ed. Kurt Werth (illus). 128pp. NF (name, address) in Good dj. *Price.* $18/£11

STILES, ROBERT. Four Years Under Marse Robert. NY, 1903. 1st ed. Pict cl. (Cvr stained, sl worn), o/w Fine. *Pratt.* $150/£94

STILES, ROBERT. Four Years Under Marse Robert. NY: Neale, 1910. Later ed. Tan cl. VG (contemp inscrip; sl soiled). *Chapel Hill.* $60/£38

STILL, ANDREW T. Autobiography. Kirksville: Privately pub'd, 1908. 2nd rev ed. Port. Fine. *Hollett.* $104/£65

STILLINGFLEET, B. J. Miscellaneous Tracts Relating to Natural History, Husbandry, and Physick. London, 1762. 2nd ed. xxxi,391pp; 11 plts. Contemp sprinkled calf (sl rubbed), gilt, leather label. VG. *Whitehart.* $208/£130

STILLMAN, DON. The Outdoor Trail of Don Stillman. Harrisburg: Stackpole, 1952. VG. *Parmer.* $15/£9

STILLMAN, J. The Story of Early Chemistry. NY: D. Appleton, c1924. Good. *Blake.* $50/£31

STILLMAN, J. D. B. The Horse in Motion, as Shown by Instantaneous Photography with a Study on Animal Mechanics. Boston: James R. Osgood, 1882. 1st ed. Edward Muybridge (photos). Teg. Pict grn cl, gilt. (Bkpl, stamp; hinges cracked; spine ends sl rubbed, faint ring to fr cvr), else VG. *Pacific*.* $374/£234

STILLMAN, J. D. B. Wanderings in the Southwest in 1855. Spokane: Arthur Clark, 1990. 1st ed. Fine. *Book Market.* $30/£19

STILLMAN, JOHN MAXSON. Theophrastus Bombastus von Hohenheim, Called Paracelsus. Chicago: Open Court, 1920. 1st ed. Port on fr cvr. Good (edges rubbed). *Glaser.* $50/£31

STILLMAN, W. J. Poetic Localities of Cambridge. Boston, 1876. 12 heliotype repros. (1st plt detached; foxed, age-dknd; spine cracked, extrems worn.) *Swann*.* $149/£93

STILLWELL, MARGARET BINGHAM. The Awakening Interest in Science During the First Century of Printing, 1450-1550. NY: Bibliographical Soc of America, 1970. 1st ed. Ltd to 1500. Internally Fine (cl dampstained). *Glaser.* $75/£47

STILLWELL, MARGARET BINGHAM. Incunabula and Americana, 1450-1800. NY: Columbia Univ, 1931. 1st ed. Silver-stamped cl. Dj. *Dawson.* $100/£63

STIMSON, LEWIS A. A Manual of Operative Surgery. Phila, 1895. 3rd ed. 598pp. Grn textured cl. NF. *Doctor's Library.* $75/£47

STIRLING, A. M. W. William De Morgan and His Wife. NY, 1922. 1st Amer ed. VG (cvrs sl scratched, bumped, tips of 2 corners chafed). *Clearwater.* $48/£30

STIRLING, A. M. W. William de Morgan and His Wife. NY: Henry Holt, 1922. VG (top edge dusty, sl mkd; spine ends, corners bumped, cvrs mkd, spine sl dknd). *Ulysses.* $72/£45

STIRLING, MRS. A. M. W. Coke of Norfolk and His Friends. London, 1908. 1st ed. 2 vols. Nice set. *Gretton.* $96/£60

STIRLING, PATRICK JAMES. The Australian and Californian Gold Discoveries, and Their Probable Consequences. Edinburgh/London: Oliver & Boyd/Simpkin, Marshall, 1853. 1st ed. 1p.l,xiii,(1),(13)-279pp. (W/o 1/2 title, apparently present in some copies.) Fldg linen-backed chart as frontis. Emb cl, gilt. (Sm lib stamps, tp sl soiled, ll evenly browned, sl spots, smudges; neatly rebacked, retaining orig backstrip, corners worn, spine dknd, edges sl faded.) Howes S1012. *Pirages.* $300/£188

STIRLING-MAXWELL, WILLIAM. Annals of the Artists of Spain. London, 1848. 1st ed. 3 vols. 8vo. Lithographed add'l tps. Later mottled calf, gilt. *Swann*.* $546/£341

STISTED, GEORGIANA M. The True Life of Captain Sir Richard F. Burton.... Written by His Niece. London: H.S. Nichols, 1896. 1st ed. 1/2-title, frontisport, xv,(i)blank,419pp. Blue cl. VG (browned adjacent to port; faded spine, lt rubbed). *Morrell.* $64/£40

STOCK, ALPHONS (ed). North American Big Game Hunters. London/Muenchen: International Sport, 1963/4. One of 250 numbered. Thick folio. Aeg. Full gilt-pict burgundy leather (lt rubbed). Slipcase (broken). *Oinonen*.* $1,000/£625

STOCK, JOHN. An Inaugural Essay on the Effects of Cold Upon the Human Body. Phila, 1797. 1st ed. 43pp. (Brittle edges.) Later wrappers. *Fye.* $100/£63

STOCKLEY, C. H. Stalking in the Himalayas and Northern India. London: Herbert Jenkins, n.d. (1936). 1st ed. Frontis, 27 plts. Blue cl (spine, corners rubbed). Internally clean (sl foxed, ink sig). *Morrell.* $64/£40

STOCKLEY, CHARLES V. M. Big Game Shooting in India, Burma, and Somaliland. London, 1913. Frontis, 8 plts. *Petersfield.* $480/£300

STOCKTON, FRANK R. The Bee-Man of Orn. Holt, Rinehart & Winston, (1964). 1st ed stated. Maurice Sendak (illus). 8vo. 46pp. NF in NF dj, price $3.50. *Davidson.* $100/£63

STOCKTON, FRANK R. The Bee-Man of Orn. NY: Holt, Rinehart & Winston, (1964). 1st ed. Sq 8vo. Maurice Sendak (illus). Cl-backed bds, color paste label. Good in full color dj. *Reisler.* $175/£109

STOCKTON, FRANK R. The Great Stone of Sardis. NY, 1898. 1st Amer ed. Dec cvrs, gilt. NF (spine sl sunned). *Polyanthos.* $35/£22

STOCKTON, FRANK R. The Vizier of the Two-Horned Alexander. NY: Century, 1899. 1st ed, 1st ptg (w/the prelims paginated in Arabic rather than Roman numerals). Teg. Dec grn cl, lettering gilt. NF. *Sumner & Stillman.* $45/£28

STOCKWELL, DAISY PAT. Land of the Oldest Hills. Caldwell, ID, 1957. 1st ed. Frontis photo port. NF in Good + dj. *Sagebrush.* $37/£23

STOCKWELL, GLENN. Fly Reels of the House of Hardy. London: Black, 1978. 1st ed. Color frontis. VF in dj. *Bowman.* $45/£28

STODDARD, ANNE. A Good Little Dog. NY: Century, (1930). 1st ed. 8vo. 16 full color illus by Berta and Elmer Hader. Color pict bds (lt shelf-rubbed). Color pict dj (marginal tears, rear cvr stained). *Reisler.* $135/£84

STODDARD, CHARLES WARREN. A Cruise Under the Crescent, from Suez to San Marco. Chicago: Rand McNally, (1898). 1st ed. Inscribed, signed. W. W. Denslow (illus). Pict cl, gilt. (Soiled), else VG. *Pacific*.* $98/£61

STODDARD, CHARLES WARREN. Poems. Bret Harte (ed). SF: Roman, 1867. 1st ed. 123pp. Contemp 1/2 morocco. *Ginsberg.* $100/£63

STODDARD, CHARLES WARREN. Summer Cruising in the South Seas. London, 1873. 1st ed. 319pp + 48pp pub's cat. (Fr hinge cracked; spine chipped w/loss.) *Edwards.* $96/£60

STODDARD, HERBERT L. The Bobwhite Quail. NY, 1931. 1st ed. Full terra-cotta buckram. Fine in dj (lt worn). *Truepenny*. $125/£78

STODDARD, HERBERT L. Memoirs of a Naturalist. Norman, OK: Univ of OK, 1969. 1st ed. 4 color plts. Off-white polished linen. Fine in VG ptd pict dj. *Biscotti*. $60/£38

STODDARD, W. L. The New Golfer's Almanac...for the Year 1910. Boston, 1909. Cl-backed pict bds (extrems worn). *Swann*. $69/£43

STODDART, ANNA M. The Life of Isabella Bird (Mrs. Bishop). John Murray, 1906. 1st Eng ed. 2 fldg color maps. All edges uncut. Dec grn cl, gilt. (Edges sl browned), o/w VG. *Sotheran*. $317/£198

STODDART, JOHN. Remarks on Local Scenery and Manners in Scotland During the Years 1799 and 1800. London: William Miller, 1801. 2 vols. xxiv,310; viii,341pp; 32 aquatint plts, fldg map. Engr eps. Contemp tree calf, gilt. (Prelims sl foxed, sl offsetting, textual browning; sl surface wear, spines worn, repairs to labels, heads, sl loss to tails.) *Edwards*. $352/£220

STODDART, THOMAS TOD. The Angler's Companion to the Rivers and Lochs of Scotland. William Blackwood, 1853. 2nd ed. Engr frontis, tp in 2nd state (tipped-in cancel), xxiii,357,20 (ads)pp; hand-color plt. Blind-stamped cl, gilt. (Lacks map; spine, edges faded, ends worn, few mks.) *Hollett*. $48/£30

STODDART, THOMAS TOD. An Angler's Rambles and Angling Songs. Edinburgh: Edmonston & Douglas, 1866. 1st ed. Dk blue cl, gilt. (Fr hinge starting), else VG. *Pacific*. $58/£36

STODDART, THOMAS TOD. Angling Songs. William Blackwood & Sons, 1889. 1st ed. Etched frontisport, ix,324,2pp. Unopened. Fine. *Hollett*. $120/£75

STODDART, THOMAS TOD. The Art of Angling as Practised in Scotland. Edinburgh, 1835. 1st ed, 1st bk. iv,156pp. (1st few ll detached, inner joint broken; shelfworn, shaken.) *Oinonen*. $70/£44

STOKER, BRAM. Dracula. NY: G&D, (1931). Photo-Play ed. VG in dj (spine foot lacks sm piece). *Pacific*. $805/£503

STOKER, BRAM. Dracula. Archibald, Constable, 1897. 1st ed. 8vo. Yellow cl ptd in red. (Eps offset; lt soiled.) *Sotheby's*. $4,232/£2,645

STOKER, BRAM. Dracula. NY, 1899. 1st Amer ed. 8vo. Pict cl (chip beneath title; spine extrems, tips rubbed). *Swann*. $862/£539

STOKER, BRAM. Dracula. NY: LEC, 1965. One of 1500. Signed by Felix Hoffmann (illus). Black cl, gilt spine. Fine in glassine, slipcase. *Pacific*. $127/£79

STOKER, BRAM. Dracula. LEC, 1965. Ltd to 1500 numbered, signed by Felix Hoffmann (illus). Fine in slipcase. *Swann*. $161/£101

STOKER, BRAM. Dracula. NY: Ptd by A. Colish, 1965. Signed by Felix Hoffmann (illus). Black linen. Fine in slipcase. *Appelfeld*. $175/£109

STOKER, BRAM. Famous Imposters. NY, 1910. 1st Amer ed. (Inner fr hinge cracked; fr cvr corner stained.) *King*. $75/£47

STOKER, BRAM. The Lair of the White Worm. W. Foulsham, 1920. Rpt. (Lt spotted; spine bumped, sunned, dull, cvrs sl warped; lacks dj.) *Tiger*. $13/£8

STOKER, BRAM. Personal Reminiscences of Henry Irving. London: Heinemann, 1906. 1st ed. 2 vols. 36 plts, incl color frontis port. (Spotted inside & out, spines faded, sl rubbed.) *Hollett*. $48/£30

STOKER, BRAM. The Watter's Mou'. London: Constable, 1895. 1st ed. 164,(2),8(ads)pp. Overall VG (lt marginal browning; spine browned, chipped, cvrs lt soiled) in grn wrappers, grn cl clamshell case. *Heritage*. $750/£469

STOKES, ADRIAN. The Quattro Cento: A Different Conception of the Italian Renaissance. Faber, 1952. VG in grn cl. *Hadley*. $56/£35

STOKES, I. N. PHELPS and DANIEL C. HASKELL. American Historical Prints. NY, 1933. *Swann*. $103/£64

STOKES, I. N. PHELPS and DANIEL HASKELL. American Historical Prints: Early Views of American Cities. NY, 1933. 1st ed. (Spine head stained.) *Swann*. $402/£251

STOKES, I. N. PHELPS. The Iconography of Manhattan Island. NY, 1967. 6 vols. 4to. Pub's cl. (Lt worn, top edge spotted.) *Oinonen*. $700/£438

STOKES, I. N. PHELPS. Phelps Stokes Collection of American Historical Prints, Early Views of American Cities.... Bulletin of NY Library, 1931. Contemp cl. *Forest*. $56/£35

STOKES, J. LORT. Discoveries in Australasia... T. & W. Boone, 1846. 1st ed. 2 vols. 8vo. Frontispieces, xii,(ii),errata leaf,521; viii,(ii),543pp; 28 engr plts, 8 fldg maps. Marbled eps; all edges marbled. Full contemp calf, gilt, catrasting leather labels. (Frontispieces, tps sl spotted; spine gilt sl rubbed), o/w VF set. *Sotheran*. $4,720/£2,950

STOKES, WILLIAM. The Diseases of the Heart and the Aorta. Phila: Lindsay & Blakiston, 1855. 2nd Amer ed. xvi,(17)-710pp. Orig sheep. Good (ex-lib; extrems worn). *Glaser*. $225/£141

STOKES, WILLIAM. A Treatise on the Diagnosis and Treatment of Diseases of the Chest. Phila, 1837. 1st Amer ed. 360pp. 1/2 leather (fr hinge cracked). *Fye*. $200/£125

STOKES, WILLIAM. A Treatise on the Diagnosis and Treatment of Diseases of the Chest. Alfred Hudson (ed). London: New Sydenham Soc, 1882. Frontisport, lv,596pp (pp 433-448 detached together). Blind emb cl (spine chipped, sm split to fr joint; edges lt dampstained, rubbed), gilt. *Edwards*. $96/£60

STONE, ALBERT H. and J. HAMMOND REED (eds). Historic Lushan. Hankow: Arthington Press, 1921. Lg fldg map at rear. VG + . *Bowman*. $65/£41

STONE, ARTHUR L. Following Old Trails. Missoula, 1913. 1st ed. Presentation from Fred C. Morgan. (Fr cvr spotted; cvr corners, spine worn), else VG. Howes S1027. *Baade*. $300/£188

STONE, CHRISTOPHER. Eton. A&C Black, 1909. 1st ed. 20 color plts by E. D. Brinton, fldg plan. Teg. (Feps browned; cl discolored, spine chipped.) *Edwards*. $48/£30

STONE, FRANK. Chelsea, Bow and Derby Porcelain Figures. Newport, (1955). *Swann*. $92/£58

STONE, GEORGE CAMERON. A Glossary of the Construction, Decoration and Use of Arms and Armor in All Countries and in All Times. Portland, 1934. 1st ed. Orig prospectus laid in. Gilt-stamped buckram. (Sl worn.) *Oinonen*. $90/£56

STONE, HERBERT L. Millions for Defense. A Pictorial History of the Races for the America's Cup. NY: Derrydale, (1934). One of 950. Color frontis. Blue cl (sl soiled). *Appelfeld*. $100/£63

STONE, HERBERT. The Timbers of Commerce and Their Identification. London, 1924. 4th imp. 186 photo-micrographs. (Lib ink stamps, bkpl, pp103-106 unbound; lt soiled, edges rubbed, accession #s.) *Edwards*. $32/£20

STONE, IRVING and JEAN (eds). I, Michelangelo, Sculptor: An Autobiography Through Letters. GC, 1962. Signed. Frontis. Dj. *Argosy*. $35/£22

STONE, IRVING. The Greek Treasure. GC: Doubleday, 1975. 1st ed. One of 350 signed. Map frontis. Pict eps. Fine in pub's paperbd slipcase. *Cady*. $35/£22

STONE, IRVING. The Greek Treasure: A Biographical Novel of Henry and Sophia Schliemann. GC: Doubleday, 1975. 1st ed. One of 350. Signed. Fine in slipcase. *Pacific*. $23/£14

STONE, IRVING. Men to Match My Mountains. NY: Doubleday, 1956. 1st ed. Fine in VG dj. *Book Market*. $20/£13

STONE, IRVING. Men to Match My Mountains. NY: Doubleday, 1956. 1st ed. This is the special 'Far West' ed, ltd in # w/special binding, and signed. Dec leatherette, gilt. Fine. *Argonaut*. $150/£94

STONE, IRVING. Men to Match My Mountains: The Opening of the Far West, 1840-1900. GC: Doubleday, 1956. 1st ed. One of ltd ed. Signed. Fine. *Pacific**. $98/£61

STONE, JULIUS F. Canyon Country. NY: Putnam, 1932. 1st ed. (Bkpl; lt soiled.) *Dumont*. $90/£56

STONE, LAWRENCE. Family and Fortune: Studies in Aristocratic Finance in the Sixteenth and Seventeenth Centuries. OUP, 1973. VG in dj. *Hadley*. $40/£25

STONE, LIVINGSTON. Domesticated Trout: How to Breed and Grow Them. Charlestown: Cold Spring Trout Ponds, 1877. 3rd ed. Inscribed. Frontis. Grn cl, gilt. NF. *Pacific**. $127/£79

STONE, LIVINGSTON. Domesticated Trout: How to Breed and Grow Them. Charlestown: Cold Spring Trout Ponds, 1896. 4th ed. Inscribed, signed, dated 1897. Brick-red cl, gilt. NF. *Pacific**. $86/£54

STONE, MARY (ed). Children's Stories That Never Grow Old. Chicago: Reilly & Lee, (1908). John R. Neill (illus). Pict cl. (Soiled, spine ends rubbed), else VG. *Pacific**. $58/£36

STONE, MARY (ed). Children's Stories That Never Grow Old. Chicago: Reilly & Britton, (1908). 1st combined ed. John R. Neill (illus). 8vo. Tan dec cl. Good. *Reisler*. $375/£234

STONE, OLIVIA M. Tenerife and Its Six Satellites. London: Marcus Ward, 1887. 1st ed. 2 vols. Demy 8vo. xvi,477; vii,459pp; 9 maps. VG (defacement of inscrips, 1 ep sl cracked at hinge) in blue cl, gilt. *Ulysses*. $720/£450

STONE, REYNOLDS. Reynolds Stone Engravings. John Murray, 1977. 1st ed. Dj (sm tear repaired). *Forest*. $88/£55

STONE, ROBERT. Children of Light. NY: Knopf, 1986. 1st ed. Purple cl over blue bds. Fine in dj (rear panel lt chipped, soiled). *Heritage*. $75/£47

STONE, ROBERT. A Hall of Mirrors. Boston: Houghton Mifflin, 1967. 1st ed, 1st bk. VG + in VG dj (soiled, 1-inch spine tear). *Lame Duck*. $200/£125

STONE, WILBUR MACEY. The Gigantic Histories of Thomas Boreman. Portland: Southworth, 1933. One of 250 signed. Order form laid in. Uncut, unopened. (Lt worn.) *Oinonen**. $120/£75

STONE, WILLIAM L. Visits to the Saratoga Battle-Grounds. Albany: Munsell, 1895. 1st ed. 344pp. Red cl (faded, worn). Good. *Cullen*. $75/£47

STONELAKE, ALFRED R. Congo Past and Present. World Dominion, 1937. 1st ed. Lg fldg map. Good in dj (frayed). *Cox*. $29/£18

STONEMAN, VERNON C. John and Thomas Seymour, Cabinetmakers in Boston, 1794-1816. Boston, 1959. Inscribed, signed. Sm folio. (Spine sl faded, spotted.) Bd slipcase. *Swann**. $92/£58

STONEY, H. BUTLER. A Residence in Tasmania: With a Descriptive Tour Through the Island from Macquarie Harbour to Circular Head. London: Smith, Elder, 1856. Tinted litho frontis, fldg engr map, 7 tinted litho plts. (Lt spotting, inscrip.) Aeg. Contemp prize binding (rubbed, scuffed), gilt spine. *Christie's**. $325/£203

STOOKEY, WALTER M. Fatal Decision. Salt Lake City, UT, 1950. 1st ed. VG + in VG dj. *Sagebrush*. $35/£22

STOPES, H. Malt and Malting. London: F.W. Lyon, 1885. 1st ed. xiv,662pp + xxiv ads; 150 woodcuts. Red cl over beveled bds. Fine. *Young*. $192/£120

STOPPARD, TOM. Is It True What They Say About Shakespeare? Oxford: OUP, 1982. Fine in stapled mustard wraps. *Lame Duck*. $25/£16

STOPPARD, TOM. Rosencrantz and Guildenstern Are Dead. London: Faber & Faber, 1967. 1st Eng ed, hb issue. VG (eps partly browned; cvrs sl bowed) in dj (sl mkd, dusty, sl creased, spine sl faded). *Ulysses*. $600/£375

STORER, JAMES S. and JOHN GREIG. The Antiquarian and Topographical Cabinet, Containing a Series of Elegant Views of the Most Interesting Objects of Curiosity in Great Britain. London: W. Clarke et al, 1807-1811. 1st ed. 10 vols. 480 copper plts. Teg. 3/4 dk red morocco, gilt, raised bands. (Sl foxed), else NF. *Pacific**. $403/£252

STORER, JAMES. History and Antiquities of the Cathedral Churches of Great Britain. London, 1814-19. 4 vols. Contemp 3/4 black polished calf (rubbed, foxed, sl stained, joints worn), gilt. *Oinonen**. $100/£63

STOREY, DAVID. The Changing Room. NY: Random House, (1972). 1st Amer ed. VF in VF dj. *Between The Covers*. $200/£125

STOREY, DAVID. Pasmore. Longman, 1972. 1st UK ed. Inscribed in 1992. NF in dj (spine sl faded). *Williams*. $32/£20

STOREY, DAVID. This Sporting Life. Longmans, 1960. 1st UK ed. VG (fr cvr sl stained through dj) in dj (edges sl worn, nicked, dusty; spine extrems sl worn strengthened to rear). *Williams*. $120/£75

STOREY, HARRY. Hunting and Shooting in Ceylon. London, 1907. 2nd ed. Frontisport, fldg map (repaired w/cellotape). (Sl foxed; extrems worn.) *Edwards*. $120/£75

STOREY, HARRY. Hunting and Shooting in Ceylon.... London: Longmans, Green, 1907. 2nd ed. Frontisport, lg fldg color map, 37 half-tone plts. Blue cl, gilt. Good (margins lt browned, upper edge sl water-stained; sl stained, rubbed). *Morrell*. $88/£55

Stories About Animals. London: Darton, 1854. 1st ed illus by Harrison Weir. Sq 8vo. (28)pp; 8 chromolitho plts. Blue blind-stamped cl, gilt. (Joints rubbed, corners knocked, upper cvr sl mkd.) *Sotheran*. $109/£68

Stories from Hans Andersen. London: Hodder & Stoughton, (1911). 1st ed. One of 750 signed by Edmund Dulac (illus). 4to. 28 mtd color plts. Teg. Gilt-stamped vellum (sl spotted, lacks ties). Good in slipcase. *Appelfeld*. $1,500/£938

STORK, BYRON C. Rawhide and Haywire. NY, 1959. 1st ed. VG in VG dj. *Woolson*. $25/£16

STORM, COLTON and HOWARD PECKHAM. Invitation to Book Collecting. NY: R.R. Bowker, 1947. 1st ed. VG. *Labordo*. $25/£16

STORM, COLTON (comp). A Catalogue of the Everett D. Graff Collection of Western Americana. Chicago: Newberry Library, 1968. 1st ed. Separate slim 4to 1972 map index laid in. Brick-red buckram, gilt spine. Fine in Fine dj. *Baltimore**. $75/£47

STORM, COLTON (comp). A Catalogue of the Everett D. Graff Collection of Western Americana. Chicago: Newberry Library, 1968. 1st ed. NF in dj (lt soiled). *Parmer*. $80/£50

STORM, JOHN. The Valadon Drama: The Life of Suzanne Valadon. NY: E.P. Dutton, 1958. 1st ed. Fine in dj (lt worn). *Hermitage*. $35/£22

Storm; or, A Collection of the Most Remarkable Casualties and Disasters Which Happen'd in the Late Dreadful Tempest, Both by Sea and Land. (By Daniel Defoe.) London: J. Nutt, 1704. 1st ed. (16),272pp (age-dknd); fldg table. Contemp paneled calf (fr joint restored but partly cracked). *Swann**. $287/£179

Story of Blue Beard. London/Chicago: Lawrence & Bullen/ Stone & Kimball, 1895. 1st ed thus. 8vo. (iv),5-61pp (eps browned); 8 engr plts by Joseph E. Southall. Teg, rest uncut. Grn dec cl (spine yellowed). *Sotheran*. $141/£88

Story of Dr. Scoresby: The Arctic Navigator. London: T. Nelson, 1886. Color frontis. Dec cl (spine rubbed). VG. *Explorer*. $24/£15

Story of Mary and Her Little Lamb as Told by Mary and Her Neighbors and Friends. Dearborn: Mr. & Mrs. Henry Ford, 1928. 1st ed. Pict bds. *Pacific**. $69/£43

Story of O. NY: Grove, (1965). 1st Amer ed. (Sl spotted), else Fine in Fine white dj (sl dknd). *Between The Covers.* $125/£78

Story of Peter Rabbit. Racine: Whitman, (1937). Ruth Easthill (illus). 12mo. Frontis (folded near spine, not affecting image). Color pict bds. *Reisler.* $75/£47

Story of Peter Rabbit. Racine, WI: Whitman, 1935. Maywill Dudley (illus). 8vo. 10pp. Good in color pict wrappers. *Reisler.* $60/£38

Story of Pinocchio. London: Octopus Books, 1979. 2nd imp. J. Pavlin & G. Seda (illus). 6 dbl-pg pop-ups. Glazed pict bds. VG. *Bookfinders.* $40/£25

Story of the Fifty-fifth Regiment. Illinois Volunteer Infantry in the Civil War. (Clinton, MA: Ptd by W.J. Coulter), 1887. 1st ed. 519pp. VG (fr joint sl cracked, cl sl worn). *Pirages.* $150/£94

Story of the Statue of Liberty. NY: Holt, Rinehart & Winston, 1986. 5 dbl-pg pop-ups, rotating wheel. Glazed pict bds. VG. *Bookfinders.* $50/£31

Story of the Three Little Pigs. USA: McLoughlin Bros, 1892. 1st ed. 16 color chromo pp ptd on linen. Good (worn, bottom cd. crumbled). *Green Meadow.* $72/£45

Story of the Three Little Pigs. Racine, WI: Whitman, 1935. Maywill Dudley (illus). 8vo. 10pp. Good in color pict wrappers. *Reisler.* $60/£38

Story of the Three Little Pigs. NY: McLoughlin Bros, n.d. (ca 1870). Little Folks Series. Sm 8vo. 6 leaves + 1pg ad rear wrapper; 5 Fine full-pg chromolithos. Pict paper wrappers. Good (wrappers lt discolored, spotted, spine reinforced). *Hobbyhorse.* $75/£47

Story of the Typewriter 1873-1923. (By Mark Twain.) Herkimer, (NY): Herkimer County Hist Soc, 1923. 1st ed. Ptd bds. VG (private lib stamps; bds bumped at tips). BAL Vol II, pg 250. *Second Life.* $150/£94

Story upon Story Every Word True. London: Raphael Tuck & Sons, (ca 1890). 4to. 16 chromolitho plts. Cl-backed color illus bds. VG in tan pict dj (margins chipped). *Reisler.* $485/£303

Storytime in Storyland. Springfield: McLoughlin Bros, (1937). Obl 4to. Cl-backed color pict bds (lower edge rubbed). Full color pict dj (dusty, rear upper edges worn). *Reisler.* $100/£63

STOTHARD, MRS. CHARLES. Letters Written During a Tour Through Normandy, Britanny, and Other Parts of France, in 1818. London: Longman, Hurst, et al, 1820. 1st ed. 322pp; 23 aquatint plts (6 color). Contemp polished calf. (Offset, sl spotted; expertly re-hinged, extrems sl rubbed), o/w VG. *Young.* $400/£250

STOTZ, CHARLES MORSE. The Early Architecture of Western Pennsylvania. NY: William Helburn, Inc. for the Buhl Foundation, 1936. One of 1000 numbered. Folio. 290pp; fldg map. Red linen (sl faded), gilt. *Karmiole.* $175/£109

STOUT, REX. And Four to Go. NY, 1958. 1st ed. Dj. *Swann**. $46/£29

STOUT, REX. The Black Mountain. London, 1955. 1st Eng ed. Very Nice in dj (sl nicked, mkd). *Clearwater.* $72/£45

STOUT, REX. Death of a Dude. NY: Viking, (1969). 1st ed. VG in dj (spine ends sl chipped). *Pacific**. $40/£25

STOUT, REX. The Golden Spiders. NY: Viking, 1953. 1st ed. Top edge stained yellow. Lt grn cl over dec bds. VG (spine sl cocked, ends sl bumped) in dj (edgeworn). *Heritage.* $100/£63

STOUT, REX. How Like a God. Morley & Mitchell Kennerley Jr, 1931. 1st UK ed, 1st bk. VG- (bds sl tired, browned). *Williams.* $77/£48

STOUT, REX. Murder by the Book. NY, 1951. 1st ed. Dj (lt worn). *Swann**. $201/£126

STOUT, REX. Prisoner's Base. NY: Viking, 1952. 1st ed. Grn bds. (Spine sl cocked, ends sl rubbed), o/w NF in dj (price-clipped, edgeworn). *Heritage.* $150/£94

STOUT, REX. Silent Speaker. NY, 1946. 1st ed. Dj (creases, 1/2-inch closed tear foot fr panel). *Swann**. $103/£64

STOUT, REX. Three Doors to Death. London: Crime Club, (1950). 1st UK ed. Red cl (top edges lt bumped). Dj (creased, spine chipped, 2-inch tear along fr flap fold). *Glenn.* $85/£53

STOUT, REX. Three Doors to Death. NY, 1950. 1st ed. Dj (spine lt sunned, extrems sl rubbed). *Swann**. $46/£29

STOUT, REX. Too Many Cooks. NY, (1938). 1st ed. 8vo. Dj (corners sl rubbed, sm chips). *Swann**. $1,035/£647

STOUT, REX. Too Many Women. NY: Viking, 1947. 1st ed. Fine in NF dj (sl chipped). *Unger.* $250/£156

STOUT, REX. Trouble in Triplicate. NY: Viking, 1949. 1st ed. Fine in VG dj (spine sl faded, ends sl worn, tear, sm scrapes to fr panel). *Mordida.* $125/£78

STOUT, WILLIAM. The Autobiography of William Stout of Lancaster 1665-1752. Manchester: University Press, 1967. 1st ed thus. Frontisport, map, fldg genealogy. VG in dj. *Hollett.* $104/£65

STOWE, HARRIET BEECHER. The Annotated Uncle Tom's Cabin. Philip Van Doren Stern (ed). NY: Paul S. Eriksson, (1964). 1st ed thus. Fine in dj (2 sm stains). *Hermitage.* $40/£25

STOWE, HARRIET BEECHER. Betty's Bright Idea. NY: J.B. Ford, 1876. 1st ed. Red cl, beveled edges, gilt. (Fep clipped; extrems worn), o/w Clean. BAL 19484. *Hermitage.* $85/£53

STOWE, HARRIET BEECHER. Dred; a Tale of the Great Dismal Swamp. Boston: Phillips, Sampson, 1856. 1st ed, 1st ptg w/'d' in 'dictatorial' aligned under terminal 'r' in 'rather' on pg 88, line 3 in vol 1, with 'the Dicksons are fewer' on pg 370, line 9 up in vol 2. 2 vols. 329pp + (66)pp ads; 370pp. Unptd eps. Blanck's binding A. VG (edges lt worn). BAL 19389. *House.* $150/£94

STOWE, HARRIET BEECHER. The Key to Uncle Tom's Cabin. Boston: John P. Jewett, 1853. 1st Amer ed. Contemp 1/4 morocco, marbled bds. (Dampstained, foxed; tips, bds rubbed.) BAL 19359. *Swann**. $57/£36

STOWE, HARRIET BEECHER. Men of Our Times. Hartford: Hartford Pub, 1868. 1st ed, state 2 of tp. 575pp + ads. Grn cl. VG (eps, cl soiled). BAL 19449. *Second Life.* $65/£41

STOWE, HARRIET BEECHER. Pink and White Tyranny. Boston: Roberts Bros, 1871. 1st ed. 331pp + ads. Good + (cocked, shelfworn; bkpl). *My Bookhouse.* $62/£39

STOWE, HARRIET BEECHER. Uncle Tom's Cabin. John Cassell, 1852. George Cruikshank (illus). Contemp 1/2 leather, marbled bds (re-spined), raised bands. Good (margins soiled, spotted; shelf-worn). *Tiger.* $128/£80

STOWE, HARRIET BEECHER. Uncle Tom's Cabin. London: Cassell, 1852. George Cruikshank (illus). Aeg. 3/4 black morocco (rubbed), gilt. *Oinonen**. $400/£250

STOWE, HARRIET BEECHER. Uncle Tom's Cabin. LEC, 1938. Ltd to 1500 numbered, signed by Miguel Covarrubias (illus). Fine in slipcase. *Swann**. $316/£198

STOWE, HARRIET BEECHER. Uncle Tom's Cabin; or, Life Among the Lowly. Boston: John P. Jewett, 1852. 1st ed, later ptg, mixed set. Vol 1, hundredth thousand; vol 2, twentieth thousand. 2 vols. Mixed orig dk brn cl, gilt. Vol 1 Good (sl aging, rippled; few sigs lt sprung; spine chipped, lt turned; vol 2 lt rippled, foxed, spine torn, chipped). *Baltimore**. $50/£31

STOWE, HARRIET BEECHER. Uncle Tom's Cabin; or, Life Among the Lowly. Boston: John P. Jewett, 1852. 1st ed, 60th thousand. 2 vols. 322; 312pp; 6 plts. Brn blind-stamped cl, gilt (expert repairs to spine, joints). VG (few text smudges, edges lt worn). *House.* $450/£281

STOWE, HARRIET BEECHER. Uncle Tom's Cabin; or, Life Among the Lowly. John P. Jewett, 1852. 1st ed, 1st ptg, w/Hobart & Robbins on c. pp. 2 vols. 12mo. Teg. Full olive grn levant morocco, gilt spine. Overall VG (bkpls each vol; joints rubbed; sm chip vol 1; upper joint vol 2 repaired; spines uniformly faded to brown). *Cummins.* $1,500/£938

STOWE, HARRIETT BEECHER. Dred: A Tale of the Great Dismal Swamp. Boston: Phillips, Sampson, 1856. 1st ed, 1st ptg. 2 vols. (Lt foxed; rebacked w/orig backstrip laid on, extrems rubbed.) BAL 19389. *Sadlon.* $175/£109

STOWELL, ROBERT F. A Thoreau Gazetteer. Calais, VT: Poor Farm Press, 1948. 1st ed. 5pp (mimeographed, stapled), 7 maps loosely laid in. VG in ptd folder. *Lucas.* $65/£41

STOY, MICHAEL S. Pea-Pod Pop-Ups. NY: Playland Books, 1985. Patricia E. Sweazey (illus). 6 dbl-pg pop-ups, complete w/3 dolls. Glazed pict bds. VG. *Bookfinders.* $50/£31

STRACHEY, LADY (ed). Memoirs of a Highland Lady. John Murray, 1928. (Spine faded.) *Hollett.* $32/£20

STRACHEY, LYTTON. Landmarks of French Literature. NY: Henry Holt, 1923. 2nd ed. VG. *Cady.* $20/£13

STRACHEY, LYTTON. Pope. NY: Harcourt, Brace, 1926. 1st Amer ed. VG in dj. *Cady.* $20/£13

STRAHAN, EDWARD (ed). The Chefs-D'Oeuvre D'Art of the International Exhibition, 1878. Phila: Gebbie & Barrie, 1878. 1st ed. Folio. Aeg. Stamped brn morocco, gilt, tooled spine. (Sl foxed; sl rubbed), else NF. *Pacific*.* $115/£72

STRAHORN, CARRIE ADELL. Fifteen Thousand Miles by Stage. NY/London: Putnam, 1911. 1st ed. Teg. Pict cvr label. (Spine gilt sl dull, sm nick to edge of cvr label), o/w Fine. Howes S1054. *Sadlon.* $400/£250

STRAHORN, CARRIE ADELL. Fifteen Thousand Miles by Stage: A Woman's Unique Experience During Thirty Years of Path Finding and Pioneering.... NY: Putnam, 1915. 2nd ed. 4 color plts by Charles M. Russell, guards. Teg. Pict color label. (Sl shaken; spine sl sunned), else NF. *Pacific*.* $138/£86

STRAIN, ISAAC G. Cordillera and Pampa, Mountain and Plain. NY, 1853. 1st ed. xi,295,(1)pp. (Foxed, soiled; sl worn, stained.) *Oinonen*.* $100/£63

STRAND, PAUL and BASIL DAVIDSON. Tir A'Mhurain, Outer Hebrides. London, (1962). 1st ed. (Foxed, offset; worn, age-dknd.) *Swann*.* $201/£126

STRAND, PAUL. The Mexican Portfolio. NY: Da Capo, (1967). 2nd ed. One of 1000 numbered, signed. Folio. 20 photogravures. Plts numbered in pencil in lower rt margin. Buckram/bd fldg box (spine sl age-dknd), slipcase (spine splitting). *Swann*.* $2,990/£1,869

STRAND, PAUL. Photographs 1915-1945. NY: MOMA, (1945). 1st ed. (Ink sig, notes; worn.) *Swann*.* $172/£108

STRAND, PAUL. Photographs of Mexico (The Mexican Portfolio). NY: Virginia Stevens, 1940. 1st ed. Signed. Folio. 20 varnished photogravures. Plts loose as issued (sl marginally age-dknd, stained, edges chipped.) Plts unaffected, each ink-numbered by hand on verso. Buckram fldg box (worn, soiled). *Swann*.* $7,475/£4,672

STRAND, PAUL. A Retrospective Monograph 1915-1968. NY: Aperture, 1971. 1st ed. 2 vols. Fine set in Fine djs. *Smith.* $300/£188

STRAND, PAUL. Time in New England. Nancy Newhall (ed). NY: OUP, 1950. 1st ed. (Edges foxed; extrems faded, corners bumped.) Dj (rubbed, chipped). *Swann*.* $115/£72

STRANG, TOM. The Northern Highlands. Edinburgh: Scottish Mountaineering Trust, 1975. 2nd ed. 15 maps. VG in dj. *Hollett.* $48/£30

STRANGE, EDWARD F. Chinese Lacquer. London, 1926. One of 600. 55 plts. *Swann*.* $149/£93

STRASSBURGER, RALPH BEAVER. Pennsylvania German Pioneers...the Original Lists of Arrivals in the Port of Philadelphia from 1727-1808. Norristown: PA German Soc, 1934. 1st ed. 3 vols. Color frontispieces (2 dbl-pg), 776; 893; 709pp + index; 24 plts. Blue cl, gilt. Fine set. *House.* $250/£156

STRATE, DAVID K. Sentinel to the Cimarron. Dodge City, 1970. 1st ptg thus. Pict wraps. Fine (sig, stamp). *Baade.* $20/£13

STRATMAN, CARL J. Bibliography of the American Theatre. Excluding New York City. (Chicago): Loyola Univ, (1965). pub's cl. VG. *Dramatis.* $40/£25

STRATTON, ARTHUR. The English Interior. London: Batsford, n.d. (1920). Folio. Gilt-dec cl. (Shelfworn; sl foxed.) *Oinonen*.* $50/£31

STRATTON, ARTHUR. The English Interior: A Review of the Decoration of English Homes from Tudor Times to the XIXth Century. Batsford, 1920. Lg folio. VG. *Hadley.* $184/£115

STRATTON, MARY. Bruges, a Record and an Impression. Batsford, 1914. 1st ed. Teg. Gilt-dec cl. *Edwards.* $32/£20

STRATTON, R. B. Captivity of the Oatman Girls: A True Story of Early Emigration in the West. Charles H. Jones (ed). Salem, OR: OR Teachers Monthly, 1909. Port. Fine in wrappers, later slipcase, chemise. *Pacific*.* $63/£39

STRATTON-PORTER, GENE. Music of the Wild. GC: Doubleday, Page, 1910. VG- (very shelfworn, 2-inch closed tear 2nd pg). *My Bookhouse.* $77/£48

STRAUB, PETER. Ghost Story. NY: Coward, McCann & Geoghegan, (1979). 1st ed. NF in dj (price-clipped). *Pacific*.* $35/£22

STRAUB, PETER. Ghost Story. NY, 1979. 1st ed. NF in NF dj. *Warren.* $40/£25

STRAUB, PETER. Julia. NY: Coward McCann, 1975. 1st US ed. (Spine sl slanted), else NF in VG + dj. *Pettler.* $60/£38

STRAUS, RALPH and ROBERT K. DENT. John Baskerville. London: Cambridge, 1907. One of 300. Frontisport, guard, 14 plts. Buckram (faded, sl rubbed, sm ink #s on spine; lib label, sm lib stamp, few marginal blind stamps), gilt. *Hollett.* $288/£180

STRAUS, RALPH. Pengard Awake. NY: D. Appleton, 1920. 1st Amer ed. Fine in dj (lt soiled, few sm tears). *Mordida.* $125/£78

STRAVINSKY, IGOR. Chronicle of My Life. Gollancz, 1936. 1st ed. 6 plts. (Spine sl faded.) *Hollett.* $40/£25

STRAWBRIDGE, ALLAN. Suspect: The War Story of a Young Artist Accused of Espionage. London: Heinemann, (1936). 1st ed. Gilt red cl. (Edges dusty), o/w VG in dj (lt smudged). *Reese.* $45/£28

STREATFEILD, NOEL. The Bell Family. Collins, 1954. 1st ed. 8vo. Shirley Hughes (illus). 255pp. VG in pict dj (lt worn). *Bookmark.* $32/£20

STREATFEILD, NOEL. The Fearless Treasure. Joseph, 1953. 1st ed. 8vo. Dorothy Braby (illus). 272pp. Illus cl. VG + in pict dj (edgeworn). *Bookmark.* $24/£15

STREATFEILD, NOEL. Harlequinade. C&W, 1943. 1st ed. Clarke Hutton (lithos). VG + in VG dj. *Green Meadow.* $72/£45

STREATFEILD, NOEL. The House in Cornwall. Dent, 1940. 1st ed. 8vo. D.L. Mays (illus). 180pp. Red/white/yellow chequer-patterned cl. VG (sl dusty). *Bookmark.* $40/£25

STREATFEILD, NOEL. Movie Shoes. Chicago: Random, 1949. 1st US ed. 5.75x8.25. Suzanne Suba (illus). 274pp. VG in dj. *Cattermole.* $35/£22

STREATFEILD, NOEL. New Town. 1960. 1st ed. 8vo. Shirley Hughes (illus). 256pp. VG in pict dj (worn). *Bookmark.* $29/£18

STREATFEILD, NOEL. Thursday's Child. Collins, 1970. 1st ed. 8vo. Peggy Fortnum (illus). 256pp. VG in pict dj (frayed). *Bookmark.* $27/£17

STREET, A. G. Farmer's Glory. London, (1934). 35 engrs by Gwendolen Raverat. Full grn morocco, gilt. VG + . *Truepenny*. $250/£156

STREET, A. G. Harvest by Lamplight. London, 1941. 1st ed. Fine in dj (sl torn). *Petersfield*. $19/£12

STREET, A. G. Hold Fast. Faber & Faber, 1946. Good (Sig; fore-edge faintly spotted, spine bumped) in dj (torn, lacks sm pieces). *Tiger*. $19/£12

STREET, ALFRED B. Frontenac: or, The Atotarho of the Iroquois. NY: Baker & Scribner, 1849. Port, xii,324pp. Orig cl. (Ex-lib, bkpl, old shelf label on spine, cl rubbed, few sigs pulled), o/w Good. *Brown*. $30/£19

STREET, ALFRED B. Woods and Waters; or, The Saranacs and Racket. NY: M. Doolady, 1860. 1st ed. Map. (Spine sunned, ends chipped, sm tear rear joint), else VG. *Pacific**. $138/£86

STREETER, E. Precious Stones and Gems. Boston: Estes & Lauriat, 1887. 4th ed, rev. xvi,347pp. (Lacks tissues, foxed, dampstain corner of frontis, tp; eps stained; rear ll sl cockled; spine label chipped.) *Blake*. $150/£94

STREETER, FLOYD BENJAMIN. Ben Thompson, Man with a Gun. NY: Frederick Fell, 1957. 1st ed. VG in dj (worn). *Labordo*. $25/£16

STREETER, FLOYD BENJAMIN. The Kaw; The Heart of a Nation. NY: Farrar & Rinehart, 1941. 1st ed. Fine in dj. *Labordo*. $45/£28

STREETER, N. R. (comp). Gems from an Old Drummer's Grip. Groton, NY: The Compiler, 1889. Port, 72pp. VG. *Brown*. $25/£16

STREETER, THOMAS W. Bibliography of Texas 1795-1845. Cambridge, 1955-1960. 5 vols. (Lib stamps, spine #s; hinges starting 1 vol.) *Dumont*. $750/£469

STREETT, WILLIAM B. Gentlemen Up. NY: Derrydale, 1930. One of 850. 15 color, 15 b/w plts. Grn cl. Fine in NF pict dj. *Biscotti*. $250/£156

STREEVER, FRED. The American Trail Hound. NY: A.S. Barnes, 1948. 1st ed. Black cl. Fine in NF pict dj. *Biscotti*. $25/£16

STRETTON, CHARLES. Sport and Sportsmen: A Book of Recollections. London, 1866. 1st ed. Frontis. Uncut, unopened, teg. 3/4 morocco (rubbed). *Oinonen**. $60/£38

STRICKLAND, AGNES. Lives of the Queens of England from the Norman Conquest. Phila: George Barrie, (1902-03). Victoria ed. One of 1000 sets. 16 vols. Teg. 3/4 dk blue morocco, marbled bds, gilt, raised bands. (Spines sl sunned, few joints lt worn, 1 spine foot worn), else VG set. *Pacific**. $431/£269

STRICKLAND, AGNES. Lives of the Queens of England, from the Norman Conquest. London: Henry Colburn, 1854. 4th ed. 8 vols. Marbled edges. Period calf, gilt, morocco spine labels. (Lacks many spine labels), else VG set. *Pacific**. $138/£86

STRICKLAND, AGNES. Lives of the Queens of England. Boston/Taggard, 1860. 7 vols. Marbled edges. 3/4 tan calf. *Appelfeld*. $500/£313

STRICKLAND, SAMUEL. Twenty-Seven Years in Canada West; or, The Experience of an Early Settler. Agnes Strickland (ed). London, 1853. 1st ed. 2 vols. (Foxed; shelfworn, spines sl frayed, chipped.) *Oinonen**. $110/£69

STRICKLAND, WILLIAM. Reports on Canals, Railways, Roads, and Other Subjects. Phila: Carey & Lea, 1826. 1st ed. Obl folio. vi,51pp; 73 Good b/w engr plts on 62 sheets, inserted errata slip at Preface. Orig black calf, tan bds, orig ptd paper label on fr cvr. (Sl aged, sl browned, incl plts, receding old dampstain at top edge of last several dozen plts; spine, corners scuffed, cracks at ends of upper joint, fr bd w/lg old stains w/partial effect on mtd label.) Howes S1075. *Baltimore**. $850/£531

STRIKER, FRAN. The Lone Ranger and the Gold Robbery. NY: G&D, 1939. 1st ed. Lone Ranger #3; lists only 3 titles. Thick ed (1st format). 5x7.5. Paul Laune (illus). 185pp. VG + (sl shelfworn) in dj (sl edgeworn). *My Bookhouse*. $62/£39

STRIKER, FRAN. The Lone Ranger and the Haunted Gulch. NY: G&D, 1941. 1st ed. Lone Ranger #6; lists only 5 titles on rear of dj. Thick book w/tan cl. 5x7.5. Paul Laune (illus). 216pp. VG + (sl shelfworn) in dj (sl edgeworn). *My Bookhouse*. $47/£29

STRIKER, FRAN. The Lone Ranger and the Mystery Ranch. NY: G&D, 1938. 1st ed. Lone Ranger #2; lists only 2 titles. Early thick format. 5x7.5. Paul Laune (illus). 199pp. VG + in dj (sl edgeworn, fingermks on rear). *My Bookhouse*. $52/£33

STRIKER, FRAN. The Lone Ranger and Tonto. NY: G&D, 1940. 1st ed. Lone Ranger #5; lists only 3 titles on dj. Early thick format. 5x7.5. Paul Laune (illus). 214pp. VG + (shelfworn) in dj (edgeworn, few sm chips). *My Bookhouse*. $62/£39

STRIKER, FRAN. The Lone Ranger on Red Butte Trail. NY: G&D, 1956. 1st ed. Last Lone Rangers in series; lists to itself. 5x7.5. 176pp. VG + (extrems sl faded) in dj (1.5-inch tear, sl faded). *My Bookhouse*. $190/£119

STRIKER, FRAN. The Lone Ranger Traps the Smugglers. NY: G&D, 1941. 1st ed. Lone Ranger #7; lists to this title on dj flap. Older thick ed. 5x7.5. 214pp. VG (corners bumped) in dj (sl edgeworn). *My Bookhouse*. $47/£29

STRIKER, FRAN. The Lone Ranger West of Maverick Pass. NY: G&D, 1951. 1st ed. Lone Ranger #13; lists to this title. 5x7.5. 208pp. VG + (sl shelfworn) in dj (sl edgeworn). *My Bookhouse*. $52/£33

STRINDBERG, AUGUST. Getting Married. Mary Sandbach (trans). Gollancz, 1972. 1st UK ed. VG in dj. *Williams*. $56/£35

STRINGER, GEORGE ALFRED. Leisure Moments in Gough Square.... Buffalo: Ulbrich & Kingsley, 1886. 1st ed. One of 300. Inscribed. 184pp + index. Grn cl (spine sl repaired, inner hinge cracked), gilt. Text VG. *Hartfield*. $145/£91

STRONG, D. E. Catalogue of the Carved Amber. British Museum, 1966. 1st ed. Color frontis. VG in dj. *Hollett*. $96/£60

STRONG, GEORGE H. The Cyclists' Road-Book of California, Containing Maps of the Principal Riding Districts.... Charles K. Melrose (comp). (SF): CA Division of the League of American Wheelmen, 1895. 2nd ed. (Lacks 1st map, w/2 preceding pp cut in 1/2, pieces present; fr cvr discolored), else VG. *Pacific**. $138/£86

STRONG, JAMES C. Wah-Kee-Nah and Her People. NY: Putnam, 1893. 1st ed. Frontisport, xiv,275pp. Brn cl, gilt. VG + (extrems sl worn). *Harrington*. $125/£78

STRONG, JAMES C. Wah-Kee-Nah and Her People: The Curious Customs, Traditions, and Legends of the North American Indians. NY/London: Putnam, 1893. 1st ed. NF. *Sadlon*. $100/£63

STRONG, L. A. G. Doyle's Rock and Other Stories. Oxford: Blackwell, 1925. 1st Eng ed, 1st issue binding variant. Blue cl stamped in red. VG in dj (sl worn). *Cady*. $30/£19

STRONG, L. A. G. The Magnolia Tree. Verses. London: A. P. Taylor, 1953. Ltd to 100 signed. Fine in heavy white paper wraps. *Cady*. $15/£9

STRONG, L. A. G. The Rolling Road. London: Hutchinson, (1956). VG in dj (edgeworn). *Bohling*. $20/£13

STRONG, L. A. G. (ed). Sixteen Portraits. National Trust, 1951. 1st ed. 8vo. 16 b/w plts by Joan Hassall (illus). (Eps foxed), else Fine in dec dj (sl worn). *Bookmark*. $40/£25

STRONG, MOSES M. (ed). History of the Territory of Wisconsin, from 1836 to 1848. Madison, WI: Democrat Ptg Co, 1885. 1st ed. Engr frontis port, 638pp. Grn cl. Good. *Karmiole*. $100/£63

STRONG, ROY. Tudor and Jacobean Portraits.... London: Nat'l Portrait Gallery, 1969. 2 vols. (Sm label on tps; shelf label removed from spines.) *Swann**. $230/£144

STRONG, SYLVESTER S. Lung, Female, and Chronic Diseases. NY: Miller & Holman, 1857. 12pp. Orig ptd wrappers. *M & S*. $85/£53

STRONG, WILLIAM E. Canadian Beaver Hunt. Norman: Univ of OK, (1960). Advance rev copy w/rev slip laid in. Ltd to 1050. Fine. *Sadlon.* $40/£25

STROOTMAN, RALPH. History of the 363rd Infantry: One Regiment of the 91st Division in WWII. Washington, 1947. 1st ed. VG. *Clark.* $65/£41

STROTHER, DAVID HUNTER. Virginia Yankee in the Civil War: The Diaries of David Hunter Strother. Cecil D. Eby, Jr. (ed). Univ of NC, (1961). Good in dj (worn). *Rybski.* $50/£31

Structure of Typical American Oil Fields; a Symposium on the Relation of Oil Accumulation to Structure. Tulsa/London: American Assoc of Petroleum Geologists/Thomas Murby, 1929?. 2nd ptg. 2 vols (of 3?). Navy blue cl. Fine. *Weber.* $50/£31

STRUEVER, STUART and FELICIA ANTONELLI HOLTON. Koster: Americans in Search of Their Prehistoric Past. NY: Anchor/Doubleday, 1979. 1st ed. VG in dj (sl worn). *Lien.* $20/£13

STRUSS, H. W. Ring Riding. NY: Appleton, 1891. 1st ed. (Few flecks of white paint on cvr.) *October Farm.* $58/£36

STRUTHERS, JOHN. Anatomical and Physiological Observations. Part I. (All published?) Edinburgh: Sutherland & Knox, 1854. 1st ed. viii,239pp. VG (cl frayed at edges). *Glaser.* $150/£94

STRUTT, JACOB GEORGE. Sylva Brittanica. London: Longman, Rees, Orme et al, (1830). 1st 8vo ed. 151pp; 50 full-pg mtd etchings. 3/4 crushed morocco, linen bds. VG (early lib label; cvrs worn). *Hartfield.* $495/£309

STRUTT, JOHN WILLIAM and WILLIAM RAMSAY. Argon, a New Constituent of the Atmosphere. Washington: Smithsonian Inst, 1896. 1st ed. Folio. (4),43pp. Grn cl. Fine. *Glaser.* $225/£141

STRUTT, JOSEPH. A Complete View of the Dress and Habits of the People of England. J. Nichols for J. Edwards, 1796-1799. 2 vols. 2 color engr frontispieces, 151 plts. Uncut. Contemp bds (sides rubbed, spines defective; lt spotted). *Sotheby's*.* $368/£230

STRUTT, JOSEPH. Glig-Gamena Angel-Deod, or the Sports and Pastimes of the People of England.... London, 1810. 2nd ed. 40 engr plts. Contemp 1/2 sheep. (Ex-lib, ink stamps; needs rebinding.) *Swann*.* $201/£126

STRUTT, JOSEPH. The Sports and Pastimes of the People of England. London, 1831. Early 1/2 morocco, gilt. *Swann*.* $138/£86

STRUTT, JOSEPH. The Sports and Pastimes of the People of England; Including the Rural and Domestic Recreations. London: Tegg, 1845. New ed. 3/4 brn morocco (rubbed). *Oinonen*.* $200/£125

STRYKER, ROY EMERSON and NANCY WOOD. In This Proud Land: America 1935-1943 as Seen in the F. S. A. Photographs. Greenwich, (1973). 1st ed. Folio. Dj (worn). *Swann*.* $103/£64

STUART, CAMPBELL. Secrets of Crewe House: The Story of a Famous Campaign. London/NY/Toronto: Hodder & Stoughton, 1920. 1st ed, 2nd imp. Red cl. (Sm ink name, fr inner hinge cracking), else VG in dj (chips, sm label, spine dknd). *Reese.* $45/£28

STUART, GRANVILLE. Forty Years on the Frontier.... Cleveland: A.H. Clark, 1925. 1st ed. 2 vols. Fine set. Howes S1096. *Labordo.* $550/£344

STUART, GRANVILLE. Forty Years on the Frontier.... Paul C. Phillips (ed). Glendale: A.H. Clark, 1967. 2nd ptg of 1-vol ed. 2 vols in 1. Blue cl. NF (rubbed). Howes S1096. *Harrington.* $100/£63

STUART, IAN. (Pseud of Alistar MacLean.) The Satan Bug. Scribner, 1962. 1st ed. (Pp edges lt soiled), else NF in pict dj (lt rubbed, rear panel sl chipped; price-clipped). *Murder.* $50/£31

STUART, JAMES. Three Years in North America. Edinburgh/London: Robert Cadell/Whittaker, 1832. 3rd ed. 2 vols. 1/2 titles, xii,525; viii,544pp; fldg map. Recent 1/2 calf, marbled sides, raised bands, red labels. VG set. *Young.* $392/£245

STUART, JAMES. Three Years in North America. Edinburgh: Cadell, 1833. 3rd, rev ed. 2 vols. Half-title, xii,525; vii,544pp; fldg map (marginal tear). Cl-backed bds (sl loss spine top vol 2). *Marlborough.* $192/£120

STUART, JAMES. Three Years in North America. London: Robert Cadell, 1833. 3rd ed, rev. 2 vols. Fldg frontis map, xii,525,(l); viii,544pp. Contemp 1/2 calf, marbled bds, leather labels. Ptr, bkslr, binder's ticket. Fine. Howes S1099. *Mott.* $250/£156

STUART, JESSE. Plowshare in Heaven. NY, (1956). 1st ed. VG in dj (sl frayed, sm spine tear). *King.* $95/£59

STUART, JOHN. Sculptured Stones of Scotland. Edinburgh: Spalding Club, 1856-67. 2 vols. Folio. (Foxed.) 1/2 morocco (scuffed). *Swann*.* $201/£126

STUART, REGINALD R. and GRACE D. Calvin B. West of the Umpaqua. (Stockton): CA Hist Foundation, 1961. One of 250. Map. Fine. *Pacific*.* $29/£18

STUART, REGINALD R. and GRACE D. Calvin B. West of the Umpqua: An Obscure Chapter in the History of Southern Oregon. (Stockton, CA): CA Hist Foundation, 1961. 1st bk ed. One of 250 ptd. Fine. *Harrington.* $55/£34

STUART, REGINALD R. San Leandro...a History. San Leandro: First Methodist Church, 1951. 1st ed. Frontis. Brick cl. Fine in pict dj (top edge chipped). *Argonaut.* $45/£28

STUART, ROBERT. The Discovery of the Oregon Trail: Robert Stuart's Narratives of His Overland Trip from Astoria in 1812-13. Philip Ashton Rollins (ed). NY: Edward Eberstadt, (1935, but 1936). Buckram. VG (spine faded). Howes S1103. *Pacific*.* $173/£108

STUART, RUTH McENERY. Napoleon Jackson. NY, 1902. 1st ed. Signed dec cl. (Ink name; rubbed.) *King.* $25/£16

STUBBS, CHARLES WILLIAM. Cambridge and Its Story. London, 1903. 1st ed. 24 tinted lithos. Marbled eps; teg. Prize calf, gilt. (Bkpl, fore-edge sl foxed, occasionally intruding onto outer margin; spine sl faded.) *Edwards.* $160/£100

STUBBS, GEORGE. The Anatomy of the Horse. London, 1938. Folio. Frontis. (Lib ink stamps, bkpl; #.) *Edwards.* $120/£75

STUDER, JACOB H. The Birds of North America. NY: Natural Science Association of America, 1888. 1st ed. Tall lg folio. Engr frontisport, 15,182,(viii)pp; 119 chromolitho plts, tissue guards. Aeg. Orig calf, gilt. (Text sl aged, few smudges, mks, sm old dampstain margin of few ll; cvrs worn, spine heavily chipped, cvrs detached, extensive peeling, wear.) *Baltimore*.* $290/£181

STUDER, JACOB H. The Birds of North America. NY: Natural Science Assoc of America, 1903. 1st ed. Folio. 119 color litho plts. Red cl. (Pg or plt edges chipped; joints, hinges cracked, insect damage to cl), else VG-. *Pacific*.* $219/£137

Studies of the Nebulae Made at the Lick Observatory, University of California at Mount Hamilton, California and Santiago, Chile. Berkeley: Univ of CA, 1918. 50 plts, fldg table. Navy blue cl. Fine. *Weber.* $100/£63

STUDLEY, VANCE. The Art and Craft of Handmade Paper. Studio Vista, 1978. Dj. *Forest.* $40/£25

STURGEON, THEODORE. Without Sorcery. (Phila): Prime Press, 1948. 1st trade ed, 1st bk. (Lower corner fep torn away; edges sl soiled; residual cellophane tape on binding.) Dj. *Kane*.* $40/£25

STURGIS, RUSSELL. A Dictionary of Architecture and Building. NY: Macmillan, 1901-1902. 1st ed. 3 vols. Lt olive buckram, gilt. Solid set (lt aged; spines, edges sl sunned, edges lt dusty). *Baltimore*.* $90/£56

STURGIS, WILLIAM BAYARD. New Lines for Flyfishers. NY: Derrydale, (1936). One of 950. Frontis, 2 photo plts. Green buckram (lt worn, edges sl sunned), gilt. *Oinonen*.* $60/£38

STURTEVANT, J. M. English Institutions and the American Rebellion. Manchester: A. Ireland, 1864. 1st ed. 32pp. VG in ptd wraps. *Chapel Hill.* $50/£31

STYLES, SHOWELL. Indestructible Jones. Faber & Faber, 1967. 1st Eng ed. NF (fep partly browned; spine ends sl faded) in dj (partly dknd). *Ulysses.* $40/£25

STYRON, ARTHUR. The Cast-Iron Man: John C. Calhoun and American Democracy. Longmans, Green, 1935. 1st ed. VG (ex-lib). *Book Broker.* $35/£22

STYRON, WILLIAM. The Confessions of Nat Turner. NY, (1967). 1st ed. VG in dj. *King.* $35/£22

STYRON, WILLIAM. The Confessions of Nat Turner. NY: Random House, 1967. 1st ed. Fine in NF dj. *Pettler.* $30/£19

STYRON, WILLIAM. Lie Down in Darkness. Indianapolis, 1951. 1st ed, 1st bk. Dj. *Swann*.* $201/£126

STYRON, WILLIAM. Lie Down in Darkness. Indianapolis, 1951. 1st ed. Dj. *Swann*.* $287/£179

STYRON, WILLIAM. Set This House on Fire. NY: Random House, (1960). 1st ed. Top edge stained red. Black cl. Fine in dj (ink name, lt chipped, soiled). *Heritage.* $75/£47

STYRON, WILLIAM. Set This House on Fire. NY: Random House, 1960. 1st ed. Fine in NF dj (price-clipped). *Pettler.* $45/£28

STYRON, WILLIAM. Set This House on Fire. NY, 1960. 1st Amer ed. Signed. Fine in dj. *Polyanthos.* $65/£41

STYRON, WILLIAM. Shadrach. L.A.: Sylvester & Orphanos, 1979. 1st ed. One of 330. Signed. Gilt-lettered cl, morocco spine label. NF. *Pacific*.* $52/£33

STYRON, WILLIAM. Shadrach. Hollywood: Sylvester & Orphanos, 1979. Ltd to 330 signed. Fine dec cl. *Truepenny.* $100/£63

STYRON, WILLIAM. Sophie's Choice. NY, (1979). 1st ed. One of 500 numbered, signed. Slipcase. *Swann*.* $201/£126

STYRON, WILLIAM. Sophie's Choice. NY: Random House, 1979. 1st ed. Signed. Fine in Fine dj. *Beasley.* $45/£28

STYRON, WILLIAM. Sophie's Choice. Franklin Center, PA: Franklin Library, 1979. True 1st ed. Fine in full leather, gilt. *Lame Duck.* $150/£94

STYRON, WILLIAM. This Quiet Dust. NY, (1982). One of 250 numbered, signed. Slipcase. *Swann*.* $92/£58

STYRON, WILLIAM. This Quiet Dust. NY, 1982. 1st Amer ed. Signed. Fine in Fine dj. *Polyanthos.* $45/£28

STYRON, WILLIAM. This Quiet Dust. London: Jonathan Cape, 1983. 1st British ed. Fine in dj. *Lame Duck.* $25/£16

STYRON, WILLIAM. This Quiet Dust. London, 1983. 1st ed. Signed. Fine in Fine dj. *Polyanthos.* $50/£31

STYRON, WILLIAM. A Tidewater Morning. London, 1993. 1st ed. Signed. Fine in Fine dj. *Polyanthos.* $30/£19

Subtyl Historyes and Fables of Esope.... SF: Grabhorn, 1930. One of 200. Full red morocco (edges rubbed). *Kane*.* $190/£119

Such Fun. (Father Tuck's 'Children's Own' Library.) Such Fun. London: Raphael Tuck, (1930). 4to. 2 full-pg color plts by Louis Wain. Cl-backed color pict bds (edges rubbed, rear hinge repaired). *Reisler.* $485/£303

SUCKLING, E. V. The Examination of Waters and Water Supplies. London: Churchill, 1944. 5th ed. 36 plts. VG. *Savona.* $40/£25

SUCKLING, JOHN. A Ballad Upon a Wedding. (Waltham Saint Lawrence): Golden Cockerel, 1927. One of 375. (Ink inscrip; spine dknd.) *Kane*.* $85/£53

SUDBURY, RICHARD. Two Gentlemen in Touraine. Chicago: Herbert S. Stone, 1899. 1st ed. 342pp. (Spine faded, extrems worn.) Contents NF. *Woolson.* $25/£16

SUDERMANN, H. The Joy of Living. Edith Wharton (trans). NY: Scribner, 1902. 1st ed in English. Teg. Gray bds, gilt. Good (sig, lt dampstain rear pastedown; cvrs, extrems rubbed; spine browned, top sl chipped). *Heritage.* $150/£94

SUDERMANN, H. The Mad Professor. Liveright, 1928. 1st ed. 2 vols. Fine in VG djs (sm chips), VG pub's slipcase (reinforced). *Fine Books.* $70/£44

SUE, EUGENE. The Mysteries of Paris. London, 1844. 3 vols. 334; 336; 296pp. Teg. Later full straight-grained calf. (Bkpls, illus toned; lacks 2 spine labels, cvrs sl worn.) *King.* $495/£309

SUE, EUGENE. The Mysteries of Paris. Chapman & Hall, 1845. 3 vols. Marbled edges. Contemp 1/2 leather, marbled bds, raised bands. Good (sl spotted, new marbled paper; rear hinge vol 1 nicked, hinges, corners rubbed). *Tiger.* $120/£75

SUE, EUGENE. The Mysteries of Paris. Charles Rochford (trans). N.d. (1844). Frontis, engr tp (1844 ink name), 533pp; 19 plts. Orig red cl, gilt. *Bickersteth.* $72/£45

SUESS, ERWIN and J. THIEDE (eds). Coastal Upwelling. NY, 1983. 2 vols. As New in dj. *Larry Price.* $49/£31

SUETONIUS. The Lives of the Twelve Caesars. LEC, 1963. Ltd to 1500 numbered, signed by Salvatore Fiume (illus) and Giovanni Mardersteig (designer). Fine in slipcase. *Swann*.* $126/£79

SUFFLING, ERNEST R. English Church Brasses. From the 13th to the 17th Century. London, 1910. Good. *Washton.* $40/£25

Suffolk Garland; or, A Collection of Poems, Songs, Tales.... Ptd & sold by John Raw, 1818. Teg, rest uncut. Half-title. Later full morocco by Birdsall, gilt. *Sotheby's*.* $147/£92

SUFFOLK, HENRY HOWARD and W. G. CRAVEN. Racing and Steeple-Chasing. Longmans, Green, 1886. 1st ed. Chromolitho frontis, xii,(420)pp. Pict cl. Nice (few sm mks, creases, sl spotted, mainly to edges). *Ash.* $120/£75

SUGDEN, A. V. and JOHN LUDLAM EDMONDSON. A History of English Wallpaper. Batsford, (1925). 70 mtd color plts. Teg. (Inscrip.) Dj (sl frayed). *Sotheby's*.* $405/£253

SUGDEN, A. V. and E. A. ENTWISLE. Potters of Darwen, 1839-1939. Manchester: Privately pub, (1939). Gilt cl, beveled bds. VG. *Hollett.* $104/£65

SUGIYAMA, KOICHI et al (eds). The Collector's Guide to Japanese Cameras. NY/Tokyo: Kodansha Internat'l, 1985. 1st ed. Fine in illus dj. *Cahan.* $85/£53

SUIDA, WILLIAM E. Studies in the History of Art. Phaidon, 1959. Tipped-in color frontis. (Lib ink stamp, label.) *Edwards.* $120/£75

SULLIVAN, EDWARD et al. Yachting. Longmans, Green, 1894. 1st ed. 2 vols. xvi,(440); xvi,456pp. Pict cl. Nice set (few ll sl creased, chipped; rear cvrs sl mkd). *Ash.* $200/£125

SULLIVAN, JOHN. G. K. Chesterton. A Bibliography. London: Univ of London, 1958. 8 plts. (Ex-lib, few stamps.) Dj. *Hollett.* $24/£15

SULLIVAN, MARK. Our Times. The United States 1900-1925. Pre-War America. Volume III of Series. NY: Scribner, 1930. Blue cl. Fine in dj (spine faded). *House.* $15/£9

SULLIVAN, MAURICE S. Jedediah Smith, Trader and Trail Breaker. NY: Press of the Pioneers, 1936. 1st ed. Fine in VG dj. *Perier.* $197/£123

SULLIVAN, MAURICE S. The Travels of Jedediah Smith: A Documentary Outline Including the Journal of the Great American Pathfinder. Santa Ana: Fine Arts, 1934. 1st ed. 12 plts, fldg facs map. Largely unopened. Pict cl. (Offset to eps; cvrs w/offset, discoloration from dj), else VG in dj. Howes S1127. *Pacific*.* $230/£144

SULLIVAN, MAY KELLOGG. The Trail of a Sourdough Life in Alaska. Boston: Richard G. Badger, 1910. 1st ed. Pict cl. (Shelfworn, spine sl sunned), else Good. *Brown.* $35/£22

SULLIVAN, MAY KELLOGG. A Woman Who Went to Alaska. Boston: Earle, 1903. Grn pict cl. VG. *Bowman*. $35/£22

SULLIVAN, WALTER. We Are Not Alone. NY: McGraw-Hill, (1964). 1st ed. NF in dj (tape-repaired). *Agvent*. $35/£22

SULLY, LANGDON. No Tears for the General—The Life of Alfred Sully, 1821-1879. Palo Alto: American West, (1974). Fine in dj. *Perier*. $25/£16

SULZBERGER, C. L. Resistentialists. NY: Harper, (1962). 1st ed. (Name), else Fine in VG dj (internal repairs, chips, tears). *Between The Covers*. $375/£234

SUMMERS, FESTUS P. The Baltimore and Ohio in the Civil War. NY, (1939). 1st ed. (Spine top sl pulled.) *Kane**. $140/£88

SUMMERS, MONTAGUE (trans). Malleus Maleficarum. Bungay: (John Rodker), 1928. One of 1275. Fore/lower edges untrimmed. Pub's red parchment spine, tan buckram sides, gilt spine. Very Nice. *Book Block*. $175/£109

SUMMERS, MONTAGUE. Covent Garden Drollery. Fortune, 1927. 1st ed. Frontis. 1/4 buckram, brn drab paper bds. (Edges sl dusty, spine sl faded), else Fine in VG dj (sl soiled, sl chipped). *Any Amount*. $64/£40

SUMMERS, MONTAGUE. The Geography of Witchcraft. London: Kegan Paul, Trench, Trubner, 1927. 1st ed. 8 plts. Blue cl, gilt. (Bkpl.) *Karmiole*. $75/£47

SUMMERS, MONTAGUE. The Playhouse of Pepys. London, 1935. 1st Eng ed. VG in dj (sl rubbed, dusty). *Clearwater*. $96/£60

SUMMERS, MONTAGUE. The Restoration Theatre. London: Kegan Paul, Trench, Trubner, 1934. 2nd issue w/spine lettered in black. 24 b/w plts. VG (prelims, edges, eps spotted; top edge dusty, internal spotting; spine ends, corners sl bumped) in dj (nicked, rubbed, dusty, sl chipped, creased, browned). *Ulysses*. $200/£125

SUMNER, CHARLES. The Promises of the Declaration of Independence: Eulogy of Abraham Lincoln...June 1, 1865. Boston: J.E. Farwell, 1865. 1st ed. variant ed. Mtd albumen frontis photo port, 67pp (1pg w/old cl repair). Contemp dk grn morocco (old wear, sl scuffed). Internally Good; cvrs Sound. *Baltimore**. $30/£19

SUMNER, CHARLES. White Slavery in the Barbary States. Boston/Cleveland/London: Jewett/Jewett, Proctor & Worthington/Low, 1853. 1st ed. 135pp. (Ex-lib stamps; rubbed, worn, edges, corners frayed, sl smudged, spotted lib spine #), o/w Good. *Worldwide*. $95/£59

SUMNER, J. B. A Treatise on the Records of Creation, and on the Moral Attributes of the Creator. London: Hatchard, (1833). 5th ed. 388; 444pp + 2pp ads. (Ex-lib; spine ends chipped.) Internally VG. *Mikesh*. $75/£47

SUMNER, WILLIAM LESLIE. The Organ, Its Evolution, Principles of Construction and Use. London, 1955. 2nd ed. (Fr cvr sl damp-mkd.) *Petersfield*. $38/£24

SUNDBERG, JOHN. Health Hints for Travelers. Phila, 1884. 1st ed. 61pp. *Fye*. $150/£94

SUNDER, JOHN E. Bill Sublette. Norman: Univ of OK, (1959). 1st ed. Dj. *Dawson*. $40/£25

Sunny Bimbo. NY: M.S. Pub, (ca 1920). Moveable shapebook. Narrow 4to. 10pp. Stiff paper cvrs. Good. *Reisler*. $90/£56

Sunshine and Shadow, Smiles and Tears, or, Pictures of Kate's Early Years. T. Nelson & Sons, 1870. 1st ed. 110x85mm. 11 color plts. Pastel-grn bds w/color pict onlay. (Mks, few sm grazes, spine neatly renewed), else VG. *Bookmark*. $72/£45

Sunshine in the Country, a Book of Rural Poetry. London: Richard Griffin, 1861. 20 albumen photos by Mr. Grundy. (Prelims detached, hinge reinforced; spine ends worn, joint cracked.) *Swann**. $373/£233

Sunshine in the Country. London: Richard Griffin, 1861. 1st ed. 20 mtd albumen prints by J. Grundy. Blue gilt-stamped cl. *Appelfeld*. $200/£125

Superman. A Pop-Up Book. NY: Random House, 1979. Curt Swan et al (illus). 3 dbl-pg pop-ups. (Mechanism repaired on 3 effects, new pull tabs.) Glazed pict bds. *Bookfinders*. $30/£19

Sure Methods of Improving Health, and Prolonging Life. London, 1828. 3rd ed. 394pp. Leather (sl worn). *Whitehart*. $80/£50

SURTEES, R. S. Jorrock's Jaunts and Jollities. London: Ackermann, 1843. 2nd ed. 8vo. 15 hand-colored plts by Henry Alken. Aeg. Fine full red morocco by Riviere, gilt fillet borders w/floral and foxhunting ornaments, spine gilt in 6 compartments. (Orig cvrs, spine bound in at end; sl worn.) Protective felt-lined cl case provided. *Oinonen**. $1,400/£875

SURTEES, R. S. Jorrock's Jaunts and Jollities. London, ca 1880. 31 Fine color plts, tissue guards. (Cl soiled.) *Argosy*. $150/£94

SURTEES, R. S. Novels. London/NY, 1929-31. One of 976 sets. 12 vols. Color frontis each vol. Red cl (spines, labels sl faded). *Kane**. $130/£81

SUSANN, JACQUELINE. Every Night, Josephine! NY, (1963). Inscribed, signed, dated 9/18/68. Dj (sl chipped). *Argosy*. $75/£47

SUSKIND, PATRICK. Perfume. NY: Knopf, 1986. 1st Amer ed. Rev slip. Fine in Fine dj. *Dermont*. $25/£16

SUTCLIFF, ROBERT. Travels in Some Parts of North America, in the Years 1804, 1805, and 1806. York: C. Peacock, 1811. 1st ed. Frontis, (xiii),293pp; 5 plts. Contemp 1/2 calf. (Sm piece out of blank margin 1 plt; corners sl rubbed, expertly rebacked), o/w VF. Howes S1145. *Mott*. $250/£156

SUTCLIFF, ROBERT. Travels in Some Parts of North America, in the Years 1804, 1805, and 1806. Phila, 1812. 1st Amer ed. Frontis. Orig bds (fr cvr loose). Howes S1145. *Swann**. $80/£50

SUTCLIFF, ROSEMARY. Dawn Wind. OUP, 1961. 1st ed. Lg 8vo. Charles Keeping (illus). 241pp. Fine in VG pict dj. *Bookmark*. $40/£25

SUTCLIFF, ROSEMARY. The Lantern Bearers. H&S, 1959. 1st ed. VG in dj. *Green Meadow*. $56/£35

SUTCLIFF, ROSEMARY. The Silver Branch. OUP, 1957. 1st ed. Lg 8vo. Charles Keeping (illus). 216pp. Fine in pict dj (sl frayed). *Bookmark*. $51/£32

SUTCLIFF, ROSEMARY. Warrior Scarlet. OUP, 1958. 1st ed. 8vo. Charles Keeping (illus). 208pp. VG (sl mks) in pict dj (worn, torn). *Bookmark*. $45/£28

SUTHERLAND, B. Romance of Seals and Engraved Gems. NY: Macmillan, c1965. VG in dj. *Blake*. $40/£25

SUTHERLAND, HALLIDAY. Hebridean Journey. Geoffrey Bles, 1947. VG in dj. *Hollett*. $32/£20

SUTHERLAND, J. The Medium of Poetry. London: Hogarth, 1934. 1st ed. (Name, address stamped on 1/2-title; eps sl browned, fore-edge sl spotted, spine edges sl chipped.) Good (lacks dj). *Virgo*. $16/£10

SUTHERLAND, ZENA (ed). The Best in Children's Books. Chicago: Univ of Chicago, 1973. 1st ed. Adv copy, pub's slip laid in. Fine in dj (sl horizontal blue line due to old style glassine protector). *Smith*. $40/£25

SUTLEY, ZACK T. The Last Frontier. NY: Macmillan, 1930. 1st ed. Fldg map. (Sl shelfworn, part of dj laid down on fr pastedown), o/w VG. *Brown*. $35/£22

SUTLEY, ZACK T. The Last Frontier. NY, 1930. 1st ed. Fldg map. (Paper clip wrinkles to map, pencil sig, feps foxed, few dog-eared corners), o/w VG. *Baade*. $50/£31

SUTTER, JOHN A. The Diary of Johann August Sutter. SF: Grabhorn, 1932. 1st ed in bk form. One of 500. 2 color ports, 3-pg facs, fldg color plt. Paper spine/cvr labels. (Cvrs lt offset), else Fine. *Argonaut*. $75/£47

SUTTER, JOHN A. New Helvetia Diary: A Record of Events Kept by John A. Sutter and His Clerks at New Helvetia, California, from September 9, 1845, to May 25, 1848. SF: Grabhorn, 1939. One of 950. 2 color plts, fac pg from diary, facs map. 1/2 linen, patterned bds, paper spine label. (Corners sl worn), else NF. Howes S1155. *Pacific**. $63/£39

SUTTON, FRED E. Hands Up! NY, 1927. Early rpt. Pict cl. (Cvrs lt soiled, faded), else VG. *Baade*. $30/£19

SUTTON, GEORGE M. Eskimo Year. NY: Macmillan, 1934. VG in VG dj. *High Latitude*. $35/£22

SUTTON, GEORGE M. High Arctic. NY: Paul, S. Ericksson, 1971. 1st ed. VG in dj. *Walcot*. $24/£15

SUTTON, MARGARET. The Black Cat's Clue. NY: G&D, 1952. Judy Bolton #23; lists to #34. 5x7.5. 210pp. Pict bds. VG (shelfworn). *My Bookhouse*. $52/£33

SUTTON, MARGARET. The Haunted Fountain. NY: G&D, 1957. Judy Bolton #28; lists 29 titles on dj flap. 5x7.5. 180pp. VG in wraparound dj (edgeworn, few sm chips). *My Bookhouse*. $52/£33

SUTTON, RICHARD L. An African Holiday. St. Louis: Mosby, 1924. 1st Amer ed. Inscribed. (Cl lt worn, spotted.) *Glenn*. $35/£22

SUTTON, RICHARD L. An African Holiday. London, 1924. NF (cl lt wrinkled fr hinge). *Grayling*. $80/£50

SUTTON, RICHARD L. and EMMY LOU. An Arctic Safari. St. Louis: C.V. Mosby, 1932. Frontis, map. (Blank fep out, cl sl worn), else VG. *High Latitude*. $65/£41

SUTTON, RICHARD L. and RICHARD L., JR. The Long Trek Around the World with Camera and Rifle. St. Louis: Mosby, 1930. 1st Amer ed. Inscribed. (Sl edgeworn.) *Glenn*. $60/£38

SUTTON, RICHARD L. Tiger Trails in Southern Asia. St. Louis, 1926. 1st ed. VG in dj (frayed, repaired). *King*. $65/£41

SUTTON, RICHARD L. Tiger Trails in Southern Asia. St. Louis: Mosby, 1926. 1st Amer ed. Inscribed. (Spine lt faded.) *Glenn*. $75/£47

SUZOR, RENAUD. Hydrophobia. An Account of M. Pasteur's System Containing a Translation of All His Communications on the Subject.... London, 1887. 1st ed. 231pp. (Ex-lib.) *Fye*. $150/£94

SUZUKI, SEIKO JUNE and MARJORIE PULLIAM. California Imprints, 1833-1862: A Bibliography. Robert Greenwood (ed). Los Gatos: Talisman, 1961. 1st ed. One of 750. Red buckram, ptd paper spine label. (Lt handled, fr hinge lt cracked; ex-lib, paper spine sticker, ink handstamps, sm ep stickers; sl rubbed, sm stains fr cvr edges.) *Baltimore**. $35/£22

SVERDRUP, OTTO. New Land. Longmans, Green, 1904. 1st UK ed. 2 vols. 2 maps in rear pocket. VG (sl worn). *Walcot*. $352/£220

SVEVO, ITALO. A Lecture Delivered in Milan in 1927 by His Friend Italo Svevo. Stanislaus Joyce (trans). New Directions, 1950. One of 1500 (of 1600). NF in wrappers, pict dj. *Maggs*. $120/£75

SWADESH, FRANCES LEON. Los Primeros Pobladores. Notre Dame, 1974. Good in dj (chipped). *Dumont*. $35/£22

SWAIN, WILLIAM PAUL. Surgical Emergencies: Together with the Emergencies Attendant of Parturition and the Treatment of Poisoning. Phila, 1874. 1st ed. 189pp. 82 wood cuts. NF (sm amount of lt pencil mks in margin; very sm top of spine tear, sl worn corners). *Doctor's Library*. $125/£78

SWAN, ABRAHAM. The British Architect; or, The Builder's Treasury of Stair-Cases.... London, 1750. 2nd ed. Folio. 59 engr plts (lacks plt 40). 19th-cent 1/2 sheep (spine, corners worn; variously browned). *Swann**. $373/£233

SWAN, JOHN A. A Trip to the Gold Mines of California in 1848. SF: Book Club of CA, 1960. 1st ed. Ltd to 400 ptd. Frontisport. Cl-backed marbled bds, gilt. Fine. *Harrington*. $80/£50

SWAN, JOHN A. A Trip to the Gold Mines of California in 1848. John A. Hussey (ed). SF: Book Club of CA, 1960. One of 400 ptd. Cl-backed marbled bds, gilt. Fine. *Pacific**. $29/£18

SWANBERG, W. A. Sickles the Incredible. NY: Scribner, 1956. Signed. (Fr cvr sl soiled), else Fine in pict dj (lt worn). *Argonaut*. $75/£47

SWANK, JAMES M. Statistics of the Iron and Steel Production of the United States. Washington: GPO, 1881. 180pp; 1 plt, 6 maps. Mod patterned bds (fragment of orig ptd wrapper bound in), black leather spine label. *Weber*. $200/£125

SWANN, PETER C. The Art of Japan from the Jomon to the Tokugawa Period. NY et al: Greystone, 1966. Rev ed. VG in dj. *Worldwide*. $35/£22

SWANN, R. A. Australia in the Antarctic. Melbourne: University Press, 1961. (Blindstamp), else VG in dj. *High Latitude*. $50/£31

SWANNER, CHARLES D. Santa Ana, a Narrative of Yesterday 1870-1910. Claremont: Saunder, (1953). 1st ed. Signed presentation copy. Grn cl. Fine in VG + pict dj. *House*. $20/£13

SWANSON, E. B. A Century of Oil and Gas in Books. NY, 1960. Good in dj. *Dumont*. $150/£94

SWANSON, FAITH H. and VIRGINIA B. RADY. Herb Garden Design. Hanover: Univ Press of New England, 1984. 1st ed. VG in dj. *Fair Meadow*. $40/£25

SWANSON, W. E. Modern Shipfitter's Handbook. NY: Cornell Maritime, 1941. VG in dj. *American Booksellers*. $35/£22

SWANTON, JOHN R. The Indian Tribes of North America. BAE Bulletin 145. Washington: GPO, 1952. VG. *Perier*. $60/£38

SWANTON, JOHN R. Tlingit Myths and Texts. Washington: GPO, 1909. 1st ed. Olive-grn cl, gilt. Fine. *Argonaut*. $75/£47

SWARTHOUT, G. They Came to Cordura. R-H, 1958. 1st ed. VG + in dj. *Fine Books*. $20/£13

SWARTZ, JOEL. Something Different to Do. (Rochester): Visual Studies Workshop, 1977. 1st ed. 8vo. (28)pp. Illus stiff bds. (Sl dusty), else Fine. *Cahan*. $50/£31

SWARZENSKI, HANNS. Monuments of Romanesque Art. The Art of Church Treasures in North-Western Europe. Chicago, 1954. 238 plts. Good. *Washton*. $85/£53

SWAYSLAND, W. Familiar Wild Birds. Cassell, (1894-1899). 4 vols. 40 color plts. Teg. Dk blue cl. Fine. *Bickersteth*. $208/£130

SWAYSLAND, W. Familiar Wild Birds. Cassell, 1903. 4 vols. 160 color plts. Good set (bkpl, fep neatly removed vol 1) in dec cl. *Cox*. $88/£55

SWEDENBORG, EMANUEL. The Generative Organs, Considered Anatomically, Physically and Philosophically. James John Garth Wilkinson (trans). William Newbery, 1852. 1st Eng ed. x,(ii),327pp. Red sprinkled, polished edges. Contemp 1/2 dk grn morocco, gilt, raised bands, morocco-grain grn cl sides. Good (lacks half-title). *Blackwell's*. $152/£95

SWEENEY, MATTHEW. A Round House. London/NY/Dublin: Allison & Busby/Raven Arts, 1983. 1st Eng ed. Inscribed presentation. VG (spine cocked, sl rubbed) in wrappers. *Ulysses*. $72/£45

SWEET, ALEXANDER E. and J. ARMOY KNOX. On a Mexican Mustang. Hartford: S.S. Scranton, 1883. 1st ed. 672pp. Good (sl browned; sl cocked). *Dumont*. $120/£75

SWEET, FREDERICK A. Miss Mary Cassatt. Norman: Univ of OK, (1966). 27 b/w, 8 color plts. VG. *Turtle Island*. $45/£28

SWEETMAN, LUKE D. Back Trailing on the Open Range. Caldwell, ID, 1951. 1st ed. Good (lacks dj). *Dumont*. $50/£31

Sweets for Leisure Hours; or, Flowers of Instruction. New Haven: S. Babcock, n.d. (ca 1835). 16mo. Full-pg wood-engr frontis, 8pp + 1pg bk list lower wrapper. Headpiece vignette signed by J.T. Howland. Grn pict paper wrappers. Near Mint. *Hobbyhorse*. $90/£56

SWEETSER, M. F. Chisholm's Mount-Desert Guide-Book. Portland: Chisholm Bros, 1888. (vi),112,(v)pp; fldg map, 5 full-pg woodcut illus. (Spine ends sl frayed.) *Hollett*. $104/£65

SWEETSER, M. F. Views of the White Mountains. Portland, ME: Chisolm Bros, 1879. 1st ed. 12 photogravure plts. NF. *Pacific**. $58/£36

SWENSON, MAY. A Cage of Spines. NY: Rinehart, (1958). 1st ed. Fine in NF dj (sm nicks, spine frayed). *Reese*. $50/£31

SWETTENHAM, FRANK. Arabella in Africa. London, 1925. 1st Eng ed. (Spine sl faded, chafed, head worn; cvr sl dust-mkd.) *Clearwater*. $80/£50

SWIFT, GRAHAM. Ever After. NY, 1992. 1st Amer ed. Signed. Fine in Fine dj. *Polyanthos*. $30/£19

SWIFT, GRAHAM. Waterland. NY, 1983. 1st ed. Fine in Fine dj. *Warren*. $35/£22

SWIFT, GRAHAM. Waterland. Heinemann, 1983. 1st ed. Black bds, gilt. Fine in dj. *Blackwell's*. $96/£60

SWIFT, JONATHAN. Gulliver's Travels into Several Remote Nations of the World. London/NY: J.M. Dent/E.P. Dutton, 1909. One of 750 containing extra color plt not in trade ed. Signed by Arthur Rackham (illus). 11x8. 13 tipped-in color plts, 2 full-pg b/w illus. Gilt-pict eps; teg. Period 3/4 gilt-ruled red levant morocco, gilt, raised bands. (Pencil inscrip; rebound, sl scuffed, sm stain to rear cvr cl), else NF. *Pacific**. $863/£539

SWIFT, JONATHAN. Gulliver's Travels. Chicago: Rand McNally, (1912). 1st ed. 12 color plts by Milo Winter. Pict eps. Grn buckram, gilt, color plt fr cvr. Fine. *House*. $125/£78

SWIFT, JONATHAN. Gulliver's Travels. London: Dent, 1909. 1st ed. Arthur Rackham (illus). Grn binding, gilt. VG (name). *Price*. $225/£141

SWIFT, JONATHAN. Gulliver's Travels. London: Cresset, 1930. 1st ed. One of 175 (of 195). 2 vols. Super-royal 4to. 12 full-pg hand-colored pen/ink plts, 5 maps by Rex Whistler. 1/2 grn morocco vellum bds, panelled spine. VF. *Maggs*. $6,400/£4,000

SWIFT, JONATHAN. The History of the Last Four Years of the Queen. London: A. Millar, 1758. 1st ed, 2nd issue. xvi,392pp. Contemp polished calf (joints sl tender), raised bands. *Young*. $104/£65

SWIFT, JONATHAN. Tale of a Tub. Phila: G.B. Zieber, 1846. 1st Amer ed. 169pp. Orig ptd wrappers, all edges red. *M & S*. $125/£78

SWIFT, JONATHAN. A Voyage to Lilliput and A Voyage to Brobdingnag Made by Lemuel Gulliver. LEC, 1950. Ltd to 1500 numbered, signed by Bruce Rogers (illus). 2 vols. 1 miniature, 1 folio. Fine in slipcase. *Swann**. $258/£161

SWIFT, JONATHAN. The Works of Dr. Jonathan Swift.... London: C. Bathurst et al, 1765-1775. 24 vols. Contemp calf, gilt spines, red/grn morocco labels. Overall VG set (contemp bkpl, gilt initials on all cvrs, some spine extrems sl chipped, hinges rubbed, few starting). *Karmiole*. $600/£375

SWIFT, JONATHAN. The Works of Jonathan Swift.... Dublin: J. Williams, 1774. 14 vols. Copper-engr tps. Period calf, gilt, raised bands, morocco labels. (Name stamped in gilt on fr cvrs, sl worn, few spine ends chipped, vol 4 w/fr cvr detached), else VG. *Pacific**. $230/£144

SWIFT, JONATHAN. The Works. Bickers & Son, 1883-1884. One of 750. 19 vols. 8vo. Engr frontis. 19th-cent tree calf by Riviere, gilt. (Bkpl.) *Sotheby's**. $2,115/£1,322

SWIFT, MARJORY and CHRISTINE T. HERRICK. Feed the Brute. NY: Frederick A. Stokes, 1926. 1st ed. Pict bds. Fine in VG- dj (dknd, extrems heavily chipped). *Pacific**. $35/£22

SWIGGETT, HOWARD. March or Die. NY, (1953). 1st ed. VG + in dj (worn, chipped). *Pratt*. $20/£13

SWINBURNE, ALGERNON CHARLES. The Age of Shakespeare. London: C&W, 1908. 1st ed. (Text sl discolored.) Teg, rest untrimmed. Dk blue cl, gilt. *Maggs*. $40/£25

SWINBURNE, ALGERNON CHARLES. Astrophel and Other Poems. London: C&W, 1894. 1st ed. One of 1500 ptd. 32pg pub's cat dated February 1894. Fine in dk grn cl, gilt. *Maggs*. $40/£25

SWINBURNE, ALGERNON CHARLES. Atalanta in Calydon, a Tragedy. London: John Camden Hotten, 1866. 3rd ed. (Fep sl torn at hinge.) Blue straight-grain cl, gilt. *Maggs*. $48/£30

SWINBURNE, ALGERNON CHARLES. Atalanta in Calydon. London: Medici Soc, 1923. 1st ed. One of 1000 ptd. Teg. Cl-backed dec bds. NF in dj. *Pacific**. $75/£47

SWINBURNE, ALGERNON CHARLES. Ballads of the English Border. William A. MacInnes (ed). London: Heinemann, 1925. 1st collected ed. Good in blue cl, gilt. *Maggs*. $32/£20

SWINBURNE, ALGERNON CHARLES. A Century of Roundels. London: C&W, 1883. 1st ed. Red hard-grain cl (sl mildewed). *Maggs*. $64/£40

SWINBURNE, ALGERNON CHARLES. A Century of Roundels. London: C&W, 1883. 1st ed. One of 1000. Dk grn cl, gilt. Fine. *Macdonnell*. $85/£53

SWINBURNE, ALGERNON CHARLES. A Channel Passage and Other Poems. London: C&W, 1904. 1st ed. VG in dk grn cl, gilt. *Maggs*. $40/£25

SWINBURNE, ALGERNON CHARLES. Charles Dickens. Theodore Watts-Dunton (ed). London: C&W, 1913. 1st ed. Teg, rest untrimmed. Fine in dk grn cl, gilt. *Maggs*. $48/£30

SWINBURNE, ALGERNON CHARLES. Chastelard. A Tragedy. London: Edward Moxon, 1865. 1st ed, 1st issue, 1st binding. One of 1000. Blue cl, gilt. Good (few mks). *Macdonnell*. $165/£103

SWINBURNE, ALGERNON CHARLES. Chastelard. A Tragedy. NY, 1866. 1st Amer ed. NF (rubbed). *Polyanthos*. $35/£22

SWINBURNE, ALGERNON CHARLES. Erechtheus. London: C&W, 1876. 1st ed. One of 1500. 32pp ads dated Oct 1875. Dk blue-grn cl. Fine. *Sumner & Stillman*. $75/£47

SWINBURNE, ALGERNON CHARLES. Erechtheus. London: C&W, 1876. 1st ed. Grn cl. VG in 1/4 brn morocco slipcase w/chemise. *Cummins*. $125/£78

SWINBURNE, ALGERNON CHARLES. Hymn to Prosperine. Golden Cockerel, 1944. One of 350. 7 wood engrs (incl frontis). Teg, rest untrimmed. Maroon buckram, grn leather label. Fine in tissue dj. *Blackwell's*. $176/£110

SWINBURNE, ALGERNON CHARLES. Laus Veneris. Golden Cockerel, 1948. 1st ed thus. One of 750. 4 full-pg woodcuts. 1/4 buckram, patterned bds. (Spine sl faded), else Fine. *Any Amount*. $64/£40

SWINBURNE, ALGERNON CHARLES. Laus Veneris.... Golden Cockerel, 1948. Ltd to 750 numbered, this copy one of 100 specially bound, w/an extra engr. Royal 8vo. 12 wood engrs by John Buckland Wright. Teg, rest untrimmed. Orig full red-brn morocco, black/gilt inlay fr cvr, spine. VG. *Sotheran*. $1,277/£798

SWINBURNE, ALGERNON CHARLES. The Letters of Algernon Charles Swinburne. Edmund Gosse and Thomas James Wise (eds). London: Heinemann, 1918. 1st ed. 2 vols. Good in blue cl (sl faded), gilt. *Maggs*. $56/£35

SWINBURNE, ALGERNON CHARLES. Locrine, a Tragedy. London: C&W, 1887. 1st ed. VG. *Reese*. $50/£31

SWINBURNE, ALGERNON CHARLES. Locrine. London: C&W, 1887. 1st ed. One of 1250. 32pp ads dated Oct 1887. Dk blue-grn cl. NF. *Sumner & Stillman*. $90/£56

SWINBURNE, ALGERNON CHARLES. Love's Cross-Currents. London: C&W, 1905. 1st ed. Teg. Dk blue buckram (spine faded), gilt. *Maggs*. $40/£25

SWINBURNE, ALGERNON CHARLES. Marino Faliero. London: C&W, 1885. 1st ed. One of 1250 ptd. 32pg pub's cat dated October 1892. Dk grn cl, gilt. *Maggs*. $64/£40

SWINBURNE, ALGERNON CHARLES. Mary Stuart. London: C&W, 1881. 1st ed. One of 1500 ptd. 32pg pub's cat dated November 1881. Dk grn cl (sl soiled, bubbled), gilt. *Maggs.* $48/£30

SWINBURNE, ALGERNON CHARLES. A Midsummer Holiday and Other Poems. London: C&W, 1884. 1st ed. One of 1500 ptd. 32pg pub's cat dated September 1884. VG in dk grn cl, gilt. *Maggs.* $40/£25

SWINBURNE, ALGERNON CHARLES. Note of an English Republican on the Muscovite Crusade. London: C&W, 1876. 1st ed. VG in gray mottled ptd wrappers (sl dust-soiled). *Maggs.* $64/£40

SWINBURNE, ALGERNON CHARLES. Note of an English Republican on the Muscovite Crusade. London: C&W, 1876. 1st ed. One of 2000. Fine in gray-grn ptd wrappers. *Macdonnell.* $100/£63

SWINBURNE, ALGERNON CHARLES. Ode on the Proclamation of the French Republic, September 4th, 1870. London: F.S. Ellis, 1870. 1st ed. Fine in orange ptd wrappers. *Maggs.* $48/£30

SWINBURNE, ALGERNON CHARLES. Ode on the Proclamation of the French Republic, September 4th, 1870. London: F.S. Ellis, 1870. 1st ed. (Fr hinge neatly reglued, spine sl dknd, corners sl soiled, worn), else VG in later chemise, orig ptd wrappers (old name). *Pacific*.* $58/£36

SWINBURNE, ALGERNON CHARLES. Poems and Ballads. London: C&W, 1889. 1st ed. One of 1000. 32pp ads dated Oct 1888. Unopened. Dk blue-grn cl. Fine. *Sumner & Stillman.* $115/£72

SWINBURNE, ALGERNON CHARLES. Poems and Ballads. Third Series. London: C&W, 1889. 1st ed. One of 1000 ptd. 32pg pub's cat dated December 1888. VG in dk grn cl, gilt. *Maggs.* $40/£25

SWINBURNE, ALGERNON CHARLES. The Queen-Mother and Rosamond. London: John Camden Hotten, 1868. 2nd ed. 32pg pub's cat dated February 1880. VG in straight-grain grn cl, gilt. *Maggs.* $72/£45

SWINBURNE, ALGERNON CHARLES. Selected Poems of Algernon Charles Swinburne. NY: Dodd, Mead, (1928). 1st Amer ed. 4to. 10 full-pg photogravure illus, dbl-pg spread by Harry Clarke. Dk black cl (spine sl rippled), gilt. Good in dj (spine split, reinforcing from below), slipcase (worn), ptd labels. *Reisler.* $350/£219

SWINBURNE, ALGERNON CHARLES. Selected Poems. London: John Lane, The Bodley Head, 1928. 1st ed illus thus. 10 Fine photogravure plts (1 dbl-pg) by Harry Clarke, guards. Uncut. Purple cl, gilt. NF in black pict dj (sl internal repair). *Sotheran.* $269/£168

SWINBURNE, ALGERNON CHARLES. Selections from A. C. Swinburne. Edmund Gosse and Thomas James Wise (eds). London: Heinemann, 1919. 1st ed. One of 525 numbered. Teg, rest untrimmed. 1/4 parchment over cream bds (extrems bumped, soiled). *Maggs.* $48/£30

SWINBURNE, ALGERNON CHARLES. The Sisters. London: C&W, 1892. 1st ed. 32pg pub's cat dated October 1891. Good in dk grn cl, gilt. *Maggs.* $40/£25

SWINBURNE, ALGERNON CHARLES. A Song of Italy. London: John Camden Hotten, 1867. 1st ed. In this copy the prelim ads are inserted between the eps. 8pp prelim undated ads, 8+(2)+6pp undated ads. Secondary cl (bright blue vertically-ribbed), w/the date '1867' at spine foot. NF (sl rubbed). *Sumner & Stillman.* $55/£34

SWINBURNE, ALGERNON CHARLES. A Song of Italy. John Camden Hotten, 1867. 1st ed. Carter: 2nd state binding, the 1st being grn cl w/Hotten's name instead of date on spine foot. 66pp, 8pg press opinions at fr, 8,(2),6pp ads. Smooth blue cl, gilt, spine foot dated 1867. *Bickersteth.* $72/£45

SWINBURNE, ALGERNON CHARLES. Songs of the Springtides. London: C&W, 1880. 1st ed, w/April 1880 ads. One of 1500. Dk grn cl, gilt. Fine. *Macdonnell.* $75/£47

SWINBURNE, ALGERNON CHARLES. Songs of Two Nations. London: C&W, 1875. 1st ed. One of 1000. Dk grn cl, gilt. Fine. *Macdonnell.* $50/£31

SWINBURNE, ALGERNON CHARLES. Songs of Two Nations. London: C&W, 1875. 1st ed. One of 1000. 32pp ads dated May 1883. Largely unopened. Dk blue-grn cl. (Cl sl bubbling), else Fine. *Sumner & Stillman.* $95/£59

SWINBURNE, ALGERNON CHARLES. Songs of Two Nations. I. A Song of Italy. II. Ode on the Proclamation of the French Republic. III. Dirae. London: C&W, 1875. 1st ed. One of 1000 ptd. 32pg pub's cat. Dk grn cl, gilt. *Maggs.* $48/£30

SWINBURNE, ALGERNON CHARLES. The Springtide of Life. London: Heinemann, 1918. 1st ed illus by Rackham. Deluxe ed. One of 765 signed by Rackham. 4to. 8 mtd color plts, guards. Teg, rest uncut. Orig white vellum-backed paper-cvrd bds, gilt. (Spine speckled, browned), o/w Very Bright. *Sotheran.* $720/£450

SWINBURNE, ALGERNON CHARLES. The Springtide of Life: Poems of Childhood. London: Heinemann, (1918). 1st ed. 4to. 8 full-pg color plts by Arthur Rackham. Dk grn cl (sl shelfworn), gilt. Dk grn dj (dknd, chipped). *Reisler.* $275/£172

SWINBURNE, ALGERNON CHARLES. Studies in Song. London: C&W, 1880. 1st ed. One of 1500 ptd. 4pp ads, pub's cat dated March 1881. Good in dk grn cl, gilt. *Maggs.* $48/£30

SWINBURNE, ALGERNON CHARLES. A Study of Victor Hugo. London: C&W, 1886. 1st ed. 32pg pub's cat dated January 1886. Dk grn cl (spine sl faded), gilt. *Maggs.* $48/£30

SWINBURNE, ALGERNON CHARLES. The Tale of Balen. London: C&W, 1896. 1st ed. 32pg pub's cat dated March 1895. VG in blue buckram, gilt. *Maggs.* $40/£25

SWINBURNE, ALGERNON CHARLES. The Tragedies. London: C&W, 1905. 5 vols. Teg, rest untrimmed. Dk blue buckram (sl soiled, spine heads sl chipped). *Maggs.* $72/£45

SWINBURNE, ALGERNON CHARLES. Tristram of Lyonesse and Other Poems. London: C&W, 1882. 1st ed. 32pg pub's cat dated May 1882. Good in dk grn cl, gilt. *Maggs.* $40/£25

SWINBURNE, CHARLES ALFRED. Life and Works of J. M. W. Turner, R.A. London, 1902. Engr frontis. Teg, rest uncut. (Tp lt spotted, marginal pencil notes, feps browned; lt faded, spine bumped.) *Edwards.* $72/£45

SWINBURNE, HENRY. Travels Through Spain, in the Years 1775-1776. London: P. Elmsly, 1779. 1st ed. 1st ed xvi,428pp; 13 engr plts (4 fldg). Contemp calf (rebacked, corners worn), red calf spine label. *Karmiole.* $450/£281

SWINDLER, MARY HAMILTON. Ancient Painting. From the Earliest Times to the Period of Christian Art. New Haven, 1929. 15 plts hors texte. Good. *Washton.* $125/£78

SWINGLER, RANDALL. The Years of Anger. London: Meridian Books, n.d. (c. 1945). 1st ed. Ptd wrappers. *Maggs.* $48/£30

SWINNERTON, FRANK. The Adventures of a Manuscript Being the Story of 'The Ragged Trousered Philanthropists.' Richards, 1956. One of 1500. Fine in ptd wraps. *Any Amount.* $10/£6

SWINNERTON, FRANK. Background with Chorus. London: Hutchinson, (1956). 1st ed. Frontisport. NF in dj. *Cady.* $15/£9

SWINNERTON, H. H. Fossils. London: Collins, 1960. 1st ed. Color frontis. VG in dj (fr flap sl mkd). *Hollett.* $64/£40

SWINSON, ARTHUR. Frederick Sander: The Orchid King. Hodder, 1970. Fine in dj (spine faded). *Hadley.* $32/£20

SWISHER, JAMES. How I Know; Or, Sixteen Years' Eventful Experience. Cincinnati, OH: The Author, 1880. 1st ed. Dec cl. VG (hinges starting, edgeworn). Howes S1183. *Labordo.* $300/£188

SWOPE, JOHN. Camera Over Hollywood. NY: Random House, 1939. 1st ed. NF. Dj (missing lg piece from fr, most of spine). *Cahan.* $175/£109

SWORD, WILEY. Shiloh: Bloody April. NY: Wm. Morrow, (1974). 1st ed. Advance proofs. NF in orig ptd wrappers. *Sadlon.* $40/£25

SYDENHAM, THOMAS. Opera Omnia. G.A. Greenhill (ed). Sydenham Soc, 1844. xxx,668pp. Teg. Orig cl. VG. *Whitehart.* $64/£40

SYKES, CHRISTOPHER. Orde Wingate. London: Collins, 1959. 1st ed. 26 plts, 12 maps. VG in dj. *Hollett.* $32/£20

SYKES, ELLA. Through Persia on a Side Saddle. London: G. Bell & Sons, 1901. Colonial Library ed. Fldg map. (Spine faded.) *Maggs.* $120/£75

SYLVESTER, DAVID. Rene Magritte. NY: Praeger, (1969). 1st US ed. 96 full-pg plts (33 color). Fine in dj. *Turtle Island.* $55/£34

SYMONDS, JOHN ADDINGTON and MARGARET. Our Life in the Swiss Highlands. A&C Black, 1892. 1st ed. x,366,(vi)pp. Fine. *Hollett.* $224/£140

SYMONDS, JOHN ADDINGTON. Anima Figura. London: Smith Elder, 1882. 1st ed. NF (cat description fep; sticker on rear, corners sl bumped). *Agvent.* $100/£63

SYMONDS, JOHN ADDINGTON. Last and First. NY, 1919. 1st Amer ed. NF (sl rubbed, spine sunned). *Polyanthos.* $25/£16

SYMONDS, JOHN ADDINGTON. The Life of Michelangelo Buonarroti. J. C. Nimmo, 1893. 1st ed. 2 vols. xxxii,469; viii,449pp; 51 plts. Teg, untrimmed. (Vol 1 eps mkd; cl sl mkd, rubbed.) *Hollett.* $72/£45

SYMONDS, JOHN ADDINGTON. New Italian Sketches. Bernhard Tauchnitz, 1884. Copyright ed. Contemp patterned bds, leather spine label, ribbon marker. VG (spine sl sunned). *Tiger.* $24/£15

SYMONDS, JOHN ADDINGTON. A Problem in Modern Ethics. London: Privately ptd, 1896. One of 100 numbered. VG (ex-lib, lib pocket, labels, sm dot on spine; bend in fr bd). *Beasley.* $60/£38

SYMONDS, JOHN ADDINGTON. Sir Philip Sidney. Macmillan, 1886. Sewn; 4pp pub's inserted ads tipped in at end (listing only first 37 titles of series). Eps coated black. Scarlet buckram. (Sl flexion creasing rear cvr), o/w VF. *Temple.* $21/£13

SYMONDS, JOHN ADDINGTON. Walt Whitman, a Study. London, 1893. VG. *Typographeum.* $85/£53

SYMONDS, JOHN ADDINGTON. Walt Whitman, a Study. London: John C. Nimmo, 1893. 1st ed, trade issue. Port. Grn cl, gilt. VG (blank eps foxed; edges sl rubbed, dknd). *Reese.* $100/£63

SYMONDS, JOHN. Conversations with Gerald. London: Duckworth, 1974. 1st Eng ed. NF (spine tail sl bumped) in dj (sl creased). *Ulysses.* $48/£30

SYMONDS, MARY and LOUISA PREECE. Needlework Through the Ages. London, 1928. 104 plts. 1/2 vellum (soiled). *Swann*.* $258/£161

SYMONDS, MARY and LOUISA PREECE. Needlework Through the Ages. Hodder & Stoughton, 1928. 103 plts. Orange cl. (Lt spotted; hinges cracked, stain fr cvr, spine sl faded.) *Sotheby's*.* $368/£230

SYMONDS, R. W. The Present State of Old English Furniture. Duckworth, 1927. VG in dj (very spotted, defective). *Hollett.* $48/£30

SYMONDS, R. W. Thomas Tompion: His Life and Work. London: B.T. Batsford, (1951). 1st ed. One of 350. Signed. Color frontis, fldg facs. Teg. 3/4 red levant morocco, gilt. (2 sm wormholes at spine foot), else Fine. *Pacific*.* $345/£216

SYMONS, A. J. A. A. J. A. Symons to Wyndham Lewis. 24 Letters. Edinburgh: Tragara, 1982. One of 120. Frontisport, 1 plt. Fine in stiff wraps, marbled dj, title label. *Any Amount.* $48/£30

SYMONS, A. J. A. Emin, Governor of Equatoria. London: Falcon Press, (1950). 2nd ed. Poor in pict bds (spine torn, defective at base). *Maggs.* $24/£15

SYMONS, A. J. A. H. M. Stanley. London: Falcon Press, 1950. 2nd Eng ed. VG in blue cl, gilt. Dj (spine ends chipped). *Maggs.* $72/£45

SYMONS, A. J. A. Inaugural Address of His Oddshippe Bro. A. J. A. Symons (Speculator). (London: Curwen), 1938. 1st ed. VG in gray ptd wrappers. *Maggs.* $104/£65

SYMONS, A. J. A. A True Recital of the Procedure of the Second Banquet Held by the Corvine Society. 'Imprimatur Magister Magn., Soc. Corv.,' 1930. Ptd wrappers. *Maggs.* $120/£75

SYMONS, ARTHUR. Aubrey Beardsley. London: J.M. Dent, 1905. New ed. Frontis, 29 b/w plts. (Materials pertaining to Beardsley tipped-in.) Externally Good. *Turtle Island.* $50/£31

SYMONS, ARTHUR. The Cafe Royal and Other Essays. (Beaumont Press, 1923.) One of 310. Uncut. VG in buckram-backed dec bds, gilt. *Cox.* $96/£60

SYMONS, ARTHUR. Confessions, a Study in Pathology. NY, 1930. 1st ed. Ltd to 542 numbered, signed. Teg. (Sl worn.) *King.* $60/£38

SYMONS, ARTHUR. The Fool of the World and Other Poems. London: Heinemann, 1906. 1st Eng ed. Good (prelims, edges spotted; sl internal spotting; eps sl browned, dusty; spine ends, corners bumped, rubbed; cvrs sl mkd). *Ulysses.* $88/£55

SYMONS, ARTHUR. The Fool of the World. Heinemann, 1906. 1st ed. VG- (eps, few ll foxed; cl sl mkd, spine cockled). *Any Amount.* $40/£25

SYMONS, ARTHUR. Great Acting in English. Privately ptd, (Ballantyne), 1907. 1st ed. 16pp, stabbed and sewn as issued. Uncut, unopened. VG in brn ptd paper wrappers. *Maggs.* $240/£150

SYMONS, ARTHUR. Knave of Hearts. Heinemann, 1913. 1st ed. (Prelims sl foxed; lower corners sl bumped), o/w VG + . *Any Amount.* $45/£28

SYMONS, ARTHUR. Love's Cruelty. Martin Secker, 1923. 1st Eng ed. VG (eps partly browned, top edge dusty; spine ends, corners sl bumped, rubbed) in dj (nicked, rubbed, sl dusty, browned). *Ulysses.* $152/£95

SYMONS, JULIAN. The 30's. Cresset, 1960. 1st UK ed. VG (ink inscrip) in dj. *Williams.* $40/£25

SYMONS, JULIAN. Conan Doyle: Portrait of an Artist. NY: Mysterious Press, (1987). 1st ed. NF in NF dj. *Gravesend.* $35/£22

SYMONS, JULIAN. The Immaterial Murder Case. Gollancz, 1945. 1st UK ed, 1st bk. Fine (spine sl faded). *Martin.* $19/£12

SYMONS, JULIAN. Mortal Consquences. NY: Harper & Row, (1972). 1st ed. VG in Good dj (worn, edges torn, price-clipped). *Gravesend.* $40/£25

SYNGE, J. M. The Shadow of the Glen and Riders to the Sea. London: Elkin Mathews, 1905. Wraps. (Sl edgeworn, few chips), else Good. *Metropolitan*.* $57/£36

SYNGE, URSULA. Weland: Smith of the Gods. London: Bodley Head, 1972. 1st ed. 5.5x8.75. Charles Keeping (illus). 94pp. Fine in dj. *Cattermole.* $40/£25

Synopsis of Modern Practical Surgery. Boston: Hewes & Sanborn, 1835. 343pp. Good (water stains, spine nick, spine damage). *Bookcell.* $30/£19

SYPHER, J. R. History of the Pennsylvania Reserve Corps. Lancaster: Elias Barr, 1865. 1st ed. 723pp (lacks orig feps; foxed); 4 Good engr port plts. Early crimson sheep, marbled bds (later red cl tape over spine, joints; worn, edges scuffed). *Baltimore*.* $80/£50

SYRETT, NETTA. The Vanishing Princess. London: David Nutt, (1909). 1st ed. Lg sq 8vo. (ii),3-93; 11 plts by Charles Robinson. Pict red cl (sm split at spine, neatly repaired). Very Nice. *Sotheran.* $109/£68

SZABAD, EMERIC. Hungary, Past and Present. Edinburgh: A&C Black, 1854. 1st ed. xiii,418pp. Aeg. Full contemp calf, raised bands, gilt. (Ink inscrip; rebacked), o/w VG. *Sotheran.* $237/£148

SZABO, ARPAD. The Beginnings of Greek Mathematics. A.M. Ungar (trans). Dordrecht/Boston: D. Reidel, 1978. 1st ed. (Fep mkd), o/w VG in dj. *Worldwide.* $65/£41

SZARKOWSKI, JOHN and MARIA MORRIS HAMBOURG. The Work of Atget: Volume 1, Old France. NY: MOMA, 1981. 1st ed. 120 plts. Blind-emb cl. NF in pict dj. *Cahan.* $150/£94

SZARKOWSKI, JOHN (ed). E. J. Bellocq: Storyville Portraits: Photographs from the New Orleans Red-Light District, Circa 1912. NY: MOMA, 1979. 34 full-pg b/w plts. Fine in pict stiff wrappers (mk lower edge). *Cahan.* $50/£31

SZARKOWSKI, JOHN (intro). New Photography USA. NY/London: MOMA/Photographers Gallery, 1972. 22 b/w photos. NF in ptd stiff wrappers. *Cahan.* $35/£22

SZARKOWSKI, JOHN. Irving Penn. NY/Boston, (1984). 1st ed. Folio. 156 repros. (Sl worn.) Dj (extrems yellowed). *Swann*.* $230/£144

SZARKOWSKI, JOHN. Mirrors and Windows. NY: MOMA, 1980 (1978). 3rd ptg. 127 plts. Fine in illus dj. *Cahan.* $45/£28

SZE, MAI-MAI. The Tao of Painting. NY: Bollingen Series/Pantheon Books, (1956). 1st ed. 2 vols. Grn cl. Fine in djs, slipcase. *Appelfeld.* $150/£94

SZILAGYI, STEVE. Photographing Fairies. NY: Ballantine, 1992. 1st ed. Uncorrected proof copy. VG in ptd wrappers. *Gravesend.* $40/£25

SZIRTES, GEORGE. Homage to Cheval. Berkhamsted: Priapus, 1980. One of 30 numbered, signed. Frontis. NF (cvrs sl mkd, corners sl creased). *Ulysses.* $56/£35

SZYK, ARTHUR. Ink and Blood: A Book of Drawings. NY: Heritage Press, 1946. One of 1500. 12 1/4 x 9. Fine in slipcase. *Pacific*.* $690/£431

SZYK, ARTHUR. The New Order. NY: Putnam, (1941). 1st ed. Fine in VG dj (spine ends, corners rubbed). *Pacific*.* $115/£72

T

Tables of Ancient Coins, Weights and Measures. (By John Arbuthnot.) London: J. Tonson, 1727. 1st ed. (10),327,(18 plts, tables, 1 fldg)pp. Orig calf (worn, nicely rebacked) w/tooled calf spine, raised bands, leather label. Contents Fine (early name, date, bkpl). *Hartfield.* $495/£309

TAFT, ROBERT. Artists and Illustrators of the Old West. NY, 1953. 1st ed. VG in dj (sl worn). *Dumont.* $75/£47

TAFT, ROBERT. Photography and the American Scene: a Social History, 1839-1889. NY: Macmillan, 1942. 1st ed, 2nd ptg. (Top, fore-edge foxed), else VG in dj. *Cahan.* $85/£53

TAGGARD, GENEVIEVE. The Life and Mind of Emily Dickinson. NY: Knopf, 1930. 1st ed, lg paper issue. One of 200 signed. 22 plts. Uncut. Blue bds. Fine. *Cummins.* $250/£156

TAGORE, RABINDRANATH. Chitra. India Soc, 1913. 1st ed. One of 500 ptd. Teg, rest uncut. White buckram, gilt. (Spine sl browned), o/w Fine. *Cox.* $29/£18

TAIBO, PACO IGNACIO II. An Easy Thing. NY: Viking, 1990. 1st ed. (Rmdr stripe to bottom edge), else Fine in dj. *Lame Duck.* $50/£31

TAIBO, PACO IGNACIO II. Life Itself. NY: Mysterious, 1990. 1st ed in English. Fine in dj w/pub's ad laid in. *Lame Duck.* $45/£28

TAILLANDIER, YVON. Indelible Miro. NY: Tudor, (1972). 1st Amer ed. 2 lithos. VG in dj (spine ends sl rubbed), slipcase. *Pacific*.* $115/£72

TAINE, H. A. History of English Literature. H. Van Laun (trans). Edinburgh: Edmonston & Douglas, 1873-1874. 4 vols. Marbled eps. Contemp 1/2 calf, marbled bds. *Bickersteth.* $200/£125

TAINE, JOHN. (Pseud of Eric Temple Bell.) The Forbidden Garden. Reading: Fantasy, 1947. 1st ed. (Stain to 1/2-title), else VG in dj (spine head chipped). *Pacific*.* $58/£36

TAINE, JOHN. (Pseud of Eric Temple Bell.) The Iron Star. L.A.: F.P.C.I., (1951). Rpt. Probable 1st binding: grn w/gold lettering. NF in VG + red 'F.P.C.I' dj (spine head lt chipped). *Other Worlds.* $40/£25

TAINE, JOHN. (Pseud of Eric Temple Bell.) The Purple Sapphire. NY: E.P. Dutton, (1924). 1st ed. Good in dj (sm corner tears, spine ends lack pieces). *Pacific*.* $58/£36

TAIT, WILLIAM. Cruise of H.M.S. Cleopatra, 1892-1895. Plymouth: C. Mansfield, n.d. (ca 1896). 1st ed. Folio. 136pp; 25 collotype plts. Pict cl, gilt. (Spine repaired.) *Maggs.* $440/£275

TAKAHASHI, SEIICHIRO. Traditional Woodblock Prints of Japan. NY/Tokyo: Weatherhill/Heibonsha, (1972). 1st ed, 5th ptg. Fldg chart. Dec stiff bds. Fine in NF dj. *Turtle Island.* $45/£28

TALBOT, CLARE RYAN. Historic California in Bookplates. L.A.: Graphic, 1936. Envelope w/collection of 30 + loose bkpls tipped onto rear cvr. (Bds worn, taped.) Internally VG. *Dumont.* $175/£109

TALBOT, ETHELBERT. My People of the Plains. NY: Harper, (1906). 1st ed. 12 photo plts. Grn cl, gilt. VG (edges lt worn). *House.* $25/£16

TALBOT, EUGENE. Interstitial Gingivitis or So-Called Pyorrhoea Alveolaris. Phila, 1899. 1st ed. 192pp. *Fye.* $150/£94

TALBOT, FRITZ B. Treatment of Epilepsy. NY: Macmillan, 1930. 1st ed. Fine. *Glaser.* $50/£31

TALBOT, THEODORE. The Journals of Theodore Talbot, 1843 and 1849-52.... Charles H. Carey (ed). Portland, OR: Metropolitan, 1931. 1st ed. Blue cl. (Sl shelfworn), else NF. Howes T13. *Pacific*.* $92/£58

TALBOT, THEODORE. The Journals of...1843 and 1849-52. (By Theodore Talbot.) Portland: Metropolitan Press, 1931. 1st ed. VG. *Book Market.* $75/£47

TALBOT, THEODORE. Soldier in the West. Letters of Theodore Talbot...1845-53. Robert Hine and Sacoie Lottinville (eds). Norman: Univ of OK, (1972). 1st ed. Map. Gray cl. NF in dj. *House.* $25/£16

TALBOT-BOOTH, E. Merchant Ships 1949-1950 Edition. NY: McGraw-Hill, 1949. Blue cl. VG. *American Booksellers.* $110/£69

TALCOTT, DUDLEY VAILL. Report of the Company. NY, 1936. 1st ed. VG in dj (taped, sm piece out). *King.* $35/£22

Tale of a Tail: A Xmas Cat-Astrophe. London: Marcus Ward, (ca 1890). Obl 12mo. 8pp pull-out panorama. Good in self-wrappers (spine lt chipped). *Reisler.* $140/£88

Tale of a Tub. (By Jonathan Swift.) London: Charles Bathurst, 1760. xvii,(1),190pp; 8 engr plts. Contemp sprinkled calf, raised bands, gilt. (Bkpl, inscrips; 1 quire, 1 plt w/sl marginal dampstain, ll evenly dknd, sl foxed; fr joint cracked, rear joint w/sm crack at top, corners sl worn, sl loss at spine.) *Pirages.* $100/£63

Tale of a Tub. (By J. Swift.) London, 1811. 322pp. Full speckled calf. (Ex-lib, tips, frontis foxed, bkpls; spine head lacks 1/2-inch), else Good. *King.* $95/£59

TALFOURD, THOMAS NOON. The Letters of Charles Lamb, with a Sketch of His Life. London, 1837. 1st ed. 2 vols. Frontisports. VG (sl rubbed, spines sunned). *Polyanthos.* $75/£47

Tall Book of Nursery Tales. Harper, (1944). 1st ed. Feodor Rojankovsky (illus). 4to. 120pp. VG in VG dj. *Davidson.* $95/£59

TALLACK, WILLIAM. The California Overland Express. L.A.: Hist Soc of Southern CA, 1935. 1st bk ed. Ltd to 150 ptd. Long fldg frontis map, photo plt, map. (Lower corners sl bumped), else NF. *Argonaut*. $275/£172

TALLACK, WILLIAM. The California Overland Express: The Longest Stage-Ride in the World. L.A.: Historical Soc of Southern CA, 1935. One of 150 ptd. Fdlg map. (Lower corners sl bumped), else NF. *Pacific**. $196/£123

TALLANT, ROBERT. Mr. Preen's Salon. GC: Doubleday, 1949. 1st ed. Fine in NF dj (sm tear crown). *Between The Covers*. $50/£31

TALLENT, ANNIE D. The Black Hills; Or, The Last Hunting Ground of the Dakotas. St. Louis, MO: Nixon-Jones Ptg, 1899. 1st ed. VG (cvr edges lt worn, spine ends tender). Howes T14. *Labordo*. $250/£156

TALLEY, THOMAS W. Negro Folk Rhymes, Wise and Otherwise, with a Study. NY: Macmillan, 1922. 1st ed. NF (spine worn). *Beasley*. $150/£94

TALLMADGE, BENJAMIN. Memoir of Col. Benjamin Tallmadge. Henry P. Johnson (ed). NY: Gillis Press, 1904. Ltd to 350. 24 plts. Vellum (spot fr cvr). Contents Fine. *Heinoldt*. $60/£38

TALMAN, JAMES J. Loyalist Narratives from Upper Canada. Toronto: Champlain Soc, 1946. One of 550 numbered. Uncut, unopened. Gilt-stamped red buckram. (Sl worn.) *Oinonen**. $70/£44

TAN, AMY. The Hundred Secret Senses. NY: Putnam, (1995). 1st ed. One of 175. Signed. As New in slipcase. *Pacific**. $69/£43

TAN, AMY. The Joy Luck Club. NY: Putnam, (1989). 1st ed, 1st bk. Fine in Fine dj. *Lenz*. $150/£94

TAN, AMY. The Kitchen God's Wife. NY, 1991. 1st Amer ed. Signed presentation. Fine (sm stamp) in Fine dj. *Polyanthos*. $45/£28

TANIZAKI, JUNICHERO. The Key. NY: Knopf, 1961. 1st Amer ed. VF in VF dj. *Between The Covers*. $150/£94

TANKERSLEY, ALLEN P. John B. Gordon: A Study in Gallantry. Atlanta: Whitehall, 1955. 1st ed. Frontisport. Gray cl. NF in dj (lt browned). *Chapel Hill*. $75/£47

TANNER, LAWRENCE E. Recollections of a Westminster Antiquary. John Baker, 1969. 1st ed. Frontis. Dj. *Forest*. $29/£18

TANNER, ROBERT G. Stonewall in the Valley. GC, (1976). 1st ed. VG+ in VG+ dj. *Pratt*. $35/£22

TANNER, V. Outlines of the Geography, Life and Customs of Newfoundland-Labrador (the Eastern Part of the Labrador Peninsula). Cambridge: At the Univ, 1947. 2 vols. 5 maps. VF in ptd djs. *High Latitude*. $500/£313

Taormina, Wilhelm von Gloeden. Pasadena: Twelvetrees, 1986. 1st ed. Dj (lt soiled). *Swann**. $103/£64

TAPLIN, WILLIAM. The Sporting Dictionary and Rural Repository of Geaneral Information Upon...the Sports of the Field. London, 1803. 2 vols. Contemp calf. (Worn, joints broken, spine labels gone, foxing.) *Oinonen**. $140/£88

TARBELL, IDA M. The History of the Standard Oil Company. NY: McClure, Phillips, 1904. 1st ed. 2 vols. Teg. Red cl, gilt. (Both vols lack fep, sm ink stamps; spot stain fr cvr vol 2.) Texts Clean. *Baltimore**. $90/£56

TARBELL, IDA M. In the Footsteps of the Lincolns. NY: Harper, 1924. 1st ed. Inscribed by Tarbell and Edwin Markham. Frontis. Blue cl. Fine in Good dj (tape-repaired on verso). *Chapel Hill*. $100/£63

TARBELL, IDA M. The Life of Abraham Lincoln. NY: Lincoln Memorial Assoc, (1900). 2 vols. Frontispieces. Red cl, gilt. Fine. *House*. $35/£22

TARBELL, IDA M. The Rising of the Tide. NY: Macmillan, 1919. 1st ed. Charcoal cl, gilt. NF in Good dj (browned, chipped). *Reese*. $50/£31

TARCOV, EDITH. Rumplestiltskin. NY: Four Winds, 1973. 1st ed. 6.25x8.25. Edward Gorey (illus). 48pp. VG in dj. *Cattermole*. $60/£38

TARG, WILLIAM. Bibliophile in the Nursery. Cleveland: World Publishing, (1957). 1st ed. Fldg frontis. NF in dj. *Pacific**. $63/£39

TARG, WILLIAM. Bibliophile in the Nursery. Cleveland: World, 1957. VG+ (shelfworn) in dj (sl worn). *My Bookhouse*. $62/£39

TARG, WILLIAM. Carousel for Bibliophiles. NY: Dueschnes, (1947). 1st ed. VG in dj (spine, extrems chipped). *Pacific**. $58/£36

TARKINGTON, BOOTH. The Fascinating Stranger. NY: Doubleday, Page, 1923. 1st trade ed. VG in dj (sl worn). *Second Life*. $85/£53

TARKINGTON, BOOTH. Lady Hamilton and Her Nelson. NY: House of Books, 1945. 1st ed. One of 300 numbered, signed. (Spine sl worn, edges mkd), else Good. *Reese*. $40/£25

TARKINGTON, BOOTH. Penrod. NY: Doubleday, Page, 1914. 1st ed, later issue. Inscribed, dated. Blue cl. (Lt worn, fr inner hinge cracked), else Fine. *Cummins*. $300/£188

TARKINGTON, BOOTH. The Plutocrat. D-P, 1927. 1st ed. Fine in VG dj. *Fine Books*. $18/£11

TARKINGTON, BOOTH. Ramsey Milholland. GC: Doubleday, Page, 1919. 1st ed, later state, w/'ou' at 215:15. Inscribed, dated 1937. Brn cl stamped in black. (Blank corner loss 1 leaf), else VG in pict dj (old tape reinforcement at inner edges, stained edges). *Reese*. $60/£38

TARLETON, BANASTRE. A History of the Campaigns of 1780 and 1781, in the Southern Provinces of North America. Dublin, 1787. Calf. Fine. *Felcone*. $600/£375

TARN, NATHANIEL. Where Babylon Ends. London/NY: Grossman/Cape Goliard, 1968. Ltd to 1400. NF in pict self-wraps. *Polyanthos*. $25/£16

TARRANT, MARGARET. The Margaret Tarrant Nursery Rhyme Book. Collins, 1944. 1st ed. Good+. *Green Meadow*. $48/£30

TARRANT, MARGARET. Nursery Rhymes. London: Ward, Lock, 1914. 1st ed. 8vo. 48 full-pg color plts. Blue cl, gilt, color paste label. (Margin of 2 prelims mkd, worn.) *Reisler*. $350/£219

TARVIN, A. H. A Century of Baseball. Standard Ptg, 1938. 1st ed. Good+. *Plapinger*. $45/£28

TASHJIAN, DICKRAN and ANN. Memorials for Children of Change. Middletown, CT: Wesleyan Univ, (1974). Fine in dj. *Turtle Island*. $75/£47

TASHJIAN, DICKRAN. Skyscraper Primitives. Middletown: Wesleyan Univ, (1975). Fine in dj. *Turtle Island*. $75/£47

TASKER, J. L. Travels in Europe and the East. York: Ptd by J.L. Foster, 1864. 1st (only?) ed. viii,9-174,(1)imprint. Gilt edges. Red ribbed cl (fr hinge cracked, sl soiled), gilt. *Morrell*. $72/£45

TASLAUANU, OCTAVIAN C. With the Austrian Army in Galicia. Skeffington, (1918). 1st Eng ed. Fldg frontis map (creased). VG (rubber stamp). *Clearwater*. $48/£30

TASSI, ROBERTO. Graham Sutherland; Complete Graphic Work. London: Thames & Hudson, 1978. Pub's dec cl. Mint in color dj. *Europa*. $96/£60

TASSIN, RAY. Stanley Vestal, Champion of the West. Glendale: A.H. Clark, 1973. 13 plts. Dj. *Heinoldt*. $30/£19

TATE, ALLEN. Mr. Pope and Other Poems. NY: Minton, Balch, 1928. 1st ed. Fine in NF dj (spine sl dknd, sm chip foot). *Beasley*. $600/£375

TATE, ALLEN. Stonewall Jackson, the Good Soldier. NY, 1928. 2nd ptg. (Sl foxed; bkpl, sl worn, spine sl faded.) *Woolman*. $100/£63

TATE, JAMES. The Lost Pilot. New Haven: Yale Univ, 1967. 1st ed, 1st bk. Rev slip laid in. Fine in Fine dj. *Lenz*. $175/£109

Tatler of California. Volume V, No. 23. L.A.: Tatler, 1912. NF in pict wrappers. *Pacific**. $92/£58

TATTERSALL, GEORGE. The Pictorial Gallery of English Race Horses. London: Bohn, 1850. All edges yellow. 3/4 red morocco by Bayntun, spine gilt in 6 compartments. (Sl foxed, soiled, few text ll w/margins restored; lt rubbed.) *Oinonen**. $475/£297

TATTERSALL, GEORGE. Sporting Architecture. London, 1841. Pub's gilt-dec cl. (Foxed, soiled, sl stains; shelfworn, spine chipped.) *Oinonen**. $150/£94

TATTERSALL, GEORGE. Sporting Architecture. London, 1841. 3/4 morocco. (Foxed, soiled, sl stains; rubbed.) *Oinonen**. $275/£172

TATUM, LAWRIE. Our Red Brothers. Phila: John C. Winston, 1899. (Extrems lt worn), else VG. *Dumont*. $125/£78

TAUBERT, SIGFRED. Bibliopola. Hamburg, 1966. 1st ed. 2 vols. Folio. 258 plts, incl 42 color facs. Red morocco labels. *Forest*. $176/£110

Tavern Anecdotes, and Reminiscences of the Origin of Signs, Clubs, Coffee-Houses, Streets, City Companies, Wards.... William Cole, (1825). Sole ed. Etched add'l vignette tp, vi,(i)-vi,(7)-296pp. Red sprinkled edges. Contemp 1/2 calf, gilt, glazed cotton sides. Good (paper fault resulting in sm hole in [C8], [G3], and [K3] affecting few letters of text, eps sl spotted, bkpl; rebacked, orig gilt-lettered label re-laid in 2nd compartment; hinges strengthened). *Blackwell's*. $240/£150

TAVERNER, ERIC. Trout Fishing from All Angles. London: Seeley, Service, 1933. NF in dj (spine ends rubbed) w/pict cvr label. *Pacific**. $58/£36

TAVERNIER, JOHN BAPTISTE. The Six Voyages...Finished in the Year 1670. J. P. (trans). Ptd for R.L. & M.P., 1678. 2 vols. Folio in 4's. (iv),2,(xvi),264; (ii),119,(3)pp. 23 plts, 1 engr. Contemp calf, raised bands. Sound (top margin lt waterstained throughout, not affecting text, browned, paper repair to blank top margin A1; rebacked, early label relaid in 2nd compartment, sides rubbed, re-cornered, recased). *Blackwell's*. $1,040/£650

TAYLOR, ALBERT PIERCE. Under Hawaiian Skies. Hawaii, 1926. 2nd ed. (Feps lt browned; spine sl rubbed, dknd.) *Edwards*. $48/£30

TAYLOR, ALFRED. On Poisons in Relation to Medical Jurisprudence and Medicine. Phila, 1859. 2nd Amer ed. 755pp. Full leather. *Fye*. $100/£63

TAYLOR, ALFRED. On Poisons in Relation to Medical Jurisprudence and Medicine. Phila: Henry C. Lea, 1875. 3rd ed. Contemp(?) sheep. (Spine rubbed; parts of 4 letters on title effaced), else Sound. *Boswell*. $125/£78

TAYLOR, ARTHUR V. (ed). Origines Golfianae. Woodstock, VT: Elm Tree, 1912. Ltd to 500 numbered. Frontis, 7 plts. Grn linen, dec bds, paper spine label. Good in pub's brn cardbd slipcase. *Karmiole*. $300/£188

TAYLOR, ARTHUR V. (ed). Origines Golfianae. Woodstock: Elm Tree, 1912. 1st ed. One of 500. Frontis. Prospectus laid in. Cl-backed dec bds, paper spine label. (Emb stamp; label rubbed), else Fine in VG slipcase (soiled, sl rubbed). *Pacific**. $920/£575

TAYLOR, BAYARD. Central Asia. Travels in Cashmere, Little Thibet and Central Asia. NY: Scribner, 1874. 1st ed. 365,6pp; fldg illus, fldg map. (Ex-lib; sl rubbed, spine ends sl frayed, sl foxed, edges sl damp-stained), o/w VG. *Worldwide*. $45/£28

TAYLOR, BAYARD. Central Asia. Travels in Cashmere, Little Thibet and Central Asia. Thomas Stevens (ed). NY: Scribner, 1892. Rev ed. vii,294pp; 16 plts. (Sl rubbed, sl foxed), o/w VG. *Worldwide*. $45/£28

TAYLOR, BAYARD. Eldorado or Adventures in the Path of Empire.... NY, 1850. 2nd Amer ed. 2 vols. 12,251; 247pp; 8 tinted engr plts. (Lt foxed, corner of 5pp torn off, affecting few words of text; fr hinge vol 1 weak, both vols w/2-inch layer of cl missing near bottom.) *Heinoldt*. $85/£53

TAYLOR, BAYARD. Eldorado, or, Adventures in the Path of Empire. NY: Putnam, 1850. 1st ed. 2 vols. xii,251; (2),247pp + 45pp ads; 8 tinted litho plts. (Foxing to plts, some contents, lt soil; spines rubbed, faded, ends sl worn, corners showing), else VG. Howes T43. *Pacific**. $1,093/£683

TAYLOR, BAYARD. Picturesque Europe, a Delineation by Pen and Pencil. NY: Appleton, (1875). 3 vols. Aeg. Pub's deluxe binding of full black morocco, gilt. Fine set. *Swann**. $431/£269

TAYLOR, BAYARD. A Visit to India, China and Japan in the Years 1853. NY: Putnam, 1860. 16th ed. Frontis, 539pp. (Ex-lib; sl soiled, foxed), o/w Good. *Worldwide*. $35/£22

TAYLOR, BENJAMIN F. Between the Gates. Chicago: S.C. Griggs, 1878. 1st ed. 292pp + ads. Brn cl (worn, soiled). Internally VG. *Parmer*. $25/£16

TAYLOR, C. R. H. A Pacific Bibliography: Printed Matter Relating to the Native Peoples of Polynesia, Melanesia and Micronesia. Wellington, NZ: Polynesian Soc, 1951. 1st ed. Photo frontis, fldg map. Fine (extrems sl rubbed). *Pacific**. $115/£72

TAYLOR, CHRISTOPHER and RICHARD MUIR. Visions of the Past. Dent, 1983. VG in dj. *Hadley*. $24/£15

TAYLOR, DICK and PAT HOWELL. Las Vegas, City of Sin? San Antonio, TX, (1963). 1st ed. Inscribed by Taylor. Dec cl. NF in VG dj. *Sagebrush*. $35/£22

TAYLOR, E. G. R. and M. W. RICHEY. The Geometrical Seaman: A Book of Early Nautical Instruments. London: Hollis & Carter, 1962. 1st ed. NF in dj. *Pacific**. $29/£18

TAYLOR, E. H. A Taxonomic Study of the Cosmopolitan Scincoid Lizards of the Genus Eumeces. Lawrence, 1935. 43 plts. Binder's buckram (sl soiled, spotted; names, pp tanned). C. F. Kauffeld's sig. *Sutton*. $100/£63

TAYLOR, EDWARD S. et al (eds). The History of Playing Cards. London: John Camden Hotten, 1865. 1st ed. 48 plts. Pict cl (shelfworn, spine tips frayed; lacks frontis, new eps). *Dramatis*. $120/£75

TAYLOR, ELEANOR ROSS. Wilderness of Ladies. NY: McDowell, Obolensky, (1960). 1st ed, 1st bk. Fine in NF dj (short mended tear on verso). *Reese*. $85/£53

TAYLOR, ELIZABETH. A Dedicated Man and Other Stories. London, 1965. 1st Eng ed. Nice in dj (sl nicked, faded). *Clearwater*. $72/£45

TAYLOR, FITCH W. Voyage Around the World, in the United States Frigate Columbia.... New Haven/NY: H. Mansfield/D. Appleton, 1842. 2nd ed. 2 vols in 1. 317; 332pp; 3 plts (1 color). Orig cl w/fr, rear bds laid down on mod cl. *Lefkowicz*. $125/£78

TAYLOR, FREDERICK WINSLOW. The Principles of Scientific Management. NY/London: Harper, 1911. 1st ed. Red cl. Very Nice (lacks fep). *M & S*. $250/£156

TAYLOR, FREDERICK. Recollections of a Horse Dealer. London: Ward & Lock, 1861. 1st ed. iv,300pp. Pub's ptd yellow bds. (Sl foxed, soiled; shelfworn, spine edges frayed.) *Oinonen**. $60/£38

TAYLOR, GRIFFITH. With Scott: the Silver Lining. London: Smith, Elder, 1916. 2 fldg maps. Dec cl (sl worn, mkd). Good. *High Latitude*. $550/£344

TAYLOR, J. E. Half-Hours in the Green Lanes. Edinburgh: Grant, 1910. 8th ed. Frontis. Pict cl. VG. *Savona*. $19/£12

TAYLOR, J. R. W. Gold from the Sea. Sydney: Aust. Pub, 1942. Grn cl. VG. *American Booksellers*. $40/£25

TAYLOR, JAMES BAYARD. Ximena; or the Battle of the Sierra Morena, and Other Poems. Phila: Herman Hooker, 1844. 1st ed. 84pp. Orig plain bds, paper label (partly rubbed away). *M & S*. $200/£125

TAYLOR, JAMES. Narrative of a Voyage to, and Travels in, Upper Canada.... Hull: John Nicholson, 1846. (Name, pp lt stained, dampstained, wrinkled, paper label chipped), else Nice. *Metropolitan**. $258/£161

TAYLOR, JEREMY. The Architectural Medal. Collonnade/British Museum, 1978. NF in dj. *Hadley*. $29/£18

TAYLOR, JEREMY. The Golden Grove. Logan Pearsall Smith (ed). Oxford: Clarendon, 1930. 1st Eng ed. NF (spine ends sl bumped) in dj (nicked, sl rubbed, mkd, dusty, browned, spine chip). *Ulysses*. $104/£65

TAYLOR, JOHN H. Taylor on Golf: Impressions, Comments and Hints. London: Hutchinson, 1902. 1st ed. Signed, dated 1902. Frontis. Dec grn cl, gilt. (Emb stamp, name; gilt sl tarnished), else NF. *Pacific**. $1,035/£647

TAYLOR, JOHN M. From the White House Inkwell. VT, 1968. 1st Amer ed. NF. *Polyanthos*. $45/£28

TAYLOR, JOHN RUSSELL. Edward Wolfe. London, 1986. Frontis port. Dj. *Edwards*. $32/£20

TAYLOR, JOHN. Pondoro. NY: S&S, 1955. Stated 1st ptg. VG + in VG dj. *Backman*. $50/£31

TAYLOR, KATHERINE AMES. Lights and Shadows of Yosemite. SF: H.S. Crocker, (1926). 1st ed. 40 photo plts. Tan cl. *Argonaut*. $60/£38

TAYLOR, KATHERINE AMES. San Francisco. (Stanford): Stanford Univ, 1929. 1st ed. Orig red wrappers (sm spine nick). NF. *House*. $25/£16

TAYLOR, LANDON. The Battle Field Reviewed: Narrow Escape from Massacre by the Indians of Spirit Lake...Rocky Mountain History and Tornado Experiences.... Chicago: The Author, 1881. 1st ed. 2 ports. (Extrems sl rubbed, sm spot to upper cvr.) Howes T70. *Sadlon*. $100/£63

TAYLOR, LOUIS. The Horse America Made. Louisville: Amer Saddle Horse Breeders, (1944). 1st ed. Blue embossed cl. VG +. *House*. $50/£31

TAYLOR, LOUIS. The Horse America Made. Harper, 1961. Good in dj (worn). *Rybski*. $20/£13

TAYLOR, MARSHALL W. The Fastest Bicycle Rider in the World. Worcester: Wormley Pub, 1928. 1st ed. VG. *Beasley*. $85/£53

TAYLOR, MART. The Gold Digger's Song Book. Cranium, 1975. One of 450. *Dawson*. $25/£16

TAYLOR, MARY L. The Tiger's Claw. London, 1956. Protected dj (frayed). *Grayling*. $88/£55

TAYLOR, MORRIS F. First Mail West. Albuquerque: Univ of NM, 1971. 1st ed. VG in dj (price-clipped). *Dumont*. $45/£28

TAYLOR, MRS. BASIL. Japanese Gardens. NY/London: Dodd, Mead/Methuen, 1912. 1st ed. 28 tipped-in pictures. Teg, untrimmed. (Name, browned; gilt faded on spine, corners bumped), else VG. *Fair Meadow*. $200/£125

TAYLOR, MRS. H. J. Yosemite Indians and Other Sketches. SF: Johnck & Seeger, 1936. 1st ed. One of 400. Paper spine label. NF (lt shelfworn) in dj. *Pacific**. $75/£47

TAYLOR, NATHANIEL W. Life on a Whaler or Antarctic Adventures in the Isle of Desolation. New London: County Hist Soc, 1929. One of 900. 16 plts. VG. *High Latitude*. $90/£56

TAYLOR, NORMAN (ed). The Garden Dictionary. Boston/NY: Houghton Mifflin, 1936. 1st ed. 20 color plts. (Foxed), else VG. *Fair Meadow*. $35/£22

TAYLOR, NORMAN (ed). Taylor's Encyclopedia of Gardening, Horticulture and Landscape Design. Boston: Houghton Mifflin, 1961. 4th ed, 1st ptg. (1st few pp wrinkled, name, lt pencil mks; shelf-worn), else VG. *Fair Meadow*. $30/£19

TAYLOR, OLIVER. Historic Sullivan: A History of Sullivan County, Tennessee.... Bristol, TN: King Ptg, 1909. 1st ed. Grn cl. VG (rear cvr sl scuffed). *Chapel Hill*. $95/£59

TAYLOR, R. R. Seeing the Elephant: The Letters of R. R. Taylor, Forty-Niner. John Walton Caughey (ed). (L.A.): Ward Ritchie, 1951. One of 250. Cl-backed bds, gilt. NF (corner sl bumped). *Pacific**. $52/£33

TAYLOR, RALPH C. Colorado South of the Border. Denver: Sage Books, 1963. Signed. VG in dj (sl worn). *Dumont*. $30/£19

TAYLOR, RAY W. Hetch Hetchy: The Story of San Francisco's Struggle to Provide a Water Supply for Her Future Needs. SF: Ricardo J. Orozco, 1926. One of 650. Signed, inscribed, tls. 16 inserted plts, 7 paginated plts. Paper spine label. *Pacific**. $196/£123

TAYLOR, RICHARD COWLING. Statistics of Coal. The Geographical and Geological Distribution of Mineral Combustibles or Fossil Fuel.... Phila: J.W. Moore, 1848. 1st ed. 6 fldg maps. (Sl foxed, top margin edge last few ll sl dampstained; spine ends, corners rubbed.) *Sadlon*. $125/£78

TAYLOR, ROBERT LEWIS. The Travels of Jaimie McPheeters. GC: Doubleday, 1958. 1st ed. (Name), else VG + in VG dj (lt chipped, lt dampstain at rear hinge). *Pettler*. $45/£28

TAYLOR, ROBERT LEWIS. Vessel of Wrath: The Life and Times of Carry Nation. (NY): NAL, (1966). 1st ed, 1st ptg. NF in dj (lt edgeworn). *Sadlon*. $35/£22

TAYLOR, SAMUEL. Angling in All Its Branches, Reduced to a Complete Science...In Three Parts. London, 1800. 1st ed, w/the half-title; there are no ads. xv,298pp. All edges yellow. Mod 3/4 morocco (lt worn, sl soiled). *Oinonen**. $100/£63

TAYLOR, TOM. Pictures of English Landscape. Text by Tom Taylor. London: Routledge, Warne & Routledge, 1863. 1st ed. 10x7.75. Birket Foster (illus), Brothers Dalziel (engrs). Aeg, gilt inner dentelles. Grn morocco, gilt, raised bands. (Foxed), else VG. *Pacific**. $115/£72

TAYLOR, WALTER (ed). The Deer of North America. Harrisburg: Stackpole, 1956. 1st ed. Color frontis. Fine. *Bowman*. $60/£38

TAYLOR, WALTER H. Four Years with General Lee. NY: Appleton, 1877. 1st ed. Frontisport, 199pp. Grn cl. (Fep excised, foxed), else VG. Howes T74. *Chapel Hill*. $95/£59

TAYLOR, WILLIAM. California Life Illustrated. NY: The Author, 1858. 1st ed. 348pp + 2pp ads; 16 full-pg woodcut plts. Blind-stamped purple cl (spine faded; some text foxed). *Karmiole*. $75/£47

TAYLOR, WILLIAM. Seven Years Street Preaching in San Francisco, California Embracing Incidents, Triumphant Death Scenes, Etc. W. P. Strickland (ed). NY: The Author, n.d. 1st ed, 22nd thousand. Signed holograph note. Frontisport. Brn cl, gilt. (Extrems sl worn), o/w NF. *Pacific**. $58/£36

TEALE, THOMAS PRIDGIN. A Treatise on Neuralgic Diseases, Dependent Upon Irritation of the Spinal Marrow and Ganglia of the Sympathetic Nerve. Phila: Carey & Hart, 1830. 1st Amer ed. iv,120pp. Orig bds, cl spine. Reading copy (heavily foxed; cvrs detached). *Glaser*. $60/£38

TEASDALE, SARA. Dark of the Moon. NY: Macmillan, 1926. 1st ed. One of 250. Signed. Parchment-backed blue bds, gilt. (Spine dknd), else VG in Fair slipcase (broken). *Pacific**. $127/£79

Teddy Bear. London: Valentine & Sons, (ca 1920). Shapebook. 3.5x6. 8 leaves. Color pict cvrs. Good. *Reisler*. $165/£103

TEDESCO, A. P. Relationship Between Type and Illustration in Books and Book Jackets. Brooklyn, (1948). Fine. *Truepenny*. $30/£19

TEERINK, H. A Bibliography of the Writings of Jonathan Swift. The Hague: Martinus Nijhoff, 1937. 1st ed. Ltd to 315 signed. Blue cl (extrems rubbed, headcaps bumped). *Maggs*. $288/£180

TEGETMEIER, WILLIAM B. The Poultry Book.... London: Routledge, 1873. New ed. Color litho tp, frontis, 28 plts. (Frontis torn at margin, lt spotting.) Orig morocco-backed cl (rubbed, spine ends torn), gilt. *Christie's**. $307/£192

TEGG, THOMAS. A Present for an Apprentice. William Tegg, 1848. 2nd ed. 8vo. Frontis by G. Cruikshank, xvii,381pp. Aeg. Pict red cl, gilt. Internally VG (spotted, dampmks, mostly to eps, cvr). *Bookmark.* $48/£30

TEGNER, ESAIAS. Frithiof's Saga. Stockholm: LEC, 1953. One of 1500. Red pastepaper bds, white buckram back, corners. Fine in matching slipcase. *Pacific*.* $40/£25

TEICHMAN, ERIC. Travels of a Consular Officer in North-West China. CUP, 1921. 1st ed. Med 8vo. xiv,219pp; 58 plts, 4 maps (2 fldg, in rear pocket). VG (cvrs sl spotted). *Ulysses.* $560/£350

TEICHMANN, HOWARD and GEORGE S. KAUFMAN. The Solid Gold Cadillac. NY: Random House, (1954). 1st ed. VF in VF dj. *Between The Covers.* $250/£156

TELL. (Pseud of Albert Buhrer.) A Rude Book. Cecil Palmer, 1926. 1st ed. Ltd to 1000. 26 full-pg caricatures. Uncut. Good in orig holland-backed bds (fr cvr sl soiled, mkd). *Cox.* $40/£25

TEMKO, A. Notre-Dame of Paris. Secker & Warburg, 1936. 22 plts. Pub's cl. VG. *Peter Taylor.* $40/£25

TEMPLE, J. Leopard in the Hills. London: Bell, 1953. 1st ed. VG+ in VG dj. *Mikesh.* $30/£19

TEMPLE, NIGEL. John Nash and the Village Picturesque. Sutton, 1979. VG in dj. *Hadley.* $40/£25

TEMPLE, PHILLIP. The Sea and the Snow. Melbourne: Cassell, 1966. VG in dj (worn, torn). *High Latitude.* $60/£38

TEMPLE, RICHARD. Oriental Experience. London: John Murray, 1883. 1st ed. xx,518pp; 5 fldg maps, 1 fldg plt. Red cl (bkpl, spine faded, sl rubbed), gilt. *Morrell.* $56/£35

TEMPLE, SETH J. Camp McClellan During the Civil War. Davenport, IA, 1928. 1st ed. 2-pg map. Good+ in ptd wraps. *Wantagh.* $25/£16

TEMPLE-PERKINS, E. A. Kingdom of the Elephant. London: A. Melrose, 1955. 1st ed. (Fep corner clipped), else NF in VG dj. *Mikesh.* $45/£28

Ten Commandments. John Winston Co, 1947. 1st ed stated. Arthur Szyk (illus). 8vo. Frontis, unpaginated; dbl-fold paper. Gray pict cl. VG. *Davidson.* $85/£53

Ten Little Mulligan Guards. NY: McLoughlin Bros, (ca 1870). Obl 4to. 12 full-color pp. Good in color pict wrappers (sl worn, spine split). *Reisler.* $750/£469

Ten Minutes Advice to Every Gentleman Going to Purchase a Horse out of a Dealer, Jockey, or, Groom's Stables.... (By Henry Bracken.) Phila, 1787. Contemp sheep. Fine. *Felcone.* $1,800/£1,125

TENGGREN, GUSTAV. Tenggren's Story Book. Golden, 1944. 4th ed. 10.3x13. 89pp. VG- (spine foot bumped, abraded for 1/2-inch, lower corners bumped) in Good+ dj (3 2-inch tears to fr, corners chipped rear). *Price.* $125/£78

TENNANT, EMMA. Black Marina. Faber, 1985. 1st UK ed. Fine in dj. *Williams.* $19/£12

TENNANT, EMMA. The Time of the Crack. Cape, 1973. 1st UK ed. Fine in dj. *Williams.* $26/£16

TENNANT, EMMA. The Time of the Crack. Cape, 1973. 1st UK ed. Signed. Fine in dj. *Williams.* $40/£25

TENNANT, JAMES EMERSON. Ceylon: An Account of the Island, Physical, Historical, and Topographical with Notices of Its Natural History, Antiquities and Productions. Longman, Green, Longman & Roberts, 1860. 5th ed. xxxix,643; xvi,669pp; 1 color fldg map. Aeg. Contemp maroon 1/2 morocco, marbled bds, gilt, raised bands. VG set (extrems sl worn). *Sotheran.* $317/£198

TENNANT, STEPHEN. Leaves from a Missionary's Notebook. Secker & Warburg, 1929. 1st ed. 62 full-pg dwgs. VG (feps mkd; bowed, edges rubbed, split to fr joint) in dj (torn, chipped, rubbed, mkd, soiled, dusty). *Ulysses.* $248/£155

TENNENT, J. EMERSON. Sketches of the Natural History of Ceylon. London, 1868. xxiii,500pp. Aeg. (Tp, frontis, head of some prelims sl stained; corners frayed, recased w/repairs to spine head.) *Edwards.* $96/£60

Tennessee. NY: Hastings House, 1939. 1st ed. VG+ in dj (lacks fr panel piece). *Labordo.* $70/£44

TENNEY, E. P. Colorado: And Homes in the New West, Comprising the Seventh Thousand of the New West, Revised and Illustrated. Boston/NY: Lee & Shepard/Charles T. Dillingham, 1880. (119)pp; fldg map. (Fr hinge weak, few spots of discoloration), else VG+ in pict cl. *Zubal*.* $30/£19

TENNEY, HORACE KENT. Vert and Venison. Privately ptd, 1924. 1st ed. Teg. 1/2-cl. (Ink name?; cvr rubbed.) *King.* $150/£94

TENNYSON, ALFRED. Demeter and Other Poems. London: Macmillan, 1889. 1st ed. Grn cl. (Joints sl rubbed), o/w Fine in 1/4 brn morocco slipcase w/chemise. *Cummins.* $125/£78

TENNYSON, ALFRED. A Dream of Fair Women. London: Grant Richards, 1900. 1st ed illus by E.J. Sullivan. Deluxe ed. One of 125. 4to. xviii,196,(i)pp; 40 engr plts, guards, 4 extra dup photogravure plts. Teg, rest uncut. Orig vellum-backed blue bds, gilt. Very Clean (corners sl bumped). *Sotheran.* $317/£198

TENNYSON, ALFRED. Guinevere and Other Poems. Boston: Dana Estes, 1912. 1st Amer ed. 4to. 24 mtd color plts by Florence Harrison. Teg. Ivory cl, gilt. Good. *Reisler.* $300/£188

TENNYSON, ALFRED. Idylls of the King. London: Edward Moxon, 1859. 1st ed, 1st issue w/verso of tp blank. 8 ad pp, (8),261pp. Aeg. Ribbed morocco, gilt, morocco spine labels, sl raised bands; bound by Bayntun. Fine. *Pacific*.* $104/£65

TENNYSON, ALFRED. Idylls of the King. LEC, 1952. Ltd to 1500 numbered, signed by Lynd Ward (illus). Fine in slipcase. *Swann*.* $115/£72

TENNYSON, ALFRED. In Memoriam, Annotated by the Author. London: Macmillan, 1905. 1st ed thus. Grn cl, gilt. Fine. *Macdonnell.* $30/£19

TENNYSON, ALFRED. The Lady of Shallot. NY: Dodd, Mead, (1881). 1st ed w/illus by Howard Pyle. 30 full-pg illus. Gray-grn pict cl. Cvrs VG (sl dusty, finger smudges; rep w/lt creases). *Baltimore*.* $300/£188

TENNYSON, ALFRED. The Lady of Shalott. NY: Dodd Mead, (1881). 1st ed. 4to. Aeg. Dk blue emb cl, gilt. VG. *Reisler.* $600/£375

TENNYSON, ALFRED. Maud, and Other Poems. London: Edward Moxon, 1855. 1st ed. Grn cl. (Spine sl faded), o/w Fine in 1/4 brn morocco slipcase w/chemise. *Cummins.* $400/£250

TENNYSON, ALFRED. The Poems of Alfred Lord Tennyson. LEC, 1974. One of 2000 signed by Reynolds Stone (illus). Fine in slipcase. *Swann*.* $230/£144

TENNYSON, ALFRED. Poems. Edward Moxon, 1842. 1st ed. One of 800. 2 vols. 12mo. 1/2-titles. Gilt edges. Later polished calf by Bedford, gilt, grn morocco labels. (Bk label.) *Sotheby's*.* $626/£391

TENNYSON, CHARLES. Alfred Tennyson. London: Macmillan, 1949. 1st ed. VG in dj (sl worn). *Hollett.* $32/£20

TENNYSON, HAROLD. The Story of a Young Sailor. London, 1918. 1st Eng ed. VG. *Clearwater.* $56/£35

TERMAN, LEWIS M. and CATHARINE MILES. Sex and Personality. Studies in Masculinity and Femininity. NY: McGraw-Hill, 1936. 1st ed. (Lib labels, pockets, stamps; sm dot), o/w Bright. *Beasley.* $45/£28

TERRELL, JOHN UPTON. Furs by Astor. NY, 1963. 1st ed. Inscribed. VG in dj (sl worn, faded). *Woolson.* $35/£22

TERRELL, JOHN UPTON. Pueblo of the Hearts. Palm Desert: Best West, (1966). 1st ed. Fine in Fine dj. *Book Market.* $20/£13

TERRELL, JOHN UPTON. Traders of the Western Morning. L.A.: Southwest Museum, 1967. 1st ed. Fine. *Harrington.* $35/£22

TERRELL, JOHN UPTON. War for the Colorado River. Arthur Clark, 1965. 1st ed. 2 vols. Frontis map. Brn cl. Fine in Fine djs. *Five Quail.* $85/£53

TERRY, ELLEN. The Story of My Life. London: Hutchinson, 1908. Port, 4 photogravures. Red cl. (Contemp presentations; text browned, spotted; rubbed), o/w Good. *Cummins.* $50/£31

TERRY, ELLEN. The Story of My Life. London: Hutchinson, 1908. One of 250 signed. 8 photogravures (few spots), 93 plts. Teg. Orig buckram (sl soiled, bubbled), gilt. *Hollett.* $120/£75

TERRY, T. PHILIP. Terry's Japanese Empire, Including Korea and Formosa. Boston/NY: Houghton Mifflin, 1914. 1st ed. 29 maps. Marbled edges. Crimson cl over thin paper bds, gilt. VG (lt aged, old document remnants mtd to fr pastedown; sl handled, corner lt bumped). *Baltimore*.* $90/£56

TERUKAZU, AKIYAMA. Japanese Painting. Geneva: Skira, 1961. Fine in color pict dj. *Petersfield.* $61/£38

TESNOHLIDEK, RUDOLF. The Cunning Little Vixen. NY, (1985). One of 250 numbered, signed by Maurice Sendak (illus). Slipcase. *Swann*.* $149/£93

TESSIER, THOMAS. How We Died. (Dublin): New Writers' Press, (1970). One of 200 numbered, signed. Fine in ptd sewn wrappers. *Dermont.* $100/£63

Testimonies Concerning the Character and Ministry of Mother Ann Lee and the First Witnesses of the Gospel of Christ's Second Appearing. Albany, 1827. 178pp. Orig 1/2 leather, paper over bds. (Name, ex-lib, stained, foxed; worn.) *Woolson.* $70/£44

TEVIS, WALTER. Far From Home. GC: Doubleday, 1981. 1st US ed. NF (spine ends sl bumped) in dj (mkd, dusty, sl creased, clipped, spotted, spine/edges browned). *Ulysses.* $104/£65

Texas. NY: Hastings House, 1940. 1st ed. VG in dj. *Labordo.* $75/£47

Texas. Being a Collection of Rare and Important Works and Manuscripts Relating to the Lone Star State. NY: Edward Eberstadt & Sons, (1963). Fine in stiff wrappers. *Argonaut.* $100/£63

TEY, JOSEPHINE. The Franchise Affair. NY: Macmillan, 1949. 1st US ed. VG+ (lt edgeworn) in dj (lt chipped, closed tears, edgeworn). *Janus.* $50/£31

THACHER, GEORGE A. Why Some Men Kill. N.p., 1919. Good (corners of cvrs, text bent) in wraps. *Baade.* $250/£156

THACHER, JAMES. The New American Dispensatory. Boston, 1810. 1st ed. 529pp. Recent 1/4 leather w/marbled bds, new eps. (Tp margins strengthened, lib stamp), o/w Fine. *Fye.* $300/£188

THACHER, JAMES. Observations on Hydrophobia, Produced by the Bite of a Mad Dog, or Other Rabid Animal. Boston, 1812. 1st ed. 302pp; 1 hand-colored plt. (Foxed; fr outer hinge cracked, spine label missing.) *Fye.* $300/£188

THACKERAY, WILLIAM MAKEPEACE. The Adventures of Philip. NY: Harper, 1862. 1st Amer bk ed. Black cl (spine tips frayed), gilt. *Macdonnell.* $165/£103

THACKERAY, WILLIAM MAKEPEACE. A Collection of Letters of W. M. Thackeray 1847-1855. London: Smith, Elder, 1887. 2nd ed. ix,190,(iv)pp. Gilt cl, beveled bds (extrems sl worn; inscrip). *Hollett.* $56/£35

THACKERAY, WILLIAM MAKEPEACE. Early and Late Papers. Boston: Ticknor & Fields, 1867. 1st Amer ed. Terra cotta cl, gilt. Fine. *Macdonnell.* $50/£31

THACKERAY, WILLIAM MAKEPEACE. The History of Henry Esmond, Esq. LEC, 1956. Ltd to 1500 numbered, signed by Edward Ardizzone (illus). Fine in slipcase. *Swann*.* $80/£50

THACKERAY, WILLIAM MAKEPEACE. The History of Pendennis. London: Bradbury & Evans, 1848-1850. 1st ed. 23 orig parts. Orig pict ptd wrappers, later morocco boxes. VG+ (some wrappers detached). *Pacific*.* $161/£101

THACKERAY, WILLIAM MAKEPEACE. The History of Pendennis. London: Bradbury & Evans, 1849-50. 1st bk ed. 2 vols. Blue-gray cl (rubbed, spines faded). VG. *Houle.* $495/£309

THACKERAY, WILLIAM MAKEPEACE. The History of Pendennis. London: Bradbury & Evans, 1849. 1st ed. 2 vols. 46 engr plts (lt offsetting). Gilt edges, inner dentelles. Full 19th-cent deep mustard wavy-grain morocco by Carss, gilt, raised bands. Very Clean set. *Young.* $176/£110

THACKERAY, WILLIAM MAKEPEACE. The History of Pendennis. Ipswich: LEC, 1961. One of 1500. Signed by Charles W. Stewart (illus). 2 vols. Blind-stamped mustard cl. Fine in glassine, slipcase. *Pacific*.* $29/£18

THACKERAY, WILLIAM MAKEPEACE. The Newcomes. Bradbury & Evans, 1854. 1st ed. 2 vols. viii,380; viii,375pp, complete w/half-titles, engr tps. Old watered silk (neatly recased), leather spine labels. *Hollett.* $296/£185

THACKERAY, WILLIAM MAKEPEACE. The Newcomes. LEC, 1954. Ltd to 1500 numbered, signed by Edward Ardizzone (illus). 2 vols. Fine in slipcase. *Swann*.* $46/£29

THACKERAY, WILLIAM MAKEPEACE. Notes of a Journey from Cornhill to Grand Cairo, by Way of Lisbon, Athens, Constantinople, and Jerusalem.... Chapman & Hall, 1846. 2nd ed. Color frontis, xi,221,(i)ads pp. Orig red pict cl, gilt. VG (sm 19th-cent cat entry fr pastedown; spine ends sl worn). *Sotheran.* $157/£98

THACKERAY, WILLIAM MAKEPEACE. The Rose and the Ring. LEC, 1942. Ltd to 1500 numbered, signed by Fritz Kredel (illus). Fine in slipcase. *Swann*.* $57/£36

THACKERAY, WILLIAM MAKEPEACE. Thackeray's Letters to an American Family. NY, 1904. 1st Amer ed. Teg. Vellum spine (sl sunned). Fine. *Polyanthos.* $30/£19

THACKERAY, WILLIAM MAKEPEACE. Thackerayana. London: C&W, 1901. New ed. Frontis. Red, gilt pict cl. NF (prelims foxed). *Turtle Island.* $55/£34

THACKERAY, WILLIAM MAKEPEACE. Vanity Fair. London: Bradbury & Evans, 1848. 1st ed, 1st issue, made up from the orig parts and w/woodcut of 'Marquis of Steyne' on p336 (w/rustic heading, p1, and 'Mr Pitt' reading on p543). Tall thick 8vo. xvi,624pp; 40 full-pg plts. Aeg. Full polished calf, gilt extra, by Riviere. VG (rebacked, w/orig spine laid down, cvrs worn) in custom-made, felt-lined solander case, morocco label. *Hartfield.* $1,095/£684

THACKERAY, WILLIAM MAKEPEACE. Vanity Fair. London: Bradbury & Evans, 1849. 2nd ed. 2 vols. Marbled edges. 3/4 red morocco, marbled bds, raised bands. Fine. *Appelfeld.* $200/£125

THACKERAY, WILLIAM MAKEPEACE. Vanity Fair. LEC, 1931. 998/1500 sets signed by John Austen (illus). 2 vols. 20 colorptd plts. 1/4 pink cl, gilt, patterned cream bds. Fine in djs w/ptd labels, matching bd slipcase w/ptd paper label (1 joint cracked). *Blackwell's.* $160/£100

THACKERAY, WILLIAM MAKEPEACE. The Virginians. Bradbury & Evans, 1858-59. 1st ed. 2 vols. viii,382; viii,376pp, complete w/2 engr tps, 39 plts. Mod 1/2 levant morocco, gilt. VG set (sl spotted). *Hollett.* $136/£85

THACKERAY, WILLIAM MAKEPEACE. The Virginians. A Tale of the Last Century. NY: Harper, 1859. 1st Amer ed. 411pp. Recent 1/2 calf. *Young.* $112/£70

THACKERAY, WILLIAM MAKEPEACE. The Works of. London: Smith, Elder, 1869-86. 22 vols. Marbled edges. Tree calf, gilt, morocco spine labels, raised bands; bound by Riviere. (1 vol w/fr cvr detached, 1 partly so; tape across 1 spine, some joints cracking), else VG set. *Pacific*.* $230/£144

THACKERAY, WILLIAM MAKEPEACE. The Works. Smith & Elder, 1869-1886. 24 vols. 8vo. Teg. Later red 1/2 morocco. (Bkpl.) *Sotheby's*.* $662/£414

THACKERAY, WILLIAM MAKEPEACE. The Works. London: Smith & Elder, 1869. 24 vols. Gilt edges. Contemp red calf, gilt. (Sl offsetting; lt rubbed.) *Christie's**. $699/£437

THACKERAY, WILLIAM MAKEPEACE. The Works. NY: Scribner, 1903-04. Kensington ed. 32 vols. Frontisport, tissue guard. Teg. Grn cl, gilt, glassine. (Some lack glassine, some glassine sl chipped), else Fine set. *Pacific**. $207/£129

THACKERAY, WILLIAM MAKEPEACE. The Works. NY/London: Harper, 1910. Centenary Biographical ed. 1st ed thus. One of 491 sets, this specially bound, limitation signed by the pub. 26 vols. Tall thick 4tos. Color illus by Howard Pyle tipped in at fr vol 1. Hand-marbled eps; teg, uncut. 3/4 red morocco, gilt extra, hand-marbled bds. (1st vol worn), else Fine set. *Hartfield*. $995/£622

THACKRAH, C. TURNER. The Effects of the Principal Arts, Trades, and Professions, and of Civic States and Habits of Living, on Health and Longevity.... Phila: Literary Rooms, 1831. 2nd Amer ed. 180pp. Period calf, morocco spine label. (Old inscrips, lacks rep, foxed), else VG. *Pacific**. $161/£101

THADEN, ROBERT E. Geology and Ore Deposits of the White Canyon Area, San Juan and Garfield Counties, Utah. Washington: USGS, 1964. 4 plts in rear pocket, 4 tables. VG + . *Five Quail*. $30/£19

THARP, LOUISE HALL. The Baroness and the General. Boston, (1962). 1st ed. VG + in VG + dj. *Pratt*. $20/£13

THARP, LOUISE HALL. The Peabody Sisters of Salem. London: Harrap, 1951. 1st ed. 11 plts. (Eps lt spotted.) Dj (sl chipped, torn). *Hollett*. $40/£25

THATCHER, B. B. Indian Biography. NY, 1832. 1st ed. 2 vols. Frontis, 324; 319pp. *Heinoldt*. $50/£31

THAYER, EMMA HOMAN. Wild Flowers of the Pacific Coast, from Original Water Color Sketches Drawn from Nature. NY: Cassell, (1887). 1st ed. 25 chromolitho plts. Aeg. Gilt-dec cl. (Adhesion damage to fr pastedown, few lib mks; spine worn, joints splitting, trace from removed label.) Internally VG. *Pacific**. $92/£58

THAYER, JAMES B. A Western Journey with Mr. Emerson. Boston: Little, Brown, 1884. 1st ed. (5),6-141pp. White wrappers. Fine in gray ptd dj (lt chipped). *Pacific**. $374/£234

THAYER, JAMES B. A Western Journey with Mr. Emerson. Richard Hoffman, 1980. One of 600. *Dawson*. $20/£13

THAYER, JANE. The Blueberry Pie Elf. Morrow, Parent's Magazine Book Club, 1961. Stated 1st ed. 4to. Seymour Fleishman (illus). Unpaginated. VG (thumbing wrinkles) in NF dj. *Price*. $35/£22

THEINER, GEORGE. A Day at the Farm. London: Bancroft, 1964. Rudolph Lukes (illus). 12pp. VG- in pict wraps. *Bookfinders*. $80/£50

THEINER, GEORGE. Who's Who at the Zoo. London: Bancroft, 1964. Rudolph Lukes (illus). 12pp. VG- in pict wraps. *Bookfinders*. $80/£50

THEOCRITUS. The Idylliums of Theocritus. Francis Fawkes (trans). London: Dryden Leach, 1767. Frontis port, lvi,(12),288pp. Calf, gilt, raised bands, morocco spine label. (Foxed; glue to spine head, fr joint), else VG. *Pacific**. $127/£79

Theodore Low de Vinne, Printer. (By Henry Lewis Bullen.) NY: Privately ptd (at The De Vinne Press), 1915. Cl spine. VG + (lt rubbed). *Zubal**. $45/£28

THEROUX, PAUL and BRUCE CHATWIN. Patagonia Revisited. Russell, 1985. 1st UK ed. Signed by Theroux. Mint in Mint dj. *Martin*. $29/£18

THEROUX, PAUL. The Black House. Boston: Houghton Mifflin, 1974. 1st ed. Signed. (Top edge sl dusty), else Fine in dj. *Reese*. $85/£53

THEROUX, PAUL. Chicago Loop. London: Hamish Hamilton, 1990. 1st Eng ed. Signed. Fine in dj. *Ulysses*. $40/£25

THEROUX, PAUL. A Christmas Card. Boston: Houghton Mifflin, 1978. 1st ed. Fine in NF dj. *Lame Duck*. $45/£28

THEROUX, PAUL. The Consul's File. Boston: Houghton Mifflin, 1977. 1st US ed. Signed. Fine in dj (sm nick). *Reese*. $45/£28

THEROUX, PAUL. Fong and the Indians. Boston: Houghton Mifflin, 1968. 1st ed. Signed. Fine in dj. *Pacific**. $109/£68

THEROUX, PAUL. Girls at Play. Boston: Hougton Mifflin, 1969. 1st ed. Signed. NF in dj. *Lame Duck*. $200/£125

THEROUX, PAUL. The Great Railway Bazaar. Boston: Houghton Mifflin, 1975. 1st ed. Signed. VG + in dj. *Lame Duck*. $225/£141

THEROUX, PAUL. Jungle Lovers. Bodley Head, 1971. 1st Eng ed. VG (top edge sl dusty; spine ends, corners sl bumped) in dj (sl creased, spotted, sl browned). *Ulysses*. $136/£85

THEROUX, PAUL. Jungle Lovers. Bodley Head, 1971. 1st UK ed. NF in dj. *Williams*. $216/£135

THEROUX, PAUL. A Kingdom by the Sea. Boston: Houghton Mifflin, 1983. One of 250 numbered, signed. Red cl. Fine in cardbd slipcase. *Antic Hay*. $150/£94

THEROUX, PAUL. London Snow. London: Wilton, 1979. 1st Eng ed. One of 450 signed by Theroux and John Lawrence (illus). Patterned cl. Fine in tissue wrapper. *Clearwater*. $120/£75

THEROUX, PAUL. London Snow. Wiltshire: Michael Russell, 1979. One of 300 (of 450) numbered, signed by Theroux and John Lawrence (illus). Fine in illus cl. Glassine dj. *Lame Duck*. $125/£78

THEROUX, PAUL. The Mosquito Coast. Boston: Houghton Mifflin, (1982). 1st ed. Signed. Fine in dj. *Cady*. $30/£19

THEROUX, PAUL. The Mosquito Coast. Boston: Houghton Mifflin, 1982. 1st trade ed. Inscribed, signed. Fine in dj. *Reese*. $40/£25

THEROUX, PAUL. The Mosquito Coast. Boston: Houghton Mifflin, 1982. One of 350 numbered, signed. Fine in cardbd slipcase. *Antic Hay*. $125/£78

THEROUX, PAUL. My Secret History. London, 1989. 1st ed. VG in dj. *Typographeum*. $30/£19

THEROUX, PAUL. My Secret History. London: Hamish Hamilton, 1989. 1st Eng ed. Signed. Fine in dj (sm nick). *Ulysses*. $56/£35

THEROUX, PAUL. The Old Patagonian Express. Boston: Houghton Mifflin, 1979. 1st Amer ed. Nice in dj. *Cady*. $20/£13

THEROUX, PAUL. Picture Palace. Hamilton, 1978. 1st UK ed. Fine in Fine dj. *Martin*. $19/£12

THEROUX, PAUL. Picture Palace. Boston: Houghton Mifflin, 1978. 1st US trade ed. Signed. NF in dj. *Reese*. $35/£22

THEROUX, PAUL. Riding the Iron Rooster, By Train Through China. London, 1988. Fine in dj. *Typographeum*. $45/£28

THEROUX, PAUL. Riding the Iron Rooster. London: Hamish Hamilton, 1988. 1st Eng ed. Fine in dj (spine head sl creased). *Ulysses*. $56/£35

THEROUX, PAUL. Sailing Through China. Russell, 1983. 1st UK ed. Signed. Mint in Mint dj. *Martin*. $26/£16

THEROUX, PAUL. Saint Jack. Boston, 1973. 1st ed. NF in NF dj. *Warren*. $35/£22

THEROUX, PAUL. Saint Jack. Boston: Houghton Mifflin, 1973. 1st ed. Signed. VG + in dj. *Lame Duck*. $150/£94

THEROUX, PAUL. Sinning with Annie. Boston: HMCo, 1972. 1st ed. Fine in Fine dj (sm tear). *Between The Covers*. $150/£94

THEROUX, PAUL. Sinning with Annie. Boston: Houghton Mifflin, 1972. 1st ed. Signed. Fine in VG + dj (chip). *Lame Duck*. $250/£156

THEROUX, PAUL. Sinning with Annie. Hamilton, 1975. 1st UK ed. Fine in VG + dj (spine sl faded, price-clipped). *Williams*. $192/£120

THEROUX, PAUL. Waldo, a Novel. Boston: Houghton Mifflin, 1967. 1st ed, 1st bk. Signed. NF in VG dj (folds rubbed). *Reese.* $200/£125

THEROUX, PAUL. Waldo. Boston: Houghton Mifflin, 1967. 1st ed, 1st bk. Signed. (Extrems rubbed), else VG + in dj (sm chip to spine foot). *Lame Duck.* $275/£172

THEROUX, PAUL. Waldo. Bodley Head, 1968. 1st UK ed. VG + in dj. *Williams.* $232/£145

THESIGER, WILFRED. Arabian Sands. Longmans, 1959. 1st ed. Signed. Fldg map in rear pocket. Cream cl, gilt. VG in dj. *Sotheran.* $176/£110

THESIGER, WILFRED. The Life of My Choice. Harper Collins, 1988. Rpt. Signed. Map. Brn cl. Dj. *Sotheran.* $48/£30

THESIGER, WILFRED. My Kenya Days. Harper Collins, 1994. 1st ed. Signed. Map. Blue cl. *Sotheran.* $48/£30

THIAN, RAPHAEL P. Notes Illustrating the Military Geography of the United States. Austin: Univ of TX, 1979. 4 fldg charts rear pocket. (Shelfworn, soiled.) Internally Good. *Dumont.* $35/£22

Think Before You Speak: or, The Three Wishes. (By Catherine Ann Dorset.) Phila: Johnson & Warner, 1810. Sq 12mo. Copper-engr frontis, 32pp + 1pg ad on lower wrapper; 5 full-pg plts. Good (2 plts browned) in ptd stiff paper wrappers (spine sl chipped). *Hobbyhorse.* $155/£97

THIRKELL, ANGELA. The Grateful Sparrow and Other Tales. Hamish Hamilton, 1935. 1st ed. Sm 4to. 117pp; 24 color plts by Ludwig Richter. Pict onlay fr bd. (Few spots, sl fingered; fr joint cracking; cl faded.) *Hollett.* $48/£30

THIRKELL, ANGELA. Happy Returns. London: Hamish Hamilton, 1952. 1st Eng ed. Fine in dj (spine sl dknd). *Ulysses.* $72/£45

Thirty Plates Illustrative of Natural Phenomena, etc. London: SPCK, 1846. Tp; 30 hand-colored plts. Good (neatly rebacked). *Henly.* $120/£75

Thirty-Fourth Annual Report of the American Colonization Society. Washington: Ptd by C. Alexander, 1851. Only ptg. 84pp. VG in ptd wraps (corners creased, lt foxed). *Chapel Hill.* $60/£38

Thirty-Six Hints to Sportsmen. (By Albany Saville.) Okehampton: Simmons, n.d. (1825). 1st ed. 18pp. Uncut. Full mottled tree calf by Sangorski & Sutcliffe (lt rubbed). *Oinonen*.* $150/£94

THIRY, PAUL and MARY. Eskimo Artifacts Designed for Use. Seattle: Superior, (1977). 1st ed. Fine in slipcase. *Perier.* $97/£61

THISSELL, G. W. Crossing the Plains in '49. Oakland, 1903. 1st ed. 11 ports. Blind-stamped cl, gilt. (Bkpl; cvrs sl worn), else NF. Howes T160. *Pacific*.* $308/£193

THOM, ADAM. The Claims to the Oregon Territory Considered. London: Smith, Elder, 1844. 44pp. VG in self wraps. Howes T161. *Perier.* $150/£94

THOM, WILLIAM. Rhymes and Recollections of a Hand-Loom Weaver. London et al, 1844. 1st ed. 128pp. Color-ptd eps. Blind/gilt-dec cl. *Marlborough.* $136/£85

THOMAS, ALAN G. Fine Books, Pleasures and Treasures. London: Weidenfeld & Nicolson, (1967). 1st ed. Presentation dated 1967; note about this being copy of the 1st state w/uncancelled pg110; author annotated pg w/correction. Fine in dj. *Oak Knoll.* $35/£22

THOMAS, ALFRED BARNABY. The Plains Indians and New Mexico 1751-1778. Albuquerque: Univ of NM, 1940. 1st ed. Fine in VG dj (spine ends, top extrems rubbed, few sm tears). *Pacific*.* $92/£58

THOMAS, BENJAMIN J. Abraham Lincoln. NY, 1952. 1st ed. Fine in dj (lt worn). *Pratt.* $35/£22

THOMAS, BERTRAM. The Arabs. GC: Doubleday, Doran, 1937. 1st ed. 18 plts, 4 maps (1 fldg). (Sl foxed; sl rubbed, soiled), o/w VG. *Worldwide.* $65/£41

THOMAS, D. H. The Southwestern Indian Detours. Phoenix, 1978. Fine in dj. *Dumont.* $35/£22

THOMAS, D. M. The White Hotel. Gollancz, 1981. 1st UK ed. Fine in dj. *Williams.* $88/£55

THOMAS, D. M. The White Hotel. London, 1981. 1st Eng ed. Inscribed. VG (2 corner tips sl bumped) in dj. *Clearwater.* $128/£80

THOMAS, DAVID. Travels Through the Western Country in the Summer of 1816.... Auburn, (NY): David Rumsey, 1819. 1st ed. 16mo. (2),320pp; fldg map; 2nd errata slip pasted in. Full contemp tree calf, leather label. Fine (sig). Howes F162. *M & S.* $950/£594

THOMAS, DOROTHY S. and RICHARD NISHIMOTO. The Spoilage. Berkeley/L.A.: Univ of CA, 1946. 1st ed. 10 charts. Fine (bkpl) in pict dj. *Argonaut.* $80/£50

THOMAS, DOROTHY. Hi-Po the Hippo. Random, 1942. 1st ed. 11.3x13.2. Ruth Gannett (illus). Unpaginated. Good (paper edges worn; spine ends worn). *Price.* $100/£63

THOMAS, DYLAN. 18 Poems. Favil Press for Saturday Referee & Parton Bookshop, 1934. 1st ed, 1st issue, 1st bk. One of 250 w/flat spine. 8vo. (Lt foxed.) Black cl. Dj (foxed, 1 sm tear lower panel, few nicks). *Sotheby's*.* $1,288/£805

THOMAS, DYLAN. 18 Poems. Sunday Referee/Parton Bookshop, 1934. 1st ed, 1st bk, 1st issue w/flat spine. One of 250. 8vo. Black cl. (Corners sl bumped.) Dj (sl foxed, spine head chipped). *Sotheby's*.* $1,472/£920

THOMAS, DYLAN. Adventures in the Skin Trade and Other Stories. New Directions, 1955. 1st ed. VG + (sl shelfworn) in dj (top worn). *My Bookhouse.* $62/£39

THOMAS, DYLAN. Adventures in the Skin Trade. London: Putnam, (1955). 1st Eng ed. Black bds, gilt. Fine in dj (spine sl faded, rear panel sl soiled). *Heritage.* $150/£94

THOMAS, DYLAN. The Beach of Falesa. NY: Stein & Day, (1963). 1st ed. Fine (spine foot sl rubbed) in Fine dj (sl rubbed). *Between The Covers.* $85/£53

THOMAS, DYLAN. A Child's Christmas in Wales. Norfolk, CT: New Directions, (1955). 1st ed. (Spine cocked), o/w NF in dj (price-clipped, spine browned). *Heritage.* $250/£156

THOMAS, DYLAN. Collected Poems 1934-1952. London: Dent, (1952). 1st ed. One of 4760. NF (sig) in VG dj (spine head worn). *Agvent.* $150/£94

THOMAS, DYLAN. Deaths and Entrances. Dent, 1946. 1st ed. Untrimmed. Orange cl, gilt. Fine in Nice dj (sm chip). *Blackwell's.* $400/£250

THOMAS, DYLAN. The Doctor and the Devils. NY: New Directions, (1953). 1st Amer ed from English sheets. VF in VF dj (internal brn paper repair). *Between The Covers.* $100/£63

THOMAS, DYLAN. Eighteen Poems. London: Fortune, 1934 [1942]. 1st Fortune Press ed (i.e. 2nd ed). Red cl, gilt. VG in dj (sl soiled). *Maggs.* $120/£75

THOMAS, DYLAN. From in Memory of Ann Jones. Llanllechid: Caseg, (1942). One of 500 ptd. (Sl foxed; 2 sm squares of brn adhesive tape to top of 2 corners.) *Clearwater.* $312/£195

THOMAS, DYLAN. In Country Sleep. NY: New Directions, (1952). 1st ed. Mtd 1/2 tone port on tp. Grey-grn bds. NF. *Cummins.* $125/£78

THOMAS, DYLAN. The Notebooks of Dylan Thomas. Ralph Maud (ed). NY: New Directions, 1967. 1st ed. VG + (1 interior spread stained due to pressed flower left behind) in dj. *Smith.* $35/£22

THOMAS, DYLAN. Portrait of the Artist as a Young Dog. London: J.M. Dent, 1940. 1st Eng ed. NF (spine foot sl bumped) in dj (nicked, sl creased, spine sl dknd). *Ulysses.* $632/£395

THOMAS, DYLAN. Quite Early One Morning. London, (1954). 1st ed. Dj (closed tear fr panel). *Swann*.* $80/£50

THOMAS, DYLAN. Quite Early One Morning. New Directions, 1954. 1st ed. VG (corners bumped) in dj (lt stained). *My Book-house*. $42/£26

THOMAS, DYLAN. Twelve More Letters. Constantine Fitzgibbon (ed). (London: J.M. Dent, 1969.) 1st ed. One of ltd ed. Frontisport. Fine. *Pacific**. $58/£36

THOMAS, DYLAN. Twenty-Five Poems. London: Dent, (1936). 1st ed. One of 730 ptd. (Eps sl foxed), else VF in gray bds. Gray ptd dj. *Bromer*. $950/£594

THOMAS, DYLAN. Under Milk Wood. NY, 1954. 1st ed, 1st state dj. NF in VG+ dj (price-clipped). *Warren*. $75/£47

THOMAS, DYLAN. Under Milk Wood. Dent, 1954. 1st UK ed. Fine (bkpl) in NF dj (spine head sl worn). *Williams*. $232/£145

THOMAS, EDITH. Babes of the Year. NY: Frederick A. Stokes, 1888. 1st ed. 8vo. Maud Humphrey (illus). 12 full-pg color plts. (Fep torn, some pp pencilled.) Cl-backed color pict bds (rubbed, worn). *Reisler*. $475/£297

THOMAS, EDITH. Children of Spring. NY: Frederick A. Stokes & Brother, 1888. 1st ed. 4to. 3 full-pg color illus by Maud Humphrey. Good in stiff paper wrappers w/serrated edge (corner clipped), sewn w/silk and gold ribbon, celluloid mold of child tied onto fr cvr. *Reisler*. $275/£172

THOMAS, EDWARD. The Chessplayer and Other Essays. Whittington, 1981. One of 350. 2 wood engrs. 1/4 buckram, marbled bds. Fine. *Michael Taylor*. $72/£45

THOMAS, EDWARD. Horae Solitariae. London, 1902. 1st Eng ed. Good (1 corner of fr cvr sl creased). *Clearwater*. $240/£150

THOMAS, EDWARD. Light and Twilight. Duckworth, 1911. Later issue red cl. VG (eps, edges spotted; spine sl faded, ends sl bumped) in dj (rubbed, spine dknd). *Ulysses*. $104/£65

THOMAS, EDWARD. A Literary Pilgrim in England. Methuen, 1917. 1st ed. 8 color, 12 monotone plts. Blue cl (lt soiled, very faded) *Cox*. $40/£25

THOMAS, EDWARD. Selected Poems. Gregynog, 1927. One of 275. VG in yellow buckram (sl soiled). *Cox*. $216/£135

THOMAS, EDWARD. A Selection of Letters to Edward Garnett. Edinburgh: Tragara, 1981. 1st Eng ed. One of 30 (of 175 numbered). Cl-backed patterned bds (spine foot sl bumped). Nice. *Clearwater*. $120/£75

THOMAS, F. W. John Randolph of Roanoke, and Other Sketches of Character, Including William Wirt. Phila: A. Hart, 1853. 1st ed. (Lt foxed, esp 1st, last ll; spine ends sl chipped, corners rubbed.) *Sadlon*. $25/£16

THOMAS, GEORGE C., JR. Golf Architecture in America: Its Strategy and Construction. L.A.: Times-Mirror, 1927. 1st ed. Signed, inscribed, initialed. 8.75x6. Color frontis. Grn cl, grn lettered. (1/2-title foxed), else NF in dj (lacks spine head piece, upper edge rear panel chipped, lacks sm piece from spine/rear joint area). *Pacific**. $3,738/£2,336

THOMAS, GILBERT. How to Enjoy Detective Fiction. Salisbury Square, London: Rockliff, 1947. 1st ed. Good+ (ink name). *Gravesend*. $40/£25

THOMAS, H. The Spanish Civil War. NY: Harper, 1961. 1st ed. VG in dj (sl dull, chipped). *Whiteson*. $24/£15

THOMAS, HARTLEY MUNRO. Songs of an Airman and Other Poems. Toronto, 1918. VG in dj (sl chipped, torn). *Clearwater*. $48/£30

THOMAS, HENRY. Typography of the Spanish XVI Century. Ernest Benn, 1926. 1st ed. 50 facs. Dec bds. Dj. *Forest*. $56/£35

THOMAS, HYLTON. The Drawings of Giovanni Battista Piranesi. London: Faber & Faber, (1954). NF in VG dj. *Turtle Island*. $35/£22

THOMAS, ISAIAH. The History of Printing in America, with a Biography of Printers, and an Account of Newspapers. Albany: Munsell, 1874. 2nd ed. 2 vols. Engr port. Uncut. Later buckram (lt worn). *Oinonen**. $100/£63

THOMAS, ISAIAH. The History of Printing in America. Barre, MA: Imprint Soc, 1970. One of 1950 numbered. Rpt w/pg from 1st ed bound in. NF in slipcase. *Dumont*. $85/£53

THOMAS, ISAIAH. The History of Printing in America. Worcester: Isaiah Thomas, June 1810. 1st ed. 2 vols. 487; 576pp; 5 facs, 2 fldg plts. Teg, untrimmed. Later 3/4 brn leather, marbled bds. (Lib mks, pp age-toned, lt offsetting from facs; sl edgeworn.) Howes T168. *Bohling*. $1,500/£938

THOMAS, J. A. W. A History of Marlboro County. Atlanta: Foote & Davies, 1897. 1st ed. 292pp; fldg map tipped in. Brn cl. VG (insect damage to outer edge of feps; spine faded). Howes T169. *Chapel Hill*. $200/£125

THOMAS, J. C. Chasin' the Trane: The Music and Mystique of John Coltrane. GC: Doubleday, 1975. 1st ed. Discography. VG in pict dj. *Petrilla*. $20/£13

THOMAS, J. J. Rural Affairs...Volume 1. Albany, NY: Luther Tucker, 1873. 440 engrs. (Rebacked w/orig backstrip laid on, corners rubbed.) *Sadlon*. $50/£31

THOMAS, J. J. Rural Affairs...Volume III. Albany, NY: Luther Tucker, 1876. (Rebacked w/orig backstrip laid on, corners rubbed.) *Sadlon*. $50/£31

THOMAS, J. P. Handling London's Underground Traffic. London's Underground, 1928. 1st ed. 16 fldg charts tipped-in. VG (bkpl; edges dusty, corners sl bumped) in dj (nicked, rubbed, mkd, sl creased, browned, spine head frayed). *Ulysses*. $120/£75

THOMAS, JOHN J. The American Fruit Culturist. NY: William Wood, 1875. Rev ed. Color litho frontis, tissue guard. Pict dk blue/black cl, gilt. (Spine ends rubbed, fr hinge starting), else VG. *Pacific**. $58/£36

THOMAS, JOSEPH B. Hounds and Hunting Through the Ages. NY, 1928. One of 750. Folio. 43 plts (6 color). Uncut. Gilt-dec red cl. (Lt worn, sl foxed, spine sl sunned.) *Oinonen**. $200/£125

THOMAS, JOSEPH B. Hounds and Hunting Through the Ages. NY: Derrydale, 1928. One of 750. Folio. 6 plts. Red cl. (Spine wrinkled), o/w Fine. *Biscotti*. $300/£188

THOMAS, JOSEPH B. Hounds and Hunting Through the Ages. NY: Derrydale, 1928. One of 750. (Spine, rear cvr spotted.) *Swann**. $316/£198

THOMAS, LATELY. A Debonair Scoundrel. NY: Holt, Rinehart & Winston, (1962). 1st ed. Fine in dj. *Argonaut*. $25/£16

THOMAS, LATELY. The Vanishing Evangelist. NY: Viking, 1959. 1st ed. Fine in VG dj. *Book Market*. $35/£22

THOMAS, LEW and PETER D'AGOSTINO (eds). Still Photography: The Problematic Model. SF: NFS Press, 1981. 1st ed. Fine in pict stiff wrappers. *Cahan*. $30/£19

THOMAS, LOWELL (ed). The Authorized Narrative of the First World Flight. Boston: Houghton Mifflin, 1925. 1st ed. VG in dj (extrems chipped, lack pieces). *Pacific**. $52/£33

THOMAS, LOWELL. Count Luckner: The Sea Devil. GC: GC Pub Co, (post-1927). Rpt. Gilt blue cl. Fine in NF pict dj. *Reese*. $22/£14

THOMAS, LOWELL. Rolling Stone. GC, 1934. Signed. (Spine, cvrs discolored.) *King*. $35/£22

THOMAS, LOWELL. With Lawrence in Arabia. NY: Century, (1924). 1st ed. Orange cl. VG. *Reese*. $30/£19

THOMAS, NORMAN. The Conscientious Objector in America. NY: Huebsch, 1923. 1st ed. Fine (rear bd sl mkd) in VG dj (soiled). *Beasley*. $125/£78

THOMAS, R. S. An Acre of Land. Newtown: Montgomeryshire Ptg, 1952. 2nd imp. VG (edges sl spotted, cvrs sl mkd, spine sl faded) in wrappers. *Ulysses*. $88/£55

THOMAS, R. S. Destinations. Warwickshire: Celandine Press, 1985. 1st ed. One of 75 signed. 3 Fine color repros, guards. Black eps; top edge trimmed, rest untrimmed. VG in orig 1/4 black leather, patterned bds, gilt. Fine cl slipcase. *Vandoros.* $250/£156

THOMAS, R. S. The Minister. Newtown, 1953. 1st ed. Fine in wrappers. *Sotheby's*.* $349/£218

THOMAS, R. S. The Mountains. NY: Chilmark, 1968. 1st ed, deluxe issue. One of 110 numbered, signed by Thomas, Reynolds Stone (engr) and John Piper (illus), w/an extra set of the engrs. Folio. 10 engrs. Orig 1/4 morocco. Slipcase. *Sotheby's*.* $478/£299

THOMAS, T. GAILLARD. A Practical Treatise on the Diseases of Women. Phila, 1891. 6th ed. 826pp. (Fr inner hinges cracked), o/w Good. *Doctor's Library.* $50/£31

THOMAS, WILLIAM S. Hunting Big Game with Gun and with Kodak. NY: Putnam, 1906. 1st ed. Teg. Brn cl, b/w photo plt on cvr. VG + . *House.* $75/£47

THOMAS, WILLIAM WIDGERY. Sweden and the Swedes. Chicago/NY, 1893. Frontisport, (iv),749pp; fldg color map. Dec cl (corners sl rubbed, spine sl rubbed s/sm repaired tear). *Edwards.* $200/£125

THOMAS-STANFORD, CHARLES. Early Editions of Euclid's Elements. London: Bibliographical Soc, 1926. 1st ed. 12 photo plts at rear. Teg; untrimmed. Tan cl, lt brn bds. (Lt handled; spine ends, joints chipped, torn; sl worn.) Text Good. *Baltimore*.* $30/£19

THOMAS-STANFORD, CHARLES. Early Editions of Euclid's Elements. London: Bibliographical Soc, 1926. 13 plts. (Lacks spine, corners bumped.) *Maggs.* $64/£40

THOMASON, JOHN W., JR. Fix Bayonets! NY: Scribner, 1926. 1st ed, 1st bk. Color frontis. Cl-backed pict bds. (Sl foxed, offset from frontis), else Fine in VG pict dj (chips, creased edge tear). *Reese.* $275/£172

THOMES, W. H. The Gold Hunter's Adventures; or, Life in Australia. Chicago: Donnelley, Loyd, 1883. 564pp + ads. Emb grn cl. (Fr hinge weak; shelfworn, spine splitting.) *Parmer.* $55/£34

THOMES, W. H. On Land and Sea, or California in the Years 1843, '44, and '45. Boston: DeWolfe, Fiske, 1884. 1st ed. 351pp. VG- (sl leaning; rubbed; corners, spine ends worn). Howes T185. *Harrington.* $75/£47

THOMES, WILLIAM H. Life in the East Indies (Ocean Life Series). Boston/NY: Lee & Shepard/Lee, Shepard & Dillingham, 1873. 354pp; 4 plts. (Few ll edges frayed; rubbed, spine ends frayed), o/w VG. *Worldwide.* $45/£28

THOMPSON, ALBERT W. They Were Open Range Days. Denver, 1946. 1st ed. One of 500. Sm map. (Lt worn.) *Woolson.* $85/£53

THOMPSON, C. The Lore and Romance of Alchemy. London: George G. Harrap, 1932. 1st ed. Good. *Blake.* $65/£41

THOMPSON, C. Poison Mysteries in History, Romance and Crime. Phila: Lippincott, 1924. 1st ed. Red cl. (Spine ends chipped, lower extrems, corners rubbed, upper corners bumped), else VG-. *Pacific*.* $29/£18

THOMPSON, C. WYVILE. The Voyage of the 'Challenger'. The Atlantic. A Preliminary Account of...H.M.S. 'Challenger' During the Year 1873 and the Early Part of the Year 1876. London, 1877. 2 vols. xv,424; xiv,396,4 ads; port, 43 plts (39 fldg). Pict cl, gilt (rebacked preserving spines). *Henly.* $280/£175

THOMPSON, DANNY and BOB FOWLER. E—6. Dillon, 1975. 1st ed. Orig trade pb ed. VG. *Plapinger.* $50/£31

THOMPSON, DUNSTAN. The Phoenix in the Desert. London: Lehman, 1951. 1st ed. 16 plts. VG in dj. *Worldwide.* $35/£22

THOMPSON, E. MAUNDE. An Introduction to Greek and Latin Palaeography. Oxford: Clarendon, 1912. 250 facs. Black cl, gilt. *Maggs.* $56/£35

THOMPSON, EDWARD (ed). Robert Graves. London: Ernest Benn, (1925). 1st ed. VG in white stapled wrappers. *Maggs.* $72/£45

THOMPSON, EDWARD. The Collected Poems of.... London: Ernest Benn, 1930. 1st ed, trade issue. (Ink inscrip, few spine nicks), else Good. *Reese.* $20/£13

THOMPSON, EDWARD. Crusader's Coast. London: Ernest Benn, 1929. 1st ed. Frontis. Tan cl. (Edges sl foxed), o/w VG in dj (lt foxed). *Reese.* $50/£31

THOMPSON, EDWARD. In Araby Orion. London: Ernest Benn, (1930). 1st ed. Gilt black cl. (Edges, eps foxed), o/w Nice in VG dj (lt foxed, sm nicks). *Reese.* $55/£34

THOMPSON, EDWARD. In Araby Orion. London, 1930. 1st Eng ed. NF (eps sl tanned) in dj. *Clearwater.* $40/£25

THOMPSON, EDWARD. An Introduction to Greek and Latin Palaeography. Oxford, 1912. 1st ed. (Ex-lib, mkd; cvrs worn.) *King.* $95/£59

THOMPSON, EDWARD. Lament for Adonis. London: Ernest Benn, (1932). 1st ed. Gilt black cl. (Fore-edge sl foxed), o/w VG in pict dj (rear foxed). *Reese.* $45/£28

THOMPSON, EDWARD. Roentgen Rays and Phenomena of the Anode and Cathode. NY, 1896. 1st ed. 190pp. Recent black cl. VF. *Fye.* $500/£313

THOMPSON, EDWARD. These Men, Thy Friends. London, 1927. 1st Eng ed. Cl-backed patterned bds. (Foxed; sl mkd, handled; no dj.) *Clearwater.* $40/£25

THOMPSON, EDWARD. These Men, Thy Friends. London: Knopf, 1927. 1st ed. (Sm ink name dated 1927, pencil erasure fep, fore-edge sl foxed), o/w NF in pict dj. *Reese.* $100/£63

THOMPSON, ERNEST SETON. Wild Animals I Have Known. Toronto: Geo. N. Morang, 1901. 1st Canadian ed. Teg. Grn gilt-stamped cl. Nice. *Appelfeld.* $50/£31

THOMPSON, GEORGE G. Bat Masterson; The Dodge City Years. Topeka, 1943. VG in ptd wraps. *Wantagh.* $45/£28

THOMPSON, GEORGE G. Bat Masterson; The Dodge City Years. Topeka: KS State Ptg Plant, 1943. 1st ed. VG in wrappers. *Labordo.* $55/£34

THOMPSON, GEORGE. Lectures on British India.... Pawtucket, RI: William & Robert Adams, 1840. 1st ed. 206pp (foxed). Orig cl-backed bds, paper label. Very Nice (sig, bkpl). *M & S.* $375/£234

THOMPSON, GEORGE. Letters and Addresses by George Thompson, During His Mission in the United States, from Oct. 1st, 1834, to Nov. 27, 1835. Boston: Isaac Knapp, 1837. 1st ed. 12,126pp. Orig cl-backed ptd bds (corner chewed). VG. *M & S.* $275/£172

THOMPSON, GEORGE. The Prison Bard. Hartford, 1848. 215pp. (Names, foxed, stained; chipped.) *Woolson.* $40/£25

THOMPSON, GEORGE. Prison Life and Reflections: Or Narrative of the Arrest, Trial, Conviction...of Work, Burr and Thompson.... Oberlin: Ptd by James M. Fitch, 1847. 1st ed. 3 parts in 1 vol. 417,(blank),(2)ads pp. (Age-spotted mainly in margins; spine ends chipped, joints splitting.) *Zubal*.* $105/£66

THOMPSON, HENRY. The Diseases of the Prostate, Their Pathology and Treatment. London, 1868. 3rd ed. 364pp. (Ex-lib.) *Fye.* $150/£94

THOMPSON, HENRY. The Motor Car, Its Nature, Use and Management. Warne, 1902. 1st ed. Pub's file copy stamp, label. Frontis, 2 plts (1 dbl-pg). Stock sheet loosely inserted. Teg. Blue pict cl, gilt. NF (1pg soiled). *Any Amount.* $136/£85

THOMPSON, HENRY. The Motor-Car. London: Warne, 1902. 1st ed. 3 plts. Blue ribbed cl (extrems sl rubbed), gilt. *Hollett.* $136/£85

THOMPSON, HERBERT (ed). A Coptic Palimpsest Containing Joshua, Judges, Ruth, Judith and Esther in the Sahidic Dialect. London/Edinburgh/NY et al: OUP, 1911. 1st ed. (Ex-lib; sl rubbed, spine ends sl frayed, lib spine sticker), o/w VG. *Worldwide*. $45/£28

THOMPSON, HUNTER S. Fear and Loathing in Las Vegas. NY: Random House, (1971). 1st ed. Black cl over gray bds. (Bd edges sl faded), o/w Fine in dj (old price sticker affixed to rear panel, edges lt browned). *Heritage*. $200/£125

THOMPSON, HUNTER S. Fear and Loathing in Las Vegas. NY, 1971. 1st ed. (Top, fore-edge spotted), o/w NF in NF dj. *Warren*. $95/£59

THOMPSON, HUNTER S. Fear and Loathing in Las Vegas. NY: Random House, 1971. 1st ed. NF (top of bds sunned, 2 sm spots pg edges) in dj. *Smith*. $225/£141

THOMPSON, HUNTER S. Fear and Loathing: On the Campaign Trail '72. SF: Straight Arrow, 1973. 1st ed. Signed by Ralph Steadman (illus). NF in dj (sl edgeworn). *Sclanders*. $120/£75

THOMPSON, HUNTER S. Generation of Swine. NY: Summit Books, 1988. 1st ed. VG+ in dj (sl edgeworn). *My Bookhouse*. $37/£23

THOMPSON, HUNTER S. Hell's Angels. NY, 1967. 1st ed. NF in NF dj (price-clipped). *Warren*. $250/£156

THOMPSON, HUNTER S. Hell's Angels. NY: Random House, 1967. 1st ed, 1st book. 8vo. Fine in dj. *Smith*. $600/£375

THOMPSON, HUNTER S. Hell's Angels: The Strange and Terrible Saga of the Outlaw Motorcycle Gangs. Allen Lane/Penguin, 1967. 1st UK ed. NF (bds sl sprung; lacks dj). *Sclanders*. $120/£75

THOMPSON, HUNTER S. Hell's Angels: The Strange and Terrible Saga of the Outlaw Motorcycle Gangs. NY: Random House, 1967. 1st ed, 1st bk. NF (inscrip) in dj. *Sclanders*. $280/£175

THOMPSON, HUNTER S. Screw Jack. CA: Neville, 1991. 1st ed. Ltd to 300 numbered, signed. Fine w/o dj as issued. *Warren*. $150/£94

THOMPSON, J. ERIC S. A Catalog of Maya Hieroglyphs. Norman: Univ of OK, (1976). 3rd ed. VG in dj. *Pacific**. $29/£18

THOMPSON, J. ERIC S. A Commentary on the Dresden Codex: A Maya Hieroglyphic Book. Phila: American Philosophical Soc, 1972. 1st ed. NF. *Pacific**. $81/£51

THOMPSON, J. ERIC S. (ed). Thomas Gage's Travels in the New World. Norman: Univ of OK, (1958). 1st US ed in over 200 years. VF in dj. *Argonaut*. $60/£38

THOMPSON, J. HARRY. Report of the Columbia Hospital for Women and Lying-In Asylum, Washington D.C. Washington, 1873. 1st ed. 430pp. (Sl water-stained last several pp.; extrems sl worn, spine end tears, rt upper corner dented). *Doctor's Library*. $75/£47

THOMPSON, JAMES WESTFALL. Byways in Bookland. Berkeley, 1935. 1st ed. Ltd to 600 numbered. (Ex-lib.) *King*. $20/£13

THOMPSON, JIM. The Kill-Off. NY: Lion Books, (1957). 1st ed. Color pict wraps. VG (top corner fr cvr, 1st few pp w/faint bending). *Baltimore**. $70/£44

THOMPSON, JIM. Pop. 1280. Greenwich, CT: Gold Medal, (1964). (Pp sl browned), else NF in wrappers. *Between The Covers*. $250/£156

THOMPSON, JIM. South of Heaven. NY: Fawcett Gold Medal, 1967. 1st ed. Pb orig. VG- (cvrs lt rubbed). *Warren*. $60/£38

THOMPSON, KAY. Eloise at Christmastime. NY: Random House, (1958). Stated 1st ed. Hilary Knight (illus). 4to. Unpaginated. VG (ink name) in dj (upper left corner torn). *Davidson*. $275/£172

THOMPSON, KAY. Eloise in Moscow. London: Max Reinhardt, (1960). 1st Eng ed. 4to. Hilary Knight (illus). Grn cl. Good in color pict dj (rear cvr lt dusty). *Reisler*. $150/£94

THOMPSON, KAY. Eloise in Moscow. S&S, 1959. Stated 1st ed. Hilary Knight (illus). Unpaginated. Good+ (rep soiled; bd corners worn, bumped). *Price*. $50/£31

THOMPSON, KAY. Eloise in Moscow. NY, 1959. 1st ed. (Bkpl), else VG in dj (sl chipped; removal mks). *King*. $150/£94

THOMPSON, KAY. Eloise in Paris. NY: S&S, 1957. 1st ed. 4to. Hilary Knight (illus). Blue bds. Color dj (spine sl dknd). *Reisler*. $175/£109

THOMPSON, KAY. Eloise. NY: S&S, 1955. 12th ptg. 4to. Hillary Knight (illus). VG- (double pg taped; lacks dj). *American Booksellers*. $40/£25

THOMPSON, MARILYN. Saying Things. Omaha: Abattoir Editions/Univ of NE, 1975. Ltd to 275 ptd. Japanese paper-cvrd bds, cl back, paper spine label. Fine in dj. *Hermitage*. $65/£41

THOMPSON, MORTON. How to Cook a Turkey. L.A., 1940. One of 400. Wrappers. *Dawson*. $50/£31

THOMPSON, R. A. Conquest of California: Capture of Sonoma by Bear Flag Men, June 14, 1846.... Santa Rosa: Sonoma Democrat Pub, 1896. 1st ed. 33pp; 4 plts. VG in red ptd wrappers (spine, edges worn, chip to fr). Howes T199. *Pacific**. $86/£54

THOMPSON, R. R. and J. B. RAMSEY. The Fifty-Second (Lowland) Division 1914-1918. Glasgow: Maclehose, Jackson, 1923. 41 plts (2 color), 10 fldg maps. Uncut. Fine. *Hollett*. $152/£95

THOMPSON, ROBERT. The Gardener's Assistant: Practical and Scientific. London: Blackie & Son, 1870. 12 color plts. 3/4 grn calf, raised bands, brn leather label. Fine. *Appelfeld*. $350/£219

THOMPSON, RUTH PLUMLY. Captain Salt in Oz. Chicago: Reilly & Lee, (1936). 1st ed. 8.75x6.5. John R. Neill (illus). 306pp. B/w pict eps. Blue cl, pict cvr label. (Spine head bumped), else VG. *Pacific**. $184/£115

THOMPSON, RUTH PLUMLY. Captain Salt in Oz. Chicago: Reilly & Lee, (1936). 1st ed. 4to. John R. Neill (illus). Med blue cl, color paste label. VG in color dj (worn, lacks pieces). *Reisler*. $450/£281

THOMPSON, RUTH PLUMLY. The Cowardly Lion of Oz. Toronto: Copp Clark, (1923). 1st Canadian ed. 9x6.5. 291pp; 12 color plts by John R. Neill. B/w pict eps. Dk grn cl, pict cvr label. VG- (lacks most of rep, hinges cracked; rubbed, spine warped). *Pacific**. $109/£68

THOMPSON, RUTH PLUMLY. The Cowardly Lion of Oz. Chicago: Reilly & Lee, (1923). 1st ed, earliest state w/non-standard ampersand in 'Reilly & Lee' imprint at spine foot. 12 color plts. (Rear inner hinge partly open; spine sl worn.) *Kane**. $130/£81

THOMPSON, RUTH PLUMLY. The Cowardly Lion of Oz. Chicago: Reilly & Lee, (1923). 1st ed, 1st state w/plts coated on the ptd side only; 1st binding w/ non-standard '&' in spine imprint. 291pp; 12 color plts by John R. Neill. B/w pict eps. Dk grn cl, pict cvr label. (Spine ends rubbed), else VG. *Pacific**. $230/£144

THOMPSON, RUTH PLUMLY. The Cowardly Lion of Oz. Chicago: Reilly & Lee, (1923). 1st ed, 1st binding w/non-standard ampersand in spine's imprint. Sq 8vo. 291pp; 12 color plts by John R. Neill. Emerald grn cl, color pict label. VG (reps lt toned; fr hinge sl loose, fr cvr plt lt rubbed). *House*. $250/£156

THOMPSON, RUTH PLUMLY. The Curious Cruise of Captain Santa. Chicago: Reilly & Lee, (1926). 1st, only ed. 9.25x7.25. John R. Neill (illus). Gray cl, pict cvr label. VG- (hinges cracked, label creased, extrems rubbed; spine, extrems torn). *Pacific**. $127/£79

THOMPSON, RUTH PLUMLY. The Giant Horse of Oz. Chicago: Reilly & Lee, (1928). 1st ed, 1st state w/misprint 'Oniberon' for 'Quiberon' in frontis caption; 'r' in 'morning' (p116, line 1) undamaged; plts coated on ptd side only. 9x6.5. 283pp; 12 color plts by John R. Neill. B/w pict eps. Brick-red cl, pict cvr label. (Hinges cracked; spine ends rubbed, label sl sunned), else VG. *Pacific**. $173/£108

THOMPSON, RUTH PLUMLY. The Giant Horse of Oz. Chicago/NY: Reilly & Lee, (1928). 1st ed, 1st state. Sm 4to. 283pp; 12 full-pg color plts by John R. Neill. Terra-cotta cl, ptd paper label. (Label rubbed), else NF. *Bromer*. $300/£188

THOMPSON, RUTH PLUMLY. The Giant Horse of Oz. Chicago: Reilly & Lee, 1928. 1st ed, 1st state, w/'Oniberon' for 'Quiberon' in frontis caption. 12 color plts. Fine. *Kane**. $170/£106

THOMPSON, RUTH PLUMLY. The Gnome King of Oz. Toronto: Copp Clarke, (1927). 1st Canadian ed. 8.75x6.5. 282pp; 11 (of 12) color plts by John R. Neill. B/w pict eps. Bright emerald cl, pict cvr label. (Lacks 1 plt, name; label rubbed, spine ends frayed, rear cvr discolored), else Good. *Pacific**. $58/£36

THOMPSON, RUTH PLUMLY. The Gnome King of Oz. Chicago: Reilly & Lee, (1927). 1st ed. 12 color plts. Lt grn cl. (Leaf smudged; rear cvr sl rubbed.) *Kane**. $140/£88

THOMPSON, RUTH PLUMLY. The Gnome King of Oz. Chicago: Reilly & Lee, (1927). 1st ed, 1st state binding in bright emerald cl (later was jade). 8.75x6.5. 282 pp; 12 color plts by John R. Neill. Pict cvr label. (Fr hinge starting; spine ends, label rubbed), else VG. *Pacific**. $161/£101

THOMPSON, RUTH PLUMLY. The Gnome King of Oz. Chicago: Reilly & Lee, (1927). 1st ed. 4to. 12 full-pg color plts by John R. Neill. Illus eps. Grn ribbed cl, color paste label. VG (sm pinhole in spine). *Reisler*. $585/£366

THOMPSON, RUTH PLUMLY. Grampa in Oz. Chicago: Reilly & Lee, (1924). 1st ed, later ptg w/broken type on p189, book measuring approx 1 5/16-inch thick. 12 color plts. *Kane**. $80/£50

THOMPSON, RUTH PLUMLY. Grampa in Oz. Chicago: Reilly & Lee, (1924). 1st ed, 1st issue w/plts coated on ptd side only; perfect type in numeral on p171 and in the last word in the next-to-last line p189; ptd on heavy stock w/sheets bulking 1-7/16 inches. 9x6.5. 271pp + (7)pp ads; 12 color plts (no color frontis as issued). B/w eps. Lt brick-red cl, pict cvr label. (Spine ends, extrems rubbed; spine sl soiled, lt worn), else VG. *Pacific**. $115/£72

THOMPSON, RUTH PLUMLY. Grampa in Oz. Chicago: Reilly & Lee, (1924). 1st ed, 1st issue w/plts coated on ptd side only; perfect type in numeral on p171 & in the last word in the next-to-the-last line on p189; ptd on heavy stock w/sheets bulking 1 7/16-inch. 9x6.5. 271,(7)ad pp (4 leaves ptd on rectos only); 12 color plts (no color frontis, as issued). B/w eps. Lt brick-red cl, pict cvr label. (Name, crease to dedication pg, hinge cracking p189; *Pacific**. $230/£144

THOMPSON, RUTH PLUMLY. Grampa in Oz. Chicago: Reilly & Lee, (1924). 1st ed. Sq 8vo. 271,(4)ads; 12 color plts by John R. Neill. Brick red cl, color pict label. VG + (sl faded). *House*. $250/£156

THOMPSON, RUTH PLUMLY. Grampa in Oz. Chicago: Reilly & Lee, (1924). 1st ed. B/w frontis, 12 color illus by John R. Neill bound in. Lt brick-red cl, pict label. VG (name) in dj (tattered). *Davidson*. $300/£188

THOMPSON, RUTH PLUMLY. Grampa in Oz. Chicago: Reilly & Lee, (1924). 1st ed. 4to. 12 full-pg color plts by John R. Neill. Brick red cl, color paste label. Nice (lt shelfworn). *Reisler*. $575/£359

THOMPSON, RUTH PLUMLY. Grampa in Oz. Chicago: Reilly & Lee, (1924, but c. 1930). 1st ed, 2nd issue w/plts coated on ptd side only & imperfect type in numeral on p171 & in the last word in the next-to-the-last line on p189. 9x6.5. 271,(7)ad pp; 12 color plts (no color frontis, as issued). B/w eps. Red cl, pict cvr label. NF in Good dj (lacks lg pieces). *Pacific**. $150/£94

THOMPSON, RUTH PLUMLY. Handy Mandy in Oz. Chicago: Reilly & Lee, (1937). 1st ed. Blue cl. (Marginal stains; rear cvr sl scratched.) *Kane**. $75/£47

THOMPSON, RUTH PLUMLY. Handy Mandy in Oz. Chicago: Reilly & Lee, (1937). 1st ed, 1st state w/picture of Handy Mandy on spine; spine imprint in semi-script 'fancy' letters. 9x6.5. John R. Neill (illus). 271pp. B/w pict eps. Orange cl, pict cvr label. VG. *Pacific**. $219/£137

THOMPSON, RUTH PLUMLY. The Hungry Tiger of Oz. Chicago: Reilly & Lee, (1926). 1st ed, 1st state w/plts coated on ptd side only; hyphen on last line p21 and the word 'two' (p252, last line) in perfect type. 9 x 6 1/2. 261,(3)pp + (2) ad ll; 12 color plts by John R. Neill. B/w pict eps. Dk grn cl, pict cvr label. (Hinges cracked at eps, ownership pg filled out, tape stain fep; extrems worn, pencil mks to cvr label, rear joint split), else Good + . *Pacific**. $52/£33

THOMPSON, RUTH PLUMLY. The Hungry Tiger of Oz. Chicago: Reilly & Lee, (1926). 1st ed, 1st state, w/plts coated on ptd side only. 12 color plts. (Name; stained.) *Kane**. $85/£53

THOMPSON, RUTH PLUMLY. The Hungry Tiger of Oz. Chicago: Reilly & Lee, (1926). 1st ed, 1st state w/plts coated on ptd side only; hyphen on last line of p21 & the word 'two' (p252, last line) in perfect type. 9x6.5. 261,(3)pp + (2)ad ll; 12 color plts by John R. Neill. B/w pict eps. Dk grn cl, pict cvr label. NF. *Pacific**. $219/£137

THOMPSON, RUTH PLUMLY. The Hungry Tiger of Oz. Chicago/NY: Reilly & Lee, (1926). 1st ed, 1st state. Sm 4to. 261pp,(3)ff; 12 full-pg color plts by John R. Neill. Grn cl, ptd paper label on fr cvr. (Extrems lt worn), else Fine. *Bromer*. $350/£219

THOMPSON, RUTH PLUMLY. Jack Pumpkinhead of Oz. Chicago: Reilly & Lee, (1929). 1st ed. 12 color plts. (Fr cvr pastedown scratched, rear cvr sl spotted.) *Kane**. $110/£69

THOMPSON, RUTH PLUMLY. Jack Pumpkinhead of Oz. Chicago: Reilly & Lee, (1929). 1st ed. 9x6.5. 252,(2)pp + (2)ad ll; 12 color plts by John R. Neill. B/w pict eps. Greenish-gray cl, pict cvr label. (Sm tear to spine head), else VG. *Pacific**. $230/£144

THOMPSON, RUTH PLUMLY. Kabumpo in Oz. Toronto: Copp Clark, (1922). 1st Canadian ed. 9x6.5. 297pp; 12 color plts by John R. Neill. B/w pict eps. Blue cl, pict cvr label. (Hinges cracked through; cvr label scratched), else VG-. *Pacific**. $69/£43

THOMPSON, RUTH PLUMLY. Kabumpo in Oz. Chicago: Reilly & Lee, (1922). 1st ed, earliest ptg w/1/2 title following ownership leaf & port at rear. 12 color plts. (Fep reglued at hinge.) *Kane**. $110/£69

THOMPSON, RUTH PLUMLY. Kabumpo in Oz. Chicago: Reilly & Lee, (1922). 1st ed, 1st state w/half-title following ownership leaf & port of Princess Dorothy on p(299); plts coated on ptd side only. 9x6.5. 297pp; 12 color plts by John R. Neill. B/w pict eps. Blue cl, pict cvr label. (Cvr label, spine ends sl rubbed, hinges starting), else VG. *Pacific**. $161/£101

THOMPSON, RUTH PLUMLY. Kabumpo in Oz. Toronto: Copp, Clark, (1922). 1st Canadian ed. 4to. John R. Neill (illus). 12 color plts, port. Blue-grn cl, color paste label (edges lt worn). *Reisler*. $450/£281

THOMPSON, RUTH PLUMLY. The Lost King of Oz. Chicago: Reilly & Lee, (1925). 1st ed. Spine imprint in boldface; plts coated on ptd side only; ptd on heavy paper stock w/sheets bulking 1-3/8 inches. 9 x 6 1/2. 280pp; 12 color plts by John R. Neill. B/w pict eps. Blue cl, pict cvr label. (Fr hinge cracked at eps, tape stains fep, ownership pg filled out w/hole; cvr label scratched; joints, extrems rubbed), else Good + . Pacific*. $75/£47

THOMPSON, RUTH PLUMLY. The Lost King of Oz. Chicago: Reilly & Lee, (1925). 1st ed, 1st ptg w/plts coated on ptd side only, later copy w/top serif of letter 'k' on p193, line 4, missing. 12 color plts. (Sm piece missing margin of plt; sl rubbed, spine tear.) Kane*. $80/£50

THOMPSON, RUTH PLUMLY. The Lost King of Oz. Chicago: Reilly & Lee, (1925). 1st ed. Spine imprint in boldface; plts coated on ptd side only; ptd on heavy paper stock w/sheets bulking 1 3/8-inch. 9x6.5. 280pp; 12 color plts by John R. Neill. B/w pict eps. Blue cl, pict cvr label. NF. Pacific*. $259/£162

THOMPSON, RUTH PLUMLY. The Lost King of Oz. Chicago: Reilly & Lee, (1925). 1st ed. Spine imprint in boldface; plts coated on ptd side only; ptd on heavy paper stock w/sheets bulking 1 3/8-inch. 9x6.5. 280pp; 12 color plts by John R. Neill. B/w pict eps. Blue cl, pict cvr label. (Name), else NF in VG dj (chipped, lacks sm pieces, few sm tears to extrems). Pacific*. $805/£503

THOMPSON, RUTH PLUMLY. Ojo in Oz. Chicago: Reilly & Lee, (1933). 1st ed, 2nd binding of putty gray cl, pub's imprint at spine foot. 12 color plts. Fine. Kane*. $200/£125

THOMPSON, RUTH PLUMLY. Ojo in Oz. Chicago: Reilly & Lee, (1933). 1st ed, 1st state binding, w/spine imprint in boldface. 9x5.5. 304pp; 12 color plts by John R. Neill. B/w pict eps. Grn cl, pict cvr label. NF. Pacific*. $259/£162

THOMPSON, RUTH PLUMLY. Ozoplaning with the Wizard of Oz. Chicago, (1939). 1st ed (w/16pp gatherings, inserted rep). John R. Neill (illus). Cl, pict color cvr label. (Cvr color run onto bottom corner 1st few pp, eps; eps soiled, stained; edges stained; cvrs worn, spine wrinkled, hinges loose.) King. $150/£94

THOMPSON, RUTH PLUMLY. Pirates in Oz. Toronto: Copp, Clark, (1931). 1st Canadian ed. 9x6.5. 280pp; 11 (of 12) color plts by John R. Neill. B/w pict eps. Grn untextured cl, pict cvr label. (Lacks plt facing p272, fr hinge starting, name; label rubbed, glue wear to spine), else VG. Pacific*. $69/£43

THOMPSON, RUTH PLUMLY. Pirates in Oz. Chicago: Reilly & Lee, (1931). 1st ed, 1st state. 9x6.5. 280pp; 12 color plts by John R. Neill. B/w pict eps. Medium-grn untextured cl, pict cvr label. (Fr hinge cracked), else VG. Pacific*. $127/£79

THOMPSON, RUTH PLUMLY. Pirates in Oz. Chicago: Reilly & Lee, (1931). 1st ed, primary binding of grn cl w/imprint at spine foot in bold type. 12 color plts. Kane*. $160/£100

THOMPSON, RUTH PLUMLY. Pirates in Oz. Chicago: Reilly & Lee, (1931). 1st ed, 1st state binding w/spine imprint in boldface. 9x6.5. 280pp; 12 color plts by John R. Neill. B/w pict eps. Medium-grn untextured cl, pict cvr label. (Label extrems sl rubbed, upper rear corner bumped), else VG. Pacific*. $161/£101

THOMPSON, RUTH PLUMLY. Pirates in Oz. Chicago: Reilly & Lee, (1931). 1st ed, spine imprint is in 1st state, in boldface type. Sq lg 8vo. 12 color plts by John R. Neill. B/w pict eps. Grn cl, color pict label fr cvr. Clean (sl handled, bkpl removed). Baltimore*. $180/£113

THOMPSON, RUTH PLUMLY. The Princess of Cozytown. Chicago: P.F. Volland, (1922). 1st ed. 9x6. Janet Laura Scott (illus). Pict bds. (Joints, extrems rubbed), else VG. Pacific*. $196/£123

THOMPSON, RUTH PLUMLY. The Princess of Cozytown. Chicago: P.F. Volland, 1922. 1st ed. 8vo. Janet Laura Scott (illus). Pict bds (edgeworn, spine faded). Pict box (missing some side pieces, faded). Reisler. $225/£141

THOMPSON, RUTH PLUMLY. The Purple Prince of Oz. Chicago: Reilly & Lee, (1932). 1st ed, 1st binding w/spine imprint in boldface. 9x6.5. 281pp; 12 color plts by John R. Neill. B/w pict eps. Dk purple cl, pict cvr label. (Bkpl; spine sunned, label w/sl smudge), else VG. Pacific*. $207/£129

THOMPSON, RUTH PLUMLY. The Royal Book of Oz. Chicago: Reilly & Lee, (1921). 1st ed. Caption plt facing p255 misprints 'Scarecorw's.' Pub's ads pp305-312. 12 color illus by John R. Neill. (Rear hinge cracked; spine, corners worn), o/w VG. Davidson. $275/£172

THOMPSON, RUTH PLUMLY. The Silver Princess in Oz. Chicago: Reilly & Lee, (1938). 1st ed, primary binding of blue cl w/illus of Handy Mandy on spine. (Stain top edge.) Kane*. $80/£50

THOMPSON, RUTH PLUMLY. The Silver Princess in Oz. Chicago: Reilly & Lee, (1938). 1st ed, 1st issue w/16-pg gatherings; illus of Handy Mandy on spine; the title, except for Oz monogram, ptd in metallic-silver ink. 9x6.5. John R. Neill (illus). B/w pict eps. Vermilion cl, pict cvr label. Fine. Pacific*. $316/£198

THOMPSON, RUTH PLUMLY. Speedy in Oz. Chicago: Reilly & Lee, (1934). 1st ed. 12 color plts. Blue cl. (Ink inscrip; spine nick.) Kane*. $90/£56

THOMPSON, RUTH PLUMLY. Speedy in Oz. Chicago: Reilly & Lee, (1934). 1st ed, 1st state w/Reilly & Lee imprint on spine in semi-script, 'fancy' letters; plts coated on ptd side only. 9x6.5. 298pp; 12 color plts by John R. Neill. B/w pict eps. Blue cl, pict cvr label. (Marginal stains to plts, tp gutter; label stained, rear cvr spotted), else VG-. Pacific*. $150/£94

THOMPSON, RUTH PLUMLY. Speedy in Oz. Chicago: Reilly & Lee, (1934). 1st ed. 12 color plts by John R. Neill. Black cl w/orange. VG. Davidson. $375/£234

THOMPSON, RUTH PLUMLY. The Wishing Horse of Oz. Chicago: Reilly & Lee, (1935). 1st ed. 12 color plts. Lavender cl. (Spine top tear), else Fine. Kane*. $140/£88

THOMPSON, RUTH PLUMLY. The Wishing Horse of Oz. Chicago: Reilly & Lee, (1935). 1st ed. 9x6.5. 297pp; 12 color plts by John R. Neill. Lavender cl, pict cvr label. NF. Pacific*. $207/£129

THOMPSON, RUTH PLUMLY. Yankee in Oz. (Kinderhook, IL): International Wizard of Oz Club, (1972). 1st, only ed. 11x8.5. Dick Martin (illus), James E. Hanff (maps). Fine in pict wrappers. Pacific*. $138/£86

THOMPSON, RUTH PLUMLY. The Yellow Knight of Oz. Chicago: Reilly & Lee, (1930). 1st ed, primary binding of brick-red cl w/pub's imprint at spine foot in bold type. 12 color plts. (Fr inner hinge re-glued; 2 rubbed spots rear cvr.) Kane*. $85/£53

THOMPSON, RUTH PLUMLY. The Yellow Knight of Oz. Chicago: Reilly & Lee, (1930). 1st ed, 1st binding, w/spine imprint in boldface. 9x6.5. 12 color plts by John R. Neill. Brick cl, pict cvr label. (Fr hinge cracked; lower edges bumped), else VG. Pacific*. $207/£129

THOMPSON, RUTH PLUMLY. The Yellow Knight of Oz. Chicago: Reilly & Lee, (1930). 1st ed. 4to. 12 full-pg color plts by John R. Neill. Brick red cl, color paste label. VG. Reisler. $585/£366

THOMPSON, SILVANUS (ed). Memorials of John Ford. London/York: Samuel Harris/William Sessions, 1877. Signed. Contemp review loosely inserted. Photo frontisport, viii,252pp. Contemp 1/2 calf, gilt, raised bands, contrasting spine label (scraped). Hollett. $152/£95

THOMPSON, SUSAN O. Caxton: An American Contribution to the Quincentenary Celebration. Stinehour, 1976. One of 1250. Dawson. $25/£16

THOMPSON, WILLIAM. Reminiscences of a Pioneer. SF, 1912. 1st ed. VG. *Perier.* $50/£31

THOMPSON, WILLIAM. Reminiscences of a Pioneer. SF, 1912. 1st ed. Frontis, 5 plts. Fine. *Harrington.* $75/£47

THOMPSON, WINFIELD M. and THOMAS W. LAWSON. The Lawson History of the America's Cup: A Record of Fifty Years. Boston: (Thomas Lawson), 1902. One of 3000. 89 plts (incl photogravure frontis), guards. Teg. Cream cl, gilt, morocco spine label. (Cvrs soiled), else VG. *Pacific*.* $161/£101

THOMSON, ALAN. Glencoe. Moffat: Lochar, 1990. 1st ed. VG in dj. *Hollett.* $32/£20

THOMSON, ARTHUR S. The Story of New Zealand. NY/Washington/London: Praeger, 1970. Rpt of 1859 ed. 2 vols in 1. VG. *Worldwide.* $30/£19

THOMSON, C. WYVILLE. The Atlantic. A Preliminary Account of the General Results of the Exploring Voyage of HMS 'Challenger' During the Year 1873 and the Early Part of the Year 1876. NY: Harper, 1878. 2 vols. 391; 340pp + ads; 106, 62 woodcuts, 42 plts, guards. Gilt-dec grn cl. NF (sl worn). *Parmer.* $350/£219

THOMSON, C. WYVILLE. The Depths of the Sea. London: Macmillan, 1873. 1st ed. xx,(iv),527,(1)imprint, 61 pub's list; 7 dbl-pg color charts, 1 fldg chart. Blue pebble cl, gilt. (Sl foxed; spine soiled, rubbed), o/w VG. *Morrell.* $88/£55

THOMSON, DAVID CLEGHORN and F. W. BATESON (eds). Oxford Poetry 1923. Oxford: Basil Blackwell, 1923. 1st ed. VG (label) in dk blue wrappers (spine head nick). *Maggs.* $48/£30

THOMSON, DAVID. A Practical Treatise on the Culture of the Pine-Apple. Edinburgh/London: William Blackwood, 1866. 1st ed. ix,53pp; 36-pg pub's cat at rear. Dk maroon blind cl, gilt. Good (sl foxed; spine ends frayed, nicked, sm tear base of fr joint, lt rippling on both cvrs). *Baltimore*.* $90/£56

THOMSON, G. (ed). Recent Advances in Conservation. Butterworths, 1963. 1st ed. Color frontis. Dj (torn). *Forest.* $40/£25

THOMSON, GEORGE. Impressions of America. Arbroath: T. Buncle, 1916. Only ed. (Cvrs bowed.) *Mott.* $40/£25

THOMSON, J. Retreats: A Series of Designs, Consisting of Plans and Elevations for Cottages, Villas, and Ornamental Buildings. London, 1833. 41 plts, incl 31 hand-colored aquatints. Contemp 1/2 roan. (Lt soiled, foxed; needs rebinding.) *Swann*.* $920/£575

THOMSON, J. H. and BOVERTON REDWOOD. Handbook on Petroleum for Inspectors Under the Petroleum Acts and for Those Engaged in the Storage, Transport, Distribution and Industrial Use of Petroleum.... London: Charles Griffin, 1901. 2 plts (1 color, 1 fldg). Maroon cl. Fine. *Weber.* $45/£28

THOMSON, J. J. Conduction of Electricity Through Gases. Cambridge: CUP, 1903. 1st ed. Grn cl (rubbed). *Weber.* $200/£125

THOMSON, JAMES (ed). Illustrated Handbook of Victoria, Australia. Melbourne, 1886. (iv),108pp; fldg map. Cl-backed wraps (edges ragged, loss to corner, spine chipped; bkpl). *Edwards.* $80/£50

THOMSON, JAMES (ed). Lectures on Peace and War: Orthopedic Surgery. (Ann Arbor: Edwards Bros), 1943. Blue cl (spine end, corner worn), o/w VG. *Weber.* $75/£47

THOMSON, JAMES. The Seasons. London: Nonesuch, 1927. Ltd to 1500. Full marbled cl, leather spine label. Fine. Leather bkpl of Barton Currie. *Truepenny.* $150/£94

THOMSON, JAMES. Vane's Story, Weddah and Om-el-Bonain and Other Poems. Reeves & Turner, 1881. 1st ed. viii,188pp. Chocolate eps. Dk grn cl, gilt, bevel-edged sides. Good (bkpl, name, fep creased; fr cvr water-mkd). *Blackwell's.* $72/£45

THOMSON, JAMES. The Works...In Three Volumes Complete. R. Baldwin et al, 1803. Frontisport, 280 (lacks prelim leaf); (iv),306,(2); (iv),308,(2)pp; 11 plts. Mod 1/4 mid brn calf, gilt, raised bands, dk grn leather label, gray bds. VG. *Blackwell's.* $160/£100

THOMSON, JOSEPH P. The Life of Jesus of Nazareth, for Young People.... Norwich, CT: Henry Bill, 1879. 690pp; 60 plts, 2 color fldg maps. Marbled eps; aeg. Orig 1/2 morocco. (Sl rubbed, soiled), o/w VG. *Worldwide.* $45/£28

THOMSON, PETER. Philadelphia Described to the Stranger and Citizen. Phila: P. Thompson, 1848. 1st ed. 72pp; hand-colored fldg map, 4 woodcut views. Orig brn cl (sl spotted, rear hinge sl frayed). *Karmiole.* $150/£94

THOMSON, SAMUEL. New Guide to Health; Or, Botanic Family Physician.... Boston: E.H. House, 1825. 2nd ed. Contemp calf, leather spine label. (Lacks feps, port, sl foxed; scuffed.) *Sadlon.* $50/£31

THOMSON, WILLIAM HANNA. Grave's Disease with and without Exophthalmic Goitre. NY, 1904. 1st ed. (Shaken; extrems sl worn, sm tear top of spine), internally VG. *Doctor's Library.* $70/£44

THOMSON, WILLIAM M. The Land and the Book. T. Nelson & Sons, 1886. xxxiv,711pp; 1 fldg map. Aeg. Dec brn cl, gilt. VG. *Sotheran.* $205/£128

THOMSON, WILLIAM M. The Land and the Book. The Holy Land. NY: Harper, 1880-1886. Popular ed. 3 vols. xx,592; xxiv,689; xxxiv,711pp. (Sl rubbed), o/w VG. *Worldwide.* $125/£78

THOMSON, WILLIAM. Kelvin's Baltimore Lectures and Modern Theoretical Physics. Robert Kargon and Peter Achinstein (eds). Cambridge: MIT Press, (1987). 1st ed thus. Frontisport. Fine in dj. *Glaser.* $60/£38

THORBURN, ARCHIBALD. A Naturalist's Sketch Book. London: Longmans & Green, 1919. 1st ed. 60 plts, of which 24 are chromolitho and 36 are in collotype. (1 plt detached.) Orig red cl (spine faded, extrems rubbed). *Christie's*.* $253/£158

THORBURN, GRANT. Men and Manners in Britain; or, A Bone to Gnaw.... NY: Wiley & Long, 1834. 1st ed. 187pp (foxed). Orig diced cl. *Mott.* $50/£31

THORBURN, J. M. India and Malaysia. Cincinnati/NY: Cranston & Curts/Hunt & Eaton, 1892. 1st ed. 562pp. Pict cl, gilt. Fine. *Sotheran.* $360/£225

THORBURN, J. S. Elements of Bedside Medicine and General Pathology on General Disease.... London, 1836. xxiv,438pp. (Eps sl foxed; rebound.) *Whitehart.* $128/£80

THOREAU, HENRY DAVID (trans). The Transmigration of the Seven Brahmans. NY: William Edwin Rudge, 1931. 1st ed, 1st ptg. One of 200 numbered. Teg. Beige striped cl, black cl spine. NF (lacks box, glassine). *Lucas.* $150/£94

THOREAU, HENRY DAVID. The Annotated Walden. Philip Van Doren Stern (ed). NY: Clarkson N. Potter, 1970. 1st ed thus. Plain tan bds, grn cl spine. VG in dj (sl tear, sl stain spine foot). *Lucas.* $50/£31

THOREAU, HENRY DAVID. Autumn: From the Journal of Henry D. Thoreau. H. G. O. Blake (ed). Boston/NY: Houghton Mifflin, 1892. 1st ed. 470pp. Teg. Grn cl. Fair (fep loose, rear inner hinge cracked; extrems worn). *Lucas.* $80/£50

THOREAU, HENRY DAVID. Cape Cod. Boston: Ticknor & Fields, 1865. 1st ed. Binding B w/sides blindstamped w/the inner rules crossed to form an 8-pointed ornament, wreath blindstamped in center and Thoreau named as 'Author of Excursions and A Week on Concord River' on spine. (Name, fr hinge cracked; spine sunned, head chipped), else VG. *Pacific*.* $374/£234

THOREAU, HENRY DAVID. Cape Cod. William Ellery Channing (ed). Boston: Ticknor & Fields, 1865. 1st ed. One of 2000. 24pp ads dated Dec 1864. Blindstamped brn 'BD' cl. Leather bkpl, private lib ink stamps of John Stuart Groves. NF (rep sl strained; spine head sl worn) in VG morocco-backed slipcase. *Sumner & Stillman.* $1,275/£797

THOREAU, HENRY DAVID. Cape Cod. Portland, ME: LEC, 1968. One of 1500 numbered, signed by R. J. Holden (illus). Pict cl (lt worn). Slipcase. *Oinonen**. $40/£25

THOREAU, HENRY DAVID. Cape Cod. Portland, ME: LEC, 1968. One of 1500. Signed by R. J. Holden (illus). Pict cl. Fine in slipcase. *Pacific**. $58/£36

THOREAU, HENRY DAVID. Cape Cod. LEC, 1968. Ltd to 1500 numbered, signed by Raymond J. Holden (illus). Fine in slipcase. *Swann**. $69/£43

THOREAU, HENRY DAVID. Collected Poems. Carl Bode (ed). Chicago: Packard, 1943. 1st ed. Dk blue cl spine, yellow-grn bds, ptd spine label. Fine in Fine dj. *Lucas.* $100/£63

THOREAU, HENRY DAVID. Consciousness in Concord. Boston: Houghton Mifflin, 1958. 1st ed, 1st ptg. Beige cl. VG in dj (sl nicks, tears). *Lucas.* $60/£38

THOREAU, HENRY DAVID. Excursions. Boston: Ticknor & Fields, 1863. 1st ed. 319pp; engr port. Blind-stamped grn cl (lt rubbed, spine top worn). *Cullen.* $450/£281

THOREAU, HENRY DAVID. Excursions. Ralph Waldo Emerson (ed). Boston, 1863. 1st ed. Frontisport. Blue-grn cl. (Few prelims sl foxed), o/w VG. BAL 20111. *Kane**. $350/£219

THOREAU, HENRY DAVID. H. D. Thoreau: A Writer's Journal. London/Melbourne/Toronto: Heinemann, (1961). 1st Eng ed thus. Blue cl. VG (pub placed black ink on c. pg to cover 1 or 2 lines of type; lacks dj). *Lucas.* $30/£19

THOREAU, HENRY DAVID. The Heart of Thoreau's Journals. Odell Shepard (ed). Boston: Houghton Mifflin, 1927. 1st ed, ltd issue. One of 300. Signed by Shepard. Uncut, unopened. Pub's compliments slip, 2 ll ink notes by Shepard laid in. Red cl, paper spine label. VG (text, edges sl foxed; fr corners bumped, label sl rubbed). BAL 20244. *Reese.* $175/£109

THOREAU, HENRY DAVID. The Journal of Henry David Thoreau. Bradford Torrey and Francis H. Allen (eds). Salt City: Peregrine Smith, 1984. 1st ed. 15 vols. Fine in wraps, boxed. *Book Market.* $150/£94

THOREAU, HENRY DAVID. Katahdin and Chesuncook. Boston/NY: Houghton Mifflin, (1909). 1st ptg thus. Grn cl. Good (sl worn, ink stain rear cvr). *Lucas.* $35/£22

THOREAU, HENRY DAVID. Letters to Various Persons. Ralph Waldo Emerson (ed). Boston: Ticknor & Fields, 1865. 1st ed. One of 2100 ptd. Brn coated eps. Orig purple dotted cl, gilt. (Sl aged, spotting 1st/last sigs, lg bkseller label; sl stains fr cvr, spine gilt dull.) BAL 5246 and 20116. *Baltimore**. $120/£75

THOREAU, HENRY DAVID. Life Without Principle. NY: Powgen Press, (1936). 1st separate ed. Red cl, paper spine label. VG. *Lucas.* $65/£41

THOREAU, HENRY DAVID. The Maine Woods. Boston: Ticknor & Fields, 1864. 1st ed. One of 1450. 24pp ads dated April 1864. Purple 'BD' cl. (Spine faded), o/w VF in VG morocco-backed slipcase. *Sumner & Stillman.* $1,450/£906

THOREAU, HENRY DAVID. The Maine Woods. Boston: Ticknor & Fields, 1868. 1st ed, 5th ptg. 328pp. Brn cl. Fair (news clipping pinned to fep, dampstain in lower gutter in 1st half of bk; browning on table of contents and facing pg; spine ends worn). *Lucas.* $75/£47

THOREAU, HENRY DAVID. Men of Concord and Some Others as Portrayed in the Journal of Henry David Thoreau. Francis H. Allen (ed). Boston: Houghton Mifflin, 1936. 1st ed, 1st ptg thus. N. C. Wyeth (illus). Grn cl. VG in dj. *Lucas.* $90/£56

THOREAU, HENRY DAVID. The Moon. Boston/NY: Houghton Mifflin, 1927. One of 500 ptd. Untrimmed. White vellum, lt purple bds, gilt. Plain paper dj (sl chipped, sm tears), lt purple bd slipcase (sl worn, spine label lt peeling). BAL 20153. *Baltimore**. $40/£25

THOREAU, HENRY DAVID. Poems of Nature. Henry Salt and Frank Sanborn (eds). Boston/NY/London: Houghton Mifflin/John Lane, Bodley Head, 1895. 1st ed. One of 250 (of 750) w/variant title imprint & spine imprint for sale in US. Unopened. Pale grn polished buckram, gilt. Good (rubbed, lt soiled, edges tanned, spine faded). *Reese.* $60/£38

THOREAU, HENRY DAVID. Sir Walter Raleigh...Lately Discovered Among His Unpublished Journals and Manuscripts. Boston: Bibliophile Soc, (1905). 1st ed. One of 489. Frontis, engr tp. 3/4 dk maroon calf, gray bds. VG (foxed, spine sl rubbed, sm scuff mk spine foot) in orange slipcase. *Lucas.* $200/£125

THOREAU, HENRY DAVID. Walden, or Life in the Woods. Boston: Ticknor & Fields, 1854. 1st ed, 1st ptg. 12mo. 357pp + 8pp pub's ads dated Oct 1854, plan of Walden. Dk brn cl. Fair (inscrip, sig starting, 1 leaf torn, but intact; text lt stained, soiled; sl warp; extrems sl worn, corners bumped, worn, spine ends chipped). *Lucas.* $3,200/£2,000

THOREAU, HENRY DAVID. Walden, or Life in the Woods. Boston: Merrymount Press for LEC, 1936. 1st ptg this ed. One of 1500 signed by Edward Steichen (photos). Black cl spine, blue bds. VG (1/4-inch tear spine top) in slipcase (top of open end broken). *Lucas.* $450/£281

THOREAU, HENRY DAVID. Walden, or Life in the Woods. LEC, 1936. Ltd to 1500 numbered, signed by Edward Steichen (photos). Fine in slipcase. *Swann**. $805/£503

THOREAU, HENRY DAVID. Walden, or Life in the Woods. Boston: LEC, 1936. One of 1500 numbered, signed. 4to. Edward Steichen (photos). Leatherette-backed bds. (Eps stained; extrems sl worn.) *Swann**. $862/£539

THOREAU, HENRY DAVID. Walden. Boston: Fields, Osgood, 1869. 1st ed, 8th ptg. 357pp. Purple cl. Good (sig, extrems worn, spine faded to brn, plan of Walden lacking, appears to have never been bound in). *Lucas.* $300/£188

THOREAU, HENRY DAVID. Walden. Boston/NY: Houghton, Mifflin, 1897. 1st ptg this ed. 2 vols. 259; 260-522pp. Teg. Gilt-dec grn cl (spines sl dknd). NF. *Lucas.* $175/£109

THOREAU, HENRY DAVID. Walden. The Ponds. (NY): Comet Press, (1949). 1st ptg thus. One of 1500. Red cl spine, white cl bds. VG in plain glassine dj (few tears, chips). *Lucas.* $35/£22

THOREAU, HENRY DAVID. A Week on the Concord and Merrimack Rivers. NY: T.Y. Crowell, (1911). 1st ed, 11th ptg. Pict grn cl. Good (bkpl, fr inner hinge cracked; spine dull). *Lucas.* $45/£28

THOREAU, HENRY DAVID. A Week on the Concord and Merrimack Rivers. Boston: Ticknor & Fields, 1868. 2nd ed, 1st ptg. 415pp. Black cl (spine ends worn, sm gouge spine middle). This copy has 'James R. Osgood & Co.' spine imprint. Good. *Lucas.* $300/£188

THOREAU, HENRY DAVID. A Week on the Concord and Merrimack Rivers. LEC, 1975. One of 2000 signed by Raymond J. Holden (illus). Fine in slipcase. *Swann**. $57/£36

THOREAU, HENRY DAVID. Where I Lived and What I Lived For. (Waltham Saint Lawrence): Golden Cockerel, 1924. 1st ed. One of 380. Vellum spine, batik-pattern paper-cvrd bds. VG (name crossed out in ink; corners worn, vellum dust-soiled). *Lucas.* $200/£125

THOREAU, HENRY DAVID. Wild Apples. Boston/NY: Houghton Mifflin, 1923. 1st ptg thus. Grn bds ptd w/tree pattern. VG in dj (sl tear spine foot). *Lucas.* $40/£25

THOREAU, HENRY DAVID. The Writings of Henry David Thoreau. Boston/NY: Houghton Mifflin, 1906. 'Walden Edition,' 1st ptg. 20 vols. 12mo. Teg. Blue ribbed cl. NF (rubber-stamped name). *Lucas.* $700/£438

THOREAU, HENRY DAVID. A Yankee in Canada, with Anti-Slavery and Reform Papers. Boston: Ticknor & Fields, 1866. 1st ed, 1st ptg. 286pp. Purplish-brn cl. Good (rear inner hinge cracked; spine ends chipped approx 1/8-inch). *Lucas.* $350/£219

THOREK, M. The Human Testis: Its Gross Anatomy, Histology, Physiology, Pathology.... Phila, 1924. 1st ed. (Ex-lib.) *Fye.* $150/£94

THOREK, M. Plastic Surgery of the Breast and Abdominal Wall. Springfield, IL, 1942. 1st ed. (Lib label remains, stamps; gilt # spine), o/w VG. *Whitehart.* $152/£95

THOREK, PHILIP. Surgical Diagnosis. Phila/Montreal: Lippincot, (1956). 1st ed. Fine. *Weber.* $50/£31

THORN, C. JORDAN. Handbook of Old Pottery and Porcelain Marks. NY: Tudor, 1947. 44 plts. VG in dj (sl defective, edges browned). *Hollett.* $48/£30

THORNBURG, NEWTON. Cutter and Bone. Boston: Little Brown, 1976. 1st ed. Fine in Fine white dj. *Pettler.* $50/£31

THORNBURG, NEWTON. Knockover. Greenwich: Fawcett, 1968. 1st ed. (2 stamps), else VG + in wrappers. *Pettler.* $25/£16

THORNBURY, GEORGE W. Songs of the Cavaliers and Roundheads. Hurst & Blackett, 1857. Frontis (dampstained), viii,328,24,14pp; 5 plts. Blind-stamped cl (worn, stained, rear joint tender, sl shaken), gilt. *Hollett.* $72/£45

THORNBURY, WALTER and EDWARD WALFORD. Old and New London. London, n.d. New ed. 6 vols. (Prelims lt browned, spines sl rubbed.) *Edwards.* $240/£150

THORNBURY, WALTER. The Life of J.M.W. Turner. Hurst & Blackett, 1862. 1st ed. 2 vols. 416; 425pp; complete w/engr frontis, 6 plts; extra illus w/33 engr plts laid or bound in. Full pebble-grain dk blue morocco (neatly rebacked), gilt. VG set (lt spotted, browned). *Hollett.* $256/£160

THORNDIKE, L. A History of Magic and Experimental Science. NY/London: Columbia Univ, 1964. 8 vols. Grn cl (upper hinge vol 1 split; sl rubbed). *Maggs.* $240/£150

THORNDIKE, RACHEL SHERMAN. The Sherman Letters. London: Sampson Low, Marston, 1894. viii,398pp. (Extrems worn), else Good. *Dumont.* $75/£47

THORNDIKE, RUSSELL. The Water Witch. London: Thornton Butterworth, 1932. 1st ed. Scarlet patterned cl. (Pinhead-sized hole in cl over fr joint), o/w Nice. *Temple.* $72/£45

THORNE, ROSS. Theatre Buildings in Australia to 1905. Sydney: Architectural Research Foundation/Univ of Sydney, (1971). One of 500. 2 vols. Pict eps. Fine in pict slipcase. *Dramatis.* $150/£94

THORNHILL, ROBERT BADHAM. The Shooting Directory. London: Longman, Hunt, Rees & Orme, 1804. 1st ed, 1st issue, pp215-220 not cancelled, half-title, color aquatint frontis, 6 color aquatint plts, 2 engr plts, 3 fldg letterpress tables. (Browning, occasional spotting.) Teg. Mod red morocco. *Christie's*.* $1,171/£732

THORNTON, J. QUINN. Oregon and California in 1848...with an Appendix.... Volume II only. NY: Harper, 1855. 2nd ed. Inscribed on piece of paper affixed to fr pastedown 1873. 6 wood-engr plts. (Contents dknd; cvrs rubbed, stained), else VG. Howes T224. *Pacific*.* $69/£43

THORNTON, JOHN L. John Abernethy. London: Privately ptd, 1953. 1st ed. 8 plts. VG in dj (defective). *Hollett.* $40/£25

THORNTON, JOHN L. and R. I. TULLY. Scientific Books, Libraries and Collectors: A Study of Bibliography and the Book Trade in Relation to Science. London: Library Assoc, 1971. 3rd ed. Frontis, 17 plts. Fine in dj. *Weber.* $45/£28

THORNTON, ROBERT DONALD. James Currie, The Entire Stranger, and Robert Burns. Oliver & Boyd, 1963. 1st ed. 17 plts (8 color). VG in dj (spine ends sl chipped). *Hollett.* $56/£35

THORNTON, THOMAS. A Sporting Tour Through the Northern Parts of England, and Great Part of the Highland of Scotland. London/Edinburgh/Glasgow: Vernor & Hood et al, 1804. 1st ed. 16 copper plts. Teg. 3/4 crushed grn morocco, marbled bds, gilt, raised bands; bound by Bayntun. (Foxed, spine sunned), else NF. *Pacific*.* $207/£129

THORP, JOHN. Letters of the Late John Thorp, of Manchester, a Minister of the Gospel in the Society of Friends. Liverpool: Ptd by James & Jonathan Smith, 1820. 1st ed. xlii,197pp. Contemp 1/2 calf (extrems sl rubbed), raised bands, red morocco label. *Young.* $72/£45

THORP, NATHAN HOWARD. Songs of the Cowboys. Boston: Houghton Mifflin, 1921. 2nd ed. Spine label. NF. *Labordo.* $75/£47

THORP, RODERICK. Nothing Lasts Forever. NY/London: W.W. Norton, (1979). 1st ed. Signed. Fine in NF dj (sm closed tear fr panel). *Bernard.* $50/£31

THORPE, NIGEL. The Glory of the Page. London, 1987. Good + in dj. *Washton.* $85/£53

Thoughts on Hunting. In a Series of Familiar Letters to a Friend. (By Peter Beckford.) Sarum, 1781. 1st ed, w/half-title. Engr frontis, 2 plts; (4) leaves, 334pp. Contemp calf (neatly rebacked at early date), spine gilt. (Sl foxed, soiled; rubbed.) *Oinonen*.* $200/£125

THRAPP, DAN L. Al Sieber, Chief of Scouts. Norman: Univ of OK, (1964). 1st ed. Fine in Fine dj. *Book Market.* $85/£53

THRAPP, DAN L. Encyclopedia of Frontier Biography. Glendale/Spokane: A.H. Clark, 1988-1994. 1st ed. 4 vols. *Dawson.* $260/£163

THRAPP, DAN L. Encyclopedia of Frontier Biography. Glendale: A.H. Clark, 1990. 2nd ptg. Ltd ed. 3 vols + supp vol. Mint set in plain white djs. *Argonaut.* $265/£166

THRAPP, DAN L. Victorio and the Mimbres Apaches. Norman, 1974. 1st ed. Fine (bkseller label) in dj (faded, edgeworn). *Baade.* $57/£36

Three Bears. NY: Charles E. Graham, (ca 1925). Shapebook. 12mo. 7 full-pg illus. Stiff pict bds. Good. *Reisler.* $45/£28

Three Generations, 1837-1949: Jules Francois Bekeart, a Gunsmith; Philip Baldwin Bekeart, His Son; Philip Kendall Bekeart, His Grandson. (Oakland), 1949. 1st ed. One of 500 ptd. Tipped-in color frontis. 1/2 cl. Fine in slipcase. *Pacific*.* $52/£33

Three Hours in Aden. Bombay, 1902. 2nd ed. 3 maps (2 fldg). Cl-backed ptd bds. *Maggs.* $400/£250

Three Little Kittens (Moveable). Boston: De Wolfe Fiske, (ca 1890). Obl 4to. 28pp. Cl-backed color pict bds (edges lt worn). *Reisler.* $225/£141

Three Little Kittens Who Lost Their Mittens: A New Ballad-Arrangement for Young Children. Phila: Henry Altemus, (1923). 16mo. 64pp; each text pg w/full-pg color plts. Cl-backed pict bds, color paste label. Good in color dj (dusty, margins worn, spine chipped). *Reisler.* $110/£69

Three Little Kittens. Akron, OH: Saalfield Pub, 1910. Cl bk. 5.75x12.5. 3 leaves (spotted, mkd). *Reisler.* $120/£75

Three Little Pigs. A Peepshow Book. London: C&W, 1977. Karen Acosta (illus). 5 scenes open to form circle. Glazed pict bds. VG. *Bookfinders.* $40/£25

Three Little Pigs. An All-Action Treasure Hour Pop-Up Book. Leicester: Brown Watson, 1983. 6 dbl-pg, fldg pop-ups by V. Kubasta. Glazed pict bds. Fine. *Bookfinders.* $40/£25

Three Rebels Write Home, Including the Letters of Edgar Allan Jackson, James Fenton Bryant, Irvin Cross Wills, and Miscellaneous Items. (Edgar Jackson, ed.) (Franklin, VA: News Pub), 1955. 1st ed. One of 150. NF in ptd gray wraps. *Chapel Hill.* $275/£172

Three Years Among the Working-Classes in the United States During the War. (By James Dawson Burn.) London: Smith, Elder, 1865. Only ed. pp xvi,309,(2) ads. Grn cl (ink spot fr cvr). Fine. *Mott.* $300/£188

Through the Land of the Aztecs. London: Sampson Low, Marston, 1892. 1st ed. x,236pp; 4 photo plts. Blue cl, gilt. (Old emb seal tp.) *Karmiole.* $75/£47

THRUM, THOMAS G. Hawaiian Almanac and Annual for 1921. Honolulu: Thos. G. Thrum, 1920. Buckram. (Ex-lib, pp browned; soiled.) *Parmer.* $60/£38

THRUM, THOMAS G. (ed). Hawaiian Folk Tales. Chicago, 1917. Frontisport. Pict cl. (Extrems sl rubbed), o/w VG. *Sagebrush.* $75/£47

THUBRON, COLIN. Among the Russians. Heinemann, 1983. 1st UK ed. Fine in dj. *Williams.* $152/£95

THUBRON, COLIN. The God in the Mountain. London, 1977. 1st Eng ed. VG (spine head, 2 corner tips sl bumped) in dj. *Clearwater.* $80/£50

THUBRON, COLIN. The God in the Mountain. Heinemann, 1977. 1st ed. VG (sm erasure fep; top edges sl faded, spine ends, corners sl bumped) in dj (sl creased, mkd, price-clipped). *Ulysses.* $88/£55

THUBRON, COLIN. Turning Back the Sun. London, 1991. Signed. VG in dj. *Typographeum.* $45/£28

THUCYDIDES. The History of the Pelponnesian War. LEC, 1974. One of 2000 signed by A. Tasson (illus). 2 vols. Fine in slipcase. *Swann*.* $161/£101

THUDICHUM, J. L. W. A Treatise on the Pathology of the Urine, Including a Complete Guide to Its Analysis. London, 1858. 1st ed. 429pp. Full leather prize binding (fr hinge cracked). *Fye.* $400/£250

THUILLIER, JACQUES. Rubens' Life of Marie De' Medici. NY: Abrams, (1967). Lg folio. (Lt worn.) Slipcase. *Oinonen*.* $60/£38

THURBER, JAMES. Alarms and Diversions. NY: S&S, 1957. 1st ed. VG + in dj (worn). *Pettler.* $15/£9

THURBER, JAMES. The Beast in Me and Other Animals. NY: Harcourt Brace, 1948. 1st ed. (Name, date), else NF in VG dj (edges chipped). *Pettler.* $30/£19

THURBER, JAMES. Further Fables for Our Time. NY: S&S, 1956. 1st ed. NF in NF dj. *Pettler.* $25/£16

THURBER, JAMES. The Last Flower. NY, 1939. 1st ed. Pict bds. Dj. *Swann*.* $69/£43

THURBER, JAMES. The Middle-Aged Man on the Flying Trapeze. NY: Harper, 1935. 1st ed. NF in dj (lt worn, spine sl dknd). *Bromer.* $250/£156

THURBER, JAMES. The Middle-Aged Man on the Flying Trapeze. NY: Harper, 1935. 1st ed. Fine in dj (sl worn). *Karmiole.* $300/£188

THURBER, JAMES. My Life and Hard Times. Harper, 1933. 1st ed. VG + in VG- dj (worn, torn, lt chipped). *Fine Books.* $195/£122

THURBER, JAMES. My World—And Welcome to It. NY, (1942). 1st ed. Inscribed. *Kane*.* $140/£88

THURBER, JAMES. Thurber's Dogs. NY: S&S, 1955. 1st ed. NF in VG dj. *Beasley.* $65/£41

THURBER, JAMES. The Wonderful O. NY: S&S, (1957). 1st ed. Blue/beige cl. VF in dj. *Appelfeld.* $50/£31

THURBER, JAMES. The Wonderful O. NY: S&S, 1957. 1st ed. VG + (worn) in dj (sl edgeworn). *My Bookhouse.* $32/£20

THURMAN, MICHAEL E. The Naval Department of San Blas. New Spain's Bastion for Alta California and Nootka 1767 to 1798. Glendale: A.H. Clark, 1967. 1st ed. Red cl. Fine. *House.* $35/£22

THWAITES, REUBEN GOLD (ed). Early Western Travels Comprising I. Memorable Days in America...II. A Visit to North America and the English Settlements in Illinois.... (By Adlard Welby.) Cleveland: A.H. Clark, 1904. Teg, others uncut. Maroon cl. *Mott.* $75/£47

THWAITES, REUBEN GOLD (ed). Early Western Travels. Cleveland, 1904-07. One of 750 numbered sets. 31 (of 32) vols (lacks vol 25). 8vo. 3/4 brn morocco, gilt. Howes T255. *Swann*.* $1,955/£1,222

THWAITES, REUBEN GOLD (ed). Original Journals of the Lewis and Clark Expedition, 1804-1806.... NY: Dodd, Mead, 1904. One of 200 sets, ptd on Van Gelder hand-made paper. 8 vols in 15, incl atlas. 12.25x9. (Offset from plts, vol 1 frontis detached but present; spines sunned, rubbed, ends worn w/a few chipped), else VG. Howes L320. *Pacific*.* $3,163/£1,977

THWAITES, REUBEN GOLD. How George Rogers Clark Won the Northwest and Other Essays in Western History. Chicago: A.C. McClurg, 1924. 4th ed. (Bkpl, ink name), else VG. *Perier.* $20/£13

TIBBLES, THOMAS HENRY. Buckskin and Blanket Days. Chicago: R.R. Donnelley, 1985. Frontis. VG. *Lien.* $30/£19

TICEHURST, NORMAN F. The Mute Swan in England. London, 1950. 31 plts (1 fldg). (Prelims lt browned, bkpl.) Dj (sl rubbed). *Edwards.* $24/£15

TIDWORTH, SIMON. Theatres. London: Pall Mall, 1973. VG in dj. *Dramatis.* $45/£28

TIDY, GORDON. Surtees on Fishing. London: Constable, 1931. 1st ed. One of 5000. 7 hand-colored facs, guards. VG (spine head sunned) in dj (spine head lacks sm piece; spine, extrems sl sunned). *Pacific*.* $46/£29

TIDYMAN, ERNEST. The Last Shaft. London: Weidenfeld & Nicolson, 1975. 1st ed. Fine in dj (spine sl faded). *Mordida.* $85/£53

TIETZE-CONRAT, E. Mantegna. London, 1955. Complete ed. Good + in dj. *Washton.* $90/£56

Tiffany Studios Collection of Notable Antique Oriental Rugs. NY: (Tiffany Studios, 1906). Ltd to 500 numbered. Color frontis; 30 b/w plts. Teg. Lt grn parchment-backed dk grn bds, spine gilt. VG (pp sl dknd; bumped; joints, spine head, foot rubbed). *Blue Mountain.* $150/£94

TIGHE, ROBERT RICHARD and JAMES EDWARD DAVIS. Annals of Windsor. London: Longmans, Brown, Green, Longmans & Roberts, 1843. 2 vols. xxviii,705; xii,752pp; 2 color fldg plan frontispieces incl 1 linen-backed, fldg plt, fldg plan. Marbled eps, teg. 1/2 calf, marbled bds. (Sl marginal browning, bkpl; rubbed, spine lt sunned.) *Edwards.* $200/£125

Tight Lines and a Happy Landing. (Balt: Reese,) 1937. 1st ed. One of 300 numbered. Signed by Alexander E. Duncan. Grn cl, striated bds. VG (eps sl aged; edgeworn). *Baltimore*.* $110/£69

TILDEN, FREEMAN. Following the Frontier with F. Jay Haynes, Pioneer Photographer of the Old West. NY: Knopf, 1964. 1st ed. Fine in dj (torn). *Argonaut.* $75/£47

TILGHMAN, ZOE A. Outlaw Days. (Oklahoma City), 1926. 1st ed. NF in pict wrappers (chip to corner). *Sagebrush.* $45/£28

TILGHMAN, ZOE A. Outlaw Days. Oklahoma City: Harlow Pub, 1926. Wraps. (Text block loose from wraps), else NF. *Dumont.* $50/£31

TILGHMAN, ZOE A. Spotlight. San Antonio, TX: Naylor, 1960. 1st ed. Fine in wrappers. *Labordo.* $40/£25

TILLER, TERENCE. The Inward Animal. London: Hogarth, (1943). 1st ed. VG in dj (sl faded). *Cady.* $15/£9

TILLER, TERENCE. Poems. London: Hogarth, (1941). 1st ed, 1st bk. Fine in dj (sl soiled). *Reese.* $50/£31

TILLETT, LESLIE (ed). Wind on the Buffalo Grass. NY, (1976). 1st ed. VG in dj (sl frayed). *King.* $45/£28

TILLEY, FRANK. Teapots and Tea. Newport: Ceramic Book Co, (1957). One of 1000. 67 leaves of plts. Teg. Red gilt cl (spine faded). *Karmiole.* $185/£116

TILLEY, ROGER. Playing Cards. (London): Octopus Bks, (1973). 1st ed. Pict cl (bumped, sl rubbed). VG. *Blue Mountain.* $20/£13

TILMAN, H. W. The Ascent of Nanda Devi. Cambridge: CUP, 1937. 1st ed. 35 plts, 2 maps (1 fldg). VG in dj (sl worn, spine dknd). *Hollett.* $192/£120

TILMAN, H. W. The Ascent of Nanda Devi. Hodder & Stoughton, 1939. 3rd ed. VG in dj (sl worn, chipped). *Hollett.* $40/£25

TILMAN, H. W. Mount Everest 1938. CUP, 1948. 1st ed. 36 plts, 4 maps. VG in dj (sl chipped, dknd). *Hollett.* $120/£75

TILMAN, H. W. Snow on the Equator. London: Travel Book Club, 1940. 4 maps. Fine in dj. *Explorer.* $64/£40

TILNEY, F. C. The Principles of Photographic Pictorialism. London: Chapman & Hall, 1930. 1st ed. 80 b/w plts. (Eps sl spotted.) Dj (sl soiled, chipped, sl loss to spine). *Edwards.* $72/£45

TILTON, CECIL G. William Chapman Ralston, Courageous Builder. Boston: Christopher Pub House, (1935). 1st ed. Blue cl, gilt. Fine in dj (spine sunned, sm tears, chips top edge). *Pacific*.* $58/£36

TILTON, J. E. (ed). The Art of Confectionery. Boston: J.E. Tilton, 1866. 1st ed. Pict grn cl, gilt. (Sm spots to tp, following few pp; spine ends, corners rubbed), else VG. *Pacific*.* $138/£86

TIMERMAN, JACOBO. Prisoner Without a Name, Cell Without a Number. London: Weidenfeld & Nicolson, 1981. 1st British ed. Fine in dj. *Lame Duck.* $45/£28

TIMLIN, WILLIAM. The Ship That Sailed to Mars. London: George G. Harrap, (1923). 4to. Unpaginated. White parchment-backed gray paper-cvrd bds, gilt. VG (few mks) in buff ptd dj (few mks, 1-inch closed tear, crease upper edge). *Sotheran.* $1,920/£1,200

TIMLIN, WILLIAM. The Ship That Sailed to Mars. London, (1923). 1st ed. 4to. 48 mtd color plts, 48 mtd ll of calligraphic text. Orig vellum-backed bds. (Lt shelfworn), o/w Excellent in gray ptd dj (sl chipped). *Heritage.* $2,000/£1,250

TIMOSHENKO, S. Theory of Elastic Stability. NY/London: McGraw-Hill, 1936. 1st ed. Black cl. Fine (bkpl). *Weber.* $100/£63

TIMPERLEY, C. H. The Printers' Manual; Containing Instructions to Learners.... H. Johnson, 1838. 1st ed. Engr frontis, 116pp. Orig cl-backed bds (spine head chipped). *Forest.* $176/£110

TIMROD, HENRY. The Poems of Henry Timrod. Paul H. Hayne (ed). NY: E.J. Hale & Son, 1873. 1st ed. 205pp. Sm broadsheet flyer for other Hale publications laid in. Dec blue cl, beveled edges. VG (pencil sig dated March 23rd, 1873, few pp roughly opened in the 'Memoir'). BAL 20327. *Chapel Hill.* $150/£94

TINDALL, WILLIAM YORK. A Reader's Guide to 'Finnegans Wake.' London: Thames & Hudson, 1969. Hb issue. NF dj (spine, edges sl dknd). *Ulysses.* $120/£75

Tinder Box. NY: Stephen Daye, 1945. 17x23 cm. Julian Wehr (engineer). 5 tab-operated plts. Pict bds. NF. *Bookfinders.* $150/£94

TING, WALLACE. Hot and Sour Soup. NY/Denmark, (1969). 1st ed. One of 1050. This copy inscribed, signed. Folio. Contents loose in folder as issued. Slipcase. *Swann*.* $138/£86

TINKER, CHAUNCEY BREWSTER. Painter and Poet. Harvard Univ, 1938. 1st Eng ed. (Name; no dj.) *Clearwater.* $136/£85

TINKHAM, GEORGE H. History of San Joaquin County, California.... L.A.: Historic Record Co, 1923. 3/4 morocco, cl. (Spine heavily, crudely repaired w/tape; hinges cracked.) Contents VG. *Pacific*.* $52/£33

TINKHAM, GEORGE H. A History of Stockton, from Its Organization up to the Present Time.... SF: W.M. Hinton, 1880. 1st ed. Orig mts albumen photo frontisport, xiv (misnumbered xvi),196,203-397pp; 6 plts. (Repairs to ep hinges; rebacked, orig spine laid on; cvrs worn), else VG. Howes T273. *Pacific*.* $288/£180

Tiny Teddies. NY: Sam'l Gabriel Sons, (ca 1910). Sq 8vo. 8pp. Linenette self-cvr (sm spot of lifted paper on fr cvr). *Reisler.* $50/£31

Tip and Top at the Farm. London: Bancroft, 1961. V. Kubasta (designer). 6 dbl-pg pop-ups. VG- in pict wraps. *Bookfinders.* $160/£100

Tip and Top at the Zoo. London: Bancroft, 1961. V. Kubasta (designer). 6 dbl-pg pop-ups. VG- in pict wraps. *Bookfinders.* $160/£100

Tip and Top Build a Motor Car. London: Bancroft, 1961. V. Kubasta (designer). 6 dbl-pg pop-ups. VG (mis-folds corrected, strengthened; 2 effects have facs replacement parts) in pict wraps. *Bookfinders.* $50/£31

Tip and Top Look at Ships. London: Bancroft, 1964. 6 dbl-pg pop-ups by V. Kubasta. VG- in pict wraps. *Bookfinders.* $160/£100

TIPPETT, TOM. When Southern Labor Stirs. NY: Cape & Smith, 1931. 1st ed. Secondary binding of tan cl. NF (stamps, faint plt removal signs on rep, bkpl) in dj (lt worn, sm spine chip). *Beasley.* $40/£25

TIPPING, H. AVRAY. English Gardens. London, 1925. Folio. Aeg. (Spine sl faded), o/w Fine. *Henly.* $232/£145

TIPPING, H. AVRAY. English Gardens. Country Life, 1925. Folio. Photo frontis. Pub's cl. *Sotheran.* $288/£180

TIPPING, H. AVRAY. English Homes of the Early Renaissance. London, n.d. Folio. (Shelfworn, torn, stained.) *Oinonen*.* $50/£31

TIPPING, H. AVRAY. English Homes. Period II—Volume I. Early Tudor, 1485-1558. London: Country Life, n.d. c.(1929). 2nd ed. Folio. (Feps lt browned; cl sl rubbed, spine sl faded.) *Edwards.* $120/£75

TIPPING, H. AVRAY. English Homes. Period III—Volumes I and II. Late Tudor and Early Stuart, 1558-1649. London: Country Life, 1929/1927. 2nd and 1st eds. 2 vols complete. Folio. (Feps sl browned; cl sl rubbed, spines lt faded.) *Edwards.* $432/£270

TIPPING, H. AVRAY. English Homes. Period IV—Volume 1 Late Stuart, 1649-1714. Country Life, 1929. Folio. 2-tone cl (sl mkd, bumped), gilt. Dj (soiled, defective in places). *Hollett.* $136/£85

TIPPING, H. AVRAY. Grinling Gibbons and the Woodwork of His Age (1648-1720). London, 1914. Folio. 1/4 cl (spine soiled, extrems worn). *Swann*.* $126/£79

TISSOT, J. JAMES. The Life of Our Lord Jesus Christ. Sampson Low, Marston, 1897. People's ed. 2 vols. xi,272; 280pp. (Sl shaken, some wax tissues torn, chipped; sm #s to spine feet.) Dj (worn, torn). *Hollett.* $224/£140

TISSOT. Onanism. A. Hume (trans). W. Wilkinson, 1767. 3rd ed. xii,184pp. 19th cent 1/2 maroon calf (spine faded). *Bickersteth.* $416/£260

Tit for Tat. (By Marion Southwood.) NY: Garret, 1856. 1st ed. 1 prelim l, pp iii,v,356,(4) ads. (Faded, sl worn.) *Mott.* $30/£19

TITCHENELL, ELSA-BRITA. Once Round the Sun. Covina, CA: Theosophical Univ, (1950). 1st ed. 8vo. 4 full-pg plts by Justin C. Gruelle. Blue cl, color paste label. Good. *Reisler.* $100/£63

TITCOMB, TIMOTHY. (Pseud of Josiah Holland.) Letters to the Jonses. NY: Scribner, 1863. 1st ed. Purple-brn cl. Good + (pencil inscrip; spine sl sunned, corners sl worn). BAL 8592. *Reese.* $125/£78

TITCOMBE, MARIANNE. The Bookbinding Career of Rachel McMasters Miller Hunt. Hunt Botanical Library, 1974. 1st ed. Frontis, 11 plts. *Forest.* $40/£25

TITLEY, NORAH M. Miniatures from Persian Manuscripts. London: British Museum, 1977. 1st ed. 41 plts. NF in dj. *Worldwide.* $125/£78

TITMARSH, M. A. (Pseud of William Makepeace Thackeray.) Doctor Birch. London, 1849. 1st ed. 49pp; 16 full-pg color plts. Finely bound in polished calf w/gilt dec spine (orig wraps bound in). (Later eps browned; fr cvr detached, spine chipped.) *King.* $300/£188

TITMARSH, M. A. (Pseud of William M. Thackeray.) The Irish Sketch-Book. London: Chapman & Hall, 1843. 1st ed. 2 vols. Engr frontispieces. Yellow-coated eps. Orig blind-stamped dk grn cl, gilt. (Frontis edges, eps sl dknd, hinge sl cracking; few mks, spine crown sl frayed), o/w Very Bright in 2 half morocco slipcases (1 damaged at top panel). *Reese.* $1,000/£625

TITTERTON, W. R. London Scenes. London: Andrew Melrose Ltd, 1920. 1st ed. Blue cl. (Spine faded through dj), o/w VG in VG dj (sl rubbed, chips). *Reese.* $30/£19

TJADER, RICHARD. The Big Game of Africa. NY: D. Appleton, 1910. 1st ed. Port, fldg map, 31 plts. Grn cl (lt rubbed). *Adelson.* $225/£141

TOBIE, HARVEY. No Man Like Joe. Portland: Binfords & Mort, (1949). 1st ed. Frontis. Fine in dj (sl chipped, lt soiled). *Argonaut.* $60/£38

TODD, BARBARA EUPHAN. Worzel Gummidge and Saucy Nancy. Hollis & Carter, 1947. 1st ed. 8vo. Color frontis by Will Nickless, 167pp. VG (spine faded, cvrs mkd). *Bookmark.* $24/£15

TODD, BARBARA EUPHAN. Worzel Gummidge at the Circus. Evans, 1956. 1st ed. 8vo. Jill Crockford (illus). 188pp. VG + in dj (worn). *Bookmark.* $40/£25

TODD, FRANK MORTON. Eradicating Plague from San Francisco. SF: Press of C.A. Murdock, 1909. 27 plts. Red cl. (Chip rep), o/w Fine. *Pacific*.* $52/£33

TODD, ROBERT. Clinical Lectures on Certain Acute Diseases. Phila, 1860. 1st Amer ed. 308pp. *Fye.* $100/£63

TODD, RUTHVEN. The Acreage of the Heart. (Glasgow): William Maclellan, (1944). 1st ed. Frontis. Fair in 1/4 red cl (corners bumped), gilt. Dj (edges torn). *Maggs.* $40/£25

TODD, RUTHVEN. Until Now. London: Fortune Press, (1942). 1st ed. Untrimmed. Black buckram (sl soiled), gilt. *Maggs.* $40/£25

TODD, W. HOGARTH. Tiger, Tiger! London, 1927. 1st ed. (Lt browned; sl worn.) *Edwards.* $40/£25

TODD, WILLIAM B. (ed). Thomas J. Wise: Centenary Studies. Austin: Univ of TX, 1959. VG + in dj. *Zubal*.* $50/£31

TOESCA, PIETRO and FERDINANDO FORLATI. Mosaics of St. Marks. CT: NYGS, 1958. Folio. 44 color plts. Mod cl (sm ink stamp), gilt. *Edwards.* $64/£40

TOESCA, PIETRO. Florentine Painting of the Trecento. Firenze/NY, n.d. 119 plts, guards. Good. *Washton.* $150/£94

TOKLAS, ALICE B. Aromas and Flavours. London: Michael Joseph, 1959. 1st Eng ed. NF (spine head sl bumped) in dj (spine head sl creased). *Ulysses.* $136/£85

TOKLAS, ALICE B. What Is Remembered. London: Michael Joseph, (1963). 1st Eng ed. VF in VF dj. *Between The Covers.* $125/£78

TOKLAS, ALICE B. What Is Remembered. NY: HRW, (1963). 1st ed. VF in VF dj. *Between The Covers.* $150/£94

TOLAND, M. B. M. Tisayac of the Yosemite. Phila: Lippincott, (1891). 1st ed. 10 plts. Blue cl, gilt. (Fr hinge cracked, extrems sl worn), o/w Fine. *Pacific*.* $58/£36

TOLKEIN, J. R. R. The Lord of the Rings. Boston: Houghton, Mifflin, 1967. 2nd ed. 3 vols. VG in djs (spine ends, corners rubbed, spine sl sunned, vol 1 spine head w/sm chip), slipcase. *Pacific*.* $127/£79

TOLKEIN, J. R. R. The Return of the King. Boston: Houghton Mifflin, 1956. 1st Amer ed. Fldg map. VG in dj (spine ends, corners sl chipped, fr flap crease rubbed). *Pacific*.* $184/£115

TOLKEIN, J. R. R. Smith of Wotton Major. Boston: Houghton, Mifflin, 1967. 1st Amer ed. Fine in NF dj (soiled, price-clipped). *Pacific*.* $63/£39

TOLKIEN, J. R. R. The Adventures of Tom Bombadil. London: George Allen & Unwin, 1962. 1st ed. 8vo. Pauline Baynes (illus). (vi),7-63pp. Pict bds. VG (ink inscrip) in Nice matching pict dj. *Sotheran.* $125/£78

TOLKIEN, J. R. R. The Adventures of Tom Bombadil. Boston: Houghton Mifflin, 1963. 1st Amer ed. Color pict bds. (Spine ends bumped), o/w Fine in dj (price-clipped, spine top lt chipped). *Heritage.* $100/£63

TOLKIEN, J. R. R. Farmer Giles of Ham. London, 1949. 1st ed. VG + in VG + dj. *Fine Books.* $185/£116

TOLKIEN, J. R. R. Farmer Giles of Ham. Boston: Houghton Mifflin, 1950. 1st US ed. 2 tri-color plts. Blue cl. (Spine faded), o/w Fine in dj (spine sunned, sl edgeworn). *Heritage.* $250/£156

TOLKIEN, J. R. R. A Middle English Vocabulary. Oxford: Clarendon, 1922. 1st ed. VG in wrappers (shelfworn, sm spot fr wrapper, spine mostly lacking). *Pacific*.* $196/£123

TOLLEY, CYRIL J. H. The Modern Golfer. NY: Knopf, 1924. 1st Amer ed. Frontisport. (Emb stamp; spine sl sunned), else VG. *Pacific*.* $98/£61

TOLLNER, MADELINE R. Netsuke: The Life and Legend of Japan in Miniature. (SF: Abbey, 1954.) 1st ed. Signed presentation. Dec black cl. Good in pict dj (sl soiled, chipped). *Karmiole.* $85/£53

TOLMACHOFF, INNOKENTY. Siberian Passage. New Brunswick: Rutger's Univ, 1949. VG in dj. *High Latitude.* $30/£19

TOLMIE, WILLIAM FRASER. Physician and Fur Trader. Vancouver: Mitchell, 1963. 1st ed. Fine in VG dj. *Perier.* $35/£22

TOLSTOI, LEO. Master and Man. A. Hulme Beaman (trans). Chapman & Hall, 1895. 1st Eng ed. 125pp. Contemp 1/2 calf (edges sl scraped), gilt. *Hollett.* $120/£75

TOLSTOY, LEO. Anna Karenina. Moscow: LEC, 1933. One of 1500. Signed by Nikolas Piskariov (illus). 2 vols. Fine in slipcase. *Pacific*.* $92/£58

TOLSTOY, LEO. Anna Karenina. LEC, 1951. Ltd to 1500 numbered, signed by Barnett Freedman (illus). 2 vols. Fine in slipcase. *Swann*.* $80/£50

TOLSTOY, LEO. Childhood, Boyhood, Youth. LEC, 1972. Ltd to 1500 numbered, signed by Fritz Eichenberg (illus). Fine in slipcase. *Swann*.* $92/£58

TOLSTOY, LEO. Resurrection. LEC, 1963. Ltd to 1500 numbered, signed by Fritz Eichenberg (illus). Fine in slipcase. *Swann*.* $92/£58

TOLSTOY, LEO. War and Peace. Constance Garnett (trans). Heinemann, 1904. 1st ed thus. 3 vols. Grn cl, gilt. VG (ink inscrips). *Williams.* $280/£175

TOLSTOY, LEO. War and Peace. Louise and Aylmer Maude (trans). Glasgow: LEC, 1938. One of 1500 ptd, signed by Barnett Freedman (illus). 6 vols. Red pict linen. Fine set in boxes. *Appelfeld.* $300/£188

TOLSTOY, LEV. Letters. R. F. Christian (ed). NY, 1978. 2 vols. VG in djs. *Typographeum.* $30/£19

Tom the Piper's Son. London: George Allen, 1901. 1st ed illus thus. Obl royal 8vo. (30)pp; 8 full-pg color plts by T. Butler-Stoney. Grn cl, pict color bds. VG (edges sl rubbed). *Sotheran.* $205/£128

Tom Thumb. (Cinderella Series.) NY: McLoughlin Bros, (ca 1880). 8vo. 8pp (incl cvrs). Clean in color pict paper wrappers. *Reisler.* $225/£141

TOMBLESON, WILLIAM and WILLIAM GRAY FEARNSIDE. Eighty Picturesque Views on the Thames and Medway. Black and Armstrong, (1834). Pict engr add'l tp, 79 engr views, w/o fldg panorama (not called for in this copy). (Some discoloration.) Aeg. Orig pub's dk grn emb cl by C. Dobson, Waterlane. (Spine ends sl bumped), o/w Fine. *Sotheby's**. $1,011/£632

TOME, PHILIP. Pioneer Life; or, Thirty Years a Hunter. Buffalo: The Author, 1854. 1st ed. 12mo. Frontis, viii,9-238pp. Orig cl-cvrd bds. (Text lt spotted, lt dampstain inner margin of text; new eps; rebacked, recased w/recent cl spine), else Good. Howes T288. *Brown*. $1,000/£625

TOMES, ROBERT. Japan and the Japanese. London: Trubner, 1859. 2nd ed. Engr frontis, viii,415,(1)blank,8 pub's list. Contemp 1/2 calf, marbled bds, gilt, black label. Good (lt browned, frontis, adjacent ll foxed; rubbed, fr hinge weak). *Morrell*. $240/£150

TOMIMAS, SHUTARO. The Open-Door Policy and the Territorial Integrity of China, with Verses in Japanese. NY: Seiler, 1919. 1st ed. Frontis. (Bkpl; sl rubbed), o/w VG. *Worldwide*. $25/£16

TOMKINSON, G. S. A Select Bibliography of the Principal Modern Presses Public and Private in Great Britain and Ireland. London: First Edition Club, 1928. 1st ed. One of 1000. Teg. 1/2 cl, morocco spine label. Fine in VG dj (extrems chipped). *Pacific**. $115/£72

TOMLINSON, CHARLES. A Peopled Landscape. London, 1963. 1st Eng ed. VG in dj w/wraparound band. *Clearwater*. $48/£30

TOMLINSON, CHARLES. Relations and Contraries. Aldington: Hand & Flower, 1951. 1st bk. (Inscrip.) Card wrappers (sl dusty). *Clearwater*. $80/£50

TOMLINSON, H. M. Illusion: 1915. NY: Harper, 1928. 1st ed in bk form. Parchment, bds, paper labels. VG. *Reese*. $30/£19

TOMLINSON, H. M. Mars His Idiot. London, 1935. 1st Eng ed. (Corners sl bumped.) Dj (sl chipped, rubbed, dusty). *Clearwater*. $48/£30

TOMLINSON, H. M. Old Junk. London: Andrew Melrose Ltd, 1918. 1st ed. Inscribed. Blue cl stamped in yellow. (Paper sl tanned), o/w VG in Fine pict dj. *Reese*. $125/£78

TOMLINSON, H. M. Thomas Hardy. NY: Crosby Gaige, 1929. One of 761. Port. Fine. *Hollett*. $56/£35

TOMLINSON, H. M. Waiting for Daylight. London (etc): Cassell, 1922. 1st ed. Gilt plum brn cl. (Lower corner worn), o/w VG in dj (lt rubbed, nicked). *Reese*. $25/£16

TOMLINSON, H. M. Waiting for Daylight. NY: Knopf, 1922. 1st US ed. One of 2000 numbered. Blue-gray cl, paper label. Fine in dj. *Reese*. $35/£22

TOMPKINS, E. P. and J. LEE DAVIS. The Natural Bridge and Its Historical Surroundings. Natural Bridge, 1939. Color frontis. VG in VG- dj. *Book Broker*. $15/£9

TOMPKINS, J. M. S. The Popular Novel in England 1770-1800. Constable, 1932. 1st ed. Dj. *Forest*. $24/£15

TOMPKINS, PETER (ed). To a Young Actress: The Letters of Bernard Shaw to Molly Tompkins. NY, 1960. 1st ed. Folio. As New in dj. *Bond*. $25/£16

TONEY, MARCUS B. Privations of a Private. Nashville: Toney, 1905. 1st ed. Dec cl. (Bkpl removed, emb stamp.) *Ginsberg*. $150/£94

TONEYAMA, KOJIN. The Popular Arts of Mexico. NY: Weatherhill, 1974. VG (some highlighting to last few pp) in dj. *Dumont*. $85/£53

Toodles. Racine: Whitman, 1936. 1st ed thus. 4to. Unpaginated. 3 pop-ups. VG (ink name) in pict wraps (lt edgeworn). *Davidson*. $65/£41

Toodles. A Magic Action Story. Racine, WI: Whitman, 1936. 4to. 3 dbl-pg pop-ups. Stiff paper wrappers (spine worn, sl splits). *Reisler*. $110/£69

TOOKE, JOHN HORNE. The Diversions of Purley. London: J. Johnson, 1798. 2nd ed. 2 vols. Frontis copper plt. 3/4 morocco, mottled bds, gilt. NF. *Pacific**. $316/£198

TOOKE, WILLIAM. View of the Russian Empire, During the Reign of Catharine the Second. London: A. Strahan, 1800. 2nd ed. 3 vols. Lg fldg b/w copperplt map. Marbled eps, edges. Period full run calf streaked in dk brn/dk grn, pairs of lt brn leather spine labels. (Sl aged, map w/sl offsetting; cvrs sl warped, lt worn, 1 label sl chipped.) *Baltimore**. $120/£75

TOOLE, JOHN KENNEDY. A Confederacy of Dunces. Baton Rouge: LA State Univ, 1980. True 1st ed w/only the one Percy blurb on rear dj panel. Fine in dj. *Pacific**. $546/£341

TOOLE, JOHN KENNEDY. A Confederacy of Dunces. Allen Lane, 1981. 1st UK ed. Fine in dj. *Williams*. $200/£125

TOOLE-STOTT, R. A Bibliography of Books on the Circus in English from 1773 to 1964. Derby: Harpur & Sons, 1964. Dj. *Forest*. $40/£25

TOOLE-STOTT, R. Circus and Allied Arts. Derby/Chippenham: Harper/Circus Friends Assoc, (1958-1971)/1992. 5 vols complete. Contents NF. 4 vols in pict djs (spines faded). *Dramatis*. $300/£188

TOOLEY, R. V. California as an Island. London: Map Collector's Series, 1964. NF in wraps (lt worn). *Dumont*. $50/£31

TOOLEY, R. V. English Books with Coloured Plates 1790 to 1860—A Bibliographical Account. Batsford, 1954. 1st ed. Good in dj. *Moss*. $64/£40

TOOLEY, R. V. English Books with Coloured Plates, 1790 to 1860. Folkestone: Dawsons, 1973. 2nd ed. Navy cl, gilt. Fine in NF dj. *Baltimore**. $35/£22

TOOLEY, R. V. Maps and Map-Makers. Batsford, 1952. 2nd ed. (Rear edge sl dampstained.) Dj (sl chipped, foxed). *Edwards*. $40/£25

TOPHAM, EDWARD. The Life of the Late John Elwes, Esquire. London: James Ridgway, 1791. 8th ed. Frontisport. (Fldg chart at back, text lt spotted.) 19th-cent 1/2 grn morocco (rubbed; sm crack lower joint, binder label). *Cummins*. $150/£94

TOPHAM, EDWARD. The Remarkable Life of John Elwes Esq. Member in Three Successive Parliaments for Berkshire. London: Anne Lemoine, 1798. New ed. Engr frontis (browned), 48pp (spotted). Later bds. *Young*. $72/£45

TOPONCE, ALEXANDER. Reminiscences of Alexander Toponce—Pioneer 1839-1923. Ogden, 1923. VG. Howes T299. *Perier*. $150/£94

TOPP, MILDRED SPURRIER. Smile Please. Boston: Houghton Mifflin, 1948. 1st ed. VG in illus dj. *Cahan*. $25/£16

TOPSELL, EDWARD. The Fowles of Heaven or History of Birdes. Austin: Univ of TX, (1972). 1st ed. Frontis. NF in dj (sl worn). *Glaser*. $100/£63

Topsy Tabbykins. Akron: Saalfield Pub, 1908. Tall 8vo. 18pp. Good in color pict stiff paper wrappers. *Reisler*. $85/£53

TORCHIANA, HENRY ALBERT VAN COENEN. Story of Mission Santa Cruz. SF: Paul Elder, 1933. 1st ed. Frontis. (Spine, lower corners sl worn), else Fine in pict dj (lt soiled). *Argonaut*. $125/£78

TORRANCE, JARED S. (comp). The Descendants of Lewis Hart and Anne Elliott. L.A.: Privately ptd, 1923. 1st ed. Teg. Paper labels. Fine. *Harrington*. $80/£50

TORRENCE, CLAYTON. Old Somerset on the Eastern Shore of Maryland. Richmond: Whittet & Shepperson, 1935. 1st ed. Untrimmed, partly unopened. Black cl, ptd paper spine label. Very Clean (few pp roughly opened). *Baltimore**. $25/£16

TORREY, BRADFORD. Field-Days in California. Boston, 1913. 1st ed. Frontis port. Dec cl. VG (1915 inscrip). *Sagebrush*. $40/£25

TORREY, F. P. Journal of the Cruise of the United States Ship Ohio. Boston, 1841. 1st ed. 120pp. 1/2 calf, contemp label fr bd. (Lt foxed; label rubbed.) *Maggs*. $280/£175

TORREY, H. D. America; or, Visions of the Rebellion. Reading, PA: Steam Press of B.F. Owen, 1862. 1st ed. 67pp. VG in wrappers (fore-edge fr wrapper clipped, sl rubbed, worn). *Brown*. $30/£19

TORREY, JOHN. A Flora of the State of New-York...with Remarks on Economical and Medicinal Properties. Albany: Carroll & Cook, 1843. 1st ed. 2 vols. 4to. 161 hand-colored plts (few sl spotted). 3/4 black morocco over marbled bds, gilt tops. Fine. *Appelfeld*. $650/£406

TOUCHSTONE, S. F. Race Horses. History of Celebrated English and French Thorough-Bred Stallions and French Mares. London, 1890. One of 525 numbered. Obl 4to. 60 color plts. Pict cl, leather back. (Shelfworn, sl shaken, sl soiled, eps w/few tears, chips.) *Oinonen**. $1,000/£625

TOULOUSE-LAUTREC, HENRI DE and MAURICE JOYANT. The Art of Cuisine. Holt, Rinehart & Winston, (c1966). 1st US ed. VG in VG dj. *Book Broker*. $45/£28

Tour in Quest of Genealogy, Through Several Parts of Wales, Somersetshire, and Wiltshire.... (By Richard Fenton.) London, 1811. Orig bds (cvrs loose; browned throughout). *Swann**. $69/£43

Tour of Doctor Syntax in Search of the Picturesque. (By William Combe.) London: Ackermann, 1838. 1st Alfred Crowquill ed. Marbled edges. Period gilt-ruled indigo calf, red morocco spine label. (Bkpl; fr corners sl rubbed), else NF. *Pacific**. $127/£79

Tour on the Prairies. (By Washington Irving.) Phila, 1835. 1st ed, 1st issue text and binding. Pub's cl (extrems worn, backstrip label chipped, rubbed; hinges cracked, rep defective). *Swann**. $69/£43

Tour on the Prairies. (By Washington Irving.) Phila, 1835. 1st US ed, 1st ptg. 36pp pub's cat. Orig cl. (3 bkpls; spine label chipped.) BAL 10140. *Kane**. $110/£69

Tour Through the Upper Provinces of Hindostan. (By Mrs. A. Deare.) London, 1823. 1st ed. 8vo. xii,291pp; fldg map. Contemp 1/2 calf. *Maggs*. $520/£325

Tour to the Caves, in the Environs of Ingleborough and Settle, in the West-Riding of Yorkshire.... (By John Hutton.) London: Richardson & Urquhart, 1780. 1st ed. iv,5-49pp. Recent 1/2 calf. Fine. *Young*. $240/£150

TOURGEE, ALBION W. The Story of a Thousand. Buffalo, 1896. 1st ed. 409 + 52pp. (Inner hinges badly cracked, lacks rep; cvr worn.) *King*. $150/£94

TOURNEUR, CYRIL. The Plays and Poems of Cyril Tourneur. John Churton Collins (ed). C&W, 1878. 1st collected ed. 2 vols. Teg. Later 1/2 morocco, banded, gilt. (Last leaf vol 1 mtd, repaired; sl mks, nicks; sl rubbed, edges sl spotted), o/w VG set. *Ash*. $400/£250

TOURNIER, MICHEL. The Erl King. Barbara Bray (trans). London: Willliam Collins Sons, 1972. 1st Eng ed. VG (top edge sl dusty; spine ends, bottom corners bumped) in dj (sl creased, spine faded, edges sl browned). *Ulysses*. $72/£45

TOURNIER, MICHEL. The Four Wise Men. Ralph Mannheim (trans). GC: Doubleday, 1982. 1st US ed. NF (spine foot, 1 corner sl bumped) in dj (sl creased, rubbed, dusty). *Ulysses*. $72/£45

TOURNIER, MICHEL. Friday or the Other Island. Norman Denny (trans). London: Collins, 1969. 1st Eng ed. VG in dj (edges sl creased). *Ulysses*. $136/£85

TOURNIER, MICHEL. The Ogre. GC: Doubleday, 1972. 1st ed in English. Pub's file copy stamp on fep. Fine in VG + dj (sl tanned, dusty). *Any Amount*. $64/£40

TOUSLEY, ALBERT S. Where Goes the River. Iowa City, IA: Te-pee, (1928). 1st ed. VG in dj. *Lien*. $45/£28

TOUSSAINT, MANUEL. Colonial Art in Mexico. Elizabeth Wilder Weismann (ed). Austin: Univ of TX, (1967). 1st ed. Fine in dj (faded). *Truepenny*. $100/£63

TOVEY, DONALD FRANCIS. Essays in Musical Analysis. OUP, 1935-44. 7 vols. VF set in djs. *Hollett*. $120/£75

TOWLE, VIRGINIA ROWE. Vigilante Woman. South Brunswick: A.S. Barnes, (1966). VG in dj. *Perier*. $25/£16

TOWLER, J. The Silver Sunbeam. NY: E. & H.T. Anthony, 1879. 4th ed. xii,373,(1)pp + (36)pp ads. (Foxed, stained, lacks fep, rep lacks lg chip; sm stain to cl, lower edge, extrems lt rubbed), o/w Good. *Cahan*. $265/£166

TOWLER, J. The Silver Sunbeam: A Practical and Theoretical Text Book on Sun Drawing and Photographic Printing.... Hastings-on-Hudson, (1969). Rpt. (Prelim lt stained.) Unptd dj (sl faded.) *Swann**. $126/£79

TOWNE, CHARLES HANSON et al. W. Somerset Maugham: Novelist, Essayist, Dramatist. NY: Doran, (n.d. 1925). 1st ed. VF in stapled wrappers. *Between The Covers*. $75/£47

TOWNE, CHARLES WAYLAND and EDWARD NORRIS WENTWORTH. Pigs from Cave to Corn Belt. Norman: Univ of OK, 1950. 1st ed. VG in Good dj. *October Farm*. $30/£19

TOWNSEND, E. D. The California Diary of General E. D. Townsend. Malcolm Edwards (ed). N.p.: Ward Ritchie, (1970). 1st ed. Black cl. Fine in Fine slipcase. *Harrington*. $40/£25

TOWNSEND, JOHN K. Narrative of a Journey Across the Rocky Mountains, to the Columbia River, and a Visit to the Sandwich Islands, Chili, &c. Phila, 1839. 1st ed. Pub's cl (backstrip defective). Howes T319. *Swann**. $402/£251

TOWNSEND, JOHN K. Narrative of a Journey Across the Rocky Mountains, to the Columbia River.... Phila: Henry Perkins, 1839. 1st ed. 352pp. Orig patterned plum cl, gilt. (Sl foxed; spine lt sunned, ends sl chipped, sl edgeworn.) Text Clean. Howes T319. *Baltimore**. $325/£203

TOWNSEND, LUTHER TRACY. History of the Sixteenth Regiment, New Hampshire Volunteers. Washington, 1897. 1st ed. 574pp. Good (inner hinges cracked, cvr sl stained.) *King*. $125/£78

TOWNSEND, R. WALTER. The Passing of the Confederate. NY/Washington: Neale, 1911. 1st ed. Gray buckram. NF. *Chapel Hill*. $95/£59

TOWNSHEND, F. TRENCH. Ten Thousand Miles of Travel, Sport, and Adventure. London: Hurst & Blackett, 1869. 1st ed. pp xiv (incl frontis),275,(18) ads. (Yellow cl lt soiled), o/w Fine. Howes T322. *Mott*. $200/£125

TOWNSHEND, JAMES. The Royal Farrier; or, The Art of Farriery Display'd. London: Isaac Fell, n.d. vi,158pp. Contemp calf. (Sl foxed, soiled, few minor tears; calf worn.) *Oinonen**. $325/£203

TOWNSHEND, R. B. Last Memories of a Tenderfoot. London: John Lane, 1926. Good. *Dumont*. $50/£31

TOWNSHEND, R. B. A Tenderfoot in Colorado. London, 1923. 1st ed. (Lt foxed), else NF in dj (sl chipped). *Dumont*. $95/£59

TOXOPEUS, KLAAS. Flying Storm. NY: Dodd, Mead, 1954. 1st ed. VG in dj. *American Booksellers*. $25/£16

TOYNBEE, ARNOLD J. The German Terror in France. London, 1917. 1st Eng ed. Card wrappers (dust-mkd, sl chipped). *Clearwater*. $40/£25

TOYNBEE, ARNOLD J. The German Terror in France. London: Hodder & Stoughton, 1917. 1st ed. Pict wrappers (sl tanned, soiled). VG. *Reese*. $50/£31

TOZIER, JOSEPHINE. The Travellers' Handbook. NY: Funk & Wagnall, 1907. Pict gray cl. VG. *American Booksellers*. $35/£22

TRACHTENBERG, MARVIN. The Campanile of Florence Cathedral, 'Giotto's Tower.' NY, 1971. 11 color plts. Good in dj. *Washton*. $125/£78

TRACY, DAVID F. The Psychologist at Bat. Sterling, 1951. 1st ed. VG in Good dj. *Plapinger.* $50/£31

TRACY, MILTON COOK and RICHARD HAVELOCK-BAILIE. The Colonizer. El Paso: Guynes Ptg, 1941. VG in Good dj. *Dumont.* $30/£19

Trade Unionism for Clerks. London: Cecil Palmer & Hayward, n.d. (1919). 1st Eng ed. VG (staple rusted; cvrs creased, sl dusty) in wrappers. *Ulysses.* $40/£25

Traditions of London, Historical and Legendary. By Waters.... (By William Russell.) London: W. Kent, 1859. 1st ed. (iv),258pp (name excised from fep, stamp, lib label). Good in blind/gilt-stamped red coarse-grained cl. *Young.* $72/£45

Tragedy of Success. (By Mary Lowell Putnam.) Boston: Ticknor & Fields, 1862. 1st ed. Patterned cl (backstrip dull, extrems rubbed). *Dramatis.* $50/£31

Tragic-Comic History of the Burial of Cock Robin. Phila: J. Bouvier for Johnson & Warner, 1811. 1st ed. Sm sq 8vo. 8 text ll, 8 engr plts, last and 1st pasted to cvrs. Orig stiff pink paper wrappers (1-inch split spine bottom, paper evenly browned). Morocco slipcase. *Swann*.* $115/£72

TRAIL, MRS. (Pseud of Catherine Parr.) The Backwoods of Canada. Nattali & Bond, (1836). Sprinkled edges. Contemp 1/2 leather, marbled bds, raised bands, leather spine label. Good (spotted; sl rubbed). *Tiger.* $104/£65

TRAIN, ARTHUR. The Earthquake. NY: Scribner, 1918. 1st ed. Gilt blue cl. (Inscrip, edges rubbed), else Good. *Reese.* $15/£9

Traits of American Indian Life and Character. By a Fur Trader. (By Duncan Finlayson.) SF: Grabhorn, 1933. One of 300. 6 plts. 1/2 cl, paper spine/cvr labels. (Bkpl; spine label worn), else NF. Howes F139. *Pacific*.* $115/£72

TRALBAUT, MARC EDO. Vincent Van Gogh. NY: Studio/Viking, (1969). Fine in dj. *Turtle Island.* $85/£53

TRALL, R. T. The New Hydropathic Cook-Book; with Recipes for Cooking on Hygenic Principles. NY, 1854. Pub's cl. (Foxing.) *Swann*.* $69/£43

Transactions of the Congress of American Physicians and Surgeons, Eighth Triennial Session, May 3 and 4, 1910. New Haven, 1910. 1st ed. Teg. Fine. *Doctor's Library.* $40/£25

Transactions of the First Pan-American Medical Congress. Washington, 1895. 1st ed. 2 vols. 2250pp. *Fye.* $250/£156

Transactions of the Medical Society of the State of New York, Volume II. Albany, 1835. 1st ed. Full leather. Good (text yellowed; extrems worn). *Doctor's Library.* $40/£25

Transatlantic Tracings, or, Sketches of Persons and Scenes in America. (By George Searle Phillips.) London: W. Tweedie, 1853. 1st ed. Frontisport, extra engr tp, 337,(2)pp. Blue cl (rubbed). Howes P314. *Mott.* $225/£141

Transport Voyage to the Mauritius and Back. (By Adam Blenkinsop.) London: J. Murray, 1851. 1st ed. Litho frontis. Aeg. (Sl worn, shaken.) *Maggs.* $264/£165

TRAPP, MARIA AUGUSTA. The Story of the Trapp Family Singers. Phila: Lippincott, (1949). 1st ed. Signed. VG in dj (lacks pieces, spine sunned). *Pacific*.* $46/£29

TRASK, JOHN B. Report of the Geology of the Coast Mountains and Part of the Sierra Nevada. (Sacramento): CA Assembly, 1854. 1st ed. (7),8-95pp. Later red cl, red morocco spine label, gilt. (Few creases, sm tears, lt foxed, spine label worn), o/w VG. *Pacific*.* $115/£72

TRASK, JOHN B. Report on the Geology of Northern and Southern California Embracing the Mineral and Agricultural Resources of Those Sections. (Sacramento): CA Senate, 1856. 1st ed. (9),10-66pp. Later black cl, morocco spine label, gilt. Fine. *Pacific*.* $86/£54

TRAUBEL, H. With Walt Whitman in Camden (March 28-July 14, 1888). Boston: Small, Maynard, 1906. 1st ed. VG (hinge cracked). *Agvent.* $45/£28

TRAUTMANN, W. and P. HAGBOLDT. Riot. Chicago: Chicago Labor Pub, 1922? 1st ed. Fine. *Beasley.* $100/£63

Travels and Adventures of Edward Brown, Esq. (By John Campbell.) London: T. Longman et al, 1752. 2nd ed. 2 vols. xvi,320; (2),318,(18)pp. Contemp calf (rubbed), red calf spine labels. *Karmiole.* $28/£18

Travels and Surprising Adventures of Baron Munchausen. (By Rudolph Erich Raspe.) London: William Tegg, 1868. 8vo. Hand-colored engr frontis, xvi,268,(4)ads pp; 21 etchings (2 dbl-pg), 5 sm woodcuts by G. Cruikshank. Teg, top edge uncut. Brn cl, gilt. NF (spine sl faded). *Sotheran.* $157/£98

Travels and Surprising Adventures of Baron Munchausen. (By Rudolph Erich Raspe.) London: William Tegg, 1868. 1st Cruikshank ed. 2 vols in 1. 8vo. Hand-colored copper-engr frontis, tissue guard, 268pp + 4pp ads; 22 copper engrs (2 dbl-pg) by George Cruikshank. Mod 3/4 black leather, 4 raised bands, maroon cl on bd, bound by Albert Y. Sielke, April 9, 1925; orig pub's labels on spine. VG (sm tear corner p25). *Hobbyhorse.* $175/£109

Travels of Cyrus. (By Andrew Michael Ramsay.) London: James Bettenham, 1730. 4th ed. xvi,(viii),363,errata,110pp. Period calf (expertly rebacked in calf), morocco spine label. (Sm stamps, ink note.) *Pacific*.* $115/£72

Travels Through the Interior Parts of America. In a Series of Letters. By an Officer. (By Thomas Anburey.) London, 1789. 1st ed. 2 vols. Lg fldg map, 6 plts, dbl-pg facs. Period calf. *Felcone.* $1,200/£750

TRAVEN, B. The Death Ship: The Story of an American Sailor. NY: Knopf, 1934. 1st Amer ed. (Partial offsetting fep; top corners sl bumped), else Fine in NF dj (lt soil, few sm tears at corners, 2 sm nicks spine foot). *Between The Covers.* $750/£469

TRAVEN, B. The Death-Ship. London: C&W, 1934. 1st British ed. (Soil, spine faded), else VG. *Pacific*.* $40/£25

TRAVERS, BEN. Five Plays. W.H. Allen, 1977. 1st UK ed. VG + in dj. *Williams.* $26/£16

TRAVERS, BENJAMIN. An Inquiry Concerning That Disturbed State of the Vital Functions Usually Denominated Constitutional Irritation. NY: The Author, 1826. 1st Amer ed. 374pp. Mod 1/4 morocco. VG (margins of 1st, last ll dampstained). *Glaser.* $175/£109

TRAVERS, JEROME D. Travers' Golf Book. NY: Macmillan, 1913. 1st ed. Tinted frontis. Dec cl, gilt, pict cvr label. (Emb stamp, lacks fep), else VG. *Pacific*.* $127/£79

TRAVERS, JEROME D. and GRANTLAND RICE. The Winning Shot. GC: Doubleday, Page, 1915. 1st ed. Pict grn/yellow cl. (Bkpl; spine head sl chipped, spine smudged), else VG. *Pacific*.* $115/£72

TRAVERS, P. L. Mary Poppins Comes Back. London: Lovat Dickson & Thompson, (1935). 1st ed. Signed presentation. 8vo. Mary Shepard (illus). White cl (dusty). Pict dj (dusty, spine dknd). *Reisler.* $575/£359

TRAVERS, P. L. Mary Poppins Comes Back. NY: Reynal & Hitchcock, 1935. 1st ed. VG (1935 name; spine tips lt rubbed). *Price.* $45/£28

TRAVERS, P. L. Mary Poppins in the Park. London: Peter Davies, (1952). 1st ed. 12mo. Mary Shepard (illus). Brn textured cl, gilt. VG in color dj (spine sl dknd). *Reisler.* $275/£172

TRAVERS, P. L. Mary Poppins. London: Gerald Howe, (1934). 1st ed. Mary Shepard (illus). Sm 8vo. Pict eps, top edge stained black. Yellow cl. (Stain across most of spine, part of rear cvr.) Pict dj (sl chipped, folds sl worn). *Baltimore*.* $180/£113

TRAVERS, P. L. Mary Poppins. NY: Reynal & Hitchcock, (1934). 1st US ed. Mary Shepard (illus). Sm 8vo. B/w pict eps; top edge stained red. Blue cl. (Sl shelfworn.) Pict dj (spine sunned, head chipped, few sm edge tears). *Baltimore*.* $230/£144

TRAVERS, P. L. Moscow Excursion. NY: Reynal & Hitchcock, (1935). 1st US ed. Scarlet cl (cvr edges, top text edge dusty, spine sl sunned), silver lettering. Nice in pict dj (sl worn, dusty, spine lt sunned). *Baltimore**. $25/£16

TRAVIS, DAVID. Photography Rediscovered: American Photography, 1900-1930. NY: Whitney Museum, 1979. 1st ed. (Stamp), else NF in illus stiff wrappers. *Cahan*. $40/£25

TRAVIS, DEMPSEY. An Autobiography of Black Chicago. Chicago: Urban Research Inst, 1981. 1st ed. Signed. Fine in dj (lt used, tears). *Beasley*. $50/£31

TRAVIS, WALTER J. Practical Golf. NY: Harper, 1902. 2nd ed. Dec grn cl, gilt. (Emb stamp; spine ends rubbed), else VG. *Pacific**. $161/£101

TREADWELL, EDWARD F. The Cattle King. NY: Macmillan, 1931. 1st ed. Tls laid in, dated 1947. Frontisport. Tan cl. Fine in ptd dec dj (lt worn, sl chipped). Howes T336. *Argonaut*. $225/£141

Treasury of Contemporary Houses and Second Treasury of Contemporary Houses. NY, 1954/1959. 2 vols. Folio. Boxed. *Heinoldt*. $50/£31

Treasury of Travel and Adventure, in North and South America, Europe, Asia, and Africa. NY: Appleton, 1865. 456pp. (Foxed, leaf frayed; sl rubbed, soiled, spine ends sl frayed), o/w Good. *Worldwide*. $35/£22

TREAT, ROGER. Walter Johnson. Messner, 1948. Later ptg. VG+ in Good+ dj. *Plapinger*. $200/£125

Treatise on the Faith and Hope of the Gospel. In Two Parts. (By Benjamin Ingham.) (London): The Author, 1770. 1st ed. viii,183pp (blank portion of last leaf torn away, not affecting text). Calf. *Young*. $112/£70

TREDGOLD, THOMAS. Elementary Principles of Carpentry. London, 1840. 3rd ed. (Ink stamps.) 47 (of 50) plts. Later cl. *Swann**. $57/£36

TREDGOLD, THOMAS. Elementary Principles of Carpentry; a Treatise on the Pressure and Equilibrium of Timber Farming.... London: J. Taylor, 1828. 2nd ed. xx,280pp; 22 full-pg engr plts. Uncut. New 1/2 calf, gilt. Very Nice (edges lt browned). *Young*. $224/£140

TREDGOLD, THOMAS. The Principles of Warming and Ventilating Public Buildings, Dwelling-Houses, Manufactories.... M. Taylor, 1836. 3rd ed. xvi,347pp (plain fep torn away); 12 engr plts (3 fldg). Yellow eps. Orig diced maroon cl (faded, stained, lacks ptd paper label). Contents Clean. *Bickersteth*. $240/£150

TREDWELL, DANIEL M. A Monograph on Privately Illustrated Books. A Plea for Bibliomania. Flatbush: Privately ptd, 1892. One of 250 numbered. Inscribed. 502pp. Uncut, unopened. (Frayed, spine chipped.) Ptd wrappers. *Oinonen**. $40/£25

TREE, HERBERT BEERBOHM. The Imaginative Faculty. London: Elkin Mathews & John Lane, 1893. Frontisport, tipped-in leaf; (iv),48pp, pub's inserted 16pp cat at end dated June 1893. Uncut. Gray bds, paper spine label. (Spine ends, corners sl worn, label chipped), o/w Good. *Temple*. $40/£25

TREE, IRIS. Poems. London, 1920. (Ep snipped, sl foxed; no dj.) *Typographeum*. $125/£78

TREECE, HENRY. 38 Poems. Fortune, n.d. (1940). 1st ed. Fine in NF dj (sl soiled). *Any Amount*. $40/£25

TREECE, HENRY. Dylan Thomas. Lindsay Drummond, 1949. 1st ed. VG (eps browned; sl mkd, spine, edges sl faded, spine foot, corner sl bumped) in dj (nicked, sl rubbed, dusty, spine, edges dknd). *Ulysses*. $88/£55

TREECE, HENRY. The Exiles. London: Faber & Faber, 1952. 1st Eng ed. VG (feps partly browned; spine ends sl bumped) in dj (nicked, sl mkd, creased, faded). *Ulysses*. $40/£25

TREECE, HENRY. Invitation and Warning. London: Faber & Faber, 1942. 1st Eng ed. VG (spine ends, corners sl bumped) in dj (sl rubbed, faded, dusty). *Ulysses*. $48/£30

TREFETHEN, JAMES B. Crusade for Wildlife. Harrisburg: Stackpole, 1961. Color frontis. Grn cl. Fine in VG color pict dj. *Biscotti*. $65/£41

TREFUSIS, VIOLET. Don't Look Round. Hutchinson, 1952. 1st ed. Good+ (rubbed). *Any Amount*. $22/£14

TRELAWNY, EDWARD JOHN. Recollections of the Last Days of Shelley and Byron. Boston: Ticknor & Fields, 1858. 1st Amer ed. VG (spine ends sl rubbed). *Clearwater*. $128/£80

TRELAWNY, EDWARD JOHN. Recollections of the Last Days of Shelley and Byron. London: Edward Moxon, 1858. 1st ed. Litho frontisport, half-title but no ads, (vi),304pp; 3 plts. 1/2 blue crushed morocco, gilt, marbled bds. *Marlborough*. $440/£275

TREMENHEERE, HUGH SEYMOUR. Notes on Public Subjects, Made During a Tour in the United States and Canada. London: John Murray, 1852. 1st ed. pp vi,(2),320,32 ads; fldg map. (Lt foxed; grn cl sl sunned), o/w NF. Howes T344. *Mott*. $250/£156

TREMLETT, MRS. HORACE. With the Tin Gods. John Lane, Bodley Head, 1915. 1st ed. 24 full-pg photo illus. All edges uncut. Maroon cl, gilt. (Sl foxed), o/w Good. *Sotheran*. $157/£98

TRENCHARD, EDWARD and STEPHEN D. Reminiscences of the Old Navy. Edgar Stanton Maclay (ed). NY/London: Putnam, 1898. 1st ed. One of 750. (xii),362pp. *Lefkowicz*. $85/£53

TRENCK, FREDERIC. The Life of Baron Frederic Trenck. Thomas Holcroft (trans). Boston: William Greenough, 1793. 4 vols in one. Frontis, (1)-107,(i)l; (1)-100; (1)-92; (1)-120pp. 19th-cent calf, gilt-lettered red leather spine label. Fair (hinges cracked, lacks fep, large hole to rep, tp fr edge tear repaired; foxed, several sigs pulled; bumped, rubbed, spine head chipped). *Blue Mountain*. $125/£78

TRENHOLM, VIRGINIA COLE. Footprints on the Frontier. (Douglas: Douglas Enterprise Co, 1945.) 1st ed. One of 1000 numbered, signed. Brick-red cl (sl shelfworn). Text Fine (rep corner creased). Ptd dj (lt rubbed). Howes T345. *Baltimore**. $100/£63

TRENT, CHRISTOPHER. Motorists' Companion on the Highways of Scotland. Newnes, 1956. 1st ed. 32 plts. VG in dj (sl worn). *Hollett*. $32/£20

TRENTON, PATRICIA and PETER H. HASSRICK. The Rocky Mountains. Norman, 1983. 1st ed. NF in dj. *Baade*. $75/£47

TRESHAM, HENRY et al. The British Gallery of Pictures. Ptd by T. Bensley & Son, 1818. Folio. 1/2-title, 25 engr plts. Later 1/2 calf (worn). *Sotheby's**. $459/£287

TRESHAM, HENRY et al. The British Gallery of Pictures. London, 1818. Large folio. 25 Fine engr plts. Contemp 3/4 morocco (rubbed, sl foxed, soiled; joints worn). Internally Sound. *Oinonen**. $550/£344

TRESHAM, HENRY et al. The British Gallery of Pictures. Longman, Hurst, Rees, Orme & Brown, 1818. Folio. Half-title, 25 engr plts. Gilt edges. Contemp calf, gilt. (Bds loose, spine head defective.) *Sotheby's**. $662/£414

TRESIDDER, MARY CURRY and DELLA TAYLOR HOSS. Trees of Yosemite. Stanford: Stanford Univ, 1932. 1st ed. Rust cl. Fine in pict dj (lt worn). *Argonaut*. $50/£31

TRESSELT, ALVIN. Wake Up, City. NY: Lothrop, Lee, & Shepard, 1966. Small 4to. Roger Duvoisin (illus). Good+ (ex-lib). *American Booksellers*. $25/£16

TREVELYAN, G. M. England Under Queen Anne. London, 1930-34. 1st eds (vol 1 and 3). 3 vols. (Vol 2 fr cvr sl spotted), o/w VG set. *Gretton*. $32/£20

TREVELYAN, G. M. Scenes from Italy's War. Boston/NY: Houghton Mifflin, 1919. 1st US ed. Frontis. Gilt red cl. Sound (ink name, edges rubbed). *Reese*. $25/£16

TREVELYAN, GEORGE OTTO. The Early History of Charles James Fox. London: Longmans, Green, 1880. 2nd ed. Teg. Full gilt-paneled vellum, beveled bds, gilt, leather spine label. Fine. *Sadlon*. $250/£156

TREVELYAN, GEORGE OTTO. The Life and Letters of Lord Macaulay. London: Longmans, Green, 1877. 2 vols. Engr frontis port. Marbled edges. Full tree calf, gilt-paneled spines, raised bands. *Appelfeld.* $150/£94

TREVELYAN, R. C. Polyphemus and Other Poems. London: R. Brimley Johnson, 1901. 1st ed. Sm 4to. Gray bds, white cl spine. VG (fep dampstained, plts sl offset; lower fore-edges sl worn, fore-edge fr bd spotted). *Maggs.* $600/£375

TREVES, FREDERIC. The Elephant Man and Other Reminiscences. NY, n.d. (c. 1918). 1st Amer ed, from British sheets. Fine in NF ptd dj (sm hole fr panel, few sm chips, tears). *Between The Covers.* $350/£219

TREVOR, ELLESTON. The Big Pick-Up. Heinemann, 1955. 1st UK ed. VG + in dj (sl worn, torn). *Williams.* $56/£35

TREVOR, WILLIAM. Angels at the Ritz. NY: Viking, 1976. 1st US ed. (Lt pencil mks), else Fine in NF dj. *Lame Duck.* $35/£22

TREVOR, WILLIAM. The Boarding House. London: Bodley Head, 1965. 1st ed. VG in dj (sl soiled, nicked). *Virgo.* $128/£80

TREVOR, WILLIAM. The Children of Dynmouth. London: Bodley Head, 1976. 1st Eng ed. NF (spine foot sl bumped, faded) in dj (sl creased, edges sl browned). *Ulysses.* $72/£45

TREVOR, WILLIAM. The Day We Got Drunk on Cake. Bodley Head, 1967. 1st UK ed. Fine in dj. *Williams.* $1,040/£650

TREVOR, WILLIAM. The Old Boys. Bodley Head, 1964. 1st UK ed. Fine in VG dj (sl yellowed, spine extrems sl worn). *Williams.* $232/£145

TREWIN, J. C. Mr. Macready. London: Harrap, 1955. 1st ed. (Sl faded.) Dj (defective). *Hollett.* $14/£9

TREXLER, HARRISON A. The Confederate Ironclad 'Virginia' ('Merrimac'). Chicago: Univ of Chicago, (1938). 1st ed. (Sm bkpl), else NF. *Chapel Hill.* $85/£53

Tricks in Magic, Illusions, and Mental Phenonema. (By H. J. Burlingame.) Chicago: Clyde, 1895. (Browned, brittle, stamp, corner of several ll chipped; spine ends abraded.) Ptd wraps. *Dramatis.* $20/£13

TRIER, WALTER. Dandy the Donkey. London: Nicholson & Watson, (1943). 1st ed. Obl 8vo. Gray cl (shaken). Full color dj (worn). *Reisler.* $175/£109

TRIMMER, J. Practical Geology and Mineralogy. Phila: Lea & Blanchard, 1842. xxviii,527pp. Orig cl. Good (new eps, lower inside margin dampstained; lt foxed; spine ends sl worn). *Blake.* $150/£94

TRIMMER, MRS. Fabulous Histories or, The History of the Robins. Ward, n.d. (c1840). 16th ed. Pub's cat. Good (sl spotted; spine bumped, rubbed, sl chipped). *Tiger.* $38/£24

TRINDER, WILLIAM MARTIN. The English Olive-Tree; or a Treatise on the Use of Oil and the Air Bath.... London: The Author, (1812). 3rd ed. Half-title present. (iv),i-v,7-72pp. Uncut. Recent calf-backed marbled bds. *Young.* $192/£120

TRIPLETT, FRANK. Conquering the Wilderness. NY: N.D. Thompson, 1885. 742pp. VG in full leather. *Perier.* $60/£38

TRIPP, C. E. Ace High the 'Frisco Detective or, The Girl Sport's Double Game. SF: Book Club of CA, 1948. One of 500 ptd. Folio. Cl-backed patterned bds. VG. *House.* $35/£22

TRIPP, EDWARD. The Tin Fiddle. NY: OUP, 1954. 1st ed. Obl 4to. Maurice Sendak (illus). Rose cl (sl dknd; fr hinge cracked). *Reisler.* $250/£156

TRIPP, F. E. British Mosses, Their Homes, Aspects, Structure and Uses. London, 1874. 2nd ed. 2 vols. Color tp, xxi,124,8 ads; color tp, 125-235pp,8 ads; 39 hand-colored plts. Partly opened. Fine. *Henly.* $192/£120

TRIPPE, SARAH L. Early History of the Six Nations of the Iroquois Confederacy with Sketch of the Life of Rev. Morton Fitch Trippe.... (Salamanca, NY: Leach, 1929.) Fine in wraps. *Cullen.* $10/£6

TRISTRAM, E. W. English Wall Painting of the Fourteenth Century. London, 1955. 1st ed. Fine. *Polyanthos.* $35/£22

TRISTRAM, W. OUTRAM. Coaching Days and Coaching Ways. London, 1893. xv,376pp. (Feps lt browned, ex-lib; chipped, spine label browned.) *Edwards.* $32/£20

TROLLOPE, ANTHONY. An Autobiography. NY: Harper, 1883. 1st US ed. Wood-engr frontisport. Dk blue cl, gilt. (Text sl aged, sm bkpl; edges sl rubbed.) *Baltimore*.* $55/£34

TROLLOPE, ANTHONY. Barchester Towers. Longman, Brown, Green et al, 1857. 1st UK ed. 3 vols. 1/2 calf. *Williams.* $1,400/£875

TROLLOPE, ANTHONY. The Belton Estate. Bernhard Tauchnitz, 1866. Copyright ed. 2 vols. Marbled edges. Contemp cl-backed bds, ribbon mkrs. Good (closed tear to 1 leaf, sl spotted; spines bumped). *Tiger.* $64/£40

TROLLOPE, ANTHONY. The Claverings. London: Smith, Elder, 1867. 1st ed. 2 vols. 8vo. (iv),314,(2); (iv),310,(2)pp. (Inner hinges sl cracked; extrems sl worn, vol 1 spine top sl repaired), else NF in grn cl, gilt. *Bromer.* $4,500/£2,813

TROLLOPE, ANTHONY. The Duke's Children. Chapman & Hall, 1880. 1st ed. 3 vols. 8vo. W/o ads at end of vol 3. Blue-grn silk-grained cl (rubbed, sl soiled, lib sticker remains fr cvrs; sl foxed). *Sotheby's*.* $589/£368

TROLLOPE, ANTHONY. Framley Parsonage. 1861. 1st ed. 3 vols. 8vo. 6 wood-engr illus by J. E. Millais; ads dated April 1861 at end of vol 3. Purple-gray grained cl (spines repaired, partly rebacked, rubbed, soiled; foxed). *Sotheby's*.* $773/£483

TROLLOPE, ANTHONY. The Golden Lion of Grandpere. Tinsley Bros, 1872. 1st ed. Ads at end. Red-brn cl (sl rubbed), cvrs blocked in black, spine in black/gilt. *Sotheby's*.* $773/£483

TROLLOPE, ANTHONY. He Knew He Was Right. Strahan, 1867. 1st ed. 2 vols. Uncut. Grn sand-grained cl, spine gilt. (Lacks plt opposite p25, half-title of vol 2 torn, remounted; sl foxed, bkseller's stamps, new eps; rubbed.) *Sotheby's*.* $368/£230

TROLLOPE, ANTHONY. Is He Popenjoy? Chapman & Hall, 1878. 1st ed. 3 vols. Pub's ads at end of vols 1, 2. Red-brn silk-grained cl (sl rubbed), dec in black/gilt. *Sotheby's*.* $1,011/£632

TROLLOPE, ANTHONY. Is He Popenjoy? Chapman & Hall, 1878. 1st UK ed. 3 vols. VG (fep, rep replaced vol 1; fep replaced vols 2, 3). *Williams.* $1,592/£995

TROLLOPE, ANTHONY. Lady Anna. Chapman & Hall, 1874. 1st bk ed. 2 vols. 8vo. viii,318; viii,314pp; w/half-titles. Teg. Recent 1/2 dk red morocco, spines w/raised bands, lettered in gilt, by Sangorski & Sutcliffe. VG. *Sotheran.* $1,117/£698

TROLLOPE, ANTHONY. The Landleaguers. C&W, 1883. 1st ed. 3 vols. 8vo. Ads at end of vol 3. White eps (sl foxed). Smooth dk grn cl, blocked in yellow, spine gilt. *Sotheby's*.* $1,747/£1,092

TROLLOPE, ANTHONY. The Last Chronicle of Barset. NY: Harper, 1867. 1st Amer ed. Grn cl, gilt. Fine. *Macdonnell.* $250/£156

TROLLOPE, ANTHONY. The Last Chronicle of Barset. London: Smith, Elder, 1867. 1st ed. 2 vols. Demy 8vo. (i-iv),(1),2-384; (i-iv),(1),2-384pp (lacks inset leaf of pub's ads); 32 full-pg wood engr plts. Contemp grn 1/2 calf, marbled bds, eps, raised bands, gilt. Fine. *Vandoros.* $600/£375

TROLLOPE, ANTHONY. The Last Chronicle of Barset. London: Smith, Elder, 1867. 1st ed. 2 vols. Demy 8vo. (i-iv),(1),2-384; (i-iv),(1),2-384pp + (385-386) inset leaf of pub's ads; 32 wood-engr plts. Yellow eps. Bound from the parts in orig bright blue sand-grained cl, gilt. Fine. *Vandoros.* $1,750/£1,094

TROLLOPE, ANTHONY. Lotta Schmidt and Other Stories. London: A. Strahan, 1867. 1st ed. 8vo. Full crimson morocco, gilt paneled spine, raised bands, aeg, by Bayntun-Riviere. Fine w/cut-out Trollope signature mtd on fep. *Appelfeld.* $650/£406

TROLLOPE, ANTHONY. Marion Fay, a Novel. Chapman & Hall, 1882. 1st ed. 3 vols. 8vo. All half-titles present. Teg. Recent 1/2 dk red morocco, spines w/raised bands, lettered in gilt, by Sangorski & Sutcliffe. VG. *Sotheran.* $1,560/£975

TROLLOPE, ANTHONY. The Noble Jilt. Michael Sadleir (ed). London: Constable, 1923. 1st ed. One of 500. Gilt-stamped cl in 19th-cent pub's style. Fine. *Swann*.* $69/£43

TROLLOPE, ANTHONY. North America. NY: Harper, 1862. 1st (Pirated) Amer ed. pp viii,623,(4) ads. (Spine, corners worn.) *Mott.* $50/£31

TROLLOPE, ANTHONY. North America. Phila: Lippincott, 1862. 1st (Authorized) Amer ed. 2 vols. 335; 334pp. Brn cl. VF. *Mott.* $200/£125

TROLLOPE, ANTHONY. An Old Man's Love. William Blackwood & Sons, 1884. 2 vols. Marbled edges. Contemp 1/2 leather, cl, raised bands, leather spine labels (sl rubbed). Good (bkpls). *Tiger.* $448/£280

TROLLOPE, ANTHONY. The Prime Minister. Chapman & Hall, 1876. 1st ed. 4 vols. 8vo. Red-brn silk-grained cl, blocked in black, spine lettered in gilt (rubbed). *Sotheby's*.* $699/£437

TROLLOPE, ANTHONY. Rachel Ray: A Novel. Chapman & Hall, n.d. (1872). New ed. Pict bds (rebacked w/orig backstrip relaid; corners rubbed). Good. *Tiger.* $48/£30

TROLLOPE, ANTHONY. Ralph the Heir. Hurst & Beckett, 1871. 1st ed. 3 vols. 8vo. Ads at beginning of vol 1, end of vol 3. Chesnut brn sand-grained cl (worn, rebacked preserving orig spines; bkpl). *Sotheby's*.* $699/£437

TROLLOPE, ANTHONY. Sir Harry Hotspur of Humblethwaite. Hurst & Blackett, 1871. 1st ed, 1st issue. Crown 8vo. Half-title, no ads. Recent 1/2 calf, banded, gilt. VG. *Ash.* $632/£395

TROLLOPE, ANTHONY. The Small House at Allington. Smith, Elder, 1864. 1st ed. Issue w/'hobbledehoya' on 1st line of p33, mispagination of p70 (both vol 1). 2 vols. Half-titles not called for, wood-engr plts after J. E. Millais, ads on endleaves. Grass-grn patterned cl (rubbed, sl stained, rebacked preserving most of orig spines; bkpl in vol 2), blocked in gilt/blind. *Sotheby's*.* $405/£253

TROLLOPE, ANTHONY. South Africa. Chapman & Hall, 1879. 1st ed thus. Fldg map. Marbled edges. Contemp 1/2 leather, marbled bds, raised bands. Good (lt spotted). *Tiger.* $56/£35

TROLLOPE, ANTHONY. The Vicar of Bullhampton. Bradbury, Evans, 1870. 1st ed in bk form. 35 wood engrs. Later full morocco, banded, gilt. Nice (lacks final ad leaf, 1 plt sl proud, few sl mks, creases; sl rubbed). *Ash.* $400/£250

TROLLOPE, ANTHONY. The Warden. London, 1855. 1st ed, 2nd binding, w/ads dated 'March, 1856.' Blindstamped brn cl (extrems lt rubbed, sl loss to spine extrems). Cl slipcase. *Swann*.* $258/£161

TROLLOPE, ANTHONY. The Warden. Longman, Brown, Green & Longmans, 1855. 1st ed. Pub's presentation copy w/blind-stamp on tp, ads at end dated September 1854. Dark brick eps w/ads for 'The Traveller's Library' and 'Works on the Arts, Manufactures and Architecture.' Pale brn grained cl (recased w/sm restoration at spine head, tear to spine top repaired; sl browned). 1/4 red morocco collector's box. *Sotheby's*.* $699/£437

TROLLOPE, ANTHONY. The West Indies and the Spanish Main. Chapman & Hall, 1859. Hand-colored frontis. Aeg. Contemp full leather, raised bands, gilt, ribbon mkr. VG (bkpl; rebacked w/orig backstrip relaid). *Tiger.* $480/£300

TROLLOPE, FRANCES. Belgium and Western Germany in 1833. London, 1834. 1st ed. 2 vols. Largely unopened. Orig bds (joints rubbed), spine labels (chipped). *Swann*.* $126/£79

TROLLOPE, FRANCES. Belgium and Western Germany in 1883. John Murray, 1835. 2nd ed. 2 vols. xii,329pp + ad leaf; viii,298pp. Uncut. VG in orig bds (worn, backstrips, paper labels chipped). *Cox.* $72/£45

TROLLOPE, FRANCES. Domestic Manners of the Americans. Paris: Baudry's Foreign Library, 1832. 1st Continental ed ('Fourth Edition' on tp). 2 vols. Later bds, leather labels. *Mott.* $75/£47

TROLLOPE, FRANCES. Domestic Manners of the Americans. NY, 1832. 1st Amer ed. ix,(1),(iii)-viii,(25)-325pp; 8 plts (lt foxed). Orig cl (spotted, spine sl chipped), paper label. *Mott.* $100/£63

TROLLOPE, FRANCES. Domestic Manners of the Americans. Donald Smalley (ed). NY: Knopf, 1949. Fine in dj. *Mott.* $40/£25

TROLLOPE, FRANCES. The Widow Barnaby. Richard Bentley, 1839. 1st ed. 3 vols. 8vo. (ii),348; (ii),380; (ii),368pp. Contemp 1/2 mid-brn calf, gilt, raised bands, dk grn leather labels, marbled bds. VG (half-titles discarded, foxed, bkpls; spines dull). *Blackwell's.* $600/£375

TROLLOPE, T. ADOLPHUS. A Summer in Brittany. Frances Trollope (ed). Henry Colburn, 1840. 2 vols. Hand-colored frontispieces, ad leaf vol 1. Postcards of Brittany tipped-in. Orig cl. VG (spines bumped, sl chipped; hinges, corners rubbed, vent rear hinge vol 1, cvrs sl mkd). *Tiger.* $264/£165

TROLLOPE, T. ADOLPHUS. A Summer in Western France. Frances Trollope (ed). London, 1841. 1st ed. 2 vols. Hand-colored frontispieces. Pub's cl. *Swann*.* $92/£58

TROTSKY, LEON. (Pseud of Lev Davidovich Bronstein.) Stalin, an Appraisal of the Man and His Influence. Charles Malamuth (ed). NY/London: Harper, (1941). 1st US ed. Frontis. Gilt black cl. (Ep gutters tanned), o/w VG + in dj (edgeworn, lt soiled, tanned, sm chips). *Reese.* $50/£31

TROTTENBERG, ARTHUR D. (ed). A Vision of Paris: The Photographs of Eugene Atget, the Words of Marcel Proust. NY, 1963. 1st ed. (Marginal stains fr pastedown, fep; dampstained, sunned.) *Swann*.* $103/£64

TROTTER, LIONEL. The Life of John Nicholson: Soldier and Administrator. London, 1898. 3rd ed. Frontisport, x,333pp + (i) pub's list; 2 plts, 3 fldg maps. (Lt browned; spine sl chipped, faded.) *Edwards.* $72/£45

TROTTER, MRS. A. F. Old Cape Colony. Constable, 1903. 1st ed. 3 ports. Teg, rest uncut. Buckram, gilt. *Cox.* $32/£20

TROTZKY, LEON. (Pseud of Lev Davidovich Bronstein.) The Bolsheviki and World Peace. NY: Boni & Liveright, 1918. 1st US ed. Charcoal cl stamped in red. (Sl offset eps), o/w NF in dj (erosion patches spine). *Reese.* $125/£78

TROTZKY, LEON. (Pseud of Lev Davidovich Bronstein.) Lenin. NY: Minton, Balch, 1925. 1st US ed. Gilt black cl. VG in dj (sl tanned, sm corner nicks). *Reese.* $85/£53

Troublesome Voyage of Captain Edward Fenton 1582-1583. Cambridge: CUP, 1959. Blue cl. Fine. *Appelfeld.* $60/£38

TROUGHTON, ELLIS. Furred Animals of Australia. NY: Angus & Robertson, 1947. 1st Amer ed. 25 color plts. Grn cl. (Shelfworn), else VG in dj (worn). *Parmer.* $40/£25

TROUSSEAU, ARMAND and H. PIDOUX. Treatise on Therapeutics. NY: William Wood, 1880. 1st Amer ed. 3 vols. 980pp. VG set. *Glaser.* $135/£84

TROUSSEAU, ARMAND. Lectures on Clinical Medicine. Phila, 1873. 1st Amer ed. 925,992pp. *Fye.* $200/£125

TROVILLION, HAL and VIOLET (comps). Love Letters of Henry VIII. Herrin, IL: Trovillion Private Press, 1936. One of 138 signed. Inserted ptd presentation card. Mtd label on bds. VG + in glassine (chipped). *Bohling.* $25/£16

TROVILLION, HAL. Some Mottoes to Live By. (Herrin, IL: Trovillion Private Press, 1954.) One of ltd ed, signed. (8)pp. VG + in ptd wraps. *Bohling.* $15/£9

TROWBRIDGE, J. T. The Desolate South 1865-1866. Gordon Carroll (ed). NY, (1956). 1st ed. Signed. (Worn, sl discolored.) *King.* $35/£22

TROWBRIDGE, J. T. Neighbors' Wives. Boston, 1867. 1st Amer ed. NF (name; sl bubbled). *Polyanthos.* $45/£28

TROYAT, HENRI. (Pseud of Lev Tarassov.) Amelie and Pierre. Mary V. Dodge (trans). NY: S&S, 1957. 1st US ed. Grn cl, black bds. VG in dj (lt worn, price-clipped). *Reese.* $25/£16

TROYAT, HENRI. (Pseud of Lev Tarassov.) Sackcloth and Ashes. Anthony Hinton (trans). London: Arco Pub, (1956). 1st British ed. Blue cl bds. Good in dj (dknd, nicked). *Reese.* $20/£13

TRUAX, CHARLES. The Mechanics of Surgery. Chicago, 1899. 1st ed. 1024pp. Internally Sound (ex-lib, bkpls, stamp; extensive tape stains on spine, hinges cracked). *Glaser.* $450/£281

TRUAX, CHARLES. The Mechanics of Surgery. SF: Norman Pub, 1988. Facs rpt of 1899 ed. As New. *Glaser.* $150/£94

True and Minute History of the Assassination of James King of Wm. at San Francisco Cal.... (By Frank Fargo.) SF: Whitton, Towne, 1856. (3),4-26pp. Ptd wrappers. (Lower rt corners last 5 leaves truncated; paper spine perished, sm chip lower edge fr wrapper, dried glue spine margins), o/w VG. Howes F31. *Pacific*.* $184/£115

True and Particular Relation of the Dreadful Earthquake Which Happened at Lima.... London: T. Osborne, 1748. 2nd ed. 5 fldg engr plts, 4 fldg maps. (Sl offsetting from plts, bkpl.) Contemp calf (rebacked, 1 corner restored). *Christie's*.* $325/£203

True Collection of the Writings of the Author of the True Born English-Man. (By Daniel Defoe.) London, 1705. 2nd ed. 2 vols. Old paneled calf. (Expertly recased, new spines.) *Argosy.* $300/£188

True Life and an Interesting History of Che-Mah. NY: NY Popular Pub Co, 1882. 14pp. (Text toned, lt dampstained; possibly lacks wraps), else Good. *Brown.* $30/£19

TRUE, FREDERICK W. The Whalebone Whales of the Western North Atlantic Compared with Those Occurring in European Waters with Some Observations on the Species of the North Pacific. Washington: Smithsonian Inst, 1904. 1st ed. 50 plts. Blue cl, gilt. (Sm stain to plt 1 margin, stamps), else Fine. *Parmer.* $395/£247

TRUETT, VELMA STEVENS. On the Hoof in Nevada. L.A.: Gehrett-Truett-Hall, 1950. 1st ed. NF. *Labordo.* $125/£78

TRUETTNER, WILLIAM H. The Natural Man Observed: A Study of Catlin's Indian Gallery. Washington, 1979. One of 500 signed. Morocco, gilt. *Swann*.* $103/£64

TRUMAN, BEN C. From the Crescent City to the Golden Gate via the Sunset Route of the Southern Pacific Company. NY: Liberty Ptg Co, 1886. 1st ed. 112,(2)pp. (Bkpl, rubberstamps), else VG in orig chromolitho wrappers (chipped, few tape repairs). *Pacific*.* $52/£33

TRUMAN, MARGARET. Murder at the Kennedy Center. NY: Random House, (1989). 1st ed. Fine in dj. *Antic Hay.* $20/£13

TRUMAN, MARGARET. Murder at the National Cathedral. NY: Random House, (1990). 1st ed. Fine in dj. *Antic Hay.* $20/£13

TRUMBO, DALTON. Johnny Got His Gun. Phila (etc): Lippincott, (1939). 1st ed. Yellow cl stamped in black. NF in VG + dj (sl sunned, smudged, sm closed tear 1 corner). *Reese.* $300/£188

TRUMBO, DALTON. The Remarkable Andrew. Phila: Lippincott, 1941. 1st ed. (Spine slant), else VG in dj (worn, edges chipped). *Pettler.* $25/£16

TRUMBO, DALTON. Washington Jitters. London: Knopf, 1936. 1st ed. Yellow cl. VG (1st/last few ll browned; extrems lt rubbed) in dj (lt chipped, soiled). *Heritage.* $125/£78

TRUMBULL, CHARLES GALLAUDET. A Pilgrimage to Jerusalem. Phila: Sunday School Times, 1905. 1st ed. 50 plts, 4 maps. Teg. (Edges sl rubbed, spine sl faded), o/w VG. *Worldwide.* $65/£41

TRUMBULL, H. CLAY. Kadesh-Barnea, Its Importance and Probable Site. NY: Scribner, 1884. 1st ed. Frontis, 478pp; 3 b/w photo plts, fldg map, lg fldg map/frontis in rear pocket. Gray-grn coated eps, teg. Dk grn cl, beveled bds, gilt. Text Good. (Hinges weak, cracked, cvrs spotted, edgeworn.) *Baltimore*.* $40/£25

Trumpet of Freedom. Boston: Oliver Ditson, 1864. 64pp incl wrapper. (Worn, stained, spine chipped away.) *Woolson.* $20/£13

TRUSLER, JOHN. Hogarth Moralized, Being a Complete Edition of Hogarth's Works.... London: Hooper & Mrs. Hogarth, 1768. Engr frontisport, viii,212pp,v,index,price-list,index of plts; 75 engrs (9 full-pg). 19th-cent calf (rebacked), gilt/blind dec. (Sm paper fault in margin of B2), o/w Fine. *Europa.* $232/£145

TRUTH, SOJOURNER. Narrative of Sojourner Truth. Boston, 1850. 1st ed. 8vo. (Last pg sl dust-soiled, margins lt stained, foxed), o/w VG in tan ptd fr wrapper (spotted, corners chipped, backstrip chipped, splitting, lacks rear wrapper). *Heritage.* $1,000/£625

TRUTH, SOJOURNER. Narrative of Sojourner Truth; a Bondswoman of Olden Time.... Frances W. Titus (ed). Boston: The Author, 1875. 1st enlgd ed. Frontis, half-title, 320pp. (Stains from tape on feps; faded, tape stains on spine.) *M & S.* $400/£250

TRUTH, SOJOURNER. Narrative of Sojourner Truth; a Bondswoman of Olden Time.... Frances W. Titus (ed). Battle Creek, MI: The Author, 1881. 1st Battle Creek ed. Frontis, half-title, 320pp. Sewn. (Lacks wrappers.) *M & S.* $275/£172

TRYNAN, KENNETH. Curtains. NY, 1961. 1st ed. (Pg edges lt foxed.) Dj (sm tears, spine sl discolored). *Woolson.* $20/£13

TRYON, THOMAS. The Way to Health, Long Life and Happiness. London: H.C. & D. Newman, 1691. 2nd ed. Small 4to. Old vellum (eps renewed). Good (sl spotted). *Appelfeld.* $600/£375

TRYON, W. S. Parnassus Corner. Boston, 1963. 1st Amer ed. Fine. *Polyanthos.* $30/£19

TSA TOKE, MONROE. The Peyote Ritual. SF: Grabhorn, (1957). One of 325. 14 color plts. 1/2 linen, dec bds. (Lt offset to eps), else Fine in dj (sl soiled). *Pacific*.* $316/£198

TSCHERING, M. Physiologic Optics. Carl Wieland (trans). Phila: Keystone, 1900. 1st Amer ed. Blue cl. VG (lt rubbed, spotted). *House.* $75/£47

TSCHICHOLD, JAN. An Illustrated History of Writing and Lettering. A. Zwemmer, 1946. 1st ed in English. 70 half-tone plts, facs. Blue bds, paper label. VG. *Cox.* $45/£28

TUCHMAN, MAURICE and STEPHANIE BARRON. David Hockney: A Retrospective. L.A./NY, (1988). Dj. *Swann*.* $57/£36

TUCKER, ANNE WILKES. Unknown Territory: Photographs by Ray K. Metzker. Houston: Aperture/Museum of Fine Arts, 1984. 1st ed. Fine in dj. *Cahan.* $125/£78

TUCKER, BENJAMIN R. The Attitude of Anarchism Toward Industrial Combinations. Detroit, MI: Laurance Labadie, 1933. 1st ed. Orig ptd wrappers, bound into lib cl. *M & S.* $75/£47

TUCKER, CHARLOTTE. The Black Cliff and Other Stories on the Parables. By A.L.O.E. NY: Robert Cater & Bros, 1864. 1st Amer ed. 8vo. 180pp; 6 engr full-pg illus. Coarse-grained grn cl, gilt, blind-stamped bds. (Corners bumped) o/w Nice. *Young.* $96/£60

TUCKER, EDWIN A. and GEORGE FITZPATRICK. Men Who Matched the Mountains. Washington, 1972. Good in dj (spine faded). *Dumont.* $25/£16

TUCKER, ELIZABETH S. Little Grown-Ups. London: Gardner, Darton, 1897. Lg 4to. 12 full-pg color plts by Maud Humphrey. Cl-backed color pict bds (edges rubbed). *Reisler.* $750/£469

TUCKER, GEORGE. A Century Hence. Donald R. Noble (ed). Charlottesville: Univ of VA, 1977. 1st ed. VG. *Brown.* $15/£9

TUCKER, JEAN (ed). Group F. 64. St. Louis: Univ of MO-St. Louis, 1978. 1st ed thus. 33 full-pg b/w photos, 10 b/w port photos. (Stamp; lt rubbed), else NF in pict stiff wrappers. *Cahan.* $45/£28

TUCKER, LUTHER et al (eds). The Cultivator and Country Gentleman, Devoted to the Practice and Science of Agriculture and Horticulture at Large.... Albany: Luther Tucker & Son, 1866. 1st eds. 2 vols (27 & 28). 3/4 calf, marbled bds, gilt. NF. *Pacific*.* $81/£51

TUCKER, PATRICK T. Riding the High Country. Caldwell, ID: Caxton Ptrs, 1933. 1st ed. NF in dj. Howes T395. *Labordo.* $175/£109

TUCKER, PATRICK T. Riding the High Country. Grace Stone Coates (ed). Caldwell: Caxton, 1933. 1st ed. Signed by Tucker and Coates. Frontis. (Fr of dj pasted to fep), else VG-. *Perier.* $150/£94

TUCKEY, C. LLOYD. Psycho-Therapeutics. NY, 1892. 3rd ed. 318 + pp. Grn cl bds. VG (extrems sl worn). *Doctor's Library.* $50/£31

TUDOR, TASHA. All for Love. NY: Philomel Books, (1984). 1st ed. Signed. Obl 4to. 93pp. Cl-backed bds. As New in full color pict dj. *Reisler.* $85/£53

TUDOR, TASHA. Around the Year. NY: OUP, 1957. 1st ed. Signed. Obl 8vo. Yellow cl, gilt. Good in full color dec dj (margins lt worn). *Reisler.* $350/£219

TUDOR, TASHA. Becky's Christmas. NY: Viking, (1961). 1st ed. 4to. Rose cl. Good in color pict dj (sl marginal tears). *Reisler.* $275/£172

TUDOR, TASHA. Corgiville Fair. NY: Crowell, 1971. Obl 4to. Fine in Fine dj. *American Booksellers.* $50/£31

TUDOR, TASHA. The Dolls' Christmas. NY: OUP, 1950. Signed. Sq 12mo. Red cl, color paste label. Good in full color pict dj (spine sl faded). *Reisler.* $275/£172

TUDOR, TASHA. Dorcas Porkus. NY: OUP, (1942). 1st ed. 16mo. Yellow bds (dusty, smudges) w/white dots, blue lettering. Text Good (some pp w/finger mks, 1945 owner statement), cvrs Sound. *Baltimore*.* $100/£63

TUDOR, TASHA. Edgar Allen Crow. NY: OUP, 1953. 1st ed. Sq 8vo. Black cl (edges lt shelfworn), color paste label. Full color dj (worn, closed tear, dusty). *Reisler.* $375/£234

TUDOR, TASHA. Mother Goose. NY: OUP, 1944. 2nd ed. 6.5x7.5. 87pp. VG (hinges sl loose) in dj (tattered, taped). *My Bookhouse.* $47/£29

TUDOR, TASHA. Take Joy! NY: World, 1966. 1st ed. 11.3x8.5 oblong. 157pp. VG (inscrip) in VG dj. *Price.* $75/£47

TUDOR, TASHA. Tasha Tudor's Seasons of Delight. A Year on an Old-Fashioned Farm. NY: Philomel Books, 1986. 5 dbl-pg pop-ups. Glazed pict bds. VG. *Bookfinders.* $40/£25

TUDOR, TASHA. A Time to Keep: The Tasha Tudor Book of Holidays. Chicago: Rand McNally, (1977). 1st ed. Lg 4to. Pink framed color pict bds (orig price sticker). *Reisler.* $85/£53

TUDOR, TASHA. Wings from the Wind. Phila: Lippincott, (1964). 1st ed. 4to. Gold cl-backed grn bds. Good in color dj. *Reisler.* $150/£94

TUFTS, ELEANOR. Luis Melendez. Columbia, 1985. 10 color plts. Good+ in dj. *Washton.* $85/£53

TUFTS, RICHARD S. The Principles Behind the Rules of Golf. Pinehurst, NC: Richard S. Tufts, (1960). 1st ed. (Emb stamp), else Fine in VG dj (extrems sl rubbed, spine head chipped). *Pacific*.* $173/£108

TULL, JETHRO. The Horse-Hoeing Husbandry.... London: William Cobbett, 1829. 12pp pub's cat at end. Orig cl-backed bds (sl rubbed; new eps). *Kane*.* $75/£47

TULL, JETHRO. The Horse-Hoing Husbandry. The Author, 1733. 2nd ed. Folio. 6 fldg engr plts, licence leaf preceding tp. Contemp 1/2 calf (rubbed, fr joint split; bkpl). *Sotheby's*.* $1,472/£920

TULLOCH, PETER A. A Window on North Ronaldsay. Kirkwall: 'Orcadian' Office, 1974. 1st ed. VG in dj. *Hollett.* $56/£35

TULLOCH, W. W. The Life of Tom Morris, with Glimpses of St. Andrews and Its Golfing Celebrities. (London): Ellesborough, (1982). Facs ed. One of 200. Signed by J.H. Neill. Aeg. Frontis. Full dk grn morocco, gilt, raised bands, calf spine & cvr labels. (Spine sl sunned), else Fine in slipcase. *Pacific*.* $207/£129

TULLOCH, W. W. The Life of Tom Morris, with Glimpses of St. Andrews and Its Golfing Celebrities. London: T. Werner Laurie, (c.1908). 1st ed. 8.75x5.5. Pict grn cl, gilt. (Emb stamp; sl shelfworn), else VG. *Pacific*.* $1,495/£934

TUMBLETY, FRANCIS. A Few Passages in the Life of Dr. Francis Tumblety, the Indian Herb Doctor, Including His Experience in the Old Capitol Prison.... Cincinnati: The Author, 1866. 1st ed. 82pp. VG in illus wrappers (lack few sm chips at edges). Howes T413. *Cahan.* $300/£188

TUNIS, EDWIN. Colonial Craftsmen and the Beginnings of American Industry. Cleveland: World Pub, (1965). 1st ed. Brn cl. NF in pict dj (lt soiled, spine ends lt chipped). *House.* $30/£19

TUNIS, EDWIN. Colonial Craftsmen and the Beginnings of American Industry. World, 1965. 9x12. 154pp. Fine in VG dj (spine tips chipped). *Price.* $45/£28

TUNIS, EDWIN. Colonial Living. Cleveland: World Pub, (1957). 1st ed. Tan cl. Fine pict dj. *House.* $40/£25

TUNNEY, GENE. A Man Must Fight. Boston: Houghton Mifflin, 1932. 1st ed. One of 550. Signed. 1/2 cl, paper spine label. (Fr hinge starting, label sl sunned), else VG. *Pacific*.* $230/£144

TUNNICLIFFE, C. F. Both Sides of the Road. Collins, (1949). 1st ed. (1 plt, few ll w/sm pin-pricks), o/w VG in dj (sl nicked). *Ash.* $80/£50

TUNNICLIFFE, C. F. Shorelands Summer Diary. Collins, (1952). 1st ed. Nice (eps sl spotted) in dj (lt worn, mkd). *Ash.* $152/£95

TUPPER, MARTIN F. Martin Tupper's Autobiography. Sampson Low, Marston, Searle, & Rivington, 1886. Frontisport, guard; xii,431,(1 blank)pp. Top/fore-edges uncut; eps coated dk chocolate. Turquoise fine diaper cl. (1st/last leaf, edges sl foxed; eps sl cracked), o/w Good. *Temple.* $80/£50

TUPPER, MARTIN F. Rides and Reveries. Peter Query (ed). Hurst & Blackett, 1858. 1st ed. x,332,xxvipp. Grained cl (neatly re-cased), gilt. *Hollett.* $104/£65

TURBERVILLE, A. S. English Men and Manners in the Eighteenth Century. Claredon, 1929. 2nd ed. (Spine lt faded.) *Edwards.* $32/£20

TURBERVILLE, A. S. (ed). Johnson's England. OUP, 1933. 1st ed. 2 vols. Gilt-dec cvrs. Fine in djs (spine sunned; price-clipped). *Polyanthos.* $75/£47

TURBEVILLE, DEBORAH. Unseen Versailles. GC: Doubleday, 1981. 1st ed. Fine in illus dj. *Cahan.* $150/£94

Turf. A Satirical Novel. London: Colburn & Bentley, 1831. 1st ed. 2 vols bound in 1. Uncut. Contemp cl-backed bds, paper spine label (chipped; shelfworn, foxed). Protective cl case provided. *Oinonen*.* $110/£69

TURGENEV, IVAN. Fathers and Sons. LEC, 1951. Ltd to 1500 numbered, signed by Fritz Eichenberg (illus). Fine in slipcase. *Swann*.* $92/£58

TURGENIEFF, IVAN. Fathers and Sons. NY: Holt, 1872. 248pp. Orig ptd wrappers (rear damaged), fr dated 1883. *M & S.* $125/£78

TURGENIEFF, IVAN. The Novels and Stories. NY: Scribner, 1903-4. 16 vols. 8vo. (Few vols dampstained.) Teg. 3/4 brn morocco (rubbed), gilt. *Oinonen*.* $850/£531

TURGENIEFF, IVAN. Smoke: A Russian Novel. Henry Holt, 1873. Good (spine bumped, chipped, sunned, corners rubbed, ring mk fr cvr). *Tiger*. $77/£48

TURGENIEFF, IVAN. Virgin Soil. Ward, Lock, n.d. (1883). Good (fore-edge lt spotted; spine bumped, chipped). *Tiger*. $29/£18

TURLEY, CHARLES. Nansen of Norway. London: Methuen, 1933. Map. VG (sl foxed). *Explorer*. $22/£14

TURNBULL, GEORGE. A Curious Collection of Ancient Paintings. London, 1744. Folio. Engr frontis, 50 engr plts. Contemp mottled calf. (Bkpl; spine ends worn, cvrs loose.) *Swann**. $488/£305

TURNBULL-KEMP, P. The Leopard. Cape Town: Timmins, 1967. 1st ed. (Ex-lib; rebacked), else Good+ in Good+ dj. *Mikesh*. $75/£47

TURNER, A. LOGAN (ed). History of the University of Edinburgh 1833-1933. Edinburgh: Oliver & Boyd, 1933. 1st ed. Teg, untrimmed. VG in dj (sl creased, chipped). *Hollett*. $56/£35

TURNER, A. LOGAN (ed). Story of a Great Hospital. Oliver & Boyd, 1937. 1st ed. 33 plts. VG. *Hollett*. $72/£45

TURNER, ALFORD (ed). The OK Corral Inquest. College Station, TX: Creative Pub, 1981. 1st ed. Fine in dj. *Labordo*. $30/£19

TURNER, C. FRANK. Across the Medicine Line. Toronto, 1973. 1st ed. Fine in dj (price-clipped). *Baade*. $65/£41

TURNER, C. H. B. (comp). Rodney's Diary and Other Delaware Records. Phila: Allen, Lane & Scott, 1911. (Lib, handstamps, spine #, sl worn), else Good. *Brown*. $25/£16

TURNER, E. B. Reminiscences of Morris, and History of the Congregational Church. Chicago, 1865. 8vo. 16pp. Mod 1/4 cl. (Orig fr wrapper bound in; fr wrapper, tp, final text leaf repaired in gutter.) *Swann**. $747/£467

TURNER, E. S. All Heaven in a Rage. NY: St. Martin's, 1965. 1st US ed. NF in dj (sl worn, price-clipped). *My Bookhouse*. $22/£14

TURNER, FREDERICK JACKSON. List of References on the History of the West. Cambridge: Harvard Univ, 1915. Wraps (chipped). Internally Good. *Dumont*. $35/£22

TURNER, FREDERICK JACKSON. Reuben Gold Thwaites. Madison: State Hist Soc of WI, 1914. 1st ed. Fine. *Labordo*. $45/£28

TURNER, J. M. W. and H. E. LLOYD. Picturesque Views of England and Wales. Longman, Orme, Brown, Green, & Longmans, 1838. 8vo. 2 vols. 96 engr plts. Contemp 1/2 morocco, gilt. (Sl spotted, dampstained; rubbed.) *Sotheby's**. $1,563/£977

TURNER, J. M. W. Liber Fluviorum: or River Scenery of France. London: Henry Bohn, 1853. 1st ed. 4to. 61 Fine steel engrs. 3/4 grn morocco, gilt paneled spine, raised bands, aeg, by Bayntun-Riviere. Clean. *Appelfeld*. $600/£375

TURNER, JIM. Lost Days. Whittington, 1981. One of 100 specials, signed, hand-colored by Miriam Macgregor (illus). 7 wood engrs. Patterned cl. Fine in slipcase. *Michael Taylor*. $192/£120

TURNER, LAURENCE. Decorative Plasterwork in Great Britain. London, (1927). Folio. (Preface leaf detached, prelims, several ll dampstained; cl stained, especially rear cvr.) *Swann**. $92/£58

TURNER, MARTHA ANNE. Old Nacogdoches in the Jazz Age. Austin: Madrona, 1976. One of 200 numbered, signed. VG in slipcase. *Dumont*. $60/£38

TURNER, SAMUEL. My Climbing Adventures in Four Continents. London, 1911. 1st ed. 1 plt (detached w/2pp). Teg. Illus cl. (Sl marginal foxing, feps browned, rear hinge cracked; corners sl bumped, spine faded, chipped.) *Edwards*. $120/£75

TURNER, T. A. Story of the Fifteenth Minnesota Volunteer Infantry. Minneapolis: Lessard Ptg Co, (1899). VG. *Wantagh*. $45/£28

TURNER, WILLIAM (ed). William Adams, an Old English Potter. London/NY, 1904. Color frontis. Marbled eps; teg. (Margins spotted; sl rubbed, spine sl bumped.) *Edwards*. $61/£38

TUROW, SCOTT. One L. NY: Putnam, (1977). 1st ed. (Rear bd bumped), else Fine in NF dj (2 sm stains, spine sl tanned). *Between The Covers*. $350/£219

TUROW, SCOTT. Presumed Innocent. Bloomsbury, 1987. 1st UK ed. Signed. (Edges sl browned), o/w Fine in Fine dj. *Martin*. $22/£14

TURRELL, CHARLES. Miniatures. London: John Lane, 1913. 6 color, 92 photogravure plts. Marbled eps; aeg. Full vellum, gilt. (Sm lib blind stamp, bkpl.) Presentation box (sl soiled, edges sl worn). *Edwards*. $400/£250

TURRELL, W. J. Ancient Angling Authors. London: Gurney & Jackson, 1910. 1st ed. Frontis. Grn cl, gilt. NF. *Pacific**. $92/£58

TURRILL, H. B. Historical Reminiscences of the City of Des Moines, Together with a Full Description of the City and County.... Des Moines: Redhead, 1857. 1st ed. 114,(30 ads)pp; 6 plts, lg fldg view (defective, about 1/2 of plt is missing). Dec cl, gilt. Howes I732. *Ginsberg*. $175/£109

TURRILL, W. B. British Plant Life. Collins, 1948. 1st ed. 8 maps. (Cl sl faded.) Dj. *Hollett*. $64/£40

Tuscarora Club's Forty-Year History 1901-1941. (Privately ptd), 1941. 1st ed. One of 100 ptd. Uncut. (Lt worn.) *Oinonen**. $400/£250

TUSSER, THOMAS. Five Hundred Points of Good Husbandry. James Tregaskis, 1931. (One of 500.) Untrimmed. Mid brn hermitage calf, gilt, raised bands, brn silk marker. Fine (eps sl browned). *Blackwell's*. $320/£200

TUTE, GEORGE. Leon Underwood: His Wood Engravings. (Woolley/Wakefield): Fleece Press, (1986). One of 200 numbered. Folio. 1/4 morocco. Cl fldg case. *Swann**. $115/£72

TUTTLE, F. Report of the U.S. Revenue Cutter Bear and the Overland Expedition for the Relief of the Whalers in the Arctic Ocean.... Washington: GPO, 1899. 1st ed. iv,144pp; 60 plts, fldg map. Good (sl rubbed). *Walcot*. $112/£70

TUTTON, A. The High Alps. London: Kegan Paul et al, 1931. 48 plts, map. (Tp spotted; spine faded.) *Hollett*. $40/£25

TUTTON, A. The High Alps: A Natural History of Snow and Ice. London: Kegan Paul, Trench, Trubner, 1931. Good. *Blake*. $60/£38

TUTUOLA, AMOS. My Life in the Bush of Ghosts. NY: Grove, 1954. True 1st ed. (Extrems lt worn), else VG+ in VG+ dj. *Lame Duck*. $75/£47

TUTUOLA, AMOS. The Palm-Wine Drinkard. Faber & Faber, 1952. 1st ed, 1st bk. NF (eps sl browned; spine ends sl bumped) in dj (sl nicked, dusty, spine sl dknd). *Ulysses*. $72/£45

TWAIN, MARK and BRET HARTE. Ah Sin. Mallette Dean, 1961. One of 450. *Dawson*. $100/£63

TWAIN, MARK and W. D. HOWELLS. The Niagara Book. Buffalo: Underhill & Nichols, 1893. 1st ed, 4th ptg, w/Canadian c. notice and no ads at rear. Grn cl, stamped in red/silver. (Hinge paper cracking), else VG. BAL 3437 and 9675. *Macdonnell*. $75/£47

TWAIN, MARK et al. After Dinner. Speeches at the Lotos Club. NY: Lotos Club, 1911. One of 950 (of 1000). NF (eps foxed, lt smudged). BAL 3469. *Agvent*. $175/£109

TWAIN, MARK et al. Lotos Leaves. Boston: Gill, 1875. 1st ed, BAL 3363: ptg 1. Dec cl. NF (sm leather bkpl, tp, Lotos plt foxed; spine tips, corners lt worn, cl sl dknd). *Agvent*. $400/£250

TWAIN, MARK. The Adventures of Huckleberry Finn (Tom Sawyer's Comrade). NY: Charles L. Webster, 1885. 1st ed, w/most of 1st issue points: 'was' for 'saw' p57; the 'Him and another Man' plt listed as being on p88; 3rd state of p155; tp a cancel; p283 conjugate w/18-3 and engr on p283 in Blanck's state 3; frontis in 1st state; final leaf a blank. Sq 8vo. E. W. Kemble (illus). Frontis, port. Clemens's 'Grasshopper' signature laid in. Orig pict grn cl (extrems lt rubbed, spine cl sl bubbled). Full grn morocco slipcase. BAL 3415. Swann*. $1,955/£1,222

TWAIN, MARK. Adventures of Huckleberry Finn (Tom Sawyer's Comrade). NY: Charles L. Webster, 1885. 1st Amer ed, w/most of 1st issue points: 'was' for 'saw' p57, the 'Him and Another Man' plt listed as being on p88; 1st state of p155, lacking final 5; tp a cancel; p283 conjugate w/18-3 and engr on p283 in Blanck's state 3; frontis in 1st state; final leaf a blank. Sq 8vo. E. W. Kemble (illus). Frontis, port. Orig pict grn cl. Superb (sm stamp fep, pp243-246 w/outer margins approx 1/4-inch shorter, undoubtedly a binder's error; sm scratch at top edge fr cvr). BAL 3415. Swann*. $4,600/£2,875

TWAIN, MARK. The Adventures of Huckleberry Finn (Tom Sawyer's Comrade...). NY: Charles L. Webster, 1885. 1st ed, w/all issue points in earliest state. The tp leaf is a cancel, w/the c. notice dated 1884 (Blank's state 2; no known copy w/state 1 of this leaf); on p13, the illus captioned 'Him and another Man' is listed as at p88 (Blank's state 1); p57, the 11th line from bottom reads: '...with the was...' (Blank's state 1); p283 is a cancel, the line on Silas Phelps's trousers is a straight line (Blank's state 3; state 1 known only in leather bound copies and no known copy of state 2); p155 is in Blank's state 1 (w/the final 5 lacking); no sig mk on p161 (Blank's only state); the final leaf is a blank; the frontisport is in Blank's state 1, w/the imprint of the Heliotype Printing Company and the tablecloth clearly visible. 8vo. 366pp. Blue cl stamped in gold/black. (Spine ends, corners lt worn, spine dknd), else Fine in blue cl clamshell box, leather labels. BAL 3415. Argonaut. $5,500/£3,438

TWAIN, MARK. The Adventures of Huckleberry Finn. C&W, 1884. 1st ed. E. W. Kemble (illus). Frontis, 32pp pub's cat dated Oct 1884 at end. New eps. Orig pict red cl. (Sl rubbed, spine sl discolored.) Sotheby's*. $459/£287

TWAIN, MARK. The Adventures of Huckleberry Finn. C&W, 1884. 1st Eng ed. 8vo. 32pg pub's cat at end dated October 1884. Frontis by E. W. Kemble. Pict red cl. (Bkpl, inscrip; spine ends sl bumped.) Sotheby's*. $1,195/£747

TWAIN, MARK. The Adventures of Huckleberry Finn. London: C&W, 1884. 1st Eng ed. BAL 3414: Issue A w/1st state ads dated Oct. 1884. 8vo. E. W. Kemble (illus). Dec red cl. VG (Cvr bottoms stained, bleeding to 1st, last few pp; rear hinge cracked but tight). BAL 3414. Agvent. $1,250/£781

TWAIN, MARK. The Adventures of Huckleberry Finn. London: C&W, 1884. 1st ed. Thick 8vo. 32-pg pub's cat dated Oct 1884 at rear. Leaf-and-vine patterned eps ptd in lt brn. Pict red cl stamped in gilt/black. Text Very Clean (lt aged), cvrs VG (spine sl rubbed.) BAL 3414. Baltimore*. $1,350/£844

TWAIN, MARK. Adventures of Huckleberry Finn. NY: Charles L. Webster, 1885. 1st US ed, mixed issue, w/following points: tp is a cancel; 'Him and another Man' listed at p88; 'with the was' p57; p155 w/2nd 5 in numeral from a different font; p283 is a cancel; frontis port in Blanck's state 1, w/imprint of Heliotype Ptg Co, tablecloth visible, sculptor's name not visible on shoulder. Pict dk grn cl, gilt. (Lt aged, foxed, few finger smudges, ink names; hinges cracked, spine ends frayed, edges lt worn, frayed.) Text Good. BAL 3415. Baltimore*. $325/£203

TWAIN, MARK. The Adventures of Huckleberry Finn. NY: Webster, 1885. 1st ed. BAL 3415: 1st issue points of pp 13, 57, 143; 2nd issue of tp, frontis, p155; 4th issue of p283. 8vo. E. W. Kemble (illus). Dec grn cl. VG (foxed, bkpl; rubbed, spine tips, corners worn). BAL 3415. Agvent. $950/£594

TWAIN, MARK. Adventures of Huckleberry Finn. NY: Charles L. Webster, 1885. 1st Amer ed, early issue: tp is a cancel; copyright notice dated 1884 (2nd state); illus captioned 'Him and another Man' (p13) listed as p88 (1st state); 11th line from bottom of p57 reads '...with the was...' (1st state); p283 is a cancel, w/corrected engr (3rd state); final 5 in p155 sl larger (3rd state); 1st state of frontis port. Dbl frontis (incl port). Grn pict cl stamped in black/gilt. VF (sl insect damage to top of fr cvr, 1/2-inch line sl bulged in lower fr cvr, [apparent defect when bound]; spine ends, corners sl rubbed; sm spot to right on tp [as manufactured]). BAL 3415. Pacific*. $9,200/£5,750

TWAIN, MARK. The Adventures of Huckleberry Finn. LEC, 1942. Ltd to 1500 numbered, signed by Thomas Hart Benton (illus). Fine in slipcase. Swann*. $575/£359

TWAIN, MARK. Adventures of Huckleberry Finn. West Hatfield: Pennyroyal, 1985. One of 350 signed by Barry Moser (illus). Folio. Separate suite of plts in cl folder. Full morocco, gilt. VG in cl slipcase. Between The Covers. $1,000/£625

TWAIN, MARK. The Adventures of Thomas Jefferson Snodgrass. Chicago: Pascal Covici, 1928. One of 375, this unnumbered. NF in Good dj (spine, rear chipped). BAL 3544. Agvent. $300/£188

TWAIN, MARK. The Adventures of Tom Sawyer. Hartford, 1876. 1st ed, 2nd ptg, BAL issue C on both wove and laid paper. Sq 8vo. Frontis. Later 1/2 blue morocco. Morocco slipcase. BAL 3369. Swann*. $690/£431

TWAIN, MARK. The Adventures of Tom Sawyer. Hartford: American Publishing, 1876. 1st Amer ed, 1st ptg on wove paper and w/prelims arranged as called for by Blanck. 275 + 4 ads pp. Blue cl, gilt. VG- (1/2-title lt stained; recased, later eps, spine faded, ends chipped). Pacific*. $1,840/£1,150

TWAIN, MARK. The Adventures of Tom Sawyer. Hartford, 1876. 1st Amer ed, 1st issue, w/fr matter paged (I)-XVI, 'THE' on 1/2 title 1/16-inch tall, ads at end dated Dec 1st, 1876, etc. 8vo. Pub's blue cl (shelfworn, sl shaken, soiled, spine sl dknd). Sound. BAL 3369. Oinonen*. $6,300/£3,938

TWAIN, MARK. The Adventures of Tom Sawyer. C&W, 1887. New ed. Pub's cat dated Jan 1888. Pict bds (rebacked w/orig backstrip relaid, shelf-worn; sig). Good. Tiger. $56/£35

TWAIN, MARK. The Adventures of Tom Sawyer. LEC, 1939. Ltd to 1500 numbered, signed by Thomas Hart Benton (illus). Fine in slipcase. Swann*. $373/£233

TWAIN, MARK. The Adventures of Tom Sawyer. Paul Elek, 1947. Keith Vaughan (illus). 232pp. Dj (sl worn, verso repaired). Hollett. $40/£25

TWAIN, MARK. The American Claimant. NY, 1892. 1st Amer ed. Pict cvrs, gilt. NF (bkpl; lt rubbed, sl soiled, spine sunned). Polyanthos. $30/£19

TWAIN, MARK. The American Claimant. NY: Charles L. Webster, 1892. 1st ed. Pict olive-grn cl, gilt. Fine (spine ends, corners sl rubbed). BAL 3434. Pacific*. $402/£251

TWAIN, MARK. The Celebrated Jumping Frog of Calaveras County.... NY, 1867. 1st ed, 1st issue, w/inserted leaf of ads before tp and unbroken type on pp21, 66, 198. 8vo. 1/2 leather, marbled bds. Very Clean (few lt spots; rebound, fr cvr nearly detached, edges rubbed, dented). BAL 3310. Kane*. $1,500/£938

TWAIN, MARK. Concerning Cats: Two Tales by.... SF: Book Club of CA, 1959. One of 450 ptd. 2 plts. 1/2 cl, dec bds, paper spine label, gilt. NF. Pacific*. $115/£72

TWAIN, MARK. Concerning Cats: Two Tales. SF: Book Club of CA, 1959. One of 450. Frontisport. Patterned bds, cl spine, paper spine label. Dawson. $100/£63

TWAIN, MARK. A Connecticut Yankee in King Arthur's Court. NY, 1889. 1st ed. Pict cl (lt rubbed; bkpl). Slipcase. Swann*. $258/£161

TWAIN, MARK. A Connecticut Yankee in King Arthur's Court. NY: Charles L. Webster, 1889. 1st ed, 2nd issue w/o the S-like ornament between THE & KING on p(59). 575,(1)pp + (2)pp ads. Pict grn cl, gilt. Fine. BAL 3429. *Pacific**. $259/£162

TWAIN, MARK. A Connecticut Yankee in King Arthur's Court. NY: LEC, 1959. One of 1500. Signed by Honore Guilbeau (illus). 1/2 cl, dec gold bds. Fine in slipcase. *Pacific**. $58/£36

TWAIN, MARK. The Curious Republic of Gondour and Other Whimsical Sketches. NY: Boni & Liveright, 1919. 1st ed. White cl-backed yellow ptd bds. Fine in dj (few sm edge chips). BAL 3527. *Macdonnell*. $250/£156

TWAIN, MARK. The Curious Republic of Gondour. NY: Boni & Liveright, 1919. 1st ed. Good (bkpl; sl soiled, worn). BAL 3527. *Second Life*. $50/£31

TWAIN, MARK. Death-Disk. NY: Edgar S. Werner, (c.1913). 1st separate ed. Fine in ptd paper wrappers. BAL 3676. *Black Sun*. $100/£63

TWAIN, MARK. A Dog's Tale. London: Anti-National Vivisection Soc, 1903. 1st separate ed. Fine in wraps. BAL 3479. *Second Life*. $200/£125

TWAIN, MARK. A Dog's Tale. NY/London: Harper, 1904. 1st Amer ed in bk form. Pict red cl. BAL 3483. *Cullen*. $95/£59

TWAIN, MARK. A Double Barrelled Detective Story. NY/London: Harper, 1902. 1st ed. Teg, untrimmed; pict eps ptd in grn. Red cl, gilt. (Few ll w/finger mks, eps lt browned, bkpl; spine sunned, sl finger smudges.) BAL 3471. *Baltimore**. $70/£44

TWAIN, MARK. A Double Barrelled Detective Story. NY: Harper, 1902. 1st ed. Teg. Red cl. Nice. *Appelfeld*. $125/£78

TWAIN, MARK. English As She Is Taught. NY: Mutual Book, (1900). 1st separate ed, 2nd issue. NF (sl offset) in gray ptd wraps. BAL 3465: second issue. *Agvent*. $350/£219

TWAIN, MARK. English as She Is Taught. Unwin, 1887. 1st ed. VG-. *Fine Books*. $295/£184

TWAIN, MARK. Europe and Elsewhere. NY: Harper, 1923. 1st ed, 1st ptg. Red cl, gilt. VF in dj (tape-reinforced, spine ends chipped). BAL 3536. *Macdonnell*. $350/£219

TWAIN, MARK. Europe and Elsewhere. A. B. Paine (intro). NY: Harper, (1923). 1st ed. 8vo. (Cvr lt dust worn), o/w Fine in Near Perfect dj (couple sl chips). BAL 3536. *Second Life*. $950/£594

TWAIN, MARK. Eve's Diary. NY: Harper, 1906. 1st ed. Pict red cl. Fine. BAL 3489. *Macdonnell*. $125/£78

TWAIN, MARK. Eve's Diary. London/NY: Harper, 1906. 1st ed. W/o period after MS on tp. Dec red cl. (Fore-edge fr cvr nicked), o/w Fine. BAL 3489. *Agvent*. $150/£94

TWAIN, MARK. Extract from Captain Stormfield's Visit to Heaven. NY: Harper, 1909. 1st ed. Red pict cl. Good. BAL 3511. *Macdonnell*. $100/£63

TWAIN, MARK. Following the Equator. Hartford: American Pub, 1897. 1st ed, 1st state (single imprint). Blue cl. VG. BAL 3451. *Second Life*. $250/£156

TWAIN, MARK. Following the Equator. Hartford: Amer Pub, 1897. 1st ed. W/single imprint, sig mk on p161. Dec blue cl. VG (sig; spine, edges lt worn). BAL 3451. *Agvent*. $300/£188

TWAIN, MARK. Following the Equator. A Journey Around the World. Hartford: American Pub, 1898. 1st ed. Dan Beard et al (illus). Teg. 3/4 brn morocco, blind tooling, raised bands. *Appelfeld*. $300/£188

TWAIN, MARK. A Horse's Tale. NY: Harper, 1907. 1st ed. (Corners bumped, spine sl pulled), o/w VG +. *My Bookhouse*. $105/£66

TWAIN, MARK. How to Tell a Story and Other Essays. NY: Harper, 1897. 1st ed. Teg, uncut. Red dec cl, gilt. NF (inscrip). BAL 3449. *Macdonnell*. $250/£156

TWAIN, MARK. The Innocents Abroad. Hartford: American Pub, 1868. 1st ed, 1st issue. Aeg. Unrecorded binding of purple cl, beveled cvrs w/gilt-decs on cvrs, spine. In addition, this cl is in a more ornate pattern than the standard cl. Good + (sl stained; fr hinge cracked, cl frayed) in custom 1/4 morocco clamshell box. *Lame Duck*. $5,000/£3,125

TWAIN, MARK. The Innocents Abroad. LEC, 1962. Ltd to 1500 numbered, signed by Fritz Kredel (illus). Fine in slipcase. *Swann**. $46/£29

TWAIN, MARK. The Innocents Abroad. NY: LEC, 1962. One of 1500 ptd. Signed by Fritz Kredel (illus). 1/2 cl, marbled bds, morocco spine label. Fine in glassine, slipcase. *Pacific**. $63/£39

TWAIN, MARK. A Letter from Mark Twain to His Publishers. SF: Penguin, 1929. 1st ed. One of 50. Frontisport by Valenti Angelo. Orig ptd wraps. BAL 3547. *Kane**. $300/£188

TWAIN, MARK. Letters from the Sandwich Islands, Written for the Sacramento Union. SF: Grabhorn, 1937. 1st ed. One of 550. 1/2 cl, bds, paper spine label. Fine. BAL 2558. *Pacific**. $173/£108

TWAIN, MARK. Life on the Mississippi. Boston: James R. Osgood, 1883. 1st Amer ed, 1st state w/p441 depicting an urn, flames and the head of Mark Twain; caption on p443 reads 'The St. Charles Hotel.' This issue, w/aeg, was more deluxe than the regular issue. 624pp. Aeg. Brn cl, gilt. (Frontis, fep nearly detached, hinge cracked before tp, few other hinges cracked; rubbed, corners, spine ends worn), else Good. BAL 3411. *Pacific**. $161/£101

TWAIN, MARK. Life on the Mississippi. Boston, 1883. 1st US ed, 1st state w/Twain in flames on p441 and 'St. Louis Hotel' on p443. Dec pub's cl (rubbed, spine ends lt worn, spine foot soiled; new eps; several sigs sl sprung). BAL 3411. *Kane**. $250/£156

TWAIN, MARK. Life on the Mississippi. Boston: Osgood, 1883. 1st ed, intermediate state A w/the cremation scene on p441 and p443 'St. Charles Hotel'. 624pp. 300 illus. Stamped brn cl. VG (bkpl, corner p441 torn off, sig sl pulled; sl worn). BAL 3411. *Second Life*. $300/£188

TWAIN, MARK. Life on the Mississippi. Boston: Osgood, 1883. 1st ed, 2nd state. Dec cl. NF (lt edgeworn). BAL 3411. *Agvent*. $300/£188

TWAIN, MARK. Life on the Mississippi. NY: LEC, 1944. One of 1200 signed by Thomas Hart Benton (illus). Frontis, 27 full-pg illus. Pict cl, leather spine, glassine in clamshell case (worn). *Dawson*. $300/£188

TWAIN, MARK. Life on the Mississippi. LEC, 1944. One of 1200 signed by Thomas Hart Benton (illus). Fine in slipcase. *Swann**. $460/£288

TWAIN, MARK. The Man That Corrupted Hadleyburg. NY: Harper, 1900. 1st ed. BAL 3459: 1st state. Frontis, 11 plts. NF (sl soiled, spotted). *Agvent*. $300/£188

TWAIN, MARK. Mark Twain on Simplified Spelling. (NY): Simplified Spelling Board, 1906. 1st ed, 2nd issue, w/broken type at p1, line 3. Single leaf folded to 4pp w/integral title. VG (vertical crease 1/2-inch from spine fold, 1/2-inch tear from spine fold at center) in bd slipcase w/fldg inner liner. *Baltimore**. $170/£106

TWAIN, MARK. Mark Twain's (Burlesque) Autobiography and First Romance. NY: Sheldon, (1871). 1st ed, 2nd state. (1)-47pp ads, pp(48) (lacks fep, tp trimmed 5/8 inch; soiled). Terra-cotta cl (worn). BAL 3326. *Cummins*. $75/£47

TWAIN, MARK. Mark Twain's (Burlesque) Autobiography and First Romance. NY: Sheldon, (1871). 1st state. 8vo. Grn cl. Superb (new eps, professional tissue repair to fr hinge before title & 3 pg corners, 1 corner clipped). *Agvent*. $750/£469

TWAIN, MARK. Mark Twain's Autobiography. NY, 1924. 1st ed, state A w/2pp ads at rear of vol 2, sigs in both vols unsigned. 2 vols. Frontisport w/ptd tissue each vol. BAL 3537. *Kane**. $55/£34

TWAIN, MARK. Mark Twain's Autobiography. NY: Harper, 1924. 1st ed. 2 vols. Frontispieces, guards. Blue cl, gilt. NF. *Pacific**. $81/£51

TWAIN, MARK. Mark Twain's Letter to the California Pioneers. Oakland: DeWitt & Snelling, 1911. 1st ed, 2nd issue w/c. notice intact and colophon unnumbered. VF in ptd wrappers. BAL 3516. *Macdonnell*. $100/£63

TWAIN, MARK. Mark Twain's Letter to William Bowen.... SF: Book Club of CA, 1938. 1st ed. One of 400 ptd. Orig prospectus laid in. BAL 3560. *Kane**. $300/£188

TWAIN, MARK. Mark Twain's Letters. NY: Harper, (1917). 1st ed, ltd issue. One of 350 sets. 2 vols. 1/4 tan linen, paper labels. Fine set. BAL 3525. *Macdonnell*. $375/£234

TWAIN, MARK. Mark Twain's Library of Humor. NY: Charles L. Webster, 1888. 1st ed, 2nd issue, w/titles arranged by authors, and 'Warm Hair' on p8 no longer credited to Twain. Floral-pattern eps. Lt gray-grn cl, gilt. (Sl shelfworn, sl rubbed; clipped owner label mtd at top of fr pastedown.) BAL 3425 and 1982. *Baltimore**. $100/£63

TWAIN, MARK. Mark Twain's Library of Humor. NY: Charles L. Webster, 1888. 1st ed, 2nd state. Brn pict cl (sl rubbed), gilt. BAL 3425. *Macdonnell*. $200/£125

TWAIN, MARK. Mark Twain's Notebook. NY: Harper, 1935. 1st ed. VG (fep offset; tp, frontis spotted, sm leather bkpl) in dj (chipped, stained). BAL 3556. *Agvent*. $150/£94

TWAIN, MARK. Mark Twain's Notebooks. NY: Harper, 1935. 1st ed. Fine. *Labordo*. $60/£38

TWAIN, MARK. Mark Twain's Sketches, New and Old. Hartford: American Pub, 1875. 1st ed, 2nd state w/footnote not repeated on p120 & lacking skit From Hospital Days on p299. Blue cl, gilt. (Sl soiled, spine ends sl worn), else VG. *Pacific**. $81/£51

TWAIN, MARK. Mark Twain's Sketches, New and Old. Hartford/Chicago: American Publishing, 1875. 1st ed, 2nd state, w/o footnote on p120, and w/o 'Hospital Days' on p299. Lt peach eps; triple feps at fr/rear. Aeg. Royal blue cl, gilt. (Lt aged; extrems frayed, spine sl dknd, sm snag, sl dusty, lt worn.) BAL 3364. *Baltimore**. $85/£53

TWAIN, MARK. Mark Twain's Sketches. C&W, 1892. New ed. Pict bds (rebacked w/orig backstrip relaid, shelf-worn; sig, few pencil notes). Good. *Tiger*. $32/£20

TWAIN, MARK. Mark Twain's Speeches. NY: Harper, 1910. 1st ed, 1st state. Red cl, gilt. (Spine sunned), else Good. BAL 3513. *Macdonnell*. $100/£63

TWAIN, MARK. Mark Twain's West. Walter Blair (ed). Chicago: R.R. Donnelley, 1983. Frontis. VG. *Lien*. $30/£19

TWAIN, MARK. Mark Twain—Howells Letters. Cambridge: Belknap, 1960. 1st ed. 2 vols. Black cl. Fine set in Fine djs. *Macdonnell*. $125/£78

TWAIN, MARK. Merry Tales. NY, 1892. 1st ed, 1st issue, w/o port, eps ptd in olive grn. (Spine ends lt worn.) BAL 3435. *Kane**. $80/£50

TWAIN, MARK. More Tramps Abroad. London, 1897. 1st British ed. (Sl foxed; sl worn.) BAL 3453. *Kane**. $60/£38

TWAIN, MARK. More Tramps Abroad. London: C&W, 1897. 1st Eng ed. Purple cl (sl edgewear). VG. BAL 3453. *Cummins*. $125/£78

TWAIN, MARK. More Tramps Abroad. London: C&W, 1897. 1st Eng ed. Pub's note tipped in. 32pg cat dated Sept 1897. Emb burgundy cl. VG (spotted, rubbed, sm discolored area to fr). BAL 3453. *Agvent*. $250/£156

TWAIN, MARK. The Mysterious Stranger. NY: Harper, (1916). 1st ed. 7 color plts by N.C. Wyeth. Teg. Black cl w/pict cvr label. (Corner repaired), else Good. *Appelfeld*. $250/£156

TWAIN, MARK. The Notorious Jumping Frog and Other Stories. Edward Wagenknecht (ed). NY: LEC, 1970. One of 1500 signed by Joseph Low (illus). VF in slipcase, glassine. *Pharos*. $125/£78

TWAIN, MARK. Old Times on the Mississippi. Toronto: Belford Bros, 1876. 1st ed, rpt C. Grn cl stamped in black. Good. BAL 3368. *Cummins*. $250/£156

TWAIN, MARK. Old Times on the Mississippi. Toronto: Belford, 1876. 1st ed. 157,(2)pp. Purple cl (spine faded). *M & S*. $300/£188

TWAIN, MARK. Personal Recollections of Joan of Arc.... London: C&W, 1896. 1st Eng ed, apparently published May 16, 1896, approx 1 month after initial US ed. 32-pg pub's cat dated March 1896 at rear. Teg, untrimmed. Dk blue cl w/fleur-de-lis pattern in blind on fr cvr, lg raised image of Joan of Arc in gilt/black at center. (Lt aged, few lt text cracks; edges sl worn, frayed, rubbed.) Text Good. BAL 3446. *Baltimore**. $110/£69

TWAIN, MARK. The Prince and the Pauper. Boston: James R. Osgood, 1882. 1st US ed, 1st ptg, w/Franklin Press imprint on tp verso; in Blanck's State A binding, w/top rosette on spine 1/8-inch below fillet. Dk grn pict cl. (Sl shaken, eps foxed; extrems frayed, worn, rear cvr rubbed.) Text Good. BAL 3402. *Baltimore**. $80/£50

TWAIN, MARK. The Prince and the Pauper. Boston: J.R. Osgood, 1882. 1st ed, 1st state w/Franklin Press imprint on c. pg. Old marbled bds over tan calf spine, corners (renewed), raised bands, red/grn leather labels, marbled edges. *Appelfeld*. $325/£203

TWAIN, MARK. The Prince and the Pauper. Boston, 1882. 1st ed, 1st binding state. Sq 4 to. Gilt-pict grn cl (extrems sl rubbed). Morocco slipcase. Fine. *Swann**. $517/£323

TWAIN, MARK. The Prince and the Pauper. Westerham, (England): LEC, 1964. One of 1500 ptd. Signed by Clarke Hutton (illus). 1/2 blue velvet, gray buckram, gilt spine label. Fine in glassine, slipcase. *Pacific**. $40/£25

TWAIN, MARK. The Prince and the Pauper. LEC, 1964. Ltd to 1500 numbered, signed by Clarke Hutton (illus). Fine in slipcase. *Swann**. $46/£29

TWAIN, MARK. Punch, Brothers, Punch! And Other Sketches. NY: Slote, Woodman, (1878). 1st ed, 2nd state. 3pp ads at rear + ad on rear pastedown. Lt blue eps w/sm ptd caricatures. Grn cl stamped in black/gilt. (Lt browned, few ll smudged; sl worn, frayed, scuffed, spotted.) BAL 3378. *Baltimore**. $110/£69

TWAIN, MARK. Roughing It. Hartford: Amer Pub, 1872. 1st state. BAL 3337: State A of p242, w/final ad leaf. Pub's imprint as listed by Blanck. 8vo. Pub's 1/2 morocco. NF (sig; spine top sl worn; joints, edges rubbed). *Agvent*. $1,750/£1,094

TWAIN, MARK. Roughing It. LEC, 1972. Ltd to 1500 numbered, signed by Noel Sickles (illus). Fine in slipcase. *Swann**. $46/£29

TWAIN, MARK. Saint Joan of Arc. NY: Harper, (1919). 1st ed thus. 4 tipped-in color plts. Pict cl (Inscrip; spine faded), else VG. *Pacific**. $35/£22

TWAIN, MARK. Simon Wheeler, Detective. Franklin Rogers (ed). NY: NY Public Library, 1963. 1st ed thus. Frontisport. Grn cl. VG. *House*. $35/£22

TWAIN, MARK. The Stolen White Elephant, Etc. Boston: James R. Osgood, 1882. 1st Amer ed. Pict tan cl. (Ep hinges repaired w/glue; spine ends, corners lt rubbed), else VG. BAL 3404. *Pacific**. $46/£29

TWAIN, MARK. The Stolen White Elephant. Boston, 1882. 1st US ed. (Foxed; soiled, spine ends sl worn.) BAL 3404. *Kane**. $80/£50

TWAIN, MARK. Three Sketches. Stamford: Overbrook, 1946. No limitation stated, but 'Printed for our Senators and Congressmen.' NF in ptd wrappers. *Black Sun*. $40/£25

TWAIN, MARK. Tom Sawyer Abroad. London: C&W, 1894. 1st Eng ed, 1st binding state, w/pict binding of lions chasing after Tom. 32-pg pub's cat dated Feb 1894 at rear. Pict red cl. (Sl foxed; spine sl turned, base sl frayed.) Cvrs VG. BAL 3440. *Baltimore**. $140/£88

TWAIN, MARK. The Tragedy of Puddn'head Wilson.... Hartford, 1894. 1st ed. Dec cl. Fine (faint sign of bkpl removal). *Swann**. $373/£233

TWAIN, MARK. A Tramp Abroad. Toronto/Montreal: Dominion News, 1880. (Pp357/358 torn out but present.) Grn pict cl (shaken, lt worn, fr hinge cracked), gilt. BAL 3626. *Cummins*. $300/£188

TWAIN, MARK. A Tramp Abroad. LEC, 1966. Ltd to 1500 numbered, signed by David Knight (illus). Fine in slipcase. *Swann**. $46/£29

TWAIN, MARK. The Writings of.... Hartford: American Pub Co, 1899-1907. One of 512. Signed. 23 (of 25) vols. Teg. 3/4 morocco, marbled bds, gilt. (Several hinges cracked; some spines, extrems sunned), else VG. *Pacific**. $920/£575

Twas the Night Before Christmas. Kenosha, WI: Samuel Lowe, 1942. Obl 4to. Series of overlapping and graduated sized pp. Good. *Reisler*. $225/£141

TWEEDIE, ALEXANDER. Clinical Illustrations of Fever. Phila: Carey & Lea, 1831. 1st Amer ed. 152pp (foxed). Orig bds (worn). *House*. $100/£63

TWEEDIE, ALEXANDER. Dissertations on Haemorrhages, Dropsy, Rheumatism, Gout, Scrofula, Etc. Phila, 1841. 1st ed. 514pp. Orig cl. (sl soiled, shaken). (Foxed), o/w Good. *Doctor's Library*. $75/£47

TWEEDIE, W. The Arabian Horse, His Country and People. William Blackwood & Sons, 1894. One of 100. Lg 4to. 7 chromolitho plts, fldg map in rear pocket. Teg. Orig 1/2 morocco (rubbed), gilt. *Sotheby's**. $3,128/£1,955

Twelve Wild Ducks, a Tale of the Norse. Phila: Henry B. Ashmead, (1859). Old Nurser's Little Library. Toybook. 12mo. 32pp. Good in color paper wrappers (lt dusty). *Reisler*. $75/£47

Twenty-Five Years of Brewing with an Illustrated History of American Beer. (NY, 1891.) 120pp. Black bds. (Dull), else VG. *Cullen*. $125/£78

Twilight Land. London: Osgood, McIlvaine, 1896. 1st ed. 8vo. Howard Pyle (illus). Engr frontis, (xii),5-369pp + (iv)pp pub's cat. Teg, rest uncut. Dk blue pict cl. Nice (sl speckled; lower cvr sl mkd, joints, spine rubbed, knocked). *Sotheran*. $109/£68

TWINN, DORIS. Reggie's Band. Warne, n.d. (1930s). 1st ed. Color frontis. Color pict bds. (Spine head lt bruised), else NF. *Any Amount*. $45/£28

TWISS, RICHARD. Travels Through Portugal and Spain in 1772 and 1773. London: Privately ptd for the Author by Robinson T. Becket & J. Robson, 1775. 1st ed. Demy 4to. vi,471pp; 6 copper engrs (2 fldg), fldg map, tailpiece. VG in orig 1/2 leather (faint accidental imprint of a later auction cat on cvrs, extrems worn, corners bruised), marbled bds (worn). *Ulysses*. $1,440/£900

TWITCHETT, DENIS and MICHAEL LOEWE. The Cambridge History of China. Cambridge: CUP, (1986). 1st ed. 9 vols. NF in djs. *Pacific**. $316/£198

Two Cousins, a Moral Story, for the Use of Young Persons, in Which Is Exemplified the Necessity of Moderation and Justice to the Attainment of Happiness. (By Mrs. Pinchard.) NY: John Tiebout, 1799. 1st Amer ed. 16mo. Engr frontis, 136pp. Leather-backed paper-cvrd bds (worn). *Reisler*. $450/£281

Two Months in the Confederate States, Including a Visit to New Orleans Under the Domination of General Butler. By an English Merchant. (By W.C. Corsan.) London: Richard Bentley, 1863. 1st ed. 8vo. 2 prelim ll, 299pp (eps cracked). Grn cl. Excellent. Howes C791. *Mott*. $500/£313

Two Years in Ava. From May 1824, to May 1826. By an Officer on the Staff of the Quarter-Master-General's Department. (By Thomas Abercrombie Trant.) London: John Murray, 1827. 1st ed. 8vo. Engr frontis, xvi,455,(1)imprint; fldg map, lg engr plan. Contemp 1/2 calf, marbled bds, black label. Sound (sl foxed; early rebacked, corners worn, hinges strengthened). *Morrell*. $720/£450

Two Yellow-Birds. Providence: Geo. P. Daniels, 1843. 12mo. 2 half-pg wood engr frontis, 24pp + 1pg ad on lower wrapper. Pink pict wrappers. (Wrappers sl spotted), else Fine. *Hobbyhorse*. $100/£63

TYLDEN, G. Horses and Saddlery. London: Allen, 1965. 1st ed. VG in VG dj. *October Farm*. $65/£41

TYLER, ANNE. The Accidental Tourist. NY: Knopf, 1985. 1st ed. Fine in Fine dj. *Pettler*. $40/£25

TYLER, ANNE. The Accidental Tourist. NY, 1985. Signed. Fine in dj (sl nicked, mkd). *Clearwater*. $136/£85

TYLER, ANNE. Breathing Lessons. NY: Knopf, 1988. 1st ed. Inscribed, signed. NF in dj. *Pacific**. $63/£39

TYLER, ANNE. Celestial Navigation. NY: Knopf, 1974. 1st ed. Fine in Fine dj. *Lenz*. $250/£156

TYLER, ANNE. Dinner at the Homesick Restaurant. NY: Knopf, 1982. 1st ed. Fine in dj. *Lame Duck*. $100/£63

TYLER, ANNE. Earthly Possessions. NY: Knopf, 1977. 1st ed. Fine in Fine dj. *Lenz*. $175/£109

TYLER, ANNE. If Morning Ever Comes. NY, 1964. 1st ed, 1st bk. 8vo. 1/4 cl. Dj (1.25-inch closed tears at joints of fr/rear spine panels; sl loss of paper at ends of panel). *Swann**. $747/£467

TYLER, ANNE. If Morning Ever Comes. Chatto, 1965. 1st UK ed, 1st bk. Fine in dj. *Williams*. $440/£275

TYLER, ANNE. Morgan's Passing. NY: Knopf, 1980. 1st ed. Fine in Fine dj. *Lenz*. $100/£63

TYLER, ANNE. Saint Maybe. NY: Knopf, 1991. 1st trade ed. Fine in dj. *Lame Duck*. $20/£13

TYLER, ANNE. A Slipping-Down Life. NY: Knopf, 1970. 1st ed. Top edge stained yellow, untrimmed. Tan cl, yellow bds, gilt. (Top edge sl dusty, sl shelfworn.) VG dj. *Baltimore**. $290/£181

TYLER, ANNE. A Slipping-Down Life. NY: Knopf, 1970. 1st ed. NF (sm bump fr cvr) in dj (sl worn). *Lenz*. $300/£188

TYLER, JOSIAH. Livingstone Lost and Found, or Africa and Its Explorers. Hartford, 1873. Pub's gilt-pict cl. (Sm tear on prelim ll; rubbed.) *Swann**. $57/£36

TYLER, JOSIAH. Livingstone Lost and Found, or Africa and Its Explorers. Hartford: Mutual Publishing, 1873. 1st ed. Grn cl, gilt. (Rear hinge, joint weak), else VG. *Pacific**. $92/£58

TYLER, RON et al. American Frontier Life. NY, 1989. NF in dj. 78 color plts. *Dumont*. $60/£38

TYLER, RON. Alfred Jacob Miller: Artist on the Oregon Trail. Fort Worth, 1982. 119 plts. VG in dj. *Dumont*. $35/£22

TYLER, RON. The Cowboy. NY, (1975). 1st ed. Simulated leather. VG + in VG dj. *Sagebrush*. $50/£31

TYLOR, C. (ed). Samuel Tuke. His Life, Work and Thoughts. London, 1900. (Pencil notes few text pp, rear inner hinge cracked.) *Whitehart*. $56/£35

TYMMS, W. R. and M. WYATT. The Art of Illuminating as Practiced in Europe from the Earliest Times. Day & Son, 1860. Chromo-litho 1/2 title, tp, colophon; 99 chromolitho plts, orig tissue quads. (Leaf corner repaired.) Aeg. 1/2 red morocco (inner hinges strengthened). Very Clean. *Moss*. $352/£220

TYMMS, W. R. and M. D. WYATT. The Art of Illuminating as Practised in Europe from the Earliest Times. London: Day & Son, (1865). 96pp; 95 plts (87 chromolitho). Blindstamped cl (spine 1/2 detached, faded, worn; bkpl), gilt. *Maggs*. $144/£90

TYMMS, W. R. and M. D. WYATT. The Art of Illuminating as Practised in Europe from the Earliest Times. London: Day & Son, 1860. Folio. Chromolitho tp, 99 chromolitho plts. Aeg. Full contemp gilt-stamped red morocco (rubbed, joints rubbed). *Oinonen**. $200/£125

TYNAN, KATHERINE and CHARLES ROBINSON. A Little Book of Courtesies. London: J.M. Dent, (1906). 1st ed. 12mo. 58pp (sl foxed, few pp w/edges cut roughly). Teg. Wine-red cl, gilt. *Reisler.* $75/£47

TYNAN, KENNETH. Bull Fever. NY, (1955). 1st ed. (Sl worn; no dj.) *Woolson.* $10/£6

TYNDALL, JOHN. Heat Considered as a Mode of Motion. London: Longman et al, 1865. 2nd ed. xx,532,32pp; fldg engr plts. Mod 1/2 morocco, gilt. VG. *Hollett.* $136/£85

TYNDALL, JOHN. Mountaineering in 1861. Longman, Green, Longman & Roberts, 1862. 1st, only ed. vi,(iv),105,8 ads pp; 2 wood-engr plts. Red-brn cl, gilt. (Ink inscrip; spine ends sl worn), o/w VG. *Sotheran.* $317/£198

TYNDALL, JOHN. New Fragments. London: Longmans, Green, 1892. 1st ed. (v),500,(1 ads),12(pub's cat)pp. Fine (lt foxed). *Glaser.* $95/£59

TYNDALL, JOHN. Tyndall's Works. NY: D. Appleton, (1872). Author's ed. One of 1000. 6 (of ?) vols. Teg. 3/4 black morocco, marbled bds, gilt spines. (Bkpls; joints, spine ends sl rubbed), else VG. *Pacific**. $69/£43

TYRELL, J. W. Across the Sub-Arctics of Canada, a Journey of 3200 Miles by Canoe and Snowshoe Through the Barren Lands. London: T. Fisher Unwin, (1898). 1st Eng ed. 280pp. Good+ (inner hinges cracked). *Walcot.* $120/£75

TYRELL, J. W. Across the Sub-Arctics of Canada. Toronto: Wm. Briggs, 1897. vi(7)-280pp; fldg map. Teg. Old 1/2 calf (rubbed). VG. *High Latitude.* $130/£81

TYRMAND, LEOPOLD. The Man with the White Eyes. NY: Knopf, 1959. 1st Amer ed. VG in Good dj. *Agvent.* $30/£19

TYRREL, HENRY. The History of the Present War with Russia: Giving Full Details of the Operations of the Allied Armies. Volumes I and II (of 3) bound together. (London): London Ptg & Pub, (c.1856). 37 steel-engr plts (incl frontis, tp), 5 dbl-pg steel engr maps. Period 3/4 morocco, mottled bds, gilt. (Ink name dated May 1st, 1857; sl shelf-rubbed), else VG. *Pacific**. $58/£36

TYRRELL, FREDERICK. A Practical Work on the Diseases of the Eye, and Their Treatment. London: Churchill, 1840. 1st ed. 2 vols. 9 plts (8 hand-color). Contemp 1/2 leather (rubbed, sl foxed, soiled; sm stain gutter vol 1, spine chip). *Oinonen**. $160/£100

TYRWHITT, R. ST. JOHN. A Handbook of Pictorial Art. London: Clarendon, 1875. 2nd ed. Color frontis, (xiv),384pp; 4 color plts. Marbled eps. Emb morocco, gilt. (Lib ink stamps, bkpl; edges, spine scuffed.) *Edwards.* $40/£25

TYSON, JAMES. A Treatise on Bright's Disease and Diabetes. Phila, 1881. 1st ed. 312pp. *Fye.* $150/£94

TYSON, PHILIP T. Report of the Secretary of War.... Washington: US Senate, 1850. 1st ed. 8.75x5.75. 127,47pp; 13 fldg maps. Mod 1/2 morocco, marbled bds, gilt spine. (Sl water damage bottom of ll, maps sl foxed), o/w VG. Howes T4551. *Pacific**. $690/£431

TYSON, R. A. and E. S. D. ALCAUSKAS (eds). Catalogue of the Hrdlicka Paleopathology Collection. CA, 1980. Thick card wrappers (edges sl worn). *Whitehart.* $64/£40

TYTLER, PATRICK F. The Northern Coasts of America, and the Hudson's Bay Territories. London: T. Nelson, 1854. Fldg engr frontis map, vi,409pp. Red-brn coated eps; aeg, w/gauffered designs. Orig full brn sheep, gilt. (Heavily browned, few pp lt chipped, map chipped at margin w/several misfolds; sl scuffed, cvrs sl bowed, hinges splitting.) Solid. *Baltimore**. $20/£13

TYTLER, PATRICK F. Progress of Discovery on the More Northern Coasts of America. NY: J.& J. Harper, 1833. Fldg map. Good (extrems worn). *Dumont.* $150/£94

TYTLER, SARAH. The Huguenot Family. Hurst & Blackett, 1867. 3 vols. Pub's cat vol 3. Good (ex-lib, traces of label removal, several ll frayed vol 1, margins soiled, spotted; spines bumped, chipped, rubbed; vol 1 recased, rebacked w/orig backstrip relaid, corners rubbed). *Tiger.* $72/£45

U

U.S. Infantry Tactics...May 1, 1861.... Phila: Lippincott, 1861. 1st ptg. 450pp + (6)pp ads. Grn cl. (Names, lt foxed), else VG+. *Chapel Hill.* $75/£47

UBIQUE. (Pseud of Parker Gillmore.) Gun, Rod, and Saddle. Personal Experiences. NY, (1869). 1st Amer ed. Frontis. Pub's gilt-pict cl. *Swann**. $115/£72

UCHARD, MARIO. My Uncle Barbassou. Vizetelly, 1888. Frontis, 40 etchings by Paul Avril. Good (fore-edge lt spotted, lower edge frontis waterstained; spine bumped, sunned). *Tiger.* $48/£30

UDAL, JOHN. In a State of Readiness. Whittington, 1988. One of 150. Inscribed. VG (sl creased) in gray ptd wrappers. *Michael Taylor.* $72/£45

UDALL, DAVID KING. Arizona Pioneer Mormon: David King Udall...1851-1938. Tuscon: AZ Silhouettes, 1959. 1st ed. Brn cl, gilt. VG (bumped) in Fair pict dj (soiled, torn at flds). *Blue Mountain.* $75/£47

UDALL, STEWART. To the Inland Empire. NY, 1987. 1st ed. Signed. Map. VG in dj (clipped). *Dumont.* $75/£47

UDELL, JOHN. Journal Kept During a Trip Across the Plains.... L.A.: N.A. Kovach, 1946. Rpt of 1868 2nd ed. 8 plts. Orange cl. VF in dj (lt soiled). *Argonaut.* $60/£38

UDEN, GRANT. A Dictionary of Chivalry. London: Longmans, 1968. 2nd ed. 6.5x9.5. Pauline Baynes (illus). 352pp. Fine in dj. *Cattermole.* $100/£63

UHLMAN, FRED. An Artist in North Wales. Paul Elek, 1946. 1st Eng ed. NF in dj remains (fr panel present). *Ulysses.* $72/£45

UKERS, WILLIAM H. The Romance of Tea: An Outline History of Tea and Tea-Drinking Through Sixteen Hundred Years. Knopf, 1936. 1st ed. VG in Good dj. *Book Broker.* $35/£22

ULANOV, BARRY and GEORGE SIMON (eds). Jazz 1954 Metronome Yearbook. NY: Metronome, 1954. 1st ed. NF in wraps. *Beasley.* $30/£19

ULANOV, BARRY and GEORGE SIMON (eds). Jazz 1955 Metronome Yearbook. NY: Metronome, 1955. 1st ed. Fine in wraps. *Beasley.* $30/£19

ULANOV, BARRY. Duke Ellington. NY: Creative Age, 1946. 2nd ptg. Fine in dj (lt used). *Beasley.* $30/£19

ULANOV, BARRY. A History of Jazz in America. NY: Viking, 1957. VG in pict dj. *Petrilla.* $25/£16

ULANOV, BARRY. The Incredible Crosby. NY: Whittlesey House, 1948. 1st ed. Fine in dj (spine dknd). *Beasley.* $100/£63

ULLMAN, JAMES RAMSEY. The Day on Fire. Cleveland: World, (1958). 1st ed. As New in VF dj (1/16-inch short). *Between The Covers.* $100/£63

ULPH, OWEN. The Fiddleback. Salt Lake City: Dream Garden, 1981. 1st ed. Fine in dj. *House.* $20/£13

ULPH, OWEN. The Fiddleback. Salt Lake City, 1981. 1st ed. One of 100. Signed. *Woolson.* $35/£22

ULTZMANN, R. The Neuroses of the Genito-Urinary System in the Male. Phila: Davis, 1890. 1st ed. VG (ex-lib). *Beasley.* $85/£53

Uncle Frank's Fables, for Good Boys and Girls. Five Volumes from the Moral and Entertaining Fables for Children Series. NY: Wm. H. Murphy, n.d. (ca 1850). Thin 12mo. 34pp each vol + 1pg ad rear cvrs; 16 wood engrs each vol. Pict paper wrappers. VG set (ink sig). *Hobbyhorse.* $225/£141

Uncle Tom's Cabin Picture Book. NY: Graham & Matlack, 1913. Toybook. Tall thin 4to. 10pp (counting cvrs). Good in stiff color pict wrappers (spine chipped, split). *Reisler.* $225/£141

Uncle Vasya Is a Hero and Other Stories of the Young Heroes...of the USSR. NY: Stalingrad Silver Ponds Club, n.d. 1st ed. VG in wraps. *Beasley.* $40/£25

Under Sail to Greenland. (By Arthur S. Allen) NY: Marchbanks, 1931. One of 900. 12plts. VG (edges sl worn). *High Latitude.* $75/£47

UNDERHILL, D. C. Underhill's New Table-Book; or, Tables of Arithmetic Made Easier. NY: Richard Marsh, 1846. Sq 12mo. Frontis, 23pp + 1pg list. Pict blue wrapper. VF. *Hobbyhorse.* $125/£78

UNDERHILL, EVELYN. Jacopone da Tody, Poet and Mystic 1228-1306. Mrs. Theodore Beck (trans). London: J.M. Dent, 1919. 1st ed. 2 plts. (Sl damped.) *Hollett.* $56/£35

UNDERHILL, FRANCIS. Driving for Pleasure. NY: Appleton, 1896. 1st ed. 1/2 leather, suede. (Edges rubbed), o/w VG. *October Farm.* $445/£278

UNDERHILL, FRANK P. Toxicology or the Effects of Poisons. Phila, 1924. 1st ed. Brn cl bds (fep removed). VG (extrems sl worn). *Doctor's Library.* $50/£31

UNDERHILL, HAROLD A. Sailing Ship Rigs and Rigging. Glasgow: Brown, Son & Ferguson, 1942. (Sl bowed from damp; fr bd stained, spine, edges worn.) *Hollett.* $56/£35

UNDERHILL, RUTH M. First Penthouse Dwellers of America. Santa Fe: Laboratory of Anthropology, (1946). 2nd, rev ed. Blue cl. Fine in dj (spine dknd, lt soiled). *Argonaut.* $60/£38

UNDERWOOD, J. CABANISS. Gilbert; Or, Then and Now. A Thrilling Story of the Life and Achievements of a Virginia Negro. Phila: Shaiffer, (1902). 1st ed. 6 plts. Fine. *Agvent.* $250/£156

UNDERWOOD, L. H. Fifteen Years Among the Top-Knots, or Life in Korea. NY: American Tract Soc, (1904). 1st ed. 42 photo plts. Dec grn linen. Good. *Karmiole.* $65/£41

UNDERWOOD, LUCIEN MARCUS. Our Native Ferns and Their Allies. NY: Henry Holt, 1896. 5th ed. xii,156pp, 4 pp ads. Grn cl, gilt. (Browned), else VG. *Fair Meadow.* $30/£19

UNDERWOOD, MICHAEL. Rosa's Dilemma. NY: St. Martin's, 1990. 1st US ed. Signed presentation. Fine in dj. *Any Amount.* $24/£15

UNDERWOOD, MICHAEL. A Treatise on the Diseases of Children, and Management of Infants from the Birth. Boston, 1806. 2nd Amer ed. 476pp. Full leather (rubbed). (Spine label missing.) *Fye.* $150/£94

UNDERWOOD, PAUL. The Kariye Djami. NY/Princeton, 1966. 3 vols. 334 plts vol 2; 218 plts vol 3. Near Mint set in dj, slipcase. *Washton.* $225/£141

UNDERWOOD, PRISCILLA. When Christmas Comes Around. London: C&W, 1915. 1st Eng ed. 4to. 6 full-pg color plts by Jessie Wilcox Smith. Cl-backed pict bds (edgeworn; fr hinge starting). *Reisler.* $400/£250

UNDERWORLD, LUCIEN. Our Native Ferns and Their Allies. Bloomington, IL: Leader Pub, 1882. 2nd ed. 134pp. Grn cl. VG. *Archer.* $15/£9

United States Bombing Survey (Pacific): Interrogations of Japanese Officials. N.p.: Naval Analysis Division, (1946). 1st ed. 2 vols. Blue cl, gilt. Fine. *Pacific*.* $63/£39

UNRUH, JOHN D. The Plains Across. Urbana: Univ of IL, 1979. 1st ed. Fine in dj. *Labordo.* $55/£34

Unsentimental Journey Through Cornwall. (By Mrs. Craik.) London, 1884. x,144pp. Aeg. (Cl sl dknd, spine sl chipped.) *Edwards.* $56/£35

UNSWORTH, BARRY. Mooncranker's Gift. London, 1973. 1st Eng ed. Very Nice (spine sl creased, 1 corner sl bumped) in dj. *Clearwater.* $72/£45

UNSWORTH, BARRY. The Partnership. London: New Authors Ltd, 1966. 1st British ed, 1st bk. NF in VG + dj. *Pettler.* $100/£63

UNSWORTH, WALT. Tiger in the Snow. The Life and Adventures of A. F. Mummery. London: Gollancz, 1967. 1st ed. 5 maps. VG in dj. *Hollett.* $32/£20

Untrodden Fields of Anthropology. Paris: Charles Carrington/La Librairie des Bibliophiles, 1896. 1st ed. 2 vols. Pub's blue cl, gilt. Wrappers bound in. (Lower corners sl rubbed, bumped, cl sl mkd), else VG + set. *Any Amount.* $200/£125

Up and Down: A Book of Changing Pictures. London: Ernest Nister, ca 1910. 8vo. 5 full-pg transformations w/pull-tabs. Cl-backed color pict bds (edgeworn). *Reisler.* $900/£563

UPDIKE, DANIEL B. In The Day's Work. Cambridge: Harvard Univ, 1924. 1st ed. Teg. (Ink inscrip; spine rubbed, bumped). *Oak Knoll.* $40/£25

UPDIKE, DANIEL B. Printing Types, Their History, Farms, and Use. Cambridge: Harvard Univ, 1966. 3rd ed, 2nd ptg. 2 vols. Fine in wrappers. *Cullen.* $100/£63

UPDIKE, DANIEL B. Some Aspects of Printing Old and New. New Haven: William Rudge, 1941. 1st ed. (Bkpl.) *Oak Knoll.* $45/£28

UPDIKE, JOHN. Assorted Prose. NY, 1965. 1st ed. VG in dj (sl discolored, chipped; spine frayed). *King.* $35/£22

UPDIKE, JOHN. Baby's First Step. Huntington Beach: James Cahill, (1993). Printer's Copy of 100. Signed. Grn cl, gilt. Fine. *Pacific*.* $46/£29

UPDIKE, JOHN. Baby's First Step. Huntington Beach: James Cahill, (1993). 1st ed. 'Author's Copy' of 126. Signed. Grn cl, gilt. As New in slipcase. *Pacific*.* $69/£43

UPDIKE, JOHN. Baby's First Step. Huntington Beach: James Cahill, (1993). 1st ed. 'Artist's Copy' of 126. Signed. Grn cl, gilt. As New. *Pacific*.* $75/£47

UPDIKE, JOHN. Bech Is Back. NY, 1982. 1st Amer ed. Signed. Fine (spine sl rubbed) in Fine dj. *Polyanthos.* $30/£19

UPDIKE, JOHN. Bech Is Back. NY, 1982. 1st ed. One of 500 numbered, signed. Dj, slipcase. *Swann*.* $46/£29

UPDIKE, JOHN. Bech Is Back. NY, 1982. 1st ed, 1st state dj w/FPT, 10/82 on fr flap, 394-52806-9 on rear panel. Fine in NF dj. *Warren.* $50/£31

UPDIKE, JOHN. Bottom's Dream. NY: Knopf, 1969. 1st ed. Fine in dj (lt used, few internal mends, sticker-dknd area 1 corner). *Beasley.* $85/£53

UPDIKE, JOHN. Buchanan Dying. NY: Knopf, 1974. 1st ed. Signed. Fine in Fine dj. *Lenz.* $100/£63

UPDIKE, JOHN. Confessions of a Wild Bore. Newton, IA: Tamazunchale Press, 1984. One of 250 numbered. Aeg. Full leather. VG. *King.* $60/£38

UPDIKE, JOHN. The Coup. NY: Knopf, 1978. 1st ed. Black topstain. VG + in dj. *Smith.* $35/£22

UPDIKE, JOHN. The Coup. NY, 1978. 1st Amer ed. Signed. Fine (sl rubbed) in NF dj. *Polyanthos.* $35/£22

UPDIKE, JOHN. The Coup. NY: Knopf, 1978. 1st ed, 1st issue w/yellow pg tops. Signed. Rev slip laid in. Fine in Fine dj. *Lenz.* $85/£53

UPDIKE, JOHN. The Coup. NY: Knopf, 1978. 1st ed, 2nd issue w/black pg tops. Signed. *Lenz.* $100/£63

UPDIKE, JOHN. Hoping for a Hoopoe. Gollancz, 1959. 1st UK ed. Mint in Mint dj. *Martin.* $54/£34

UPDIKE, JOHN. Hoping for a Hoopoe. London: Gollancz, 1959. 1st British ed, 1st bk. Signed. Fine in Fine dj. *Lenz*. $175/£109

UPDIKE, JOHN. Hub Fans Bid Kid Adieu. Northridge: Lord John, 1977. One of 300 numbered, signed. Cl, patterned bds. Fine in custom blue linen 2-part slipcase w/leather spine labels. *Dermont*. $300/£188

UPDIKE, JOHN. Hugging the Shore: Essays and Criticisms. NY: Knopf, 1983. 1st ed. Signed. Fine in dj. *Pacific**. $23/£14

UPDIKE, JOHN. Impressions. Hollywood: Sylvester & Orphanos, 1985. Ltd to 330 signed. 14 color plts. Fine dec cl. *Truepenny*. $250/£156

UPDIKE, JOHN. Marry Me. NY, 1976. 1st ed. One of 300 numbered, signed. Slipcase. *Swann**. $80/£50

UPDIKE, JOHN. Marry Me. Franklin Center, PA: Franklin Library, 1976. Franklin Library ltd 1st ed. Signed. Fine in full leather, gilt. *Lame Duck*. $150/£94

UPDIKE, JOHN. Marry Me. Andre Deutsch, 1977. 1st ed. Fine (edges sl spotted) in dj. *Ulysses*. $56/£35

UPDIKE, JOHN. Midpoint and Other Poems. NY, 1969. 1st Amer ed. Signed. Fine in dj (spine sl rubbed). *Polyanthos*. $35/£22

UPDIKE, JOHN. Midpoint. NY: Knopf, 1969. One of 350 numbered, signed. Fine in dj, NF slipcase. *Smith*. $150/£94

UPDIKE, JOHN. A Month of Sundays. NY: Knopf, 1975. 1st trade ed. Signed. Fine in dj. *Pacific**. $46/£29

UPDIKE, JOHN. The Music School. NY, 1966. 1st ed, 1st issue (pg 46 l. 15: 'The state...'). VG in dj (spine dknd, soiled back panel). *King*. $150/£94

UPDIKE, JOHN. The Music School. London: Andre Deutsch, 1967. 1st Eng ed. Fine in dj (nick). *Ulysses*. $88/£55

UPDIKE, JOHN. Of the Farm. NY: Knopf, 1965. 1st ed. Signed. Fine in Fine dj. *Lenz*. $125/£78

UPDIKE, JOHN. Picked-Up Pieces. NY, (1975). 1st ed. One of 250 numbered, signed. Dj, slipcase. *Swann**. $57/£36

UPDIKE, JOHN. Picked-Up Pieces. NY: Knopf, 1975. 1st ed. Signed. Fine in Fine dj. *Lenz*. $85/£53

UPDIKE, JOHN. The Poorhouse Fair. NY: Knopf, 1959. 1st ed. NF in dj (spine head, extrems sl creased, sm scrape rear flap). *Pacific**. $109/£68

UPDIKE, JOHN. Rabbit at Rest. NY, 1990. 1st Amer ed. Signed. Fine in Fine dj. *Polyanthos*. $30/£19

UPDIKE, JOHN. Rabbit at Rest. NY: Knopf, 1990. 1st ed. Signed. Fine in dj. *Pacific**. $52/£33

UPDIKE, JOHN. Rabbit at Rest. NY: Knopf, 1990. One of 350 numbered, signed. Fine in clear acetate dj, slipcase. *Lenz*. $275/£172

UPDIKE, JOHN. Rabbit Is Rich. NY: Knopf, 1981. 1st ed. Signed. (Spine head sl rubbed), else NF in dj. *Pacific**. $63/£39

UPDIKE, JOHN. Rabbit Is Rich. NY: Knopf, 1981. 1st ed. Signed, inscribed. Dj (crown sl creased). *Swann**. $138/£86

UPDIKE, JOHN. Rabbit is Rich. NY: Knopf, 1981. 1st ed. Inscribed. (Blind-stamp 1st 3 pp), else NF in VG + dj (rear panel edge sl torn). *Lame Duck*. $150/£94

UPDIKE, JOHN. Rabbit Redux. NY, 1971. 1st ed. Inscribed. Dj. *Swann**. $126/£79

UPDIKE, JOHN. Rabbit Redux. NY: Knopf, 1971. 1st ed. One of 350 signed. Top edge stained red. Blue cl over white cl, gilt. Fine in pub's cardboard case (lt worn). *Heritage*. $275/£172

UPDIKE, JOHN. Rabbit, Run. Pennsylvania: Franklin Mint, (1977). One of unspecified #, signed. Jerry Pinkney (illus). Gilt-dec red leather. *Swann**. $57/£36

UPDIKE, JOHN. Rabbit, Run. NY: Knopf, 1960. 1st ed. (Fore-edge lt foxed), else NF in VG + dj (spine sl faded, lt foxed). *Lame Duck*. $375/£234

UPDIKE, JOHN. Roger's Version. NY, 1986. 1st ed. One of 350 numbered, signed. 1/4 cl. Mylar dj, slipcase. *Swann**. $80/£50

UPDIKE, JOHN. The Same Door. NY: Knopf, 1959. 1st ed. Signed. Fine in dj (sl worn). *Lenz*. $350/£219

UPDIKE, JOHN. Talk from the Fifties. Northridge: Lord John, 1979. 1st ed. One of 300 numbered, signed. *Swann**. $92/£58

UPDIKE, JOHN. Telephone Poles and Other Poems. London, 1964. 1st Eng ed. As New (lacks dj). *Bond*. $50/£31

UPDIKE, JOHN. Three Texts for Early Ipswich. Ipswich: 17th Century Day Committee, 1968. 1st ed. Fine in stapled wrappers. *Between The Covers*. $75/£47

UPDIKE, JOHN. Trust Me: Short Stories. NY: Knopf, 1987. 1st ed. Signed. Fine in dj. *Pacific**. $29/£18

UPDIKE, JOHN. The Twelve Terrors of Christmas. NY: Gotham Book Mart, (1994). 1st trade ed. Signed by Updike and Gorey (illus). Fine in pict wrappers. *Pacific**. $75/£47

UPDIKE, JOHN. The Witches of Eastwick. Franklin Center: Franklin Library, 1984. 1st ed. Signed. Gilt-dec grn morocco. (Sl dampstaining to extrems of signed leaf; sl wear to gilt along fore-edges), else VG. *Pacific**. $63/£39

UPFIELD, A. Madman's Bend. Heinemann, 1963. 1st ed. Fine in NF dj. *Fine Books*. $45/£28

UPFIELD, A. The Sands of Windee. A&R, 1958. 1st Eng ed. VG + in VG dj (lt worn, torn). *Fine Books*. $45/£28

UPHAM, CHARLES WENTWORTH. Life Explorations and Public Services of John Charles Fremont. Boston: Ticknor & Fields, 1856. 356pp. VG (shelfworn, very foxed). *My Bookhouse*. $52/£33

UPHAM, ELIZABETH. Little Brown Bear Goes to School. NY: Platt & Munk, 1955. 4to. Marjorie Hartwell (illus). VG. *American Booksellers*. $40/£25

UPHAM, ELIZABETH. Little Brown Bear. NY: Platt & Munk, 1942. 4vo. Marjorie Hartwell (illus). VG. *American Booksellers*. $40/£25

Ups and Downs: A Book of Transformation Pictures. London: Ernest Nister, (ca 1893). Sq 8vo. 6 full-pg tab-activated slat transformation plts. Cl-backed color pict bds. (Eps replaced, lt overall wear.) *Reisler*. $750/£469

UPSON, THEODORE F. With Sherman to the Sea. Oscar O. Winther (ed). Baton Rouge: LA State Univ, 1943. 1st ed. Frontis. Brn cl. (Neat sig), else VG in dj. *Chapel Hill*. $85/£53

UPTON, BERTHA. The Adventures of Borbee and the Wisp. London: Longmans, Green, 1908. 1st ed. Lg sq 4to. Cl-backed pict bds (rubbed). *Reisler*. $400/£250

UPTON, BERTHA. The Golliwogg at the Sea-Side. London: Longmans, Green, 1898. 1st ed. Florence K. Upton (illus). Obl 4to. Cl-backed color pict bds (edges lt worn, dusty). Nice. *Reisler*. $400/£250

UPTON, BERTHA. The Golliwogg's Air-Ship. Longmans, Green, 1902. 1st ed. Obl 4to. 64pp; 30 Fine color litho plts (1 dbl-pg) by Florence Upton. Cl-backed pict bds (sl browned, corners sl worn). Internally Fine. *Sotheran*. $317/£198

UPTON, BERTHA. The Golliwogg's Auto-Go-Cart. London: Longmans, Green, 1901. 1st ed. Obl 4to. Florence Upton (illus). 66pp (fr hinge expertly strengthened, rep replaced w/facs); 30 Fine color litho plts (1 dbl-pg). Cl-backed pict bds (corner tips worn, edges rubbed, lt soiled, sm scratches). Internally Very Clean. *Sotheran*. $237/£148

UPTON, BERTHA. The Golliwogg's Circus. NY, 1903. Obl 8.5x11. 64pp; 30 full-pg color plts by Florence K. Upton. Cl-backed pict bds. (Few sl margin tears, smudges; cvrs rubbed, spotted; sl musty odor.) *King*. $350/£219

UPTON, BERTHA. The Golliwogg's Circus. London: Longmans, Green, 1903. 1st ed. Oblong 4to. Cl-backed color illus bds (edges sl dusty). Clean. *Reisler*. $400/£250

UPTON, EMORY. The Military Policy of the United States. Washington, 1904. VG. *Pratt.* $45/£28

UPTON, RICHARD (ed). Fort Custer on the Big Horn, 1877-1898. Glendale, CA: A.H. Clark, 1973. 1st ed. VG. *Lien.* $50/£31

UPWARD, EDWARD. In the Thirties. London, 1962. 1st Eng ed. Very Nice (cvr edges sl bumped) in dj (sl rubbed). *Clearwater.* $64/£40

URANN, C. A. Centennial History of Cleveland. Cleveland, 1896. 120pp. Pict cl (soiled). *Zubal*.* $17/£11

URBAN, JOHN W. My Experiences Mid Shot and Shell and in Rebel Den.... Lancaster, PA: Published for the Author, 1882. 1st ed. 633pp (browned, inner hinges cracked). Pict cl (sl speckled). *King.* $45/£28

URBAN, MARTIN. Emil Nolde: Catalogue Raisonne of the Oil-Paintings. (London/NY, 1987-90.) 2 vols. Djs. *Swann*.* $230/£144

URE, ANDREW. Dictionary of Arts, Manufactures, and Mines.... Robert Hunt (ed). London: Longman, Green et al, 1863. 5th ed. 3 vols. x,909; 740; 1078pp. Marbled edges, eps. Contemp 1/2 calf, gilt, raised bands. Excellent set (some hinges just cracking, few spots 1 bd). *Hollett.* $352/£220

URE, DAVID. The History of Rutherglen and East-Kilbride. Glasgow: David Niven, 1793. 1st ed. vi,(ii),334,(xxii, sub's list)pp; complete w/21 plts (1 aquatint, 1 fldg). Uncut. Orig bds (spine sl chipped, worn). VG (tp water-stained, few spots, dampstains). *Hollett.* $280/£175

URE, PETER (ed). The Chronicle History of Perkin Warbeck. Methuen, 1968. 1st Eng ed. NF (spine ends sl bumped) in dj. *Ulysses.* $32/£20

URIBE, C. ANDRES. Brown Gold. NY: RH, 1954. 1st ed. VG in Good dj (internally tape repaired). *Archer.* $15/£9

URIS, LEON. Exodus Revisited. GC: Doubleday, 1960. 1st ed. Inscribed. NF in NF dj (rubbed, few tears). *Unger.* $150/£94

URIS, LEON. Exodus. Wingate, 1959. 1st UK ed. VG in dj (edges sl worn). *Williams.* $40/£25

URIS, LEON. Mila 18. GC: Doubleday, 1961. 1st ed. Pub's file copy stamp on fep. (Top edge sl dusty), else Fine in VG dj (soiled, few sm closed marginal tears). *Any Amount.* $40/£25

URIS, LEON. Mila 18. GC: Doubleday, 1961. 1st ed. (Name fep, fr dj flap), else VG in VG dj. *Pettler.* $40/£25

URQUHART, DAVID. The Pillars of Hercules; Or, A Narrative of Travels in Spain and Morocco. Richard Bentley, 1850. 1st ed. 2 vols in 1. xi,464pp. Recent speckled 1/2 calf, marbled bds, raised bands, gilt. Good (bkpl, ink inscrip, sl browned throughout). *Sotheran.* $477/£298

USLAR PIETRI, ARTURO. The Red Lances. Harriet de Onis (trans). NY: Knopf, 1963. 1st US ed. (Sm, sl whitish spots to stain of pp top edges), else Fine in VG + dj (few nicks). *Lame Duck.* $65/£41

USTINOV, PETER. The Love of Four Colonels. NY: Dramatists Play Service, (1953). 1st Amer ed. VF in VF dj. *Between The Covers.* $150/£94

USTINOV, PETER. Romanoff and Juliet. NY: Random House, (1958). 1st Amer ed. VF in VF dj. *Between The Covers.* $125/£78

UTLEY, ROBERT M. Billy the Kid, a Short and Violent Life. Lincoln: Univ of NE, (1989). 1st ed. Fine in Fine dj. *Book Market.* $38/£24

UTLEY, ROBERT M. Cavalier in Buckskin. Norman: Univ of OK, (1988). 1st ed. VG in dj. *Lien.* $30/£19

UTLEY, ROBERT M. Custer and the Great Controversy. L.A.: Westernlore, 1962. 1st ed. Inscribed, signed presentation. Fine in dj (sm cut fr panel). *Pacific*.* $35/£22

UTLEY, ROBERT M. Custer Battlefield. Washington: US Dept of Interior, 1969. 1st ed. Fine in wrappers. *Labordo.* $15/£9

UTLEY, ROBERT M. Fort Davis. Washington, 1965. VG + in pict wraps. *Pratt.* $7/£4

UTLEY, ROBERT M. Fort Union National Monument, New Mexico. Washington, 1962. (Rear cvr corner creased), else VG + in pict wrappers. *Sagebrush.* $22/£14

UTLEY, ROBERT M. Frontier Regulars. NY: Macmillan, (1973). 1st ed. Fine in dj. *Perier.* $50/£31

UTLEY, ROBERT M. Frontier Regulars: The United States Army and the Indian, 1866-1891. NY: Macmillan, (1973). 1st ed. Inscribed, signed presentation. Fine in dj. *Pacific*.* $81/£51

UTLEY, ROBERT M. High Noon in Lincoln. Albuquerque: Univ of NM, (1987). 1st ed. Fine in dj. *Lien.* $40/£25

UTLEY, ROBERT M. Last Days of the Sioux Nation. New Haven, (1963). 1st ed. Fine in dj (sl faded). *Pratt.* $50/£31

UTLEY, ROBERT M. The Last Days of the Sioux Nation. New Haven: Yale Univ, 1963. 1st ed. Inscribed, signed presentation. NF in VG dj (spine faded, title re-lettered). *Pacific*.* $29/£18

UTLEY, ROBERT M. Life in Custer's Cavalry. New Haven, 1977. 1st ed. VG in dj (sl rubbed). *King.* $35/£22

UTTLEY, ALISON. Country Things. Faber, 1946. 1st ed. C.F. Tunnicliffe (illus). VG in VG dj. *Green Meadow.* $40/£25

UTTLEY, ALISON. The Flower Show. London: Heinemann, (1955). 1st ed. 8vo. 13 full-pg color plts by Katherine Wigglesworth. Color pict bds (lower edges lt worn). Color dj (sm chip spine head). *Reisler.* $75/£47

UTTLEY, ALISON. From Spring to Spring. Kathleen Lines (ed). Faber, 1978. 1st ed thus. 8vo. Shirley Hughes (illus). 131pp. Fine in VG pict dj. *Bookmark.* $27/£17

UTTLEY, ALISON. Gray Rabbit Finds a Shoe. London: Collins, (1960). 1st ed. 12mo. 64pp. Margaret Tempest (illus). Red pict bds. VG in color pict dj. *Reisler.* $60/£38

UTTLEY, ALISON. The Gypsy Hedgehogs. London: Heinemann, (1953). 1st ed. 12mo. Katherine Wigglesworth (illus). 69pp. Color pict bds. Good in color pict dj (corners sl chipped). *Reisler.* $85/£53

UTTLEY, ALISON. Hare and the Rainbow. London: Collins, (1975). 1st ed. 12mo. 63pp; 15 full-pg color plts by Katherine Wigglesworth. Full color pict bds. VG/ *Reisler.* $65/£41

UTTLEY, ALISON. Here's a New Day. Faber, 1956. 1st ed. C.F. Tunnicliffe (illus). Fine in Fine dj. *Green Meadow.* $56/£35

UTTLEY, ALISON. Little Grey Rabbit Goes to the Sea. Collins Clear-Type Press, (1954). 1st ed. Margaret Tempest (illus). 12mo. Color illus bds. Good in full color dj (spine sl worn). *Reisler.* $85/£53

UTTLEY, ALISON. Little Red Fox and the Unicorn. Heinemann, 1962. 1st ed. Lg 8vo. Katherine Wigglesworth (illus). 63pp. VG. *Bookmark.* $40/£25

UTTLEY, ALISON. Moldy Warp the Mole. London: Collins, (1940). 1st ed. 12mo. Margaret Tempest (illus). 88pp. Color pict bds (edges lt worn). *Reisler.* $75/£47

UTTLEY, ALISON. Moonshine and Magic. Faber, 1932. 1st ed. Lg 8vo. 206pp; 8 color plts, 9 full-pg illus by William Townsend. Pict cl. Sound (mkd, spine worn). *Bookmark.* $51/£32

UTTLEY, ALISON. Secret Places and Other Essays. London, 1972. Dj (sm tear). *Petersfield.* $26/£16

UTTLEY, ALISON. Snug and Serena Go to Town. Heinemann, 1961. 1st ed. Lg 8vo. Katherine Wigglesworth (illus). 63pp. VG. *Bookmark.* $40/£25

UTTLEY, ALISON. Snug and Serena Pick Cowslips. London: Heinemann, (1950). 1st ed. 8vo. 72pp; 20 full-pg color illus by Katherine Wigglesworth. Color illus bds (lt edgeworn). Color dj (edgeworn, spine chip). *Reisler.* $60/£38

UZANNE, OCTAVE. The Book-Hunter in Paris. London: Elliot Stock, 1895. Cheaper ed. Maroon cl (spine faded, 1st quire loose), gilt. *Maggs.* $35/£22

UZANNE, OCTAVE. Fashion...from 1797 to 1897. London, 1898. 100 hand-colored plts. (Cl worn, shaken.) *Swann**. $201/£126

UZANNE, OCTAVE. The Sunshade—The Glove—The Muff. J.C. Nimmo & Bain, 1883. 1st Eng ed. viii,138pp (feps browned). Pict grn cl (sl mkd). *Hollett*. $192/£120

V

VACHELL, HORACE ANNESLEY. Fishpingle. London: John Murray, 1917. 1st Eng ed. 8pp pub's ads. Good (inscrip, top edge dusty, spotted; top corners bumped, cvrs sl mkd, spine sl faded, severe crack between first 2 gatherings). *Ulysses*. $40/£25

VACHELL, HORACE ANNESLEY. John Verney. London: John Murray, 1911. 1st Eng ed. 6pp pub's ads. Good (eps partly browned; spine ends, corners sl bumped, rubbed, cvrs sl mkd, spine sl dknd) in dj (edges sl spotted). *Ulysses*. $40/£25

VACHELL, HORACE ANNESLEY. Life and Sport on the Pacific Slope. Hodder & Stoughton, 1900. 1st ed. 11 photo plts. Teg. Pale grn cl, gilt. Fine (lt spotted; joints sl rubbed). *Sotheran*. $237/£148

VACHELL, HORACE ANNESLEY. The Quicksands of Pactolus. Holt, 1896. 1st ed. VG+ in yellow cl. *Fine Books*. $45/£28

VACHELL, HORACE ANNESLEY. Quinneys. London: John Murray, 1914. 1st Eng ed. Als tipped onto fep dated October 10th, 1924 on headed notepaper. 8pp pub's ads. Good (top edge dusty, spotted; cvrs sl mkd, edges sl rubbed, spine ends, corners sl bumped). *Ulysses*. $56/£35

VACHELL, HORACE ANNESLEY. Sport and Life on the Pacific Slope. London: Eveleigh Nash, 1908. 1st ed. Frontisport. Grn cl, gilt. (Bkpl, lacks fep, frontis detached), else VG. *Pacific**. $98/£61

VACHSS, ANDREW. Sacrifice. NY, 1991. 1st ed. Fine in Fine dj. *Warren*. $30/£19

VACHSS, ANDREW. Strega. NY: Knopf, 1987. 1st ed. Fine (rmdr mk) in Fine dj. *Beasley*. $40/£25

VACHSS, ANDREW. Strega. Collins, 1988. 1st UK ed. (Margins sl yellowed), else Fine in dj. *Any Amount*. $26/£16

VACHTOVA, LUDMILA. Frank Kupka: Pioneer of Abstract Art. NY, (1968). Dj (price-clipped). *Swann**. $316/£198

VAIL, I. E. Three Years on the Blockade. NY: Abbey, (1902). 1st ed. Red cl. (Faded), else VG. *Chapel Hill*. $200/£125

VAILE, P. A. Golf on the Green. NY: John Wanamaker, 1915. 1st ed. Pict grn cl, gilt. (Emb stamp; spine ends sl rubbed), else NF. *Pacific**. $127/£79

VAILE, P. A. The New Golf. NY: E.P. Dutton, 1917. 2nd ed. Grn cl, gilt. VG (C.B. Clapcott pencil initials, # fr pastedown, emb stamp). *Pacific**. $29/£18

VAILE, P. A. The Soul of Golf. London: Macmillan, 1912. 1st ed. Grn cl, gilt. (C.B. Clapcott pencil initials, # fr pastedown, emb stamps; upper corners sl bumped), else VG. *Pacific**. $288/£180

VAILLANT, GEORGE C. Indian Arts in North America. NY/London: Harper, 1939. Color frontis, 96 full-pg b/w plts. Pict cl bds (worn, discolored). *Metropolitan**. $28/£18

VALENS, E. G. Magnet. Cleveland/NY, (1964). 1st ed. Berenice Abbott (photos). (Bkpl.) Dj (chipped, lt worn). *Swann**. $103/£64

VALENS, E. G. Motion. Cleveland: The World Pub, 1965. 1st ed. 36 b/w photos by Berenice Abbott. (Fep creased), else VG in pict dj. *Cahan*. $175/£109

VALENTINER, WILHELM R. The Art of the Low Countries. Studies. NY, 1914. 84 plts hors texte. 1/2 cl (sl worn). *Washton*. $50/£31

VALENTINER, WILHELM R. Rembrandt Paintings in America. NY, 1931. One of 200 numbered. Signed, inscribed. Folio. Frontisport, 175 plts w/guards. Full gilt-stamped leather (rubbed, spine tips worn). Plain brn dj. *Oinonen**. $100/£63

VALENTINI, ENZO. Letters and Drawings by an Italian Volunteer and Soldier. Fernanda Bellachioma (trans). Constable, 1917. 1st Eng ed. Pict bds. Good (name; spine, corners rubbed). *Clearwater*. $56/£35

VALENZUELA, LUISA. Strange Things Happen Here. NY: Harcourt Brace Jovanovich, 1979. 1st US ed. NF in VG+ dj. *Lame Duck*. $45/£28

VALERY, PAUL. Degas Dance Drawing. (NY): Lear Pub, (1948). 1st ed in English. One of 1200 numbered. Color frontis, 3 add'l color plts tipped-in. VG. *Turtle Island*. $65/£41

VALERY, PAUL. Eupalinos or the Architect. William Stewart (trans). London, 1932. One of 250 numbered, signed. Gilt-pict cl. *Swann**. $230/£144

VALIN, JONATHAN. Day of Wrath. Congdon, 1982. 1st ed. VF in dj (lt nicked). *Murder*. $30/£19

VALIN, JONATHAN. Dead Letter. Dodd, 1981. 1st ed. Fine in dj (lt worn). *Murder*. $35/£22

VALIN, JONATHAN. Life's Work. Delacorte, 1986. 1st ed. Fine in dj. *Murder*. $25/£16

VALLANCE, AYMER et al. Great Masters of Decorative Art: Sir Edward Burne-Jones, William Morris, Walter Crane. London: Art Journal, 1900. 1st ed. Aeg. Dec cl, gilt. (Bkpl; soiled), else VG. *Pacific**. $150/£94

VALLANCE, AYMER. The Old Colleges of Oxford. Batsford, n.d. c.(1912). Folio. Frontis, 50 plts. Teg. (Upper bd, spine stained; spine chipped, joints partly splitting, corners rubbed w/cl loss.) *Edwards*. $120/£75

VALLANCE, AYMER. William Morris: His Art, His Writings and His Public Life. London: George Bell, 1897. 1st ed. Frontis port, xiv,(2),462pp. Marbled eps; aeg. Full dk blue morocco ruled/tooled in gilt, raised bands, gilt-ruled turn-ins, red morocco doublures. (Lib bkpl, rubberstamp; spine ends, corners sl scuffed), else NF. *Pacific**. $316/£198

VALLENTIN, ANTONINA. Leonardo da Vinci. E. W. Dickes (trans). W.H. Allen, 1952. 1st Eng ed. 31 plts. VG. *Hollett*. $40/£25

VALLERY-RADOT, RENE. The Life of Pasteur. R. L. Devonshire (trans). Westminster: Archibald Constable, 1902. 1st ed in English. 2 vols. Port. Blue cl, gilt. VG (text lt foxed). *House*. $75/£47

VALLI, ERIC and DIANE SUMMERS. Dolpo. NY: Aperture Foundation, 1986. 1st ed. Obl folio. VG. *Worldwide*. $40/£25

VALLIER, DORA. Henri Rousseau. NY: Abrams, ca 1962. Color mtd repros. Dj. *Swann**. $57/£36

Valuable Library of Books in Fonthill Abbey. A Catalogue of the...Library...Which Will Be Sold by Auction, by Mr. Phillips.... London, 1823. (xii),391pp. (Bd binding worn, cvrs detached.) *Zubal**. $100/£63

Valuable Secrets in Arts and Trades; or, Approved Directions from the Best Artists. London: J. Barker et al, n.d. (c. 1800). New, improved ed. Tp, preface, 351 + 3pp ads. Contemp 1/2-calf (rebacked retaining orig spine; worn, label cracked). *Europa*. $360/£225

VAMBERY, ARMINIUS. Travels in Central Asia. London, 1864. 12 plts, lg fldg map (1/4 missing). Teg. 1/2 grn morocco. (Backstrip faded.) *Petersfield*. $240/£150

VAN ALLSBURG, CHRIS. The Polar Express. Boston: Houghton Mifflin, 1985. 1st ed. Obl 8vo. VG in VG dj. *Davidson*. $150/£94

VAN ALLSBURG, CHRIS. The Z Was Zapped. Boston: Houghton Mifflin, 1987. 1st ed. 4to. Unpaginated. Fine in Fine dj. *Davidson.* $85/£53

VAN BUREN, A. DE PUY. Jottings of a Year's Sojourn in the South.... Battle Creek, MI: (Review & Herald Print), 1859. 1st ed. 320pp. Lt grn cl. VG (faded, foxed). Howes V15. *Chapel Hill.* $300/£188

VAN CLEVE, CHARLOTTE OUISCONSIN. Three Score Years and Ten. Minneapolis: Harrison & Smith, 1888. 1st ed, 2nd state, w/copyright notice on tp verso, not on ptd slip. Port, 176pp. (Sides rubbed, worn, scuffed), else Good. Howes V21. *Brown.* $60/£38

VAN COURT, DEWITT. The Making of Champions in California. L.A.: Premier Ptg, (1926). 1st ed. Brick cl, gilt. Fine. *Argonaut.* $150/£94

VAN DE PASS, CRISPIN. Hortus Floridus. Spencer Savage (trans). Cresset, 1928/9. One of 500 numbered. 2 vols. Morocco-backed Cockerell bds. VG set (bkpl; extrems sl worn) in djs (tanned, brittle, sl chipped). *Clearwater.* $400/£250

VAN DE WATER, FREDERIC F. Glory-Hunter: A Life of General Custer. Indianapolis: Bobbs-Merrill, (1934). 1st ed. VG (bkpl). Howes V27. *Pacific*.* $173/£108

VAN DENBURGH, ELIZABETH DOUGLAS. My Voyage in the United States Frigate 'Congress', 1845-1846. NY: Desmond Fitzgerald, (1913). 1st ed. 11 plts, facs. Teg. Pict grn cl. VG + (lt worn). *House.* $50/£31

VAN DENBURGH, J. The Reptiles of Western North America. SF, 1922. 2 vols. (3 index pp vol 2 repaired w/tape; sm tear to 1 pg fore-edge.) 128 plts. Binder's buckram. *Sutton.* $250/£156

VAN DER HOEVEN, J. Handbook of Zoology. Cambridge, 1856-58. 2 vols. 24 plts. xvi,(1),853; xxiv,(1),775pp. (Worn, faded, few spots to cvrs, spine heads professionally repaired.) *Sutton.* $150/£94

VAN DER MEER and J. McGOWAN. Sailing Ships. Viking, 1984. 1st ed. Borge Svensson (illus). Mint. *Green Meadow.* $40/£25

VAN DER MEER, RON. The World's First Ever Pop-Up Games Book. NY: Delacorte, 1982. 4 dbl-pg pop-ups, rotating wheel. Glazed pict bds. VG. *Bookfinders.* $45/£28

VAN DER POST, LAURENS. First Catch Your Eland. London: Hogarth, 1977. 1st Eng ed. Fine (spine ends sl bumped) in dj (spine faded). *Ulysses.* $40/£25

VAN DER POST, LAURENS. Flamingo Feather. NY, 1955. 1st ed. VG in dj (rear panel stained). *Typographeum.* $20/£13

VAN DER POST, LAURENS. The Hunter and the Whale. London, 1967. 1st ed. Signed presentation. Fine in dj (spine sl rubbed). *Polyanthos.* $50/£31

VAN DER POST, LAURENS. A Portrait of All the Russias. London, 1967. 1st ed. VG in dj (sl torn). *Typographeum.* $35/£22

VAN DER POST, LAURENS. Venture to the Interior. Hogarth, 1952. 1st ed. Signed presentation. Lt blue cl. (Sl faded), else NF. *Any Amount.* $35/£22

VAN DER STRAETEN, E. The Romance of the Fiddle. Rebman, 1911. 1st ed. 37 plts. Teg. (Eps sl browned; cl sl worn, soiled.) *Hollett.* $56/£35

VAN DERSAL, WILLIAM R. Ornamental American Shrubs. NY: OUP, 1942. 1st ed. (Foxed, pencil notes), else VG. *Fair Meadow.* $30/£19

VAN DIEREN, BERNARD. Down Among the Dead Men. OUP, 1935. 1st ed. (Spine sl faded.) *Hollett.* $48/£30

VAN DINE, S. S. The Bishop Murder Case. NY: Scribner, 1929. 1st ed. VG in dj (lacks spine pieces, extrems chipped, spine browned, sl leaning). *Pacific*.* $29/£18

VAN DINE, S. S. The Greene Murder Case. NY: Scribner, 1928. 1st ed. VG in dj (spine ends, extrems heavily chipped, sm tears extrems). *Pacific*.* $58/£36

VAN DINE, S. S. The Greene Murder Case. NY: Scribner, 1928. 1st ed. Woodcut frontis. Untrimmed. Black cl. (Fr cvr lt spotted, sl edgeworn.) Text Good in dj (sl worn, chipped, sm tears some folds). *Baltimore*.* $75/£47

VAN DINE, S. S. The Kennel Murder Case. NY: Scribner, 1933. 1st ed. VG in dj (spine head, corners chipped, foot rubbed, spine sl leaning). *Pacific*.* $75/£47

VAN DINE, S. S. The Scarab Murder Case. London/Toronto/Melbourne/Sydney: Cassell, 1930. 1st ed. Lg fldg plan. Dull purple rexine. (Prelims, last 2 leaves sl foxed; spine ends nicked), o/w Nice. *Temple.* $30/£19

VAN DINE, S. S. The Scarab Murder Case. NY: Scribner, 1930. 1st ed. (Spine leaning), else VG in dj (spine ends chipped, sm tear to foot). *Pacific*.* $69/£43

VAN DOREN, CARL. (ed). The Borzoi Reader. NY: Knopf, 1936. 1st ed. Red dec cl, gilt. VG (fep creased; lt bumped, cvr edges dknd) in dj (spine dknd, rear cvr soiled). *Blue Mountain.* $50/£31

VAN DORSTEN, J. A. Thomas Basson 1555-1613 English Printer at Leiden. Univ of Leiden, 1961. 1st ed. 5 plts. Dj. *Forest.* $35/£22

VAN DRUTEN, JOHN. The Druid Circle. NY: Dramatists Play Service, (1948). 1st ed. VF in dj (sm faint spot), o/w VF. *Between The Covers.* $150/£94

VAN DRUTEN, JOHN. I've Got Sixpence. NY: Dramatists Play Service, (1953). 1st ed. VF in VF dj (sl shortened). *Between The Covers.* $125/£78

VAN DRUTEN, JOHN. The Mermaids Singing. NY: Dramatists Play Service, (1946). 1st ed. VF in VF dj. *Between The Covers.* $150/£94

VAN DUYN, MONA. A Time of Bees. Chapel Hill: Univ of NC, 1964. 1st trade ed. Inscribed. VG (crayon price) in dj (price-clipped). *Hermitage.* $75/£47

VAN DYKE, HENRY. The First Christmas Tree. NY: Scribner, 1897. 1st ed. 8vo. (12),76pp; 4 photogravure plts by Howard Pyle. Teg. Gilt-pict grn cl. NF (cvrs sl faded). *House.* $120/£75

VAN DYKE, HENRY. The Travel Diary of an Angler. NY: Derrydale, 1929. 1st ed. One of 750. Signed by R. L. Boyer (illus). Photogravure frontis. Cl-backed bds, paper cvr label. (Sl soil), else NF. *Pacific*.* $127/£79

VAN DYKE, HENRY. The Travel Diary of an Angler. NY: Derrydale, 1929. One of 750. Frontis orig etching signed by Ralph Boyer. Blue cl backed over lt blue paper-cvrd bds. Fine. *Biscotti.* $150/£94

VAN DYKE, HENRY. The Works of Henry Van Dyke. NY: Scribner, 1920-1927. Avalon ed. One of 504 numbered, vol 1 frontis signed by Van Dyke, limitation pg signed by pub. 18 vols. Gravure frontis each vol. Red linen, paper spine labels, tan bds. Good. *Karmiole.* $300/£188

VAN DYKE, JOHN C. The Desert. NY: Scribner, 1901. 1st ed. Frontis. Brn cl, gilt. Fine. *Pacific*.* $98/£61

VAN DYKE, JOHN C. The Desert: Further Studies in Natural Appearances. NY: Scribner, 1918. 1st illus ed. Teg. Brn cl, gilt. Fine. *Harrington.* $75/£47

VAN DYKE, JOHN C. Rembrandt and His School. NY, 1923. (Sl rubbed.) *Washton.* $50/£31

VAN DYKE, JOHN. The Autobiography. Peter Wild (ed). Salt Lake City: Univ of UT, (1993). 1st ed. Fine in Fine dj. *Book Market.* $35/£22

VAN DYKE, THEODORE S. Millionaires of a Day. NY: Fords, Howard, Hulbert, 1890. 1st ed. (iv),208pp + 12pp pub's cat. (Inner hinges weak, pencil mks; lt worn, soiled.) *Dawson.* $100/£63

VAN DYNE, EDITH. (Pseud of L. Frank Baum.) Aunt Jane's Nieces and Uncle John. Chicago: Reilly & Britton, (1911). 1st ed, 1st state. Frontis by E. A. Nelson. Dec cl, oval pict cvr label. (Sm glue repair to edge of rear cvr), else VG. *Pacific**. $40/£25

VAN DYNE, EDITH. (Pseud of L. Frank Baum.) Aunt Jane's Nieces and Uncle John. Chicago: Reilly & Britton, (1911). 1st ed, 1st state w/ads on 1/2-title verso listing 6 titles in this series, as well as The Daring Twins & Annabel. Frontis by E. A. Nelson. Dec cl, oval pict cvr label. (Bkpl; sl soiled), else NF. *Pacific**. $138/£86

VAN DYNE, EDITH. (Pseud of L. Frank Baum.) Aunt Jane's Nieces at Work. Chicago: Reilly & Britton, (1909). 1st ed, 1st state w/author's credits on tp listing all 3 previous titles. Frontis by E. A. Nelson. Dec cl, oval pict cvr label. (Bkpl; spine leaned), o/w NF. *Pacific**. $46/£29

VAN DYNE, EDITH. (Pseud of L. Frank Baum.) Aunt Jane's Nieces in Society. Chicago: Reilly & Britton, (1910). 1st ed, 1st state w/ads on 1/2-title verso listing only 5 titles in this series & 'Annabel'; pub's announcement at end for The Girl Graduate, 14th ed. Frontis by E. A. Nelson. Dec cl, oval pict cvr label. VG. *Pacific**. $115/£72

VAN DYNE, EDITH. (Pseud of L. Frank Baum.) Aunt Jane's Nieces in the Red Cross. Chicago: Reilly & Britton, (1915). 1st ed, 1st state w/single c. notice. Frontis by Norman P. Hall. Dec cl, oval pict cvr label. (Inscrip dated 1915; sl spotted, label lt scratched), else VG. *Pacific**. $81/£51

VAN DYNE, EDITH. (Pseud of L. Frank Baum.) Aunt Jane's Nieces in the Red Cross. Chicago: Reilly & Britton, (1915). 1st ed, 1st state w/ single c. notice. Frontis by Norman P. Hall. Dec cl, oval pict cvr label. NF (old inscrip dated 1916, bkpl). *Pacific**. $109/£68

VAN DYNE, EDITH. (Pseud of L. Frank Baum.) Aunt Jane's Nieces in the Red Cross. Chicago: Reilly & Britton, (1918). 2nd ed. Frontis. Tan cl stamped in purple/blue-grn w/pict vignette. Schiller bkpl laid in. Good (ink name, sl soiled). *Reese*. $55/£34

VAN DYNE, EDITH. (Pseud of L. Frank Baum.) Aunt Jane's Nieces in the Red Cross. Chicago: Reilly & Britton, (1918). 2nd ed. Frontis by Norman P. Hall. Dec cl, oval pict cvr label. (Bkpl), else NF. *Pacific**. $138/£86

VAN DYNE, EDITH. (Pseud of L. Frank Baum.) Aunt Jane's Nieces on the Ranch. Chicago: Reilly & Britton, (1913). 1st ed, 1st ptg, w/ads on 1/2-title verso listing 8 titles through this one. Frontis by E. A. Nelson. Dec cl, oval pict cvr label. VG. *Pacific**. $69/£43

VAN DYNE, EDITH. (Pseud of L. Frank Baum.) Aunt Jane's Nieces on Vacation. Chicago: Reilly & Britton, (1912). 1st ed, 1st state w/ad on 1/2-title verso listing 7 titles. 7.5x5. Frontis by Emile Nelson, 305,(1)pp + (8)ad ll. Tan cl, pict cvr label. (Foxed), else VG in dj (soiled). *Pacific**. $104/£65

VAN DYNE, EDITH. (Pseud of L. Frank Baum.) Aunt Jane's Nieces Out West. Chicago: Reilly & Britton, (1914). 1st ed w/Series List of 9 titles, through Aunt Jane's Nieces Out West, to 1/2-title verso. Frontis by James McCracken. Dec cl, oval pict cvr label. NF. *Pacific**. $86/£54

VAN DYNE, EDITH. (Pseud of L. Frank Baum.) Mary Louise Adopts a Soldier. Chicago: Reilly & Lee, (1919). 1st ed. Frontis. Blue cl stamped in black. Schiller bkpl laid in. VG (few sm rubs, smudges). *Reese*. $125/£78

VAN DYNE, EDITH. (Pseud of L. Frank Baum.) Mary Louise. Chicago: Reilly & Britton, (1916). 1st ed, 1st state. Frontis by J. Allen St. John, 267pp. Blue cl. Primary binding w/the title stamped in white, outlined in blue w/dbl rule blindstamped at bottom of fr cvr & spine. (Tp lt foxed, rear hinge starting; spine foot sl rubbed), else VG. *Pacific**. $150/£94

VAN GOGH, VINCENT. The Complete Letters of Vincent Van Gogh with Reproductions of All the Drawings in the Correspondence. Greenwich: NYGS, (1959). 2nd ed. 3 vols. NF set (spines lt sunned) in orig ptd slipcase. *Captain's Bookshelf*. $175/£109

VAN GOGH, VINCENT. Letters to an Artist. Rela van Messel (trans). NY: Viking, 1936. One of 650. Cl w/Japanese wood veneer paper. NF in slipcase. *Turtle Island*. $55/£34

VAN GOGH, VINCENT. Letters to Emile Bernard. Douglas Lord (ed). NY: MOMA, 1937. Frontis, 32 plts. (Label faded), else VG. *Turtle Island*. $75/£47

VAN GREENAWAY, PETER. The Medusa Touch. Stein & Day, 1973. 1st ed. NF in dj (lt rubbed, edges sl worn). *Murder*. $40/£25

VAN GULIK, R. H. The Gibbon in China—An Essay in Chinese Animal Lore. Leiden, Holland: E.J. Brill, 1967. Folio. Complete w/the 45 r.p.m. record rear pocket. Blue bds, gilt. Fine. *Williams*. $160/£100

VAN GULIK, ROBERT. The Chinese Maze Murders. The Hague, 1956. 1st ed. Pict eps. Dj (white portions sl discolored; spine head, tips sl worn), wrap-around band ptg Agatha Christie's endorsement. *Swann**. $345/£216

VAN GULIK, ROBERT. The Given Day: An Amsterdam Mystery. (San Antonio: Dennis McMillan), 1984. One of 300. Signed by Janwillem Van de Wetering (postscript). Fine in dj. *Pacific**. $150/£94

VAN GULIK, ROBERT. The Monkey and the Tiger. London: Heinemann, 1965. 1st Eng ed. Fine in dj (price-clipped). *Mordida*. $125/£78

VAN GULIK, ROBERT. Necklace and Calabash: A Chinese Detective Story. NY: Scribner, 1967. 1st US ed. Fine in NF dj (price-clipped, few closed tears). *Janus*. $35/£22

VAN GULIK, ROBERT. The Phantom of the Temple. NY: Scribner, 1966. 1st US ed. Fine in Fine dj. *Unger*. $100/£63

VAN GUNDY, JOHN C. Reminiscences of Frontier Life on the Upper Neosho in 1855 and 1856. Topeka: College Press, 1925. Port, 1 plt. NF in orig stiff wraps. Howes V33. *Brown*. $75/£47

VAN HENGEL, STEVEN J. H. Early Golf. N.p., (1982). 1st ed. Fine in dj. *Pacific**. $75/£47

VAN KEMPEN, N. G. The History and Topography of Holland and Belgium. London: Geo. Virtue, (1837). 1st ed. Fldg map, 62 Fine steel engrs by W. H. Bartlett. Aeg. Contemp gilt-stamped red morocco, richly gilt paneled spine, raised bands. Fine. *Appelfeld*. $350/£219

VAN LAREN, A. J. Cactus. L.A., 1935. One of 1500. 134 color plts tipped-in. Dec brn buckram. (Inner hinges starting), else Fine. *Brooks*. $115/£72

VAN LAREN, A. J. Succulents Other than Cacti. L.A., 1934. Abbey San Encino ed. One of 1000. Signed by John Thomas Howell. 145 color plts tipped-in. (Rear cvr sl soiled), else NF. *Brooks*. $125/£78

VAN LOON, HENDRIK. History with a Match. NY: David MacKay, 1917. 1st ed. 7.75x10. 126pp. Good. *Cattermole*. $75/£47

VAN MARLE, RAIMOND and CHARLOTTE. The Development of the Italian Schools of Painting. NY: Hacker, 1970. 19 vols. *Christie's**. $442/£276

VAN NOSTRAND, JEANNE. A Pictorial and Narrative History of Monterey, Adobe Capital of California, 1770-1847. SF: CA Hist Soc, 1968. 1st ed. 40 plts. Pict eps. Fine in Fine dj (spine sl dknd). *Harrington*. $100/£63

VAN NOSTRAND, JEANNE. A Pictorial and Narrative History of Monterey, Adobe Capital of California, 1770-1847. SF: CA Hist Soc, 1968. 1st ed. 40 plts. Fine in dj. *Argonaut*. $125/£78

VAN NOSTRAND, JEANNE. San Francisco, 1806-1906 in Contemporary Paintings, Drawings and Watercolors. SF: Book Club of CA, 1975. Ltd to 500 ptd. 54 plts. Prospectus, omission slip laid in. Tan linen, gilt. *Pacific**. $98/£61

VAN PATTEN, NATHAN. Catalogue of the Memorial Library of Music Stanford University. Stanford: Stanford Univ, 1950. 1st ed. Extra illus tp. Red cl, gilt. Good. *Karmiole*. $65/£41

VAN RAVENSWAAY, CHARLES. Drawn from Nature. Washington: Smithsonian, 1984. 95 full-pg color plts. As New. *Quest*. $70/£44

VAN RAVENSWAAY, CHARLES. Drawn from Nature: The Botanical Art of Joseph Prestele and His Sons. Washington: Smithsonian, 1984. 1st ed. Fine in wraps. *Archer*. $30/£19

VAN STOCKUM, HILDA. The Borrowed House. FSG, 1975. 1st ed. 215pp. NF in NF dj. *Price*. $32/£20

VAN SWIETEN, GERARD. The Commentaries Upon the Aphorisms of Dr. Herman Boerhaave. London. (1757 to 1765). 1st ed. Includes vols. VI-X, XII, and XIV. Contemp calf. *Doctor's Library*. $400/£250

VAN TRAMP, JOHN C. Prairie and Rocky Mountain Adventures or Life in the Far West. Columbus, OH: Gilmore & Brush, (1858). 626,(6)pp. Marbled eps, edges. Orig full emb leather, gilt. (Sl shelfworn, fr joint cracked), else VG +. Howes V43. *Pacific**. $75/£47

VAN URK, JOHN BLAN. The Story of American Foxhunting. NY: Derrydale, (1940-41). One of 950 sets. 2 vols. Uncut, teg. Red burlap, gilt-lettered labels. (Sl worn, spines sl sunned.) *Oinonen**. $225/£141

VAN URK, JOHN BLAN. The Story of American Foxhunting. NY: Derrydale, (1941). One of 950 sets. Inscribed, signed. 2 vols. Folio. (Spines faded.) *Swann**. $201/£126

VAN VECHTEN, CARL. Parties. Scenes from Contemporary New York Life. NY: Knopf, 1930. 1st ed. (Spine cocked), o/w Fine in dj (spine faded, extrems lt worn, few internal mends). *Jaffe*. $125/£78

VAN VECHTEN, CARL. The Tattooed Countess. NY: Knopf, 1924. 1st ed, trade issue. (Pencil erased fep), o/w Nice in pict dj (lt used, spine sl chipped, sm nicks). *Reese*. $100/£63

VAN VOGT, A. E. The Book of Ptath. Reading, PA: Fantasy, 1947. 1st trade ed. (Cvrs sl dknd), else Good in dj (rubbed, edges chipped). *King*. $65/£41

VAN VOGT, A. E. The House That Stood Still. (NY): Greenberg, (1950). 1st ed. VG in dj (spine ends, extrems sl chipped, rubbed). *Pacific**. $29/£18

VAN VOGT, A. E. The Mind Cage. NY: S&S, 1957. 1st ed. (Pp sl browned), else Fine in dj. *Pacific**. $23/£14

VAN VOGT, A. E. The Mixed Men. NY: Gnome, (1952). 1st ed. Blue cl. VG in dj (spine ends rubbed, sm tear fr panel). *Pacific**. $40/£25

VAN VOGT, A. E. and E. MAYNE HULL. Out of the Unknown. L.A.: Fantasy, (1948). 1st ed. (Offset from binder's glue to eps), else VG in dj (spine ends chipped, extrems rubbed, crease fr panel). *Pacific**. $46/£29

VAN VOGT, A. E. and E. MAYNE HULL. Out of the Unknown. L.A.: Fantasy Pub, (1948). 1st ed. (Ink name; sl worn), else Good in dj (used w/edges torn, extrems frayed). *King*. $65/£41

VAN VOGT, A. E. Slan. Sauk City: Arkham House, 1946. 1st ed, 1st bk. One of 4000. VG in dj (spine ends chipped, rear joint rubbed). *Pacific**. $127/£79

VAN VOGT, A. E. The Voyage of the Space Beagle. NY: S&S, 1950. 1st ed. Advance copy w/label tipped-in to fep. VG in dj (spine head, extrems chipped). *Pacific**. $69/£43

VAN VOGT, A. E. The Weapon Makers. Providence, (1943). 1st ed. Frontis. Fine in dj. *Swann**. $287/£179

VAN VOGT, A. E. The Weapon Makers. NY: Greenberg, (1952). VG in dj. *Pacific**. $29/£18

VAN VOGT, A. E. The Weapon Makers. Weidenfeld, 1954. 1st UK ed. Fine (ink name) in VG dj (edges sl worn). *Williams*. $40/£25

VAN VOGT, A. E. The Weapon Shops of Isher. Weidenfeld, 1952. 1st UK ed. VG + (ink name) in dj (sm closed tear). *Williams*. $56/£35

VAN VOGT, A. E. The World of A. NY: S&S, 1948. 1st ed. VG in dj (spine ends, extrems rubbed). *Pacific**. $81/£51

VAN VOLLENHOVEN, HANNA. The Night Before Christmas: A Spoken Song or Recitation. Boston: Boston Music, 1923. 4to. Grace Drayton (illus). 14pp. Good in full color paper wrappers. *Reisler*. $165/£103

VAN WINKLE, WILLIAM MITCHELL. Henry William Herbert (Frank Forester): a Bibliography of His Writings 1832-1858. Portland: Southworth-Anthoensen, 1936. One of 250 ptd. 2 copies of prospectus laid in. Uncut, unopened. (Lt worn.) *Oinonen**. $120/£75

VAN WINKLE, WILLIAM MITCHELL. Henry William Herbert (Frank Forester): a Bibliography of His Writings 1832-1858. Portland, ME: Southworth-Anthoenson, 1936. 1st ed. Ltd to 300. Uncut. 1/4 black cl, grn buckram-cvrd bds (gilt faded). Fine. *Biscotti*. $165/£103

VAN WYCK, WILLIAM. Robinson Jeffers. L.A.: Ward Ritchie, 1938. One of 250 ptd. VG + in dj (chipped). *Smith*. $60/£38

VAN, MELVIN. The Big Heart. SF, (1957). 1st ed. Ruth Bernhard (photos). (Extrems sl worn.) Dj (rubbed, sl soiled). *Swann**. $103/£64

VANBRUGH, JOHN. The Complete Works of Sir John Vanbrugh.... Bonamy Dobree and Geoffrey Webb (eds). Bloomsbury: Nonesuch, 1927. One of 1300 numbered sets (of 1410). 4 vols. Paper spine labels. VG set (eps lt foxed; few mks to bds, spines uniformly sunned). *Reese*. $175/£109

VANCE, JACK. To Live Forever. NY: Ballantine, (1956). 1st ed. (Top edge soiled), else NF in dj (traces of staining from old dj protector, esp to rear panel). *Other Worlds*. $500/£313

VANCE, JACK. Vandals of the Void. Phila: John C. Winston, (1953). 1st ed. NF in dj (sm tear upper fr panel). *Pacific**. $127/£79

VANCOUVER, GEORGE. A Voyage of Discovery to the North Pacific Ocean, and Round the World. John Stockdale, 1801. New ed. 6 vols. 8vo. 1 (of 2) fldg engr maps (laid down, repaired), 17 fldg engr plts (spotted). Later tree calf, gilt. (Sl marginal dampstaining vol 1.) *Sotheby's**. $1,288/£805

VANDENHOFF, GEORGE. Leaves from an Actor's Note-book. NY: D. Appleton, 1860. 1st ed. Blind-stamped cl (extrems rubbed, spine ends frayed; bkpls, highlighting marginalia throughout). *Dramatis*. $50/£31

VANDERBILT, CORNELIUS, JR. Ranches and Ranch Life in America. NY, 1969. Good in dj (sl worn). *Dumont*. $30/£19

VANDERBILT, WILLIAM K. Taking One's Own Ship Around the World. NY, 1929. One of 200 numbered, specially bound; this copy out-of-series. 1/4 morocco (soiled, backstrip partly dknd). *Swann**. $115/£72

VANDERBILT, WILLIAM K. West Made East, with the Loss of a Day. NY: Privately ptd, 1933. 1st ed. One of 200 ptd. Teg. 1/2 morocco, gilt-dec bds. (Rear cvr discolored), else VG. *Pacific**. $196/£123

VANDERCOOK, JOHN W. King Cane. NY/London: Harper & Row, 1939. 1st ed. Cl spine. VG in dj (tattered). *Worldwide*. $35/£22

VANDERPOEL, EMILY NOYES. American Lace and Lace-Makers. New Haven, 1924. Sm folio. 111 plts (incl color frontis). Pict cl (extrems rubbed, sl foxed). *Swann**. $69/£43

VANDIVER, FRANK. Mighty Stonewall. NY: McGraw-Hill, (1957). 1st ed. Brn bds, red cl back. (Sig; top edge lt spotted), else Fine in VG dj. *Chapel Hill*. $75/£47

VANDIVER, FRANK. Rebel Brass. Baton Rouge: LA State Univ, (1956). 1st ed. One of unspecified # signed. Red bds. NF in dj (lt faded, chipped). *Chapel Hill.* $60/£38

VANNORSDALL, HARRY H. Trees of Ohio. Wilmington, OH, 1958. Fine. *Brooks.* $39/£24

VANSITTART, PETER. The Death of Robin Hood. Peter Owen, 1981. 1st UK ed. VG + in dj. *Williams.* $29/£18

VAQUEZ, HENRI. Diseases of the Heart. Phila, 1924. American ed. (Extrems sl worn), o/w Good. *Doctor's Library.* $60/£38

VARDON, HARRY et al. Success at Golf. Boston: Little, Brown, 1914. 2nd Amer ed. Frontis. Grn cl, gilt. (Sl red offset to fr cvr), else VG. *Pacific*.* $161/£101

VARDON, HARRY. The Complete Golfer. NY: McClure, Philips, 1908. 10th Amer ed, 1st bk. Frontisport. Grn cl, gilt. VG (emb stamp). *Pacific*.* $75/£47

VARDON, HARRY. The Gist of Golf. NY: George H. Doran, (1922). 1st Amer ed. (Spine ends sl rubbed), else NF. *Pacific*.* $69/£43

VARDON, HARRY. How to Play Golf. NY: George W. Jacobs, (1912). 1st Amer ed. Grn cl. NF (emb stamp, sig). *Pacific*.* $98/£61

VARDON, HARRY. My Golfing Life. London: Hutchinson, (1933). 1st ed. Dk grn cl, gilt. (Emb stamp; spine head torn), else VG in Good dj (very chipped, spine ends, lower extrems lack pieces). *Pacific*.* $345/£216

VARENDONCK, J. The Evolution of the Conscious Faculties. London: Allen & Unwin, 1923. 1st ed. VG (joints frayed, spine ends worn). *Beasley.* $45/£28

VARENDONCK, J. The Psychology of Daydreams. London: Allen & Unwin, 1921. 1st ed. VG (bkpl; joints frayed, spine ends worn, sm sticker fr bd). *Beasley.* $65/£41

VARGAS LLOSA, MARIO. Captain Pantoja and the Special Service. London: Jonathan Cape, 1978. 1st British ed. NF in dj. *Lame Duck.* $50/£31

VARGAS LLOSA, MARIO. Conversation in the Cathedral. NY: Harper & Row, 1975. 1st ed. Fine in dj. *Lame Duck.* $175/£109

VARGAS LLOSA, MARIO. The Cubs and Other Stories. NY: Harper & Row, 1979. 1st US ed. Fine in dj. *Lame Duck.* $75/£47

VARGAS LLOSA, MARIO. The Cubs. NY: Harper & Row, 1979. 1st US ed. Fine in Fine dj. *Pettler.* $30/£19

VARGAS LLOSA, MARIO. The Green House. NY, 1968. 1st Amer ed. Fine (spine rubbed) in dj (few sm chips). *Polyanthos.* $25/£16

VARGAS LLOSA, MARIO. The Green House. London: Jonathan Cape, 1969. 1st British ed. NF in dj (edges lt worn). *Lame Duck.* $100/£63

VARGAS LLOSA, MARIO. The Real Life of Alejandro Mayta. NY: FSG, 1986. 1st US ed. Fine in dj (fr cvr lower forecorner bump). *Lame Duck.* $25/£16

VARGAS LLOSA, MARIO. The Real Life of Alejandro Mayta. London: Faber & Faber, 1986. 1st British ed. Fine in NF dj. *Lame Duck.* $35/£22

VARGAS LLOSA, MARIO. The Real Life of Alejandro Mayta. Faber, 1986. 1st UK ed. NF (pp sl browned) in dj. *Williams.* $45/£28

VARGAS LLOSA, MARIO. The Time of the Hero. NY, 1966. 1st Amer ed. Fine in Fine dj. *Polyanthos.* $50/£31

VARGAS LLOSA, MARIO. The Time of the Hero. NY: Grove, 1966. 1st US ed. (Cl, edges sl soiled), else VG + in dj. *Lame Duck.* $85/£53

VARGAS LLOSA, MARIO. The Time of the Hero. L. Kemp (trans). London, 1967. VG in dj (dknd). *Typographeum.* $42/£26

VARGAS LLOSA, MARIO. The War of the End of the World. NY, (1984). 1st ed in English. One of 250 numbered, signed. Slipcase. *Swann*.* $80/£50

VARLEY, JOHN. Blue Champagne. Arlington Heights: Dark Harvest, 1986. One of 300 numbered, signed by Varley and Todd Cameron Hamilton (illus). (Sl worn.) Dj, slipcase. *Oinonen*.* $30/£19

VARLEY, JOHN. Blue Champagne. Niles: Dark Harvest, 1986. 1st ed. One of 300. Signed by Varley and Todd Cameron Hamilton (illus). Fine in dj, slipcase. *Pacific*.* $52/£33

VARLEY, JOHN. The Persistence of Vision. NY: Dial, (1978). 1st ed. Fine in dj (spine foot sl bumped). *Levin.* $95/£59

VARLO, CHARLES. A New System of Husbandry. Phila: The Author, 1785. 1st Amer ed. 2 vols. Fldg table. Full contemp calf, leather labels. (Vol 2 has duplicate sig; worn, scuffed; text lt spotted), o/w VG set. Howes V54. *Brown.* $250/£156

VARNUM, CHARLES. I, Varnum. Glendale: A.H. Clark, 1982. 1st ed. One of 350. Buckram, gilt. *Dawson.* $100/£63

VASARI, GIORGIO. Lives of the Most Eminent Painters. Verona: LEC, 1966. One of 1500. Signed by Giovanni Mardersteig (designer). 2 vols. Brn buckram. Fine in djs, marbled slipcase. *Pacific*.* $115/£72

VASARI, GIORGIO. Lives of the Most Eminent Painters. LEC, 1966. Ltd to 1500 numbered, signed by Giovanni Mardersteig (designer). 2 vols. Fine in slipcase. *Swann*.* $316/£198

VASARI, GIORGIO. Lives of the Most Eminent Painters. Marilyn Aaronberg Lavin (ed). NY: Heritage, 1967. 2 vols. 19 color plts; 13 color plts. Cl-backed patterned bds. VF set in slipcases. Salloch bkpl. *Europa.* $72/£45

VASSILEVA-POPOVA, JULIA G. (ed). Physical and Chemical Bases of Biological Information Transfer. NY: Plenum, (1975). 1st ed. Red cl. Fine in dj. *House.* $50/£31

VASSILIKOS, VASSILIS. Z. Macdonald, 1968. 1st UK ed. Fine in VG dj (edges sl worn). *Williams.* $29/£18

VASSOS, JOHN. Contempo: This American Tempo, Creations by.... NY: Dutton, 1929. 1st ed. Dk blue cl (sl rubbed). VG. *Houle.* $150/£94

Vathek. (By William Beckford.) London: W. Clarke, 1816. 3rd ed. Engr frontis (browned), (iv),234pp (sl spotted). Contemp red 1/2-morocco, marbled sides. *Young.* $120/£75

VAUGHAN WILLIAMS, RALPH. National Music. OUP, 1934. 1st ed. (Spine, edges dknd.) *Hollett.* $40/£25

VAUGHAN WILLIAMS, RALPH. Some Thoughts on Beethoven's Choral Symphony. OUP, 1953. 1st ed. VG in dj. *Hollett.* $40/£25

VAUGHAN, ALEX J. Modern Bookbinding.... Leicester: Raithby, Lawrence, 1929. 1st ed. Good (marginal stamps). *Cox.* $32/£20

VAUGHAN, BILL. Half the Battle. NY: S&S, (1967). 1st ed. Signed. NF in NF dj. *Glenn.* $35/£22

VAUGHAN, T. W. Recent Madreporaria of the Hawaiian Islands and Laysan. Washington, 1907. 96 plts. Buckram, wraps bound in. (Lacks tp, sm lib stamp.) *Henly.* $38/£24

VAUGHAN, THOMAS. The Works of Thomas Vaughan: Eugenius Philalethes. Arthur Edward Waite (ed). London: Theosophical Soc of England, 1919. 1st ed. (Sm sliver gone from spine head), else NF in buckram, morocco spine label. *Captain's Bookshelf.* $150/£94

VAUGHAN, WILLIAM. The Catechism of Man. Phila: Mathew Carey, 1794. Amer ed. 34pp. Sewn as issued. (Tp soiled, spotted, red stain in most outer blank margins), else Good. *Brown.* $45/£28

VAUGHN, J. W. The Battle of Platte Bridge. Norman, 1963. 1st ed. Fine in dj (price-clipped). *Baade.* $50/£31

VAUGHN, J. W. Indian Fights. Norman: Univ of OK, (1966). 1st ed. Dj. *Dawson.* $45/£28

VAUGHN, J. W. The Reynolds Campaign on Powder River. Norman: Univ of OK, (1961). 1st ed. Brn cl. Fine in NF dj. *Harrington*. $70/£44

VAUGHN, J. W. With Crook at the Rosebud. Harrisburg: Stackpole, (1956). 1st ed. Dj (top edge lt worn). *Dawson*. $50/£31

VAVRA, ROBERT. Tiger Flower. NY: Reynal, 1968. 4to. Fleur Cowles (illus). VG in VG dj. *American Booksellers*. $35/£22

VAZQUEZ, PEDRO RAMIREZ. The National Museum of Anthropology, Mexico. NY: Abrams, (1968). Folio. Fine in illus dj (worn). *Metropolitan**. $86/£54

VEATCH, A. C. Evolution of the Congo Basin. Geological Soc, 1935. 1st ed. 10 color fldg maps, photo plts. Maroon cl, gilt. VG. *Larry Price*. $49/£31

VECSEY, GEORGE. One Sunset a Week. The Story of a Coal Miner. NY: Saturday Review Edition, 1974. 2nd ptg. NF in NF dj. *Beasley*. $25/£16

VEECK, BILL and ED LINN. The Hustler's Handbook. Putnam, 1965. 1st ed. VG + in VG dj (spine faded). *Plapinger*. $45/£28

VEECK, BILL and ED LINN. Veeck as in Wreck. Putnam, 1962. 1st ed. Signed by Veeck. VG + in Good + dj. *Plapinger*. $200/£125

VEITCH, HENRY NEWTON. Sheffield Plate. London: Bell, 1908. (Sl worn, lt foxed, cvrs sl spotted.) *Oinonen**. $40/£25

VEITCH, JAMES. Hortus Veitchii, a History of the Rise and Progress of the Nurseries of Messrs. James Veitch and Sons.... London: James Veitch & Sons, 1906. (Edges through, extrems sl worn, fading.) Contents Very Fine. *Metropolitan**. $299/£187

VEITCH, JAMES. Veitch's Manual of the Coniferae. London, 1900. 2nd ed. 30 plts. Pict gilt cl. Fine. *Henly*. $96/£60

VELIKOVSKY, IMMANUEL. Worlds in Collision. NY: Macmillan, 1950. 1st ed, 1st ptg, 1st bk. Dj (chipped). *M & S*. $75/£47

VELPEAU, A. A Treatise on the Diseases of the Breast and Mammary Region. London, 1856. 1st ed in English. 608pp. (Ex-lib; spine head torn.) Fine internally. *Fye*. $200/£125

Venetians. (By M. E. Braddon.) Simpkin, Marshall, Hamilton, et al, 1893. Stereotyped ed. Sprinkled edges. Later cl (hinges, corners sl rubbed). Good. *Tiger*. $32/£20

VENNER, TOBIAS. A Briefe and Accurate Treatise of Tobacco. SF: Book Club of CA, 1931. One of 200 ptd. Dec bds, brn morocco spine (sl discolored; bkpl). Slipcase. *Karmiole*. $200/£125

VENTURI, ADOLFO. North Italian Painting of the Quattrocento; Lombardy, Piedmont, Liguria. Florence/Paris: Pantheon/Pegasus, 1930. 80 plts hors-texte, guards. Teg. Orig red 1/2 leather, gilt. VF. *Europa*. $80/£50

VENTURI, LIONELLO. Marc Chagall. NY, (1945). 1st ed. One of 1500 numbered. 2 tipped-in color plts, 44 full-pg b/w plts. W/errata slip. (Extrems heavily rubbed.) *King*. $95/£59

VER BECK, FRANK. Little Black Sambo and the Tiger Kitten. Phila: Henry Altemus, (1926). 1st ed. 12mo. 64pp. Cl-backed pict bds, color paste label. Full color dj (lacks pieces along edges, picture intact). *Reisler*. $175/£109

VER BECK, FRANK. Little Black Sambo and the Tiger Kitten. NY: Platt & Munk, (1935). Pict color label. (Pp 5-8 damaged.) Dj (lg chip out of rear cvr). *King*. $125/£78

VERCEL, ROGER. Captain Conan. Warre Bradley Wells (trans). NY: Henry Holt, (1935). 1st US ed. Blue cl. VG in pict dj (lt nicked, sunned). *Reese*. $45/£28

VEREA, F. G. Guide for the American in the Phillipines.... F. C. Fisher (trans). Manila: Chofrey Comp., 1899. (12),289pp; complete w/7 fldg maps. Cl spine, ptd bds. (Text brittle; spine worn, bds rubbed, lettering dull), else Good. *Brown*. $100/£63

VERGER, PIERRE. Indians of Peru. Text by Luis E. Valcarcel. Lake Forest, IL: Pocahontas Press, 1950. 1st ed. 87 halftones. (Cl sl soiled), else VG. *Cahan*. $50/£31

VERHOEFF, MARY. The Kentucky River Navigation. Louisville: Filson Club, 1917. 3 fldg maps, 21 plts. Mod cl w/orig ptd fr wrap bound in. Nice. *Bohling*. $135/£84

VERKAUF, WILLY. Dada. London/NY: Academy/St. Martin's, (1975). NF in illus wrappers. *Turtle Island*. $55/£34

VERMES, GEZA (trans). Dead Sea Scrolls. LEC, 1966. Ltd to 1500 numbered, signed by Shagra Weil (illus). Fine in slipcase. *Swann**. $172/£108

VERNE, JULES. Among the Cannibals. Ward, Lock, n.d. (rpt c1890). Pub's illus cat. Pict cl. Good (sl spotted; spine bumped). *Tiger*. $24/£15

VERNE, JULES. Around in the World in Eighty Days. Sampson Low, Marston, Low, et al, 1873. Pub's cat dated October 1873. Aeg. Pict cl (rebacked w/orig backstrip relaid, corners badly rubbed; sl spotted, new eps). *Tiger*. $192/£120

VERNE, JULES. Around the World in Eighty Days. LEC, 1962. Ltd to 1500 numbered, signed by Edward A. Wilson (illus). Fine in slipcase. *Swann**. $69/£43

VERNE, JULES. Around the World in Eighty Days. L.A.: LEC, 1962. One of 1500 ptd. Signed by Edward A. Wilson (illus). 1/2 vellum, marbled bds, gilt spine label. Fine in glassine, slipcase. *Pacific**. $138/£86

VERNE, JULES. Around the World in Eighty Days. L.A.: LEC, 1963. One of 1500. Signed by Edward A. Wilson (illus). 1/2 vellum, marbled bds, gilt spine label. Fine in glassine, slipcase. *Pacific**. $98/£61

VERNE, JULES. The Baltimore Gun Club. Edward Roth (trans). Phila: King & Bard, (1874). 1st Amer ed. Frontis. Grn cl, gilt. Good (extrems rubbed, spine ends frayed, cl worn). *Pacific**. $138/£86

VERNE, JULES. The Cryptogram. Sampson Low, Marston, n.d. (rpt c1890). Pict cl. VG (spine bumped, rear cvr unevenly sunned). *Tiger*. $54/£34

VERNE, JULES. Dick Sands. Sampson Low, Marston, Searle, et al, 1882. Author's illus ed. Pict cl. Good (fore-edge lt spotted, new eps; spine bumped). *Tiger*. $48/£30

VERNE, JULES. From the Earth to the Moon and Around the Moon. LEC, 1970. Ltd to 1500 numbered, signed by Robert Shore (illus). 2 vols. Fine in slipcase. *Swann**. $34/£21

VERNE, JULES. In Search of the Castaways. Phila: Lippincott, (1873). 1st Amer ed. Blue dec cl. (Spine ends sl rubbed), else NF. *Pacific**. $207/£129

VERNE, JULES. A Journey to the Center of the Earth. LEC, 1966. Ltd to 1500 numbered, signed by Edward A. Wilson (illus). Fine in slipcase. *Swann**. $80/£50

VERNE, JULES. Meridiana: The Adventures of Three Englishmen and Three Russians in South Africa. NY: Scribner, Armstrong, 1874. 1st Amer ed, ptg B in red cl on lighter paper. (Soiled, spine dknd, ends frayed), else VG-. *Pacific**. $52/£33

VERNE, JULES. Michael Strogoff, the Courier of the Czar. Scribner, Armstrong, 1877. 1st Amer ed. VG- (cvrs lt worn). *Fine Books*. $250/£156

VERNE, JULES. Michael Strogoff. NY: Scribner, (1927). 1st ed. 4to. 9 full-pg color plts by N. C. Wyeth. Black cl, gilt, color paste label. Good in dj w/color paste label, ptd list of titles rear cvr. *Reisler*. $335/£209

VERNE, JULES. Mistress Branican. A. Estoclet (trans). NY: Cassell, (1891). 1st Amer ed. Pict grn cl. (Spine ends sl rubbed, spine head sl bumped, lower fr joint scuffed), else VG. *Pacific**. $126/£79

VERNE, JULES. The Mysterious Island. LEC, 1959. Ltd to 1500 numbered, signed by Edward A. Wilson (illus). Fine in slipcase. *Swann**. $57/£36

VERNE, JULES. The Mysterious Island. Balt: LEC, 1959. One of 1500 copies lettered 'F.D.F' from Garamond Press. Signed by Edward A. Wilson (illus). Pict cl. Fine in slipcase. *Pacific**. $75/£47

VERNE, JULES. Their Island Home. Sampson Low, Marston, (1923). 1st Eng ed. (Lacks fep, news clipping pasted to fr paste-down), else VG. *Fine Books*. $55/£34

VERNE, JULES. The Tour of the World in Eighty Days. George M. Towle (trans). Boston: James R. Osgood, 1873. 1st Amer trade ed. Brick-red cl, gilt. (Spine ends sl rubbed), else NF. *Pacific**. $431/£269

VERNE, JULES. Twenty Thousand Leagues Under the Sea. L.A.: LEC, 1956. One of 1500. Signed by Edward A. Wilson (illus). 1/2 grn morocco, pict bds, gilt-lettered spine label. Fine in slipcase. *Pacific**. $63/£39

VERNE, JULES. Twenty Thousand Leagues Under the Sea. LEC, 1956. Ltd to 1500 numbered, signed by Edward A. Wilson (illus). Fine in slipcase. *Swann**. $80/£50

VERNE, JULES. The Wreck of the Chancellor. Boston: James R. Osgood, 1875. 1st Amer ed. Brick-red cl, gilt. (Lower corner fep creased; spine ends sl frayed, extrems rubbed), else VG. *Pacific**. $46/£29

VERNE, JULES. The Wreck of the Chancellor. Boston: James R. Osgood, 1875. 1st Amer ed. Blue cl, gilt. (Sm tear fep top; spine ends, extrems rubbed, spine sl leaning), else VG. *Pacific**. $52/£33

VERNEY, JOHN. Friday's Tunnel. Collins, 1959. 1st ed. 8vo. 320pp. VG + in pict dj. *Bookmark*. $56/£35

VERNON, WILLIAM TECUMSEH. The Upbuilding of a Race, or The Rise of a Great People. Quindaro, KS: Industrial Students Printers, 1904. 1st ed. Signed, inscribed. Port. (Cl worn, soiled), else Good. *Brown*. $125/£78

VERRILL, A. E. Monograph of the Shallow-Water Starfishes of the North Pacific Coast. Washington, 1914. 2 vols. 110 plts. Text vol unopened. Slipcases (worn). *Sutton*. $295/£184

VERRILL, A. HYATT. The Bridge of Light. Reading: Fantasy Press, 1950. 1st ed. One of 300. Signed. Fine in NF dj. *Pacific**. $52/£33

VERTREES, H. Pearls and Pearling. NY: Fur New, c1913. 1st ed. Pict cl. Good (eps foxed; cvrs rubbed). *Blake*. $65/£41

VERY, JONES. Poems...with an Introductory Memoir. Boston: Houghton Mifflin, 1883. 2nd ed. 160pp. Brn cl w/floral decs. NF. *Lucas*. $100/£63

VERY, LYDIA. Poems. Andover: Draper, 1856. 1st ed, 1st bk. 222pp. Drab cl (sl dusted). VG. *Second Life*. $275/£172

VERY, LYDIA. Red Riding Hood. (Boston: Louis Prang & Co), 1863. 12mo. (8)pp. Full-color chromolitho cardbd wrappers. (Lt foxing inside rear wrapper), else VF. *Bromer*. $375/£234

VESALIUS, ANDREAS. The Epitome.... L. R. Lind (trans). NY: Macmillan, 1949. 1st complete ed in English. 25 plts. VG. *Glaser*. $95/£59

VESSEY, JOHN HENRY. Mr. Vessey of England. Being the Incidents and Reminiscences of Travel...Through the United States and Canada in the Year 1859. Brian Waters (ed). NY: Putnam, (1956). 1st ed. Fine in dj. *Mott*. $35/£22

VESTAL, STANLEY. Dobe Walls. Boston, 1929. 1st ed. (Soiled, corners lt worn.) Internally VG. *Baade*. $35/£22

VESTAL, STANLEY. Dodge City Queen of the Cowtowns. (London): Peter Nevill, (1955). 1st British ed. Blue bds. VG in color pict dj (sm scrape fr cvr, spine ends lt chipped). *House*. $30/£19

VESTAL, STANLEY. Fandango. NY: Houghton Mifflin, 1927. 1st ed, 1st bk. Fine in dj. *Labordo*. $125/£78

VESTAL, STANLEY. Fandango: Ballads of the Old West. Boston: Houghton Mifflin, 1927. 1st ed. (Inscrip; spine ends rubbed), else VG in dj (rubbed, price-clipped; spine, extrems faded). *Pacific**. $69/£43

VESTAL, STANLEY. Happy Hunting Grounds. Chicago: Lyons & Canrahan, 1928. 1st ed. Pict cl. VG + . *Labordo*. $100/£63

VESTAL, STANLEY. Kit Carson; The Happy Warrior of the Old West. Boston, 1928. Inscribed. NF in dj (clipped, lt worn). *Dumont*. $200/£125

VESTAL, STANLEY. The Missouri. NY: Farrar & Rinehart, 1945. 1st ed. NF in dj. *Labordo*. $75/£47

VESTAL, STANLEY. New Sources of Indian History. Norman, 1934. 1st ed. Internally Fine (sm emb name top 1st 3 ll; back-strip, edges faded, top sl frayed). *Baade*. $125/£78

VESTAL, STANLEY. Queen of the Cowtowns: Dodge City. NY, 1952. Good in dj. *Dumont*. $40/£25

VESTAL, STANLEY. Short Grass Country. Erskine Caldwell (ed). NY: Duell, Sloan & Pearce, 1941. 1st ed. VG + in dj (worn). *Labordo*. $75/£47

VESTAL, STANLEY. Wagons West. NY: American Pioneer Trails Assoc, 1946. 1st ed. Fine in wrappers. *Labordo*. $45/£28

VETROMILE, EUGENE. A Tour in Both Hemispheres; Or, Travels Around the World. NY: D&J Sadlier, 1880. 1st ed. Pebbled cl over beveled bds (spine ends sl rubbed, few sm lightened spots), gilt. *Sadlon*. $100/£63

VICAIRE, G. Bibliographie Gastronomique. London, 1954. 2nd ed. Errata. VG in dj (edges frayed). *King*. $95/£59

Vicar of Wakefield. A Tale. Supposed to Be Written By Himself. (By Oliver Goldsmith.) Glasgow: Ptd by J. & M. Robertson, 1790. 2 vols in 1. 143; 138pp (foxed). Old 1/2 calf (rebacked), gilt. *Young*. $120/£75

VICKERS, GEORGE E. Gettysburg. A Poem. Phila: Ptd by Thomas R. Davis, 1890. 1st ed. 36pp. VG in wraps (sl worn). *Brown*. $25/£16

VICTOR, FRANCES FULLER. The River of the West. Hartford/Toledo: R.W. Bliss, 1870. 1st ed. Steel-engr frontis port, 602pp. Brn coated eps. Orig pub's full sheep, 2 black leather spine labels. (Sl foxed, aged, eps dusty; sl worn, lt scuffed.) Howes V89. *Baltimore**. $100/£63

VICTOR, RALPH. Boy Scouts Patrol. NY: A.L. Chatterton, (1911). 1st ed. Pict cvr label. NF. *Pacific**. $46/£29

Victory Division in Europe: Story of the Fifth Armored Division. Gotha, Germany, 1945. Good in wraps (torn). *Clark*. $75/£47

VIDAL, GORE. 1876. NY: RH, (1976). One of 300 numbered, signed. Fine in slipcase. *Agvent*. $150/£94

VIDAL, GORE. The Best Man: A Play About Politics. Boston: LB, (1960). 1st ed. Fine in NF dj (foot sl rubbed). *Between The Covers*. $125/£78

VIDAL, GORE. Creation. NY: Random House, 1981. 1st Amer ed. One of 500 signed. Brn cl. Fine in pub's paper bd slipcase. *Cady*. $50/£31

VIDAL, GORE. Dark Green, Bright Red. John Lehmann, 1950. 1st ed. VG (spine sl mkd) in dj (nicked, sl torn, rubbed, creased, dusty, edges sl dknd). *Ulysses*. $152/£95

VIDAL, GORE. Empire. NY: Random House, (1987). 1st ed. One of 250. Signed. Burgundy cl, gilt. Fine in slipcase. *Pacific**. $40/£25

VIDAL, GORE. Homage to Daniel Shays. Collected Essays 1952-1972. NY, 1972. 1st Amer ed. Fine (sl rubbed) in dj (sm nick, price-clipped). *Polyanthos*. $30/£19

VIDAL, GORE. Julian. Boston: LB, (1964). 1st ed. Fine in Fine dj. *Between The Covers*. $250/£156

VIDAL, GORE. Kalki. London: Heinemann, 1978. 1st Eng ed. NF in dj. *Cady*. $15/£9

VIDAL, GORE. Reflections Upon a Sinking Ship. Boston: LB, (1968). 1st ed. VF in VF dj. *Between The Covers*. $200/£125

VIDAL, GORE. Rocking the Boat. Boston: LB, (1962). 1st ed. VF in VF dj (price-clipped, sl rubbed). *Between The Covers*. $200/£125

VIDAL, GORE. Romulus. NY: Grove, 1966. 1st Amer ed. Fine in dj (price-clipped). *Polyanthos.* $35/£22

VIDAL, GORE. Sex Is Politics. Hollywood: Sylvester & Orphanos, 1979. Ltd to 330 signed. Fine dec cl. *Truepenny.* $100/£63

VIDAL, GORE. A Thirsty Evil. NY, 1956. 1st Amer ed. VG in VG dj. *Polyanthos.* $30/£19

VIDAL, GORE. Two Sisters. Boston: LB, (1970). 1st ed. (Fep sl sticker shadow), else VF in VF dj (sl rubbed). *Between The Covers.* $150/£94

VIDAL, GORE. Visit to a Small Planet and Other Television Plays. Boston, 1956. 1st Amer ed. Fine (name, fep offset; sl rubbed) in dj (rubbed, few sm chips, sl soiled). *Polyanthos.* $30/£19

VIDAL, GORE. Visit to a Small Planet and Other Television Plays. Boston: Little Brown, 1956. 1st ed. VG in VG dj (clear tape repaired tears). *Pettler.* $40/£25

VIEBIG, CLARA. The Sleeping Army, a Story of Prussian and Pole. Gilbert Waterhouse (trans). London: Ernest Benn, 1929. 1st British ed. Grn cl stamped in orange. (Pencil note fep), o/w Fine in pict dj. *Reese.* $60/£38

VIELE, TERESA GRIFFIN. Following the Drum. NY, 1858. 1st ed. 256, (10 ads)pp. Ptd bds (worn, faded). Howes V92. *Dumont.* $275/£172

VIERECK, GEORGE SYLVESTER and PAUL ELDREDGE. The Invincible Adam. NY: Liveright, (1932). 1st ed. One of 100. Signed. NF in VG dj (spine ends chipped, head lacks sm pieces, long tears real panel, spine). *Pacific*.* $75/£47

View of the Valley of the Mississippi. (By Robert Baird.) Phila: H.S. Tanner, 1834. 2nd ed (so stated). 372pp; 15 Good engr maps, frontis map w/orig hand-coloring. Orig purple muslin, ptd paper spine label. (Fr hinge nearly split, sl browned, foxed, bottom margin 1 pg lacks sm piece, most maps browned; lib, white ink # on spine, perf stamp tp, 1 leaf; ink stamps, bkpl; spine sunned, chipped, rear cvr sl stained.) Text VG, cvrs Clean. Howes B45. *Baltimore*.* $240/£150

Views of American Slavery, Taken a Century Ago. Phila: Association of Friends for the Diffusion of Religious and Useful Knowledge, 1858. 138pp. (Sl shelf-worn), o/w VG. *Brown.* $40/£25

Views of Society and Manners in America; in a Series of Letters from That Country to a Friend in England. (By Fanny D'Arusmont.) NY, 1821. 1st Amer ed. xii,387pp (foxed, part of fep torn away). Contemp roan-backed bds (worn). *Oinonen*.* $60/£38

VILLA, SILVIO. The Unbidden Guest. NY: Macmillan, 1923. Later, probably 2nd, imp. Signed, inscribed 1926. Gilt red cl. Fine in pict dj. *Reese.* $30/£19

Village Annals, Containing Austerus and Humanus. Phila: Johnson & Warner, 1814. 12mo. Full-pg wood-engr frontis, 35pp; 7 full-pg cuts. Frontis, last pg pasted down on wrappers. Orig yellow stiff paper wrappers speckled w/gold. Fine (bkpl). *Hobbyhorse.* $200/£125

VILLARREAL, JOSE ANTONIO. Pocho. GC: Doubleday, 1959. 1st ed, 1st bk. Fine in Fine dj. *Agvent.* $75/£47

VILLASENOR, VICTOR. Rain of Gold. Houston: Arte Publico, 1991. 1st ed. NF in dj. *Smith.* $50/£31

VILLIERS, FREDERIC. Villiers, His Five Decades of Adventure. NY/London: Harper & Bros, (1920). 1st ed. 2 vols. NF in djs (few sm spine chips). *Sadlon.* $40/£25

VILLIERS, GEORGE. The Rehearsal: With a Key, or Critical View of the Authors...and Their Writings, Exposed in This Play. London: T. Waller, 1768. 17th ed, but 1st thus. 81pp + 3 ads. Calf-backed bds. Good. *Young.* $24/£15

VILLIMKOVA, M. and D. DARBOIS. Egyptian Jewellery. London: Hamlyn, 1969. VG. *Blake.* $50/£31

VILLON, FRANCOIS. The Ballads of.... SF: Windsor Press, 1927. Ltd to 200 numbered. Vellum. (Cvrs dknd, lacks tie.) *King.* $35/£22

VILLON, FRANCOIS. The Lyrical Poems of Francois Villon. LEC, 1979. One of 2000 signed by Stephen Harvard (calligrapher). Fine in slipcase. *Swann*.* $46/£29

VILLON, FRANCOIS. The Lyrics of Francois Villon. (NY): LEC, 1933. One of 1500 signed by Howard Simon (illus). 30 woodcuts. Teg, deckle-edged. Tan cl, spine label (sm piece out). VG (lt foxed, illus offset, sm stain contents pp) in brn cardbd slipcase (rubbed, chipped). *Blue Mountain.* $25/£16

VINCE, S. The Elements of Astronomy. Phila, 1811. 1st Amer ed. 242pp; fldg plt. Contemp tree calf. Very Nice. *M & S.* $85/£53

VINCENT, IRENE VONGEHR. The Sacred Oasis. Chicago: Univ of Chicago, (1953). Color frontis, fldg map. VG in dj. *Turtle Island.* $50/£31

VINE, FRED T. Cakes and How to Make Them. British Baker, n.d. (c.1914). 4th ed. Good in ptd linen. *Cox.* $29/£18

VINES, SHERARD (ed). Whips and Scorpions. London: Wishart, 1932. 1st ed. (Reps spotted, 2pp badly ptd.) Dj (sl browned, chipped). *Hollett.* $72/£45

VINGE, JOAN. The Snow Queen. NY: Dial, (1980). 1st ed. NF in NF dj. *Levin.* $125/£78

VIOLA, HERMAN J. Diplomats in Buckskin. Washington, 1981. 1st ed. (Inscrip, very sl waterstain top last few pp), else Fine in dj. *Baade.* $40/£25

VIOLA, JEROME. The Painting and Teaching of Philip Pearlstein. NY: Watson-Guptill, (1982). 83 color plts. NF in dj. *Turtle Island.* $100/£63

VIOSCA, PERCY. Pondfish Culture. New Orleans, 1937. Blue cl. (Edges chipped), else VG. *Larry Price.* $17/£11

VIRCHOW, RUDOLF. Disease, Life, and Man. Lelland J. Rather (trans). Stanford Univ, 1958. 1st ed thus. Good (ex-lib). *Glaser.* $35/£22

VIRGIL. The Aeneid. LEC, 1944. One of 1100 signed by Carlotta Petrina (illus). Fine in slipcase. *Swann*.* $34/£21

VIRGIL. The Eclogues. LEC, 1960. Ltd to 1500 numbered, signed by Marcel Vertes (illus). Fine in slipcase. *Swann*.* $57/£36

VIRGIL. The Eclogues. NY: LEC, 1960. One of 1500. Signed by Vertes (illus). Pict cl. Fine in glassine, slipcase. *Pacific*.* $69/£43

VIRGIL. The Georgics. William Sotheby (trans). London, 1800. 229pp. Marbled edges. Contemp full calf, gilt spine. *Argosy.* $200/£125

VIRGIL. The Georgics. NY, 1931. One of 1200. 20 engrs. Uncut. Fine (sl rubbed). *Polyanthos.* $60/£38

VIRGIL. The Georgics. LEC, 1952. Ltd to 1500 numbered, signed by Bruno Bramanti (illus) and Giovanni Mardersteig (designer). Fine in slipcase. *Swann*.* $40/£25

VIRGIL. The Georgics. Verona: LEC, 1952. One of 1500. Signed by Bruno Bramanti (illus) & Giovanni Mardersteig (ptr). 1/2 grn cl, patterned bds. Fine in slipcase. *Pacific*.* $75/£47

Virginia Highway Historical Markers: The Tourist Guide Book of Virginia Featuring the Inscriptions of the Official Markers Along the Historic and Romantic Highways.... Strasburg, VA: Shenandoah Pub House, 1931. Map. Orig ptd wrappers (spine head chip, sl edgeworn). *Sadlon.* $25/£16

Virginia Illustrated. (By David Hunter Strother.) NY: Harper, 1857. 1st ed. 300pp. (Spine worn.) Howes S1084. *M & S.* $175/£109

VISCHER, EDWARD. Edward Vischer's Drawings of the California Missions, 1861-1878. SF: Book Club of CA, 1982. One of 600 ptd. 44 color plts. Fine in dj. *Pacific*.* $40/£25

VISCHER, EDWARD. Missions of Upper California, 1872. SF: Winterburn, 1872. 1st ed. (7),4-44,viii,ivpp. Fine in white wrappers, laid in stiff tan wrappers (sl soiled, dknd). *Pacific*.* $86/£54

Visit to the Antipodes: with Some Reminiscences of a Sojourn in Australia. (By Edward Lloyd.) Smith, Elder, 1846. 1st ed. Litho frontisport. Pub's cl, gilt. *Sotheby's**. $202/£126

Visit to the Celestial City. (By Nathaniel Hawthorne.) Phila: American Sunday-School Union No. 146 Chestnut St, (1845?). (2nd ed.) 54pp + ads; 4 full-pg lithos inserted. (Numeral worn; soiled, heavily foxed.) *M & S*. $150/£94

VISSCHER, WILLIAM L. The Pony Express. Chicago, (1908). 1st ed. (Worn, sl dirty.) *Woolson*. $30/£19

VISSCHER, WILLIAM L. The Pony Express. Chicago: Charles T. Powner, 1946. VG in dj (worn). *Lien*. $18/£11

VISSCHER, WILLIAM L. A Thrilling and Truthful History of the Pony Express.... Chicago, (1908). 1st ed. Pict cl. (Blindstamp; cvr heavily soiled), else Good. *King*. $40/£25

VITKOVICK, VICTOR. A Tour of Soviet Uzbekistan. Moscow: Foreign Languages Pub House, 1954. Fldg map. (Sl rubbed, spine ends rubbed, frayed), o/w VG. *Worldwide*. $25/£16

VIVIAN, A. P. G. The Phantom Brigade; or The Contemptible Adventurers. London: Ernest Benn, (1930). 1st ed, 2nd imp. Red cl, gilt. VG in pict dj (sl foxed, nicked). *Reese*. $30/£19

VIVIAN, A. PENDARVIS. Wanderings in the Western Land. London: Sampson Low et al, 1879. 1st ed. Frontis (detached), xvi,426,blank pp + 32pp ads; 2 fldg maps, 8 full-pg wood engrs. Pict terracotta cl, gilt. Good + (rubberstamp, bkpl, old mks; spine rubbed, ends frayed, trace of old spine #, vertical crease fr cvr). *Pacific**. $58/£36

VIVIAN, H. HUSSEY. Notes of a Tour in America. From August 7th to November 17th, 1877. London: Edward Stanford, 1878. 1st ed. Fldg frontis map, 6 prelim ll, 260pp (sl browned at edges). Pict grn cl, gilt. *Mott*. $125/£78

VIZETELLY, HENRY (ed). Paris in Peril. London: Tinsley Bros, 1882. 1st ed. 2 vols. vi,267; vi,263pp; 16 full-pg b/w plts. Blue-grn cl, gilt. (Lt aged, lg bkpls; sl rubbed.) Text VG. *Baltimore**. $80/£50

VOGLIOTTI, GABRIEL R. The Girls of Nevada. NJ: Citadel, (1975). Fine in Fine dj. *Book Market*. $25/£16

VOGT, CHRISTIAN. In Camera: Eighty-Two Images by Fifty-Two Women. Geneva: Robinson, 1982. 1st ed. 82 b/w photos. NF in dj. *Cahan*. $75/£47

Vogue's Contemporary Cookery. London: Conde-Nast, 1947. 1st Eng ed. Card wrappers (spine head sl worn). *Clearwater*. $64/£40

Voice of the Yukon. Vancouver, BC: Wrigley, August, 1930. VG in illus wrapper. *High Latitude*. $35/£22

VOIGT, F. A. Combed Out. NY: Dial, 1929. 1st US ed. Red cl stamped in black/blind. NF in pict dj (lt worn). *Reese*. $60/£38

Volcano Under the City. NY, 1887. 1st ed. 350,(ii)pp; fldg color map. (Lt soiled, few sm spots.) *Wantagh*. $65/£41

VOLK, KURT (ed). The Oldest Christmas Story. N.p.: Kurt H. Volk, 1938. One of 500. Signed. Silk-cvrd bds, gilt. Fine in box. *Pacific**. $75/£47

VOLKMANN, DANIEL G. Fifty Years of the McCloud River Club. SF: Privately ptd, 1951. 1st ed. One of 150 ptd. Frontis fldg map. Cl-backed dec bds, paper cvr label. NF. *Pacific**. $230/£144

VOLKMANN, DANIEL G. Memories of a Fishing Journey to New Zealand Made in 1950 by Dean and Helen Witter...as Narrated in Letters to Family and Friends. SF: Privately ptd, 1950. 1st ed. One of 100 ptd. Fldg frontis map. Flexible marbled bds, paper cvr label. Fine in glassine. *Pacific**. $316/£198

VOLLMAN, WILLIAM T. An Afghanistan Picture Show. NY: FSG, (1992). 1st ed. Fine in Fine dj. *Agvent*. $35/£22

VOLLMAN, WILLIAM T. Butterfly Stories. Deutsch, 1993. 1st UK ed. Pb orig. Mint in ptd wraps as issued. *Martin*. $26/£16

VOLLMAN, WILLIAM T. Thirteen Stories and Thirteen Epitaphs. NY: Pantheon, 1991. 1st US ed. Signed. Fine in dj. *Lame Duck*. $100/£63

VOLLMAN, WILLIAM T. You Bright and Risen Angels. Deutsch, 1987. 1st UK ed, 1st bk. One of 2500. Fine in Fine dj. *Martin*. $93/£58

VOLNEY, C. F. View of the Climate and Soil of the United States.... London: J. Johnson, 1804. 1st British ed. xxiv,iii-vi,503,(i)pp; 2 fldg plts, 2 Good fldg maps in rear pocket. Recent brn buckram, later ptd paper spine label. (Sl browned, offset, lt foxing; 1 fldg plt lacks left third; maps sl browned w/lt offsetting, 1 map rebacked and partly split along 1 fold, chipped at margins w/sl loss of image rt edge, lg map w/paper repairs along sides on reverse.) Howes V141. *Baltimore**. $100/£63

VOLNEY, M. The Ruins; or, A Survey of the Revolutions of Empires. London: T.T. & J. Tegg, 1834. Frontis, rear fldg map, chart. Period diced calf, gilt spine, morocco spine label. (Lacks part of fldg chart; extrems rubbed), else VG. *Pacific**. $35/£22

VOLTAIRE. Candide. NY, 1927. One of 250. Signed by Clara Tice (etchings). 10 color etchings w/ptd tissue inter-leaves. Full red morocco (spine ends worn, outer hinges sl flaked), gilt. *Kane**. $250/£156

VOLTAIRE. Candide. NY: Random House, 1928. 1st Kent ed. One of 95 signed by Rockwell Kent (illus). 4to. Teg. Ptd linen bds over maroon morocco spine, raised bands. Fine in box. *Appelfeld*. $2,000/£1,250

VOLTAIRE. The History of the Russian Empire Under Peter the Great. London: J. Nourse et al, (1763). 1st ed in English. 2 vols. 2 frontispieces, (2),xxiii,(1),329,(5); (2),xvi,(4),328,(20)pp; 2 fldg maps. Calf. (Bkpl; glue to spine ends, joints, needs rebinding), else VG. *Pacific**. $173/£108

VOLTAIRE. The History of the War of Seventeen Hundred and Forty One. London: J. Nourse, 1756. 2nd ed. 2 parts in 1. (4),260pp. Period calf, later morocco spine label. VG. *Pacific**. $35/£22

VOLTAIRE. The History of Zadig, or Destiny. LEC, 1952. Ltd to 1500 numbered. Fine in slipcase. *Swann**. $115/£72

VOLTAIRE. The Ignorant Philosopher. David Williams (trans). Fielding & Walker, 1779. 1st Eng ed. iii,50pp (corner cut from top of tp, w/o text loss). Old full polished calf (rather scraped, fr hinge cracked but cords holding), gilt. *Hollett*. $136/£85

VOLTAIRE. The Princess of Babylon. London: Nonesuch, 1927. Teg. Marbled bds, vellum spine, corners. *Appelfeld*. $95/£59

VON ARNIM, ELIZABETH BEAUCHAMP. Elizabeth and Her German Garden. Chicago: Henneberry, 1901. Alberta Hall (illus). Unpaginated. Gray cl, gilt. Red ribbon marker. VG (inscrip partly crossed out; corners sl bumped). *Price*. $75/£47

VON BERG, GUSTAVE. From Kapuvar to California, 1893. Feathered Serpent Press, 1979. One of 500. *Dawson*. $30/£19

VON BLIXEN-FINECKE, BROR. African Hunter. NY: Knopf, 1938. 1st Amer ed. (Extrems sl dampstained), else VG in dj (extrems sl dampstained, fr panel scrape). *Pacific**. $69/£43

VON BODE, WILHELM. Italian Renaissance Furniture. NY, 1931. Good. *Washton*. $50/£31

VON BOEHN, MAX. Dolls and Puppets. Harrap, 1932. 1st ed. 30 color plts (labels removed from pastedowns, title relaid). Lib cl, gilt. *Hollett*. $64/£40

VON BORCKE, HEROS. Memoirs of the Confederate War for Independence. NY: Peter Smith, 1938. Photo rpt of 1866 ed. 2 vols. Lg fldg map at rear of vol 2. (Lt aging; pencil notes feps 1 vol.) Blue cl (lt rubbed, dusty), gilt (sl dull). *Baltimore**. $90/£56

VON BULOP, BARONESS. My Royal Past. London: Batsford, 1939. 1st Eng ed. Color frontis by Cecil Beaton. VG (bkpl, edges spotted; spine ends sl bumped) in dj (nicked, chipped, rubbed, spotted, sl frayed, creased, price-clipped, sl dknd, #s written on lower flap). *Ulysses*. $120/£75

VON BULOW, HANS. Letters of Hans von Bulow. Richard Eckart (ed). Hannah Waller (trans). Knopf, 1931. One of 1000. VG. *Hollett.* $72/£45

VON DER VOGELWEIDE, WALTHER. Songs and Sayings. F. Betts (trans). Oxford, n.d. 1st ed. (Lack part of label; no dj.) *Typographeum.* $45/£28

VON ECKARDT, HANS. Russia. NY: Knopf, 1932. 1st ed. 13 maps. VG + (pencil notes). *Beasley.* $40/£25

VON ENGEL, ALFRED. Ionized Gases. Oxford: Clarendon, 1955. VG in dj (worn). *Weber.* $45/£28

VON FOERSTER, HEINZ and JAMES W. BEAUCHAMP (eds). Music by Computers. NY: John Wiley, (1969). 1st ed. Complete w/4 records rear pocket. Fine in dj. *Glaser.* $135/£84

VON FOERSTER, HEINZ (ed). Cybernetics.... NY: Josiah Macy Foundation, (1952). 1st ed. Fine in dj. *Glaser.* $125/£78

VON GOETHE, J. W. Faust: A Tragedy. NY: Cape & Smith, (1930). One of 490. Signed by Lynd Ward (illus) & Alice Raphael (trans). Frontis. Teg. Cl-backed dec bds, gilt. (Spine sunned), else NF in slipcase. *Pacific*.* $316/£198

VON GOETHE, J. W. Goethe's Theory of Colours; translated from the German: with notes by Charles Lock Eastlake. London: John Murray, 1840. 1st Eng ed. 8vo. xlviii,423pp + 16pp ads (dated April 1840), 1/2-title; 4 litho plts (3 hand-colored). Orig dk grn straight-grain cl, ptd paper spine label. (Heavy offset browning pp216-217), o/w Fine. *Weber.* $2,700/£1,688

VON GOETHE, J. W. Wilhelm Meister's Apprenticeship. NY: Riverside, 1959. Signed by William Sharp (illus). Full cream cl, blocked in gilt floral design; gilt/maroon. Boxed. *Appelfeld.* $100/£63

VON GOETHE. Letters from Goethe. M. von Herzfeld & C. Melvil Sym (trans). Edinburgh: University Press, 1957. 1st ed. 14 plts, 2 fldg maps. VG in dj (sl torn, chipped). *Hollett.* $72/£45

VON GRIMMELHAUSEN, JOHAN. The Adventures of Simplicissimus. LEC, 1981. One of 2000 signed by Fritz Eichenberg (illus). Fine in slipcase. *Swann*.* $34/£21

VON HAGEN, VICTOR W. Ecuador and the Galapagos Islands. Norman: Univ of OK, 1949. 3 maps. (Spine lt chipped.) *Archaeologia.* $65/£41

VON HAGEN, VICTOR W. Maya Explorer: John Lloyd Stephens and the Lost Cities of Central America and Yucatan. Norman: Univ of OK, (1947). Fine in Fine dj. *Book Market.* $20/£13

VON HAMMER, JOSEPH. The History of the Assassins. London, 1835. *Swann*.* $126/£79

VON HAXTHAUSEN, BARON. The Russian Empire. Robert Farie (trans). London: Chapman and Hall, 1856. 1st ed in English. 2 vols. 1/2-titles, xxvii,(i)blank,432pp; viii,463,(1)imprint. Grn blindstamped cl (spine splits repaired). VG set. *Morrell.* $176/£110

VON HOFFMAN, NICHOLAS. Mississippi Notebook. NY: David White, (1964). 1st ed. VG in ptd dj. *Petrilla.* $30/£19

VON HUMBOLDT, A. Aspects of Nature in Different Lands and Different Climates; with Scientific Elucidations. Mrs. Sabine (trans). London, 1849. 1st Eng ed. 2 vols. Diced grn calf, gilt. Good. *Henly.* $77/£48

VON KARMAN, THEODORE. Aerodynamics; Selected Topics in the Light of Their Historical Development. Ithaca: Cornell Univ, (1954). 4 ports. Blue cl. Fine. *Weber.* $60/£38

VON KOSEWITZ, W. F. Eccentric Tales. London, 1827. 1st ed. 20 hand-colored aquatint plts by George Cruikshank. Floral silk doublures, eps; uncut. Later 19th-cent purple morocco (spine faded), gilt. *Swann*.* $488/£305

VON KOTZEBUE, OTTO. A New Voyage Round the World, in the Years 1823, 24, 25, and 26. London: Henry & Richard Bentley, 1830. 1st ed in English. 2 vols. 7.5x4.5. 2 copper-engr frontispieces, (8),341pp + (2)pp ads; (4),362pp + (1)pg ads; 2 fldg engr maps, fldg plan. Marbled eps. 19th-cent 3/4 morocco, cl, gilt, raised bands. (Lt foxing/offset to tps, frontispieces; fldg maps mtd on linen backing; joints, spines sl rubbed), else NF, w/sm binder's labels of McHutchison Bros., Melbourne, on fr pastedowns. Howes K259. *Pacific*.* $1,955/£1,222

VON KURR, JOHANN GOTTLIEB. The Mineral Kingdom. Edinburgh: Edmonston & Douglas, 1859. 1st ed in English. 24 hand-colored litho plts (tp lt spotted). Contemp calf-backed cl bds (spine lt faded, corners bumped). *Christie's*.* $990/£619

VON LANGSDORFF, GEORGE H. Voyages and Travels in Various Parts of the World, During the Years 1803, 1804, 1805, 1806, and 1807. London: Henry Colburn, 1813-14. 1st ed. 2 parts in 1. 4to. xxi,(3),362,(6); (8),386,(6)pp; 21 copper-engr plts, incl frontispieces and 2 plts of sheet music; fldg copper-engr map. Period full calf (rebacked w/mod calf), gilt, morocco spine label. (Offset from plts w/foxing to them and adjacent pp; sm hole lower margin 1st tp), else NF. *Pacific*.* $2,300/£1,438

VON LUDENDORF, ERICH. My War Memories 1914-1918. London: Hutchinson, (1919). 1st British ed. 2 vols. Gilt blue cl (sl sunned, lt spotted). Good set. *Reese.* $75/£47

VON NEUMANN, JOHN and OSKAR MORGENSTERN. Theory of Games and Economic Behavior. Princeton, NJ: Princeton Univ, 1944. 1st ed. Complete w/corrigenda slip laid in. VG. *Glaser.* $375/£234

VON NEUMANN, JOHN. The Computer and the Brain. New Haven: Yale Univ, (1958). 1st ed, 2nd ptg. Fine in dj. *Glaser.* $60/£38

VON NOSTRAND, JEANNE. Edward Vischer's Drawings of the California Missions 1861-1878. SF: Book Club of CA, 1982. One of 600 ptd. Fine in dj. *Pacific*.* $86/£54

VON RICHTHOFEN, WALTER. Cattle-Raising on the Plains of North America. NY: D. Appleton, 1885. 1st ed. Grn cl. (Lt stain to bottom edge of text; cvrs sl worn), o/w NF. Howes R273. *Labordo.* $475/£297

VON RICHTHOFEN, WALTER. Cattle-Raising on the Plains. NY: D. Appleton, 1885. 1st ed. 102,(6) ads pp. (Few sl spots), else Fine. Howes R273. *Dumont.* $650/£406

VON SCHILLER, JOHANN CHRISTOPH. William Tell. Zurich: LEC, 1951. One of 1500. Signed by Charles Hug (illus). Cl-backed wood veneer bds, gilt. Fine in slipcase. *Pacific*.* $29/£18

VON SIMPSON, OTTO. The Gothic Cathedral: Origins of Gothic Architecture and the Medieval Concept of Order. Pantheon/Bollingen, 1962. 2nd ed. 3 tipped-in color plts. VG in glassine wraps. *Hadley.* $48/£30

VON SIMPSON, OTTO. Sacred Fortress. Byzantine Art and Statecraft in Ravenna. Chicago, 1948. 48 plts. (Cl sl spotted.) *Washton.* $50/£31

VON TROIL, UNO. Letters on Iceland. London, 1780. Frontis, engr fldg map. Contemp sheep (needs rebinding; ink lib stamps). *Swann*.* $316/£198

VON UNRUH, FRITZ. The Way of Sacrifice. C. A. Macartney (trans). London: Knopf, 1928. 1st ed. Gilt black cl. (Relevant items affixed to eps, few fox mks), else VG in dj (lt edgeworn). *Reese.* $65/£41

VON WINNING, HASSO. Pre-Colombian Art of Mexico and Central America. NY: Abrams, n.d. Folio. 595 plts. Pict dj (discolored). *Metropolitan*.* $230/£144

VON WRANGELL, F. Narrative of an Expedition to the Polar Sea, in the Years 1820, 1821, 1822, and 1823. Edward Sabine (ed). London: James Madden, 1840. 1st Eng ed. cxxxvii,413pp; fldg map. Contemp 1/2 calf (worn). VG (few ll foxed, browned; sm lib stamps). *Explorer.* $232/£145

VONNEGUT, KURT. Breakfast of Champions. (NY): Delacorte, (1973). 1st ed. Fine in dj (spine sunned). *Pacific**. $40/£25

VONNEGUT, KURT. Canary in a Cat House. NY: Gold Medal, 1961. 1st ed. Pb orig. NF. *Warren*. $150/£94

VONNEGUT, KURT. Deadeye Dick. NY: Delacorte, (1982). 1st ed. One of 350 signed. Aeg. Maroon cl, gilt. Fine in pub's open-end slipcase. *Heritage*. $150/£94

VONNEGUT, KURT. Galapagos. NY, (1985). 1st ed. One of 500 numbered, signed. Slipcase. *Swann**. $138/£86

VONNEGUT, KURT. Jailbird. NY, (1979). 1st ed. One of 500 numbered, signed. Slipcase. *Swann**. $138/£86

VONNEGUT, KURT. Palm Sunday. NY, (1981). 1st ed. One of 500 numbered, signed. Slipcase. *Swann**. $138/£86

VONNEGUT, KURT. Player Piano. NY: Scribner, 1952. 1st ed, 1st bk. VG (stamps, lib label removed, tape mks) in Nice dj (sl faded). *Second Life*. $300/£188

VONNEGUT, KURT. Player Piano. NY: Scribner, 1952. 1st ed, 1st bk, w/Scribner's A and seal. Grn bds, silver-stamped spine. VG (eps sl browned; spine faded) in dj (sl browned, soiled). *Heritage*. $350/£219

VONNEGUT, KURT. Player Piano. Macmillan, 1953. 1st Eng ed, 1st bk. (Cvrs soiled), else VG in dj (chipped). *Fine Books*. $125/£78

VONNEGUT, KURT. The Sirens of Titan. Boston: HMCo, 1961. 1st hb ed. Fine in Fine dj (sl rubbed, white spine lettering subtly dknd). *Between The Covers*. $1,500/£938

VONNEGUT, KURT. Slapstick. NY, (1976). 1st ed. One of 250 numbered, signed. Slipcase. *Swann**. $138/£86

VONNEGUT, KURT. Slaughterhouse Five. NY, (1969). 1st ed. Dj (sl soiled, skewed). *Swann**. $103/£64

VONNEGUT, KURT. Welcome to the Monkey House. NY: Delacorte, 1968. 1st ed. Fine in dj. *Lame Duck*. $450/£281

VOORN, HENK. Old Ream Wrappers. North Hills: Bird & Bull, 1969. 1st ed. One of 375. 1/2 red morocco, marbled bds, gilt. Fine. *Pacific**. $63/£39

VOORSANGER, WILLIAM C. Medical Memoirs. SF: Ptd by Lawton & Alfred Kennedy, 1965. One of 500. Unopened. Grn cl, gilt. Fine. *Parmer*. $45/£28

VOORSANGER, WILLIAM C. Medical Memoirs: The Reminiscences of.... SF: (Privately ptd), 1965. 1st ed. One of 500 ptd. Grn cl. Fine. *Harrington*. $35/£22

VOOUS, K. H. Atlas of European Birds. London, 1960. 419 maps, 355 gravure plts. Dj (chipped). *Edwards*. $40/£25

VORIS, W. R. Notes on Some Early Grabhorn Items Together with Some More or Less Impertinent Comments. Tucson, 1939. Wraps (lt worn). *Dumont*. $125/£78

VOSBURGH, W. S. Cherished Portraits of Thoroughbred Horses. NY: Derrydale, 1929. Ltd to 300 unnumbered. Folio. 68 b/w plts. Bound by Sangorski and Sutcliffe in full crimson morocco, gilt, spine w/raised bands. NF in slipcase. *Biscotti*. $1,750/£1,094

VOSBURGH, W. S. Cherry and Black. The Career of Mr. Pierre Lorillard on the Turf. N.p.: (Devinne Press) for Pierre Lorillard, 1916. Uncut, teg. (Sl worn.) *Oinonen**. $50/£31

VOSBURGH, W. S. et al. Thoroughbred Types. 1900-1925. NY, 1926. One of 250 numbered. Sm folio. Linen-backed bds. (Sl worn.) *Oinonen**. $130/£81

Voyage of the Chelyuskin by Members of the Expedition. C&W, 1935. 1st ed. Good (spine sl rubbed). *Walcot*. $32/£20

Voyage of the Chelyuskin. By Members of the Expedition. NY: Macmillan, 1935. VG in dj. *High Latitude*. $45/£28

VOZNESENSKY, ANDREI. Dogalypse. San Francisco Poetry Reading. SF: City Lights, 1972. 1st ed. Fine in wraps. *Beasley*. $25/£16

VREDENBURG, EDRIC (ed). My Book of Favourite Fairy Tales. Phila: David McKay, (n.d.). 1st Amer ed. 4to. 12 full-pg color plts by Jennie Harbour. Blue cl, gilt. Good. *Reisler*. $285/£178

VREDENBURG, EDRIC et al. Golden Locks and Pretty Frocks. London: Raphael Tuck & Sons, (1914). 8vo. Agnes Richardson (illus). 12 full-pg color plts. Cl-backed illus bds (edges lt worn), color paste label. *Reisler*. $335/£209

VREDENBURG, EDRIC. Tinker, Tailor. London: Raphael Tuck & Sons, (1914). 4to. 136pp + ads; 12 full-pg color plts by Louis Wain. Cl-backed pict bds, color paste label. Very Nice (long description by orig buyer; few spots rear cvr). *Reisler*. $1,500/£938

VRING, GEORGE VON DER. Private Suhren: The Story of a German Rifleman. Fred Hall (trans). NY/London: Harper, 1928. 1st US ed. Dec eps. Blue cl stamped in yellow. VG in dj (lt chipped) w/pub's rev stamp on fr. *Reese*. $50/£31

VUILLIER, GASTON. A History of Dancing from the Earliest Ages to Our Own Times. Heinemann, 1898. 1st Eng ed. xvi,446pp; 20 plts, guards. VG (few spots, mks, joints tender; sl worn, dknd, few sm nicks to extrems). *Hollett*. $288/£180

VULLIAMY, LEWIS. Examples of Ornamental Sculpture in Architecture. London, n.d. c.(1823). Tall thin folio. Engr tp, 40 plts. Contemp 1/2 calf, marbled bds, gilt. (Ex-lib; ep labels, spotted, hinges reinforced; calf worn, rebacked.) *Edwards*. $160/£100

VYNER, ROBERT. A Treatise on Fox-Hunting...the General Management of Hounds. Wm. C.A. Blew (ed). London: Nimmo, 1892. New ed. 12 hand-colored plts. 3/4 mod leather (lt worn). *Oinonen**. $130/£81

W

WABER, BERNARD. An Anteater Named Arthur. Boston: HMCo, 1967. 1st ed. 8.5x10. 32pp. Fine in dj. *Cattermole*. $125/£78

WABER, BERNARD. Good-Bye, Funny Dumpy-Lumpy. Boston: HMCo, 1977. 1st ed. 7.5x9.25. 64pp. VG in dj. *Cattermole*. $25/£16

WACKER, PETER O. The Musconetcong Valley of New Jersey. New Brunswick: Rutgers Univ, (1968). 1st ed. Dj. *Heinoldt*. $15/£9

WADD, WILLIAM. Mems. Maxims, and Memoirs. London: Callow & Wilson, 1827. (iv),303,(i)pp; 3 plts (foxed). Early cl-backed bds (corner rubbed, backstrip lacks some cl), spine label (chipped). *Edwards*. $136/£85

WADDELL, HELEN. Beasts and Saints. Constable, 1942. 3rd imp. Robert Gibbings (illus). Dec blue cl. VG (eps, fore-edges foxed; sl faded) in dj (worn). *Whittle*. $22/£14

WADDELL, HELEN. New York City. (Newtown: Gregynog), 1935. Ltd to 350. Booklet. Full-pg wood engr. Fine in ptd wrappers (lt foxed). *Bromer*. $85/£53

WADDELL, JOSEPH A. Annals of Augusta County, Virginia, with Reminiscences.... William Ellis Jones, 1886. 1st ed. Frontis map, 374pp. Cl w/leather spine label (rebound, new eps). Internally Sound (pp waterstained, browned). Good. Howes W2. *Book Broker*. $100/£63

WADDELL, JOSEPH A. Annals of Augusta County, Virginia, with...a Diary of the War, 1861-5, and a Chapter on Reconstruction. Richmond, 1886-88. 1st ed. 2 vols, incl supp. Uncut. (Ex-lib, vol 1 worn, shaken, inner hinge broken; vol 2 inner joints tape-repaired.) Howes W2. *Oinonen**. $40/£25

WADDELL, MARTIN. The Hidden House. NY: Philomel, 1990. 1st ed. 9.5x7.75. Angela Barrett (illus). 32pp. VG (ink name) in dj. *Cattermole*. $25/£16

WADE, AUBREY. The War of the Guns. Western Front, 1917 and 1918. Batsford, 1936. 1st Eng ed. Fine (1/2-title hinge tender, fore-edges foxed) in VG pict dj. *Clearwater.* $88/£55

WADE, MASON. Francis Parkman, Heroic Historian. NY: Viking, 1942. 1st ed. Maroon cl, gilt. Fine in VG dj (spine foot chipped). *Harrington.* $30/£19

WADSWORTH, EDWARD. The Black Country. Ovid, 1920. 1st ed. (One of 400, of 450.) Folio. 20 plts (12 collotype), woodcut head-piece. 1/4 pale gray linen, pale grn bds (fr cvr lt soiled). Good in dj (lt soiled). *Blackwell's.* $480/£300

WAESON, WILBUR J. Bridge Architecture. NY: William Helburn, (1927). Paper bds, cl spine. Fine (stain on fore-edge; bumped, sl discolored). *Metropolitan*.* $86/£54

WAGENKNECHT, EDWARD. Mark Twain, the Man and His Work. New Haven: Yale Univ, 1935. 1st ed. Red cl, gilt. NF. BAL II:253. *Macdonnell.* $60/£38

Waggles. A Nodding Head Book. London: Rainbow Books, n.d. (195?). 4 characters, each w/nodding head on wire spring. VG in pict wraps. *Bookfinders.* $85/£53

WAGNER, ANTHONY R. Historic Heraldry of Britain. OUP, 1948. 2nd imp. Color frontis, 28 plts. (Eps lt spotted; spine lt faded.) Dj (lt soiled, sl ragged). *Edwards.* $40/£25

WAGNER, CLINTON. Habitual Mouth-Breathing: Its Causes, Effects, and Treatment. Albany: Edgar S. Werner, 1884. 2nd ed. (Upper extrems sl dknd), else VG in ptd wrappers. *Pacific*.* $98/£61

WAGNER, FRITS A. Indonesia. NY: McGraw-Hill, (1959). 61 tipped-in color plts, 36 b/w plts, maps. Fine in VG slipcase. *Turtle Island.* $50/£31

WAGNER, HENRY R. California Imprints, August 1846-June 1851. Berkeley, CA, 1922. 1st ed. VG in wrappers. *Labordo.* $250/£156

WAGNER, HENRY R. The Cartography of the Northwest Coast of America to the Year 1800. Berkeley: Univ of CA, 1937. 1st ed. 2 vols. Black cl, gilt. (2 leaves vol 2 w/marginal creases, sm edge tear), else NF in djs (spines sl sunned, sl corner nicks, vol 1 price-clipped), new slipcase w/orig label pasted on. *Pacific*.* $431/£269

WAGNER, HENRY R. Collecting: Especially Books. (L.A.), 1968. Ltd to 400 ptd. (Lib ink stamp), o/w VG +. Bkpl of W.J. Holliday, Jr. *Truepenny.* $35/£22

WAGNER, HENRY R. Juan Rodriguez Cabrillo: Discoverer of the Coast of California. SF: CA Hist Soc, 1941. 1st ed. One of 750 ptd. Frontis. 1/2 linen, paper spine label. Fine. Howes W8. *Pacific*.* $92/£58

WAGNER, HENRY R. Juan Rodriguez Cabrillo: Discoverer of the Coast of California. SF: CA Historical Soc, 1941. 1st ed. One of 750 ptd. Frontis. 1/2 linen, paper spine label. Fine. Howes W8. *Pacific*.* $98/£61

WAGNER, HENRY R. The Library of Fernando Colon. N.p.: Fine Arts Press, 1934. Frontis. Wraps in coarse paper. (Sig, browned, lt fold at corner), else VG. *Dumont.* $100/£63

WAGNER, HENRY R. The Life and Writings of Bartolome de las Casas. Albuquerque: Univ of NM, 1967. 1st ed. Frontis. (Bkpl), else NF in dj. *Dumont.* $40/£25

WAGNER, HENRY R. Marco Polo's Narrative Becomes Propaganda to Inspire Colon. Stockholm, 1949. Inscribed. Wraps. VG. *Dumont.* $50/£31

WAGNER, HENRY R. The Plains and the Rockies. Charles L. Camp (ed). SF: Grabhorn, 1937. 2nd ed. One of 600. Paper spine label. (Spine faded), else VG. *Pacific*.* $109/£68

WAGNER, HENRY R. The Plains and the Rockies. Charles L. Camp (ed). SF: Grabhorn, 1937. 2nd ed. One of 600. Red cl, leather spine label (faded). NF (corner bumped). *Harrington.* $135/£84

WAGNER, HENRY R. The Plains and the Rockies. SF: Grabhorn, 1937. Ltd to 600. Paper spine label (rubbed). (Spine ends sl rubbed, lower joint sl spotted.) *Sadlon.* $150/£94

WAGNER, HENRY R. The Plains and the Rockies. Columbus: Long's College Book Co, 1953. 3rd ed. 32 full-pg illus. Later buckram. *Dawson.* $75/£47

WAGNER, HENRY R. The Plains and the Rockies. Charles L. Camp (ed). Columbus: Long's College Book Co, 1953. 3rd ed. (Spine, joints lt rubbed), else NF. *Pacific*.* $104/£65

WAGNER, HENRY R. The Plains and the Rockies. Robert H. Becker (ed). SF: John Howell Books, 1982. 4th ed. Buckram, gilt. Fine (sl rubbed). *Pacific*.* $98/£61

WAGNER, HENRY R. The Plains and the Rockies. SF: John Howell, 1982. 4th ed. (Lt worn.) *Oinonen*.* $100/£63

WAGNER, HENRY R. The Plains and the Rockies. Robert H. Becker (ed). SF: John Howell-Books, 1982. 4th ed. Frontis. VF. *Argonaut.* $150/£94

WAGNER, HENRY R. The Rise of Fernando Cortes. (Berkeley, CA): Cortes Soc, 1944. Ltd to 300. 18 plts (1 fldg). Gray cl. Good. *Karmiole.* $150/£94

WAGNER, HENRY R. Sixty Years of Book Collecting. L.A.: Ptd for the Roxburghe and Zamorano Clubs, 1952. One of 200. Photo frontisport. Patterned bds, paper cvr label. *Dawson.* $100/£63

WAGNER, HENRY R. Spanish Explorations in the Strait of Juan de Fuca. Santa Ana: Fine Arts, 1933. 1st ed. One of 425. 13 facs maps. Black cl, gilt. (Fr hinge sl tender; fldg map facing p39 cut at fold during binding process, repaired), else NF. *Pacific*.* $403/£252

WAGNER, HENRY R. The Plains and the Rockies. SF: Grabhorn, 1937. One of 600. Gilt spine label. NF (bkpl, accession # to 2 pp). *Bohling.* $150/£94

WAGNER, RICHARD. Letters of Richard Wagner. John N. Burke (ed). Gollancz, 1951. 1st ed. VG in dj (sl chipped, soiled). *Hollett.* $72/£45

WAGNER, RICHARD. My Life. London: Constable, 1911. 2 vols. 2 ports. Partly unopened. (Spine faded.) *Hollett.* $48/£30

WAGNER, RICHARD. Parsifal. London: Harrap, (1912). 1st ed illus by Willy Pogany. 16 mtd color plts. Uncut. Gray pict cl, gilt. Fine. *Sotheran.* $400/£250

WAGNER, RICHARD. The Rhinegold and the Valkyrie. London: Heinemann, 1910. 1st Rackham trade ed. 34 Fine tipped-in color plts by Arthur Rackham, guards. Gilt-dec cl. (Bkpl, 1 tissue guard detached but present; spine sunned, shelf-rubbed, corner bumped), else VG. *Pacific*.* $230/£144

WAGNER, RICHARD. The Rhinegold and the Valkyrie. London/NY: Heinemann/Doubleday, 1910. 1st trade ed. 32 tipped-in color plts by Arthur Rackham. Gilt-pict bds, blue cl. Fine in pict protective box. *Cullen.* $275/£172

WAGNER, RICHARD. Richard to Minna Wagner. William Ashton Ellis (trans). H. Grevel, 1909. 1st ed. 2 vols. 2 ports. (Spines faded.) *Hollett.* $104/£65

WAGNER, RICHARD. The Ring of the Niblung. London: Heinemann, 1939. 1st ed thus w/both vols combined. 4to. (ii),3-159; (x),3-181pp; 48 color plts by Arthur Rackham. Pict eps. Mid-blue cl stamped in darker blue. (Fore-edge of bk block sl speckled; fr cvrs sl shadowed.) *Sotheran.* $269/£168

WAGNER, RICHARD. The Ring of the Niblung: A Trilogy. NY: Doubleday, Page, (1911). 1st Amer Rackham trade ed. 26 color plts by Arthur Rackham, guards. 1/2 cl, pict bds, gilt. (Bkpl; sl soiled, spine ends chipped), else VG. *Pacific*.* $115/£72

WAGNER, RICHARD. Siegfried and the Twilight of the Gods. London: Heinemann, 1911. 1st Rackham trade ed, Amer issue w/secondary publisher Doubleday's imprint on spine. 30 tipped-in color plts by Arthur Rackham, ptd tissue guards. 1/2 cl, gilt-pict bds. (1 plt creased; spine sl sunned, corners showing), else VG. *Pacific**. $86/£54

WAGNER, RICHARD. Siegfried and the Twilight of the Gods. Margaret Armour (trans). London: Heinemann, 1911. 1st Eng trade ed. 30 VG tipped-in color plts by Arthur Rackham, guards. Pict eps. Gilt-stamped brn buckram. Text Clean (pp sl aged, ink inscrip), cvrs VG (sl rubbed, rear cvr sl worn). *Baltimore**. $110/£69

WAGNER, RICHARD. Siegfried and the Twilight of the Gods. Margaret Armour (trans). London: Heinemann, 1911. Ltd to 1150 signed by Arthur Rackham. 4to. 30 mtd color plts on brn paper. Teg. Orig pict vellum, gilt. (Lt spotted, browned, sig; lacks ties, lt stained.) *Christie's**. $515/£322

WAGNER, RICHARD. Tannhauser. London: G.G. Harrap, (1911). 1st ed illus by Willy Pogany. 16 mtd full-color plts. Dk grn dec cl, gilt. (Gilt dull), o/w Sound. *Sotheran.* $301/£188

WAGNER, WILLIAM F. Letters of William F. Wagner, Confederate Soldier. Joe M. Hatley and Linda B. Huffman (eds). Wendell, (1983). 1st ed. Fine. *Pratt.* $25/£16

WAGONER, DAVID. Through the Forest. NY, 1987. 1st Amer ed. Fine in Fine dj. *Polyanthos.* $25/£16

WAGSTAFF, ALEXANDER E. (ed). Life of David S. Terry. SF: Continental Pub Co, 1892. 1st ed. Frontis, 526pp (browning); 5 full-pg photo illus. Grn cl. *Dawson.* $250/£156

WAHL, JAN. Cobweb Castle. Holt, Rinehart & Wilson, 1968. 1st ed. 7x7. Edward Gorey (illus). Fine in VG dj (flap corner clipped). *Price.* $50/£31

WAHL, JAN. Hello Elephant. NY: Holt, Rinehart & Winston, (1964). 1st Amer ed. Obl 12mo. Edward Ardizzone (illus). Gray-grn pict bds. Color dj (sl worn). *Reisler.* $50/£31

WAHL, LOREN. The Invisible Glass. NY: Greenberg, (1950). 1st ed. VF in dj (lt rubbed, 1/8 inch short), o/w Fine. *Between The Covers.* $85/£53

WAHL, LOREN. The Invisible Glass. Washington: Guild, 1965. New ed, possible 1st issue sheets. (Sm fore-edge abrasion w/sm tear to edges few pp, Greenberg pub info on c. pg obliterated; corners bumped), else Fine in VF dj (sl rubbed). *Between The Covers.* $50/£31

WAHLSTEDT, JACOBUS J. Iter in America. Upsala, 1725. (Lt foxed, few edges bent, no bds.) *Metropolitan**. $431/£269

WAIN, JOHN. Strike the Father Dead. NY: St. Martins, (1962). 1st Amer ed. VF in Fine dj (sl rubbed). *Between The Covers.* $65/£41

WAIN, JOHN. A Word Carved on a Sill. London: Routledge & Kegan Paul, 1956. 1st ed. Fine in pale mauve patterned bds. Dj. *Maggs.* $64/£40

WAIN, LOUIS. Merry Times. London: Raphael Tuck & Sons, (ca 1890). Lg 4to. 12 full-pg color illus by Louis Wain. Good in color pict stiff wrappers (spine worn, lt folds at margins). *Reisler.* $800/£500

WAIN, LOUIS. Pussyland Pictures. London: Raphael Tuck & Sons, (ca 1912). 4to. 14pp. Good in full color stiff paper wrappers. *Reisler.* $485/£303

WAIN, LOUIS. Such Fun. London: Raphael Tuck, (1930). 1st ed. Royal 8vo. Color frontis, (92),(i)pp; 1 color plt. Cl-backed pict bds. *Sotheran.* $400/£250

WAIN, LOUIS. With Louis Wain to Fairyland. London: Raphael Tuck & Sons, (1903). 1st ed. Lg 4to. Louis Wain (illus). Cl-backed color pict bds (edgeworn, rubbed). *Reisler.* $2,650/£1,656

WAINWRIGHT, A. The Central Highlands. Kendal: Westmorland Gazette, (1977). 1st ed. (Inscrip.) Dj. *Hollett.* $120/£75

WAINWRIGHT, A. The Eastern Highlands. Kendal: Westmorland Gazette, (1978). 1st ed. (Inscrip.) Dj. *Hollett.* $120/£75

WAINWRIGHT, A. The North-Western Highlands. Kendal: Westmorland Gazette, (1976). 1st ed. (Inscrip.) Dj. *Hollett.* $120/£75

WAINWRIGHT, A. The Western Highlands. Kendal: Westmorland Gazette, (1976). 1st ed. (Inscrip.) Dj. *Hollett.* $120/£75

WAINWRIGHT, CHARLES S. A Diary of Battle. Allan Nevins (ed). NY, (1962). 1st ed. VG + in dj (sl worn, sm piece torn off). *Pratt.* $70/£44

WAINWRIGHT, DAVID. The Piano Makers. London: Hutchinson, 1975. 1st ed. Color frontis. VG in dj. *Hollett.* $40/£25

WAINWRIGHT, J. M. The Land of Bondage. NY: Appleton, 1852. 1st ed. xx,190pp; 28 steel-engr plts. Aeg. Orig full morocco, gilt. (Edges rubbed, sl scuffed, fr cvr detached), o/w VG. *Worldwide.* $145/£91

WAINWRIGHT, JOHN. A Nest of Rats. NY: St. Martin's, (1977). 1st Amer ed. Rev copy w/inserted rev notice. NF in dj. *Antic Hay.* $25/£16

WAIT, BENJAMIN. Letters from Van Dieman's Land, Written During Four Years Imprisonment for Political Offences Committed in Upper Canada. Buffalo: A.W. Wilgus, 1843. 1st ed. Frontis, 356pp; map. Contemp calf, leather label. (Lt spotted; worn, scuffed), else Good. Howes W16. *Brown.* $250/£156

WAITE, ARTHUR EDWARD. Azoth: Or the Star in the East: Embracing the First Matter of the Magnum Opus. London: Theosophical Publ, 1893. 1st ed. xvi,239pp. (Worn, fore-edge spotted, inner hinges exposed), o/w VG. *Middle Earth.* $195/£122

WAITE, ARTHUR EDWARD. A New Encyclopedia of Freemasonry: And of Cognate Instituted Mysteries, Their Rites, Literature, and History. London: Rider, 1921. 2 vols. 16 full-pg plts. NF. *Middle Earth.* $295/£184

WAKEFIELD, DAN. New York in the Fifties. Boston, 1992. 1st Amer ed. Fine in Fine dj. *Polyanthos.* $25/£16

WAKEFIELD, ELIZA. Five Hundred Charades, from History, Geography and Biography. John W. Parker, 1835. Half-title present, 128,7,(1)pp, pub's cat at end. Figured pink cotton (faded, worn, sm splits to backstrip). Good (label? removed from fep recto, bkpl, tear to fore-edge of final blank). *Blackwell's.* $192/£120

WAKEFIELD, H. RUSSELL. The Clock Strikes Twelve. Sauk City: Arkham House, 1946. 1st Amer ed. (Name), else NF in dj (spine sl faded). *Pacific**. $40/£25

WAKEFIELD, PRISCILLA. Mental Improvement; or, The Beauty and Wonders of Nature and Art. London: Harvey & Darton, 1823. 12th ed. 2 vols. 12mo. viii,243; iv,245pp + 2pp ads. Marbled paper on bds, 3/4 red roan spine. VF complete set (ink names tps; cvr lt soiled, corner rubbed). *Hobbyhorse.* $300/£188

WAKEFIELD, W. The Happy Valley. London: Sampson Low, 1879. 1st ed. xii,300pp; 8 full-pg lithos, fldg map. Teg. Contemp crimson dec calf, gilt. VG (tear in map repaired, plts sl spotted; joints repaired, new spine labels, sl rubbed). *Morrell.* $192/£120

WAKELEY, C. P. G. and J. B. HUNTER. Rose and Carless' Manual of Surgery. London, 1937. 15th ed. Special Coronation Edition. 2 vols. 29 plts. Leather. VG. *Whitehart.* $64/£40

WAKEMAN, EDGAR. The Log of an Ancient Mariner. SF: Bancroft, 1878. 1st ed. Litho frontisport, 378pp; 1 plt. Gilt-pict cl. (Spine sl faded), else Fine. Howes W23. *Argonaut.* $225/£141

WAKOSKI, DIANE. The Fable of the Lion and the Scorpion. WI: Pentagram, (1975). Ltd to 1000. Signed presentation. Fine in ptd wraps. *Polyanthos.* $25/£16

WAKOSKI, DIANE. The Man Who Shook Hands. NY, 1978. 1st Amer ed. Signed. Fine in Fine dj. *Polyanthos.* $30/£19

WALCOTT, DEREK. Poems of the Caribbean. LEC, 1983. One of 2000 signed by Walcott and Romare Bearden (illus). Fine in slipcase. *Swann**. $546/£341

WALCOTT, DEREK. Selected Poems. NY, 1964. 1st Amer ed. Fine in NF dj. *Warren*. $100/£63

WALCOTT, DEREK. Selected Poems. NY: FSG, 1964. 1st ed. Inscribed. NF in dj. *Lame Duck*. $250/£156

WALCOTT, MACKENZIE E. C. Scot-Monasticon. The Ancient Church of Scotland. Virtue, Spalding & Daldy, 1874. xxvii,428pp; 24 steel-engr plts, color map. Paper spine label. (Lt spotted; sl soiled, corners sl bumped), o/w VG. *Hollett*. $224/£140

WALDBERG, PATRICK. Rene Magritte. A. Wainhouse (trans). Brussels: De Rache, 1965. 1st ed. Frontisport. Dec cl. VF in dj (torn). *Europa*. $136/£85

WALDEN, ARTHUR T. A Dog-Puncher on the Yukon. Boston: Houghton Mifflin, 1928. 1st ed. Signed, 1928. VG in dj (defective). *High Latitude*. $55/£34

WALDEN, HOWARD T. Angler's Choice. NY: Macmillan, 1947. 1st ed. Pict eps. Grn cl. NF in VG pict dj. *Biscotti*. $25/£16

WALDEN, HOWARD T. Big Stony. NY: Derrydale, (1940). One of 550. Gilt dec cl, color label. (Bkpl.) *Kane**. $160/£100

WALDEN, HOWARD T. Big Stony. NY: Derrydale, 1940. One of 550 numbered. Signed. Black cl, gilt. Fine. *Biscotti*. $275/£172

WALDEN, HOWARD T. Upstream and Down. NY: Derrydale, 1938. One of 950 numbered. Signed by the author and Milton C. Weiler (illus). Black cl. (Gilt poor), o/w Fine. Issued boxed. *Biscotti*. $275/£172

WALDEN, J. B. and L. PAINE. The Long Whip. Chapman & Hall, 1937. 1st ed. Good (sl rubbed). *Walcot*. $24/£15

WALDMAN, ANNE. West Indies Poems. (NY): Adventures in Poetry, (1972). One of 300. Folio. Fine in stapled wrappers. *Between The Covers*. $100/£63

WALDMAN, DIANE. Roy Lichtenstein. NY, (1971). 183 plts. (Sl loose), else VG in dj (edge tears). *King*. $150/£94

WALDO, EDNA LAMOORE. Dakota: An Informal Study of Territorial Days. Caldwell: Caxton Ptrs, 1936. 1st ed. Signed. VG in dj (spine head chipped, price-clipped). *Pacific**. $52/£33

WALDO, S. PUTNAM. Biographical Sketches of Distinguished American Naval Heroes of the War of the Revolution.... Hartford: Silas Andrus, 1823. 1st ed. 392pp; 3 engr plts. Contemp calf, gilt spine (joints worn; foxed). Emb stamp of W.M.P. Dunne. Howes W26. *Lefkowicz*. $225/£141

WALDO, S. PUTNAM. The Life and Character of Stephen Decatur. Middletown, CT: Clark & Lyman, 1822. 2nd ed. 372,(367)-378pp; 3 (of 4) plts. Recent 1/2 cl. (Foxed, tp margin repaired, tears to margins last 5 ll restored w/loss; few lines of text pp 63-64 highlighted.) HowesW27. *Lefkowicz*. $50/£31

WALDORF, J. A Kid on the Comstock. Palo Alto: American West, c1970. Pub's file copy. Dj. *Blake*. $25/£16

WALDRON, T. J. and JAMES GLEESON. The Frogmen. London: Evans, 1951. VG in dj. *American Booksellers*. $28/£18

WALES, GEORGE. Etchings and Lithographs of American Ships. Boston: Goodspeed, 1927. One of 500. 1 etching, 1 litho, each signed; 75 repros. (Sl worn.) Dj. *Oinonen**. $130/£81

WALEY, ARTHUR (trans). Lady Who Loved Insects. Blackamore, 1929. One of 550. NF in slipcase (browned). *Williams*. $77/£48

WALEY, ARTHUR. Life and Times of Po Chu-I 772-846 A.D. London, (1951). 2nd imp. Port, map. NF in VG dj. *Agvent*. $25/£16

WALEY, ARTHUR. Yuan Mei: Eighteenth Century Chinese Poet. London: Geo. Allen, (1958). 2nd imp. Port. NF in VG dj. *Agvent*. $25/£16

WALFORD, EDWARD. Greater London.... Cassell, 1894/95. 2 vols. xvi,576; xii,560pp. Dec cl, gilt (Vol 1 early ll sl water-stained), o/w Good. *Cox*. $56/£35

WALFORD, EDWARD. Londiniana. Hurst & Blackett, 1879. 1st Eng ed. 2 vols. VG (lib stamp, # in ink each tp; top edge dusty; cocked, spine ends sl bumped, extrems sl rubbed, spines faded). *Ulysses*. $136/£85

WALFORD, LIONEL A. Marine Game Fishes of the Pacific Coast from Alaska to the Equator. Berkeley: Univ of CA, 1937. 1st ed. Lt blue cl, gilt. (Spine ends sl rubbed), else VG. *Pacific**. $52/£33

WALKER, AGNES. Manual of Needlework and Cutting Out. Blackie, 1902. 3rd ed. 2 fldg samplers. Dec cl (worn, mkd). VG. *Whittle*. $19/£12

WALKER, ALEXANDER. Beauty: Illustrated Chiefly by an Analysis and Classification of Beauty in Woman. London: Henry G. Bohn, 1846. 2nd ed. 22 mtd lithos. Blind-stamped cl, gilt. (Sl foxed; spine ends sl worn), else VG. *Pacific**. $52/£33

WALKER, ALICE. Meridian. Deutsch, 1976. 1st UK ed. NF in VG dj (spine sl faded). *Williams*. $72/£45

WALKER, ALICE. The Same River Twice. NY: Scribner, 1996. 1st ed. Signed. Fine in dj. *Smith*. $40/£25

WALKER, ALICE. The Temple of My Familiar. San Diego, 1989. 1st Amer ed. Fine (spine sl rubbed) in Fine dj. *Polyanthos*. $25/£16

WALKER, ALICE. The Third Life of Grange Copeland. NY: HBJ, (1970). 1st ed. Fine in Fine dj (rear sl foxed). *Agvent*. $350/£219

WALKER, ALICE. You Can't Keep a Good Woman Down. NY/London: Harcourt Brace Jovanovich, (1981). 1st ed. Tan cl, mauve bds, gilt spine. (Ink sig, sl shelfworn.) NF dj. *Baltimore**. $140/£88

WALKER, C. F. Chalk Stream Flies. London, 1953. 1st ed. 4 color plts. Dj. *Petersfield*. $48/£30

WALKER, DESMOND GREER. Malformations of the Face. Edinburgh/London: E.& S. Livingstone, 1961. (Lt freckled, possibly by insects, on cvrs), else Fine. *Weber*. $150/£94

WALKER, EGBERT. Flora of Okinawa and the Southern Ryukyu Islands. Washington: Smithsonian Inst, 1976. 1st ed. Fine in NF dj. *Archer*. $45/£28

WALKER, ERNEST. A History of Music in England. J. A. Westrup (ed). Oxford: Clarendon, 1952. 3rd ed. VG in dj. *Hollett*. $40/£25

WALKER, FRANKLIN. The Seacoast of Bohemia. Santa Barbara: Peregrine Smith, 1973. 1st rev ed. NF in dj (sl soiled). *Pacific**. $40/£25

WALKER, GERALD. Cruising. NY: Stein & Day, (1970). 1st ed. VF in Fine black dj (extrems sl rubbed). *Between The Covers*. $150/£94

WALKER, HENRY P. The Wagonmasters. Norman: Univ of OK, (1966). 1st ed. Color frontis. Good (ex-lib). *Lien*. $35/£22

WALKER, J. G. and O. L. SHEPHERD. The Navajo Reconnaissance. L.A.: Westernlore, 1964. VG in dj. *Dumont*. $35/£22

WALKER, J. HUBERT. Mountain Days in the Highlands and Alps. Edward Arnold, 1937. 1st ed, 1st bk. 64 plts, 2 sketch maps. Uncut. VG in dj (torn, spine dknd, head defective). *Hollett*. $72/£45

WALKER, JOHN. Joseph Mallord William Turner. NY, 1976. 1st ed. 56 tipped-in color illus. Dj. *Edwards*. $40/£25

WALKER, JOSEPH C. An Historical Essay on the Dress of the Ancient and Modern Irish. Dublin, 1788. 14 plts, incl frontis. Contemp 1/2 calf. (Lt dampstained; needs rebinding.) *Swann**. $287/£179

WALKER, MARGARET. For My People. LEC, 1992. One of 400 signed by Walker and Elisabeth Catlett (illus). Fine in slipcase. *Swann**. $747/£467

WALKER, MARGARET. How I Wrote Jubilee. Chicago, (1972). 1st ed. VG in wraps. *King.* $65/£41

WALKER, MARGARET. Jubilee. Boston, 1966. 1st ed. Dj (lt worn, spine sunned). *Swann*.* $57/£36

WALKER, MARY E. Hit. NY, (1871). 1st ed. 177pp. (Binding, frontis waterstained.) *M & S.* $275/£172

WALKER, MARY JO. The F. Stanley Story. Santa Fe, 1985. One of 700 signed. Frontis. NF in dj. *Dumont.* $30/£19

WALKER, MARY WILLIS. The Red Scream. NY: Doubleday, (1994). 1st ed. Signed. Fine in dj. *Pacific*.* $86/£54

WALKER, R. A. Le Morte D'Arthur. London: Privately ptd, 1945. Ltd to 350. VG in orig wraps. *Edrich.* $19/£12

WALKER, R. A. (ed). The Best of Beardsley. London: Bodley Head, (1948). 1st ed. 134 b/w plts. Yellow illus cl. VG. *Turtle Island.* $60/£38

WALKER, RALPH. Ralph Walker, Architect. NY: Henahan House, 1957. One of 1000. 2-tone cl, paper spine label. Good in slipcase. *Karmiole.* $100/£63

WALKER, STELLA A. British Sporting Art in the Twentieth Century. London, 1989. 1st ed. 24 color plts. Dj. *Edwards.* $40/£25

WALKER, TODD. Three Soliloquies,.... N.p.: Todd Walker, 1977. 1st ed. Ltd to 500. 43 b/w photos. Fine in illus stiff wrappers. *Cahan.* $85/£53

WALKER, W. S. Between the Tides. Los Gatos, CA: W.S. & Glenn Walker, 1885. 1st ed. Frontisport, (4),250pp. (Contents dknd, sm chip lower gutter of tp, frontis, few other early ll; extrems lt worn), else VG. *Pacific*.* $35/£22

WALKLEY, A. B. Playhouse Impressions. London: T. Fisher Unwin, 1892. 1st ed. (Spine sunned, ends rubbed.) *Dramatis.* $25/£16

WALL, JOHN F. Famous Running Horses. Washington: Infantry Journal, 1949. 1st ed. VG. *October Farm.* $65/£41

WALL, JOHN F. Thoroughbred Bloodlines. An Elementary Study. Columbia, SC: Privately ptd, (1946). 3rd ed rev in 1 vol. One of 1000 numbered. Folio. (Sl worn.) *Oinonen*.* $90/£56

WALLACE, A. R. Darwinism: an Exposition of the Theory of Natural Selection. London: Macmillan, (1912). 3rd ed. Frontisport, map. VG + . *Mikesh.* $60/£38

WALLACE, A. R. Island Life of the Phenomena and Causes of Insular Faunas and Floras. London, 1895. 2nd, rev ed. xx,563pp; 3 maps. (Sm grease mk affecting few pp), o/w Fine. *Henly.* $77/£48

WALLACE, A. R. Island Life. London: Macmillan, 1892. 2nd ed. xx,563pp; 26 maps. (Extrems sl worn.) *Hollett.* $104/£65

WALLACE, A. R. My Life. London: Chapman & Hall, 1908. (Spine sl faded.) *Hollett.* $40/£25

WALLACE, A. R. A Narrative of Travels on the Amazon and Rio Negro. Ward, Lock, 1889. 2nd ed. xiv,(i),363pp. 1/2 hard-grain morocco, gilt, marbled bds, raised bands. (Prize label on pastedown; sl rubbed.) *Hollett.* $120/£75

WALLACE, ANDREW. Sources and Readings in Arizona History. Tucson, 1965. (Pencil notes), else Good. *Dumont.* $30/£19

WALLACE, BETTY. History with the Hide Off. Denver, 1965. Inscribed. VG (extrems lt worn). *Baade.* $60/£38

WALLACE, BRENTON. Patton and His Third Army. Harrisburg, 1951. VG in VG dj. *Clark.* $45/£28

WALLACE, DAVID FOSTER. Girl with Curious Hair. NY: Norton, 1989. 1st ed. Fine in Fine dj. *Beasley.* $50/£31

WALLACE, DILLON. Saddle and Camp in the Rockies. NY, 1911. (Extrems worn), else Good. *Dumont.* $85/£53

WALLACE, EDWARD S. The Great Reconnaissance. Boston, 1955. 1st ed. Map. Good in dj (torn). *Dumont.* $35/£22

WALLACE, EDWARD S. The Great Reconnaissance: Soldiers, Artists and Scientists on the Frontier, 1848-1861. Boston: Little, Brown, (1955). 1st ed. Map. Fine in dj (sl chipped). *Argonaut.* $50/£31

WALLACE, H. F. British Deer Heads. London, 1913. One of 600. White buckram. (Lt foxed.) *Grayling.* $208/£130

WALLACE, H. F. Stalks Abroad. London, 1908. (Lt rubbed, mkd.) *Grayling.* $96/£60

WALLACE, HUGH N. The Navy, the Company, and Richard King. British Exploration in the Canadian Arctic, 1829-1860. Montreal: McGill-Queen's Univ, 1980. 14 maps. VG (rear bd sl stained). *Explorer.* $32/£20

WALLACE, IRVING. The Fabulous Originals. NY: Knopf, 1955. 1st ed. As New in dj. *Smith.* $50/£31

WALLACE, LEW. Ben-Hur. NY: Harper, 1892. Garfield ed. 2 vols. Orange cl, gilt. (Sl soiled), else NF in VG box (cracked). *Pacific*.* $58/£36

WALLACE, LEW. Ben-Hur. LEC, 1960. Ltd to 1500 numbered, signed by Joe Mugnaini (illus). Fine in slipcase. *Swann*.* $46/£29

WALLACE, LEW. Ben-Hur. NY: LEC, 1960. 3938/1500. Signed by Joe Mugnaini (illus). 1/2 leather, natural linen, leather cvr label. Fine in glassine, slipcase. *Pacific*.* $52/£33

WALLACE, PHILIP B. Colonial Ironwork in Old Philadelphia. NY, (1930). Folio. (Lt worn.) *Oinonen*.* $80/£50

WALLACE, PHILLIP B. Colonial Churches and Meeting Houses: Pennsylvania, New Jersey and Delaware. NY: Architectural Book Pub, (1931). 1st ed. 291 photo plts. Blue cl. Fine in dj. *Karmiole.* $100/£63

WALLACE, RICHARD W. The Etchings of Salvator Rosa. Princeton, 1979. Good in dj (corners sl bumped). *Washton.* $55/£34

WALLACE, WILLIAM S. (ed). A Journey Through New Mexico's First Judicial District in 1864. L.A.: Westernlore, 1956. One of 350. (Spine faded), else VG. *Dumont.* $60/£38

WALLER, AUGUSTUS D. Eight Lectures on the Signs of Life. London, 1903. 1st ed. *Fye.* $200/£125

WALLER, AUGUSTUS D. An Introduction to Human Physiology. London, 1893. 2nd ed. 632pp. (Pencil notations; spine, outer hinges worn.) *Fye.* $100/£63

WALLER, AUGUSTUS D. Lectures on Physiology. First Series: On Animal Electricity. London, 1897. 1st ed. 144pp. *Fye.* $300/£188

WALLER, IRENE. Thread: An Art Form. Studio Vista, 1973. 1st ed. Good + (ex-lib, stamp mks) in dj. *Whittle.* $40/£25

WALLER, ROBERT JAMES. The Bridges of Madison County. (NY): Warner Books, (1992). 1st ed. Fine in Fine dj. *Lenz.* $125/£78

WALLER, ROBERT JAMES. Love in Black and White. Stevenson, 1992. 1st UK ed. One of 3000 ptd. Mint in Mint dj. *Martin.* $40/£25

WALLER, ROBERT JAMES. Love in Black and White. Sinclair, 1992. One of 3000. Fine in dj. *Any Amount.* $72/£45

WALLIS, FRANK E. How to Know Architecture. NY, 1910. 1st Amer ed. Teg, uncut. NF. *Polyanthos.* $45/£28

WALLIS, HENRY. The Cloud Kingdom. London: John Lane, (1905). 1st ed. Charles Robinson (illus). 8vo. Teg. Grn cl, gilt. Fine in illus dj (edges, spine chipped). *Reisler.* $485/£303

WALLIS, J. P. R. The Northern Goldfield Diaries of Thomas Baines, 1869-72. London, 1946. 1st ed. Frontisport, 7 color plts, 24 b/w plts, 5 maps (4 fldg). Teg. *Edwards.* $224/£140

WALLMO, O. C. (ed). Mule and Black-Tailed Deer of North America. Lincoln, 1981. 1/2 cl. Dj. *Sutton.* $40/£25

WALMSLEY, HUGH MULLENEUX. Stories of the Battle Field; and Sketches in Algeria. London, ca 1860. (Bkpl; hinges cracked.) *Swann*.* $201/£126

WALPOLE, HORACE. Anecdotes of Painting in England. London, 1828. 5 vols. 80 plts. 3/4 gilt-stamped leather (shelfworn, chipped). *Oinonen**. $160/£100

WALPOLE, HORACE. The Castle of Otranto. Vernor & Hood, 1804. New ed. Wood-engr frontis, xvi,179pp; 11 plts. Red sprinkled edges. Contemp 1/2 marbled calf, gilt, dk blue label, marbled bds. Good (browned, contemp presentation note). *Blackwell's*. $80/£50

WALPOLE, HORACE. The Castle of Otranto. UK: LEC, 1975. One of 2000. Signed by W.S. Lewis (intro). Fine in glassine dj in Fine box. *Polyanthos*. $60/£38

WALPOLE, HORACE. Historic Doubts on the Life and Reign of King Richard the Third. London: J. Dodsley, 1768. 2nd ed. Frontisport, xvi,134,(2)pp; 1 plt. Contemp speckled calf (sl scuffed), red morocco spine label. (Foxed.) *Karmiole*. $175/£109

WALPOLE, HORACE. Horace Walpole's Fugitive Verses. W. S. Lewis (ed). London, 1931. 1st ed. Ltd to 500 (this copy unnumbered). Buckram. VG. *Gretton*. $64/£40

WALPOLE, HORACE. Horace Walpole's Letters to Sir Horace Mann. Lord Dover (ed). London, 1833. 1st ed thus. 3 vols rebound as 1. Early 20th-cent blue cl. *Gretton*. $32/£20

WALPOLE, HORACE. Horace Walpole's Letters to the Countess of Ossory. (By Horace Walpole.) London, 1903. 3 vols. Uncut. Paper cvrs. Fine. *Gretton*. $48/£30

WALPOLE, HORACE. The Letters of Horace Walpole, Fourth Earl of Orford. Mrs. Paget Toynbee (ed). London, 1903-05. 1st ed. 15 vols (of 16), vol 5 not present. Grn cl. VG (pencil notes). *Gretton*. $120/£75

WALPOLE, HORACE. The Letters of Horace Walpole. Peter Cunningham (ed). Edinburgh, 1906. 9 vols. 64 steel-engr plts. Red cl. VG. *Gretton*. $168/£105

WALPOLE, HORACE. Letters. Peter Cunningham (ed). Bickers & Son, 1877. 9 vols. 8vo. 9 engr frontispieces, 30 engr plts. Teg. Contemp red 1/2 morocco, gilt spines. (Sl foxed at ends, bkpl; pp130-131 vol 7 torn.) *Sotheby's**. $810/£506

WALPOLE, HORACE. Memoirs of the Reign of King George the Third. London, 1894. Ltd to 1000. 4 vols. 14 addt'l 18th-cent engr ports inserted. Dk red cl. Good + . *Gretton*. $96/£60

WALPOLE, HORACE. A Notebook of Horace Walpole. Wilmarth Lewis (ed). NY: William E. Rudge, 1927. 1st ed. One of 500. Fine (bkpl) in VG cl case (breaks at fr, rear joint; spine snag). *Reese*. $125/£78

WALPOLE, HORACE. A Prayer for My Son. Macmillan, 1936. 1st ed. Fine in VG + dj. *Fine Books*. $24/£15

WALPOLE, HORACE. A Selection of the Letters of Horace Walpole. W.S. Lewis (ed). London, 1926. 1st ed. 2 vols. VG-. *Gretton*. $72/£45

WALPOLE, HORACE. Some Unpublished Letters of Horace Walpole. Spencer Walpole (ed). London, 1902. 1st ed. Fine. *Gretton*. $24/£15

WALPOLE, HUGH. The Cathedral. NY, (1922). Lg paper ed. Ltd to 500 numbered, signed. Teg. (Ink inscrip w/pictures affixed to fep; spine sl stained, hinges cracked.) Dj (heavily chipped, soiled). *King*. $35/£22

WALPOLE, HUGH. John Cornelius, His Life and Adventures. London: Macmillan, 1937. 1st ed. Gilt grn cl dec in blind. Fine in dj (spine sl dknd, sl chip at crown). *Reese*. $30/£19

WALPOLE, HUGH. A Letter to a Modern Novelist. London: Hogarth, 1932. 1st ed. VG wrappers (sl soiled). *Virgo*. $40/£25

WALPOLE, HUGH. Seven Pillars of Wisdom. T. E. Lawrence in Life and Death. London: Bertram Rota, 1985. 1st ed. One of 100. Ptd wrappers. *Maggs*. $80/£50

WALPOLE, HUGH. Vanessa. London: Macmillan, 1933. 1st ed. One of 315 signed. Unopened. Paper spine label. (Fore-edge sl foxed), o/w Fine in dj (sl foxed, mend at top of 1 joint). *Reese*. $50/£31

WALSDORF, JOHN J. (ed). Men of Printing. Pennyroyal, (1976). Ltd to 300. 8 port engrs by Barry Moser. Marbled bds, tan backstrip. VG (lt rubbed). *Truepenny*. $300/£188

WALSH, C. C. Early Days of the Western Range. Boston: Sherman, French, 1917. 1st ed. VG + . Howes W64. *Labordo*. $185/£116

WALSH, HENRY COLLINS. The Last Cruise of the Miranda. NY: Transatlantic Pub, 1896. 232pp. VG (white spine lt soiled). *High Latitude*. $85/£53

WALSH, JAMES J. Psychotherapy. NY, 1912. 1st ed. Red textured cl. NF. *Doctor's Library*. $75/£47

WALSH, ROBERT. Constantinople and the Scenery of the Seven Churches of Asia Minor Illustrated. London: Fisher, n.d. First Series. Pub's gilt-stamped morocco (rubbed, foxed, sl stained, soiled). *Oinonen**. $160/£100

WALSH, STUART P. How to Run a Patrol: A Manual for Patrol Leaders. Tuckahoe: Boycraft Co, (1929). 6th ed. Pict grn wrappers. Fine. *Pacific**. $35/£22

WALSH, T. J. The History of Opera. London, 1981. 1st ed. NF in NF dj. *Polyanthos*. $25/£16

WALSINGHAM, THOMAS DE GREY and RALPH PAYNE-GALLWEY. Shooting. Longmans, Green, 1886. 1st ed. 2 vols. (xvi),(360); (xiv),348pp. Dec cl, gilt. Nice set (sl shaken; sl spotted, mainly edges). *Ash*. $160/£100

WALTER, JAMES. Shakespeare's True Life. London: Longman et al, 1890. 1st ed. Inscribed. iv,395pp. Aeg. Dk-brn morocco, gilt. *Young*. $80/£50

WALTER, RICHARD. Anson's Voyage Round the World. London: Martin Hopkinson, 1928. One of 1500. Amer issue, w/imprint of Charles E. Lauriat on spine. 4 fldg charts. Teg. 1/2 cl, gilt. NF (sl shelfworn, corner sl bumped). *Pacific**. $173/£108

WALTERS, HENRY. Incunabula Typographica. Balt, 1906. 1st ed. Color frontis. Teg, untrimmed. Full lt brn calf, raised bands, partly exposed rawhide thongs, gilt. (Sm lib # stamped on tp, ink handstamps rep.) Cvrs VG (lt rubbed). *Baltimore**. $110/£69

WALTERS, MINETTE. The Sculptress. London: Macmillan, (1993). Uncorrected proof. Signed. As New in wrappers. *Pacific**. $98/£61

WALTHER, ERIC. Echeveria. SF, 1972. Ivory buckram. Fine. *Brooks*. $45/£28

WALTON, ALAN HULL. Love Recipes, Old and New. London: Touchstream Books, (1956). One of 1375. 12 plts. Fine in dj. *Perier*. $85/£53

WALTON, ELIJAH. The Camel: Its Anatomy, Proportions and Paces. London: Day & Son, 1865. Frontis, 94 litho plts, 22 color (few soiled at margins and detached, lib stamps on verso some plts, emb lib stamps, lib label). Aeg. Orig cl (scuffed, spine sl worn, inner hinges broken), gilt. *Christie's**. $3,421/£2,138

WALTON, EVANGELINE. Witch House. Sauk City: Arkham House, 1945. 1st ed. Fine in Fine dj. *Other Worlds*. $100/£63

WALTON, IZAAK. The Compleat Angler, The Lives of Donne, Wotton, Hooker, Herbert and Sanderson, with Love and Truth and Miscellaneous Writings. Geoffrey Keynes (ed). (London): Nonesuch, 1929. One of 1600. Full calf. Fine. *Lenz*. $300/£188

WALTON, IZAAK. The Compleat Angler, the Lives of Donne, Wotton, Hooker, Herbert and Sanderson.... Geoffrey Keynes (ed). Nonesuch, 1929. One of 1600. 6 copper-engr ports. Marbled eps; teg on the rough, rest untrimmed. Orig natural russet-red niger morocco, gilt, raised bands. Fine in matching marbled bd slipcase. *Blackwell's*. $440/£275

WALTON, IZAAK. The Compleat Angler. London: Hodder & Stoughton, (1911). 1st ed illus by James Thorpe. Deluxe ed. One of 250 signed by Thorpe. 4to. xvi,166pp; 25 mtd color plts, guards. Teg, rest uncut. Pub's grn crushed morocco (spine discolored; browned, sl rubbed), gilt. Very Clean. *Sotheran.* $429/£268

WALTON, IZAAK. The Compleat Angler. London: Eyre & Spottiswoode, 1930. Ltd to 450 numbered, signed by Frank Adams (illus). Folio. Frontis. 1/4 vellum, marbled bds. Fine in pub's box. *Karmiole.* $200/£125

WALTON, IZAAK. The Compleat Angler. London, 1931. 1st ed thus. One of 775 numbered, signed by Arthur Rackham (illus). Eps, 12 full-pg color plts, guards, b/w chapter headings. Teg, unopened. Full vellum, gilt. VG (fr cvr worn, soiled, spine sl dknd) in slipcase (sl worn, split, soiled). *Ulysses.* $1,040/£650

WALTON, IZAAK. The Compleat Angler. London: George G. Harrap, 1931. 1st deluxe ed. Ltd to 775 numbered, signed by Arthur Rackham (illus). 4to. 12 color plts, guards. Teg, rest uncut. Full white vellum, gilt. (Spine crease), o/w Fine in slipcase w/numbered spine label. *Sotheran.* $1,117/£698

WALTON, IZAAK. The Compleat Angler. LEC, 1948. Ltd to 1500 numbered, signed by Douglas Gorsline (illus). Fine in slipcase. *Swann*.* $161/£101

WALTON, IZAAK. The Compleat Angler; or, Contemplative Man's Recreation. London: Thomas Hope, 1760. 1st Hawkins ed. 2 parts in 1. lvi,xxii,303,(1); xlvii,iv,ii,iv,128,(8)pp; 14 copper-engr plts, incl frontis. Mod calf, gilt, raised bands. NF. *Pacific*.* $431/£269

WALTON, IZAAK. The Compleat Angler; or, Contemplative Man's Recreation. London: J.C. Nimmo & Bain, 1883. 6 etchings, 2 ports, guards. Teg. Dk blue cl, gilt. (Sm tear spine head), else NF. *Pacific*.* $259/£162

WALTON, IZAAK. The Compleat Angler; or, Contemplative Man's Recreation. London: C&W, 1887. 4th Nicolas ed. Pict gilt-stamped maroon cl, morocco spine label. NF. *Pacific*.* $127/£79

WALTON, IZAAK. The Compleat Angler; or, Contemplative Man's Recreation. NY: D. Appleton, 1925. 7th Thorpe ed. 21 color plts by James Thorpe. (Extrems, cvrs rubbed), else VG. *Pacific*.* $46/£29

WALTON, IZAAK. The Compleat Angler; or, The Contemplative Man's Recreation. NY: LEC, 1948. One of 1500. Signed by Douglas W. Gorsline (illus). 1/2 parchment, gilt. Fine. *Pacific*.* $138/£86

WALTON, IZAAK. The Complete Angler of Izaak Walton and Charles Cotton. London: John Major, 1824. 2nd Major ed. Bds, paper spine label. VG. *Pacific*.* $150/£94

WALTON, IZAAK. The Complete Angler or Contemplative Man's Recreation. London: Samuel Bagster, 1893. Tercentenary ed. One of 350 numbered sets. 2 vols. Gilt-pict cl (lt worn), gilt vellum backs. Cl djs (sl frayed). *Oinonen*.* $130/£81

WALTON, IZAAK. The Complete Angler or the Contemplative Man's Recreation. Chiswick: Caradoc, 1905. One of 350 numbered. Etched frontis, extra tp. Uncut. Blind-stamped calf (rubbed, dried). Internally Sound. *Oinonen*.* $80/£50

WALTON, IZAAK. The Complete Angler, or Contemplative Man's Recreation. London: Rivington, 1784. 4th Hawkins ed. 12 engr plts. Mod 3/4 leather (lt worn, sl stained, soiled, foxed), most of early calf spine laid on. *Oinonen*.* $120/£75

WALTON, IZAAK. The Complete Angler, or Contemplative Man's Recreation.... London: Bagster, 1815. 2nd Bagster ed. Sheets are 8-5/8 inches tall this copy. Later 3/4 morocco (rubbed, sl browned, soiled). *Oinonen*.* $60/£38

WALTON, IZAAK. The Complete Angler. London: C. Rivington et al, 1797. Old brn calf (expertly rebacked), raised bands, red leather label. Nice (sig of Gustave Dore). *Appelfeld.* $250/£156

WALTON, IZAAK. The Complete Angler. London, 1815. 14 engr plts. Contemp 1/2 sheep (rebacked), spine in 6 compartments, red morocco lettering piece, gilt. (Foxed, offset.) *Swann*.* $149/£93

WALTON, IZAAK. The Complete Angler. London: John Major, 1823. 1st Major ed, lg paper copy. 8vo. 13 mtd India-proof engr plts, engr leaf of music. Grn levant, gilt, by Birdsall (spine faded to brn). *Swann*.* $575/£359

WALTON, IZAAK. The Complete Angler. London: John Major, 1824. 2nd Major ed. 14 copper-engr plts. (Spotting 1st few ll, o/w Clean.) Contemp black 1/2 morocco, gilt. *Christie's*.* $171/£107

WALTON, IZAAK. The Complete Angler. NY, 1847. 1st Amer ed. Orig cl (spine faded, ends chipped, paper shelf label; clean tear across 1 leaf, lib stamps on tp, bkpl). *Swann*.* $201/£126

WALTON, IZAAK. The Complete Angler. London, 1856. 3/4 morocco, gilt. (Lt dampstaining in margins.) *Swann*.* $115/£72

WALTON, IZAAK. The Complete Angler. London: Nattali & Bond, 1860. 2nd Nicolas rpt. 2 vols. Frontis. Grn crushed levant, gilt extra, by Wright. *Swann*.* $373/£233

WALTON, IZAAK. The Complete Angler. London, 1889. 8 etched plts. Mod 3/4 grn morocco, gilt. *Swann*.* $126/£79

WALTON, IZAAK. The Complete Angler. Privately ptd for the Navarre Soc, 1925. 8vo. Silk eps; aeg. Full crushed grn morocco by Bayntun Riviere, gilt. Slipcase. *Sotheby's*.* $699/£437

WALTON, IZAAK. The Complete Angler. 'Ephemera' (ed). London: Ingram/Cooke, 1853. New ed. Mod 1/2 brn calf, marbled sides. *Petersfield.* $64/£40

WALTON, IZAAK. The Complete Angler...with...a Bibliographical Note and a Notice of Cotton and His Writings, by the American Editor. NY: Dodd, Mead, (1880-i.e.1888). New ed. 2 vols. Gilt-pict dec grn cl (lt worn, sl soiled, foxed; lib bkpls). *Oinonen*.* $160/£100

WALTON, IZAAK. The Complete Angler; Or Contemplative Man's Recreation.... London: Ptd by Samuel Bagster, 1808. 1st Bagster ed. Add'l engr tp, 14 full-pg engr plts. Marbled eps; aeg. 3/4 leather (recently rebound), marbled bds. Nice. *Hartfield.* $485/£303

WALTON, WILLIAM M. Life and Adventures of Ben Thompson, the Famous Texan. Austin: Steck, 1956. Rpt ed. Fine (no slipcase). Howes W82. *Labordo.* $40/£25

WALTON, WILLIAM M. Life and Adventures of Ben Thompson. Houston, 1954. Rpt of 1884 ed. Ltd to 1000. Fine. Howes W82. *Baade.* $45/£28

WAMBAUGH, JOSEPH. The Onion Field. NY: Delacorte, 1973. 1st ed. NF in VG + dj (price-clipped). *Pettler.* $15/£9

Wanderings in West Africa from Liverpool to Fernando Po. (By Richard F. Burton.) London, 1863. 1st ed. 2 vols. 8vo. Frontis, viii,(ii),303; (vi),205pp; fldg map. Fine. *Maggs.* $1,280/£800

Wanderings of a Pilgrim. (By Fanny Parks.) London: Pelham Richardson, 1850. 2 vols. 4to. xxxv,479pp; 20 chromolithos, 28 lithos, fldg litho panorama in rear pocket vol 1. (Pp181-2 torn, some ll chipped to margins; list of plts vol 2 repaired to inner margin, replaced outer margin; sm wormholes lower margin vol 2 from pp329-353 affecting 1 plain plt but no text; lt browned, soiled.) Gilt-illus cl (corners softening, sympathetically rebacked w/orig spines repaired, laid down). *Edwards.* $1,088/£680

WANDREI, DONALD. Dark Odyssey. St. Paul, (1931). 1st ed. One of 400. Signed, inscribed. (Spine extrems lt rubbed.) *Swann*.* $103/£64

WANDREI, DONALD. The Web of Easter Island. Sauk City: Arkham House, (1948). 1st ed. NF in dj. *Pacific*.* $63/£39

WANG, TSENG-TSU. Bamboo. Berkeley: Gillick, 1945. Fine in dj. *Turtle Island.* $125/£78

WANGERIN, WALTER, JR. The Book of the Dun Cow. NY, 1978. 1st ed, 1st bk. Fine in NF dj (price-clipped). *Warren*. $35/£22

WANLOCK, ROBERT. Moorland Rhymes. Dumfries: John Anderson, 1874. vi,256pp (eps spotted). Orig cl (sl rubbed), gilt. *Hollett*. $40/£25

WANSEY, HENRY. The Journal of an Excursion to the United States of America, in the Summer of 1794. Salisbury: J. Easton, 1796. 1st ed, 2nd issue w/caption on frontisport changed, and an eyelash added. Silhouette frontisport, (iii)-xiii,(3),290,(12)pp, aquatint plt. Period 3/4 calf, marbled bds. (Tp, frontis, few other places foxed, bkpls, label; rubbed, spine worn), else VG. Howes W86. *Pacific**. $184/£115

War Letters of a Disbanded Volunteer. (By Jos. Barber.) NY: Frederic A. Brady, 1864. 1st ed. Frontis, 312,(1 pub's list)pp. VG (fr pp marginally stained, sl foxed; spine sl worn). *Wantagh*. $75/£47

WARBURTON, J. et al. History of the City of Dublin. London, 1818. 2 vols. Contemp calf. (Offsetting from plts to text; needs rebinding.) *Swann**. $402/£251

WARD, ARTEMAS (ed). The Grocer's Encyclopedia. NY, 1911. 1st ed. (One pg detached w/frayed edges; shaken, cvrs heavily worn.) *King*. $65/£41

WARD, CYRIL. Royal Gardens. London, 1912. 1st ed. (Spine sl rubbed.) *Edwards*. $72/£45

WARD, ELIZABETH. No Dudes Few Women. Albuquerque: Univ of NM, 1951. VG in dj (chipped). *Dumont*. $45/£28

WARD, EVELYN D. The Children of Bladensfield. NY, (1978). 1st of this ed. Fine in dj. *Wantagh*. $30/£19

WARD, FREDERICK. Nobody Called Me Mine: Black Memories. (Plattsburgh, NY): Tundra Books, 1977. 1st ed. Letter laid in from Ward. VG + in dj. *Petrilla*. $45/£28

WARD, H. and W. ROBERTS. Romney, a Biographical and Critical Essay with a Catalogue Raisonne of His Works. London: Agnew, 1904. One of 350. 2 vols. 46; 24 plts. 1/2 leather (corners worn, spine ends chaffed; lib stamps). *Ars Artis*. $480/£300

WARD, H. SNOWDEN and CATHARINE. The Real Dickens Land with an Outline of Dickens's Life. Chapman & Hall, 1904. Good (prize plt; spine bumped, chipped). *Tiger*. $48/£30

WARD, HERBERT. Mr. Poilu. London, 1916. 1st Eng ed. 46 tipped-in plts. VG (inscrip; sl faded, mkd). *Clearwater*. $40/£25

WARD, JAMES. Historic Ornament. London, 1897. 2 vols. xx,409,(iii)ads; xvi,411,(v)ads pp. Uncut. Dec black cl, gilt. (Tp vol 2 sl spotted, few margins sl thumbed, hinges tender; edges rubbed, upper bd vol 2 sl warped, head sl bumped.) *Edwards*. $48/£30

WARD, JAMES. Psychological Principles. Cambridge: CUP, 1918. 1st ed. Brn cl, gilt. Fine (sl worn). *House*. $250/£156

WARD, JONATHAN. American Slavery, and the Means of Its Abolition. Boston: Perkins & Marvin, 1840. 1st ed. 26pp. Orig ptd wrappers (wrinkled). *M & S*. $175/£109

WARD, LYND. Gods' Man. NY: Cape & Smith, (1929). 1st ed. One of 409. Signed. Teg. Black cl, pict cvr label, paper spine label. (Stamps; spine sl sunned), else NF in slipcase. *Pacific**. $374/£234

WARD, LYND. Gods' Man. NY: Jonathan Cape & Harrison Smith, (1930). Ltd to 409 signed. Teg. Black cl, illus paste label on cvr and spine. Good in pub's slipcase (worn, rubbed, lacks sides). *Reisler*. $475/£297

WARD, LYND. Madman's Drum: A Novel in Woodcuts. NY: Cape & Smith, (1930). 1st ed. Cl-backed dec bds, paper spine label. VG in dj (sl soiled, spine ends sl rubbed). *Pacific**. $161/£101

WARD, LYND. Song Without Words. NY: Random House, 1936. 1st ed. One of 1250. Signed. Parchment-backed foil-cvrd bds. (Spine dknd, ends, extrems sl rubbed, fr hinge starting), else VG. *Pacific**. $196/£123

WARD, LYND. Vertigo: A Novel in Woodcuts. NY: Random House, (1937). 1st ed. Dec cl. (Price-clipped, spine foot sl rubbed), else NF in dj. *Pacific**. $184/£115

WARD, LYND. Wild Pilgrimage. NY: Harrison Smith, (1932). 1st ed. Brick red linen, paper labels. Fine in dj. *Appelfeld*. $350/£219

WARD, LYND. Wild Pilgrimage. NY: Harrison Smith & Robert Haas, 1932. 1st ed. 4to. Orange cl, b/w paste labels on cvr and spine. Good in black/orange illus dj (chip spine head, overall wear). *Reisler*. $225/£141

WARD, MRS. E. M. Mrs. E. M. Ward's Reminiscences. Elliott O'Donnell (ed). London: Sir Isaac Pitman, 1911. 1st ed. 6 photogravure plts. Teg. Gilt cl, beveled bds. *Hollett*. $40/£25

WARD, MRS. HUMPHRY and C. E. MONTAGUE. William Thomas Arnold: Journalist and Historian. Manchester: University Press, 1907. VG (inscrip; cvrs mkd, edges rubbed). *Ulysses*. $128/£80

WARD, MRS. HUMPHRY. The Case of Richard Meynell. Smith, Elder, 1911. Pub's cat. Good (lt spotted, sig; spine bumped). *Tiger*. $29/£18

WARD, MRS. HUMPHRY. Fenwick's Career. Smith, Elder, 1906. Good (last ad leaf waterstained, new eps, fore-edge sl spotted; spine bumped, sunned, cvrs sl mkd). *Tiger*. $29/£18

WARD, MRS. HUMPHRY. The Marriage of William Ashe. Smith, Elder, 1905. VG (sig; spine bumped). *Tiger*. $32/£20

WARD, NED. A Vade Mecum for Malt-Worms: Or, a Guide to Good Fellows. London: Ptd by T. Bickerston, 1866. 2nd ed. 48pp. (Spine sunned.) *Young*. $120/£75

WARD, R. H. The Offenders. Cassell, 1960. 1st ed. NF in dj. *Any Amount*. $29/£18

WARD, ROWLAND. Rowland Ward's Records of Big Game. London, 1910. 6th ed. (Sl shelfworn, sl soiled.) *Oinonen**. $110/£69

WARD, ROWLAND. Rowland Ward's Records of Big Game. London, 1962. 11th ed. (Lt worn.) *Oinonen**. $60/£38

WARD, ROWLAND. Rowland Ward's Records of Big Game. London, 1971. 14th ed. (Bkpl; scuffed, soiled.) *Oinonen**. $30/£19

WARD, ROWLAND. The Sportsman's Handbook to Practical Collecting...of Trophies and Specimens.... London, 1900. 8th ed. Leather-cvrd bds (worn at corners, spine w/loss, joints cracked; sl spotted, ink notes, fr hinge tender). *Edwards*. $56/£35

WARD, SUSAN HAYES. History of Broadway Tabernacle Church from 1840 to 1900. NY, 1901. 1st ed. Frontis. (Lt dampstain to corner of 1st 60pp; stain to fr cvr corner.) *Heinoldt*. $15/£9

WARD-JACKSON, PETER. English Furniture Designs of the Eighteenth-Century. HMSO, 1958. 1st ed. 366 plts. Buckram, gilt. VG in dj. *Hollett*. $72/£45

WARDE, BEATRICE. The Crystal Goblet. Henry Jacob (ed). London: Sylvan, 1955. Ptd presentation slip. VG in dj (sl chipped). *Michael Taylor*. $40/£25

WARDLE, THOMAS. Kashmir: Its New Silk Industry. London/Leek, 1904. 1st ed. Frontisport, 45 plts. (Fore-edge of later pp chipped; spine sl faded, recased, new eps.) *Edwards*. $240/£150

WARDROP, A. E. Modern Pig Sticking. London, 1930. 2nd ed. Frontis. NF in dj (chipped). *Grayling*. $96/£60

WARDWELL, ALLEN. Ancient Eskimo Ivories of the Bering Strait. NY: Hudson Hills, (1986). 1st ed. VF in dj. *Perier*. $45/£28

WARE, CAROLINE F. Greenwich Village, 1920-1930. Boston, 1935. 1st ed. *Heinoldt.* $25/£16

WARE, FABIAN. The Immortal Heritage. Cambridge, 1937. 1st Eng ed. (Spine, some edges sl faded.) *Clearwater.* $24/£15

WARE, JOSEPH. The Emigrant's Guide to California. Princeton: Princeton Univ, 1932. Facs of orig tp, 1 other plt, fldg facs map. (Spine foot sl bumped), else NF. Howes W104. *Pacific*.* $52/£33

WARE, WILLIAM R. An Outline of a Course of Architectural Instruction. Boston: Press of John Wilson & Sons, 1866. 1st ed. 36pp (sl aged, few lt pencil notes). Ptd salmon wraps (separated along spine but still together at top thread; sl chipped, dusty; sm later ink handstamp date fr wrapper). *Baltimore*.* $80/£50

WARHOL, ANDY and PAT HACKETT. Popism: The Warhol '60s. NY: Harcourt Brace, 1980. 1st ed. NF in VG dj. *Pettler.* $40/£25

WARHOL, ANDY. Andy Warhol's Index (Book). NY: Random House, 1967. 1st ed. 1/4 cl, bds, pict plastic cvr label. (Sl soiled), else NF. *Pacific*.* $316/£198

WARHOL, ANDY. Andy Warhol's Index Book. (NY, 1967.) Stiff wrappers. *Swann*.* $103/£64

WARHOL, ANDY. Andy Warhol. Boston: Boston Book & Art, (1968). Orig wrappers. *Swann*.* $138/£86

WARHOL, ANDY. From A to B and Back Again. The Philosophy of Andy Warhol. Cassell/Dempsey, 1975. 1st UK ed. NF in dj (spine sl faded). *Sclanders.* $24/£15

WARHOL, ANDY. The Philosophy of Andy Warhol (From A to B and Back Again). NY, (1975). 1st ed. Initialed. VG in dj (sl worn). *King.* $150/£94

WARHOL, ANDY. The Philosophy of Andy Warhol, from A to B and Back Again. NY: Harcourt, Brace, (1975). 1st ed. Signed (w/initials). Fine in dj. *Pacific*.* $98/£61

WARING, GUY. My Pioneer Past. Boston: Bruce Humphries, (1936). 1st ed. Fine in Poor dj. *Perier.* $45/£28

WARING, HOLBURT. The Surgical Management of Malignant Disease. London, 1928. 1st ed. 10 color plts. *Fye.* $75/£47

WARING, J. B. Art Treasures of the United Kingdom from the Art Treasures Exhibition, Manchester. London: Day & Son, 1858. Folio. Chromolitho tp, 100 chromolitho plts by F. Bedford. Full polished calf, gilt. (Sm piece cut tp; worn, rubbed, fr cvr detached.) *Kane*.* $375/£234

WARING, J. B. Ceramic Art in Remote Ages. London, 1874. Folio. Color illus tp,tp,(ii),ii,127pp; 51 (of 55) plts. Aeg. Black cl, gilt. (Lib ink stamp, label remains fep, lt spotted; lt soiled, rubbed, rebacked w/much of orig spine laid down.) *Edwards.* $64/£40

WARING, J. B. Masterpieces of Industrial Art and Sculpture at the International Exhibition, 1862. London, 1863. 1st ed. 3 vols. Folio. 304 chromolitho plts, incl add'l titles (few marginally sl foxed). Pub's gilt-blocked leather (rear joints restored, hinges renewed, tears, spines rubbed). *Swann*.* $1,495/£934

WARNER, C. A. Texas Oil and Gas Since 1543. Houston: Gulf Pub, 1939. 1st ed. VG in dj (sl chipped). *Dumont.* $275/£172

WARNER, CHARLES DUDLEY. Backlog Studies. Boston, 1899. 1st Amer ed. Teg, uncut. 1/2 leather, marbled cvrs, gilt. Fine (sl rubbed). *Polyanthos.* $35/£22

WARNER, CHARLES DUDLEY. Backlog Studies. MA, 1899. One of 250. Teg, uncut. NF (bkpl; sl rubbed, spine sunned). *Polyanthos.* $45/£28

WARNER, CHARLES DUDLEY. On Horseback. Boston/NY: Houghton Mifflin, 1888. 1st ed. 1890 signed ink presentation. (iii),331pp + 15pg pub's cat. Pict brn cl. (Sl browned, few pp roughly opened; sl rubbed, worn.) BAL 21168. *Baltimore*.* $25/£16

WARNER, EZRA J. Generals in Gray. (Baton Rouge): LA State Univ, (1959). 1st ed. Tls to Arnold Gates, dated 21 April, 1955, laid in. Add'l tls from Carl Haverlin to Gates laid in. Gray cl. Fine in NF dj (sl edgeworn). *Chapel Hill.* $95/£59

WARNER, F. W. Guide Book and Street Manual of San Francisco, California. SF: F.W. Warner, 1882. 170,(5ads)pp. Black cl, gilt. (Stamp; hinges cracked, cvrs lt faded, worn), o/w VG. *Pacific*.* $69/£43

WARNER, GERTRUDE C. The Box-Car Children. Chicago: Rand-McNally, (1924). 1st ed. 8vo. 4 full-pg color plts by Dorothy Lake Gregory. Dk clue cl, gilt, color paste label. NF in full color pub's box. *Reisler.* $275/£172

WARNER, J. J. et al. An Historical Sketch of Los Angeles County, California from the Spanish Occupancy.... (L.A.): Louis Lewin, 1876. 1st ed. 5.5x8.5. (5),6-88pp. Ptd wrappers. (Paper dknd, fr joint split at ends), o/w Fine in cl-cvrd clamshell box. *Pacific*.* $920/£575

WARNER, J. J. et al. An Historical Sketch of Los Angeles County, California from the Spanish Occupancy.... L.A.: O.W. Smith, 1936. Frontisports. Cl-backed ptd bds. (Lt blue dye spattered on fr pg edges, margin of rear cvr), o/w VG. *Pacific*.* $40/£25

WARNER, MATT. The Last of the Bandit Riders. Caldwell, 1940. 1st ed. Pict cl. VG (lib cancellation, stamps; rear pocket removed; spine ends starting to fray) in dj (flaps glued to fep). Howes W112. *Baade.* $50/£31

WARNER, OPIE L. A Pardoned Lifer. Life of George Sontag.... San Bernardino, CA: Index Print, 1901. 1st ed. VG (cvrs worn). *Labordo.* $135/£84

WARNER, RALPH. Dutch and Flemish Flower and Fruit Painters of XVIIth and XVIIIth Centuries. London, (1928). 1/2 morocco, gilt. *Swann*.* $69/£43

WARNER, REX. The Wild Goose Chase. London, 1939. 1st ed. NF in NF dj (strip of internal tape). *Warren.* $35/£22

WARNER, RICHARD. A Second Walk Through Wales. London, 1799. viii,365,(ii)pp + 8pp pub's ads; 2 aquatint plts. Leather-backed marbled bds. (Lt sporadic foxing; rebound.) *Edwards.* $120/£75

WARNER, RICHARD. A Walk Through Some of the Western Countries of England. Bath: Ptd by R. Cruttwell, 1800. 1st ed. vi,222pp; 12 vignette maps, 2 tinted plts. Contemp 1/2 calf (extrems sl worn). *Young.* $120/£75

WARNER, SYLVIA TOWNSEND. Elinor Barley. (London): Cresset, 1930. One of 350 numbered, signed. 5 Fine b/w plts by I. R. Hodgkins. Teg. Vellum, marbled bds, gilt. (Bkpl; edges scuffed, scraped.) *Baltimore*.* $110/£69

WARNER, SYLVIA TOWNSEND. A Moral Ending and Other Stories. Chiswick, 1931. One of 550 signed. Frontis. Teg. Fine in Fine glassine dj. *Polyanthos.* $60/£38

WARNER, SYLVIA TOWNSEND. T. H. White. London: Cape/C&W, 1967. 1st ed. VG in dj (sl rubbed). *Hollett.* $48/£30

WARREN, B. H. Report on the Birds of Pennsylvania. Harrisburg, 1888. 1st ed. xii,260pp (eps foxed, inscrip, pg edges foxed, pp tanned); 50 plts (49 color). (Lt worn, soiled, sm stains.) *Sutton.* $75/£47

WARREN, B. H. Report on the Birds of Pennsylvania. Harrisburg, 1890. 2nd ed. 100 litho plts. Later buckram (sl worn, sl soiled, frayed). *Oinonen*.* $100/£63

WARREN, CHARLES. The Supreme Court in United States History. Boston: Little, Brown, 1923. 1st ed, later ptg. 3 vols. Untrimmed. Maroon cl, gilt. (Spines lt sunned, cvrs lt worn.) Texts Clean. *Baltimore*.* $30/£19

WARREN, EDWARD. The Life of John Warren, M.D., Surgeon-General During the War of the Revolution. Boston: Noyes, Holmes, 1874. 1st ed. Frontisport, 15,568pp. Fine. *M & S.* $250/£156

WARREN, G. O. Trackless Regions. Oxford/NY, 1917. (Sl faded, some extrems chafed.) *Clearwater.* $40/£25

WARREN, HENRY CLARKE. Buddhism in Translations. Cambridge, MA: Harvard Univ, 1906. 4th ptg. Ltd to 500. 1 plt. Teg. (1 leaf frayed; sl rubbed), o/w VG. *Worldwide*. $45/£28

WARREN, J. MASON. Surgical Observations, with Cases and Operations. NY, 1867. 1st ed. 630pp. (Inner hinges cracked; 1-inch piece from spine top.) Internally Fine. *Fye*. $600/£375

WARREN, JANE S. The Morning Star. Boston: American Tract Soc, (1860). Probable 1st ed. (2),309pp + (6)pp ads. VG (ink inscrip dated 1860; lt aged, shelfworn). *Pacific**. $23/£14

WARREN, JOHN C. Hernia, Strangulated and Reducible. Boston, 1881. 1st Amer ed. 280pp. *Fye*. $150/£94

WARREN, JOHN C. Physical Education and the Preservation of Health. Boston: William D. Ticknor, 1846. 2nd ed. iv(ads),90pp. Orig limp cl. VG. *Glaser*. $125/£78

WARREN, JOHN. C. Physical Education and the Preservation of Health. Boston, 1846. 1st ed. 90pp. *Fye*. $200/£125

WARREN, ROBERT PENN. All the King's Men. (NY): Dramatist's Play Service, (1960). 1st DPS ed. (Soft corner crease), else Fine in ptd wrappers. *Reese*. $30/£19

WARREN, ROBERT PENN. All the King's Men. NY: Harcourt, Brace, 1946. 1st ed. VG + (inscrip) in VG dj (sl chipped). *Unger*. $750/£469

WARREN, ROBERT PENN. All the King's Men. LEC, 1989. One of 600 signed by Warren and Hank O'Neal (photos). 2 vols. Fine in slipcase. *Swann**. $575/£359

WARREN, ROBERT PENN. Audubon: A Vision. NY: Random House, (1969). 1st ltd ed. One of 300 numbered, signed on inserted limitation leaf. Top edge stained lt blue. Dk blue cl, gilt. Fine in Fine dj. *Baltimore**. $100/£63

WARREN, ROBERT PENN. Chief Joseph of the Nez Perce. NY, (1983). 1st ed. One of 250 numbered, signed. Slipcase. *Swann**. $161/£101

WARREN, ROBERT PENN. The Circus in the Attic. NH: HB&Co, (1947). 1st ed. Signed. (Pg edges sl soiled), else Fine in VG dj (white spine dknd). *Between The Covers*. $375/£234

WARREN, ROBERT PENN. Jefferson Davis Gets His Citizenship Back. (Lexington): Univ of KY, (1980). 1st ed in bk form. Fine in dj. *Reese*. $40/£25

WARREN, ROBERT PENN. John Greenleaf Whittier's Poetry. Minneapolis: Univ of MN, 1971. 1st ed. Signed. NF in dj (spine panel sl rubbed). *Lame Duck*. $175/£109

WARREN, ROBERT PENN. Promises. Poems 1954-6. London: Eyre & Spottiswoode, 1959. 1st British ed. Fine in NF dj. *Reese*. $35/£22

WARREN, ROBERT PENN. Remember the Alamo. NY, 1958. 1st ed. NF (inscrip) in NF dj. *Warren*. $65/£41

WARREN, ROBERT PENN. Rumor Verified. NY, (1981). 1st ed. One of 250 numbered, signed. Slipcase. *Swann**. $69/£43

WARREN, ROBERT PENN. Selected Poems. 1923-1975. NY: Random House, (1975). 1st ed. Ltd to 250 signed. VF in black cl. Slipcase. *Bromer*. $225/£141

WARREN, ROBERT PENN. Who Speaks for the Negro? NY: Random House, (1965). 1st ed. VG in ptd dj. *Petrilla*. $40/£25

WARREN, ROBERT PENN. Wilderness. London: Eyre & Spottiswoode, (1962). 1st British ed. NF in dj. *Reese*. $35/£22

WARREN, SIDNEY. Farthest Frontier. NY, 1949. 1st ed. VG in dj (sl worn). *Woolson*. $15/£9

WARREN, WILLIAM F. Paradise Found. Boston: Houghton Mifflin, 1886. 8th ed. xxiv,505pp; map. VG. *High Latitude*. $65/£41

WARREN, WILLIAM THORN. Winchester Illustrated. Winchester: Warren's Library, 1905. Tipped-in frontis. VG. *Hollett*. $104/£65

WASEURTZ AF SANDELS, G. M. A Sojourn in California by the King's Orphan: The Travels and Sketches of G. M. Waseurtz af Sandels...Who Visited California in 1842-1843. Helen Putnam Van Sicklen (ed). SF: Book Club of CA, 1945. 1st ed. One of 300 ptd. 1/2 cl, patterned bds, paper spine label. Fine. Howes W125. *Pacific**. $104/£65

WASHBURN, CHARLES G. The Life of John W. Weeks. Houghton, 1928. Good in dj (worn, chipped). *Rybski*. $40/£25

WASHBURN, WILCOMBE E. The Indian in America. NY: Harper, (1975). 1st ed. 3 maps, 16 plts. Blue cl. Fine in pict dj. *House*. $20/£13

WASHBURNE, E. B. Recollections of a Minister to France 1869-1877. NY: Scribner, 1887. 1st ed. 2 vols. Teg. Beveled bds. (1st, last ll sl foxed; spines lightened, ends chipped, cvrs rubbed, lt soiled.) *Sadlon*. $30/£19

WASHINGTON, BOOKER T. Character Building. Toronto: William Briggs, 1902. 1st Canadian ed. VG (ex-lib w/all mks). *Beasley*. $50/£31

WASHINGTON, BOOKER T. The Future of the American Negro. Boston: Small, Maynard, 1902. 1st ed. Red cl, gilt. (Old name; spine sunned, ends sl rubbed), else VG. *Pacific**. $46/£29

WASHINGTON, BOOKER T. The Man Farthest Down. GC: Doubleday, Page, 1912. 1st ed. VG + (inner hinges starting) in VG- dj (loss to spine extrems). *Lame Duck*. $750/£469

WASHINGTON, BOOKER T. My Larger Education. H&S, 1911. 1st Eng ed. (Crease along fr cvr), else VG + . *Fine Books*. $50/£31

WASHINGTON, BOOKER T. Up from Slavery. NY: Doubleday, 1901. 1st ed. VG + (sm tear to tp gutter; spine tips lt worn). *Agvent*. $175/£109

WASHINGTON, BOOKER T. Up from Slavery. NY: LEC, 1970. One of 1500 ptd. Signed by Denver Gillen (illus). 3/4 gray buckram, brn bds. Fine in glassine, slipcase. *Pacific**. $63/£39

WASHINGTON, BOOKER T. Up from Slavery. NY: LEC, 1970. One of 1500. Signed by Denver Gillen (illus). (Bkpl), o/w Fine in NF slipcase. *Agvent*. $85/£53

WASHINGTON, BOOKER T. Working with the Hands. NY: Doubleday, 1904. 1st ed. NF (sl edgeworn). *Agvent*. $200/£125

WASHINGTON, GEORGE. Letters and Recollections of G.W....to Tobias Lear and Others Between 1790-1799.... Constable, 1906. (Edges browned; cvr sl warped, spotted, fr hinge broken.) Internally Sound. *Book Broker*. $65/£41

WASHINGTON, GEORGE. Letters from George Washington to Tobias Lear...Reprinted from the Originals in the Collection of Mr. William K. Bixby of St. Louis, Missouri. Rochester, NY: Privately ptd, 1905. Ltd to 300. Signed, inscribed by Bixby. Paper spine label, cvr label. (Cvr edges lightened.) *Sadlon*. $75/£47

WASHINGTON, GEORGE. Washington and the West Being...Diary of September 1784. A.H. Clark, 1911. (Ex-lib; cvrs soiled.) *Book Broker*. $45/£28

WASHINGTON, M. BUNCH. The Art of Romare Bearden: The Prevalence of Ritual. NY, (1972). 1st ed. Dj. *Swann**. $258/£161

Washingtoniana: Containing a Sketch of the Life and Death of the Late Gen. George Washington; with a Collection of Elegant Eulogies, Orations, Poems &c. Lancaster: William Hamilton, 1802. 1st ed. Frontis. 320,78,(401)-411pp. Period sheep. (Ink inscrip dated 1901, frontis detached, chipped, lacks part of image; sl rubbed, joints splitting), else VG. *Pacific**. $127/£79

Wasp. Special Number: Past and Present of San Francisco. SF, Aug. 29, 1896. Special issue. (Contents detached from pict wrappers as a unit), else VG. *Pacific**. $46/£29

WASSERMAN, DALE et al. Man of la Mancha. NY: Random House, (1966). 1st ed. Fine in dj (rubbed, few sm tears). *Between The Covers*. $200/£125

WASSERMANN, AUGUST. Immune Sera: Haemolysins, Cyto- toxins, and Precipitins. NY, 1904. 1st ed in English. (Ex-lib.) Fye. $125/£78

WASSON, VALENTINA PAVLOVNA and R. GORDON. Mush- rooms, Russia and History. NY: Pantheon, (1957). One of 512 numbered sets. 2 vols. Lg 4to. 82 pochoir color plts. Teg. Grn cl, red cl spine labels. Fine set in slipcase. Karmiole. $2,250/£1,406

WASSON, VALENTINA PAVLOVNA and R. GORDON. Mush- rooms, Russia and History. NY: Pantheon, (1957). 1st ed. One of 512 designed by Mardersteig, ptd by the Stamperia Val- donega. Teg. Grn cl, gilt. Fine in acetate, slipcase. Pacific*. $978/£611

WATERER, JOHN W. Leather: In Life, Art and Industry. London: Faber & Faber, 1946. 1st ed. VG in buckram. Michael Taylor. $48/£30

WATERER, JOHN W. Leather: In Life, Art and Industry. Faber, 1946. 1st ed. 110 plts. VG in dj (shabby). Whittle. $77/£48

WATERFIELD, HERMIONE and CHRISTOPHER FORBES. Faberge. Imperial Eggs and Other Fantasies. NY, 1978. 1st Amer ed. Fine in NF dj. Polyanthos. $45/£28

WATERHOUSE, ELLIS. Gainsborough. (London): Edward Hul- ton, 1958. NF in Good dj (tears, lacks pieces). Turtle Island. $85/£53

WATERHOUSE, KEITH. Billy Liar. NY: W.W. Norton, 1960. 1st US ed. VG+ in VG dj (spine top sl worn, rear sl inked). My Bookhouse. $42/£26

WATERMAN, JOSEPH M. With Sword and Lancet, the Life of General Hugh Mercer. Richmond, 1941. 1st ed. Fine in dj (worn, chipped). Pratt. $27/£17

WATERMAN, THOMAS TILESTON and JOHN A. BARROWS. Domestic Colonial Architecture of Tidewater Virginia. NY: Scribner, 1932. (Lt worn.) Slipcase (broken). Oinonen*. $170/£106

WATERMAN, THOMAS TILESTON. The Mansions of Virginia 1706-1776. Univ of NC, (1946). 2nd ptg. Signed. VG- (box sl worn). Book Broker. $50/£31

WATERS, ETHEL. To Me It's Wonderful. NY: Harper & Row, (1972). 1st ed. VG in pict dj. Petrilla. $20/£13

WATERS, FRANK. Book of the Hopi. NY: Viking, 1964. 2nd ptg. Inscribed. VG in dj (sl worn, soiled). Dumont. $85/£53

WATERS, FRANK. The Earp Brothers of Tombstone. NY: Clark- son N. Potter, 1960. 1st ed. VG in dj (clipped, spine tape-re- paired). Dumont. $50/£31

WATERS, FRANK. The Man Who Killed the Deer. London: Neville Spearman, 1962. 1st Eng ed. Inscribed. VG in dj (sl worn). Dumont. $35/£22

WATERS, FRANK. The Man Who Killed the Deer. Flagstaff: Northland, 1965. Ltd to 1250 numbered. Signed; also signed by Lawrence Clark Powell (intro). (Spine sl faded), else NF in slipcase (sl worn). Dumont. $150/£94

WATERS, FRANK. Midas of the Rockies. NY: Covici Friede, 1937. 1st ed. Inscribed. Good in dj (worn). Dumont. $95/£59

WATERS, FRANK. People of the Valley. Denver: Sage Books, n.d. (1962). Inscribed. VG in dj (sl soiled). Dumont. $50/£31

WATERS, FRANK. Pumpkin Seed Point. Chicago, 1970. 2nd ptg. Brn cl. VG+ in dj (chipped, damp). Five Quail. $25/£16

WATERS, FRANK. The Story of Mrs. Virgil Earp. NY: Clarkson N. Potter, 1960. 1st ed. VG+ in dj. Labordo. $55/£34

WATERS, FRANK. The Woman at Otowi Crossing. Denver: Alan Swallow, 1966. 1st ed, 1st state. Inscribed. VG in dj (lt worn). Dumont. $85/£53

WATERS, FRANK. The Yogi of Cockroach Court. NY: Rinehart, 1947. 1st ed. Red bds. Fine in dj (lt used). Dermont. $200/£125

WATERS, FRANK. The Yogi of Cockroach Court. NY: Rinehart, 1947. 1st ed. Red bds. NF in NF dj. House. $200/£125

WATERS, ROBERT S. North American Big Game. Pittsburgh: Boone & Crockett Club, 1971. 1st ed. Color frontis. Pict eps. Grn cl. Fine in NF pict dj. Biscotti. $75/£47

WATKIN, LAWRENCE. Thomas Jones and His Nine Lives. Har- court, Brace, 1941. 1st ed. 7x9. Janice Holland (illus). 102pp. VG in Good dj (edgeworn). Price. $30/£19

WATKINS, J. SPENCER. Lucky Montana Cowpoke. NY, 1958. 1st ed. Signed. VG in VG dj. Woolson. $15/£9

WATKINS, LUCY. Henry and Eliza. NY: Borradaile, 1823. 1st ed. VG (frontis removed, crudely partly hand-colored). Second Life. $85/£53

WATKINS-PITCHFORD, D. J. Recollections of a 'Longshore Gun- ner. Ipswich: Boydell, 1979. VG. Hollett. $32/£20

WATKINSON, RAY. William Morris as Designer. Studio Vista, 1967. 26 color plts. Protected dj (browned). Edwards. $48/£30

WATSON, B. A. A Treatise on Amputations of the Extremities and Their Complications. Phila: P. Blakiston, Son, 1885. 1st ed. xix,762pp + 32pp Feb 1886 pub's cat; 2 Fine chromolitho plts. Teg. Dk brn cl, gilt. (Few pp w/finger smudges; sl dusty, rubbed.) Text Clean, cvrs VG. Baltimore*. $100/£63

WATSON, DOUGLAS S. California in the Fifties. SF: John How- ell Books, 1936. One of 1000. 50 plts. Paper cvr label. VG. Pa- cific*. $230/£144

WATSON, DOUGLAS S. California in the Fifties: Fifty Views of Cities and Mining Towns in California and the West.... SF: John Howell Books, 1936. One of 100 on Alexandra Japan paper, w/accompanying portfolio of plts. 12x18.25. 50 plts, 50 add'l duplicate plts loose in cl folder, as issued. 3/4 morocco, paper cvr label. (Extrems scuffed), else NF in dj (worn, torn). Pacific*. $575/£359

WATSON, DOUGLAS S. An Hour's Walk Through Yerba Buena. SF: Yerba Buena Chapter of E. Clampus Vitus, 1937. Ltd to 100 ptd. Street plan frontis. NF in gray ptd wrapper. Pa- cific*. $35/£22

WATSON, DOUGLAS S. West Wind. Morongo Valley, CA, 1984. One of 999. Fldg map. NF in dj. Dumont. $50/£31

WATSON, ERNEST W. and NORMAN KENT (eds). The Relief Print. NY, 1945. Fine in dj (lt worn). Truepenny. $45/£28

WATSON, HELEN O. Chanco, a U.S. Army Homing Pigeon. NY, 1928. 1st ed. 16 photo plts. VG in dj (torn). Larry Price. $30/£19

WATSON, JAMES D. The Double Helix. NY: Atheneum, 1968. 1st ed. Fine in Fine dj (crown bumped). Unger. $150/£94

WATSON, JOHN F. Annals of Philadelphia, and Pennsylvania, in the Olden Time.... Phila: Edwin S. Stuart, 1898. 3 vols. Engr frontispieces. Crimson cl, gilt. (Few hinges lt cracked; sl worn, rubbed.) Text Clean, cvrs VG. Howes W169. Baltimore*. $90/£56

WATSON, MARGARET. Silver Theatre: Amusements of Ne- vada's Mining Frontier 1580 to 1864. Glendale: Arthur Clark, 1964. 1st ed. Fine in Fine dj. Book Market. $20/£13

WATSON, ROBERT SPENCE. The History of the Literary and Philosophical Society of Newcastle-upon-Tyne (1793-1896). London: Walter Scott, 1897. 1st ed. xii,384pp + iv subs list; fldg linen-backed table. Dec eps. Lib buckram. (Lt marginal brown- ing; lib #s, bkpl; rebound, spine discolored.) Edwards. $152/£95

WATSON, ROBERT. The History of the Reign of Philip the Sec- ond of Spain. London: W. Strahan et al, 1778. 2 vols. Full pol- ished calf, red/grn leather spine labels. (Ink sig; sl rubbed, 1 spine top worn.) Kane*. $150/£94

WATSON, ROBERT. The History of the Reign of Philip the Third, King of Spain. London: G.G.J. & J. Robinson, 1793. 3rd ed. 2 vols. (iv),460; (ii),389,(18)pp. Contemp calf (neatly rehinged, new labels). VG set. Young. $93/£58

WATSON, T. Mineral Resources of Virginia. Lynchburg: VA Jamestown Exposition Commission, 1907. (Recent eps, 10 pp w/ink notes), else Good. *Blake.* $125/£78

WATSON, W. PETRIE. Japan, Aspects and Destinies. London, 1904. 2 fldg maps. Teg. Dec cl. (Feps lt foxed; spine sl discolored.) *Edwards.* $80/£50

WATSON, WARREN N. Early Fire-Making Methods and Devices. (Washington: Gibson Bros, 1939.) 1st ed. 7 photo plts. Red cl. Good. *Karmiole.* $75/£47

WATSON, WILLIAM (ed). Chinese Ivories. Sotheby, 1984. 8 color plts. VG in dj. *Hollett.* $64/£40

WATSON, WILLIAM. The Eloping Angels. London: Elkin Mathews/John Lane, 1893. 1st ed. 7pp ads dated 1893. Black cl, gilt. Fine. *Sumner & Stillman.* $70/£44

WATSON, WILLIAM. Excursions in Criticism. London/NY: Elkin Mathews & John Lane/Macmillan, 1893. Blank before 1/2-title, imprint leaf at end; (xii),166,(ii)pp. Teg, rest uncut. Grayish-fawn buckram, gilt. (Spine sl faded, rear cvr sl mkd), o/w VG. *Temple.* $19/£12

WATSON, WILLIAM. The Father of the Forest. London/Chicago: John Lane/Stone & Kimball, 1895. 1st ed. 16pp ads dated 1895. Olive grn cl. VG+ (sl shelfworn, discolored). *Sumner & Stillman.* $45/£28

WATSON, WILLIAM. Lachrymae Musarum and Other Poems. London, 1892. 1st ed. Uncut. NF (bkpl; sl rubbed). *Polyanthos.* $25/£16

WATSON, WILLIAM. Life in the Confederate Army. NY: Scribner & Welford, 1888. 1st Amer ed. 456pp. Gold cl. Good (description pasted to fep; few sigs sl pulled, spine loose, rear hinge cracked). Howes W173. *Chapel Hill.* $250/£156

WATSON, WILLIAM. Poems. London, 1892. 1st ed. Uncut. NF (bkpl; sl rubbed). *Polyanthos.* $25/£16

WATT, GEORGE. Indian Art at Delhi 1903. London: John Murray, 1904. Frontis, 86 plts. Teg, rest uncut. Emb cl. (Lib ink stamps, bkpl; lt soiled, joints rubbed, head split, spine faded, head bumped.) *Edwards.* $192/£120

WATT, ROBERT. Bibliotheca Britannica. Edinburgh: Constable, 1824. 1st ed. 4 vols bound in 2. Contemp blind-tooled calf (vol 2 rebacked, orig spine laid down), gilt spine labels. *Karmiole.* $350/£219

WATTS, ALAN. The Joyous Cosmology. NY: Pantheon, 1962. 1st ed. Fine in NF dj (2 tears spine head). *Beasley.* $50/£31

WATTS, ALAN. This Is It and Other Essays on Zen and Spiritual Experiences. NY: Pantheon, 1960. 1st ed. Fine in dj (lt used, tear, lt soil). *Beasley.* $40/£25

WATTS, C. C. In Mid-Atlantic. London: SPCK, 1936. 1st ed. Card cvrs. VG+ in dj. *Walcot.* $48/£30

WATTS, WILLIAM LORD. Across the Vatna Jokull; or, Scenes in Iceland. London, 1876. 2 maps, 2 plts. Dec cl. *Swann*.* $172/£108

WATTS-DUNTON, THEODORE. Henry Thoreau and Other Children of the Open Air. Cedar Rapids, IA: Torch Press, 1910. 1st ed. Gray bds (spine ends sl worn). VG. *Lucas.* $45/£28

WAUGH, ALEC. The Balliols. London (etc): Cassell, (1934). 1st ed. Pink textured cl, gilt. Fine in VG pict dj (sm chips, tears). *Reese.* $35/£22

WAUGH, ALEC. Hot Countries. NY: Farrar & Rinehart, 1930. 1st ed. Lynd Ward (illus). (Sl rubbed, soiled), o/w VG. *Worldwide.* $18/£11

WAUGH, ALEC. In Praise of Wine. London: Cassell, (1959). 1st ed. NF in dj (price-clipped). *Glenn.* $45/£28

WAUGH, ALEC. Kept: A Story of Post-War London. NY: Albert & Charles Boni, 1925. 1st US ed, 3rd imp. Grn cl. Fine in pict dj (lt dust-soiled, sm nick). *Reese.* $20/£13

WAUGH, ALEC. The Prisoners of Mainz. London: Chapman & Hall, 1919. 1st ed. Frontis. Gray cl, ptd spine label. VF in pict dj. *Reese.* $275/£172

WAUGH, ALEC. Resentment Poems. London: Grant Richards, 1918. 1st ed. Paper label. VG in dj (sl frayed, fr panel fore-edge lt discolored). *Reese.* $125/£78

WAUGH, ARTHUR and THOMAS HATTON. Nonesuch Dickensiana. Bloomsbury: Nonesuch, 1937. 1st ed. Blue cl, gilt. NF. *Pacific*.* $28/£18

WAUGH, ARTHUR. A Hundred Years of Publishing, Behind the Story of Chapman and Hall Ltd. Chapman & Hall, 1930. 41 plts. Good. *Moss.* $38/£24

WAUGH, EVELYN. Basil Seal Rides Again; or The Rake's Regress. Boston: Little, Brown, 1963. 1st US ed. Ltd to 1000 signed. Fine in pub's buckram. Acetate wrapper. *Lame Duck.* $325/£203

WAUGH, EVELYN. Basil Seal Rides Again; or, The Rake's Progress. London: Chapman & Hall, 1963. 1st ed, ltd issue. One of 750 numbered, signed. 4to. Color frontis. Teg, rest untrimmed. NF in blue cl, gilt. *Vandoros.* $595/£372

WAUGH, EVELYN. Black Mischief. London, (1932). 1st ed. 8vo. Dj. *Swann*.* $1,092/£683

WAUGH, EVELYN. Black Mischief. London: Chapman & Hall, 1932. 1st ed. Frontis map. Red/black cl, gilt. VG in dj (spine sl dknd). *Maggs.* $600/£375

WAUGH, EVELYN. Black Mischief. Chapman & Hall, 1932. 1st ed. 8vo. Frontis map. Black/red cl. VG in dj (sl worn). *Sotheran.* $680/£425

WAUGH, EVELYN. Black Mischief. Chapman & Hall, 1932. 1st ed. Crown 8vo. Frontis map. Pink marbled cl, gilt. Fine (bkpl) in dj (backstrip panel sl sunned). *Blackwell's.* $800/£500

WAUGH, EVELYN. Black Mischief. Chapman & Hall, 1932. 1st ed. Ltd to 250 numbered, signed. 8vo. Teg. Purple cl (spine faded), gilt medallion fr cvr. Dj (sm tear). *Sotheby's*.* $1,195/£747

WAUGH, EVELYN. Brideshead Revisited. London: Chapman & Hall, (1946). 1st Australian ed, ptd in Melbourne. (Offset to pastedowns, ll evenly browned.) Dj (rubbed, internal paper tape repair spine head). *Swann*.* $115/£72

WAUGH, EVELYN. Brideshead Revisited. The Sacred and Profane Memories of Captain Charles Ryder. London: Chapman & Hall, 1945. Rev ed. Pale red cl (sl rubbed, lettering faded). VG in dj (creased, spine ends defective). *Maggs.* $120/£75

WAUGH, EVELYN. Brideshead Revisited. The Sacred and Profane Memories of Captain Charles Ryder. London: Chapman & Hall, 1960. New, rev ed. Fine in blue cl, gilt. Dj. *Maggs.* $160/£100

WAUGH, EVELYN. Decline and Fall. London: Chapman & Hall, 1928. 1st ed. 8vo. Fine in black/red cl, gilt. Dj (spine sl browned). *Maggs.* $4,800/£3,000

WAUGH, EVELYN. The Diaries of Evelyn Waugh. Michael Davie (ed). London: Weidenfeld & Nicolson, 1976. 1st ed. VG in brn cl. Dj. *Maggs.* $32/£20

WAUGH, EVELYN. Edmund Campion. Longmans, Green, 1935. 1st ed. Orange buckram. VG in dj. *Maggs.* $264/£165

WAUGH, EVELYN. Edmund Campion. Longmans, 1935. 1st UK ed. VG (spine sl faded, lt stained) in dj. *Williams.* $440/£275

WAUGH, EVELYN. A Handful of Dust. London: Chapman & Hall, 1934. 1st ed. 8vo. Frontis. Good in red/black cl, gilt. Dj (sl soiled, creased, repaired tears), 1/4 black morocco slipcase. *Maggs.* $2,960/£1,850

WAUGH, EVELYN. A Handful of Dust. Chapman & Hall, 1934. 1st ed. Signed, dated Nov. 1934. 8vo. Frontis. Repaired Book Society wrap-around band inserted. Patterned bds. Fine in dj. *Sotheby's*.* $3,680/£2,300

WAUGH, EVELYN. Helena. Chapman & Hall, 1950. 1st ed. Good. *Whiteson.* $19/£12

WAUGH, EVELYN. Helena. Chapman & Hall, 1950. 1st ed. (Spine foot sl rubbed), o/w VG in dj (chipped, nicked, spine foot lacks sm piece). *Virgo.* $48/£30

WAUGH, EVELYN. The Holy Places. Queen Anne, 1952. One of 950. Reynolds Stone (illus). (Cvrs sl mkd, extrems rubbed), o/w VG in dj (sl soiled, browned, sl nicked, edges chipped). *Virgo.* $208/£130

WAUGH, EVELYN. The Letters. Mark Amory (ed). London: Weidenfeld & Nicolson, 1980. 1st ed. As New in red cl. Dj. *Maggs.* $32/£20

WAUGH, EVELYN. A Little Order, a Selection from His Journalism. Donat Gallagher (ed). London, 1977. 1st ed. VG in dj. *Gretton.* $16/£10

WAUGH, EVELYN. Love Among the Ruins. Chapman & Hall, 1953. 1st ed. (Pp sl yellowed), o/w VG in VG dj (spine ends, corners sl rubbed). *Virgo.* $56/£35

WAUGH, EVELYN. Love Among the Ruins. London: Chapman & Hall, 1953. 1st ed. One of 350. Signed. Teg. Red cl, gilt. (Spine sl sunned), else NF. *Pacific*.* $196/£123

WAUGH, EVELYN. Love Among the Ruins. Chapman & Hall, 1953. One of 350 numbered, signed. Buckram. Glassine dj (sm tear). *Sotheby's*.* $442/£276

WAUGH, EVELYN. The Loved One. Chapman & Hall, (1948). 1st ed. VG in dj (lt soiled, sl chipped). *Cox.* $40/£25

WAUGH, EVELYN. The Loved One. Boston: Little, Brown, 1948. 1st Amer ed. VG in lilac cl (sl faded). Dj. *Maggs.* $48/£30

WAUGH, EVELYN. Mr. Loveday's Little Outing and Other Sad Stories. London: Chapman & Hall, (1936). 1st ed. 8vo. Frontis. Red/black cl, gilt. VG in dj (dusty, sm nicks). *Maggs.* $1,600/£1,000

WAUGH, EVELYN. Mr. Loveday's Little Outing and Other Sad Stories. Boston: Little, Brown, 1936. 1st Amer ed. One of 750. Fine in orange-red cl. Dj (sl nicked). *Maggs.* $352/£220

WAUGH, EVELYN. Mr. Loveday's Little Outing. London: Chapman & Hall, (1936). 1st ed. NF. *Black Sun.* $135/£84

WAUGH, EVELYN. Mr. Loveday's Little Outing. NY: Little, Brown, 1936. One of 700 (of 750). NF (fep sl foxed) in dj (lt soiled). *Black Sun.* $350/£219

WAUGH, EVELYN. Ninety-Two Days. Duckworth, 1934. 1st ed, 1st issue. Frontisport, map. Dj (strengthened, spine head defective, sm tears). *Sotheby's*.* $2,208/£1,380

WAUGH, EVELYN. Officers and Gentlemen. Boston, 1955. 1st Amer ed. NF in VG+ dj. *Warren.* $40/£25

WAUGH, EVELYN. Officers and Gentlemen. L-B, 1955. 1st Amer ed. (Sm nicks lower corner), else NF in VG+ dj (2 closed tears, rear panel faded). *Fine Books.* $45/£28

WAUGH, EVELYN. PRB: An Essay on Pre-Raphaelite Brotherhood 1847-54. Dalrymple, 1982. 1st ed thus. One of 475. Fine in glassine dj. *Virgo.* $160/£100

WAUGH, EVELYN. Put Out More Flags. Chapman & Hall, 1942. 1st ed. Good. *Cox.* $24/£15

WAUGH, EVELYN. Put Out More Flags. Chapman & Hall, 1942. 1st UK ed. VG in dj (sl chipped, mainly spine head). *Williams.* $232/£145

WAUGH, EVELYN. Put Out More Flags. Chapman & Hall, 1942. 1st ed. 8vo. Buckram. Fine (bkpl? removed from ep) in Fine dj. *Sotheby's*.* $626/£391

WAUGH, EVELYN. Remote People. London: Duckworth, 1931. 1st ed. Inscribed presentation. 8vo. 2 fldg maps. Fine (bkpl) in maroon cl, gilt. Plain grn dj (edges sl chipped). *Maggs.* $3,200/£2,000

WAUGH, EVELYN. Robbery Under Law. Chapman & Hall, 1939. 1st ed. 8vo. Dj (repaired, sl defective). *Sotheby's*.* $736/£460

WAUGH, EVELYN. Rossetti. NY: Dodd, Mead, 1928. 1st US ed. NF in VG- dj (top edge fr panel chipped, 1-inch loss to foot, 1/2-inch loss to spine head). *Lame Duck.* $275/£172

WAUGH, EVELYN. Scoop. Chapman & Hall, 1933. 1st UK ed, 2nd state dj, w/o 'Daily Beast' heading on fr cvr. NF (fr cvr bumped) in VG dj (sl rubbed, edges worn). *Williams.* $760/£475

WAUGH, EVELYN. Scoop. Chapman & Hall, 1933. 1st UK ed, 1st issue w/misprint last line of pg 88; 1st issue dj w/'aily Beas' newspaper title on fr panel. VG in dj (rubbed, creased, worn, few closed tears, edges sl chipped). *Williams.* $952/£595

WAUGH, EVELYN. Scoop. London: Chapman & Hall, 1933. 1st ed. Inscribed presentation. 8vo. Black/red cl, gilt. *Maggs.* $3,200/£2,000

WAUGH, EVELYN. Scoop. Chapman & Hall, 1938. 1st ed. (Foxed, eps, edges browned; spine sl faded, ends rubbed; lacks dj), o/w Good. *Virgo.* $56/£35

WAUGH, EVELYN. Scoop. London, 1964. Reset ed. Fine in dj. *Clearwater.* $48/£30

WAUGH, EVELYN. Scoop. Folio Soc, 1982. 1st UK ed. Mint in slipcase. *Martin.* $19/£12

WAUGH, EVELYN. Scott-King's Modern Europe. Chapman, 1947. 1st UK ed. NF in VG dj (sl worn, sl torn). *Martin.* $26/£16

WAUGH, EVELYN. Sword of Honour. London: Chapman & Hall, (1965). 1st ed. Errata sheet tipped in. Fine in dj (spine sl dknd). *Lenz.* $150/£94

WAUGH, EVELYN. Sword of Honour. London, 1965. 1st Eng ed. W/errata slip. VG in dj (sl tanned). *Clearwater.* $240/£150

WAUGH, EVELYN. They Were Still Dancing. NY: Farrar & Rhinehart, 1932. 1st Amer ed, 2nd issue. VG in yellow cl. Dj (spine ends sl chipped). *Maggs.* $360/£225

WAUGH, EVELYN. They Were Still Dancing. F&R, 1932. 1st Amer ed. (Sl black residue bottom edge of cvr), else NF in VG+ dj (sl dust-soiled). *Fine Books.* $450/£281

WAUGH, EVELYN. A Tourist in Africa. Chapman, 1960. 1st UK ed. (Few tears fr panel), o/w Fine in Fine dj. *Martin.* $29/£18

WAUGH, EVELYN. A Tourist in Africa. Chapman & Hall, 1960. 1st ed. VG in dj (sl browned, chipped). *Virgo.* $32/£20

WAUGH, EVELYN. A Tourist in Africa. London, 1960. 1st ed. Dj (price-clipped, spine tanned). *Swann*.* $46/£29

WAUGH, EVELYN. Unconditional Surrender. London: C&H, 1961. 1st ed. Fine in dj. *Between The Covers.* $85/£53

WAUGH, EVELYN. Unconditional Surrender. London: Chapman & Hall, 1961. 1st Eng ed. Signed. VG (feps sl browned; cvrs mkd) in dj (sl rubbed, mkd, dusty, edges sl browned). *Ulysses.* $520/£325

WAUGH, EVELYN. Vile Bodies. Chapman & Hall, 1930. 1st UK ed. NF. *Williams.* $400/£250

WAUGH, EVELYN. Vile Bodies. Chapman & Hall, 1930. 1st ed. 8vo. Patterned cl. Dj (strengthened, sm spine tears). *Sotheby's*.* $4,048/£2,530

WAUGH, EVELYN. Waugh in Abyssinia. Longmans Green, 1936. 1st ed. (Sm ink mk p2; bds sl strained, sl grubby, spine mk; lacks dj), o/w Good. *Virgo.* $160/£100

WAUGH, EVELYN. Waugh in Abyssinia. Longmans, Green, 1936. 1st ed. Inscribed presentation. 8vo. 1st issue dj (spine head sl defective). *Sotheby's*.* $1,656/£1,035

WAUGH, EVELYN. Wine in Peace and War. London: Saccone & Speed, (1947). 1st ed. VG in cream bds (sm puncture to fr joint, glue seepage stains to eps). *Maggs.* $160/£100

WAUGH, F. A. The American Apple Orchard. NY: OJ, 1917. Grn cl, gilt. VG. *Larry Price.* $40/£25

WAUGH, FRANCIS G. The Athenaeum Club and Its Associations. London: Privately ptd, (ca 1900). One of 50. *Marlborough*. $80/£50

WAUGH, FREDERICK J. The Clan of Munes. NY: Scribner, 1916. 1st ed. Obl lg 4to. Color dec cl (fr hinge starting). Clean in pict dj (lacks pieces, dusty). *Reisler*. $685/£428

WAUGH, HILLARY. The Priscilla Copperwaite Case. London: Gollancz, 1986. 1st ed. Fine in dj. *Murder*. $40/£25

WAUGH, IDA. Ideal Heads. Phila: Sunshine, 1890. 1st ed. Sm folio. 24 litho plts by Waugh, 1 b/w dwg by Jessie Wilcox Smith. Aeg. Brn cl (spine, corners worn), gilt. *Reisler*. $400/£250

WAUGH, NORAH. Corsets and Crinolines. Batsford, 1954. 1st ed. (Lt spotted.) Dj (edges sl ragged). *Edwards*. $120/£75

WAUTERS, A. J. Stanley's Emin Pasha Expedition. London: John C. Nimmo, 1890. 1st ed. Frontisport, xvii,(i)blank,378,(31) pub's list; fldg map, 32 engr plts. Brn cl, gilt. Generally Good (sl foxed, lib plt; label removed fr cvr, fr hinge weak.) *Morrell*. $88/£55

WAY, FREDERICK, JR. The Saga of the Delta Queen. Picture Marine Pub, (1951). 1st ed. (Eps foxed.) Dj (worn). *Rybski*. $25/£16

WAY, THOMAS R. and PHILIP NORMAN. The Ancient Halls of the City Guilds. NY, 1903. One of 100 signed by Way. 30 litho plts. Gilt-pict cl. *Swann**. $138/£86

WAY, THOMAS R. Memories of James McNeill Whistler. London: John Lane, 1912. 1st ed. 38 plts, ptd tissue guards. (Soiled, spine dknd, ends chipped), else VG. *Pacific**. $58/£36

WAY, W. IRVING. Migratory Books. SF: Ernest Dawson, 1924. One of 500. Wrappers in dj, paper cvr label, matching shipping envelope. *Dawson*. $50/£31

WAYLAND, FRANCIS. A Memoir of the Life and Labors of the Rev. Adoniram Judson. NY: Shedon, 1861. 2 vols in 1. Frontis, 544; 404pp. (Lib spine #; edges rubbed, spine torn, ends chipped), o/w VG. *Worldwide*. $35/£22

WAYLAND, JOHN W. The Pathfinder of the Seas: The Life of Matthew Fontaine Maury. Garrett & Massie, (c1930). Good + (spine frayed, rear hinge torn). *Book Broker*. $45/£28

WAYLAND, JOHN W. Stonewall Jackson's Way: Route—Method—Achievement. Verona: McClure, 1969. 3rd ptg (so stated). Gray-grn coated cl, port fr cvr. Very Clean (sl worn, rubbed). *Baltimore**. $75/£47

WAYMAN, JOHN HUDSON. A Doctor on the California Trail. Denver: Old West, 1971. 1st ed. Frontis, fldg map. Fine. *Parmer*. $39/£24

WAYNE, HENRY C. The Sword Exercise, Arranged for Military Instruction. Wash: Gideon, 1850. 23 plts. (Rebacked, worn, lt dampstained.) *Oinonen**. $100/£63

We Read More Pictures. Chicago: Scott Foresman, 1951. 2 vols. 11.5x8.5. VG (pencil mks, worn) in wraps. *My Bookhouse*. $52/£33

WEALE, J. A Dictionary of Terms. R. Hunt (ed). London: Crosby Lockwood, 1876. 5th ed. xii,569pp + ads. (Hinges weak), else Good. *Blake*. $65/£41

WEARIN, OTHA D. Clarence Arthur Ellsworth. Shenandoah, IA, 1967. One of 750. Signed. Folio. Dj. *Heinoldt*. $75/£47

WEATHERLY, F. E. Apes and Scrapes. London: Hildesheimer & Faulkner, (ca 1890). Obl 12mo. 5 full-pg color plts by H.R. Miller and H.H. Couldery. Good in stiff color paper wrappers. *Reisler*. $60/£38

WEATHERLY, F. E. Touch and Go. A Book of Transformation Pictures.... London/NY: Nister/Dutton, (1894). 4to. (10)ff; 8 chromolitho transforming illus, each slatted so that when one pulls the tab, it dissolves to be replaced by another picture. Cl-backed bds w/chromolitho illus. (Foxing, wear to extrems and tabs, inner hinges carefully mended w/tape.) Complete, w/all pictures Fine and in working condition. *Bromer*. $975/£609

WEATHERWAX, PAUL. Indian Corn in Old America. NY: Macmillan, 1954. 1st ptg. VG in dj (worn). *Dumont*. $40/£25

WEAVER, JOHN D. The Brownsville Raid. NY: W.W. Norton, (1970). 1st ed. VG in illus dj. *Petrilla*. $25/£16

WEAVER, LAWRENCE (ed). Houses and Gardens by E. L. Lutyens. London, 1914. Folio. 1/2 cl (soiled, extrems worn, sl cocked). *Swann**. $287/£179

WEAVER, LAWRENCE. Luytens Houses and Gardens. London: Country Life, 1921. 1st ed. Frontis port. Grn buckram, grn bds (edges sl rubbed), gilt, ptd paper label fr cvr. VG (fr hinge cracked). *Baltimore**. $60/£38

WEAVER, LAWRENCE. Luytens Houses and Gardens. London: Country Life, 1921. 1st ed w/smaller format and added preface. Frontis, 146 photo engrs, plans. Paper label on fr bd. (Sl bowed), else Fine. *Quest*. $90/£56

WEAVER, MIKE. Alvin Langdon Coburn. Symbolist Photographer 1882-1966. NY: Aperture, 1986. 1st ed. Fine in dj. *Smith*. $45/£28

WEBB, CHARLES. The Graduate. NY: NAL, 1963. 1st ed. VG in VG dj. *Unger*. $125/£78

WEBB, CLIFFORD. The Go-to-Bed Book. Warne, 1935. 1st ed. Pub's file copy stamp on fep. 4 color plts. NF in VG pict dj (soiled, frayed). *Any Amount*. $56/£35

WEBB, DANIEL. An Enquiry into the Beauties of Painting; and into the Merits of the Most Celebrated Painters.... London: Dodsley, 1760. 1st ed. xv,200pp. Contemp full calf, gilt. (Pencil underlining; rebacked), o/w Fine. *Europa*. $136/£85

WEBB, F. R. Manual of the Canvas Canoe: Its Construction. NY: Forest & Stream, 1898. 1st ed. Mustard cl, gilt. (Soiled, spine head rubbed, sm tears tp), else VG. *Pacific**. $161/£101

WEBB, JAMES. Fields of Fire. Englewood Cliffs: Prentice-Hall, 1978. 1st ed, 1st bk. VG + (sl shelfworn) in dj (sl worn, sl faded). *My Bookhouse*. $37/£23

WEBB, JANE. The Mummy! A Tale of the Twenty-second Century. Henry Colburn, 1827. 1st ed. 3 vols. 12mo. Half-titles in vols 2, 3. Old 1/2 calf (partly restored, rebacked). *Sotheby's**. $2,576/£1,610

WEBB, LAURA S. Custer's Immortality: A Poem, with Biographical Sketches. (NY: Evening Post Stream Presses, n.d.) 1st ed. Steel-engr frontisport, 72pp; fldg map, facs letter dated July 26, 1876. Aeg. Gilt-dec cl. (Hinges repaired, resulting in rep tear), else VG. *Pacific**. $150/£94

WEBB, M. I. Michael Rysbrack. Country Life, 1954. 1st ed. 95 plts. VG in dj. *Hollett*. $72/£45

WEBB, MARY. Armour Wherein He Trusted. NY: Dutton, (1929). 1st Amer ed. Fine in VG + dj (extrems sl chipped). *Between The Covers*. $125/£78

WEBB, MARY. The Golden Arrow. London: Constable, 1916. 1st ed. Inscribed presentation. 8vo. (Spine sl dknd, joints lt worn, lt vertical spine crease, binding sl cracked, corners sl bumped.) *Maggs*. $720/£450

WEBB, MARY. Gone to Earth. London: Constable, (1917). 1st ed. Aeg. 3/4 red morocco, gilt, raised bands; bound by Sangorski & Sutcliffe. (Spine sl sunned), else NF. *Pacific**. $40/£25

WEBB, MARY. The House in Dormer Forest. London: Hutchinson, n.d. (1920). 1st ed. Inscribed. Brn cl. Fr panel of dj pasted to fep. VG. *Maggs*. $240/£150

WEBB, MARY. Precious Bane, a Novel. London: Cape, (1924). 1st ed. 1924 inscribed presentation. Grn cl, gilt. VG + (sl faded) in 1/2 morocco slipcase. *Reese*. $450/£281

WEBB, W. E. Buffalo Land. Cincinnati/Chicago: E. Hannaford, 1872. 1st ed. 503pp. Recent brn coated cl, mottled bds, gilt-lettered cl spine label. (Sl browned, lt spot stains, foxing, old dampstain to margins of 1st 60pp, trimmed orig fr blank w/undated signed ink presentation by publisher.) *Baltimore**. $55/£34

WEBB, W. L. Battles and Biographies of Missourians or the Civil War Period of Our State. Kansas City, MO: Hudson-Kimberly, 1900. 1st ed. Frontisport, add'l ports (incl 19 bound in at rear). Grn cl. VG. *Chapel Hill.* $300/£188

WEBB, WALTER PRESCOTT. Flat Top. El Paso, TX: Carl Hertzog, 1960. 1st ed. One of 200 cl-bound. VF. *Labordo.* $150/£94

WEBB, WALTER PRESCOTT. The Great Plains. Boston: Gin, (1931). 2nd issue, w/o errors on p10. Silver pict cl. NF. Howes W193. *Sadlon.* $40/£25

WEBB, WALTER PRESCOTT. The Texas Rangers, a Century of Frontier Defense. Boston: Houghton Mifflin, 1935. 1st ed, 1st state. VG in dj (chipped, worn). Howes W194. *Labordo.* $175/£109

WEBB, WALTER PRESCOTT. The Texas Rangers. Boston, 1935. Not 1st ed. Reading copy. VG (sig, add'l inked notes, bkpl; fabric torn about 1-inch at lower fr joint, cvrs sl spotted). Howes W194. *Baade.* $30/£19

WEBB, WALTER PRESCOTT. The Texas Rangers: A Century of Frontier Defence. Boston: Houghton Mifflin, 1935. 1st ed. (Spine sl dull), else NF in dj (chipped, lt worn). Howes W194. *Pacific*.* $161/£101

WEBB, WILLIAM SEWARD. California and Alaska and Over the Canadian Pacific Railway. NY, 1890. One of 500 numbered. Teg, uncut. Pub's morocco stamped in blind/gilt. (Rubbed.) *Oinonen*.* $325/£203

WEBB, WILLIAM SEWARD. California and Alaska. And Over the Canadian Pacific Railway. NY: Putnam, 1891. 2nd ed. xiv,268pp; 12 full-pg photo plts. Dec rose cl. *Karmiole.* $100/£63

WEBBER, BYRON. James Orrock, R.I. C&W, 1903. One of 500. 2 vols. Sm folio. Teg, uncut. Dec cl, gilt extra. (Few spots.) *Hollett.* $152/£95

WEBER, BRUCE. Bear Pond. NY, (1990). 1st ed. Contents Clean. Dj (corners bumped, rear inner flap creased). *Swann*.* $402/£251

WEBER, BRUCE. Bruce Weber. NY, (1989). 1st ed. Folio. (Sl worn.) Dj, wrapper (sl worn). *Swann*.* $230/£144

WEBER, BRUCE. Let's Get Lost. NY, 1988. 1st ed. Fine in orig oversize wraps (short tear at corner fr panel). *Warren.* $150/£94

WEBER, BRUCE. Looking Good. NY: Hawthorn, 1977. 1st ed. NF (fep corner creased) in dj (few closed tears). *Smith.* $125/£78

WEBER, BRUCE. O Rio de Janeiro, a Photographic Journal. (NY, 1986.) 1st ed. Folio. (Sig fep.) Photo-pict stiff wrappers, acetate wrapper. *Swann*.* $632/£395

WEBER, CARL J. A Bibliography of Jacob Abbott. Waterville: Colby College, 1948. (Lt worn.) Dj (edges sl stained, frayed). *Oinonen*.* $160/£100

WEBER, DAVID J. The Californios Versus Jedediah Smith, 1826-1827. Spokane: Arthur Clark, 1990. 1st ed. Ltd to 1000. Fine. *Book Market.* $40/£25

WEBER, FRANCIS J. A Bibliography of California Bibliographies. L.A.: Ward Ritchie, (1968). 1st ed. Ltd to 500. Fine in Fine slipcase. *Book Market.* $75/£47

WEBER, FRANCIS J. The Peninsular California Missions, 1808-1880. L.A., 1979. One of 300. Blue cl, gilt. (Owner stamps), o/w Fine. *Parmer.* $55/£34

WEBER, FRANCIS J. Readings in California Catholic History. L.A.: Westernlore, 1967. 1st ed. Fine in Fine dj. *Book Market.* $50/£31

WEBER, LENORA MATTINGLY. Wind on the Prairie. Boston: LBCo, 1929. 1st ed, 1st bk. 5.75x8. Kurt Wiese (illus). 276pp. Good. *Cattermole.* $40/£25

WEBSTER, A. D. British Orchids. London, 1898. 2nd, enlgd ed. 132pp + (iii)pp ads. (Bkpl; eps sl browned.) *Edwards.* $64/£40

WEBSTER, C. K. (ed). Britain and the Independence of Latin America 1812-1830. OUP, 1938. 2 vols. *Edwards.* $80/£50

WEBSTER, CAROLINE LE ROY. Mr. W. and I, Being the Authentic Diary.... Binghamton: Ives Washburn, c. 1942. VG in dj (worn). *Parmer.* $35/£22

WEBSTER, DANIEL. The Rhode Island Question. Mr. Webster's Argument...January 27th, 1848. Washington: J. & G.S. Gideon, 1848. 1st ed. 20pp (top margin stained). Orig ptd fr wrapper, sewn. *M & S.* $175/£109

WEBSTER, E. B. Fishing in the Olympics. Port Angeles: Evening News, (1923). 1st ed. VG. *Pacific*.* $40/£25

WEBSTER, FRANK V. The Newsboy Partners. NY: Cupples & Leon, 1909. 5x7.5. 203pp. (Shelfworn), else VG + in dj (edge-worn). *My Bookhouse.* $42/£26

WEBSTER, JOHN. Introduction to Fungi. Cambridge: CUP, 1970. 1st ed. Fine in VG dj. *Archer.* $30/£19

WEBSTER, NOAH. The Elementary Spelling-Book. NY: D. Appleton, (ca 1860). 168pp (bkseller stamp). Ptd blue bds, tan cl spine. Cvr title has imprint of H.H. Bancroft & Co, rear cvr is ad for Bancroft Co. *Dawson.* $75/£47

WECHSELMANN, WILHELM. The Treatment of Syphilis with Salvarsan. NY, 1911. 1st ed in English. 16 color plts. *Fye.* $200/£125

WECHSLER, HERMAN J. Great Prints and Printmakers. London, 1967. 1st UK ed. 16 tipped-in color plts. (Bkpl; spine head sl faded.) Dj (sl ragged). *Edwards.* $48/£30

WEDEL, W. R. An Introduction to Pawnee Archeology. BAE Bulletin 112. Washington: GPO, 1936. (Rear cvr sl creased), else Good in wraps. *King.* $35/£22

WEDEL, W. R. et al. River Basin Surveys Papers. Washington: Smithsonian, 1953. 1st ed. 56 plts, fldg map. Cl w/orig wraps bound in. (Ex-lib), else Fine. *Mikesh.* $25/£16

WEEGEE. Naked City. NY, (1945). 1st ed. (1/2-title creased, fore-edge soiled; dampstained.) *Swann*.* $201/£126

WEEGEE. Weegee, an Autobiography. NY, (1961). 1st ed. 116 repros. (Prelims, ep, rear pastedown sl foxed; spine ends bumped.) Dj (torn, soiled). *Swann*.* $126/£79

Week at Harrogate. A Poem: In a Series of Letters. (By Barbara Hoole.) Knaresborough: Ptd (for the Author) at Hargrove's Office, 1812. 1st ed. Half-title present, engr frontis (offset to tp), 84pp. Untrimmed. Ptd buff bds, pub's ads rear cvr. Good (loss to backstrip tail, sl loss to head). *Blackwell's.* $136/£85

WEEKS, DONALD (ed). Frederick Rolfe and the Times 4-12 February 1901. Edinburgh: Tragara, 1977. Ltd to 175 numbered. VG in wraps. *King.* $35/£22

WEEKS, DONALD. Frederick William Rolfe, Christchurch, and the Artist. Edinburgh: Tragara, 1980. One of 120. Signed. NF in wrappers (edges sl creased). *Ulysses.* $56/£35

WEEKS, DONALD. Frederick William Rolfe, the 1903 Conclave and Hartwell de la Garde Grissell. Edinburgh: Tragara, 1982. One of 110. Signed. Fine in wrappers (edges sl creased). *Ulysses.* $40/£25

WEEKS, DONALD. Rolfe Without Frederick. Edinburgh: Tragara, 1983. One of 110. Signed. Fine in wrappers. *Ulysses.* $56/£35

WEEKS, E. The Moise Salmon Club. Barre, MA: Barre Pub, 1971. 1st ed. Ltd to 1500 signed. This copy not signed. 1/4 dark blue buckram, blue-grn buckram-cvrd bds. Fine in Fine slipcase. *Biscotti.* $160/£100

WEEKS, E. The Moisie Salmon Club. Barre: Barre Publishers, 1971. 1st ed. One of 1500 ptd. Color frontis. Silver-dec cl. Fine in slipcase. *Pacific*.* $92/£58

WEEKS, E. Writers and Friends. L-B, 1981. 1st ed. Fine in dj. *Fine Books.* $18/£11

WEEKS, EDWIN. From the Black Sea Through Persia and India. NY, 1896. Frontisport, xii,437pp + (ii)pub's ads. Teg. Gilt-dec cl (corner sl frayed w/sl cl loss, spine sl chipped). *Edwards.* $200/£125

WEGENROTH, STOW. Stow Wegenroth's New England. Barre: Barre Publishers, 1969. 1st ed. One of 350. Signed on orig litho at rear. 1/4 cl, bds, gilt. Fine in slipcase. *Pacific**. $374/£234

WEGMANN, EDWARD. The Design and Construction of Dams. London, 1900. 4th ed, 1st thousand. Frontis, 11 plts, 86 fldg plts, 24 tables. (Hinges tender; rebacked, orig spine laid down, corners rubbed.) *Edwards*. $120/£75

WEHR, JULIAN. Animated Antics in Playland. OH/NY: Saalfield, 1946. Julian Wehr (engineer). 20x26 cm. 4pp animations. Spiral binding (broken, strengthened w/scotch tape). Internally VG. *Bookfinders*. $65/£41

WEHR, JULIAN. Animated Nursery Tales. NY: G&D, (1943). 8vo. 6 moveable images. Illus yellow cvr, spiral back. Good in color dj (dusting, marginal wear). *Reisler*. $225/£141

WEHR, JULIAN. Mother Goose Panorama. McLoughlin Bros, 1957. 10 heavy bd reversible panels which fold into 2-sided panorama. Pict bds. VG-. *Bookfinders*. $60/£38

WEIBEL, M. A Guide to the Minerals of Switzerland. NY: Wiley-Interscience, c1966. VG. *Blake*. $100/£63

WEIBERT, DON. Custer, Cases and Cartridges. Billings, MT: Don Weibert, (1989). 1st ed. Ltd to 1000. Signed by Henry and Don Weibert. Obl folio. Fine in dj. *Lien*. $175/£109

WEICHERT, CHARLES K. Anatomy of the Chordates. NY, 1951. 1st ed. Olive cl, gilt. VG. *Larry Price*. $35/£22

WEIDENMANN, JACOB. Beautifying Country Homes. A Handbook of Landscape Gardening. NY: OJ, (1870). Folio. 24 color litho plts. (Cvrs worn, spotted; shaken, sl foxed, soiled; inner joints broken.) Internally Sound, Clean. *Oinonen**. $750/£469

WEIGELT, CURT H. Sienese Painting of the Trecento. Firenze/NY, 1930. Sm folio. 120 collotype plts, guards. Good. *Washton*. $145/£91

WEILERSTEIN, SADIE ROSE. Ten and a Kid. Doubleday, 1961. 1st ed. Janina Domanska (illus). 182pp. VG (bottom corner bumped) in Good+ dj (1.5-inch chip across spine head, corner sl chipped). *Price*. $32/£20

WEINBAUM, STANLEY G. The Black Flame. Reading: Fantasy, 1948. 1st ed, trade issue. VG (top edge lt stained, spine cocked) in dj (lt chipped, rear panel foxed). *Other Worlds*. $35/£22

WEINBAUM, STANLEY G. The Dark Other. L.A.: F.P.C.I., 1950. 1st ed, 1st binding. Blue cl. (Corners bumped), else NF in NF dj (rear panel fold, flap edges damaged). Bkpl of Oswald Train. *Other Worlds*. $50/£31

WEINBERGER, BERNARD WOLF. An Introduction to the History of Dentistry in America. St. Louis, 1948. 1st ed. 2 vols. (Lt worn, sl foxed.) Dj (soiled, edgeworn). *Oinonen**. $250/£156

WEINHARDT, CARL J. (intro). The Most of John Held, Jr. Brattleboro, VT: Stephen Greene, (1972). Orig ed. NF in dj. *Turtle Island*. $65/£41

WEINSTEIN, MICHAEL. Precious and Semi-Precious Stones. London: Pitman, 1929. Color frontis, 16 plts. VG. *Hollett*. $40/£25

WEINTHAL, LEO (ed). The Story of the Cape to Cairo Railway and River Route from 1887 to 1922. London: Pioneer Publishing, (1923-26). 4to. 5 vols incl index and map folder. 12 fldg color litho maps. Contemp 1/2 morocco, gilt. (Label pasted in, bkpl.) *Christie's**. $1,080/£675

WEIR, IRENE. Robert W. Weir. NY: House of Field-Doubleday, (1947). Orig ed. VG in dj (water-stained). *Turtle Island*. $45/£28

WEIR, ROBERT and J. MORAY BROWN. Riding and Polo. London: Longmans, Green, 1891. 2nd ed. Teg. 3/4 blue morocco, orange cl, gilt. (Foxed; spine ends scuffed), else VG. *Pacific**. $46/£29

WEIS, NORMAN D. Ghost Towns of the Northwest. Caldwell: Caxton, 1971. 1st ed. (Name stamp), else Fine in dj. *Perier*. $25/£16

WEISBACH, WERNER. Spanish Baroque Art. Cambridge, 1941. 1st Eng ed. Nice in dj (sl frayed, foxed). *Clearwater*. $40/£25

WEISBERG, HAROLD. Oswald in New Orleans. NY, (1967). 1st ed. VG in wraps. *King*. $25/£16

WEISBERGER, BERNARD A. Reporters for the Union. Boston: Little, Brown, 1953. 1st ed. Good in dj (wrapper rubbed, nicked). *Brown*. $15/£9

WEISBORD, ALBERT. The Conquest of Power. NY: Covici-Friede, 1937. 1st ed. 2 vols. Fine (spine sl sunned) in djs (lt used). *Beasley*. $125/£78

WEISHAUS, JOEL. Oxherding. SF: Cranium, (1971). One of 750. 9 loose sigs, facing orig tipped-in block prints by Arthur Okamura. Block ptd paper portfolio w/ribbon ties. *Turtle Island*. $95/£59

WEISMANN, AUGUST. Essays Upon Heredity and Kindred Biological Problems. Oxford, 1891. 2nd ed. 2 vols. 471; 226pp. (Ex-lib.) *Fye*. $125/£78

WEISS, HARRY B. Country Doctor: Cornelius Wilson Larison. Trenton, NJ, 1953. VG in ptd wrappers. *Doctor's Library*. $20/£13

WEISS, PETER. Bodies and Shadows. NY: Delacorte, (1969). 1st Amer ed. VF in VF dj. *Between The Covers*. $100/£63

WEISS, PETER. The Leavetaking. HBW, 1962. 1st Amer ed. NF in dj. *Fine Books*. $25/£16

WEISS, PETER. The Persecution and Assassination of Jean-Paul Marat as Performed by the Inmates of the Asylum of Charenton Under the Direction of the Marquis de Sade. NY: Atheneum, 1965. 1st Amer ed. VF in VF dj. *Between The Covers*. $350/£219

WEISS, SAMUEL. Diseases of the Liver, Gall Bladder, Ducts, and Pancreas. Their Diagnosis and Treatment. NY, 1935. 1st ed. *Fye*. $100/£63

WEITZMANN, KURT et al. A Treasury of Icons. NY: Harry N. Abrams, (1967). 1st ed. 58 mtd color plts. Natural linen, gilt. Good in color-illus dj. *Karmiole*. $150/£94

WEIZMANN, C. and R. GOTTHEIL. What Is Zionism? London: The Zionist Organization, 1918. NF. *Edrich*. $19/£12

WELCH, DENTON. Extracts from His Published Works. J. Brooke (ed). London, 1963. VG in dj (sl soiled). *Typographeum*. $35/£22

WELCH, DENTON. In Youth Is Pleasure. London, 1944. 1st Eng ed. VG (cvrs sl foxed) in dj (sl nicked, mkd). *Clearwater*. $96/£60

WELCH, DENTON. The Journals of Denton Welch. Michael De-la-Noy (ed). Allison & Busby, 1984. 1st unabridged ed. VG in dj. *Virgo*. $32/£20

WELCH, DENTON. A Last Sheaf. (Eric Oliver, ed). Lehmann, 1951. 1st Eng ed. Nice (spine sl sunned) in dj (sl rubbed, 1 sm hole rear panel). *Clearwater*. $88/£55

WELCH, DENTON. A Voice Through a Cloud. London: John Lehmann, 1950. 1st ed. Red cl. Fine in dj. *Maggs*. $88/£55

WELCH, STUART CARY. Indian Paintings and Painted Sketches. Asia Soc, 1976. 1st ed. Dj. *Edwards*. $72/£45

WELCH, WILLIAM. Papers and Addresses. Balt, 1920. 1st ed. 3 vols. *Fye*. $300/£188

WELD, ISAAC. Travels Through the States of North America, and the Provinces of Upper and Lower Canada During the Years 1795, London: Stockdale, 1799. 1st ed. Sm folio. 24,464pp; 14 plts. 3 add'l contemp maps laid in. 3/4 leather. (Lacks 2 plts, erratum slip; tp, frontis repaired, corner torn off preface pg.) *Heinoldt*. $400/£250

WELD, ISAAC. Travels Through the States of North America, and the Provinces of Upper and Lower Canada During the Years 1795, 1796, and 1797. John Stockdale, 1800. 3rd ed. 2 vols. 8vo. viii,376pp; 11 plts, 3 maps (1 color). Full contemp marbled calf, black leather label. VG set (extrems sl rubbed). *Sotheran*. $1,117/£698

WELD, ISAAC. Travels Through the States of North America, and the Provinces of Upper and Lower Canada, During the Years 1795, 1796, and 1797. London: John Stockdale, 1799. 1st ed. 4to. 16 engr plts, maps. Contemp 1/2 sheep. (Lt foxed, marginally affecting some plts; sm lib stamp; needs rebacking.) Howes W235. *Swann**. $632/£395

WELD, ISAAC. Travels Through the States of North America, and the Provinces of Upper and Lower Canada, During the Years 1795, 1796, and 1797. London, 1807. 2 vols. 16 maps, plts. Contemp tree calf (1 cvr loose). *Swann**. $138/£86

WELLCOME, HENRY S. The Story of Metlakahtla. London: Saxon, 1887. 4th ed. 483pp. Good (cvr stained). *Perier*. $50/£31

WELLER, ALLEN S. Art USA Now. Lee Nordness (ed). Lucerne, (1962). 2 vols. (Sl rubbed.) Slipcase (rubbed). *King*. $100/£63

WELLER, CHARLES E. Yesterday. Indianapolis: The Author, 1921. 1st ed. Port. (Shelfworn, spotted, spine lettering faded), else Good. *Brown*. $25/£16

WELLES, GIDEON. Diary of Gideon Welles. Boston, (1911). 1st ed. 3 vols. Frontis each vol. Orig djs (spines dknd; vol 3 in fragments). *Kane**. $110/£69

WELLES, GIDEON. Diary of Gideon Welles. Boston, 1911. 1st ed. 3 vols. (Sl worn, bkpls; all sl cockeyed.) Howes W240. *Woolman*. $40/£25

WELLES, GIDEON. Letter of the Secretary of the Navy...the Capture of Forts Jackson, St. Philip, and the City of New Orleans.... Washington: GPO, 1862. 37th Congress, 2d Session, SED 56. 107pp (sl aging); 3 VG fldg b/w litho maps (lt mis-folded, few sm tears), 2 hand-color litho plts (1 nearly detached, sm chunk missing 1 margin). Recent olive buckram (sl rubbed). *Baltimore**. $50/£31

WELLES, S. P. A New Species of Elasmosaur from the Aptian of Colombia and a Review of the Cretaceous Pleisours. Berkeley: Univ of CA, 1962. 1st ed. 4 plts. Fine in wraps. *Mikesh*. $25/£16

WELLESLEY, DOROTHY. Early Light, the Collected Poems of.... London: Rupert Hart-Davis, 1955. 1st ed. Fine in dj (lt sunned, nicked). *Reese*. $30/£19

WELLING, WILLIAM. Photography in America: The Formative Years, 1839-1900. NY: Crowell, (1978). 1st ed. NF in VG dj. *Baltimore**. $70/£44

WELLINGTON, BARRET R. The Mystery of Elizabeth Canning, as Found in the Testimony of the Old Bailey Trials and Other Records. NY: J. Ray Peck, 1940. *Boswell*. $75/£47

WELLINGTON, DUKE OF. The Dispatches of Field Marshal the Duke of Wellington.... Lieut. Colonel Gurwood (comp). John Murray, 1837-1839. New ed. 8vo. 13 vols. (Some spotting.) Contemp diced calf (extrems worn; bkpl), gilt. *Sotheby's**. $1,104/£690

WELLINGTON, DUKE OF. The Speeches of the Duke of Wellington in Parliament. John Murray, 1854. 1st ed. 2 vols. xiv,760; 759pp (blindstamps on tps). Later 1/2 calf (rubbed, scraped), gilt. Good set. *Hollett*. $136/£85

WELLINGTON, EVELYN. A Descriptive and Historical Catalogue of the Collection of Pictures and Sculpture at Apsley House, London. London: Longman, Green, 1901. One of 400. 2 vols. 51 mtd photo-engrs. Aeg. 1/2 vellum, gilt, cream buckram, gilt escutcheon. VG set. *Europa*. $472/£295

WELLMAN, MANLY WADE. The Beasts from Beyond. Manchester: World/Sydney, (1950). 1st ed. (Diagonal cvr crease, sm closed tear spine edge), else NF in pict wrappers. *Other Worlds*. $75/£47

WELLMAN, MANLY WADE. Rebel Boast: First at Bethel—Last at Appomattox. NY: Henry Holt, (1956). 1st ed. Black cl. Fine in VG dj. *Chapel Hill*. $50/£31

WELLMAN, MANLY WADE. Worse Things Waiting. Chapel Hill: Carcosa, 1973. 1st ed. NF in dj. *Pacific**. $63/£39

WELLMAN, MANLY WADE. Worse Things Waiting. Chapel Hill: Carcosa, 1973. 1st ed. (Trace of bkpl removal), else Fine in dj. *Other Worlds*. $100/£63

WELLMAN, PAUL I. The Callaghan, Yesterday and Today. Encinal, TX: Callaghan Land and Pastoral Co, n.d. 1st ed. VG+ in wrappers. *Labordo*. $225/£141

WELLMAN, PAUL I. Death on Horseback. Phila: Lippincott, 1947. VG in dj (sl worn). *Dumont*. $35/£22

WELLMAN, PAUL I. The Trampling Herd. NY, 1951. VG in dj (chipped). *Heinoldt*. $18/£11

WELLMAN, PAUL I. The Trampling Herd: The Story of the Cattle Range in America. NY: Carrick & Evans, (1939). 1st ed. Inscribed. (Top of rear cvr sl rippled.) *Sadlon*. $30/£19

WELLS, CAROLYN. Christmas ABC. NY: McLoughlin Bros, 1911. Lg 4to. 4 full-pg color illus. Color illus paper wrappers (worn, spine chipped). *Reisler*. $275/£172

WELLS, CAROLYN. Folly for the Wise. Indianapolis: Bobbs-Merrill, (1904). 1st ed. Binding design by Margaret Armstrong. Blue cl stamped in white/gilt. (Lt worn), o/w VG. *Hermitage*. $75/£47

WELLS, E. HAZARD. Magnificence and Misery. GC: Doubleday, 1984. 1st ed. VG in dj. *Perier*. $35/£22

WELLS, EDWARD L. Hampton and His Cavalry in '64. Richmond: B.F. Johnson, 1899. 1st ed. Frontisport, 429,xivpp+(4)pp ads. Gilt-pict blue cl. (Edges lt rubbed, spine sl faded), else VG. Howes W245. *Chapel Hill*. $375/£234

WELLS, H. G. '42 to '44: A Contemporary Memoir Upon Human Behavior During the Crisis of the World Revolution. London: Secker & Warburg, (1944). 1st ed. Teg. Grn cl. NF (ink name, dated 1944; edges sl bumped) in dj (sl worn, sm chips). *Antic Hay*. $150/£94

WELLS, H. G. The Adventures of Tommy. Harrap, 1929. 1st ed. Tall 4to. 45pp. Cl spine, illus bds. VG. *Bookmark*. $72/£45

WELLS, H. G. The Adventures of Tommy. George G. Harrap, 1929. 1st ed. Sq 4to. 45pp; 20pp facs ms and color illus. Pict cl-backed bds (lower edges sl dknd). VF in dj (edges sl worn). *Hollett*. $224/£140

WELLS, H. G. Anne Veronica: A Modern Love Story. T. Fisher Unwin, 1909. Good (sl spotted; spine bumped, hinges, corners rubbed). *Tiger*. $38/£24

WELLS, H. G. Apropos of Dolores. London: Cape, (1938). 1st Eng ed. Pink cl. VG (ink name, sm bkseller label) in dj (worn, chipped). *Antic Hay*. $50/£31

WELLS, H. G. The Autocracy of Mr. Parham: His Remarkable Adventures in This Changing World. London: Heinemann, (1930). 1st Eng ed. Red cl. VG (edges foxed, lower corner fep missing) in dj (sl edgeworn, soiled). *Antic Hay*. $85/£53

WELLS, H. G. The Bulpington of Blup. London: Hutchinson, (1932). 1st ed. Pub's cat. Pict eps. Black cl, gilt. Fine in dj (sl sunned, tears, nicks, sm chip foot of 1 joint). *Reese*. $45/£28

WELLS, H. G. The Bulpington of Blup. Hutchinson, (1932). 1st UK ed. VG in dj (edges, spine sl worn). *Williams*. $64/£40

WELLS, H. G. Christina Alberta's Father. London: Cape, (1925). 1st Eng ed. Red cl. VG (sm stain top edge, eps browned) in dj (sl worn, price-clipped, spine sl browned). *Antic Hay*. $125/£78

WELLS, H. G. The Country of the Blind and Other Stories. London: Thomas Nelson & Sons, (1911). 1st ed. Color frontis. Blue cl, gilt. (Spine sl dknd, head chipped, foot rubbed), else VG. *Pacific**. $46/£29

WELLS, H. G. The Croquet Player. London: C&W, 1936. 1st Eng ed. Dec cl. NF in dj (sm chip, few sm holes, spine sl browned). *Antic Hay*. $125/£78

WELLS, H. G. The Croquet Player. NY: Viking, 1937. 1st ed. VG in illus cl, dj (lg closed tear fr panel, chip). *Smith*. $30/£19

WELLS, H. G. The Croquet Player. NY: Viking, 1937. 1st Amer ed. Gray/black cl. Fine in Fine dj. *Sumner & Stillman*. $65/£41

WELLS, H. G. Crux Ansata: An Indictment of the Roman Catholic Church. NY: Agora, (1944). 1st Amer ed. Frontis photo port. Orange cl, gilt. VG in dj (nicked). *Houle.* $125/£78

WELLS, H. G. The Dream. NY: Macmillan, 1924. 1st Amer ed. Red cl. Fine. *Sumner & Stillman.* $45/£28

WELLS, H. G. The First Men in the Moon. Indianapolis: Bowen-Merrill, (1901). 1st Amer ed. Gilt-lettered pict cl. (Sl insect damage to cl), else VG. *Pacific*.* $150/£94

WELLS, H. G. The First Men in the Moon. Newnes, 1901. 1st UK ed, 2nd issue in dk-blue cl, gilt. VG (sm ink name, sm blindstamp; gilt lettering faded). *Williams.* $176/£110

WELLS, H. G. The First Men in the Moon. London, 1901. 1st ed. Blue cl (lt rubbed, spine sl dknd). *Swann*.* $258/£161

WELLS, H. G. Floor Games. London: Frank Palmer, 1911. 1st ed. 8vo. (ix),10-71pp. Dk blue cl, onlaid pict label to upper cvr. Very Clean (fore-edge sl speckled). *Sotheran.* $157/£98

WELLS, H. G. The Food of the Gods and How It Came to Earth. London: Macmillan, 1904. 1st ed. Final ads dated 20.09.04. Good in blind-blocked sage grn cl, gilt. *Maggs.* $80/£50

WELLS, H. G. The Food of the Gods and How It Came to Earth. London, 1904. 1st ed. Colonial issue. Blue cl. (Lt foxing, sl discoloration fr cvr.) *Swann*.* $161/£101

WELLS, H. G. The Future in America. NY: Harper, (1906). 1st ed. VG (sig, pencil notes reps). *Mott.* $30/£19

WELLS, H. G. H.G. Wells in Love, Postscript to an Experiment in Autobiography. London, 1984. 1st ed. Fine in dj. *Petersfield.* $24/£15

WELLS, H. G. The History of Mr. Polly. NY: Duffield, 1910. 1st Amer ed. Red cl, gilt. VG. *Macdonnell.* $30/£19

WELLS, H. G. The Holy Terror. Michael Joseph, 1939. 1st UK ed. NF in dj. *Williams.* $72/£45

WELLS, H. G. In the Days of the Comet. London, 1906. 1st ed. Colonial issue. Blue cl. (Eps lt foxed.) *Swann*.* $149/£93

WELLS, H. G. The Invisible Man. London, 1897. 1st ed. Pict red cl. (Pp evenly browned, fr hinge partly cracked; cl lt soiled.) *Swann*.* $488/£305

WELLS, H. G. The Invisible Man. NY: LEC, 1967. One of 1500. Signed. Red buckram, gilt spine. Fine in slipcase. *Pacific*.* $52/£33

WELLS, H. G. Joan and Peter, the Story of an Education. London (etc): Cassell, (1918). 1st ed. Forest grn cl stamped in gilt/blind. (Sm sliver losses at fep fore-edge), else VG in dj (defective). *Reese.* $75/£47

WELLS, H. G. Joan and Peter: The Story of an Education. London: Cassell, (1918). 1st Eng ed, w/ptr's code 'F.150.818' on p748. Dec grn cl. VG (eps sl foxed, ink name) in dj (worn, lt foxed, few sm tears, tear along fr flap professionally repaired on interior w/archival tape, spine sl dknd). *Antic Hay.* $275/£172

WELLS, H. G. The King Who Was a King. London: Ernest Benn, 1929. 1st Eng ed. NF (spine ends sl bumped) in dj (sl rubbed, nicked, creased, dusty, spine sl dknd). *Ulysses.* $104/£65

WELLS, H. G. The King Who Was a King: The Book of a Film. London: Ernest Benn, (1929). 1st Eng ed, earliest binding w/spine stamped in gilt. Brn cl. VG (top edge, fore-edge foxed) in dj (sl worn, nick). *Antic Hay.* $125/£78

WELLS, H. G. Kipps, the Story of a Simple Soul. London: Macmillan, 1905. 1st ed. VG in grn cl, gilt. *Maggs.* $88/£55

WELLS, H. G. Little Wars. London: Frank Palmer, (1913). 1st ed. Red cl, pict cvr label. VG (white cvr lettering discolored from bleeding of red cvrs, spine head lacks piece, lettering worn off). *Pacific*.* $187/£117

WELLS, H. G. Meanwhile: The Picture of a Lady. Leipzig: Bernhard Tauchnitz, 1927. Hb issue. NF (spine sl dknd). *Ulysses.* $48/£30

WELLS, H. G. Men Like Gods. Cassell, 1923. 1st UK ed. VG in dj (edges sl worn, spine browned, rear panel lacks sm corner). *Williams.* $120/£75

WELLS, H. G. Mr. Belloc Objects to 'The Outline of History.' London: Watts, 1926. 1st Eng ed. Red cl. NF in dj (sl browned). *Antic Hay.* $85/£53

WELLS, H. G. Mr. Blettsworthy on Rampole Island. London: Ernest Benn, 1928. 1st ed. Brn cl. Fine in NF dj (sl soiled). *Sumner & Stillman.* $115/£72

WELLS, H. G. Mr. Blettsworthy on Rampole Island. London: Ernest Benn, 1928. 1st ed. Brn cl (sm stains), gilt. Pict dj. *Maggs.* $120/£75

WELLS, H. G. Mr. Britling Sees It Through. London (etc): Cassell, (1916). 1st ed. Grn cl, gilt, dec in blind. (Early ink name; spine gilt sl patinated), o/w VG in dj (lt soiled), 1/2 calf slipcase (spine faded). *Reese.* $175/£109

WELLS, H. G. The New America: The New World. London: Cresset, (1935). 1st ed. Fine in dj. *Mott.* $25/£16

WELLS, H. G. The Plattner Story. Bernard Tauchnitz, 1900. Copyright ed. Sprinkled edges. Contemp 1/2 leather over cl. VG (spine sl sunned). *Tiger.* $45/£28

WELLS, H. G. The Sea Lady. London: Methuen, 1902. 1st ed. Primary binding: red cl. VG + (prelim ll foxed; fore-corners bumped, spine sl dknd). *Sumner & Stillman.* $275/£172

WELLS, H. G. The Secret Places of the Heart. London: Cassell, 1922. 1st ed. VF in grn cl, gilt. Dj. *Maggs.* $120/£75

WELLS, H. G. Select Conversations with an Uncle. Merriam, 1895. 1st Amer ed. (Spine, cvrs dust-soiled; 1st several pp torn in gutter), else VG. *Fine Books.* $275/£172

WELLS, H. G. Seven Famous Novels. NY, 1934. 1st ed. NF in VG + dj (spine head chipped). *Warren.* $40/£25

WELLS, H. G. The Soul of a Bishop. London: Cassell, (1917). 1st ed. Grn cl, gilt. Fine in NF dj. *Macdonnell.* $125/£78

WELLS, H. G. The Soul of a Bishop. NY: Macmillan, 1917. 1st US ed. Frontis. Gilt red cl. (Ink name, lt foxed early/late), else VG in pict dj (worn, lacks a strip at lower edge). *Reese.* $60/£38

WELLS, H. G. The Soul of a Bishop. NY: Macmillan, 1917. 1st Amer ed. Red cl, gilt. VF in VG dj. *Macdonnell.* $85/£53

WELLS, H. G. Star Begotten: A Biological Fantasia. London: C&W, 1937. 1st Eng ed, w/gilt spine lettering. Black cl. NF in dj (sl edgeworn, lt browned, few nicks). *Antic Hay.* $150/£94

WELLS, H. G. Star-Begotton: A Biological Fantasia. NY: Viking, 1937. 1st Amer ed. (Spine head sl rubbed), else NF in dj. *Pacific*.* $98/£61

WELLS, H. G. Tales of Space and Time. Bernhard Tauchnitz, 1900. Copyright ed. Sprinkled edges. Contemp 1/2 leather over cl. VG (stamp; spine sl sunned). *Tiger.* $58/£36

WELLS, H. G. The Time Machine. London, 1895. 1st ed, 2nd binding, w/trimmed edges from remainder of wrappered issue. Sm 8vo. Tan cl, pict stamped in purple. *Swann*.* $747/£467

WELLS, H. G. The Time Machine. London, 1895. 1st ed, earliest binding. Sm 8vo. Tan cl (lt tanned) pict stamped in purple. *Swann*.* $1,380/£863

WELLS, H. G. Tono-Bungay. London: Macmillan, 1909. 1st ed, 1st issue, w/8pp ads dated 1.09. 8vo. VG in lt grn cl, gilt. *Maggs.* $72/£45

WELLS, H. G. The Undying Fire. Cassell, n.d. (1919). 1st ed. VG (edges browned, spine ends, corners bumped, fr hinge cracked) in dj (nicked, chipped, rubbed, dusty, sl creased, mkd, torn, dknd, spine, edges browned, spine head frayed). *Ulysses.* $152/£95

WELLS, H. G. War and the Future: Italy, France and Britain at War. London (etc): Cassell, 1917. 1st ed. Red cl stamped in gilt/blind. (Eps, edges lt foxed), o/w VG in dj. *Reese.* $175/£109

WELLS, H. G. The War in the Air. London, 1908. 1st ed. Colonial issue. Red cl. (Lt foxing.) *Swann**. $201/£126

WELLS, H. G. The War in the Air. NY: Macmillan, 1908. 1st Amer ed. 20 plts. Gray cl. Good (cvrs rubbed, faded). *Heritage*. $300/£188

WELLS, H. G. The War of the Worlds and The Time Machine. LEC, 1964. Ltd to 1500 numbered, signed by Joe Mugnaini (illus). 2 vols. Fine in slipcase. *Swann**. $149/£93

WELLS, H. G. The War of the Worlds. London: Heinemann, 1898. 1st ed, later state binding. Red cl. Good (lacks fep, old name; cl spotted, corners, spine ends well rubbed; spine, rear cvr stained). *Pacific**. $150/£94

WELLS, H. G. The War of the Worlds. London, 1898. 1st ed, Currey's 1st state of ads. 8vo. Gray cl (spine sl dknd). *Swann**. $747/£467

WELLS, H. G. Washington and the Hope of Peace. London: W. Collins, 1922. 1st Eng ed. VG (nameplt; spine ends sl bumped, scuffed) in dj (sl dknd, sl nicked, rubbed). *Ulysses*. $120/£75

WELLS, H. G. What Is Coming? London: Cassell, 1916. 1st Eng ed. VG (paper browned; spine ends sl bumped, edges sl rubbed). *Ulysses*. $88/£55

WELLS, H. G. What Is Coming? London (etc): Cassell, 1916. 1st ed. Grn cl stamped in gilt/blind. (Cl sl sunned through dj), o/w NF in NF pict dj (spine crown sl frayed). *Reese*. $175/£109

WELLS, H. G. The Wheels of Chance. London: J.M. Dent, 1896. 1st ed, 1st issue w/p314 blank except for imprint and the 10pp of ads dated October 1896. All copies of this ed have no pp1 and 2 due to an error in pagination. 40 illus by J. Ayton Symington. Teg, rest untrimmed. Good in red buckram (spine faded), gilt. *Maggs*. $192/£120

WELLS, H. G. The Wheels of Chance: A Bicycling Idyll. NY: Macmillan, 1896. 1st Amer ed. Pict cl. (Spine sl leaning, image rubbed), else VG. *Pacific**. $52/£33

WELLS, H. G. The Wife of Sir Isaac Harman. London: Macmillan, 1914. 1st Eng ed, w/code '2H' at base of p465. Teg. Emb grn cl. VG (offsetting feps). *Antic Hay*. $125/£78

WELLS, H. G. The Works of H.G. Wells. NY: Scribner, 1924-27. Atlantic ed. One of 1050 sets. Signed. 16 vols (partial set). Frontisport. Teg. Paper spine labels. Fine in glassine (chipped), slipcases. *Pacific**. $207/£129

WELLS, H. G. World Brain. London: Methuen, (1928). 1st Eng ed. Orange cl. VG (ink name) in dj (browned, chipped, price-clipped). *Antic Hay*. $150/£94

WELLS, H. G. The World of William Clissold. NY: George H. Doran, 1926. 1st ed. 2 vols. NF in grn cl, gilt. *Smith*. $45/£28

WELLS, H. G. The World of William Clissold. London: Ernest Benn, 1926. One of 188 sets signed in vol 1. 3 vols. Teg. White cl spine, dk grn cl, gilt. VG set (spines sl soiled, extrems lt rubbed). *Heritage*. $500/£313

WELLS, H. P. Fly-Rods and Fly-Tackle. NY: Harper, 1885. 1st ed. 364pp + ads. Fine. *Bowman*. $150/£94

WELLS, HELEN. The Clue of the Carved Ruby. NY: G&D, 1961. 1st ed. Vicki Barr #14; lists only to this title. 5x7.5. 179pp. VG + (sl shelfworn) in dj (sl edgeworn, price-clipped). *My Bookhouse*. $52/£33

WELLS, HENRY P. The American Salmon Fisherman. NY: Harper, 1886. 1st ed. Frontis. Grn cl, gilt. NF (spine head sl rubbed). *Pacific**. $138/£86

WELLS, HENRY P. City Boys in the Woods. NY: Harper, (1889). 1st ed. Pict cl, gilt. (Soiled, insect damage cvr extrems), else VG. *Pacific**. $29/£18

WELLS, HENRY P. Fly-Rods and Fly-Tackle. NY, (1885). Frontis. Gilt-pict cl. *Swann**. $201/£126

WELLS, HENRY P. Fly-Rods and Fly-Tackle: Suggestions as to Their Manufacture and Use. NY: Harper, 1885. 1st ed. NF. *Pacific**. $345/£216

WELLS, JAMES W. Exploring and Travelling Three Thousand Miles Through Brazil. London: Sampson Low, Marston, Searle & Rivington, 1887. 2nd ed. 2 vols. Frontispieces, xix,411; xii,386pp + 32pp pub's cat; 2 fldg maps, 3 sections. Dec cl. (Prelims lt browned; sm gouges fr bd vol 1, spines sl rubbed.) *Edwards*. $360/£225

WELLS, LEE E. The Big Die. NY, 1952. 1st ed. Inscribed. VG in VG dj. *Sagebrush*. $35/£22

WELLS, LEE E. The Long Noose. London, (1953). 1st British ed. Inscribed. Signed photo of Wells laid in. Dec cl. NF in Good + dj (chipped). *Sagebrush*. $50/£31

WELLS, LEE E. Spanish Range. NY, (1951). 1st ed. Inscribed. Related newspaper clippings laid in. Good (corner bumped, cl lt creased) in Good dj. *Sagebrush*. $35/£22

WELLS, MARGARET. Margaret Wells: A Selection of Her Wood Engravings. Wakefield: Fleece, 1985. Ltd to 200 ptd. 15 full-pg engrs. Yellow cl. VF. *Truepenny*. $125/£78

WELLS, WILLIAM CHARLES. An Essay on Dew, and Several Appearances Connected With It. London: Taylor & Hessey, 1814. 1st ed. (4),146pp,16ads. 1/4 morocco fldg case w/gilt spine lettering, orig two-toned bds w/paper spine label. (Fr joint starting, corners bumped, spine label rubbed.) *Glaser*. $950/£594

WELSH, CHARLES (ed). Character Portraits from Dickens. C&W, 1908. Frontisport. Good (sig; spine bumped, sl sunned, cvrs unevenly sunned). *Tiger*. $29/£18

WELSH, IRVINE. Trainspotting. Secker & Warburg, 1993. 1st UK ed. Fine in self-wrappers. *Williams*. $192/£120

WELTY, EDWIN A. Ballads of the Bivouac and the Border. Buffalo: Peter Paul Book Co, 1896. 1st ed. Inscribed. Aeg. Pict cl (spine ends worn, white spot to lower cvr), gilt. *Sadlon*. $20/£13

WELTY, EUDORA. Acrobats in a Park. Northridge: Lord John, 1980. 1st ed. One of 300 numbered, signed. 1/4 cl. *Swann**. $92/£58

WELTY, EUDORA. The Bride of the Innisfallen and Other Stories. NY: Harcourt Brace, (1955). 1st ed, 2nd issue, w/the 5 dates on the c. pg. Inscribed presentation. Grn cl over grn/blue mottled bds. (Feps lt browned; spine ends sl rubbed), o/w Fine in dj (spine sl browned). *Heritage*. $300/£188

WELTY, EUDORA. The Bride of the Innisfallen and Other Stories. London, 1955. 1st Eng ed. (Spine foot, 1 corner tip sl bumped.) Dj (rubbed, creased, dust-mkd, price-clipped to '12s.6d' for a later issue). *Clearwater*. $88/£55

WELTY, EUDORA. The Collected Stories of Eudora Welty. NY: Harcourt Brace, (1980). One of 500 numbered, signed. Fine in Fine slipcase. *Lenz*. $450/£281

WELTY, EUDORA. Delta Wedding. NY, (1946). 1st ed. Dj (edges lt rubbed). *Swann**. $201/£126

WELTY, EUDORA. The Eye of the Story. NY: Random House, (1977). 1st ed. One of 300 signed. Fine in slipcase. *Hermitage*. $250/£156

WELTY, EUDORA. The Eye of the Story. Selected Essays and Reviews. NY: Random House, (1977). 1st ed, trade issue. NF in dj. *Reese*. $30/£19

WELTY, EUDORA. The Golden Apples. NY: HB, (1949). 1st ed. Fine in Fine dj (spine sl tanned). *Between The Covers*. $200/£125

WELTY, EUDORA. Ida M'Toy. Urbana: Univ of IL, (1979). One of 350 signed. Red cl, gilt. Fine. *Heritage*. $200/£125

WELTY, EUDORA. Ida M'Toy. Urbana: Univ of IL, (1979). One of 350 numbered, signed. Fine. *Lenz*. $250/£156

WELTY, EUDORA. Losing Battles. NY: Random House, (1970). 1st ed, trade issue. VG + (sl sunned) in dj. *Reese*. $35/£22

WELTY, EUDORA. The Ponder Heart. NY: Harcourt, Brace, (1954). 1st ed. Inscribed, signed. VG in dj (spine ends rubbed, sm tear, crease to upper joint). *Pacific**. $104/£65

WELTY, EUDORA. The Robber Bridegroom. West Hatfield, MA: Pennyroyal, 1987. 1st this ed. One of 150 numbered, signed by Welty & Barry Moser (woodcuts). Lg 8vo. Full red blind-stamped morocco, gilt. Fine. *Reese.* $600/£375

WELTY, EUDORA. Women!! Make Turban in Own Home! N.p.: Palaemon Press, (1979). 1st ed. One of 200 numbered, signed. Grn bds. *Swann*.* $80/£50

WENTWORTH, EDWARD NORRIS. America's Sheep Trails, History, Personalities. Ames, IA: IA State College, 1948. 1st ed. Inscribed, signed. VG+ in dj. *Labordo.* $125/£78

WENTWORTH, EDWARD NORRIS. America's Sheep Trails: History, Personalities. IA State College, 1948. 1st ed. Very Clean in dj (chipped, repaired). *Rybski.* $85/£53

WENTWORTH, LADY. The Crabbet Arabian Stud. London, n.d. Cl-backed color pict bds. *Edwards.* $24/£15

WENTWORTH, LADY. Horses in the Making. London: Allen & Unwin, 1951. 1st ed. VG in Good+ dj. *October Farm.* $30/£19

WENTWORTH, PATRICIA. Ladies' Bane. Phila: Lippincott, 1952. 1st ed. NF (corners sl bumped) in dj (sl worn). *Janus.* $45/£28

WENTZ, ROBY. Eleven Western Presses. L.A.: LA Club of Ptg House Craftsmen, 1956. 1st ed. Cream bds, black cl backstrip. Fine. *Harrington.* $100/£63

WENTZ, ROBY. The Grabhorn Press. Grace Hoper, 1981. One of 750. *Dawson.* $85/£53

WERFEL, FRANZ. Class Reunion. NY, 1929. 1st Amer ed. Fine (spine sl cocked) in dj (spine sunned, few nicks, price-clipped). *Polyanthos.* $25/£16

WERFEL, FRANZ. The Forty Days of Musa Dagh. Geoffrey Dunlop (trans). NY: Viking, 1934. 1st US ed. Gilt red cl. NF in VG dj (sm tears). *Reese.* $45/£28

WERFEL, FRANZ. Paul Among the Jews. Paul Levertoff (trans). London: Grey Walls, 1943. 1st Eng ed. VG (cvrs faded; spine ends, corners sl bumped) in dj (nicked, spotted, rubbed, dusty, sl chipped, creased, browned). *Ulysses.* $88/£55

WERNE, FERDINAND. African Wanderings. London: Traveller's Library, 1852. 1st Eng ed. xi,267pp; map. *Maggs.* $456/£285

WERNER, HERMAN. On the Western Frontier with the United States Cavalry Fifty Years Ago. N.p., (1934). 1st ed. Frontisport. Blue ptd wrappers. Fine. Howes W259. *Harrington.* $45/£28

WERNER, JANE. Walt Disney's Living Desert. NY: S&S, (1954). 1st ed. Fine. *Book Market.* $30/£19

WERNER, M. R. Orderly! NY: Jonathan Cape & Harrison Smith, (1930). 1st ed. White cl, black bds. (Ink name, spine foot sl dknd), else VG in dj (used, 2 chips, spine tear). *Reese.* $45/£28

WERNER, M. R. Orderly! London, 1930. 1st Eng ed. VG (no dj). *Clearwater.* $48/£30

WESCHLER, HERTA. Collage. Robert E. Wolf (trans). NY: Abrams, (1968). Fine in dj (spine sunned). *Metropolitan*.* $28/£18

WESCOTT, GLENWAY. Images of Truth: Rememberances and Criticism. NY: Harper, (1962). 1st ed. As New in As New dj. *Between The Covers.* $150/£94

WESKER, ARNOLD. Said the Old Man to the Young Man. London: Cape, 1978. 1st Eng ed. Inscribed. NF (spine foot, 2 corners sl bumped) in dj (nicked, sl dusty, spine faded). *Ulysses.* $72/£45

WESSEL, KLAUS. Byzantine Enamels. Shannon: Irish Univ, 1969. 23 color plts. VG in dj, slipcase. *Hollett.* $64/£40

WESSON, DOUGLAS B. I'll Never Be Cured and I Don't Much Care.... NY: J.H. Sears, (1928). 1st ed. Frontis map. Orange cl. (Stamp; spine, upper rear cvr sl spotted, head rubbed), else VG. *Pacific*.* $63/£39

West India Sketch Book. (By Trelawney Wentworth.) London: Whittaker, 1834. 1st ed. 2 vols. 10 engr and litho plts, some colored, 1 map, 1 chart. Contemp blue calf (lt rubbed, corners bumped), gilt, contrasting lettering-pieces. *Christie's*.* $469/£293

WEST, ANTHONY. Gloucestershire. Faber, 1939. 1st ed. VG in dj (torn, chipped). *Hadley.* $56/£35

WEST, ANTHONY. On a Dark Night. London: Eyre & Spottiswood, (1949). 1st Eng ed. VG in dj. *Cady.* $60/£38

WEST, CHARLES. An Inquiry into the Pathological Importance of Ulceration of the Os Uteri. Phila, 1854. 1st Amer ed. 88pp. *Fye.* $125/£78

WEST, ELLIOTT. The Saloon on the Rocky Mountain Mining Frontier. Univ of NE, (1979). 1st ed. Good in dj. *Rybski.* $35/£22

WEST, HERBERT FAULKNER (ed). Mr. Emerson Writes a Letter About Walden. (Hanover): Thoreau Soc & Friends of Dartmouth Library, 1954. 1st ed, 1st issue. (15)pp incl facs. Wrappers. VG. *Lucas.* $25/£16

WEST, JOHN O. Jose Cisneros—An Artists Journey. El Paso: Texas Western Press, 1993. One of 100 signed by West & Cisneros. Fine in dj, slipcase. *Dumont.* $150/£94

WEST, LEONARD. The Natural Trout Fly and Its Imitation. St. Helens: Privately ptd, (1913). 1st ed. 16 plts. Prospectus w/extra color plt laid in. Grn cl, gilt. (Inscrip; piece of cl lacking from fr cvr affecting title), else VG. *Pacific*.* $52/£33

WEST, NATHANIEL. The Dream Life of Balso Snell. Paris: Contact Editions, (1931). 1st ed, 1st bk. Ltd to 500. VF in stiff ptd wrappers, glassine, chemise, slipcase. *Bromer.* $3,000/£1,875

WEST, NATHANIEL. Miss Lonelyhearts. NY, (1933). 1st ed. 8vo. (Bkpl.) *Swann*.* $920/£575

WEST, RAY B., JR. Kingdom of the Saints. NY, 1957. 1st ed. Good (inscrip) in dj (clipped). Bkpl of Cecil B. deMille. *Dumont.* $50/£31

WEST, REBECCA. The Return of the Soldier. Nisbet, 1918. 1st ed. (Prelims sl spotted; spine ends sl rubbed), else VG. *Any Amount.* $80/£50

WEST, REBECCA. The Return of the Soldier. NY: Century, 1918. 1st ed in bk form. Frontis. Gray cl stamped in purple. (Pencil erasures ep), o/w Nice in pict dj (dust-soiled, frayed). *Reese.* $225/£141

WEST, REBECCA. The Return of the Soldier. NY: Century, 1918. 1st ed, 1st bk. Frontis, 4 full-pg illus. (Top edge lt foxed), else Fine in pict dj (lt chipped, soiled). *Bromer.* $325/£203

WESTELL, W. PERCIVAL and H. E. TURNER. The Hedge I Know. London, 1909. 16 color plts. Grn dec cl. (Edgeworn), else Good. *Larry Price.* $16/£10

WESTERBY, HERBERT. The History of Pianoforte Music. Kegan Paul et al, 1924. 1st ed. VG. *Hollett.* $40/£25

WESTERMAN, PERCY F. The Amir's Ruby. Blackie, (1932). 1st ed. Lg 8vo. 224pp; 4 mono plts by W. Edward Wigfull. Pict cl. VG+. *Bookmark.* $32/£20

WESTERMARCK, EDWARD. Marriage Ceremonies in Morocco. London: Macmillan, 1914. 1st ed. NF (2 lib stickers). *Beasley.* $75/£47

Westerner's Brand Book, Los Angeles Corral, (1953). Brand Book 5. L.A., (1953). Orig 1st ed. Ltd to 400. Inscribed by Frank A. Schilling. VG. *Sagebrush.* $60/£38

Westerner's Brand Book. Los Angeles Corral, (1957). Brand Book 7. W.W. Robinson (ed). (1957.) 1st ed. Ltd to 475. Fine in Fine dj. *Book Market.* $60/£38

Westerner's Brand Book. Los Angeles Corral, 1963. Brand Book 10. 1963. 1st ed. Ltd to 525. Signed by 19 Westerners. Fine in Fine dj. *Book Market.* $50/£31

Westerner's Brand Book. Los Angeles Corral, 1964. Brand Book 11. Russ Leadabrand (ed). 1964. 1st ed. Ltd to 525. Signed by 25 Westerners. Fine (lacks dj). *Book Market.* $150/£94

WESTERVELT, W. D. Hawaiian Legends of Gods and Ghosts. Boston/London: Ellis/Constable, 1915. 1st ed. This copy signed. Gray dec cl. (Fep taped, mkd; fr hinge cracked, spine faded.) *Parmer.* $125/£78

WESTFALL, RICHARD S. Never at Rest: A Biography of Isaac Newton. Cambridge/NY et al: CUP, (1980). Fine in dj. *Weber.* $75/£47

WESTMACOTT, MARY. (Pseud of Agatha Christie.) The Burden. Heinemann, 1956. 1st UK ed. Fine in VG dj (price-clipped, spine sl faded, couple nicks strengthened to rear). *Williams.* $152/£95

WESTMACOTT, MARY. (Pseud of Agatha Christie.) A Daughter's a Daughter. Heinemann, 1952. 1st UK ed. VG in dj (sl loss to spine, few sm closed tears). *Williams.* $64/£40

WESTON, CHARIS WILSON and EDWARD. California and the West. NY: Duell, Sloan & Pearce, 1940. 1st ed. (Bds spotted, rear bd creased.) Internally Good. *Dumont.* $95/£59

WESTON, EDWARD. Edward Weston Nudes. (NY): Aperture, 1977. 1st ed, trade issue. Fine in dj. *Pacific*.* $109/£68

WESTON, EDWARD. My Camera on Point Lobos. Boston, 1950. 1st ed. Special bound stiff wraps. (Corners sl worn), else VG in dj (partial). *King.* $250/£156

WESTON, EDWARD. My Camera on Point Lobos. Yosemite Nat'l Park/Virginia Adams, 1950. 1st ed. Folio. Fine (lacks dj) in orig black bds, plastic spiral binding. *Smith.* $350/£219

WESTON, FRANK. The Black Slaves of Prussia: An Open Letter Addressed to General Smuts. Boston/NY: Houghton Mifflin, 1918. 1st US ptg. Ptd self-wrappers. (Lib receipt stamp fr wrapper), else VG. *Reese.* $30/£19

WESTON, GEORGE M. The Progress of Slavery in the United States. Washington: The Author, 1857. 1st ed. Sig of John W. Hasbrouck. viii,301pp. Dk brn blind cl, gilt, paper spine label. (Ex-lib, bkpl, ink stamps, sl aged; hinges cracked; edges frayed, worn, torn; joints partly split.) *Baltimore*.* $35/£22

WESTON, WILLIAM. The Art and Process of Carbon Printing. NY: G. Gennert, 1896. 64pp,(8) ads. (Stamp, fep separating; joint sl separated at spine base, sm spine #), else VG. *Cahan.* $175/£109

WESTOVER, WENDELL. Suicide Battalions. NY/London: Putnam, 1929. 1st ed. Frontis. Pict eps. Gilt black cl. NF in pict dj (lt edgeworn, nicked). *Reese.* $125/£78

WESTROP, H. M. A Manual of Precious Stones and Antique Gems. London, 1874. 1st ed. Frontis, xvi,165pp. Pict gilt cl (spine sl faded), o/w Fine. *Henly.* $58/£36

WESTROPP, M. S. DUDLEY. Irish Glass. Herbert Jenkins, (1920). 1st ed. 40 plts. (Cl sl faded.) *Hollett.* $192/£120

WESTROPP, M. S. DUDLEY. Irish Glass...XVIth Century to the Present Day. London, (1920). (Spine faded, label removed.) *Swann*.* $230/£144

WESTWOOD, THOMAS and T. SATCHELL. Bibliotheca Piscatoria: A Catalogue of Books on Angling, the Fisheries, and Fish-Culture. London: W. Satchell, 1883. 1st ed. (Bkpls, fr hinge cracked, spine ends chipped), else VG. *Pacific*.* $460/£288

WESTWOOD, THOMAS. A New Bibliotheca Piscatoria; or, General Catalogue of Angling and Fishing Literature. London: Field Office, 1861. 1st ed. Grn cl, gilt. (Spine dull, spots fr cvr), else VG. *Pacific*.* $138/£86

WETHERED, JOYCE. Golfing Memories and Methods. London: Hutchinson, (1933). 3rd ed. Grn cl. NF (emb stamp, tipped-in bkpl). *Pacific*.* $115/£72

WETHERED, NEWTON. Mediaeval Craftsmanship and the Modern Amateur, More Particularly with Reference to Metal and Enamel. London: Longmans, Green, 1923. 1st ed. Frontis, 31 plts. Emb cl. VG (sm gouge to spine). *Glaser.* $85/£53

WETHERED, ROGER and JOYCE. Golf from Two Sides. London: Longmans, Green, 1925. 3rd ed. Blue cl. (Sig, emb stamp; shelfworn), else VG. *Pacific*.* $75/£47

WETHEY, HAROLD E. The Paintings of Titian. London: Phaidon, 1969-75. 3 vols. 4to. Djs. *Christie's*.* $883/£552

WETHEY, HAROLD E. The Paintings of Titian. London, 1971. Complete ed. 275 plts. Good + in dj (sl worn). *Washton.* $350/£219

WETZEL, CHARLES M. American Fishing Books. A Bibliography from the Earliest Times up to 1948. Together with a History of Angling and Angling Literature in America. Newark, DE, 1950. One of 200 ptd. 3/4 goatskin. VF. *Felcone.* $1,500/£938

WETZEL, CHARLES M. Trout Flies: Naturals and Imitations. Harrisburg: Stackpole, (1955). 1st ed. NF in dj (rear panel lacks sm piece, price-clipped). *Pacific*.* $104/£65

WEXLEY, JOHN. The Judgement of Julius and Ethel Rosenberg. NY: Cameron & Kahn, 1955. 1st ed. Rockwell Kent (illus). Errata slip laid in. VG + (sl shelfworn) in Kent dj (sl edgeworn). *My Bookhouse.* $77/£48

WEYBRIGHT, VICTOR and HENRY SELL. Buffalo Bill and the Wild West. London: Hamish Hamilton, (1956). 1st ed. Fldg map. Brn cl. Fine in dj. *Karmiole.* $75/£47

WEYGANDT, CORNELIUS. The Wissahickon Hills. Univ of PA, 1930. 10 photo plts. Grn cl, gilt. VG. *Larry Price.* $30/£19

WHALE, GEORGE and JOHN SARGEAUNT (eds). Johnson Club Papers. By Various Hands. Fisher Unwin, 1920. (2nd series.) Good (cvrs sl mkd). *Clearwater.* $56/£35

Whaling Directory of the United States in 1869. New Bedford, 1869. 8vo. 14pp of hand-colored lithos. *Swann*.* $1,035/£647

WHANSLAW, H. W. A Second Bench Book of Puppetry. Redhill: Wells Gardner, Darton, (1957). Color frontis. Dec eps. (Spine lettering partly rubbed off.) *Dramatis.* $25/£16

WHARTON, EDITH. The Age of Innocence. NY: D. Appleton, 1920. 1st ed. Red cl. (Sm old name; spine sunned, sm spot fr cvr, rehinged), else VG. *Pacific*.* $63/£39

WHARTON, EDITH. The Age of Innocence. NY: D. Appleton, 1920. 1st ed. Red cl. (Offset from laid-in news clipping to feps, 2 pinholes to fep), else NF. *Pacific*.* $196/£123

WHARTON, EDITH. The Age of Innocence. LEC, 1974. One of 2000 signed by Lawrence Beall Smith (illus). Fine in slipcase. *Swann*.* $34/£21

WHARTON, EDITH. A Backward Glance. NY: D. Appleton, 1934. 1st ed. Blue cl, gilt. Fine. *Pacific*.* $86/£54

WHARTON, EDITH. The Children. NY: D. Appleton, 1928. 1st ed. NF. *Pacific*.* $75/£47

WHARTON, EDITH. The Children. NY: Appleton, 1928. 1st ed. VG ('1' at end of text; shelfworn) in dj (lacks few chunks). *My Bookhouse.* $82/£51

WHARTON, EDITH. The Custom of the Country. Macmillan, 1913. Teg. Good (fore-edge lt spotted; spine bumped, hinges, corners rubbed). *Tiger.* $40/£25

WHARTON, EDITH. The Custom of the Country. NY: Scribner, 1913. 1st ed. NF (lt rubbed). *Between The Covers.* $175/£109

WHARTON, EDITH. Ethan Frome. Macmillan, 1911. Good (fore-edge spotted; spine bumped, badly sunned). *Tiger.* $45/£28

WHARTON, EDITH. Ethan Frome. NY, 1911. 1st ed. Red cl. *Swann*.* $258/£161

WHARTON, EDITH. Ethan Frome. NY: Scribner, 1911. 1st ed, 1st ptg, w/4pp ads and blank leaf at end. Red cl, gilt. NF (fore-edge, eps sl foxed; spine sl dknd, corners lt rubbed). *Heritage*. $300/£188

WHARTON, EDITH. Ethan Frome. NY: Scribner, 1922. One of 2000. Frontis. Tan paper over bds, brn cl spine, paper label. Fine in orig box (lacks top). *Cummins*. $150/£94

WHARTON, EDITH. Ethan Frome. LEC, 1939. Ltd to 1500 numbered, signed by Henry Varnum Poor (illus). Fine in slipcase. *Swann**. $172/£108

WHARTON, EDITH. Fighting France from Dunkerque to Belfort. NY: Scribner, 1915. 1st ed, US issue. Frontis. Red cl, gilt. (Ink name; cl sl soiled), else Good. *Reese*. $55/£34

WHARTON, EDITH. French Ways and Their Meaning. NY: D. Appleton, 1919. 1st ed. Grn cl, gilt. NF. *Pacific**. $98/£61

WHARTON, EDITH. The Fruit of the Tree. NY: Scribner, 1907. 1st ed. Untrimmed. Red cl (couple letters chipped off cvr), gilt. VG. *Second Life*. $100/£63

WHARTON, EDITH. The Glimpses of the Moon. NY: D. Appleton, 1922. 1st ed. Blue cl, gilt. (Spine crease), else VG. *Pacific**. $69/£43

WHARTON, EDITH. The Greater Inclination. NY, 1899. 1st ed. Gilt-pict bds (tips rubbed, spine top chipped). *Swann**. $138/£86

WHARTON, EDITH. The House of Mirth. Macmillan, 1905. 1st UK ed. VG (ink name, sl foxed; cvrs sl rubbed). *Williams*. $104/£65

WHARTON, EDITH. The House of Mirth. LEC, 1975. One of 2000 signed by Lily Harmon (illus). Fine in slipcase. *Swann**. $57/£36

WHARTON, EDITH. In Morocco. NY: Scribner, 1920. 1st US ed. Color dec cl. VG (spine ends bumped, scuffed, corners sl bumped, cvrs sl rubbed at edges). *Ulysses*. $312/£195

WHARTON, EDITH. Italian Backgrounds. NY: Scribner, 1905. 1st ed. Teg. Grn cl, gilt. (Bkpl), else NF. *Pacific**. $207/£129

WHARTON, EDITH. Italian Villas and Their Gardens. NY: Century, 1904. 1st ed. 26 VG plts by Maxfield Parrish. Teg, untrimmed. Dk grn cl, gilt. (Edges sl worn, scattered sm stains.) *Baltimore**. $250/£156

WHARTON, EDITH. Italian Villas and Their Gardens. NY: Century, 1904. 1st ed. 10.5x7. Color frontis, 25 plts by Maxfield Parrish, ptd tissue guards. Teg. Pict grn cl, gilt. (Offset, inscrip), else NF. *Pacific**. $748/£468

WHARTON, EDITH. Madame de Treymes. NY: Scribner, 1907. 1st ed. Teg. Brn cl, gilt. (Bkpl traces fep, owner label; corners sl rubbed), else NF. *Hermitage*. $85/£53

WHARTON, EDITH. Madame de Treymes. NY: Scribner, 1907. 1st ed. (Spine extrems sl rubbed), else Fine (lacks dj). *Between The Covers*. $200/£125

WHARTON, EDITH. The Mother's Recompense. NY: D. Appleton, 1925. 1st ed. Red cl, gilt. (Bkpl), else Fine. *Pacific**. $35/£22

WHARTON, EDITH. A Motor-Flight Through France. NY: Scribner, 1908. 1st ed. Fine (lacks dj). *Between The Covers*. $285/£178

WHARTON, EDITH. The Old Maid. NY: Grosset & Dunlap, (c. 1939). 1st ed. (Fep corner clipped), else VF in VF dj. *Between The Covers*. $125/£78

WHARTON, EDITH. Quartet: Four Stories. Kentfield: Allen, 1975. One of 140. Prospectus laid in. 1/4 cl, dec bds. Fine. *Pacific**. $219/£137

WHARTON, EDITH. The Reef. NY: D. Appleton, 1912. 1st ed. Red cl, gilt. VG. *Second Life*. $100/£63

WHARTON, EDITH. Sanctuary. NY: Scribner, 1903. 1st ed. Grn cl (sl faded), gilt. *Second Life*. $150/£94

WHARTON, EDITH. A Son at the Front. NY: Scribner, 1923. 1st ed. Red cl, gilt. Fine. *Pacific**. $98/£61

WHARTON, EDITH. The Valley of Decision. NY: Scribner, 1902. 1st ed. 2 vols. Teg. VG set (sl rubbed, spines sl cocked). *Jaffe*. $150/£94

WHARTON, HENRY. The Life of John Smith, English Soldier. Laura Polanyi Striker (trans). V.H.S., (c1957). Inscribed by Striker. VG in VG dj. *Book Broker*. $35/£22

WHARTON, JAMES B. Squad. NY: Coward-McCann, 1928. 1st ed. Grn cl stamped in red. NF in pict dj (sl foxed). *Reese*. $55/£34

WHARTON, JAMES B. Squad. London, 1929. 1st Eng ed. Pict dj (repaired). *Clearwater*. $136/£85

WHARTON, WILLIAM. Birdy. NY: Knopf, 1979. 1st ed. Signed. Fine in NF dj. *Lame Duck*. $125/£78

WHARTON, WILLIAM. A Midnight Clear. NY: Knopf, 1982. 1st ed. Signed. Fine in NF dj. *Lame Duck*. $75/£47

WHARTON, WILLIAM. Scumbler. NY: Knopf, 1984. 1st ed. Fine in Fine dj. *Between The Covers*. $45/£28

What's Cookin' By the Kate Crutcher Players. Hollywood: Murray & Gee, (1944). Fine. *Perier*. $37/£23

What's That? London: Dean's Rag Book, (1903). 8vo. 10pp. Rose-pink cl, sewn spine, full color pict decs. Very Nice (1 corner w/sm fold). *Reisler*. $75/£47

WHEAT, CARL I. Books of the California Gold Rush. SF: Colt Press, 1949. 1st ed. One of 500. Untrimmed. Red buckram, ptd yellow bds, ptd paper spine label. (Lib ink handstamps, adhesive remnant from card pocket at rep; edges, spine sl worn, label chipped.) *Baltimore**. $80/£50

WHEAT, CARL I. Mapping the American West 1540-1857. Worcester: American Antiquarian Soc, 1954. Wraps. Fine in VG dj. *Book Market*. $100/£63

WHEAT, CARL I. Mapping the Trans-Mississippi West. SF, 1957-63. 1st ed. 5 vols in 6. Fine set. *Dumont*. $3,750/£2,344

WHEAT, CARL I. Mapping the Trans-Mississippi West. Vol V, Part II. SF, 1963. 1st ed. Fine. *Dumont*. $450/£281

WHEAT, CARL I. Mapping the Transmississippi West, 1540-1861. SF: Inst of Hist Cartography, 1957-63. 1st ed. One of 1000 sets. 5 vols in 6. 14x10. Orig prospectuses laid into 2 vols. Tan buckram, simulated grn morocco backstrips. Fine. *Harrington*. $3,500/£2,188

WHEAT, CARL I. Mapping the Transmississippi West...1540-1861. SF: Inst for Hist Cartography, 1957-1967. 1st ed. One of 1000 sets. 5 vols in 6. 14x10. Vol 1 ptd by Grabhorn; vols 2-5 by Taylor & Taylor & James. 1/2 cl, buckram, gilt. Fine. *Pacific**. $4,025/£2,516

WHEAT, CARL I. The Maps of the California Gold Region, 1848-1857. SF: Grabhorn, 1942. 1st ed. One of 300. 14x9.25. 1/2 cl, linen, paper spine label. (Offset to eps; spine sl sunned, soiled), else VG. Howes W312. *Pacific**. $1,380/£863

WHEAT, CARL I. The Pioneer Press of California. Oakland: Biobooks, 1948. One of 450 ptd. 3 tipped-in facs. Cl-backed marbled bds, paper spine label. (Offset from newspaper facs to corresponding pp; spine foot lt rubbed, sm chip to label), else NF. *Pacific**. $138/£86

WHEATLEY, DENNIS and J. G. LINKS. File on Bolitho Blane. Crimefile Number 1. NY: Morrow, 1936. 1st US ed. All clues present, but solution opened. VG+ (bd corners chipped). *Janus*. $65/£41

WHEATLEY, DENNIS. The Memoirs 1897-1977. London, 1977,1978,1979. 1st eds. Fine in djs. *Gretton*. $29/£18

WHEATLEY, DENNIS. The Sultan's Daughter. London: Hutchinson, 1963. 1st ed. Fine in NF dj. *Unger*. $45/£28

WHEATLEY, DENNIS. They Used Dark Forces. Hutchinson, 1964. 1st ed. Fine in dj. *Any Amount*. $24/£15

WHEATLEY, DENNIS. Vendetta in Spain. London: Hutchinson, 1961. 1st ed. Fine in NF dj (creased). *Unger.* $45/£28

WHEATLEY, HENRY B. Round About Piccadilly and Pall Mall. Smith, Elder, 1870. 1st ed. Frontis, xii,405pp. Pict cl (spine faded), gilt. *Cox.* $24/£15

WHEATON, HENRY. History of the Northmen, or Danes and Normans, from the Earliest Times to the Conquest of England by William of Normandy. Phila: Carey & Lea, 1831. 1st ed. Recent tan cl (foxed). *Sadlon.* $40/£25

WHEELER, A. A Short Catalogue of Books Printed in England and English Books Printed Abroad Before 1641 in the Library of Wadham College Oxford. Longmans, 1929. VG in dj (sl torn). *Moss.* $42/£26

WHEELER, DANIEL. Extracts from the Letters and Journal of Daniel Wheeler, Now Engaged in a Religious Visit.... London: Harvey & Darton, 1839. 1st complete ed. 4 parts in 1. 300pp. Orig blindstamped cl (spine ends, corners, fr joint worn), gilt. Internally NF. *Pacific*.* $127/£79

WHEELER, E. L. Scientific Glassblowing. NY: Interscience, 1958. Dj. *Weber.* $25/£16

WHEELER, GEORGE M. Memoir Upon the Voyages, Discoveries, Explorations, and Surveys to the West Coast of North America and Interior of the United States West of the Mississippi River.... Washington, 1889. 481-745pp; 10 maps. (Sl chipped; rebound), else VG. *Dumont.* $185/£116

WHEELER, GEORGE M. Report upon Geographical and Geological Explorations and Surveys West of the One Hundredth Meridian. Vol III, Geology. Washington, 1875. 585pp; 12 plts (1 fldg). Presentation card tipped inside fr wrap. Wraps (spine faded, hinges repaired). Internally VG. *Dumont.* $100/£63

WHEELER, GEORGE M. Report upon Geographical and Geological Explorations and Surveys West of the One Hundredth Meridian. Volume V—Zoology. Washington: Engineer Dept, US Army, 1875. 22,(326)pp; 13 plts. Ptd gray wrappers (spine worn, resewn). *Dawson.* $60/£38

WHEELER, GEORGE M. Report upon United States Geographical Surveys West of the One Hundredth Meridian...Volume VII. Archaeology. Washington: GPO, 1879. xxi,497pp. (Bds unevenly faded), else Nice. *Dumont.* $125/£78

WHEELER, HOMER W. Buffalo Days. Indianapolis: Bobbs-Merrill, (1925). Good (spine ends lt worn). Howes W322. *Lien.* $45/£28

WHEELER, HOMER W. Buffalo Days. NY: A.L. Burt, 1925. (Sl shelfworn), else VG. *Dumont.* $40/£25

WHEELER, KEITH. The Pacific Is My Beat. NY, 1943. 1st ed. Map. VG in Poor dj. *Clark.* $24/£15

WHEELER, L. N. The Foreigner in China. Chicago: Griggs, 1881. 1st ed. 268pp. (Spine ends sl rubbed), o/w VG. *Worldwide.* $65/£41

WHEELER, OLIN D. The Trail of Lewis and Clark, 1804-1904: A Story of the Great Exploration Across the Continent in 1804-06.... NY: Putnam, 1904. 1st ed. 2 vols. Teg. Red cl, gilt. (Sl shelfworn, fr hinge cracking each vol, vol I w/scrape to fore-edge fr cvr), else VG +. Howes W325. *Pacific*.* $259/£162

WHEELER, OPAL and SYBIL DEUCHER. Edward Mac Dowell and His Cabin in the Pines. Dutton, 1940. 1st ed. Mary Greenwalt (illus). 1/2 cl, illus bds. VG + (stray grn mk bottom edge, 1 corner sl worn). *Price.* $30/£19

WHEELER, R. E. M. Prehistoric and Roman Wales. OUP, 1925. 1st ed. (Sl pencil mks to margins; spine faded.) *Edwards.* $40/£25

WHEELER, RICHARD. Sword over Richmond. NY, (1986). 1st ed. Fine in Fine dj. *Pratt.* $20/£13

WHEELER, W. M. The Social Insects, Their Origin and Evolution. London, 1928. 48 plts. Fine in dj. *Henly.* $45/£28

WHEELOCK, JOHN HALL. The Gardener and Other Poems. NY, (1961). Signed. *Argosy.* $25/£16

WHEILDON, WILLIAM W. New History of the Battle of Bunker Hill, June 17, 1775, Its Purpose, Conduct, and Result. Boston: Lee & Shepard, 1875. 2nd ed. Presentation copy. 56pp; map. (Spine worn), else Good in ptd wraps (sl dust-soiled). *Brown.* $30/£19

WHELEN, TOWNSEND. Telescopic Rifle Sights. Plantersville: S.A.T.P, (1944). Stated 2nd ed. Frontis. Fine (tape mks, name, date) in dj (edges reinforced w/yellowed tape, scuffed), protective cvr. *Backman.* $25/£16

Where and How to Build. NY: Hubert, Pirsson, ca 1884. 82pp, 10pp ads. Lt grn-brn cl. Cvrs Good (corners sl worn, spine ends frayed; pp lt aged, several text cracks, portion of 1 sig loose, fr hinge cracked; lacks corner of fep, 1/2 of rep). *Baltimore*.* $260/£163

Where Men Only Dare to Go! Or the Story of a Boy Company (C.S.A.). By an Ex-Boy. (By Royal W. Figg.) Richmond: Whittet & Shepperson, 1885. 1st ed. Multiple-port frontis, 263pp. Brn cl, gilt. NF. *Chapel Hill.* $400/£250

WHERRY, JOSEPH. The Totem Pole Indians. NY: Wilfred Funk, (1964). Fine in Fine dj. *Perier.* $25/£16

WHEWELL, WILLIAM. History of the Inductive Sciences, from the Earliest to the Present Times. London: John Parker, 1837. 1st ed. 3 vols. 8vo. xxxvi,437,(2); xi,(1),534,(2); xii,624pp. Complete w/all 1/2-titles, errata ll. Mod 3/4 calf, marbled bds, morocco spine labels. NF (contemp ink underlining, notes vol 1). *Glaser.* $750/£469

WHIBLEY, CHARLES. American Sketches. London: William Blackwood, 1908. 1st ed. Red cl (spine sl worn). *Mott.* $50/£31

WHIBLEY, CHARLES. A Book of Scoundrels. London: Heinemann, 1892. Later issue. viii,283,(i)pp; pub's inserted 32-pg cat dated Aug 1896 at end. Uncut. Black coarse buckram. (Neat restoration spine head), o/w VG. *Temple.* $29/£18

WHIFFEN, THOMAS. The North-West Amazons. London: Constable, 1915. 1st ed. Frontis; 54 plts, 5 maps (2 lg fldg). Blue cl. Good. *Karmiole.* $125/£78

WHIGHAM, H. J. How to Play Golf. Chicago: Herbert S. Stone, 1897. 1st ed. Blue cl. (Name clipped from upper corner of tp; spine head chipped, sm bump to upper fr cvr corner), else VG. *Pacific*.* $259/£162

WHIGHAM, H. J. Manchuria and Korea. London: Isbister, 1904. 1st ed. Map, 12 plts. Yellow cl (waterstained, rubbed, cl holed at fr cvr foot), gilt. Internally Clean (lib stamps). *Morrell.* $56/£35

WHINNEY, MARGARET and RUPERT GUNNIS. The Collection of Models by John Flaxman R. A. at University College London. London, 1967. 24 plts. Good+ in dj (worn). *Washton.* $65/£41

WHIPPLE, A. W. The Whipple Report: Journal of an Expedition...September 11 to December 11, 1849. L.A.: Westernlore, 1961. Ltd to 900. Fine in Fine dj. *Book Market.* $50/£31

WHIPPLE, A. B. C. Yankee Whalers in the South Seas. NY, 1954. 1st ed. Dec cl (spine head worn). VG. *Larry Price.* $17/£11

WHIPPLE, GEORGE. Typhoid Fever: Its Causation, Transmission and Prevention. NY, 1908. 1st ed. *Fye.* $100/£63

WHIPPLE, GUY MONTROSE. Manual of Mental and Physical Tests. Issued in the Series Classics in Psychology. NY: Arno Press, 1973. Facs rpt of 1914 ed. 2 vols in 1. Ptd gray cl. VG. *Gach.* $50/£31

WHIPPLE, GUY MONTROSE. Manual of Mental and Physical Tests. Part I. Simpler Processes. Part II. Complex Processes. Balt: Warwick & York, 1914/1915. 2nd rev, enlgd ed. 2 vols. Ptd panelled red cl. VG set. *Gach.* $65/£41

WHISHAW, FRANCIS. The Railways of Great Britain and Ireland Practically Described and Illustrated. London, 1842. 2nd ed. xxix,500,lxivpp; 20 plts (incl fldg map). Later lib buckram. (Ex-lib, stamps, bkpl, plts chipped, stained, repaired; soiled, worn.) *Bohling.* $85/£53

WHISTHALER, JOHANNA S. By Water to the Columbian Exposition. Schenectady, 1894. (132)pp; fldg map. Good. *Zubal**. $28/£18

WHISTLER, HUGH. Popular Handbook of Indian Birds. London, 1928. 1st ed. 17 plts (4 color). Good. *Henly*. $51/£32

WHISTLER, HUGH. Popular Handbook of Indian Birds. London, 1941. 3rd ed. Rev, enlgd. 21 plts (6 color). Teg. (Fep, rep lt waterstained; spine lt faded, creased). *Edwards*. $24/£15

WHISTLER, JAMES MCNEILL. The Lithographs of Whistler. NY: Kennedy, 1914. One of 400 ptd. Lg 4to. Over 166 loose plts in portfolio ptd separate cat. Brn linen folder (soiled, ties worn). *Appelfeld*. $650/£406

WHISTLER, JAMES MCNEILL. Ten O'Clock, a Lecture. Portland, ME: Thomas Bird Mosher, 1920. Ltd to 25 numbered, ptd on Japan vellum. Port. (Bkpl; cvrs heavily rubbed.) *King*. $100/£63

WHISTLER, LAURENCE. Oho! Bodley Head, 1946. 1st ed. 15 full-pg faces by Rex Whistler. Illus eps. Colorptd bds. VG (ink sig; lib shelf #) in dj. *Blackwell's*. $104/£65

WHISTLER, LAURENCE. Oho! London: John Lane, The Bodley Head, 1946. 1st ed. Slim royal 8vo. (32)pp; 15 ports by Rex Whistler. Pict eps. Pict bds. Fine in dj (lower wrap sl spotted). *Sotheran*. $125/£78

WHITAKER, CHARLES HARRIS (ed). Bertram Grosvenor Goodhue—Architect and Master of Many Arts. NY, 1925. Folio. (Few ll loose; backstrip spotted.) *Swann**. $92/£58

WHITAKER, JOHN. The Ancient Cathedral of Cornwall. London: John Stockdale, 1804. 1st ed. 2 vols. 348; 434pp; 2 plts (offset, foxed). Contemp marbled bds, calf corners. (Lt foxed, lib bkpls; corners sl worn, rebacked in mod calf.) *Edwards*. $280/£175

WHITAKER, W. and W. TOPLEY. The Geological Record...1874-1884. London, 1875-1889. 8 vols. (Worn, 1 vol spine, chipped), o/w Good set. *Henly*. $256/£160

White House Gallery of Official Portraits of the Presidents. NY/Washington: Gravure Company of America, 1907. 1st ed. One of unspecified number. Lg folio. 24 full-pg Fine b/w gravure repros, tissue guards. Teg. Full dk brn sheep over beveled bds, lg circular mtd gold-colored metal seal. (Lt aged, few ll at fr partly torn, few plts dusty, dknd at margin edges; lacks spine, cvrs detached, worn, scuffed.) *Baltimore**. $230/£144

White Partner. Wiggins, Teape & Alex Pirie, 1924. 1st ed. 18 tipped-in paper samples. Cl-backed dec bds. *Forest*. $72/£45

WHITE, ALAIN and BOYD L. SLOANE. The Stapelieae. Pasadena: Abbey San Encino, 1937. 2nd ed. 3 vols. 39 color plts. VG (spine edges sl rubbed). *Brooks*. $375/£234

WHITE, ALMA. The Titanic Tragedy: God Speaking to the Nations. Bound Brook, NJ, 1912. 1st ed. (Worn, spine ends frayed, hinges broken.) *King*. $95/£59

WHITE, ARTHUR S. A Bibliography of Regimental Histories of the British Army. Society for Army Historical Research, 1965. 1st ed. Dj. *Forest*. $72/£45

WHITE, BENJAMIN. The Remarkable Mr. Franklin. Kansas City: Hallmark Cards, n.d. (1975). Carol Bryan (illus). 5 dbl-pg popups, rotating wheel, tab-operated mechanicals. Glazed pict bds. VG. *Bookfinders*. $55/£34

WHITE, BENJAMIN. Silver. Its History and Romance. London, 1917. 1st ed. *Edwards*. $96/£60

WHITE, C. The Flower Drawings of Jan Van Huysum. Leigh-on-Sea: Lewis, 1964. 64 plts. Good. *Ars Artis*. $56/£35

WHITE, C. C. No Quittin' Sense. Austin, 1969. 1st ed. Dj (price-clipped). *Swann**. $103/£64

WHITE, CHRISTINE SCHULTZ and BENTON R. WHITE. Now the Wolf Has Come. College Station, (1996). 1st ed. Fine in dj. *Pratt*. $20/£13

WHITE, CHRISTOPHER. The Dutch Pictures in the Collection of Her Majesty the Queen. London, 1982. Good+ in dj, slipcase. *Washton*. $165/£103

WHITE, CLAYTON and OTIS BENSON. Physics and Medicine of the Upper Atmosphere. Albuquerque, 1952. 1st ed. *Fye*. $150/£94

WHITE, E. B. Charlotte's Web. NY: Harper & Bros, (1952). 1st ed. 8vo. Garth William (illus). Wheat cl. Good in color pict dj (edges worn, chipped). *Reisler*. $400/£250

WHITE, E. B. Letters of.... NY: H&R, (1976). 1st ed. VG in VG dj. *Agvent*. $25/£16

WHITE, E. B. Stuart Little. NY, (1945). 1st ed. Dj (chipped, spine dknd). *Swann**. $92/£58

WHITE, E. B. Stuart Little. NY: Harper, (1945). 1st ed. VG in dj (extrems sl dknd, tape repair to sm tear on rear panel). *Pacific**. $161/£101

WHITE, EDMUND. The Beautiful Room Is Empty. NY, 1988. 1st Amer ed. Signed. Fine in Fine dj. *Polyanthos*. $25/£16

WHITE, EDMUND. The Beautiful Room Is Empty. London: Picador/Pan, 1988. 1st UK ed. Pub's wraparound band (worn) laid in. Fine in NF dj. *Lame Duck*. $35/£22

WHITE, EDMUND. A Boy's Own Story. NY, 1982. 1st Amer ed. Signed presentation. Fine in Fine dj. *Polyanthos*. $35/£22

WHITE, EDMUND. Caracole. NY, 1985. 1st Amer ed. Signed. Fine in Fine dj. *Polyanthos*. $30/£19

WHITE, EDMUND. Forgetting Elena. NY: Random House, 1973. 1st ed, 1st bk. NF in NF dj. *Pettler*. $50/£31

WHITE, EDMUND. States of Desire. Travels in Gay America. NY: Dutton, 1980. 1st ed. Signed. Fine in dj (lt used, vertical spine crease). *Beasley*. $75/£47

WHITE, EDWARD. American Orchid Culture. NY: De la Mare, 1948. 3rd ed. Ltr ptg. VG. *Archer*. $30/£19

WHITE, FRANK H. Panorama of the Tabernacle. London: S.W. Partridge, ca 1874. 12 chromolitho plts. Fldg gilt-dec bds (sl edgeworn). *Metropolitan**. $258/£161

WHITE, FREDERICK. The Spicklefisherman: and Others. NY: Derrydale, 1928. One of 740. Vellum cl backed over marbled paper-cvrd bds. Fine in orig patterned glassine wrapper. *Biscotti*. $175/£109

WHITE, GERALD T. Baptism in Oil: Stephen F. Peckham in Southern California, 1865-66. Ward Ritchie, 1984. One of 500. *Dawson*. $40/£25

WHITE, GILBERT. The Natural History and Antiquities of Selborne, in the County of Southampton. London: Bickers, (1881). 3rd ed. 568pp + 16pp ads; fldg chart. Teg. Pict cl, gilt. (Extrems rubbed), else VG. *Mikesh*. $60/£38

WHITE, GILBERT. The Natural History and Antiquities of Selborne. London: Swan Sonneschein, ca 1890. Full grn polished calf w/arms of Highgate School stamped in gilt on cvr, gilt paneled spine, raised bands, marbled edges. Nice. *Appelfeld*. $200/£125

WHITE, GILBERT. The Natural History of Selborne. London, 1825. 2 vols. 351; 2,364pp; 4 plts (one hand-colored). Uncut. (Orig bds, labels sl worn.) *Henly*. $144/£90

WHITE, GILBERT. The Natural History of Selborne. London: C.&J. Rivington, et al, 1825. 2nd ed thus. 2 vols. Color frontis, viii,351; 364pp; 3 engr plts. Contemp calf (rebacked), twin labels. *Young*. $192/£120

WHITE, GILBERT. The Natural History of Selborne. London: C. and J. Rivington, 1825. New ed. 2 vols. Frontispieces (1 hand-colored) viii,351pp; (iv),364pp; 2 plts. (Sl spotted, bkpl, pp13-14 in vol 2 torn, repaired; hinges reinforced.) Marbled eps, 1/2 calf w/cl bds, sympathetically rebacked in mod calf w/raised bands, leather labels. *Edwards*. $200/£125

WHITE, GILBERT. The Natural History of Selborne. E. Jesse (ed). London, 1854. Frontis, xxiv,416pp (sl spotted, fr joint open but solid); 40 hand-colored engrs. 1/2 morocco (spine head chipped, fr outer hinge sl split). *Sutton.* $150/£94

WHITE, GILBERT. The Natural History of Selborne. Ipswich: LEC, 1972. One of 1500 signed by John Nash (illus). Box. *Kane*.* $65/£41

WHITE, GILBERT. The Natural History of Selborne. LEC, 1972. Ltd to 1500 numbered, signed by John Nash (illus). Fine in slipcase. *Swann*.* $126/£79

WHITE, GILBERT. The Writings of Gilbert White of Selbourne. H. J. Massingham (ed). London: Nonesuch, 1938. One of 850 sets. 2 vols. Wood engr tps, xxx,(2),311; viii,356pp; 2 fldg maps. (Lt foxed to margins, edges, prelims, final ll.) *Marlborough.* $768/£480

WHITE, HELEN McCANN (ed). Ho! For the Gold Fields. St. Paul: MN Hist Soc, 1966. 1st ed. VG in dj. *Lien.* $25/£16

WHITE, HENRY ALEXANDER. Robert E. Lee and the Southern Confederacy 1807-1870. NY/London: Putnam, 1910. 3rd ed. Red cl. (Sig; 1/4-inch tear at spine top), else VG. *Chapel Hill.* $65/£41

WHITE, HENRY C. The Life and Art of Dwight William Tryon. Boston: Houghton Mifflin, 1930. 1st ed. Black cl (corners rubbed). *Karmiole.* $100/£63

WHITE, HENRY C. The Life and Art of Dwight William Tryon. Boston, 1930. 1/4 cl (extrems worn, hinges just starting). *Swann*.* $161/£101

WHITE, HENRY. Geology, Oil Fields, and Minerals, of Canada West: How and Where to Find Them. Toronto: W.C. Chewett, 1865. 1st ed. 12mo. 109pp; 2 lg color litho fldg maps (few tears). Orig cl, black paper label fr cvr. Excellent. *M & S.* $1,750/£1,094

WHITE, J. CLAUDE. Sikhim and Bhutan, Twenty-One Years on the North-East Frontier, 1887-1908. London, 1909. Map. (Rubber stamp, lib label; rebacked w/orig backstrip replaced, corner sl rubbed.) *Petersfield.* $352/£220

WHITE, J. M. Marshal of France. London: Hamilton, (1962). Frontis; 8 plts. Good. *Stewart.* $48/£30

WHITE, JAMES E. A Life Span and Reminiscences of Railway Mail Service. Phila: Deemer & Jaisohn, (1910). 1st ed. Good. *Lien.* $50/£31

WHITE, KATHERINE KEOGH. The King's Mountain Men. Ruebush, 1924. 1st ed. Ltd to 500. Good- (tp tipped back in; acidic paper browned, brittle; pencil checks throughout). *Book Broker.* $125/£78

WHITE, KENNETH. Karel Appel: Works on Paper. Abbeville, 1980. Nice in dj (torn, repaired). *Rybski.* $110/£69

WHITE, LAWRENCE GRANT. Sketches and Designs by Stanford White. NY: Architectural Book Publishing, Paul Wenzel & Maurice Krakow, 1920. 1st ed. Tall folio. Color frontis, 56 plts. Teg. Brn cl, gilt. (Sl handled, lt foxed; sl rubbed, lt shelfworn.) Text VG. *Baltimore*.* $180/£113

WHITE, LESLIE A. Pioneers in American Anthropology. Albuquerque: Univ of NM, 1940. 1st ed. One of 400 numbered sets. 2 vols. Frontisports. Untrimmed, mostly unopened. Crimson cl, gilt. Clean (ex-lib, white tape spine stickers, ink stamps, card pockets; sl sunned, shelfworn). *Baltimore*.* $90/£56

WHITE, LUKE. Henry William Herbert and the American Publishing Scene: 1831-1858. Newark, NJ: Cateret Book Club, 1943. 1st ed. Ltd to 200 numbered. Issued w/repro of Forester letter in pocket inside rear panel. Grn buckram. NF. *Biscotti.* $200/£125

WHITE, MINOR. Mirrors, Messages, Manifestations. NY, (1969). 1st ed. Folio. (Eps age-dknd, lacks pamphlet; extrems sl worn, age-dknd.) Dj (rubbed, chipped). *Swann*.* $126/£79

WHITE, NEWMAN IVEY. Shelley. NY, 1940. 1st ed. (Joints splitting.) Djs, slipcase (worn). *Woolson.* $30/£19

WHITE, OWEN P. The Autobiography of a Durable Sinner. NY: Putnam, (1942). 1st ed. Signed. VG in dj (sl worn). Howes W363. *Lien.* $100/£63

WHITE, OWEN P. Lead and Likker. NY: Minton, Balch, 1932. 1st ed. VG + in dj (worn). *Labordo.* $85/£53

WHITE, OWEN P. Them Was the Days; from El Paso to Prohibition. NY: Minton, Balch, 1925. 1st ed. VG (no dj). *Labordo.* $50/£31

WHITE, PHILO. Narrative of a Cruize in the Pacific to South America and California on the U.S. Sloop-of-War 'Dale' 1841-1843. Denver: Old West, (1965). 1st ed. One of 1000 ptd. Folio. 2 full-pg color plts, 4 b/w plts. Grn cl. Fine. *House.* $50/£31

WHITE, PHILO. Narrative of a Cruize in the Pacific to South America and California on the U.S. Sloop-of-War 'Dale,' 1841-1843. Charles L. Camp (ed). Denver: Fred A. Rosenstock, (1965). 1st ed. One of 1000 ptd. 5 plts (2 color). (Top edge fr cvr sl sunned), else Fine. *Pacific*.* $29/£18

WHITE, RUTH. Yankee from Sweden, the Dream and the Reality in the Days of John Ericsson. NY, (1960). 1st ed. VG + in dj (sl worn). *Pratt.* $25/£16

WHITE, SAMUEL. History of the American Troops During the Late War Under the Command of Colonels Fenton and Campbell. Rochester, NY, 1896. One of 300. 107pp. Howes W370. *Cullen.* $150/£94

WHITE, STEWART EDWARD. African Camp Fires. GC: Doubleday, Page, 1913. 1st ed. Frontis. Dec multi-color cvr, gilt. VG + (spine edges lt chipped). *Backman.* $65/£41

WHITE, STEWART EDWARD. Arizona Nights. NY: McClure, 1907. 1st ed. N. C. Wyeth (illus). Pict cvr label. (Old name; rear cvr, extrem of fr cvr insect-damaged, soiled, spine worn), else VG-. *Pacific*.* $40/£25

WHITE, STEWART EDWARD. Conjuror's House: A Romance of the Free Forest. NY: McClure, Phillips, 1903. 1st ed. Pict cl (spine sl dull), gilt. *Sadlon.* $20/£13

WHITE, T. A Treatise on the Struma or Scrofula, Commonly Called the King's Evil. London, 1787. 2nd ed. viii,100pp. Mod 1/2 leather, marbled bds. (Ex-lib, ink mks, marginal pencil lines), o/w Good. *Whitehart.* $224/£140

WHITE, T. H. America at Last. The American Journal of T. H. White. NY: Putnam, 1965. 1st ed. VG + in dj. *Any Amount.* $24/£15

WHITE, T. H. The Elephant and the Kangaroo. NY, (1947). 1st ed. VG in dj (rubbed, sl soiled, frayed, price-clipped). *King.* $75/£47

WHITE, T. H. The Elephant and the Kangaroo. NY: Putnam, 1947. 1st US ed. (Spine ends sl rubbed), o/w VG in dj (sl rubbed, discolored, internally repaired, corners, spine ends sl chipped). *Virgo.* $96/£60

WHITE, T. H. Farewell Victoria. NY: Smith & Haas, 1934. 1st ed, 1st issue binding. NF in NF dj (1/4-inch loss to spine head, extrems chipped). *Warren.* $40/£25

WHITE, T. H. The Godstone and the Blackymor. London: Cape, 1959. 1st ed. 5.5x8. Edward Ardizzone (illus). 224pp. Fine in dj. *Cattermole.* $45/£28

WHITE, T. H. The Goshawk. London: Cape, 1951. 1st ed. VG + in Good + dj. *Mikesh.* $60/£38

WHITE, T. H. The Green Bay Tree; or, The Wicked Man Touches Wood. (Cambridge: W. Heffer & Sons, 1929.) 1st ed, 1st bk. Illus paper wrappers (sm snag). *Black Sun.* $200/£125

WHITE, T. H. The Ill-Made Knight. NY: Putnam, 1940. 1st ed. NF in VG dj (spine foot chipped, sm tears to lower joints, spine head, extrems sl rubbed). *Pacific*.* $230/£144

WHITE, T. H. The Master. Collins, 1942. 1st ed. 256pp (few sl spots). Mod 1/2 morocco, gilt. Dj (lacks flaps) tipped in at end. *Hollett.* $136/£85

WHITE, T. H. The Sword in the Stone. London: Collins, 1938. 1st ed. 8vo. Black cl. Overall VG (eps lt browned; edges, 1st/last few ll lt foxed; cvrs sl bubbled) in dj (spine browned, sl edge-worn). *Heritage.* $650/£406

WHITE, T. H. The Sword in the Stone. London: Collins, 1938. 1st ed. (Outer edges lt foxed), else Fine in dj (2 sm chips). *Bromer.* $950/£594

WHITE, T. H. The Witch in the Wood. NY: Putnam, 1939. 1st ed. VG in dj (spine ends, corners chipped, spine sunned, flap tips clipped). *Pacific*.* $138/£86

WHITE, THOMAS. The Beauties of Occult Science Investigated. London: Anne Davis, 1810. 1st ed. 436pp. Later 1/2 calf, cl, morocco spine label. VG + (spine, cvr lt rubbed). *Middle Earth.* $696/£435

WHITE, WALTER. A Rising Wind. NY, 1945. 1st ed. Dj. *Swann*.* $57/£36

WHITE, WILLIAM B. Theory and Practice of Pianoforte Building. NY: Edward Lyman Bill, 1906. 1st ed. 2-tone cl (extrems sl rubbed), gilt. *Hollett.* $120/£75

WHITE, WILLIAM S. Contributions to a History of the Richmond Howitzer Battalion. Richmond, VA, 1883. Pamphlet no 2. 89-304pp. (Spine tape, cvrs chipped, soiled.) Wraps. *King.* $200/£125

WHITE, WILLIAM. Directory of Staffordshire. London, 1851. 2nd ed. 800pp + ads. Contemp full dec calf. Sound (lacks map). *Gretton.* $72/£45

WHITEHEAD, ALFRED NORTH and BERTRAND RUSSELL. Principia Mathematica. Cambridge: CUP, 1910. 1st ed. Vol 1 (of 3) only. xiii,(3),666pp. Blue cl, gilt. (Ink name, sl shaken; lt worn, cl sl rippled), else VG. *Pacific*.* $1,265/£791

WHITEHEAD, ALFRED NORTH and BERTRAND RUSSELL. Principia Mathematica. CUP, 1950. 2nd ed (3rd rpt). 3 vols. Blue lib buckram, gilt. VG set (sm lib stamps, pencil underlining; cl sl mkd). *Hollett.* $240/£150

WHITEHEAD, G. KENNETH. Deer and Their Management in the Deer Parks of Great Britain and Ireland. Country Life, 1950. 1st ed. VG in dj (edges sl chipped). *Hollett.* $240/£150

WHITEHEAD, G. KENNETH. The Deer Stalking Grounds of Great Britain and Ireland. London, 1960. Frontis, 12 maps. (Note), o/w VG in dj. *Petersfield.* $200/£125

WHITEHEAD, G. KENNETH. The Wild Goats of Great Britain and Ireland. London, 1972. Fine in dj. *Petersfield.* $40/£25

WHITEHEAD, HENRY S. Jumbee and Other Uncanny Tales. Sauk City: Arkham House, 1944. 1st ed. VG in dj (spine head rubbed, sm piece lacking rear panel corner). *Pacific*.* $98/£61

WHITEHEAD, HENRY S. Jumbee and Other Uncanny Tales. (Sauk City): Arkham House, 1944. 1st ed. VG + in VG dj (spine sl faded). Bkpl of Oswald Train. *Other Worlds.* $300/£188

WHITEHEAD, JOHN. Exploration of Mount Kina Balu, North Borneo. London: Gurney & Jackson, 1893. 4to. x,(ii),317pp; 11 color plts, 20 sepia plts, 1 b/w plt. Teg. (Lt marginal browning, sl loss fep fore-edge, bkpl; spine sl rubbed, chipped.) *Edwards.* $2,400/£1,500

WHITEHEAD, JOHN. Guardian of the Grail. (London): Jarrolds, 1959. 1st Eng ed. VG (spine ends sl bumped, head faded) in dj (nicked, sl rubbed, dusty, spine faded, edges sl browned). *Ulysses.* $56/£35

WHITEHEAD, JOHN. This Solemn Mockery. Arlington Books, 1973. 1st ed. 8 plts. Dj (rubbed). *Forest.* $35/£22

WHITEHEAD, P. J. P. and P. I. EDWARDS. Chinese Natural History Drawings. British Museum, 1974. Issued in a ltd ed of 400 numbered copies. Folio. 20 Fine collotype color plts. 1/4 goatskin leather over dec buckram. Fine in velvet-lined buckram portfolio box. *Sutton.* $325/£203

WHITEHEAD, P. J. P. Forty Drawings of Fishes. British Museum, 1968. Folio. Frontisport, 35 plts. Dj (sl chipped, soiled). *Edwards.* $160/£100

WHITEHEAD, P. J. P. and P. I. EDWARDS. Chinese Natural History Drawings. London, 1974. One of 400. Folio. 20 plts. Teg. Gilt-edged morocco-backed buckram w/gilt device, spine. Velveteen lined buckram drop-down-box w/black device. *Edwards.* $240/£150

WHITEHOUSE, H. L. K. Towards an Understanding of the Mechanism of Heredity. London: Edward Arnold, (1965). 1st ed. Grn bds. VG + in dj (rubbed). *House.* $40/£25

WHITEHOUSE, J. HOWARD (ed). To the Memory of Ruskin. Cambridge: CUP, 1934. Uncut, unopened. Mod holland-backed bds, orig paper label preserved. VG. *Hollett.* $56/£35

WHITEHURST, FRED. Hark Away. Sketches of Hunting, Coaching, Fishing, Etc. London: Tinsley Bros, 1879. (vii),319pp. 3/4 calf, spine gilt. (Rubbed.) *Oinonen*.* $70/£44

WHITELEY, DEREK PEPYS. George du Maurier. London: Art & Technics, 1948. VG in dj (spine faded, edges taped on verso). *Hollett.* $48/£30

WHITELY, IKE. Rural Life in Texas. Atlanta: Jas. P. Harrison, 1891. 1st ed. Copyright slip, 1-iv,1-82,83-86 ads, 87-88 blank pp. Orig pict yellow wraps. (Paper browned; soiled, chipped, rear corner gone, spine chipped w/loss), else Good. Howes W377. *Brown.* $100/£63

WHITEMAN, PAUL. Records for the Millions. David A. Stein (ed). NY: Hermitage, 1948. 1st ed. VG in pict dj. *Petrilla.* $40/£25

WHITESIDE, JAMES. Italy in the Nineteenth Century. London: Richard Bentley, 1849. 2nd ed, rev. 3 vols. 3 frontispieces, xxviii,341; xii,335; xi,346pp. Contemp navy-blue 1/2 calf, raised bands. Very Nice set. *Young.* $152/£95

WHITFORD, WILLIAM CLARKE. Colorado Volunteers in the Civil War; The New Mexico Campaign in 1862. Denver, 1906. (Lt worn), else VG. Howes W378. *Dumont.* $250/£156

WHITHARD, PHILIP. Illuminating and Missal-Painting on Paper and Vellum. Crosby Lockwood, 1909. 1st ed. Extra color frontis; color plt. Grn dec cl. (Sl foxed), o/w VG. *Whittle.* $61/£38

WHITING, LILLIAN. The Land of Enchantment from Pike's Peak to the Pacific. Boston, 1906. 1st ed. Teg, fore-edge untrimmed. Grn cl, gilt. (Hinges cracked, corner bumped), o/w VG. *Five Quail.* $35/£22

WHITING, PERRY. Autobiography of Perry Whiting. Boston: Christopher Pub, (1938). VG. *Lien.* $15/£9

WHITING, ROBERT. The Chrysanthemum and the Bat. Dodd, Mead, 1977. 1st ed. Fine in VG dj. *Plapinger.* $85/£53

WHITLOCK, BRAND. Lafayette. NY/London: D. Appleton, 1929. 1st ed. 2 vols. Teg. Gilt-dec cl. NF. *Sadlon.* $25/£16

Whitman Mother Goose: A Complete Collection of Nursery Rhyme Favorites. Racine: Whitman, (1922). 12.25x9. Cl-backed pict bds. VG. *Pacific*.* $46/£29

WHITMAN, ALFRED. Nineteenth Century Mezzotinters: Samuel Cousins. London: Bell, 1904. One of 600. 36 plts. (Spine tear, sl worn.) *Ars Artis.* $80/£50

WHITMAN, ALFRED. Samuel Cousins. George Bell & Sons, 1904. Ltd to 600. 34 plts. (Cl worn.) *Hollett.* $104/£65

WHITMAN, WALT. Autobiographia. NY: Charles Webster, 1892. 1st ed, 1st issue, primary binding. Frontis. Olive grn cl, gilt. Fine (crease fep). BAL 21639. *Macdonnell.* $100/£63

WHITMAN, WALT. The Correspondence of Walt Whitman, 1842-1875. Edwin H. Miller (ed). NY: NY Univ, 1961. 1st ed. 2 vols. Fine set in djs. *Macdonnell.* $65/£41

WHITMAN, WALT. Leaves of Grass. Boston, (1860). 3rd ed, later issue. NF (ex-lib, sl rubbed). *Polyanthos.* $150/£94

WHITMAN, WALT. Leaves of Grass. Brooklyn, 1856. 2nd ed. 12mo. 20 add'l poems not in 1855 1st ed. Grn cl. VG (lt foxed; spine head, foot neatly restored, hinges expertly repaired) in 1/4 grn morocco slipcase. *Heritage.* $3,500/£2,188

WHITMAN, WALT. Leaves of Grass. LEC, 1942. Ltd to 1500 numbered, signed by Edward Weston (photos). 2 vols. Fine in slipcase. *Swann*.* $460/£288

WHITMAN, WALT. Leaves of Grass. Mount Vernon: Peter Pauper, n.d. (1950). Ltd to 1100. Folio. 1/4 morocco, pict bds. Fine (bkpl) in slipcase (lt worn, soiled). *Truepenny.* $350/£219

WHITMAN, WALT. Leaves of Grass: Comprising All the Poems Written by Walt Whitman Following the Arrangement of the Edition of 1891-'2. NY: Random House, 1930. One of 400 ptd by the Grabhorn Press. 14.5x9.75. 37 woodcuts by Valenti Angelo. 1/2 red niger morocco, Philippine mahogany bds, raised bands. (Spine sl browned, leather sl crackled, extrems sl rubbed), else VG in later clamshell box. *Pacific*.* $748/£468

WHITMAN, WALT. Memories of President Lincoln. Portland, ME: Thomas B. Mosher, 1912. One of 300. Good. *Cullen.* $85/£53

WHITMAN, WALT. November Boughs. Phila: David McKay, 1888. 1st ed, later lg paper issue. Mostly unopened; teg. Grn cl. VF. *Appelfeld.* $300/£188

WHITMAN, WALT. Songs of the Open Road. LEC, 1990. One of 550 signed by Aaron Siskind (photos). Fine in slipcase. *Swann*.* $517/£323

WHITMAN, WALT. Specimen Days and Collect. Phila, 1882-1883. 1st ed, 1st issue. (Inner hinges cracked; spine head frayed, cvrs soiled.) *King.* $300/£188

WHITMAN, WALT. Specimen Days in America. Walter Scott, 1887. New rev ed. Good (fore-edge lt spotted; spine bumped, paper label rubbed). *Tiger.* $22/£14

WHITMAN, WALT. Specimen Days. Boston, 1971. Mtd repro. Dj (worn). *Swann*.* $80/£50

WHITNEY, CASPAR. On Snow Shoes to the Barren Grounds. London, 1896. 1st British ed. 324pp; 15 full-pg plts by Frederic Remington. Teg. Pict cl. VG. *Truepenny.* $200/£125

WHITNEY, CASPAR. On Snow-Shoes to the Barren Grounds. London, 1896. x,323pp (feps foxed, pp71/2 damaged w/sl loss, ex-lib, pen mk spine head). Illus cl (spine sl rubbed, sm split lower joint head). *Edwards.* $96/£60

WHITNEY, CASPAR. On Snow-Shoes to the Barren Grounds. NY: Harper & Bros, 1896. x,324pp. Teg. Dec cl. VG (new eps). *High Latitude.* $125/£78

WHITNEY, DAVID (ed). Andy Warhol: Portraits of the 70s. (NY, 1979.) One of 200 numbered, signed by Warhol. Slipcase. *Swann*.* $488/£305

WHITNEY, HARRY. Hunting with the Eskimos. NY: Century, 1910. 1st ed. 64 photo plts. Teg. Blue cl, gilt, paper label. (Spine gilt lt rubbed), o/w VG. *House.* $70/£44

WHITNEY, HARRY. Hunting with the Eskimos. NY, 1910. One of 150 numbered. Signed. 1/2 morocco. *Swann*.* $402/£251

WHITNEY, J. D. Contributions to American Geology, Volume I: The Auriferous Gravels of the Sierra Nevada of California. CUP, 1880. 1st ed. xvi,569pp; 3 heliotype plts, dbl-pg plt, 20 maps, diags, sections, plans. Uncut, teg. Grn pebble cl, gilt. Fine (flap detached from rear map pocket but present). *Pacific*.* $230/£144

WHITNEY, J. D. Geological Survey of California, J. D. Whitney, State Geologist. (Sacramento): Legislature of CA, 1865. 1st ed. 10.25x7.75. xxvii,(1),498pp; 9 plts. Grn pebbled cl, gilt. (Hinges cracking.) *Pacific*.* $1,840/£1,150

WHITNEY, J. D. Geological Survey of California, J. D. Whitney, State Geologist. (Sacramento): CA State Legislature, 1869. 1st ed. 9x6.5. (5),vi-vii,(2),10-155pp; 8 wood-engr plts, tissue guards, 2 fldg maps, one in each fr/rear pockets. Grn cl, gilt. (Ink sig; spine top sl worn), o/w VF. *Pacific*.* $1,265/£791

WHITNEY, J. D. Geological Survey of California, J. D. Whitney, State Geologist. (Sacramento): CA Legislature, 1871. 2nd ed, 1st ptg. (v),vi-vii,(9)-133pp; 2 fldg maps. Blue cl, gilt. (Bkpl, lib #s, sm waterstain 2 ep corners; extrems lt worn), o/w VG. *Pacific*.* $230/£144

WHITNEY, J. D. Geological Survey of California, J. D. Whitney, State Geologist. (Sacramento): CA Legislature, 1874. 3rd ed, 1st ptg. (v),vi-vii,(9)-186pp; 3 maps (2 fldg). Aeg. Brn cl, gilt. (Lacks map; extrems sl worn, ink stain rear cvr margin extending across gilt edges), o/w VG. *Pacific*.* $207/£129

WHITNEY, J. P. Silver Mining Regions of Colorado. With Some Account of the Different Processes No Being Introduced for Working the Gold Ores That Territory (wrapper title). NY: D. Van Nostrand, 1865. 1st ed. 107pp. Mod 1/2 buckram, marbled bds. (2 spots of adhesion residue to blank portion of preface pg; lacks rear wrapper), else NF in ptd fr wrapper. Howes W388. *Pacific*.* $1,265/£791

WHITTAKER, FREDERICK. A Complete Life of Gen. George A. Custer. NY: Sheldon, (1876). 1st ed. Steel-engr frontis, x,648pp. Gilt-pict cl. (Inscrips, dated 1879, 1904; spine ends frayed, corners sl worn, rear hinge repaired w/glue), else VG. *Pacific*.* $173/£108

WHITTEMORE, EDWARD. Jericho Mosaic. NY: Norton, 1987. 1st ed. Fine in NF dj. *Pettler.* $40/£25

WHITTEMORE, EDWARD. Quin's Shanghai Circus. NY: Holt Rinehart, 1974. 1st ed, 1st bk. (Spine sl slanted), else Fine in VG + dj. *Pettler.* $45/£28

WHITTEMORE, MARGARET. Historic Kansas, a Centenary Sketchbook. Lawrence: Univ of KS, 1954. 1st ed. NF (sig) in dj (edges faded). *Glenn.* $45/£28

WHITTICK, ARNOLD. History of Cemetery Sculpture. Volume 1 (apparently all pub). London, 1938. One of 500. Frontis, 51 plts. (1st, last few ll lt spotted, wrinkled.) Dj (sl soiled, chipped). *Edwards.* $200/£125

WHITTIER, JOHN GREENLEAF. Miriam. Boston: Fields, Osgood, 1871. 1st ed. Brn cl, gilt: BAL's suggested 2nd binding, w/the FRO monogram at spine foot. (Spine sl faded), o/w Fine. *Maggs.* $80/£50

WHITTIER, JOHN GREENLEAF. The Poems of John Greenleaf Whittier. LEC, 1945. Ltd to 1500 numbered, signed by Raymond J. Holden (illus). Fine in slipcase. *Swann*.* $40/£25

WHITTIER, JOHN GREENLEAF. The Poetical Works of John Greenleaf Whittier. W. Garrett Horder (ed). London: Henry Frowde, 1898. Frontisport, xv,(1),598pp. Marbled eps; aeg. Contemp tree calf, gilt, raised bands, black morocco label. (Lg bkpl; joints, 1 corner sl worn, fr joint sl cracked, spine sl unevenly faded). Internally Fine. *Pirages.* $25/£16

WHITTIER, JOHN GREENLEAF. A Sabbath Scene. Boston, 1854. 1st ed. Glazed letterpress wrappers. *Swann*.* $46/£29

WHITTING, P. D. Byzantine Coins. NY: Putnam, 1973. 1st ed. VG in dj. *Worldwide.* $60/£38

WHITWORTH, CHARLES. An Account of Russia as It Was in the Year 1710. Ptd at Strawberry Hill, 1758. 1st ed. One of 700. 8vo. All edges sprinkled. Full contemp polished calf, gilt. VG (bkpl; hinges sl rubbed). *Hartfield.* $895/£559

WHITWORTH, R. The Electric Organ. London: Musical Opinion, 1930. 1st ed. 8 plts. 9pp photostat on 'The Art of Voicing' loosely inserted. (Spine sl faded, neatly recased.) *Hollett.* $72/£45

Who Are We? N.K. Fairbank Co, 1908. Shapebook. 16mo. 6pp. Good in color illus paper wrappers. *Reisler.* $185/£116

WHYMPER, EDWARD. The Ascent of the Matterhorn. London, 1880. 1st ed thus. xxii,325pp; 2 fldg maps (1 color), 14 plts. Pict cl, gilt. (Sl dust soiled, lt edgeworn.) *Maggs.* $280/£175

WHYMPER, EDWARD. Travels Amongst the Great Andes of the Equator. London, 1892. 2nd ed. xxiv,456pp; 20 plts, 4 maps (2 fldg, 1 in rear pocket). (Lib bkpl, label remains fep, blindstamp to tp; lacks top portion fep; cl soiled, label remains fr bd, spine discolored.) *Edwards.* $88/£55

WHYMPER, FREDERICK. Travel and Adventure in the Territory of Alaska. Readex Microprint, (1966). Facs of 1868 London ed. Fine. *Perier.* $40/£25

WHYTE-MELVILLE, GEORGE JOHN. The Brookes of Bridlemere. London: Chapman & Hall, 1864. 1st ed. 3 vols. Contemp reddish-brn 1/2 calf (spine heads sl rubbed). VG set. *Young.* $216/£135

WIATER, STANLEY (ed). After the Darkness. Balt: Maclay & Assoc, 1993. One of 750. Signed by all contributors. As New in slipcase. *Pacific*.* $35/£22

WIATER, STANLEY (ed). Night Visions 7. Arlington Hts: Dark Harvest, 1989. 1st ed. One of 550. Signed by all contributors & ed. Fine in dj, slipcase. *Pacific*.* $46/£29

WICKER, TOM. Unto This Hour. NY, (1984). 1st ed. VG + in VG + dj. *Pratt.* $17/£11

WICKERSHAM, JAMES. Old Yukon. Washington: Washington Law Book, 1938. 1st ed. Signed (stamped?), w/Wickersham's bkpl. (Spine w/discolored spots.) *Perier.* $50/£31

WICKERSHAM, JAMES. Old Yukon. St. Paul: West Pub, 1973. 8th ptg. Sketch, greeting signed by Ruth Allman (author's niece). Color travel pamphlet laid in. Fine. *Perier.* $40/£25

WICKES, CHARLES. Illustrations of the Spires and Towers of the Mediaeval Churches of England. London: John Weale, 1853-55. 2 vols. 52 litho plts. (Spotting, emb lib stamps, bkpl.) Orig cl (spines sl worn), gilt. *Christie's*.* $154/£96

WICKES, GEORGE (ed). Lawrence Durrell and Henry Miller: a Private Correspondence. NY: Dutton, 1963. 1st ed. As New in As New dj. *Between The Covers.* $125/£78

WICKHAM, CONSTANCE. The Teddy Bear Book. London: Collins, (1937). 4to. 8 full-pg color plts by A. E. Kennedy. Grn cl, gilt. (Lt spotted.) *Reisler.* $125/£78

WICKHAM, GLYNNE. Early English Stages 1300-1660. London: Routledge & Kegan Paul, 1963-1972. 1st Eng ed. 2 vols in 3. Buckram (1 spine head snagged). Fine set in djs (edges sl rubbed). *Ulysses.* $240/£150

WICKHOFF, FRANZ. Roman Art. London, 1900. 1st ed. 14 plts. Uncut. NF (sl rubbed). *Polyanthos.* $75/£47

WICKSTEAD, PHILIP H. Our Lady's Tumbler. Portland, ME: Thomas B. Mosher, 1900. Ltd to 450. (Foxed; book sl bent.) Stiff wraps. *King.* $35/£22

WIDEMAN, JOHN EDGAR. Hiding Place. London: Allison & Busby, (1984). 1st UK ed. Fine in Fine dj. *Agvent.* $100/£63

WIDEMAN, JOHN EDGAR. The Lynchers. NY: HB, (1973). 1st ed. (Sl sticker shadow on pastedown.) Dj (sm closed tear). *Agvent.* $150/£94

WIDEMAN, JOHN EDGAR. Sent for You Yesterday. NY: Avon, (1983). True 1st ed. Fine in wraps (sl creased). *Agvent.* $65/£41

WIDEMAN, JOHN EDGAR. Sent for You Yesterday. London: A&B, (1984). 1st UK ed. Fine in Fine dj. *Agvent.* $100/£63

WIDENER, HARRY ELKINS. A Catalogue of the Books and Manuscripts of Robert Louis Stevenson in the Library of the Late Harry Elkins Eidener. Phila: Privately ptd, 1913. One of 150 numbered. Uncut. Full black morocco (lt rubbed). *Oinonen*.* $160/£100

WIDMER, JACK. The American Quarter Horse. NY: Scribner, (1959). 1st ed. VG in dj (sl worn). *Lien.* $35/£22

Widow of the Wood. (By Benjamin Victor.) London: C. Corbett, 1755. 1st ed. (ii),iv,208,(1) ad leaf pp (1 gathering loose). 20th-cent 1/4 calf, raised bands, red label. *Young.* $288/£180

WIEDERSEIM, GRACE G. The Tiny Tots. Their Adventures. NY: Frederick A. Stokes, (1909). 1st ed. Lg 4to. 12 full-pg color plts. Cl-backed color illus bds (edges rubbed, worn). *Reisler.* $275/£172

WIENER, NORBERT. Cybernetics: or, Control and Communication in the Animal and the Machine. NY: John Wiley, (1948). 1st ed, 1st ptg. Fine. *Glaser.* $400/£250

WIENER, NORBERT. Cybernetics: or, Control and Communication in the Animal and the Machine. NY: John Wiley, (1948). 1st ed, 1st ptg. 8vo. (Dj edges sl worn), o/w Fine in dj. *Glaser.* $600/£375

WIENER, NORBERT. Cybernetics: or, Control and Communication in the Animal and the Machine. NY: MIT Press/John Wiley, 1961. 2nd ed. VG in dj. *Glaser.* $275/£172

WIENER, NORBERT. God and Golem, Inc. A Comment on Certain Points Where Cybernetics Impinges on Religion. Cambridge: MIT Press, (1964). 1st ed. Fine in dj (sl rubbed). *Glaser.* $75/£47

WIENERS, JOHN. A Letter to Charles Olson. Brooklyn: Charters/Portents 11, 1968. One of 300. Fldg broadside, sealed w/sticker and strip of tissue. Fine. *Beasley.* $30/£19

WIENERS, JOHN. Nerves. Cape Goliard, 1970. 1st ed. Fine in dj. *Fine Books.* $35/£22

WIERZBICKI, F. P. California As It Is and As It May Be; or, A Guide to the Gold Region. SF: Grabhorn, 1933. One of 500. 1/2 cl, paper spine label. Fine. Howes W405. *Pacific*.* $104/£65

WIESE, KURT. You Can Write Chinese. NY: Random, 1945. 1st ed. 10x8. 64pp. Cl spine, pict bds. Good. *Cattermole.* $50/£31

WIESEL, ELIE. The Accident. NY, 1962. 1st ed. Fine in NF dj. *Warren.* $85/£53

WIESEL, ELIE. From the Kingdom of Memory: Reminiscences. NY, (1990). Signed, inscribed. Dj (sl rubbed). *Argosy.* $60/£38

WIESEL, ELIE. The Gates of the Forest. NY, 1966. 1st ed. Fine in Fine dj. *Warren.* $50/£31

WIESEL, ELIE. The Golem. NY, (1983). 1st ed. One of 250 numbered, signed by Wiesel and Mark Podwal (illus). Slipcase. *Swann*.* $126/£79

WIESEL, ELIE. The Jews of Silence. NY, 1966. 1st ed. Fine in NF dj. *Warren.* $50/£31

WIESEL, ELIE. The Town Beyond the Wall. NY, 1964. 1st ed. VG + in Fine dj. *Warren.* $65/£41

WIESNER, WILLIAM. Arresto the Great Presents the Book of Magic. NY: G&D, (1944). 5 mechanical slides and/or tabs. Pict spiral bds. (Worn, pp loose), else Good in dj (chipped, torn, repaired). *King.* $85/£53

WIGGIN, KATE DOUGLAS and NORA A. SMITH (eds). The Arabian Nights. NY: Scribner, 1909. 1st ed. 4to. 12 full-pg color plts by Maxfield Parrish. Teg. Black cl (lt shelfworn), gilt, full color paste label (rubbed). *Reisler.* $225/£141

WIGGIN, KATE DOUGLAS and NORA A. SMITH (eds). The Arabian Nights. NY: Scribner, 1933. 9.25x6.75. 9 color plts by Maxfield Parrish. Black cl, pict cvr label. (Emb name; spine lettering rubbed off), else VG. *Pacific*.* $69/£43

WIGGIN, KATE DOUGLAS. The Birds' Christmas Carol. Boston: Houghton Mifflin, 1912. 1st ed thus. Katharine Wireman (illus). 8vo. 91pp. Grn cl bds, gilt. VG in VG dj. *Davidson.* $125/£78

WIGGIN, KATE DOUGLAS. Marm Lisa. Boston, 1896. 1st Amer ed. Pict cvrs. NF (spine sl rubbed). *Polyanthos.* $30/£19

WIGGIN, KATE DOUGLAS. New Chronicles of Rebecca. Boston, 1907. 1st Amer ed. Pict cvrs. Fine. *Polyanthos.* $30/£19

WIGGIN, KATE DOUGLAS. Penelope's Irish Experiences. Boston, 1901. 1st ed. (Ink name, bkpl; spine dknd; worn.) *King.* $20/£13

WIGGIN, KATE DOUGLAS. Rebecca of Sunnybrook Farm. Boston/NY: Houghton Mifflin, 1903. 1st ed, 1st state. 8vo. 327pp. Pict grn cl. VG (bottom edge tp sl torn, blind-stamp; plt removed rep; bumped, spine chipped). *Blue Mountain.* $50/£31

WIGHT, D. B. The Androscoggin River Valley. Charles E. Tuttle, (1967). 1st ed. Nice in dj, slipcase. *Rybski.* $45/£28

WIGHT, JOHN. More Mornings at Bow Street: A New Collection of Humorous and Entertaining Reports. London: James Robbins, 1827. 1st ed. George Cruikshank (illus). xvi,264pp. Aeg. Later full calf, gilt, morocco labels. Bound by Morrell. Fine (lacks ads, sl aging). *Pacific*.* $115/£72

WIGHT, JOHN. Mornings at Bow Street: A Selection of the Most Humorous and Entertaining Reports.... London: Charles Baldwin, 1824. 1st ed, later issue w/o imprint on tp verso, plts lettered, lacks ad. x,279,(1)pp; 11 plts by George Cruikshank. Aeg. Later full calf, gilt, morocco labels. Bound by Morrell. Fine (lt foxed). *Pacific*.* $115/£72

WIGHTMANN, MARY (ed). Roman Trier and the Treveri. London, 1970. 1st ed. 8 maps, 24 plts. Dj (sl soiled) in protective cellophane. *Edwards.* $56/£35

WIGHTWICK, GEORGE. The Palace of Architecture. James Fraser, 1840. 219pp. VG + in orig grn dec cl. *Hadley.* $280/£175

WIGLITTLE, A. Ten Years a Police Court Judge. NY, 1884. 229pp. (Worn, lacks part of spine.) Wraps. *King.* $12/£8

WILBERFORCE, WILLIAM. A Practical View of the Prevailing Religious System of Professed Christians...Contrasted with Real Christianity. Dublin: B. Dugdale, 1801. Early ed. Contemp calf, morocco spine label. (Glue to upper joints), else VG. *Pacific*.* $52/£33

WILBRAHAM, RICHARD. Travels in the Trans-Caucasian Provinces of Russia. London: John Murray, 1839. 1st ed. 1/2-title, engr frontis, xvii,(i)list,477pp; fldg map, 4 litho plts, errata slip before 1st pg. Contemp calf, gilt, red label gilt. Good (plts, map sl spotted; sl rubbed). *Morrell.* $336/£210

WILBUR, RICHARD. More Opposites. NY, 1991. 1st Amer ed. Signed. Fine in Fine dj. *Polyanthos.* $25/£16

WILBUR, RICHARD. Poems, 1943-1956. London: Faber & Faber, 1957. 1st Eng ed. VG (nameplt, feps browned; top edge spotted, sl dusty; spine ends, corners sl bumped) in dj (nicked, sl rubbed, creased, soiled, dusty, browned). *Ulysses.* $104/£65

WILBY, THOMAS W. A Motor Tour Through Canada. London, 1914. 1st ed. 21 photo plts. (Lt rubbed.) *Maggs.* $192/£120

WILCOX, COLLIN. Dead Aim. NY: Random House, 1971. 1st ed. Fine (stamp) in VG + dj (sm closed tear, scratched, inside fr flap creased). *Janus.* $35/£22

WILCOX, COLLIN. The Disappearance. NY: Random House, 1970. 1st ed. NF (letter H stamped to fep; lt edgeworn) in dj (closed tear inside fr flap). *Janus.* $35/£22

WILCOX, COLLIN. The Lonely Hunter. NY: Random House, 1969. 1st ed. NF (edges lt foxed) in NF dj. *Janus.* $50/£31

WILCOX, COLLIN. Power Plays. NY: Random House, 1979. 1st ed. Fine (price fep) in Fine dj. *Janus.* $45/£28

WILCOX, COLLIN. The Third Figure. NY: Dodd, Mead, 1968. 1st ed. Fine in dj (lt rubbed, few sm closed tears). *Janus.* $75/£47

WILCOX, JAMES. Miss Undine's Living Room. NY: Harper & Row, 1987. 1st ed. Fine in Fine dj. *Pettler.* $50/£31

WILD, FRANK. Shackleton's Last Voyage. Cassell, 1923. 1st ed. Gilt-pict cl (spine sl dull). VG. *Walcot.* $280/£175

WILD, FRANK. Shackleton's Last Voyage. London: Cassell, 1923. 1st ed. Good (worn, ink mk rear bd). *Explorer.* $320/£200

WILD, JOHN ROBERT FRANCIS. Shackleton's Last Voyage. The Story of the Quest...from the Official Journal and Private Diary Kept by Dr. A. H. Macklin. Cassell, 1923. 1st ed. Half-title, color frontis. Pub's dec blue cl (spine sl rubbed, edges spotted; 1923 inscrip), gilt. *Sotheby's*.* $626/£391

WILDE, JOHANNES. Italian Drawings in the Department of Prints and Drawings in the British Museum. London, 1953. 53 plts. Good + in dj (worn). *Washton.* $75/£47

WILDE, OSCAR. The Ballad of Reading Gaol. NY: E.P. Dutton, 1928. 1st Vassos ed. One of 200 signed by Vassos (illus). Teg. Blue cl. *Appelfeld.* $150/£94

WILDE, OSCAR. The Ballad of Reading Gaol. LEC, 1937. Ltd to 1500 numbered, signed by Zhenya Gay (illus). Fine in slipcase. *Swann*.* $80/£50

WILDE, OSCAR. The Birthday of the Infanta. NY, 1929. 1st ed thus. Signed by Pamela Bianco (illus). Silver dec cl. (Sl faded), else VG. *Whiteson.* $72/£45

WILDE, OSCAR. Complete Writings of Oscar Wilde. NY: Nottingham Soc, n.d. Edition de Luxe. One of 1000 sets. 10 vols. Teg; unopened. Orig 3/4 morocco, gilt. (Spine heads sl worn, few sm tears, sm chip.) Contents Fine. *Pacific*.* $184/£115

WILDE, OSCAR. De Profundis. Methuen, 1905. 1st ed, early issue w/February Methuen cat. 151pp + 40pp cat. Uncut. VG (1st, last ll, edges lt spotted) in blue cl, gilt. *Cox.* $88/£55

WILDE, OSCAR. De Profundis. Methuen, 1905. 1st UK ed, 1st issue w/inserted ads dated February 1905. VG (spine head sl worn, rear cvr sl stained). *Williams.* $176/£110

WILDE, OSCAR. De Profundis. Methuen, 1905. Ltd to 200. 8vo. Teg; uncut. White buckram bds (spine dust-soiled; bkpl), gilt. *Sotheby's*.* $773/£483

WILDE, OSCAR. The Fisherman and His Soul. (SF: Ransoffs, 1939.) One of 200 ptd. 1/2 yellow cl, marbled bds, morocco spine label. (Soiled), else VG. *Pacific*.* $115/£72

WILDE, OSCAR. The Happy Prince. London: Horace Marshall, (1948). 1st ed. Slim 4to. 16 color plts by H. Paul, 78 rpm record in rear pocket. Orig brn buckram bds, lg onlaid color plt upper cvr. Fine. *Sotheran.* $205/£128

WILDE, OSCAR. The Happy Prince. London, 1889. 2nd ed. Walter Crane & Jacob Hood (illus). Pict white bds (edges sl tanned, tips lt bumped). *Swann*.* $172/£108

WILDE, OSCAR. The Happy Prince. Stamford, CT: Overbrook, 1936. One of 250. Dec bds, cl spine, tips. Fine in slipcase (sl faded). *Black Sun.* $350/£219

WILDE, OSCAR. A House of Pomegranates. London: James R. Osgood, McIlvaine, 1891. One of 500. VG (hinges cracking, lacks feps; soiled, cup rings fr cvr, spine ends chipped, extrems dknd, repair to rear joint cl). *Pacific*.* $115/£72

WILDE, OSCAR. A House of Pomegranates. NY: Moffat, Yard, 1918. 1st ed. Good (cvrs soiled, spotted). *Agvent.* $150/£94

WILDE, OSCAR. An Ideal Husband. London, 1899. 1st ed. One of 1000 ptd. Sm 4to. Pale purple cl, gilt. (Sl skewed, sl discoloration fr cvr.) *Swann*.* $632/£395

WILDE, OSCAR. An Ideal Husband. Leonard Smithers, 1899. 1st ed. One of 100 signed. 4to. Uncut, partly unopened. Lt brn-red linen bds, gilt. *Sotheby's*.* $3,312/£2,070

WILDE, OSCAR. The Importance of Being Earnest. Smithers, 1899. One of 1000 ptd. VG (spine extrems sl bumped, cvrs browned). *Williams.* $552/£345

WILDE, OSCAR. Impressions of America. Stuart Mason (ed). Sunderland: Keystone, 1906. 1st ed. One of 500. Orig ptd wrappers (faded). Slipcase. *Mott.* $100/£63

WILDE, OSCAR. Intentions. London, 1891. 1st ed. One of 1500 ptd. Grn cl, gilt. (Spine faded, sl skewed.) *Swann*.* $149/£93

WILDE, OSCAR. Lady Windermere's Fan and The Importance of Being Ernest. LEC, 1973. Ltd to 1500 numbered, signed by Tony Walton (illus). Fine in slipcase. *Swann*.* $126/£79

WILDE, OSCAR. Lady Windermere's Fan. Paris (London), 1903. Rpt. Pale purple cl (pinpricks to fr cvr). *Swann**. $80/£50

WILDE, OSCAR. Letters to Graham Hill. Edinburgh: Privately ptd at Tragara Press, 1978. Mkd 'printer's proof copy.' NF in wrappers (edges sl creased). *Ulysses*. $104/£65

WILDE, OSCAR. Lord Arthur Savile's Crime and Other Stories. London: James Osgood, McIlvaine, 1891. 1st ed. One of 2000. Tan ptd flexible bds. VG (sm chip to spine foot, joints worn). *Macdonnell*. $400/£250

WILDE, OSCAR. Lord Arthur Savile's Crime and Other Stories. London: James R. Osgood, McIlvaine, 1891. 1st ed. 8vo. Uncut. Salmon pink paper bds (sl soiled, spine foot chipped, restored). Fair. *Maggs*. $560/£350

WILDE, OSCAR. The Picture of Dorian Gray. Ward Lock, 1891. 1st ed. Lg paper ed. One of 250 signed. Misprint p208 corrected. 8vo. All edges uncut. Rough gray beveled bds, gilt, fr cvr w/55 'butterfly designs' by Charles Ricketts, artist's monogram w/in a rectangle, white parchment spine (worn). *Sotheby's**. $2,944/£1,840

WILDE, OSCAR. The Picture of Dorian Gray. LEC, 1957. Ltd to 1500 numbered, signed by Lucille Corcos (illus). Fine in slipcase. *Swann**. $149/£93

WILDE, OSCAR. The Picture of Dorian Gray. Ward Lock, n.d. (1891). 1st ed. Misprint 'nd' for 'and' p208. 8vo. 8pp ads at end. All edges uncut. Rough gray beveled bds, gilt, fr cvr w/10 'butterfly designs' by Charles Ricketts, white parchment spine. Fine. *Sotheby's**. $2,024/£1,265

WILDE, OSCAR. Poems. Boston: Roberts Bros, 1881. 1st Amer ed. VG (1 pg offset from clipping; spine rubbed). *Agvent*. $150/£94

WILDE, OSCAR. Poems. London: David Bogue, 1881. 1st ed. One of 250 ptd. (10),229pp. Teg, rest untrimmed. Vellum, gilt. (Lacks fep, extrem pg edges sl dknd, worn; rubbed, soiled, discolored, spine ends worn), o/w VG. *Pacific**. $575/£359

WILDE, OSCAR. Poems. David Bogue, 1881. 1st ed. One of 250. 8vo. (Eps offset.) White parchment (soiled), gilt. *Sotheby's**. $736/£460

WILDE, OSCAR. Poems. Elkin Mathews/John Lane, 1892. Author's ed. Ltd to 220 signed. 8vo. Orig prelims cut out, replaced by new 1/2-title, tp. Dec tp, eps designed by Charles Ricketts. Violet cl, gilt. (Outer prelim margins sl dampstained; bds sl water-damaged, sm spine tears.) *Sotheby's**. $2,208/£1,380

WILDE, OSCAR. Salome. London, 1907. 16 plts by Aubrey Beardsley (incl tp and plt list). (Feps browned.) *Swann**. $287/£179

WILDE, OSCAR. Salome. Alfred Bruce Douglas (trans). Portland, ME: Thomas B. Mosher, 1911. One of 500. Gray paper-cvrd bds; deckled-edged. Good + (worn, stains; spine dknd, rubbed; spine label dknd). *Blue Mountain*. $25/£16

WILDE, OSCAR. Salome. (SF: Grabhorn, 1927.) One of 195 ptd. Signed, numbered by Valenti Angelo (illus). Frontis. (Adhesion residue from removed bkpl; cvrs sl browned), else VG. *Pacific**. $69/£43

WILDE, OSCAR. Salome. Alfred Douglas (trans). LEC, 1938. Ltd to 1500 numbered, signed by Andre Derain (illus). French orig and Eng version. Together, 2 vols. Rene Ben Sussan (designer). Fine in slipcase. *Swann**. $345/£216

WILDE, OSCAR. The Short Stories of Oscar Wilde. LEC, 1968. Ltd to 1500 numbered, signed by James Hill (illus). Fine in slipcase. *Swann**. $92/£58

WILDE, OSCAR. The Sphinx (Poems). London: Bodley Head, 1920. One of 1000 ptd. 4to. Alastair (illus). 12 full-pg plts by Alastair. Gilt-stamped white linen (sl soiled; sm adhesive residue mks eps). VG. *Appelfeld*. $650/£406

WILDE, OSCAR. The Writings of Oscar Wilde. NY: Gabriel Wells, 1925. Lg paper ed. One of 575. 12 vols. Blue bds, gilt. (Extrems lt rubbed), else NF in VG djs (spine labels spotted). *Pacific**. $431/£269

WILDENSTEIN, GEORGES. Ingres. London, 1954. (Corners of some plts repaired.) Dj (sl worn). *Washton*. $150/£94

WILDENSTEIN, GEORGES. Ingres. Phaidon, 1956. 2nd ed. Tipped-in color frontis, 7 tipped-in color plts. (Ink notes; spine faded.) *Edwards*. $120/£75

WILDENSTEIN, GEORGES. The Paintings of Fragonard. (London): Phaidon, (1960). Complete ed. 133 full-pg plts (15 color). VG. *Turtle Island*. $125/£78

WILDER SMITH, A. E. The Drug Users. The Psychopharmacology of Turning On. Wheaton, IL: Harold Shaw, 1969. 1st ed. NF in dj. *Sclanders*. $32/£20

WILDER, DANIEL W. The Annals of Kansas. Topeka: KS Publishing House, 1875. 1st ed. Grn cl (extrems lt worn). Howes W411. *Glenn*. $145/£91

WILDER, G. P. Flora of Rarotonga. Honolulu, 1931. 8 plts. Later 1/2 leather (worn; eps dknd, sm tear tp margin, pp tanned). *Sutton*. $40/£25

WILDER, LAURA INGALLS. The Long Winter. NY: Harper & Bros, (1940). 1st ed. 8vo. Color frontis, 16 full-pg b/w dwgs by Helen Sewell & Mildred Boyle. Brn cl. Good in color pict dj. *Reisler*. $400/£250

WILDER, LOUISE BEEBE. Adventures in My Garden and Rock Garden. GC: Doubleday, Page, 1929. Cl pict bd. (Name, pencil notes; bds scuffed), else Good + . *Fair Meadow*. $40/£25

WILDER, LOUISE BEEBE. The Garden in Color. NY: Macmillan, 1937. 1st ed. 320 color plts. (Eps foxed, bkpl removed; spine worn), else VG. *Fair Meadow*. $45/£28

WILDER, LOUISE BEEBE. Pleasures and Problems of a Rock Garden. GC: GC Pub, c. 1937. (Foxed, eps browned), else VG in dj (rubbed). *Fair Meadow*. $40/£25

WILDER, MITCHELL A. Santos. Colorado Springs: Taylor Museum, (1943). Orig ed. 64 full-pg plts. Red pict cl. Nice (offset from news clipping on contents pg; spine sl faded). *Turtle Island*. $125/£78

WILDER, ROBERT. The Sound of Drums and Cymbals. London: Allen, (1974). 1st Eng ed. (Copyright info obliterated), else As New in dj. *Between The Covers*. $100/£63

WILDER, THORNTON. The Alcestiad, or a Life in the Sun. NY: Harper, (1977). 1st ed. VF in VF dj (lt rubbed, sm tear). *Between The Covers*. $150/£94

WILDER, THORNTON. The Bridge of San Luis Rey. NY: A&C Boni, 1928. 8th ptg. Inscribed 1931. *Cummins*. $200/£125

WILDER, THORNTON. The Bridge of San Luis Rey. NY: A&C Boni, 1929. One of 1100 ptd. Signed by Wilder & Rockwell Kent (illus). Morocco spine label. (Soiled, spine sl sunned), else VG in slipcase. *Pacific**. $173/£108

WILDER, THORNTON. The Bridge of San Luis Rey. NY: LEC, 1962. One of 1500 ptd. Signed by Jean Charlot (illus). 1/2 black morocco, pict buckram. Fine in glassine, slipcase. *Pacific**. $58/£36

WILDER, THORNTON. The Bridge of San Luis Rey. NY: LEC, 1962. One of 1500 numbered, signed by Jean Charlot (illus). 1/4 morocco. Slipcase. *Swann**. $103/£64

WILDER, THORNTON. The Bridge of San Luis Rey. LEC, 1962. Ltd to 1500 numbered, signed by Jean Charlot (illus). Fine in slipcase. *Swann**. $138/£86

WILDER, THORNTON. The Cabala. London: Longmans, Green, 1926. 1st Eng ed, 1st bk. VG (edges spotted; spine ends sl bumped) in dj (rubbed, dusty, frayed, mkd, spine dknd). *Ulysses*. $200/£125

WILDER, THORNTON. The Eighth Day. NY/London: Evanston/Harper & Row, 1967. 1st ed. Ltd to 500 signed. Ptd spine label. Fine in pub's slipcase (sl dusty). *Cahan*. $150/£94

WILDER, THORNTON. Heaven's My Destination. NY: Harper, 1935. 1st ed. Fine in VG dj (crown sl chipped). *Between The Covers*. $85/£53

WILDER, THORNTON. The Ides of March. NY/London: Harper, (1948). 1st trade ed. VG + in dj (spine ends sl worn, rear panel lt soiled). *Bernard*. $40/£25

WILDER, THORNTON. Our Town. LEC, 1975. One of 2000 signed by Wilder and Robert J. Lee (illus). Fine in slipcase. *Swann**. $80/£50

WILDER, THORNTON. Theophilus North. NY: Harper, (1973). 1st ed. VF in VF dj. *Between The Covers*. $125/£78

WILDRAKE (ed). The New Sporting Almanack, a Manual of Instruction and Amusement. London: Ackermann, 1845. Extra pict tp, 10 engr plts. Pub's cl. (Sl stains, foxing; sl worn.) *Oinonen**. $80/£50

WILDRIDGE, T. TINDALL. The Grotesque in Church Art. A. Brown & Sons, n.d. (c.1900). 2nd ed. Teg. (Feps sl browned; cl sl rubbed, cockled.) *Hollett*. $120/£75

WILE, FREDERIC WILLIAM. Men Around the Kaiser. London: Heinemann, 1914. (Spotted.) Wrappers (sl spotted, upper hinge cracked). *Hollett*. $40/£25

WILENSKI, R. H. Flemish Painters, 1430-1830. London: Faber & Faber, (1960). 1st ed. 2 vols. Red cl. Good in djs. *Karmiole*. $150/£94

WILENSKI, R. H. The Study of Art. London: Faber & Faber, 1936. 1st Eng ed. VG (prelims, edges, contents spotted; spine sl faded, foot sl bumped, edges sl rubbed) in dj (nicked, sl rubbed, creased, torn, dusty, price-clipped, browned). *Ulysses*. $58/£36

WILENSKY, ABRAHAM O. Osteomyelitis: Its Pathogenesis, Symptomatology and Treatment. NY, 1934. 1st ed. Fldg graph. Grn cl. NF. *Doctor's Library*. $100/£63

WILENTZ, ELIAS (ed). The Beat Scene. NY: Corinth, 1960. 1st Amer ed. NF (lt rubbed) in wrappers. *Warren*. $30/£19

WILEY, BELL IRVIN. The Common Soldier of the Civil War. NY, (1973). 1st ed. Fine in dj (sl worn). *Pratt*. $30/£19

WILEY, BELL IRVIN. The Life of Johnny Reb, the Common Soldier of the Confederacy. Indianapolis: Bobbs-Merrill, (1943). 1st ed. Red cl. VG + (name) in VG dj (edgeworn). *Chapel Hill*. $95/£59

WILEY, BELL IRVIN. The Road to Appomattox. Memphis: Memphis State College, (1956). Signed. Fine in pict dj. *Argonaut*. $50/£31

WILEY, C. H. Adventures of Old Dan Tucker, and His Son Walter. London: Willoughby, n.d. (ca 1851). Mod cl. (Tp torn, soiled, cello-tape repairs verso, few plts; soiled, stained.) *Oinonen**. $30/£19

WILEY, HUGH. The Prowler. NY, 1924. 1st ed. Cl-backed patterned bds. Dj (price-clipped). *Swann**. $92/£58

WILEY, MARGARET L. The Subtle Knot. Creative Scepticism in Seventeenth-Century England. Allen & Unwin, 1952. 1st ed. (Sl marginal ink ruling, eps spotted.) Dj. *Edwards*. $29/£18

WILEY, WILLIAM H. and SARA KING WILEY. The Yosemite, Alaska, and the Yellowstone. London: Offices of 'Engineering,' (1893). 1st ed. xix,230pp; 3 maps (1 fldg). Later cl. (Contents stained, ex-lib, mks; rebound), else Good + . *Pacific**. $62/£39

WILHELM, KATE. Sweet, Sweet Poison. St. Martin, 1990. 1st ed. Fine in dj (edges lt worn). *Murder*. $25/£16

WILKE, KARL. Prisoner Halm. Indianapolis: Bobbs-Merrill, (ca 1931). 1st US ed. Gray cl. (Eps lt foxed), o/w NF in pict dj (sl wear, nicks, creases along top edge). *Reese*. $50/£31

WILKES, CHARLES. Autobiography of Rear Admiral Charles Wilkes, U. S. N., 1798-1877. Washington: Dept. of the Navy, 1978. 1st ed. VG. *High Latitude*. $35/£22

WILKES, CHARLES. Columbia River to the Sacramento. Oakland: Biobooks, 1958. 1st CA ed. One of 600. Fldg map. Black cl, gilt. Fine. *House*. $30/£19

WILKES, CHARLES. Narrative of the United States Expedition. During the Years 1838, 1839, 1840, 1841, 1842. Volumes 1-3, and 5 (of 5) only. Phila: Lea & Blanchard, 1845. 1st ed. 4 vols. lx,434; xvi,476; xvi,438; xvi,558pp; 49 steel-engr plts, 8 dbl-pg maps. Full morocco. (Vol 5 marginally damp-stained, some plts affected; edges rubbed, sl scuffed, lt shaken), o/w VG. *Worldwide*. $480/£300

WILKES, M. V. Automatic Digital Computers. NY: John Wiley, (1956). 1st Amer ed. 9 plts (1 fldg). NF. *Glaser*. $250/£156

WILKESON, SAMUEL. Wilkeson's Puget Sound. NY, 1870?. 1st ed. Pamphlet. 47pp. Good in wraps (detached but present, sl chipped, torn). Howes W420. *Brown*. $75/£47

WILKIE, FRANC B. Pen and Powder. Boston, 1888. 1st ed. 383pp. (Ex-lib, foxed; cvrs worn.) *King*. $125/£78

WILKINS, GEORGE H. Flying the Arctic. NY/London: Putnam/Knickerbocker, 1928. 2nd ptg. Fine (dj laid down on eps). *Explorer*. $40/£25

WILKINS, H. ST. CLAIR. Reconnoitring in Abyssinia. London, 1870. Fldg map in rear pocket, 10 color litho plts. (Bkpl; fr joint split, spine head frayed.) *Swann**. $345/£216

WILKINS, HUBERT. Under the North Pole. N.p.: Brewer, Warren, & Putnam, 1931. Deluxe ed of 275 numbered, signed by Wilkins & Sloan Danenho wer. Frontis port (faded). Teg. Good (lt soil, edges sl worn). *High Latitude*. $195/£122

WILKINS, JAMES F. An Artist on the Overland Trail. John Francis McDermott (ed). San Marino: Huntington Library, 1968. 50 full-pg repros. Dj. *Dawson*. $50/£31

WILKINS, JAMES H. (ed). The Great Diamond Hoax. SF, 1913. Frontis. Gray-grn cl, gilt. VG. *Five Quail*. $75/£47

WILKINS, THURMAN. Clarence King. NY: Macmillan, 1958. 1st ed. 5 plts. Fine in dj (few sm edge tears, lt tape stain lower fr panel). *Argonaut*. $75/£47

WILKINS, W. H. The Romance of Isabel Lady Burton. London, 1897. 1st ed. 2 vols. 1/2 morocco (edges worn). *Maggs*. $200/£125

WILKINS, WILLIAM GLYDE. Charles Dickens in America. NY: Scribner, 1912. 1st ed, Amer issue w/cancel-title. *Mott*. $25/£16

WILKINS, WILLIAM. The Antiquities of Magna Graecia. CUP, 1807. 73 engr plts and plans, 1 dbl-pg, incl 21 sepia aquatints. (Tp lt creased, soiled, lt mainly marginal soil, short tear 1 leaf, sm emb and ink lib stamps, bkpl.) Contemp 1/2 calf (rubbed). *Christie's**. $1,171/£732

WILKINS, WILLIAMS. Atheniensia, or Remarks on the Topography and Buildings of Athens. John Murray, 1816. 1st ed. Engr dbl-pg map, dbl-pg plt (sl offsetting onto tp, 2 other ll). Teg. Contemp maroon 1/2 morocco (rubbed). *Sotheby's**. $478/£299

WILKINS-FREEMAN, MARY E. Collected Ghost Stories. Sauk City: Arkham House, 1974. 1st ed. Fine in Fine dj. *Other Worlds*. $20/£13

WILKINSON, CHARLES. Epitome of the History of Malta and Gozo. London: William Miller and W. Bulmer, 1804. 1st, only ed. 1/2-title, xii,210pp; fldg engr map, errata slip at end. Orig blue bds (upper joint cracked, spine head worn, sl rubbed), paper spine label. Internally VG. *Morrell*. $304/£190

WILKINSON, GERALD (ed). Turner's Early Sketchbooks. London: Barrie & Jenkins, (1975). 2nd ptg. NF in dj. *Turtle Island*. $75/£47

WILKINSON, J. GARDNER. Manners and Customs of the Ancient Egyptians. London: John Murray, 1841-1842. 6 vols. Vols 1, 2 & 3 are 2nd ed, others 1st ed, 2nd series & supp vols. Uniform calf, gilt, morocco spine labels, raised bands. (Expertly rebacked, spine ends, extrems rubbed), else VG. *Pacific**. $690/£431

WILKINSON, J. GARDNER. A Second Series of the Manners and Customs of the Ancient Egyptians, including Their Religion, Agriculture, etc.... London: John Murray, 1841. 1st ed. 3 vols. 67 litho plts (2 color). Orig gilt-dec cl. (Fr hinge vol 1 strengthened w/paper tape, cvrs rubbed, faded), else VG set. Pacific*. $259/£162

WILKINSON, J. V. S. The Lights of Canopus. London: Studio, n.d. (ca 1930). 1st ed. 36 tipped-in color plts. Teg. (Bkpl; sl faded), o/w VG. Worldwide. $95/£59

WILKINSON, MRS. A Lady's Life and Travels in Zululand and the Transvaal During Cetewayo's Reign. London: J.T. Hayes, 1882. 1st ed. 1/2-title, mtd frontis photo, viii,(i)contents,(i)blank,264pp. Grn cl, gilt. (Few ll margins lt foxed; fr cvr scratch), o/w VG. Morrell. $200/£125

WILKINSON, SAMUEL. In the Land of the North. London, n.d. c.(1905). (Lt browned, spine sl faded.) Edwards. $32/£20

WILKS, MARK. Historical Sketches of the South of India, in an Attempt to Trace the History of Mysoor. London, 1810-17. 1st ed. 3 vols. 2 fldg hand-colored engr maps, half-title in vol 1 (lacking in 2nd; not called for in 3rd). Contemp calf (rebacked, vol 1 fr joint starting). Swann*. $460/£288

WILLANS, GEOFFREY. Back in the Jug Agane. London: Max Parrish, 1959. 1st Eng ed. VG (spine head sl bumped, gilt lettering oxidised) in dj (torn, internally repaired, sl rubbed, sm chip). Ulysses. $48/£30

WILLARD, DANIEL E. Montana: the Geological Story. Lancaster, PA, 1935. 1st ed. (Name clipped fep; lt worn.) Woolson. $40/£25

WILLARD, DANIEL E. The Story of the Prairies. Chicago, 1907. (Shelfworn.) Internally Good. Dumont. $35/£22

WILLCOCKS, J. From Kabul to Kumassi. London, 1904. (Lt rubbed, sm spine snag.) Grayling. $96/£60

WILLEFORD, CHARLES. The Burnt Orange Heresy. NY, 1971. 1st ed. Fine in NF dj. Warren. $150/£94

WILLEFORD, CHARLES. Cockfighter Journal: The Story of a Shooting. Santa Barbara: Neville, 1989. 1st ed. One of 300 ptd. Signed by James Lee Burke (foreword). Pict cl. As New. Pacific*. $81/£51

WILLEFORD, CHARLES. I Was Looking for a Street. VT: Countryman, 1988. 1st ed. NF in NF dj. Warren. $30/£19

WILLEFORD, CHARLES. Proletarian Laughter. Yonkers: Alicat Bookshop Press, 1948. 1st ed, 1st bk. Pict stiff wrappers. (Interior extrems sl faded), else NF. Pacific*. $75/£47

WILLERT, JAMES. After Little Bighorn: 1876 Campaign Rosters. La Mirada, CA: James Willert, (1985). #26h of a ltd ed. Inscribed, signed presentation. Dec fabricoid. Fine. Pacific*. $29/£18

WILLEY, BENJAMIN G. Incidents in White Mountain History. Boston/Dover, NH: Nathaniel Noyes/Edmund J. Lane, 1856. 1st ed. 307pp; lg fldg map inserted at rear (fragile). (Spine chipped.) M & S. $450/£281

WILLEY, GORDON R. (ed). Archaeology of Southern Mesoamerica. Austin: Univ of TX, (1965). 2 vols. Djs. Archaeologia. $85/£53

WILLIAM, HAROLD. Book Clubs and Printing Societies of Great Britain and Ireland. London: First Edition Club, 1929. 1st ed. One of 175 ptd. Dec cl. (Extrems soiled), else VG. Pacific*. $46/£29

WILLIAMS, A. D. Spanish Colonial Furniture. Milwaukee, 1941. (Emb stamps), else Good in dj (chipped). Dumont. $85/£53

WILLIAMS, A. F. The Genesis of the Diamond. London: Ernest Benn, 1932. 2 vols. 221 plts. VG (spine faded, lettering rubbed 1 vol). Blake. $400/£250

WILLIAMS, A. F. The Genesis of the Diamond. London, 1932. Roy 8vo. 2 vols. 221 plts (30 color), fldg map. VF. Henly. $480/£300

WILLIAMS, AARON. The Harmony Society, at Economy, Penn'a. Founded by George Rapp, A.D. 1805. Pittsburgh: W.S. Haven, 1866. 1st ed. 16mo. 182pp (1869 inscrip). Orig cl. Very Bright. Howes W445. M & S. $1,350/£844

WILLIAMS, ALFRED B. Hampton and His Red Shirts. Charleston, (1935). Port. Good+. Wantagh. $45/£28

WILLIAMS, ALFRED B. Hampton and His Red Shirts. Charleston: Walker, Evans & Cogswell, (1935). 2nd ed. Red cl. NF in VG dj. Chapel Hill. $95/£59

WILLIAMS, ALFRED. Folk Songs of the Thames. Duckworth, 1923. 1st ed. (Cl sl faded, 2 sm stains), else VG+. Any Amount. $48/£30

WILLIAMS, ALFRED. A Wiltshire Village. London, 1944. 1st Eng ed. (Foxed, margins pencil-lined; cocked, edges sl rubbed.) Clearwater. $48/£30

WILLIAMS, ALICE LAIDLAW. Sunday Suppers. NY: Duffield, 1912. 1st ed. Brn cl. VG (fore-edge stained; lt rubbed, stained). Blue Mountain. $15/£9

WILLIAMS, ARTHUR JOHN. How to Avoid Law. Cassell, (1885). 1st ed thus. 192pp. Recent 1/2 calf. Young. $80/£50

WILLIAMS, B. S. The Orchid-Grower's Manual. London, 1877. 5th ed. xi,336,24 ads; fldg color, 33 plain plts (19 dbl-pg). (Rebacked preserving spine, sl soiled.) Henly. $67/£42

WILLIAMS, BEN AMES. Fraternity Village. Boston: Houghton Mifflin, 1949. 1st ed. Red cl. NF in NF color pict dj. Biscotti. $40/£25

WILLIAMS, BEN AMES. The Happy End. NY: Derrydale, 1939. One of 1250 numbered. 1/4 coarse tan linen, blue-grn cl-cvrd bds. Fine. Biscotti. $225/£141

WILLIAMS, BEN AMES. Time of Peace. Boston, 1942. 1st ed. Fine (lacks dj). Bond. $17/£11

WILLIAMS, CANNING. The Story of the Hive. London: A&C Black, 1928. Frontis. Gray cl, gilt. Good (hinges weak, heavy edgewear). Larry Price. $15/£9

WILLIAMS, CHARLES H. (ed). New Foundling Hospital for Wit. (Charles Hanbury Williams, ed.) London: J. Debrett, 1784. 6 vols. 3/4 dk grn calf, marbled bds, gilt. VG set (bkpls, old note). Pacific*. $81/£51

WILLIAMS, CHARLES. All the Way. NY: Dell, 1958. 1st ed. Pb orig. Fine in wrappers. Mordida. $50/£31

WILLIAMS, CHARLES. James I. London, 1934. 1st Eng ed. Inscribed. (Cvrs faded, mkd; extrems sl chafed; lacks dj.) Clearwater. $120/£75

WILLIAMS, CHARLES. Poetry at Present. Oxford, 1930. 1st Eng ed. Fine in dj (sunned). Clearwater. $120/£75

WILLIAMS, CHARLES. A Practical Treatise on the Diseases of the Respiratory Organs. Phila, 1845. 508pp. Full calf (sl scuffed). (Ex-lib, foxed), o/w Good. Doctor's Library. $85/£53

WILLIAMS, CHARLES. The Region of the Summer Stars. London: Editions Poetry London, 1944. 1st Eng ed. Nice in dj (sl foxed, price-clipped, internally strengthened w/tape). Clearwater. $56/£35

WILLIAMS, CHARLES. War in Heaven. Gollancz, 1930. 1st ed. Black cl (sl mkd). VG (ep sl offset, name) in pale blue self wraps (edges sunned). Any Amount. $35/£22

WILLIAMS, CLARA ANDREWS. The Teddy Bears. NY: Frederick A. Stokes, 1907. 1st ed. Obl lg 4to. 16 full-pg color plts by George Alfred Williams. Cl-backed color pict bds (worn, dusty, hinges weak; margins sl spotted). Reisler. $750/£469

WILLIAMS, D. E. The Life and Correspondence of Sir Thomas Lawrence, Kt President of the Royal Academy.... London: Henry Colburn, 1831. 1st ed. 2 vols. 2 frontispieces, xxiv,473; viii,586pp. Contemp 1/2 calf. Good. Young. $120/£75

WILLIAMS, F. B. Index of Dedications and Commendatory Verses in English Books Before 1641. Bibliographical Soc, 1962. 1st ed. VG. Cox. $24/£15

WILLIAMS, FRANCIS EDGAR. Orokaiva Society. London: OUP/Humphrey Milford, 1930. 1st ed. 2 frontispieces, 36 photo plts, fldg map. Blue cl, gilt. Good. *Karmiole*. $85/£53

WILLIAMS, FREDERICK WELLS. Anson Burlingame and the First Chinese Mission to Foreign Powers. NY: Scribner, 1912. 1st ed. Frontisport. (Cl sl rubbed, rear cvr w/2 sm nicks), o/w VG. *Worldwide*. $25/£16

WILLIAMS, G. The Diamond Mines of South Africa. NY: B.F. Buck, 1906. 2nd ed. 2 vols. Teg. VG set. *Blake*. $450/£281

WILLIAMS, G. The Diamond Mines of South Africa. NY: Macmillan, c1902. 1st ed. Teg. Dec cl. Good (blind-stamp, margins lt dampstained). *Blake*. $450/£281

WILLIAMS, GLYNDWR (ed). Andrew Graham's Observations on Hudson's Bay, 1767-91. London: Hudson's Bay Record Soc, 1969. 1st ltd ed. Fine. *Perier*. $75/£47

WILLIAMS, H. NOEL. The Fascinating Duc de Richelieu. London: Methuen, (1910). 17 plts. (Gilt, spine faded.) *Stewart*. $64/£40

WILLIAMS, H. NOEL. Queens of the French Stage. NY: Scribner, 1905. Frontisport. Teg. (Lt shelf-worn.) *Dramatis*. $25/£16

WILLIAMS, H. NOEL. The Women Bonapartes. London: Methuen, (1908). 2 vols. 36 plts. (Ex-lib on fep.) *Stewart*. $80/£50

WILLIAMS, HAROLD. Book Clubs and Printing Societies of Great Britain and Ireland. First Edition Club, 1929. 1st ed. One of 750. Patterned cl (edges sl soiled). Good. *Maggs*. $80/£50

WILLIAMS, HELEN MARIA. A Narrative of the Events Which Have Taken Place in France. Phila: Thomas, 1816. 1st US ed. 245pp. Uncut. Orig ptd bds (cvrs near detached). VG. *Second Life*. $250/£156

WILLIAMS, HENRY SMITH. The History of the Art of Writing. London/NY: Merrill & Baker, (1902). Folio. 225 facs plts. In orig parts, loose in 4 cl portfolios (worn), as issued. *Oinonen**. $110/£69

WILLIAMS, HENRY T. (ed). Window Gardening. NY: Henry T. Williams, 1874. Grn cl, gilt. VG. *Pacific**. $35/£22

WILLIAMS, HUGH WILLIAM. Select Views in Greece. Longman, 1829. 1st ed. 2 vols. 4to. 64 engr plts, 1/2-titles. Gilt edges. Contemp red 1/2 morocco (worn, cvr detached). *Sotheby's**. $883/£552

WILLIAMS, HUGH WILLIAM. Travels in Italy, Greece, and the Ionian Islands, in a Series of Letters.... Edinburgh: Constable, 1820. 1st ed. 2 vols. 8vo. 20 engr plts (2 fldg, offset). Contemp calf (lacks labels, joints rubbed). *Sotheby's**. $643/£402

WILLIAMS, IOLO A. Early English Watercolours and Some Cognate Drawings by Artists Born Not Later Than 1785. London, 1952. (Sl worn.) Dj (chipped, frayed). *Oinonen**. $50/£31

WILLIAMS, IOLO A. The Elements of Book Collecting. Elkin Matthews & Marrot, 1927. 1st ed. VG. *Moss*. $19/£12

WILLIAMS, J. R. Born Thirty Years Too Soon. NY: Scribner, 1945. 1st ed. VG in dj. *Labordo*. $75/£47

WILLIAMS, J. R. Bull of the Woods. NY: Scribner, 1944. 1st ed. VG (spine bottom worn). *Labordo*. $60/£38

WILLIAMS, JOANNA GOTTFRIED. The Art of Gupta India: Empire and Province. Princeton Univ, (1982). Dj (corners bumped). *Argosy*. $60/£38

WILLIAMS, JOHN A. Captain Blackman. GC: Doubleday, 1972. 1st ed. Fine in VG+ dj. *Bernard*. $45/£28

WILLIAMS, JOHN A. The Man Who Cried I Am. Boston: LB, (1967). 1st ed. VG in dj (edgeworn, sm peeled spot from sticker). *Agvent*. $75/£47

WILLIAMS, JOHN H. Yosemite and Its High Sierra. Tacoma/SF: John H. Williams, 1914. 1st ed. 8 color plts. Color pict label. (Lacks fep), else VG. *Pacific**. $63/£39

WILLIAMS, JOHN H. Yosemite and Its High Sierra. Tacoma/SF: John H. Williams, 1914. 1st ed. 8 color plts, fldg map inside rear cvr. Beige cl, color illus tipped to fr cvr. Fine. *Pacific**. $138/£86

WILLIAMS, JOHN. The Redeemed Captive Returning to Zion.... Boston, 1795. 6th ed. Contemp sheep (needs rebinding). Howes W461. *Swann**. $201/£126

WILLIAMS, K. L. Systematics and Natural History of the American Milk Snake. Milwaukee, 1978. 1st ed. 8 color plts. Pb (lt worn). *Sutton*. $50/£31

WILLIAMS, KEITH. The English Newspaper. Springwood Books, 1977. 1st ed. *Forest*. $29/£18

WILLIAMS, LEONARD. The Land of the Dons. London, 1902. 1st ed. Frontisport. (Bkpl.) *Edwards*. $72/£45

WILLIAMS, LLEW. The Dalton Brothers in Their Oklahoma Cave. Chicago, 1893. Early ptg or variant on 1st ed. Pict cl. NF (sig, address). Howes W473. *Baade*. $75/£47

WILLIAMS, MARGERY. Velveteen Rabbit. NY: Holt, 1983. 4to. Michael Hague (illus). Fine in Fine dj. *American Booksellers*. $30/£19

WILLIAMS, MARTIN (ed). Jazz Panorama. NY: Crowell-Collier, 1962. 1st ed. NF in dj (sl worn). *Beasley*. $65/£41

WILLIAMS, MARTIN. Jazz Masters of New Orleans. NY: Macmillan, (1967). 1st ed. VG in pict dj. *Petrilla*. $35/£22

WILLIAMS, MARY FLOYD. History of the San Francisco Committee of Vigilance of 1851. Berkeley: Univ of CA, 1921. 1st ed. Frontis, 2 ports, 1 facs. Dk blue cl, gilt. Fine (sm bkpl, tp foxed). *Argonaut*. $150/£94

WILLIAMS, MRS. H. DWIGHT. A Year in China; and a Narrative of Capture and Imprisonment. NY, 1864. *Swann**. $57/£36

WILLIAMS, ORLO. Three Naughty Children. Duckworth, 1922. 1st ed. 4to. J.R. Monsell (illus). 111pp. Cl spine, pict bds. (Extrems worn, sl rubbed), else VG. *Bookmark*. $48/£30

WILLIAMS, R. JAMES. Pussy-Cats ABC. London: Dean's Rag Book, (ca 1920). 8vo. 6 ll (counting cvrs). Pinking shears edges. Sewn cl binding. VG. *Reisler*. $200/£125

WILLIAMS, RALPH COPLESTONE. Bibliography of the Seventeenth-Century Novel in France. NY, 1931. 1st Amer ed. NF. *Polyanthos*. $30/£19

WILLIAMS, ROLAND. Where the World Is Quiet. Witherby, 1965. 1st ed. 16 color plts. VG in dj (price-clipped). *Hollett*. $19/£12

WILLIAMS, S. WELLS. The Middle Kingdom. NY: Scribner, 1883. Rev ed. 2 vols. xxvi,836; xii,775pp; 2 fldg plts (1 color), fldg map in rear pocket. (Lib spine #s,; edges rubbed, vol 2 spine sl nicked), o/w VG. *Worldwide*. $95/£59

WILLIAMS, SAMUEL COLE. History of the Lost State of Franklin. Johnson City, TN: Watauga, 1924. Frontis. (Shelfworn), else Good. Howes W482. *Dumont*. $125/£78

WILLIAMS, TENNESSEE. 27 Wagons Full of Cotton. Norfolk: New Directions, (1953). 1st ed thus. NF (eps lt browned) in dj (sl worn, soiled, scratch on rear panel). *Antic Hay*. $45/£28

WILLIAMS, TENNESSEE. Androgyne, Mon Amour. NY, (1977). 1st ed. One of 200 numbered, signed. Color frontis. Slipcase. *Swann**. $230/£144

WILLIAMS, TENNESSEE. Androgyne, Mon Amour. (NY, 1977.) 1st hb ed. VG in dj (sl worn). *King*. $25/£16

WILLIAMS, TENNESSEE. Baby Doll. NY: New Directions, (1956). 1st ed. VF in VF dj (fr spine edge sl rubbed). *Between The Covers*. $300/£188

WILLIAMS, TENNESSEE. Baby Doll. London: S&W, 1957. 1st Eng ed. VF in VF dj. *Between The Covers*. $150/£94

WILLIAMS, TENNESSEE. Cat on a Hot Tin Roof. (NY): New Directions, (1955). 1st ed. VG in dj (extrems chipped, rubbed, price-clipped). *Pacific**. $46/£29

WILLIAMS, TENNESSEE. Cat on a Hot Tin Roof. NY: New Directions, n.d. (c. 1955). 1st Amer ed. (Rear cvr sl mkd, top edges sl faded, lower edge shelfworn), o/w VG in dj (soiled, corners, spine ends heavily chipped). *Virgo*. $72/£45

WILLIAMS, TENNESSEE. Dragon Country. NY: New Directions, (1970). 1st ed. VF in VF dj. *Between The Covers*. $125/£78

WILLIAMS, TENNESSEE. The Eccentricities of a Nightingale and Summer and Smoke. (NY): New Directions, (1965). 1st ed. Lt blue cl. NF (sl faded) in dj. *Antic Hay*. $150/£94

WILLIAMS, TENNESSEE. The Glass Menagerie. NY: Random House, (1945). 1st ed. Fine. *Pacific**. $196/£123

WILLIAMS, TENNESSEE. The Glass Menagerie. NY: Random House, (1945). 1st ed. NF in dj (sl edgeworn, few creases, nicks, sm tears). *Antic Hay*. $350/£219

WILLIAMS, TENNESSEE. Hard Candy. (Norfolk): New Directions, (1954). Ltd ed. VG (spine dknd; lacks slipcase). *Antic Hay*. $85/£53

WILLIAMS, TENNESSEE. I Rise in Flame, Cried the Phoenix. Norfolk, (1951). 1st ed. One of 300 numbered, signed. Slipcase. *Swann**. $488/£305

WILLIAMS, TENNESSEE. In the Winter of Cities. (NY): New Directions, (1956). 1st ed. (Extrems sl dknd), else Fine in dj. *Pacific**. $35/£22

WILLIAMS, TENNESSEE. In the Winter of Cities. (Norfolk): New Directions, (1956). 1st trade ed. NF (eps sl discolored) in dj (sl worn, browned). *Antic Hay*. $100/£63

WILLIAMS, TENNESSEE. It Happened the Day the Sun Rose. Hollywood: Sylvester & Orphanos, 1981. Ltd to 330 signed. Fine debossed cl. *Truepenny*. $250/£156

WILLIAMS, TENNESSEE. Kingdom of Earth: The Seven Descents of Myrtle. NY: New Directions, (1968). 1st ed. VF in VF dj. *Between The Covers*. $150/£94

WILLIAMS, TENNESSEE. The Knightly Quest. NY: New Directions, (1966). 1st ed. VF in VF white dj. *Between The Covers*. $175/£109

WILLIAMS, TENNESSEE. Memoirs. NY, 1975. 1st ed. One of 400 numbered, signed. Slipcase. *Swann**. $230/£144

WILLIAMS, TENNESSEE. The Milk Train Doesn't Stop Here Anymore. NY: New Directions, 1964. 2nd issue w/pp 19-22 tipped-in and Scene Two starting on pg 21. VF in VF- dj (lt scuff rear cvr). *Between The Covers*. $125/£78

WILLIAMS, TENNESSEE. Moise and the World of Reason. NY: S&S, (1975). 1st ed. Fine in dj. *Antic Hay*. $25/£16

WILLIAMS, TENNESSEE. Moise and the World of Reason. NY: S&S, (1975). 1st trade ed. Black cl. Fine in dj (top edge sl browned). *Heritage*. $50/£31

WILLIAMS, TENNESSEE. One Arm and Other Stories. (Norfolk): New Directions, (1949). 1st ed, 2nd state, w/the copyright notice in Williams' name. Buckram, dec bds. VG (sm crack fr hinge) in cardbd slipcase (cracked). *Antic Hay*. $150/£94

WILLIAMS, TENNESSEE. Orpheus Descending, with Battle of Angels. NY: New Directions, (1958). 1st ed. VF in Fine dj (fr cvr sm internally repaired scrape). *Between The Covers*. $125/£78

WILLIAMS, TENNESSEE. Out Cry. NY: New Directions, (1973). 1st ed. Orange cl, spine gilt. NF in pict white dj (soiled). *Blue Mountain*. $45/£28

WILLIAMS, TENNESSEE. A Perfect Analysis Given by a Parrot. (NY): Dramatists Play Service, (1961). 1st ed. VG (sl worn, browned) in ptd blue wraps. *Antic Hay*. $85/£53

WILLIAMS, TENNESSEE. The Remarkable Rooming-House of Mme. le Monde. NY: Albondocani, 1984. Ltd to 150 numbered. Pub's prospectus laid in. Fine in sewn marbled wraps. *Antic Hay*. $85/£53

WILLIAMS, TENNESSEE. The Roman Spring of Mrs. Stone. (NY): New Directions, (1950). 1st trade ed. Black cl. Fine (spine ends sl rubbed) in dj (rear panel sl soiled, top edge sl creased). *Heritage*. $125/£78

WILLIAMS, TENNESSEE. The Roman Spring of Mrs. Stone. (NY, 1950.) 1st ed. Ltd to 500 numbered, signed. Vellum backed patterned bds. (Spine sl dknd), else Good in slipcase (stained, split). *King*. $250/£156

WILLIAMS, TENNESSEE. The Rose Tattoo. (NY): New Directions, (1951). 1st ed, 1st issue binding. Rose cl lettered in black on spine. NF (lt text browning) in dj (sl chipped, soiled). *Heritage*. $250/£156

WILLIAMS, TENNESSEE. The Rose Tattoo. NY: New Directions, 1951. 1st ed. NF in dj. *Smith*. $85/£53

WILLIAMS, TENNESSEE. Small Craft Warnings. (NY): New Directions, (1972). 1st ed. As New in dj. *Between The Covers*. $150/£94

WILLIAMS, TENNESSEE. Small Craft Warnings. London: Secker & Warburg, 1973. 1st ed. Fine in dj. *Smith*. $45/£28

WILLIAMS, TENNESSEE. Steps Must Be Gentle. NY: Targ Editions, (1980). 1st ed thus. One of 350 signed. Marbled bds. Fine in plain dj, as issued. *Reese*. $150/£94

WILLIAMS, TENNESSEE. A Streetcar Named Desire. (NY): New Directions, (1947). 1st ed. Pink ptd bds (sl faded; name). Pink ptd dj (sl faded, sl chipped). *Second Life*. $350/£219

WILLIAMS, TENNESSEE. A Streetcar Named Desire. LEC, 1983. One of 2000 signed by Al Hirschfeld (illus). Fine in slipcase. *Swann**. $172/£108

WILLIAMS, TENNESSEE. Suddenly Last Summer. NY, (1958). 1st ed. Frontis. Dj. *Swann**. $230/£144

WILLIAMS, TENNESSEE. Summer and Smoke. (NY): New Directions, (1948). 1st ed. Blue-gray cl. NF in VG dj (sl dknd, sl rubbed). *Reese*. $75/£47

WILLIAMS, TENNESSEE. Summer and Smoke. (NY): New Directions, (1948). 1st ed. VG in dj (spine, extrems sunned, ends chipped). *Pacific**. $75/£47

WILLIAMS, TENNESSEE. Summer and Smoke. London: John Lehmann, (1952). 1st Eng ed. Orange cl. (Eps lt browned, bkpl), o/w Fine in dj (lt chipped, soiled). *Heritage*. $125/£78

WILLIAMS, TENNESSEE. Sweet Bird of Youth. (NY): New Directions, (1959). 1st ed. Frontis. NF in dj (spine sl sunned, sm tears to extrems). *Pacific**. $52/£33

WILLIAMS, TENNESSEE. Sweet Bird of Youth. London: Secker & Warburg, (1959). 1st Eng ed. Rust-colored cl. (Spine ends sl bumped), o/w Fine in dj (uneven fading, price-clipped). *Heritage*. $85/£53

WILLIAMS, TENNESSEE. Tennessee Williams' Letters to Donald Windham 1940-65. Donald Windham (ed). Verona, (Italy: For Sandy M. Campbell), 1976. One of 500 numbered. This copy signed by Windham. Plain white wraps in pict dj. Fine in slipcase (sl worn). *Antic Hay*. $250/£156

WILLIAMS, TENNESSEE. The Theater of Tennessee Williams. Volume 6. NY: New Directions, (1981). 1st ed. VF in VF dj. *Between The Covers*. $125/£78

WILLIAMS, TENNESSEE. Three Plays of Tennessee Williams. NY: New Directions, (1964). 1st ed thus. VF in VF dj (sl rubbed). *Between The Covers*. $125/£78

WILLIAMS, TENNESSEE. Where I Live: Selected Essays. (NY): New Directions, (1978). 1st ed. Fine in ptd wraps. *Antic Hay*. $25/£16

WILLIAMS, URSULA. Secrets of the Wood. George C. Harrap, 1955. 1st ed. 127pp. NF (spine foot sl bumped) in NF dj. *Price*. $40/£25

WILLIAMS, WILLIAM CARLOS and JOHN SANFORD. A Correspondence. Santa Barbara: Oyster, 1984. 1st ed. Ltd to 500 hb. VG in dj. *King*. $17/£11

WILLIAMS, WILLIAM CARLOS. The Clouds, Aigeltinger, Russia, &c. (Aurora, NY): Wells College Press/Cummington Press, 1948. One of 310. Cl, paper spine label. Fine. *Pacific**. $207/£129

WILLIAMS, WILLIAM CARLOS. The Great American Novel. Paris: Three Mountains, 1923. 1st ed. One of 300. Grn cl, ptd paper spine label. VG (eps, bds, spine label sl browned). *Heritage*. $650/£406

WILLIAMS, WILLIAM CARLOS. In the American Grain. NY: Boni, 1925. 1st ed. VG (lacks dj). *Agvent*. $150/£94

WILLIAMS, WILLIAM CARLOS. Life Among the Passaic River. Norfolk: New Directions, 1938. 1st ed. NF in dj (soiled, sl dknd, spine head chipped). *Pacific**. $52/£33

WILLIAMS, WILLIAM CARLOS. Paterson (Book Five). (NY): New Directions, (1958). 1st ed. Tan cl. (Cvr edges sl browned), o/w Fine in dj (sl chipped, soiled). *Heritage*. $150/£94

WILLIAMS, WILLIAM CARLOS. Paterson (Book Two). (NY): New Directions, (1948). 1st ed. NF in VG dj (spine, extrems dknd, tape repair to verso). *Pacific**. $69/£43

WILLIAMS, WILLIAM CARLOS. A Recognizable Image. Bram Dijkstra (ed). NY: New Directions, (1978). 1st ed. Fine in dj. *Turtle Island*. $50/£31

WILLIAMS, WILLIAM CARLOS. Selected Essays. NY: Random House, (1954). 1st ed. Fine in dj (sl worn). *Lenz*. $125/£78

WILLIAMS, WILLIAM CARLOS. White Mule. Norfolk: New Directions, 1937. 1st ed. (Eps lt stained, sig), else VF in white cl. Dj (lt soiled). *Bromer*. $250/£156

WILLIAMS, WILLIAM. Journal of the Life, Travels and Gospel Labours of.... Cincinnati: Lodge, L'Hommedieu & Hammond, 1828. 1st ed. 272pp. Full leather (joints worn). Good. Howes W490. *Book Broker*. $175/£109

WILLIAMS, WILLIAM. Journal of the Life, Travels, and Gospel Labours.... Cincinnati: Lodge, L'Hommedieu, & Hammond, 1828. 1st ed. 272pp. Orig calf, black leather spine label. (Lt browned, foxed, edges sl rippled, eps browned, foxed, portion of bkpl; sl worn, scuffed.) Cvrs Sound. Howes W490. *Baltimore**. $130/£81

WILLIAMS, RALPH VAUGHAN. See VAUGHAN WILLIAMS, RALPH

WILLIAMS-WOOD, CYRIL. Staffordshire Pot Lids and Their Potters. London: Faber & Faber, 1972. 1st ed. Color frontis, 8 color plts, 72 b/w plts at rear. Dj (spine head sl chipped). *Edwards*. $72/£45

WILLIAMSON, G. The Book of Amber. London: Ernest Benn, 1932. VG. *Blake*. $250/£156

WILLIAMSON, G. The Orchids of South Central Africa. London, 1977. 2 maps. Dj (chipped). *Sutton*. $85/£53

WILLIAMSON, G. C. George Morland. London: Bell, 1904. 49 plts. Teg. (1-inch stain fr cvr.) *Ars Artis*. $72/£45

WILLIAMSON, G. C. The History of Portrait Miniatures. 1531-1860. London, 1904. Ltd to 520. 2 vols. 104 plts. Teg. Gilt-dec cl. (Sm lib ink stamps; soiled.) *Edwards*. $200/£125

WILLIAMSON, H. A Clear Water Stream. Faber, 1958. 1st UK ed. Fine in NF dj. *Martin*. $29/£18

WILLIAMSON, H. Methods of Book Design, the Practice of an Industrial Craft. London: OUP, 1956. 16 plts. Red cl (spine sl faded). *Maggs*. $48/£30

WILLIAMSON, HAROLD. Winchester, The Gun That Won the West. Washington: Combat Forces, (1952). 1st ed. VG in dj. *Perier*. $60/£38

WILLIAMSON, HAROLD. Winchester, the Gun That Won the West. Washington: Combat Forces Press, 1952. 1st ed. VG in dj (chipped, worn). *Labordo*. $65/£41

WILLIAMSON, HENRY (ed). A Soldier's Diary of the Great War. (By Douglas Herbert Bell.) London, 1929. 1st Eng ed. Nice (spine sl bumped) in dj (sl nicked). *Clearwater*. $88/£55

WILLIAMSON, HENRY. The Beautiful Years. Faber, 1929. 1st rev ed. One of 200 signed. NF (spine faded). *Williams*. $120/£75

WILLIAMSON, HENRY. The Children of Shallowford. London, 1939. 1st ed. Fine (lacks dj). *Petersfield*. $26/£16

WILLIAMSON, HENRY. Devon Holiday. Jonathan Cape, 1935. 1st ed. (Paper-clip mk on final ll), o/w Good in dj (chipped). *Cox*. $32/£20

WILLIAMSON, HENRY. The Dream of Fair Women.... London: Faber & Faber, (1931). 1st ed, trade issue. Gilt brn cl. (Lower corner bumped), o/w Nice in Good dj (lt foxed, sm edge tears, sm internal mends). *Reese*. $50/£31

WILLIAMSON, HENRY. The Flax of Dream. London, 1936. 1st Eng ed. Nice (inscrip) in dj (grubby, chipped, spine tanned). *Clearwater*. $96/£60

WILLIAMSON, HENRY. A Fox Under My Cloak. London: MacDonald, (1955). 1st ed. Tan cl stamped in red. VG in pict dj (worn, discolored). *Reese*. $85/£53

WILLIAMSON, HENRY. A Fox Under My Cloak. London, 1955. 1st Eng ed. VG in dj. *Clearwater*. $120/£75

WILLIAMSON, HENRY. The Golden Virgin. London: MacDonald, (1957). 1st ed. Gilt red cl. Fine in NF pict dj. *Reese*. $75/£47

WILLIAMSON, HENRY. The Golden Virgin. London, 1957. 1st Eng ed. VG in dj. *Clearwater*. $96/£60

WILLIAMSON, HENRY. How Dear Is Life. London: MacDonald, (1954). 1st ed. Blue cl, gilt. NF in pict dj. *Reese*. $95/£59

WILLIAMSON, HENRY. How Dear Is Life. London, 1954. 1st Eng ed. (Spine sl offset, faded.) Dj (sl faded, chipped). *Clearwater*. $88/£55

WILLIAMSON, HENRY. In the Woods. Llandeilo: St. Albert's, 1960. One of 1000. This copy one of 50 signed, specially bound. Buckram. VG (sl mkd). *Clearwater*. $200/£125

WILLIAMSON, HENRY. Love and the Loveless. London, 1958. 1st Eng ed. VG in dj (sl nicked). *Clearwater*. $96/£60

WILLIAMSON, HENRY. Love and the Loveless: A Soldier's Tale. London: MacDonald, (1958). 1st ed. Gilt grn cl (faded). VG in Fine pict dj. *Reese*. $75/£47

WILLIAMSON, HENRY. The Old Stag. Putnam, 1926. 1st UK ed. NF (pp sl browned, edges foxed) in VG+ dj. *Williams*. $120/£75

WILLIAMSON, HENRY. The Pathway. Cape, 1931. 1st ed thus. One of 200 signed. VG+ (spine sl faded). *Williams*. $120/£75

WILLIAMSON, HENRY. Scribbling Lark. Faber, 1949. 1st ed. Good (sl faded) in dj (chipped). *Cox*. $29/£18

WILLIAMSON, HENRY. The Story of a Norfolk Farm. London, 1941. 2nd imp. VG in dj. *Gretton*. $27/£17

WILLIAMSON, HENRY. A Test to Destruction. London: MacDonald, (1960). 1st ed. Gilt red cl. (Top edge sl foxed), else NF in dj (sl dknd). *Reese*. $65/£41

WILLIAMSON, HENRY. A Test to Destruction. London, 1960. 1st Eng ed. Nice (fore-edges sl foxed) in dj. *Clearwater*. $72/£45

WILLIAMSON, HENRY. The Village Book. London: Cape, (1930). 1st Eng ed. Orange-tan cl, gilt. VG. *Cady*. $25/£16

WILLIAMSON, HENRY. The Village Book. London: Cape, 1930. 1st Eng ed. One of 504 signed. Teg. Vellum backed grn cl bds, gilt. (Bd edges sl faded), else VG. *Cady*. $85/£53

WILLIAMSON, HENRY. The Village Book. Cape, 1930. One of 504 signed. Vellum-backed bds. VG+. *Williams*. $104/£65

WILLIAMSON, HENRY. The Wet Flanders Plain. Beaumont, (1929). One of 320 numbered. Holland-backed patterned bds (corners sl chafed). VG. *Clearwater*. $144/£90

WILLIAMSON, HENRY. The Wet Flanders Plain. London: Beaumont, 1929. 1st ed. One of 400 (of 480). Patterned bds, cl spine. Fine. *Maggs*. $160/£100

WILLIAMSON, HUGH ROSS. Gods and Mortals in Love. London: Country Life, (1935). 1st ed. 4to. (vi),7-82pp; 9 color plts by Edmund Dulac. Flecked loose-weave cl. Fine. *Sotheran*. $205/£128

WILLIAMSON, HUGH ROSS. Gods and Mortals in Love. London: Country Life, (1935). 1st ed. 4to. (x),11-82pp; 9 color plts by Edmund Dulac. Textured blue cl. Fine in Excellent lt blue pict dj (spine sl browned). *Sotheran*. $352/£220

WILLIAMSON, JACK and JAMES E. GUNN. Star Bridge. NY: Gnome, (1955). 1st ed/ Fine in NF dj (spine lt sunned, foot frayed, 2 sm areas of wear). *Other Worlds*. $60/£38

WILLIAMSON, JACK. The Green Girl. NY: Avon, (1950). 1st ed. NF in pict wrappers. *Other Worlds*. $40/£25

WILLIAMSON, JAMES A. The Cabot Voyages and Bristol Discovery Under Henry VII. Cambridge: CUP, 1962. Blue cl. Fine. *Appelfeld*. $60/£38

WILLIAMSON, JAMES J. Mosby's Rangers. NY, 1896. Time-Life 1982 Collector's Library of Civil War rpt. Leather, gilt. Fine. *Pratt*. $30/£19

WILLIAMSON, JAMES J. Mosby's Rangers: A Record of the Operations of the Forty-Third Battalion Virginia Cavalry from Its Organization to the Surrender.... NY: Ralph B. Kenyon, 1896. 1st ed. 8vo. Frontis, 511pp. Blue-gray pebbled cl, gilt. VG+ (spine sl faded). Howes W498. *Chapel Hill*. $575/£359

WILLIAMSON, JOHN. Ferns of Kentucky. Louisville, KY: John P. Morton, 1878. 1st ed. v,6-154pp, 1 pg ads. Emb grn bds. (Browned; corners bumped, spine sl worn), else VG. *Fair Meadow*. $65/£41

WILLIAMSON, KENNETH. The Atlantic Islands, a Study of the Faeroe Life and Scene. London, 1948. 4 maps. Fine in dj (sl soiled). *Petersfield*. $42/£26

WILLIAMSON, R. S. and W. H. HEUER. Report upon the Removal of Blossom Rock, in San Francisco Harbor, California. Washington: GPO, 1871. 1st ed. Litho tp vignette, 40pp; 11 litho plts (1 fldg). Fine (bkpls; lower corners, spine ends sl worn). *Argonaut*. $400/£250

WILLIAMSON, THOMAS. Oriental Field Sports. London: H.R. Young, 1819. 2nd ed. 2 vols in 1. Sm thick folio. Sepia engr frontis, xv,306; (iii),239,(xi)pp; 40 Good hand-colored aquatint plts. Marbled eps. Contemp dk grn morocco, gilt, raised bands. (Sl aged, lt browned, sl foxed, lt pencil mks few pp; plts lt aged, sl smudges; fr cvr detached, extrems worn, scuffed, spine ends chipped.) *Baltimore**. $850/£531

WILLIAMSON, WILLIAM CRAWFORD. Reminiscences of a Yorkshire Naturalist. London: George Redway, 1896. 1st ed. xii,228pp. Teg, uncut. (Eps spotted; fore-edge of lower bd sl damped.) *Hollett*. $88/£55

WILLIS, CARRIE HUNTER. Golden Days in Old Virginia. Dietz, 1938. Paper cvrs covered w/cl. (Ex-lib.) *Book Broker*. $25/£16

WILLIS, FREDERICK L. H. Alcott Memoirs, Posthumously Compiled from Papers, Journals, and Memoranda of the Late Dr. Frederick L. H. Willis. Boston: Richard G. Badger, (1915). 1st ed. Red cl, paper spine label. VG (sl rubbed). *Lucas*. $60/£38

WILLIS, GEORGE. Little Boy Blues. NY: Dutton, 1947. 1st ed. VG in pict dj. *Petrilla*. $25/£16

WILLIS, N. P. American Scenery. London: George Virtue, 1840. 2 vols. 2 engr tps, port, engr map hand-colored in outline, 116 (of 117) plts (lt spotted throughout, heavier on tps). Contemp 1/2 calf (spines scuffed, extrems rubbed), gilt, later morocco lettering pieces. *Christie's**. $432/£270

WILLIS, N. P. American Scenery. London: George Virtue, 1840. 2 vols bound in 1. 4to. 2 hand-colored engr title vignettes, port, engr map, 117 hand-colored engr plts. (Few short tears not affecting plts, lt spotting.) Contemp red morocco (rubbed, recornered), gilt, mod red morocco spine gilt. *Christie's**. $685/£428

WILLIS, N. P. American Scenery. George Virtue, 1840. 2 vols. 4to. Engr frontis port, 117 engr plts, map. Gilt edges. Contemp pict blind-stamped morocco, gilt spines. *Sotheby's**. $1,067/£667

WILLIS, N. P. American Scenery. London: George Virtue, 1840. 2 vols. 140; 105pp. Gilt edges. 1/2 calf, gilt. VG (marginal foxing). *Cullen*. $1,200/£750

WILLIS, N. P. American Scenery. J.S. Virtue, n.d. 4to. 2 vols in 5 parts. 2 add'l engr pict tps, map, 117 plts (1 plt loose in part 4, w/o port—presumably never present in this copy), ptd tps at end of final vol, ads. *Sotheby's**. $589/£368

WILLIS, N. P. Canadian Scenery. J.S. Virtue, n.d. 2 vols in 5 parts. 4to. 2 add'l engr pict tps, map, 117 plts, w/o port—presumably never present in this copy, ptd tps at end of vol 5, ads. Edges gilt. Orig cl, gilt. (Sl soiled, spine sl worn.) *Sotheby's**. $773/£483

WILLIS, N. P. Picturesque American Scenery. Boston: Estes & Lauriat, 1883. 1st ed. Sm folio. (iii),92pp; 25 VG b/w steel-engr plts, guards. Aeg. Lt olive cl, beveled bds. (Inscrip, sl foxed; lt frayed, sl dusty, sm stain fr cvr.) Cvrs VG. *Baltimore**. $85/£53

WILLIS, N. P. and J. STIRLING COYNE. The Scenery and Antiquities of Ireland. James S. Virtue, n.d. 5 vols. 2 engr tps, 118 engr plts, engr map. Gilt edges. Pub's cl, gilt. (Sl spotting.) *Sotheby's**. $405/£253

WILLIS, N. P. Summer Cruise in the Mediterranean, on Board an American Frigate. NY: Scribner, 1853. 1st ed. 396pp. VG (cvrs sl faded, spine ends worn). *Lefkowicz*. $125/£78

WILLIS, THOMAS. The Anatomy of the Brain and Nerves. William Feindel (ed). Montreal: McGill Univ, 1965. Tercentenary ed. One of 2000 sets. 2 vols. Sm folio. Fldg plt, facs. Untrimmed. Cream linson vellum. Fine in matching bd slipcase. *Blackwell's*. $240/£150

WILLISTON, GEORGE F. Here They Dug the Gold. London: Eyre & Spottiswoode, (1950). 1st Eng ed. 2 maps. Dj (price-clipped, corners chipped). *Glenn*. $35/£22

WILLISTON, TERESA PEIRCE. Japanese Fairy Tales. Rand McNally, 1904. 1st series. Sq 8vo. 74pp; 8 full-pg color plts. Dec cl. (Edges lt creased.) *Hollett*. $48/£30

WILLKIE, WENDELL L. One World. LEC, 1944. Ltd to 1500 numbered, signed. Fine in slipcase. *Swann**. $80/£50

WILLOUGHBY, HUGH L. Across the Everglades. Phila: Lippincott, 1904. Blue cl. VG. *American Booksellers*. $40/£25

WILLOUGHBY, VERA. Horati Carminum Libri IV. London: Peter Davies, 1926. One of 500. Black cl. Fine in VG gold paper dj (lacks 3-inch by 1-inch piece rear wrapper). *Maggs*. $80/£50

WILLOX, D. With the British Bowlers in Canada 1906. Glasgow, n.d. Frontisport. Teg. Orig cl, spine gilt. *Edwards*. $96/£60

WILLS, ALFRED. Wanderings Among the High Alps. Oxford: Blackwell, 1937. 16 plts. (Fore-edges, feps sl spotted.) Dj (spine sl stained, head frayed). *Hollett*. $56/£35

WILLS, MARY and H. IRWIN. Roadside Flower of Texas. Austin: Univ of TX, 1961. 1st ed. NF in VG- dj. *Archer*. $25/£16

WILLS, MARY ALICE. The Confederate Blockade of Washington, D.C. 1861-1862. Parsons, WV, (1975). 1st ed. Fine in dj. *Pratt*. $32/£20

WILLSHIRE, WILLIAM HUGHES. An Introduction to the Study and Collection of Ancient Prints. London, 1877. 2nd ed. 2 vols. 2 frontispieces (1 fldg), x,373; viii,305pp; fldg plt. Lib morocco-backed cl (rebound). (Lib blind/ink stamps, bkpls removed; spines rubbed.) *Edwards*. $120/£75

WILLSON, BECKLES. In the Ypres Salient...June 2-16, 1916. London, (1916). 1st Eng ed. Card wrappers (joint tender). *Clearwater*. $32/£20

WILLSON, D. WYNNE. Early Closing. London: Constable, (1931). 1st ed. Nice. *Cady*. $15/£9

WILLSON, JAMES L. and CHARLES ROBB. The Metals in Canada. Montreal: Dawson, 1861. 80pp; fldg table. Ptd wrappers (soiled, stained; sl worn, lt marginal dampstains last 1/2 of bk). *Oinonen**. $80/£50

WILLUGHBY, FRANCIS. The Ornithology. John Martyn, 1678. 1st ed in English. Folio. 78 (of 80) engr plts, 2 ptd tables. (Several plts w/portions of image torn away, others w/marginal repairs; sl discolored.) Mod 1/2 calf. *Sotheby's**. $589/£368

WILLYAMS, COOPER. A Voyage Up the Mediterranean. London: J. White, 1802. 1st ed. 4to. Engr dedication, fldg hand-colored aquatint map, plan, 40 plts. Contemp 1/2 calf, marbled bds. (Fr joints cracked but cords holding, rubbed; new eps.) *Christie's**. $757/£473

WILMER, WILLIAM HOLLAND. Atlas Fundus Oculi. NY, 1934. 1st ed. 100 full-pg color plts. (Ex-lib, inner hinges cracking; extrems sl worn), o/w Good. *Doctor's Library*. $150/£94

WILMERDING, JOHN. A History of American Marine Painting. Salem: Peabody Museum, (1968). 1st ed. (Lt worn.) Dj. *Oinonen**. $80/£50

Wilson's Tales of the Borders. Ettrick, 1947. (Top edge spotted.) Dj (sl chipped). *Hollett*. $24/£15

WILSON, A. N. Hilaire Belloc. Hamish Hamilton, 1984. 1st ed. Signed presentation. NF (inscrip) in dj. *Virgo*. $27/£17

WILSON, A. N. Love Unknown. Hamilton, 1986. 1st UK ed. Fine in Fine dj. *Martin*. $10/£6

WILSON, A. N. The Sweets of Pimlico. London, 1977. 1st Eng ed, 1st bk. VG (spine sticker) in dj (sl rubbed, price-clipped). *Clearwater*. $72/£45

WILSON, A. N. Unguarded Hours. Secker, 1978. 1st UK ed. NF in dj. *Williams*. $128/£80

WILSON, ANDREW. The Abode of Snow. Edinburgh: William Blackwood, 1875. 1st ed. Tinted litho frontis, xxvi,475,(1)imprint; fldg map (torn, repaired). Later red straight-grained 1/2 calf, marbled bds. VG (lib plt removed; sl rubbed, spine repaired). *Morrell*. $272/£170

WILSON, ANGUS. Anglo-Saxon Attitudes. London, 1956. VG in dj. *Typographeum*. $18/£11

WILSON, ANGUS. As If By Magic. Secker, 1973. 1st UK ed. Signed. NF in dj (spine label). *Williams*. $40/£25

WILSON, ANGUS. The Wrong Set and Other Stories. London, 1949. 1st Eng ed, 1st bk. Nice (spine sl sunned) in dj (sl tanned, rubbed). *Clearwater*. $104/£65

WILSON, BLANCHE NICHOLS. Minnetonka Story. Minneapolis: Colwell, 1950. (Ink name), else VG in dj. *Perier*. $30/£19

WILSON, CAROL GREEN. Alice Eastwood's Wonderland. SF: CA Academy of Sciences, (1955). 1st ed. One of 2000 ptd. Frontisport. Unopened. Grn cl. Fine. *Harrington*. $35/£22

WILSON, CHARLES W. From Korti to Khartum. Edinburgh: Blackwood, 1885. 1st ed. xxvii, 313pp; fldg map. Aeg. Contemp blue calf, gilt. VG (sm lib stamp; sl rubbed). *Morrell*. $192/£120

WILSON, CHARLES W. Picturesque Palestine, Sinai and Egypt. London: J.S. Virtue, (1880-84). 4 vols. 38 engr plts, 2 dbl-pg litho maps at end vol 4. (Lt spotting, frontispieces re-bound.) Mod lib cl. *Christie's**. $216/£135

WILSON, CHARLES W. Picturesque Palestine. NY, (1881-83). 2 vols. 1/2 morocco. (Sl dampstaining 1 vol.) *Swann**. $172/£108

WILSON, CLAUDE. Mountaineering. George Bell & Sons, 1893. 1st ed. vi,(i),208,(vi) ads pp (ads also ptd on pastedown eps). Pict cl. VG. *Sotheran*. $61/£38

WILSON, COLIN. Bernard Shaw—a Reassessment. Hutchinson, 1969. 1st UK ed. Fine in dj. *Williams*. $40/£25

WILSON, COLIN. Brandy of the Damned. London, 1964. 1st Eng ed. Very Nice (fep sl chafed) in dj (sl rubbed, price-clipped). *Clearwater*. $56/£35

WILSON, COLIN. The Mind Parasites. Sauk City, WI: Arkham House, 1967. 1st US ed. One of 3045. NF in dj. *Bernard*. $60/£38

WILSON, COLIN. Religion and the Rebel. Gollancz, 1957. 1st UK ed. Fine (edges foxed) in VG dj (closed tear to rear panel). *Williams*. $38/£24

WILSON, COLIN. Ritual in the Dark. Gollancz, 1960. 1st ed. (Corners sl bumped, top edge sl dusty), else VG + in dj (nicked, sl soiled). *Any Amount*. $40/£25

WILSON, COLIN. The World of Violence. London, 1963. 1st ed. Signed. VG. *Typographeum*. $65/£41

WILSON, DANIEL. The Archaeology and Prehistoric Annals of Scotland. Edinburgh: Sutherland & Knox, 1851. 1st ed. xxvi,714pp (bkpl); 6 engr plts. Orig dec cl (rebacked in matching levant morocco), gilt. *Hollett*. $224/£140

WILSON, DANIEL. Prehistoric Man.... Cambridge: Macmillan, 1862. 1st ed. 2 vols. Color frontispieces, xviii,488; vi,(500)pp; map. Bound w/o half-titles. Contemp 1/2 morocco. VG set (lt pencil notes, few sl creases; sl worn). *Ash*. $400/£250

WILSON, E. Diary of the 'Terra Nova' Expedition to the Antarctic 1910-1912. Blandford, 1972. 1st ed. VG + in dj. *Walcot*. $48/£30

WILSON, E. (ed). Diary of the 'Discovery' Expedition to the Antarctic Regions 1901-1904. Ann Savours (ed). Blandford, 1966. 1st ed. Map. (Cellotape mks fr pastedown), o/w VG in dj. *Walcot*. $72/£45

WILSON, E. H. If I Were to Make a Garden. Boston: Stratford, 1931. 1st ed. Frontisport. Teg. (Sm snag to spine), else Fine. *Quest*. $110/£69

WILSON, E. H. Plantae Wilsonianae. Charles Sprague Sargent (ed). Portland, OR: Dioscorides Press, 1988. Rpt. 3 vols. Fine in djs. *Archer*. $100/£63

WILSON, EARL et al. Betio Beachhead. NY, 1945. VG. *Clark*. $30/£19

WILSON, EDMUND. The American Earthquake. GC, 1958. 1st ed. Good in dj (used). *King*. $35/£22

WILSON, EDMUND. The Bit Between My Teeth. NY, (1965). 1st ed. VG in dj (used). *King*. $35/£22

WILSON, EDMUND. The Boys in the Back Room: Notes on California Novelists. Colt, 1941. 1st ltd ed of 1500. NF (lacks acetate dj). *Authors Of The West*. $150/£94

WILSON, EDMUND. The Devils and Canon Barham. NY, (1973). 1st ed. VG in dj (sl used) *King*. $25/£16

WILSON, EDMUND. The Duke of Palermo and Other Plays. NY, (1969). 1st Amer ed. Fine in dj. *Polyanthos*. $40/£25

WILSON, EDMUND. The Forties. NY, (1983). 1st ed. VG in dj (sl torn). *King*. $25/£16

WILSON, EDMUND. Night Thoughts. NY: Farrar, Straus & Cudahy, (1961). 1st ed. Gilt blue cl. VG in dj (corner chip). *Reese*. $30/£19

WILSON, EDMUND. Three Reliques of Ancient Western Poetry. Boston: Todd, 1951. 1st ed. Inscribed. Red wrappers, paper label. (Spine split at fold), o/w Fine. *Cummins*. $150/£94

WILSON, EDMUND. A Window on Russia. NY: Farrar, 1972. 1st ed. Fine in Fine dj. *Beasley*. $25/£16

WILSON, EDWARD A. The Pirate's Treasure. NY: P.F. Volland, 1926. 1st ed. 8vo. Unpaginated. Illus eps. VG in box (torn). *Davidson*. $95/£59

WILSON, EDWARD A. The Pirate's Treasure: The Strange Adventures of Jack Adams on the Spanish Main. NY: Volland, 1926. 4to. Good. *American Booksellers*. $40/£25

WILSON, EDWARD L. (ed). Photographic Mosaics. Phila: Benerman & Wilson, 1873. 1st ed. 192pp incl + 48pp ads (lacks fep, lt aging). Grn cl (lt worn, frayed; fr joint partly torn), gilt. Cvrs Good. *Baltimore**. $75/£47

WILSON, EDWARD L. (ed). Photographic Mosaics: Annual Record of Photographic Progress. NY: Edward L. Wilson, 1900. 1st ed. Frontis, guard, 60 full-pg b/w photos. VG in illus stiff wrappers (spine chipped, sl soiled). *Cahan*. $75/£47

WILSON, ELIJAH NICHOLAS. Among the Shoshones. Salt Lake City, (1910). 1st ed. 8 plts. *Kane**. $275/£172

WILSON, ELIJAH NICHOLAS. Among the Shoshones. Salt Lake City, 1910. 2nd ed. Frontis, port. (1 leaf w/closed tear; edgeworn, fr hinge cracked), o/w VG. *Benchmark*. $115/£72

WILSON, ERASMUS. Cleopatra's Needle. London: Brain, (1877). xvi,214pp. Pict cl, gilt. (Bkpl, inscrip; sm tear at spine.) *Archaeologia*. $75/£47

WILSON, ERNEST H. Aristocrats of the Garden. Boston: Stratford, 1926. 1st ed. Teg. VG (fr hinge reglued). *Archer*. $45/£28

WILSON, ERNEST H. Aristocrats of the Garden. Boston: Stratford, 1932. 1st ed thus. 2 vols. Teg. NF in VG djs. *Archer*. $60/£38

WILSON, ERNEST H. China: Mother of Gardens. Boston: Stratford, 1929. 1st ed. Fldg map. Teg. Black cl w/gold graining, gold flecked orange fep. (Bkpl sl mkd facing fep), else VG. *Fair Meadow*. $300/£188

WILSON, ERNEST H. China: Mother of Gardens. Boston: Stratford, 1929. 1st ed. Teg. (Bkpl), else NF. *Archer*. $375/£234

WILSON, ERNEST H. More Aristocrats of the Garden. Boston: Stratford, 1928. 1st ed. Teg. VG + in dj (chipped, dampstained). *Archer*. $40/£25

WILSON, ERNEST H. A Naturalist in Western China. NY: Doubleday, Page, 1914. 2nd ptg. 2 vols. Fldg map. (Lib stamp; spine #s neatly cvrd), o/w VG. *Archer*. $375/£234

WILSON, ERNEST H. Plant Hunting. Boston: Stratford, 1927. 1st ed. 2 vols. (Spines sl rubbed), o/w Fine. *Archer*. $250/£156

WILSON, HARRY LEON. So This Is Golf! NY: Cosmopolitan Book Co, 1923. 1st ed. Cvr label. (Offset to fr pastedown; corners sl bumped), else VG. *Pacific**. $46/£29

WILSON, HELENA CALISTA and ELSIE REED MITCHELL. Vagabonding at Fifty from Siberia to Turkestan. NY: Coward-McCann, 1929. 1st US ed. Frontis map, 15 plts. (Cl sl rubbed, soiled), o/w VG. *Worldwide*. $35/£22

WILSON, HENRY and JAMES CAULFIELD. The Book of Wonderful Characters: Memoirs and Anecdotes of Remarkable and Eccentric Persons in All Ages and Countries. London: John Camden Hotten, (1869). Hand-colored frontisport, xxii,416pp; 59 plts. Orig 1/2 calf, marbled paper sides, raised bands, gilt, honey-colored morocco label. (Inscrip, sig, 7 plts trimmed close at bottom, affecting edge of caption, sl stained, smudged; joints cracked, leather sl worn, paper sides sl chafed.) *Pirages*. $85/£53

WILSON, HORACE HAYMAN. The History of British India. From 1805 to 1835. London, 1845-1848. 3 vols. Marbled eps, edges. Contemp calf (sympathetic reinforcement to corners, edges rubbed), rebacked in mod calf (rubbed w/sl surface wear), gilt, morocco spine labels. *Edwards*. $240/£150

WILSON, IRIS HIGBIE. William Wolfskill, 1798-1866. Glendale: A.H. Clark, 1965. 1st ed. Frontis. Red cl. *Dawson*. $50/£31

WILSON, J. J. Narrative of Discovery and Adventure in Africa, from the Earliest Ages to the Present Time. NY: Harper, (1834). Family Lib ed. Fldg frontis map, 359pp; full-pg engr repro. (Lt foxed), else VG. *Mikesh*. $60/£38

WILSON, J. LEIGHTON. Western Africa: Its History, Condition, and Prospects. NY: Harper, 1856. 1st ed. 527pp; dbl-pg map. Blind red cl, gilt. (Lt aged, sl foxed, bkpls; chipped, frayed, sl worn.) Text Clean. *Baltimore**. $35/£22

WILSON, JAMES. Biography of the Blind. Birmingham, 1838. 4th ed. lxii,300pp. Orig cl, gilt. *Bickersteth*. $35/£22

WILSON, JAMES. A Complete Dictionary of Astrology. London, 1819. 1st ed. xxv,411pp. VG (nicely rebound). *Middle Earth*. $175/£109

WILSON, JAMES. Lectures on the Blood, and on the Anatomy, Physiology and Surgical Pathology of the Vascular System of the Human Body. London, 1819. 1st ed. 429pp. Orig bds (fr bd detached, spine chipped). *Fye*. $300/£188

WILSON, JAMES. Lowland Scotch. OUP, 1915. 1st ed. Frontisport. (Feps lt browned, might lack fep, bkpl; cl lt discolored, ink spots fr bd.) *Edwards*. $80/£50

WILSON, JAMES. A Missionary Voyage to the Southern Pacific Ocean. London: T. Chapman, 1799. 1st ed. 6 engr plts, 7 fldg maps. (Some plts dampstained and browned, few tears, margin 1 fldg map brittle, few ll spotted.) Contemp 1/2 calf, marbled bds (worn, damage to spine). *Christie's**. $325/£203

WILSON, JOHN A. Adventures of Alf. Wilson. Washington: Nat'l Tribune, 1897. 237pp + 16pp pub's cat. Good + (browned) in wrappers (extrems worn). *House*. $65/£41

WILSON, JOHN DOVER. Milestones on the Dover Road. London: Faber, 1969. 1st ed. 15 plts. VG in dj (spine faded). *Hollett*. $32/£20

WILSON, JOHN MACKAY. Tales of the Borders. Gteshead-on-Tyne: Adam, n.d. (c.1870). 3 vols. Aeg. 1/2 grn morocco (sl mkd), gilt. Nice set. *Hollett*. $152/£95

WILSON, JOHN. The Royal Philatelic Collection. London, (1925). Thick sm folio. Crimson morocco, gilt. (Cvrs sl bowed.) *Swann**. $172/£108

WILSON, JOSEPH. The Black Phalanx; A History of the Negro Soldiers of the United States in the Wars of 1775-1812, 1861-'65. Hartford: Amer Pub, 1888. 1st ed. Frontisport, 528pp; 56 plts. Dec cl. VG (cheap paper dknd, sl brittle; lacks sm pieces of cl, rear cvr). *Agvent*. $500/£313

WILSON, JOYCE LANCASTER (ed). The Work and Play of Adrian Wilson: A Bibliography with Commentary. Austin: W. Thomas Taylor, 1983. One of 325 ptd. Frontis, tipped-in ephemera. 1/4 levant morocco, gilt. Fine. *Pacific**. $173/£108

WILSON, JUNE. Green Shadows. London: Hodder & Stoughton, 1951. 1st Eng ed. 6 b/w plts. VG (edges sl spotted, spine ends sl bumped) in dj (rubbed, chipped, sl mkd). *Ulysses*. $40/£25

WILSON, JUNE. Green Shadows. The Life of John Clare. London: Hodder & Stoughton, 1951. 1st ed. 6 plts. VG in dj (edges sl worn, chipped). *Hollett*. $56/£35

WILSON, MONA. The Life of William Blake. London: Nonesuch, 1927. 1st ed. One of 1480 ptd. 1/4 parchment, marbled bds, gilt. (Stamp; extrems rubbed), else VG. *Pacific**. $127/£79

WILSON, MONA. The Life of William Blake. London: Rupert Hart-Davis, 1948. 1st trade ed. 6 plts. (Fore-edge spotted; spine faded.) *Hollett*. $40/£25

WILSON, NEILL C. Silver Stampede: The Career of Death Valley's Hell-Camp, Old Panamint. NY: Macmillan, c1937. VG in VG dj. *Blake*. $45/£28

WILSON, NEILL C. and FRANK J. TAYLOR. Southern Pacific. NY: McGraw Hill, (1952). 1st ed. Signed by both authors. Good. *Lien*. $35/£22

WILSON, NEILL C. Treasure Express. NY: Macmillan, 1936. 1st ed. Inscribed, signed. VG + in dj (chipped). *Labordo*. $75/£47

WILSON, R. McNAIR. The Beloved Physician: Sir James Mackenzie. NY: Macmillan, (1928). Port. Brn cl. VG + . *House*. $25/£16

WILSON, RICHARD (retold by). The Russian Story Book. London: Macmillan, 1916. 1st ed. 8vo. 16 full-pg color plts by Frank C. Pape. Red cl (sl dknd), gilt. *Reisler*. $125/£78

WILSON, RICHARD. An Italian Sketchbook. Denys Sutton (ed). London: Mellon/Routledge, 1968. 2 vols. Uniform pub's cl. Fine set in slipcase. *Europa*. $77/£48

WILSON, ROBERT A. Ben K. Green—A Descriptive Bibliography.... Flagstaff: Northland, (1977). 1st ed. Fine in dj. *Perier*. $40/£25

WILSON, ROBERT ANDERSON. Mexico: Its Peasants and Its Priests. NY: Harper, 1856. New ed. Woodcut frontis, xiv,418pp. Purple cl (faded), gilt. *Karmiole.* $75/£47

WILSON, ROMER (ed). Red Magic. London: Jonathan Cape, (1930). 1st ed. 8vo. 8 full-pg color plts by Kay Nielson. Red cl, gilt. Good. *Reisler.* $750/£469

WILSON, RUFUS ROCKWELL. Out of the West. NY: Press of the Pioneers, 1933. Good (bkpl, lib pocket on rep; shelfworn). *Dumont.* $85/£53

WILSON, S. S. A Narrative of a Greek Mission; or Sixteen Years in Malta and Greece.... John Snow, 1839. 1st ed. Frontis, xiii,596,(ii) ads pp. Uncut. Recent blue 1/2 calf, blue cl sides, raised bands, gilt. VG. *Sotheran.* $360/£225

WILSON, T. P. CAMERON. Magpies in Picardy. Poetry Bookshop, 1919. 1st Eng ed. Cl-backed pict bds. (Rubber stamp; edges rubbed.) *Clearwater.* $56/£35

WILSON, THOMAS. The Swastika. Washington: GPO, 1896. 1st ed. Later cl. VG. *Pacific*.* $69/£43

WILSON, WARREN et al. The Recovery of Jerusalem. NY: Appleton, 1871. 1st ed. xxiv,435pp; 22 plts (7 fldg). (Ex-lib, plt torn along fold; edges rubbed, lib spine #), o/w Good. *Worldwide.* $50/£31

WILSON, WILLIAM RAE. Travels in Egypt and the Holy Land. London: Longman, Hurst, Rees, 1823. 1st ed. Frontis, xi,(i),544pp; 8 aquatints. Marbled edges. Contemp polished calf, gilt. VG (lt waterstain affecting frontis, upper plt margins; spine repaired w/new label). *Morrell.* $352/£220

WILSON, WILLIAM RAE. Travels in Egypt and the Holy Land. London, 1824. 2nd ed. 6 (of 12) aquatint plts. Contemp 1/2 calf (extrems worn, spine ends chipped). *Swann*.* $172/£108

WILSON, WILLIAM. The Post-Chaise Companion; or, Traveller's Directory Through Ireland. Dublin: The Author, 1786. Engr tp, frontis (mtd), 3 fldg plts, fldg map. Contemp calf (worn, cvrs detached; opening ll loose). *Swann*.* $103/£64

WILSON, WOODROW. A History of the American People. NY, 1918. One of 400 numbered, signed sets. 10 vols. 8vo. 3/4 morocco, gilt. *Swann*.* $1,495/£934

WILSON, WOODROW. A History of the American People. NY: William H. Wise, 1931. 5 vols. (Spines dull.) *Sadlon.* $20/£13

WILSTACH, FRANK JENNERS. Wild Bill Hickok, the Prince of Pistoleers. GC: Doubleday, Page, 1926. 1st ed. NF in dj. *Labordo.* $125/£78

WILSTACH, PAUL. Hudson River Landings. NY: Tudor, 1937. New ed. Red/grn cl. VG. *American Booksellers.* $25/£16

WILTSE, CHARLES M. John C. Calhoun. Indianapolis: Bobbs-Merrill, (1944-49-51). 1st ed of vols 1, 3; 2nd ptd of vol 2. Red/blue cl. (Bkpls, vol 1 spine sunned), else VG; Poor dj on vol 3. *Chapel Hill.* $80/£50

WILTSEE, ERNEST A. Gold Rush Steamers (of the Pacific). SF: Grabhorn, 1938. Ltd to 500. Color frontis, 16 plts, 4-pg facs letter. Linen over red cl, paper spine label. Fine. *Karmiole.* $250/£156

WILTSEE, ERNEST A. Gold Rush Steamers (of the Pacific). SF: Grabhorn, 1938. 1st ed. Ltd to 500. Color frontis, 33 plts. Brick-red cl, tan cl backstrip, ptd paper spine label. VF. *Argonaut.* $350/£219

WILTSEE, ERNEST A. Gold Rush Steamers. SF: Grabhorn, 1938. 1st ed. One of 500. Color frontis. Linen-backed cl, paper spine label. Fine. *Harrington.* $300/£188

WILTSEY, NORMAN B. Brave Warriors. Caldwell: Caxton, 1963. 1st ed. Frontis. Tan cl. Dj (lt edgeworn). *Dawson.* $40/£25

WINANT, LEWIS. Firearms Curiosa. NY: Bonanza Books, (1950). Frontis. NF (inscrip) in VG + dj. *Backman.* $20/£13

WINCHELL, A. Preadamites. Chicago: Griggs, 1880. 1st ed. Engr frontis, 500pp; 3 fldg color maps, charts. VG. *Mikesh.* $60/£38

WIND, EDGAR. Pagan Mysteries in the Renaissance. Faber & Faber, 1958. 1st ed. 77 b/w plts. *Edwards.* $56/£35

WIND, EDGAR. Pagan Mysteries in the Renaissance. NY, 1968. Rev ed. Red buckram. *Washton.* $45/£28

WIND, HERBERT WARREN. The Story of American Golf. NY: Farrar, Straus, 1948. 1st ed. Grn cl. Good in slipcase (worn). *Karmiole.* $150/£94

WINDELER, BERNARD. Sailing-ships and Barges of the Western Mediterranean and Adriatic Seas. Haslewood, 1926. One of 450. Sm folio. Copperplt-engr tp,xv,81,(1)pp; map, 17 plts (16 hand-colored). Untrimmed. 1/4 cream canvas, gilt, orange cl sides. Fine in bd slipcase w/ptd label. *Blackwell's.* $800/£500

WINDHAM, DONALD. Two People. NY: Coward-McCann, (1965). 1st ed. VF in dj. *Between The Covers.* $250/£156

WINDISCH-GRAETZ, MATHILDE. The Spanish Riding School. London, 1956. 1st ed. Color frontis. Dj (lt soiled, chipped). *Edwards.* $26/£16

WINDSOR, EDWARD, DUKE OF. A King's Story. NY: Putnam, 1951. One of 385 signed. Silk eps; teg. Red morocco w/raised bands, gilt. Fine (fr joint sl rubbed) in buckram slipcase. *Ulysses.* $880/£550

Wine, Women and War: A Diary of Disillusionment. (By Howard Vincent O'Brien.) London: Heinemann, (1927). 1st British ed. Yellow cl. (Eps offset; edge dkng), o/w VG + in pict dj (dknd, lt soiled). *Reese.* $50/£31

WINES, E. C. The State of the Prisons and of the Child-Saving Institutions in the Civilized World. Cambridge: CUP/John Wilson, 1880. (ii),xxiv,719,(3)pp. Pebbled ruled grn cl. Fine. *Gach.* $200/£125

WINGATE, GEORGE W. Through the Yellowstone Park on Horseback. NY: OJ, 1886. 1st ed. 250pp + (6)pp ads; fldg color litho map loose in rep pocket. Blue cl, gilt. (2pp w/offset from newsclippings; spine sl sunned, ends sl frayed), else VG +. *Pacific*.* $98/£61

WINGET, D. H. Anecdotes of 'Buffalo Bill' That Have Never Appeared in Print. Chicago: Historical Pub, 1927. 2nd ed. Flexible suede leather, gilt. VF. Howes W564. *Labordo.* $95/£59

WINGLER, HANS M. The Bauhaus. (Cambridge, 1969.) Folio. Slipcase. *Swann*.* $161/£101

Winkle's Architectural and Picturesque Illustrations of the Cathedral Churches of England and Wales. London: Effingham Wilson & Charles Tilt, 1836-1842. Lg paper copy. 3 vols. Lg 4to. Robert Garland (illus). Engr frontis each vol, xx,144; viii,140; xii,160pp; 178 mtd engr plts. Aeg. 3/4 grn squeezed morocco, marbled bds, gilt. Fine set. *House.* $900/£563

WINKLER, ERNEST W. (ed). Check List of Texas Imprints, 1846-1860. Austin: TX State Hist Assoc, 1949, 1963, (1964). 1st eds. 2 vols. Untrimmed, partly unopened. Red buckram. Very Clean set in djs (sl rubbed). *Baltimore*.* $150/£94

WINN, MARY DAY. The Macadam Trail. NY: Knopf, 1931. 1st ed. Color frontis. Good. *Lien.* $30/£19

WINSHIP, GEORGE PARKER. John Carter Brown Library: A History. Providence: Merrymount, 1914. VG (bkpl). *Truepenny.* $55/£34

WINSHIP, GEORGE PARKER. The Merrymount Press of Boston. Vienna: Herbert Reichner, 1929. One of 350 numbered. Signed, inscribed presentation, w/als laid in. 'Extra-illustrated' w/pieces of Merrymount ephemera loosely inserted. Paper label. (Lt worn, spine head torn.) *Oinonen*.* $140/£88

WINSHIP, GEORGE PARKER. Printing in the Fifteenth Century. Phila: University of PA, 1940. 1st ed. Fine in dj (soiled). *Oak Knoll.* $65/£41

WINSOR, JUSTIN. The Kohl Collection of Maps Relating to America. Washington, 1904. Internally Good (edges worn, lib stamp). *Dumont.* $175/£109

WINSOR, JUSTIN. The Memorial History of Boston...1630-1880. Boston, 1880-81. 4 vols. 1/2 calf. (Several hinges cracked.) *Swann**. $149/£93

WINSTON, ROBERT W. High Stakes and Hair Triggers. NY: Henry Holt, (1930). 1st ed. Frontisport, map. Burgundy cl. Fine in NF dj. *Chapel Hill*. $125/£78

WINTER, CARL. The Fitzwilliam Museum. An Illustrated Survey. London: Trianon, 1958. One of 1500. Frontis port, 107 plts (7 color). *Edwards*. $64/£40

WINTER, DOUGLAS E. (ed). Prime Evil. West Kingston: Donald M. Grant, 1988. 1st ed. One of 1000. Signed by all contributors, Thomas Canty (illus) & Winter. Black morocco, gilt. Fine in clamshell box. *Pacific**. $173/£108

WINTER, MARION HANNAH. The Pre-Romantic Ballet. (London): Pitman, (1975). VG in color pict dj (price-clipped). *Dramatis*. $65/£41

WINTER, NEVIN O. Texas the Marvellous: The State of the Six Flags. Boston: Page, 1916. 1st ed, blind-stamped 'Presentation Copy' on tp. Signed presentation. Fldg map. Pict eps; teg, untrimmed, partly unopened. Pict navy cl. Text Very Clean, cvrs VG. *Baltimore**. $80/£50

WINTER, WILLIAM. Life and Art of Edwin Booth. NY: Macmillan, 1893. 1st ed. Orig contemp photo of Booth inserted. Teg. 3/4 red polished calf, gilt paneled spine, raised bands. Fine. *Appelfeld*. $125/£78

WINTERICH, JOHN T. The Grolier Club 1884-1967. NY: Grolier Club, 1967. Ltd to 2000. NF in NF box. *Polyanthos*. $30/£19

WINTERICH, JOHN T. (ed). Squads Write! NY, 1931. 1st Amer ed. NF. *Polyanthos*. $35/£22

WINTERNITZ, M. C. (ed). Collected Studies on the Pathology of War Gas Poisoning. New Haven: Yale Univ, 1920. 1st ed. 41 color plts. Fine. *Glaser*. $125/£78

WINTERRY, VIVENNE TALLAL. Fritz Henle's Rollei. NY, (1950). 1st ed. VG in dj (chipped, torn). *King*. $35/£22

WINTERS, YVOR. The Anatomy of Nonsense. Norfolk: New Directions, 1943. 1st ed. VG in dj. *Smith*. $25/£16

WINTERS, YVOR. Edwin Arlington Robinson. New Directions, (1946). 1st ed. Fine in Fine dj. *Dermont*. $35/£22

WINTERS, YVOR. The Journey and Other Poems. Ithaca, NY: Dragon Press, 1931. 1st ed. Wraps (soiled). *King*. $35/£22

WINTERSON, JEANETTE. Boating for Beginners. Methuen, 1985. 1st ed. NF (spine ends sl bumped) in dj. *Ulysses*. $200/£125

WINTERSON, JEANETTE. The Passion. London: Bloomsbury, 1987. 1st Eng ed. NF (sl abrasion 1/2-title; spine head sl bumped) in dj. *Ulysses*. $88/£55

WINTERSON, JEANETTE. Sexing the Cherry. Bloomsbury, 1989. 1st ed. Fine in dj. *Virgo*. $40/£25

WINTERSON, JEANETTE. Sexing the Cherry. London: Bloomsbury, 1989. 1st ed. Fine in dj. *Smith*. $75/£47

WINTHER, OSCAR OSBURN. A Classified Bibliography of the Periodical Literature of the Trans-Mississippi West (1811-1957). Bloomington, 1961. (Edges soiled.) Internally VG. *Dumont*. $40/£25

WINTHER, OSCAR OSBURN. The Old Oregon Country. Stanford, CA: Stanford Univ, (1950). 1st ed, 2nd issue. Tan cl. (Inscrip), o/w Fine in Fine dj. *Harrington*. $100/£63

WINTHER, OSCAR OSBURN. Via Western Express and Stage Coach. Stanford Univ, (1945). 2nd ptg. VG in dj (edgeworn). *Perier*. $30/£19

WINTHER, OSCAR OSBURN. Via Western Express and Stagecoach. Stanford: Stanford Univ, (1945). 1st ed. Fine in dj. *Argonaut*. $35/£22

WINTHROP, ROBERT P. Cast and Wrought: The Architectural Metalwork of Richmond, Virginia. Valentine Museum, 1980. Signed by Winthrop and Margot Gayle (forward). VG- in Good-dj. *Book Broker*. $45/£28

WINTHROP, THEODORE. The Canoe and the Saddle or Klalam and Klickatat.... John H. Williams (ed). Tacoma: John H. Williams, 1913. Rev ed, 1st ptg. Color frontis, 16 color plts. Maroon cl, gilt-stamped vellum spine. Fine. Howes W584. *Argonaut*. $300/£188

WIRGIN, JAN. Sung Ceramic Designs. London, 1979. 104 b/w plts. *Edwards*. $88/£55

WIRT, MILDRED A. The Vanishing Houseboat. NY: Cupples & Leon, 1939. Penny Parker #2; lists only 6 titles. Older thick ed. 5.5.x7.5. 204pp. VG (sl shelfworn) in dj (edgeworn). *My Bookhouse*. $42/£26

WIRT, MILDRED A. The Wishing Well. NY: Cupples & Leon, 1942. 1st ed. Penny Parker #8; last title listed. 5.5.x8. 206pp. VG (shelfworn) in dj (worn). *My Bookhouse*. $52/£33

WIRT, WILLIAM. Sketches of the Life and Character of Patrick Henry. Phila: James Webster, 1817. 1st ed. Port (dampstain to verso; sl foxing mainly to 1st ll). Orig calf (scuffed, lower fr joint starting), leather spine label. Howes W586. *Sadlon*. $35/£22

Wisdom in Miniature; or, The Young Gentleman and Lady's Magazine. Phila: John Adams, 1805. 24mo. Full-pg woodcut frontis, 32pp; 12 half-pg woodcuts. Frontis, last pg ads pasted down on wrappers. Buff stiff paper wrappers. VF in orig glassine dj. *Hobbyhorse*. $250/£156

WISE, ARTHUR and FRANCIS I. LORD. Bands and Drummer Boys of the Civil War. NY, (1966). 1st ed. VG + in dj (sl worn). *Pratt*. $40/£25

WISE, GEORGE. Campaigns and Battles of the Army of Northern Virginia. NY: Neale, 1916. 1st ed. Frontisport, port. Red buckram. (Bkpl, sm stamp), else VG. *Chapel Hill*. $275/£172

WISE, HENRY A. Los Gringos; or, An Inside View of Mexico and California; with Wanderings in Peru, Chili, and Polynesia. NY: Putnam, 1850. 2nd Amer ed. 3/4 polished calf, marbled bds, gilt, raised bands (extrems sl rubbed; few ll lt foxed). Howes W593. *Sadlon*. $75/£47

WISE, HERBERT A. and PHYLLIS FRASER (eds). Great Tales of Terror and the Supernatural. NY, (1944). 1st ed. VG in dj (heavily chipped; split). *King*. $35/£22

WISE, HUGH D. Tigers of the Sea. NY: Derrydale, 1937. One of 950 numbered. Grn cl. Fine in NF pict dj. *Biscotti*. $175/£109

WISE, JENNINGS C. The Long Arm of Lee. Lynchburg: J.P. Bell, 1915. 1st ed. 2 vols. (Bkpl.) Crimson cl (sl worn, rubbed; few hinges split), gilt. Text Clean. *Baltimore**. $150/£94

WISE, JENNINGS C. The Long Arm of Lee. Lynchburg, VA, 1915. 2 vols. (Bkpl taped inside each vol; spine lettering faded.) *Kane**. $170/£106

WISE, JENNINGS C. The Military History of the Virginia Military Institute from 1839 to 1865. Lynchburg: J.P. Bell, 1915. 1st ed. Tipped-in errata slip; fldg map. (Sl aging.) Ribbed crimson cl (recently recased w/new eps, blanks; sl worn), gilt. Text Clean. *Baltimore**. $50/£31

WISE, JOHN S. The End of an Era. Boston/NY: Houghton Mifflin, (1899). Stated 'fourteenth impression.' Teg. (Spine ends, corners sl rubbed.) *Sadlon*. $20/£13

WISE, THOMAS J. A Bibliography of the Writings in Prose and Verse of Algernon Swinburne. London/NY: Heinemann/Gabriel Wells, 1927. 1st ed. One of 780. Untrimmed, unopened. Grn buckram, ptd paper spine label. (Few pp roughly opened.) Cvrs Clean in plain ptd dj (sl dusting, wear). *Baltimore**. $65/£41

WISE, THOMAS J. A Bibliography of the Writings in Prose and Verse of Samuel Taylor Coleridge. London: Bib Soc, 1913. 13 plts. Partly unopened, uncut. Canvas-backed bds (spine faded). *Maggs*. $64/£40

WISE, THOMAS J. and JAMES P. SMART. A Complete Bibliography of the Writings in Prose and Verse of John Ruskin. London: For Subscribers Only, 1893. One of 250. 2 vols. Frontisport. Teg, rest uncut. 3/4 morocco. Upper wrappers bound in. (Margins pencilled, sl foxed; rubbed, corners worn.) *Oinonen**. $90/£56

WISE, THOMAS J. A Swinburne Library. London: For Private Circulation, 1925. One of 170. Signed presentation. Uncut. (Lt worn.) *Oinonen**. $100/£63

WISE, THOMAS J. (ed). A Conrad Library: A Catalogue of Printed Books, Manuscripts and Autograph Letters by Joseph Conrad. London: Privately ptd, 1928. 1st ed. One of 180. 70 plts (incl frontisport). Teg. Red cl, gilt. (Feps offset; spine sunned), else NF. *Pacific**. $207/£129

WISEMAN, HERBERT. Singing Together. London: Faber & Faber, 1946. 1st ed. Obl 4to. Walter Trier (illus). Full color pict bds (corners sl mkd). Full color dj (dusty, few spots). *Reisler*. $185/£116

WISSLER, CLARK. Indian Cavalcade or Life on the Old Time Indian Reservations. NY: Sheridan House, 1938. 1st ed. VG+ in dj (tape-repaired). *Labordo*. $85/£53

WISTAR, CASPAR. A System of Anatomy for the Use of Students of Medicine. Phila: Thomas Dobson, 1811. 1st ed. 2 vols. Lg fldg table. VG set (text browned, spine labels restored) in contemp full calf. *Captain's Bookshelf*. $750/£469

WISTAR, ISAAC JONES. Autobiography 1827-1905. Phila: Wistar Inst, (1937). Lg paper ed. Fine in Fine dj. *Book Market*. $30/£19

WISTAR, ISAAC JONES. Autobiography of Isaac Jones Wistar 1827-1905. Phila: Wistar Inst, 1937. Frontisport, 6 plts, fldg map. Blue buckram, gilt. VG+ (lt rubbed). Howes W598. *House*. $35/£22

WISTER, OWEN. The Pentecost of Calamity. NY: Macmillan, 1915. Reddish bds, paper labels. (Ink inscrip, label; corners sl worn), else VG in dj (chipped, foxed). *Reese*. $30/£19

WISTER, OWEN. The Virginian. LEC, 1951. Ltd to 1500 numbered, signed by William Moyers (illus). Fine in slipcase. *Swann**. $57/£36

WISTER, OWEN. Watch Your Thirst. NY: Macmillan, 1923. 1st ed. One of 1000. Signed. VG in dj. *Labordo*. $95/£59

With a Highland Regiment in Mesopotamia, 1916-1917. (By H.J. Blampied.) Bombay, Times Press, 1918. (Hinges sl tender, extrems sl bumped.) *Clearwater*. $72/£45

With Rod and Whip. (The Medical Pub Co), (1903, but probably 1950s). Good in dj (defective). *King*. $22/£14

WITHERBY, H. F. (ed). A Practical Handbook of British Birds. Witherby, 1920-1924. 1st ed. 2 vols. Teg. Later full morocco, banded, extra gilt. VG set (few sl mks; sl sunned). *Ash*. $400/£250

WITHERBY, H. F. et al. The Hand-Book of British Birds. H.F. & G. Witherby, 1943-4. 2nd imp. 5 vols. 147 plts. Good set in blue cl. Djs (worn). *Cox*. $120/£75

WITHERS, ALEXANDER S. Chronicles of Border Warfare; or A History of the Settlement by the Whites, of North-Western Virginia.... Clarksburg, VA: Joseph Israel, 1831. 1st ed. 319,(2)pp. Period calf, leather spine label. (Foxed, stained), else VG-. *Pacific**. $230/£144

WITHERS, R. M. Liliums in Australia. Victoria: Aust Lilim Soc, 1967. 1st ed. Lg fold-out. VG (ex-libris). *Larry Price*. $75/£47

WITKIN, JOEL-PETER. Joel-Peter Witkin: Forty Photographs. SF: Museum of Modern Art, 1985. 1st ed. 25 full-pg plts. (Corner lt creased), else NF in illus stiff wrappers (lt soiled). *Cahan*. $50/£31

WITKIN, LEE D. and BARBARA LONDON. The Photograph Collector's Guide. Boston: NYGS, (1979). 1st ed. Maroon cl. Very Clean in dj (lt worn, price-clipped, chipped; scratch). *Baltimore**. $120/£75

WITKOP, PHILIPP (ed). German Students' War Letters. London: Methuen, (1929). 1st British ed. Red cl, gilt. Fine in VG dj (spine, edges faded). *Reese*. $65/£41

WITTEMANN, A. Fort Leavenworth, Kansas. NY, 1894. 38 photogravures. (Ink inscrip, last photo w/badly chipped margins; sl soiled, sl stained, cvrs worn.) *King*. $40/£25

WITTENMYER, ANNIE. Under the Guns: A Woman's Reminiscences of the Civil War. Boston: E.B. Stillings, 1895. 1st ed. Frontisport, (xiii),272pp (lt aging). Aeg. Dk grn cl, beveled bds, gilt. VG. *Baltimore**. $90/£56

WITTGENSTEIN, LUDWIG. Remarks on the Foundations of Mathematics. G. H. von Wright et al (eds). Oxford: Blackwell, 1956. 1st Eng ed. Nice (stamp) in dj. *Clearwater*. $120/£75

WITTKOWER, R. The Drawings of the Carracci. London/Oxford: Phaidon, 1952. Frontis, 84 plts. (Spine sl faded.) Internally VF. *Europa*. $112/£70

WODEHOUSE, P. G. and GUY BOLTON. Anything Goes, a Musical Comedy. S. French, 1936. 1st ed. Good+ (foxed, lt ink stain to 1 prelim pg) in wraps (soiled). *Any Amount*. $58/£36

WODEHOUSE, P. G. Aunts Aren't Gentlemen. London: Barrie & Jenkins, 1974. 1st ed. Blue cl, gilt. Fine in Fine pict dj (price-clipped). *Vandoros*. $135/£84

WODEHOUSE, P. G. Baa, Baa, Black Sheep. London, 1930. 1st ed. Ptd gray wrappers (discoloration; early sig on cvr and tp). *Swann**. $115/£72

WODEHOUSE, P. G. Bachelors Anonymous. NY: S&S, (1974). 1st Amer ed. Blue cl. Fine in dj (rear panel edge sl soiled). *Heritage*. $60/£38

WODEHOUSE, P. G. Bill the Conqueror. London, (1924). 1st ed. Yellow cl. (Edges lt foxed.) *Swann**. $80/£50

WODEHOUSE, P. G. The Cat-Nappers. NY: S&S, (1974). 1st Amer ed. Brn cl. (Pencil notes rep), o/w Fine in dj (lt browned). *Heritage*. $75/£47

WODEHOUSE, P. G. Cocktail Time. London: Herbert Jenkins, 1958. 1st Eng ed. NF (spine ends sl bumped) in dj (nicked, rubbed, sl torn, dusty, price-clipped). *Ulysses*. $152/£95

WODEHOUSE, P. G. Company for Henry. London: Herbert Jenkins, 1967. 1st Eng ed. Fine in dj. *Ulysses*. $104/£65

WODEHOUSE, P. G. Eggs, Beans and Crumpets. London, (1940). 1st ed. Orange cl. Dj (few short closed tears, lt edgewear). *Swann**. $230/£144

WODEHOUSE, P. G. Eggs, Beans and Crumpets. NY: Doubleday, Doran, 1940. 1st US ed. Grn pict cl. (Extrems sl dknd), o/w VG+ in pict dj (worn, edges nicked, frayed; rear panel soiled, loss at spine ends). *Any Amount*. $104/£65

WODEHOUSE, P. G. A Few Quick Ones. London: Herbert Jenkins, (1959). 1st Eng ed. Variant grn cl. Fine in dj (lt rubbed, price-clipped). *Glenn*. $85/£53

WODEHOUSE, P. G. A Few Quick Ones. London: Herbert Jenkins, 1959. 1st Eng ed. NF (spine foot sl bumped) in dj (nicked, rubbed, dusty, price-clipped, sl dknd). *Ulysses*. $152/£95

WODEHOUSE, P. G. Galahad at Blandings. London: Herbert Jenkins, 1965. 1st Eng ed. Fine in red cl, gilt, Fine pict dj. *Vandoros*. $175/£109

WODEHOUSE, P. G. The Girl in Blue. London: Barrie & Jenkins, 1970. 1st Eng ed. Fine in dj (price-clipped). *Ulysses*. $88/£55

WODEHOUSE, P. G. Golf Without Tears. NY: George H. Doran, (1924). 1st Amer ed. (Soiled, spine ends sl rubbed), else VG. *Pacific**. $63/£39

WODEHOUSE, P. G. He Rather Enjoyed It. NY: George H. Doran, (1925). 1st Amer ed. (Spine sl dknd), else NF. *Pacific**. $35/£22

WODEHOUSE, P. G. Heavy Weather. London: Herbert Jenkins, 1933. 1st Eng ed. Fine in blue cl (lacks dj). *Vandoros*. $350/£219

WODEHOUSE, P. G. Ice in the Bedroom. Jenkins, 1961. 1st Eng ed. Inscribed presentation. Crown 8vo. Red bds, 1st issue, w/backstrip gilt-lettered. Good (fr cvr stain) in dj (spine faded). *Blackwell's.* $616/£385

WODEHOUSE, P. G. Indiscretions of Archie. Leipzig: Bernhardt Tauchitz, 1929. 1st Tauchnitz ed. Orig wrappers (spine browned, few marginal tears). VG. *Glenn.* $125/£78

WODEHOUSE, P. G. The Intrusion of Jimmy. NY, (1910). 1st ed. Cl, color pict label. Good+ (ink name; sl rubbed, soiled, frayed, label sl chipped). *King.* $350/£219

WODEHOUSE, P. G. Jeeves and the Tie That Binds. NY: S&S, (1971). 1st Amer ed. Yellow cl. Fine in dj (lt soiled). *Heritage.* $75/£47

WODEHOUSE, P. G. Jeeves and the Tie That Binds. NY: S&S, 1971. 1st ed. VG+ (bkpl) in dj (sl worn). *My Bookhouse.* $52/£33

WODEHOUSE, P. G. Jeeves in the Offing. London: Herbert Jenkins, 1960. 1st Eng ed, 1st issue. Fine in fine pict dj w/paper coated w/clear plastic; flaps are uncoated. *Vandoros.* $225/£141

WODEHOUSE, P. G. Laughing Gas. London, (1936). 1st ed. Gray cl (spine lt discolored). *Swann*.* $57/£36

WODEHOUSE, P. G. Leave It to Psmith. London, 1924. 1st ed. Grn cl. (Foxing; spine sl faded.) *Swann*.* $69/£43

WODEHOUSE, P. G. The Little Nugget. NY: W.J. Watt, (1914). 1st Amer ed. 8vo. Frontis, 2 plts. Black cl, gilt. VG (2 ink names, lt foxed, browned; spine sl faded). *Heritage.* $600/£375

WODEHOUSE, P. G. Lord Emsworth. H. Jenkins, 1937. 1st ed. (Spine sl tanned), else Fine in VG 2nd issue dj (lt chipped). *Fine Books.* $675/£422

WODEHOUSE, P. G. The Luck of the Bodkins. Herbert Jenkins, (1935). 1st ed. Red cl. VG. *Ash.* $104/£65

WODEHOUSE, P. G. The Man with Two Left Feet. London: Barrie & Jenkins, 1971. NF (spine foot sl bumped) in dj (sl rubbed, price-clipped). *Ulysses.* $56/£35

WODEHOUSE, P. G. The Mating Season. Jenkins, (1949). 1st ed. (Sl mkd), else VG. *Whiteson.* $29/£18

WODEHOUSE, P. G. Mulliner Nights. M&S, 1933. 1st Canadian ed. NF in VG dj (lt worn, torn, chipped). *Fine Books.* $375/£234

WODEHOUSE, P. G. Nothing Serious. GC: Doubleday, 1951. 1st US ed. Fine in dj (lt used, sl worn, spine head tears). *Beasley.* $100/£63

WODEHOUSE, P. G. The Old Reliable. Jenkins, 1951. 1st ed. VG. *Whiteson.* $32/£20

WODEHOUSE, P. G. Pearls, Girls and Monty Bodkin. London: Barrie & Jenkins, 1972. 1st Eng ed. Fine in dj (sl nicked, price-clipped). *Ulysses.* $88/£55

WODEHOUSE, P. G. A Pelican at Blandings. London: Herbert Jenkins, 1969. 1st ed. Black cl, silver-lettered spine. Fine in dj. *Vandoros.* $200/£125

WODEHOUSE, P. G. The Plot That Thickened. NY: S&S, (1973). 1st Amer ed. Yellow eps. Brn cl, gilt. Fine in dj. *Heritage.* $75/£47

WODEHOUSE, P. G. Psmith in the City. London, 1910. 1st ed. Pict cl. (Ex-lib?, lacks part of fep, ink inscrip; cvrs heavily worn, spotted.) *King.* $450/£281

WODEHOUSE, P. G. Quick Service. London, (1940). 1st ed. Colonial issue. Blue-grn cl. Dj stating 'Herbert Jenkins Colonial Library' on spine (internal archival repair to head, sl creased). *Swann*.* $201/£126

WODEHOUSE, P. G. Quick Service. NY: Doubleday, Doran, 1940. 1st US ed. Top edge stained red, untrimmed. Tan cl. (Sl old stain fr cvr w/similar stain at edges of feps.) Color pict dj (sl chipped, lt stain fr flap fold). *Baltimore*.* $40/£25

WODEHOUSE, P. G. The Return of Jeeves. NY: S&S, 1954. 1st Amer ed. Nice (few sl mks) in dj (sl sunned, chipped, lacks sm piece). *Ash.* $120/£75

WODEHOUSE, P. G. Service with a Smile. London: Herbert Jenkins, 1962. 1st Eng ed. Fine in dj (price-clipped). *Ulysses.* $152/£95

WODEHOUSE, P. G. Service with a Smile. London: Herbert Jenkins, 1962. 1st Eng ed. Red buckram, gilt. Fine in NF color pict dj. *Vandoros.* $175/£109

WODEHOUSE, P. G. The Small Bachelor. London, (1927). 1st ed. Blue cl. (Scattered foxing; lt rubbed.) *Swann*.* $69/£43

WODEHOUSE, P. G. The Small Bachelor. NY, (1927). 1st Amer ed. Pict dj (spine edges lt rubbed). *Swann*.* $316/£198

WODEHOUSE, P. G. Something Fishy. London: Herbert Jenkins, 1957. 1st Eng ed. Fine in dj (price-clipped, sl rubbed). *Ulysses.* $152/£95

WODEHOUSE, P. G. Something Fishy. London: Herbert Jenkins, 1957. 1st ed. Fine in purplish-red cl, NF color pict dj. *Vandoros.* $195/£122

WODEHOUSE, P. G. Spring Fever. London: Herbert Jenkins, (1948). 1st Eng ed. Orange cl. Fine in Fine pict dj. *Vandoros.* $250/£156

WODEHOUSE, P. G. Spring Fever. GC: Doubleday, 1948. 1st ed. Reddish-brn cl. Fine in Fine pict dj (price-clipped). *Vandoros.* $275/£172

WODEHOUSE, P. G. Stiff Upper Lip, Jeeves. London: Herbert Jenkins, 1963. 1st Eng ed. NF (spine foot sl bumped) in dj (sl rubbed, sl creased). *Ulysses.* $152/£95

WODEHOUSE, P. G. Stiff Upper Lip, Jeeves. London: Herbert Jenkins, 1963. 1st Eng ed. Red buckram, gilt. Fine in Fine color pict dj. *Vandoros.* $225/£141

WODEHOUSE, P. G. Summer Lightning. Toronto: McClelland & Stewart, (1929). 1st Canadian ed. Red cl. VG (ink name, bkpl offsetting to fep; spine ends rubbed) in dj (tears, tape-repaired, spine faded). *Heritage.* $300/£188

WODEHOUSE, P. G. Summer Moonshine. London: Herbert Jenkins, (1938). 1st Eng ed. 8vo. Red cl. VG (eps lt browned, sm emb bkseller stamp; spine cocked) in dj (lt edgeworn). *Heritage.* $650/£406

WODEHOUSE, P. G. Sunset at Blandings. London: C&W, 1977. 1st Eng ed. Fine (spine head sl bumped) in dj. *Ulysses.* $72/£45

WODEHOUSE, P. G. Ukridge. London: Herbert Jenkins, 1924. 1st ed. Grn cl. NF (lacks dj). *Vandoros.* $275/£172

WODEHOUSE, P. G. Uncle Dynamite. Herbert Jenkins, (1948). 1st ed. (Spine faded.) *Hollett.* $56/£35

WODEHOUSE, P. G. Uncle Dynamite. London, (1948). 1st ed. Orange cl. Dj (spine extrems lt worn). *Swann*.* $138/£86

WODEHOUSE, P. J. Very Good, Jeeves. NY: Doubleday, 1930. 1st US ed. Orange cvr (sl soiled). VG. *Second Life.* $65/£41

WOHL, ANTHONY S. Endangered Lives. Public Health in Victorian Britain. London: J.M. Dent, (1983). 1st ed. Fine in dj. *Glaser.* $40/£25

WOJNAROWICZ, DAVID. Close to the Knives. NY, 1991. 1st ed. Pb orig. NF in wraps. *Warren.* $35/£22

WOJNAROWICZ, DAVID. Memories That Smell Like Gasoline. CA: Artspace, 1992. 1st ed. Fine w/o dj as issued. *Warren.* $30/£19

WOLBERG, LEWIS R. Micro-Art, Art Images in a Hidden World. NY: Abrams, n.d. Fine in illus dj (sl scratched). *Metropolitan*.* $28/£18

WOLF, EDWIN and JOHN F. FLEMING. Rosenbach. A Biography. Cleveland/NY: World, 1960. 1st trade ed. Inscribed by Fleming. Dj (spine lightened, extrems frayed). *Zubal*.* $50/£31

WOLF, EDWIN and JOHN F. FLEMING. Rosenbach: A Biography. Cleveland: World, (1960). 2nd ptg. Red cl. Fine in NF dj (sl rubbed). *Harrington*. $45/£28

WOLF, JOSEPH and DANIEL GIRAUD ELLIOT. The Life and Habits of Wild Animals. Alexander Macmillan, 1874. 1st ed. Folio. 20 wood-engr plts. Gilt edges. Contemp crimson full morocco, gilt. *Sotheby's**. $442/£276

WOLF, SIMON. The American Jew as Patriot, Soldier, and Citizen. Phila/NY/Chicago/Washington: Brentano's, 1895. 1st ed. Frontis, xii,(1 errata),(1),576,(10 ads). Good + . *Wantagh*. $125/£78

WOLFE, ALFRED. In Alaskan Waters. Caldwell, ID: Caxton, 1942. VG in dj. *American Booksellers*. $70/£44

WOLFE, GENE. The Castle of the Other. NY, 1982. 1st ed. One of 520 signed. Fine in Fine dj. *Warren*. $100/£63

WOLFE, GENE. The Claw of the Conciliator. NY: Timescape, (1981). 1st ed. Inscribed. Fine in Fine dj. *Other Worlds*. $75/£47

WOLFE, HUMBERT. Circular Saws. London: Chapman & Hall, 1923. 1st ed. Fine in black cl, blue paper spine label. Dj (skilfully backed). *Maggs*. $320/£200

WOLFE, LINNIE MARSH. Son of the Wilderness. The Life of John Muir. NY: Knopf, 1947. Blue cl. NF in dj. *House*. $20/£13

WOLFE, THOMAS. From Death to Morning. NY, 1935. 1st Amer ed. NF (spine sunned). *Polyanthos*. $45/£28

WOLFE, THOMAS. From Death to Morning. NY: Scribner, 1935. 1st ed, 1st ptg. Maroon cl, gilt. Fine in NF dj (lt used). *Macdonnell*. $150/£94

WOLFE, THOMAS. The Hills Beyond. NY, (1941). 1st ed. Black cl. VG (extrems sl rubbed, spine sl faded) in dj (lt soiled, extensive repairs). *Heritage*. $100/£63

WOLFE, THOMAS. Look Homeward, Angel. A Story of the Buried Life. NY: Scribner, 1929. 1st ed, 1st bk. Fine in blue cl. 1st issue dj (chipped w/some loss). *Bromer*. $750/£469

WOLFE, THOMAS. A Note on Experts: Dexter Vespasian Joyner. NY: House of Books, 1939. 1st ed. Ltd to 300. VF in brn cl, gilt. *Bromer*. $275/£172

WOLFE, THOMAS. A Note on Experts: Dexter Vespasian Joyner. NY: House of Books, 1939. One of 300. Brn cl, gilt. (Spine faded), o/w Fine. *Heritage*. $300/£188

WOLFE, THOMAS. Of Time and the River. NY: Scribner, 1935. 1st ed. Fine in dj (chipped). *Second Life*. $125/£78

WOLFE, THOMAS. Of Time and the River. NY: Scribner, 1935. 1st ed. Fine in NF dj. *Karmiole*. $350/£219

WOLFE, THOMAS. The Portable Thomas Wolfe. Maxwell Geismar (ed). NY: Viking, 1946. 1st ed. VF in VF dj. *Between The Covers*. $125/£78

WOLFE, THOMAS. The Story of a Novel. NY: Scribner, 1936. 1st ed. Fine in NF dj (spine sunned, head lt worn). *Beasley*. $85/£53

WOLFE, THOMAS. The Story of a Novel. NY: Scribner, 1936. 1st ed. Red cl. Dj (spine faded, extrems sl chipped, lt soiled, ink date stamp fr flap). *Heritage*. $100/£63

WOLFE, THOMAS. The Web and the Rock. NY: Harper, 1939. 1st ed. VG in dj (sl nicked). *Second Life*. $125/£78

WOLFE, THOMAS. The Web and the Rock. NY: Harper, 1939. 1st ed. Blue cl. (Spine extrems, 2 corners bumped), o/w NF in dj (chipped). *Heritage*. $150/£94

WOLFE, THOMAS. You Can't Go Home Again. NY: Scribner, (1940). 1st ed. VG (cl sl soiled) in dj (extrems chipped). *Second Life*. $125/£78

WOLFE, THOMAS. You Can't Go Home Again. NY: Harper, (1940). 1st ed. Fine in blue cl. Dj (sm chips, edges lt worn). *Bromer*. $150/£94

WOLFE, TOM. The Bonfire of the Vanities. NY, 1987. 1st ed. Signed. Fine in Fine dj. *Warren*. $60/£38

WOLFE, TOM. The Kandy-Colored Tangerine-Flake Streamline Baby. NY: Farrar Straus, (1965). 1st ed, 1st bk. Signed. Fine in Fine dj. *Lenz*. $200/£125

WOLFE, TOM. The Mid-Atlantic Man. London: Weidenfeld & Nicolson, 1969. VG (spine ends sl bumped) in dj (sl rubbed, nicked). *Ulysses*. $64/£40

WOLFE, TOM. The Painted Word. NY: FSG, 1975. 1st ed. Signed. VG + in dj. *Lame Duck*. $150/£94

WOLFE, TOM. The Pump House Gang. NY, 1968. 1st Amer ed. Fine (name, sl rubbed) in Fine dj. *Polyanthos*. $25/£16

WOLFE, TOM. The Purple Decades. NY: FSG, (1982). One of 450 numbered, signed. Fine in cardbd slipcase. *Antic Hay*. $100/£63

WOLFE, TOM. The Purple Decades: A Reader. NY: FSG, (1982). 1st ed. One of 450. Signed. NF in slipcase (sunned). *Pacific**. $46/£29

WOLFE, TOM. Radical Chic and Mau-Mauing the Flak Catchers. NY: FSG, (1970). 1st ed. Cream cl. (Spine ends sl rubbed), o/w Fine in dj (lt soiled). *Heritage*. $50/£31

WOLFE, TOM. Radical Chic and Mau-Mauing the Flak Catchers. NY: FSG, 1970. 1st ed. Signed. (2 fingerprints to 1st pp), else NF in dj (spine sl tanned). *Lame Duck*. $125/£78

WOLFE, TOM. Radical Chic and Mau-Mauing the Flak Catchers. London: Michael Joseph, 1971. 1st Eng ed. Fine (spine head sl bumped) in dj (sl rubbed). *Ulysses*. $72/£45

WOLFE, TOM. The Right Stuff. NY: Farrar Straus, (1979). 1st ed. Signed. Fine in Fine dj. *Lenz*. $100/£63

WOLFENSTINE, MANFRED R. The Manual of Brands and Marks. Norman: Univ of OK, 1970. 1st ed. VF in dj. *Labordo*. $50/£31

WOLFENSTINE, MANFRED R. The Manual of Brands and Marks. Norman, 1970. 1st ed. VG in dj. *Dumont*. $60/£38

WOLFENSTINE, MANFRED R. The Manual of Brands and Marks. Ramon F. Adams (ed). Norman: Univ of OK, (1970). 1st ed. 74 plts. Brick red cl. Nice reading copy (fore-edge fr bd very bumped; corners, spine ends sl bumped) in dj (lt chipped, spine faded). *Harrington*. $35/£22

WOLFERT, IRA. American Guerrilla in the Philippines. NY, 1945. 1st ed. VG + in dj (worn, sm piece torn from spine). *Pratt*. $20/£13

WOLFF, GEOFFREY. Black Sun. NY: Random House, 1976. 1st ed. Fine in Fine dj. *Pettler*. $20/£13

WOLFF, GEOFFREY. Providence. NY: Viking, 1986. 1st ed. Fine in Fine dj. *Pettler*. $15/£9

WOLFF, GEOFFRY. The Final Club. NY, 1990. 1st ed. NF in NF dj. *Warren*. $30/£19

WOLFF, MARITTA. The Big Nickelodeon. NY: Random House, (1956). 1st ed. (Fore-edge sl smudged), else VF in VF dj (rubbed). *Between The Covers*. $100/£63

WOLFF, TOBIAS. This Boy's Life: A Memoir. NY: Atlantic Monthly, (1989). 1st ed. Fine in Fine dj. *Between The Covers*. $85/£53

WOLFF, TOBIAS. Ugly Rumours. London: Allen & Unwin, 1975. 1st Eng ed, 1st bk. (Lib stamps; label removed fep, sm note ep; corners sl bumped), o/w VG in VG dj (sl chipped). *Virgo*. $136/£85

WOLFF, WERNER. Island of Death (Easter Island). NY: J.J. Augustin, 1948. 20 b/w plts. Black cl. (Eps offset), else VG in dj remnant. *Parmer*. $85/£53

WOLHUTER, HARRY. Memories of a Game Ranger. (Johannesburg, 1948.) (Spine faded.) *Swann**. $172/£108

WOLLASTON, NICHOLAS. The Man on the Ice Cap: The Life of August Courtauld. London: Constable, 1980. Fine in dj. *Explorer*. $19/£12

WOLLE, MURIEL. The Bonanza Trail. Bloomington, 1953. 1st ed. Signed. VG in dj (torn, chipped). *King*. $25/£16

WOLLE, MURIEL. Montana Pay Dirt. Denver, 1963. 1st ed. VG (sig) in dj (sig, sl worn, soiled). *Baade*. $125/£78

WOLLE, MURIEL. Stampede to Timberline. Boulder, CO: The Author, (1949). 1st ed. Inscribed. Errata slip. Gray-grn cl. Fine in Good dj (chipped, closed tears). *Harrington*. $45/£28

WOLLEY, CHARLES. A Two Years' Journal in New York and Part of Its Territories in America. Cleveland: Burrows Bros, 1902. Rpt of 1701 ed. One of 250. 2 plts. Paper-cvrd bds. VG (bkpl). Howes W620. *Brown*. $65/£41

WOLLHEIM, RICHARD. A Family Romance. London: Cape, 1969. 1st ed. Fine in Fine dj. *Beasley*. $35/£22

WOLLMAN, JOHN. A Journal of the Life...His Last Epistle. Phila: Friends Bookstore, 1845. Orig old calf (rubbed, foxing). *Metropolitan**. $28/£18

WOLLSTONECRAFT, MARY. Letters Written During a Short Residence.... London: J. Johnson, 1796. 1st ed. 8vo. (iv),262,ivpp + ad leaf. (Tp resized, emb stamp rolled out, 1840 inscrip; sl dknd), else VG in contemp mottled calf (neatly re-backed) w/leather label. *Second Life*. $1,250/£781

WOLLSTONECRAFT, MARY. Original Stories from Real Life. London: J. Johnson, 1791. 2nd ed. 175pp + 3pp bk list. Period-style full polished morocco, leather label, gilt. VG. *Hartfield*. $385/£241

WOLLSTONECRAFT, MARY. A Vindication of the Rights of Woman; with Strictures on Political and Moral Subjects. London: Johnson, 1792. 2nd ed. 4to. Mod calf. *Rostenberg & Stern*. $1,275/£797

WOLOSHUK, NICHOLAS. E. Irving Couse, 1866-1936. Santa Fe, 1976. Signed. *Swann**. $92/£58

WOLOSHUK, NICHOLAS. Edward Borein: Drawings and Paintings of the Old West. Volume 2 only. Santa Fe, 1974. One of 2000 numbered, signed. (Top edge sl bumped.) Dj (chipped, torn). *Swann**. $115/£72

WOLPERT, STANLEY. Nine Hours to Rama. NY: Random House, (1962). 1st ed. NF in dj. *Bernard*. $20/£13

WOLSELEY, VISCOUNTESS. Some Sussex Byways. Medici Soc, 1920. 1st ed. 8 tipped-in color plts, guards. Uncut. Coarse-weave cl (faded), gilt. *Hollett*. $104/£65

WOLTERS, RICHARD A. The Labrador Retriever. L.A.: Peterson Prints, (1981). Color frontis. NF. *Backman*. $20/£13

WOLVERTON, F. G. Five Months' Sport in Somali Land. London: Chapman & Hall, 1894. 1st ed. 1/2-title, (vi),108pp; fldg map. Recent 1/4 calf, red label. VG (blind/ink lib stamps). *Morrell*. $144/£90

WOMACK, J. J. The Civil War Diary of Capt. J. J. Womack. McMinnville, TN: Womack Pub, 1961. 1st ed. Port. VG (edges, spine lt sunned) in stiff blue-white ptd wraps. *Chapel Hill*. $65/£41

WOMACK, JACK. Ambient. NY, 1987. 1st ed. Signed. Fine in Fine dj. *Warren*. $50/£31

WOMACK, JACK. Terraplane. NY: Weidenfeld & Nicolson, 1988. 1st ed. Fine in dj. *Lame Duck*. $45/£28

Wonder Woman. A Pop-Up Book. NY: Random House, 1980. Ross Andru & Dick Giordano (illus). 4 dbl-pg pop-ups. Glazed pict bds. VG. *Bookfinders*. $40/£25

Wonderful Adventures of Paul Bunyan. LEC, 1945. Ltd to 1500 numbered, signed by Everett Gee Jackson (illus). Fine in slipcase. *Swann**. $57/£36

Wonders of the Circus: Men, Monkeys, and Dogs. NY: McLoughlin Bros, (1905). 1st ed. 10.75x9. Cl-backed pict chromolitho bds. Fine. *Pacific**. $138/£86

WONG, QUINCEY J. Chinese Hunter. NY, (1939). NF in yellow buckram. *Grayling*. $208/£130

WOOD, C. F. Yachting Cruise in the South Seas. Henry S. King, 1875. 1st ed. (iv),221pp (1st/last few ll lt browned). Emb cl (spine sl rubbed, frayed). *Edwards*. $136/£85

WOOD, CHARLES. Glories of Spain. Macmillan, 1901. 1st ed. Pict grn cl, gilt. (Sm rub-mk to spine), o/w NF. *Sotheran*. $205/£128

WOOD, CHARLES. In the Valley of the Rhone. London, 1900. 2nd ed. (Bkpl.) *Edwards*. $56/£35

WOOD, DEAN EARL. The Old Santa Fe Trail from the Missouri River. Kansas City: E.L. Mendenhall, (1955). Panoramic ed. (Bkpl, inscrip.) *Glenn*. $35/£22

WOOD, ED, JR. Watts...After. Aqoura, CA: PAD Library, 1967. 1st ed. VG + in illus wraps. *Lame Duck*. $150/£94

WOOD, EDWARD J. Curiosities of Clocks and Watches. London, 1866. 1st ed. Frontis, x,443pp (margins lt browned). Uncut. Emb cl (spine faded), gilt. *Edwards*. $88/£55

WOOD, ELIZABETH L. Pete French, Cattle King. Portland, OR: Binfords & Mort, 1951. 1st ed. VG + in dj (chipped). *Labordo*. $40/£25

WOOD, ERIC FISHER. The Note-Book of an Intelligence Officer. NY: Century, 1917. 1st ed. Port. Gilt grn cl. (Lt foxed), else VG. *Reese*. $50/£31

WOOD, FRANCES HARTSON and EVA PAINE KITCHEL. Warp and Woof: Or, New Frames for Old Pictures. Boonton, NJ: F.H. Wood, 1890. 1st ed. 431pp. Dec cl (spine ends lt rubbed). *Petrilla*. $50/£31

WOOD, GEORGE B. and FRANKLIN BACHE. The Dispensatory of the United States of America. Phila, 1847. 7th ed. 1368pp. Full leather. *Fye*. $125/£78

WOOD, GEORGE B. and FRANKLIN BACHE. The Dispensatory of the United States of America. Phila, 1854. 10th ed. 1480pp. (Ex-lib, foxed; rebound in lib binding), o/w Good. *Doctor's Library*. $90/£56

WOOD, GEORGE B. A Treatise on the Practice of Medicine. Phila, 1849. 2nd ed. 1 vol (of 2). 806pp. Full calf. (Ex-lib, shaken, fep removed, foxed w/sl water-staining; re-backed w/leather strip), o/w Good. *Doctor's Library*. $30/£19

WOOD, H. C. Therapeutics: It's Principles and Practice. Phila, 1891. 8th ed. 937pp. (Shaken; extrems sl worn). Internally Good. *Doctor's Library*. $60/£38

WOOD, HARRY B. Golfing Curios and 'The Like.' Manchester: Pride Pub, (1980). Rpt. Calf, gilt. (Emb stamp; corners sl bumped), else NF in dj. *Pacific**. $104/£65

WOOD, HARVEY. Personal Recollections of Harvey Wood. Pasadena, CA: (Castle Press), 1955. 2nd ed. One of 200. Signed by John B. Goodman III (illus). 2 fldg facs. Cl-backed gray-grn dec bds. NF in dk grn plain paper shipping wrapper (faded). *Harrington*. $100/£63

WOOD, HERBERT. The Shores of Lake Aral. London, 1876. 2 maps. (Sm tp corner torn; eps, tp faint foxed.) *Petersfield*. $152/£95

WOOD, J. G. Animate Creation; Popular Edition of 'Our Living World,' a Natural History. Joseph B. Holder (ed). NY: Selmar Hess, (1885). 1st ed thus. 3 vols. Aeg. Dec brn cl, gilt. (Tears to tissue guard of frontis vol 1), else NF set. *Pacific**. $288/£180

WOOD, J. G. The Illustrated Natural History. London, 1872. 1/2 calf, cl bds, gilt raised bands, marbled eps, edges. (Margins lt browned, bkpls; rubbed, sl surface loss.) *Edwards*. $160/£100

WOOD, J. MAXWELL. Smuggling in the Solway and Around the Galloway Sea-board. Dumfries: J. Maxwell & Son, 1908. Frontis, 12 plts, route-map. Pict cl, beveled bds (sl rubbed, faded, few mks to fr fore-edge). *Hollett*. $104/£65

WOOD, J. N. Travel and Sport in Turkestan. London, 1910. Route-map. Pict cl, (rear cvr sl scratched; eps foxed), gilt. *Petersfield*. $192/£120

WOOD, JOHN PHILIP. Memoirs of the Life of John Law of Lauriston. Edinburgh: Adam Black, 1824. 2nd ed. Engr frontis-port, (iv),234pp+ad leaf. Marbled eps; teg, untrimmed. Later grn morocco, marbled bds, gilt. (Sl browned, foxed, ex-lib, bkpl, blindstamp, ink stamp tp; spine head chipped, sl worn, scuffed.) Howes W634. *Baltimore**. $110/£69

WOOD, JOSEPHINE and LILLY DE JONGH OSBORNE. Indian Costumes of Guatemala. Graz, Austria: Akademische Druck-und Verlagsanstalt, 1966. 1st ed. 60 Fine tipped-in color plts, fldg map. Gray linen. Good in dj. *Karmiole*. $100/£63

WOOD, LAWSON. Lawson Wood's Merry Monkeys. London: Birn Bros, (ca 1940s). 4to. 84pp; 16 full-pg color plts. Cl-backed color pict bds. Good in color pict dj (mkd, margins lt worn). *Reisler*. $225/£141

WOOD, LAWSON. Nursery Rhyme Pets. (The Jumble Books). Dundee: Valentine & Sons, (ca 1920). 6.5x11.25. 3-tiered flap transformation. Stiff paper color illus bds (rubbed, corners worn). *Reisler*. $385/£241

WOOD, MARGARET. The English Mediaeval House. London, 1965. 1st ed. Buckram, gilt. Fine in dj, plastic cvr. *Whittle*. $32/£20

WOOD, MRS. HENRY. The Master of Greylands: A Novel. Richard Bentley, 1890. 25th thousand. (Spine bumped, chipped, sunned; ring mk fr cvr, shaken.) *Tiger*. $13/£8

WOOD, MRS. HENRY. Oswald Cray. A&C Black, 1864. 3 vols. (Several ll frayed at edge; rebacked w/orig backstrip relaid, re-cased; shelf-worn.) *Tiger*. $72/£45

WOOD, MRS. HENRY. Verner's Pride. Bradbury & Evans, 1863. 3 vols. Good (sl spotted, new eps; recased, rebacked w/orig backstrips relaid, corners rubbed, cvrs sl mkd). *Tiger*. $88/£55

WOOD, PETER. Unbelievable Years. Playa del Rey: Little Page, (1969). (Ink name), else VG in dj. *Perier*. $25/£16

WOOD, PETER. Unbelievable Years. Playa Del Rey: Little Page Press, (1969). Signed, inscribed. Fine in dj. *Perier*. $30/£19

WOOD, RICHARD G. Stephen Harriman Long 1784-1864. Glendale: A.H. Clark, 1966. 1st ed. Frontisport, fldg map. Blue cl. Fine. *House*. $35/£22

WOOD, RICHARD G. Stephen Harriman Long, 1784-1864. Glendale: A.H. Clark, 1966. 1st ed. Fldg map. Blue cl. Fine. *Harrington*. $50/£31

WOOD, STERLING A. et al. History of the 313 Infantry in World War II. Washington Infantry Jour., (1947). Nice (cvrs faded). *Rybski*. $85/£53

WOOD, SUMNER GILBERT. The Taverns and Turnpikes of Blandford, 1733-1833. N.p.: The Author, 1908. Fldg map. VG. *Zubal**. $15/£9

WOOD, T. MARTIN. George du Maurier. NY: McBride, Nast, 1913. Teg, uncut. (Prelims spotted; spine head sl frayed.) *Hollett*. $40/£25

WOOD, TED. Corkscrew. London: Collins, 1987. 1st ed. VG+ (corners sl bumped) in dj (sl edgeworn). *My Bookhouse*. $20/£13

WOOD, WILLIAM MAXWELL. A Shoulder to the Wheel of Progress: Being Essays, Lectures and Miscellanies upon Themes of the Day. Buffalo: Derby, Orton & Mulligan, 1853. 1st ed. Inscribed. (Spine ends, corners sl rubbed, fore-edge lt foxed.) *Sadlon*. $75/£47

WOOD, WILLIAM NATHANIEL. Reminiscences of Big I. Bell I. Wiley (ed). McCowat-Mercer, 1956. VG in VG dj. *Book Broker*. $45/£28

WOODARD, DAVID. The Narrative of Capt. David Woodard and Four Seamen.... London: J. Johnson, 1805. 2nd ed. xxxii,234pp; port (port, tp washed), 2 fldg maps (1 repaired), 2 plts. New tan cl, red morocco label. *Adelson*. $325/£203

WOODARD, DAVID. The Narrative of Captain Woodard and Four Seamen.... J. Johnson, 1804. 1st ed. Engr frontis, xl,248pp; 2 fldg maps, 2 engr plts. Orig maroon cl, gilt. (Ink lib stamp; sl faded, worn), o/w Good. *Sotheran*. $448/£280

WOODCOCK, GEORGE. Imagine the South. Pasadena: Untide Press, (1947). One of 1000. Dec wrappers. *Dawson*. $40/£25

WOODCOCK, H. D. and J. COUTTS. Lilies: Their Culture and Management. London, 1935. 1st ed. Color frontis. Gray cl, gilt. VG. *Larry Price*. $49/£31

WOODESON, JOHN. Mark Gertler: Biography of a Painter, 1891-1939. London: Sidgwick & Jackson, 1972. 1st Eng ed. VG (spine ends, corners bumped) in dj (nicked, sl torn, creased, price-clipped). *Ulysses*. $120/£75

WOODFORDE, CHRISTOPHER. English Stained and Painted Glass. Oxford, 1954. Color frontis, 80 plts. Good in dj (worn). *Washton*. $85/£53

WOODFORDE, JOHN. The Strange Story of False Teeth. Universe Books, (1970). (Sl underlined.) *Rybski*. $20/£13

WOODFORDE, JOHN. The Strange Story of False Teeth. London: Routledge & Kegan Paul w/Reckitt & Sons, 1968. VG. *Hollett*. $48/£30

WOODGATE, M. V. The Abbe Edgeworth (1745-1807). Longmans, Green, 1946. Frontis. Good (sig; spine bumped) in dj (chipped). *Tiger*. $19/£12

WOODHAM-SMITH, CECIL. The Great Hunger, Ireland 1845-49. London, 1962. 1st ed. VG in dj (sl frayed). *Typographeum*. $28/£18

WOODHEAD, CONSTANCE (retold by). The Little Red Hen. F. Warne 'Sunbeam Stories,' (1950). 1st ed thus. 12mo. 62pp; 4 color plts by Grace Lodge. Pict bds. VG (sl rubbed). *Bookmark*. $27/£17

WOODHEAD, CONSTANCE (retold by). Rumpelstiltskin. F. Warne 'Sunbeam Stories,' (1950). 1st ed thus. 12mo. 62pp; 4 color plts by Grace Lodge. Pict bds. VG (sl rubbed). *Bookmark*. $27/£17

WOODHOUSE, CHARLES PLATTEN. The World's Master Potters. Newton Abbot: David & Charles, (1974). 83 plts. NF in dj. *Turtle Island*. $45/£28

WOODHOUSE, S. C. Crude Ditties. Ptd at the Motley Press for Swan Sonnenschein, 1903. 1st ed. 32mo. 103pp; 24 color plts by Augusine J. MacGregor. Pict cl. VG (dustmks). *Bookmark*. $128/£80

Woodman's Hut (Harlequinade). London: G. Martin, (ca 1810). 3x7.5. 4pp, each w/dbl flap overlay. Good. *Reisler*. $3,000/£1,875

WOODRELL, DANIEL. Under the Bright Lights. NY: Holt, 1986. 1st ed. Fine in Fine dj (2 spine nicks). *Unger*. $75/£47

WOODROW, G. The Biographical Gallery, Comprising 240 Portraits. London, 1836. Pub's cl. (Ex-lib, label fr pastedown.) *Swann**. $103/£64

WOODRUFF, ELIZABETH. Stories from a Magic World. Springfield, (MA): McLoughlin Bros, (1938). Lg 4to. 6 full-pg color plts by Gustaf Tenggren. Red cl, black lettering, full color paste label. (Cl worn, lt mkd.) *Reisler*. $250/£156

WOODRUFF, HIRAM. The Trotting Horse of America. NY, 1868. 1st ed. 412pp; port. (Name label, inner hinges cracked; spine top frayed, cvrs dknd.) *King*. $50/£31

WOODRUFF, WILLIAM EDWARD. With the Light Guns in '61-65. Little Rock, AR: Central Ptg, 1903. 1st ed. Dec red cl. Nice (cvrs lt spotted). Howes W650. *Chapel Hill*. $500/£313

WOODS, DANIEL B. Sixteen Months at the Gold Diggings. NY: Harper, 1851. 1st ed. Blindstamped brn cl, gilt. Fine. Howes W651. *Labordo*. $675/£422

WOODS, DAVID. The Fireside Book of Horse Racing. NY: S&S, 1963. 1st ed. VG in Fair dj. *October Farm*. $30/£19

WOODS, EDGAR. Albemarle County in Virginia. (Michie, c1901). Good (foxed; cvrs spotted, soiled). *Book Broker.* $85/£53

WOODS, JAMES CHAPMAN. Old and Rare Books, an Elementary Lecture. London: Elliot Stock, 1885. 1st ed. Paper cvrd limp bds. Ptd paper jacket (part chipped off, spotted.) *Oak Knoll.* $40/£25

WOODS, JOHN. Two Years' Residence on the English Prairie of Illinois. Chicago: R.R. Donnelley, 1968. Frontis, map. VG. *Lien.* $25/£16

WOODS, JOSEPH. The Tourist's Flora. London, 1850. Frontis, lxxxii,503pp (margins lt browned). 1/2 morocco, cl bds. *Edwards.* $64/£40

WOODS, ROBERT ARCHEY. English Social Movements. NY: Scribner, 1891. 1st ed. Inscribed. Fine (spine sl mkd). *Beasley.* $85/£53

WOODS, SARA. A Thief or Two. NY: St. Martin's, (1977). 1st Amer ed. NF in dj. *Antic Hay.* $17/£11

WOODS, STUART. Run Before the Wind. Norton, 1983. 1st ed. (Cvrs lt worn), else NF in dj. *Murder.* $55/£34

WOODSON, CARTER. Negro Makers of History. Washington: Associated Pub, 1928. 1st ed. VG (worn). *Beasley.* $75/£47

Woodstock Vermont: A Few Notes, Historical and Other, Concerning the Town and Village. Woodstock: Elm Tree, 1910. Ptd wrappers (sm tear, top fore-edge lower cvr creased). *Sadlon.* $15/£9

Woodstock; or, The Cavalier.... (By Walter Scott.) Edinburgh, 1826. 1st ed. 3 vols. 1/2 title each vol. Orig bds (vol 1 joints cracked, spines chipped), ptd paper spine labels. *Kane*.* $120/£75

WOODVILLE, WILLIAM. Medical Botany, Containing Systematic and General Descriptions, with Plates, of All the Medicinal Plants, Indigenous and Exotic.... London: James Phillips, 1790-94. 4 vols (3 + suppl). 274 hand-colored copper plts. Period 3/4 morocco, marbled bds, gilt. (Marginal tears few plts; cvrs detached w/crude leather reinforcements), else VG. *Pacific*.* $1,955/£1,222

WOODWARD, A. B. The Presidency of the United States. NY: Derick Van Veghten, 1825. (2nd ed.) 88pp. (Stained, browned, lacks wraps.) Howes W658. *M & S.* $150/£94

WOODWARD, ARTHUR. A Brief History of Navajo Silversmithing. Flagstaff: Northern AZ Soc of Science & Art Museum, 1946. 2nd ed. VG in VG dj. *Book Market.* $35/£22

WOODWARD, DAVID. Five Centuries of Map Printing. Chicago: Univ of Chicago, (1975). 1st ed. Color frontis. Fine in dj (price-clipped). *Pacific*.* $75/£47

WOODWARD, H. The History of the Geological Society of London. London: Longmans, Green, 1908. (Outside edges of pp ends w/lib stamp), else VG. *Blake.* $150/£94

WOODWARD, H. Stanford's Geological Atlas of Great Britain and Ireland and Photographic Supplement. London: Stanford, 1913. 4th ed. 2 vols. VG. *Savona.* $45/£28

WOODWARD, JOHN and GEORGE BURNETT. A Treatise on Heraldry, British and Foreign. London: W. & A.K. Johnson, 1892. 1st ed. 2 vols. 57 plts (47 color). Teg. 3/4 brn morocco, raised bands. Fine. *Appelfeld.* $150/£94

WOODWARD, JOHN. An Essay Towards a Natural History of the Earth, and Terrestrial Bodyes, Especially Minerals. London, 1723. 3rd ed. 8vo. (xii),304,1 pub's ad. Contemp calf. (Rebacked; prelims top edge sl dampstained.) *Henly.* $576/£360

WOODWARD, JOSEPH. Report on Epidemic Cholera and Yellow Fever in the Army of the United States During the Year 1867. Washington, 1868. 1st ed. 156pp. Wrappers. *Fye.* $125/£78

WOODWARD, W. E. Meet General Grant. NY, 1928. Rpt. Pict cl. VG + . *Pratt.* $20/£13

WOODY, CLARA T. and MILTON SCHWARTZ. Globe, Arizona. Tucson, 1977. (Inscrip, tape offset on 1/2-title), o/w NF in pict wraps. *Baade.* $75/£47

WOOLEN, WILLIAM WATSON. The Inside Passage to Alaska, 1792-1920. Cleveland: A.H. Clark, 1924. 1st ed. One of 1000 sets. 2 vols. (Ex-lib, mks.) *Perier.* $150/£94

WOOLF, LEONARD. An Autobiography. London: Hogarth, 1964/1969. Vols 3, 5 1st eds; vols 1, 2, 4 rpts. 5 vols. VG in djs (sl soiled, nicked). *Virgo.* $120/£75

WOOLF, LEONARD. Diaries in Ceylon 1908-1911. London: Hogarth, 1963. 1st ed thus. (Spine sl bumped), o/w VG in dj (sl soiled, nicked). *Virgo.* $56/£35

WOOLF, LEONARD. The Hotel. Hogarth, 1939. One of 1000 ptd. Fine (name; spine sl faded) in Fine dj. *Martin.* $45/£28

WOOLF, LEONARD. The International Post-War Settlement. (London): Fabian Publications Ltd & Gollancz, (1944). 1st ed. VG in ptd blue wraps. *Antic Hay.* $25/£16

WOOLF, LEONARD. Quack, Quack. London: Hogarth, 1935. 1st ed. (Cvrs sl soiled, spine sl faded, sl shelf worn), o/w VG (lacks dj). *Virgo.* $32/£20

WOOLF, LEONARD. Stories of the East. London: Hogarth, 1921. 1st ed. One of 300 ptd. Good (pp edges dusty, metal stapling rusty; cvrs soiled, yapped edges creased) in buff paper wrappers. *Virgo.* $560/£350

WOOLF, VIRGINIA and L. S. Two Stories. Richmond: Hogarth, 1917. 1st ed, 1st publication of the Hogarth Press. Ltd to 150. 8vo. Dora Carrington (woodcuts). (Sl soiled.) Red/white Japanese paper wrappers, one of several types of colored paper used (edges sl frayed, outer edges sl smudged). Collector's fldg box (sl dampstained). *Sotheby's*.* $6,992/£4,370

WOOLF, VIRGINIA. Beau Brummell. NY, 1930. One of 550 numbered, signed. Sm folio. 1/4 cl. Slipcase (extrems worn). *Swann*.* $431/£269

WOOLF, VIRGINIA. Beau Brummell. NY: Rimington & Hooper, 1930. 1st separate ed. One of 550 signed. Lg 4to. 2 full-pg illus. Teg, rest untrimmed. Pale gray bds, pink linen, gilt backstrip (faded), variant pale pink ptd paper label w/dk pink ptd design at center of fr cvr. VG (spine faded) in grn bd slipcase (sl soiled, chipped) w/orig ptd paper label (chipped). *Blackwell's.* $640/£400

WOOLF, VIRGINIA. Between the Acts. London: Hogarth, 1941. 1st ed. VF in blue cl. Dj (sm closed tear). *Bromer.* $475/£297

WOOLF, VIRGINIA. The Captain's Death Bed and Other Essays. London: Hogarth, 1950. 1st Eng ed. Purple cl, gilt. VG (eps, cvrs browned) in dj (price-clipped, lt browned, soiled). *Heritage.* $100/£63

WOOLF, VIRGINIA. The Common Reader. Second Series. London: Hogarth, 1932. 1st ed. Grn cl (sl soiled, sl nick, stain). *Cummins.* $135/£84

WOOLF, VIRGINIA. The Diary of Virginia Woolf. Anne Olivier Bell (ed). Volumes 1-5 (Complete). London: Hogarth, 1977-1984. 1st ed. NF in djs. *Smith.* $350/£219

WOOLF, VIRGINIA. Granite and Rainbow. NY: Harcourt, Brace, 1958. 1st Amer ed. Fine in dj. *Hermitage.* $60/£38

WOOLF, VIRGINIA. Jacob's Room. NY: Harcourt, Brace, (1923). 1st US ed. One of 1500 ptd. Orange cl, paper spine label. Good (bkpl, label sl rubbed, lt pencil notes). *Reese.* $85/£53

WOOLF, VIRGINIA. A Letter to a Young Poet. London: Hogarth, 1932. 1st ed, issued as Hogarth Letters No. 8. VG in pict wrappers (spine sl tanned). *Reese.* $100/£63

WOOLF, VIRGINIA. The Mark on the Wall. Richmond: Hogarth, 1919. 1st separate ed. Ltd to 1000. Fine (lt foxed) in wrappers. *Bromer.* $950/£594

WOOLF, VIRGINIA. The Moment and Other Essays. Hogarth, 1947. 1st UK ed. Near Mint in NF (spine, fr wrappers faded) dj. *Martin.* $38/£24

WOOLF, VIRGINIA. Monday or Tuesday. Richmond: Hogarth, 1921. 1st ed. One of 1000. 8vo. Vanessa Bell (illus). Bds w/woodcut design, cl spine. *Sotheby's**. $1,011/£632

WOOLF, VIRGINIA. Mrs. Dalloway. Hogarth, 1925. 1st ed. Mid brn cl, gilt. Good (margins sl browned; spine lt faded). *Blackwell's*. $480/£300

WOOLF, VIRGINIA. Night and Day. NY: George H. Doran, (1920). 1st Amer ed. Grn cl. (Spine ends sl rubbed), else NF. *Pacific**. $109/£68

WOOLF, VIRGINIA. Night and Day. NY: George H. Doran, (1920). 1st Amer ed. (Edges sl rubbed; lacks dj), else Fine. *Hermitage*. $275/£172

WOOLF, VIRGINIA. Night and Day. Duckworth, 1919. 1st ed, w/misprints uncorrected on pp199, 236, 269, 400, and 483. 8vo. (Bkpl.) *Sotheby's**. $589/£368

WOOLF, VIRGINIA. On Being Ill. (Richmond): Hogarth, 1930. 1st separate ed. One of 250 numbered, signed in purple ink. 8vo. Marbled eps. Vellum spine. Dj (sl defective). *Sotheby's**. $1,141/£713

WOOLF, VIRGINIA. Orlando. Leipzig: Bernhard Tauchnitz, 1929. 1st Tauchnitz ed. Orig wrappers (spine browned, few marginal tears). VG. *Glenn*. $85/£53

WOOLF, VIRGINIA. Orlando: A Biography. Hogarth, 1928. Good (fore-edge spotted; spine bumped, sunned w/repaired nick, cvrs unevenly sunned) in glassine dj (creased) in purpose-made bk box (initials). *Tiger*. $128/£80

WOOLF, VIRGINIA. Orlando: A Biography. NY: Crosby Gaige, 1928. 1st ed. One of 800 (of 861) numbered, signed. 8vo. Partly unopened. Black cl, gilt. Fine in glassine dj. *Sotheby's**. $810/£506

WOOLF, VIRGINIA. Reviewing. London: Hogarth, 1939. VG in orig wraps. *Edrich*. $32/£20

WOOLF, VIRGINIA. A Room of One's Own. NY/London, 1929. 1st ed, Amer issue. One of 492 numbered, signed. Tall 8vo. Uncut. (Sm Random House bk label.) *Swann**. $920/£575

WOOLF, VIRGINIA. A Room of One's Own. NY/London: Fountain/Hogarth, 1929. 1st ed. One of 492 numbered, signed. Lg 8vo. (4 sm tape offset mks feps; spine, edges sl sunned, ends sl dull), else VG. *Reese*. $950/£594

WOOLF, VIRGINIA. A Room of One's Own. NY/London: Fountain/Hogarth, 1929. 1st ed. One of 492 numbered, signed in purple ink. 8vo. Partly unopened. Fine in glassine dj. *Sotheby's**. $1,563/£977

WOOLF, VIRGINIA. Street Haunting. SF: Westgate, 1930. Ltd to 500 signed. Gray paper bds, blue leather spine (rubbed, sl dknd). NF in pub's gray slipcase (bottom edge cracked). *Hermitage*. $1,000/£625

WOOLF, VIRGINIA. Three Guineas. London: Hogarth, 1938. 1st ed. 5 half-tone plts. Yellow cl. (Sl soiled, spine sl dull), o/w VG in dj. *Cummins*. $150/£94

WOOLF, VIRGINIA. To the Lighthouse. NY: Harcourt, Brace, 1927. 1st US ed. One of 4000 ptd. (Pp lt foxed, top edge dknd), else NF in NF dj (lt soiled). *Lame Duck*. $950/£594

WOOLF, VIRGINIA. The Voyage Out. NY: Doran, (1920). 1st US ed, 1st bk. Grn cl (corners sl worn; text sl aged). *Baltimore**. $70/£44

WOOLF, VIRGINIA. The Voyage Out. Duckworth, 1915. 1st ed, 1st bk. 8vo. Duff Cooper copy, Rex Whistler bkpl. *Sotheby's**. $810/£506

WOOLF, VIRGINIA. The Voyage Out. London: Duckworth, 1915. 1st ed. (Edge lt rubbed), o/w Clean. *Hermitage*. $1,500/£938

WOOLF, VIRGINIA. Walter Sickert: A Conversation. Hogarth, 1934. 1st ed. VG in pale blue wrappers (sl soiled). *Virgo*. $72/£45

WOOLF, VIRGINIA. The Waves. London: Hogarth, 1931. 1st ed. Purple bds. (Foxed, lacks dj.) *Warren*. $85/£53

WOOLF, VIRGINIA. The Waves. London, 1931. 1st ed. Dj (spine extrems chipped). *Swann**. $172/£108

WOOLF, VIRGINIA. The Waves. London: Hogarth, 1931. 1st ed. (1st, last pp, edges sl spotted; spine ends, corners sl rubbed), o/w VG in dj (browned, sl soiled, internally sl stained, corners nicked, chipped, 1 1/2-inch closed tear top edge spine). *Virgo*. $560/£350

WOOLF, VIRGINIA. A Writer's Diary. London: Hogarth, 1953. 1st ed. Fine in dj (lt worn). *Cummins*. $125/£78

WOOLF, VIRGINIA. A Writer's Diary. NY: Harcourt Brace, 1954. 1st US ed. VG (shelfworn) in dj (price-clipped, sl worn). *My Bookhouse*. $52/£33

WOOLF, VIRGINIA. A Writer's Diary. Leonard Woolf (ed). NY: Harcourt Brace, (1954). 1st ed. NF (pg edges sl dknd) in dj (sm tear). *Lenz*. $85/£53

WOOLF, VIRGINIA. The Years. Hogarth, 1937. 1st ed. Good (feps foxed, blindstamped address; cvrs sl rubbed, spine sl scratched; lacks dj). *Virgo*. $56/£35

WOOLF, VIRGINIA. The Years. London: Hogarth, 1937. 1st ed. (Eps sl foxed), else Fine in Vanessa Bell illus dj (sl foxed, 1 sm nick to lower edge). *Cahan*. $300/£188

WOOLF, VIRGINIA. The Years. Hogarth, 1937. 1st ed. (Pg edges sl browned, eps sl spotted, offsetting; cvrs sl soiled, rubbed, spine sl faded), o/w VG in dj (browned, spotted, corners, spine ends chipped, top edge frayed). *Virgo*. $320/£200

WOOLF, VIRGINIA. The Years. London: Hogarth, 1937. 1st ed. Pale jade-grn cl. Fine in dj (closed tears, 2 sm chips, spine sl dknd). *Bromer*. $425/£266

WOOLF, VIRGINIA. The Years. London: Hogarth, 1937. 1st ed. 8vo. Jade grn cl, gilt. Fine (bkpl) in Fine pict dj. *Vandoros*. $650/£406

WOOLLCOTT, ALEXANDER. The Command Is Forward. NY: Century, 1919. 1st ed. Frontis. Straw cl. (Spine sl dknd, ends lt worn), o/w VG. *Reese*. $50/£31

WOOLLEY, C. LEONARD. Dead Towns and Living Men. NY: OUP, 1929. 1st ed. Frontis. (Sig.) *Archaeologia*. $45/£28

WOOLLEY, C. LEONARD. The Development of Sumerian Art. Faber & Faber, 1935. 1st ed. 72 plts. Teg, rest uncut. (Ex-lib, stamp, spine #s; sl soiled, worn.) *Edwards*. $61/£38

WOOLLEY, C. LEONARD. A Forgotten Kingdom. Balt: Penguin, (1953). 24 plts. Dj. *Archaeologia*. $35/£22

WOOLLEY, C. LEONARD. Ur of the Chaldees. London: Ernest Benn, (1950). 16 plts, map. Dj (tattered). *Archaeologia*. $35/£22

WOOLLEY, H. The Piggy Wiggies. London: Raphael Tuck & Sons, (1948). 8vo. 18pp. Color pict stiff bds (lt edgeworn). *Reisler*. $285/£178

WOOLLEY, L. H. California, 1849-1913. Oakland: DeWitt & Snelling, 1913. 1st ed. Frontisport. Gray wrappers. (Losses to wrapper spine ends, sl rubbed, chipped), o/w VG + . *Harrington*. $65/£41

WOOLLEY, RALF R. The Green River and Its Utilization. Washington: USGS, 1930. 35 plts, incl lg map in pocket. Orange wraps. (Spine rebuilt), o/w VG + . *Five Quail*. $60/£38

WOOLLEY, REGINALD MAXWELL. Catalogue of the Manuscripts of Lincoln Cathedral Chapter Library. OUP, 1927. 1st ed. Dj. *Forest*. $40/£25

WOOLMAN, JOHN. A Journal of the Life, Gospel Labors, and Christian Experiences of That Faithful Minister of Jesus Christ.... Phila: T.E. Chapman, 1837. 396pp. Full leather (spine gone, fr cvr detached, rear hinge broken; tp sewn on, rep tear). *Book Broker*. $150/£94

WOOLMAN, JOHN. A Journal of the Life, Gospel Labours, and Christian Experiences.... Phila: T.E. Chapman, 1837. (1st, last ll sl foxed.) Recent 1/2 calf over cl. *Sadlon*. $40/£25

WOOLRICH, CORNELL. Night Webs. NY, 1971. 1st ed. NF (top edge lt spotted) in NF dj. *Warren*. $45/£28

WOOLRICH, CORNELL. Rendezvous in Black. NY, 1948. 1st ed. VG + (name, date) in VG dj (chipped, rubbed). *Warren*. $35/£22

WOOLSEY, GAMEL. Collected Poems. Warren House, 1984. 1st ltd ed. One of 500. Fine in dj. *Virgo*. $24/£15

WOOLSEY, GAMEL. The Letters of Gamel Woolsey to Llewelyn Powys, 1930-1939. Kenneth Hopkins (ed). Warren House, 1983. 1st ed. Fine in dj. *Virgo*. $24/£15

WOOTON, E. O. Cacti in New Mexico. (Las Cruces), 1911. Orig ed. 18 full-pg b/w photos. Self wraps, staplebound. *Brooks*. $35/£22

WOOTON, E. O. Certain Desert Plants as Emergency Stock Feed. Washington: GPO, 1918. 8 plts. VG in wraps. *Perier*. $20/£13

WOOTON, E. O. Trees and Shrubs of New Mexico. Las Cruces, NM, 1913. (Few pp chipped at edges w/no loss of text; rebound in hb.) *Dumont*. $40/£25

WORCESTER, G. R. G. The Junks and Sampans of the Yangtze. Annapolis: Naval Inst, (1979). 2nd ed. VG in dj (spine ends sl chipped). *Pacific**. $40/£25

WORCESTER, G. R. G. The Junks and Sampans of the Yangtze. Shanghai: Inspectorate General of Customs, 1947-48. 1st ed. 2 vols. 2 frontispieces. Grn cl, gilt. Good. *Karmiole*. $450/£281

WORCESTER, G. R. G. The Junks and Sampans of the Yangtze. Annapolis: Naval Inst., 1971. Folio. Tan cl. VG. *American Booksellers*. $55/£34

WORDSWORTH, CHRISTOPHER. Athens and Attica: Journal of a Residence There. London: John Murray, 1836. 1st ed. 1/2-title, (xii),285pp; 2 fldg maps, 3 litho plts, fldg table. Mod Cockerill marbled bds, early black leather spine label. (Maps frayed, torn, repaired w/o loss; bkpl, edges sl browned.) *Morrell*. $88/£55

WORDSWORTH, CHRISTOPHER. Greece, Pictorial, Descriptive and Historical. William S. Orr, 1839. 1st ed. xxvii,356pp; 28 steel-engr plts. Contemp full calf (neatly rebacked), red label, gilt. VG (upper margin corner sl dampstained throughout, not affecting plts; sl rubbed, scuffed). *Sotheran*. $416/£260

WORDSWORTH, JOHN. The Letters of John Wordsworth. Cornell Univ, 1969. Good in dj (chipped, price clipped w/closed tears). *Tiger*. $26/£16

WORDSWORTH, WILLIAM. Our English Lakes, Mountains and Waterfalls. London: Bennett, 1864. True 1st ed. Aeg. Orig dec bds, later cl on spine, later eps. VG. *Martin*. $264/£165

WORDSWORTH, WILLIAM. The Poems of William Wordsworth. LEC, 1973. One of 2000 signed by John O'Connor (illus). Fine in slipcase. *Swann**. $46/£29

WORDSWORTH, WILLIAM. Poems...Including Lyrical Ballads, and the Miscellaneous Pieces of the Author. Longman, Hurst, Rees, Orme & Brown, 1815. 1st ed. 2 vols. Half-titles not called for, engr frontispieces by Bromley and Reynolds. (Lt foxed.) Aeg. 1/2 red morocco, gilt, by Bayntun's. Slipcase. *Sotheby's**. $442/£276

WORDSWORTH, WILLIAM. The Poetical Works. London: Edward Moxon, 1840,1842,1851. New ed. 8 vols. Sm 8vo. Frontisport vol 1. Aeg. Full grn hard-grain morocco, gilt. VF set (bkpls). *Maggs*. $2,240/£1,400

WORDSWORTH, WILLIAM. Yarrow Revisited, and Other Poems. London: Longman et al/Edward Moxon, 1835. 1st ed. 12mo. 12,(ii),xvi,350,(4)pp. W/half-title, final 2 ad ll, 12pg Longman's cat dated July, 1835. (Lacks tipped-in errata slip, bkpl; extrems rubbed), else Fine in orig brn bds, paper spine label intact. Morocco-backed slipcase, chemise. *Bromer*. $850/£531

Workhouse Boy; Containing His Letters, with a Short Account of Him. London: RTS, (n.d.). Only ed. Frontis, 72pp. Good in orig ptd wrappers (soiled). *Young*. $56/£35

WORKMAN, BENJAMIN. The American Accountant. Phila: William Young, 1796. 3rd ed. 220,(4)pp. Contemp calf (worn; spine head chipped; fr hinge cracked). *Karmiole*. $200/£125

Works of Quintus Horatius Flaccus Illustrated Chiefly from the Remains of Ancient Art. With a Life by the Rev. Henry Hart Milman. London: John Murray, 1849. Owen Jones (illus). (6),490,xivpp. Marbled eps; teg. Mod 3/4 gilt-ruled morocco, marbled bds, gilt, raised bands. Bkpl of William Savidge. Fine. *Pacific**. $403/£252

World's Columbian Exposition Reproduced. Chicago: Rand McNally, 1894. 1st ed. Blue cl, gilt. NF. *Pacific**. $63/£39

WORMALD, FRANCIS and C. E. WRIGHT (eds). The English Library Before 1700. Athlone/Univ of London, 1958. 1st ed. Frontis, 22 plts. Dj. *Forest*. $61/£38

WORMALD, FRANCIS. Collected Writings. I. Studies in Medieval Art from the Sixth to the Twelfth Centuries. London/NY, 1984. Good. *Washton*. $55/£34

WORMALD, FRANCIS. The Winchester Psalter. London: Harvey Miller & Medcalf, 1973. Sm folio. Tipped-in color frontis, 3 tipped-in color illus. Blue cl. Dj (sl creased). *Maggs*. $48/£30

WORRALL, JOHN. Bibliotheca Legum or a Catalogue of the Common and Statute Law Books of This Realm.... London, 1782. (xvi),204,(2)pp. Contemp sheep, mod calf back (rubbed, browned, edges sl frayed). *Oinonen**. $120/£75

WORSLEY, F. A. Shackleton's Boat Journey. W.W. Norton, 1977. 1st ed. VG + in dj. *Walcot*. $22/£14

WORSLEY, F. A. Under Sail in the Frozen North. Phila: David McKay, 1927. Lg fldg map. VG. *High Latitude*. $50/£31

WORST, EDWARD F. Foot-Power Loom Weaving. Milwaukee: Bruce Pub Co, 1924. 3rd ed. VG. *Hollett*. $72/£45

WORSWICK, CLARK and AINSLIE EMBREE. The Last Empire: Photography in British India, 1855-1911. Millerton: Aperture, 1976. Fine in dj. *Cahan*. $60/£38

WORTLEY, EMMELINE STUART. Travels in the United States, etc., During 1849 and 1850. NY, 1851. 1st Amer ed. Pub's cl. (Foxed throughout.) Howes W687. *Swann**. $69/£43

WORTLEY, ROTHESAY STUART. Letters from a Flying Officer. London: Humphrey Milford/OUP, 1928. 1st ed. Photogravure frontis. Red cl, black bds. (Fore-edge lt foxed), o/w Fine in dj. *Reese*. $85/£53

WOTTON, HENRY. Reliquiae Wottonianae: Or, A Collection of Lives, Letters, Poems; with Characters of Sundry Personages.... London: B. Tooke & T. Sawbridge, 1685. 4th ed. Frontis port, (82),713pp. Period calf, gilt. (Frontis lacks lower marginal piece, bkpl; glue to joints), else VG. *Pacific**. $173/£108

WOUK, HERMAN. Aurora Dawn. James Barrie, 1947. 1st UK ed. NF in VG + dj (sm closed tear, extrems sl worn). *Any Amount*. $56/£35

WOUK, HERMAN. The Caine Mutiny Court-Martial. GC: Doubleday, 1954. 1st ed in play form. Fine in pict dj (sl rubbed). *Bromer*. $110/£69

WOUK, HERMAN. Inside, Outside. Boston: Little, Brown, (1985). One of 1565 numbered, signed. Fine in mylar dj, slipcase. *Agvent*. $125/£78

WRAXHALL, NATHANIEL. Memoirs of the King of France, of the Race of Valois...to which is added, A Tour Through the Western, Southern, and Interior Provinces of France. London: Edward & Charles Dilly, 1777. 1st ed. 2 vols. 3/4 calf, marbled bds, morocco spine labels. (Fr joints starting, lacks half of spine label, corners rubbed), else VG. *Pacific**. $58/£36

WRAY, W. FITZWATER. Across France in War Time. London, (1916). 1st Eng ed. Nice (sl mkd). *Clearwater*. $88/£55

WREDDEN, J. The Microscope, Its Theory and Applications. NY: Grune & Stratton, 1948. Good (ex-lib, mks). *Blake*. $50/£31

WREN, LASSITER and RANDLE McKAY. The Baffle Book. GC: Doubleday, Doran, 1928. 1st ed. Dk brn buckram. (Rear cvr lt rubbed), o/w Nice. *Temple.* $32/£20

WREN, P. C. Fort in the Jungle. London, (1936). 1st ed. (Bkpl.) Pict dj. *Swann*.* $46/£29

WRIGHT, B. C. (ed). The 1st Cavalry Division in World War II. Tokyo, (1947). 2nd ptg. Wraps. (Stained.) *King.* $50/£31

WRIGHT, BENJAMIN C. San Francisco's Ocean Trade, Past and Future. SF: A. Carlisle, 1911. 1st ed. 12 plts. Grn cl, gilt. Fine (extrems lt rubbed). *Argonaut.* $75/£47

WRIGHT, BETTY REN (adapted by). A Christmas Carol Pop-Up Book. NY: Rand McNally, 1986. 3 dbl-pg pop-ups, 2 pop-ups by Victor G. Ambrus. Glazed pict bds. Fine. *Bookfinders.* $30/£19

WRIGHT, BLANCHE FISHER. Our Child's Favorites. Chicago: Rand-McNally, (1913). 1st ed. 12 x 9 3/4. Pict cvr label. (Sl soiled), else NF. *Pacific*.* $58/£36

WRIGHT, CHARLES S. British (Terra Nova) Antarctic Expedition 1910-1913. London: Harrison & Sons, 1921. VG (bkpl) in ptd paper wrapper (sl worn, chipped). *Explorer.* $32/£20

WRIGHT, DARE. The Doll and the Kitten. NY: Doubleday, 1960. 1st ed. 8.75x12. 32pp. Cl spine, pict bds. VG in dj. *Cattermole.* $100/£63

WRIGHT, DARE. Holiday for Edith and the Bears. GC: Doubleday, (1958). 1st ed. Lg 4to. Cl-backed photo illus bds (lower edge sl faded). Color dj. *Reisler.* $125/£78

WRIGHT, E. W. Lewis and Dryden's Marine History of the Pacific Northwest. Portland: Lewis & Dryden Ptg, 1895. 1st ed. 494pp. VG (recased w/orig spine laid on). Howes W693. *Perier.* $525/£328

WRIGHT, E. W. Lewis and Dryden's Marine History of the Pacific Northwest. NY: Antiquarian Press, 1961. One of 750. Buckram. Fine. *Pacific*.* $109/£68

WRIGHT, E. W. Lewis and Dryden's Maritime History of the Pacific Northwest. Portland, OR: LD, 1895. 1st ed. Folio. 493pp. Orig full leather, gilt. VG. *American Booksellers.* $375/£234

WRIGHT, EDWARD. Some Observations Made in Travelling Through France, Italy, &c. in the Years MDCCXX, MDCCXXI, and MDCCXXII.... London: A. Millar, 1764. 2nd ed. 2 vols. 4to. 40 engr plts by Vandergucht, woodcut plt, fldg plan. Contemp vellum, gilt. Cl slipcases. *Swann*.* $747/£467

WRIGHT, ELIZUR, JR. A Lecture on Tobacco, Delivered in the Chapel of the Western Reserve College, Hudson, Ohio, May 29, 1832. Cleveland, (OH): By Order of the Students, 1832. 1st ed. 12mo. 14pp. Orig plain wraps (corner sl chewed). *M & S.* $625/£391

WRIGHT, FRANK LLOYD. An American Architecture. Edgar Kaufmann (ed). NY, 1955. 1st Amer ed. Fine in dj (sl rubbed). *Polyanthos.* $95/£59

WRIGHT, FRANK LLOYD. An Autobiography. Faber, 1945. 1st ed. VG in VG dj (sl chipped). *Hadley.* $88/£55

WRIGHT, FRANK LLOYD. An Autobiography. London: Faber, 1945. 1st ed. (Spine top faded.) Dj (torn, defective). *Hollett.* $72/£45

WRIGHT, FRANK LLOYD. Buildings, Plans, and Designs. NY: Horizon, (1963). Folio. 100 plts. Unbound plts, text booklet laid in paper sleeve in 1/2 cl portfolio as issued. (Last 13 leaves, rear sleeve cvr browned, dampstained; extrems rubbed.) *Swann*.* $690/£431

WRIGHT, FRANK LLOYD. The Disappearing City. NY, 1932. 1st ed. (Cl faded, discolored.) *Swann*.* $92/£58

WRIGHT, FRANK LLOYD. Drawings for a Living Architecture. NY, 1959. 1st ed. VG in dj (extrems worn, lt faded, soiled). *Truepenny.* $500/£313

WRIGHT, FRANK LLOYD. Drawings for a Living Architecture. NY, 1959. 1st ed. Obl folio. (Lt worn.) Dj (missing pieces from spine, fr panel). *Swann*.* $546/£341

WRIGHT, FRANK LLOYD. The Future of Architecture. NY: Horizon, 1953. 1st ed. VG in dj (spine ends, corners chipped, tear lower fr panel). *Pacific*.* $69/£43

WRIGHT, FRANK LLOYD. The Future of Architecture. NY: Horizon, 1953. 1st ed. Red cl over beige linen. (Blank corner p305 torn.) Dj. *Karmiole.* $85/£53

WRIGHT, FRANK LLOYD. Genius and the Mobocracy. NY, (1949). 1st ed. Inscribed, signed. 4to. (Cl soiled.) Dj (chipped). *Swann*.* $747/£467

WRIGHT, FRANK LLOYD. Modern Architecture; Being, The Kahn Lectures for 1930. Princeton, 1931. Frontis (loose; ex-lib; bds worn). *Swann*.* $46/£29

WRIGHT, FRANK LLOYD. The Natural House. NY: Horizon Press, 1954. 1st ed. White cl. Good in dj (sl chipped). *Karmiole.* $85/£53

WRIGHT, FRANK LLOYD. The Story of the Tower. NY: Horizon Press, 1956. 1st ed. Ink presentation from one of the tenants of the tower. 2 fldg color photo plts. Black cl, gilt. (Sl foxed; sl shelfworn.) Cvrs VG in dj (lt chipped, several noticeable tears). *Baltimore*.* $65/£41

WRIGHT, FRANK LLOYD. A Testament. London: Architectural Press, 1957. 1st Eng ed. NF (cvrs sl bowed) in dj (sl rubbed, creased). *Ulysses.* $232/£145

WRIGHT, G. FREDERICK. The Ice Age in North America. NY, 1889. 1st ed. 622pp + index. Pict cl. (Ex-lib; outer hinges torn, cvrs worn, dknd.) *King.* $60/£38

WRIGHT, G. N. China Illustrated, Its Scenery, Architecture, Social Habits.... Fisher & Son, (1843). 1st ed. 4 vols bound in 2. 4to. 96; 72; 68; 52pp; 124 steel-engr plts. Contemp red 1/2 calf, red cl sides, gilt, raised bands. (Upper left margin vols 1&2 sl dampstained, not affecting images or text; extrems sl rubbed), o/w Very Clean set. *Sotheran.* $1,840/£1,150

WRIGHT, HAROLD BELL. Helen of the Old House. NY, 1921. 1st ed. VG. *Sagebrush.* $60/£38

WRIGHT, HAROLD BELL. The Mine with the Iron Door. NY, 1923. 1st ed. (Spine dull, cvrs worn, soiled), else Good. *King.* $20/£13

WRIGHT, HAROLD BELL. The Mine with the Iron Door. NY: Appleton, 1923. 1st ed. VG + ('1' at end of text; sl shelfworn) in dj (ragged, chipped). *My Bookhouse.* $62/£39

WRIGHT, HAROLD BELL. When a Man's a Man. NY: A.L. Burt, 1916. Photoplay ed. (Lower edge very shelfworn), else VG in dj (very ragged). *My Bookhouse.* $22/£14

WRIGHT, HAROLD BELL. The Winning of Barbara Worth. Chicago, (1911). 1st ed. Frontis, map. (Frontis sl sticking to tp, pp485-86 and 509-10 repaired w/archival tape), o/w VG. *Sagebrush.* $60/£38

WRIGHT, HAROLD BELL. The Winning of Barbara Worth. Chicago: Book Supply Co, 1911. Maroon cl, gilt. VG +. *Five Quail.* $50/£31

WRIGHT, HARRY. A Short History of Golf in Mexico and Mexico City Country Club. NY: Privately ptd, 1938. One of a ltd ed. Signed. Supplement laid in. Dec cl, paper cvr label. Fine. *Pacific*.* $230/£144

WRIGHT, HORACE J. and WALTER P. Beautiful Flowers and How to Grow Them. T.C. & E.C. Jack, 1909. 1st ed. 2 vols. 100 color plts. Contemp 1/2 grn calf (backs rubbed, worn). Contents VG (ex-libris). *Cox.* $40/£25

WRIGHT, ISA L. The Remarkable Tale of a Whale (a Rollicking Nonsense Rhyme). Joliet: P.F. Volland, (1930). 13th ed. 12mo. John Held, Jr. (illus). Full color pict bds (spine sl worn). *Reisler.* $125/£78

WRIGHT, J. British Carboniferous Crinoidea. London, 1950-60. 2 vols. 83 plts. 10 pts as issued, complete. Good. *Henly.* $72/£45

WRIGHT, J. Mushrooms for the Million. London, 1886. 4th ed. 126pp. Brn cl, gilt. VG. *Larry Price.* $40/£25

WRIGHT, J. E. B. Mountain Days in the Isle of Skye. Moray, 1934. 1st ed. 63 plts. VG. *Hollett.* $72/£45

WRIGHT, JOHN. Early Bibles of America. Gay & Bird, 1893. 1st ed. Frontis, 4 plts. Teg. (Hinges torn.) *Forest.* $32/£20

WRIGHT, JULIA McNAIR. Among the Alaskans. Phila: Presbyterian Board of Pub, c. 1883. 351pp; 2 maps. VG (lib bkpl; cl sl soiled, mkd). *High Latitude.* $75/£47

WRIGHT, LYLE H. American Fiction, 1774-1900. San Marino: Huntington Library, 1969-1978. 3 vols. 2nd rev ed of vol 1, 3rd ptgs of vols 2-3. (Sl handled.) Djs (soiled, handled, spines lt sunned). *Baltimore*.* $80/£50

WRIGHT, MARCUS J. (ed). General Officers of the Confederate Army. NY: Neale Pub, 1911. 1st ed. (Ink inscrip, fep roughly removed; cvrs heavily soiled, sm tears, frayed, spotted.) *King.* $95/£59

WRIGHT, MRS. D. GIRAUD. A Southern Girl in '61. NY: Doubleday, Page, 1905. 1st ed. Frontis. Teg. Pict grn cl. NF (neat sig). *Chapel Hill.* $150/£94

WRIGHT, NOEL. Quest for Franklin. London/Melbourne/Toronto: Heinemann, 1959. Fine in dj. *Explorer.* $19/£12

WRIGHT, R. R., JR. et al. Encyclopaedia of the African Methodist Episcopal Church. Phila, 1947. (Spine sl smudged, spine edges worn.) *Rybski.* $100/£63

WRIGHT, RICHARD. The Color Curtain. Cleveland, 1956. 1st Amer ed. Fine in Fine dj. *Polyanthos.* $60/£38

WRIGHT, RICHARD. The Outsider. NY: Harper, (1953). 1st ed. Black cl, dec bds. (Extrems sl rubbed, cl lt spotted), o/w NF in dj (rear panel scraped, edgeworn). *Heritage.* $75/£47

WRIGHT, RICHARD. The Outsider. London: Angus & Robertson, 1954. 1st Eng ed. VG (feps partly browned, sm label mk; spine ends sl bumped) in dj (price-clipped, edges sl rubbed, sm tear). *Ulysses.* $152/£95

WRIGHT, RICHARD. White Man, Listen! GC: Doubleday, 1957. 1st ed. Black cl. VG (ink inscrip, eps lt browned; spine ends rubbed) in dj (edgeworn, sl browned). *Heritage.* $125/£78

WRIGHT, RICHARDSON. The Gardener's Bed-Book. Phila: Lippincott, 1929. 1st ed. (Browned), else VG. *Fair Meadow.* $30/£19

WRIGHT, ROBERT M. Dodge City the Cowboy Capital. N.p., n.d. (ca 1930). (Sl shelfworn), else VG. Howes W707. *Dumont.* $95/£59

WRIGHT, ROBERT M. Dodge City: The Cowboy Capital and the Great Southwest.... Privately ptd, 1913. 1st ed. Pict cl. (Sig, address fep; lacks fep, frontis loose; fr, rear hinge open; extrems worn.) Howes W706. *Baade.* $150/£94

WRIGHT, S. FOWLER. The Throne of Saturn. Sauk City: Arkham House, 1949. 1st US ed. Fine in Fine dj. *Other Worlds.* $75/£47

WRIGHT, S. FOWLER. The World Below. Chicago: Shasta, (1949). One of 1000. NF in dj. *Pacific*.* $23/£14

WRIGHT, THOMAS (ed). Early Travels in Palestine. London: H.G. Bohn, 1848. Engr frontis, (xxxi),517pp. Orig blindstamped cl (spine damage, fr hinge cracked). *Maggs.* $240/£150

WRIGHT, THOMAS. A History of Caricature and Grotesque. London: Virtue Bros, n.d. (1864). Pict cvrs, gilt. NF (spine tips professionally repaired). *Polyanthos.* $60/£38

WRIGHT, THOMAS. The Life of William Blake. Olney, Bucks: T. Wright, 1929. 1st ed. 2 vols. 135 plts (2 color). Grn linen. Fine. *Appelfeld.* $200/£125

WRIGHT, THOMAS. The Life of William Blake. Olney, Bucks.: Thomas Wright, 1929. 1st ed. 2 vols. Fine set in VG djs (spines sunned). *Turtle Island.* $225/£141

WRIGHT, THOMAS. The Picturesque Beauties of Great Britain: A Series of Views from Original Drawings. London: Virtue, 1834. Fldg map, colored in outline (splits). (Foxed; worn, lacks spine piece.) Internally Sound. *Oinonen*.* $230/£144

WRIGHT, THOMAS. The Ruins of the Roman City of Vriconium, at Wroxeter, Near Shrewsbury. Shrewsbury: J.O. Sandford, 1864. 4th ed. 101,(3)pp; 16 plts (incl extra engr tp, fldg plan). Yellow eps w/ads. Paper label. VG. *Cox.* $32/£20

WRIGHT, WILLIAM. An Account of Palmyra and Zenobia with Travels and Adventures in Bashan and the Desert. Thomas Nelson & Sons, 1895. 1st ed. xviii,394pp; 32 full-pg, 4 fldg illus. Marbled eps; all edges marbled. Full red calf, contemp prize binding, gilt, raised bands. (Prelims lt foxed), o/w Fine. *Sotheran.* $317/£198

WRIGLEY, AMMON. Rakings Up. Rochdale: E. Wrigley, 1949. 1st ed. (Eps sl spotted; sl string-mkd, bumped.) *Hollett.* $72/£45

WROTH, LAWRENCE C. The Colonial Printer. NY: Grolier Club, 1931. One of 300. Uncut, unopened. (Lt worn.) *Oinonen*.* $110/£69

WROTH, LAWRENCE C. The Colonial Printer. Portland, 1938. 2nd ed. One of 1500. Uncut, unopened. (Lt worn.) Slipcase (broken, stains). *Oinonen*.* $90/£56

WROTH, LAWRENCE C. A History of Printing in Colonial Maryland, 1686-1776. Balt: Typothetae of Balt, 1922. 1st ltd ed. One of 125 numbered, signed. Marbled eps; teg, untrimmed. Contemp full lt brn levant morocco by Bayntun, raised bands, gilt. Fine (lt foxing fr/rear blanks) in fleece-lined cl-cvrd bd box (dust-soiled, sl worn) w/inner liner. *Baltimore*.* $220/£138

WROTH, LAWRENCE C. William Parks. Richmond: William Parks Club, 1926. 1st ed. One of 300 numbered, w/unsigned ink presentation by Wroth. Untrimmed. Brn cl, ptd paper labels. (Text lt aged; rubbed, spine label browned and scraped.) *Baltimore*.* $110/£69

WUERTH, LOUIS A. Catalogue of the Lithographs of Joseph Pennell. Boston, 1931. One of 425 numbered. 1/4 sheep. Dj, pub's 2-piece box (imperfect). *Swann*.* $287/£179

WULFF, LEE. The Atlantic Salmon. NY: A.S. Barnes, (1958). 1st ed. One of 200. Signed. 11x8.25. 1/4 chieftan goatskin, marbled bds, gilt. (Spine sl dull), else NF in VG slipcase. *Pacific*.* $690/£431

WUNDERLICH, C. A. and EDWARD SEGUIN. Medical Thermometry, and Human Temperature. NY, 1871. 1st ed. 280pp. *Fye.* $200/£125

WURLITZER, RUDOLPH. Nog. NY, (1968). 1st ed, 1st bk. VG in dj (sl insect-spotted). *King.* $35/£22

Wyatt Earp's Personal Diagram of Prominent Historical Events...Circa 1881-82, Arizona Territory. MacLean, VA: US Marshal's Foundation, 1989. 1st ed. Folder w/4 diagrams. Fine. *Labordo.* $50/£31

WYATT, THOMAS. Life and Letters of Sir Thomas Wyatt. Kenneth Muir (ed). Liverpool: Liverpool Univ, 1963. 1st Eng ed. B/w frontis. Advance rev slip, postcard from Karl Miller loosely inserted. Good (2pp, fore-edge sl soiled; top edge dusty; spine ends, corners bumped, cvrs sl cocked) in dj (nicked, rubbed, spotted, soiled, dusty, sl chipped, creased, torn, browned). *Ulysses.* $72/£45

WYATT, THOMAS. Memoirs of the Generals, Commodores, and Other Commanders...During the Wars of the Revolution and 1812. Phila, 1848. 1st ed. 14 plts. Contemp 3/4 leather (worn, joints broken; foxed, browned). *Oinonen*.* $70/£44

WYCHERLEY, WILLIAM. The Complete Works of.... Montague Summers (ed). Soho: Nonesuch, 1924. One of 800 sets. 4 vols. Untrimmed. Paper labels. Fine set. *Second Life.* $250/£156

WYCHERLEY, WILLIAM. The Country Wife. Hutchinson, 1934. One of 1000 signed by Steven Spurrier (illus). Sm folio. 8 color plts. Uncut. Good in yellow linen-backed dec bds (backstrip sl rubbed, soiled), paper label. *Cox.* $40/£25

WYCHERLEY, WILLIAM. Miscellany Poems.... C. Brome et al, 1704. 1st ed, 1st issue. Folio in 4's. Mezzotint frontisport, xlvi,(ii)errata leaf,438pp. Red sprinkled edges. Contemp 'Cambridge-pane' calf (expertly rebacked to match, corners sl rubbed, hinges strengthened), raised bands, red leather label, gilt. Good (bkpl). Internally VF. *Blackwell's.* $920/£575

WYCKOFF, CAPWELL. The Sea Runners' Cache. NY: A.L. Burt, 1935. 5x8. 253pp. VG (erased pencil inscrip to 1/2-title, shelfworn) in dj (worn). *My Bookhouse.* $37/£23

WYETH, ANDREW. The Four Seasons. NY, (1963). One of 500 numbered, signed. Folio. Cl portfolio case, contents loose as issued. Pub's box (sl crushed). *Swann*.* $402/£251

WYETH, ANDREW. Wyeth at Kuerners. Boston: Houghton Mifflin, 1976. 1st ed. Fine in dj. *Pacific*.* $40/£25

WYETH, BETSY JAMES. The Stray. NY: FSG, (1979). 1st ed. Red cl. Fine in color pict dj. *House.* $30/£19

WYETH, JAMIE. Jamie Wyeth. Boston, 1980. One of 500 numbered, signed. 1/2 morocco. Cl slipcase. *Swann*.* $103/£64

WYETH, JOHN ALLAN. Life of General Nathan Bedford Forrest. NY: Harper, 1899. 1st ed. Frontisport, 656pp. Sig of Charles M. Blackford. Teg. Gray cl. (Spine lt soiled), else VG + . Howes W716. *Chapel Hill.* $450/£281

WYLIE, ELINOR. Nets to Catch the Wind. London: Knopf, 1928. 1st British ed. Parchment over bds. (Spine dknd), else Fine in NF dj (2 sm internal mends). BAL 23484. *Reese.* $100/£63

WYLIE, ELINOR. The Orphan Angel. NY: Knopf, 1926. 1st ed. One of 30 (of 190) signed. Vellum, gilt. (Spine sl dknd), o/w Fine in mod custom slipcase. *Hermitage.* $350/£219

WYLIE, ELINOR. Trivial Breath. London/NY: Knopf, 1928. 1st ed, ltd issue. One of 100 numbered, signed. Dec cl. NF in glassine wrapper (chipped). BAL 23518. *Reese.* $250/£156

WYLIE, ELINOR. The Venetian Glass Nephew. NY: Doran, 1925. 1st ed. Ltd to 250 lg paper copies signed. VF (inscrip) in dj (lt chipped), slipcase (defective). *Bromer.* $125/£78

WYLLYS, RUFUS K. Arizona. Phoenix, 1950. 1st ed. Ltd to 408 signed by Wyllys, illus, cartographer. This copy w/o #, orig ms pg or designer's sig called for in numbered ed. (Ink inscrip, pencil sig; cvrs faded along narrow margin at top), else Fine in dj (sl chipped, sl shorter than bk). *Baade.* $50/£31

WYLLYS, RUFUS K. Arizona: The History of a Frontier State. Phoenix, AZ: Hobson & Herr, (1950). 1st ed. Pict eps. VG in dj. *Lien.* $50/£31

WYMAN, LELAND C. The Sandpaintings of the Kayenta Navajo. Albuquerque: Univ of NM, 1952. Good in wraps. *Dumont.* $50/£31

WYMAN, MORRILL. Autumnal Catarrh (Hay Fever) with Illustrative Maps. NY, 1876. 221pp. *Fye.* $150/£94

WYMAN, WALKER D. Nothing But Prairie and Sky. Norman, 1954. 1st ed. Good in dj (sl worn). *Dumont.* $35/£22

WYMAN, WALKER D. Nothing but Prairie and Sky. Norman, 1954. 1st ed. Fine in dj. *Baade.* $40/£25

WYMAN, WALKER D. (ed). California Emigrant Letters. NY: Bookman Assoc, (1952). VG in dj (sl worn). *Lien.* $15/£9

WYNDHAM, JOHN. The Chrysalids. Michael Joseph, 1955. 1st UK ed. VG (ink name) in dj (edges sl worn). *Williams.* $64/£40

WYNDHAM, JOHN. Jizzle. Dobson, 1954. 1st UK ed, 1st issue dj w/blurbs about two other bks on rear panel. VG (spine sl bumped) in dj (price-clipped, sm closed tears). *Williams.* $152/£95

WYNDHAM, JOHN. The Midwich Cuckoos. NY: Ballantine, (1957). 1st Amer ed. VG in dj (spine ends rubbed, lower fr corner chipped). *Pacific*.* $403/£252

WYNDHAM, JOHN. Trouble with Lichen. London: Michael Joseph, 1960. 1st ed. NF in dj (spine, flap fold rubbed). *Else Fine.* $50/£31

WYNDHAM, RICHARD. A Book of Towers and Other Buildings of Southern Europe.... Haslewood Books, 1928. 1st ed. One of 337 (of 350). Folio. 24 copperplt engrs. Untrimmed. Orig 1/4 cream vellum, gilt, tan bds, cream vellum-tipped corners. (Cvrs dust-soiled.) *Blackwell's.* $320/£200

WYNN, MARCIA RITTENHOUSE. Desert Bonanza. Culver City, CA, 1949. Good (name). *Dumont.* $75/£47

Wyoming. NY: OUP, 1941. 1st ed. VG + in dj. *Labordo.* $125/£78

Wyoming. NY: OUP, 1948. 3rd ptg. Good in dj (sl chipped). *Dumont.* $45/£28

WYSS, JOHANN. The Swiss Family Robinson. Boston: Munroe & Francis, 1832. 395pp + 5pp ads; map. Orig leather spine, marbled bds. (Browned; shelfworn, rubbed, lt worn), else VG. *Brown.* $175/£109

WYSS, JOHANN. The Swiss Family Robinson. Ipswich: LEC, 1963. One of 1500. Signed by David Gentleman (illus). 1/2 buckram, grasscloth-cvrd bds, morocco spine label. Fine in glassine, slipcase. *Pacific*.* $40/£25

WYSUPH, C. L. Jackson Pollock. NY: Horizon, (1970). Orig ed. 83 full-pg plts (16 color). NF in color illus stiff wrappers. *Turtle Island.* $45/£28

WYTHE, JOSEPH H. The Microscopist. Phila, 1853. 2nd ed. 212pp; 2 plts. (Bkpls, inscrips, bottom of fr hinge torn, spine faded.) *King.* $40/£25

X

X, EX-PRIVATE. (Pseud of Alfred McClelland Burrage.) War Is War. London, 1930. 1st Eng ed. VG in dj (sl torn, nicked). *Clearwater.* $136/£85

X, MALCOLM. (Pseud of Malcolm Little.) The Autobiography of Malcolm X. NY: Grove, (1965). 1st ed. 8vo. Fine in VG dj (price-clipped, 1.75-inch open tear to fr panel). *Agvent.* $800/£500

XAVIER, PAUL. The Anarchist Papers. Berkeley: Undermine, 1969. 1st ed. One of 1000. Fine in wraps. *Beasley.* $25/£16

XENEPHON. The Anabasis. Henry G. Dakyns (trans). Athens: LEC, 1969. One of 1500 ptd. Signed by A. Tassos (illus). Fine in glassine, slipcase. *Pacific*.* $52/£33

XENOPHON. The Anabasis of Xenophon. LEC, 1969. Ltd to 1500 numbered, signed by A. Tassos (illus). Fine in slipcase. *Swann*.* $103/£64

XENOPHON. Xenophon's History of the Affairs of Greece, by the Translator of Thucydides. London: Benjamin White, 1770. 1st ed in English. Fldg frontis map, vi (p vi misnumbered iv),329,(5)pp. Calf, gilt, morocco spine labels. (Bkpl; joints cracked through, fr cvr nearly detached, writing on spine), else VG. *Pacific*.* $109/£68

Y

Y. The Odyssey of a Torpedoed Transport. Grace F. Norton (trans). Boston/NY: Houghton Mifflin, 1923. 1st this ed. Yellow cl. Fine in dj (lt edgeworn). *Reese.* $50/£31

Yale in the World War. New Haven: Yale Univ, 1925. 1st ed. 2 vols. Unopened. (Spine ends sl rubbed), o/w Fine. *Sadlon.* $45/£28

YANEZ, AUGUSTIN. The Lean Lands. Austin: Univ of TX, 1968. 1st US ed. NF in VG dj (price-clipped, few mended edge-tears). *Lame Duck.* $65/£41

YARDLEY, HERBERT O. The Education of a Poker Player. Sphere, 1970. 1st pb ed. VG. *Williams.* $19/£12

YARRELL, WILLIAM. A History of British Birds. John Van Voorst, 1843. 1st ed. 3 vols. W/half-titles, xxxii,525; (4),669; (4),528pp; 520 wood-engrs. Good set (bkpls) in contemp 1/2 tan calf (sl rubbed), marbled sides. *Cox.* $152/£95

YARRELL, WILLIAM. A History of British Birds. London, 1843. 1st ed. 3 vols. Pub's cat vol 3. Good (bkpl). *Henly.* $179/£112

YARRELL, WILLIAM. A History of British Birds. London, 1845. 2nd ed. 3 vols. 535 wood engrs. Uncut. (Margins lt browned, lacks fep vol 1; hinges cracked, cl lt soiled, rubbed, spines sl bumped.) *Edwards.* $96/£60

YARRELL, WILLIAM. A History of British Fishes. London, 1836. 1st ed. 2 vols. (Cl rebacked preserving spines.) *Henly.* $120/£75

YARRELL, WILLIAM. A History of British Fishes. London: John Van Voorst, 1836. 1st ed. 2 vols. xxxvi,408; 472pp. 19th-cent polished calf, gilt. VF set. *Karmiole.* $250/£156

YARRELL, WILLIAM. A History of British Fishes. London: John Van Voorst, 1836/1839. 1st ed. 2 vols + suppl (3 vols complete). 3/4 brn calf, raised bands, leather labels. Supp in orig grn cl. Good. *Appelfeld.* $250/£156

YARROW, WILLIAM and LOUIS BOUCHE. Robert Henri, His Life and Works. NY: Privately ptd, 1921. Folio. 41 plts. Bds (rebacked retaining most of discolored backstrip). *Swann*.* $138/£86

YARWOOD, DOREEN. The Architecture of England from Prehistoric Times to the Present Day. Batsford, 1963. 1st ed. NF in dj. *Hadley.* $45/£28

YARWOOD, DOREEN. The English Home. London: Batsford, 1956. 1st ed. Color frontis. Dj (sl chipped). *Edwards.* $32/£20

YASHIMA, TARO. Seashore Story. Viking, 1967. 1st ed. 10.2x9.2. Unpaginated. VG in dj (chipped, torn). *Price.* $65/£41

YASHIRO, YUKIO. Sandro Botticelli. London, 1925. One of 630 numbered sets. 3 vols. Sm folio. 291 plts. (Soiling, staining to cvrs, 1 spine label rubbed.) *Swann*.* $517/£323

YATES, DORNFORD. Gale Warning. Ward Lock, 1939. 1st UK ed. VG (sl cocked) in dj (price-clipped, few closed tears). *Williams.* $64/£40

YATES, ELIZABETH. Once in the Year. Coward McCann, 1947. 1st ed. Nora S. Unwin (illus). Unpaginated. Pict lib binding. VG (1947 inscrip) in VG dj (sm chip to spine). *Price.* $30/£19

YATES, JAMES. An Account of the Art of Weaving Among the Ancients. Part 1. London: Taylor & Walton, 1843. One of 250 ptd. Inscribed presentation, dated Nov 19th, 1848. xvi,(ii),472pp; 16 plts (2 hand-colored). Orig cl, gilt. (Foxing to plts, lib stamp on tp, last leaf; extrems sl worn, bds damp-cockled.) *Hollett.* $192/£120

YATES, RAYMOND F. Boys Book of Model Boats. NY: Appleton-Century, 1943. VG in dj. *American Booksellers.* $35/£22

YATES, RICHARD and MARY MARSHALL. The Lower Colorado River. Yuma, 1974. Tan cl. Fine. *Five Quail.* $40/£25

YATES, RICHARD. Revolutionary Road. Boston: Little, Brown, (1961). 1st ed, 1st bk. Fine in dj (sm chip on rear, 2 sm tears). *Agvent.* $150/£94

YATES, RICHARD. A Special Providence. NY: Knopf, 1969. 1st ed. NF in NF dj (sm crease fr panel top). *Agvent.* $75/£47

YATES, WILLIAM HOLT. The Modern History and Condition of Egypt. London, 1843. 1st ed. 2 vols. lxxxviii,512; viii,644pp; 14 litho plts, 2 engr fldg maps. VG set (tps sl mkd) in orig cl. *Ulysses.* $960/£600

YATES, WILLIAM. An Account of New Zealand. London: R.B. Seeley & W. Burnside, 1835. 2nd ed. Frontisport, (viii),310,(x)pp; 9 plts (1 hand-colored), dbl-pg map. (Prelims sl spotted, bkpl.) Grn cl (spine head, fr joint frayed, sl worn.) *Edwards.* $240/£150

YATO, TAMOTSU. Naked Festival. NY/Tokyo: Walker/Weatherhill, 1969. 1st Amer ed. Fine in illus dj (fr panel lacks lg piece). *Cahan.* $125/£78

YAVAPAI COWBELLES OF ARIZONA. Echoes of the Past. Prescott, 1964. VG in dj. *Dumont.* $35/£22

YCAS, M. The Biological Code. Amsterdam: North-Holland Pub, 1969. 1st ed. Grn cl. Fine in dj. *House.* $75/£47

YEALLAND, LEWIS R. Hysterical Disorders of Warfare. London: Macmillan, 1918. 1st ed. (Fep excised, bkpl remains), o/w NF. *Beasley.* $50/£31

YEARNS, W. BUCK and JOHN G. BARRETT (eds). North Carolina Civil War Documentary. Chapel Hill: Univ of NC, (1980). 1st ed. Black cl. (Rev's bkpl, copy of rev affixed to rear pastedown), else Fine in dj. *Chapel Hill.* $45/£28

YEARSLEY, ANN. The Royal Captives. Phila: Robert Campbell, 1795. 1st Amer ed. 2 vols in 1. iv,128; 122pp. Contemp calf. (Lacks fep, text spotted, toned; rubbed, bds sl buckled), else Good. *Brown.* $75/£47

YEATS, JOHN BUTLER. Early Memories: Some Chapters of Autobiography. Dublin: Cuala, 1923. 1st ed. One of 500. (Tp gutter torn.) Linen-backed bds, ptd spine label. *Maggs.* $80/£50

YEATS, W. B. The Cat and the Moon and Certain Poems. Dublin: The Cuala, 1924. 1st ed. One of 500 ptd. Blue-grey bds over linen spine, paper label. Good. *Appelfeld.* $300/£188

YEATS, W. B. The Cat and the Moon and Certain Poems. Dublin: Cuala, 1924. 1st ed. One of 500. Signed. Mostly unopened. Blue bds, linen spine, spine label (chipped). *Appelfeld.* $500/£313

YEATS, W. B. Cathleen Ni Hoolihan. Caradoc, 1902. 1st ed. (Bkpl.) Leather spine (head sl worn). *Sotheby's*.* $405/£253

YEATS, W. B. The Celtic Twilight. London: Lawrence & Bullen, 1893. Grn cl. (Lt foxed, hinges split; corners curled, worn.) *Metropolitan*.* $172/£108

YEATS, W. B. The Celtic Twilight. London: Lawrence & Bullen, 1893. 1st ed. 1st issue binding, w/pub's name in uppercase only. Frontis. Uncut. Straight-grain grn cl, gilt. (Joints cracked, binding sl tilted, spine sl faded.) *Maggs.* $320/£200

YEATS, W. B. Collected Poems. London, 1950. 2nd ed. Dj. *Clearwater.* $72/£45

YEATS, W. B. The Death of Synge, and Other Passages from an Old Diary. Dublin: Cuala, 1928. One of 400. Beige cl over gray bds, ptd paper spine label. NF (bkpl; cl lt soiled) in glassine wrapper. *Heritage.* $500/£313

YEATS, W. B. Deirdre. Stratford-on-Avon: Shakespeare Head Press, 1914. 2nd theatre ed. Fine in brn ptd wrappers. *Dermont.* $35/£22

YEATS, W. B. Early Poems and Stories. London: Macmillan, 1925. 1st ed. One of 2908 ptd. Pict eps. Dec grn cl. (Lt foxed, extrems sl rubbed), o/w Fine in dj. *Jaffe.* $350/£219

YEATS, W. B. A Fool Moon in March. Macmillan, 1935. 1st ed. (Eps lt offset), else NF in NF dj (closed tear). *Any Amount.* $88/£55

YEATS, W. B. Four Years. Churchtown, Dundrum: Cuala, 1921. One of 400. Beige linen over blue bds, ptd paper spine label. VG (feps browned, bkpl; spine, label sl browned) in glassine wrapper. *Heritage.* $300/£188

YEATS, W. B. The Green Helmet: An Heroic Farce. Stratford-upon-Avon: Shakespeare Head, 1911. 1st ed. Signed. Wrappers. *Sotheby's*.* $478/£299

YEATS, W. B. The Herne's Egg. London, 1938. 1st Eng ed. Nice (sm mk fep edge; spine, cvr edges sl faded; lacks dj). *Clearwater.* $56/£35

YEATS, W. B. The Hour-Glass, Cathleen Ni Houlihan, the Pot of Broth. London: A.H. Bullen, 1904. 1st ed. 1/2 cl, paper spine label. (Soiled; spine label, extrems rubbed), else VG. *Pacific*.* $75/£47

YEATS, W. B. Ideas of Good and Evil. NY, 1903. 1st Amer ed from Eng sheets. One of 520 for the Amer pub. Blue cl, gilt. (Lt rubbed, tips bumped.) *Swann*.* $115/£72

YEATS, W. B. Ideas of Good and Evil. London, 1903. 1st Eng ed. One of 1490. Good (foxed; 2 corners chafed, spine label sl rubbed). *Clearwater.* $120/£75

YEATS, W. B. In the Seven Woods, Being Poems Chiefly of the Irish Heroic Age. Dun Emer, 1903. 1st ed. (One of 325.) Signed. 8vo. Linen (browned). Dj (partly defective). *Sotheby's*.* $1,288/£805

YEATS, W. B. The King's Threshold: A Play in Verse. NY: Privately ptd, 1904. 1st ed. One of 100. This copy signed. 8vo. Acetate dj, slipcase. *Sotheby's*.* $1,379/£862

YEATS, W. B. The Letters of W. B. Yeats. Allan Wade (ed). London: Rupert Hart-Davis, 1954. 1st Eng ed. 11 b/w plts. VG (edges sl browned; spine ends, corners sl bumped, fr cvr sl creased) in dj (nicked, creased, mkd, frayed, worn, sl torn, sl browned). *Ulysses.* $152/£95

YEATS, W. B. Letters on Poetry to Dorothy Wellesley. London, 1940. 1st Eng ed. Very Nice in dj (sl nicked, rubbed). *Clearwater.* $48/£30

YEATS, W. B. Letters. Allan Wade (ed). NY, 1955. 1st ed, Amer issue. Very Nice in dj (sl nicked, rubbed). *Clearwater.* $88/£55

YEATS, W. B. On Baile's Strand. Dublin: Maunsel, 1905. 1st Irish ed. Volume VI of Abbey Theatre series. Pict wrappers. (Soiled, spine dknd), else VG. *Pacific*.* $115/£72

YEATS, W. B. On the Boiler. Dublin: Cuala, (1939). 2nd ptg. VG in blue wrappers (edges sl faded, creased). *Heritage.* $200/£125

YEATS, W. B. The Player Queen. London, 1922. 1st Eng ed. One of 1000. Card wrappers (sl mkd, dusty, spine sl chafed, ptd price at fr wrapper foot neatly changed in ink). *Clearwater.* $88/£55

YEATS, W. B. Plays for an Irish Theatre. London/Stratford-upon-Avon: A.H. Bullen, 1911. 1st ed. 1/2 cl, paper spine label; new-looking label tipped to rear pastedown. (Spine dknd, label chipped), else VG. *Pacific*.* $259/£162

YEATS, W. B. Plays for an Irish Theatre. London: A.H. Bullen, 1911. 1st Eng ed. Spare title label. Good (fore-edges some pp nicked, hinges cracked, top edge dusty; spine ends, corners bumped) in dj (torn, worn, chipped, spotted, frayed, soiled, dknd, internally repaired, browned, lacks few sm pieces). *Ulysses.* $360/£225

YEATS, W. B. Poems 1899-1905. Bullen, 1906. 1st ed. Blue dec cl, gilt. (Inscrip, bkpl; fr bd sl mkd, lower corners sl bumped), else NF. *Any Amount.* $208/£130

YEATS, W. B. The Poems of William Butler Yeats. LEC, 1970. Ltd to 1500 numbered, signed by Robin Jacques (illus). Fine in slipcase. *Swann*.* $69/£43

YEATS, W. B. Poems. T.F. Unwin, 1899. 2nd ed. Frontis, port. Blue dec cl, gilt. (Few ll sl foxed; corners bumped, spine end sl bruised), else NF. *Any Amount.* $176/£110

YEATS, W. B. The Poems. Macmillan, 1949. Ltd to 350 signed. 2 vols. 8vo. Prospectus laid in. Grn cl, gilt. Slipcase. *Sotheby's*.* $1,435/£897

YEATS, W. B. Reveries Over Childhood and Youth. Churchtown, Dundrum: Cuala, 1915. One of 425. Unopened. (Extrems sl worn.) *Metropolitan*.* $172/£108

YEATS, W. B. Reveries Over Childhood and Youth. NY: Macmillan, 1916. 1st Amer ed. Dec cl-backed bds. NF (bkpls). *Agvent.* $125/£78

YEATS, W. B. Sophocles' King Oedipus. London: Macmillan, 1928. 1st ed. VF in ptd wrappers. *Maggs.* $256/£160

YEATS, W. B. Three Things. London: Ariel Poems, (1929). 1st Eng ed. Fine in pict card wrappers. *Clearwater.* $48/£30

YEATS, W. B. Three Things. London, 1929. 1st ed. One of 500 lg paper copies, signed. Pale blue bds (worn, most spine chipped away), gilt. *Kane*.* $35/£22

YEATS, W. B. The Tower. NY, 1928. 1st Amer ed. (Name, ex-lib; extrems sl worn, dull.) *Woolson.* $40/£25

YEATS, W. B. The Wanderings of Oisin and Other Poems. London: Kegan, Paul, Trench, 1889. 1st ed. Ltd to 500. 8vo. 156pp. VF (lower rear cvr w/sm marred area) in navy cl, gilt. *Bromer.* $2,500/£1,563

YEATS, W. B. The Wild Swans at Coole, Other Verses and a Play in Verse. Churchtown, Dundrum: Cuala, 1917. Ltd to 400. (Sl faded, paper label nicked.) *Metropolitan*.* $201/£126

YEATS, W. B. The Winding Stair and Other Poems. London: Macmillan, 1933. 1st British ed. Dec grn cl. VG. *Pacific*.* $75/£47

YEATS, W. B. The Winding Stair. NY: Fountain Press, 1929. 1st ltd ed. One of 642 numbered, signed. Teg, untrimmed. Navy cl, gilt. VG (ep edges sl discolored; few lt spots fr cvr). *Baltimore*.* $325/£203

YEATS, W. B. (ed). Fairy and Folk Tales of the Irish Peasantry. London: Walter Scott, n.d. Early ed. Blue cl, paper spine label. (Spine head frayed, foot rubbed, label soiled), else VG. *Pacific*.* $81/£51

YEATS, W. B. (ed). Irish Fairy and Folk Tales. London: Walter Scott, (1893). 1st illus ed. 8vo. xviii,326,(vi)pp; 12 monochrome plts by James Torrance. Pict grn eps; aeg. Variant binding: Grn/blue cl, gilt, spine wraps round to rear bd, w/onlaid rectangular white cl lettering label. VG (sl shaken; label browned, spine sl rubbed). *Sotheran.* $253/£158

YEATS, W. B. (ed). Samhain. Dublin, 1901/1903. 2 vols. Later brn wrappers. (Bkpls.) *Swann*.* $138/£86

YEE, CHIANG. The Silent Traveller in Dublin. Methuen, 1953. 1st ed. VG in VG dj. *Green Meadow.* $32/£20

Yellow Book: An Illustrated Quarterly. London/NY, 1894-97. 13 vols (all issued). 8vo. Orig pict yellow cl (soiled). *Swann*.* $747/£467

Yellow Submarine. NY: Signet, 1968. 1st ed. Fine in wraps. *Warren.* $35/£22

YENDYS, SYDNEY. (Pseud of Sydney Dobell.) The Roman. London: Richard Bentley, 1852. 2nd ed. Contemp 3/4 grn leather (ends worn); marbled bds, eps, edges. VG. *Dramatis.* $35/£22

YEOMAN, JOHN. Beatrice and Vanessa. Hamilton, 1974. 1st ed. 4to. Quentin Blake (illus). VG in pict dj. *Bookmark.* $29/£18

YEVTUSHENKO, YEVGENY. Flowers and Bullets. SF: City Lights, 1970. 1st ed. Yellow wraps ptd in red ink. Fine. *Beasley.* $30/£19

YOAKUM, H. History of Texas from Its First Settlement in 1685 to Its Annexation to the United States in 1846. NY: Redfield, 1856. 2nd ed. 2 vols. 482; 576pp; 4 maps (2 fldg), 5 plts, fldg facs. Rebacked w/new leather spines, 2 red spine labels, w/hubs, gilt. (Foxed, ex-lib, inner hinges reinforced), o/w VG. Howes Y10. *New Hampshire*.* $390/£244

Yogi Bear and the Beaver Dam. A Yogi Bear Pop-Up Book. NY: Modern Promotions, 1974. Authorized ed. 4 dbl-pg pop-ups. Glazed pict bds (lt worn). *Bookfinders.* $30/£19

YONGE, CHARLOTTE M. The History of Sir Thomas Thumb, by the Author of 'The Heir of Redcliffe'.... Edinburgh: Thomas Constable, 1855. 1st ed. Sm 4to. Jane Blackburn (illus). Wood-engr frontis, (iv),vii,(i) blank,142pp; 3 plts, guards. Cream eps; gilt edges. Orig morocco-grain pale grn cl, gilt, by John Gray, w/his blue ptd ticket on rear pastedown. VG (early inscrip; lt soiled). *Blackwell's.* $248/£155

YONGE, CHARLOTTE M. The Little Duke. Macmillan, 1930. New ed. 1st ed thus. 181pp; 3 color, 7 b/w plts by Marguerite de Angeli. VG. *Price.* $45/£28

YONGE, CHARLOTTE M. Magnum Bonum or Mother Carey's Brood. Macmillan, 1879. 1st ed. 3 vols. No half-titles called for, ad leaf at end of vol 3. Grn cl. (Ink inscrips; lt red ink stain top margin pg[iii] vol 1.) *Bickersteth.* $88/£55

YONGE, CHARLOTTE M. An Old Woman's Outlook in a Hampshire Village. London, 1892. 285pp. Blue cl, gilt. Good (lib spine # removed). *Larry Price.* $15/£9

YORKE, PHILIP. The Royal Tribes of Wales. Wrexham: John Painter, 1799. 1st ed. 12 plts (offset onto opposing pg). 1/2 morocco, marbled bds (worn, rubbed, inner hinges strengthened w/binder's tape). *Kane*.* $110/£69

YORKE, PHILIP. The Royal Tribes of Wales. Wrerham: John Painter, 1799. 1st ed. vii,(3),192,2 + (1)ad pg; 13 copper-engr ports, incl frontis, guards. Contemp diced russia, gilt-roll borders, expertly rebacked in calf, gilt, morocco spine label. (New cl-backed eps, bkpl; adhesion residue to cvrs), else VG. *Pacific*.* $138/£86

YOSHIDA, TETSURO. The Japanese House and Garden. Marcus G. Sims (trans). NY, 1955. 1st US ed. Color frontis, map. (Lt spotted; fr bd head lt waterstained.) Dj (sl chipped). *Edwards.* $120/£75

YOSHIKAWA, EIJI. The Heike Story. NY, 1956. 1st Amer ed. Fine (sl rubbed) in dj (sl rubbed). *Polyanthos.* $45/£28

YOST, KARL. Charles M. Russell, the Cowboy Artist: A Bibliography. Pasadena: Trail's End, (1948). 1st ed. One of 500. Maroon cl, gilt. Fine. *Baltimore*.* $80/£50

YOST, NELLIE S. The Call of the Range. Denver: Sage Books, (1966). Beige cl. Dj. *Dawson.* $45/£28

YOST, NELLIE S. (ed). Boss Cowman: The Recollections of Ed Lemmon 1857-1946. Lincoln, 1969. 1st ed. VG in VG dj. *Woolson.* $40/£25

Young Bird-Catchers, and Other Stories. Boston: Henry A. Young, n.d. (ca 1870). 16mo. 63pp; 3 full-pg wood engrs incl frontis. Red blind-stamped cl, gilt. Good (sm bk dealer label inside fr cvr; bds lt discolored, chipped). *Hobbyhorse.* $75/£47

Young Samurai, Bodybuilders of Japan. NY, (1967). 1st ed. Tamotsu Yato (photos). Contents Clean. *Swann*.* $373/£233

YOUNG, ANDREW et al. The Paintings of James McNeill Whistler. New Haven/London, 1980. 2 vols. Djs. *Swann*.* $115/£72

YOUNG, ART. Art Young. John Nicholas Beffel (ed). NY: Sheridan House, 1939. 1st ed. Frontis photo port. Red cl. *Turtle Island.* $50/£31

YOUNG, ARTHUR. The Farmer's Calendar. London: Richard Phillips, 1809. 8th ed. 2 plts. Contemp calf bds. (Inscrip dated 1815, 1st 2 ll sl browned, 1 leaf w/3-inch tear, margin inelegantly repaired, no text loss, sl marginal worming; corners worn, sides sl mkd, recently neatly rebacked, retaining orig black morocco spine label.) *Pirages.* $125/£78

YOUNG, ARTHUR. Travels During the Years 1787, 1788, and 1789. London: For W. Richardson, 1794. 2nd ed. 2 vols. 3 fldg engr maps (spotted). Contemp 1/2 calf (rebacked retaining orig spines, corners repaired). *Sotheby's*.* $331/£207

YOUNG, EDWARD. The Complaint and the Consolation; or, Night Thoughts. R. Noble for R. Edwards, 1797. 1st ed. Folio. 43 engr pict borders by William Blake. Uncut. Morocco-backed bds. (Lacks explanation leaf, spotting, sm tears lower edge few ll, edges soiled, browned, owner notes tipped to fep; spine, corners rubbed.) *Sotheby's*.* $4,784/£2,990

YOUNG, EDWARD. The Complaint, and the Consolation; or Night Thoughts. London: R. Noble, 1797. 1st Blake ed. This copy complete w/the 'Explanation of the Engravings' following the text, a leaf sl smaller than the rest of the bk. 16.5x12.25. viii,(2),95,(2)pp; 43 copper-engrs by William Blake (incl 4 frontispieces). Teg. 19th-cent 3/4 gilt-ruled morocco, marbled bds. (Sl offset from illus, sl foxed, few pp trimmed to the edge of the illus but apparently as issued; extrems sl rubbed, sl edgworn), o/w VG. *Pacific*.* $4,600/£2,875

YOUNG, EDWARD. One of Our Submarines. London: Davis, 1952. VG in dj. *American Booksellers.* $40/£25

YOUNG, EGERTON R. My Dogs in the Northland. London: S.W. Partridge, 1903. 2nd ed. Grn dec cl (sl worn). Good. *Explorer.* $16/£10

YOUNG, FRANCIS BRETT. Black Roses. London: Heinemann, 1929. 1st ed. Ltd to 525 signed. Unopened. VG in full vellum gilt. *Cady.* $60/£38

YOUNG, FRANCIS BRETT. Jim Redlake. London: Heinemann, (1930). 1st ed. Gilt blue cl. NF in pict dj. *Reese.* $45/£28

YOUNG, FRANCIS BRETT. Marching on Tanga. London: W. Collins Sons, (1917). 1st ed. Frontis, fldg map. Slate blue cl, gilt. (Bkpl, eps sl tanned, edges lt foxed), o/w Nice in pict dj (lt rubbed, dust-mkd). *Reese.* $250/£156

YOUNG, FRANCIS BRETT. Mr. and Mrs. Penington. Heinemann, 1931. 1st ed. Signed. VG (top edge sl dusty, spine ends, corners sl bumped, fore-edge sl spotted) in dj (worn). *Ulysses.* $40/£25

YOUNG, FRANK C. Across the Plains in '65. Denver, CO: Privately ptd, 1905. Ltd ed. One of 200. Fldg map. Teg. Maroon cl, gilt. (Sl rubbed), else VG. Howes Y125. *Glenn.* $250/£156

YOUNG, G. O. Alaskan-Yukon Trophies Won and Lost. Huntington, WV, 1947. 1st ed. (Sl rubbed.) Dj (chipped). *Kane*.* $110/£69

YOUNG, GEOFFREY WINTHROP. Mountain Craft. Methuen, 1943. 4th ed. 8 plts. VG in dj (few sm edge chips). *Hollett.* $56/£35

YOUNG, GERALD. The Witch's Kitchen. London: George G. Harrap, (1910). 1st ed. Sq 8vo. Frontis (sm closed tear to extreme margin, repaired in verso), (xi),2-223,(ii)ads pp; 8 color plts by Willy Pogany. Pict eps. Grn dec cl, gilt, circular pict label onlaid to fr cvr. VG. *Sotheran.* $317/£198

YOUNG, HERBERT V. Ghosts of Cleopatra Hill. Jerome, AZ: Jerome Hist Soc, (1964). 1st ed. VG + in wraps. *Book Market.* $15/£9

YOUNG, HERBERT V. Ghosts of Cleopatra Hill. Men and Legends of Old Jerome. Jerome, AZ: Jerome Hist Soc, (1964). One of 500. Signed. VG in dj. *Perier.* $45/£28

YOUNG, HUGH HAMPTON. Genital Abnormalities, Hermaphroditism and Related Adrenal Diseases. Balt: Williams & Wilkins, 1937. 1st ed. Frontis. Blue cl. Fine. *Weber.* $225/£141

YOUNG, JAMES REID (ed). Scottish Mountaineering Club General Guide-Book. Edinburgh: S.M.C., 1933. 3rd ed. Photogravure frontis. Red cl (spine, edges sl faded), gilt. *Hollett.* $56/£35

YOUNG, JENNIE J. The Ceramic Art. NY, 1878. 1st Amer ed. Fine (rebound in buckram). *Polyanthos.* $75/£47

YOUNG, JESSE BOWMAN. The Battle of Gettysburg. NY/London: Harper, 1913. 1st ed. Frontisport. Blue cl. VG + . *Chapel Hill.* $175/£109

YOUNG, JOHN P. Journalism in California. SF: Chronicle Pub Co, (1915). 1st bk ed. Frontis, 50 plts. Marbled eps. Gray cl, gilt. VG + (extrems sl worn, spine sl dknd). *Harrington.* $50/£31

YOUNG, JOHN. Around the World with General Grant. NY: American News, (1879). 1st ed. 2 vols. Fldg engr frontis map vol 2. Marbled edges, eps. Orig brn leather, pebbled cl, gilt. (Cvrs detached vol 1, spine chipped, lt scuffed, vol 2 sl worn.) Contents VG. Baltimore*. $15/£9

YOUNG, JOHN. Around the World with General Grant...1877, 1878, 1879. NY, (1879). 2 vols. Pub's 1/2 calf. (Lt dampstained; extrems rubbed.) Swann*. $115/£72

YOUNG, JOHN. A Catalogue of the Celebrated Collection of Pictures of the Late John Angerstein.... London: John Young et al, 1823. Tps, 98pp; 42 guarded plts. Contemp morocco-backed bds. (Edges sl worn), o/w Fine. Europa. $184/£115

YOUNG, JOHN. A Catalogue of the Pictures at Grosvenor House, London; With Etchings from the Whole Collection. London, 1820. 46 engr plts. (Sl foxed, offset.) Roan back (binding loose, worn, spine chipped, torn). Oinonen*. $120/£75

YOUNG, JOHN. The Letters of Agricola on the Principles of Vegetation and Tillage.... Halifax: Holland, 1822. 1st ed. 402,(10)pp(foxed, spotted)+index. Uncut. Orig bds (rubbed, sl soiled, fr hinge repaired), ptd paper label (rubbed). Mott. $350/£219

YOUNG, JOHN. San Francisco: A History of the Pacific Metropolis. SF: S.J. Clarke, (1912). One of an unspecified # signed. 2 vols. Teg. 3/4 morocco. (Leather sl scuffed), o/w Fine. Pacific*. $104/£65

YOUNG, JOSEPH L. Mosaics: Principles and Practice. Reinhold, 1963. 1st ed. Color frontis. VG +. Whittle. $13/£8

YOUNG, M. Bibliography of Memory. Chilton, 1961. Good in dj. Moss. $48/£30

YOUNG, OTIS E., JR. Black Powder and Hand Steel. Norman, 1976. 1st ed. Fine in dj (sl rubbed). Baade. $32/£20

YOUNG, PETER. Himalayan Holiday. Herbert Jenkins, (1945). 1st ed. 3 maps (1 fldg). (Edges sl faded.) Dj (sl rubbed, faded). Hollett. $40/£25

YOUNG, PHILIP and CHARLES W. MANN. The Hemingway Manuscripts. An Inventory. Univ Park: PA Univ, (1969). One of 300 numbered. Leather-backed bds. Fine in pub's slipcase. Cady. $35/£22

YOUNG, R. The Banket. London: Gurney & Jackson, 1917. 28 plts. Good (lt foxed). Blake. $150/£94

YOUNG, S. HALL. Adventures in Alaska. NY: Fleming H. Revell, (1919). (Ink inscrip), else VG. Perier. $45/£28

YOUNG, S. HALL. Alaska Days with John Muir. NY: Fleming H. Revell, (1915). VG. Perier. $50/£31

YOUNG, STANLEY P. and EDWARD A. GOLDMAN. The Puma. Washington: Amer Wildlife Inst, 1946. 1st ed. Color frontis. Grn cl. Fine in color, pict dj (lt chipped). House. $65/£41

YOUNG, STANLEY P. and EDWARD A. GOLDMAN. The Wolves of North America. Washington: American Wildlife Inst, 1944. One of 100 specially bound in buffalo leather. Inscribed by Young. (Lt worn, leather dried out), else VG. Dumont. $650/£406

YOUNG, THOMAS. Outlines of Experiments and Inquiries Respecting Sound and Light. (London): W. Bulmer, 1800. 1st ed. 8vo. 47pp; 5 fldg plts. Fine in mod stiff wrappers. Glaser. $950/£594

YOUNG, WILLIAM E. Shark! Shark! NY: Gotham House, 1933. 1st ed. Helen Sewell (illus). Brn sharkskin, beige linen, gilt. Good. Karmiole. $85/£53

YOUNGBLOOD, CHARLES L. A Mighty Hunter. Chicago: Rand, McNally, 1890. 362pp + 3pp ads. (Browned; extrems sl worn), else Good. Howes Y38. Dumont. $195/£122

YOUNGER, COLE. The Story of Cole Younger by Himself. Houston, 1955. Rpt in ltd ed of 1903 ed. NF. Howes Y35. Baade. $85/£53

YOUNGER, COLE. The Story of Cole Younger, by Himself. Houston: Frontier, 1955. Rpt ed. NF. Howes Y35. Labordo. $50/£31

YOUNGHUSBAND, FRANCIS. Kashmir. London: A&C Black, 1909. 1st ed. 70 color plts, color fldg map. Teg. Maroon dec cl, gilt. (Sl foxed; spine ends rubbed, sm split upper joint.) Morrell. $32/£20

YOUNGHUSBAND, FRANK E. The Heart of a Continent: A Narrative of Travels in Manchuria, Across the Gobi Desert...1884.... London, 1896. (1.5 inches missing from backstrip top), o/w Sound. Petersfield. $86/£54

YOUNGHUSBAND, G. J. and F. E. The Relief of Chitral. London: Macmillan, 1895. 3rd imp. viii,183pp + (1 blank, 4 ads); color map, 2 fldg plans, 21 plts. Pub's cl. Marlborough. $176/£110

YOUNGMAN, W. E. Gleanings from Western Prairies. Cambridge (England): Jones & Piggott, 1882. Only ed. xv,214pp + 1 leaf ads. Blue cl, gilt. Mott. $100/£63

YOUNGSON, A. J. The Scientific Revolution in Victorian Medicine. NY: Holmes & Meier, (1979). 1st ed. Fine in dj. Glaser. $25/£16

Youngster's Diary; or, Youth's Remembrancer of Natural Events, for Every Month of the Year. Alnwick: W. Davison, (ca 1815). 3.25x5.25. 36pp; 35 woodcuts by Thomas Bewick. Good in ptd paper wrappers w/dec woodcuts on both cvrs. Reisler. $500/£313

YOURCENAR, MARGUERITE. Memoirs of Hadrian. G. Frick (trans). London, 1955. 1st ed. VG in dj (sl soiled, torn). Typographeum. $28/£18

Youth's Cabinet of Nature, for the Year; Containing Curious Particulars Characteristic of Each Month. NY: Samuel Wood, 1814. Rpt of 1812 ed. 12mo. 52pp + 1pg list on lower wrapper; 1 VF half-pg wood engr, 12 half-pg engrs as head-pieces. Orig dec stiff buff paper wrappers (lt stains). Fine. Hobbyhorse. $125/£78

YOYOTTE, JEAN. Treasures of the Pharaohs. Geneva: Skira, (1968). Folio. 120 tipped-in plts. (Bkpl; corner bumped.) Archaeologia. $150/£94

Yukon Territory, Its History and Resources. Ottawa: Minister of the Interior, 1916. (Rebound, sl musty.) Perier. $125/£78

YULE, HENRY (ed). The Book of Ser Marco Polo, the Venetian.... John Murray, 1875. 2nd ed. 2 vols. (xlii),444; (xxii),606pp. Nice set (eps cracked, few mks, nicks, sl shaken; sl worn). Ash. $400/£250

YULE, HENRY. Cathay and the Way Thither. Henri Cordier (ed). London: Hakluyt Soc, 1913-1916. 2nd rev ed. 4 vols. 8vo. 2 lg fldg maps. Blindstamped cl (spine sl faded). Maggs. $800/£500

YUMOTO, JOHN M. The Samurai Sword. Tokyo/Rutland, VT: Charles E. Tuttle, 1958. 1st ed. 49 plts. VG in dj. Hollett. $72/£45

YUTANG, LIN. Imperial Peking. Seven Centuries of China, with an Essay on the Art of Peking, by Peter C. Swann. NY: Crown, 1961. 1st ed. VG in dj (lacks sm piece). Worldwide. $45/£28

YZENDOORN, REGINALD. History of the Catholic Mission in the Hawaiian Islands. Honolulu: Honolulu Star-Bulletin, 1927. Frontis, 29 plts. Dec fabricoid (extrems sl rubbed). Karmiole. $85/£53

Z

ZABRISKIE, GEORGE A. The Pathfinder. Ormond Beach, FL, 1947. VG in dj (chipped). Dumont. $65/£41

ZAGOSKIN, MICHAEL. Tales of Three Centuries. Jeremiah Curtin (trans). Boston: Little, Brown, 1891. 1st Amer ed. Nice. Cady. $25/£16

ZAHARIAS, BABE DIDRICKSON. This Life I've Led: My Autobiography. Harry Paxton (ed). NY: A.S. Barnes, (1955). 1st ed. Signed. NF in dj (spine ends sl chipped). Pacific*. $1,035/£647

ZAMMIT, THEMISTOCLES. Malta. Valletta: Ptd at 'The Malta Herald' Office, 1929. 2nd ed. 8 plts. Sound (rather browned; joints, hinges cracked). Morrell. $88/£55

Zamorano 80. NY, 1969. Rpt. VG. Dumont. $55/£34

ZANGWILL, ISRAEL. Italian Fantasies. London: Heinemann, 1910. 1st Eng ed. Color frontis. Buckram. NF (bkpl, edges lt spotted; spine ends sl bumped) in dj (sl rubbed, spine sl dknd). Ulysses. $88/£55

ZANGWILL, ISRAEL. The King of Schnorrers: Grotesques and Fantasies. Heinemann, 1894. Pub's cat dated December 1894. Good (fore-edge lt spotted, ink inscrip, dusty; spine bumped, dknd). Tiger. $29/£18

ZANUCK, D. and D. RUNYON. Tunis Expedition. R-H, 1943. 1st ed. NF in VG + dj. Fine Books. $55/£34

ZELAZNY, ROGER. The Changing Land. SF: Underwood-Miller, 1981. 1st ed. One of 200. Signed by Zelazny and Thomas Canty (illus). Frontis. Fine in dj. Pacific*. $58/£36

ZELAZNY, ROGER. Creatures of Light and Darkness. GC: Doubleday, 1969. 1st ed. (Traces of bkpl removal), else Fine in dj (chip fr panel, lt edgeworn). Else Fine. $65/£41

ZELAZNY, ROGER. Dilvish, the Damned. SF: Underwood/Miller, 1983. 1st ed. One of 333. Signed. Pict cl. Fine in dj. Pacific*. $58/£36

ZELAZNY, ROGER. The Guns of Avalon. London: Faber & Faber, (1974). 1st British ed. Signed. NF in djs. Pacific*. $58/£36

ZELAZNY, ROGER. Nine Princes in Amber. London: Faber & Faber, (1972). 1st British ed. Signed. Fine in dj. Pacific*. $127/£79

ZELAZNY, ROGER. Nine Princes in Amber. GC: Doubleday, 1970. 1st ed. NF in dj (spine ends sl rubbed, sm tear, crease to lower fr panel, sm spots to part of fr panel). Pacific*. $1,150/£719

ZELAZNY, ROGER. Nine Princes in Amber. GC: Doubleday, 1970. 1st ed. Signed, w/signed holograph postcard laid-in. Fine in dj. Pacific*. $1,610/£1,006

ZERI, FEDERICO. Italian Paintings in the Walters Art Gallery. Balt: Walters Art Gallery Coll, 1976. 2 vols. 299 plts. Good. Washton. $65/£41

ZICHY, MIHALY. The Erotic Drawings of Mihaly Zichy. NY: Grove, (1969). 1st ed. 40 plts. NF in Good dj (sl rubbed, soiled; spine ends, inner corners of cvrs tape mkd). Blue Mountain. $65/£41

ZIEBER, EUGENE. Heraldry in America. Phila: Bailey, Banks & Biddle, 1909. 2nd ed. Brick-red cl, gilt. (Spine ends, joints rubbed), else VG. Pacific*. $52/£33

ZIEGLER, GILLETE. The Court of Versailles in the Reign of Louis XIV. S. W. Taylor (trans). London: Allen, 1966. Good. Stewart. $32/£20

ZIGROSSER, CARL. The Complete Etchings of John Marin. Phila: Museum of Art, 1969. Presentation copy. VG in ptd wrappers. Turtle Island. $135/£84

ZIGROSSER, CARL. Rockwellkentiana. NY: Harcourt, Brace, 1933. 1st ed. VG. Perier. $60/£38

ZIGROSSER, CARL. Rockwellkentiana: A Few Words and Many Pictures by R. K.... NY: Harcourt, Brace, 1933. 1st ed. VG. Perier. $60/£38

ZILAHY, LAJOS. The Deserter. George Halasz (trans). GC: Doubleday, Doran, 1932. 1st US ed. Orange cl. VG (pencil inscrip) in foil-finish dj (dust-spotted, lt frayed). Reese. $45/£28

ZIMMER, DAVE. Crosby, Stills and Nash. The Authorized Biography. NY: St. Martin's, 1984. 1st ed. NF in wraps. Sclanders. $16/£10

ZIMMER, JOSEPH. The History of the 43rd Infantry Division. Baton Rouge, 1946. 1st ed. VG. Clark. $95/£59

ZIMMERMAN, PAUL. The Los Angeles Dodgers. Coward McCann, 1960. 1st ed. Fine in Fine dj. Plapinger. $50/£31

ZIMMERMAN, WILLIAM. Waterfowl of North America. Louisville: Frame House Gallery, (1974). 1st ed. One of 1000. Signed. Obl elephant folio. 42 color plts, 2 extra plts laid in loose, signed. 1/2 grn morocco, cl, metal seal fr cvr. (Sl stains fr cvr), else NF. Pacific*. $316/£198

ZINKEISEN, DORIS. Designing for the Stage. London/NY: Studio, n.d. (c.1938). Color frontis. 45 tipped-in illus. (Spine sl faded), o/w Good. Europa. $64/£40

ZITELLA. 59 of '86. Letters Written to the Lebanon Courier, During the Summer of 1886. Lebanon: Worth & Reinoehl, ptrs, 1886. 1st ed in bk form. 72pp. (Fr hinge starting; cl lt worn), else Good. Brown. $100/£63

ZOBELEIN, JENNIFER. Dinosaurs. Kansas City: Hallmark, n.d. (1971). Dennis Anderson (illus). 4 dbl-pg pop-ups, wheel. Glazed pict bds. VG in VG dj. Bookfinders. $75/£47

ZOGBAUM, RUFUS F. Horse, Foot, and Dragoons. NY: Harper, 1888. 1st ed. (3)-176pp. Teg. Dec blue cl, gilt. (Hinges sl cracking at eps; sl rubbed, extrems worn), else NF. Pacific*. $196/£123

ZOGBAUM, RUFUS F. Horse, Foot, and Dragoons. Sketches of Army Life at Home and Abroad. NY: Harper, 1888. 1st ed. Tissue frontis, 176pp. Teg. Color, pict blue cl, gilt. VG (frontis tear expertly repaired, edges worn, spine ends lt worn). House. $120/£75

ZOLA, EMILE. The Attack on the Mill. Heinemann, 1895. 1st ed thus. Pub's cat dated October 1894. Dec beveled bds. Good (bkpl, sl spotted, fr joint cracked; spine bumped). Tiger. $88/£55

ZOLA, EMILE. Germinal. E. A. Vizetelly (ed). London, 1901. 1st ed. (Backstrip faded, foxed; no dj.) Typographeum. $15/£9

ZOLA, EMILE. Nana. LEC, 1948. 1st ed thus. One of 1500 signed by Bernard Lamotte (illus). Fine in glassine dj, slipcase. Fine Books. $55/£34

ZOLA, EMILE. Nana: A Realistic Novel. Vizetelly, 1886. New ed. Ad leaf; 24 tinted plts. Good (fore-edge spotted, corner torn fep; spine bumped, hinges sl rubbed). Tiger. $96/£60

ZOLA, EMILE. Savage Paris. David Hughes and Marie-Jacqueline Mason (trans). Elek Books, 1955. 1st ed thus. (Pencil inscrip, bkpl; sm splash mks fr, rear edges), else Good in Pagram dj (sl chipped). Tiger. $40/£25

ZOLOTOW, CHARLOTTE. The Sky Was Blue. NY: Harper & Row, 1963. 1st ed. 8.25x10.5. Garth Williams (illus). 32pp. Cl spine, pict bds. VG in dj. Cattermole. $50/£31

ZOLTAN, JANOS. Cicatrix Optima: Techniques for Ideal Wound Healing. Balt/London/Tokyo: University Park, (1977). Folio. (Sig.) Weber. $75/£47

ZORN, FRIEDRICH ALBERT. Grammar of the Art of Dancing. Boston, 1905. 1st Amer ed. (Pg offset; rear cvr sl stained), else VG. King. $125/£78

ZOUCH, THOMAS. The Life of Isaac Walton; Including Notices of His Contemporaries. London: Septimus Prowett, 1823. Frontis port. Several extra illus tipped in. Contemp 3/4 calf (neatly rebacked, rubbed, sl foxed). Protective morocco-backed cl case. Oinonen*. $180/£113

ZUCKER, A. E. The Chinese Theater. Boston: Little, Brown, 1925. One of 750. 4 orig mtd hand-colored silk paintings, 17 add'l full-pg plts. Teg. Dec yellow/black cl (spine lt soiled). Slipcase. Karmiole. $175/£109

ZUKOFSKY, LOUIS. A-24. NY: Grossman, 1972. 1st ed. Fine in VG + dj (extrems worn). Lame Duck. $45/£28

ZUKOFSKY, LOUIS. Autobiography. NY, 1970. 1st Amer ed. Fine in dj (spine sl rubbed). *Polyanthos*. $25/£16

ZWEIG, ARNOLD. The Case of Sergeant Grischa. NY: Viking, 1928. 1st US ed. Pub's promo flyer laid in. Gilt black cl. (Sm ink note), o/w NF in pict dj (price-clipped, sm edge tear). *Reese*. $65/£41

ZWEIG, ARNOLD. The Case of Sergeant Grischa. Eric Sutton (trans). London: Martin Secker, 1928. 1st British ed. Yellow cl stamped in brn. (Cl sl foxed), o/w VG in dj (spine sl dknd). *Reese*. $100/£63

ZWEIG, STEFAN. Amerigo: A Comedy of Errors in History. NY: Viking, 1942. 1st Amer ed. (Fep top corner clipped), else VF in VF dj. *Between The Covers*. $150/£94

ZWEIG, STEFAN. The Buried Candelabrum. NY: Viking, 1937. 1st Amer ed. Signed. (Fep top corner clipped), else VF in VF dj (extrems sl rubbed). *Between The Covers*. $350/£219

ZWEIG, STEFAN. The Buried Candelabrum. Oxford: Phaidon, 1944. VG (eps spotted) in dj (sl dusty, rubbed, nicked, spine sl dknd, internally tape-mkd). *Ulysses*. $58/£36

ZWEIG, STEFAN. Conqueror of the Seas: The Story of Magellan. NY: Viking, 1938. 1st Amer ed. (Fep corner clipped), else Fine in Fine black dj (sl rubbed). *Between The Covers*. $125/£78

ZWEIG, STEFAN. The Invisible Collection. (NY: Pynson Printers), 1926. 1st ed. Inscribed, initialed by Elmer Adler (ptr). Cl dec papercvrd bds in unptd glassine dj. VF (edges sl dknd) *Between The Covers*. $200/£125

ZWEIG, STEFAN. Jeremiah: a Drama in Nine Scenes. NY: Viking, 1939. 1st rev ed in English. VF in VF dj (fr cvr sm wrinkle). *Between The Covers*. $150/£94

ZWEIG, STEFAN. Master Builders: A Typology of the Spirit. NY: Viking, 1939. 1st Amer ed. (Fep corner clipped), else VF in VF dj. *Between The Covers*. $125/£78

ZWEIG, STEFAN. The Right to Heresy: Castellio Against Calvin. NY: Viking, 1936. 1st ed. (Fep corner clipped), else VF in VF dj (lt rubbed). *Between The Covers*. $150/£94

ZWEIG, STEFAN. The Royal Game. J. Sutcliffe (trans). London, 1981. VG in dj. *Typographeum*. $20/£13

ZWEIG, STEFAN. The World of Yesterday: An Autobiography. NY: Viking, 1943. 1st ed. (Fep corner clipped), else VF in VF dj (sm spine smudge). *Between The Covers*. $100/£63